Main groups | Transition metals | Main groups

Metals | Metalloids | Nonmetals

	1A[a] 1	2A 2	3B 3	4B 4	5B 5	6B 6	7B 7	8B 8	8B 9	8B 10	1B 11	2B 12	3A 13	4A 14	5A 15	6A 16	7A 17	8A 18
1	1 **H** 1.008																	2 **He** 4.003
2	3 **Li** 6.94	4 **Be** 9.012											5 **B** 10.81	6 **C** 12.01	7 **N** 14.01	8 **O** 16.00	9 **F** 19.00	10 **Ne** 20.18
3	11 **Na** 22.99	12 **Mg** 24.31											13 **Al** 26.98	14 **Si** 28.09	15 **P** 30.97	16 **S** 32.06	17 **Cl** 35.45	18 **Ar** 39.95
4	19 **K** 39.10	20 **Ca** 40.08	21 **Sc** 44.96	22 **Ti** 47.87	23 **V** 50.94	24 **Cr** 52.00	25 **Mn** 54.94	26 **Fe** 55.85	27 **Co** 58.93	28 **Ni** 58.69	29 **Cu** 63.55	30 **Zn** 65.38	31 **Ga** 69.72	32 **Ge** 72.63	33 **As** 74.92	34 **Se** 78.97	35 **Br** 79.90	36 **Kr** 83.80
5	37 **Rb** 85.47	38 **Sr** 87.62	39 **Y** 88.91	40 **Zr** 91.22	41 **Nb** 92.91	42 **Mo** 95.95	43 **Tc** [98]	44 **Ru** 101.07	45 **Rh** 102.91	46 **Pd** 106.42	47 **Ag** 107.87	48 **Cd** 112.41	49 **In** 114.82	50 **Sn** 118.71	51 **Sb** 121.76	52 **Te** 127.60	53 **I** 126.90	54 **Xe** 131.29
6	55 **Cs** 132.91	56 **Ba** 137.33	57 **La** 138.91	72 **Hf** 178.49	73 **Ta** 180.95	74 **W** 183.84	75 **Re** 186.21	76 **Os** 190.23	77 **Ir** 192.22	78 **Pt** 195.08	79 **Au** 196.97	80 **Hg** 200.59	81 **Tl** 204.38	82 **Pb** 207.2	83 **Bi** 208.98	84 **Po** [208.98]	85 **At** [209.99]	86 **Rn** [222.02]
7	87 **Fr** [223.02]	88 **Ra** [226.03]	89 **Ac** [227.03]	104 **Rf** [261.11]	105 **Db** [262.11]	106 **Sg** [266.12]	107 **Bh** [264.12]	108 **Hs** [269.13]	109 **Mt** [268.14]	110 **Ds** [271]	111 **Rg** [272]	112 **Cn** [285]	113 **Nh** [284]	114 **Fl** [289]	115 **Mc** [289]	116 **Lv** [292]	117 **Ts** [294]	118 **Og** [294]

Lanthanide series	58 **Ce** 140.12	59 **Pr** 140.91	60 **Nd** 144.24	61 **Pm** [145]	62 **Sm** 150.36	63 **Eu** 151.96	64 **Gd** 157.25	65 **Tb** 158.93	66 **Dy** 162.50	67 **Ho** 164.93	68 **Er** 167.26	69 **Tm** 168.93	70 **Yb** 173.05	71 **Lu** 174.97
Actinide series	90 **Th** 232.04	91 **Pa** 231.04	92 **U** 238.03	93 **Np** [237.05]	94 **Pu** [244.06]	95 **Am** [243.06]	96 **Cm** [247.07]	97 **Bk** [247.07]	98 **Cf** [251.08]	99 **Es** [252.08]	100 **Fm** [257.10]	101 **Md** [258.10]	102 **No** [259.10]	103 **Lr** [262.11]

[a] The labels on top (1A, 2A, etc.) are common American usage. The labels below these (1, 2, etc.) are those recommended by the International Union of Pure and Applied Chemistry.

Atomic masses in brackets are the masses of the longest-lived or most important isotope of radioactive elements.

List of Elements with Their Symbols and Atomic Masses

Element	Symbol	Atomic Number	Atomic Mass
Actinium	Ac	89	227.03[a]
Aluminum	Al	13	26.98
Americium	Am	95	243.06[a]
Antimony	Sb	51	121.76
Argon	Ar	18	39.95
Arsenic	As	33	74.92
Astatine	At	85	209.99[a]
Barium	Ba	56	137.33
Berkelium	Bk	97	247.07[a]
Beryllium	Be	4	9.012
Bismuth	Bi	83	208.98
Bohrium	Bh	107	264.12[a]
Boron	B	5	10.81
Bromine	Br	35	79.90
Cadmium	Cd	48	112.41
Calcium	Ca	20	40.08
Californium	Cf	98	251.08[a]
Carbon	C	6	12.01
Cerium	Ce	58	140.12
Cesium	Cs	55	132.91
Chlorine	Cl	17	35.45
Chromium	Cr	24	52.00
Cobalt	Co	27	58.93
Copernicium	Cn	112	285[a]
Copper	Cu	29	63.55
Curium	Cm	96	247.07[a]
Darmstadtium	Ds	110	271[a]
Dubnium	Db	105	262.11[a]
Dysprosium	Dy	66	162.50
Einsteinium	Es	99	252.08[a]
Erbium	Er	68	167.26
Europium	Eu	63	151.96
Fermium	Fm	100	257.10[a]
Flerovium	Fl	114	289[a]
Fluorine	F	9	19.00
Francium	Fr	87	223.02[a]
Gadolinium	Gd	64	157.25
Gallium	Ga	31	69.72
Germanium	Ge	32	72.63
Gold	Au	79	196.97
Hafnium	Hf	72	178.49
Hassium	Hs	108	269.13[a]
Helium	He	2	4.003
Holmium	Ho	67	164.93
Hydrogen	H	1	1.008
Indium	In	49	114.82
Iodine	I	53	126.90
Iridium	Ir	77	192.22
Iron	Fe	26	55.85
Krypton	Kr	36	83.80
Lanthanum	La	57	138.91
Lawrencium	Lr	103	262.11[a]
Lead	Pb	82	207.2
Lithium	Li	3	6.94
Livermorium	Lv	116	292[a]
Lutetium	Lu	71	174.97
Magnesium	Mg	12	24.31
Manganese	Mn	25	54.94
Meitnerium	Mt	109	268.14[a]
Mendelevium	Md	101	258.10[a]
Mercury	Hg	80	200.59
Molybdenum	Mo	42	95.95
Moscovium	Mc	115	289[a]
Neodymium	Nd	60	144.24
Neon	Ne	10	20.18
Neptunium	Np	93	237.05[a]
Nickel	Ni	28	58.69
Nihonium	Nh	113	284[a]
Niobium	Nb	41	92.91
Nitrogen	N	7	14.01
Nobelium	No	102	259.10[a]
Oganesson	Og	118	294[a]
Osmium	Os	76	190.23
Oxygen	O	8	16.00
Palladium	Pd	46	106.42
Phosphorus	P	15	30.97
Platinum	Pt	78	195.08
Plutonium	Pu	94	244.06[a]
Polonium	Po	84	208.98[a]
Potassium	K	19	39.10
Praseodymium	Pr	59	140.91
Promethium	Pm	61	145[a]
Protactinium	Pa	91	231.04
Radium	Ra	88	226.03[a]
Radon	Rn	86	222.02[a]
Rhenium	Re	75	186.21
Rhodium	Rh	45	102.91
Roentgenium	Rg	111	272[a]
Rubidium	Rb	37	85.47
Ruthenium	Ru	44	101.07
Rutherfordium	Rf	104	261.11[a]
Samarium	Sm	62	150.36
Scandium	Sc	21	44.96
Seaborgium	Sg	106	266.12[a]
Selenium	Se	34	78.97
Silicon	Si	14	28.09
Silver	Ag	47	107.87
Sodium	Na	11	22.99
Strontium	Sr	38	87.62
Sulfur	S	16	32.06
Tantalum	Ta	73	180.95
Technetium	Tc	43	98[a]
Tellurium	Te	52	127.60
Tennessine	Ts	117	294[a]
Terbium	Tb	65	158.93
Thallium	Tl	81	204.38
Thorium	Th	90	232.04
Thulium	Tm	69	168.93
Tin	Sn	50	118.71
Titanium	Ti	22	47.87
Tungsten	W	74	183.84
Uranium	U	92	238.03
Vanadium	V	23	50.94
Xenon	Xe	54	131.293
Ytterbium	Yb	70	173.05
Yttrium	Y	39	88.91
Zinc	Zn	30	65.38
Zirconium	Zr	40	91.22

[a]Mass of longest-lived or most important isotope.

FIFTH EDITION

Chemistry

A MOLECULAR APPROACH

Nivaldo J. Tro

Pearson

Director, Physical Science Portfolio Management: Jeanne Zalesky
Executive Courseware Portfolio Manager, General Chemistry: Terry Haugen
Courseware Portfolio Manager Assistant: Harry Misthos
Executive Field Marketing Manager: Christopher Barker
Senior Product Manager: Elizabeth Bell
Courseware Director, Content Development: Barbara Yien
Senior Analyst, Courseware Development: Matthew Walker
Specialist, Art Courseware Development: Laura Southworth
Managing Producer, Science: Kristen Flathman
Senior Content Producer, Science: Beth Sweeten
Director MasteringChemistry Content Development: Amir Said
MasteringChemistry Senior Content Producer: Margaret Trombley
MasteringChemistry Content Producer: Meaghan Fallano
Rich Media Content Producer: Paula Iborra
Production Management and Composition: codeMantra
Design Manager: Maria Gugleilmo Walsh
Interior/Cover Designer: Elise Lansdon
Illustrator: Lachina Creative
Manager, Rights & Permissions: Ben Ferrini
Photo Research & Management: SPi Global
Senior Procurement Specialist: Stacey Weinberger
Cover and Chapter Opening Illustrations: Quade Paul

Library of Congress Cataloging-in-Publication Data
Names: Tro, Nivaldo J.
Title: Chemistry : a molecular approach / Nivaldo J. Tro
Description: Fifth edition. | Hoboken, NJ : Pearson Education, Inc., [2020] | Includes index.
Identifiers: LCCN 2018036311 (print) | LCCN 2018038617 (ebook) | ISBN 9780134988894 (ebook) | ISBN 9780134874371 (student edition)
Subjects: LCSH: Chemistry, Physical and theoretical—Textbooks.
Classification: LCC QD453.3 (ebook) | LCC QD453.3 .T759 2020 (print) | DDC 540—dc23
LC record available at https://lccn.loc.gov/2018036311

9 2021

Pearson

ISBN-10: 0-13-526562-2 / ISBN-13: 978-0-13-526562-8 (High School Binding)

About the Author

Nivaldo Tro has been teaching college Chemistry since 1990 and is currently teaching at Santa Barbara City College. He received his Ph.D. in chemistry from Stanford University for work on developing and using optical techniques to study the adsorption and desorption of molecules to and from surfaces in ultrahigh vacuum. He then went on to the University of California at Berkeley, where he did postdoctoral research on ultrafast reaction dynamics in solution. Professor Tro has been awarded grants from the American Chemical Society Petroleum Research Fund, the Research Corporation, and the National Science Foundation to study the dynamics of various processes occurring in thin adlayer films adsorbed on dielectric surfaces. Professor Tro lives in Santa Barbara with his wife, Ann, and their four children, Michael, Ali, Kyle, and Kaden. In his leisure time, Professor Tro enjoys mountain biking, surfing, and being outdoors with his family.

To Michael, Ali, Kyle, and Kaden

Brief Contents

1	Matter, Measurement, and Problem Solving	1
2	Atoms and Elements	48
3	Molecules and Compounds	90
4	Chemical Reactions and Chemical Quantities	138
5	Introduction to Solutions and Aqueous Reactions	166
6	Gases	210
7	Thermochemistry	262
8	The Quantum-Mechanical Model of the Atom	310
9	Periodic Properties of the Elements	350
10	Chemical Bonding I: The Lewis Model	392
11	Chemical Bonding II: Molecular Shapes, Valence Bond Theory, and Molecular Orbital Theory	436
12	Liquids, Solids, and Intermolecular Forces	494
13	Solids and Modern Materials	540
14	Solutions	578
15	Chemical Kinetics	630
16	Chemical Equilibrium	682
17	Acids and Bases	730
18	Aqueous Ionic Equilibrium	786
19	Free Energy and Thermodynamics	846
20	Electrochemistry	896
21	Radioactivity and Nuclear Chemistry	946
22	Organic Chemistry	988
23	Biochemistry	1036
24	Chemistry of the Nonmetals	1070
25	Metals and Metallurgy	1108
26	Transition Metals and Coordination Compounds	1134

Appendix I Common Mathematical Operations in Chemistry A-1
Appendix II Useful Data A-5
Appendix III Answers to Selected Exercises A-15
Appendix IV Answers to In-Chapter Practice Problems A-53
Glossary G-1
Photo and Text Credits C-1
Index I-1

Interactive eText Media Contents

KEY CONCEPT VIDEOS (KCVs)

1.1 Atoms and Molecules
1.3 Classifying Matter
1.6 Units and Significant Figures
1.7 Significant Figures in Calculations
1.8 Solving Chemical Problems
2.3 Atomic Theory
2.6 Subatomic Particles and Isotope Symbols
2.7 The Periodic Law and the Periodic Table
2.9 The Mole Concept
3.5 Naming Ionic Compounds
3.6 Naming Molecular Compounds
4.2 Writing and Balancing Chemical Equations
4.3 Reaction Stoichiometry
4.4 Limiting Reactant, Theoretical Yield, and Percent Yield
5.2 Solution Concentration
5.5 Reactions in Solutions
6.3 Simple Gas Laws and Ideal Gas Law
6.6 Mixtures of Gases and Partial Pressures
6.8 Kinetic Molecular Theory
7.3 The First Law of Thermodynamics
7.4 Heat Capacity
7.6 The Change in Enthalpy for a Chemical Reaction
7.9 Determining the Enthalpy of Reaction from Standard Enthalpies of Formation
8.2 The Nature of Light
8.4 The Wave Nature of Matter
8.5A Quantum Mechanics and the Atom: Orbitals and Quantum Numbers
8.5B Atomic Spectroscopy
9.3 Electron Configurations
9.4 Writing an Electron Configuration Based on an Element's Position on the Periodic Table
9.6 Periodic Trends in the Size of Atoms and Effective Nuclear Charge
10.5 The Lewis Model for Chemical Bonding
10.6 Electronegativity and Bond Polarity
10.7 Writing Lewis Structures for Molecular Compounds
10.8 Resonance and Formal Charge
10.9 Exceptions to the Octet Rule and Expanded Octets
11.2 VSEPR Theory
11.3 VSEPR Theory: The Effect of Lone Pairs
11.5 Molecular Shape and Polarity
11.6 Valence Bond Theory
11.7 Valence Bond Theory: Hybridization
12.3 Intermolecular Forces
12.5 Vaporization and Vapor Pressure
12.7 Heating Curve for Water
12.8 Phase Diagrams
13.3 Unit Cells: Simple Cubic, Body-Centered Cubic, and Face-Centered Cubic
14.4 Solution Equilibrium and the Factors Affecting Solubility
14.5 Solution Concentration: Molarity, Molality, Parts by Mass and Volume, Mole Fraction
14.6 Colligative Properties
15.2 The Rate of a Chemical Reaction
15.3 The Rate Law for a Chemical Reaction
15.4 The Integrated Rate Law
15.5 The Effect of Temperature on Reaction Rate
15.6 Reaction Mechanisms
16.3 The Equilibrium Constant
16.7 The Reaction Quotient
16.8 Finding Equilibrium Concentrations from Initial Concentrations
16.9 Le Châtelier's Principle
17.3 Definitions of Acids and Bases
17.4 Acid Strength and the Acid Ionization Constant
17.5 The pH Scale
17.6 Finding the $[H_3O^+]$ and pH of Strong and Weak Acid Solutions
17.8 The Acid–Base Properties of Ions and Salts
18.2A Buffers
18.2B Finding pH and pH Changes in Buffer Solutions
18.4A The Titration of a Strong Acid with a Strong Base
18.4B The Titration of a Weak Acid and a Strong Base
19.3 Entropy and the Second Law of Thermodynamics
19.6 The Effect of ΔH, ΔS, and T on Reaction Spontaneity
19.7 Standard Molar Entropies
20.3 Voltaic Cells
20.4 Standard Electrode Potentials
20.5 Cell Potential, Free Energy, and the Equilibrium Constant
21.3 Types of Radioactivity

INTERACTIVE WORKED EXAMPLES (IWEs)

1.5 Determining the Number of Significant Figures in a Number
1.6 Significant Figures in Calculations
1.8 Unit Conversion
1.9 Unit Conversions Involving Units Raised to a Power
1.10 Density as a Conversion Factor
1.12 Problems with Equations
2.3 Atomic Numbers, Mass Numbers, and Isotope Symbols
2.5 Atomic Mass
2.8 The Mole Concept—Converting between Mass and Number of Atoms
2.9 The Mole Concept
3.3 Writing Formulas for Ionic Compounds
3.11 Using the Nomenclature Flowchart to Name Compounds
3.13 The Mole Concept—Converting between Mass and Number of Molecules
3.15 Using Mass Percent Composition as a Conversion Factor
3.16 Chemical Formulas as Conversion Factors
3.18 Obtaining an Empirical Formula from Experimental Data
3.21 Determining an Empirical Formula from Combustion Analysis
4.2 Balancing Chemical Equations
4.3 Balancing Chemical Equations Containing a Polyatomic Ion
4.4 Stoichiometry
4.6 Limiting Reactant and Theoretical Yield
5.1 Calculating Solution Concentration
5.2 Using Molarity in Calculations
5.3 Solution Dilution
5.4 Solution Stoichiometry
5.5 Predicting Whether an Ionic Compound Is Soluble
5.6 Writing Equations for Precipitation Reactions
5.9 Writing Equations for Acid–Base Reactions Involving a Strong Acid
5.11 Acid–Base Titration
5.13 Assigning Oxidation States
6.5 Ideal Gas Law I
6.7 Density
6.8 Molar Mass of a Gas
6.10 Partial Pressures and Mole Fractions
6.11 Collecting Gases over Water
6.12 Gases in Chemical Reactions
6.15 Graham's Law of Effusion
7.2 Temperature Changes and Heat Capacity
7.3 Thermal Energy Transfer
7.5 Measuring ΔE_{rxn} in a Bomb Calorimeter
7.7 Stoichiometry Involving ΔH
7.8 Measuring ΔH_{rxn} in a Coffee-Cup Calorimeter
7.9 Hess's Law
7.11 ΔH°_{rxn} and Standard Enthalpies of Formation
8.2 Photon Energy
8.3 Wavelength, Energy, and Frequency
8.5 Quantum Numbers I
8.7 Wavelength of Light for a Transition in the Hydrogen Atom
9.2 Writing Orbital Diagrams
9.4 Writing Electron Configurations from the Periodic Table
9.5 Atomic Size
9.6 Electron Configurations and Magnetic Properties for Ions
9.8 First Ionization Energy
10.4 Writing Lewis Structures
10.6 Writing Lewis Structures for Polyatomic Ions
10.7 Writing Resonance Structures
10.8 Assigning Formal Charges
10.9 Drawing Resonance Structures and Assigning Formal Charge for Organic Compounds
10.10 Writing Lewis Structures for Compounds Having Expanded Octets
10.11 Calculating ΔH_{rxn} from Bond Energies
11.1 VSEPR Theory and the Basic Shapes
11.2 Predicting Molecular Geometries
11.4 Predicting the Shape of Larger Molecules
11.5 Determining Whether a Molecule Is Polar
11.8 Hybridization and Bonding Scheme
11.10 Molecular Orbital Theory
12.1 Dipole–Dipole Forces
12.2 Hydrogen Bonding
12.3 Using the Heat of Vaporization in Calculations
12.5 Using the Two-Point Form of the Clausius–Clapeyron Equation to Predict the Vapor Pressure at a Given Temperature
13.3 Relating Unit Cell Volume, Edge Length, and Atomic Radius
13.4 Relating Density to Crystal Structure
14.2 Henry's Law
14.3 Using Parts by Mass in Calculations
14.4 Calculating Concentrations
14.5 Converting between Concentration Units
14.6 Calculating the Vapor Pressure of a Solution Containing a Nonelectrolyte and Nonvolatile Solute
14.9 Boiling Point Elevation
14.12 Calculating the Vapor Pressure of a Solution Containing an Ionic Solute
15.1 Expressing Reaction Rates
15.2 Determining the Order and Rate Constant of a Reaction
15.4 The First-Order Integrated Rate Law: Determining the Concentration of a Reactant at a Given Time
15.8 Using the Two-Point Form of the Arrhenius Equation
15.9 Reaction Mechanisms
16.1 Expressing Equilibrium Constants for Chemical Equations

16.3 Relating K_p and K_c
16.5 Finding Equilibrium Constants from Experimental Concentration Measurements
16.7 Predicting the Direction of a Reaction by Comparing Q and K
16.8 Finding Equilibrium Concentrations When You Know the Equilibrium Constant and All but One of the Equilibrium Concentrations of the Reactants and Products
16.9 Finding Equilibrium Concentrations from Initial Concentrations and the Equilibrium Constant
16.12 Finding Equilibrium Concentrations from Initial Concentrations in Cases with a Small Equilibrium Constant
16.14 The Effect of a Concentration Change on Equilibrium
17.1 Identifying Brønsted–Lowry Acids and Bases and Their Conjugates
17.3 Calculating pH from $[H_3O^+]$ or $[OH^-]$
17.5 Finding the $[H_3O^+]$ of a Weak Acid Solution
17.7 Finding the pH of a Weak Acid Solution in Cases Where the *x is small* Approximation Does Not Work
17.8 Finding the Equilibrium Constant from pH
17.9 Finding the Percent Ionization of a Weak Acid
17.12 Finding the $[OH^-]$ and pH of a Weak Base Solution
17.14 Determining the pH of a Solution Containing an Anion Acting as a Base
17.16 Determining the Overall Acidity or Basicity of Salt Solutions
18.2 Calculating the pH of a Buffer Solution as an Equilibrium Problem and with the Henderson–Hasselbalch Equation
18.3 Calculating the pH Change in a Buffer Solution after the Addition of a Small Amount of Strong Acid or Base
18.4 Using the Henderson–Hasselbalch Equation to Calculate the pH of a Buffer Solution Composed of a Weak Base and Its Conjugate Acid
18.6 Strong Acid–Strong Base Titration pH Curve
18.7 Weak Acid–Strong Base Titration pH Curve
18.8 Calculating Molar Solubility from K_{sp}
18.12 Predicting Precipitation Reactions by Comparing Q and K_{sp}
19.2 Calculating ΔS for a Change of State
19.3 Calculating Entropy Changes in the Surroundings
19.4 Calculating Gibbs Free Energy Changes and Predicting Spontaneity from ΔH and ΔS
19.5 Calculating Standard Entropy Changes (ΔS°_{rxn})
19.6 Calculating the Standard Change in Free Energy for a Reaction Using $\Delta G^\circ_{rxn} = \Delta H^\circ_{rxn} - T\Delta S^\circ_{rxn}$
19.10 Calculating ΔG_{rxn} under Nonstandard Conditions
19.11 The Equilibrium Constant and ΔG°_{rxn}
20.2 Half-Reaction Method of Balancing Aqueous Redox Equations in Acidic Solution
20.3 Balancing Redox Reactions Occurring in Basic Solution
20.4 Calculating Standard Potentials for Electrochemical Cells from Standard Electrode Potentials of the Half-Reactions
20.6 Relating ΔG° and E°_{cell}
21.1 Writing Nuclear Equations for Alpha Decay
21.2 Writing Nuclear Equations for Beta Decay, Positron Emission, and Electron Capture
21.4 Radioactive Decay Kinetics
21.5 Radiocarbon Dating
22.3 Naming Alkanes

Contents

PREFACE xxi

1 Matter, Measurement, and Problem Solving 1

1.1 Atoms and Molecules 1
1.2 The Scientific Approach to Knowledge 3
THE NATURE OF SCIENCE *Thomas S. Kuhn and Scientific Revolutions* 5
1.3 The Classification of Matter 5
The States of Matter: Solid, Liquid, and Gas 6
Classifying Matter by Composition: Elements, Compounds, and Mixtures 7 Separating Mixtures 8
1.4 Physical and Chemical Changes and Physical and Chemical Properties 9
1.5 Energy: A Fundamental Part of Physical and Chemical Change 12
1.6 The Units of Measurement 13
Standard Units 14 The Meter: A Measure of Length 14 The Kilogram: A Measure of Mass 14 The Second: A Measure of Time 14 The Kelvin: A Measure of Temperature 15 Prefix Multipliers 17 Derived Units: Volume and Density 17 Volume 18 Density 18 Calculating Density 19
CHEMISTRY AND MEDICINE *Bone Density* 20
1.7 The Reliability of a Measurement 20
Counting Significant Figures 22 Exact Numbers 22 Significant Figures in Calculations 23 Precision and Accuracy 25
CHEMISTRY IN YOUR DAY *Integrity in Data Gathering* 26
1.8 Solving Chemical Problems 26
Converting from One Unit to Another 26 General Problem-Solving Strategy 28 Units Raised to a Power 30 Order-of-Magnitude Estimations 31 Problems Involving an Equation 32
1.9 Analyzing and Interpreting Data 33
Identifying Patterns in Data 33 Interpreting Graphs 34

CHAPTER IN REVIEW Self-Assessment Quiz 36 Terms 37 Concepts 38 Equations and Relationships 38 Learning Outcomes 38

EXERCISES Review Questions 39 Problems by Topic 39 Cumulative Problems 43 Challenge Problems 45 Conceptual Problems 45 Questions for Group Work 46 Data Interpretation and Analysis 46 Answers to Conceptual Connections 47

2 Atoms and Elements 48

2.1 Brownian Motion: Atoms Confirmed 49
2.2 Early Ideas about the Building Blocks of Matter 51
2.3 Modern Atomic Theory and the Laws That Led to It 51
The Law of Conservation of Mass 51 The Law of Definite Proportions 52 The Law of Multiple Proportions 53 John Dalton and the Atomic Theory 54
CHEMISTRY IN YOUR DAY *Atoms and Humans* 54
2.4 The Discovery of the Electron 55
Cathode Rays 55 Millikan's Oil Drop Experiment: The Charge of the Electron 56
2.5 The Structure of the Atom 57
2.6 Subatomic Particles: Protons, Neutrons, and Electrons in Atoms 59
Elements: Defined by Their Numbers of Protons 60 Isotopes: When the Number of Neutrons Varies 61 Ions: Losing and Gaining Electrons 63
CHEMISTRY IN YOUR DAY *Where Did Elements Come From?* 64
2.7 Finding Patterns: The Periodic Law and the Periodic Table 65
Modern Periodic Table Organization 66 Ions and the Periodic Table 68
CHEMISTRY AND MEDICINE *The Elements of Life* 69
2.8 Atomic Mass: The Average Mass of an Element's Atoms 69
Mass Spectrometry: Measuring the Mass of Atoms and Molecules 70
CHEMISTRY IN YOUR DAY *Evolving Atomic Masses* 72

2.9 Molar Mass: Counting Atoms by Weighing Them 73
The Mole: A Chemist's "Dozen" 73 Converting between Number of Moles and Number of Atoms 74 Converting between Mass and Amount (Number of Moles) 75

CHAPTER IN REVIEW Self-Assessment Quiz 78 Terms 79 Concepts 80 Equations and Relationships 80 Learning Outcomes 81

EXERCISES Review Questions 81 Problems by Topic 82 Cumulative Problems 85 Challenge Problems 86 Conceptual Problems 87 Questions for Group Work 88 Data Interpretation and Analysis 88 Answers to Conceptual Connections 89

3 Molecules and Compounds 90

3.1 Hydrogen, Oxygen, and Water 91

3.2 Chemical Bonds 93
Ionic Bonds 93 Covalent Bonds 94

3.3 Representing Compounds: Chemical Formulas and Molecular Models 94
Types of Chemical Formulas 94
Molecular Models 96

3.4 An Atomic-Level View of Elements and Compounds 96

3.5 Ionic Compounds: Formulas and Names 100
Writing Formulas for Ionic Compounds 100 Naming Ionic Compounds 101 Naming Binary Ionic Compounds Containing a Metal That Forms Only One Type of Cation 102 Naming Binary Ionic Compounds Containing a Metal That Forms More Than One Kind of Cation 103 Naming Ionic Compounds Containing Polyatomic Ions 104 Hydrated Ionic Compounds 105

3.6 Molecular Compounds: Formulas and Names 106
Naming Molecular Compounds 106 Naming Acids 107 Naming Binary Acids 108 Naming Oxyacids 108
CHEMISTRY IN THE ENVIRONMENT *Acid Rain* 108

3.7 Summary of Inorganic Nomenclature 109

3.8 Formula Mass and the Mole Concept for Compounds 111
Molar Mass of a Compound 111 Using Molar Mass to Count Molecules by Weighing 111

3.9 Composition of Compounds 113
Mass Percent Composition as a Conversion Factor 114
Conversion Factors from Chemical Formulas 116
CHEMISTRY AND MEDICINE *Methylmercury in Fish* 118

3.10 Determining a Chemical Formula from Experimental Data 118
Determining Molecular Formulas for Compounds 120
Combustion Analysis 121

3.11 Organic Compounds 123
Hydrocarbons 124 Functionalized Hydrocarbons 125

CHAPTER IN REVIEW Self-Assessment Quiz 127 Terms 128 Concepts 128 Equations and Relationships 129 Learning Outcomes 129

EXERCISES Review Questions 129 Problems by Topic 130 Cumulative Problems 134 Challenge Problems 135 Conceptual Problems 135 Questions for Group Work 136 Data Interpretation and Analysis 136 Answers to Conceptual Connections 136

4 Chemical Reactions and Chemical Quantities 138

4.1 Climate Change and the Combustion of Fossil Fuels 139

4.2 Writing and Balancing Chemical Equations 141

4.3 Reaction Stoichiometry: How Much Carbon Dioxide? 145
Making Pizza: The Relationships among Ingredients 145
Making Molecules: Mole-to-Mole Conversions 146
Making Molecules: Mass-to-Mass Conversions 146

4.4 Stoichiometric Relationships: Limiting Reactant, Theoretical Yield, Percent Yield, and Reactant in Excess 149
Calculating Limiting Reactant, Theoretical Yield, and Percent Yield 151 Calculating Limiting Reactant, Theoretical Yield, and Percent Yield from Initial Reactant Masses 152

4.5 Three Examples of Chemical Reactions: Combustion, Alkali Metals, and Halogens 155
Combustion Reactions 155 Alkali Metal Reactions 156
Halogen Reactions 156

CHAPTER IN REVIEW Self-Assessment Quiz 158 Terms 159 Concepts 159 Equations and Relationships 159 Learning Outcomes 159

EXERCISES Review Questions 160 Problems by Topic 160 Cumulative Problems 163 Challenge Problems 164 Conceptual Problems 164 Questions for Group Work 165 Data Interpretation and Analysis 165 Answers to Conceptual Connections 165

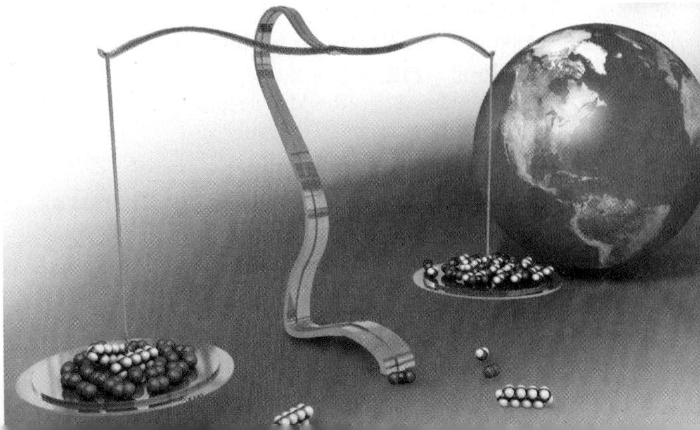

5 Introduction to Solutions and Aqueous Reactions 166

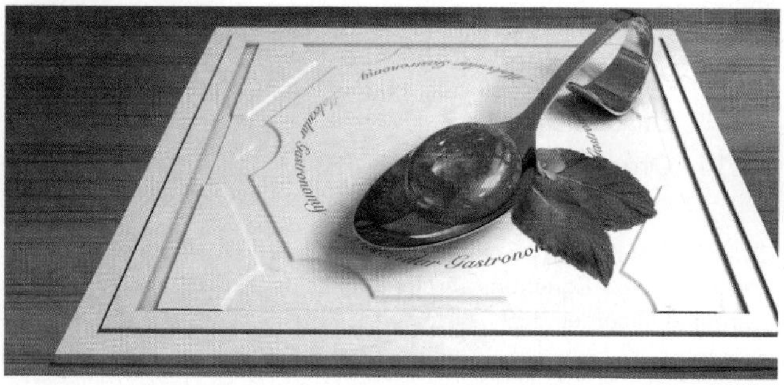

5.1 Molecular Gastronomy and the Spherified Cherry 167
5.2 Solution Concentration 168
Solution Concentration 168 Using Molarity in Calculations 170 Solution Dilution 171
5.3 Solution Stoichiometry 173
5.4 Types of Aqueous Solutions and Solubility 175
Electrolyte and Nonelectrolyte Solutions 175
The Solubility of Ionic Compounds 177
5.5 Precipitation Reactions 179
5.6 Representing Aqueous Reactions: Molecular, Ionic, and Net Ionic Equations 183
5.7 Acid–Base Reactions 185
Acid–Base Reactions 185 Acid–Base Titrations 189
5.8 Gas-Evolution Reactions 191
5.9 Oxidation–Reduction Reactions 193
Oxidation States 194 Identifying Redox Reactions 196 The Activity Series: Predicting Whether a Redox Reaction Is Spontaneous 198
CHEMISTRY IN YOUR DAY *Bleached Blonde* 199

CHAPTER IN REVIEW Self-Assessment Quiz 201 Terms 202 Concepts 202 Equations and Relationships 203 Learning Outcomes 203

EXERCISES Review Questions 204 Problems by Topic 204 Cumulative Problems 206 Challenge Problems 207 Conceptual Problems 207 Questions for Group Work 208 Data Interpretation and Analysis 208 Answers to Conceptual Connections 209

6 Gases 210

6.1 Supersonic Skydiving and the Risk of Decompression 211
6.2 Pressure: The Result of Molecular Collisions 212
Pressure Units 213 The Manometer: A Way to Measure Pressure in the Laboratory 214
CHEMISTRY AND MEDICINE *Blood Pressure* 215
6.3 The Simple Gas Laws: Boyle's Law, Charles's Law, and Avogadro's Law 215
Boyle's Law: Volume and Pressure 216
Charles's Law: Volume and Temperature 218
CHEMISTRY IN YOUR DAY *Extra-Long Snorkels* 219
Avogadro's Law: Volume and Amount (in Moles) 221
6.4 The Ideal Gas Law 222
6.5 Applications of the Ideal Gas Law: Molar Volume, Density, and Molar Mass of a Gas 225
Molar Volume at Standard Temperature and Pressure 225
Density of a Gas 226 Molar Mass of a Gas 227
6.6 Mixtures of Gases and Partial Pressures 228
Deep-Sea Diving and Partial Pressures 231
Collecting Gases over Water 233
6.7 Gases in Chemical Reactions: Stoichiometry Revisited 235
Molar Volume and Stoichiometry 236
ANALYZING AND INTERPRETING DATA *Good News about Our Nation's Air Quality* 238
6.8 Kinetic Molecular Theory: A Model for Gases 238
How Kinetic Molecular Theory Explains Pressure and the Simple Gas Laws 239 Kinetic Molecular Theory and the Ideal Gas Law 240 Temperature and Molecular Velocities 242
6.9 Mean Free Path, Diffusion, and Effusion of Gases 245
6.10 Real Gases: The Effects of Size and Intermolecular Forces 246
The Effect of the Finite Volume of Gas Particles 247
The Effect of Intermolecular Forces 248 Van der Waals Equation 249 Real Gases 249

CHAPTER IN REVIEW Self-Assessment Quiz 250 Terms 251 Concepts 251 Equations and Relationships 252 Learning Outcomes 252

EXERCISES Review Questions 253 Problems by Topic 253 Cumulative Problems 257 Challenge Problems 259 Conceptual Problems 260 Questions for Group Work 260 Data Interpretation and Analysis 260 Answers to Conceptual Connections 261

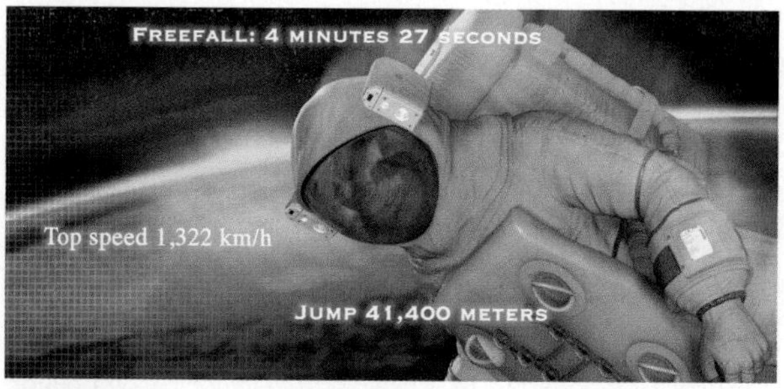

7 Thermochemistry 262

7.1 Chemical Hand Warmers 263
7.2 The Nature of Energy: Key Definitions 264
Types of Energy 264 Energy Conservation and Energy Transfer 265 Units of Energy 265
7.3 The First Law of Thermodynamics: There Is No Free Lunch 267
Internal Energy 267
CHEMISTRY IN YOUR DAY *Redheffer's Perpetual Motion Machine* 267
Heat and Work 270

7.4 Quantifying Heat and Work 272
Heat 272 Temperature Changes and Heat Capacity 272 Thermal Energy Transfer 274 Work: Pressure–Volume Work 276

7.5 Measuring ΔE for Chemical Reactions: Constant-Volume Calorimetry 278

7.6 Enthalpy: The Heat Evolved in a Chemical Reaction at Constant Pressure 281
Exothermic and Endothermic Processes: A Molecular View 283 Stoichiometry Involving ΔH: Thermochemical Equations 283

7.7 Constant-Pressure Calorimetry: Measuring ΔH_{rxn} 285

7.8 Relationships Involving ΔH_{rxn} 286

7.9 Determining Enthalpies of Reaction from Standard Enthalpies of Formation 289
Standard States and Standard Enthalpy Changes 289 Calculating the Standard Enthalpy Change for a Reaction 291

7.10 Energy Use and the Environment 294
Energy Consumption 294 Environmental Problems Associated with Fossil Fuel Use 295 Air Pollution 295 Global Climate Change 296
CHEMISTRY IN THE ENVIRONMENT *Renewable Energy* 298

CHAPTER IN REVIEW Self-Assessment Quiz 299 Terms 300 Concepts 300 Equations and Relationships 301 Learning Outcomes 301

EXERCISES Review Questions 302 Problems by Topic 302 Cumulative Problems 306 Challenge Problems 307 Conceptual Problems 308 Questions for Group Work 308 Data Interpretation and Analysis 309 Answers to Conceptual Connections 309

8 The Quantum-Mechanical Model of the Atom 310

8.1 Schrödinger's Cat 311

8.2 The Nature of Light 312
The Wave Nature of Light 313
The Electromagnetic Spectrum 315
CHEMISTRY AND MEDICINE *Radiation Treatment for Cancer* 317
Interference and Diffraction 317 The Particle Nature of Light 318

8.3 Atomic Spectroscopy and the Bohr Model 322
CHEMISTRY IN YOUR DAY *Atomic Spectroscopy, a Bar Code for Atoms* 324

8.4 The Wave Nature of Matter: The de Broglie Wavelength, the Uncertainty Principle, and Indeterminacy 325
The de Broglie Wavelength 327 The Uncertainty Principle 328 Indeterminacy and Probability Distribution Maps 329

8.5 Quantum Mechanics and the Atom 331
Solutions to the Schrödinger Equation for the Hydrogen Atom 331 Atomic Spectroscopy Explained 334

8.6 The Shapes of Atomic Orbitals 337
s Orbitals ($l = 0$) 337 *p* Orbitals ($l = 1$) 340 *d* Orbitals ($l = 2$) 340 *f* Orbitals ($l = 3$) 340 The Phase of Orbitals 341 The Shape of Atoms 342

CHAPTER IN REVIEW Self-Assessment Quiz 342 Terms 343 Concepts 343 Equations and Relationships 344 Learning Outcomes 344

EXERCISES Review Questions 344 Problems by Topic 345 Cumulative Problems 346 Challenge Problems 347 Conceptual Problems 348 Questions for Group Work 348 Data Interpretation and Analysis 349 Answers to Conceptual Connections 349

9 Periodic Properties of the Elements 350

9.1 Nerve Signal Transmission 351

9.2 The Development of the Periodic Table 352

9.3 Electron Configurations: How Electrons Occupy Orbitals 353
Electron Spin and the Pauli Exclusion Principle 354 Sublevel Energy Splitting in Multielectron Atoms 354 Coulomb's Law 355 Shielding 356 Penetration 356 Electron Spatial Distributions and Sublevel Splitting 356 Electron Configurations for Multielectron Atoms 358

9.4 Electron Configurations, Valence Electrons, and the Periodic Table 361
Orbital Blocks in the Periodic Table 362 Writing an Electron Configuration for an Element from Its Position in the Periodic Table 363 The Transition and Inner Transition Elements 364

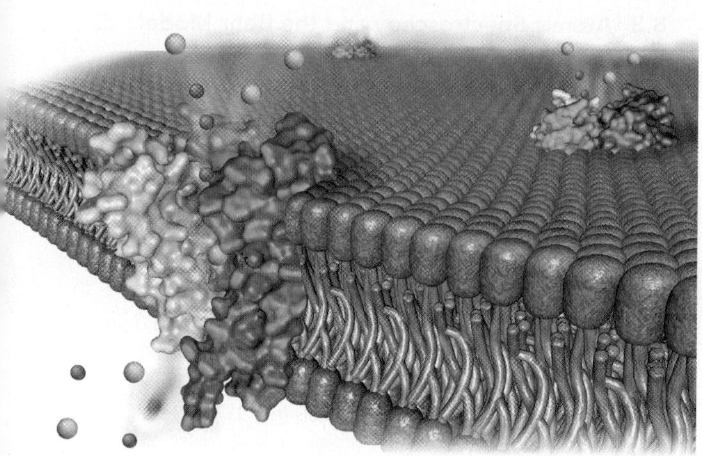

9.5 The Explanatory Power of the Quantum-Mechanical Model 365

9.6 Periodic Trends in the Size of Atoms and Effective Nuclear Charge 366
Effective Nuclear Charge 368 Atomic Radii and the Transition Elements 369

9.7 Ions: Electron Configurations, Magnetic Properties, Ionic Radii, and Ionization Energy 371
Electron Configurations and Magnetic Properties of Ions 371 Ionic Radii 373 Ionization Energy 375 Trends in First Ionization Energy 375 Exceptions to Trends in First Ionization Energy 377 Trends in Second and Successive Ionization Energies 378

9.8 Electron Affinities and Metallic Character 379
Electron Affinity 379 Metallic Character 380

9.9 Periodic Trends Summary 383

CHAPTER IN REVIEW Self-Assessment Quiz 383 Terms 384 Concepts 384 Equations and Relationships 385 Learning Outcomes 385

EXERCISES Review Questions 386 Problems by Topic 387 Cumulative Problems 388 Challenge Problems 389 Conceptual Problems 390 Questions for Group Work 390 Data Interpretation and Analysis 391 Answers to Conceptual Connections 391

10 Chemical Bonding I: The Lewis Model 392

10.1 Bonding Models and AIDS Drugs 393

10.2 Types of Chemical Bonds 394

10.3 Representing Valence Electrons with Dots 396

10.4 Ionic Bonding: Lewis Symbols and Lattice Energies 397
Ionic Bonding and Electron Transfer 397 Lattice Energy: The Rest of the Story 398 The Born–Haber Cycle 398 Trends in Lattice Energies: Ion Size 401 Trends in Lattice Energies: Ion Charge 401 Ionic Bonding: Models and Reality 402
CHEMISTRY AND MEDICINE *Ionic Compounds in Medicine* 403

10.5 Covalent Bonding: Lewis Structures 404
Single Covalent Bonds 404 Double and Triple Covalent Bonds 404 Covalent Bonding: Models and Reality 405

10.6 Electronegativity and Bond Polarity 406
Electronegativity 407 Bond Polarity, Dipole Moment, and Percent Ionic Character 408

10.7 Lewis Structures of Molecular Compounds and Polyatomic Ions 410
Writing Lewis Structures for Molecular Compounds 410 Writing Lewis Structures for Polyatomic Ions 412

10.8 Resonance and Formal Charge 412
Resonance 412 Formal Charge 414

10.9 Exceptions to the Octet Rule: Odd-Electron Species, Incomplete Octets, and Expanded Octets 417
Odd-Electron Species 418 Incomplete Octets 418
CHEMISTRY IN THE ENVIRONMENT *Free Radicals and the Atmospheric Vacuum Cleaner* 419
Expanded Octets 420

10.10 Bond Energies and Bond Lengths 422
Bond Energy 422 Using Average Bond Energies to Estimate Enthalpy Changes for Reactions 423 Bond Lengths 424

10.11 Bonding in Metals: The Electron Sea Model 425
CHEMISTRY IN THE ENVIRONMENT *The Lewis Structure of Ozone* 426

CHAPTER IN REVIEW Self-Assessment Quiz 427 Terms 428 Concepts 428 Equations and Relationships 429 Learning Outcomes 429

EXERCISES Review Questions 430 Problems by Topic 430 Cumulative Problems 432 Challenge Problems 434 Conceptual Problems 434 Questions for Group Work 434 Data Interpretation and Analysis 435 Answers to Conceptual Connections 435

11 Chemical Bonding II: Molecular Shapes, Valence Bond Theory, and Molecular Orbital Theory 436

11.1 Morphine: A Molecular Imposter 437

11.2 VSEPR Theory: The Five Basic Shapes 438
Two Electron Groups: Linear Geometry 439
Three Electron Groups: Trigonal Planar Geometry 439
Four Electron Groups: Tetrahedral Geometry 439
Five Electron Groups: Trigonal Bipyramidal Geometry 441
Six Electron Groups: Octahedral Geometry 441

11.3 VSEPR Theory: The Effect of Lone Pairs 442
Four Electron Groups with Lone Pairs 442 Five Electron Groups with Lone Pairs 444 Six Electron Groups with Lone Pairs 445

11.4 VSEPR Theory: Predicting Molecular Geometries 447
Representing Molecular Geometries on Paper 449 Predicting the Shapes of Larger Molecules 449

11.5 Molecular Shape and Polarity 450
Vector Addition 452
CHEMISTRY IN YOUR DAY *How Soap Works* 454

11.6 Valence Bond Theory: Orbital Overlap as a Chemical Bond 455

11.7 Valence Bond Theory: Hybridization of Atomic Orbitals 457
sp^3 Hybridization 458 sp^2 Hybridization and Double Bonds 460
CHEMISTRY IN YOUR DAY *The Chemistry of Vision* 464
sp Hybridization and Triple Bonds 464 sp^3d and sp^3d^2 Hybridization 466 Writing Hybridization and Bonding Schemes 467

11.8 Molecular Orbital Theory: Electron Delocalization 470
Linear Combination of Atomic Orbitals (LCAOs) 471
Period Two Homonuclear Diatomic Molecules 475
Second-Period Heteronuclear Diatomic Molecules 480
Polyatomic Molecules 482

CHAPTER IN REVIEW Self-Assessment Quiz 483 Terms 484 Concepts 484 Equations and Relationships 484 Learning Outcomes 485

EXERCISES Review Questions 485 Problems by Topic 486 Cumulative Problems 488 Challenge Problems 490 Conceptual Problems 491 Questions for Group Work 491 Data Interpretation and Analysis 492 Answers to Conceptual Connections 492

12 Liquids, Solids, and Intermolecular Forces 494

12.1 Water, No Gravity 495

12.2 Solids, Liquids, and Gases: A Molecular Comparison 496
Differences between States of Matter 496
Changes between States 498

12.3 Intermolecular Forces: The Forces That Hold Condensed States Together 499
Dispersion Force 500 Dipole–Dipole Force 502 Hydrogen Bonding 505 Ion–Dipole Force 507
CHEMISTRY AND MEDICINE *Hydrogen Bonding in DNA* 508

12.4 Intermolecular Forces in Action: Surface Tension, Viscosity, and Capillary Action 509
Surface Tension 509 Viscosity 511
CHEMISTRY IN YOUR DAY *Viscosity and Motor Oil* 511
Capillary Action 511

12.5 Vaporization and Vapor Pressure 512
The Process of Vaporization 512 The Energetics of Vaporization 514 Vapor Pressure and Dynamic Equilibrium 515 Temperature Dependence of Vapor Pressure and Boiling Point 517 The Clausius–Clapeyron Equation 518 The Critical Point: The Transition to an Unusual State of Matter 521

12.6 Sublimation and Fusion 522
Sublimation 522 Fusion 523 Energetics of Melting and Freezing 523

12.7 Heating Curve for Water 524

12.8 Phase Diagrams 527
The Major Features of a Phase Diagram 527 Navigation within a Phase Diagram 528 The Phase Diagrams of Other Substances 529

12.9 Water: An Extraordinary Substance 529
CHEMISTRY IN THE ENVIRONMENT *Water Pollution* 531

CHAPTER IN REVIEW Self-Assessment Quiz 531 Terms 532 Concepts 532 Equations and Relationships 533 Learning Outcomes 533

EXERCISES Review Questions 534 Problems by Topic 534 Cumulative Problems 537 Challenge Problems 537 Conceptual Problems 538 Questions for Group Work 538 Data Interpretation and Analysis 539 Answers to Conceptual Connections 539

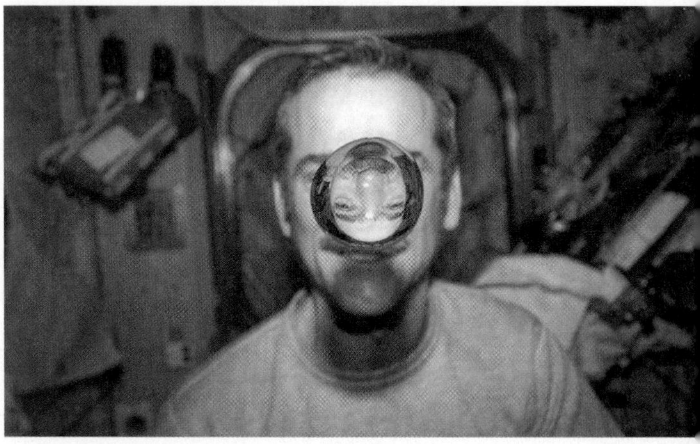

13 Solids and Modern Materials 540

13.1 **Friday Night Experiments: The Discovery of Graphene** 541

13.2 **X-Ray Crystallography** 542

13.3 **Unit Cells and Basic Structures** 545
Cubic Unit Cells 545 Closest-Packed Structures 551

13.4 **The Fundamental Types of Crystalline Solids** 552
Molecular Solids 553
CHEMISTRY IN YOUR DAY *Chocolate, An Edible Material* 554
Ionic Solids 555 Atomic Solids 555

13.5 **The Structures of Ionic Solids** 556

13.6 **Network Covalent Atomic Solids: Carbon and Silicates** 558
Carbon 558 Silicates 561

13.7 **Ceramics, Cement, and Glass** 561
Ceramics 561 Cement 562 Glass 563

13.8 **Semiconductors and Band Theory** 563
Molecular Orbitals and Energy Bands 563 Doping: Controlling the Conductivity of Semiconductors 565

13.9 **Polymers and Plastics** 565
CHEMISTRY IN YOUR DAY *Kevlar* 568

CHAPTER IN REVIEW Self-Assessment Quiz 569 Terms 570 Concepts 570 Equations and Relationships 571 Learning Outcomes 571

EXERCISES Review Questions 571 Problems by Topic 572 Cumulative Problems 575 Challenge Problems 576 Conceptual Problems 576 Questions for Group Work 576 Data Interpretation and Analysis 577 Answers to Conceptual Connections 577

14 Solutions 578

14.1 **Thirsty Solutions: Why You Shouldn't Drink Seawater** 579

14.2 **Types of Solutions and Solubility** 581
Nature's Tendency toward Mixing: Entropy 582
The Effect of Intermolecular Forces 582

14.3 **Energetics of Solution Formation** 586
Energy Changes in Solution Formation 586 Aqueous Solutions and Heats of Hydration 588

14.4 **Solution Equilibrium and Factors Affecting Solubility** 589
The Temperature Dependence of the Solubility of Solids 591 Factors Affecting the Solubility of Gases in Water 591

14.5 **Expressing Solution Concentration** 594
CHEMISTRY IN THE ENVIRONMENT *Lake Nyos* 594
Molarity 595 Molality 596 Parts by Mass and Parts by Volume 596 Using Parts by Mass (or Parts by Volume) in Calculations 597 Mole Fraction and Mole Percent 598
CHEMISTRY IN THE ENVIRONMENT *The Dirty Dozen* 598

14.6 **Colligative Properties: Vapor Pressure Lowering, Freezing Point Depression, Boiling Point Elevation, and Osmotic Pressure** 601
Vapor Pressure Lowering 602 Vapor Pressures of Solutions Containing a Volatile (Nonelectrolyte) Solute 605
Freezing Point Depression and Boiling Point Elevation 608
CHEMISTRY IN YOUR DAY *Antifreeze in Frogs* 611
Osmotic Pressure 611

14.7 **Colligative Properties of Strong Electrolyte Solutions** 613
Strong Electrolytes and Vapor Pressure 614
Colligative Properties and Medical Solutions 615

14.8 **Colloids** 616

CHAPTER IN REVIEW Self-Assessment Quiz 619 Terms 620 Concepts 620 Equations and Relationships 621 Learning Outcomes 621

EXERCISES Review Questions 622 Problems by Topic 623 Cumulative Problems 626 Challenge Problems 627 Conceptual Problems 628 Questions for Group Work 628 Data Interpretation and Analysis 629 Answers to Conceptual Connections 629

15 Chemical Kinetics 630

15.1 Catching Lizards 631

15.2 The Rate of a Chemical Reaction 632
Definition of Reaction Rate 632 Measuring Reaction Rates 636

15.3 The Rate Law: The Effect of Concentration on Reaction Rate 637
The Three Common Reaction Orders (n = 0, 1, and 2) 637 Determining the Order of a Reaction 638 Reaction Order for Multiple Reactants 640

15.4 The Integrated Rate Law: The Dependence of Concentration on Time 642
The Integrated Rate Law 642 The Half-Life of a Reaction 646

15.5 The Effect of Temperature on Reaction Rate 650
The Arrhenius Equation 650 The Activation Energy, Frequency Factor, and Exponential Factor 651 Arrhenius Plots: Experimental Measurements of the Frequency Factor and the Activation Energy 652 The Collision Model: A Closer Look at the Frequency Factor 655

15.6 Reaction Mechanisms 656
Rate Laws for Elementary Steps 657 Rate-Determining Steps and Overall Reaction Rate Laws 658 Mechanisms with a Fast Initial Step 659

15.7 Catalysis 661
Homogeneous and Heterogeneous Catalysis 663
Enzymes: Biological Catalysts 664
CHEMISTRY AND MEDICINE *Enzyme Catalysis and the Role of Chymotrypsin in Digestion* 666

CHAPTER IN REVIEW Self-Assessment Quiz 667 Terms 669 Concepts 669 Equations and Relationships 670 Learning Outcomes 670

EXERCISES Review Questions 670 Problems by Topic 671 Cumulative Problems 676 Challenge Problems 678 Conceptual Problems 679 Questions for Group Work 680 Data Interpretation and Analysis 680 Answers to Conceptual Connections 681

16 Chemical Equilibrium 682

16.1 Fetal Hemoglobin and Equilibrium 683

16.2 The Concept of Dynamic Equilibrium 685

16.3 The Equilibrium Constant (*K*) 688
Expressing Equilibrium Constants for Chemical Reactions 688
The Significance of the Equilibrium Constant 689
CHEMISTRY AND MEDICINE *Life and Equilibrium* 690
Relationships between the Equilibrium Constant and the Chemical Equation 691

16.4 Expressing the Equilibrium Constant in Terms of Pressure 692
Relationship Between K_p and K_c 693 Units of K 694

16.5 Heterogeneous Equilibria: Reactions Involving Solids and Liquids 695

16.6 Calculating the Equilibrium Constant from Measured Equilibrium Concentrations 696

16.7 The Reaction Quotient: Predicting the Direction of Change 699

16.8 Finding Equilibrium Concentrations 701
Finding Equilibrium Concentrations from the Equilibrium Constant and All but One of the Equilibrium Concentrations of the Reactants and Products 702
Finding Equilibrium Concentrations from the Equilibrium Constant and Initial Concentrations or Pressures 703
Simplifying Approximations in Working Equilibrium Problems 707

16.9 Le Châtelier's Principle: How a System at Equilibrium Responds to Disturbances 711
The Effect of a Concentration Change on Equilibrium 712
The Effect of a Volume (or Pressure) Change on Equilibrium 714 The Effect of a Temperature Change on Equilibrium 716

CHAPTER IN REVIEW Self-Assessment Quiz 718 Terms 719 Concepts 719 Equations and Relationships 720 Learning Outcomes 720

EXERCISES Review Questions 721 Problems by Topic 722 Cumulative Problems 725 Challenge Problems 727 Conceptual Problems 727 Questions for Group Work 728 Data Interpretation and Analysis 728 Answers to Conceptual Connections 729

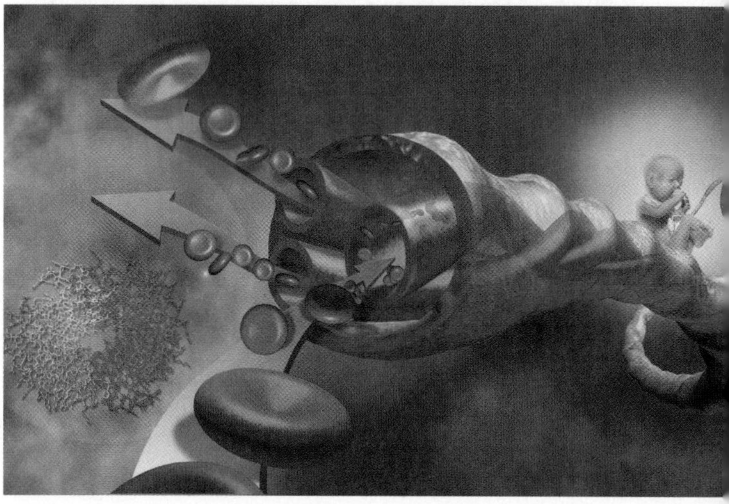

17 Acids and Bases 730

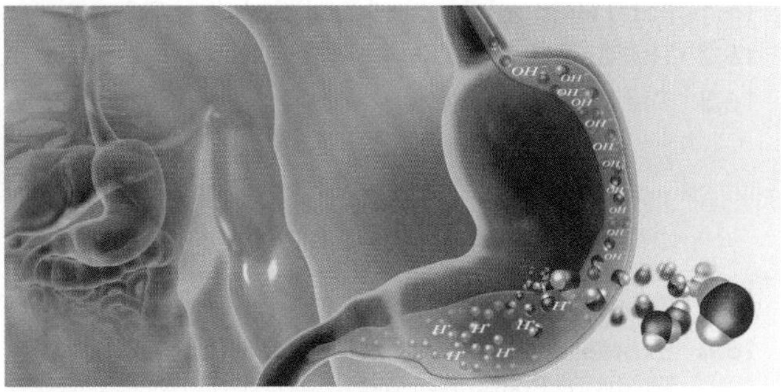

17.1 Heartburn 731

17.2 The Nature of Acids and Bases 732

17.3 Definitions of Acids and Bases 734
The Arrhenius Definition 734 The Brønsted–Lowry Definition 735

17.4 Acid Strength and the Acid Ionization Constant (K_a) 737
Strong Acids 737 Weak Acids 738 The Acid Ionization Constant (K_a) 739

17.5 Autoionization of Water and pH 740
The pH Scale: A Way to Quantify Acidity and Basicity 742
pOH and Other p Scales 743
CHEMISTRY AND MEDICINE *Ulcers* 744

17.6 Finding the $[H_3O^+]$ and pH of Strong and Weak Acid Solutions 745
Strong Acids 745 Weak Acids 745 Percent Ionization of a Weak Acid 750 Mixtures of Acids 751

17.7 Base Solutions 754
Strong Bases 754 Weak Bases 754
Finding the $[OH^-]$ and pH of Basic Solutions 756
CHEMISTRY AND MEDICINE *What's in My Antacid?* 758

17.8 The Acid–Base Properties of Ions and Salts 758
Anions as Weak Bases 759 Cations as Weak Acids 762
Classifying Salt Solutions as Acidic, Basic, or Neutral 763

17.9 Polyprotic Acids 765
Finding the pH of Polyprotic Acid Solutions 766 Finding the Concentration of the Anions for a Weak Diprotic Acid Solution 768

17.10 Acid Strength and Molecular Structure 770
Binary Acids 770 Oxyacids 771

17.11 Lewis Acids and Bases 772
Molecules That Act as Lewis Acids 772 Cations That Act as Lewis Acids 773

17.12 Acid Rain 773
Effects of Acid Rain 774 Acid Rain Legislation 775

CHAPTER IN REVIEW Self-Assessment Quiz 775 Terms 776 Concepts 776 Equations and Relationships 777 Learning Outcomes 778

EXERCISES Review Questions 778 Problems by Topic 779 Cumulative Problems 782 Challenge Problems 784 Conceptual Problems 784 Questions for Group Work 784 Data Interpretation and Analysis 784 Answers to Conceptual Connections 785

18 Aqueous Ionic Equilibrium 786

18.1 The Danger of Antifreeze 787

18.2 Buffers: Solutions That Resist pH Change 788
Calculating the pH of a Buffer Solution 790 The Henderson–Hasselbalch Equation 791 Calculating pH Changes in a Buffer Solution 794 The Stoichiometry Calculation 794 The Equilibrium Calculation 794
Buffers Containing a Base and Its Conjugate Acid 798

18.3 Buffer Effectiveness: Buffer Range and Buffer Capacity 799
Relative Amounts of Acid and Base 799 Absolute Concentrations of the Acid and Conjugate Base 800
Buffer Range 801
CHEMISTRY AND MEDICINE *Buffer Effectiveness in Human Blood* 802
Buffer Capacity 802

18.4 Titrations and pH Curves 803
The Titration of a Strong Acid with a Strong Base 804
The Titration of a Weak Acid with a Strong Base 808
The Titration of a Weak Base with a Strong Acid 813
The Titration of a Polyprotic Acid 814
Indicators: pH-Dependent Colors 814

18.5 Solubility Equilibria and the Solubility Product Constant 817
K_{sp} and Molar Solubility 817
CHEMISTRY IN YOUR DAY *Hard Water* 819
K_{sp} and Relative Solubility 820 The Effect of a Common Ion on Solubility 820 The Effect of pH on Solubility 822

18.6 Precipitation 823
Selective Precipitation 824

18.7 Qualitative Chemical Analysis 826
Group 1: Insoluble Chlorides 827 Group 2: Acid-Insoluble Sulfides 827 Group 3: Base-Insoluble Sulfides and Hydroxides 828 Group 4: Insoluble Phosphates 828 Group 5: Alkali Metals and NH_4^+ 828

18.8 Complex Ion Equilibria 829
The Effect of Complex Ion Equilibria on Solubility 831
The Solubility of Amphoteric Metal Hydroxides 832

CHAPTER IN REVIEW Self-Assessment Quiz 833 Terms 834 Concepts 834 Equations and Relationships 835 Learning Outcomes 835

EXERCISES Review Questions 836 Problems by Topic 837 Cumulative Problems 842 Challenge Problems 843 Conceptual Problems 843 Questions for Group Work 844 Data Interpretation and Analysis 844 Answers to Conceptual Connections 845

19 Free Energy and Thermodynamics 846

19.1 Cold Coffee and Dead Universes 847

19.2 Spontaneous and Nonspontaneous Processes 848

19.3 Entropy and the Second Law of Thermodynamics 850
Entropy 852 The Entropy Change upon the Expansion of an Ideal Gas 854

19.4 Entropy Changes Associated with State Changes 856
Entropy and State Change: The Concept 857 Entropy and State Changes: The Calculation 858

19.5 Heat Transfer and Changes in the Entropy of the Surroundings 860
The Temperature Dependence of ΔS_{surr} 861 Quantifying Entropy Changes in the Surroundings 861

19.6 Gibbs Free Energy 863
The Effect of ΔH, ΔS, and T on Spontaneity 864

19.7 Entropy Changes in Chemical Reactions: Calculating ΔS°_{rxn} 867
Defining Standard States and Standard Entropy Changes 867 Standard Molar Entropies (S°) and the Third Law of Thermodynamics 867 Calculating the Standard Entropy Change (ΔS°_{rxn}) for a Reaction 871

19.8 Free Energy Changes in Chemical Reactions: Calculating ΔG°_{rxn} 871
Calculating Standard Free Energy Changes with $\Delta G^\circ_{rxn} = \Delta H^\circ_{rxn} - T\Delta S^\circ_{rxn}$ 872 Calculating ΔG°_{rxn} with Tabulated Values of Free Energies of Formation 873
CHEMISTRY IN YOUR DAY *Making a Nonspontaneous Process Spontaneous* 875
Calculating ΔG°_{rxn} for a Stepwise Reaction from the Changes in Free Energy for Each of the Steps 875
Why Free Energy Is "Free" 876

19.9 Free Energy Changes for Nonstandard States: The Relationship between ΔG°_{rxn} and ΔG_{rxn} 878
Standard versus Nonstandard States 878 The Free Energy Change of a Reaction under Nonstandard Conditions 878 Standard Conditions 878 Equilibrium Conditions 879 Other Nonstandard Conditions 880

19.10 Free Energy and Equilibrium: Relating ΔG°_{rxn} to the Equilibrium Constant (K) 881
The Relationship between ΔG°_{rxn} and K 881 The Temperature Dependence of the Equilibrium Constant 883

CHAPTER IN REVIEW Self-Assessment Quiz 884 Terms 885 Concepts 885 Equations and Relationships 886 Learning Outcomes 886

EXERCISES Review Questions 887 Problems by Topic 888 Cumulative Problems 891 Challenge Problems 892 Conceptual Problems 893 Questions for Group Work 893 Data Interpretation and Analysis 894 Answers to Conceptual Connections 894

20 Electrochemistry 896

20.1 Lightning and Batteries 897

20.2 Balancing Oxidation–Reduction Equations 898

20.3 Voltaic (or Galvanic) Cells: Generating Electricity from Spontaneous Chemical Reactions 901
The Voltaic Cell 902 Current and Potential Difference 903 Anode, Cathode, and Salt Bridge 904 Electrochemical Cell Notation 905

20.4 Standard Electrode Potentials 905
Predicting the Spontaneous Direction of an Oxidation–Reduction Reaction 910 Predicting Whether a Metal Will Dissolve in Acid 913

20.5 Cell Potential, Free Energy, and the Equilibrium Constant 913
The Relationship between ΔG° and E°_{cell} 914
The Relationship between E°_{cell} and K 916

20.6 Cell Potential and Concentration 917
Cell Potential under Nonstandard Conditions: The Nernst Equation 917 Concentration Cells 920
CHEMISTRY AND MEDICINE *Concentration Cells in Human Nerve Cells* 922

20.7 Batteries: Using Chemistry to Generate Electricity 922
Dry-Cell Batteries 922 Lead–Acid Storage Batteries 923 Other Rechargeable Batteries 924 Fuel Cells 925
CHEMISTRY IN YOUR DAY *The Fuel-Cell Breathalyzer* 926

20.8 Electrolysis: Driving Nonspontaneous Chemical Reactions with Electricity 926
Predicting the Products of Electrolysis 929 Stoichiometry of Electrolysis 932

20.9 Corrosion: Undesirable Redox Reactions 933
Corrosion of Iron 934 Preventing the Corrosion of Iron 935

CHAPTER IN REVIEW Self-Assessment Quiz 936 Terms 937 Concepts 937 Equations and Relationships 938 Learning Outcomes 938

EXERCISES Review Questions 939 Problems by Topic 939 Cumulative Problems 943 Challenge Problems 944 Conceptual Problems 944 Questions for Group Work 944 Data Interpretation and Analysis 945 Answers to Conceptual Connections 945

21 Radioactivity and Nuclear Chemistry 946

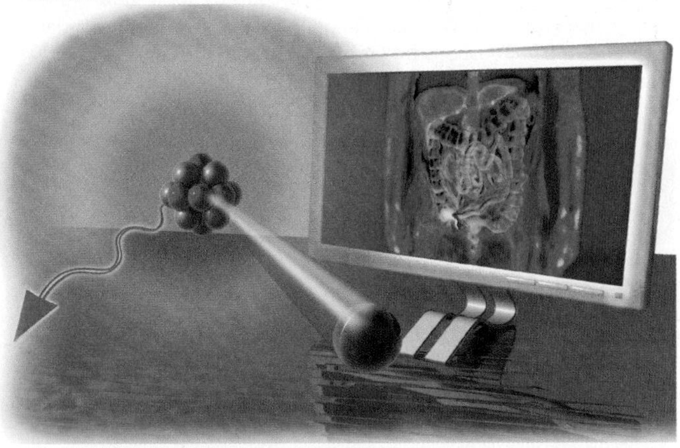

21.1 Diagnosing Appendicitis 947

21.2 The Discovery of Radioactivity 948

21.3 Types of Radioactivity 949
Alpha (α) Decay 950 Beta (β) Decay 951 Gamma (γ) Ray Emission 952 Positron Emission 952 Electron Capture 953

21.4 The Valley of Stability: Predicting the Type of Radioactivity 954
Magic Numbers 956 Radioactive Decay Series 956

21.5 Detecting Radioactivity 957

21.6 The Kinetics of Radioactive Decay and Radiometric Dating 958
The Integrated Rate Law 960 Radiocarbon Dating: Using Radioactivity to Measure the Age of Fossils and Artifacts 961
CHEMISTRY IN YOUR DAY *Radiocarbon Dating and the Shroud of Turin* 963
Uranium/Lead Dating 963 The Age of Earth 964

21.7 The Discovery of Fission: The Atomic Bomb and Nuclear Power 965
The Manhattan Project 965 Nuclear Power: Using Fission to Generate Electricity 967 Problems with Nuclear Power 968

21.8 Converting Mass to Energy: Mass Defect and Nuclear Binding Energy 969
Mass Defect and Nuclear Binding Energy 969 The Nuclear Binding Energy Curve 971

21.9 Nuclear Fusion: The Power of the Sun 971

21.10 Nuclear Transmutation and Transuranium Elements 972

21.11 The Effects of Radiation on Life 974
Acute Radiation Damage 974 Increased Cancer Risk 974 Genetic Defects 974 Measuring Radiation Exposure and Dose 975

21.12 Radioactivity in Medicine and Other Applications 976
Diagnosis in Medicine 977 Radiotherapy in Medicine 978 Other Applications 978

CHAPTER IN REVIEW Self-Assessment Quiz 979 Terms 980 Concepts 980 Equations and Relationships 981 Learning Outcomes 981

EXERCISES Review Questions 982 Problems by Topic 982 Cumulative Problems 984 Challenge Problems 985 Conceptual Problems 986 Questions for Group Work 986 Data Interpretation and Analysis 987 Answers to Conceptual Connections 987

22 Organic Chemistry 988

22.1 Fragrances and Odors 989

22.2 Carbon: Why It Is Unique 990
CHEMISTRY IN YOUR DAY *Vitalism and the Perceived Differences between Organic and Inorganic Compounds* 991

22.3 Hydrocarbons: Compounds Containing Only Carbon and Hydrogen 992
Drawing Hydrocarbon Structures 993 Stereoisomerism and Optical Isomerism 995 Rotation of Polarized Light 996 Chemical Behavior in a Chiral Environment 997

22.4 Alkanes: Saturated Hydrocarbons 998
Naming Alkanes 999

22.5 Alkenes and Alkynes 1002
Naming Alkenes and Alkynes 1003 Geometric (Cis–Trans) Isomerism in Alkenes 1006

22.6 Hydrocarbon Reactions 1007
Reactions of Alkanes 1007 Reactions of Alkenes and Alkynes 1008

22.7 Aromatic Hydrocarbons 1010
Naming Aromatic Hydrocarbons 1010 Reactions of Aromatic Compounds 1012

22.8 Functional Groups 1013

22.9 Alcohols 1014
Naming Alcohols 1014 About Alcohols 1014 Alcohol Reactions 1014

22.10 Aldehydes and Ketones 1016
Naming Aldehydes and Ketones 1017 About Aldehydes and Ketones 1017 Aldehyde and Ketone Reactions 1018

22.11 Carboxylic Acids and Esters 1019
Naming Carboxylic Acids and Esters 1019 About Carboxylic Acids and Esters 1019 Carboxylic Acid and Ester Reactions 1020

22.12 Ethers 1021
Naming Ethers 1021 About Ethers 1022

22.13 Amines 1022
Amine Reactions 1022

CHAPTER IN REVIEW Self-Assessment Quiz 1023 Terms 1024 Concepts 1024 Equations and Relationships 1025 Learning Outcomes 1026

EXERCISES Review Questions 1027 Problems by Topic 1027 Cumulative Problems 1032 Challenge Problems 1034 Conceptual Problems 1034 Questions for Group Work 1035 Data Interpretation and Analysis 1035 Answers to Conceptual Connections 1035

23 Biochemistry 1036

23.1 Diabetes and the Synthesis of Human Insulin 1037

23.2 Lipids 1038
Fatty Acids 1038 Fats and Oils 1040 Other Lipids 1041

23.3 Carbohydrates 1043
Simple Carbohydrates: Monosaccharides and Disaccharides 1043 Complex Carbohydrates 1045

23.4 Proteins and Amino Acids 1046
Amino Acids: The Building Blocks of Proteins 1047
Peptide Bonding between Amino Acids 1049

23.5 Protein Structure 1050
Primary Structure 1052 Secondary Structure 1052
Tertiary Structure 1053 Quaternary Structure 1054

23.6 Nucleic Acids: Blueprints for Proteins 1054
The Basic Structure of Nucleic Acids 1054
The Genetic Code 1056

23.7 DNA Replication, the Double Helix, and Protein Synthesis 1058
DNA Replication and the Double Helix 1058
Protein Synthesis 1059

CHEMISTRY AND MEDICINE *The Human Genome Project* 1060

CHAPTER IN REVIEW Self-Assessment Quiz 1061 Terms 1062 Concepts 1062 Learning Outcomes 1063

EXERCISES Review Questions 1064 Problems by Topic 1064 Cumulative Problems 1067 Challenge Problems 1068 Conceptual Problems 1068 Questions for Group Work 1068 Data Interpretation and Analysis 1069 Answers to Conceptual Connections 1069

24 Chemistry of the Nonmetals 1070

24.1 Insulated Nanowires 1071

24.2 The Main-Group Elements: Bonding and Properties 1072

24.3 Silicates: The Most Abundant Matter in Earth's Crust 1074
Quartz 1074 Aluminosilicates 1075 Individual Silicate Units, Silicate Chains, and Silicate Sheets 1075

24.4 Boron and Its Remarkable Structures 1078
Elemental Boron 1078 Boron–Halogen Compounds: Trihalides 1079 Boron–Oxygen Compounds 1079
Boron–Hydrogen Compounds: Boranes 1080

24.5 Carbon, Carbides, and Carbonates 1081
Amorphous Carbon 1081 Carbides 1082 Carbon Oxides 1083 Carbonates 1084

24.6 Nitrogen and Phosphorus: Essential Elements for Life 1085
Elemental Nitrogen and Phosphorus 1085 Nitrogen Compounds 1086 Phosphorus Compounds 1089

24.7 Oxygen 1091
Elemental Oxygen 1091 Uses for Oxygen 1092 Oxides 1092 Ozone 1093

24.8 Sulfur: A Dangerous but Useful Element 1093
Elemental Sulfur 1094 Hydrogen Sulfide and Metal Sulfides 1095 Sulfur Dioxide 1096 Sulfuric Acid 1096

24.9 Halogens: Reactive Elements with High Electronegativity 1097
Elemental Fluorine and Hydrofluoric Acid 1098
Elemental Chlorine 1099 Halogen Compounds 1099

CHAPTER IN REVIEW Self-Assessment Quiz 1101 Terms 1102 Concepts 1102 Learning Outcomes 1103

EXERCISES Review Questions 1103 Problems by Topic 1103 Cumulative Problems 1105 Challenge Problems 1106 Conceptual Problems 1106 Questions for Group Work 1106 Data Interpretation and Analysis 1107 Answers to Conceptual Connections 1107

25 Metals and Metallurgy 1108

25.1 Vanadium: A Problem and an Opportunity 1109

25.2 The General Properties and Natural Distribution of Metals 1110

25.3 Metallurgical Processes 1112
Separation 1112 Pyrometallurgy 1112
Hydrometallurgy 1113 Electrometallurgy 1114
Powder Metallurgy 1115

25.4 Metal Structures and Alloys 1116
Alloys 1116 Substitutional Alloys 1116 Alloys with Limited Solubility 1118 Interstitial Alloys 1119

25.5 Sources, Properties, and Products of Some of the 3*d* Transition Metals 1121
Titanium 1121 Chromium 1122 Manganese 1123
Cobalt 1124 Copper 1125 Nickel 1125
Zinc 1126

CHAPTER IN REVIEW Self-Assessment Quiz 1126 Terms 1128
Concepts 1128 Equations and Relationships 1128
Learning Outcomes 1129

EXERCISES Review Questions 1129 Problems by Topic 1129
Cumulative Problems 1131 Challenge Problems 1131
Conceptual Problems 1131 Questions for Group Work 1132
Data Interpretation and Analysis 1132 Answers to Conceptual Connections 1133

26 Transition Metals and Coordination Compounds 1134

26.1 The Colors of Rubies and Emeralds 1135

26.2 Properties of Transition Metals 1136
Electron Configurations 1136 Atomic Size 1138
Ionization Energy 1138 Electronegativity 1139
Oxidation States 1139

26.3 Coordination Compounds 1140
Naming Coordination Compounds 1143

26.4 Structure and Isomerization 1145
Structural Isomerism 1145 Stereoisomerism 1147

26.5 Bonding in Coordination Compounds 1150
Valence Bond Theory 1150 Crystal Field Theory 1151

26.6 Applications of Coordination Compounds 1155
Chelating Agents 1156 Chemical Analysis 1156
Coloring Agents 1156 Biomolecules 1156
Hemoglobin and Cytochrome C 1157

CHAPTER IN REVIEW Self-Assessment Quiz 1159 Terms 1159
Concepts 1160 Equations and Relationships 1160
Learning Outcomes 1160

EXERCISES Review Questions 1161 Problems by Topic 1161
Cumulative Problems 1163 Challenge Problems 1163
Conceptual Problems 1164 Questions for Group Work 1164
Data Interpretation and Analysis 1164 Answers to Conceptual Connections 1165

Appendix I Common Mathematical Operations in Chemistry A-1

Appendix II Useful Data A-5

Appendix III Answers to Selected Exercises A-15

Appendix IV Answers to In-Chapter Practice Problems A-53

Glossary G-1

Photo and Text Credits C-1

Index I-1

Preface

To the Student

As you begin this course, I invite you to think about your reasons for enrolling in it. Why are you taking general chemistry? More generally, why are you pursuing a college education? If you are like most college students taking general chemistry, part of your answer is probably that this course is required for your major and that you are pursuing a college education so you can get a good job some day. Although these are good reasons, I would like to suggest a better one. I think the primary reason for your education is to prepare you to *live a good life*. You should understand chemistry—not for what it can *get* you—but for what it can *do* to you. Understanding chemistry, I believe, is an important source of happiness and fulfillment. Let me explain.

Understanding chemistry helps you to live life to its fullest for two basic reasons. The first is *intrinsic*: through an understanding of chemistry, you gain a powerful appreciation for just how rich and extraordinary the world really is. The second reason is *extrinsic*: understanding chemistry makes you a more informed citizen—it allows you to engage with many of the issues of our day. In other words, understanding chemistry makes *you* a deeper and richer person and makes your country and the world a better place to live. These reasons have been the foundation of education from the very beginnings of civilization.

How does chemistry help prepare you for a rich life and conscientious citizenship? Let me explain with two examples. My first one comes from the very first page of Chapter 1 of this book. There, I ask the following question: What is the most important idea in all of scientific knowledge? My answer to that question is this: **the behavior of matter is determined by the properties of molecules and atoms**. That simple statement is the reason I love chemistry. We humans have been able to study the substances that compose the world around us and explain their behavior by reference to particles so small that they can hardly be imagined. If you have never realized the remarkable dependence of the world we *can* see on the world we *cannot*, you have missed out on a fundamental truth about our universe. To have never encountered this truth is like never having read a play by Shakespeare or seen a sculpture by Michelangelo—or, for that matter, like never having discovered that the world is round. It robs you of an amazing and unforgettable experience of the world and the human ability to understand it.

My second example demonstrates how science literacy helps you to be a better citizen. Although I am largely sympathetic to the environmental movement, a lack of science literacy within some sectors of that movement and the resulting anti-environmental backlash create confusion that impedes real progress and opens the door to what could be misinformed policies. For example, I have heard conservative pundits say that volcanoes emit more carbon dioxide—the most significant greenhouse gas—than does petroleum combustion. I have also heard a liberal environmentalist say that we have to stop using hair spray because it is causing holes in the ozone layer that will lead to global warming. Well, the claim about volcanoes emitting more carbon dioxide than petroleum combustion can be refuted by the basic tools you will learn to use in Chapter 4 of this book. We can easily show that volcanoes emit only 1/50th as much carbon dioxide as petroleum combustion. As for hair spray depleting the ozone layer and thereby leading to global warming, the chlorofluorocarbons that deplete ozone have been banned from hair spray since 1978, and ozone depletion has nothing to do with global warming anyway. People with special interests or axes to grind can conveniently distort the truth before an ill-informed public, which is why we all need to be knowledgeable.

So this is why I think you should take this course. Not just to satisfy the requirement for your major and not just to get a good job some day, but to help you to lead a fuller life and to make the world a little better for everyone. I wish you the best as you embark on the journey to understanding the world around you at the molecular level. The rewards are well worth the effort.

To the Professor

First and foremost, thanks to all of you who adopted this book in its previous editions. You helped to make this book one of the most popular general chemistry textbooks in the world. I am grateful beyond words. Second, I have listened carefully to your feedback on the previous edition. The changes you see in this edition are the direct result of your input, as well as my own experience using the book in my general chemistry courses. If you have reviewed content or have contacted me directly, you will likely see your suggestions reflected in the changes I have made. Thank you.

Higher education in science is changing. Foremost among those changes is a shift toward *active learning*. A flood of recent studies has demonstrated that General Chemistry students learn better when they are active in the learning process. However, implementing active learning can be a difficult and time-consuming process. One of my main goals in this revision is to give you, the professor, a range of tools to easily implement active learning in your class. My goal is simple: *I want to make it easy for you to engage your students in active learning before class, during class, and after class.*

- **BEFORE CLASS** Although the term *active learning* has been applied mainly to in-class learning, the main idea—*that we learn better when we are actively engaged*—applies to all of learning. I have developed two main tools to help students prepare for class in an active way. The first tool is a complete library of 3- to 6-minute *Key Concept Videos* (*KCVs*) that, with this edition, span virtually all of the key concepts in a general chemistry course. The videos introduce a key concept and encourage active learning because they stop in the middle and pose a question that must be answered before the video continues playing. Each video also has an associated follow-up question that can be assigned using Mastering Chemistry. You can assign a video before each one of your classes to get your students thinking about the concepts for that day. A second tool for use before class is *active reading*. Each chapter in the book now contains 10–12 *Conceptual Connection* questions. These questions are live in the ebook, assignable in Mastering Chemistry, and contain wrong answer feedback. Instead of passively reading the assigned material with no accountability, you can now encourage your students to engage in *active reading*, in which they read a bit and then answer a question that probes their comprehension and gives them immediate feedback.
- **DURING CLASS** By delivering some content through key concept videos and active reading before class, you can make room in your lecture to pose questions to your students that make the class experience active as well. This book features two main tools for in-class use. The first tool is *Learning Catalytics*, which allows you to pose many different types of questions to your students during class. Instead of passively listening to your lecture, students interact with the concepts you present through questions you pose. Your students can answer the questions individually, or you can pair them with a partner or small group. A second tool for in-class use is the *Questions for Group Work*. These questions appear in the end-of-chapter material and are specifically designed to be answered in small groups.
- **AFTER CLASS** Active learning can continue after class with two additional tools. The first is another library of 3- to 6-minute videos called *Interactive Worked Examples (IWEs)*. Each IWE video walks a student through the solution to a chemistry problem. Like the KCVs, the IWE video stops in the middle and poses a question that must be answered before the video continues playing. Each video also has an associated follow-up problem that can be assigned using Mastering Chemistry. The second tool for after (or outside of) class active learning is *Active Exam Preparation*. Research studies suggest that students who take a pretest before an exam do better on the exam, especially if the pretest contains immediate feedback. Each chapter in this book contains a *Self-Assessment Quiz* that you can use to easily make a pretest for any of your exams. The *Self-Assessment Quizzes* are live in the ebook, assignable in Mastering Chemistry, and contain wrong answer feedback. Simply choose the questions that you want from each of the quizzes that span the chapters on your exam, and you can create an assignable pretest that students can use to actively prepare for your exams.

Although we have added many active learning tools to this edition and made other changes as well, the book's goal remains the same: *to present a rigorous and accessible treatment of general chemistry in the context of relevance.* Teaching general chemistry would be much easier if all of our students had exactly the same level of preparation and ability. But alas, that is not the case. My own courses are populated with students with a range of backgrounds and abilities in chemistry. The challenge of successful teaching, in my opinion, is figuring out how to instruct and challenge the best students while not losing those with lesser backgrounds and abilities. My strategy has always been to set the bar relatively high, while at the same time providing the motivation and support necessary to reach the high bar. That is exactly the philosophy of this book. We do not have to compromise rigor in order to make chemistry accessible to our students. In this book, I have worked hard to combine rigor with accessibility—to create a book that does not dilute the content and yet can be used and understood by any student willing to put in the necessary effort.

Chemistry: A Molecular Approach* is first and foremost a *student-oriented book. My main goal is to motivate students and get them to achieve at the highest possible level. As we all know, many students take general chemistry because it is a requirement; they do not see the connection between chemistry and their lives or their intended careers. *Chemistry: A Molecular Approach* strives to make those connections consistently and effectively. Unlike other books, which often teach chemistry as something that happens only in the laboratory or in industry, this book teaches chemistry in the context of relevance. It shows students *why* chemistry is important to them, to their future careers, and to their world.

Second, *Chemistry: A Molecular Approach* is a *pedagogically driven book.* In seeking to develop problem-solving skills, a consistent approach (Sort, Strategize, Solve, and Check) is applied, usually in a two- or three-column format. In the two-column format, the left column shows the student how to analyze the problem and devise a solution strategy. It also lists the steps of the solution, explaining the rationale for each one, while the right column shows the implementation of each step. In the three-column format, the left column outlines the general procedure for solving an important category of problems that is then applied to two side-by-side examples. This strategy allows students to see both the general pattern and the slightly different ways in which the procedure may be applied in differing contexts. The aim is to help students understand both the *concept of the problem* (through the formulation of an explicit conceptual plan for each problem) and the *solution to the problem.*

Third, *Chemistry: A Molecular Approach* is a *visual book.* Wherever possible, I use images to deepen the student's insight into chemistry. In developing chemical principles, multipart images help show the connection between everyday processes visible to the unaided eye and what atoms and molecules are actually doing. Many of these images have three parts: macroscopic, molecular, and symbolic. This combination helps students to see the relationships between the formulas they write down on paper (symbolic), the world they see around them (macroscopic), and the atoms and molecules that compose that world (molecular). In addition, most figures are designed to teach rather than just to illustrate. They are rich with annotations and labels intended to help the student grasp the most important processes and the principles that underlie them. In this edition, the art program has been thoroughly revised in two major ways. First, navigation of the more complex figures has been reoriented to track from left to right whenever possible. Second, figure captions have been migrated into the image itself as an "author voice" that explains the image and guides the reader through it. The resulting images are rich with information but also clear and quickly understood.

Fourth, *Chemistry: A Molecular Approach* is a "big-picture" book. At the beginning of each chapter, a short paragraph helps students to see the key relationships between the different topics they are learning. Through a focused and concise narrative, I strive to make the basic ideas of every chapter clear to the student. Interim summaries are provided at selected spots in the narrative, making it easier to grasp (and review) the main points of important discussions. And to make sure that students never lose sight of the forest for the trees, each chapter includes several *Conceptual Connections,* which ask them to think about concepts and solve problems without doing any math. I want students to learn the concepts, not just plug numbers into equations to churn out the right answer. This philosophy is also integral to the *Key Concept Videos,* which concisely reinforce student appreciation of the core concepts in each chapter.

Lastly, *Chemistry: A Molecular Approach* is a book that delivers the depth of coverage faculty want. We do not have to cut corners and water down the material in order to get our students interested. We have to meet them where they are, challenge them to the highest level of achievement, and support them with enough pedagogy to allow them to succeed.

I hope that this book supports you in your vocation of teaching students chemistry. I am increasingly convinced of the importance of our task. Please feel free to contact me with any questions or comments about the book.

Nivaldo J. Tro
nivatro@gmail.com

What's New in This Edition?

The book has been extensively revised and contains more small changes than can be detailed here. The most significant changes to the book and its supplements are listed below:

- **NEW INTERACTIVE VIDEOS** I have added 16 new *Key Concept Videos (KCVs)* and 24 new *Interactive Worked Examples (IWEs)* to the media package that accompanies the book. *The video library now contains nearly 200 interactive videos.* These tools are designed to help professors engage their students in active learning.
- **NEW IN-CHAPTER QUESTIONS WITH FEEDBACK** I have added approximately 67 new *Conceptual Connection* questions throughout the book and have changed the format to multiple choice (with wrong answer feedback in the ebook or through Mastering Chemistry). Each chapter now has 10–12 of these embedded assignable questions. These questions transform the reading process from passive to active and hold students accountable for reading assignments.
- **NEW *MISSED THIS?* FEATURE** I have added a new feature called *MISSED THIS?* to the *Self-Assessment Quizzes* and to the *Problems by Topic* section of the end-of-chapter problems. This feature lists the resources that students can use to learn how to answer the question or solve the problem. The resources include chapter sections to read, *Key Concept Videos (KCVs)* to watch, and *Interactive Worked Examples (IWEs)* to view. Students often try to solve an assigned question or problem before doing any reading or reviewing; they seek resources only *after* they have missed the question or problem. The *MISSED THIS?* feature guides them to reliable resources that provide just-in-time instruction.
- **NEW FOR PRACTICE FEEDBACK** I have enhanced 64 of the in-chapter *For Practice* problems (which immediately follow an in-chapter worked example) with feedback that can be accessed in the ebook or through Mastering Chemistry.
- **REVISED ART PROGRAM** The art program has been extensively revised. Navigation of the more complex figures has been reoriented to track from left to right, and many figure captions have been broken up and have been moved into the image itself as an "author voice" that explains the image and guides the reader through it.
- **REVISED DATA INTERPRETATION AND ANALYSIS QUESTIONS** The *Data Interpretation and Analysis* questions that accompany each chapter have been extensively revised to make them clearer and more accessible to students.
- **NEW SECTION ON DATA INTERPRETATION AND ANALYSIS** I have added a new section to Chapter 1 (Section 1.9) on the general topic of analyzing and interpreting data. This section introduces the skills required to address many of the revised data interpretation and analysis questions.
- **NEW HOW TO . . . FEATURE** All guidance for essential skills such as problem-solving techniques, drawing Lewis structures, and naming compounds is now presented in a consistent, step-by-step numbered list called *How To...*
- **REVISED CHAPTER 4** Chapter 4 in the previous edition covered both stoichiometry and chemical reactions in solution. In this edition, this content has been

expanded slightly and has been divided into two more focused chapters, so that Chapter 4 is now focused on stoichiometry and Chapter 5 on chemical reactions in solution. This new organization lessens the cognitive load for students and allows each chapter to be more direct and focused. All subsequent chapters have been renumbered accordingly.

- **NEW ACTIVITY SERIES CONTENT** I added a new subsection to Section 5.9 entitled *The Activity Series: Predicting Whether a Redox Reaction Is Spontaneous.* The new section includes new figures, tables, and a new worked example.
- **NEW READY-TO-GO LEARNING MODULES** These online modules offer students easy access to the best Tro content in Mastering Chemistry without needing to have it assigned.
- **NEW TWO-TIER OBJECTIVES** A system of two-tier objectives is being applied to the text and to the Mastering Chemistry assets. The two tiers are Learning Objectives, or LOs, and Enabling Objectives, or EOs. The LOs are broad, high-level objectives that summarize the overall learning goal, while the EOs are the building block skills that enable students to achieve the LO. The learning objectives are given in the Learning Outcomes table at the end of the chapter.
- **REVISED DATA** All the data throughout the book have been updated to reflect the most recent measurements available. These updates include Figure 4.2: *Carbon Dioxide in the Atmosphere*; Figure 4.3: *Global Temperatures*; the unnumbered figure in Section 7.10 of *U.S. Energy Consumption*; Figure 7.12: *Energy Consumption by Source*; Table 7.6: *Changes in National Average Pollutant Levels, 1990–2016*; Figure 15.19: *Ozone Depletion in the Antarctic Spring*; Figure 17.15: *Sources of U.S. Energy*; Figure 17.16: *Acid Rain*; and Figure 17.18: *U.S. Sulfur Dioxide Pollutant Levels.*
- **REVISED CHAPTER OPENERS** Many chapter-opening sections and (or) the corresponding art—including Chapters 1, 3, 4, 5, 6, 7, 10, 11, 18, 19, 20, and 22—have been replaced or modified.

Acknowledgments

The book you hold in your hands bears my name on the cover, but I am really only one member of a large team that carefully crafted this book. Most importantly, I thank my editor, Terry Haugen. Terry is a great editor and friend. He gives me the right balance of freedom and direction and always supports me in my endeavors. Thanks, Terry, for all you have done for me and for general chemistry courses throughout the world. Thanks also to Matt Walker, my new developmental editor on this project. Matt is creative, organized, and extremely competent. He has made significant contributions to this revision and has helped me with the many tasks that must be simultaneously addressed and developed during a revision as significant as this one. Matt, I hope this is only the beginning of a long and fruitful collaboration. I also owe a special debt of gratitude to Barbara Yien and Laura Southworth. Barbara was involved in many parts of content development, and Laura played a critical role in the revision of the art program. Many thanks to the both of you!

Thanks also to my media editor, Paula Iborra. Paula has been instrumental in helping me craft and develop the Key Concept Videos, Interactive Worked Examples, and other media content that accompany this text. Gracias, Paula.

I am also grateful to Harry Misthos, who helped with organizing reviews, as well as numerous other tasks associated with keeping the team running smoothly. I am also grateful to Jeanne Zalesky, Editor-in-Chief for Physical Sciences. She has supported me and my projects and allowed me to succeed. Thanks also to Adam Jaworski, who oversees science courseware at Pearson. I am grateful to have his wise and steady, yet innovative, hand at the wheel, especially during the many changes that are happening within educational publishing. I am also grateful to my marketing managers, Chris Barker and Elizabeth Bell. Chris and I go way back and have worked together in many different ways. Chris, thanks for all you do to promote my books. Elizabeth is a marketing manager extraordinaire. She has endless energy and ideas for marketing this book. I have enjoyed working with her over the last several years and wish to congratulate her on the recent birth of her first child. Congratulations, Elizabeth! I continue to owe a special word of thanks to Glenn and Meg Turner of Burrston House, ideal collaborators whose contributions to the first edition of the book were extremely important and much appreciated. Quade Paul, who makes my ideas come alive with his art, has been with us from the beginning, and I owe a special debt of gratitude to him. I am also grateful to Maria Guglielmo Walsh and Elise Lansdon for their creativity and hard work in crafting the design of this text. Finally, I would like to thank Beth Sweeten and the rest of the Pearson production team. They are a first-class operation—this text has benefited immeasurably from their talents and hard work. I also thank Francesca Monaco and her coworkers at CodeMantra. I am a picky author and Francesca is endlessly patient and a true professional. I am also greatly indebted to my copy editor, Betty Pessagno, for her dedication and professionalism over many projects, and to Eric Schrader for his exemplary photo research. And of course, I am continually grateful for Paul Corey, with whom I have now worked for over 18 years and 16 projects. Paul is a man of incredible energy and vision, and it is my great privilege to work with him. Paul told me many years ago (when he first signed me on to the Pearson team) to dream big, and then he provided the resources I needed to make those dreams come true. *Thanks, Paul.* I would also like to thank my first editor at Pearson, Kent Porter-Hamann. Kent and I spent many good years together writing books, and I continue to miss her presence in my work.

I am also grateful to those who have supported me personally while working on this book. First on that list is my wife, Ann. Her patience and love for me are beyond description, and without her, this book would never have been written. I am also indebted to my children, Michael, Ali, Kyle, and Kaden, whose smiling faces and love of life always inspire me. I come from a large Cuban family whose closeness and support most people would envy. Thanks to my parents, Nivaldo and Sara; my siblings, Sarita, Mary, and Jorge; my siblings-in-law, Nachy, Karen, and John; and my nephews and nieces, Germain, Danny, Lisette, Sara, and Kenny. These are the people with whom I celebrate life.

I am especially grateful to Michael Tro, who put in many hours proofreading my manuscript, working problems and quiz questions, and organizing appendices. Michael, you are amazing—it is my privilege to have you work with me on this project.

I would like to thank all of the general chemistry students who have been in my classes throughout my 29 years as a professor. You have taught me much about teaching that is now in this book.

Lastly, I am indebted to the many reviewers, listed on the following pages, whose ideas are embedded throughout this book. They have corrected me, inspired me, and sharpened my thinking on how best to teach this subject we call chemistry. I deeply appreciate their commitment to this project. I am particularly grateful to Corey Beck who has played an important role in developing the objectives for this edition. I am also grateful to the accuracy of reviewers who tirelessly checked page proofs for correctness.

Reviewers of the Fifth Edition

Vanessa Castleberry, *Baylor University*
Andrew Frazer, *University of Central Florida*
Alton Hassell, *Baylor University*
Barry Lavine, *Oklahoma State University*
Diana Leung, *The University of Alabama*
Lauren McMills, *Ohio University*
David Perdian, *Broward College*
Daniele Ramella, *Temple University*
Shuai Sun, *University of Kansas*
Dennis Taylor, *Clemson University*
Tara Todd, *Vanderbilt University*

Reviewers of Previous Editions

Patricia G. Amateis, *Virginia Tech*
Margaret R. Asirvatham, *University of Colorado*
Paul Badger, *Robert Morris University*
Monica H. Baloga, *Florida Institute of Technology*
Rebecca Barlag, *Ohio University*
Mufeed M. Basti, *North Carolina Agricultural & Technological State University*
Amy E. Beilstein, *Centre College*
Donald Bellew, *The University of New Mexico*
Maria Benavides, *University of Houston, Downtown*
Kyle A. Beran, *University of Texas of the Permian Basin*
Thomas Bertolini, *University of Southern California*
Christine V. Bilicki, *Pasadena City College*
Silas C. Blackstock, *The University of Alabama*
Robert E. Blake, *Texas Tech University*
Angela E. Boerger, *Loyola University Chicago*
Robert S. Boikess, *Rutgers University*
Paul Brandt, *North Central College*
Michelle M. Brooks, *College of Charleston*
Gary Buckley, *Cameron University*
Joseph H. Bularzik, *Purdue University, Calumet*
Cindy M. Burkhardt, *Radford University*
Andrew E. Burns, *Kent State University at Stark*
Kim C. Calvo, *The University of Akron*
Stephen C. Carlson, *Lansing Community College*
David A. Carter, *Angelo State University*
Ferman Chavez, *Oakland University*
Eric G. Chesloff, *Villanova University*
Ted Clark, *The Ohio State University*
William M. Cleaver, *The University of Vermont*
Charles T. Cox Jr., *Georgia Institute of Technology*
J. Ricky Cox, *Murray State University*
Samuel R. Cron, *Arkansas State University*
Guy Crundwell, *Central Connecticut State University*
Darwin B. Dahl, *Western Kentucky University*
Robert F. Dias, *Old Dominion University*
Daniel S. Domin, *Tennessee State University*
Bonnie Dixon, *University of Maryland*
Alan D. Earhart, *Southeast Community College*
Jack Eichler, *University of California, Riverside*
Amina K. El-Ashmawy, *Collin College*
Joseph P. Ellison, *United States Military Academy at West Point*
Joseph M. Eridon, *Central New Mexico Community College*
Deborah B. Exton, *The University of Oregon*
William A. Faber, *Grand Rapids Community College*
Michael Ferguson, *Honolulu Community College*
Maria C. Fermin-Ennis, *Gordon College*
Oscar Navarro Fernandez, *University of Hawaii at Manoa*
Jan Florian, *Loyola University Chicago*
Andy Frazer, *University of Central Florida*
Candice E. Fulton, *Midwestern State University*
Ron Garber, *California State University at Long Beach*
Carlos D. Garcia, *The University of Texas at San Antonio*
Eric S. Goll, *Brookdale Community College*
Robert A. Gossage, *Acadia University*
Pierre Y. Goueth, *Santa Monica College*
Thomas J. Greenbowe, *Iowa State University*
Victoria Guarisco, *Middle Georgia State University*
Christin Gustafson, *Illinois Central College*
Jason A. Halfen, *University of Wisconsin-Eau Claire*
Nathan Hammer, *University of Mississippi*
Michael D. Hampton, *University of Central Florida*
Tamara Hanna, *Texas Tech University*
Lois Hansen-Polcar, *Cuyahoga Community College-Western Campus*
Tony Hascall, *Northern Arizona University*
Elda Hegmann, *Kent State University*
Monte L. Helm, *Fort Lewis College*
David E. Henderson, *Trinity College*
Susan K. Henderson, *Quinnipiac University*
Peter M. Hierl, *The University of Kansas*
Paula Hjorth-Gustin, *San Diego Mesa College*
Angela Hoffman, *University of Portland*
Todd A. Hopkins, *Butler University*
Byron E. Howell, *Tyler Junior College*
Ralph Isovitsch, *Xavier University of Louisiana*
Kenneth C. Janda, *University of California, Irvine*
Milt Johnston, *University of South Florida*
Jason A. Kautz, *University of Nebraska-Lincoln*
Catherine A. Keenan, *Chaffey College*
Steven W. Keller, *University of Missouri*
Resa Kelly, *San Jose State University*
Chulsung Kim, *Georgia Gwinnett College*
Louis J. Kirschenbaum, *University of Rhode Island*
Mark Knecht, *University of Kentucky*
Bette Kreuz, *University of Michigan-Dearborn*
Sergiy Kryatov, *Tufts University*
Richard H. Langley, *Stephen F. Austin State University*
Clifford B. Lemaster, *Boise State University*
Sarah Lievens, *University of California, Davis*
Robley Light, *Florida State University*
Adam List, *Vanderbilt University*
Christopher Lovallo, *Mount Royal University*
Eric Malina, *University of Nebraska-Lincoln*
Benjamin R. Martin, *Texas State University*
Lydia J. Martinez-Rivera, *University of Texas at San Antonio*
Marcus T. McEllistrem, *University of Wisconsin-Eau Claire*
Danny G. McGuire, *Cameron University*
Charles W. McLaughlin, *University of Nebraska, Lincoln*
Curt L. McLendon, *Saddleback College*
Lauren McMills, *Ohio University*

Robert C. McWilliams, *United States Military Academy*
Behnoush Memari, *Broward College*
David H. Metcalf, *University of Virginia*
Ray Mohseni, *East Tennessee State University*
Elisabeth A. Morlino, *University of the Sciences, Philadelphia*
Nancy Mullins, *Florida State College at Jacksonville*
James E. Murphy, *Santa Monica College*
Maria C. Nagan, *Truman State University*
Edward J. Neth, *University of Connecticut*
Aric Opdahl, *University of Wisconsin La Crosse*
Kenneth S. Overway, *Bates College*
Greg Owens, *University of Utah*
Naresh Pandya, *University of Hawaii*
George Papadantonakis, *The University of Illinois at Chicago*
Gerard Parkin, *Columbia University*
Jessica Parr, *University of Southern California*
Yasmin Patell, *Kansas State University*
Tom Pentecost, *Grand Valley State University*
David Perdian, *Broward College*
Glenn A. Petrie, *Central Missouri State*
Norbert J. Pienta, *University of Iowa*
Louis H. Pignolet, *University of Minnesota*
Jerry Poteat, *Georgia Perimeter College*
Valerie Reeves, *University of New Brunswick*
Dawn J. Richardson, *Colin College*
Thomas G. Richmond, *University of Utah*
Dana L. Richter-Egger, *University of Nebraska*
Jason Ritchie, *University of Mississippi*
Christopher P. Roy, *Duke University*
A. Timothy Royappa, *University of West Florida*
Stephen P. Ruis, *American River College*
Raymond Sadeghi, *The University of Texas at San Antonio*
Alan E. Sadurski, *Ohio Northern University*
Thomas W. Schleich, *University of California, Santa Cruz*
Rod Schoonover, *CA Polytechnic State University*
Mark Schraf, *West Virginia University*
John Selegue, *University of Kentucky*
Tom Selegue, *Pima Community College, West*
Susan Shadle, *Boise State University*
Anju H. Sharma, *Stevens Institute of Technology*
Sherril A. Soman, *Grand Valley State University*
Michael S. Sommer, *University of Wyoming*
Jie S. Song, *University of Michigan, Flint*
Clarissa Sorensen, *Central New Mexico Community College*
Mary Kay Sorenson, *University of Wisconsin, Milwaukee*
Stacy E. Sparks, *University of Texas, Austin*
Richard Spinney, *Ohio State University*
William H. Steel, *York College of Pennsylvania*
Vinodhkumar Subramaniam, *East Carolina University*
Jerry Suits, *University of Northern Colorado*
Tamar Y. Susskind, *Oakland Community College*
Uma Swamy, *Florida International University*
Ryan Sweeder, *Michigan State University*
Dennis Taylor, *Clemson University*
Jacquelyn Thomas, *Southwestern College*
Kathleen Thrush Shaginaw, *Villanova University*
Lydia Tien, *Monroe Community College*
David Livingstone Toppen, *California State University Northridge*
Marcy Towns, *Purdue University*
Harold Trimm, *Broome Community College*
Frank Tsung, *Boston College*
Laura VanDorn, *University of Arizona*
Susan Varkey, *Mount Royal College*
Ramaiyer Venkatraman, *Jackson State University*
John B. Vincent, *University of Alabama, Tuscaloosa*
Kent S. Voelkner, *Lake Superior College*
Sheryl K. Wallace, *South Plains College*
Wayne E. Wesolowski, *University of Arizona*
Sarah E. West, *Notre Dame University*
John Wiginton, *University of Mississippi*
Kurt J. Winkelmann, *Florida Institute of Technology*
Troy D. Wood, *University of Buffalo*
Servet M. Yatin, *Quincy College*
Kazushige Yokoyama, *SUNY Geneseo*
Lin Zhu, *IUPUI*

Chapter 13, Solids and Modern Materials, Advisory Board

Michael Burand, *Oregon State University*
Christopher Collison, *Rochester Institute of Technology*
Jordan Fantini, *Denison University*
Melissa Hines, *Cornell University*
Raymond Schaak, *Penn State University*
Jennifer Shanoski, *Merritt College*
Jim Zubricky, *University of Toledo*

Focus Group Participants

We would like to thank the following professors for contributing their valuable time to meet with the author and the publishing team in order to provide a meaningful perspective on the most important challenges they face in teaching general chemistry. They gave us insight into creating a general chemistry text that successfully responds to those challenges.

Focus Group 13

Kim Cortes, *Kennesaw State University*
Patrick Daubenmire, *Loyola University - Chicago*
Michael Dianovsky, *South Dakota State University*
Deborah Exton, *University of Oregon*
Joel Goldberg, *University of Vermont*
Edith Preciosa Kippenhan, *University of Toledo*
Thomas Mullen, *University of North Florida*
Tricia Shepherd, *St. Edward's University*

Focus Groups 1–12

Corey Beck, *Ohio University*
Jennifer Duis, *Northern Arizona University*
Alton Hassell, *Baylor University*
Tina Huang, *University of Illinois*
Amy Irwin, *Monroe Community College*
Maria Korolev, *University of Florida*
Jennifer Schwartz Poehlmann, *Stanford University*
John Selegue, *University of Kentucky*
Sarah Siegel, *Gonzaga University*
Jeff Statler, *University of Utah*
Michael R. Abraham, *University of Oklahoma*
Ramesh D. Arasasingham, *University of California, Irvine*
James A. Armstrong, *City College of San Francisco*
Silas C. Blackstock, *University of Alabama*
Roberto A. Bogomolni, *University of California, Santa Cruz*
Stacey Brydges, *University of California San Diego*
Kenneth Capps, *Central Florida Community College*
Stephen C. Carlson, *Lansing Community College*
Charles E. Carraher, *Florida Atlantic University*
Kenneth Caswell, *University of South Florida*
Robert Craig Taylor, *Oakland University*
Darwin B. Dahl, *Western Kentucky University*
Mohammed Daoudi, *University of Central Florida*
Kate Deline, *College of San Mateo*
Stephanie Dillon, *Florida State University*
Ralph C. Dougherty, *Florida State University*
William Eck, *University of Wisconsin, Marshfield/Wood County*
Robert J. Eierman, *University of Wisconsin, Eau Claire*
Amina K. El-Ashmawy, *Collin County Community College*
William A. Faber, *Grand Rapids Community College*
Richard W. Frazee, *Rowan University*
Barbara A. Gage, *Prince George's Community College*
Simon Garrett, *California State University, Northridge*
Raymond F. Glienna, *Glendale Community College*
Eric S. Goll, *Brookdale Community College*
Pierre Y. Goueth, *Santa Monica College*

W. Tandy Grubbs, *Stetson University*
Jerome E. Haky, *Florida Atlantic University*
Jason A. Halfen, *University of Wisconsin, Eau Claire*
John A. W. Harkless, *Howard University*
Paul I. Higgs, *Barry University*
Norris W. Hoffman, *University of South Alabama*
Tony Holland, *Wallace Community College*
Todd A. Hopkins, *Butler University*
Moheb Ishak, *St. Petersburg College, St. Petersburg*
Kamal Ismail, *CUNY, Bronx Community College*
Greg M. Jorgensen, *American River College*
Sharon K. Kapica, *County College of Morris*
Jason Kautz, *University of Nebraska, Lincoln*
Mark Kearley, *Florida State University*
Catherine A. Keenan, *Chaffey College*
Steven W. Keller, *University of Missouri, Columbia*
Ellen Kime-Hunt, *Riverside Community College, Riverside Campus*
Peter J. Krieger, *Palm Beach Community College, Lake Worth*
Roy A. Lacey, State *University of New York, Stony Brook*
David P. Licata, *Coastline Community College*
Michael E. Lipschutz, *Purdue University*
Patrick M. Lloyd, CUNY, *Kingsborough Community College*
Boon H. Loo, *Towson University*
James L. Mack, *Fort Valley State University*
Jeanette C. Madea, *Broward Community College, North*
Joseph L. March, *University of Alabama, Birmingham*
Jack F. McKenna, *St. Cloud State University*
Curtis L. McLendon, *Saddleback College*
Dianne Meador, *American River College*
David Metcalf, *University of Virginia*
John A. Milligan, *Los Angeles Valley College*
Alice J. Monroe, *St. Petersburg College, Clearwater*
Elisabeth A. Morlino, *University of the Sciences, Philadelphia*
Heino Nitsche, *University of California at Berkeley*
Pedro Patino, *University of Central Florida*
Jeremy Perotti, *Nova Southeastern University*
Norbert J. Pienta, *University of Iowa*
Jayashree Ranga, *Salem State University*
Cathrine E. Reck, *Indiana University*
Thomas Ridgway, *University of Cincinnati*
Jil Robinson, *Indiana University*
Richard Rosso, *St. John's University*
Steven Rowley, *Middlesex County College*
Benjamin E. Rusiloski, *Delaware Valley College*
Karen Sanchez, *Florida Community College, Jacksonville*
David M. Sarno, CUNY, *Queensborough Community College*
Reva A. Savkar, *Northern Virginia Community College*
Thomas W. Schleich, *University of California, Santa Cruz*
Donald L. Siegel, *Rutgers University, New Brunswick*
Mary L. Sohn, *Florida Institute of Technology*
Sherril Soman-Williams, *Grand Valley State University*
Allison Soult, *University of Kentucky*
Louise S. Sowers, *Richard Stockton College of New Jersey*
Anne Spuches, *East Carolina University*
William H. Steel, *York College of Pennsylvania*
Uma Swamy, *Florida International University*
Richard E. Sykora, *University of South Alabama*
Galina G. Talanova, *Howard University*
Claire A. Tessier, *University of Akron*
Kathleen Thrush Shaginaw, *Villanova University*
John Vincent, *University of Alabama*
Gary L. Wood, *Valdosta State University*
Servet M. Yatin, *Quincy College*
James Zubricky, *University of Toledo*

Actively Engage Students to Become Expert Problem Solvers and Critical Thinkers

Nivaldo Tro's *Chemistry: A Molecular Approach* presents chemistry visually through multi-level images—macroscopic, molecular, and symbolic representations—to help students see the connections between the world they see around them, the atoms and molecules that compose the world, and the formulas they write down on paper. The **5th Edition** pairs digital, pedagogical innovation with insights from learning design and educational research to create an active, integrated, and easy-to-use framework. The new edition introduces a fully integrated book and media package that streamlines course setup, actively engages students in becoming expert problem solvers, and makes it possible for professors to teach the general chemistry course easily and effectively.

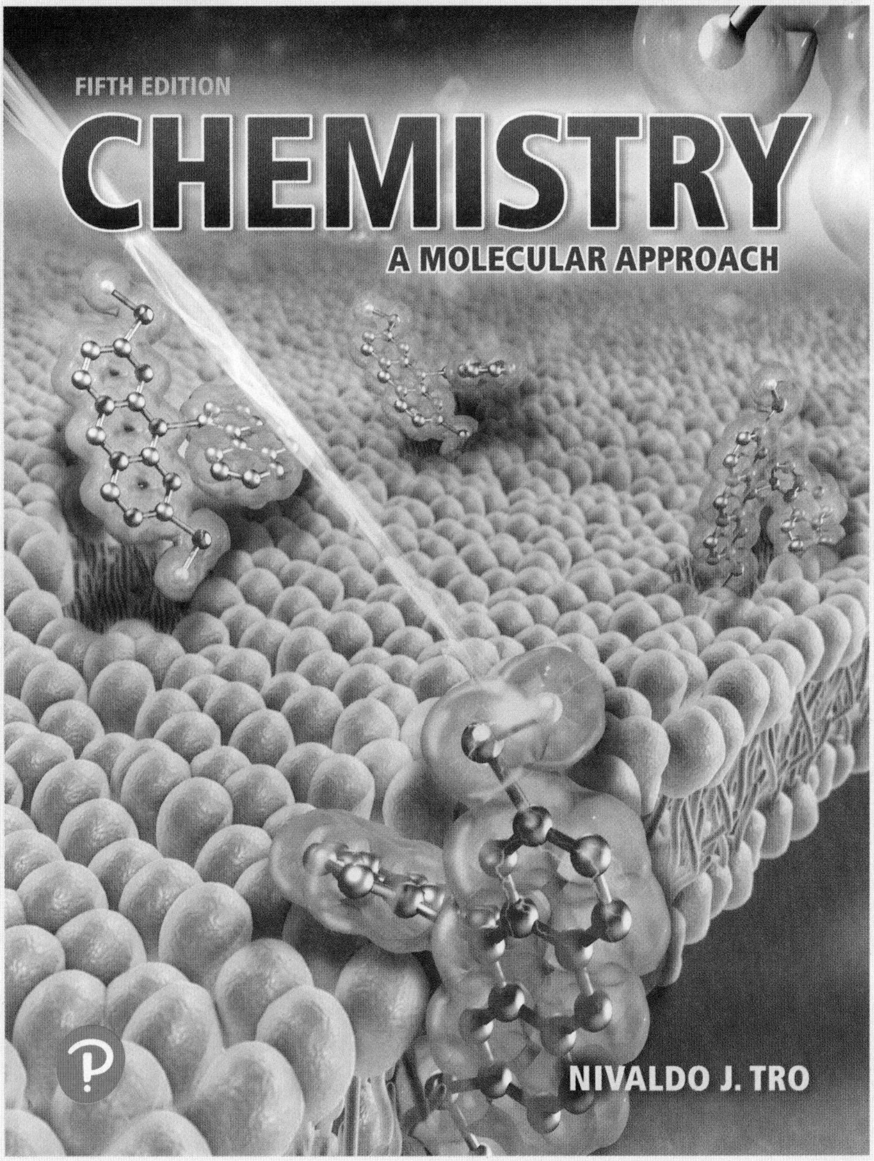

Learn core concepts...

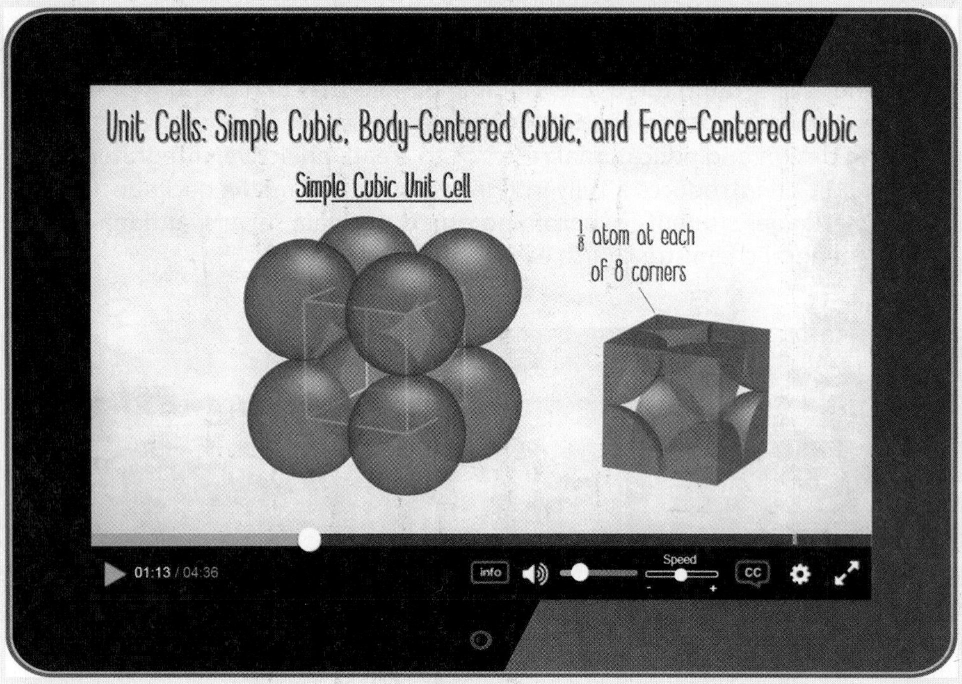

Key Concept Videos combine artwork from the textbook with 2D and 3D animations to create a dynamic on-screen viewing and learning experience. The 5th edition includes **16 new** videos, for a total of **74**.

These short videos include **narration and brief live-action clips of author Nivaldo Tro** explaining every key concept in general chemistry. All Key Concept Videos are available on mobile devices, embedded in Pearson eText, and are assignable in Mastering Chemistry.

before students even come to class

Newly Interactive Conceptual Connections allow students to interact with all conceptual connections within the Pearson eText, so that they can study on their own and test their understanding in real time. **Complete with answer-specific feedback written by the author himself**, these interactives help students extinguish misconceptions and deepen their understanding of important topics, making reading an active experience.

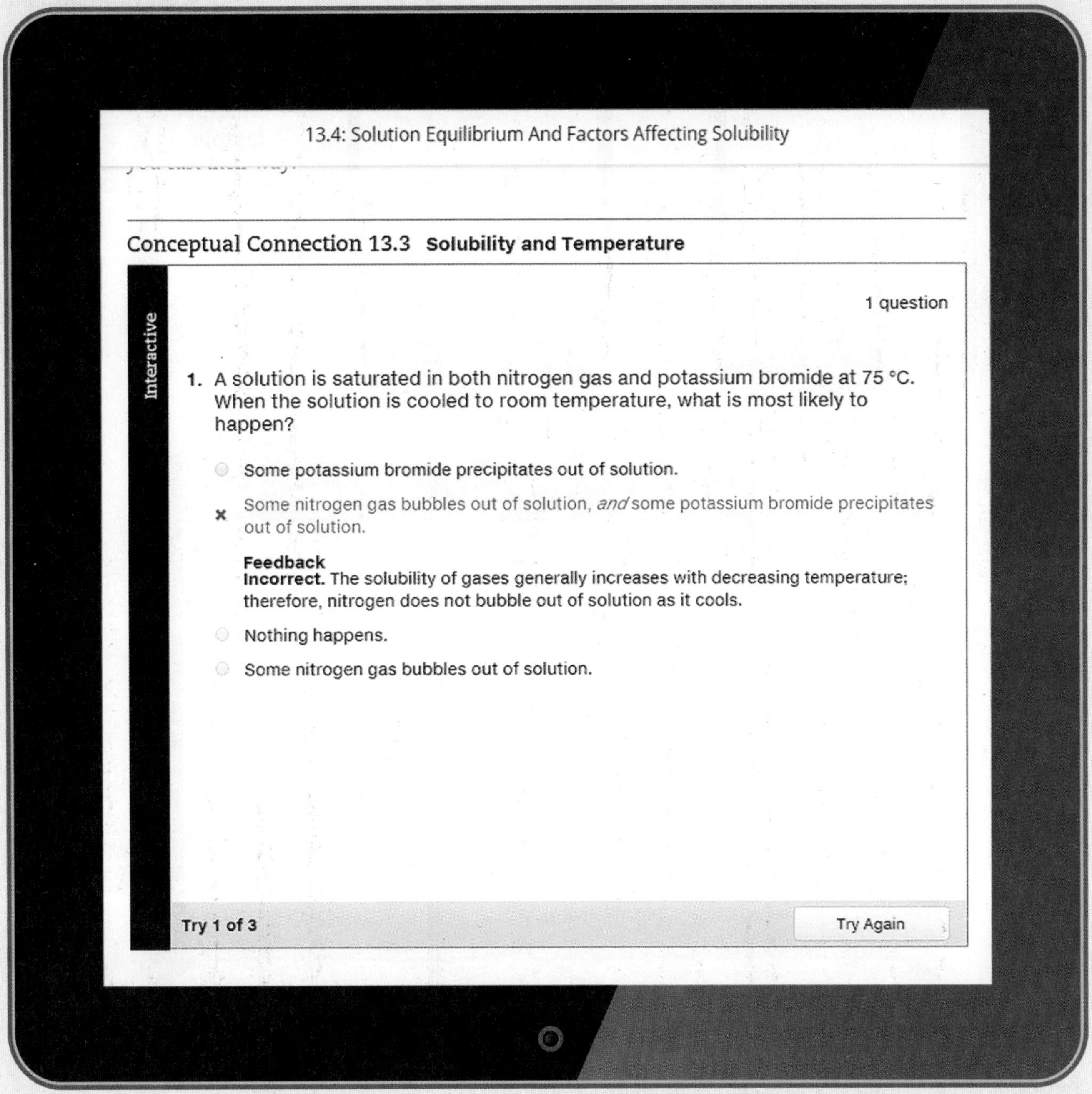

Actively engage students...

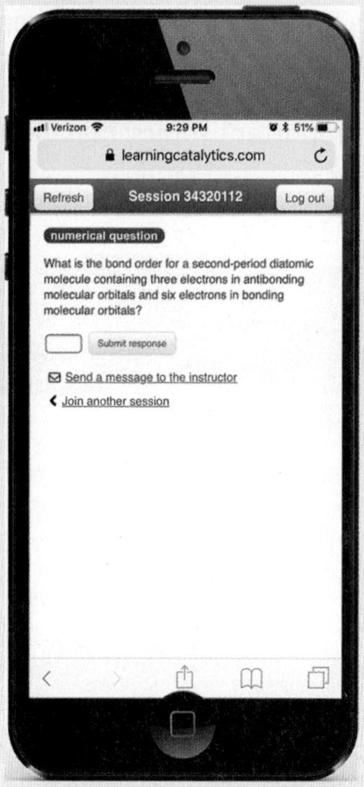

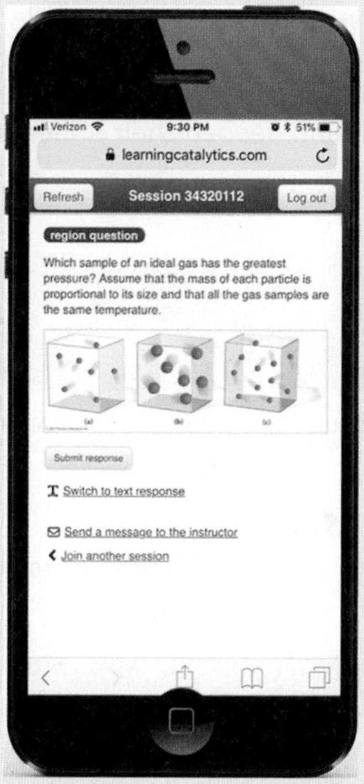

With Learning Catalytics, you'll hear from every student when it matters most. You pose a variety of questions that help students recall ideas, apply concepts, and develop critical-thinking skills. Your students respond using their own smartphones, tablets, or laptops.

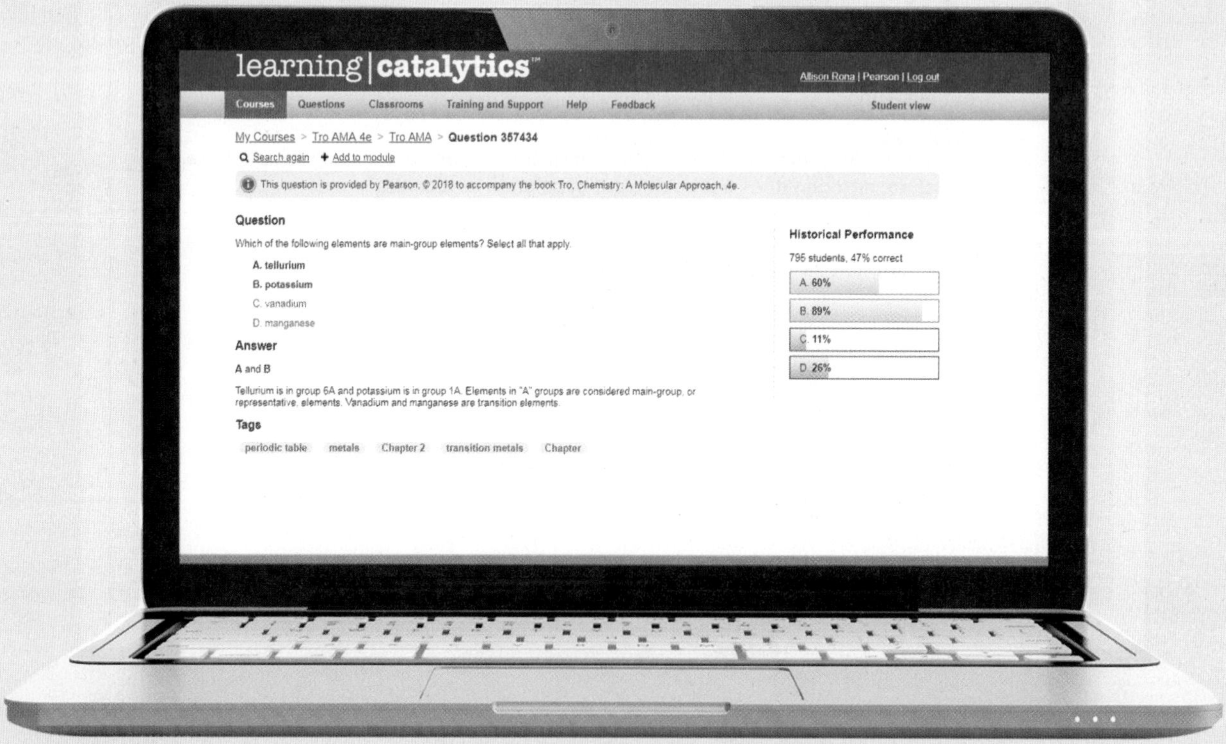

You can monitor responses with real-time analytics and find out what your students do — and don't — understand. Then, you can adjust your teaching accordingly, and even facilitate peer-to-peer learning, helping students stay motivated and engaged. **Learning Catalytics includes prebuilt questions for every key topic in General Chemistry.**

with in-class activities

QUESTIONS FOR GROUP WORK

Active Classroom Learning

Discuss these questions with the group and record your consensus answer.

139. Explain why 1-propanol ($CH_3CH_2CH_2OH$) is miscible in both water (H_2O) and hexane (C_6H_6) when hexane and water are barely soluble in each other.

140. Have each group member make a flashcard with one of the following on the front: ΔH_{soln}, $\Delta H_{lattice}$, $\Delta H_{solvent}$, ΔH_{mix}, and $\Delta H_{hydration}$. On the back of the card, each group member should describe (in words) the ΔH process his or her card lists and how that ΔH relates to other ΔH values mathematically. Each member presents his or her ΔH to the group. After everyone has presented, members should trade cards and quiz each other.

141. Complete the following table by adding *increases, decreases*, or *no effect*:

	Increasing Temperature	Increasing Pressure
solubility of gas in water		
solubility of a solid in water		

142. When 13.62 g (about one tablespoon) of table sugar (sucrose, $C_{12}H_{22}O_{11}$) is dissolved in 241.5 mL of water (density 0.997 g/mL), the final volume is 250.0 mL (about one cup). Have each group member calculate one of the following for the solution and present his or her answer to the group:

a. mass percent
b. molarity
c. molality

143. Calculate the expected boiling and freezing point for the solution in the previous problem. If you had to bring this syrup to the boiling point for a recipe, would you expect it to take much more time than it takes to boil the same amount of pure water? Why or why not? Would the syrup freeze in a typical freezer (−18 °C)? Why or why not?

p. 628

Questions for Group Work allow students to collaborate and apply problem-solving skills on questions covering multiple concepts. The questions can be used in or out of the classroom, and the goal is to foster collaborative learning and encourage students to work together as a team to solve problems. All questions for group work are pre-loaded into Learning Catalytics for ease of assignment.

Numerous ideas for in-class activities can be found in the Ready-to-Go Teaching Modules in the Instructor Resources in Mastering Chemistry. There, instructors will find the most effective activities, problems, and questions from the text, Mastering, and Learning Catalytics, to use in class.

Kinesthetic Activity: Polarity

5 - 10 minutes
Average time for activity

In groups, students model molecules using rope (representing bond dipoles) to show which molecular shapes are polar or nonpolar. This activity can be done at the front of the classroom or in small groups. Example: For trigonal planar, have one student stand in the middle holding the ends of three ropes. Have three other students stand in a trigonal planar arrangement around the middle student and pull equally on the ropes. Since all the ropes (dipole moments) cancel out, the middle student does not get pulled in any direction; this illustrates that the trigonal planar shape is nonpolar. Other shapes that can be shown include: linear, bent, trigonal planar, square planar, T-shaped.

Master problem-solving...

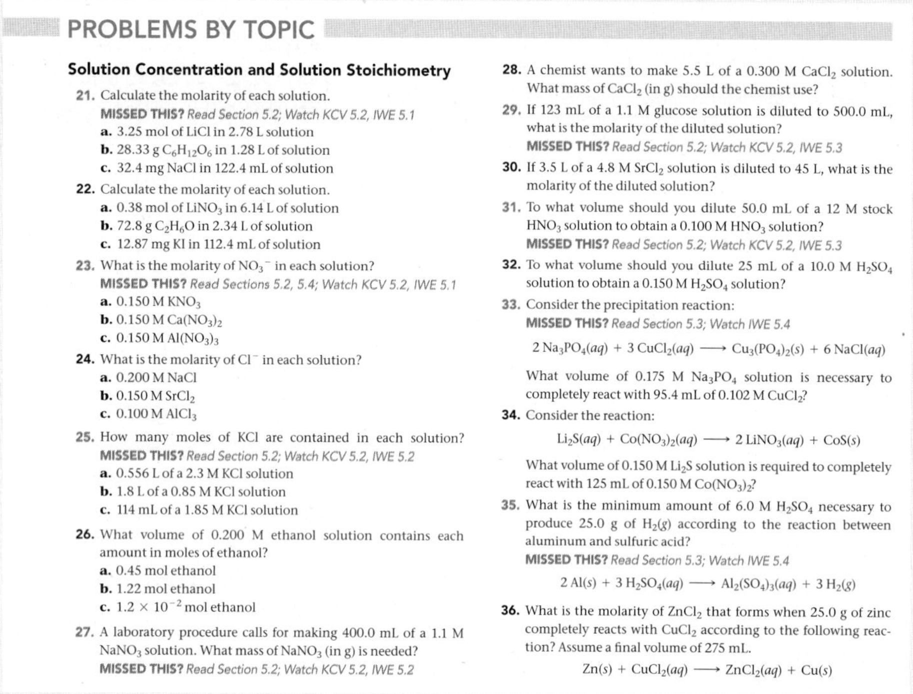

PROBLEMS BY TOPIC

Solution Concentration and Solution Stoichiometry

21. Calculate the molarity of each solution.
MISSED THIS? *Read Section 5.2; Watch KCV 5.2, IWE 5.1*
a. 3.25 mol of LiCl in 2.78 L solution
b. 28.33 g $C_6H_{12}O_6$ in 1.28 L of solution
c. 32.4 mg NaCl in 122.4 mL of solution

22. Calculate the molarity of each solution.
a. 0.38 mol of $LiNO_3$ in 6.14 L of solution
b. 72.8 g C_2H_6O in 2.34 L of solution
c. 12.87 mg KI in 112.4 mL of solution

23. What is the molarity of NO_3^- in each solution?
MISSED THIS? *Read Sections 5.2, 5.4; Watch KCV 5.2, IWE 5.1*
a. 0.150 M KNO_3
b. 0.150 M $Ca(NO_3)_2$
c. 0.150 M $Al(NO_3)_3$

24. What is the molarity of Cl^- in each solution?
a. 0.200 M NaCl
b. 0.150 M $SrCl_2$
c. 0.100 M $AlCl_3$

25. How many moles of KCl are contained in each solution?
MISSED THIS? *Read Section 5.2; Watch KCV 5.2, IWE 5.2*
a. 0.556 L of a 2.3 M KCl solution
b. 1.8 L of a 0.85 M KCl solution
c. 114 mL of a 1.85 M KCl solution

26. What volume of 0.200 M ethanol solution contains each amount in moles of ethanol?
a. 0.45 mol ethanol
b. 1.22 mol ethanol
c. 1.2×10^{-2} mol ethanol

27. A laboratory procedure calls for making 400.0 mL of a 1.1 M $NaNO_3$ solution. What mass of $NaNO_3$ (in g) is needed?
MISSED THIS? *Read Section 5.2; Watch KCV 5.2, IWE 5.2*

28. A chemist wants to make 5.5 L of a 0.300 M $CaCl_2$ solution. What mass of $CaCl_2$ (in g) should the chemist use?

29. If 123 mL of a 1.1 M glucose solution is diluted to 500.0 mL, what is the molarity of the diluted solution?
MISSED THIS? *Read Section 5.2; Watch KCV 5.2, IWE 5.3*

30. If 3.5 L of a 4.8 M $SrCl_2$ solution is diluted to 45 L, what is the molarity of the diluted solution?

31. To what volume should you dilute 50.0 mL of a 12 M stock HNO_3 solution to obtain a 0.100 M HNO_3 solution?
MISSED THIS? *Read Section 5.2; Watch KCV 5.2, IWE 5.3*

32. To what volume should you dilute 25 mL of a 10.0 M H_2SO_4 solution to obtain a 0.150 M H_2SO_4 solution?

33. Consider the precipitation reaction:
MISSED THIS? *Read Section 5.3; Watch IWE 5.4*

$$2\,Na_3PO_4(aq) + 3\,CuCl_2(aq) \longrightarrow Cu_3(PO_4)_2(s) + 6\,NaCl(aq)$$

What volume of 0.175 M Na_3PO_4 solution is necessary to completely react with 95.4 mL of 0.102 M $CuCl_2$?

34. Consider the reaction:

$$Li_2S(aq) + Co(NO_3)_2(aq) \longrightarrow 2\,LiNO_3(aq) + CoS(s)$$

What volume of 0.150 M Li_2S solution is required to completely react with 125 mL of 0.150 M $Co(NO_3)_2$?

35. What is the minimum amount of 6.0 M H_2SO_4 necessary to produce 25.0 g of $H_2(g)$ according to the reaction between aluminum and sulfuric acid?
MISSED THIS? *Read Section 5.3; Watch IWE 5.4*

$$2\,Al(s) + 3\,H_2SO_4(aq) \longrightarrow Al_2(SO_4)_3(aq) + 3\,H_2(g)$$

36. What is the molarity of $ZnCl_2$ that forms when 25.0 g of zinc completely reacts with $CuCl_2$ according to the following reaction? Assume a final volume of 275 mL.

$$Zn(s) + CuCl_2(aq) \longrightarrow ZnCl_2(aq) + Cu(s)$$

p. 204

NEW! MISSED THIS? appears in the end-of-chapter Self-Assessment Quizzes and each odd-numbered Problems by Topic exercise. *MISSED THIS?* provides sections to read and videos to watch to help students remediate where necessary.

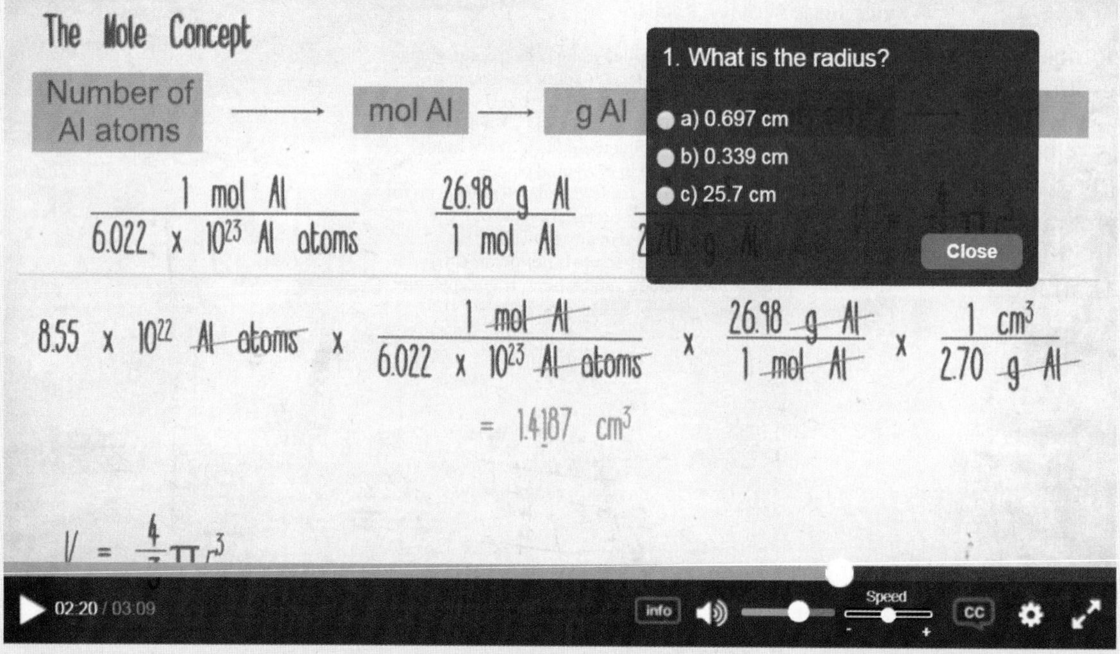

Interactive Worked Examples are digital versions of select worked examples from the text that instruct students how to break down problems using Tro's "Sort, Strategize, Solve, and Check" technique. The Interactive Worked Examples pause in the middle and require the student to interact by completing a step in the example. Each example has a follow-up question that is assignable in Mastering Chemistry. There are 24 new Interactive Worked Examples for a total of 125.

with tools students can use after class

Solutions and Factors Affecting Solubility   Chapter 13

Overview | Prepare | Practice

Prepare

Pre-Class Preparation

The following are appropriate assignments for students to complete before class:

- Section 13.2 Types of Solutions and Solubility (pp. 540–544)
- Section 13.3 Energetics of Solution Formation (pp. 544–548)
- Section 13.4 Solution Equilibrium and Factors Affecting Solubility (pp. 548–552)
- Key Concept Video: Solution Equilibrium and Factors Affecting Solubility
- MasteringChemistry Pre-Built Assignment "Chapter 13 Ready-To-Go Teaching Module Before Class: Solutions and Factors Affecting Solubility"

Videos

The Key Concept Video explains how a solid dissolves in a solvent, as well as the formation of an equilibrium at which point the rate of dissolution equals the rate of recrystallization. It illustrates how temperature and pressure can affect the solubility of solids and gases in liquids. The video also asks students to consider factors affecting solubility.

Key Concept Video: Solution Equilibrium and Factors Affecting Solubility

Dynamic Study Modules

NEW! Ready-to-Go Practice Modules in the Mastering Chemistry Study Area help students master the toughest topics (as identified by professors and fellow students completing homework and practicing for exams). Key Concept Videos, Interactive Worked Examples, and problem sets with answer-specific feedback are all in one easy to navigate place to keep students focused and give them the scaffolded support they need to succeed.

Newly Interactive Self-Assessment Quizzes, complete with answer-specific feedback, allow students to quiz themselves within the Pearson eText, so that they can study on their own and test their understanding in real time. The Self-Assessment Quizzes are also assignable in Mastering Chemistry. Professors can use questions from these quizzes to prepare a pretest on Mastering Chemistry. Research has shown that this kind of active exam preparation improves students' exam scores.

Self-Assessment Quiz > Chapter 4

Self-Assessment Quiz

Chapter 4: Molecules and Compounds

1 What is the empirical formula of the compound with the molecular formula $C_{10}H_8$?

- CH
- C_5H_3
- C_5H_4
- C_2H_4

Incorrect. Remember that the subscripts in the molecular formula must equal *n* times the subscripts in the empirical formula (where *n* is an integer).

Teach with art based on learning design principles

Extensively updated art program better directs students' attention to key elements in the art and promotes understanding of the processes depicted. Dozens of figures in the 5th Edition were reviewed by learning design specialists to ensure they are clearly navigable for students and now include more helpful annotations and labels to help readers focus on key concepts.

180 **CHAPTER 5** Introduction to Solutions and Aqueous Reactions

Precipitation Reaction

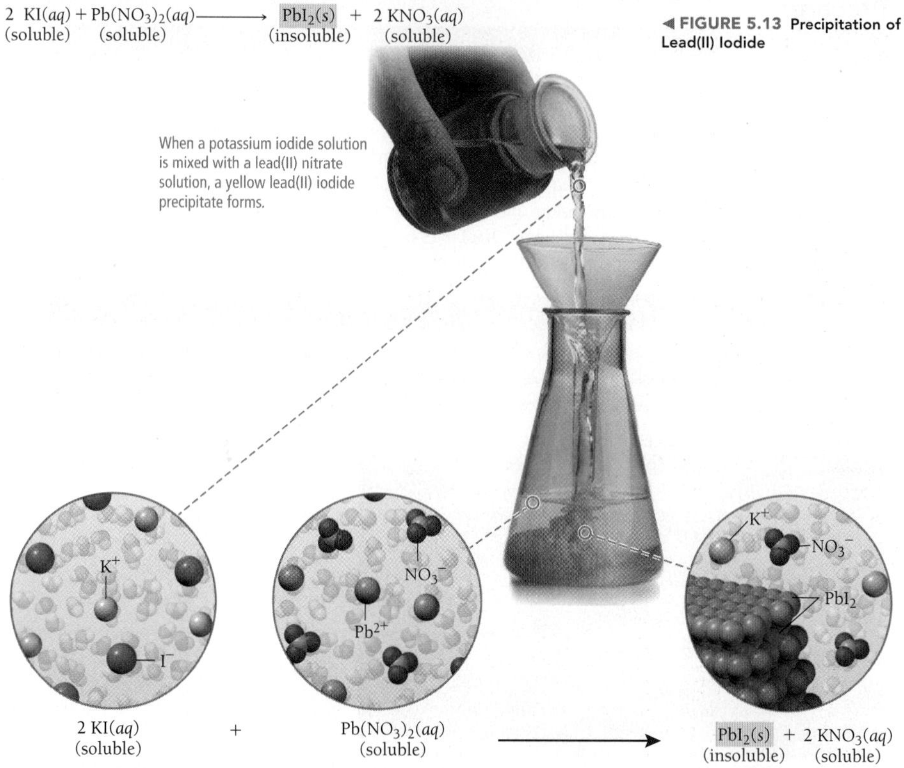

◀ **FIGURE 5.13** **Precipitation of Lead(II) Iodide**

Precipitation reactions do not always occur when two aqueous solutions are mixed. For example, if we combine solutions of $KI(aq)$ and $NaCl(aq)$, nothing happens (Figure 5.14▶):

$$KI(aq) + NaCl(aq) \not\longrightarrow \text{NO REACTION}$$

The key to predicting precipitation reactions is to understand that *only insoluble compounds form precipitates*. In a precipitation reaction, two solutions containing soluble compounds combine and an insoluble compound precipitates. Consider the precipitation reaction described previously:

$$\underset{\text{soluble}}{2\,KI(aq)} + \underset{\text{soluble}}{Pb(NO_3)_2(aq)} \longrightarrow \underset{\text{insoluble}}{PbI_2(s)} + \underset{\text{soluble}}{2\,KNO_3(aq)}$$

KI and $Pb(NO_3)_2$ are both soluble, but the precipitate, PbI_2, is insoluble. Before mixing, $KI(aq)$ and $Pb(NO_3)_2(aq)$ are both dissociated in their respective solutions:

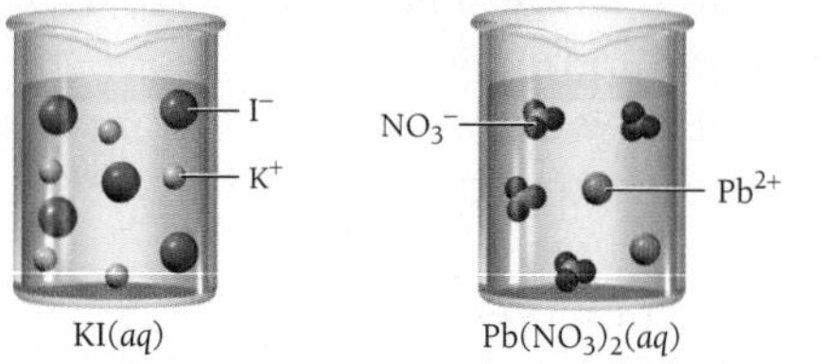

Tro's multipart images help students see the relationship between the formulas they write down on paper (symbolic), the world they see around them (macroscopic), and the atoms and molecules that compose the world (molecular).

The instant that the solutions come into contact, all four ions are present:

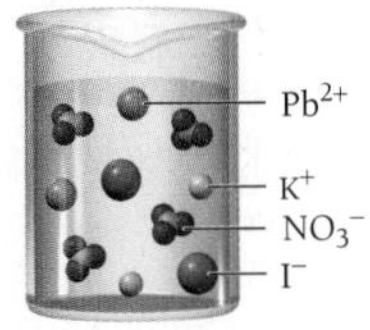

KI(*aq*) and $Pb(NO_3)_2$(*aq*)

Now, new compounds—one or both of which might be insoluble—are possible. Specifically, the cation from either compound can pair with the anion from the other to form possibly insoluble products:

Original compounds		Possible products
K I	⟶	KNO_3
Pb $(NO_3)_2$		PbI_2

If the possible products are both soluble, no reaction occurs and no precipitate forms. If one or both of the possible products are insoluble, a precipitation reaction occurs. In this case, KNO_3 is soluble, but PbI_2 is insoluble. Consequently, PbI_2 precipitates.

To predict whether a precipitation reaction will occur when two solutions are mixed and to write an equation for the reaction, we use the procedure that follows. The steps are outlined in the left column, and two examples illustrating how to apply the procedure are shown in the center and right columns.

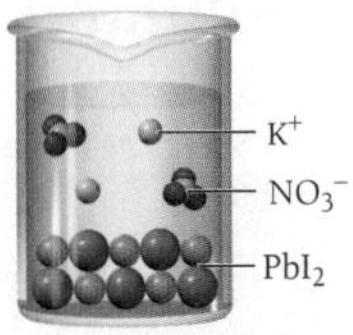

PbI_2(s) and KNO_3(*aq*)

No Reaction

KI(*aq*) + NaCl(*aq*) —✕→ No reaction

◀ **FIGURE 5.14 No Precipitation**

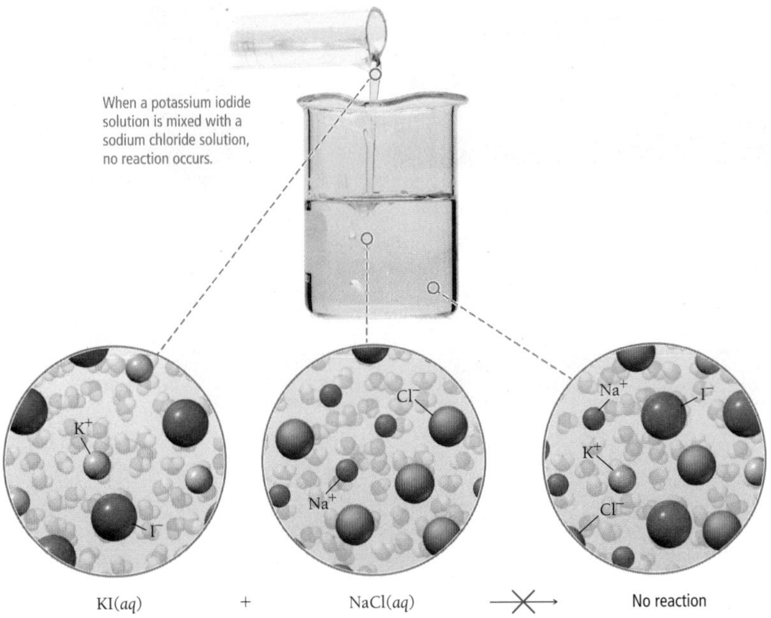

pgs. 180–181

Deliver trusted content with Pearson eText

Pearson eText is a simple-to-use, mobile-optimized, personalized reading experience available within Mastering. It allows students to easily highlight, take notes, and review key vocabulary all in one place—even when offline. Seamlessly integrated videos, rich media, and interactive self-assessment questions engage students and give them access to the help they need, when they need it. Pearson eText is available within Mastering when packaged with a new book; students can also purchase Mastering with Pearson eText online.

Improve learning with Dynamic Study Modules

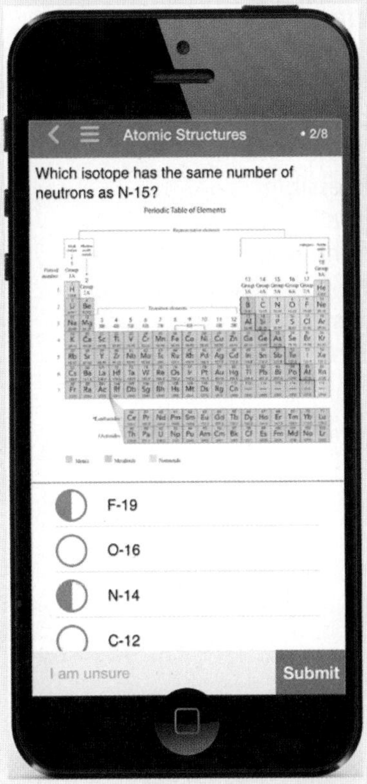

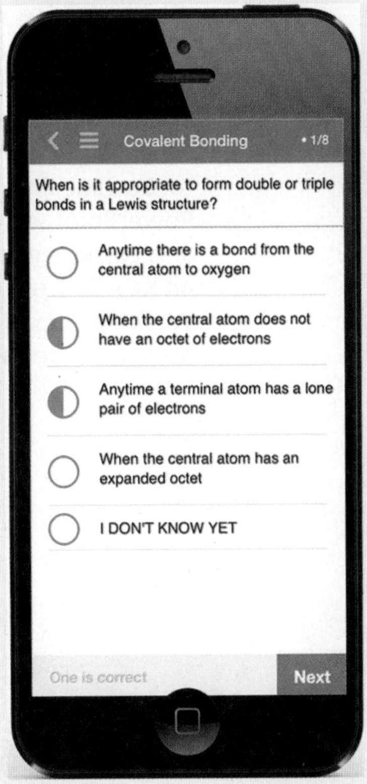

Dynamic Study Modules in Mastering Chemistry help students study effectively—and at their own pace—by keeping them motivated and engaged. The assignable modules rely on the latest research in cognitive science, using methods—such as adaptivity, gamification, and intermittent rewards—to stimulate learning and improve retention.

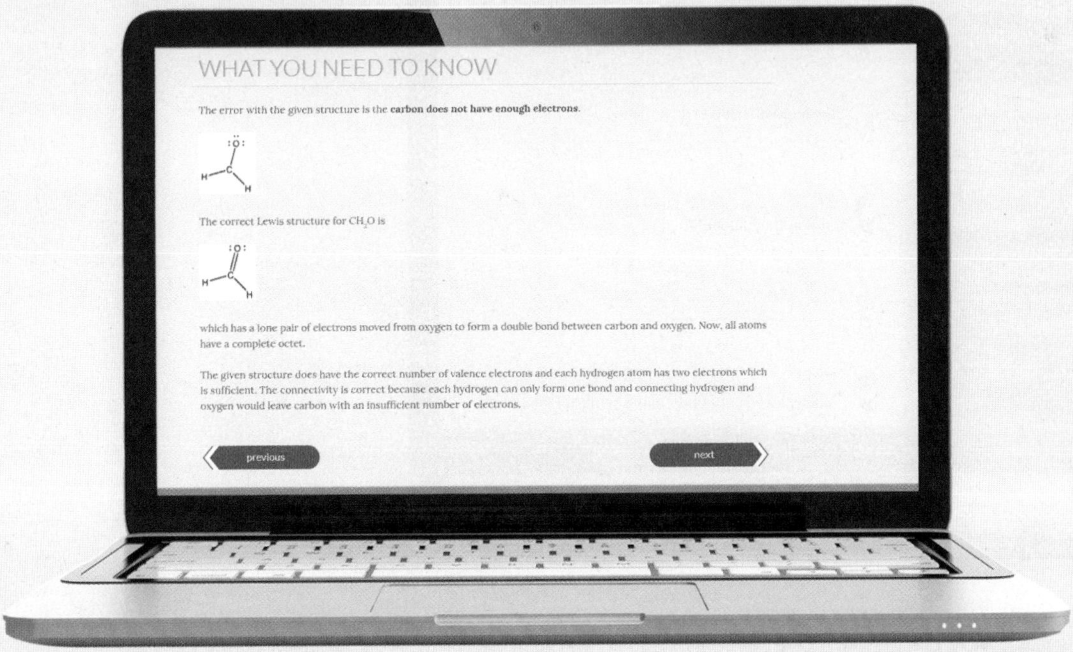

Each module poses a series of questions about a course topic. These question sets adapt to each student's performance and offer personalized, targeted feedback to help them master key concepts. With **Dynamic Study Modules,** students build the confidence they need to deepen their understanding, participate meaningfully, and perform better—in and out of class.

Instructor support you can rely on

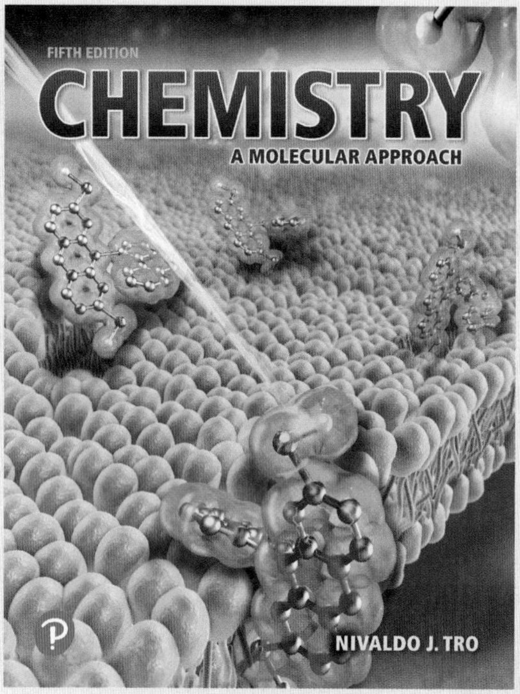

Chemistry: A Molecular Approach includes a full suite of instructor support materials in the Instructor Resources area in Mastering Chemistry. Resources include new Ready-to-Go Teaching Modules; accessible PowerPoint lecture outlines; all images and worked examples from the text; all Key Concept Videos and Interactive Worked Examples; plus an instructor resource manual and test bank.

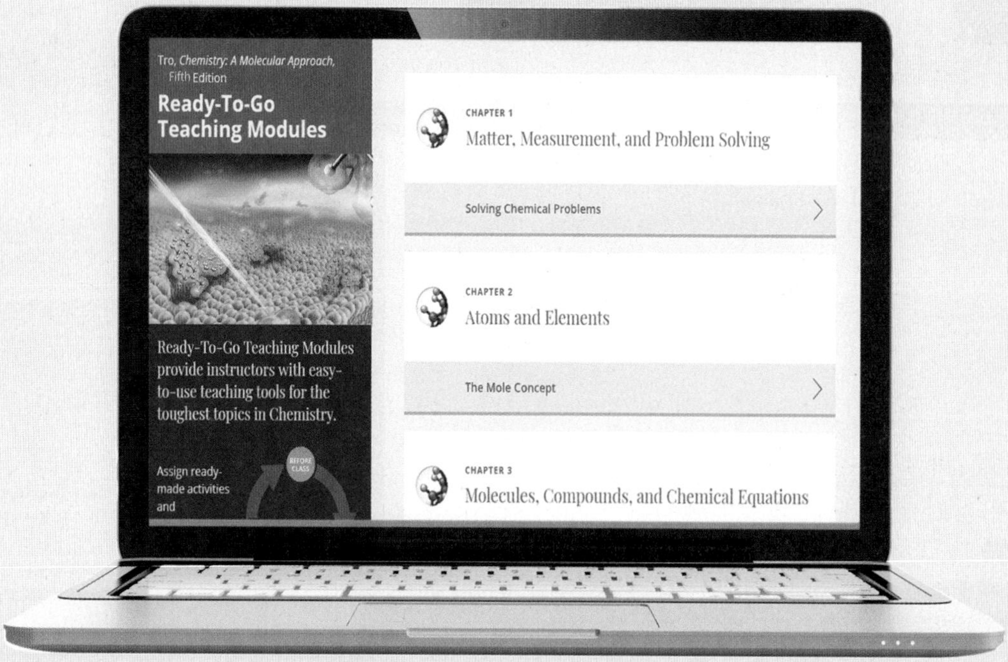

Ready-to-Go Study Tools provide organized material for every tough topic in General Chemistry. The modules – created for and by instructors – provide easy-to-use before and after class assignments, in-class activities with clicker questions, and questions in Learning Catalytics™. The modules are easily accessed via Mastering Chemistry.

Teaching and Learning Materials

Support for the AP Curriculum

A complete correlation chart to the College Board's AP® Chemistry Curriculum Framework that corresponds with the chapters and sections within *Chemistry: A Molecular Approach 5e, AP® Edition* can be found online at www.PearsonSchool.com. We also provide tips for the AP Chemistry exam, information on the AP curriculum and Science Practices along with other helpful details to prepare you and your students for course and exam success.

For the Instructor

Most of the teacher supplements and resources for this text are available electronically to qualified adopters within Mastering.

Instructor's Resource Manual

Organized by chapter, this useful guide includes objectives, lecture outlines, references to figures and solved problems, as well as teaching tips. Prepared by Michael Ferguson.

Instructor's Resource Materials

This resource contains the following:

- All illustrations, tables, and photos from the text in JPEG format.
- Three pre-built PowerPoint Presentations (lecture, worked examples, and images).
- TestGen / TestBank—The Test Bank, prepared by Christine Hermann, contains more than 3,000 multiple choice, matching, and short answer questions. The TestGen version of the Test Bank, which allows you to create and tailor exams to your needs.

Instructor's Manual for Laboratory Manual

This manual provides solutions to the questions asked before each experiment in the accompanying Laboratory Manual, and provides background and suggestions for the instructor directing the lab.

Solutions Manual

Prepared by Kathy Shaginaw, this manual contains step-by-step solutions to all end-of-chapter exercises. With instructor permission, this manual may be made available to students.

For the Student

The following resources are available for purchase.

Pearson's Test Prep Series for AP® Chemistry

The test prep workbook contains concise content summaries of each chapter that are relevant to the AP Chemistry Exam, test taking tips, multiple-choice and free-response practice questions, a practice exam with scoring guidelines, and answers and detailed explanations of all questions and answers.

Laboratory Manual

Prepared by John B. Vincent and Erica Livingston, this manual contains experiments with a focus on real-world applications. Each experiment covers one or more topics discussed within a chapter of the textbook.

Study Guide

This Study Guide, prepared by Jennifer Shanoski, presents the major concepts, theories, and applications discussed in the text in a comprehensive and accessible manner.

Selected Solutions Manual

Prepared by Kathy Shaginaw, the selected solutions manual for students contains complete, step-by-step solutions to selected odd-numbered, end-of-chapter problems.

Mastering Chemistry Access

Mastering Chemistry is the most advanced, most widely \used online chemistry tutorial and homework program available. Mastering Chemistry, with Pearson eText, utilizes the Socratic method to coach students through problem-solving techniques, offering hints and simpler questions on request to help students learn, not just practice. Tutorials guide students through the most challenging chemistry topics and help them make connections.

Upon textbook purchase, students and teachers are granted access to Mastering Chemistry with Pearson eText. High school teachers can obtain preview or adoption access to Mastering Chemistry in one of the following ways:

Preview Access

- Teachers can request preview access online by visiting www.PearsonSchool.com/Access_Request. Select Science, choose Initial Access, and complete the form under Option 2. Preview Access information will be sent to the teacher via e-mail.

Adoption Access

- With the purchase of this program, a Pearson Adoption Access Card with Instructor Manual will be delivered with your textbook purchase. (ISBN: 978-0-13-354087-1)
- Ask your sales representative for a Pearson Adoption Access Card with Instructor Manual. (ISBN: 978-0-13-354087-1)

OR

- Visit PearsonSchool.com/Access_Request, select Science, choose initial Access, and complete the form under Option 3—MyLab/Mastering Class Adoption Access. Teacher and Student access information will be sent to the teacher via e-mail.

Students, ask your teacher for access

Pearson reserves the right to change and/or update technology platforms, including possible edition updates to customers during the term of access. This will allow Pearson to continue to deliver the most up-to-date content and technology to customers. Customer will be notified of any change prior to the beginning of the new school year.

The most incomprehensible thing about the universe is that it is comprehensible.

—ALBERT EINSTEIN (1879–1955)

CHAPTER 1 Matter, Measurement, and Problem Solving

What do you think is the most important idea in all of human knowledge? This question has many possible answers—some practical, some philosophical, and some scientific. If we limit ourselves to scientific answers, mine would be this: **the properties of matter are determined by the properties of atoms and molecules**. Atoms and molecules determine how matter behaves—if they were different, matter would be different. The properties of water molecules determine how water behaves, the properties of sugar molecules determine how sugar behaves, and the properties of the molecules that compose our bodies determine how our bodies behave. The understanding of matter at the molecular level gives us unprecedented control over that matter. For example, our understanding of the details of the molecules that compose living organisms has revolutionized biology over the last 50 years.

This image portrays the Disneyland ride, *Adventure Thru Inner Space*. The premise of the ride is that you enter a microscope and get shrunk down to the size of an atom. The red and white spheres shown here depict oxygen and hydrogen atoms bound together to form water molecules.

1.1 Atoms and Molecules 1

1.2 The Scientific Approach to Knowledge 3

1.3 The Classification of Matter 5

1.4 Physical and Chemical Changes and Physical and Chemical Properties 9

1.5 Energy: A Fundamental Part of Physical and Chemical Change 12

1.6 The Units of Measurement 13

1.7 The Reliability of a Measurement 20

1.8 Solving Chemical Problems 26

1.9 Analyzing and Interpreting Data 33

LEARNING OUTCOMES 38

1.1 Atoms and Molecules

WATCH **NOW!**

KEY CONCEPT VIDEO 1.1
Atoms and Molecules

As I sat in the "omnimover" and listened to the narrator's voice telling me that I was shrinking down to the size of an atom, I grew apprehensive but curious. Just minutes before, while waiting in line, I witnessed what appeared to be full-sized humans entering a microscope and emerging from the other end many times smaller. I was seven years old, and I was about to ride *Adventure Thru Inner Space*, a Disneyland ride (in Tomorrowland) that simulated what it would be like to shrink to the size of an atom. The ride began with darkness and shaking, but then the shaking stopped and giant snowflakes appeared. The narrator explained that you were in the process of shrinking to an ever-smaller size (which explains why the snowflakes grew larger and larger). Soon, you entered the wall of the snowflake itself and began to see water molecules all around you. These also grew larger as you continued your journey into inner space and eventually ended up within the atom itself. Although this Disneyland ride bordered on being corny, and although it has since been shut down, it was my favorite ride as a young child.

That ride sparked my interest in the world of atoms and molecules, an interest that has continued and grown to this day. I am a chemist because I am obsessed with the connection between the "stuff" around us and the atoms and molecules that compose that stuff. More specifically, I love the idea that we humans have been able to figure out the connection between the *properties of the stuff* around us and the *properties of atoms and molecules*. **Atoms** are submicroscopic particles that are the fundamental building blocks of ordinary matter. Free atoms are rare in nature; instead they bind together in specific geometrical arrangements to form **molecules**. A good example of a molecule is the water molecule, which I remember so well from the Disneyland ride.

Water molecule

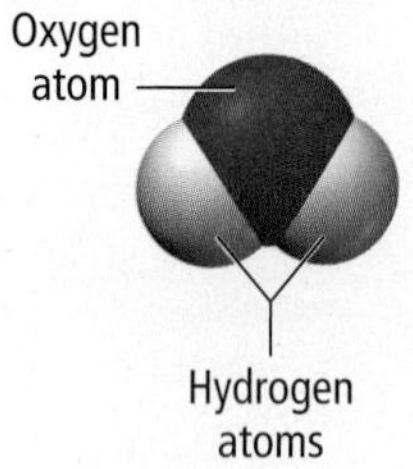

A water molecule is composed of one oxygen atom bound to two hydrogen atoms in the shape shown at left. The exact properties of the water molecule—the atoms that compose it, the distances between those atoms, and the geometry of how the atoms are bound together—determine the properties of water. If the molecule were different, water would be different. For example, if water contained two oxygen atoms instead of just one, it would be a molecule like this:

Hydrogen peroxide molecule

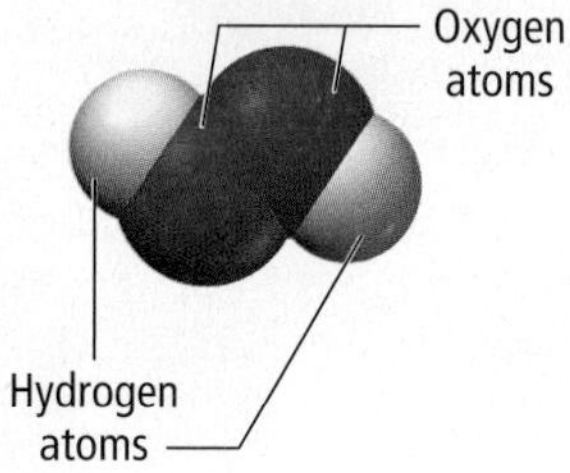

The hydrogen peroxide we use as an antiseptic or bleaching agent is considerably diluted.

This molecule is hydrogen peroxide, which you may have encountered if you have ever bleached your hair. A hydrogen peroxide molecule is composed of *two* oxygen atoms and two hydrogen atoms. This seemingly small molecular difference results in a huge difference in the properties of water and hydrogen peroxide. Water is the familiar and stable liquid we all drink and bathe in. Hydrogen peroxide, in contrast, is an unstable liquid that, in its pure form, burns the skin on contact and is used in rocket fuel. When you pour water onto your hair, your hair simply becomes wet. However, if you put diluted hydrogen peroxide on your hair, a chemical reaction occurs that strips your hair of its color.

The details of how specific atoms bond to form a molecule—in a straight line, at a particular angle, in a ring, or in some other pattern—as well as the type of atoms in the molecule, determine everything about the substance that the molecule composes. If we want to understand the substances around us, we must understand the atoms and molecules that compose them—this is the central goal of chemistry. A good simple definition of **chemistry** is

Chemistry—the science that seeks to understand the behavior of matter by studying the behavior of atoms and molecules.

The term *atoms* in this definition can be interpreted loosely to include atoms that have lost or gained electrons.

Throughout this book, we explore the connection between atoms and molecules and the matter they compose. We seek to understand how differences on the atomic or molecular level affect the properties on the macroscopic level. Before we move on, let's examine one more example that demonstrates this principle. Consider the structures of graphite and diamond.

Graphite is the slippery black substance (often called pencil lead) that you have probably used in a mechanical pencil. Diamond is the brilliant gemstone found in jewelry. Graphite and diamond are both composed of exactly the same atoms—carbon atoms. The striking differences between the substances are a result of how those atoms are arranged. In graphite, the atoms are arranged in sheets. The atoms within each sheet are tightly bound to each other, but the sheets are *not* tightly bound to other sheets. Therefore the sheets can slide past each other, which is why the graphite in a pencil leaves a trail as you write. In diamond, by contrast, the carbon atoms are all bound together in a three-dimensional structure where layers are strongly bound to other layers, resulting in the strong, nearly unbreakable substance. This example illustrates how even the same atoms can compose vastly different substances when they are bound together in different patterns. Such is the atomic and molecular world—small differences in atoms and molecules can result in large differences in the substances that they compose.

1.2 The Scientific Approach to Knowledge

Although some Greek philosophers, such as Aristotle, did use observation to attain knowledge, they did not emphasize experiment and measurement to the extent that modern science does.

Throughout history, humans have approached knowledge about the physical world in different ways. For example, the Greek philosopher Plato (427–347 B.C.E.) thought that the best way to learn about reality was—not through the senses—but through reason. He believed that the physical world was an imperfect representation of a perfect and transcendent world (a world beyond space and time). For him, true knowledge came, not through observing the real physical world, but through reasoning and thinking about the ideal one.

The *scientific* approach to knowledge, however, is exactly the opposite of Plato's. Scientific knowledge is empirical—it is based on *observation* and *experiment*. Scientists observe and perform experiments on the physical world to learn about it. Some observations and experiments are qualitative (noting or describing how a process happens), but many are quantitative (measuring or quantifying something about the process). For example, Antoine Lavoisier (1743–1794), a French chemist who studied combustion (burning), made careful measurements of the mass of objects before and after burning them in closed containers. He noticed that there was no change in the total mass of material within the container during combustion. In doing so, Lavoisier made an important *observation* about the physical world.

▲ French chemist Antoine Lavoisier with his wife, Marie, who helped him in his work by illustrating his experiments and translating scientific articles from English. Lavoisier, who also made significant contributions to agriculture, industry, education, and government administration, was executed during the French Revolution.
(The Metropolitan Museum of Art)

Observations often lead scientists to formulate a **hypothesis**, a tentative interpretation or explanation of the observations. For example, Lavoisier explained his observations on combustion by hypothesizing that when a substance burns, it combines with a component of air. A good hypothesis is *falsifiable*, which means that it makes predictions that can be confirmed or refuted by further observations. Scientists test hypotheses by **experiments**, highly controlled procedures designed to generate observations that confirm or refute a hypothesis. The results of an experiment may support a hypothesis or prove it wrong—in which case the scientist must modify or discard the hypothesis.

In some cases, a series of similar observations leads to the development of a **scientific law**, a brief statement that summarizes past observations and predicts future ones. Lavoisier summarized his observations on combustion with the **law of conservation of mass**, which states, "In a chemical reaction, matter is neither created nor destroyed." This statement summarized his observations on chemical reactions and predicted the outcome of future observations on reactions. Laws, like hypotheses, are also subject to experiments, which can support them or prove them wrong.

Scientific laws are not *laws* in the same sense as civil or governmental laws. Nature does not follow laws in the way that we obey the laws against speeding or running a stop sign. Rather, scientific laws *describe* how nature behaves—they are generalizations about what nature does. For that reason, some people find it more appropriate to refer to them as *principles* rather than *laws*.

One or more well-established hypotheses may form the basis for a scientific **theory**. A scientific theory is a model for the way nature is and tries to explain not merely what nature does but why. As such, well-established theories are the pinnacle of scientific knowledge, often predicting behavior far beyond the observations or laws from which they were developed. A good example of a theory is the **atomic theory** proposed by English chemist John Dalton (1766–1844). Dalton explained the law of conservation of mass, as well as other laws and observations of the time, by proposing that matter is composed of small, indestructible particles called atoms. Since these particles are merely rearranged in chemical changes (and not created or destroyed), the total amount of mass remains the same. Dalton's theory is a model for the physical world—it gives us insight into how nature works and, therefore, *explains* our laws and observations.

In Dalton's time, people thought atoms were indestructible. Today, because of nuclear reactions, we know that atoms can be broken apart into their smaller components.

Finally, the scientific approach returns to observation to test theories. For example, scientists can test the atomic theory by trying to isolate single atoms or by trying to image them (both of which, by the way, have already been accomplished). Theories are validated by experiments; however, theories can never be conclusively proven because some new observation or experiment always has the potential to reveal a flaw. Notice that the scientific approach to knowledge begins with observation and ends with observation. An experiment is in essence a highly controlled procedure for generating critical observations designed to test a theory or hypothesis. Each new set of observations has the potential to refine the original model. Figure 1.1▼ summarizes one way to map the scientific approach to knowledge. Scientific laws, hypotheses, and theories are all subject to continued experimentation. If a law, hypothesis, or theory is proved wrong by an experiment, it must be revised and tested with new experiments. Over time, the scientific community eliminates or corrects poor theories and laws, and valid theories and laws—those consistent with experimental results—remain.

Established theories with strong experimental support are the most powerful pieces of scientific knowledge. You may have heard the phrase "That is just a theory," as if theories are easily dismissible. Such a statement reveals a deep misunderstanding of the nature of a scientific theory. Well-established theories are as close to truth as we get in science. The idea that all matter is made of atoms is "just a theory," but it has over 200 years of experimental evidence to support it. It is a powerful piece of scientific knowledge on which many other scientific ideas are based.

One last word about the scientific approach to knowledge: some people wrongly imagine science to be a strict set of rules and procedures that automatically leads to inarguable, objective facts. This is not the case. Even our diagram of the scientific approach to knowledge is only an idealization of real science, useful to help us see the key distinctions of science. Real science requires hard work, care, creativity, and even a bit of luck.

▼ **FIGURE 1.1 The Scientific Approach to Knowledge**

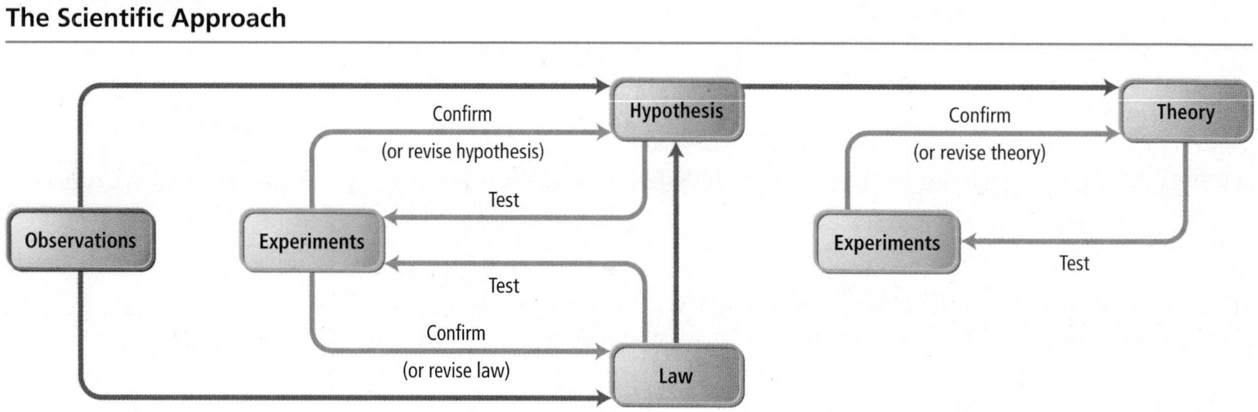

Scientific theories do not just arise out of data—men and women of genius and creativity craft theories. A great theory is not unlike a master painting, and many see a similar kind of beauty in both. (For more on this aspect of science, see the accompanying box entitled *Thomas S. Kuhn and Scientific Revolutions*.)

LAWS AND THEORIES Which statement best explains the difference between a law and a theory?

(a) A law is truth; a theory is mere speculation.
(b) A law summarizes a series of related observations; a theory gives the underlying reasons for them.
(c) A theory describes *what* nature does; a law describes *why* nature does it.

1.1 Cc Conceptual Connection

ANSWER **NOW!**

THE NATURE OF SCIENCE | Thomas S. Kuhn and Scientific Revolutions

When scientists talk about science, they often talk in ways that imply that theories are "true." Further, they talk as if they arrive at theories in logical and unbiased ways. For example, a theory central to chemistry that we have discussed in this chapter is John Dalton's atomic theory—the idea that all matter is composed of atoms. Is this theory "true"? Was it reached in logical, unbiased ways? Will this theory still be around in 200 years?

The answers to these questions depend on how we view science and its development. One way to view science—let's call it the *traditional view*—is as the continual accumulation of knowledge and the building of increasingly precise theories. In this view, a scientific theory is a model of the world that reflects what is *actually in* nature. New observations and experiments result in gradual adjustments to theories. Over time, theories get better, giving us a more accurate picture of the physical world.

In the twentieth century, a different view of scientific knowledge began to develop. A book by Thomas Kuhn (1922–1996), published in 1962 and entitled *The Structure of Scientific Revolutions*, challenged the traditional view. Kuhn's ideas came from his study of the history of science, which, he argued, does not support the idea that science progresses in a smooth, cumulative way. According to Kuhn, science goes through fairly quiet periods that he called *normal science*. In these periods, scientists make their data fit the reigning theory, or paradigm. Small inconsistencies are swept aside during periods of normal science. However, when too many inconsistencies and anomalies develop, a crisis emerges. The crisis brings about a *revolution* and a new reigning theory. According to Kuhn, the new theory is usually quite different from the old one; it not only helps us to make sense of new or anomalous information, but it also enables us to see accumulated data from the past in a dramatically new way.

Kuhn further contended that theories are held for reasons that are not always logical or unbiased, and that theories are not *true* models—in the sense of a one-to-one mapping—of the physical world. Because new theories are often so different from the ones they replace, he argued, and because old theories always make good sense to those holding them, they must not be "True" with a capital *T*; otherwise "truth" would be constantly changing.

Kuhn's ideas created a controversy among scientists and science historians that continues to this day. Some, especially postmodern philosophers of science, have taken Kuhn's ideas one step further. They argue that scientific knowledge is *completely* biased and lacks any objectivity. Most scientists, including Kuhn, would disagree. Although Kuhn pointed out that scientific knowledge has *arbitrary elements*, he also said, "*Observation . . . can and must drastically restrict the range of admissible scientific belief, else there would be no science.*" In other words, saying that science contains arbitrary elements is quite different from saying that science itself is arbitrary.

QUESTION *In his book, Kuhn stated, "A new theory . . . is seldom or never just an increment to what is already known." From your knowledge of the history of science, can you think of any examples that support Kuhn's statement? Do you know of any instances in which a new theory or model was drastically different from the one it replaced?*

1.3 The Classification of Matter

WATCH **NOW!**
KEY CONCEPT VIDEO 1.3 *Classifying Matter*

Matter is anything that occupies space and has mass. Your desk, your chair, and even your body are all composed of matter. Less obviously, the air around you is also matter—it too occupies space and has mass. We call a specific instance of matter—such as air, water, or sand—a **substance**. We classify matter according to its **state** (its physical form) and its **composition** (the basic components that make it up).

The state of matter changes from solid to liquid to gas with increasing temperature.

The States of Matter: Solid, Liquid, and Gas

Matter exists in three different states: **solid**, **liquid**, and **gas**. In *solid matter*, atoms or molecules pack closely to each other in fixed locations. Although the atoms and molecules in a solid vibrate, they do not move around or past each other. Consequently, a solid has a fixed volume and rigid shape. Ice, aluminum, and diamond are examples of solids. Solid matter may be **crystalline**, in which case its atoms or molecules are in patterns with long-range, repeating order (Figure 1.2▼), or it may be **amorphous**, in which case its atoms or molecules do not have any long-range order. Table salt and diamond are examples of *crystalline* solids; the well-ordered geometric shapes of salt and diamond crystals reflect the well-ordered geometric arrangement of their atoms (although this is not the case for *all* crystalline solids). Examples of *amorphous* solids include glass and plastic. In *liquid matter*, atoms or molecules pack about as closely as they do in solid matter, but they are free to move relative to each other, giving liquids a fixed volume but not a fixed shape. Liquids assume the shape of their containers. Water, alcohol, and gasoline are all substances that are liquids at room temperature.

Glass and other amorphous solids can be thought of, from one point of view, as intermediate between solids and liquids. Their atoms are fixed in position at room temperature, but they have no long-range structure and do not have distinct melting points.

Crystalline Solid:
Atoms are arranged in a regular three-dimensional pattern

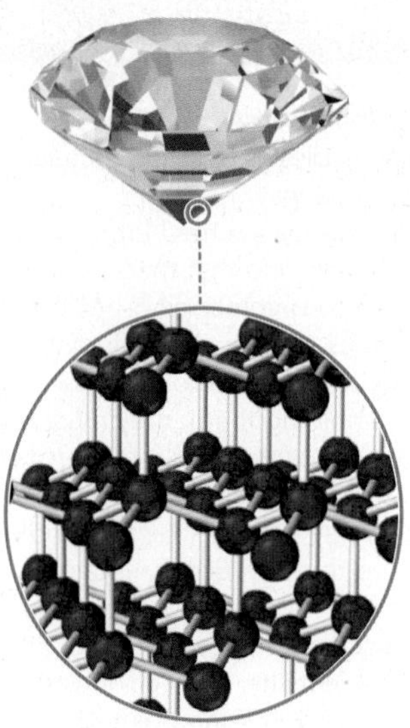

Diamond
C (*s*, diamond)

▲ **FIGURE 1.2 Crystalline Solid** Diamond (first discussed in Section 1.1) is a crystalline solid composed of carbon atoms arranged in a regular, repeating pattern.

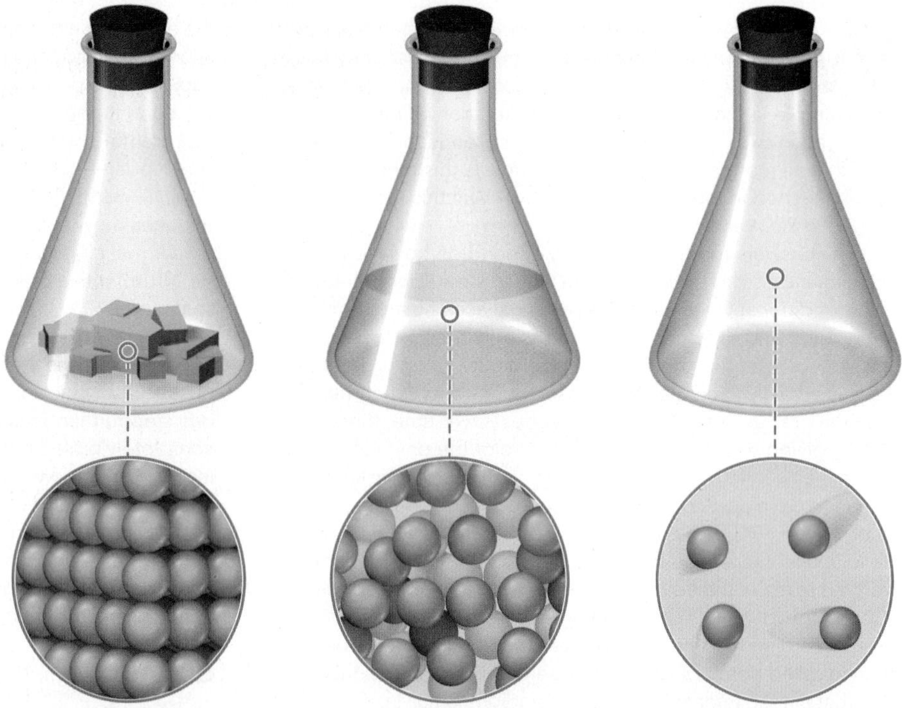

Solid matter **Liquid matter** **Gaseous matter**

▲ In a solid, the atoms or molecules are fixed in place and can only vibrate. In a liquid, although the atoms or molecules are closely packed, they can move past one another, allowing the liquid to flow and assume the shape of its container. In a gas, the atoms or molecules are widely spaced, making gases compressible as well as fluid (able to flow).

In *gaseous matter*, atoms or molecules have a lot of space between them and are free to move relative to one another, making gases *compressible* (Figure 1.3▶). When you squeeze a balloon or sit down on an air mattress, you force the atoms and molecules into a smaller space so that they are closer together. Gases always assume the shape *and* volume of their containers. Substances that are gases at room temperature include helium, nitrogen (the main component of air), and carbon dioxide.

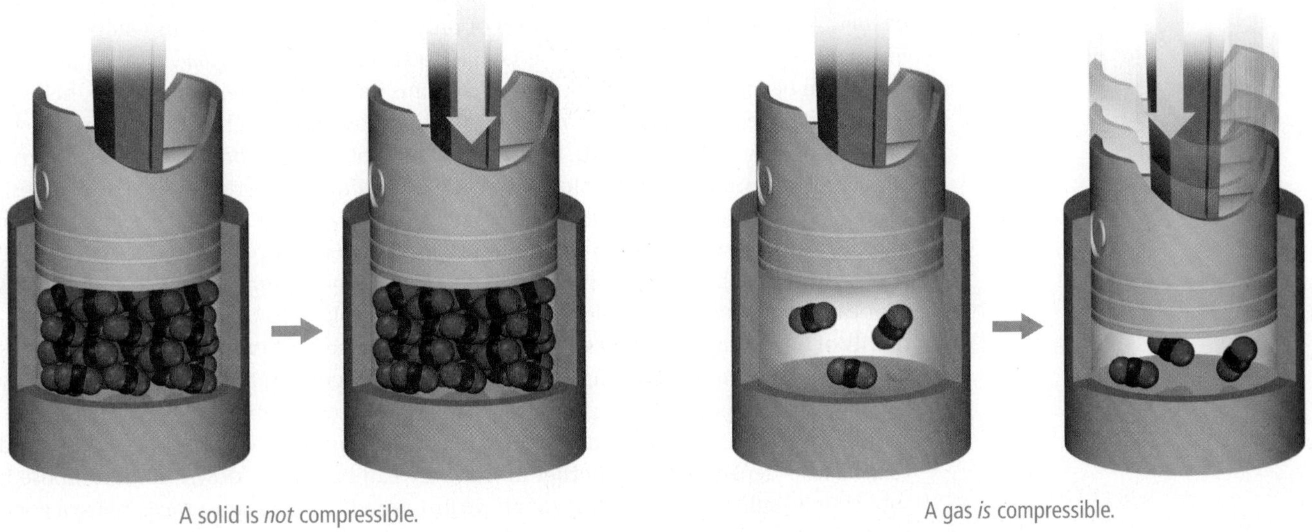

▲ **FIGURE 1.3 The Compressibility of Gases** Gases can be compressed—squeezed into a smaller volume—because there is so much empty space between atoms or molecules in the gaseous state.

Classifying Matter by Composition: Elements, Compounds, and Mixtures

In addition to classifying matter according to its state, we classify it according to its composition, as shown in the following chart:

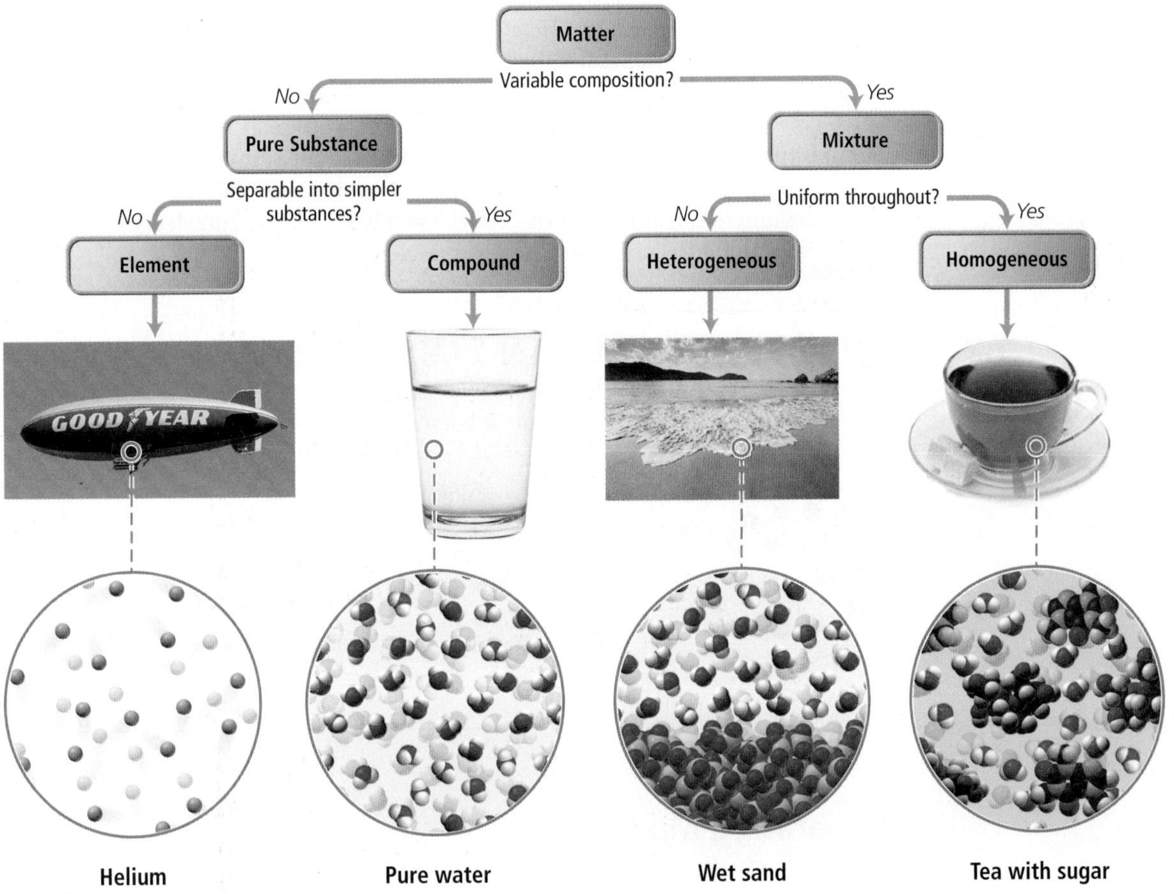

The first division in the classification of matter is between a *pure substance* and a *mixture*. A **pure substance** is made up of only one component, and its composition is invariant (it does not vary from one sample to another). The *components* of a pure substance can be individual atoms or groups of atoms joined together. For example, helium, water, and table salt (sodium chloride) are all pure substances. Each of these substances is made up of only one component: helium is made up of helium atoms, water is made up of water molecules, and sodium chloride is made up of sodium chloride units. The composition of a pure sample of any one of these substances is always exactly the same (because you can't vary the composition of a substance made up of only one component).

A **mixture**, by contrast, is composed of two or more components in proportions that can vary from one sample to another. For example, sweetened tea, composed primarily of water molecules and sugar molecules (with a few other substances mixed in), is a mixture. We can make tea slightly sweet (a small proportion of sugar to water) or very sweet (a large proportion of sugar to water) or any level of sweetness in between.

We categorize pure substances themselves into two types—*elements* and *compounds*—depending on whether or not they can be broken down (or decomposed) into simpler substances. Helium, which we just noted is a pure substance, is also a good example of an **element**, a substance that cannot be chemically broken down into simpler substances. Water, also a pure substance, is a good example of a **compound**, a substance composed of two or more elements (in this case, hydrogen and oxygen) in a fixed, definite proportion. On Earth, compounds are more common than pure elements because most elements combine with other elements to form compounds.

All known elements are listed in the periodic table in the inside front cover of this book.

We also categorize mixtures into two types—heterogeneous and homogeneous—depending on how *uniformly* the substances within them mix. Wet sand is a **heterogeneous mixture**, one in which the composition varies from one region of the mixture to another. Sweetened tea is a **homogeneous mixture**, one with the same composition throughout. Homogeneous mixtures have uniform compositions because the atoms or molecules that compose them mix uniformly. Heterogeneous mixtures are made up of distinct regions because the atoms or molecules that compose them separate. Here again we see that the properties of matter are determined by the atoms or molecules that compose it.

Classifying a substance according to its composition is not always obvious and requires that we either know the true composition of the substance or are able to test it in a laboratory. For now, we focus on relatively common substances that you are likely to have encountered. Throughout this course, you will gain the knowledge to understand the composition of a larger variety of substances.

ANSWER **NOW!**

1.2 Cc Conceptual Connection

PURE SUBSTANCES AND MIXTURES In these images, a blue circle represents an atom of one type of element, and a red square represents an atom of a second type of element. Which image is a pure substance?

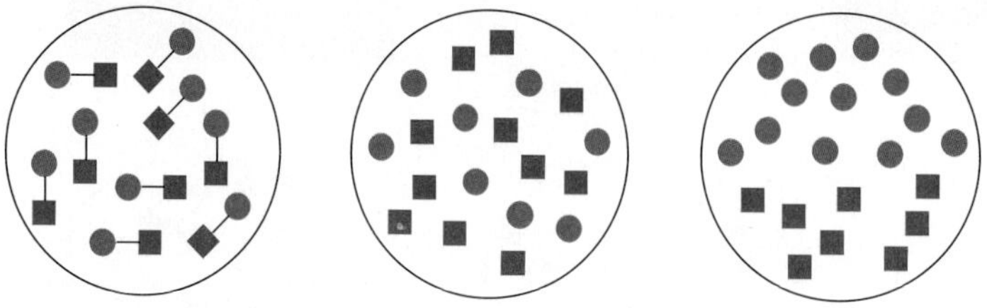

(a) (b) (c) None of the these (d)

Separating Mixtures

Chemists often want to separate a mixture into its components. Such separations can be easy or difficult, depending on the components in the mixture. In general, mixtures are separable because the different components have different physical or chemical properties. We can use various techniques that exploit these differences to achieve

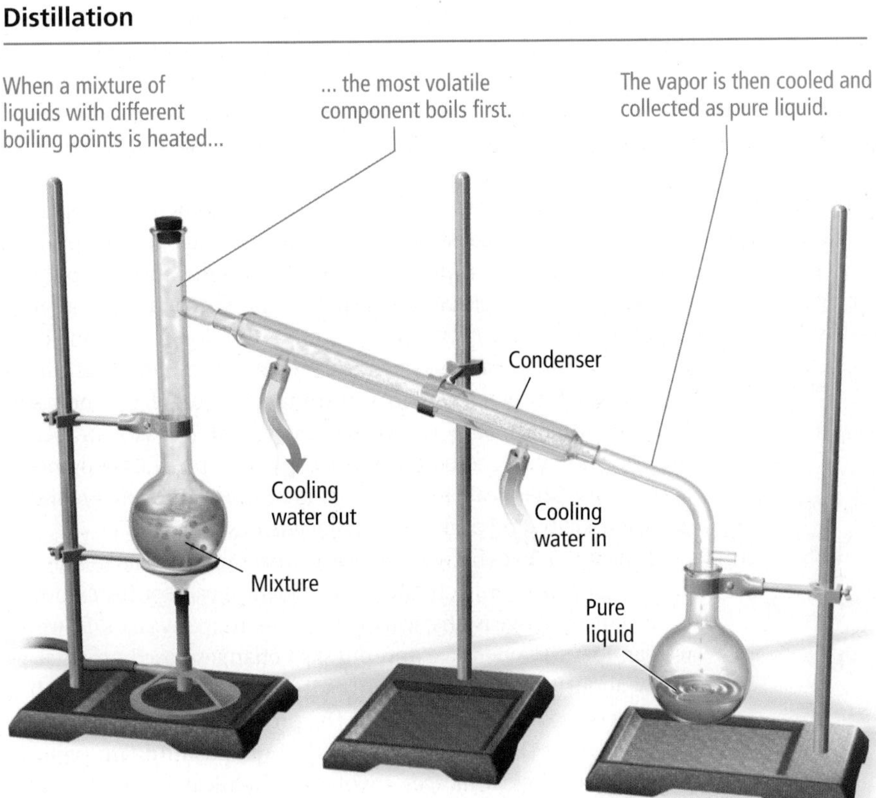

▲FIGURE 1.4 **Separating Substances by Distillation**

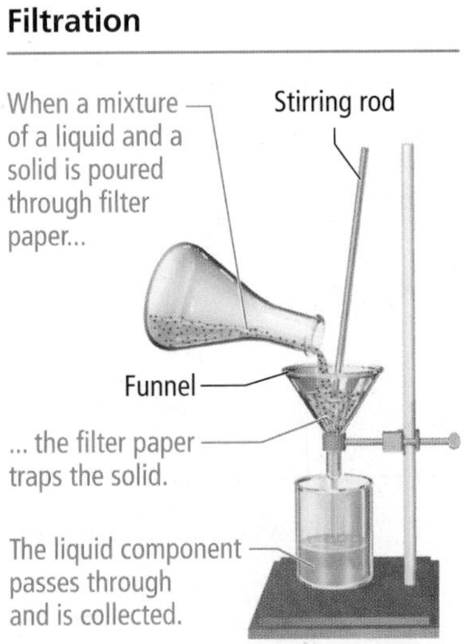

▲ FIGURE 1.5 **Separating Substances by Filtration**

separation. For example, we can separate a mixture of sand and water by **decanting**—carefully pouring off—the water into another container. A homogeneous mixture of liquids can usually be separated by **distillation**, a process in which the mixture is heated to boil off the more **volatile** (easily vaporizable) liquid. The volatile liquid is then recondensed in a condenser and collected in a separate flask (Figure 1.4▲). If a mixture is composed of an insoluble solid and a liquid, we can separate the two by **filtration**, in which the mixture is poured through filter paper in a funnel (Figure 1.5▲).

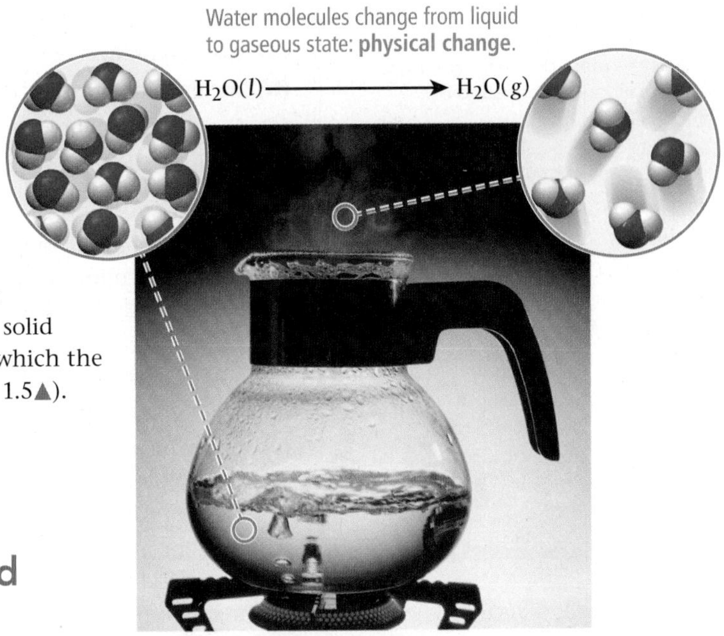

▲ FIGURE 1.6 **Boiling, a Physical Change** When water boils, it turns into a gas but does not alter its chemical identity—the water molecules are the same in both the liquid and gaseous states. Boiling is a physical change, and the boiling point of water is a physical property.

1.4 Physical and Chemical Changes and Physical and Chemical Properties

Every day we witness changes in matter: ice melts, iron rusts, gasoline burns, fruit ripens, and water evaporates. What happens to the molecules or atoms that compose these substances during such changes? The answer depends on the type of change. Changes that alter only state or appearance, but not composition, are **physical changes**. The atoms or molecules that compose a substance *do not change* their identity during a physical change. For example, when water boils, it changes its state from a liquid to a gas, but the gas remains composed of water molecules, so this is a physical change (Figure 1.6▲).

A physical change results in a different form of the same substance, while a chemical change results in a completely different substance.

In contrast, changes that alter the composition of matter are **chemical changes**. During a chemical change, atoms rearrange, transforming the original substances into different substances. For example, the rusting of iron is a chemical change. The atoms that compose iron (iron atoms) combine with oxygen molecules from air to form iron oxide, the orange substance we call rust (Figure 1.7◀). Figure 1.8▶ illustrates other examples of physical and chemical changes.

Physical and chemical changes are manifestations of physical and chemical properties. A **physical property** is a property that a substance displays without changing its composition, whereas a **chemical property** is a property that a substance displays only by changing its composition via a chemical change. The smell of gasoline is a physical property—gasoline does not change its composition when it exhibits its odor. The flammability of gasoline, in contrast, is a chemical property—gasoline does change its composition when it burns, turning into completely new substances (primarily carbon dioxide and water). Physical properties include odor, taste, color, appearance, melting point, boiling point, and density. Chemical properties include corrosiveness, flammability, acidity, toxicity, and other such characteristics.

The differences between physical and chemical changes are not always apparent. Only chemical examination can confirm whether a particular change is physical or chemical. In many cases, however, we can identify chemical and physical changes based on what we know about the changes. Changes in the state of matter, such as melting or boiling, or changes in the physical condition of matter, such as those that result from cutting or crushing, are typically physical changes. Changes involving chemical reactions—often evidenced by temperature or color changes—are chemical changes.

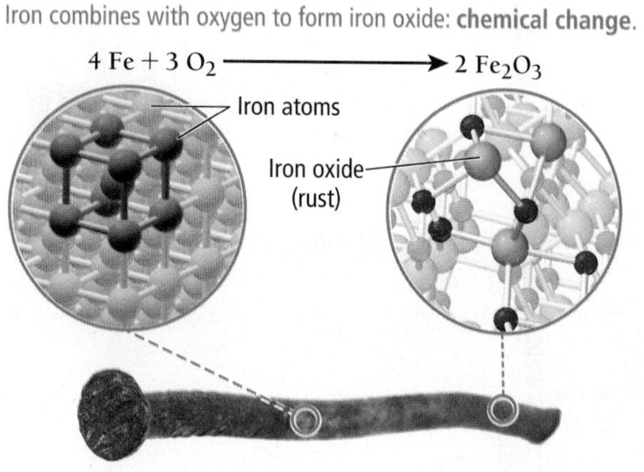

▲ **FIGURE 1.7 Rusting, a Chemical Change** When iron rusts, the iron atoms combine with oxygen atoms to form a different chemical substance, the compound iron oxide. Rusting is a chemical change, and the tendency of iron to rust is a chemical property. A more detailed exploration of this reaction can be found in Section 20.9.

EXAMPLE 1.1 Physical and Chemical Changes and Properties

Determine whether each change is physical or chemical. What kind of property (chemical or physical) is demonstrated in each case?

(a) the evaporation of rubbing alcohol
(b) the burning of lamp oil
(c) the bleaching of hair with hydrogen peroxide
(d) the formation of frost on a cold night

SOLUTION

(a) When rubbing alcohol evaporates, it changes from liquid to gas, but it remains alcohol—this is a physical change. The volatility (the ability to evaporate easily) of alcohol is therefore a physical property.

(b) Lamp oil burns because it reacts with oxygen in air to form carbon dioxide and water—this is a chemical change. The flammability of lamp oil is therefore a chemical property.

(c) Applying hydrogen peroxide to hair changes pigment molecules in hair that give it color—this is a chemical change. The susceptibility of hair to bleaching is therefore a chemical property.

(d) Frost forms on a cold night because water vapor in air changes its state to form solid ice—this is a physical change. The temperature at which water freezes is therefore a physical property.

Answers to For Practice and For More Practice problems can be found in Appendix IV.

FOR PRACTICE 1.1 Determine whether each change is physical or chemical. What kind of property (chemical or physical) is demonstrated in each case?

(a) A copper wire is hammered flat.
(b) A nickel dissolves in acid to form a blue-green solution.
(c) Dry ice sublimes without melting.
(d) A match ignites when struck on a flint.

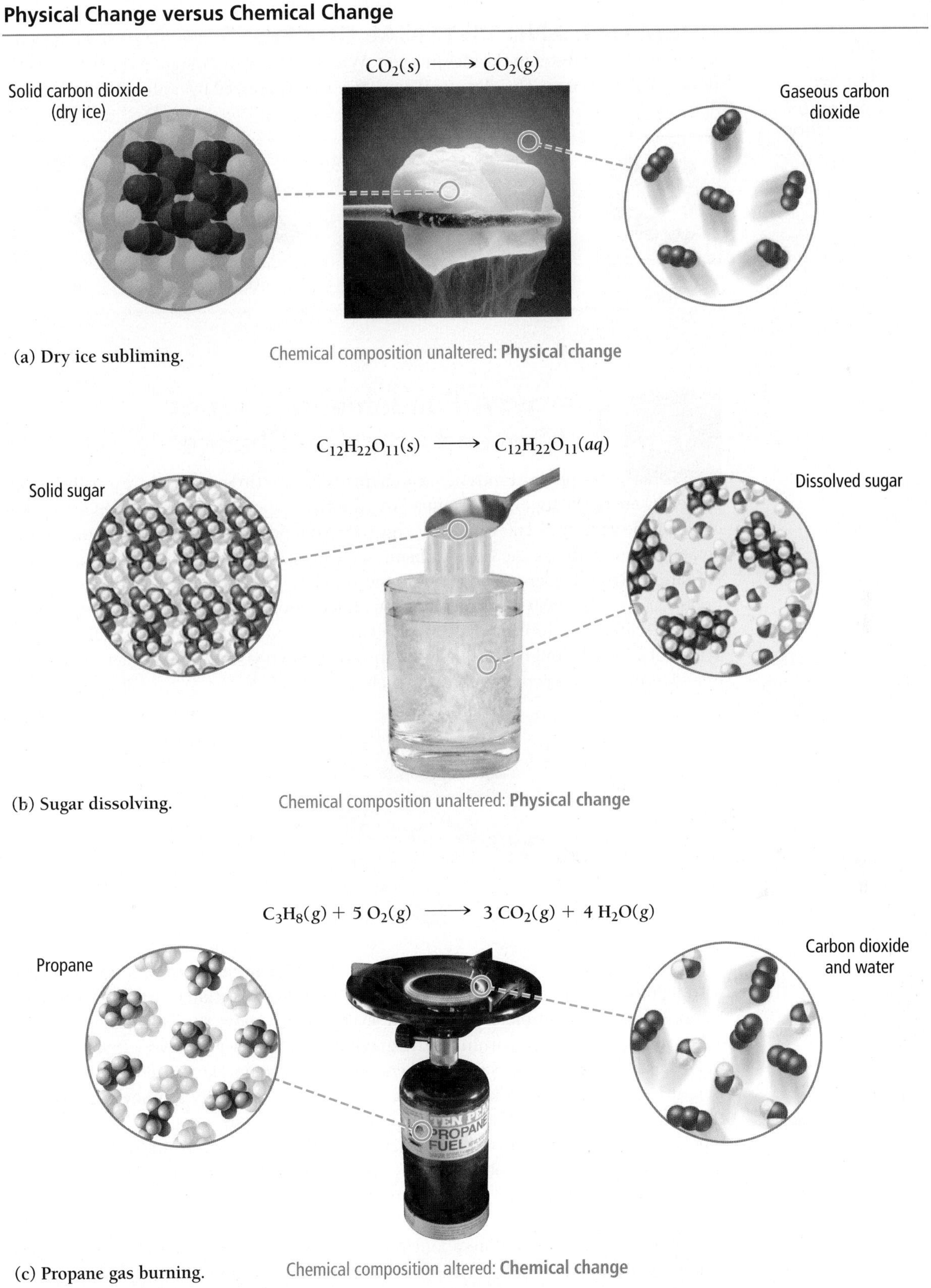

▲ **FIGURE 1.8 Physical and Chemical Changes** **(a)** The sublimation (the state change from a solid to a gas) of dry ice (solid CO_2) is a physical change. **(b)** The dissolution of sugar is a physical change. **(c)** The burning of propane is a chemical change.

ANSWER **NOW!**

1.3 Cc Conceptual Connection

CHEMICAL AND PHYSICAL CHANGES The diagram on the left represents liquid water molecules in a pan. Which of the three diagrams (a, b, or c) best represents the water molecules after they have been vaporized by boiling?

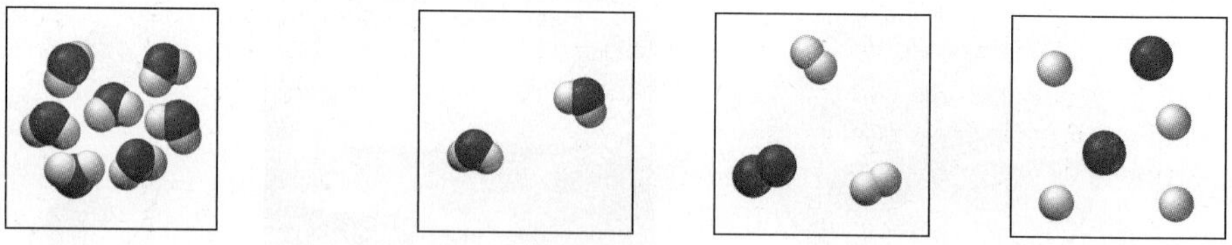

(a) **(b)** **(c)**

1.5 Energy: A Fundamental Part of Physical and Chemical Change

The physical and chemical changes discussed in Section 1.4 are usually accompanied by energy changes. For example, when water evaporates from your skin (a physical change), the water molecules absorb energy from your body, making you feel cooler. When you burn natural gas on the stove (a chemical change), energy is released, heating the food you are cooking. Understanding the physical and chemical changes of matter—that is, understanding chemistry—requires that you understand energy changes and energy flow.

The scientific definition of **energy** is *the capacity to do work*. **Work** is defined as the action of a force through a distance. For instance, when you push a box across the floor or pedal your bicycle across the street, you have done work.

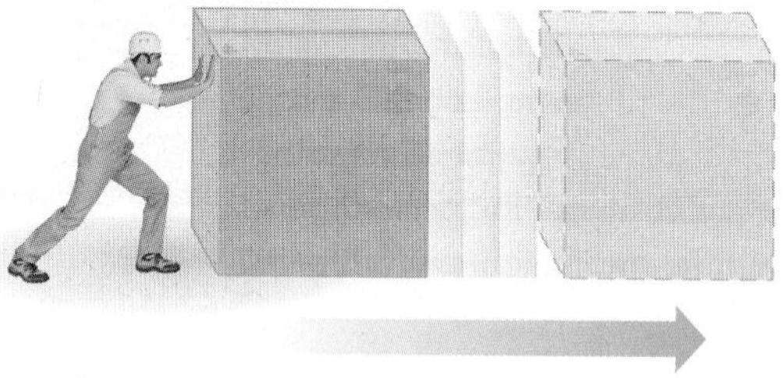

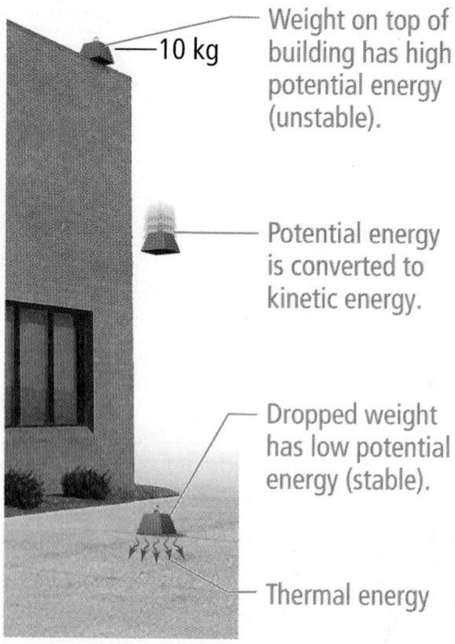

▲ **FIGURE 1.9 Energy Conversions** Gravitational potential energy is converted into kinetic energy when the weight is dropped. The kinetic energy is converted mostly to thermal energy when the weight strikes the ground.

The *total energy* of an object is a sum of its **kinetic energy** (the energy associated with its motion) and its **potential energy** (the energy associated with its position or composition). For example, a weight held several meters above the ground has potential energy due to its position within Earth's gravitational field (Figure 1.9◀). If you drop the weight, it accelerates, and its potential energy is converted to kinetic energy. When the weight hits the ground, its kinetic energy is converted primarily to **thermal energy**, the energy associated with the temperature of an object. Thermal energy is actually a type of kinetic energy because it is associated with the motion of the individual atoms or molecules that make up an object. When the weight hits the ground, its kinetic energy is essentially transferred to the atoms and molecules that compose the ground, raising the temperature of the ground ever so slightly.

The first principle to note about how energy changes as the weight falls to the ground is that *energy is neither created nor destroyed*. The potential energy of the weight becomes kinetic energy as the weight accelerates toward the ground. The kinetic energy then becomes thermal energy when the weight hits the ground. The total amount of thermal energy that is released through the process is exactly equal to the initial potential energy of the weight. The idea that energy is neither created nor destroyed is known as the **law of conservation of energy**. Although energy can change from one type into another, and although it can flow from one object to another, the *total quantity* of energy does not change—it remains constant.

In Chapter 21 we will discuss how energy conservation is actually part of a more general law that allows for the interconvertibility of mass and energy.

The second principle to note about the raised weight and its fall is *the tendency of systems with high potential energy to change in a way that lowers their potential energy*. For this reason, objects or systems with high potential energy tend to be *unstable*. The weight lifted several meters from the ground is unstable because it contains a significant amount of potential energy. Unless restrained, the weight will naturally fall, lowering its potential energy (due to its position in Earth's gravitational field). We can harness some of the raised weight's potential energy to do work. For example, we can attach the weight to a rope that turns a paddle wheel or spins a drill as the weight falls. After the weight falls to the ground, it contains less potential energy—it has become more *stable*.

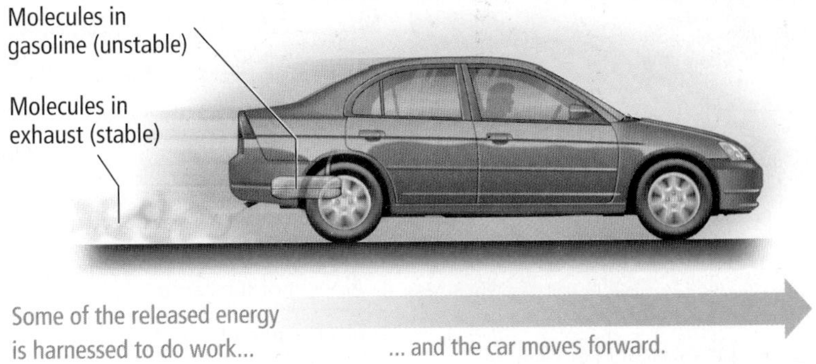

▲ **FIGURE 1.10 Using Chemical Energy to Do Work** The compounds produced when gasoline burns have less chemical potential energy than the gasoline molecules.

Some chemical substances are like a raised weight. For example, the molecules that compose gasoline have a relatively high potential energy—energy is concentrated in them just as energy is concentrated in the raised weight. The molecules in the gasoline tend to undergo chemical changes (specifically combustion) that lower the molecules' potential energy. As the energy of the molecules is released, some of it can be harnessed to do work, such as moving a car forward (Figure 1.10▲). The molecules that result from the chemical change have less potential energy than the original molecules in gasoline and are more stable.

Chemical potential energy, such as the energy contained in the molecules that compose gasoline, arises primarily from electrostatic forces between the electrically charged particles (protons and electrons) that compose atoms and molecules. We will learn more about those particles, as well as the properties of electrical charge, in Chapter 2, but for now, know that molecules contain specific, usually complex, arrangements of these charged particles. Some of these arrangements—such as the one within the molecules that compose gasoline—have a much higher potential energy than others. When gasoline undergoes combustion, the arrangement of these particles changes, creating molecules with much lower potential energy and transferring a great deal of energy (mostly in the form of heat) to the surroundings.

Summarizing Energy:

- Energy is always conserved in a physical or chemical change; it is neither created nor destroyed.
- Systems with high potential energy tend to change in ways that lower their potential energy, transferring energy to the surroundings.

ENERGY What type of energy is chemical energy?

(a) kinetic energy
(b) thermal energy
(c) potential energy

1.4 Cc Conceptual Connection

ANSWER **NOW!**

1.6 The Units of Measurement

WATCH **NOW!**

KEY CONCEPT VIDEO 1.6 *Units and Significant Figures*

In 1999, NASA lost the $125 million *Mars Climate Orbiter*. The chairman of the commission that investigated the disaster concluded, "The root cause of the loss of the spacecraft was a failed translation of English units into metric units." As a result, the orbiter—which was supposed to monitor weather on Mars—descended too far into the Martian atmosphere and burned up. In chemistry as in space exploration, **units**—standard quantities used to specify measurements—are critical. If we get them wrong, the consequences can be disastrous.

▲ The $125 million *Mars Climate Orbiter* was lost in 1999 because two groups of engineers used different units.

TABLE 1.1 ■ SI Base Units

Quantity	Unit	Symbol
Length	Meter	m
Mass	Kilogram	kg
Time	Second	s
Temperature	Kelvin	K
Amount of substance	Mole	mol
Electric current	Ampere	A
Luminous intensity	Candela	cd

The two most common unit systems are the **metric system**, used in most of the world, and the **English system**, used in the United States. Scientists use the **International System of Units (SI)**, which is based on the metric system.

Standard Units

The abbreviation *SI* comes from the French, *Système International d'Unités.*

Table 1.1 shows the standard SI base units. In this chapter, we focus on the first four of these units: the *meter*, the standard unit of length; the *kilogram*, the standard unit of mass; the *second*, the standard unit of time; and the *kelvin*, the standard unit of temperature.

The Meter: A Measure of Length

The **meter (m)** is slightly longer than a yard (1 yard is 36 inches, while 1 meter is 39.37 inches).

Thus, a 100-yard (yd) football field measures only 91.4 m. The meter was originally defined as 1/10,000,000 of the distance from the equator to the North Pole (through Paris). The International Bureau of Weights and Measures now defines it more precisely as the distance light travels through a vacuum in a certain period of time, 1/299,792,458 second. A tall human is about 2 m tall, and the Empire State Building stands 443 m tall (including its mast).

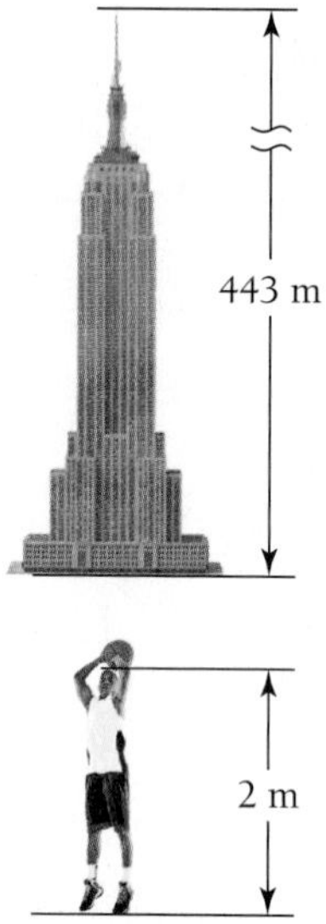

▲ The Empire State Building is 443 m tall. A basketball player stands about 2 m tall.

The Kilogram: A Measure of Mass

The **kilogram (kg)**, defined as the mass of a metal cylinder kept at the International Bureau of Weights and Measures at Sèvres, France, is a measure of *mass*, a quantity different from *weight*. The **mass** of an object is a measure of the quantity of matter within it, while the weight of an object is a measure of the *gravitational pull* on its matter. If you could weigh yourself on the moon, for example, its weaker gravity would pull on you with less force than does Earth's gravity, resulting in a lower weight. A 130-pound (lb) person on Earth would weigh only 21.5 lb on the moon. However, a person's mass—the quantity of matter in his or her body—remains the same on every planet. One kilogram of mass is the equivalent of 2.205 lb of weight on Earth, so expressed in kilograms, a 130-lb person has a mass of approximately 59 kg and this book has a mass of about 2.5 kg. A second common unit of mass is the gram (g). One gram is 1/1000 kg. A nickel (5¢) has a mass of about 5 g.

▲ A nickel (5 cents) weighs about 5 g.

The Second: A Measure of Time

If you live in the United States, the **second (s)** is perhaps the SI unit most familiar to you. The International Bureau of Weights and Measures originally defined the second in terms of the day and the year, but a second is now defined more precisely as the duration of 9,192,631,770 periods of the radiation emitted from a certain transition in a cesium-133 atom. (We discuss transitions and the emission of radiation by atoms in Chapter 8.)

Scientists measure time on a large range of scales. The human heart beats about once every second, the age of the universe is estimated to be about 4.32×10^{17} s (13.7 billion years), and some molecular bonds break or form in time periods as short as 1×10^{-15} s.

The Kelvin: A Measure of Temperature

The **kelvin (K)** is the SI unit of **temperature**. The temperature of a sample of matter is a measure of the average kinetic energy—the energy due to motion—of the atoms or molecules that compose the matter. The molecules in a *hot* glass of water are, on average, moving faster than the molecules in a *cold* glass of water. Temperature is a measure of this molecular motion.

Temperature also determines the direction of thermal energy transfer, what we commonly call *heat*. Thermal energy transfers from hot objects to cold ones. For example, when you touch another person's warm hand (and yours is cold), thermal energy flows *from his or her hand to yours*, making your hand feel warmer. However, if you touch an ice cube, thermal energy flows *out of your hand* to the ice, cooling your hand (and possibly melting some of the ice cube).

Figure 1.11▼ shows the three common temperature scales. The most common in the United States is the **Fahrenheit (°F) scale**, shown on the left in Figure 1.11. On the Fahrenheit scale, water freezes at 32 °F and boils at 212 °F at sea level. Room temperature is approximately 72 °F. The Fahrenheit scale was originally determined by assigning 0 °F to the freezing point of a concentrated saltwater solution and 96 °F to normal body temperature.

Normal body temperature on the modern Farhenheit scale is 98.6 °F.

Scientists and citizens of most countries other than the United States typically use the **Celsius (°C) scale**, shown in the middle in Figure 1.11. On this scale, pure water freezes at 0 °C and boils at 100 °C (at sea level). Room temperature is approximately 22 °C. The Fahrenheit scale and the Celsius scale differ both in the size of their respective degrees and the temperature each designates as "zero." Both the Fahrenheit and Celsius scales allow for negative temperatures.

The SI unit for temperature is the kelvin, shown in Figure 1.11. The **Kelvin scale** (sometimes also called the *absolute scale*) avoids negative temperatures by assigning 0 K to the coldest temperature possible, absolute zero. Absolute zero (–273.15 °C or –459 °F) is the temperature at which molecular motion virtually stops. Lower temperatures do not exist. The size of the kelvin is identical to that of the Celsius degree; the only difference is

Molecular motion does not *completely* stop at absolute zero because of the uncertainty principle in quantum mechanics, which we discuss in Chapter 8.

Temperature Scales

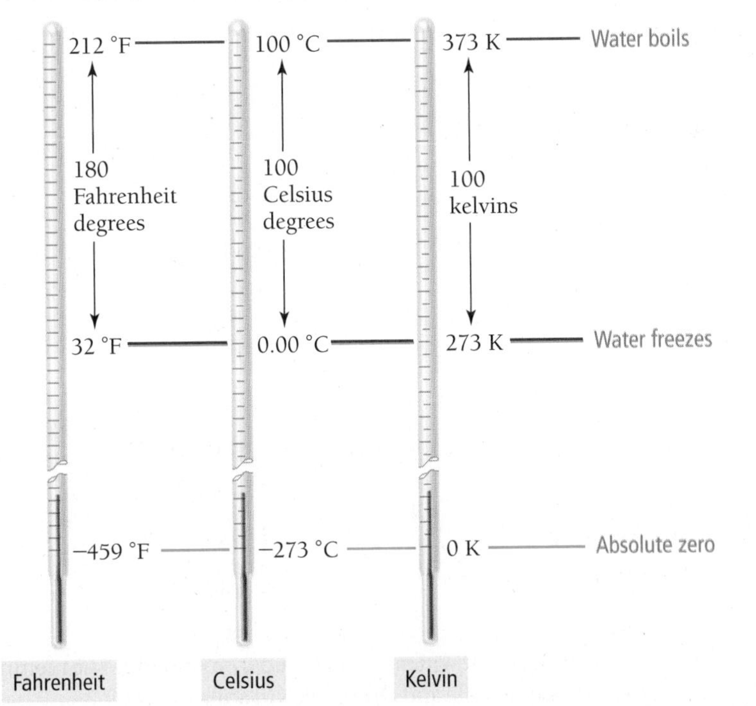

◀ **FIGURE 1.11 Comparison of the Fahrenheit, Celsius, and Kelvin Temperature Scales** The Fahrenheit degree is five-ninths the size of the Celsius degree and the kelvin. The zero point of the Kelvin scale is absolute zero (the lowest possible temperature), whereas the zero point of the Celsius scale is the freezing point of water.

The Celsius Temperature Scale

0 °C – Water freezes

10 °C – Brisk fall day

22 °C – Room temperature

45 °C – Summer day in Death Valley

the temperature that each scale designates as zero. We can convert between the temperature scales with these formulas:

Note that we give Kelvin temperatures in kelvins (*not* "degrees Kelvin") or K (*not* °K).

$$°C = \frac{(°F - 32)}{1.8}$$

$$K = °C + 273.15$$

ANSWER **NOW!**

1.5 Cc Conceptual Connection

TEMPERATURE SCALES Which temperature scale has no negative temperatures?

(a) Kelvin
(b) Celsius
(c) Fahrenheit

Throughout this book, we provide examples worked out in formats that are designed to help you develop problem-solving skills. The most common format uses two columns to guide you through the worked example. The left column describes the thought processes and steps used in solving the problem, while the right column shows the implementation. Example 1.2 follows this two-column format.

EXAMPLE 1.2 Converting between Temperature Scales

A sick child has a temperature of 40.00 °C. What is the child's temperature in **(a)** K and **(b)** °F?

SOLUTION

(a) Begin by finding the equation that relates the quantity that is given (°C) and the quantity you are trying to find (K).	$K = °C + 273.15$
Since this equation gives the temperature in K directly, substitute in the correct value for the temperature in °C and calculate the answer.	$K = °C + 273.15$ $K = 40.00 + 273.15 = 313.15\ K$
(b) To convert from °C to °F, first find the equation that relates these two quantities.	$°C = \frac{(°F - 32)}{1.8}$
Since this equation expresses °C in terms of °F, solve the equation for °F.	$°C = \frac{(°F - 32)}{1.8}$ $1.8(°C) = (°F - 32)$ $°F = 1.8(°C) + 32$
Now substitute °C into the equation and calculate the answer. *Note: The number of digits reported in this answer follows significant figure conventions, covered in Section 1.7.*	$°F = 1.8(°C) + 32$ $°F = 1.8(40.00\ °C) + 32 = 104.00\ °F$

FOR PRACTICE 1.2 Gallium is a solid metal at room temperature, but it will melt to a liquid in your hand. The melting point of gallium is 85.6 °F. What is this temperature on **(a)** the Celsius scale and **(b)** the Kelvin scale?

Prefix Multipliers

Scientific notation (see Appendix IA) allows us to express very large or very small quantities in a compact manner by using exponents. For example, the diameter of a hydrogen atom is 1.06×10^{-10} m. The International System of Units uses the **prefix multipliers** listed in Table 1.2 with the standard units. These multipliers change the value of the unit by powers of 10 (just like an exponent does in scientific notation). For example, the kilometer has the prefix *kilo* meaning 1000 or 10^3. Therefore,

$$1 \text{ kilometer} = 1000 \text{ meters} = 10^3 \text{ meters}$$

Similarly, the millimeter has the prefix *milli* meaning 0.001 or 10^{-3}.

$$1 \text{ millimeter} = 0.001 \text{ meters} = 10^{-3} \text{ meters}$$

TABLE 1.2 ■ SI Prefix Multipliers

Prefix	Symbol	Multiplier	
exa	E	1,000,000,000,000,000,000	(10^{18})
peta	P	1,000,000,000,000,000	(10^{15})
tera	T	1,000,000,000,000	(10^{12})
giga	G	1,000,000,000	(10^{9})
mega	M	1,000,000	(10^{6})
kilo	k	1000	(10^{3})
deci	d	0.1	(10^{-1})
centi	c	0.01	(10^{-2})
milli	m	0.001	(10^{-3})
micro	μ	0.000001	(10^{-6})
nano	n	0.000000001	(10^{-9})
pico	p	0.000000000001	(10^{-12})
femto	f	0.000000000000001	(10^{-15})
atto	a	0.000000000000000001	(10^{-18})

When reporting a measurement, choose a prefix multiplier close to the size of the quantity you are measuring. For example, to state the diameter of a hydrogen atom, which is 1.06×10^{-10} m, use picometers (106 pm) or nanometers (0.106 nm) rather than micrometers or millimeters. Choose the prefix multiplier that is most convenient for a particular number.

PREFIX MULTIPLIERS Which prefix multiplier is most appropriate for reporting a measurement of 5.57×10^{-5} m?

(a) mega
(b) milli
(c) micro
(d) kilo

1.6 Cc Conceptual Connection

ANSWER **NOW!**

Derived Units: Volume and Density

A **derived unit** is a combination of other units. For example, the SI unit for speed is meters per second (m/s), a derived unit. Notice that this unit is formed from two other SI units—meters and seconds—put together. You are probably more familiar with speed measured in miles/hour or kilometers/hour—these are also examples of derived units. Two other common derived units are those for volume (SI base unit is m^3) and density (SI base unit is kg/m^3).

Relationship between Length and Volume

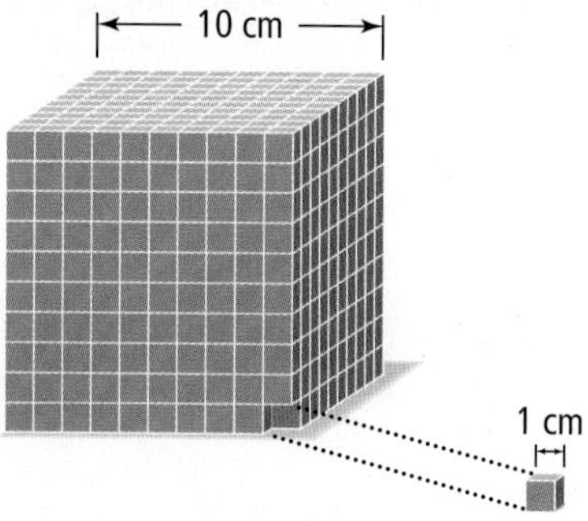

A 10-cm cube contains 1000 1-cm cubes.

▲ **FIGURE 1.12 The Relationship between Length and Volume** A cube with a 10-cm edge has a volume of (10 cm)^3 or 1000 cm^3, and a cube with a 100-cm edge has a volume of (100 cm)^3 = 1,000,000 cm^3.

Volume

Volume is a measure of space. Any unit of length, when cubed (raised to the third power), becomes a unit of volume. The cubic meter (m^3), cubic centimeter (cm^3), and cubic millimeter (mm^3) are all units of volume. The cubic nature of volume is not always intuitive, and studies have shown that our brains are not naturally wired to process abstract concepts such as volume. For example, consider this question: how many small cubes measuring 1 cm on each side are required to construct a large cube measuring 10 cm on a side?

The answer to this question, as you can see by carefully examining the unit cube in Figure 1.12◀, is 1000 small cubes. When we go from a linear, one-dimensional distance to three-dimensional volume, we must raise both the linear dimension *and* its unit to the third power (not multiply by 3). Thus, the volume of a cube is equal to the length of its edge cubed.

$$\text{volume of cube} = (\text{edge length})^3$$

Other common units of volume in chemistry are the **liter (L)** and the **milliliter (mL)**. One milliliter (10^{-3} L) is equal to 1 cm^3. A gallon of gasoline contains 3.785 L. Table 1.3 lists some common units—for volume and other quantities—and their equivalents.

TABLE 1.3 ■ Some Common Units and Their Equivalents

Length	Mass	Volume
1 kilometer (km) = 0.6214 mile (mi)	1 kilogram (kg) = 2.205 pounds (lb)	1 liter (L) = 1000 mL = 1000 cm^3
1 meter (m) = 39.37 inches (in) = 1.094 yards (yd)	1 pound (lb) = 453.59 grams (g)	1 liter (L) = 1.057 quarts (qt)
1 foot (ft) = 30.48 centimeters (cm)	1 ounce (oz) = 28.35 grams (g)	1 U.S. gallon (gal) = 3.785 liters (L)
1 inch (in) = 2.54 centimeters (cm) (exact)		

Density

An old riddle asks, "Which weighs more, a ton of bricks or a ton of feathers?" The answer is neither—they both weigh the same (1 ton). If you answered bricks, you confused weight with density. The **density (*d*)** of a substance is the ratio of its mass (*m*) to its volume (*V*).

The *m* in the equation for density is in italic type, meaning that it stands for mass rather than for meters. In general, the symbols for units such as meters (m), seconds (s), or kelvins (K) appear in regular type while those for variables such as mass (*m*), volume (*V*), and time (*t*) appear in italics.

$$\text{Density} = \frac{\text{mass}}{\text{volume}} \quad \text{or} \quad d = \frac{m}{V}$$

Density is a characteristic physical property of substances (see Table 1.4) that depends on temperature. Density is an example of an **intensive property**, one that is *independent* of the amount of the substance. The density of aluminum, for example, is the same whether you have a gram or a kilogram. Intensive properties are often used to identify substances because these properties depend only on the type of substance, not on the amount of it. For example, from Table 1.4 you can see that pure gold has a density of 19.3 g/cm^3. One way to determine whether a substance is pure gold is to determine its density and compare it to 19.3 g/cm^3. Mass, in contrast, is an **extensive property**, one that depends on the amount of the substance. If you know only the mass of a sample of gold, that information alone will not allow you to identify it as gold.

The units of density are those of mass divided by volume. Although the SI-derived unit for density is kg/m^3, the density of liquids and solids is most often expressed in g/cm^3 or g/mL. (Remember that cm^3 and mL are equivalent units: 1 cm^3 = 1 mL.) Aluminum is among the least dense metals with a density of 2.7 g/cm^3, while platinum is one of the densest metals with a density of 21.4 g/cm^3.

Calculating Density

We can calculate the density of a substance by dividing the mass of a given amount of the substance by its volume. For example, suppose a small nugget we suspect to be gold has a mass of 22.5 g and a volume of 2.38 cm^3. To find its density, we divide the mass by the volume:

$$d = \frac{m}{V} = \frac{22.5\ \text{g}}{2.38\ \text{cm}^3} = 9.45\ \text{g/cm}^3$$

In this case, the density reveals that the nugget is not pure gold because the density of gold is 19.3 g/cm^3.

TABLE 1.4 ■ The Density of Some Common Substances at 20 °C

Substance	Density (g/cm^3)
Charcoal (from oak)	0.57
Ethanol	0.789
Ice	0.917 (at 0 °C)
Water	1.00 (at 4 °C)
Sugar (sucrose)	1.58
Table salt (sodium chloride)	2.16
Glass	2.6
Aluminum	2.70
Titanium	4.51
Iron	7.86
Copper	8.96
Lead	11.4
Mercury	13.55
Gold	19.3
Platinum	21.4

EXAMPLE 1.3 Calculating Density

A man receives a platinum ring from his fiancée. Before the wedding, he notices that the ring feels a little light for its size, and so he decides to determine its density. He places the ring on a balance and finds that it has a mass of 3.15 g. He then finds that the ring displaces 0.233 cm^3 of water. Is the ring made of platinum? (Note: The volume of irregularly shaped objects is often measured by the displacement of water. To use this method, the object is placed in water and the change in volume of the water is measured. This increase in the total volume represents the volume of water *displaced* by the object and is equal to the volume of the object.)

Set up the problem by writing the important information that is *given* as well as the information that you are asked to *find*. In this case, we need to find the density of the ring and compare it to that of platinum.

Note: In Section 1.8, we discuss this standardized way of setting up problems.

GIVEN: $m = 3.15\ \text{g}$

$V = 0.233\ \text{cm}^3$

FIND: Density in g/cm^3

Next, write down the equation that defines density.

EQUATION $d = \frac{m}{V}$

Solve the problem by substituting the correct values of mass and volume into the expression for density.

SOLUTION

$$d = \frac{m}{V} = \frac{3.15\ \text{g}}{0.233\ \text{cm}^3} = 13.5\ \text{g/cm}^3$$

The density of the ring is much too low to be platinum (platinum density is 21.4 g/cm^3), and the ring is therefore a fake.

FOR PRACTICE 1.3 The woman in Example 1.3 is shocked that the ring is fake and returns it. She buys a new ring that has a mass of 4.53 g and a volume of 0.212 cm^3. Is the new ring genuine?

FOR MORE PRACTICE 1.3 A metal cube has an edge that is 11.4 mm long and a mass of 6.67 g. Calculate the density of the metal and use Table 1.4 to determine the likely identity of the metal.

1.7 Cc Conceptual Connection ANSWER **NOW!**

DENSITY The density of copper decreases as temperature increases (as does the density of most substances). Which change occurs in a sample of copper when it is warmed from room temperature to 95 °C?

(a) The sample becomes lighter.
(b) The sample becomes heavier.
(c) The sample expands.
(d) The sample contracts.

CHEMISTRY AND MEDICINE | Bone Density

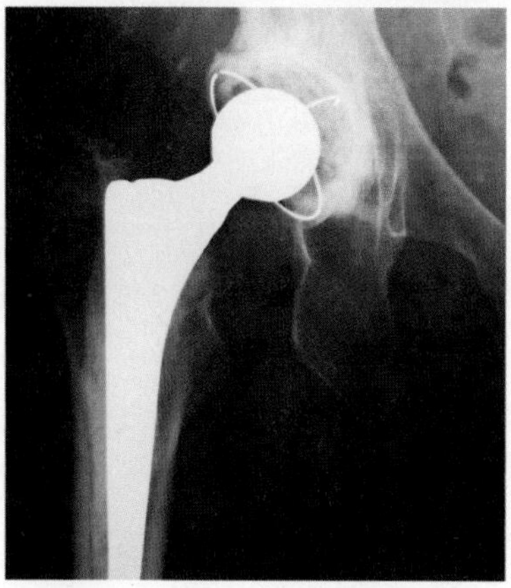

Osteoporosis—which means *porous bone*—is a condition in which bone density becomes low. The healthy bones of a young adult have a density of about 1.0 g/cm^3. Patients suffering from osteoporosis, however, can have bone densities as low as 0.22 g/cm^3. These low densities indicate that the bones have deteriorated and weakened, resulting in increased susceptibility to fractures, especially hip fractures. Patients suffering from osteoporosis can also experience height loss and disfiguration such as dowager's hump, a condition in which the patient becomes hunched over due to compression of the vertebrae. Osteoporosis is most common in postmenopausal women, but it can also occur in people (including men) who have certain diseases, such as insulin-dependent diabetes, or who take certain medications, such as prednisone. Osteoporosis is usually diagnosed and monitored with hip X-rays. Low-density bones absorb less of the X-rays than do high-density bones, producing characteristic differences in the X-ray image. Treatments for osteoporosis include calcium and vitamin D supplements, drugs that prevent bone weakening, exercise and strength training, and, in extreme cases, hip-replacement surgery.

QUESTION *Suppose you find a large animal bone in the woods, too large to fit in a beaker or flask. How might you approximate its density?*

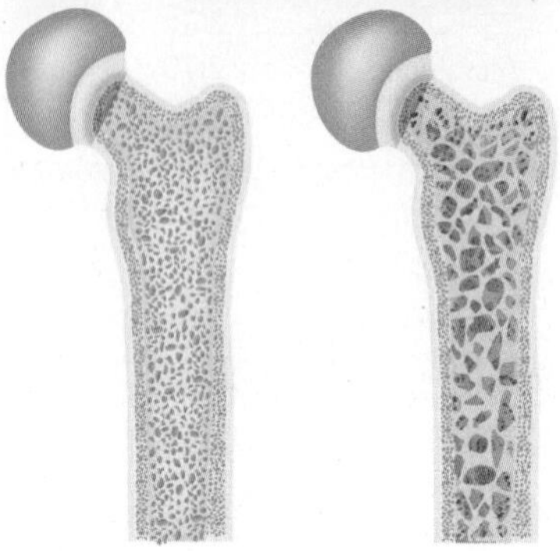

◀ Top: Severe osteoporosis can necessitate surgery to implant an artificial hip joint, seen in this X-ray image. Bottom: Views of the bone matrix in a normal bone (left) and one weakened by osteoporosis (right).

1.7 The Reliability of a Measurement

Carbon monoxide is a colorless gas emitted by motor vehicles and found in polluted air. The table shown here lists carbon monoxide concentrations in Los Angeles County as reported by the U.S. Environmental Protection Agency (EPA) over the period 1990–2017:

Year	Carbon Monoxide Concentration (ppm)*
1990	9.9
1995	9.0
2000	7.4
2005	2.8
2010	1.9
2017	1.1

*Second maximum, 8 hour average; ppm = parts per million (Pasadena Site 06-037-2005)

The first thing you should notice about these values is that they decrease over time. For this decrease, we can thank the Clean Air Act and its amendments, which have resulted in more efficient engines and specially blended fuels and consequently in cleaner air in all major U.S. cities over the last 30 years. The second thing you might notice is the number of digits to which the measurements are reported. The number of digits in a reported measurement indicates the certainty associated with that measurement. A less certain measurement of carbon monoxide levels might be reported as follows:

Year	Carbon Monoxide Concentration (ppm)
1990	10
1995	9
2000	7
2005	3
2010	2
2017	1

Notice that the first set of data is reported to the nearest 0.1 ppm, while the second set is reported to the nearest 1 ppm. Scientists report measured quantities in an agreed-upon standard way. The number of reported digits reflects the certainty in the measurement: more digits, more certainty; fewer digits, less certainty. Numbers are usually written so that the uncertainty is in the last reported digit. (We assume that uncertainty to be ± 1 in the last digit unless otherwise indicated.) By reporting the 2010 carbon monoxide concentration as 1.9 ppm, the scientists mean 1.9 ± 0.1 ppm. The carbon monoxide concentration is between 1.8 and 2.0 ppm—it might be 2.0 ppm, for example, but it could not be 3.0 ppm. In contrast, if the reported value was 2 ppm (as in the second set of measurements), this would mean 2 ± 1 ppm, or between 1 and 3 ppm. In general,

Scientific measurements are reported so that every digit is certain except the last, which is estimated.

For example, consider the following reported number:

5.213

(certain: 5.21; estimated: 3)

The first three digits are certain; the last digit is estimated.

The number of digits reported in a measurement depends on the measuring device. Consider weighing a pistachio nut on two different balances (Figure 1.13▶). The balance on the top has marks every 1 g, while the balance on the bottom has marks every 0.1 g. For the balance on the top, we mentally divide the space between the 1- and 2-g marks into ten equal spaces and estimate that the pointer is at about 1.2 g. We then write the measurement as 1.2 g, indicating that we are sure of the "1" but we have estimated the ".2." The balance on the bottom, with marks every *tenth* of a gram, requires that we write the result with more digits. The pointer is between the 1.2-g mark and the 1.3-g mark. We again divide the space between the two marks into ten equal spaces and estimate the third digit. For the figure shown, we report 1.27 g.

Estimation in Weighing

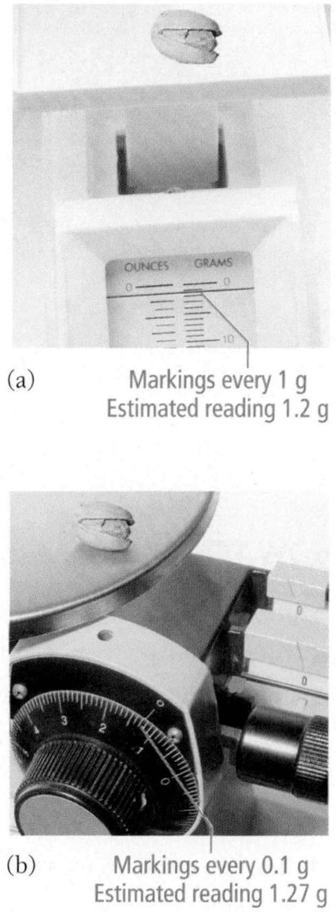

▲ **FIGURE 1.13 Estimation in Weighing** **(a)** This scale has markings every 1 g, so we mentally divide the space into ten equal spaces to estimate the last digit. This reading is 1.2 g. **(b)** Because this balance has markings every 0.1 g, we estimate to the hundredths place. This reading is 1.27 g.

EXAMPLE 1.4 Reporting the Correct Number of Digits

The graduated cylinder shown in the right margin has markings every 0.1 mL. Report the volume (which is read at the bottom of the meniscus) to the correct number of digits. (Note: The meniscus is the crescent-shaped surface at the top of a column of liquid.)

SOLUTION

Since the bottom of the meniscus is between the 4.5 and 4.6 mL markings, mentally divide the space between the markings into ten equal spaces and estimate the next digit. In this case, you should report the result as 4.57 mL.

What if you estimated a little differently and wrote 4.56 mL? In general, a one-unit difference in the last digit is acceptable because the last digit is estimated and different people might estimate it slightly differently. However, if you wrote 4.63 mL, you would have misreported the measurement.

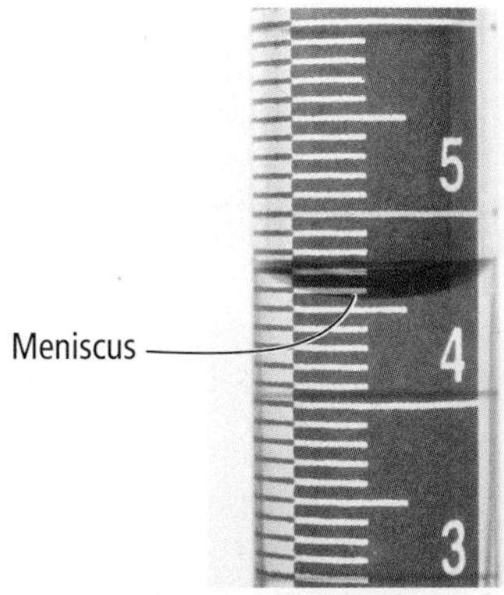

FOR PRACTICE 1.4 Record the temperature on the thermometer shown in the right margin to the correct number of digits.

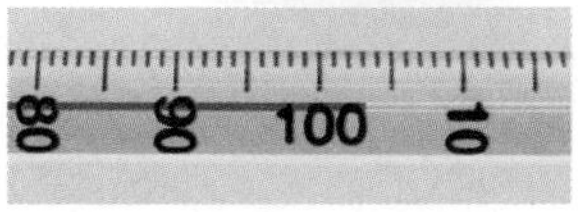

Counting Significant Figures

The precision of a measurement—which depends on the instrument used to make the measurement—must be preserved, not only when recording the measurement, but also when performing calculations that use the measurement. We can accomplish the preservation of this precision by using *significant figures*. In any reported measurement, the non-place-holding digits—those that are not simply marking the decimal place—are called **significant figures** (or **significant digits**). *The greater the number of significant figures, the greater the certainty of the measurement.* For example, the number 23.5 has three significant figures while the number 23.56 has four. To determine the number of significant figures in a number containing zeroes, we distinguish between zeroes that are significant and those that simply mark the decimal place. For example, in the number 0.0008, the leading zeroes (zeroes to the left of the first nonzero digit) mark the decimal place but *do not* add to the certainty of the measurement and are therefore not significant; this number has only one significant figure. In contrast, the trailing zeroes (zeroes at the end of a number) in the number 0.000800 *do add* to the certainty of the measurement and are therefore counted as significant; this number has three significant figures.

HOW TO: *Determine the Number of Significant Figures in a Given Value*

Significant Figure Rules	Examples	
1. All nonzero digits are significant.	28.03	0.0540
2. Interior zeroes (zeroes between two nonzero digits) are significant.	408	7.0301
3. Leading zeroes (zeroes to the left of the first nonzero digit) are not significant. They only serve to locate the decimal point.	(0.00)32 — not significant	(0.0000)6 — not significant
4. Trailing zeroes (zeroes at the end of a number) are categorized as follows:		
• Trailing zeroes after a decimal point are always significant.	45.000	3.5600
• Trailing zeroes before a decimal point (and after a nonzero number) are always significant.	140.00	2500.55
• Trailing zeroes before an *implied* decimal point are ambiguous and should be avoided by using scientific notation.	1200	ambiguous
	1.2×10^3	2 significant figures
	1.20×10^3	3 significant figures
	1.200×10^3	4 significant figures
• Some textbooks put a decimal point after one or more trailing zeroes if the zeroes are to be considered significant. We avoid that practice in this book, but you should be aware of it.	1200.	4 significant figures (common in some textbooks)

Exact Numbers

Exact numbers have no uncertainty and thus do not limit the number of significant figures in any calculation. We can regard an exact number as having an unlimited number of significant figures. Exact numbers originate from three sources:

- From the accurate counting of discrete objects. For example, 3 atoms means 3.00000. . . atoms.
- From defined quantities, such as the number of centimeters in 1 m. Because 100 cm is defined as 1 m,

$$100 \text{ cm} = 1 \text{ m means } 100.00000... \text{ cm} = 1.0000000... \text{ m}$$

- From integral numbers that are part of an equation. For example, in the equation $radius = \frac{diameter}{2}$, the number 2 is exact and therefore has an unlimited number of significant figures.

WATCH **NOW!**

INTERACTIVE WORKED EXAMPLE 1.5

EXAMPLE 1.5 Determining the Number of Significant Figures in a Number

How many significant figures are in each number?

(a) 0.04450 m **(b)** 5.0003 km **(c)** 10 dm = 1 m **(d)** 1.000×10^5 s **(e)** 0.00002 mm **(f)** 10,000 m

SOLUTION

(a) 0.04450 m	*Four significant figures.* The two 4s and the 5 are significant (Rule 1). The trailing zero is after a decimal point and is therefore significant (Rule 4). The leading zeroes only mark the decimal place and are therefore not significant (Rule 3).
(b) 5.0003 km	*Five significant figures.* The 5 and 3 are significant (Rule 1), as are the three interior zeroes (Rule 2).
(c) 10 dm = 1 m	*Unlimited significant figures.* Defined quantities have an unlimited number of significant figures.
(d) 1.000×10^5 s	*Four significant figures.* The 1 is significant (Rule 1). The trailing zeroes are after a decimal point and therefore significant (Rule 4).
(e) 0.00002 mm	*One significant figure.* The 2 is significant (Rule 1). The leading zeroes only mark the decimal place and are therefore not significant (Rule 3).
(f) 10,000 m	*Ambiguous.* The 1 is significant (Rule 1), but the trailing zeroes occur before an implied decimal point and are therefore ambiguous (Rule 4). Without more information, you would assume one significant figure. It is better to write this as 1×10^5 to indicate one significant figure or as 1.0000×10^5 to indicate five (Rule 4).

FOR PRACTICE 1.5 How many significant figures are in each number?

(a) 554 km **(b)** 7 pennies **(c)** 1.01×10^5 m **(d)** 0.00099 s **(e)** 1.4500 km **(f)** 21,000 m

Significant Figures in Calculations

WATCH **NOW!**

KEY CONCEPT VIDEO 1.7
Significant Figures in Calculations

When we use measured quantities in calculations, the results of the calculation must reflect the precision of the measured quantities. We should not lose or gain precision during mathematical operations. Follow these rules when carrying significant figures through calculations.

HOW TO: *Determine Significant Figures in Calculated Quantities*

Rules for Calculations

1. In multiplication or division, the result carries the same number of significant figures as the factor with the fewest significant figures.
2. In addition or subtraction, the result carries the same number of decimal places as the quantity with the fewest decimal places.

Examples

1.052 (4 sig. figures) × 12.504 (5 sig. figures) × 0.53 (2 sig. figures) = 6.7208 = 6.7 (2 sig. figures)

2.0035 (5 sig. figures) ÷ 3.20 (3 sig. figures) = 0.626094 = 0.626 (3 sig. figures)

```
 2.34|5
 0.07|
 2.99|75
 5.41|25 = 5.41

  5.9|
 −0.2|21
  5.6|79 = 5.7
```

In addition and subtraction, it is helpful to draw a line next to the number with the fewest decimal places. This line determines the number of decimal places in the answer.

—*Continued on the next page*

Rules for Calculations	**Examples**
3. When rounding to the correct number of significant figures, round down if the last (or leftmost) digit dropped is four or less; round up if the last (or leftmost) digit dropped is five or more.	Rounding to two significant figures: 5.37 rounds to 5.4 5.34 rounds to 5.3 5.35 rounds to 5.4 5.349 rounds to 5.3 Notice in the last example (5.349) that only the *leftmost digit being dropped* (in this example, the 4) determines how you round the number. You ignore all the digits to the right of the leftmost digit you are dropping (in this example, you ignore the 9).
4. To avoid rounding errors in multistep calculations, round only the final answer—do not round intermediate steps. If you write down intermediate answers, keep track of significant figures by underlining the least significant digit.	$6.78 \times 5.903 \times (5.489 - 5.01)$ $= 6.78 \times 5.903 \times 0.4\underline{7}9$ $= 19.1707$ $= 19$ underline least significant digit

A few books recommend a slightly different rounding procedure for cases in which the last digit is 5. However, the procedure presented here is consistent with electronic calculators and will be used throughout this book.

Notice that for multiplication or division, the quantity with the fewest *significant figures* determines the number of *significant figures* in the answer, but for addition and subtraction, the quantity with the fewest *decimal places* determines the number of *decimal places* in the answer. In multiplication and division, we focus on significant figures, but in addition and subtraction we focus on decimal places. When a problem involves addition or subtraction, the answer may have a different number of significant figures than the initial quantities. Keep this in mind in problems that involve both addition or subtraction and multiplication or division. For example,

$$\frac{1.002 - 0.999}{3.754} = \frac{0.003}{3.754}$$
$$= 7.99 \times 10^{-4}$$
$$= 8 \times 10^{-4}$$

The answer has only one significant figure, even though the initial numbers had three or four.

WATCH **NOW!**
INTERACTIVE WORKED EXAMPLE 1.6

EXAMPLE 1.6 Significant Figures in Calculations

Perform each calculation to the correct number of significant figures.

(a) $1.10 \times 0.5120 \times 4.0015 \div 3.4555$

(b)
$$\begin{array}{r} 0.355 \\ +105.1 \\ -100.5820 \\ \hline \end{array}$$

(c) $4.562 \times 3.99870 \div (452.6755 - 452.33)$

(d) $(14.84 \times 0.55) - 8.02$

SOLUTION

(a) Round the intermediate result (in blue) to three significant figures to reflect the three significant figures in the quantity with the fewest significant figures (1.10).	$1.10 \times 0.5120 \times 4.0015 \div 3.4555$ $= 0.65219$ $= 0.652$
(b) Round the intermediate answer (in blue) to one decimal place to reflect the quantity with the fewest decimal places (105.1). Notice that 105.1 is *not* the quantity with the fewest significant figures, but it has the fewest decimal places and therefore determines the number of decimal places in the answer.	$\begin{array}{r} 0.355 \\ +105.1 \\ -100.5820 \\ \hline 4.8730 \end{array} = 4.9$

(c) Mark the intermediate result to two decimal places to reflect the number of decimal places in the quantity within the parentheses having the fewest number of decimal places (452.33). Round the final answer to two significant figures to reflect the two significant figures in the least precisely known quantity (0.3455).	$4.562 \times 3.99870 \div (452.6755 - 452.33)$ $= 4.562 \times 3.99870 \div 0.3455$ $= 52.79904$ $= 53$ 2 places of the decimal
(d) Mark the intermediate result to two significant figures to reflect the number of significant figures in the quantity within the parentheses having the fewest number of significant figures (0.55). Round the final answer to one decimal place to reflect the one decimal place in the least precisely known quantity (8.162).	$(14.84 \times 0.55) - 8.02 = 8.162 - 8.02$ $= 0.142$ $= 0.1$

FOR PRACTICE 1.6 Perform each calculation to the correct number of significant figures.

(a) $3.10007 \times 9.441 \times 0.0301 \div 2.31$

(b)
$$\begin{array}{r} 0.881 \\ +132.1 \\ -\ 12.02 \\ \hline \end{array}$$

(c) $2.5110 \times 21.20 \div (44.11 + 1.223)$

(d) $(12.01 \times 0.3) + 4.811$

Precision and Accuracy

Scientists often repeat measurements several times to increase confidence in the result. We distinguish between two different kinds of certainty—accuracy and precision—associated with such measurements. **Accuracy** refers to how close the measured value is to the actual value. **Precision** refers to how close a series of measurements are to one another or how reproducible they are. A series of measurements can be precise (close to one another in value and reproducible) but not accurate (not close to the true value). Consider the results of three students who repeatedly weighed a lead block known to have a true mass of 10.00 g (indicated by the solid horizontal blue line on the graphs in the accompanying figure).

	Student A	Student B	Student C
Trial 1	10.49 g	9.78 g	10.03 g
Trial 2	9.79 g	9.82 g	9.99 g
Trial 3	9.92 g	9.75 g	10.03 g
Trial 4	10.31 g	9.80 g	9.98 g
Average	**10.13 g**	**9.79 g**	**10.01 g**

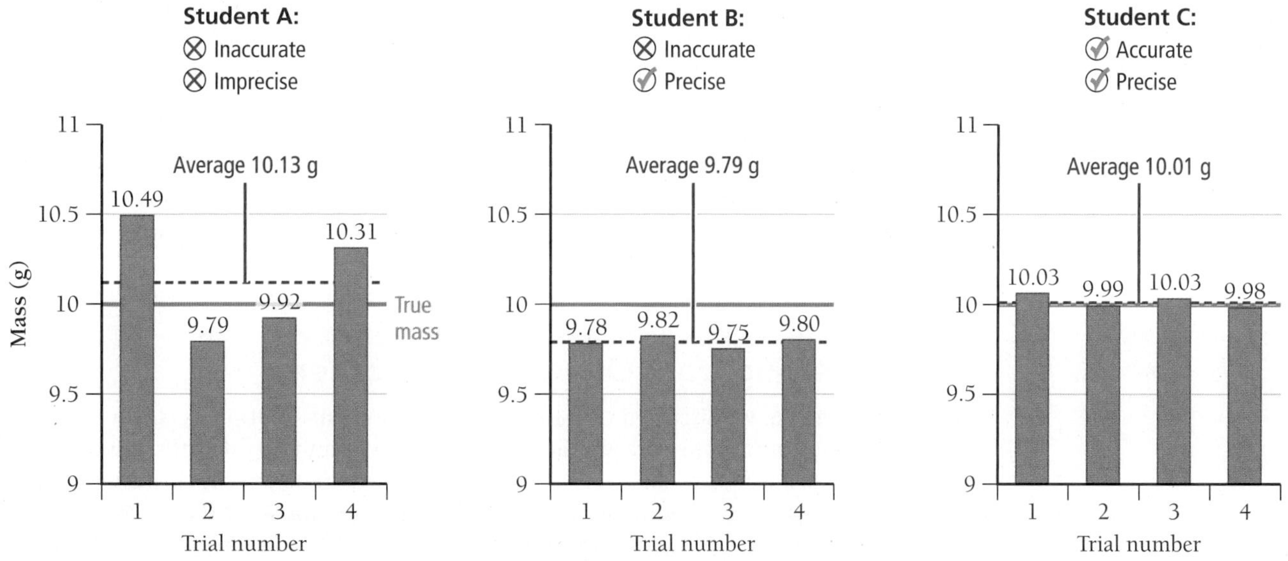

▲ Measurements are said to be precise if they are consistent with one another, but they are accurate only if they are close to the actual value.

- The results of student A are both inaccurate (not close to the true value) and imprecise (not consistent with one another). The inconsistency is the result of **random error**, error that has equal probability of being too high or too low. Almost all measurements have some degree of random error. Random error can, with enough trials, average itself out.
- The results of student B are precise (close to one another in value) but inaccurate. The inaccuracy is the result of **systematic error**, error that tends to be either too high or too low. In contrast to random error, systematic error does not average out with repeated trials. For instance, if a balance is not properly calibrated, it will systematically read too high or too low.
- The results of student C display little systematic error or random error—they are both accurate and precise.

CHEMISTRY IN YOUR DAY | Integrity in Data Gathering

Most scientists spend many hours collecting data in the laboratory. Often, the data do not turn out exactly as the scientist had expected (or hoped). A scientist may then be tempted to "fudge" the results. For example, suppose you are expecting a particular set of measurements to follow a certain pattern. After working hard over several days or weeks to make the measurements, you notice that a few of them do not quite fit the pattern that you anticipated. You might find yourself wishing that you could simply change or omit the "faulty" measurements. Altering data in this way is considered highly unethical in the scientific community and, when discovered, is punished severely.

In 2004, Dr. Hwang Woo Suk, a stem cell researcher at the Seoul National University in South Korea, published a research paper in *Science* (a highly respected research journal) claiming that he and his colleagues had cloned human embryonic stem cells. As part of his evidence, he showed photographs of the cells. The paper was hailed as an incredible breakthrough, and Dr. Hwang traveled the world lecturing on his work. *Time* magazine even included him on its "people that matter" list for 2004. Several months later, however, one of his coworkers revealed that the photographs were fraudulent. According to the coworker, the photographs came from a computer data bank of stem cell photographs, not from a cloning experiment. A university panel investigated the results and confirmed that the photographs and other data had indeed been faked. Dr. Hwang was forced to resign his prestigious post at the university.

Although not common, incidents like this do occur from time to time. They are damaging to a community that is largely built on trust. A scientist's peers (other researchers in similar fields) review all published research papers, but usually they are judging whether the data support the conclusion—they assume that the experimental measurements are authentic. The pressure to succeed sometimes leads researchers to betray that trust. However, over time, the tendency of scientists to reproduce and build upon one another's work results in the discovery of the fraudulent data. When that happens, the researchers at fault are usually banished from the community and their careers are ruined.

WATCH **NOW!**

KEY CONCEPT VIDEO 1.8
Solving Chemical Problems

1.8 Solving Chemical Problems

Learning to solve problems is one of the most important skills you will acquire in this course. No one succeeds in chemistry—or in life, really—without the ability to solve problems. Although no simple formula applies to every chemistry problem, you can learn problem-solving strategies and begin to develop some chemical intuition. Many of the problems you will solve in this course are *unit conversion problems,* where you are given one or more quantities and asked to convert them into different units. Other problems require that you use *specific equations* to get to the information you are trying to find. In the sections that follow, you will find strategies to help you solve both of these types of problems. Of course, many problems contain both conversions and equations, requiring the combination of these strategies, and some problems may require an altogether different approach.

Converting from One Unit to Another

In Section 1.6, we discussed the SI unit system, the prefix multipliers, and a few other units. Knowing how to work with and manipulate these units in calculations is central to solving chemical problems. In calculations, units help to determine correctness. Using units as a guide to solving problems is called **dimensional analysis**. Units should always be included in calculations; they are multiplied, divided, and canceled like any other algebraic quantity.

Consider converting 12.5 inches (in) to centimeters (cm). We know from Table 1.3 that 1 in = 2.54 cm (exact), so we can use this quantity in the calculation.

$$12.5\ \cancel{\text{in}} \times \frac{2.54\ \text{cm}}{1\ \cancel{\text{in}}} = 31.8\ \text{cm}$$

The unit, in, cancels, and we are left with cm as our final unit. The quantity $\frac{2.54\ \text{cm}}{1\ \text{in}}$ is a **conversion factor**—a fractional quantity with the units we are *converting from* on the bottom and the units we are *converting to* on the top. Conversion factors are constructed from any two equivalent quantities. In this example, 2.54 cm = 1 in, so we construct the conversion factor by dividing both sides of the equality by 1 in and canceling the units.

$$2.54\ \text{cm} = 1\ \text{in}$$

$$\frac{2.54\ \text{cm}}{1\ \text{in}} = \frac{1\ \cancel{\text{in}}}{1\ \cancel{\text{in}}}$$

$$\frac{2.54\ \text{cm}}{1\ \text{in}} = 1$$

Because the quantity $\frac{2.54\ \text{cm}}{1\ \text{in}}$ is equivalent to 1, multiplying by the conversion factor affects only the units, not the actual quantity. To convert the other way, from centimeters to inches, we must—using units as a guide—use a different form of the conversion factor. If we accidentally use the same form, we will get the wrong result, indicated by erroneous units. For example, suppose that we want to convert 31.8 cm to inches.

$$31.8\ \text{cm} \times \frac{2.54\ \text{cm}}{1\ \text{in}} = \frac{80.8\ \text{cm}^2}{\text{in}}$$

The units in the answer (cm^2/in), as well as the value of the answer, are obviously wrong. When we solve a problem, we always look at the final units. Are they the desired units? We must always look at the magnitude of the numerical answer as well. Does it make sense? In this case, our mistake was the form of the conversion factor. It should have been inverted so that the units cancel as follows:

$$31.8\ \cancel{\text{cm}} \times \frac{1\ \text{in}}{2.54\ \cancel{\text{cm}}} = 12.5\ \text{in}$$

We can invert conversion factors because they are equal to 1 and the inverse of 1 is 1. Therefore,

$$\frac{2.54\ \text{cm}}{1\ \text{in}} = 1 = \frac{1\ \text{in}}{2.54\ \text{cm}}$$

Most unit conversion problems take the following form:

$$\text{Information given} \times \text{conversion factor(s)} = \text{information sought}$$

$$\cancel{\text{Given unit}} \times \frac{\text{desired unit}}{\cancel{\text{given unit}}} = \text{desired unit}$$

In this book, we diagram problem solutions using a *conceptual plan*. A conceptual plan is a visual outline that helps us to see the general flow of the problem solution. For unit conversions, the conceptual plan focuses on units and the conversion from one unit to another. The conceptual plan for converting in to cm is:

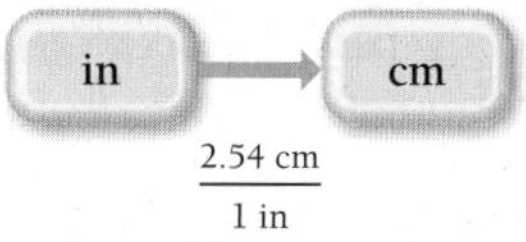

The conceptual plan for converting the other way, from cm to in, is just the reverse, with the reciprocal conversion factor:

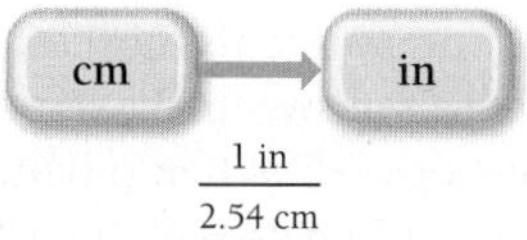

Each arrow in a conceptual plan for a unit conversion has an associated conversion factor, with the units of the previous step in the denominator and the units of the following step in the numerator. In the following section, we incorporate the idea of a conceptual plan into an overall approach to solving numerical chemical problems.

General Problem-Solving Strategy

In this book, we introduce a standard problem-solving procedure that you can adapt to many of the problems encountered in general chemistry and beyond. One of the difficulties beginning students encounter when trying to solve problems in general chemistry is not knowing where to begin. To solve any problem, you must assess the information given in the problem and devise a way to determine the requested information. In other words, you must do the following:

- Identify the starting point (the ***given*** information).
- Identify the end point (what you must ***find***).
- Devise a way to get from the starting point to the end point using what is given as well as what you already know or can look up. (As we just discussed, this is the ***conceptual plan***.)

In graphic form, we can represent this progression as:

Given ⟶ Conceptual Plan ⟶ Find

Although no problem-solving procedure is applicable to all problems, the following four-step procedure can be helpful in working through many of the numerical problems you will encounter in this book.

1. **Sort.** Begin by sorting the information in the problem. *Given* information is the basic data provided by the problem—often one or more numbers with their associated units. *Find* indicates what information you will need for your answer.
2. **Strategize.** This is usually the most challenging part of solving a problem. In this process, you must develop a *conceptual plan*—a series of steps that take you from the given information to the information you are trying to find. You have already seen conceptual plans for simple unit conversion problems. Each arrow in a conceptual plan represents a computational step. On the left side of the arrow is the quantity you had before the step, on the right side of the arrow is the quantity you have after the step, and below the arrow is the information you need to get from one to the other—the relationship between the quantities.

Most problems can be solved in more than one way. The solutions in this book tend to be the most straightforward but certainly are not the only way to solve the problem.

Often such relationships take the form of conversion factors or equations. These may be given in the problem, in which case you will have written them down under "Given" in step 1. Usually, however, you will need other information—which may include physical constants, formulas, or conversion factors—to help get you from what you are given to what you must find. This information comes from what you have learned or can look up in the chapter or in tables within the book.

In some cases, you may get stuck at the strategize step. If you cannot figure out how to get from the given information to the information you are asked to find, you might try working backward. For example, you can look at the units of the quantity you are trying to find and attempt to find conversion factors to get to the units of the given quantity. You may even try a combination of strategies; work forward, backward, or some of both. If you persist, you will develop a strategy to solve the problem.

3. **Solve.** This is the easiest part of solving a problem. Once you set up the problem properly and devise a conceptual plan, you simply follow the plan to solve the problem. Carry out any mathematical operations (paying attention to the rules for significant figures in calculations) and cancel units as needed.
4. **Check.** This is the step beginning students most often overlook. Experienced problem solvers always ask, "Does this answer make sense? Are the units correct? Is the number of significant figures correct?" When solving multistep problems, errors can easily creep into the solution. You can catch most of these errors by simply

checking the answer. For example, suppose you are calculating the number of atoms in a gold coin and end up with an answer of 1.1×10^{-6} atoms. Could the gold coin really be composed of one-millionth of one atom?

In Examples 1.7 and 1.8, this problem-solving procedure is applied to unit conversion problems. The procedure is summarized in the left column, and two examples of applying the procedure are provided in the middle and right columns. This three-column format is used in selected examples throughout this text. It allows you to see how to apply a particular procedure to two different problems. Work through one problem first (from top to bottom) and then see how you can apply the same procedure to the other problem. Recognizing the commonalities and differences between problems is a key part of developing problem-solving skills.

WATCH **NOW!** INTERACTIVE WORKED EXAMPLE VIDEO 1.8

HOW TO: *Solve Unit Conversion Problems*	**Unit Conversion** **EXAMPLE 1.7** Convert 1.76 yards to centimeters.	**Unit Conversion** **EXAMPLE 1.8** Convert 1.8 quarts to cubic centimeters.
SORT Begin by sorting the information in the problem into *given* and *find*.	**GIVEN:** 1.76 yd **FIND:** cm	**GIVEN:** 1.8 qt **FIND:** cm^3
STRATEGIZE Devise a *conceptual plan* for the problem. Begin with the *given* quantity and symbolize each conversion step with an arrow. Below each arrow, write the appropriate conversion factor for that step. Focus on the units. The conceptual plan should end at the *find* quantity and its units. In these examples, the other information you need consists of relationships between the various units.	**CONCEPTUAL PLAN** $\text{yd} \xrightarrow[\frac{1\text{ m}}{1.094\text{ yd}}]{} \text{m} \xrightarrow[\frac{1\text{ cm}}{10^{-2}\text{ m}}]{} \text{cm}$ **RELATIONSHIPS USED** $1.094\text{ yd} = 1\text{ m}$ $1\text{ cm} = 10^{-2}\text{ m}$ (These conversion factors are from Tables 1.2 and 1.3.)	**CONCEPTUAL PLAN** $\text{qt} \xrightarrow[\frac{1\text{ L}}{1.057\text{ qt}}]{} \text{L} \xrightarrow[\frac{1\text{ mL}}{10^{-3}\text{ L}}]{} \text{mL} \xrightarrow[\frac{1\text{ cm}^3}{1\text{ mL}}]{} \text{cm}^3$ **RELATIONSHIPS USED** $1.057\text{ qt} = 1\text{ L}$ $1\text{ mL} = 10^{-3}\text{ L}$ $1\text{ mL} = 1\text{ cm}^3$ (These conversion factors are from Tables 1.2 and 1.3.)
SOLVE Follow the conceptual plan. Begin with the *given* quantity and its units. Multiply by the appropriate conversion factor(s), canceling units, to arrive at the *find* quantity.	**SOLUTION** $1.76\,\cancel{\text{yd}} \times \frac{1\,\cancel{\text{m}}}{1.094\,\cancel{\text{yd}}} \times \frac{1\text{ cm}}{10^{-2}\,\cancel{\text{m}}}$ $= 160.8775\text{ cm}$	**SOLUTION** $1.8\,\cancel{\text{qt}} \times \frac{1\,\cancel{\text{L}}}{1.057\,\cancel{\text{qt}}} \times \frac{1\,\cancel{\text{mL}}}{10^{-3}\,\cancel{\text{L}}} \times \frac{1\text{ cm}^3}{1\,\cancel{\text{mL}}}$ $= 1.70293 \times 10^3\text{ cm}^3$
Round the answer to the correct number of significant figures following the rules in Section 1.7. Remember that exact conversion factors do not limit significant figures.	$160.8775\text{ cm} = 161\text{ cm}$	$1.70293 \times 10^3\text{ cm}^3 = 1.7 \times 10^3\text{ cm}^3$
CHECK Check your answer. Are the units correct? Does the answer make sense?	The units (cm) are correct. The magnitude of the answer (161) makes sense because a centimeter is a much smaller unit than a yard.	The units (cm^3) are correct. The magnitude of the answer (1700) makes sense because a cubic centimeter is a much smaller unit than a quart.
	FOR PRACTICE 1.7 Convert 288 cm to yards.	**FOR PRACTICE 1.8** Convert 9255 cm^3 to gallons.

Units Raised to a Power

When building conversion factors for units raised to a power, remember to raise both the number and the unit to the power. For example, to convert from in^2 to cm^2, we construct the conversion factor as follows:

$$2.54\ \text{cm} = 1\ \text{in}$$
$$(2.54\ \text{cm})^2 = (1\ \text{in})^2$$
$$(2.54)^2\ \text{cm}^2 = 1^2\ \text{in}^2$$
$$6.45\ \text{cm}^2 = 1\ \text{in}^2$$
$$\frac{6.45\ \text{cm}^2}{1\ \text{in}^2} = 1$$

Example 1.9 demonstrates how to use conversion factors involving units raised to a power.

WATCH **NOW!**

INTERACTIVE WORKED EXAMPLE 1.9

EXAMPLE 1.9 Unit Conversions Involving Units Raised to a Power

Calculate the displacement (the total volume of the cylinders through which the pistons move) of a 5.70-L automobile engine in cubic inches.

SORT Sort the information in the problem into *given* and *find*.

GIVEN: 5.70 L
FIND: in^3

STRATEGIZE Write a conceptual plan. Begin with the given information and devise a path to the information that you are asked to find. For cubic units, you must cube the conversion factors.

CONCEPTUAL PLAN

$$\text{L} \xrightarrow{\frac{1\ \text{mL}}{10^{-3}\ \text{L}}} \text{mL} \xrightarrow{\frac{1\ \text{cm}^3}{1\ \text{mL}}} \text{cm}^3 \xrightarrow{\frac{(1\ \text{in})^3}{(2.54\ \text{cm})^3}} \text{in}^3$$

RELATIONSHIPS USED

$$1\ \text{mL} = 10^{-3}\ \text{L}$$
$$1\ \text{mL} = 1\ \text{cm}^3$$
$$2.54\ \text{cm} = 1\ \text{in}$$

(These conversion factors are from Tables 1.2 and 1.3.)

SOLVE Follow the conceptual plan to solve the problem. Round the answer to three significant figures to reflect the three significant figures in the least precisely known quantity (5.70 L). These conversion factors are all exact and therefore do not limit the number of significant figures.

SOLUTION

$$5.70\ \cancel{\text{L}} \times \frac{1\ \cancel{\text{mL}}}{10^{-3}\ \cancel{\text{L}}} \times \frac{1\ \cancel{\text{cm}^3}}{1\ \cancel{\text{mL}}} \times \frac{(1\ \text{in})^3}{(2.54\ \cancel{\text{cm}})^3}$$
$$= 347.835\ \text{in}^3 = 348\ \text{in}^3$$

CHECK The units of the answer are correct, and the magnitude makes sense. The unit cubic inches is smaller than liters, so the volume in cubic inches should be larger than the volume in liters.

FOR PRACTICE 1.9 How many cubic centimeters are there in 2.11 yd^3?

FOR MORE PRACTICE 1.9 A vineyard has 145 acres of Chardonnay grapes. A particular soil supplement requires 5.50 g for every square meter of vineyard. How many kilograms of the soil supplement are required for the entire vineyard? ($1\ \text{km}^2 = 247$ acres)

WATCH **NOW!**

INTERACTIVE WORKED EXAMPLE 1.10

EXAMPLE 1.10 Density as a Conversion Factor

The mass of fuel in a jet must be calculated before each flight to ensure that the jet is not too heavy to fly. A 747 is fueled with 173,231 L of jet fuel. If the density of the fuel is 0.768 g/cm^3, what is the mass of the fuel in kilograms?

SORT Begin by sorting the information in the problem into *given* and *find*.

GIVEN: fuel volume = 173,231 L
density of fuel = 0.768 g/cm^3
FIND: mass in kg

STRATEGIZE Draw the conceptual plan by beginning with the given quantity—in this case the volume in liters (L). The overall goal of this problem is to find the mass. You can convert between volume and mass using density (g/cm^3). However, you must first convert the volume to cm^3. After you convert the volume to cm^3, use the density to convert to g. Finally, convert g to kg.

CONCEPTUAL PLAN

$$\text{L} \xrightarrow{\frac{1\ \text{mL}}{10^{-3}\ \text{L}}} \text{mL} \xrightarrow{\frac{1\ \text{cm}^3}{1\ \text{mL}}} \text{cm}^3 \xrightarrow{\frac{0.768\ \text{g}}{\text{cm}^3}} \text{g} \xrightarrow{\frac{1\ \text{kg}}{1000\ \text{g}}} \text{kg}$$

RELATIONSHIPS USED

$1\ \text{mL} = 10^{-3}\ \text{L}$

$1\ \text{mL} = 1\ \text{cm}^3$

$d = 0.768\ \text{g/cm}^3$

$1000\ \text{g} = 1\ \text{kg}$

(These conversion factors are from Tables 1.2 and 1.3.)

SOLVE Follow the conceptual plan to solve the problem. Round the answer to three significant figures to reflect the three significant figures in the density.

SOLUTION

$$173{,}231\ \cancel{\text{L}} \times \frac{1\ \cancel{\text{mL}}}{10^{-3}\ \cancel{\text{L}}} \times \frac{1\ \cancel{\text{cm}^3}}{1\ \cancel{\text{mL}}} \times \frac{0.768\ \cancel{\text{g}}}{1\ \cancel{\text{cm}^3}} \times \frac{1\ \text{kg}}{1000\ \cancel{\text{g}}}$$
$$= 1.33 \times 10^5\ \text{kg}$$

CHECK The units of the answer (kg) are correct. The magnitude makes sense because the mass (1.33×10^5 kg) is similar in magnitude to the given volume (173,231 L or 1.73231×10^5 L), as expected for a density close to 1 ($0.768\ \text{g/cm}^3$).

FOR PRACTICE 1.10 Backpackers often use canisters of white gas to fuel a cooking stove's burner. If one canister contains 1.45 L of white gas and the density of the gas is $0.710\ \text{g/cm}^3$, what is the mass of the fuel in kilograms?

FOR MORE PRACTICE 1.10 A drop of gasoline has a mass of 22 mg and a density of $0.754\ \text{g/cm}^3$. What is its volume in cubic centimeters?

Order-of-Magnitude Estimations

Calculation is an integral part of chemical problem solving. But precise numerical calculation is not always necessary, or even possible. Sometimes data are only approximate; other times we may not need a high degree of precision—a rough estimate or a simplified "back of the envelope" calculation is enough. We can also use approximate calculations to get an initial feel for a problem or to make a quick check to see whether our solution is "in the right ballpark."

One way to make such estimates is to simplify the numbers so that they can be manipulated easily. The technique known as *order-of-magnitude estimation* is based on focusing only on the exponential part of numbers written in scientific notation, according to these guidelines:

- If the decimal part of the number is less than 5, just drop it. Thus, 4.36×10^5 becomes 10^5 and 2.7×10^{-3} becomes 10^{-3}.
- If the decimal part is 5 or more, round it up to 10 and rewrite the number as a power of 10. Thus, 5.982×10^7 becomes $10 \times 10^7 = 10^8$, and 6.1101×10^{-3} becomes $10 \times 10^{-3} = 10^{-2}$.

When we make these approximations, we are left with powers of 10, which are easier to multiply and divide. Of course, our answer is only as reliable as the numbers used to get it, so we should not assume that the results of an order-of-magnitude calculation are accurate to more than an order of magnitude.

Suppose, for example, that we want to estimate the number of atoms that an immortal being could have counted in the 14 billion (1.4×10^{10}) years that the universe has been in existence, assuming a counting rate of ten atoms per second. Since a year has 3.2×10^7 seconds, we can approximate the number of atoms counted as follows:

$$\underset{\text{(number of years)}}{10^{10}\ \cancel{\text{years}}} \times \underset{\text{(number of seconds per year)}}{10^7\ \frac{\cancel{\text{seconds}}}{\cancel{\text{years}}}} \times \underset{\text{(number of atoms counted per second)}}{10^1\ \frac{\text{atoms}}{\cancel{\text{second}}}} \approx 10^{18}\ \text{atoms}$$

A million trillion atoms (10^{18}) may seem like a lot, but as we discuss in Chapter 2, a speck of matter made up of a million trillion atoms is nearly impossible to see without a microscope.

In our general problem-solving procedure, the last step is to check whether the results seem reasonable. Order-of-magnitude estimations often help us catch the kinds of mistakes that can happen in a detailed calculation, such as entering an incorrect exponent or sign into a calculator or multiplying when we should have divided.

Problems Involving an Equation

We can solve problems involving equations in much the same way as problems involving conversions. Usually, in problems involving equations, we must find one of the variables in the equation, given the others. The *conceptual plan* concept outlined earlier can be used for problems involving equations. For example, suppose we are given the mass (m) and volume (V) of a sample and asked to calculate its density. The conceptual plan shows how the *equation* takes us from the *given* quantities to the *find* quantity:

$$m, V \rightarrow d \qquad d = \frac{m}{V}$$

Here, instead of a conversion factor under the arrow, this conceptual plan has an equation. The equation shows the *relationship* between the quantities on the left of the arrow and the quantities on the right. Note that at this point the equation need not be solved for the quantity on the right (although in this particular case it is). The procedure that follows, as well as the two examples, offer guidance for developing a strategy to solve problems involving equations. We again use the three-column format. Work through one problem from top to bottom and then see how you can apply the same general procedure to the second problem.

WATCH **NOW!**

INTERACTIVE WORKED EXAMPLE VIDEO 1.12

HOW TO: *Solve Problems Involving Equations*	**Problems with Equations** **EXAMPLE 1.11** Find the radius (r) in centimeters of a spherical water droplet with a volume (V) of 0.058 cm^3. For a sphere, $V = (4/3)\pi r^3$.	**Problems with Equations** **EXAMPLE 1.12** Find the density (in g/cm^3) of a metal cylinder with a mass (m) of 8.3 g, a length (l) of 1.94 cm, and a radius (r) of 0.55 cm. For a cylinder, $V = \pi r^2 l$.
SORT Begin by sorting the information in the problem into *given* and *find*.	**GIVEN:** $V = 0.058\ cm^3$ **FIND:** r in cm	**GIVEN:** $m = 8.3$ g $l = 1.94$ cm $r = 0.55$ cm **FIND:** d in g/cm^3
STRATEGIZE Write a conceptual plan for the problem. Focus on the equation(s). The conceptual plan shows how the equation takes you from the *given* quantity (or quantities) to the *find* quantity. The conceptual plan may have several parts, involving other equations or required conversions. In these examples, you use the geometrical relationships given in the problem statements as well as the definition of density, $d = m/V$, which you learned in this chapter.	**CONCEPTUAL PLAN** $V \rightarrow r \qquad V = \frac{4}{3}\pi r^3$ **RELATIONSHIPS USED** $V = \frac{4}{3}\pi r^3$	**CONCEPTUAL PLAN** $l, r \rightarrow V \qquad V = \pi r^2 l$, $m, V \rightarrow d \qquad d = m/V$ **RELATIONSHIPS USED** $V = \pi r^2 l$ $d = \frac{m}{V}$

SOLVE Follow the conceptual plan. Solve the equation(s) for the *find* quantity (if it is not already). Gather each of the quantities that must go into the equation in the correct units. (Convert to the correct units if necessary.) Substitute the numerical values and their units into the equation(s) and calculate the answer. Round the answer to the correct number of significant figures.	**SOLUTION** $V = \frac{4}{3}\pi r^3$ $r^3 = \frac{3}{4\pi}V$ $r = \left(\frac{3}{4\pi}V\right)^{1/3}$ $= \left(\frac{3}{4\pi}0.058 \text{ cm}^3\right)^{1/3}$ $= 0.24013 \text{ cm}$ $0.24013 \text{ cm} = 0.24 \text{ cm}$	**SOLUTION** $V = \pi r^2 l$ $= \pi(0.55 \text{ cm})^2 (1.94 \text{ cm})$ $= 1.\underline{8}436 \text{ cm}^3$ $d = \frac{m}{V}$ $= \frac{8.3 \text{ g}}{1.\underline{8}436 \text{ cm}^3} = 4.50195 \text{ g/cm}^3$ $4.50195 \text{ g/cm}^3 = 4.5 \text{ g/cm}^3$
CHECK Check your answer. Are the units correct? Does the answer make sense?	The units (cm) are correct and the magnitude makes sense.	The units (g/cm^3) are correct. The magnitude of the answer seems correct for one of the lighter metals (see Table 1.4).
	FOR PRACTICE 1.11 Find the radius (r) of an aluminum cylinder that is 2.00 cm long and has a mass of 12.4 g. For a cylinder, $V = \pi r^2 l$.	**FOR PRACTICE 1.12** Find the density, in g/cm^3, of a metal cube with a mass of 50.3 g and an edge length (l) of 2.65 cm. For a cube, $V = l^3$.

1.9 Analyzing and Interpreting Data

In Section 1.2, we saw that Lavoisier saw patterns in a series of related measurements. Sets of measurements constitute scientific *data*, and learning to analyze and interpret data is an important scientific skill.

Identifying Patterns in Data

Suppose you are an early chemist trying to understand the composition of water. You know that water is composed of the elements hydrogen and oxygen. You do several experiments in which different samples of water are decomposed into hydrogen and oxygen and you get the following results:

Sample	Mass of Water Sample	Mass of Hydrogen Formed	Mass of Oxygen Formed
A	20.0 g	2.2 g	17.8 g
B	50.0 g	5.6 g	44.4 g
C	100.0 g	11.1 g	88.9 g

Do you notice any patterns in these data? Perhaps the easiest pattern to see is that the sum of the masses of oxygen and hydrogen always sum to the mass of the water sample. For example, for the first water sample, 2.2 g hydrogen + 17.8 g oxygen = 20.0 g water. The pattern is the same for the other samples. Another pattern, which is a bit more difficult to see, is that the ratio of the masses of oxygen and hydrogen is the same for each sample.

Sample	Mass of Hydrogen Formed	Mass of Oxygen Formed	$\frac{\text{Mass Oxygen}}{\text{Mass Hydrogen}}$
A	2.2 g	17.8 g	8.1
B	5.6 g	44.4 g	7.9
C	11.1 g	88.9 g	8.01

The ratio is 8—the small variations are due to experimental error, which is common in all measurements and observations.

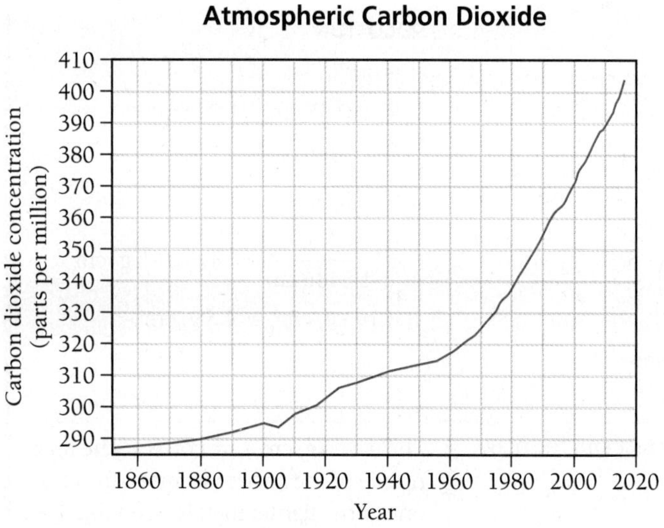

▲ **FIGURE 1.14 Atmospheric Carbon Dioxide Levels from 1860 to Present.**

Seeing patterns in data is a creative process that requires you to not just merely tabulate laboratory measurements, but to see relationships that may not always be obvious. The best scientists see patterns that others have missed. As you learn to interpret data in this course, be creative and try looking at data in new ways.

Interpreting Graphs

Data are often visualized using graphs or images and scientists must constantly analyze and interpret graphs. For example, the graph in Figure 1.14◀ shows the concentration of carbon dioxide in Earth's atmosphere as a function of time. Carbon dioxide is a greenhouse gas that has been rising as result of the burning of fossil fuels (such as gasoline and coal). When you look at a graph such as this one, you should first examine the *x* and *y* axes and make sure you understand what each axis represents. You should also examine the numerical range of the axes. In Figure 1.14 the *y* axis does not begin at zero in order to better display the change that is occurring. How would this graph look different if the *y* axis began at zero instead of at 290? Notice also that, in this graph, the increase in carbon dioxide has not been constant over time. The rate of increase—represented by the slope of the line—has intensified since about 1960.

EXAMPLE 1.13 Interpreting Graphs

Examine the graph in Figure 1.14 and answer each question.

(a) What was the concentration of carbon dioxide in 1960?

(b) What was the concentration in 2010?

(c) How much did the concentration increase between 1960 and 2010?

(d) What is the average rate of increase over this time?

(e) If the average rate of increase from part d remains constant, estimate the carbon dioxide concentration in 2050. (Use the concentration in 2010 as your starting point.)

SOLUTION

(a) To determine the concentration of carbon dioxide in 1960, draw a vertical line at the year 1960. At the point where the vertical line intersects the carbon dioxide concentration curve, draw a horizontal line. The point where the horizontal line intercepts the *y* axis represents the concentration in 1960. So, the concentration in 1960 was 317 ppm.

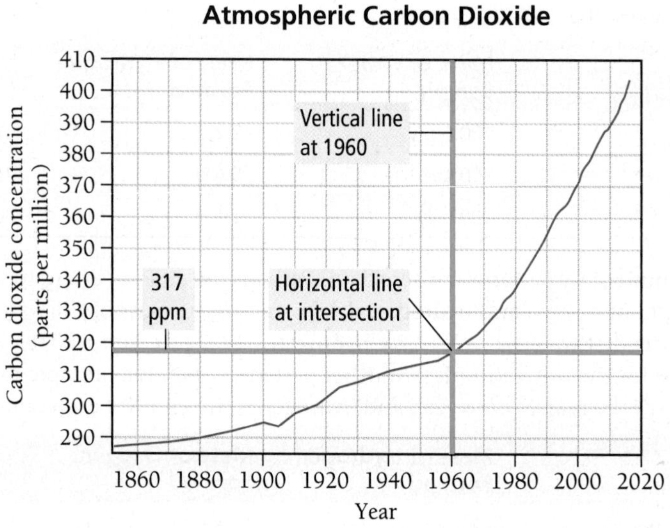

(b) Apply the same procedure as in part a, but now shift the vertical line to the year 2010. The concentration in the year 2010 was 389 ppm.	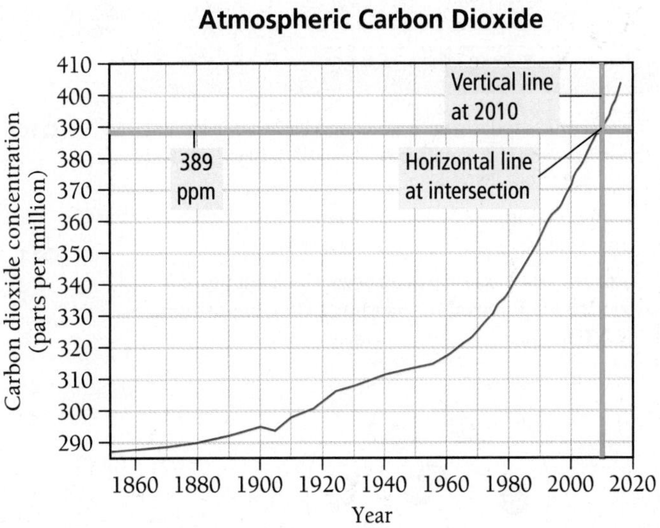
(c) The increase in the carbon dioxide concentration is the difference between the two concentrations. When calculating changes in quantities such as this, take the final quantity minus the initial quantity.	Increase in concentration = concentration in 2010 − concentration in 1960 = 389 ppm − 317 ppm = 72 ppm
(d) The average rate of increase over this time is the change in the concentration divided by the number of years that passed. Determine the number of years that have passed, which is equal to the final year minus the initial year.	Number of years = final year − initial year = 2010 − 1960 = 50 years
Determine the average rate of increase by dividing the change in concentration from part c by the number of years that you just calculated.	$\text{Average rate} = \dfrac{\text{change in concentration}}{\text{number of years}}$ $= \dfrac{72\text{ ppm}}{50\text{ years}}$ $= \dfrac{1.4\text{ ppm}}{\text{year}}$
(e) Determine the increase in concentration between 2010 and 2050 by multiplying the number of years that pass in that time interval by the average rate of change from part d. Lastly, determine the concentration in 2050 by adding the increase between 2010 and 2050 to the concentration in 2010.	$\text{Increase} = 40\text{ years} \times \dfrac{1.4\text{ ppm}}{\text{year}}$ = 56 ppm Concentration in 2050 = 389 ppm + 56 ppm = 445 ppm

FOR PRACTICE 1.13 What was the average rate of increase in carbon dioxide concentration between 1880 and 1920? Why might that rate be different than the rate between 1960 and 2010?

QUIZ YOURSELF **NOW!**

Self-Assessment Quiz

Q1. A chemist mixes sodium with water and witnesses a violent reaction between the metal and water. This is best classified as
MISSED THIS? *Read Section 1.2*

a) an observation.
b) a law.
c) a hypothesis.
d) a theory.

Q2. This image represents a particulate view of a sample of matter. Classify the sample according to its composition.
MISSED THIS? *Read Section 1.3; Watch KCV 1.3*

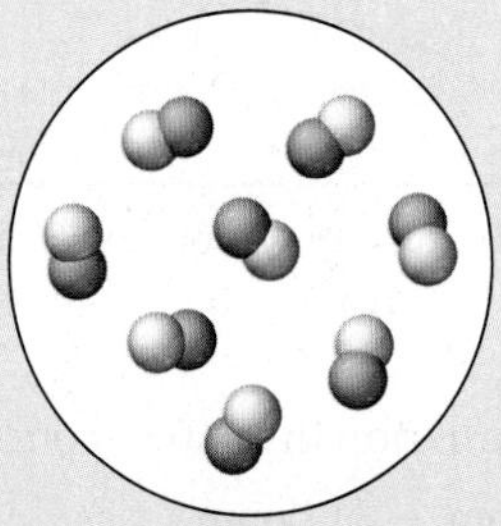

a) The sample is a pure element.
b) The sample is a homogeneous mixture.
c) The sample is a compound.
d) The sample is a heterogeneous mixture.

Q3. Which change is a physical change?
MISSED THIS? *Read Section 1.4*

a) wood burning
b) iron rusting
c) dynamite exploding
d) gasoline evaporating

Q4. Which property of rubbing alcohol is a chemical property?
MISSED THIS? *Read Section 1.4*

a) density (0.786 g/cm^3)
b) flammability
c) boiling point (82.5 °C)
d) melting point (−89 °C)

Q5. Convert 85.0 °F to K.
MISSED THIS? *Read Section 1.6; Watch KCV 1.3*

a) 181.1 K
b) 358 K
c) 29.4 K
d) 302.6 K

Q6. Express the quantity 33.2×10^{-4} m in mm.
MISSED THIS? *Read Section 1.6; Watch KCV 1.3*

a) 33.2 mm
b) 3.32 mm
c) 0.332 mm
d) 3.32×10^{-6} mm

Q7. What is the mass of a 1.75 L sample of a liquid that has a density of 0.921 g/mL?
MISSED THIS? *Read Section 1.6; Watch KCV 1.10*

a) 1.61×10^3 g
b) 1.61×10^{-3} g
c) 1.90×10^3 g
d) 1.90×10^{-3} g

Q8. Perform the calculation to the correct number of significant figures. **MISSED THIS?** *Read Section 1.7; Watch KCV 1.6, 1.7, IWE 1.5, 1.6*

$$(43.998 \times 0.00552)/2.002$$

a) 0.121
b) 0.12
c) 0.12131
d) 0.1213

Q9. Perform the calculation to the correct number of significant figures. **MISSED THIS?** *Read Section 1.7; Watch KCV 1.6, 1.7, IWE 1.5, 1.6*

$$(8.01 - 7.50)/3.002$$

a) 0.1698867
b) 0.17
c) 0.170
d) 0.1699

Q10. Convert 1285 cm^2 to m^2.
MISSED THIS? *Read Section 1.8; Watch IWE 1.9*

a) 1.285×10^7 m^2
b) 12.85 m^2
c) 0.1285 m^2
d) 1.285×10^5 m^2

Q11. The first diagram depicts a compound in its liquid state. Which of the other diagrams best depicts the compound after it has evaporated into a gas?
MISSED THIS? *Read Section 1.4*

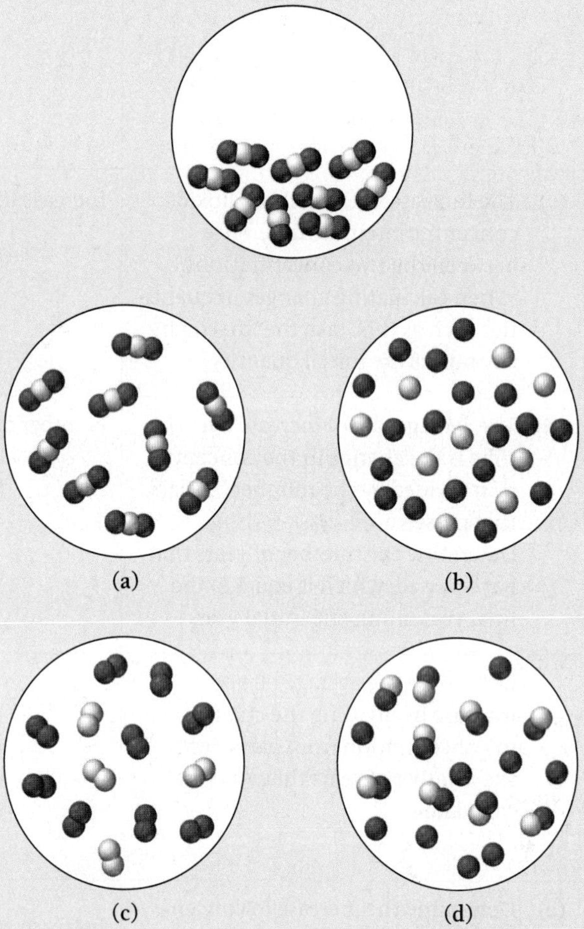

Q12. Three samples, each of a different substance, are weighed, and their volume is measured. The results are tabulated. List the substances in order of decreasing density.
MISSED THIS? *Read Section 1.6*

	Mass	Volume
Substance I	10.0 g	10.0 mL
Substance II	10.0 kg	12.0 L
Substance III	12.0 mg	10.0 μL

a) III > II > I
b) I > II > III
c) III > I > II
d) II > I > III

Q13. A solid metal sphere has a radius of 3.53 cm and a mass of 1.796 kg. What is the density of the metal in g/cm^3? (The volume of a sphere is $V = \frac{4}{3}\pi r^3$.)
MISSED THIS? *Read Section 1.6; Watch IWE 1.12*

a) 34.4 g/cm^3 b) 0.103 g/cm^3
c) 121 g/cm^3 d) 9.75 g/cm^3

Q14. The gas mileage of a certain German automobile is 22 km/L. Convert this quantity to miles per gallon.
MISSED THIS? *Read Section 1.8; Watch KCV 1.8*

a) 9.4 mi/gal b) 1.3×10^2 mi/gal
c) 52 mi/gal d) 3.6 mi/gal

Q15. A wooden block has a volume of 18.5 in^3. Express the volume of the cube in cm^3.
MISSED THIS? *Read Section 1.8; Watch KCV 1.8, IWE 1.9*

a) 303 cm^3 b) 47.0 cm^3
c) 1.13 cm^3 d) 7.28 cm^3

Q16. The graph that follows shows the area of a circle as a function of its radius. What is the radius of a circle that has an area of 155 square inches?
MISSED THIS? *Read Section 1.9*

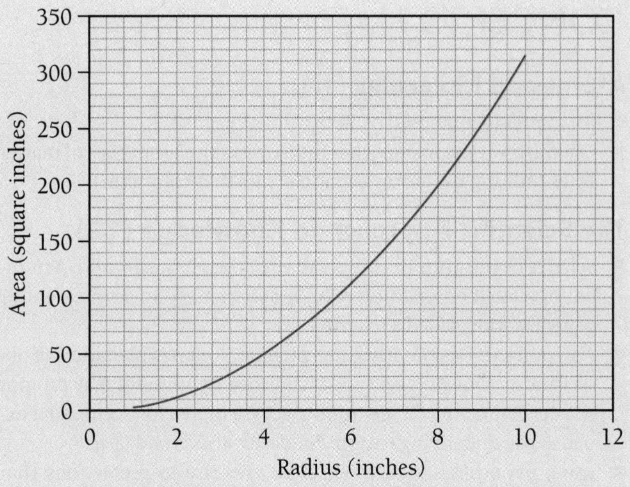

a) 7.0 inches b) 6.5 inches
c) 6.8 inches d) 6.2 inches

Answers: **1.** (a) **2.** (c) **3.** (d) **4.** (b) **5.** (d) **6.** (b) **7.** (a) **8.** (a) **9.** (b) **10.** (c) **11.** (a) **12.** (c) **13.** (d) **14.** (c) **15.** (a) **16.** (a)

CHAPTER 1 IN REVIEW

TERMS

Section 1.1
atoms (2)
molecules (2)
chemistry (2)

Section 1.2
hypothesis (3)
experiments (3)
scientific law (3)
law of conservation of mass (3)
theory (4)
atomic theory (4)

Section 1.3
matter (5)
substance (5)
state (5)
composition (5)
solid (6)
liquid (6)
gas (6)
crystalline (6)
amorphous (6)
pure substance (8)
mixture (8)
element (8)
compound (8)
heterogeneous mixture (8)
homogeneous mixture (8)
decanting (9)
distillation (9)
volatile (9)
filtration (9)

Section 1.4
physical change (9)
chemical change (10)
physical property (10)
chemical property (10)

Section 1.5
energy (12)
work (12)
kinetic energy (12)
potential energy (12)
thermal energy (12)
law of conservation of energy (12)

Section 1.6
units (13)
metric system (14)
English system (14)
International System of Units (SI) (14)
meter (m) (14)
kilogram (kg) (14)
mass (14)
second (s) (14)
kelvin (K) (15)
temperature (15)
Fahrenheit (°F) scale (15)
Celsius (°C) scale (15)
Kelvin scale (15)
prefix multipliers (17)
derived unit (17)
volume (*V*) (18)
liter (L) (18)
milliliter (mL) (18)
density (*d*) (18)
intensive property (18)
extensive property (18)

Section 1.7
significant figures (significant digits) (22)
exact numbers (22)
accuracy (25)
precision (25)
random error (26)
systematic error (26)

Section 1.8
dimensional analysis (26)
conversion factor (27)

CONCEPTS

Atoms and Molecules (1.1)

- All matter is composed of atoms and molecules.
- Chemistry is the science that investigates the properties of matter by examining the atoms and molecules that compose it.

The Scientific Approach to Knowledge (1.2)

- Science begins with the observation of the physical world. A number of related observations can be summarized in a statement or generalization called a scientific law.
- A hypothesis is a tentative interpretation or an explanation of observations. One or more well-established hypotheses may prompt the development of a scientific theory, a model for nature that explains the underlying reasons for observations and laws.
- Laws, hypotheses, and theories all give rise to predictions that can be tested by experiments, carefully controlled procedures designed to produce critical new observations. If scientists cannot confirm the predictions, they must modify or replace the law, hypothesis, or theory.

The Classification of Matter (1.3)

- We classify matter according to its state (solid, liquid, or gas) or according to its composition (pure substance or mixture).
- A pure substance can either be an element, which cannot be chemically broken down into simpler substances, or a compound, which is composed of two or more elements in fixed proportions.
- A mixture can be either homogeneous, with the same composition throughout, or heterogeneous, with different compositions in different regions.

The Properties of Matter (1.4)

- We classify the properties of matter into two types: physical and chemical. Matter displays its physical properties without changing its composition.
- Changes in matter in which composition does not change are physical changes. Changes in matter in which composition does change are chemical changes.

Energy (1.5)

- In chemical and physical changes, matter often exchanges energy with its surroundings. In these exchanges, the total energy is always conserved; energy is neither created nor destroyed.
- Systems with high potential energy tend to change in the direction of lower potential energy, releasing energy into the surroundings.

The Units of Measurement and Significant Figures (1.6, 1.7)

- Scientists use SI units, which are based on the metric system. The SI base units include the meter (m) for length, the kilogram (kg) for mass, the second (s) for time, and the kelvin (K) for temperature.
- Derived units are formed from a combination of other units. Common derived units include those for volume (cm^3 or m^3) and density (g/cm^3).
- The number of digits in a reported measurement reflects the uncertainty in the measurement. Significant figures are the non–place-holding digits in a reported number.

EQUATIONS AND RELATIONSHIPS

Relationship between Kelvin (K) and Celsius (°C) Temperature Scales (1.6)

$$K = °C + 273.15$$

Relationship between Celsius (°C) and Fahrenheit (°F) Temperature Scales (1.6)

$$°C = \frac{(°F - 32)}{1.8}$$

Relationship between Density (d), Mass (m), and Volume (V) (1.6)

$$d = \frac{m}{V}$$

LEARNING OUTCOMES

Chapter Objectives	Assessment
Apply the scientific approach (1.2)	Exercises 33–36
Classify matter according to its composition (1.3)	Exercises 37–42
Classify the properties and changes in matter as chemical or physical (1.4)	Example 1.1 **For Practice** 1.1 **Exercises** 43–50
Compare the Fahrenheit, Celsius, and Kelvin temperature scales (1.6)	Example 1.2 **For Practice** 1.2 **Exercises** 51–54
Express measurements using appropriate prefix multipliers (1.6)	Exercises 55–64
Apply the density relationship to problems involving mass and volume (1.6)	Example 1.3 **For Practice** 1.3 **For More Practice** 1.3 **Exercises** 65–72
Determine the number of significant figures in a measurement or reported number (1.7)	Examples 1.4, 1.5 **For Practice** 1.4, 1.5 **Exercises** 73–82
Determine the number of significant figures in the result of a given calculation (1.7)	Example 1.6 **For Practice** 1.6 **Exercises** 83–90
Convert between units using dimensional analysis (1.8)	Examples 1.7, 1.8, 1.9, 1.10 **For Practice** 1.7, 1.8, 1.9, 1.10 **For More Practice** 1.9, 1.10 **Exercises** 91–104
Solve problems involving equations (1.8)	Examples 1.11, 1.12 **For Practice** 1.11, 1.12

EXERCISES

Mastering Chemistry provides end-of-chapter exercises, feedback-enriched tutorial problems, animations, and interactive activities to encourage problem-solving practice and deeper understanding of key concepts and topics.

REVIEW QUESTIONS

1. Explain this statement in your own words and give an example. *The properties of the substances around us depend on the atoms and molecules that compose them.*

2. Explain the main goal of chemistry.

3. Describe the scientific approach to knowledge. How does it differ from other approaches?

4. Explain the differences between a hypothesis, a law, and a theory.

5. What observations did Antoine Lavoisier make? What law did he formulate?

6. What theory did John Dalton formulate?

7. What is wrong with the expression "That is just a theory," if by *theory* the speaker is referring to a scientific theory?

8. What are two different ways to classify matter?

9. How do solids, liquids, and gases differ?

10. What is the difference between a crystalline solid and an amorphous solid?

11. Explain the difference between a pure substance and a mixture.

12. Explain the difference between an element and a compound.

13. Explain the difference between a homogeneous and a heterogeneous mixture.

14. What kind of mixtures can be separated by filtration?

15. Explain how distillation is used to separate mixtures.

16. What is the difference between a physical property and a chemical property?

17. What is the difference between a physical change and a chemical change? List some examples of each.

18. Explain the significance of the law of conservation of energy.

19. What kind of energy is chemical energy? In what way is an elevated weight similar to a tank of gasoline?

20. What are the standard SI base units of length, mass, time, and temperature?

21. What are the three common temperature scales? Does the size of a degree differ among them?

22. What are prefix multipliers? List some examples.

23. What is a derived unit? List an example.

24. Explain the difference between density and mass.

25. Explain the difference between *intensive* and *extensive* properties.

26. What is the meaning of the number of digits reported in a measured quantity?

27. When multiplying or dividing measured quantities, what determines the number of significant figures in the result?

28. When adding or subtracting measured quantities, what determines the number of significant figures in the result?

29. What are the rules for rounding off the results of calculations?

30. Explain the difference between precision and accuracy.

31. Explain the difference between random error and systematic error.

32. What is dimensional analysis?

PROBLEMS BY TOPIC

Note: *Answers to all odd-numbered Problems, numbered in blue, can be found in Appendix III. Exercises in the Problems by Topic section are paired, with each odd-numbered problem followed by a similar even-numbered problem. Exercises in the Cumulative Problems section are also paired, but more loosely. Challenge Problems and Conceptual Problems, because of their nature, are unpaired.*

The Scientific Approach to Knowledge

33. Classify each statement as an observation, a law, or a theory. **MISSED THIS?** *Read Section 1.2*

a. All matter is made of tiny, indestructible particles called atoms.

b. When iron rusts in a closed container, the mass of the container and its contents does not change.

c. In chemical reactions, matter is neither created nor destroyed.

d. When a match burns, heat is released.

34. Classify each statement as an observation, a law, or a theory.

a. Chlorine is a highly reactive gas.

b. If elements are listed in order of increasing mass of their atoms, their chemical reactivities follow a repeating pattern.

c. Neon is an inert (or nonreactive) gas.

d. The reactivity of elements depends on the arrangement of their electrons.

35. A chemist decomposes several samples of carbon monoxide into carbon and oxygen and weighs the resultant elements. The results are shown in the table. **MISSED THIS?** *Read Section 1.2*

Sample	Mass of Carbon (g)	Mass of Oxygen (g)
1	6	8
2	12	16
3	18	24

a. Do you notice a pattern in these results?

Next, the chemist decomposes several samples of hydrogen peroxide into hydrogen and oxygen. The results are shown in the table.

Sample	Mass of Hydrogen (g)	Mass of Oxygen (g)
1	0.5	8
2	1	16
3	1.5	24

b. Do you notice a similarity between these results and those for carbon monoxide in part a?

c. Can you formulate a law from your observations in a and b?

d. Can you formulate a hypothesis that might explain your law in c?

36. When astronomers observe distant galaxies, they can tell that most of them are moving away from one another. In addition, the more distant the galaxies, the more rapidly they are likely to be moving away from each other. Can you devise a hypothesis to explain these observations?

The Classification and Properties of Matter

37. Classify each substance as a pure substance or a mixture. If it is a pure substance, classify it as an element or a compound. If it is a mixture, classify it as homogeneous or heterogeneous.
MISSED THIS? *Read Section 1.3; Watch KCV 1.3*

a. sweat b. carbon dioxide
c. aluminum d. vegetable soup

38. Classify each substance as a pure substance or a mixture. If it is a pure substance, classify it as an element or a compound. If it is a mixture, classify it as homogeneous or heterogeneous.

a. wine b. beef stew
c. iron d. carbon monoxide

39. Complete the table.
MISSED THIS? *Read Section 1.3; Watch KCV 1.3*

Substance	Pure or mixture	Type
aluminum	pure	element
apple juice	______	______
hydrogen peroxide	______	______
chicken soup	______	______

40. Complete the table.

Substance	Pure or mixture	Type
water	pure	compound
coffee	______	______
ice	______	______
carbon	______	______

41. Determine whether each molecular diagram represents a pure substance or a mixture. If it represents a pure substance, classify the substance as an element or a compound. If it represents a mixture, classify the mixture as homogeneous or heterogeneous.
MISSED THIS? *Read Section 1.3; Watch KCV 1.3*

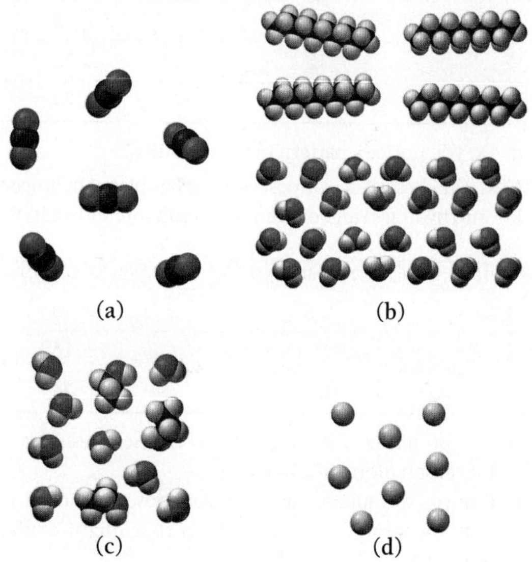

42. Determine whether each molecular diagram represents a pure substance or a mixture. If it represents a pure substance, classify the substance as an element or a compound. If it represents a mixture, classify the mixture as homogeneous or heterogeneous.

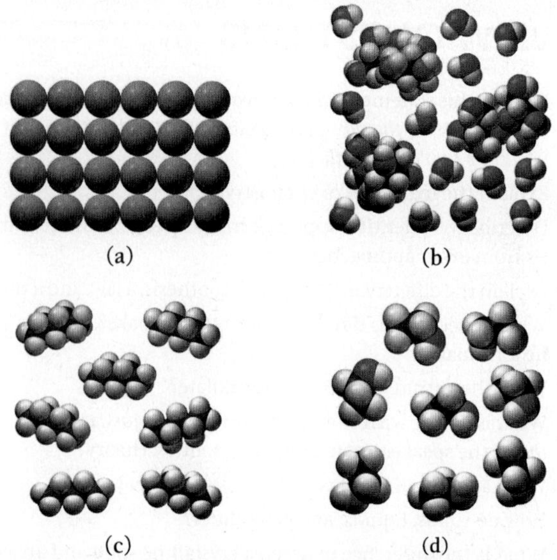

43. Classify each of the listed properties of isopropyl alcohol (also known as rubbing alcohol) as physical or chemical.
MISSED THIS? *Read Section 1.4*

a. colorless b. flammable
c. liquid at room temperature d. density = 0.79 g/mL
e. mixes with water

44. Classify each of the listed properties of ozone (a pollutant in the lower atmosphere but part of a protective shield against UV light in the upper atmosphere) as physical or chemical.

a. bluish color
b. pungent odor
c. very reactive
d. decomposes on exposure to ultraviolet light
e. gas at room temperature

45. Classify each property as physical or chemical.
MISSED THIS? *Read Section 1.4*

a. the tendency of ethyl alcohol to burn
b. the shine on silver
c. the odor of paint thinner
d. the flammability of propane gas

46. Classify each property as physical or chemical.

a. the boiling point of ethyl alcohol
b. the temperature at which dry ice evaporates
c. the tendency of iron to rust
d. the color of gold

47. Classify each change as physical or chemical.
MISSED THIS? *Read Section 1.4*

a. Natural gas burns in a stove.
b. The liquid propane in a gas grill evaporates because the valve was left open.
c. The liquid propane in a gas grill burns in a flame.
d. A bicycle frame rusts on repeated exposure to air and water.

48. Classify each change as physical or chemical.

a. Sugar burns when heated in a skillet.
b. Sugar dissolves in water.
c. A platinum ring becomes dull because of continued abrasion.
d. A silver surface becomes tarnished after exposure to air for a long period of time.

49. Based on the molecular diagram, classify each change as physical or chemical. **MISSED THIS?** *Read Section 1.4*

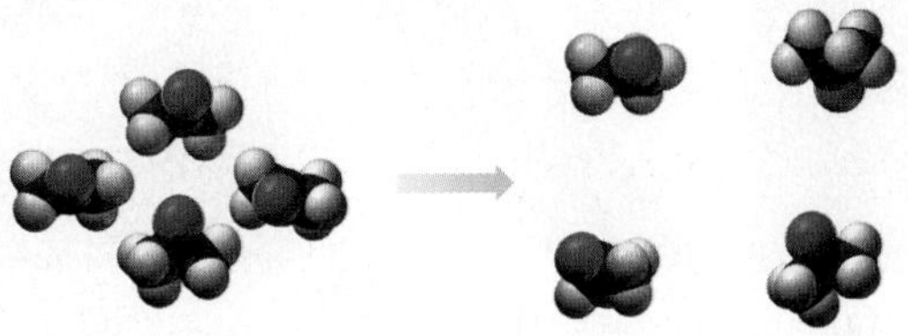

(a)

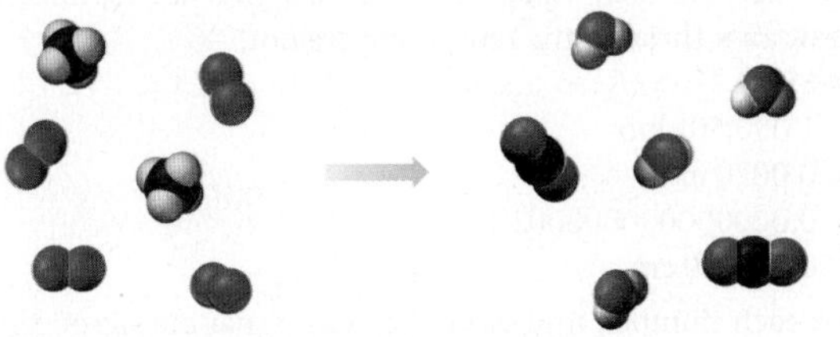

(b)

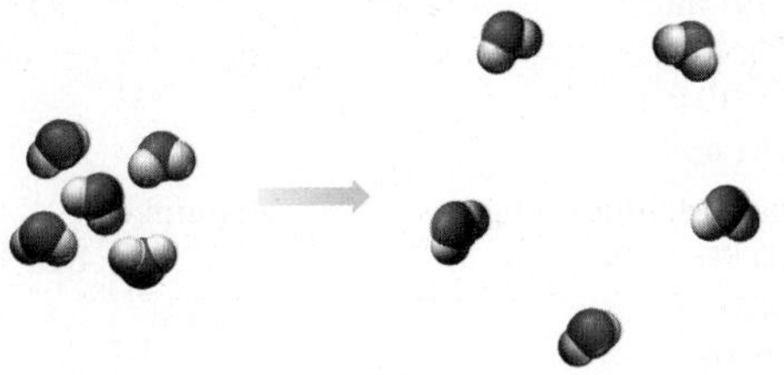

(c)

50. Based on the molecular diagram, classify each change as physical or chemical.

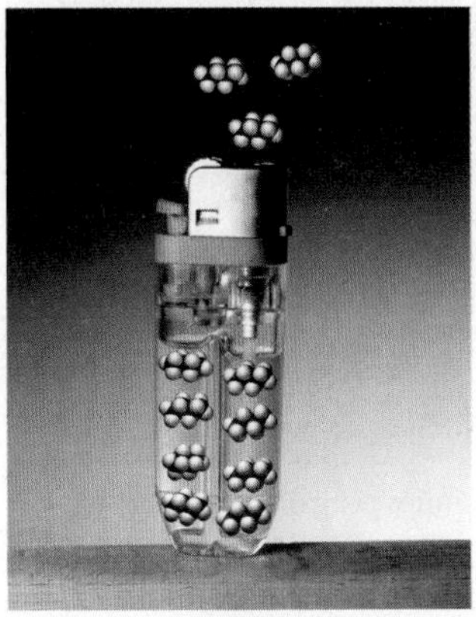

(a)

(b)

(c)

Units in Measurement

51. Convert each temperature.
MISSED THIS? *Read Section 1.6; Watch KCV 1.6*
- **a.** 32 °F to °C (temperature at which water freezes)
- **b.** 77 K to °F (temperature of liquid nitrogen)
- **c.** −109 °F to °C (temperature of dry ice)
- **d.** 98.6 °F to K (body temperature)

52. Convert each temperature.
- **a.** 212 °F to °C (temperature of boiling water at sea level)
- **b.** 22 °C to K (approximate room temperature)
- **c.** 0.00 K to °F (coldest temperature possible, also known as absolute zero)
- **d.** 2.735 K to °C (average temperature of the universe as measured from background black body radiation)

53. The coldest ground-level temperature ever measured on Earth is −128.6 °F, recorded on July 21, 1983, in Antarctica. Convert that temperature to °C and K.
MISSED THIS? *Read Section 1.6; Watch KCV 1.6*

54. The warmest temperature ever measured in the United States is 134 °F, recorded on July 10, 1913, in Death Valley, California. Convert that temperature to °C and K.

55. Use the prefix multipliers to express each measurement without exponents. **MISSED THIS?** *Read Section 1.6; Watch KCV 1.6*
- **a.** 1.2×10^{-9} m
- **b.** 22×10^{-15} s
- **c.** 1.5×10^{9} g
- **d.** 3.5×10^{6} L

56. Use prefix multipliers to express each measurement without exponents.
- **a.** 38.8×10^{5} g
- **b.** 55.2×10^{-10} s
- **c.** 23.4×10^{11} m
- **d.** 87.9×10^{-7} L

57. Use scientific notation to express each quantity with only base units (no prefix multipliers).
MISSED THIS? *Read Section 1.6; Watch KCV 1.6*
- **a.** 4.5 ns
- **b.** 18 fs
- **c.** 128 pm
- **d.** 35 μm

58. Use scientific notation to express each quantity with only base units (no prefix multipliers).
- **a.** 35 μL
- **b.** 225 Mm
- **c.** 133 Tg
- **d.** 1.5 cg

59. Complete the table.
MISSED THIS? *Read Section 1.6; Watch KCV 1.6*

a. 1245 kg	1.245×10^{6} g	1.245×10^{9} mg
b. 515 km	_______dm	_______cm
c. 122.355 s	_______ms	_______ks
d. 3.345 kJ	_______J	_______mJ

60. Complete the table.

a. 355 km/s	_______cm/s	_______m/ms
b. 1228 g/L	_______g/mL	_______kg/mL
c. 554 mK/s	_______K/s	_______μK/ms
d. 2.554 mg/mL	_______g/L	_______μg/mL

61. Express the quantity 254,998 m in each unit.
MISSED THIS? *Read Section 1.6; Watch KCV 1.6*
a. km
b. Mm
c. mm
d. cm

62. Express the quantity 556.2×10^{-12} s in each unit.
a. ms b. ns c. ps d. fs

63. How many 1-cm squares would it take to construct a square that is 1 m on each side? **MISSED THIS?** *Read Section 1.6*

64. How many 1-cm cubes would it take to construct a cube that is 4 cm on edge?

Density

65. A new penny has a mass of 2.49 g and a volume of 0.349 cm^3. Is the penny made of pure copper? Explain your answer.
MISSED THIS? *Read Section 1.6; Watch KCV 1.6*

66. A titanium bicycle frame displaces 0.314 L of water and has a mass of 1.41 kg. What is the density of the titanium in g/cm^3?

67. Glycerol is a syrupy liquid often used in cosmetics and soaps. A 3.25 L sample of pure glycerol has a mass of 4.10×10^3 g. What is the density of glycerol in g/cm^3?
MISSED THIS? *Read Section 1.6; Watch KCV 1.6*

68. A supposedly gold nugget displaces 19.3 mL of water and has a mass of 371 g. Could the nugget be made of gold?

69. Ethylene glycol (antifreeze) has a density of 1.11 g/cm^3.
MISSED THIS? *Read Section 1.6; Watch KCV 1.6, IWE 1.10*
a. What is the mass in g of 417 mL of ethylene glycol?
b. What is the volume in L of 4.1 kg of ethylene glycol?

70. Acetone (nail polish remover) has a density of 0.7857 g/cm^3.
a. What is the mass in g of 28.56 mL of acetone?
b. What is the volume in mL of 6.54 g of acetone?

71. A small airplane takes on 245 L of fuel. If the density of the fuel is 0.821 g/mL, what mass of fuel has the airplane taken on?
MISSED THIS? *Read Section 1.6; Watch KCV 1.6, IWE 1.10*

72. Human fat has a density of 0.918 g/cm^3. How much volume (in cm^3) is gained by a person who gains 10.0 lb of pure fat?

The Reliability of a Measurement and Significant Figures

73. Read each measurement to the correct number of significant figures. Laboratory glassware should always be read from the bottom of the meniscus. **MISSED THIS?** *Read Section 1.7*

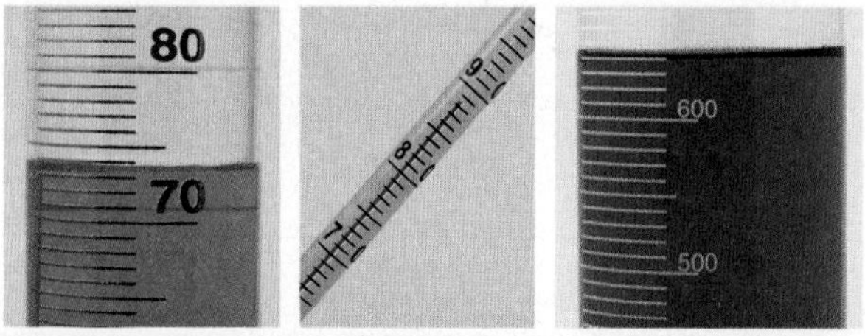

(a) (b) (c)

74. Read each measurement to the correct number of significant figures. Laboratory glassware should always be read from the bottom of the meniscus. Digital balances normally display mass to the correct number of significant figures for that particular balance.

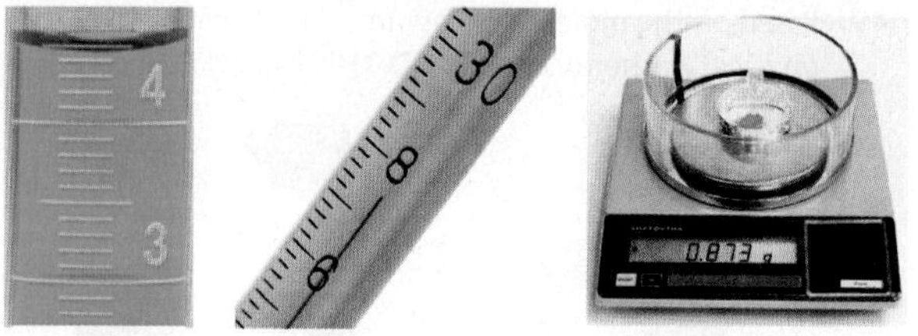

(a) (b) (c)

75. For each number, underline the zeroes that are significant and draw an **x** through the zeroes that are not.
MISSED THIS? *Read Section 1.7; Watch KCV 1.6, IWE 1.5*
a. 1,050,501 km
b. 0.0020 m
c. 0.000000000000002 s
d. 0.001090 cm

76. For each number, underline the zeroes that are significant and draw an **x** through the zeroes that are not.
a. 180,701 mi
b. 0.001040 m
c. 0.005710 km
d. 90,201 m

77. How many significant figures are in each number?
MISSED THIS? *Read Section 1.7; Watch KCV 1.6, IWE 1.5*
a. 0.000312 m
b. 312,000 s
c. 3.12×10^5 km
d. 13,127 s
e. 2000

78. How many significant figures are in each number?
a. 0.1111 s
b. 0.007 m
c. 108,700 km
d. 1.563300×10^{11} m
e. 30,800

79. Which numbers are exact (and therefore have an unlimited number of significant figures)?
MISSED THIS? *Read Section 1.7; Watch KCV 1.6, IWE 1.5*
a. $\pi = 3.14$
b. 12 in = 1 ft
c. EPA gas mileage rating of 26 miles per gallon
d. 1 gross = 144

80. Indicate the number of significant figures in each number. If the number is an exact number, indicate an unlimited number of significant figures.
a. 325,365,189 (July 4, 2017 U.S. population)
b. 2.54 cm = 1 in
c. 11.4 g/cm^3 (density of lead)
d. 12 = 1 dozen

81. Round each number to four significant figures.
MISSED THIS? *Read Section 1.7; Watch KCV 1.7*
a. 156.852
b. 156.842
c. 156.849
d. 156.899

82. Round each number to three significant figures.
a. 79,845.82
b. 1.548937×10^7
c. 2.3499999995
d. 0.000045389

Significant Figures in Calculations

83. Calculate to the correct number of significant figures. **MISSED THIS?** *Read Section 1.7; Watch KCVs 1.6, 1.7, IWEs 1.5, 1.6*
a. $9.15 \div 4.970$
b. $1.54 \times 0.03060 \times 0.69$
c. $27.5 \times 1.82 \div 100.04$
d. $(2.290 \times 10^6) \div (6.7 \times 10^4)$

84. Calculate to the correct number of significant figures.
a. $89.3 \times 77.0 \times 0.08$
b. $(5.01 \times 10^5) \div (7.8 \times 10^2)$
c. $4.005 \times 74 \times 0.007$
d. $453 \div 2.031$

85. Calculate to the correct number of significant figures. **MISSED THIS?** *Read Section 1.7; Watch KCVs 1.6, 1.7, IWEs 1.5, 1.6*
a. $43.7 - 2.341$
b. $17.6 + 2.838 + 2.3 + 110.77$
c. $19.6 + 58.33 - 4.974$
d. $5.99 - 5.572$

86. Calculate to the correct number of significant figures.
a. $0.004 + 0.09879$
b. $1239.3 + 9.73 + 3.42$
c. $2.4 - 1.777$
d. $532 + 7.3 - 48.523$

87. Calculate to the correct number of significant figures. **MISSED THIS?** *Read Section 1.7; Watch KCVs 1.6, 1.7, IWEs 1.5, 1.6*
a. $(24.6681 \times 2.38) + 332.58$
b. $(85.3 - 21.489) \div 0.0059$
c. $(512 \div 986.7) + 5.44$
d. $[(28.7 \times 10^5) \div 48.533] + 144.99$

88. Calculate to the correct number of significant figures.
a. $[(1.7 \times 10^6) \div (2.63 \times 10^5)] + 7.33$
b. $(568.99 - 232.1) \div 5.3$
c. $(9443 + 45 - 9.9) \times 8.1 \times 10^6$
d. $(3.14 \times 2.4367) - 2.34$

89. A flask containing 11.7 mL of a liquid weighs 132.8 g with the liquid in the flask and 124.1 g when empty. Calculate the density of the liquid in g/mL to the correct number of significant digits. **MISSED THIS?** *Read Section 1.6; Watch KCV 1.7, IWE 1.6*

90. A flask containing 9.55 mL of a liquid weighs 157.2 g with the liquid in the flask and 148.4 g when empty. Calculate the density of the liquid in g/mL to the correct number of significant digits.

Unit Conversions

91. Perform each unit conversion.
MISSED THIS? *Read Section 1.8; Watch KCV 1.8, IWE 1.8*
a. 27.8 L to cm^3
b. 1898 mg to kg
c. 198 km to cm

92. Perform each unit conversion.
a. 28.9 nm to μm
b. 1432 cm^3 to L
c. 1211 Tm to Gm

93. Perform each unit conversion.
MISSED THIS? *Read Section 1.8; Watch KCV 1.8, IWE 1.8*
a. 154 cm to in
b. 3.14 kg to g
c. 3.5 L to qt
d. 109 mm to in

94. Perform each unit conversion.
a. 1.4 in to mm
b. 116 ft to cm
c. 1845 kg to lb
d. 815 yd to km

95. A runner wants to run 10.0 km. Her running pace is 7.5 mi per hour. How many minutes must she run?
MISSED THIS? *Read Section 1.8; Watch KCV 1.8, IWE 1.8*

96. A cyclist rides at an average speed of 18 mi per hour. If she wants to bike 212 km, how long (in hours) must she ride?

97. A certain European automobile has a gas mileage of 17 km/L. What is the gas mileage in miles per gallon?
MISSED THIS? *Read Section 1.8; Watch KCV 1.8, IWE 1.8*

98. A gas can holds 5.0 gal of gasoline. Express this quantity in cm^3.

99. A house has an area of 195 m^2. What is its area in each unit?
MISSED THIS? *Read Section 1.8; Watch KCV 1.8, IWE 1.9*
a. km^2
b. dm^2
c. cm^2

100. A bedroom has a volume of 115 m^3. What is its volume in each unit?
a. km^3
b. dm^3
c. cm^3

101. The average U.S. farm occupies 435 acres. How many square miles is this? (1 acre = 43,560 ft^2, 1 mile = 5280 ft)
MISSED THIS? *Read Section 1.8; Watch KCV 1.8, IWE 1.9*

102. Total U.S. farmland occupies 954 million acres. How many square miles is this? (1 acre = 43,560 ft^2, 1 mi = 5280 ft). Total U.S. land area is 3.537 million square miles. What percentage of U.S. land is farmland?

103. An acetaminophen suspension for infants contains 80 mg/0.80 mL suspension. The recommended dose is 15 mg/kg body weight. How many mL of this suspension should be given to an infant weighing 14 lb? (Assume two significant figures.)
MISSED THIS? *Read Section 1.8; Watch KCV 1.8, IWE 1.8*

104. An ibuprofen suspension for infants contains 100 mg/5.0 mL suspension. The recommended dose is 10 mg/kg body weight. How many mL of this suspension should be given to an infant weighing 18 lb? (Assume two significant figures.)

CUMULATIVE PROBLEMS

105. There are exactly 60 seconds in a minute, exactly 60 minutes in an hour, exactly 24 hours in a mean solar day, and 365.24 solar days in a solar year. How many seconds are in a solar year? Give your answer with the correct number of significant figures.

106. Determine the number of picoseconds in 2.0 hours.

107. Classify each property as intensive or extensive.
a. volume
b. boiling point
c. temperature
d. electrical conductivity
e. energy

108. At what temperatures are the readings on the Fahrenheit and Celsius thermometers the same?

109. Suppose you design a new thermometer called the X thermometer. On the X scale the boiling point of water is 130 °X, and the freezing point of water is 10 °X. At what temperature are the readings on the Fahrenheit and X thermometers the same?

110. On a new Jekyll temperature scale, water freezes at 17 °J and boils at 97 °J. On another new temperature scale, the Hyde scale, water freezes at 0 °H and boils at 120 °H. If methyl alcohol boils at 84 °H, what is its boiling point on the Jekyll scale?

111. Force is defined as mass times acceleration. Starting with SI base units, derive a unit for force. Using SI prefixes, suggest a convenient unit for the force resulting from a collision with a 10-ton trailer truck moving at 55 mi per hour and for the force resulting from the collision of a molecule of mass around 10^{-20} kg moving almost at the speed of light (3×10^8 m/s) with the wall of its container. (Assume a 1-second deceleration time for both collisions.)

112. A temperature measurement of 25 °C has three significant figures, while a temperature measurement of −196 °C has only two significant figures. Explain.

113. Do each calculation without your calculator and give the answers to the correct number of significant figures.

a. $1.76 \times 10^{-3}/8.0 \times 10^2$

b. $1.87 \times 10^{-2} + 2 \times 10^{-4} - 3.0 \times 10^{-3}$

c. $[(1.36 \times 10^5)(0.000322)/0.082](129.2)$

114. The value of the euro was recently $1.15 U.S., and the price of 1 liter of gasoline in France is 1.42 euro. What is the price of 1 gallon of gasoline in U.S. dollars in France?

115. A thief uses a can of sand to replace a solid gold cylinder that sits on a weight-sensitive, alarmed pedestal. The can of sand and the gold cylinder have exactly the same dimensions (length = 22 and radius = 3.8 cm).

a. Calculate the mass of each cylinder (ignore the mass of the can itself). (density of gold = 19.3 g/cm^3, density of sand = 3.00 g/cm^3)

b. Does the thief set off the alarm? Explain.

116. The proton has a radius of approximately 1.0×10^{-13} cm and a mass of 1.7×10^{-24} g. Determine the density of a proton. For a sphere, $V = (4/3)\pi r^3$.

117. The density of titanium is 4.51 g/cm^3. What is the volume (in cubic inches) of 3.5 lb of titanium?

118. The density of iron is 7.86 g/cm^3. What is its density in pounds per cubic inch (lb/in^3)?

119. A steel cylinder has a length of 2.16 in, a radius of 0.22 in, and a mass of 41 g. What is the density of the steel in g/cm^3?

120. A solid aluminum sphere has a mass of 85 g. Use the density of aluminum to find the radius of the sphere in inches.

121. A backyard swimming pool holds 185 cubic yards (yd^3) of water. What is the mass of the water in pounds?

122. An iceberg has a volume of 7655 ft^2. What is the mass of the ice (in kg) composing the iceberg (at 0 °C)?

123. The Toyota Prius, a hybrid electric vehicle, has an EPA gas mileage rating of 52 mi/gal in the city. How many kilometers can the Prius travel on 15 L of gasoline?

124. The Honda Insight, a hybrid electric vehicle, has an EPA gas mileage rating of 41 mi/gal in the city. How many kilometers can the Insight travel on the amount of gasoline that would fit in a soda can? The volume of a soda can is 355 mL.

125. The single proton that forms the nucleus of the hydrogen atom has a radius of approximately 1.0×10^{-13} cm. The hydrogen atom itself has a radius of approximately 52.9 pm. What fraction of the space within the atom is occupied by the nucleus?

126. A sample of gaseous neon atoms at atmospheric pressure and 0 °C contains 2.69×10^{22} atoms per liter. The atomic radius of neon is 69 pm. What fraction of the space do the atoms themselves occupy? What does this reveal about the separation between atoms in the gaseous phase?

127. The diameter of a hydrogen atom is 212 pm. Find the length in kilometers of a row of 6.02×10^{23} hydrogen atoms. The diameter of a ping pong ball is 4.0 cm. Find the length in kilometers of a row of 6.02×10^{23} ping pong balls.

128. The world record in the men's 100-m dash is 9.58 s, and in the 100-yd dash it is 9.07 s. Find the speed in mi/hr of the runners who set these records. (Assume three significant figures for 100 m and 100 yd.)

129. Table salt contains 39.33 g of sodium per 100 g of salt. The U.S. Food and Drug Administration (FDA) recommends that adults consume less than 2.40 g of sodium per day. A particular snack mix contains 1.25 g of salt per 100 g of the mix. What mass of the snack mix can an adult consume and still be within the FDA limit? (Assume three significant figures for 100 g.)

130. Lead metal can be extracted from a mineral called galena, which contains 86.6% lead by mass. A particular ore contains 68.5% galena by mass. If the lead can be extracted with 92.5% efficiency, what mass of ore is required to make a lead sphere with a 5.00-cm radius?

131. A length of #8 copper wire (radius = 1.63 mm) has a mass of 24.0 kg and a resistance of 2.061 ohm per km (Ω/km). What is the overall resistance of the wire?

132. Rolls of aluminum foil are 304 mm wide and 0.016 mm thick. What maximum length of aluminum foil can be made from 1.10 kg of aluminum?

133. Liquid nitrogen has a density of 0.808 g/mL and boils at 77 K. Researchers often purchase liquid nitrogen in insulated 175 L tanks. The liquid vaporizes quickly to gaseous nitrogen (which has a density of 1.15 g/L at room temperature and atmospheric pressure) when the liquid is removed from the tank. Suppose that all 175 L of liquid nitrogen in a tank accidentally vaporized in a lab that measured 10.00 m × 10.00 m × 2.50 m. What maximum fraction of the air in the room could be displaced by the gaseous nitrogen?

134. Mercury is often used in thermometers. The mercury sits in a bulb on the bottom of the thermometer and rises up a thin capillary as the temperature rises. Suppose a mercury thermometer contains 3.380 g of mercury and has a capillary that is 0.200 mm in diameter. How far does the mercury rise in the capillary when the temperature changes from 0.0 °C to 25.0 °C? The density of mercury at these temperatures is 13.596 g/cm^3 and 13.534 g/cm^3, respectively.

CHALLENGE PROBLEMS

135. A force of 2.31×10^4 N is applied to a diver's face mask that has an area of 125 cm^2. Find the pressure in atm on the face mask.

136. The SI unit of force is the newton, derived from the base units by using the definition of force, $F = ma$. The dyne is a non-SI unit of force in which mass is measured in grams and time is measured in seconds. The relationship between the two units is 1 dyne $= 10^{-5}$ N. Find the unit of length used to define the dyne.

137. Kinetic energy can be defined as $\frac{1}{2}mv^2$ or as $\frac{3}{2}PV$. Show that the derived SI units of each of these terms are those of energy. (Pressure is force/area and force is mass × acceleration.)

138. In 1999, scientists discovered a new class of black holes with masses 100 to 10,000 times the mass of our sun that occupy less space than our moon. Suppose that one of these black holes has a mass of 1×10^3 suns and a radius equal to one-half the radius of our moon. What is the density of the black hole in g/cm^3? The radius of our sun is 7.0×10^5 km, and it has an average density of 1.4×10^3 kg/m^3. The diameter of the moon is 2.16×10^3 mi.

139. Suppose that polluted air has carbon monoxide (CO) levels of 15.0 ppm. An average human inhales about 0.50 L of air per breath and takes about 20 breaths per minute. How many milligrams of carbon monoxide does the average person inhale in an 8-hour period at this level of carbon monoxide pollution? Assume that the carbon monoxide has a density of 1.2 g/L. (*Hint*: 15.0 ppm CO means 15.0 L CO per 10^6 L air.)

140. Nanotechnology, the field of building ultrasmall structures one atom at a time, has progressed in recent years. One potential application of nanotechnology is the construction of artificial cells. The simplest cells would probably mimic red blood cells, the body's oxygen transporters. Nanocontainers, perhaps constructed of carbon, could be pumped full of oxygen and injected into a person's bloodstream. If the person needed additional oxygen—due to a heart attack perhaps, or for the purpose of space travel—these containers could slowly release oxygen into the blood, allowing tissues that would otherwise die to remain alive. Suppose that the nanocontainers were cubic and had an edge length of 25 nm.

a. What is the volume of one nanocontainer? (Ignore the thickness of the nanocontainer's wall.)

b. Suppose that each nanocontainer could contain pure oxygen pressurized to a density of 85 g/L. How many grams of oxygen could each nanocontainer contain?

c. Air typically contains about 0.28 g of oxygen per liter. An average human inhales about 0.50 L of air per breath and takes about 20 breaths per minute. How many grams of oxygen does a human inhale per hour? (Assume two significant figures.)

d. What is the minimum number of nanocontainers that a person would need in his or her bloodstream to provide 1 hour's worth of oxygen?

e. What is the minimum volume occupied by the number of nanocontainers calculated in part d? Is such a volume feasible, given that total blood volume in an adult is about 5 L?

141. Approximate the percent increase in waist size that occurs when a 155-lb person gains 40.0 lb of fat. Assume that the volume of the person can be modeled by a cylinder that is 4.0 ft tall. The average density of a human is about 1.0 g/cm^3, and the density of fat is 0.918 g/cm^3.

142. A box contains a mixture of small copper spheres and small lead spheres. The total volume of both metals is measured by the displacement of water to be 427 cm^3, and the total mass is 4.36 kg. What percentage of the spheres are copper?

CONCEPTUAL PROBLEMS

143. A volatile liquid (one that easily evaporates) is put into a jar, and the jar is then sealed. Does the mass of the sealed jar and its contents change upon the vaporization of the liquid?

144. The diagram shown first represents solid carbon dioxide, also known as dry ice. Which of the other diagrams best represents the dry ice after it has sublimed into a gas?

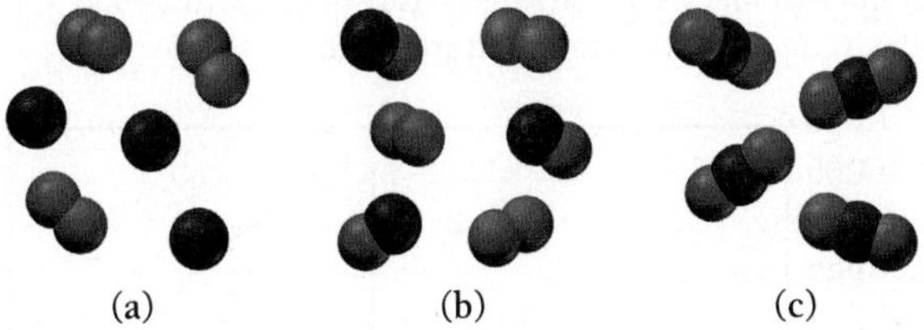

(a) (b) (c)

145. A cube has an edge length of 7 cm. If it is divided into 1-cm cubes, how many 1-cm cubes are there?

146. Substance A has a density of 1.7 g/cm^3. Substance B has a density of 1.7 kg/m^3. Without doing any calculations, determine which substance is more dense.

147. For each box, examine the blocks attached to the balances. Based on their positions and sizes, determine which block is more dense (the dark block or the lighter-colored block), or if the relative densities cannot be determined. (Think carefully about the information being shown.)

148. Let a triangle represent atoms of element A and a circle represent atoms of element B.

a. Draw an atomic-level view of a homogeneous mixture of elements A and B.

b. Draw an atomic view of the compound AB in a liquid state (molecules close together).

c. Draw an atomic view of the compound AB after it has undergone a physical change (such as evaporation).

d. Draw an atomic view of the compound after it has undergone a chemical change (such as decomposition of AB into A and B).

149. Identify each statement as being most like an observation, a law, or a theory.

a. All coastal areas experience two high tides and two low tides each day.

b. The tides in Earth's oceans are caused mainly by the gravitational attraction of the moon.

c. Yesterday, high tide in San Francisco Bay occurred at 2:43 A.M. and 3:07 P.M.

d. Tides are higher at the full moon and new moon than at other times of the month.

QUESTIONS FOR GROUP WORK

Active Classroom Learning

Discuss these questions with the group and record your consensus answer.

150. Using white and black circles to represent different kinds of atoms, make a drawing that accurately represents each sample of matter: a solid element, a liquid compound, and a heterogeneous mixture. Make a drawing (clearly showing *before* and *after*) depicting your liquid compound undergoing a physical change. Make a drawing depicting your solid element undergoing a chemical change.

151. Look up the measurement of the approximate thickness of a human hair.

a. Convert the measurement to an SI unit (if it isn't already).

b. Write it in scientific notation.

c. Write it without scientific notation.

d. Write it with an appropriate prefix on a base unit.

Now repeat these steps using the distance from Earth to the sun.

152. The following statements are all true.

a. Jessica's house is 5 km from the grocery store.

b. Jessica's house is 4.73 km from the grocery store.

c. Jessica's house is 4.73297 km from the grocery store.

How can all the statements be true? What does the number of digits in each statement communicate? What sort of device would Jessica need to make the measurement in each statement?

153. One inch is equal to 2.54 cm. Draw a line that is 1 in long, and mark the centimeters on the line. Draw a cube that is 1 in on each side. Draw lines on each face of the cube that are 1 cm apart. How many cubic centimeters are there in 1 in^3?

154. Convert the height of each member in your group from feet and inches to meters. Once you have your heights in meters, calculate the sum of all the heights. Use appropriate rules for significant figures at each step.

DATA INTERPRETATION AND ANALYSIS

Density of Water

155. The density of a substance can change with temperature. The graph that follows displays the density of water from −150 °C to 100 °C. Examine the graph and answer the questions.

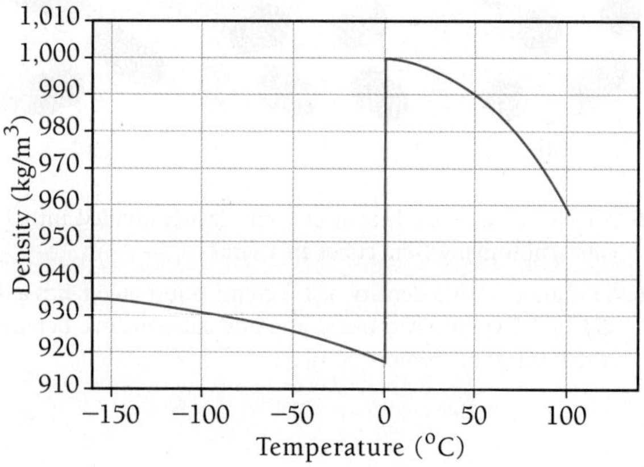

a. Water undergoes a large change in density at 0 °C as it freezes to form ice. Calculate the percent change in density that occurs when liquid water freezes to ice at 0 °C.

(*Hint*: % change $= \dfrac{\text{final value} - \text{initial value}}{\text{initial value}} \times 100\%$)

b. Calculate the volume (in cm^3) of 54 g of water at 1 °C and the volume of the same mass of ice at −1 °C. What is the change in volume?

c. Antarctica contains 26.5 million cubic kilometers of ice. Assume the temperature of the ice is −20 °C. If all of this ice were heated to 1 °C and melted to form water, what volume of liquid water would form?

d. A 1.00-L sample of water is heated from 1 °C to 100 °C. What is the volume of the water after it is heated?

Cc ANSWERS TO CONCEPTUAL CONNECTIONS

Laws and Theories

1.1 **(b)** A law only summarizes a series of related observations; a theory gives the underlying reasons for them.

Pure Substances and Mixtures

1.2 **(a)** This image is a pure substance. More specifically, because it contains two different type of atoms bonded together, it is a pure compound.

Chemical and Physical Changes

1.3 View **(a)** best represents the water after vaporization. Vaporization is a physical change, so the molecules must remain the same before and after the change.

Energy

1.4 **(c)** Chemical energy is a type of potential energy that results from the electrostatic forces between the charged particles that compose atoms and molecules.

Temperature Scale

1.5 **(a)** The Kelvin scale has no negative temperatures because 0 Kelvin is the coldest possible temperature. Lower temperatures do not exist. Both the Celsius scale and the Fahrenheit scale have negative temperatures.

Prefix Multipliers

1.6 **(c)** The prefix micro (10^{-6}) is appropriate. The measurement would be reported as 55.7 μm.

Density

1.7 **(c)** The copper sample expands. However, because its mass remains constant while its volume increases, its density decreases.

These observations have tacitly led to the conclusion which seems universally adopted, that all bodies of sensible magnitude . . . are constituted of a vast number of extremely small particles, or atoms of matter . . . .

—JOHN DALTON (1766–1844)

CHAPTER 2 Atoms and Elements

If you cut a piece of graphite from the tip of a pencil into smaller and smaller pieces, how far could you go? Could you divide it forever? Would you eventually run into some basic particles that were no longer divisible, not because of their sheer smallness, but because of the nature of matter? This fundamental question about the nature of matter has been asked by thinkers for over two millennia. Their answers have varied over time. On the scale of everyday objects, matter appears continuous, or infinitely divisible. And until about 200 years ago, many scientists thought that matter was indeed continuous—but they were proven wrong. If you were to divide the graphite from your pencil tip into smaller and smaller pieces (far smaller than the eye could see), you would eventually end up with individual carbon atoms. The word *atom* comes from the Greek *atomos*, meaning "indivisible." You cannot divide a carbon atom into smaller pieces and still have carbon. Atoms compose all ordinary matter—if you want to understand matter, you must begin by understanding atoms.

Scottish botanist Robert Brown observed random motion in tiny particles suspended in water. This motion later confirmed the particulate nature of matter.

2.1 Brownian Motion: Atoms Confirmed 49

2.2 Early Ideas about the Building Blocks of Matter 51

2.3 Modern Atomic Theory and the Laws That Led to It 51

2.4 The Discovery of the Electron 55

2.5 The Structure of the Atom 57

2.6 Subatomic Particles: Protons, Neutrons, and Electrons in Atoms 59

2.7 Finding Patterns: The Periodic Law and the Periodic Table 65

2.8 Atomic Mass: The Average Mass of an Element's Atoms 69

2.9 Molar Mass: Counting Atoms by Weighing Them 73

LEARNING OUTCOMES 81

2.1 Brownian Motion: Atoms Confirmed

In 1827, Scottish botanist Robert Brown (1773–1858) looked through his microscope at water-suspended particles that had come from pollen grains. He noticed that the particles were in continuous motion. Any one particle traveled a random, jittery path through the liquid water. Brown initially thought that the particles might be alive and were perhaps the male sexual cells of plants (similar to sperm). However, similar particles from plants long dead exhibited the same jittery motion, and so did dust from pulverized stones. Brown concluded that the source of the motion must not come from the particles themselves. What was causing this motion?

The definitive answer to this question did not come until 1905, when Albert Einstein (1879–1955) developed a theory that quantitatively explained what was by then called *Brownian motion*. Einstein's model explained that the particle motion was the result of molecular bombardments of the particles due to the thermal energy of the surrounding water. In other words, the water molecules in liquid water—constantly in motion due to thermal energy—were continuously battering the pollen and dust particles, causing them to jump around and move. In Einstein's model, the jittering pollen particles are like a beach ball that is thrown into a crowd at a graduation ceremony. As the eager graduates strike the ball over and over again, the ball moves through the crowd in a jittery random path. The difference is that, in the case of Brownian motion, the "crowd" is composed of molecules much too small to see.

In 1908, French physicist Jean Perrin (1870–1942) conducted experimental measurements to test Einstein's model. His measurements confirmed that Einstein's model was valid. In 1926, Perrin was awarded the Nobel Prize in Physics. During the award speech, the presenter said, "the object of the researches of Professor Jean Perrin which have gained for him the Nobel Prize in Physics for 1926 was to put a definite end to the long struggle regarding the real existence of molecules." In other words, the work of Einstein, and then Perrin, removed any lingering doubt about the particulate nature of matter.

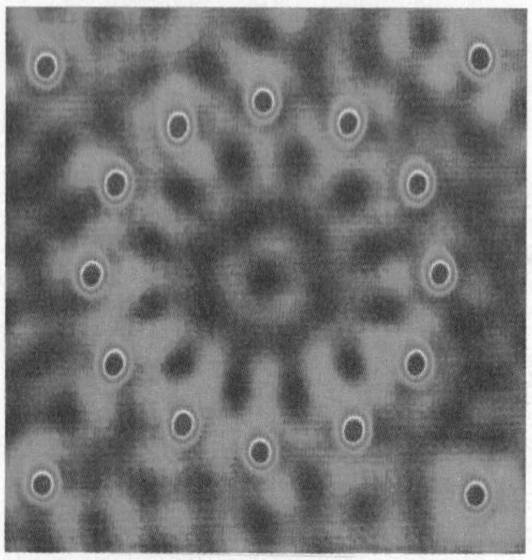

▲ **FIGURE 2.1 Imaging Atoms** 12 cobalt atoms arranged in a circle on a copper surface.

In Einstein's day, the existence of atoms was inferred from the jittery motion first witnessed by Brown. Today, with a type of microscope called a scanning tunneling microscope (STM), we can form images of atoms themselves. In fact, STM can be used to *pick up and move* individual atoms, allowing structures and patterns to be made one atom at a time. Figure 2.1◀, for example, shows 12 cobalt atoms arranged in a circle on a copper surface. If all of the words in the books in the Library of Congress—38 million books occupying 840 miles of shelves—were written in letters the size of this circle, they would fit into an area of about five square millimeters. Scientists at IBM have also succeeded in making a short video entitled *A Boy and His Atom*, in which the main character (a boy) is animated using a few dozen atoms. In the video, which has been viewed millions of times on YouTube, the boy plays with an atom like a real boy would play with a ball.

As we discussed in Chapter 1, it was only 200 years ago that John Dalton proposed his atomic theory, and about 100 years ago that the theory was confirmed through the work of Einstein and Perrin. Yet today we can image atoms, move them, and even build tiny machines out of just a few dozen atoms (an area of research called nanotechnology). These atomic machines, and the atoms that compose them, are almost unimaginably small. To get an idea of the size of an atom, imagine picking up a grain of sand at a beach. That grain contains more atoms than you could count in a lifetime. In fact, the number of atoms in one sand grain far exceeds the number of grains on an entire beach.

The exact number of naturally occurring elements is controversial because some elements that were first discovered when they were synthesized are believed to also be present in trace amounts in nature.

In spite of their small size, atoms are the key to connecting the macroscopic and microscopic worlds. An *atom* is the smallest identifiable unit of an *element*. There are about 91 different naturally occurring elements. In addition, scientists have succeeded in making over 20 synthetic elements (elements not found in nature). In this chapter, we learn about atoms: what they are made of, how they differ from one another, and how they are structured. We also learn about the elements that are composed of these different kinds of atoms and about some of their characteristic properties. We will also discuss how the elements can be organized in a way that reveals patterns in their properties and helps us to understand what underlies those properties.

2.2 Early Ideas about the Building Blocks of Matter

The first people to propose that matter was composed of small, indestructible particles were Leucippus (fifth century B.C., exact dates unknown) and his student Democritus (460–370 B.C.). These Greek philosophers theorized that matter is ultimately composed of small, indivisible particles they named *atomos*. Democritus wrote, "Nothing exists except atoms and empty space; everything else is opinion." Leucippus and Democritus proposed that many different kinds of atoms exist, each different in shape and size, and that they move randomly through empty space. Other influential Greek thinkers of the time, such as Plato and Aristotle, did not embrace the atomic ideas of Leucippus and Democritus. Instead, Plato and Aristotle held that matter had no smallest parts and that different substances were composed of various proportions of fire, air, earth, and water. Since there was no experimental way to test the relative merits of the competing ideas, Aristotle's view prevailed, largely because he was so influential. The idea that matter is composed of atoms took a back seat in intellectual thought for nearly 2000 years.

In the sixteenth century, modern science began to emerge. A greater emphasis on observation led Nicolaus Copernicus (1473–1543) to publish *On the Revolution of the Heavenly Orbs* in 1543. The publication of that book—which proposed that the sun, not Earth, is at the center of the universe—marks the beginning of what we now call the *scientific revolution*. The next 200 years—and the work of scientists such as Francis Bacon (1561–1626), Johannes Kepler (1571–1630), Galileo Galilei (1564–1642), Robert Boyle (1627–1691), and Isaac Newton (1642–1727)—brought rapid advancement as the scientific approach became the established way to learn about the physical world. By the early 1800s, certain observations led the English chemist John Dalton (1766–1844) to offer convincing evidence that supported the early atomic ideas of Leucippus and Democritus. However, debate continued about whether atoms actually exist until the description of Brownian motion by Einstein in 1905 and subsequent experimental verification of the description in 1908 by Perrin (see Section 2.1).

2.3 Modern Atomic Theory and the Laws That Led to It

WATCH **NOW!**
KEY CONCEPT VIDEO 2.3
Atomic Theory

Recall the discussion of the scientific approach to knowledge from Chapter 1. The *atomic theory* (the idea that all matter is composed of atoms) grew out of observations and laws. The three most important laws that led to the development and acceptance of the atomic theory are the law of conservation of mass, the law of definite proportions, and the law of multiple proportions.

The Law of Conservation of Mass

In 1789, as we saw in Chapter 1, Antoine Lavoisier formulated the **law of conservation of mass**, which states:

In a chemical reaction, matter is neither created nor destroyed.

In other words, when a chemical reaction occurs, the total mass of the substances involved in the reaction does not change. For example, consider the reaction between sodium and chlorine to form sodium chloride. The combined mass of the sodium and chlorine that react (the *reactants*) exactly equals the mass of the sodium chloride that forms (the *product*). This law is consistent with the idea that matter is composed of small, indestructible particles. The particles rearrange during a chemical reaction, but the amount of matter is conserved because the particles themselves are indestructible (at least by chemical means).

We will see in Chapter 21 that the law of conservation of mass is a slight oversimplification. However, the changes in mass in ordinary chemical processes are so minute that they can be ignored for all practical purposes.

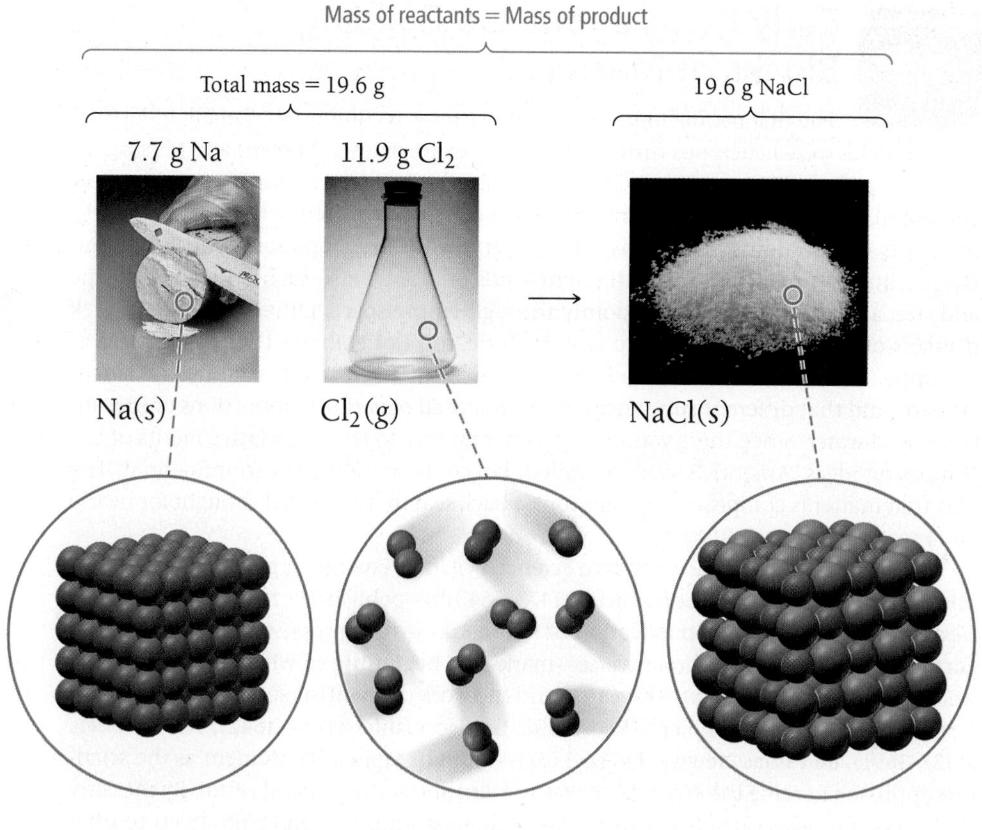

ANSWER **NOW!**

2.1 Cc Conceptual Connection

THE LAW OF CONSERVATION OF MASS When a log completely burns in a campfire, the mass of the ash is much less than the mass of the log. What happens to the matter that composed the log?

(a) The matter that composed the log reacts to form gases that are released into the air.
(b) The matter that composed the log is converted into energy.
(c) The matter that composed the log is still present in the ashes but has a much lower mass.

The Law of Definite Proportions

In 1797, the French chemist Joseph Proust (1754–1826) made observations on the composition of compounds. He found that the elements composing a given compound always occur in fixed (or definite) proportions in all samples of the compound. In contrast, the components of a mixture can be present in any proportions whatsoever. Proust summarized his observations in the **law of definite proportions**:

The law of definite proportions is sometimes called the law of constant composition.

> **All samples of a given compound, regardless of their source or how they were prepared, have the same proportions of their constituent elements.**

For example, the decomposition of 18.0 g of water results in 16.0 g of oxygen and 2.0 g of hydrogen, or an oxygen-to-hydrogen mass ratio of:

$$\text{Mass ratio} = \frac{16.0\text{ g O}}{2.0\text{ g H}} = 8.0 \text{ or } 8{:}1$$

This ratio holds for any sample of pure water, regardless of its origin. The law of definite proportions applies to every compound. Consider ammonia, a compound composed of nitrogen and hydrogen. Ammonia contains 14.0 g of nitrogen for every 3.0 g of hydrogen, resulting in a nitrogen-to-hydrogen mass ratio of 4.7.

$$\text{Mass ratio} = \frac{14.0\text{ g N}}{3.0\text{ g H}} = 4.7 \text{ or } 4.7{:}1$$

Again, this ratio is the same for every sample of ammonia. The law of definite proportions also hints at the idea that matter is composed of atoms. Compounds have definite proportions of their constituent elements because the atoms that compose them, each with its own specific mass, occur in a definite ratio. Since the ratio of atoms is the same for all samples of a particular compound, the ratio of masses is also the same.

LAW OF DEFINITE PROPORTIONS We just saw that the mass ratio of nitrogen to hydrogen in ammonia is 4.7:1. If a sample of ammonia contains 10.0 g of H, how many grams of N does it contain?

(a) 4.7 **(b)** 9.4 **(c)** 14 **(d)** 47

Cc 2.2 Conceptual Connection

ANSWER **NOW!**

EXAMPLE 2.1 Law of Definite Proportions

Two samples of carbon dioxide are decomposed into their constituent elements. One sample produces 25.6 g of oxygen and 9.60 g of carbon, and the other produces 21.6 g of oxygen and 8.10 g of carbon. Show that these results are consistent with the law of definite proportions.

SOLUTION

To show this, for both samples calculate the mass ratio of one element to the other by dividing the mass of one element by the mass of the other. For convenience, divide the larger mass by the smaller one.	For the first sample: $\frac{\text{Mass oxygen}}{\text{Mass carbon}} = \frac{25.6}{9.60} = 2.67 \text{ or } 2.67{:}1$ For the second sample: $\frac{\text{Mass oxygen}}{\text{Mass carbon}} = \frac{21.6}{8.10} = 2.67 \text{ or } 2.67{:}1$

The ratios are the same for the two samples, so these results are consistent with the law of definite proportions.

FOR PRACTICE 2.1 Two samples of carbon monoxide are decomposed into their constituent elements. One sample produces 17.2 g of oxygen and 12.9 g of carbon, and the other sample produces 10.5 g of oxygen and 7.88 g of carbon. Show that these results are consistent with the law of definite proportions.

Answers to For Practice and For More Practice Problems can be found in Appendix IV.

The Law of Multiple Proportions

In 1804, John Dalton published his **law of multiple proportions**:

> **When two elements (call them A and B) form two different compounds, the masses of element B that combine with 1 g of element A can be expressed as a ratio of small whole numbers.**

Dalton suspected that matter was composed of atoms, so that when two elements A and B combine to form more than one compound, an atom of A combines with either one, two, three, or more atoms of B (AB_1, AB_2, AB_3, etc.). Therefore, the masses of B that react with a fixed mass of A are always related to one another as small whole-number ratios. Consider the compounds carbon monoxide and carbon dioxide. Carbon monoxide and carbon dioxide are two compounds composed of the same two elements: carbon and oxygen. We saw in Example 2.1 that the mass ratio of oxygen to carbon in carbon dioxide is 2.67:1; therefore, 2.67 g of oxygen reacts with 1 g of carbon. In carbon monoxide, however, the mass ratio of oxygen to carbon is 1.33:1, or 1.33 g of oxygen to every 1 g of carbon.

The ratio of these two masses is itself a small whole number.

$$\frac{\text{Mass oxygen to 1 g carbon in carbon dioxide}}{\text{Mass oxygen to 1 g carbon in carbon monoxide}} = \frac{2.67}{1.33} = 2$$

Carbon dioxide

Mass oxygen that combines with 1 g carbon = 2.67 g

Carbon monoxide

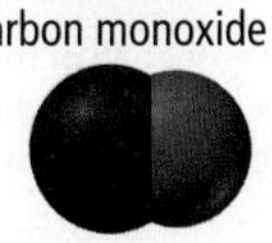

Mass oxygen that combines with 1 g carbon = 1.33 g

With the help of the molecular models in the margin on the preceding page, we can see why the ratio is 2:1—carbon dioxide contains two oxygen atoms to every carbon atom, while carbon monoxide contains only one. Of course, neither John Dalton nor Joseph Proust had access to any kind of modern instrumentation that could detect individual atoms—Dalton supported his atomic ideas primarily by using the *masses* of samples.

EXAMPLE 2.2 Law of Multiple Proportions

Nitrogen forms several compounds with oxygen, including nitrogen dioxide and dinitrogen monoxide. Nitrogen dioxide contains 2.28 g oxygen to every 1.00 g nitrogen, while dinitrogen monoxide contains 0.570 g oxygen to every 1.00 g nitrogen. Show that these results are consistent with the law of multiple proportions.

SOLUTION

Calculate the ratio of the mass of oxygen from one compound to the mass of oxygen in the other. Always divide the larger of the two masses by the smaller one.	$\frac{\text{Mass oxygen to 1 g nitrogen in nitrogen dioxide}}{\text{Mass oxygen to 1 g nitrogen in dinitrogen monoxide}} = \frac{2.28}{0.570} = 4.00$

The ratio is a small whole number (4); these results are consistent with the law of multiple proportions.

FOR PRACTICE 2.2 Hydrogen and oxygen form both water and hydrogen peroxide. The decomposition of a sample of water forms 0.125 g hydrogen to every 1.00 g oxygen. The decomposition of a sample of hydrogen peroxide forms 0.0625 g hydrogen to every 1.00 g oxygen. Show that these results are consistent with the law of multiple proportions.

John Dalton and the Atomic Theory

In 1808, John Dalton explained the laws we just discussed with his **atomic theory**:

In Section 2.6, we will see that, contrary to Dalton's theory, all atoms of a given element do not have exactly the same mass.

1. Each element is composed of tiny, indestructible particles called atoms.
2. All atoms of a given element have the same mass and other properties that distinguish them from the atoms of other elements.
3. Atoms combine in simple, whole-number ratios to form compounds.
4. Atoms of one element cannot change into atoms of another element. In a chemical reaction, atoms only change the way they are *bound together* with other atoms.

Today, the evidence for the atomic theory is overwhelming. Matter is indeed composed of atoms.

CHEMISTRY IN YOUR DAY | Atoms and Humans

You and I are composed of atoms. We get those atoms from the food we eat. Yesterday's cheeseburger contributes to today's skin, muscle, and hair. Not only are we made of atoms, but we are made of *recycled* atoms. The carbon atoms that compose our bodies were used by other living organisms before we got them. And they will be used by still others when we are done with them. In fact, it is likely that at this moment, your body contains some (over one trillion*) carbon atoms that were at one time part of your chemistry professor.

The idea that humans are composed of atoms acting in accord with the laws of chemistry and physics has significant implications and raises important questions. If atoms compose our brains, for example, do those atoms determine our thoughts and emotions? Are our feelings caused by atoms acting according to the laws of chemistry and physics?

*This calculation assumes that all of the carbon atoms metabolized by your professor over the last 40 years have been uniformly distributed into atmospheric carbon dioxide, and subsequently incorporated into the plants you have eaten.

Richard Feynman (1918–1988), a Nobel Prize–winning physicist, said that "The most important hypothesis in all of biology is that everything that animals do, atoms do. In other words, there is nothing that living things do that cannot be understood from the point of view that they are made of atoms acting according to the laws of physics." Indeed, biology has undergone a revolution in the last 50 years, mostly through investigation of the atomic and molecular basis for life. Some people have seen the atomic view of life as a devaluation of human life. We have always wanted to distinguish ourselves from everything else, and the idea that we are made of the same basic particles as all other matter takes something away from that distinction . . . or does it?

QUESTION *Do you find the idea that you are made of recycled atoms disturbing? Why or why not? Reductionism is the idea that complex systems can be understood by understanding their parts. Is reductionism a good way to understand humans? Is it the only way?*

THE LAWS OF DEFINITE AND MULTIPLE PROPORTIONS

2.3 Cc Conceptual Connection — ANSWER NOW!

Which statement best captures one of the differences between the law of definite proportions and the law of multiple proportions?

(a) The law of definite proportions applies to two or more samples of the *same compound*, while the law of multiple proportions applies to two *different compounds* containing the same two elements (A and B).

(b) The law of definite proportions applies to two *different compounds* containing the same two elements (A and B), while the law of multiple proportions applies to two or more samples of the *same compound*.

(c) None of the above. Both laws apply to multiple samples of the same compound.

2.4 The Discovery of the Electron

By the end of the nineteenth century, scientists were convinced that matter is made up of atoms, the permanent, supposedly indestructible building blocks that compose everything. However, further experiments revealed that the atom itself is composed of even smaller, more fundamental particles.

Cathode Rays

In the late 1800s, an English physicist named J. J. Thomson (1856–1940), working at Cambridge University, performed experiments to probe the properties of **cathode rays**. Thomson constructed a partially evacuated glass tube called a **cathode ray tube**, shown in Figure 2.2▼. Thomson then applied a high electrical voltage between two electrodes at either end of the tube. He found that a beam of particles, called cathode rays, traveled from the negatively charged electrode (which is called the cathode) to the positively charged one (which is called the anode).

Thomson found that the particles that compose the cathode ray have the following properties: they travel in straight lines; they are independent of the composition of the material from which they originate (the cathode); and they carry a negative **electrical charge**. Electrical charge is a fundamental property of some of the particles that compose atoms and results in attractive and repulsive forces—called *electrostatic forces*—between those particles. The area around a charged particle where these forces exist is called an *electric field*. The characteristics of electrical charge are summarized in the figure in the margin. You have probably experienced excess electrical charge when brushing your hair on a dry day. The brushing action causes the accumulation of charged particles in your hair, which repel each other, making your hair stand on end.

J. J. Thomson measured the charge-to-mass ratio of the cathode ray particles by deflecting them using electric and magnetic fields, as shown in Figure 2.3▶. The value he measured, -1.76×10^8 coulombs (C) per gram, implied that the cathode ray particle

Properties of Electrical Charge

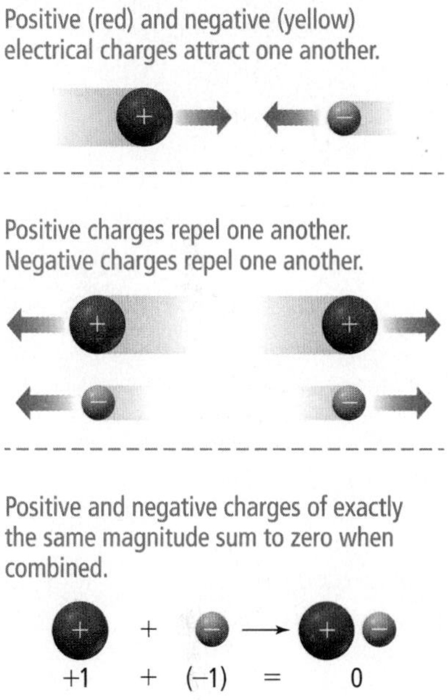

For a full explanation of electrical voltage, see Chapter 20.

The coulomb (C) is the SI unit for charge.

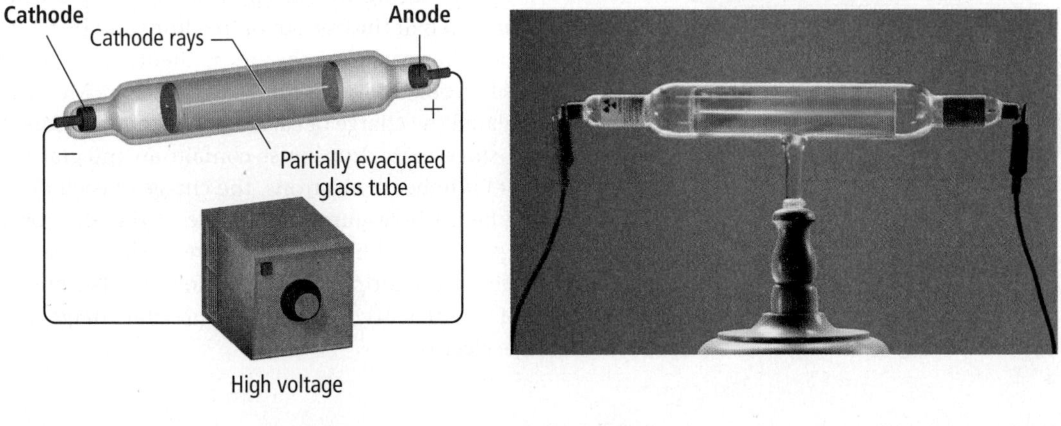

◀ **FIGURE 2.2**
Cathode Ray Tube

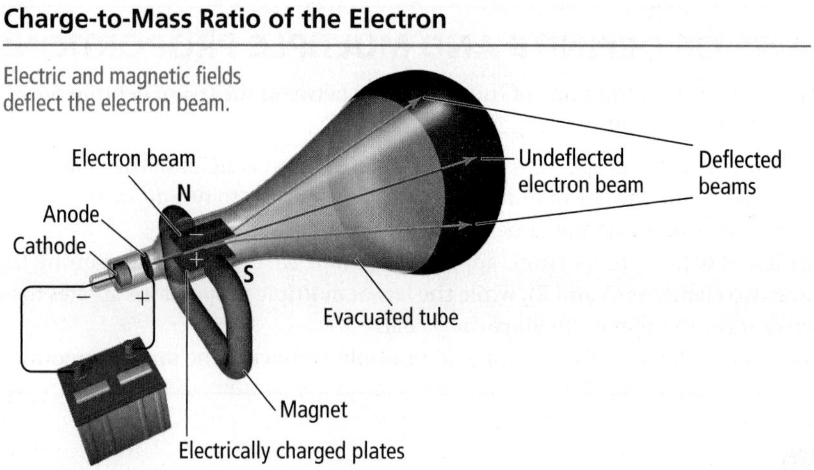

▶ **FIGURE 2.3 Thomson's Measurement of the Charge-to-Mass Ratio of the Electron** J. J. Thomson used electric and magnetic fields to deflect the electron beam in a cathode ray tube. By measuring the strengths at which the effects of the two fields (electric and magnetic) cancel exactly, leaving the beam undeflected, he was able to calculate the charge-to-mass ratio of the electron.

was about 2000 times lighter (less massive) than hydrogen, the lightest known atom. These results were revolutionary—the indestructible atom could apparently be chipped!

J. J. Thomson had discovered the **electron**, a negatively charged, low-mass particle present within all atoms. He wrote, "We have in the cathode rays matter in a new state, a state in which the subdivision of matter is carried very much further . . . a state in which all matter . . . is of one and the same kind; this matter being the substance from which all the chemical elements are built up."

Millikan's Oil Drop Experiment: The Charge of the Electron

In 1909, American physicist Robert Millikan (1868–1953), working at the University of Chicago, performed his now famous oil drop experiment in which he deduced the charge of a single electron. The apparatus for the oil drop experiment is shown in Figure 2.4▼.

In his experiment, Millikan sprayed oil into fine droplets using an atomizer. The droplets were allowed to fall under the influence of gravity through a small hole into the lower portion of the apparatus where Millikan viewed them with the aid of a light source and a viewing microscope. During their fall, the drops acquired electrons Millikan had produced by bombarding the air in the chamber with ionizing radiation (a kind of energy described in Chapter 8). The electrons imparted a negative charge to the drops. In the lower portion of the apparatus, Millikan could create an electric field between two metal plates. Since the lower plate was negatively charged, and since Millikan could vary the strength of the electric field, he could slow or even reverse the free fall of the negatively charged drops. (Remember that like charges repel each other.)

By measuring the strength of the electric field required to halt the free fall of the drops and by figuring out the masses of the drops themselves (determined from their radii and density), Millikan calculated the charge of each drop. He then reasoned that, since each drop must contain an integral (or whole) number of electrons, the charge of each drop must be a whole-number multiple of the electron's charge. Indeed, Millikan was correct; the measured charge on any drop is always a whole-number multiple of -1.60×10^{-19} C, the fundamental charge of a single electron.

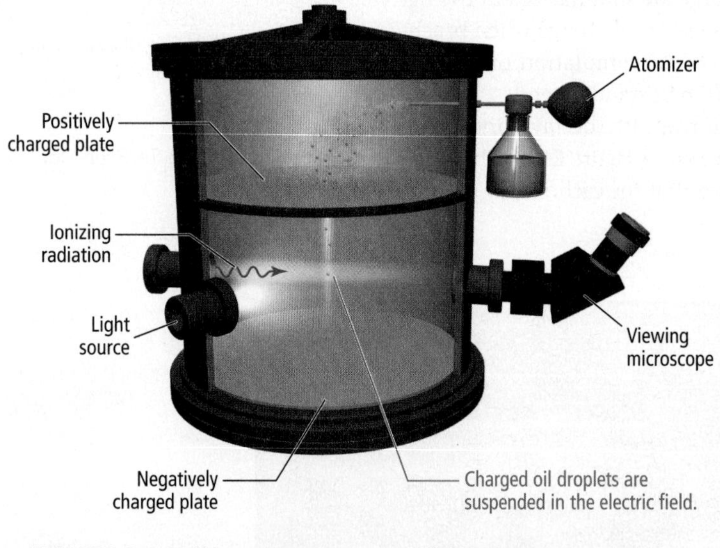

▲ **FIGURE 2.4 Millikan's Measurement of the Electron's Charge** Millikan calculated the charge on oil droplets falling in an electric field. He found that it was always a whole-number multiple of -1.60×10^{-19} C, the charge of a single electron.

With this number in hand and knowing Thomson's mass-to-charge ratio for electrons, we can deduce the mass of an electron:

$$\cancel{\text{charge}} \times \frac{\text{mass}}{\cancel{\text{charge}}} = \text{mass}$$

$$-1.60 \times 10^{-19}\,\cancel{C} \times \frac{\text{g}}{-\,1.76 \times 10^{8}\,\cancel{C}} = 9.10 \times 10^{-28}\,\text{g}$$

As Thomson had correctly determined, this mass is about 2000 times less than hydrogen, the lightest atom.

Why did scientists work so hard to measure the charge of the electron? Since the electron is a fundamental building block of matter, scientists want to know its properties, including its charge. The magnitude of the charge of the electron is of tremendous importance because it determines how strongly an atom holds its electrons. On one hand, imagine how matter would be different if electrons had a much smaller charge, so that atoms held them more loosely. Many atoms might not even be stable. On the other hand, imagine how matter would be different if electrons had a much greater charge, so that atoms held them more tightly. Since atoms form compounds by exchanging and sharing electrons (more on this in Chapter 3), there could be fewer compounds or maybe even none. Without the abundant diversity of compounds, life would not be possible. So, the magnitude of the charge of the electron—even though it may seem like an insignificantly small number—has great importance.

THE MILLIKAN OIL DROP EXPERIMENT Suppose that one of Millikan's oil drops has a charge of -4.8×10^{-19} C. How many excess electrons does the drop contain?

(a) 1 **(b)** 2 **(c)** 3 **(d)** 4

2.4 Cc Conceptual Connection

ANSWER **NOW!**

2.5 The Structure of the Atom

The discovery of negatively charged particles within atoms raised a new question. Since atoms are charge-neutral, they must contain a positive charge that neutralizes the negative charge of the electrons—but how do the positive and negative charges fit together? Are atoms just a jumble of even more fundamental particles? Are they solid spheres? Do they have some internal structure? J. J. Thomson proposed that the negatively charged electrons were small particles held within a positively charged sphere.

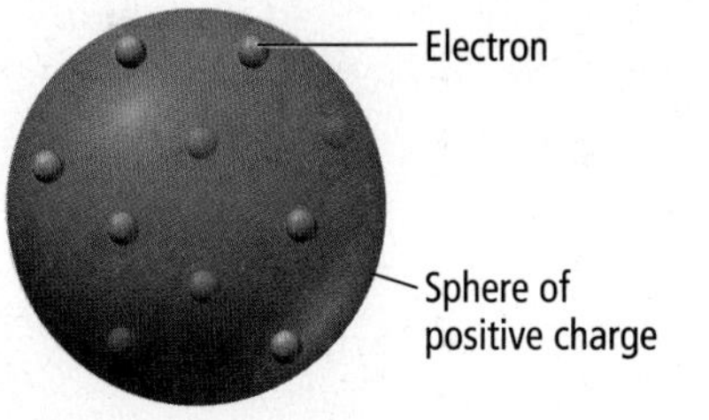

Plum-pudding model

This model, the most popular of the time, became known as the plum-pudding model. The model suggested by Thomson, to those of us not familiar with plum pudding (an English dessert), was like a blueberry muffin; the blueberries are the electrons, and the muffin is the positively charged sphere.

The discovery of **radioactivity**—the emission of small energetic particles from the core of certain unstable atoms—by scientists Henri Becquerel (1852–1908) and Marie Curie (1867–1934) at the end of the nineteenth century allowed researchers to experimentally probe the structure of the atom. At the time, scientists had identified three different types of radioactivity: alpha (α) particles, beta (β) particles, and gamma (γ) rays. We will discuss these and other types of radioactivity in more detail in Chapter 21. For now, just know that α particles are positively charged and that they are by far the most massive of the three.

In 1909, Ernest Rutherford (1871–1937), who had worked under Thomson and subscribed to his plum-pudding model, performed an experiment in an attempt to confirm Thomson's model. Instead, Rutherford's experiment, which employed α particles, proved Thomson wrong. In the experiment, Rutherford directed the positively charged α particles at an ultrathin sheet of gold foil, as shown in Figure 2.5▶.

Alpha particles are about 7000 times more massive than electrons.

▶ **FIGURE 2.5 Rutherford's Gold Foil Experiment**

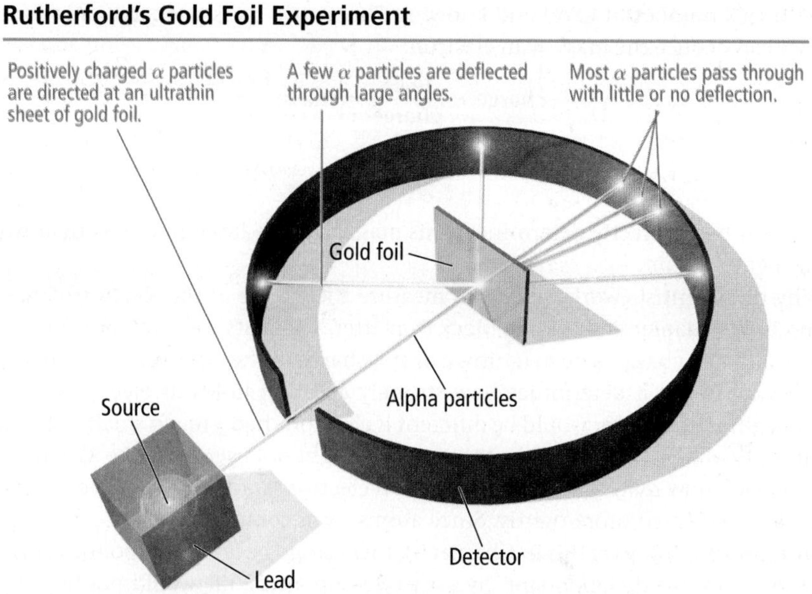

These particles were to act as probes of the gold atoms' structure. If the gold atoms were indeed like blueberry muffins or plum pudding—with their mass and charge spread throughout the entire volume of the atom—Rutherford reasoned that these speeding probes would pass right through the gold foil with minimum deflection.

Rutherford and his coworkers performed the experiment, but the results were not what they expected. The majority of the particles did pass directly through the foil, but some particles were deflected, and some (approximately 1 in 20,000) even bounced back. The results puzzled Rutherford, who wrote that they were "about as credible as if you had fired a 15-inch shell at a piece of tissue paper and it came back and hit you." What sort of atomic structure could explain this odd behavior? Rutherford created a new model—a modern version of which is shown in Figure 2.6▼ alongside the plum-pudding model—to explain his results.

Rutherford realized that to account for the deflections he observed, the mass and positive charge of an atom must be concentrated in a space much smaller than the size of the atom itself. He concluded that, in contrast to the plum-pudding model, matter must not be as uniform as it appears. It must contain large regions of empty space dotted with small regions of very dense matter. Building on this idea, he proposed the **nuclear theory** of the atom, with three basic parts:

1. Most of the atom's mass and all of its positive charge are contained in a small core called the **nucleus**.
2. Most of the volume of the atom is empty space, throughout which tiny, negatively charged electrons are dispersed.
3. There are as many negatively charged electrons outside the nucleus as there are positively charged particles (named **protons**) within the nucleus, so the atom is electrically neutral.

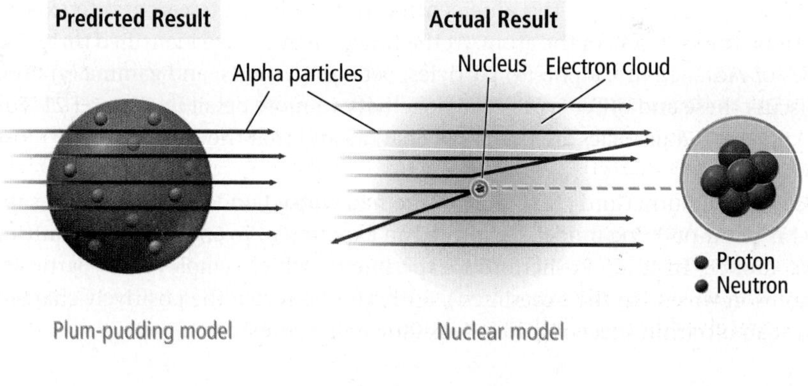

▶ **FIGURE 2.6 The Nuclear Atom** Rutherford's results could not be explained by the plum-pudding model. Instead, they suggest that the atom has a small, dense nucleus.

Although Rutherford's model was highly successful, scientists realized that it was incomplete. For example, hydrogen atoms contain one proton, and helium atoms contain two, yet a hydrogen atom has only one-fourth the mass of a helium atom. Why? The helium atom must contain some additional mass. Later work by Rutherford and one of his students, British scientist James Chadwick (1891–1974), demonstrated that the previously unaccounted for mass was due to **neutrons**, neutral particles within the nucleus. The mass of a neutron is similar to that of a proton, but a neutron has no electrical charge. The helium atom is four times as massive as the hydrogen atom because its nucleus contains two protons *and two neutrons* (while hydrogen contains only one proton and no neutrons).

The dense nucleus contains over 99.9% of the mass of the atom but occupies very little of its volume. For now, we can think of the electrons that surround the nucleus in analogy to the water droplets that make up a cloud—their mass is almost negligibly small, but they are dispersed over a very large volume. Consequently, an atom, like a cloud, is mostly empty space.

Rutherford's nuclear theory was a success and is still valid today. The revolutionary part of this theory is the idea that matter—at its core—is much less uniform than it appears. If the nucleus of the atom were the size of the period at the end of this sentence, the average electron would be about 10 meters away. Yet the period would contain nearly all of the atom's mass. Imagine what matter would be like if atomic structure were different. What if matter were composed of atomic nuclei piled on top of each other like marbles in a box? Such matter would be incredibly dense; a single grain of sand composed of solid atomic nuclei would have a mass of 5 million kilograms (or a weight of about 11 million pounds). Astronomers believe there are some objects in the universe composed of such matter—neutron stars.

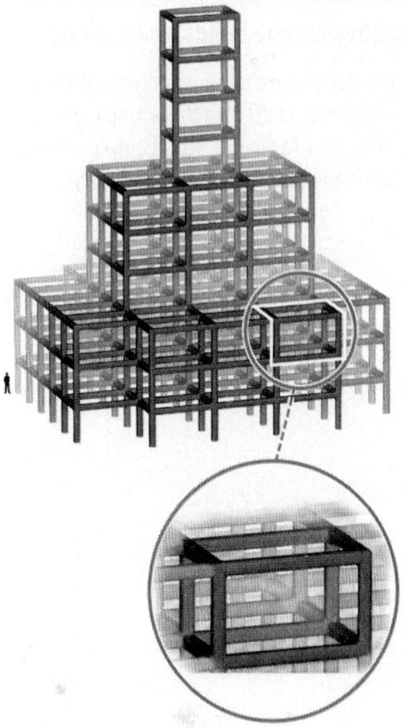

If matter really is mostly empty space, as Rutherford suggested, then why does it appear so solid? Why can we tap our knuckles on a table and feel a solid thump? Matter appears solid because the variation in its density is on such a small scale that our eyes cannot see it. Imagine a scaffolding 100 stories high and the size of a football field as shown in the margin. The volume of the scaffolding is mostly empty space. Yet if you viewed it from an airplane, it would appear as a solid mass. Matter is similar. When you tap your knuckle on the table, it is much like one giant scaffolding (your finger) crashing into another (the table). Even though they are both primarily empty space, one does not fall into the other.

2.6 Subatomic Particles: Protons, Neutrons, and Electrons in Atoms

WATCH **NOW!**

KEY CONCEPT VIDEO 2.6
Subatomic Particles and Isotope Symbols

All atoms are composed of the same subatomic particles: protons, neutrons, and electrons. Protons and neutrons, as we discussed earlier, have nearly identical masses. In SI units, the mass of the proton is 1.67262×10^{-27} kg, and the mass of the neutron is 1.67493×10^{-27} kg. A more common unit to express these masses is the **atomic mass unit (amu)**, defined as 1/12 the mass of a carbon atom that contains six protons and six neutrons. The mass of a proton or neutron is approximately 1 amu. Electrons, by contrast, have an almost negligible mass of 0.00091×10^{-27} kg or 0.00055 amu.

If a proton had the mass of a baseball, an electron would have the mass of a rice grain.

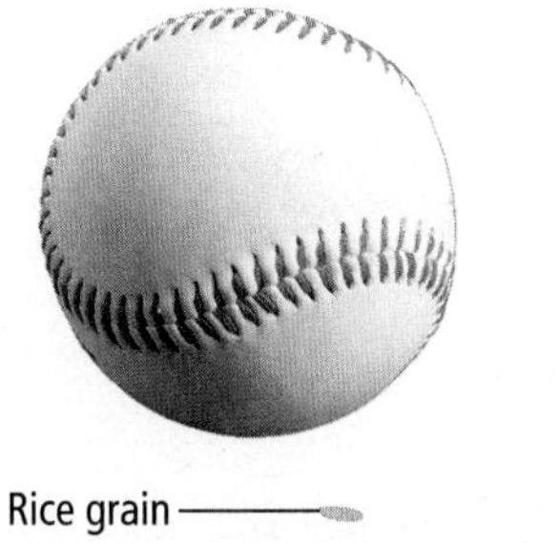

The proton and the electron both have electrical *charge*. We know from Millikan's oil drop experiment that the electron has a charge of -1.60×10^{-19} C. In atomic (or relative) units, the electron is assigned a charge of −1 and the proton is assigned a charge of +1. *The charge of the proton and the charge of the electron are equal in magnitude but opposite in sign,* so that when the two particles are paired, the charges sum to zero. The neutron has no charge.

Matter is usually charge-neutral (it has no overall charge) because protons and electrons are normally present in equal numbers. When matter does acquire charge imbalances, these imbalances usually equalize quickly, often in dramatic ways. For example, the shock you receive when touching a doorknob during dry weather is the equalization

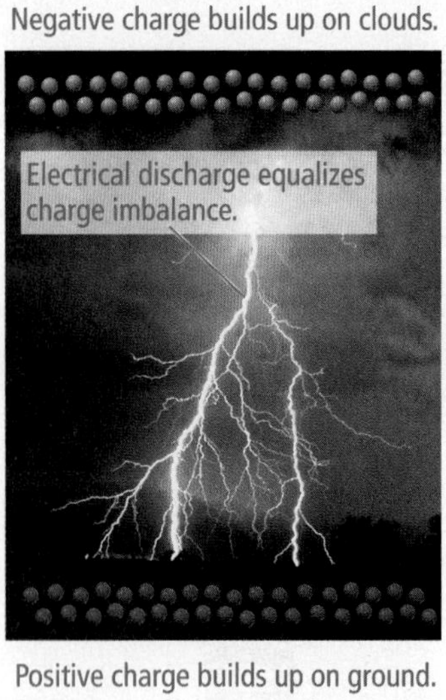

▲ When the normal charge balance of matter is disturbed, as happens during an electrical storm, it quickly equalizes, often in dramatic ways.

of a charge imbalance that developed as you walked across the carpet. Lightning is an equalization of charge imbalances that develop during electrical storms.

A sample of matter—even a tiny sand grain—composed of only protons or only electrons would be unstable due to extraordinarily strong repulsive forces within it. Luckily, matter is not that way. Table 2.1 summarizes the properties of protons, neutrons, and electrons.

TABLE 2.1 ■ Subatomic Particles

	Mass (kg)	Mass (amu)	Charge (relative)	Charge (C)
Proton	1.67262×10^{-27}	1.00727	+1	$+1.60218 \times 10^{-19}$
Neutron	1.67493×10^{-27}	1.00866	0	0
Electron	0.00091×10^{-27}	0.00055	−1	-1.60218×10^{-19}

Elements: Defined by Their Numbers of Protons

If all atoms are composed of the same subatomic particles, what makes the atoms of one element different from those of another? The answer is the *number* of these particles. The most important number to the *identity* of an atom is the number of protons in its nucleus. *The number of protons defines the element.* For example, an atom with two protons in its nucleus is a helium atom, an atom with six protons in its nucleus is a carbon atom (Figure 2.7▼), and an atom with 92 protons in its nucleus is a uranium atom. The number of protons in an atom's nucleus is its **atomic number** and is given the symbol *Z*. The atomic numbers of known elements range from 1 to 118 (although evidence for the synthesis of additional elements is currently being considered), as shown in the periodic table of the elements (Figure 2.8▶). In the periodic table, described in more detail in Section 2.7, the elements are arranged so that those with similar properties are in the same column.

Each element, identified by its unique atomic number, is represented with a unique **chemical symbol**, a one- or two-letter abbreviation listed directly below its atomic number on the periodic table. The chemical symbol for helium is He; for carbon, the symbol is C; and for uranium, it is U. The chemical symbol and the atomic number always go together. If the atomic number is 2, the chemical symbol *must be* He. If the atomic number is 6, the chemical symbol *must be* C. This is another way of saying that the number of protons defines the element.

Most chemical symbols are based on the English name of the element. For example, the symbol for sulfur is S; for oxygen, O; and for chlorine, Cl. Several of the oldest known

The Number of Protons Defines the Element

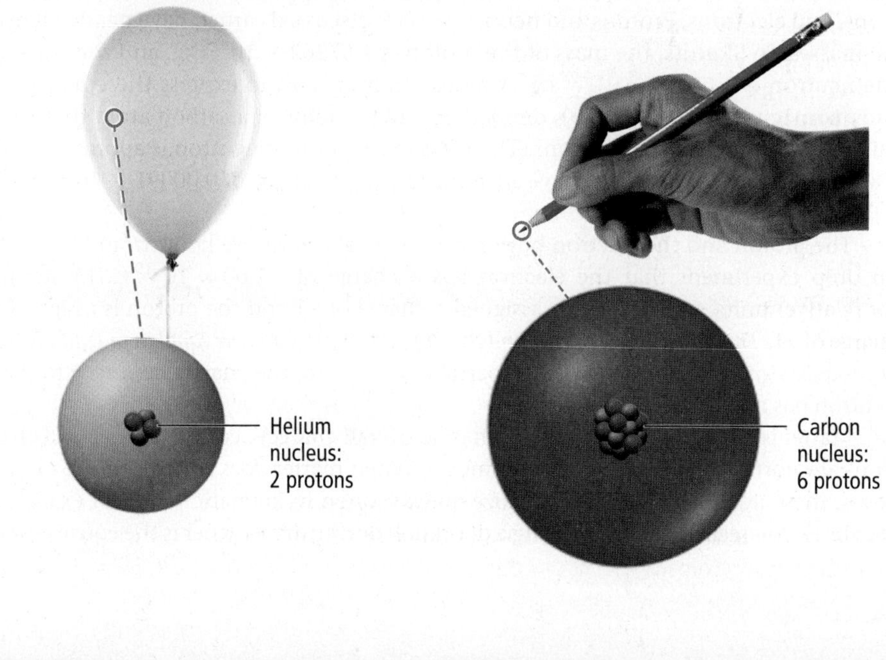

▶ **FIGURE 2.7 How Elements Differ** Each element is defined by a unique atomic number (*Z*), the number of protons in the nucleus of every atom of that element.

The Periodic Table

Atomic number (Z)
4
Be — Chemical symbol
beryllium — Name

1 H hydrogen																	2 He helium
3 Li lithium	4 Be beryllium											5 B boron	6 C carbon	7 N nitrogen	8 O oxygen	9 F fluorine	10 Ne neon
11 Na sodium	12 Mg magnesium											13 Al aluminum	14 Si silicon	15 P phosphorus	16 S sulfur	17 Cl chlorine	18 Ar argon
19 K potassium	20 Ca calcium	21 Sc scandium	22 Ti titanium	23 V vanadium	24 Cr chromium	25 Mn manganese	26 Fe iron	27 Co cobalt	28 Ni nickel	29 Cu copper	30 Zn zinc	31 Ga gallium	32 Ge germanium	33 As arsenic	34 Se selenium	35 Br bromine	36 Kr krypton
37 Rb rubidium	38 Sr strontium	39 Y yttrium	40 Zr zirconium	41 Nb niobium	42 Mo molybdenum	43 Tc technetium	44 Ru ruthenium	45 Rh rhodium	46 Pd palladium	47 Ag silver	48 Cd cadmium	49 In indium	50 Sn tin	51 Sb antimony	52 Te tellurium	53 I iodine	54 Xe xenon
55 Cs cesium	56 Ba barium	57 La lanthanum	72 Hf hafnium	73 Ta tantalum	74 W tungsten	75 Re rhenium	76 Os osmium	77 Ir iridium	78 Pt platinum	79 Au gold	80 Hg mercury	81 Tl thallium	82 Pb lead	83 Bi bismuth	84 Po polonium	85 At astatine	86 Rn radon
87 Fr francium	88 Ra radium	89 Ac actinium	104 Rf rutherfordium	105 Db dubnium	106 Sg seaborgium	107 Bh bohrium	108 Hs hassium	109 Mt meitnerium	110 Ds darmstadtium	111 Rg roentgenium	112 Cn copernicium	113 Nh nihonium	114 Fl flerovium	115 Mc moscovium	116 Lv livermorium	117 Tn tennessine	118 Og oganesson
				58 Ce cerium	59 Pr praseodymium	60 Nd neodymium	61 Pm promethium	62 Sm samarium	63 Eu europium	64 Gd gadolinium	65 Tb terbium	66 Dy dysprosium	67 Ho holmium	68 Er erbium	69 Tm thulium	70 Yb ytterbium	71 Lu lutetium
				90 Th thorium	91 Pa protactinium	92 U uranium	93 Np neptunium	94 Pu plutonium	95 Am americium	96 Cm curium	97 Bk berkelium	98 Cf californium	99 Es einsteinium	100 Fm fermium	101 Md mendelevium	102 No nobelium	103 Lr lawrencium

▲ **FIGURE 2.8 The Periodic Table** Each element is represented by its symbol and atomic number. Elements in the same column have similar properties.

elements, however, have symbols based on their original Latin names. For example, the symbol for sodium is Na from the Latin *natrium*, and the symbol for tin is Sn from the Latin *stannum*. Early scientists often gave newly discovered elements names that reflect their properties. For example, argon originates from the Greek word *argos* meaning inactive, referring to argon's chemical inertness (it does not react with other elements). Chlorine originates from the Greek word *chloros* meaning pale green, referring to chlorine's pale green color. Other elements, including helium, selenium, and mercury, are named after figures from Greek or Roman mythology or astronomical bodies. Still others (such as europium, polonium, and berkelium) are named for the places where they were discovered or where their discoverers were born. More recently, elements have been named after scientists; for example, curium for Marie Curie, einsteinium for Albert Einstein, and rutherfordium for Ernest Rutherford.

ATOMIC NUMBER Which element contains 50 protons in its nucleus?

(a) tin **(b)** vanadium

(c) manganese **(d)** fermium

2.5 Cc Conceptual Connection

ANSWER **NOW!**

Isotopes: When the Number of Neutrons Varies

All atoms of a given element have the same number of protons; however, they do not necessarily have the same number of neutrons. Since neutrons have nearly the same mass as protons (1 amu), this means that—contrary to what John Dalton originally proposed in

96
Cm
curium

▲ Element 96 is named curium, after Marie Curie, co-discoverer of radioactivity.

his atomic theory—all atoms of a given element *do not* have the same mass. For example, all neon atoms contain 10 protons, but they may contain 10, 11, or 12 neutrons. All three types of neon atoms exist, and each has a slightly different mass. Atoms with the same number of protons but different numbers of neutrons are **isotopes**. Some elements, such as beryllium (Be) and aluminum (Al), have only one naturally occurring isotope, while other elements, such as neon (Ne) and chlorine (Cl), have two or more.

The relative amount of each different isotope in a naturally occurring sample of a given element is roughly constant. For example, in any natural sample of neon atoms, 90.48% of them are the isotope with 10 neutrons, 0.27% are the isotope with 11 neutrons, and 9.25% are the isotope with 12 neutrons. These percentages are the **natural abundance** of the isotopes. Each element has its own characteristic natural abundance of isotopes. However, advances in mass spectrometry (see Section 2.8) have allowed accurate measurements that reveal small but significant variations in the natural abundance of isotopes for many elements.

The sum of the number of neutrons and protons in an atom is its **mass number**. We represent mass number with the symbol A.

$$A = \text{number of protons (p)} + \text{number of neutrons (n)}$$

For neon, with 10 protons, the mass numbers of the three different naturally occurring isotopes are 20, 21, and 22, corresponding to 10, 11, and 12 neutrons, respectively.

We symbolize isotopes using the notation:

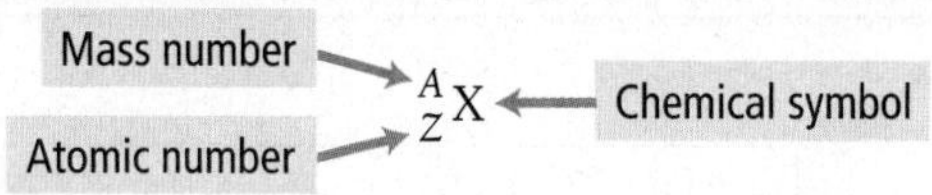

where X is the chemical symbol, A is the mass number, and Z is the atomic number. Therefore, the symbols for the neon isotopes are:

$$^{20}_{10}\text{Ne} \quad ^{21}_{10}\text{Ne} \quad ^{22}_{10}\text{Ne}$$

Notice that the chemical symbol, Ne, and the atomic number, 10, are redundant: if the atomic number is 10, the symbol must be Ne. The mass numbers, however, are different for the different isotopes, reflecting the different number of neutrons in each one.

A second common notation for isotopes is the chemical symbol (or chemical name) followed by a dash and the mass number of the isotope.

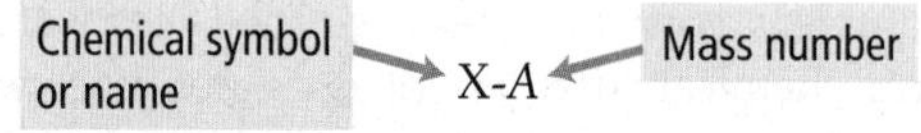

In this notation, the neon isotopes are:

Ne-20 Ne-21 Ne-22
neon-20 neon-21 neon-22

We summarize the neon isotopes in the following table:

Symbol	Number of Protons	Number of Neutrons	A (Mass Number)	Natural Abundance (%)
Ne-20 or $^{20}_{10}$Ne	10	10	20	90.48
Ne-21 or $^{21}_{10}$Ne	10	11	21	0.27
Ne-22 or $^{22}_{10}$Ne	10	12	22	9.25

Notice that all isotopes of a given element have the same number of protons (otherwise they would be different elements). Notice also that the mass number is the *sum* of the number of protons and the number of neutrons. The number of neutrons in an isotope is therefore the difference between the mass number and the atomic number (A–Z). The different isotopes of an element generally exhibit the same chemical behavior—the three isotopes of neon, for example, all exhibit chemical inertness.

MASS NUMBER AND ATOMIC NUMBER An argon isotope has a mass number of 40 ($A = 40$). How many neutrons does it contain?

(a) 40 **(b)** 18 **(c)** 22

2.6 Cc Conceptual Connection — ANSWER **NOW!**

WATCH **NOW!**

INTERACTIVE WORKED EXAMPLE 2.3

EXAMPLE 2.3 Atomic Numbers, Mass Numbers, and Isotope Symbols

(a) What are the atomic number (Z), mass number (A), and symbol of the chlorine isotope with 18 neutrons?

(b) How many protons, electrons, and neutrons are present in an atom of $^{52}_{24}\text{Cr}$?

SOLUTION

(a) Look up the atomic number (Z) for chlorine on the periodic table. The atomic number specifies the number of protons.	$Z = 17$, so chlorine has 17 protons.
The mass number (A) for an isotope is the sum of the number of protons and the number of neutrons.	$A =$ number of protons + number of neutrons $= 17 + 18 = 35$
The symbol for an isotope is its chemical symbol with the atomic number (Z) in the lower left corner and the mass number (A) in the upper left corner.	$^{35}_{17}\text{Cl}$
(b) For any isotope (in this case $^{52}_{24}\text{Cr}$) the atomic number located at the lower left indicates the number of protons. Since this is a neutral atom, the number of electrons equals the number of protons.	Number of protons $= Z = 24$ Number of electrons $= 24$ (neutral atom)
The number of neutrons is equal to the mass number (upper left) minus the atomic number (lower left).	Number of neutrons $= 52 - 24 = 28$

FOR PRACTICE 2.3

(a) What are the atomic number, mass number, and symbol for the carbon isotope with seven neutrons?

(b) How many protons and neutrons are present in an atom of $^{39}_{19}\text{K}$?

ISOTOPES Carbon has two naturally occurring isotopes: C-12 (natural abundance is 98.93%) and C-13 (natural abundance is 1.07%). If circles represent protons and squares represent neutrons, which image best represents the C-13 isotope?

(a) 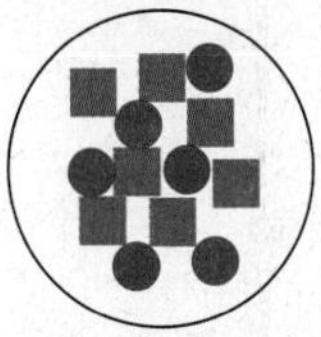 (b) 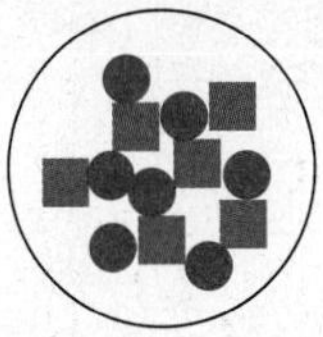 (c) 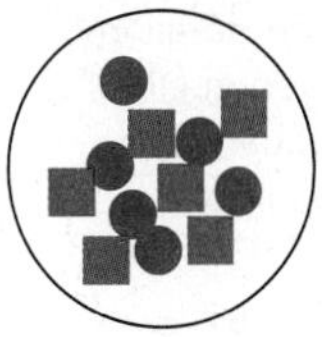

2.7 Cc Conceptual Connection — ANSWER **NOW!**

Ions: Losing and Gaining Electrons

The number of electrons in a neutral atom is equal to the number of protons in its nucleus (designated by its atomic number Z). During chemical changes, however, atoms can lose or gain electrons and become charged particles called **ions**. For example, neutral lithium (Li) atoms contain three protons and three electrons; however, in many chemical reactions lithium atoms lose one electron (e^-) to form Li^+ ions.

$$\text{Li} \longrightarrow \text{Li}^+ + 1\text{e}^-$$

The charge of an ion is indicated in the upper right corner of the chemical symbol. Since the Li^+ ion contains three protons and only two electrons, its charge is 1+ (ion charges are written as the magnitude first followed by the sign of the charge; for a charge of 1+, the 1 is usually dropped and the charge is written as simply +).

Ions can also be negatively charged. For example, neutral fluorine (F) atoms contain nine protons and nine electrons; however, in many chemical reactions fluorine atoms gain one electron to form F^- ions.

$$F + 1e^- \longrightarrow F^-$$

The F^- ion contains 9 protons and 10 electrons, resulting in a charge of 1− (written simply as −). For many elements, such as lithium and fluorine, the ion is much more common than the neutral atom. In fact, lithium and fluorine occur in nature mostly as ions.

Positively charged ions, such as Li^+, are **cations**, and negatively charged ions, such as F^-, are **anions**. Ions behave quite differently than their corresponding atoms. Neutral sodium atoms, for example, are extremely unstable, reacting violently with most things they contact. Sodium cations (Na^+), by contrast, are relatively inert—we eat them all the time in sodium chloride (table salt). In ordinary matter, cations and anions always occur together, so that matter is charge neutral overall.

A useful mnemonic device is, "a negative ion is an anion."

ANSWER **NOW!**

2.8 Cc Conceptual Connection

IONS How many electrons are present in the O^{2-} anion?

(a) 6

(b) 8

(c) 10

CHEMISTRY IN YOUR DAY | Where Did Elements Come From?

We find ourselves on a planet containing many different kinds of elements. If it were otherwise, we would not exist and would not be here to reflect on why. Where did these elements come from? The story of element formation is as old as the universe itself, and we have to go back to the very beginning to tell the story.

The birth of the universe is described by the Big Bang theory, which asserts that the universe began as a hot, dense collection of matter and energy that expanded rapidly. As it expanded, it cooled, and within the first several minutes, subatomic particles formed the first atomic nuclei: hydrogen and helium. These two elements were (and continue to be) the most abundant in the universe. As the universe continued expanding, some of the hydrogen and helium clumped together under the influence of gravity to form *nebulae* (clouds of gas) that eventually gave birth to stars and galaxies. These stars and galaxies became the nurseries where all other elements formed.

Stars are fueled by nuclear fusion, which we will discuss in more detail in Chapter 21. Under the conditions within the core of a star, hydrogen nuclei can combine (or fuse) to form helium. Fusion gives off enormous quantities of energy, which is why stars emit so much heat and light. The fusion of hydrogen to helium can fuel a star for billions of years.

After it burns through large quantities of hydrogen, if a star is large enough, the helium that builds up in its core can in turn fuse to form carbon. The carbon then builds up in the core and (again, if the star is large enough) can fuse to form even heavier elements. The fusion process ends with iron, which has a highly stable nucleus. By the time iron is formed, however, the star is near the end of its existence and may enter a phase of expansion, transforming into a *supernova*. Within a supernova, which is in essence a large exploding star, a shower of neutrons allows the lighter elements (which formed during the lifetime of the star through the fusion processes just described) to capture extra neutrons. These neutrons can transform into protons (through processes that we discuss in Chapter 21), contributing ultimately to the formation of elements heavier than iron, all the way up to uranium. As the supernova continues to expand, the elements present within it are blown out into space, where they can incorporate into other nebulae and perhaps even eventually form planets that orbit stars like our own sun.

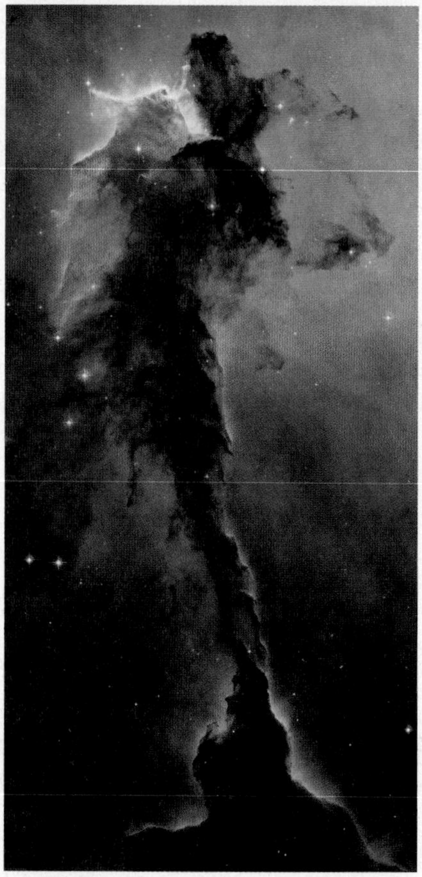

▲ Stars are born in nebulae such as the Eagle Nebula (also known as M16). This image was taken by the Hubble Space Telescope and shows a gaseous pillar in a star-forming region of the Eagle Nebula.

THE NUCLEAR ATOM, ISOTOPES, AND IONS In light of the nuclear model for the atom, which statement is true?

(a) For a given element, the size of an isotope with more neutrons is larger than one with fewer neutrons.

(b) For a given element, the size of an atom is the same for all of the element's isotopes.

2.9 Cc Conceptual Connection

ANSWER **NOW!**

2.7 Finding Patterns: The Periodic Law and the Periodic Table

WATCH **NOW!**

KEY CONCEPT VIDEO 2.7
The Periodic Law and the Periodic Table

The modern periodic table grew out of the work of Dmitri Mendeleev (1834–1907), a nineteenth-century Russian chemistry professor. In his time, scientists had discovered about 65 different elements, and chemists had identified many of the properties of these elements—such as their relative masses, their chemical activity, and some of their physical properties. However, no one had developed any systematic way of organizing them.

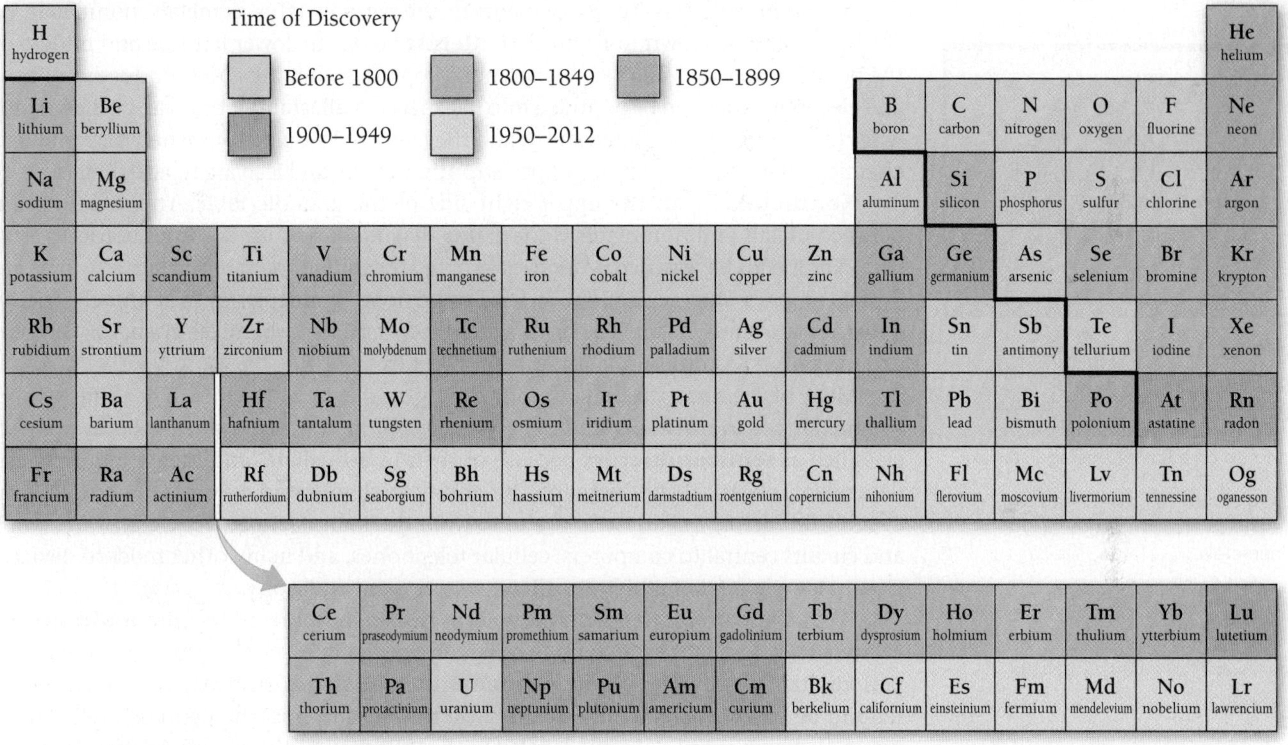

▲ Many of the elements that we know today were discovered during Mendeleev's lifetime.

In 1869, Mendeleev noticed that certain groups of elements had similar properties. He also found that when he listed elements in order of increasing mass, these similar properties recurred in a periodic pattern (Figure 2.9▼). Mendeleev summarized these observations in the **periodic law**:

When the elements are arranged in order of increasing mass, certain sets of properties recur periodically.

To be periodic means to exhibit a repeating pattern.

Mendeleev organized the known elements in a table consisting of a series of rows in which mass increases from left to right. He arranged the rows so that elements with similar properties fall in the same vertical columns (Figure 2.10▶).

The Periodic Law

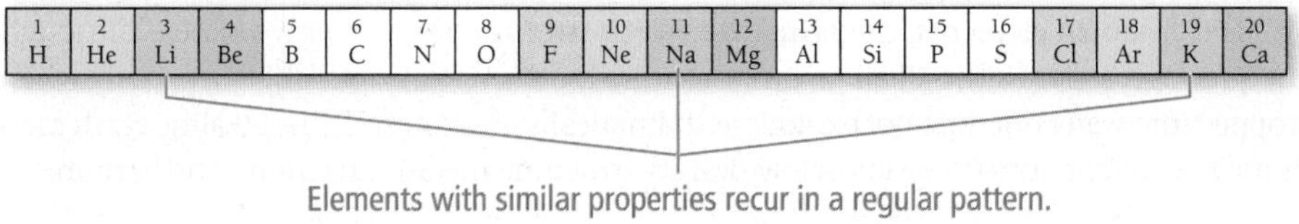

◀ **FIGURE 2.9 Recurring Properties** These elements are listed in order of increasing atomic number. Elements with similar properties are represented with the same color. Notice that the colors form a repeating pattern, much like musical notes form a repeating pattern on a piano keyboard.

A Simple Periodic Table

Elements with similar properties fall into columns.

1 H							2 He
3 Li	4 Be	5 B	6 C	7 N	8 O	9 F	10 Ne
11 Na	12 Mg	13 Al	14 Si	15 P	16 S	17 Cl	18 Ar
19 K	20 Ca						

▲ **FIGURE 2.10 Making a Periodic Table** We can arrange the elements in Figure 2.9 in a table in which atomic number increases from left to right and elements with similar properties (as represented by the different colors) are aligned in columns.

▲ Dmitri Mendeleev, a Russian chemistry professor who proposed the periodic law and arranged early versions of the periodic table, was honored on a Soviet postage stamp.

Since many elements had not yet been discovered, Mendeleev's table contained some gaps, which allowed him to predict the existence (and even the properties) of yet undiscovered elements. For example, Mendeleev predicted the existence of an element he called eka-silicon, which fell below silicon on the table and between gallium and arsenic (*eka* means the one beyond). In 1886, eka-silicon was discovered by German chemist Clemens Winkler (1838–1904), who named it germanium, after his home country.

Modern Periodic Table Organization

Mendeleev's original listing evolved into the modern periodic table shown in Figure 2.11▶. In the modern table, elements are listed in order of increasing atomic number rather than increasing relative mass. The modern periodic table also contains more elements than Mendeleev's original table because more have been discovered since his time. Mendeleev's periodic law was based on observation. Like all scientific laws, the periodic law summarizes many observations but does not give the underlying reason for the observations—only theories do that. For now, we accept the periodic law as it is, but in Chapters 8 and 9 we will examine a powerful theory—called quantum mechanics—that explains the law and gives the underlying reasons for it.

We can broadly classify the elements in the periodic table as metals, nonmetals, or metalloids, as shown in Figure 2.11. **Metals** lie on the lower left side and middle of the periodic table and share some common properties: they are good conductors of heat and electricity, they can be pounded into flat sheets (malleability), they can be drawn into wires (ductility), they are often shiny, and they tend to lose electrons when they undergo chemical changes. Chromium, copper, strontium, gold, and lead are typical metals.

Nonmetals lie on the upper right side of the periodic table. The dividing line between metals and nonmetals is the zigzag diagonal line running from boron to astatine. Nonmetals have varied properties—some are solids at room temperature, others are liquids or gases—but typically they tend to be poor conductors of heat and electricity, and they all tend to gain electrons when they undergo chemical changes. Oxygen, carbon, sulfur, bromine, and iodine are nonmetals.

Many of the elements that lie along the zigzag diagonal line that divides metals and nonmetals are **metalloids** and exhibit mixed properties. Several metalloids are also classified as **semiconductors** because of their intermediate (and highly temperature-dependent) electrical conductivity. Our ability to change and control the conductivity of semiconductors makes them useful to us in the manufacture of the electronic chips and circuits central to computers, cellular telephones, and many other modern devices. Good examples of metalloids are silicon, arsenic, and antimony.

Metalloids are sometimes called semimetals.

We can also divide the periodic table, as shown in Figure 2.12▶, into **main-group elements**, whose properties tend to be largely predictable based on their position in the periodic table, and **transition elements** or **transition metals**, whose properties tend to be less predictable based simply on their position in the periodic table. Main-group elements are in columns labeled with a number and the letter A. Transition elements are in columns labeled with a number and the letter B. An alternative numbering system does not use letters, but only the numbers 1–18. Both numbering systems are shown in most of the periodic tables in this book. Each column within the main-group regions of the periodic table is a **family** or **group** of elements.

The elements within a group usually have similar properties. For example, the group 8A elements, called the **noble gases**, are mostly unreactive. The most familiar noble gas is probably helium, used to fill buoyant balloons. Helium is chemically stable—it does not combine with other elements to form compounds—and is therefore safe to put into balloons. Other noble gases are neon (often used in electronic signs), argon (a small component of our atmosphere), krypton, and xenon.

The group 1A elements, the **alkali metals**, are all reactive metals. A marble-sized piece of sodium explodes violently when dropped into water. Lithium, potassium, and rubidium are also alkali metals.

Alkali metals

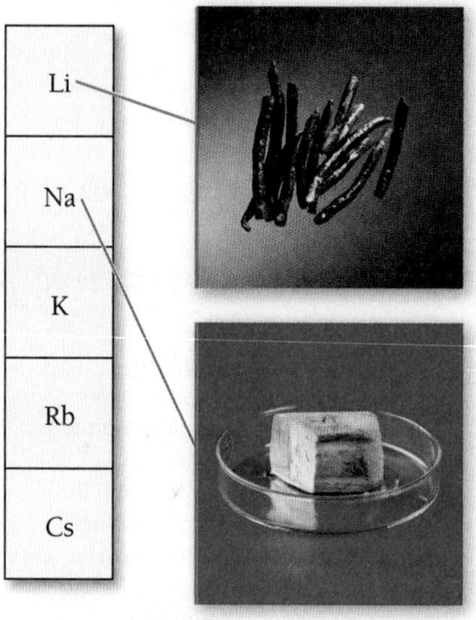

The group 2A elements, the **alkaline earth metals**, are also fairly reactive, although not quite as reactive as the alkali metals. Calcium, for example, reacts fairly vigorously when dropped into water but does not explode as dramatically as sodium. Other alkaline earth metals include magnesium (a common low-density structural metal), strontium, and barium.

Major Divisions of the Periodic Table

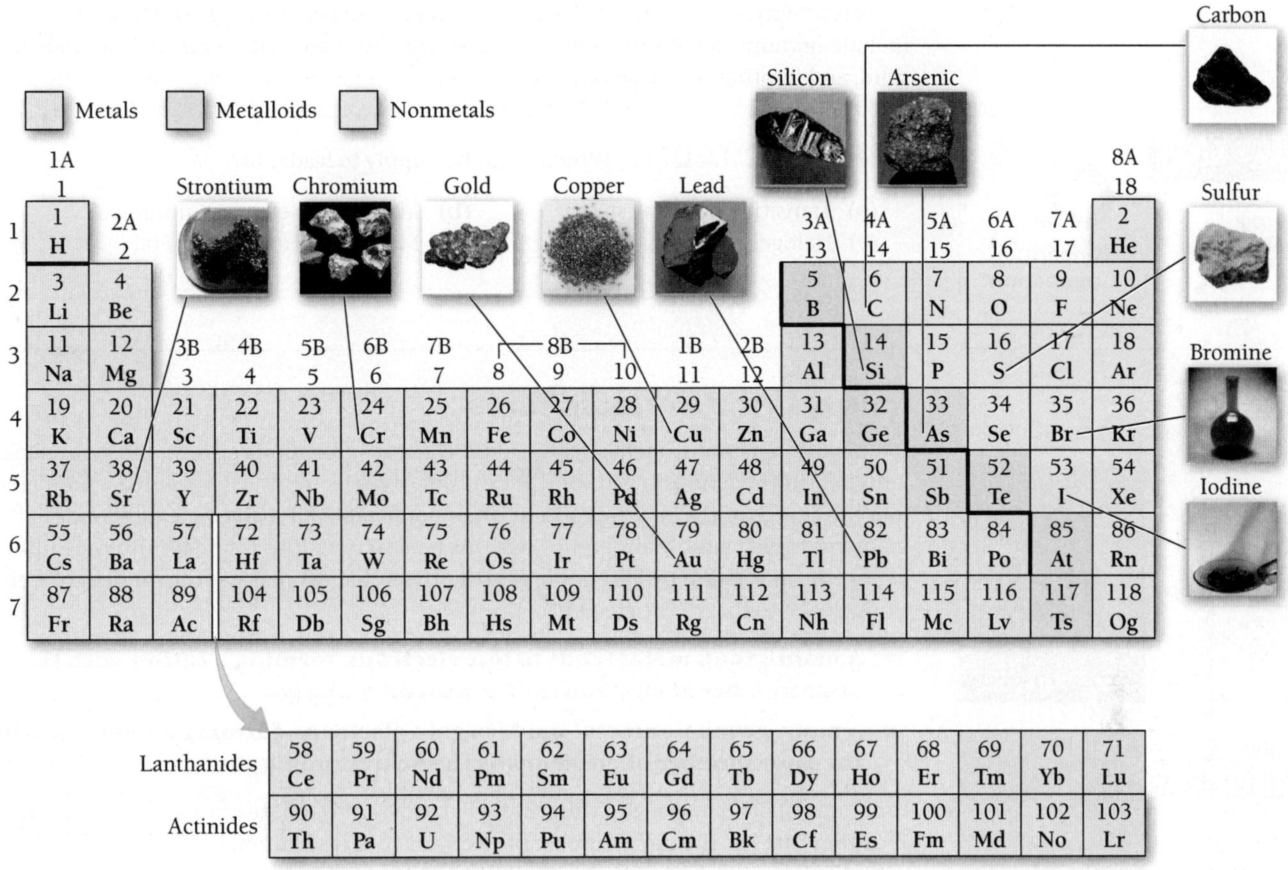

▲ FIGURE 2.11 Metals, Nonmetals, and Metalloids The elements in the periodic table fall into these three broad classes.

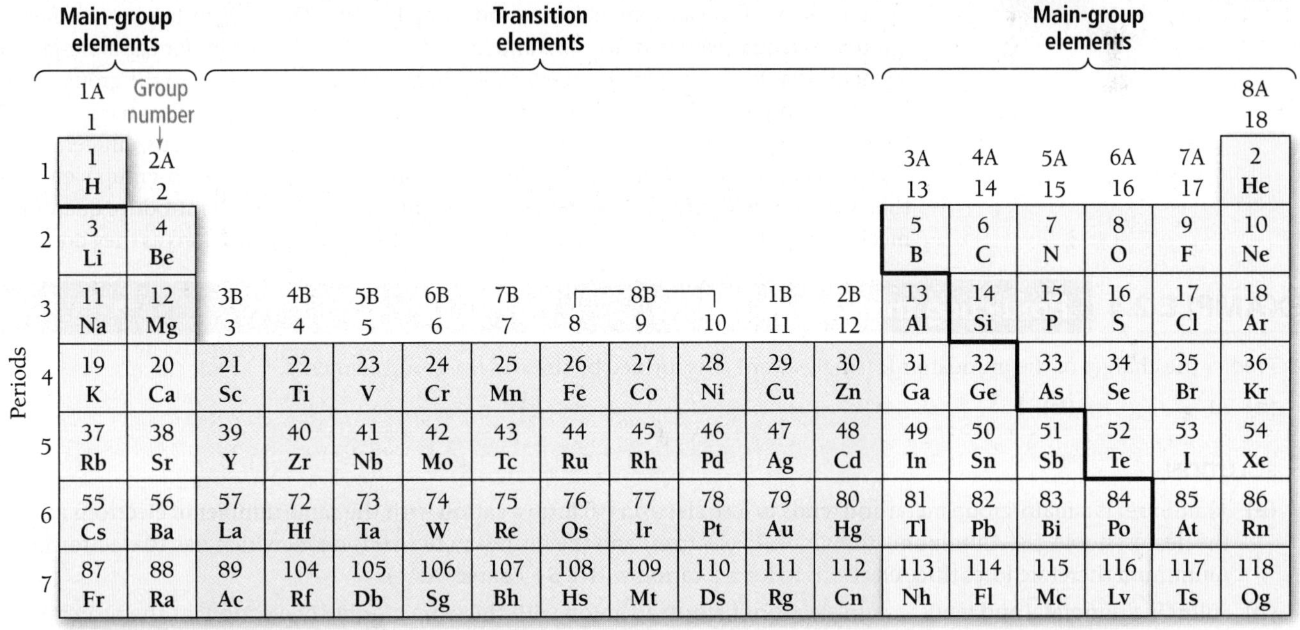

▲ FIGURE 2.12 The Periodic Table: Main-Group and Transition Elements The elements in the periodic table fall into columns. The two columns at the left and the six columns at the right comprise the main-group elements. Each of these eight columns is a group or family. The properties of main-group elements can generally be predicted from their position in the periodic table. The properties of the elements in the middle of the table, known as transition elements, are less predictable.

The group 7A elements, the **halogens**, are very reactive nonmetals. One of the most familiar halogens is chlorine, a greenish-yellow gas with a pungent odor. Because of its reactivity, chlorine is used as a sterilizing and disinfecting agent. Other halogens include bromine, a red-brown liquid that easily evaporates into a gas; iodine, a purple solid; and fluorine, a pale-yellow gas.

ANSWER NOW!

2.10 Cc Conceptual Connection

PERIODIC TABLE Which terms best apply to lead (Pb)?

(a) Transition element; metal
(b) Main-group element; nonmetal
(c) Halogen; nonmetal
(d) Main-group element; metal

Halogens

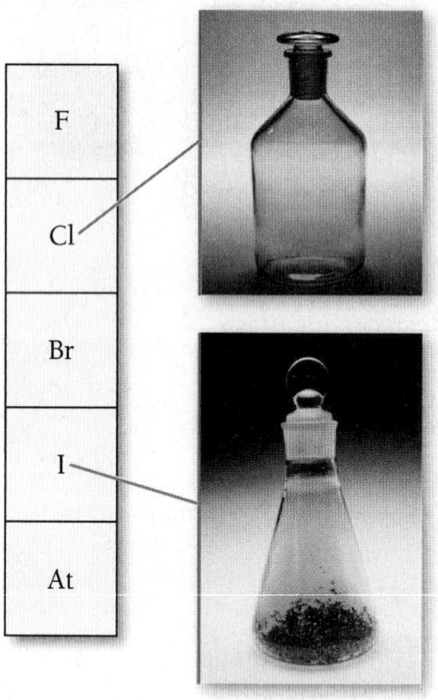

Ions and the Periodic Table

In chemical reactions, metals tend to lose electrons (forming cations) and nonmetals tend to gain them (forming anions). The number of electrons lost or gained, and therefore the charge of the resulting ion, is often predictable for a given element, especially main-group elements. Main-group elements tend to form ions that have the same number of electrons as the nearest noble gas (i.e., the noble gas that has the number of electrons closest to that of the element).

- **A main-group metal tends to lose electrons, forming a cation with the same number of electrons as the nearest noble gas.**
- **A main-group nonmetal tends to gain electrons, forming an anion with the same number of electrons as the nearest noble gas.**

For example, lithium, a metal with three electrons, tends to lose one electron, forming a 1+ cation that has the same number of electrons (two) as helium. Chlorine, a nonmetal with 17 electrons, tends to gain one electron, forming a 1− anion that has the same number of electrons (18) as argon.

In general, the alkali metals (group 1A) tend to lose one electron and form 1+ ions. The alkaline earth metals (group 2A) tend to lose two electrons and form 2+ ions. The halogens (group 7A) tend to gain one electron and form 1− ions. The oxygen family nonmetals (group 6A) tend to gain two electrons and form 2− ions. More generally, for the main-group elements that form cations with predictable charge, the charge is equal to the group number. For main-group elements that form anions with predictable charge, the charge is equal to the group number minus eight. Transition elements may form various different ions with different charges. Figure 2.13▶ shows the ions formed by the main-group elements that form ions with predictable charges. In Chapters 8 and 9, we will introduce quantum-mechanical theory, which more fully explains *why* these groups form ions as they do.

EXAMPLE 2.4 Predicting the Charge of Ions

Predict the charges of the monoatomic (single atom) ions formed by these main-group elements.

(a) Al **(b)** S

SOLUTION

(a) Aluminum is a main-group metal and tends to lose electrons to form a cation with the same number of electrons as the nearest noble gas. Aluminum atoms have 13 electrons and the nearest noble gas is neon, which has 10 electrons. Aluminum therefore loses three electrons to form a cation with a 3+ charge (Al^{3+}).

(b) Sulfur is a nonmetal and tends to gain electrons to form an anion with the same number of electrons as the nearest noble gas. Sulfur atoms have 16 electrons and the nearest noble gas is argon, which has 18 electrons. Sulfur therefore gains two electrons to form an anion with a 2− charge (S^{2-}).

FOR PRACTICE 2.4 Predict the charges of the monoatomic ions formed by these main-group elements.

(a) N **(b)** Rb

Elements That Form Ions with Predictable Charges

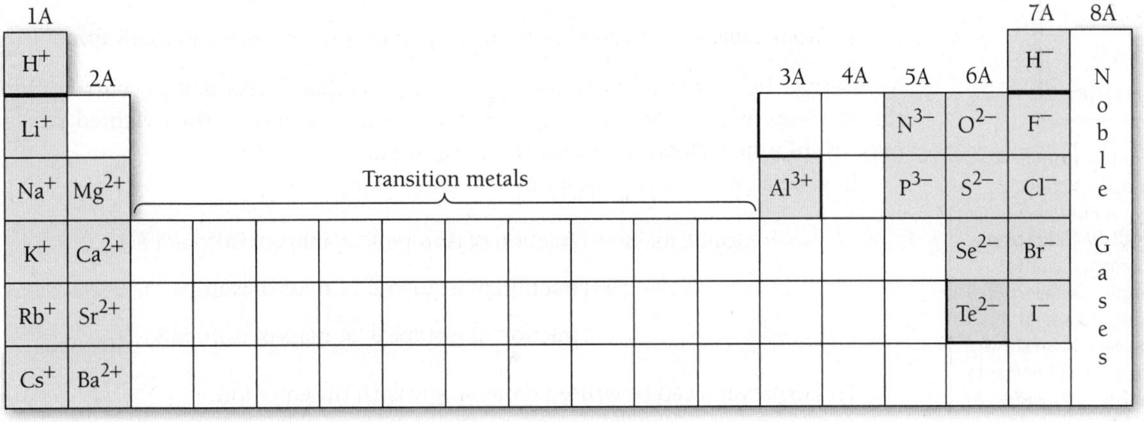

▲ **FIGURE 2.13 Elements That Form Ions with Predictable Charges**

CHEMISTRY AND MEDICINE | The Elements of Life

What kind of atoms compose us? In terms of mass, our bodies are 65% oxygen (because of the large amount of water), 18% carbon, and 10% hydrogen, with a few other elements present in smaller quantities, as shown in Figure 2.14▶ and Table 2.2. Because the atoms of different elements have different masses (more on this in Sections 2.8 and 2.9), if we consider number of atoms (instead of mass), hydrogen comes in first (because hydrogen atoms are so light), with oxygen second and carbon third.

TABLE 2.2 ■ Approximate Percent Elemental Composition of Humans

Element	% by Mass	% by Number of Atoms
Oxygen	65	26.4
Carbon	18	9.2
Hydrogen	10	62.3
Nitrogen	3	1.4
Calcium	1.5	0.2
Phosphorus	1	0.3
Other	1.5	0.2

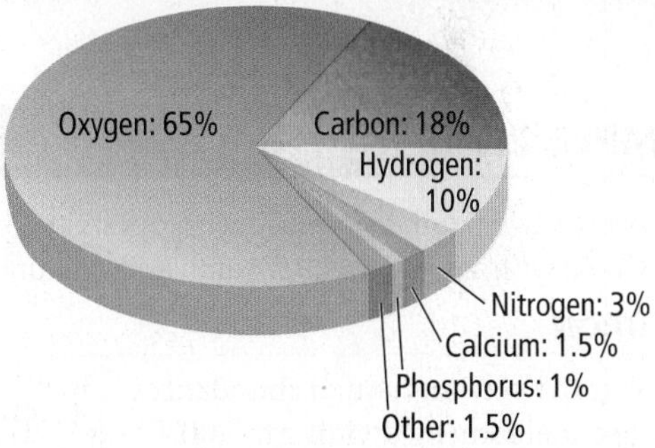

▲ **FIGURE 2.14 Elemental Composition of Humans (by Mass)**

Much of the *chemistry* of life revolves not around oxygen or hydrogen but around carbon, an element that forms a disproportionately large number of compounds with a few other elements such as hydrogen, oxygen, and nitrogen. We will explore the chemistry of carbon—called organic chemistry—briefly in Chapter 3 and in more detail in Chapter 22.

2.8 Atomic Mass: The Average Mass of an Element's Atoms

An important part of Dalton's atomic theory is that all atoms of a given element have the same mass. In Section 2.6, we learned that because of isotopes, the atoms of a given element often have different masses, so Dalton was not completely correct. We can, however, calculate an average mass—called the **atomic mass**—for each element.

Atomic mass is sometimes called *atomic weight* or *standard atomic weight.*

The atomic mass of each element is listed directly beneath the element's symbol in the periodic table and represents the average mass of the isotopes that compose that element, *weighted according to the natural abundance of each isotope.* For example, the periodic table lists the atomic mass of chlorine as 35.45 amu. Naturally occurring chlorine

17
Cl
35.45
chlorine

consists of 75.77% chlorine-35 atoms (mass 34.97 amu) and 24.23% chlorine-37 atoms (mass 36.97 amu). We can calculate its atomic mass accordingly:

$$\text{Atomic mass} = 0.7577(34.97\text{ amu}) + 0.2423(36.97\text{ amu}) = 35.45\text{ amu}$$

Notice that the atomic mass of chlorine is closer to 35 than 37. Naturally occurring chlorine contains more chlorine-35 atoms than chlorine-37 atoms, so the weighted average mass of chlorine is closer to 35 amu than to 37 amu.

In this book, we use the atomic masses recommended by the International Union of Pure and Applied Chemistry (IUPAC) for users needing an atomic mass value for an unspecified sample. Detailed studies of the atomic masses of many samples, however, have shown that atomic masses are not constants of nature because the exact isotopic abundances in any given sample depend on the history of the sample (see the Chemistry in Your Day box later in this section).

In general, we calculate the atomic mass as follows:

$$\begin{aligned}\text{Atomic mass} &= (\text{fraction of isotope 1} \times \text{mass of isotope 1})\\ &+ (\text{fraction of isotope 2} \times \text{mass of isotope 2})\\ &+ (\text{fraction of isotope 3} \times \text{mass of isotope 3}) + \ldots\end{aligned}$$

This expression can be written more simply with the equation:

$$\text{Atomic mass} = \sum_n (\text{fraction of isotope } n) \times (\text{mass of isotope } n)$$

where the fractions of each isotope are the percent natural abundances converted to their decimal values. The concept of atomic mass is useful because it allows us to assign a characteristic mass to each element, and, as we will see shortly, it allows us to quantify the number of atoms in a sample of that element.

When we use percentages in calculations, we convert them to their decimal value by dividing by 100.

WATCH **NOW!**

INTERACTIVE WORKED EXAMPLE 2.5

EXAMPLE 2.5 Atomic Mass

Copper has two naturally occurring isotopes: Cu-63 with a mass of 62.9291 amu and a natural abundance of 69.17%, and Cu-65 with a mass of 64.9278 amu and a natural abundance of 30.83%. Calculate the atomic mass of copper.

SOLUTION

Convert the percent natural abundances into decimal form by dividing by 100.	$\text{Fraction Cu-63} = \frac{69.17}{100} = 0.6917$ $\text{Fraction Cu-65} = \frac{30.83}{100} = 0.3083$
Calculate the atomic mass using the equation given in the text.	$\text{Atomic mass} = 0.6917(62.9296\text{ amu}) + 0.3083(64.9278\text{ amu})$ $= 43.5284\text{ amu} + 20.0172\text{ amu} = 63.5456 = 63.55\text{ amu}$

FOR PRACTICE 2.5 Magnesium has three naturally occurring isotopes with masses of 23.99 amu, 24.99 amu, and 25.98 amu and natural abundances of 78.99%, 10.00%, and 11.01%, respectively. Calculate the atomic mass of magnesium.

FOR MORE PRACTICE 2.5 Gallium has two naturally occurring isotopes: Ga-69 with a mass of 68.9256 amu and a natural abundance of 60.11%, and Ga-71. Use the atomic mass of gallium from the periodic table to find the mass of Ga-71.

ANSWER **NOW!**

2.11 Cc Conceptual Connection

ATOMIC MASS Recall from Conceptual Connection 2.7 that carbon has two naturally occurring isotopes: C-12 (natural abundance is 98.93%; mass is 12.0000 amu) and C-13 (natural abundance is 1.07%; mass is 13.0034 amu). Without doing any calculations, determine which mass is closest to the atomic mass of carbon.

(a) 12.00 amu **(b)** 12.50 amu **(c)** 13.00 amu

Mass Spectrometry: Measuring the Mass of Atoms and Molecules

The masses of atoms and the percent abundances of isotopes of elements are measured using **mass spectrometry**, a technique that separates particles according to their mass. In a mass spectrometer, such as the one in Figure 2.15▶, the sample (containing the

Mass Spectrometer

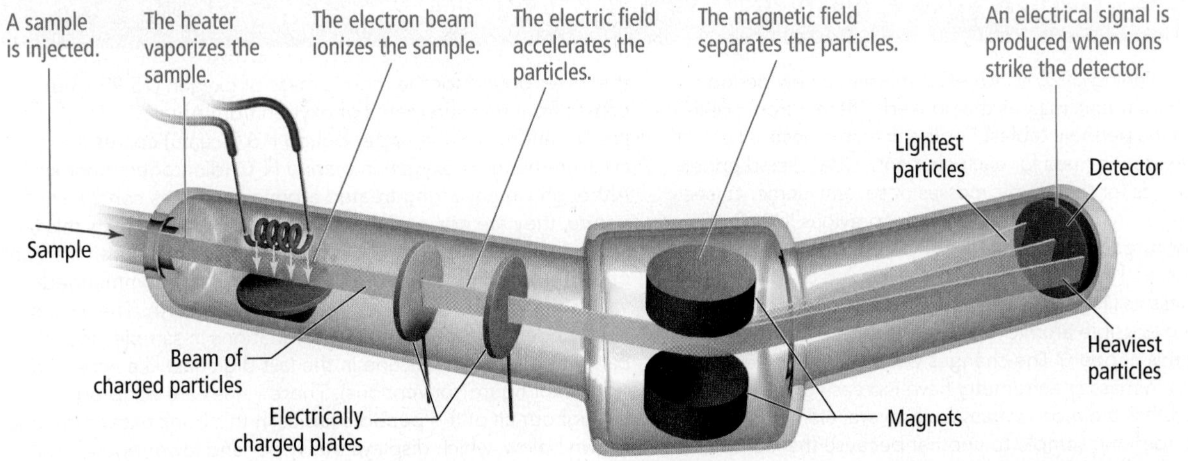

▲FIGURE 2.15 The Mass Spectrometer Atoms are converted to positively charged ions, accelerated, and passed through a magnetic field that deflects their path. The heaviest ions undergo the least deflection.

atoms whose mass is to be measured) is injected into the instrument and vaporized. The vaporized atoms are ionized by an electron beam—the electrons in the beam collide with the atoms, removing electrons and creating positively charged ions. The ions are then accelerated into a magnetic field. When ions drift through a magnetic field, they experience a force that bends their trajectory. The amount of bending depends on the mass of the ions—the trajectories of lighter ions are bent more than those of heavier ones.

In the right side of the spectrometer in Figure 2.15▲, you can see three different paths, each corresponding to ions of different mass. Finally, the ions strike a detector and produce an electrical signal that is recorded. The result is the separation of the ions according to their mass, producing a mass spectrum such as the one in Figure 2.16▶. The *position* of each peak on the *x*-axis indicates the *mass of the isotope* that was ionized, and the *intensity* (indicated by the height of the peak) indicates the *relative abundance of that isotope.*

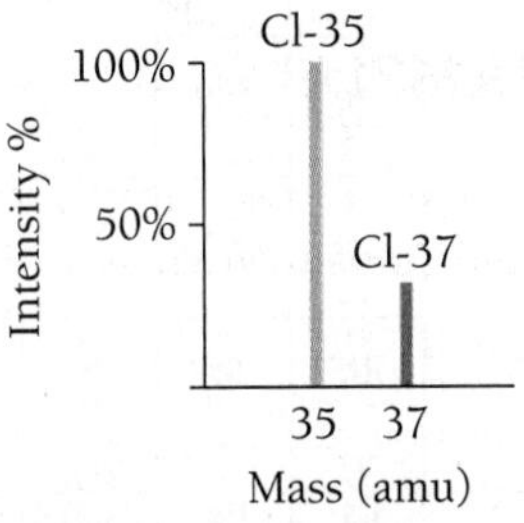

▲FIGURE 2.16 The Mass Spectrum of Chlorine The position of each peak on the *x*-axis indicates the mass of the isotope. The intensity (or height) of the peak indicates the relative abundance of the isotope. The intensity of the highest peak is usually set to 100%, and the intensity of all other peaks is reported relative to the most intense one.

The mass spectrum of an elemental sample can be used to determine the atomic mass of that sample of the element. For example, consider the mass spectrum of a naturally occurring sample of silver:

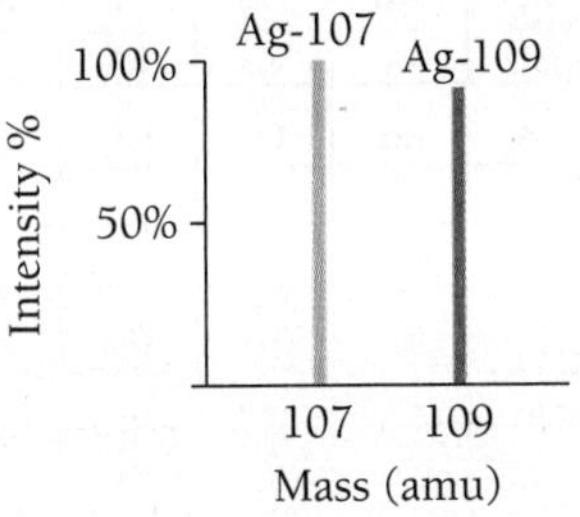

The two peaks correspond to the two isotopes of silver. We can determine the percent abundance of each isotope from the intensity of each line. However, the *total* intensity must be *normalized*—it must be made to equal 100%. We can accomplish this by dividing the intensity of each peak by the total intensity:

$$\text{Abundance of Ag-107} = \frac{100.0\%}{100.0\% + 92.90\%} \times 100\% = 51.84\%$$

$$\text{Abundance of Ag-109} = \frac{92.90\%}{100.0\% + 92.90\%} \times 100\% = 48.16\%$$

Then we can calculate the atomic mass of silver:

$$\begin{aligned}\text{Ag atomic mass} &= 0.5184(106.905\text{ amu}) + 0.4816(108.904\text{ amu}) \\ &= 55.4\underline{1}95\text{ amu} + 52.4\underline{4}82\text{ amu} = 107.8677 = 107.87\text{ amu}\end{aligned}$$

Mass spectrometry can also be used on molecules. Because molecules often fragment (break apart) during ionization, the mass spectrum of a molecule usually contains many peaks representing the masses of different parts of the molecule, as well as a peak

CHEMISTRY IN YOUR DAY | Evolving Atomic Masses

At the beginning of 2011, IUPAC published a new periodic table with atomic masses that looked different from previous IUPAC periodic tables. For the first time, instead of listing a single atomic mass for each element, IUPAC listed upper and lower bounds for the atomic masses of several elements (see the periodic table in this box). For example, previous IUPAC periodic tables reported the atomic mass of O (rounded to four significant figures) as 16.00. However, the new periodic table reports the atomic mass as [15.99, 16.00] denoting the upper and lower bounds for the possible atomic masses of terrestrial oxygen.

Why did this happen? The changes were necessary because developments in mass spectrometry have increasingly demonstrated that the atomic masses of several elements are not constant from one sample to another because the isotopic composition is not constant from one sample to another. In other words, the isotopic composition of a sample of a given element can vary depending on the source of the sample. For example, the lower bound for the atomic mass of oxygen (15.99 amu) comes from measurements of oxygen from Antarctic precipitation, and the upper bound (16.00 amu) comes from measurements of oxygen in marine N_2O (dinitrogen monoxide). Although we have long treated atomic masses as *constants of nature*, they are not, and the new periodic table reflects this fact.

So what do we do if we need an atomic mass for an element of unknown or unspecified origin? IUPAC has recommended values that apply to most samples found on Earth. The values are rounded so that atomic mass variations in samples found on Earth are plus or minus one in the last digit (just like accepted significant figure conventions). These values are adopted throughout all of the periodic tables in this book except the one shown below, which displays the upper and lower bounds for those elements in which variation occurs. For further reading, see IUPAC. *Pure Appl. Chem.* **2011**, 83(2), 359–396.

IUPAC Periodic Table of the Elements

Key: atomic number / **Symbol** / name / conventional atomic weight / standard atomic weight

1	2	3	4	5	6	7	8	9	10	11	12	13	14	15	16	17	18
1 **H** hydrogen 1.008 [1.0078, 1.0082]																	2 **He** helium 4.0026
3 **Li** lithium 6.94 [6.938, 6.997]	4 **Be** beryllium 9.0122											5 **B** boron 10.81 [10.806, 10.821]	6 **C** carbon 12.011 [12.009, 12.012]	7 **N** nitrogen 14.007 [14.006, 14.008]	8 **O** oxygen 15.999 [15.999, 16.000]	9 **F** fluorine 18.998	10 **Ne** neon 20.180
11 **Na** sodium 22.990	12 **Mg** magnesium 24.305 [24.304, 24.307]											13 **Al** aluminium 26.982	14 **Si** silicon 28.085 [28.084, 28.086]	15 **P** phosphorus 30.974	16 **S** sulfur 32.06 [32.059, 32.076]	17 **Cl** chlorine 35.45 [35.446, 35.457]	18 **Ar** argon 39.948
19 **K** potassium 39.098	20 **Ca** calcium 40.078(4)	21 **Sc** scandium 44.956	22 **Ti** titanium 47.867	23 **V** vanadium 50.942	24 **Cr** chromium 51.996	25 **Mn** manganese 54.938	26 **Fe** iron 55.845(2)	27 **Co** cobalt 58.933	28 **Ni** nickel 58.693	29 **Cu** copper 63.546(3)	30 **Zn** zinc 65.38(2)	31 **Ga** gallium 69.723	32 **Ge** germanium 72.630(8)	33 **As** arsenic 74.922	34 **Se** selenium 78.971(8)	35 **Br** bromine 79.904 [79.901, 79.907]	36 **Kr** krypton 83.798(2)
37 **Rb** rubidium 85.468	38 **Sr** strontium 87.62	39 **Y** yttrium 88.906	40 **Zr** zirconium 91.224(2)	41 **Nb** niobium 92.906	42 **Mo** molybdenum 95.95	43 **Tc** technetium	44 **Ru** ruthenium 101.07(2)	45 **Rh** rhodium 102.91	46 **Pd** palladium 106.42	47 **Ag** silver 107.87	48 **Cd** cadmium 112.41	49 **In** indium 114.82	50 **Sn** tin 118.71	51 **Sb** antimony 121.76	52 **Te** tellurium 127.60(3)	53 **I** iodine 126.90	54 **Xe** xenon 131.29
55 **Cs** caesium 132.91	56 **Ba** barium 137.33	57-71 lanthanoids	72 **Hf** hafnium 178.49(2)	73 **Ta** tantalum 180.95	74 **W** tungsten 183.84	75 **Re** rhenium 186.21	76 **Os** osmium 190.23(3)	77 **Ir** iridium 192.22	78 **Pt** platinum 195.08	79 **Au** gold 196.97	80 **Hg** mercury 200.59	81 **Tl** thallium 204.38 [204.38, 204.39]	82 **Pb** lead 207.2	83 **Bi** bismuth 208.98	84 **Po** polonium	85 **At** astatine	86 **Rn** radon
87 **Fr** francium	88 **Ra** radium	89-103 actinoids	104 **Rf** rutherfordium	105 **Db** dubnium	106 **Sg** seaborgium	107 **Bh** bohrium	108 **Hs** hassium	109 **Mt** meitnerium	110 **Ds** darmstadtium	111 **Rg** roentgenium	112 **Cn** copernicium	113 **Nh** nihonium	114 **Fl** flerovium	115 **Mc** moscovium	116 **Lv** livermorium	117 **Ts** tennessine	118 **Og** oganesson

57 **La** lanthanum 138.91	58 **Ce** cerium 140.12	59 **Pr** praseodymium 140.91	60 **Nd** neodymium 144.24	61 **Pm** promethium	62 **Sm** samarium 150.36(2)	63 **Eu** europium 151.96	64 **Gd** gadolinium 157.25(3)	65 **Tb** terbium 158.93	66 **Dy** dysprosium 162.50	67 **Ho** holmium 164.93	68 **Er** erbium 167.26	69 **Tm** thulium 168.93	70 **Yb** ytterbium 173.05	71 **Lu** lutetium 174.97
89 **Ac** actinium	90 **Th** thorium 232.04	91 **Pa** protactinium 231.04	92 **U** uranium 238.03	93 **Np** neptunium	94 **Pu** plutonium	95 **Am** americium	96 **Cm** curium	97 **Bk** berkelium	98 **Cf** californium	99 **Es** einsteinium	100 **Fm** fermium	101 **Md** mendelevium	102 **No** nobelium	103 **Lr** lawrencium

INTERNATIONAL UNION OF PURE AND APPLIED CHEMISTRY

For notes and updates to this table, see www.iupac.org. This version is dated 28 November 2016.

representing the mass of the molecule as a whole. The fragments that form upon ionization, and therefore the corresponding peaks that appear in the mass spectrum, are specific to the molecule, so a mass spectrum is like a molecular fingerprint. Mass spectroscopy can be used to identify an unknown molecule and to determine how much of it is present in a particular sample. For example, mass spectrometry has been used to detect organic (carbon-containing) compounds present in meteorites, a puzzling observation that some scientists speculate may be evidence of life outside of our planet.

Most scientists think that the carbon compounds in meteorites probably formed in the same way as the first organic molecules on Earth, indicating that the formation of organic molecules may be common in the universe.

Since the early 1990s, researchers have also successfully applied mass spectrometry to biological molecules, including proteins (the workhorse molecules in cells) and nucleic acids (the molecules that carry genetic information). For a long time, these molecules could not be analyzed by mass spectrometry because they were difficult to vaporize and ionize without being destroyed, but modern techniques have overcome this problem. A tumor, for example, can now be instantly analyzed by mass spectrometry to determine whether it contains specific proteins associated with cancer.

2.9 Molar Mass: Counting Atoms by Weighing Them

WATCH **NOW!**

KEY CONCEPT VIDEO 2.9

The Mole Concept

Shrimp are normally sold by *count*, which indicates the number of shrimp per pound. For example, 41–50 count shrimp means that there are between 41 and 50 shrimp per pound. The smaller the count, the larger the shrimp. Big tiger prawns have counts as low as 10–15, which means that each shrimp can weigh up to 1/10 of a pound. One advantage of categorizing shrimp in this way is that we can count the shrimp by weighing them. For example, two pounds of 41–50 count shrimp contains between 82 and 100 shrimp.

A similar (but more precise) concept exists for atoms. Counting atoms is much more difficult than counting shrimp, yet as chemists we often need to know the number of atoms in a sample of a given mass. Why? *Because chemical processes happen between particles*. For elements, those particles are atoms. For example, when hydrogen and oxygen combine to form water, two hydrogen atoms combine with one oxygen atom to form one water molecule. If we want to know how much hydrogen to react with a given mass of oxygen to form water, we need to know the number of atoms in the given mass of oxygen. We also need to know the mass of hydrogen that contains exactly twice that number of atoms.

As another example, consider intravenous fluids—fluids that are delivered to patients by directly dripping them into veins. These fluids are saline (sodium chloride) solutions that must have a specific number of sodium and chloride ions per liter of fluid. The number of particles in the fluid directly influences the properties of the fluid. Administering an intravenous fluid with the wrong number of sodium and chloride ions could be fatal.

Atoms are far too small to count by any ordinary means. As we noted earlier, even if you could somehow count atoms, and counted them 24 hours a day for as long as you lived, you would barely begin to count the number of atoms in something as small as a sand grain. Therefore, if we want to know the number of atoms in anything of ordinary size, we count them by weighing.

The Mole: A Chemist's "Dozen"

When we count large numbers of objects, we often use units such as a dozen (12 objects) or a gross (144 objects) to organize our counting and to keep our numbers more manageable. With atoms, quadrillions of which may be in a speck of dust, we need a much larger number for this purpose. The chemist's "dozen" is the **mole** (abbreviated mol). A mole is the *amount* of material containing 6.02214×10^{23} particles.

$$1 \text{ mol} = 6.02214 \times 10^{23} \text{ particles}$$

This number is **Avogadro's number**, named after Italian physicist Amedeo Avogadro (1776–1856), and is a convenient number to use when working with atoms, molecules, and ions. In this book, we usually round Avogadro's number to four significant figures

Twenty-two copper pennies contain approximately 1 mol of copper atoms.

Before 1982, when they became almost all zinc with only a copper coating, pennies were mostly copper.

One tablespoon of water contains approximately 1 mol of water molecules.

One tablespoon is approximately 15 mL; one mol of water occupies 18 mL.

or 6.022×10^{23}. Notice that the definition of the mole is an *amount* of a substance. We often refer to the number of moles of substance as the *amount* of the substance.

The first thing to understand about the mole is that it can specify Avogadro's number of anything. For example, one mole of marbles corresponds to 6.022×10^{23} marbles, and one mole of sand grains corresponds to 6.022×10^{23} sand grains. *One mole of anything is* 6.022×10^{23} *units of that thing.* One mole of atoms, ions, or molecules, however, makes up objects of everyday sizes. Twenty-two copper pennies, for example, contain approximately 1 mol of copper atoms, and 1 tablespoon of water contains approximately 1 mol of water molecules.

The second, and more fundamental, thing to understand about the mole is how it gets its specific value.

The value of the mole is equal to the number of atoms in exactly 12 g of pure carbon-12 (12 g C = 1 mol C atoms = 6.022×10^{23} C atoms).

The definition of the mole gives us a relationship between mass (grams of carbon) and number of atoms (Avogadro's number). This relationship, as we will see shortly, allows us to count atoms by weighing them.

Converting between Number of Moles and Number of Atoms

Converting between number of moles and number of atoms is similar to converting between dozens of eggs and number of eggs. For eggs, you use the conversion factor 1 dozen eggs = 12 eggs. For atoms, you use the conversion factor 1 mol atoms = 6.022×10^{23} atoms. The conversion factors take the following forms:

$$\frac{1 \text{ mol atoms}}{6.022 \times 10^{23} \text{ atoms}} \quad \text{or} \quad \frac{6.022 \times 10^{23} \text{ atoms}}{1 \text{ mol atoms}}$$

Example 2.6 demonstrates how to use these conversion factors in calculations.

EXAMPLE 2.6 Converting between Number of Moles and Number of Atoms

Calculate the number of copper atoms in 2.45 mol of copper.

SORT You are given the amount of copper in moles and asked to find the number of copper atoms.

GIVEN: 2.45 mol Cu
FIND: Cu atoms

STRATEGIZE Convert between number of moles and number of atoms by using Avogadro's number as a conversion factor.

CONCEPTUAL PLAN

mol Cu → Cu atoms

$$\frac{6.022 \times 10^{23} \text{ Cu atoms}}{1 \text{ mol Cu}}$$

RELATIONSHIPS USED

$6.022 \times 10^{23} = 1$ mol (Avogadro's number)

SOLVE Follow the conceptual plan to solve the problem. Begin with 2.45 mol Cu and multiply by Avogadro's number to get to the number of Cu atoms.

SOLUTION

$$2.45 \cancel{\text{mol Cu}} \times \frac{6.022 \times 10^{23} \text{ Cu atoms}}{1 \cancel{\text{mol Cu}}} = 1.48 \times 10^{24} \text{ Cu atoms}$$

CHECK Since atoms are small, it makes sense that the answer is large. The given number of moles of copper is almost 2.5, so the number of atoms is almost 2.5 times Avogadro's number.

FOR PRACTICE 2.6 A pure silver ring contains 2.80×10^{22} silver atoms. How many moles of silver atoms does it contain?

SOLVE Follow the conceptual plan to solve the problem. Begin with 3.10 g Cu and multiply by the appropriate conversion factors to arrive at the number of Cu atoms.	**SOLUTION** $3.10\ \text{g Cu} \times \dfrac{1\ \text{mol Cu}}{63.55\ \text{g Cu}} \times \dfrac{6.022 \times 10^{23}\ \text{Cu atoms}}{1\ \text{mol Cu}} = 2.94 \times 10^{22}\ \text{Cu atoms}$

CHECK The answer (the number of copper atoms) is less than 6.022×10^{23} (1 mol). This is consistent with the given mass of copper atoms, which is less than the molar mass of copper.

FOR PRACTICE 2.8 How many carbon atoms are there in a 1.3-carat diamond? Diamonds are a form of pure carbon. (1 carat = 0.20 g)

FOR MORE PRACTICE 2.8 Calculate the mass of 2.25×10^{22} tungsten atoms.

Notice that numbers with large exponents, such as 6.022×10^{23}, are almost unbelievably large. Twenty-two copper pennies contain 6.022×10^{23} or 1 mol of copper atoms, but 6.022×10^{23} pennies would cover Earth's entire surface to a depth of 300 m. Even objects small by everyday standards occupy a huge space when we have a mole of them. For example, a grain of sand has a mass of less than 1 mg and a diameter of less than 0.1 mm, yet 1 mol of sand grains would cover the state of Texas to a depth of several feet. For every increase of 1 in the exponent of a number, the number increases by a factor of 10, so 10^{23} is incredibly large. Of course 1 mol has to be a large number if it is to have practical value because atoms are so small.

WATCH **NOW!**
INTERACTIVE WORKED EXAMPLE 2.9

EXAMPLE 2.9 The Mole Concept

An aluminum sphere contains 8.55×10^{22} aluminum atoms. What is the sphere's radius in centimeters? The density of aluminum is $2.70\ \text{g/cm}^3$.

SORT You are given the number of aluminum atoms in a sphere and the density of aluminum. You are asked to find the radius of the sphere.

GIVEN: 8.55×10^{22} Al atoms
$d = 2.70\ \text{g/cm}^3$

FIND: radius (r) of sphere

STRATEGIZE The heart of this problem is density, which relates mass to volume; though you aren't given the mass directly, you are given the number of atoms, which you can use to find mass.

1. Convert from number of atoms to number of moles using Avogadro's number as a conversion factor.
2. Convert from number of moles to mass using molar mass as a conversion factor.
3. Convert from mass to volume (in cm^3) using density as a conversion factor.
4. Once you calculate the volume, find the radius from the volume using the formula for the volume of a sphere.

CONCEPTUAL PLAN

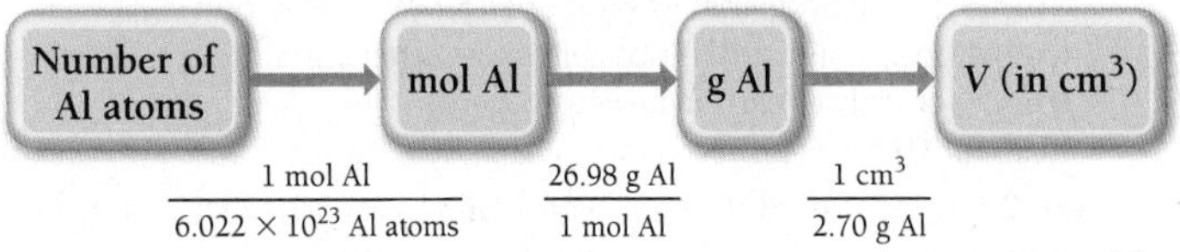

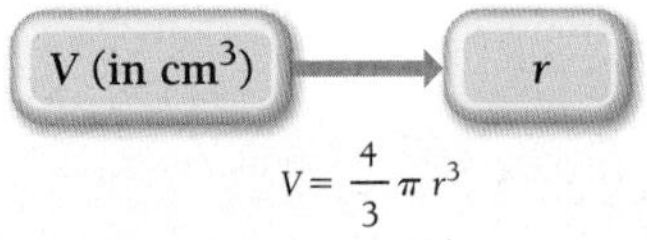

RELATIONSHIPS AND EQUATIONS USED

$6.022 \times 10^{23} = 1$ mol (Avogadro's number)

26.98 g Al = 1 mol Al (molar mass of aluminum)

$2.70\ \text{g/cm}^3$ (density of aluminum)

$V = \frac{4}{3}\pi r^3$ (volume of a sphere)

—*Continued on the next page*

Continued—

SOLVE	SOLUTION
Finally, follow the conceptual plan to solve the problem. Begin with 8.55×10^{22} Al atoms and multiply by the appropriate conversion factors to arrive at volume in cm^3.	$8.55 \times 10^{22}\ \text{Al atoms} \times \dfrac{1\ \text{mol Al}}{6.022 \times 10^{23}\ \text{Al atoms}} \times \dfrac{26.98\ \text{g Al}}{1\ \text{mol Al}} \times \dfrac{1\ \text{cm}^3}{2.70\ \text{g Al}} = 1.4\underline{1}87\ \text{cm}^3$
Then solve the equation for the volume of a sphere for *r* and substitute the volume to calculate *r*.	$V = \dfrac{4}{3}\pi r^3$ $r = \sqrt[3]{\dfrac{3V}{4\pi}} = \sqrt[3]{\dfrac{3(1.4\underline{1}87\ \text{cm}^3)}{4\pi}} = 0.697\ \text{cm}$

CHECK The units of the answer (cm) are correct. The magnitude cannot be estimated accurately, but a radius of about one-half of a centimeter is reasonable for just over one-tenth of a mole of aluminum atoms.

FOR PRACTICE 2.9 A titanium cube contains 2.86×10^{23} atoms. What is the edge length of the cube? The density of titanium is $4.50\ g/cm^3$.

FOR MORE PRACTICE 2.9 Find the number of atoms in a copper rod with a length of 9.85 cm and a radius of 1.05 cm. The density of copper is $8.96\ g/cm^3$.

ANSWER **NOW!**

2.12 Cc Conceptual Connection

THE MOLE Without doing any calculations, determine which sample contains the most atoms.

(a) a 1-g sample of copper
(b) a 1-g sample of carbon
(c) a 10-g sample of uranium

QUIZ YOURSELF **NOW!**

Self-Assessment Quiz

Q1. Two samples of a compound containing elements A and B are decomposed. The first sample produces 15 g of A and 35 g of B. The second sample produces 25 g of A and what mass of B?
MISSED THIS? *Read Section 2.3; Watch KCV 2.3*

a) 11 g b) 58 g c) 21 g d) 45 g

Q2. A compound containing only carbon and hydrogen has a carbon-to-hydrogen mass ratio of 11.89. Which carbon-to-hydrogen mass ratio is possible for another compound composed only of carbon and hydrogen?
MISSED THIS? *Read Section 2.3; Watch KCV 2.3*

a) 2.50 b) 3.97 c) 4.66 d) 7.89

Q3. Which idea came out of Rutherford's gold foil experiment?
MISSED THIS? *Read Section 2.5*

a) Atoms contain protons and neutrons.
b) Matter is composed of atoms.
c) Elements have isotopes.
d) Atoms are mostly empty space.

Q4. A student re-creates the Millikan oil drop experiment and tabulates the relative charges of the oil drops in terms of a constant, α.

Drop #1	α
Drop #2	$\frac{3}{2}\alpha$
Drop #3	$\frac{5}{2}\alpha$
Drop #4	3α

What charge for the electron (in terms of α) is consistent with these data?
MISSED THIS? *Read Section 2.4*

a) $\frac{1}{2}\alpha$ b) α c) $\frac{3}{2}\alpha$ d) 2α

Q5. Determine the number of protons and neutrons in the isotope Fe-58.
MISSED THIS? *Read Section 2.6; Watch KCV 2.6, IWE 2.3*

a) 26 protons and 58 neutrons
b) 32 protons and 26 neutrons
c) 26 protons and 32 neutrons
d) 58 protons and 58 neutrons

Q6. An isotope of an element contains 82 protons and 122 neutrons. What is the symbol for the isotope?
MISSED THIS? *Read Section 2.6; Watch KCV 2.6, IWE 2.3*

a) $^{204}_{82}Pb$ b) $^{122}_{82}Pb$ c) $^{122}_{40}Zr$ d) $^{204}_{40}Zr$

Q7. Determine the number of electrons in the Cr^{3+} ion.
MISSED THIS? *Read Section 2.6*

a) 24 electrons b) 27 electrons
c) 3 electrons d) 21 electrons

Q8. Which pair of elements do you expect to be most similar in their chemical properties?
MISSED THIS? *Read Section 2.7; Watch KCV 2.7*

a) K and Fe b) O and Si
c) Ne and N d) Br and I

Q9. Which element is *not* a main-group element?
MISSED THIS? *Read Section 2.7; Watch KCV 2.7*

a) Se b) Mo c) Sr d) Ba

Q10. What is the charge of the ion most commonly formed by S?
MISSED THIS? *Read Section 2.7*

a) 2+ b) + c) − d) 2−

Q11. A naturally occurring sample of an element contains only two isotopes. The first isotope has a mass of 68.9255 amu and a natural abundance of 60.11%. The second isotope has a mass of 70.9247 amu. Find the atomic mass of the element.
MISSED THIS? *Read Section 2.8; Watch IWE 2.5*

a) 70.13 amu
b) 69.72 amu
c) 84.06 amu
d) 69.93 amu

Q12. Which sample contains the greatest number of atoms?
MISSED THIS? *Read Section 2.9; Watch KCV 2.9, IWE 2.8*

a) 14 g C
b) 49 g Cr
c) 102 g Ag
d) 202 g Pb

Q13. Determine the number of atoms in 1.85 mL of mercury. (The density of mercury is 13.5 g/mL.) **MISSED THIS?** *Read Section 2.9; Watch KCV 2.9, IWE 2.8, 2.9*

a) 3.02×10^{27} atoms
b) 4.11×10^{20} atoms
c) 7.50×10^{22} atoms
d) 1.50×10^{25} atoms

Q14. A 20.0 g sample of an element contains 4.95×10^{23} atoms. Identify the element.
MISSED THIS? *Read Section 2.9; Watch KCV 2.9, IWE 2.8*

a) Cr b) O c) Mg d) Fe

Q15. Copper has two naturally occurring isotopes with masses 62.94 amu and 64.93 amu and has an atomic mass of 63.55 amu. Which mass spectrum (of those shown at right) is most likely to correspond to a naturally occurring sample of copper? **MISSED THIS?** *Read Section 2.9*

a)
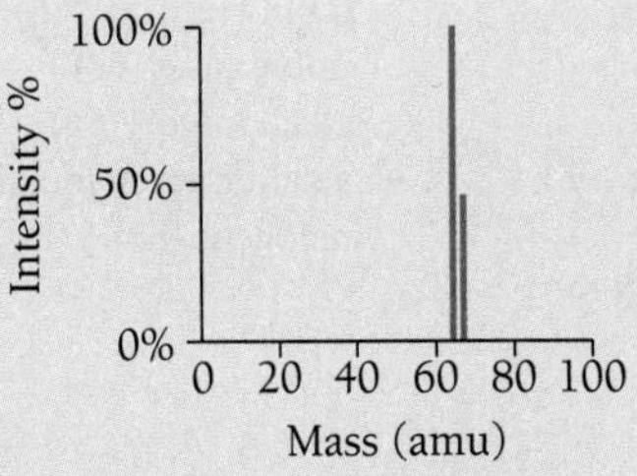

b)
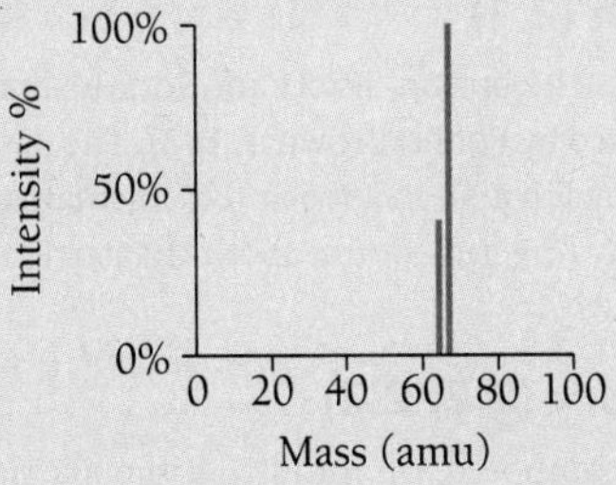

c)
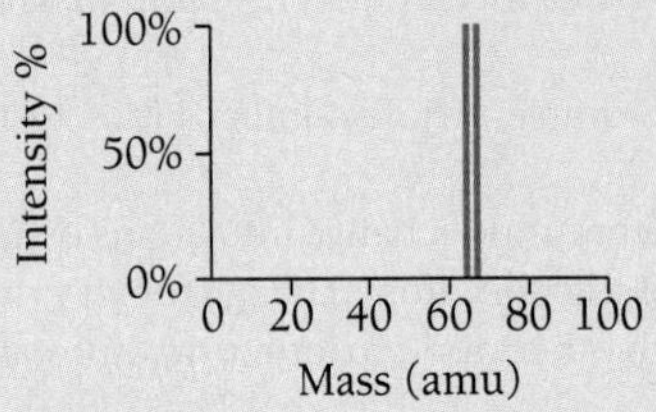

d)
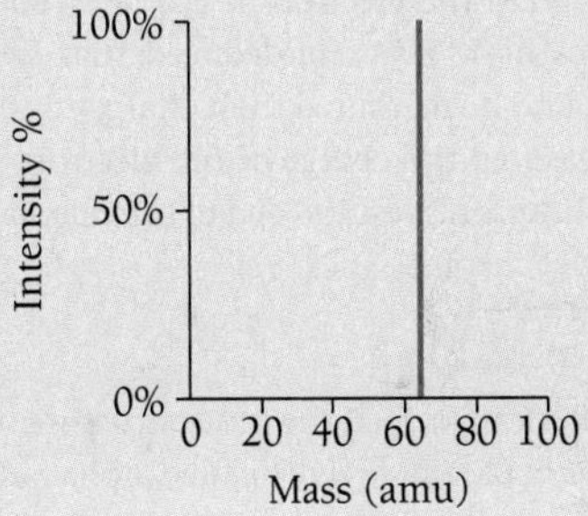

Answers: **1.** (b) **2.** (b) **3.** (d) **4.** (a) **5.** (c) **6.** (a) **7.** (d) **8.** (d) **9.** (b) **10.** (d) **11.** (b) **12.** (a) **13.** (c) **14.** (c) **15.** (a)

CHAPTER 2 IN REVIEW

TERMS

Section 2.3
law of conservation of mass (51)
law of definite proportions (52)
law of multiple proportions (53)
atomic theory (54)

Section 2.4
cathode rays (55)
cathode ray tube (55)
electrical charge (55)
electron (56)

Section 2.5
radioactivity (57)
nuclear theory (58)
nucleus (58)
proton (58)
neutrons (59)

Section 2.6
atomic mass unit (amu) (59)
atomic number (*Z*) (60)
chemical symbol (60)
isotope (62)
natural abundance (62)
mass number (*A*) (62)
ion (63)
cation (64)
anion (64)

Section 2.7
periodic law (65)
metal (66)

nonmetal (66)
metalloid (66)
semiconductor (66)
main-group elements (66)
transition elements (transition metals) (66)
family (group) (66)
noble gases (66)
alkali metals (66)
alkaline earth metals (66)
halogens (68)

Section 2.8
atomic mass (69)
mass spectrometry (70)

Section 2.9
mole (mol) (73)
Avogadro's number (73)
molar mass (75)

CONCEPTS

Brownian Motion (2.1)

- Brownian motion is the erratic, jittery motion of small particles that was first observed by Robert Brown in 1827. The description of Brownian motion by Einstein in 1905 and confirmation by Perrin in 1908 removed any lingering doubt about the particulate nature of matter.

The Atomic Theory (2.2, 2.3)

- Each element is composed of indestructible particles called atoms.
- All atoms of a given element have the same mass and other properties.
- Atoms combine in simple, whole-number ratios to form compounds.
- Atoms of one element cannot change into atoms of another element. In a chemical reaction, atoms change the way that they are bound together with other atoms to form a new substance.

The Electron (2.4)

- J. J. Thomson discovered the electron in the late 1800s through experiments with cathode rays. He deduced that electrons are negatively charged, and he measured their charge-to-mass ratio.
- Robert Millikan measured the charge of the electron, which—in conjunction with Thomson's results—led to the calculation of the mass of an electron.

The Nuclear Atom (2.5)

- In 1909, Ernest Rutherford probed the inner structure of the atom by working with a form of radioactivity called alpha radiation and developed the nuclear theory of the atom.
- Nuclear theory states that the atom is mainly empty space, with most of its mass concentrated in a tiny region called the nucleus and most of its volume occupied by relatively light electrons.

Subatomic Particles (2.6)

- Atoms are composed of three fundamental particles: the proton (1 amu, +1 charge), the neutron (1 amu, 0 charge), and the electron (~0 amu, −1 charge).
- The number of protons in the nucleus of the atom is its atomic number (Z) and defines the element.
- The sum of the number of protons and neutrons is the mass number (A).
- Atoms of an element that have different numbers of neutrons (and therefore different mass numbers) are isotopes.
- Atoms that lose or gain electrons become charged and are ions. Cations are positively charged and anions are negatively charged.

The Periodic Table (2.7)

- The periodic table tabulates all known elements in order of increasing atomic number.
- The periodic table is arranged so that similar elements are grouped together in columns.
- Elements on the left side and in the center of the periodic table are metals and tend to lose electrons in chemical changes.
- Elements on the upper right side of the periodic table are nonmetals and tend to gain electrons in chemical changes.
- Elements located on the boundary between metals and nonmetals are metalloids.

Atomic Mass and the Mole (2.8, 2.9)

- The atomic mass of an element, listed directly below its symbol in the periodic table, is a weighted average of the masses of the naturally occurring isotopes of the element.
- One mole of an element is the amount of that element that contains Avogadro's number (6.022×10^{23}) of atoms.
- Any sample of an element with a mass (in grams) that equals its atomic mass contains one mole of the element. For example, the atomic mass of carbon is 12.011 amu; therefore, 12.011 g of carbon contains 1 mol of carbon atoms.

EQUATIONS AND RELATIONSHIPS

Relationship between Mass Number (A), Number of Protons (p), and Number of Neutrons (n) (**2.6**)

$$A = \text{number of protons (p)} + \text{number of neutrons (n)}$$

Atomic Mass (**2.8**)

$$\text{Atomic mass} = \sum_n (\text{fraction of isotope } n) \times (\text{mass of isotope } n)$$

Avogadro's Number (**2.9**)

$$1 \text{ mol} = 6.0221421 \times 10^{23} \text{ particles}$$

LEARNING OUTCOMES

Chapter Objectives	Assessment
Apply the mass laws that are the basis of modern atomic theory (2.3)	Examples 2.1, 2.2 **For Practice** 2.1, 2.2 **Exercises** 29–38
Describe the experiments that led to the discovery of the electron and its charge (2.4)	Exercises 43–46
Explain the structure of an atom (2.5)	Exercises 39–42
Describe the properties of subatomic particles and interpret isotope symbols (2.6)	Example 2.3 **For Practice** 2.3 **Exercises** 47–58
Relate the periodic law to the organization of the periodic table (2.7)	**Exercises** 63–70
Predict the charge of ions (2.7)	Example 2.4 **For Practice** 2.4 **Exercises** 59–62
Determine the atomic mass of atoms (2.8)	Example 2.5 **For Practice** 2.5 **For More Practice** 2.5 **Exercises** 71–80
Apply the mole concept (2.9)	Examples 2.6, 2.7, 2.8, 2.9 **For Practice** 2.6, 2.7, 2.8, 2.9 **For More Practice** 2.7, 2.8, 2.9 **Exercises** 81–94

EXERCISES

Mastering Chemistry provides end-of-chapter exercises, feedback-enriched tutorial problems, animations, and interactive activities to encourage problem-solving practice and deeper understanding of key concepts and topics.

REVIEW QUESTIONS

1. What is Brownian motion? How is it related to the development of the idea that matter is particulate?
2. Summarize the history of the atomic idea. How was Dalton able to convince others to accept an idea that had been controversial for 2000 years?
3. State and explain the law of conservation of mass.
4. State and explain the law of definite proportions.
5. State and explain the law of multiple proportions. How is the law of multiple proportions different from the law of definite proportions?
6. What are the main ideas in Dalton's atomic theory? How do they help explain the laws of conservation of mass, of constant composition, and of definite proportions?
7. How and by whom was the electron discovered? What basic properties of the electron were reported with its discovery?
8. Explain Millikan's oil drop experiment and how it led to the measurement of the electron's charge. Why is the magnitude of the charge of the electron so important?
9. Describe the plum-pudding model of the atom.
10. Describe Rutherford's gold foil experiment. How did the experiment prove that the plum-pudding model of the atom was wrong?
11. Describe Rutherford's nuclear model of the atom. What was revolutionary about his model?
12. If matter is mostly empty space, as suggested by Rutherford, then why does it appear so solid?
13. List the three subatomic particles that compose atoms and give the basic properties (mass and charge) of each.
14. What defines an element?
15. Explain the difference between Z (the atomic number) and A (the mass number).
16. Where do elements get their names?
17. What are isotopes? What is percent natural abundance of isotopes?
18. Describe the two different notations used to specify isotopes and give an example of each.
19. What is an ion? A cation? An anion?
20. State the periodic law. How did the periodic law lead to the periodic table?
21. Describe the characteristic properties of metals, nonmetals, and metalloids.
22. List the characteristic properties of each group.
    a. noble gases
    b. alkali metals
    c. alkaline earth metals
    d. halogens
23. How do you predict the charges of ions formed by main-group elements?
24. What is atomic mass? How is it calculated?
25. Explain how a mass spectrometer works.
26. What kind of information can be determined from a mass spectrum?
27. What is a mole? How is the mole concept useful in chemical calculations?
28. Why is the mass corresponding to a mole of one element different from the mass corresponding to a mole of another element?

PROBLEMS BY TOPIC

Note: Answers to all odd-numbered Problems, numbered in blue, can be found in Appendix III. Exercises in the Problems by Topic section are paired, with each odd-numbered problem followed by a similar even-numbered problem. Exercises in the Cumulative Problems section are also paired, but somewhat more loosely. (Challenge Problems and Conceptual Problems, because of their nature, are unpaired.)

The Laws of Conservation of Mass, Definite Proportions, and Multiple Proportions

29. A hydrogen-filled balloon is ignited, and 1.50 g of hydrogen reacts with 12.0 g of oxygen. How many grams of water vapor form? (Assume that water vapor is the only product.)
MISSED THIS? *Read Section 2.3; Watch KCV 2.3*

30. An automobile gasoline tank holds 21 kg of gasoline. When the gasoline burns, 84 kg of oxygen is consumed, and carbon dioxide and water are produced. What is the total combined mass of carbon dioxide and water that is produced?

31. Two samples of carbon tetrachloride are decomposed into their constituent elements. One sample produces 38.9 g of carbon and 448 g of chlorine, and the other sample produces 14.8 g of carbon and 134 g of chlorine. Are these results consistent with the law of definite proportions? Explain your answer.
MISSED THIS? *Read Section 2.3; Watch KCV 2.3*

32. Two samples of sodium chloride are decomposed into their constituent elements. One sample produces 6.98 g of sodium and 10.7 g of chlorine, and the other sample produces 11.2 g of sodium and 17.3 g of chlorine. Are these results consistent with the law of definite proportions? Explain your answer.

33. The mass ratio of sodium to fluorine in sodium fluoride is 1.21:1. A sample of sodium fluoride produces 28.8 g of sodium upon decomposition. How much fluorine (in grams) forms?
MISSED THIS? *Read Section 2.3; Watch KCV 2.3*

34. Upon decomposition, one sample of magnesium fluoride produces 1.65 kg of magnesium and 2.57 kg of fluorine. A second sample produces 1.32 kg of magnesium. How much fluorine (in grams) does the second sample produce?

35. Two different compounds containing osmium and oxygen have the following masses of oxygen per gram of osmium: 0.168 and 0.3369 g. Show that these amounts are consistent with the law of multiple proportions.
MISSED THIS? *Read Section 2.3; Watch KCV 2.3*

36. Palladium forms three different compounds with sulfur. The mass of sulfur per gram of palladium in each compound is listed here. Show that these masses are consistent with the law of multiple proportions.

Compound	Grams S per Gram Pd
A	0.603
B	0.301
C	0.151

37. Sulfur and oxygen form both sulfur dioxide and sulfur trioxide. When samples of these are decomposed, the sulfur dioxide produces 3.49 g oxygen and 3.50 g sulfur, while the sulfur trioxide produces 6.75 g oxygen and 4.50 g sulfur. Calculate the mass of oxygen per gram of sulfur for each sample and show that these results are consistent with the law of multiple proportions.
MISSED THIS? *Read Section 2.3; Watch KCV 2.3*

38. Sulfur and fluorine form several different compounds including sulfur hexafluoride and sulfur tetrafluoride. Decomposition of a sample of sulfur hexafluoride produces 4.45 g of fluorine and 1.25 g of sulfur, while decomposition of a sample of sulfur tetrafluoride produces 4.43 g of fluorine and 1.87 g of sulfur. Calculate the mass of fluorine per gram of sulfur for each sample and show that these results are consistent with the law of multiple proportions.

Atomic Theory, Nuclear Theory, and Subatomic Particles

39. Which statements are *consistent* with Dalton's atomic theory as it was originally stated? Why?
MISSED THIS? *Read Section 2.3; Watch KCV 2.3*

a. Sulfur and oxygen atoms have the same mass.
b. All cobalt atoms are identical.
c. Potassium and chlorine atoms combine in a 1:1 ratio to form potassium chloride.
d. Lead atoms can be converted into gold.

40. Which statements are *inconsistent* with Dalton's atomic theory as it was originally stated? Why?

a. All carbon atoms are identical.
b. An oxygen atom combines with 1.5 hydrogen atoms to form a water molecule.
c. Two oxygen atoms combine with a carbon atom to form a carbon dioxide molecule.
d. The formation of a compound often involves the destruction of one or more atoms.

41. Which statements are *consistent* with Rutherford's nuclear theory as it was originally stated? Why?
MISSED THIS? *Read Section 2.5*

a. The volume of an atom is mostly empty space.
b. The nucleus of an atom is small compared to the size of the atom.
c. Neutral lithium atoms contain more neutrons than protons.
d. Neutral lithium atoms contain more protons than electrons.

42. Which statements are *inconsistent* with Rutherford's nuclear theory as it was originally stated? Why?

a. Since electrons are smaller than protons and since a hydrogen atom contains only one proton and one electron, it must follow that the volume of a hydrogen atom is mostly due to the proton.
b. A nitrogen atom has seven protons in its nucleus and seven electrons outside of its nucleus.
c. A phosphorus atom has 15 protons in its nucleus and 150 electrons outside of its nucleus.
d. The majority of the mass of a fluorine atom is due to its nine electrons.

43. A chemist in an imaginary universe, where electrons have a different charge than they do in our universe, performs the Millikan oil drop experiment to measure the electron's charge. The charges of several drops are recorded here. What is the charge of the electron in this imaginary universe?
MISSED THIS? *Read Section 2.4*

Drop #	Charge
A	-6.9×10^{-19} C
B	-9.2×10^{-19} C
C	-11.5×10^{-19} C
D	-4.6×10^{-19} C

44. Imagine a unit of charge called the *zorg*. A chemist performs the oil drop experiment and measures the charge of each drop in zorgs. Based on the results shown here, what is the charge of the electron in zorgs (z)? How many electrons are in each drop?

Drop #	Charge
A	-4.8×10^{-9} z
B	-9.6×10^{-9} z
C	-6.4×10^{-9} z
D	-12.8×10^{-9} z

45. On a dry day, your body can accumulate static charge from walking across a carpet or from brushing your hair. If your body develops a charge of $-15\ \mu C$ (microcoulombs), how many excess electrons has it acquired? What is their collective mass? **MISSED THIS?** *Read Section 2.4*

46. How many electrons are necessary to produce a charge of -1.0 C? What is the mass of this many electrons?

47. Which statements about subatomic particles are true? **MISSED THIS?** *Read Section 2.4, 2.5*
   a. If an atom has an equal number of protons and electrons, it will be charge-neutral.
   b. Electrons are attracted to protons.
   c. Electrons are much lighter than neutrons.
   d. Protons have twice the mass of neutrons.

48. Which statements about subatomic particles are false?
   a. Protons and electrons have charges of the same magnitude but opposite signs.
   b. Protons have about the same mass as neutrons.
   c. Some atoms don't have any protons.
   d. Protons and neutrons have charges of the same magnitude but opposite signs.

49. How many electrons does it take to equal the mass of a proton? **MISSED THIS?** *Read Section 2.4*

50. A helium nucleus has two protons and two neutrons. How many electrons does it take to equal the mass of a helium nucleus?

Isotopes and Ions

51. Write isotopic symbols in the form X-*A* (e.g., C-13) for each isotope. **MISSED THIS?** *Read Section 2.6; Watch KCV 2.6*
   a. the silver isotope with 60 neutrons
   b. the silver isotope with 62 neutrons
   c. the uranium isotope with 146 neutrons
   d. the hydrogen isotope with one neutron

52. Write isotopic symbols in the form $^{A}_{Z}X$ for each isotope.
   a. the copper isotope with 34 neutrons
   b. the copper isotope with 36 neutrons
   c. the potassium isotope with 21 neutrons
   d. the argon isotope with 22 neutrons

53. Determine the number of protons and the number of neutrons in each isotope.
MISSED THIS? *Read Section 2.6; Watch KCV 2.6, IWE 2.3*
   a. $^{14}_{7}N$ b. $^{23}_{11}Na$ c. $^{222}_{86}Rn$ d. $^{208}_{82}Pb$

54. Determine the number of protons and the number of neutrons in each isotope.
   a. $^{40}_{19}K$ b. $^{226}_{88}Ra$ c. $^{99}_{43}Tc$ d. $^{33}_{15}P$

55. The amount of carbon-14 in ancient artifacts and fossils is often used to establish their age. Determine the number of protons and the number of neutrons in carbon-14 and write its symbol in the form $^{A}_{Z}X$.
MISSED THIS? *Read Section 2.6; Watch KCV 2.6, IWE 2.3*

56. Uranium-235 is used in nuclear fission. Determine the number of protons and the number of neutrons in uranium-235 and write its symbol in the form $^{A}_{Z}X$.

57. Determine the number of protons and the number of electrons in each ion.
MISSED THIS? *Read Section 2.6; Watch KCV 2.6, IWE 2.3*
   a. Ni^{2+} b. S^{2-} c. Br^{-} d. Cr^{3+}

58. Determine the number of protons and the number of electrons in each ion.
   a. Al^{3+} b. Se^{2-} c. Ga^{3+} d. Sr^{2+}

59. Predict the charge of the ion formed by each element.
MISSED THIS? *Read Section 2.7*
   a. O b. K c. Al d. Rb

60. Predict the charge of the ion formed by each element.
   a. Mg b. N c. F d. Na

61. Fill in the blanks to complete the table.
MISSED THIS? *Read Section 2.6; Watch KCV 2.6, IWE 2.3*

Symbol	Ion Formed	Number of Electrons in Ion	Number of Protons in Ion
Ca	Ca^{2+}	____	____
____	Be^{2+}	2	____
Se	____	____	34
In	____	____	49

62. Fill in the blanks to complete the table.

Symbol	Ion Formed	Number of Electrons in Ion	Number of Protons in Ion
Cl	____	____	17
Te	____	54	____
Br	Br^{-}	____	____
____	Sr^{2+}	____	38

The Periodic Table and Atomic Mass

63. Write the name of each element and classify it as a metal, nonmetal, or metalloid.
MISSED THIS? *Read Section 2.7; Watch KCV 2.7*
   a. K b. Ba c. I d. O e. Sb

64. Write the symbol for each element and classify it as a metal, nonmetal, or metalloid.
   a. gold b. fluorine c. sodium d. tin e. argon

65. Determine whether or not each element is a main-group element. **MISSED THIS?** *Read Section 2.7; Watch KCV 2.7*
   a. tellurium
   b. potassium
   c. vanadium
   d. manganese

66. Determine whether or not each element is a transition element.
   a. Cr b. Br c. Mo d. Cs

67. Classify each element as an alkali metal, alkaline earth metal, halogen, or noble gas.
MISSED THIS? *Read Section 2.7; Watch KCV 2.7*
a. sodium b. iodine
c. calcium d. barium
e. krypton

68. Classify each element as an alkali metal, alkaline earth metal, halogen, or noble gas.
a. F b. Sr c. K d. Ne e. At

69. Which pair of elements do you expect to be most similar? Why?
MISSED THIS? *Read Section 2.7; Watch KCV 2.7*
a. N and Ni b. Mo and Sn
c. Na and Mg d. Cl and F
e. Si and P

70. Which pair of elements do you expect to be most similar? Why?
a. nitrogen and oxygen
b. titanium and gallium
c. lithium and sodium
d. germanium and arsenic
e. argon and bromine

71. Gallium has two naturally occurring isotopes with the following masses and natural abundances:
MISSED THIS? *Read Section 2.8*

Isotope	Mass (amu)	Abundance (%)
Ga-69	68.92558	60.108
Ga-71	70.92470	39.892

Sketch the mass spectrum of gallium.

72. Magnesium has three naturally occurring isotopes with the following masses and natural abundances:

Isotope	Mass (amu)	Abundance (%)
Mg-24	23.9850	78.99
Mg-25	24.9858	10.00
Mg-26	25.9826	11.01

Sketch the mass spectrum of magnesium.

73. The atomic mass of fluorine is 18.998 amu, and its mass spectrum shows a large peak at this mass. The atomic mass of chlorine is 35.45 amu, yet the mass spectrum of chlorine does not show a peak at this mass. Explain the difference.
MISSED THIS? *Read Section 2.8*

74. The atomic mass of copper is 63.546 amu. Do any copper isotopes have a mass of 63.546 amu? Explain.

75. An element has two naturally occurring isotopes. Isotope 1 has a mass of 120.9038 amu and a relative abundance of 57.4%, and isotope 2 has a mass of 122.9042 amu. Find the atomic mass of this element and identify it.
MISSED THIS? *Read Section 2.8; Watch IWE 2.5*

76. An element has four naturally occurring isotopes with the masses and natural abundances given here. Find the atomic mass of the element and identify it.

Isotope	Mass (amu)	Abundance (%)
1	135.90714	0.19
2	137.90599	0.25
3	139.90543	88.43
4	141.90924	11.13

77. Bromine has two naturally occurring isotopes (Br-79 and Br-81) and has an atomic mass of 79.904 amu. The mass of Br-81 is 80.9163 amu, and its natural abundance is 49.31%. Calculate the mass and natural abundance of Br-79.
MISSED THIS? *Read Section 2.8; Watch IWE 2.5*

78. Silicon has three naturally occurring isotopes (Si-28, Si-29, and Si-30). The mass and natural abundance of Si-28 are 27.9769 amu and 92.2%, respectively. The mass and natural abundance of Si-29 are 28.9765 amu and 4.67%, respectively. Find the mass and natural abundance of Si-30.

79. Use the mass spectrum of europium to determine the atomic mass of europium.
MISSED THIS? *Read Section 2.8; Watch IWE 2.5*

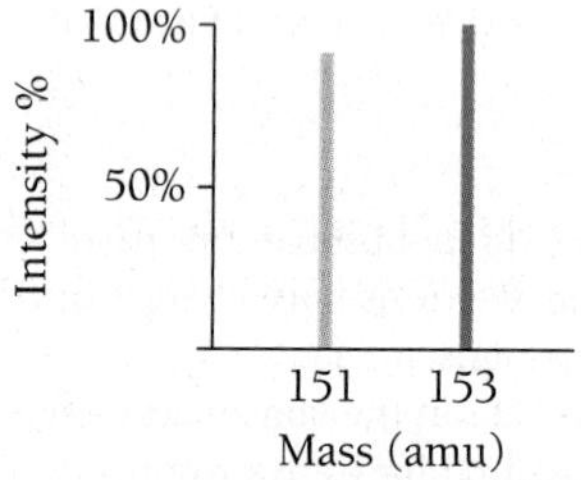

80. Use the mass spectrum of rubidium to determine the atomic mass of rubidium.

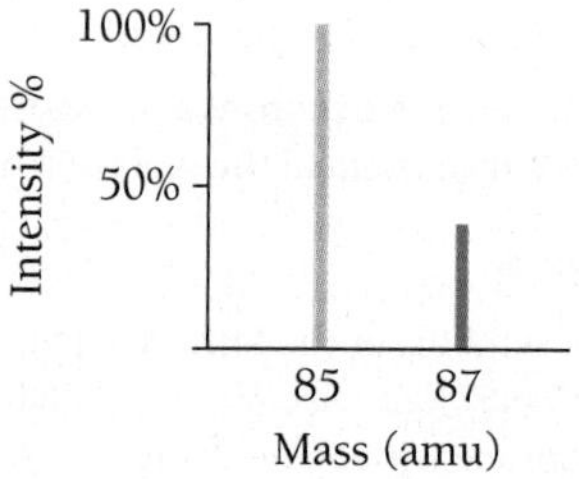

The Mole Concept

81. How many sulfur atoms are there in 5.52 mol of sulfur?
MISSED THIS? *Read Section 2.9; Watch KCV 2.9*

82. How many moles of aluminum do 3.7×10^{24} aluminum atoms represent?

83. What is the amount, in moles, of each elemental sample?
MISSED THIS? *Read Section 2.9; Watch KCV 2.9*
a. 11.8 g Ar b. 3.55 g Zn
c. 26.1 g Ta d. 0.211 g Li

84. What is the mass, in grams, of each elemental sample?
a. 2.3×10^{-3} mol Sb
b. 0.0355 mol Ba
c. 43.9 mol Xe
d. 1.3 mol W

85. How many silver atoms are there in 3.78 g of silver?
MISSED THIS? *Read Section 2.9; Watch KCV 2.9, IWE 2.8*

86. What is the mass of 4.91×10^{21} platinum atoms?

87. Calculate the number of atoms in each sample.
MISSED THIS? *Read Section 2.9; Watch KCV 2.9, IWE 2.8*
a. 5.18 g P b. 2.26 g Hg
c. 1.87 g Bi d. 0.082 g Sr

88. Calculate the number of atoms in each sample.
a. 14.955 g Cr b. 39.733 g S
c. 12.899 g Pt d. 97.552 g Sn

89. Calculate the mass, in grams, of each sample.
MISSED THIS? *Read Section 2.9; Watch KCV 2.9, IWE 2.8*
a. 1.1×10^{23} gold atoms
b. 2.82×10^{22} helium atoms
c. 1.8×10^{23} lead atoms
d. 7.9×10^{21} uranium atoms

90. Calculate the mass, in kg, of each sample.
a. 7.55×10^{26} cadmium atoms
b. 8.15×10^{27} nickel atoms
c. 1.22×10^{27} manganese atoms
d. 5.48×10^{29} lithium atoms

91. How many carbon atoms are there in a diamond (pure carbon) with a mass of 52 mg?
MISSED THIS? *Read Section 2.9; Watch KCV 2.9, IWE 2.8*

92. How many helium atoms are there in a helium blimp containing 536 kg of helium?

93. Calculate the average mass, in grams, of one platinum atom.
MISSED THIS? *Read Section 2.9; Watch KCV 2.9, IWE 2.8*

94. Scientists at the National Institute for Standards and Technology (NIST) wrote the initials of their agency with 70 individual cobalt atoms (as shown below). Calculate the total mass of these letters in grams.

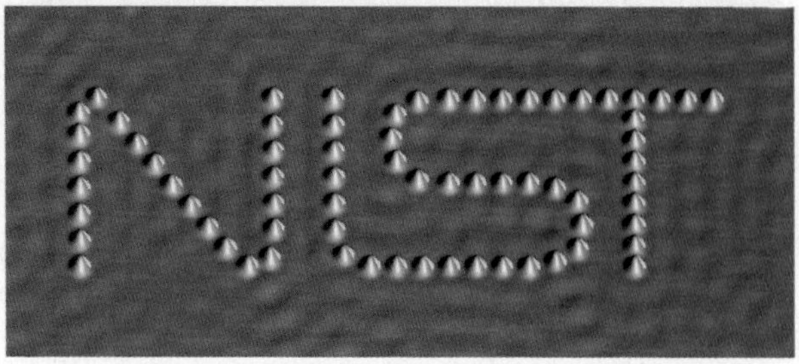

CUMULATIVE PROBLEMS

95. A 7.83 g sample of HCN contains 0.290 g of H and 4.06 g of N. Find the mass of carbon in a sample of HCN with a mass of 3.37 g.

96. The ratio of sulfur to oxygen by mass in SO_2 is 1.0:1.0.
a. Find the ratio of sulfur to oxygen by mass in SO_3.
b. Find the ratio of sulfur to oxygen by mass in S_2O.

97. The ratio of oxygen to carbon by mass in carbon monoxide is 1.33:1.00. Find the formula of an oxide of carbon in which the ratio by mass of oxygen to carbon is 2.00:1.00.

98. The ratio of the mass of a nitrogen atom to the mass of an atom of ^{12}C is 7:6, and the ratio of the mass of nitrogen to oxygen in N_2O is 7:4. Find the mass of 1 mol of oxygen atoms.

99. An α particle, $^4He^{2+}$, has a mass of 4.00151 amu. Find the value of its charge-to-mass ratio in C/kg.

100. Naturally occurring iodine has an atomic mass of 126.9045 amu. A 12.3849 g sample of iodine is accidentally contaminated with an additional 1.00070 g of ^{129}I, a synthetic radioisotope of iodine used in the treatment of certain diseases of the thyroid gland. The mass of ^{129}I is 128.9050 amu. Find the apparent "atomic mass" of the contaminated iodine.

101. Use the mass spectrum of lead to estimate the atomic mass of lead. Estimate the mass and percent intensity values from the graph to three significant figures.

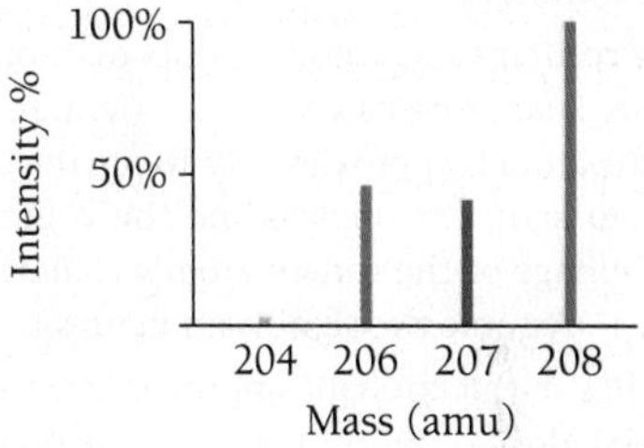

102. Use the mass spectrum of mercury to estimate the atomic mass of mercury. Estimate the masses and percent intensity values from the graph to three significant figures.

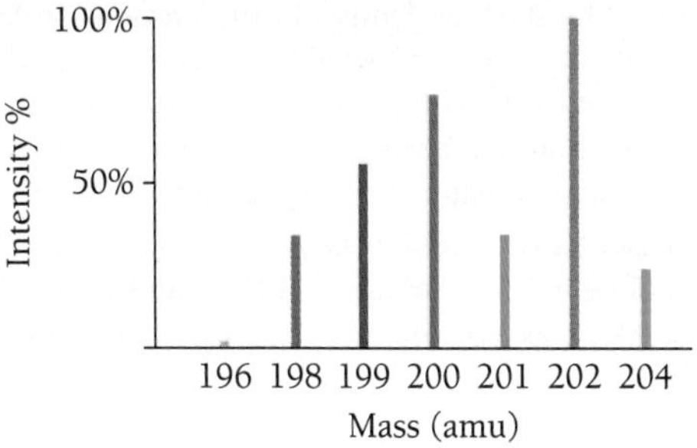

103. Nuclei with the same number of *neutrons* but different mass numbers are called *isotones*. Write the symbols of four isotones of ^{236}Th.

104. Fill in the blanks to complete the table.

Symbol	Z	A	Number of p	Number of e^-	Number of n	Charge
Si	14	____	____	14	14	____
S^{2-}	____	32	____	____	____	2−
Cu^{2+}	____	____	____	____	34	2+
____	15	____	____	15	16	____

105. Fill in the blanks to complete the table.

Symbol	Z	A	Number of p	Number of e^-	Number of n	Charge
____	8	____	____	____	8	2−
Ca^{2+}	20	____	____	____	20	____
Mg^{2+}	____	25	____	____	13	2+
N^{3-}	____	14	____	10	____	____

106. Neutron stars are composed of solid nuclear matter, primarily neutrons. Assume the radius of a neutron is approximately 1.0×10^{-13} cm. Calculate the density of a neutron. [*Hint*: For a sphere $V = (4/3)\pi r^3$.] Assuming that a neutron star has the same density as a neutron, calculate the mass (in kg) of a small piece of a neutron star the size of a spherical pebble with a radius of 0.10 mm.

107. Carbon-12 contains six protons and six neutrons. The radius of the nucleus is approximately 2.7 fm (femtometers), and the radius of the atom is approximately 70 pm (picometers). Calculate the volume of the nucleus and the volume of the atom. What percentage of the carbon atom's volume is occupied by the nucleus? (Assume two significant figures.)

108. A penny has a thickness of approximately 1.0 mm. If you stacked Avogadro's number of pennies one on top of the other on Earth's surface, how far would the stack extend (in km)? [For comparison, the sun is about 150 million km from Earth, and the nearest star (Proxima Centauri) is about 40 trillion km from Earth.]

109. Consider the stack of pennies in the previous problem. How much money (in dollars) would this represent? If this money were equally distributed among the world's population of 7.0 billion, how much would each person receive? Would each person be a millionaire? A billionaire? A trillionaire?

110. The mass of an average blueberry is 0.75 g, and the mass of an automobile is 2.0×10^3 kg. Find the number of automobiles whose total mass is the same as 1.0 mol of blueberries.

111. Suppose that atomic masses were based on the assignment of a mass of 12.000 g to 1 mol of carbon, rather than 1 mol of ^{12}C. What would the atomic mass of oxygen be? (The atomic masses of carbon and oxygen based on the assignment of 12.000 g to 1 mol of ^{12}C are 12.011 amu and 15.9994 amu, respectively.)

112. A pure titanium cube has an edge length of 2.78 in. How many titanium atoms does it contain? Titanium has a density of 4.50 g/cm^3.

113. A pure copper sphere has a radius of 0.935 in. How many copper atoms does it contain? [The volume of a sphere is $(4/3)\pi r^3$, and the density of copper is 8.96 g/cm^3.]

114. What is the radius (in cm) of a pure copper sphere that contains 1.14×10^{24} copper atoms? [The volume of a sphere is $(4/3)\pi r^3$, and the density of copper is 8.96 g/cm^3.]

115. What is the edge length (in cm) of a titanium cube that contains 2.55×10^{24} titanium atoms? The density of titanium is 4.50 g/cm^3.

116. Boron has only two naturally occurring isotopes. The mass of boron-10 is 10.01294 amu, and the mass of boron-11 is 11.00931 amu. Calculate the relative abundances of the two isotopes.

117. Lithium has only two naturally occurring isotopes. The mass of lithium-6 is 6.01512 amu, and the mass of lithium-7 is 7.01601 amu. Calculate the relative abundances of the two isotopes.

118. Common brass is a copper and zinc alloy containing 37.0% zinc by mass and having a density of 8.48 g/cm^3. A fitting composed of common brass has a total volume of 112.5 cm^3. How many atoms (copper and zinc) does the fitting contain?

119. A 67.2 g sample of a gold and palladium alloy contains 2.49×10^{23} atoms. What is the composition (by mass) of the alloy?

120. Naturally occurring chlorine is composed of two isotopes: 75.76% Cl-35 (mass 34.9688 amu) and 24.24% Cl-37 (mass 36.9659 amu). Naturally occurring oxygen is composed of three isotopes: 99.757% O-16 (mass 15.9949 amu), 0.038% O-17 (mass 16.9991 amu), and 0.205% O-18 (mass 17.9991 amu). The compound dichlorine monoxide is composed of two chlorine atoms and one oxygen atom bonded together to form the Cl_2O molecule. How many Cl_2O molecules of different masses naturally exist? Give the masses of the three most abundant Cl_2O molecules.

121. Silver is composed of two naturally occurring isotopes: Ag-107 (51.839%) and Ag-109. The ratio of the masses of the two isotopes is 1.0187. What is the mass of Ag-107?

122. The U.S. Environmental Protection Agency (EPA) sets limits on healthful levels of air pollutants. The maximum level that the EPA considers safe for lead air pollution is 1.5 μg/m^3. If your lungs were filled with air containing this level of lead, how many lead atoms would be in your lungs? (Assume a total lung volume of 5.50 L.)

123. Pure gold is usually too soft for jewelry, so it is often alloyed with other metals. How many gold atoms are in an 0.255-ounce, 18 K gold bracelet? (18 K gold is 75% gold by mass.)

CHALLENGE PROBLEMS

124. In Section 2.9, it was stated that 1 mol of sand grains would cover the state of Texas to several feet. Estimate how many feet by assuming that the sand grains are roughly cube-shaped, each one with an edge length of 0.10 mm. Texas has a land area of 268,601 square miles.

125. Use the concepts in this chapter to obtain an estimate for the number of atoms in the universe. Make the following assumptions: **(a)** All of the atoms in the universe are hydrogen atoms in stars. (This is not a ridiculous assumption because over three-fourths of the atoms in the universe are in fact hydrogen.

Gas and dust between the stars represent only about 15% of the visible matter of our galaxy, and planets compose a far tinier fraction.) **(b)** The sun is a typical star composed of pure hydrogen with a density of 1.4 g/cm^3 and a radius of 7×10^8 m. **(c)** Each of the roughly 100 billion stars in the Milky Way galaxy contains the same number of atoms as our sun. **(d)** Each of the 10 billion galaxies in the visible universe contains the same number of atoms as our Milky Way galaxy.

126. Below is a representation of 50 atoms of a fictitious element called pearsonium (Ps). The red spheres represent Ps-296, the blue spheres Ps-297, and the green spheres Ps-298.

a. Assuming that the sample is statistically representative of a naturally occurring sample, calculate the percent natural abundance of each Ps isotope.

b. Draw the mass spectrum for a naturally occurring sample of Ps.

c. The mass of each Ps isotope is measured relative to C-12 and tabulated. Use the mass of C-12 to convert each of the masses to amu and calculate the atomic mass of Ps.

Isotope	Mass
Ps-296	$24.6630 \times \text{Mass}(^{12}\text{C})$
Ps-297	$24.7490 \times \text{Mass}(^{12}\text{C})$
Ps-298	$24.8312 \times \text{Mass}(^{12}\text{C})$

127. The ratio of oxygen to nitrogen by mass in NO_2 is 2.29. The ratio of fluorine to nitrogen by mass in NF_3 is 4.07. Find the ratio of oxygen to fluorine by mass in OF_2.

128. Naturally occurring cobalt consists of only one isotope, ^{59}Co, whose relative atomic mass is 58.9332. A synthetic radioactive isotope of cobalt, ^{60}Co, has a relative atomic mass of 59.9338 and is used in radiation therapy for cancer. A 1.5886 g sample of cobalt has an apparent "atomic mass" of 58.9901. Find the mass of ^{60}Co in this sample.

129. A 7.36 g sample of copper is contaminated with an additional 0.51 g of zinc. Suppose an atomic mass measurement was performed on this sample. What would be the measured atomic mass?

130. The ratio of the mass of O to the mass of N in N_2O_3 is 12:7. Another binary compound of nitrogen has a ratio of O to N of 16:7. What is its formula? What is the ratio of O to N in the next member of this series of compounds?

131. Naturally occurring magnesium has an atomic mass of 24.312 and consists of three isotopes. The major isotope is ^{24}Mg, natural abundance 78.99%, relative atomic mass 23.98504. The next most abundant isotope is ^{26}Mg, relative atomic mass 25.98259. The third most abundant isotope is ^{25}Mg, whose natural abundance is in the ratio of 0.9083 to that of ^{26}Mg. Find the relative atomic mass of ^{25}Mg.

CONCEPTUAL PROBLEMS

132. Which answer is an example of the law of multiple proportions? Explain.

a. Two different samples of water are found to have the same ratio of hydrogen to oxygen.

b. When hydrogen and oxygen react, the mass of water formed is exactly equal to the mass of hydrogen and oxygen that reacted.

c. The mass ratio of oxygen to hydrogen in water is 8:1. The mass ratio of oxygen to hydrogen in hydrogen peroxide (a compound that only contains hydrogen and oxygen) is 16:1.

133. Lithium has two naturally occurring isotopes: Li-6 (natural abundance 7.5%) and Li-7 (natural abundance 92.5%). Using circles to represent protons and squares to represent neutrons, draw the nucleus of each isotope. How many Li-6 atoms are present, on average, in a 1000-atom sample of lithium?

134. As we saw in the previous problem, lithium has two naturally occurring isotopes: Li-6 (natural abundance 7.5%; mass 6.0151 amu) and Li-7 (natural abundance 92.5%; mass 7.0160 amu). Without doing any calculations, determine which mass is closest to the atomic mass of Li.

a. 6.00 amu b. 6.50 amu c. 7.00 amu

135. The mole is defined as the amount of a substance containing the same number of particles as exactly 12 g of C-12. The amu is defined as 1/12 of the mass of an atom of C-12. Why is it important that both of these definitions reference the same isotope? What would be the result, for example, of defining the mole with respect to C-12, but the amu with respect to Ne-20?

136. Without doing any calculations, determine which of the samples contains the greatest amount of the element in moles. Which contains the greatest mass of the element?

a. 55.0 g Cr b. 45.0 g Ti c. 60.0 g Zn

137. The atomic radii of the isotopes of an element are identical to one another. However, the atomic radii of the ions of an element are significantly different from the atomic radii of the neutral atom of the element. Explain.

QUESTIONS FOR GROUP WORK

Active Classroom Learning

Discuss these questions with the group and record your consensus answer.

138. The table shown here includes data similar to those used by Mendeleev when he created the periodic table. On a small card, write the symbol, atomic mass, and a stable compound formed by each element. Without consulting a periodic table, arrange the cards so that atomic mass increases from left to right and elements with similar properties are above and below each other. Copy the periodic table you have invented onto a piece of paper. There is one element missing. Predict its mass and a stable compound it might form.

Element	Atomic Mass	Stable Compound
Be	9	$BeCl_2$
S	32	H_2S
F	19	F_2
Ca	40	$CaCl_2$
Li	7	LiCl
Si	28	SiH_4
Cl	35.4	Cl_2
B	10.8	BH_3
Ge	72.6	GeH_4
N	14	NF_3
O	16	H_2O
Ga	69.7	GaH_3
As	75	AsF_3
C	12	CH_4
K	39	KCl
Mg	24.3	$MgCl_2$
Se	79	H_2Se
Al	27	AlH_3
Br	80	Br_2
Na	23	NaCl

139. In a naturally occurring sample, 19.8% of boron atoms have five neutrons and 80.2% have six neutrons. What is the mass number of each boron isotope? Sketch a sample of 10 atoms that is nearly representative of a natural sample. What is the average mass of the atoms in your drawing? What is the atomic mass of boron? (Boron-10 has a mass of 10.01294 amu, and boron-11 has a mass of 11.00931 amu.)

140. In complete sentences, describe the similarities and differences between:

a. different isotopes of an element

b. a neutral atom and an ion of the same element

141. Calculate the mass in grams of one mole of each of the following (the mass of a single item is given in parentheses): electrons (9.10938×10^{-28} g), protons (1.67262×10^{-24} g), neutrons (1.67493×10^{-24} g), atoms of carbon-12 (1.992646×10^{-23} g), and doughnuts (74 g). Compare the mass of one mole of carbon-12 atoms to the sum of the masses of the particles that it contains. If the doughnut mentioned in this question were made entirely of carbon, how many atoms would it contain?

DATA INTERPRETATION AND ANALYSIS

Lead Air Quality

142. The U.S. Environmental Protection Agency (U.S. EPA) monitors air quality in the United States. Lead is among the pollutants regularly monitored and regulated. Lead is released into the atmosphere primarily by the processing of metal ores containing lead and by lead-based battery manufacturing. The effects of too much exposure to lead include neurological damage and cardiovascular disease. Because of the Clear Air Act and its amendments, the amounts of lead in air have been decreasing for many years. The chart below shows the lead concentration in air in the United States from 2000 to 2016. Examine the data and answer the questions that follow.

Lead Air Quality

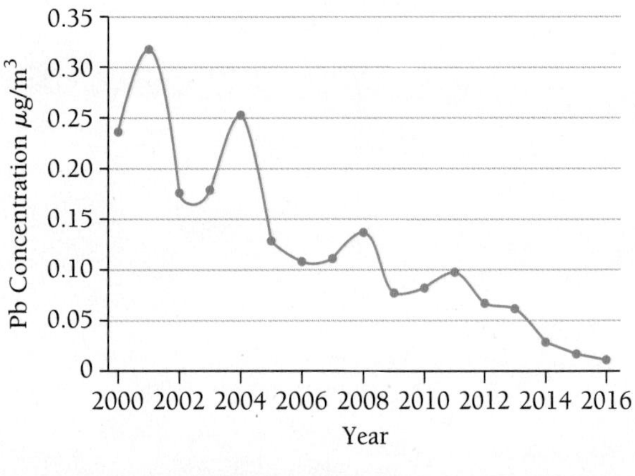

Source: U.S. EPA Air Trends (http://www3.epa.gov/airtrends/lead.html)

a. Determine the lead concentrations in 2000 and in 2016.

b. Calculate the percent change in lead concentration that occurred from 2000 to 2016. *Hint:* Calculate the percent change with the following equation:

$$\text{percent change} = \frac{(\text{final concentration} - \text{initial concentration})}{\text{initial concentration}} \times 100\%$$

c. How many lead atoms were in one cubic centimeter of air in 2011?

d. Examine the mass spectrum for lead shown below. How many Pb-206 atoms were in one cubic centimeter of air in 2011?

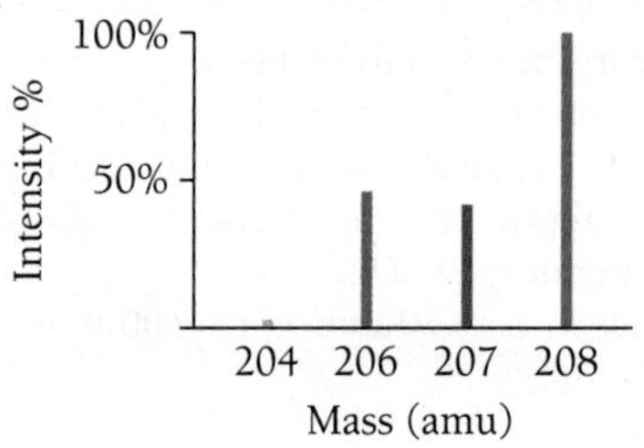

Cc ANSWERS TO CONCEPTUAL CONNECTIONS

The Law of Conservation of Mass

2.1 **(a)** Most of the matter that composed the log undergoes a chemical change by reacting with oxygen molecules in the air. The products of the reaction (mostly carbon dioxide and water) are released as gases into the air.

Law of Definite Proportions

2.2 **(d)** If the sample contains 10 g H, then it must contain 47 g N for a nitrogen-to-hydrogen ratio of 4.7:1.

The Laws of Definite and Multiple Proportions

2.3 **(a)** The law of definite proportions applies to two or more samples of the *same compound* and states that the ratio of one element to the other is always the same. The law of multiple proportions applies to two *different compounds* containing the same two elements (A and B) and states that the masses of B that combine with 1 g of A are always related to each other as a small whole-number ratio.

The Millikan Oil Drop Experiment

2.4 **(c)** The drop contains three excess electrons ($3 \times (-1.6 \times 10^{-19}\text{ C}) = -4.8 \times 10^{-19}\text{ C}$).

Atomic Number

2.5 **(a)** Tin (Sn) has atomic number 50 and therefore contains 50 protons in its nucleus.

Mass Number and Atomic Number

2.6 **(c)** The number of neutrons is equal to the mass number minus the atomic number. Since the atomic number of argon is 18, the number of neutrons is $40 - 18 = 22$.

Isotopes

2.7 **(a)** Carbon-13 has 6 protons ($Z = 6$) and 7 neutrons. The image must therefore contain 6 circles and 7 squares.

Ions

2.8 **(c)** Since the atomic number of oxygen is 8, it contains 8 protons. In order for the anion to have an overall charge of 2–, it must contain 10 electrons.

The Nuclear Atom, Isotopes, and Ions

2.9 **(b)** The number of neutrons in the nucleus of an atom does not affect the atom's size because the nucleus is miniscule compared to the atom itself.

The Periodic Table

2.10 **(d)** Lead is both a main-group element and a metal.

Atomic Mass

2.11 **(a)** Since 98.93% of the atoms are C-12, we would expect the atomic mass to be very close to the mass of the C-12 isotope.

The Mole

2.12 **(b)** The carbon sample contains more atoms than the copper sample because carbon has a lower molar mass than copper. Carbon atoms are lighter than copper atoms, so a 1-g sample of carbon contains more atoms than a 1-g sample of copper. The carbon sample also contains more atoms than the uranium sample because even though the uranium sample has 10 times the mass of the carbon sample, a uranium atom is more than 10 times as massive (238 g/mol for uranium versus 12 g/mol for carbon).

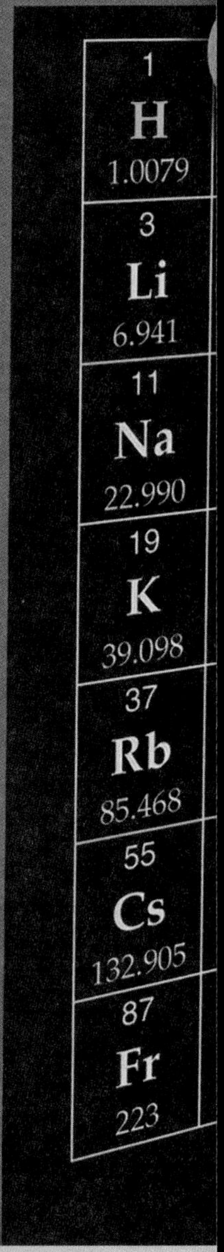

Almost all aspects of life are engineered at the molecular level, and without understanding molecules we can only have a very sketchy understanding of life itself.

—FRANCIS HARRY COMPTON CRICK (1916–2004)

CHAPTER 3 Molecules and Compounds

How many different substances exist? Recall from Chapter 2 that about 91 different elements exist in nature, so there are at least 91 different substances. However, the world would be dull—not to mention lifeless—with only 91 different substances. Fortunately, elements combine with each other to form *compounds.* Just as combinations of only 26 letters in our English alphabet allow for an almost limitless number of words, each with its own specific meaning, combinations of the 91 naturally occurring elements allow for an almost limitless number of compounds, each with its own specific properties. The great diversity of substances that we find in nature is a direct result of the ability of elements to form compounds. Life, for example, could not exist with just 91 different elements. It takes compounds, in all of their diversity, to make life possible.

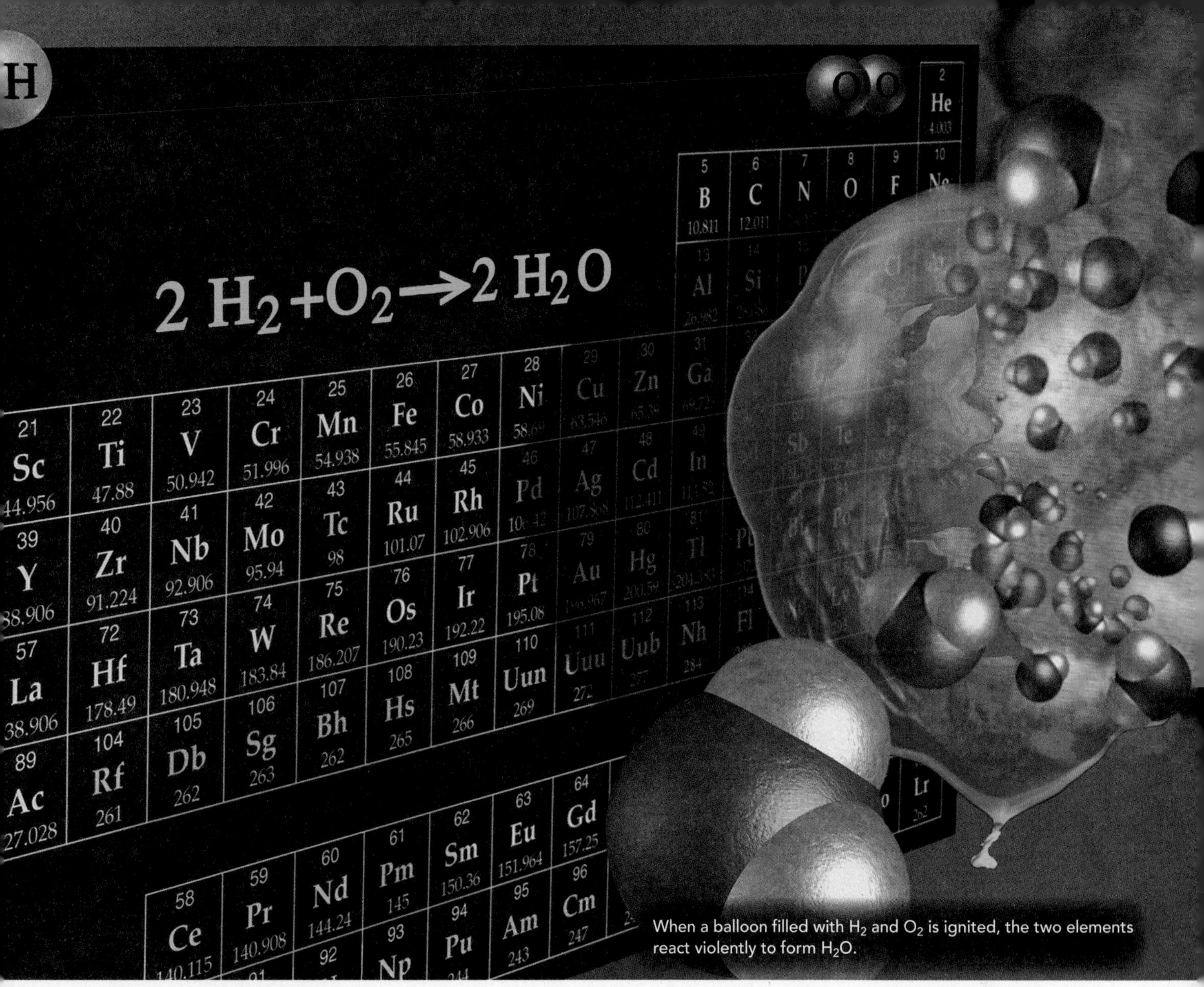

When a balloon filled with H_2 and O_2 is ignited, the two elements react violently to form H_2O.

3.1 Hydrogen, Oxygen, and Water 91
3.2 Chemical Bonds 93
3.3 Representing Compounds: Chemical Formulas and Molecular Models 94
3.4 An Atomic-Level View of Elements and Compounds 96
3.5 Ionic Compounds: Formulas and Names 100
3.6 Molecular Compounds: Formulas and Names 106
3.7 Summary of Inorganic Nomenclature 109
3.8 Formula Mass and the Mole Concept for Compounds 111
3.9 Composition of Compounds 113
3.10 Determining a Chemical Formula from Experimental Data 118
3.11 Organic Compounds 123
LEARNING OUTCOMES 129

3.1 Hydrogen, Oxygen, and Water

Hydrogen (H_2) is an explosive gas used as a fuel in rocket engines. Oxygen (O_2), also a gas, is a natural component of the air on Earth. Oxygen itself is not flammable but must be present for combustion (burning) to occur. Hydrogen and oxygen both have extremely low boiling points, as you can see from the table that follows.

Selected Properties	Hydrogen	Oxygen	Water
Boiling Point	−253 °C	−183 °C	100 °C
State at Room Temperature	Gas	Gas	Liquid
Flammability	Explosive	Necessary for combustion	Used to extinguish flame

When hydrogen and oxygen combine to form the compound water (H_2O), however, a dramatically different substance results. First of all, water is a liquid rather than a gas at room temperature, and its boiling point is hundreds of degrees higher than the boiling points of hydrogen and oxygen. Second, instead of being flammable (like hydrogen gas) or supporting combustion (like oxygen gas), water actually smothers flames. Water is nothing like the hydrogen and oxygen from which it forms. The dramatic difference between the elements hydrogen and oxygen and the compound water is typical of the differences between elements and the compounds that they form. *When two or more elements combine to form a compound, an entirely new substance results.*

Consider as another example common table salt, a highly stable compound composed of sodium and chlorine. Elemental sodium, by contrast, is a highly reactive, silvery metal that can explode on contact with water. Elemental chlorine is a corrosive, greenish-yellow gas that can be fatal if inhaled. Yet the compound formed from the combination of these two elements is sodium chloride (or table salt), a flavor enhancer that tastes great on steak.

Although some of the substances that we encounter in everyday life are elements, most are compounds. As we discussed in Chapter 1, a compound is different from a mixture of elements. In a compound, elements combine in fixed, definite proportions; in a mixture, elements can mix in any proportions whatsoever. Consider the difference between a hydrogen–oxygen mixture and water in Figure 3.1▼. A hydrogen–oxygen mixture can have any proportions of hydrogen and oxygen gas. Water, by contrast, is composed of water molecules that always contain two hydrogen atoms to every one oxygen atom. Water has a definite proportion of hydrogen to oxygen.

In this chapter, you will learn about compounds: how to represent them, how to name them, how to distinguish between their different types, and how to write chemical equations showing how they form and change. You will also learn how to quantify

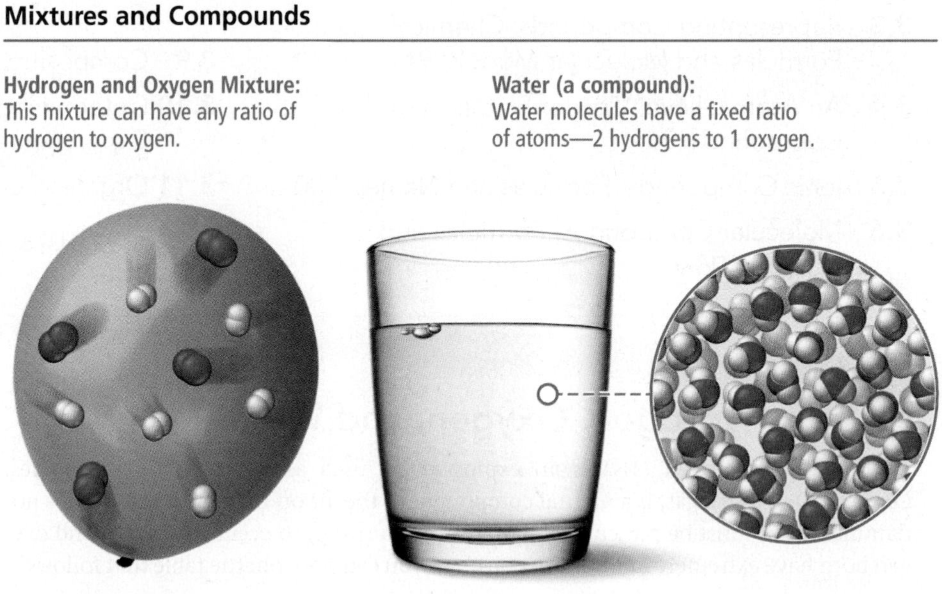

▶ **FIGURE 3.1 Mixtures and Compounds**

the elemental composition of a compound. This is important in determining how much of a particular element is contained within a particular compound. For example, patients with high blood pressure (hypertension) often have to reduce their sodium ion intake. The sodium ion is normally consumed in the form of sodium chloride, so a hypertension patient needs to know how much sodium is present in a given amount of sodium chloride. Similarly, an iron-mining company needs to know how much iron it can recover from a given amount of iron ore. This chapter provides the tools to understand and answer these kinds of questions.

3.2 Chemical Bonds

Compounds are composed of atoms held together by *chemical bonds*. Chemical bonds form because of the attractions between the charged particles (the electrons and protons) that compose atoms. We discuss these interactions in more detail in Chapter 10 (see Section 10.2). For now, remember that, as we discussed in Section 2.4, charged particles exert electrostatic forces on one another: like charges repel and opposite charges attract. These forces are responsible for chemical bonding.

We can broadly classify most chemical bonds into two types: ionic and covalent. *Ionic bonds*—which occur between metals and nonmetals—involve the *transfer* of electrons from one atom to another. *Covalent bonds*—which occur between two or more nonmetals—involve the *sharing* of electrons between two atoms.

Ionic Bonds

Recall from Chapter 2 that metals have a tendency to lose electrons and that nonmetals have a tendency to gain them. Therefore, when a metal interacts with a nonmetal, it can transfer one or more of its electrons to the nonmetal. The metal atom then becomes a *cation* (a positively charged ion), and the nonmetal atom becomes an *anion* (a negatively charged ion), as shown in Figure 3.2▼. These oppositely charged ions attract one another by electrostatic forces and form an **ionic bond**. The result is an **ionic compound**, which in the solid phase is composed of a lattice—a regular three-dimensional array—of alternating cations and anions.

▼ **FIGURE 3.2** The Formation of an Ionic Compound

The Formation of an Ionic Compound

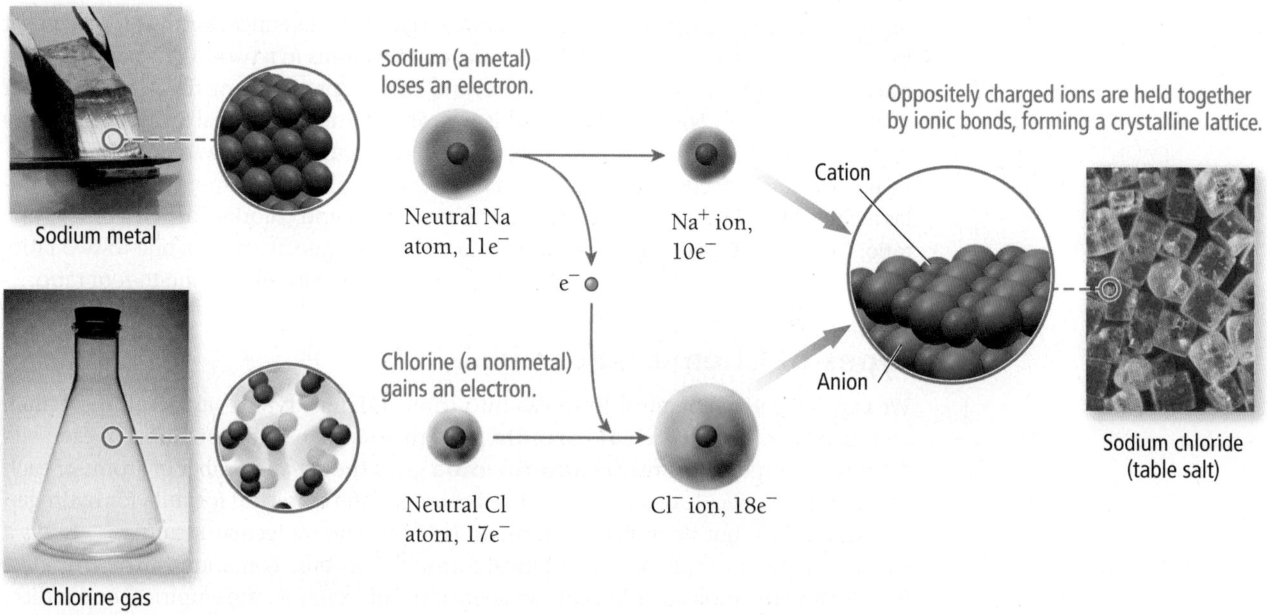

Covalent Bonds

When a nonmetal bonds with another nonmetal, neither atom transfers its electron to the other. Instead the bonding atoms *share* some of their electrons. The shared electrons have lower potential energy than they do in the isolated atoms because they interact with the nuclei of both atoms. The bond is a **covalent bond**, and the covalently bound atoms compose a *molecule*. Each molecule is independent of the others—the molecules are themselves not covalently bound to one another. Therefore, we call covalently bonded compounds **molecular compounds**.

We can begin to understand the stability of a covalent bond by considering the most stable (or lowest potential energy) configuration of a negative charge interacting with two positive charges (which are separated by some small distance). Figure 3.3▼ shows that the lowest potential energy occurs when the negative charge lies *between* the two positive charges because in this arrangement the negative charge can interact with *both positive charges*. Similarly, shared electrons in a covalent chemical bond hold the bonding atoms together by attracting the positively charged nuclei of both bonding atoms.

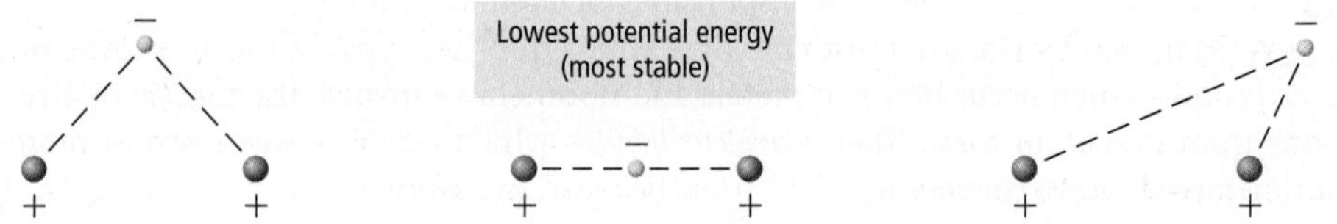

▶ **FIGURE 3.3 The Stability of a Covalent Bond** The potential energy of a negative charge interacting with two positive charges is lowest when the negative charge is between the two positive charges.

ANSWER **NOW!**

3.1 Cc Conceptual Connection

TYPES OF CHEMICAL BONDS What type of bond—ionic or covalent—forms between nitrogen and oxygen?

(a) Ionic
(b) Covalent

3.3 Representing Compounds: Chemical Formulas and Molecular Models

The quickest and easiest way to represent a compound is with its **chemical formula**, which indicates the elements present in the compound and the relative number of atoms or ions of each element. For example, H_2O is the chemical formula for water—it indicates that water consists of hydrogen and oxygen atoms in a two-to-one ratio. The formula contains the symbol for each element and a subscript indicating the relative number of atoms of the element. A subscript of 1 is typically omitted. Chemical formulas generally list the more metallic (or more positively charged) elements first, followed by the less metallic (or more negatively charged) elements. Other examples of common chemical formulas include NaCl for sodium chloride, indicating sodium and chloride ions in a one-to-one ratio; CO_2 for carbon dioxide, indicating carbon and oxygen atoms in a one-to-two ratio; and CCl_4 for carbon tetrachloride, indicating carbon and chlorine in a one-to-four ratio.

Types of Chemical Formulas

We can categorize chemical formulas into three different types: empirical, molecular, and structural. An **empirical formula** gives the *relative* number of atoms of each element in a compound. A **molecular formula** gives the *actual* number of atoms of each element in a molecule of a compound. For example, the empirical formula for hydrogen peroxide is HO, but its molecular formula is H_2O_2. The molecular formula is always a whole-number multiple of the empirical formula. For some compounds, the empirical formula and the molecular formula are identical. For example, the empirical and molecular formula for water is H_2O because water molecules contain two hydrogen atoms and one oxygen atom, and no simpler whole-number ratio can express the relative number of hydrogen atoms to oxygen atoms.

A **structural formula** uses lines to represent covalent bonds and shows how atoms in a molecule connect or bond to each other. The structural formula for H_2O_2 is:

$$\text{H—O—O—H}$$

We can also write structural formulas to convey a sense of the molecule's geometry. For example, we can write the structural formula for hydrogen peroxide as:

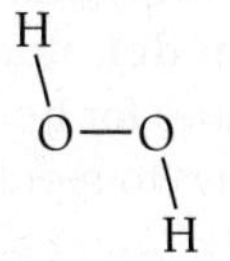

This version of the formula represents the approximate angles between bonds, giving a sense of the molecule's shape.

Structural formulas can also depict the different types of bonds that occur within molecules. For example, consider the structural formula for carbon dioxide:

$$\text{O=C=O}$$

The two lines between each carbon and oxygen atom represent a double bond, which is generally stronger and shorter than a single bond (represented by a single line). A single bond corresponds to one shared electron pair, while a double bond corresponds to two shared electron pairs. We will learn more about single, double, and even triple bonds in Chapter 10.

The type of formula we use depends on how much we know about the compound and how much we want to communicate. A structural formula communicates the most information, while an empirical formula communicates the least.

STRUCTURAL FORMULAS Select the structural formula for water.

3.2 Cc Conceptual Connection — ANSWER **NOW!**

(a) H—O **(b)** H—H

(c) H—O—H **(d)** H_2O

EXAMPLE 3.1 Molecular and Empirical Formulas

Write empirical formulas for the compounds represented by the molecular formulas.

(a) C_4H_8 **(b)** B_2H_6 **(c)** CCl_4

SOLUTION

To determine the empirical formula from a molecular formula, divide the subscripts by the greatest common factor (the largest number that divides exactly into all of the subscripts).

(a) For C_4H_8, the greatest common factor is 4. The empirical formula is therefore CH_2.

(b) For B_2H_6, the greatest common factor is 2. The empirical formula is therefore BH_3.

(c) For CCl_4, the only common factor is 1, so the empirical formula and the molecular formula are identical.

FOR PRACTICE 3.1 Write the empirical formula for the compounds represented by each molecular formula.

(a) C_5H_{12} **(b)** Hg_2Cl_2 **(c)** $C_2H_4O_2$

Answers to For Practice and For More Practice problems can be found in Appendix IV.

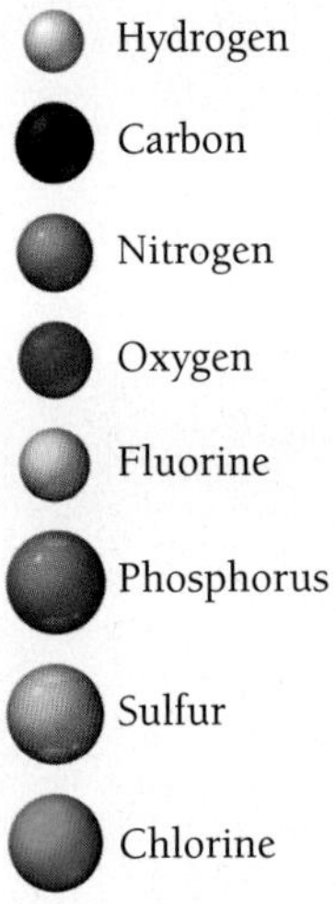

Molecular Models

A *molecular model* is a more accurate and complete way to specify a compound. A **ball-and-stick molecular model** represents atoms as balls and chemical bonds as sticks; how the two connect reflects a molecule's shape. The balls are typically color-coded to specific elements. For example, carbon is customarily black, hydrogen is white, nitrogen is blue, and oxygen is red. (For a complete list of colors of elements in the molecular models used in this book, see Appendix IIA.)

In a **space-filling molecular model**, atoms fill the space between each other to more closely represent our best estimates for how a molecule might appear if scaled to visible size. Consider the following ways to represent a molecule of methane, the main component of natural gas:

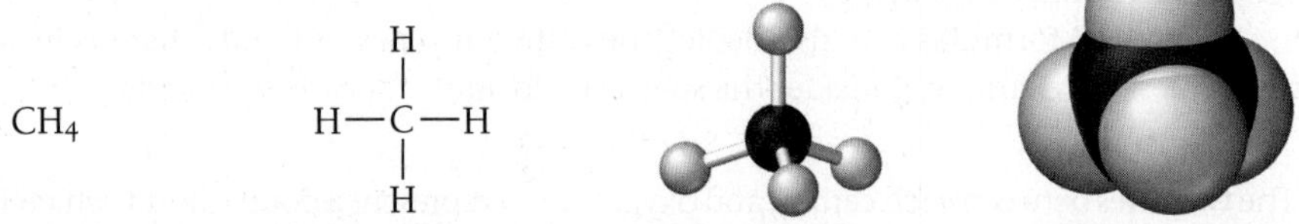

Molecular formula | Structural formula | Ball-and-stick model | Space-filling model

The molecular formula of methane indicates the number and type of each atom in the molecule: one carbon atom and four hydrogen atoms. The structural formula indicates how the atoms connect: the carbon atom bonds to the four hydrogen atoms. The ball-and-stick model clearly portrays the geometry of the molecule: the carbon atom sits in the center of a *tetrahedron* formed by the four hydrogen atoms. And finally, the space-filling model gives the best sense of the relative sizes of the atoms and how they merge together in bonding.

Throughout this book, you will see molecules represented in all of these ways. As you look at these representations, keep in mind what you learned in Chapter 1: that the details about a molecule—the atoms that compose it, the lengths of the bonds between atoms, the angles of the bonds between atoms, and its overall shape—determine the properties of the substance that the molecule composes. Change any of these details and those properties change. Table 3.1 shows various compounds represented in the different ways we have just discussed.

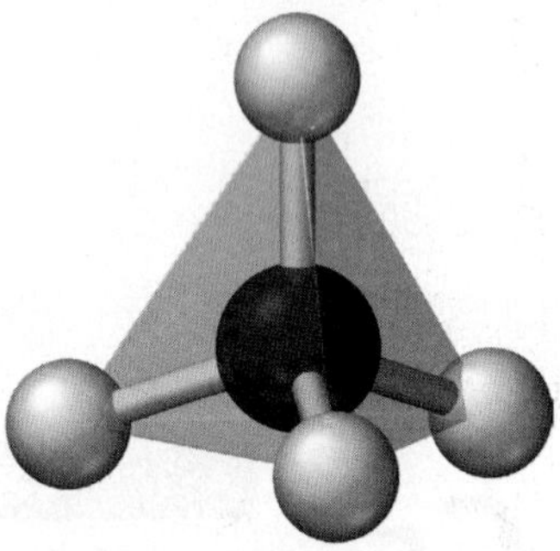

▲ A tetrahedron is a three-dimensional geometrical shape characterized by four equivalent triangular faces.

ANSWER **NOW!**

3.3 Cc Conceptual Connection

REPRESENTING MOLECULES Based on what you learned in Chapter 2 about atoms, what part of the atom do you think the spheres in the molecular space-filling models shown in Table 3.1 represent? If you were to superimpose a nucleus on one of these spheres, how big would you draw it?

(a) Each sphere represents the hard outer shell of an atom. The nucleus would be too small to see on the same scale.
(b) Each sphere represents the electron cloud of the atom. The nucleus would be too small to see on the same scale.
(c) Each sphere represents the nucleus of an atom. The nucleus is the same size as the sphere.

3.4 An Atomic-Level View of Elements and Compounds

Recall from Chapter 1 that we categorize pure substances as either elements or compounds. We can subcategorize elements and compounds according to the basic units that compose them, as shown in Figure 3.4▶. Elements may be either atomic or molecular. Compounds may be either molecular or ionic.

Atomic elements exist in nature with single atoms as their basic units. Most elements fall into this category. For example, helium is composed of helium atoms, aluminum is composed of aluminum atoms, and iron is composed of iron atoms. **Molecular elements** do not normally exist in nature with single atoms as their basic units.

TABLE 3.1 ■ Benzene, Acetylene, Glucose, and Ammonia

Name of Compound	Empirical Formula	Molecular Formula	Structural Formula	Ball-and-Stick Model	Space-Filling Model
Benzene	CH	C_6H_6	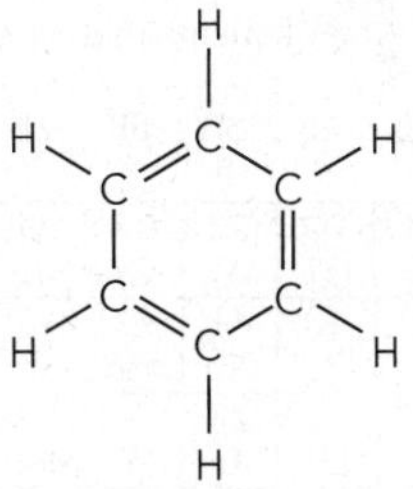	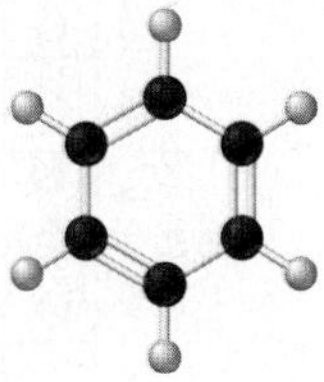	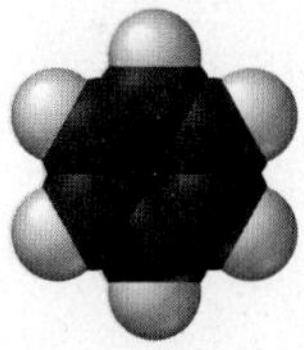
Acetylene	CH	C_2H_2	H—C≡C—H		
Glucose	CH_2O	$C_6H_{12}O_6$	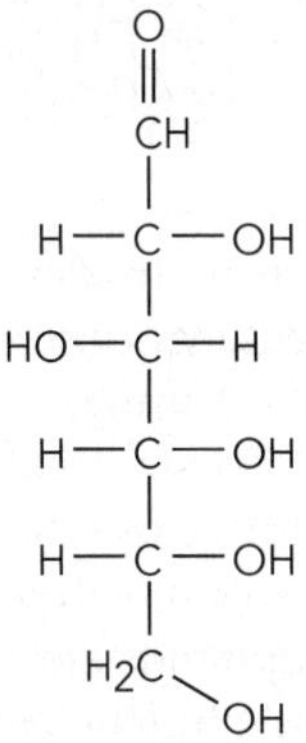	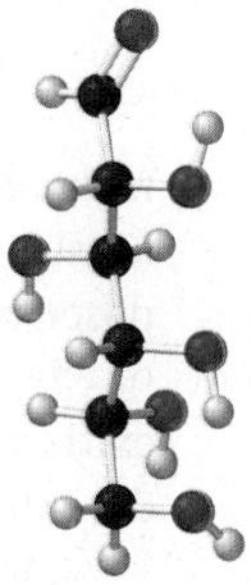	
Ammonia	NH_3	NH_3	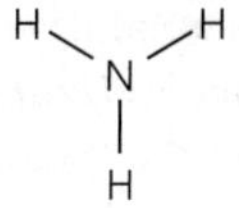		

Classification of Elements and Compounds

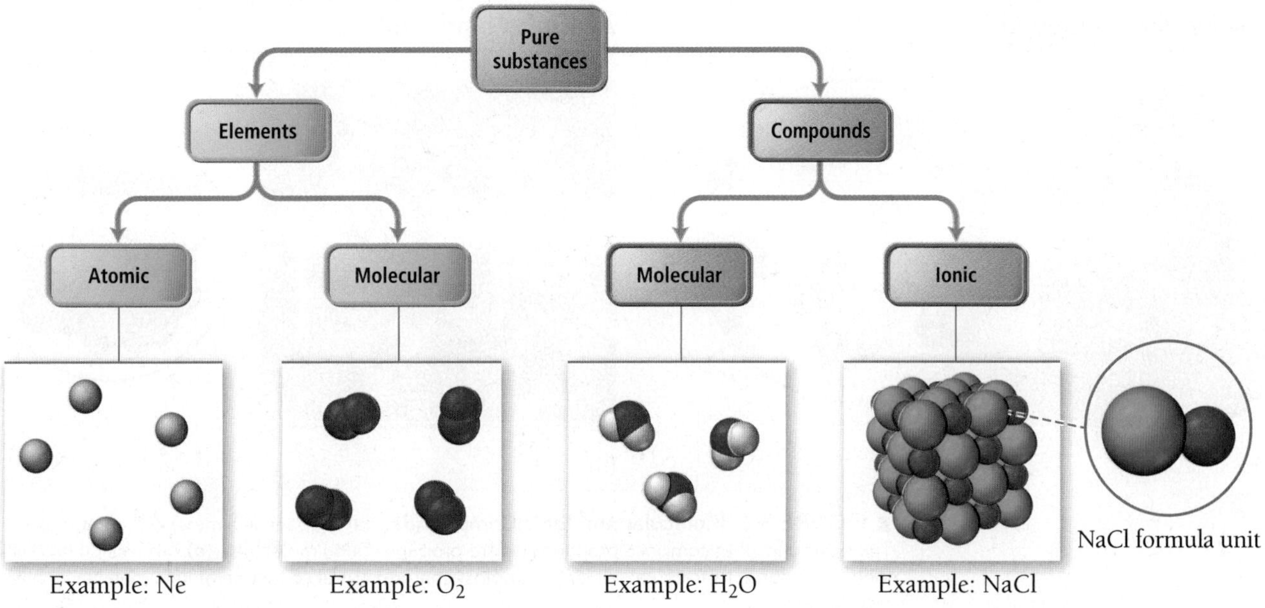

▲ **FIGURE 3.4 A Molecular View of Elements and Compounds**

Molecular Elements

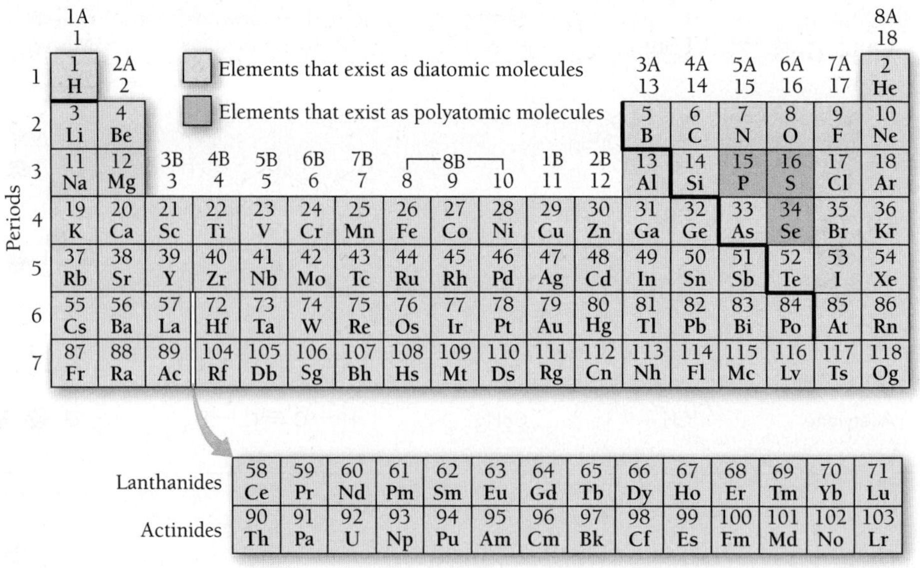

▶ **FIGURE 3.5 Molecular Elements** The highlighted elements exist primarily as diatomic molecules (yellow) or polyatomic molecules (light orange).

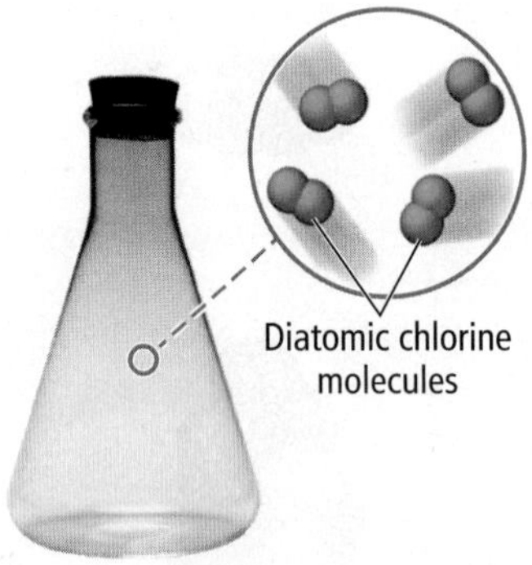

▲ The basic units that compose chlorine gas are diatomic molecules (Cl_2).

Instead, they exist as molecules—two or more atoms of the element bonded together. Most molecular elements exist as *diatomic* molecules. For example, hydrogen is composed of H_2 molecules, nitrogen is composed of N_2 molecules, and chlorine is composed of Cl_2 molecules. A few molecular elements exist as *polyatomic molecules*. Phosphorus exists as P_4, and sulfur exists as S_8. Figure 3.5▲ shows the elements that exist primarily as diatomic or polyatomic molecules.

Molecular compounds are usually composed of two or more covalently bonded nonmetals. The basic units of molecular compounds are molecules composed of the constituent atoms. For example, water is composed of H_2O molecules, dry ice is composed of CO_2 molecules, and propane (often used as a fuel for grills) is composed of C_3H_8 molecules as illustrated in Figure 3.6(a)▼.

Ionic compounds are usually composed of a metal ionically bonded to one or more nonmetals. The basic unit of an ionic compound is the **formula unit**, the smallest, electrically neutral collection of ions. A formula unit is not a molecule—it does not usually exist as a discrete entity but rather as part of a larger lattice. For example, the ionic

Some ionic compounds, such as K_2NaPO_4, contain more than one type of metal ion.

People occasionally refer to formula units as molecules. This is incorrect because ionic compounds do not contain distinct molecules.

A Molecular Compound

(a)

An Ionic Compound

(b)

▲ **FIGURE 3.6 Molecular and Ionic Compounds** **(a)** Propane is a molecular compound. The basic units that compose propane gas are propane (C_3H_8) molecules. **(b)** Table salt (NaCl) is an ionic compound. Its formula unit is the simplest charge-neutral collection of ions: one Na^+ ion and one Cl^- ion.

compound table salt, with the formula unit NaCl, is composed of Na^+ and Cl^- ions in a one-to-one ratio. In table salt, Na^+ and Cl^- ions exist in a three-dimensional alternating array. Because ionic bonds are not directional, no one Na^+ ion pairs with a specific Cl^- ion. Rather, as illustrated in Figure 3.6(b)◀, any one Na^+ cation is surrounded by Cl^- anions and vice versa.

Many common ionic compounds contain ions that are themselves composed of a group of covalently bonded atoms with an overall charge. For example, the active ingredient in household bleach is sodium hypochlorite, which acts to chemically alter color-causing molecules in clothes (bleaching action) and to kill bacteria (disinfection). Hypochlorite is a **polyatomic ion**—an ion composed of two or more atoms—with the formula ClO^-. (Note that the charge on the hypochlorite ion is a property of the whole ion, not just the oxygen atom; this is true for all polyatomic ions.) The hypochlorite ion is often found as a unit in other compounds as well (such as KClO and $Mg(ClO)_2$). Other common compounds that contain polyatomic ions include sodium bicarbonate ($NaHCO_3$), also known as baking soda; sodium nitrite ($NaNO_2$), an inhibitor of bacterial growth in packaged meats; and calcium carbonate ($CaCO_3$), the active ingredient in antacids such as TUMS®.

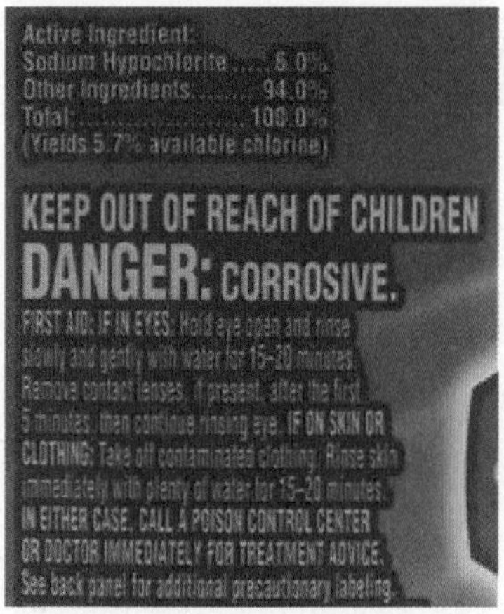

▲ Polyatomic ions are common in household products such as bleach, which contains sodium hypochlorite (NaClO).

A MOLECULAR VIEW OF ELEMENTS AND COMPOUNDS

3.4 Cc Conceptual Connection — ANSWER NOW!

Classify the substance represented by the molecular view shown here.

(a) Atomic element
(b) Molecular element
(c) Molecular compound
(d) Ionic compound

EXAMPLE 3.2 Classifying Substances as Atomic Elements, Molecular Elements, Molecular Compounds, or Ionic Compounds

Classify each of the substances as an atomic element, molecular element, molecular compound, or ionic compound.

(a) xenon **(b)** $NiCl_2$ **(c)** bromine **(d)** NO_2 **(e)** $NaNO_3$

SOLUTION

(a) Xenon is an element. It is not a molecular element (see Figure 3.5); therefore, it is an atomic element.

(b) $NiCl_2$ is a compound composed of a metal (nickel is on the left side of the periodic table) and nonmetal (chlorine is on the right side of the periodic table); therefore, it is an ionic compound.

(c) Bromine is one of the elements that exists as a diatomic molecule (see Figure 3.5); therefore, it is a molecular element.

(d) NO_2 is a compound composed of a nonmetal and a nonmetal; therefore, it is a molecular compound.

(e) $NaNO_3$ is a compound composed of a metal and a polyatomic ion; therefore, it is an ionic compound.

FOR PRACTICE 3.2 Classify each of the substances as an atomic element, molecular element, molecular compound, or ionic compound.

(a) fluorine **(b)** N_2O **(c)** silver **(d)** K_2O **(e)** Fe_2O_3

ANSWER NOW!

3.5 Cc Conceptual Connection

IONIC AND MOLECULAR COMPOUNDS Which statement best summarizes the difference between ionic and molecular compounds?

(a) Molecular compounds contain highly directional covalent bonds, which result in the formation of molecules. Ionic compounds contain nondirectional ionic bonds, which result (in the solid state) in the formation of ionic lattices.

(b) Molecular compounds and ionic compounds both contain molecules as their smallest identifiable unit, but in ionic compounds the molecules are smaller.

(c) A molecular compound is composed of covalently bonded molecules. An ionic compound is composed of ionically bonded molecules (in the solid phase).

WATCH **NOW!**

KEY CONCEPT VIDEO 3.5
Naming Ionic Compounds

3.5 Ionic Compounds: Formulas and Names

Ionic compounds occur throughout Earth's crust as minerals. Examples include limestone ($CaCO_3$), a type of sedimentary rock; gibbsite [$Al(OH)_3$], a mineral; and soda ash (Na_2CO_3), a natural deposit. We can also find ionic compounds in the foods that we eat. Examples include sodium chloride (NaCl), which is table salt; calcium carbonate ($CaCO_3$), a source of calcium necessary for bone health; and potassium chloride (KCl), a source of potassium necessary for fluid balance and muscle function. Ionic compounds are generally very stable because the attractions between cations and anions within ionic compounds are strong and because each ion interacts with several oppositely charged ions in the crystalline lattice.

▲ Ionic compounds are common in food and consumer products such as reduced-sodium salt (a mixture of NaCl and KCl) and TUMS® ($CaCO_3$).

▲ Calcite (left) is the main component of limestone, marble, and other forms of calcium carbonate ($CaCO_3$) commonly found in Earth's crust. Trona (right) is a crystalline form of hydrated sodium carbonate ($Na_2CO_3 \cdot NaHCO_3 \cdot 2\,H_2O$).

Writing Formulas for Ionic Compounds

See Figure 2.13 to review the elements that form ions with a predictable charge.

Since ionic compounds are charge-neutral, and since many elements form only one type of ion with a predictable charge, we can deduce the formulas for many ionic compounds from their constituent elements. For example, the formula for the ionic compound composed of sodium and chlorine must be NaCl because in compounds Na always forms 1+ cations and Cl always forms 1− anions. In order for the compound to be charge-neutral, it must contain one Na^+ cation for every one Cl^- anion. The formula for the ionic compound composed of *calcium* and chlorine, however, is $CaCl_2$ because Ca always forms 2+ cations and Cl always forms 1− anions. In order for this compound to be charge-neutral, it must contain one Ca^{2+} cation for every two Cl^- anions.

Summarizing Ionic Compound Formulas:

- Ionic compounds always contain positive and negative ions.
- In a chemical formula, the sum of the charges of the positive ions (cations) must equal the sum of the charges of the negative ions (anions).
- The formula of an ionic compound reflects the smallest whole-number ratio of ions.

To write the formula for an ionic compound, follow the procedure in the left column. Two examples of how to apply the procedure are provided in the center and right columns.

WATCH **NOW!**
INTERACTIVE WORKED EXAMPLE VIDEO 3.3

HOW TO: *Write Formulas for Ionic Compounds*	**EXAMPLE 3.3** **Writing Formulas for Ionic Compounds** Write the formula for the ionic compound that forms between aluminum and oxygen.	**EXAMPLE 3.4** **Writing Formulas for Ionic Compounds** Write the formula for the ionic compound that forms between calcium and oxygen.
1. Write the symbol for the metal cation and its charge followed by the symbol for the nonmetal anion and its charge. Determine charges from the element's group number in the periodic table (refer to Figure 2.13).	Al^{3+} O^{2-}	Ca^{2+} O^{2-}
2. Adjust the subscript on each cation and anion to balance the overall charge.	Al^{3+} O^{2-} ↓ Al_2O_3	Ca^{2+} O^{2-} ↓ CaO
3. Check that the sum of the charges of the cations equals the sum of the charges of the anions.	cations: 2(3+) = 6+ anions: 3(2−) = 6− The charges cancel.	cations: 2+ anions: 2− The charges cancel.
	FOR PRACTICE 3.3 Write the formula for the compound formed between potassium and sulfur.	**FOR PRACTICE 3.4** Write the formula for the compound formed between aluminum and nitrogen.

Naming Ionic Compounds

Some ionic compounds—such as NaCl (table salt) and $NaHCO_3$ (baking soda)—have **common names**, which are nicknames of sorts learned by familiarity. However, chemists have developed **systematic names** for different types of compounds including ionic ones. Even if you are not familiar with a compound, you can determine its systematic name from its chemical formula. Conversely, you can deduce the formula of a compound from its systematic name.

Before naming an ionic compound you must identify it as one. Remember, *ionic compounds are usually composed of metals and nonmetals*; any time you see a metal and one or more nonmetals together in a chemical formula, assume that you have an ionic compound. Ionic compounds can be categorized into two types, depending on the metal in the compound. The first type contains a metal whose charge is invariant from one compound to another. Whenever the metal in this first type of compound forms an ion, the ion always has the same charge.

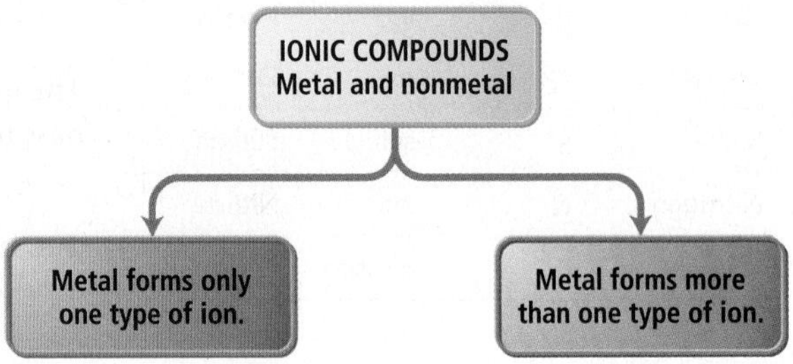

Since the charge of the metal in this first type of ionic compound is always the same, it need not be specified in the name of the compound. Sodium, for instance, has a 1+ charge in all of its compounds. Figure 3.7▶ lists some examples of these types of metals; the charges of these metals can be inferred from their group number in the periodic table.

Metals Whose Charge Is Invariant from One Compound to Another

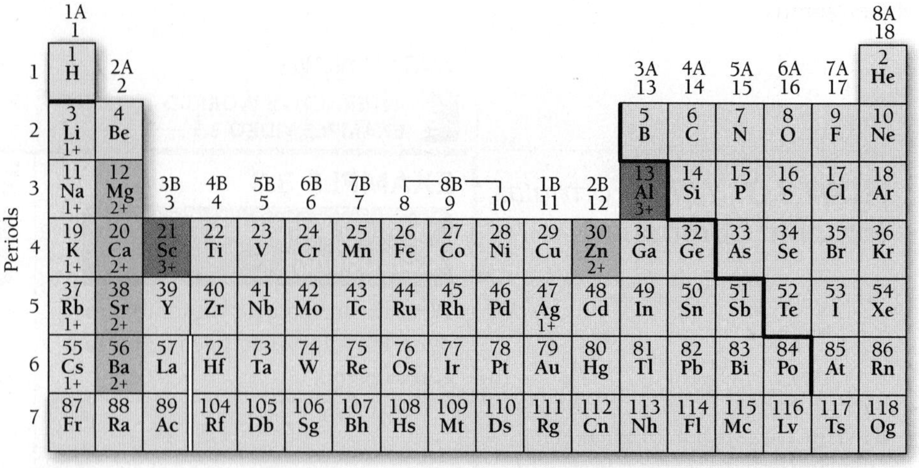

▲ **FIGURE 3.7 Metals with Invariant Charges** The metals highlighted in this table form cations with the same charges in all of their compounds. (Note that silver sometimes forms compounds with other charges, but these are rare.)

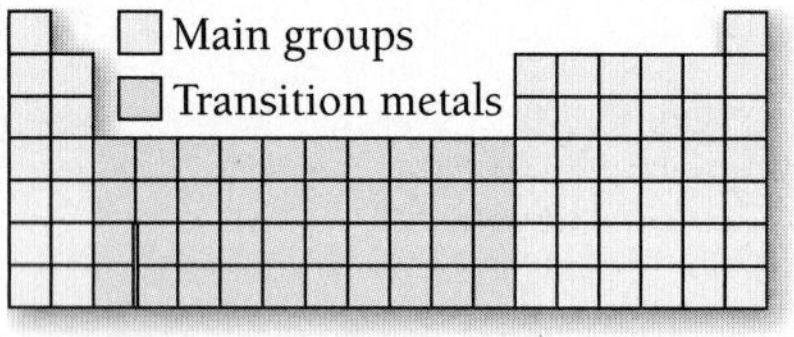

▲ **FIGURE 3.8 Transition Metals** Metals that can have different charges in different compounds are usually (but not always) transition metals.

The second type of ionic compound contains a metal with a charge that can differ in different compounds. In other words, the metal in this second type of ionic compound can form more than one kind of cation (depending on the compound), and its charge must therefore be specified for a given compound. Iron, for instance, forms a 2+ cation in some of its compounds and a 3+ cation in others. Metals of this type are often *transition metals* (Figure 3.8◀). However, some transition metals, such as Zn and Ag, form cations with the same charge in all of their compounds, and some main-group metals, such as Pb and Sn, form more than one type of cation.

ANSWER **NOW!**

3.6 Cc Conceptual Connection

TYPES OF METALS Which metal has the same charge in all of its compounds?

(a) Fe **(b)** Mo
(c) Pb **(d)** Sr

Naming Binary Ionic Compounds Containing a Metal That Forms Only One Type of Cation

Binary compounds contain only two different elements. The names of binary ionic compounds take the form:

name of cation (metal)	base name of anion (nonmetal) + *-ide*

For example, the name for KCl consists of the name of the cation, *potassium*, followed by the base name of the anion, *chlor*, with the ending *-ide*. Its full name is *potassium chloride*.

KCl potassium chloride

The name for CaO consists of the name of the cation, *calcium*, followed by the base name of the anion, *ox*, with the ending *-ide*. Its full name is *calcium oxide*.

CaO calcium oxide

The base names for various nonmetals and their most common charges in ionic compounds are shown in Table 3.2.

TABLE 3.2 ■ Some Common Monoatomic Anions

Nonmetal	Symbol for Ion	Base Name	Anion Name
Fluorine	F^-	fluor	Fluoride
Chlorine	Cl^-	chlor	Chloride
Bromine	Br^-	brom	Bromide
Iodine	I^-	iod	Iodide
Oxygen	O^{2-}	ox	Oxide
Sulfur	S^{2-}	sulf	Sulfide
Nitrogen	N^{3-}	nitr	Nitride
Phosphorus	P^{3-}	phosph	Phosphide

EXAMPLE 3.5 Naming Ionic Compounds Containing a Metal That Forms Only One Type of Cation

Name the compound $CaBr_2$.

SOLUTION

The cation is *calcium*. The anion is from bromine, which becomes *bromide*. The correct name is *calcium bromide*.

FOR PRACTICE 3.5 Name the compound Ag_3N.

FOR MORE PRACTICE 3.5 Write the formula for rubidium sulfide.

Naming Binary Ionic Compounds Containing a Metal That Forms More Than One Kind of Cation

For these types of metals, the name of the cation is followed by a Roman numeral (in parentheses) that indicates the charge of the metal in that particular compound. For example, we distinguish between Fe^{2+} and Fe^{3+} as follows:

Note that there is no space between the name of the cation and the parenthetical number indicating its charge.

Fe^{2+}	iron(II)
Fe^{3+}	iron(III)

The full names for compounds containing metals that form more than one kind of cation have the form:

name of cation (metal) (**charge of cation (metal) in Roman numerals in parentheses**) **base name of anion (nonmetal) + *-ide***

You can determine the charge of the metal cation by inference from the sum of the charges of the nonmetal anions—remember that the sum of all the charges in the compound must be zero. Table 3.3 shows some of the metals that form more than one cation and their most common charges. For example, in $CrBr_3$, the charge of chromium must be 3+ in order for the compound to be charge-neutral with three Br^- anions. The cation is named:

Cr^{3+} chromium(III)

The full name of the compound is:

$CrBr_3$ chromium(III) bromide

Similarly, in CuO the charge of copper must be 2+ in order for the compound to be charge-neutral with one O^{2-} anion. The cation is therefore named:

Cu^{2+} copper(II)

The full name of the compound is:

CuO copper(II) oxide

TABLE 3.3 ■ Some Metals That Form Cations with Different Charges

Metal	Ion	Name	Older Name*
Chromium	Cr^{2+}	Chromium(II)	Chromous
	Cr^{3+}	Chromium(III)	Chromic
Iron	Fe^{2+}	Iron(II)	Ferrous
	Fe^{3+}	Iron(III)	Ferric
Cobalt	Co^{2+}	Cobalt(II)	Cobaltous
	Co^{3+}	Cobalt(III)	Cobaltic
Copper	Cu^{+}	Copper(I)	Cuprous
	Cu^{2+}	Copper(II)	Cupric
Tin	Sn^{2+}	Tin(II)	Stannous
	Sn^{4+}	Tin(IV)	Stannic
Mercury	Hg_2^{2+}	Mercury(I)	Mercurous
	Hg^{2+}	Mercury(II)	Mercuric
Lead	Pb^{2+}	Lead(II)	Plumbous
	Pb^{4+}	Lead(IV)	Plumbic

*An older naming system substitutes the names found in this column for the name of the metal and its charge. Under this system, chromium(II) oxide is named chromous oxide. Additionally, the suffix *-ous* indicates the ion with the lesser charge, and *-ic* indicates the ion with the greater charge. We will *not* use the older system in this text.

EXAMPLE 3.6 Naming Ionic Compounds Containing a Metal That Forms More Than One Kind of Cation

Name the compound $PbCl_4$.

SOLUTION

The charge on Pb must be 4+ for the compound to be charge-neutral with four Cl^- anions. The name for $PbCl_4$ is the name of the cation, *lead*, followed by the charge of the cation in parentheses *(IV)* and the base name of the anion, *chlor*, with the ending *-ide*. The full name is *lead(IV) chloride*.

$PbCl_4$ lead(IV) chloride

FOR PRACTICE 3.6 Name the compound FeS.

FOR MORE PRACTICE 3.6 Write the formula for ruthenium(IV) oxide.

Naming Ionic Compounds Containing Polyatomic Ions

We name ionic compounds that contain a polyatomic ion in the same way as other ionic compounds, except that we use the name of the polyatomic ion whenever it occurs. Table 3.4 lists common polyatomic ions and their formulas. For example, $NaNO_2$ is named according to its cation, Na^+ *(sodium)*, and its polyatomic anion, NO_2^- *(nitrite)*. Its full name is *sodium nitrite*.

$NaNO_2$ sodium nitrite

$FeSO_4$ is named according to its cation *iron*, its charge *(II)*, and its polyatomic ion *sulfate*. Its full name is *iron(II) sulfate*.

$FeSO_4$ iron(II) sulfate

If the compound contains both a polyatomic cation and a polyatomic anion, use the names of both polyatomic ions. For example, NH_4NO_3 is *ammonium nitrate*.

NH_4NO_3 ammonium nitrate

You should be able to recognize polyatomic ions in a chemical formula, so become familiar with the ions listed in Table 3.4. Most polyatomic ions are **oxyanions**, anions containing oxygen and another element. Notice that when a series of oxyanions contains different numbers of oxygen atoms, they are named systematically according to

TABLE 3.4 ■ Some Common Polyatomic Ions

Name	Formula	Name	Formula
Acetate	$C_2H_3O_2^-$	Hypochlorite	ClO^-
Carbonate	CO_3^{2-}	Chlorite	ClO_2^-
Hydrogen carbonate (or bicarbonate)	HCO_3^-	Chlorate	ClO_3^-
Hydroxide	OH^-	Perchlorate	ClO_4^-
Nitrite	NO_2^-	Permanganate	MnO_4^-
Nitrate	NO_3^-	Sulfite	SO_3^{2-}
Chromate	CrO_4^{2-}	Hydrogen sulfite (or bisulfite)	HSO_3^-
Dichromate	$Cr_2O_7^{2-}$	Sulfate	SO_4^{2-}
Phosphate	PO_4^{3-}	Hydrogen sulfate (or bisulfate)	HSO_4^-
Hydrogen phosphate	HPO_4^{2-}	Cyanide	CN^-
Dihydrogen phosphate	$H_2PO_4^-$	Peroxide	O_2^{2-}
Ammonium	NH_4^+		

the number of oxygen atoms in the ion. If there are only two ions in the series, the one with more oxygen atoms has the ending *-ate* and the one with fewer has the ending *-ite*. For example, NO_3^- is *nitrate* and NO_2^- is *nitrite.*

NO_3^- nitr*ate*

NO_2^- nitr*ite*

If there are more than two ions in the series, then the prefixes *hypo-*, meaning *less than,* and *per-*, meaning *more than,* are used. So ClO^- is hypochlorite (less oxygen than chlorite), and ClO_4^- is perchlorate (more oxygen than chlorate).

ClO^- *hypo*chlor*ite*
ClO_2^- chlor*ite*
ClO_3^- chlor*ate*
ClO_4^- *per*chlor*ate*

Other halides (halogen ions) form similar series with similar names. Thus, IO_3^- is iodate and BrO_3^- is bromate.

EXAMPLE 3.7 Naming Ionic Compounds That Contain a Polyatomic Ion

Name the compound $Li_2Cr_2O_7$.

SOLUTION

The name for $Li_2Cr_2O_7$ is the name of the cation, *lithium*, followed by the name of the polyatomic ion, *dichromate*. Its full name is *lithium dichromate*.

$Li_2Cr_2O_7$ lithium dichromate

FOR PRACTICE 3.7 Name the compound $Sn(ClO_3)_2$.

FOR MORE PRACTICE 3.7 Write the formula for cobalt(II) phosphate.

3.7 Cc Conceptual Connection ANSWER NOW!

POLYATOMIC IONS Identify the polyatomic ion and its charge in each compound: KNO_2, $CaSO_4$, $Mg(NO_3)_2$.

(a) NO_2^-, SO_4^{2-}, and NO_3^-
(b) K^+, Ca^{2+}, and Mg^{2+}
(c) K^+, Ca^{2+}, Mg^{2+}, NO_2^-, SO_4^{2-}, and NO_3^-
(d) NO_2^{2-}, SO_4^-, and NO_3^{2-}

Hydrated Ionic Compounds

The ionic compounds called **hydrates** contain a specific number of water molecules associated with each formula unit. For example, the formula for epsom salts is $MgSO_4 \cdot 7\,H_2O$, and its systematic name is magnesium sulfate heptahydrate. The seven H_2O molecules associated with the formula unit are *waters of hydration.* Waters of hydration can usually be removed by heating the compound. Figure 3.9▶ shows a sample of cobalt(II) chloride hexahydrate ($CoCl_2 \cdot 6\,H_2O$) before and after heating. The hydrate is pink and the anhydrous salt (the salt without any associated water molecules) is blue. Hydrates are named just as other ionic compounds, but they are given the additional name "*prefix*hydrate," where the *prefix* indicates the number of water molecules associated with each formula unit.

Common hydrated ionic compounds and their names are as follows:

$CaSO_4 \cdot \frac{1}{2}H_2O$ calcium sulfate hemihydrate
$BaCl_2 \cdot 6\,H_2O$ barium chloride hexahydrate
$CuSO_4 \cdot 5\,H_2O$ copper(II) sulfate pentahydrate

Hydrate | Anhydrous

$CoCl_2 \cdot 6\,H_2O$ | $CoCl_2$

▲ **FIGURE 3.9 Hydrates** Heating pink cobalt(II) chloride hexahydrate removes the waters of hydration to produce blue cobalt(II) chloride.

Common hydrate prefixes
hemi = 1/2
mono = 1
di = 2
tri = 3
tetra = 4
penta = 5
hexa = 6
hepta = 7
octa = 8

WATCH **NOW!**

KEY CONCEPT VIDEO 3.6
Naming Molecular Compounds

3.6 Molecular Compounds: Formulas and Names

In contrast to ionic compounds, the formula for a molecular compound *cannot* readily be determined from its constituent elements because the same combination of elements may form many different molecular compounds, each with a different formula. For example, carbon and oxygen form both CO and CO_2, and hydrogen and oxygen form both H_2O and H_2O_2. Nitrogen and oxygen form all of the following molecular compounds: NO, NO_2, N_2O, N_2O_3, N_2O_4, and N_2O_5. In Chapter 10, we will discuss the stability of these various combinations of the same elements. For now, we focus on naming a molecular compound based on its formula and writing its formula based on its name.

Naming Molecular Compounds

Like ionic compounds, many molecular compounds have common names. For example, H_2O and NH_3 have the common names *water* and *ammonia*. However, the sheer number of existing molecular compounds—numbering in the millions—necessitates a systematic approach to naming them.

The first step in naming a molecular compound is identifying it as one. Remember, *molecular compounds are composed of two or more nonmetals*. In this section, we discuss how to name binary (two-element) molecular compounds. Their names have the form:

prefix	name of 1st element	prefix	base name of 2nd element + *-ide*

When writing the name of a molecular compound, as when writing the formula, we first list the more metal-like element (toward the left and bottom of the periodic table). Generally, we write the name of the element with the smaller group number first. If the two elements lie in the same group, then we write the element with the greater row number first. The prefixes given to each element indicate the number of atoms present:

These prefixes are the same as those used in naming hydrates.

mono = 1	hexa = 6
di = 2	hepta = 7
tri = 3	octa = 8
tetra = 4	nona = 9
penta = 5	deca = 10

If there is only one atom of the *first element* in the formula, the prefix *mono-* is normally omitted. For example, we name NO_2 according to the first element, *nitrogen*, with no prefix because *mono-* is omitted for the first element, followed by the prefix *di-*, to indicate two oxygen atoms, and the base name of the second element, *ox*, with the ending *-ide*. Its full name is *nitrogen dioxide*.

NO_2 nitrogen dioxide

When a prefix ends with "o" and the base name begins with "o," the first "o" is often dropped. For example, mono-oxide becomes *monoxide*.

We name the compound N_2O, sometimes called laughing gas, similarly except that we use the prefix *di-* before nitrogen to indicate two nitrogen atoms and the prefix *mono-* before oxide to indicate one oxygen atom. Its full name is *dinitrogen monoxide*.

N_2O dinitrogen monoxide

EXAMPLE 3.8 Naming Molecular Compounds

Name each compound.

(a) NI_3 **(b)** PCl_5 **(c)** P_4S_{10}

SOLUTION

(a) The name of the compound is the name of the first element, *nitrogen*, followed by the base name of the second element, *iod*, prefixed by *tri-* to indicate three and given the suffix *-ide*.

NI_3 nitrogen triiodide

(b) The name of the compound is the name of the first element, *phosphorus*, followed by the base name of the second element, *chlor*, prefixed by *penta-* to indicate five and given the suffix *-ide*.

PCl_5 phosphorus pentachloride

(c) The name of the compound is the name of the first element, *phosphorus*, prefixed by *tetra-* to indicate four, followed by the base name of the second element, *sulf*, prefixed by *deca-* to indicate ten and given the suffix *-ide*.

P_4S_{10} tetraphosphorus decasulfide

FOR PRACTICE 3.8 Name the compound N_2O_5.

FOR MORE PRACTICE 3.8 Write the formula for phosphorus tribromide.

3.8 Cc Conceptual Connection — ANSWER NOW!

NOMENCLATURE The compound NCl_3 is nitrogen trichloride, but $AlCl_3$ is simply aluminum chloride. Why?

(a) The name forms differ because NCl_3 is an ionic compound and $AlCl_3$ is a molecular compound. Prefixes such as *mono-*, *di-*, and *tri-* are used for ionic compounds but not for molecular compounds.

(b) The name forms differ because NCl_3 is a molecular compound and $AlCl_3$ is an ionic compound. Prefixes such as *mono-*, *di-*, and *tri-* are used for molecular compounds but not for ionic compounds.

Naming Acids

We can define acids in a number of ways, as we will discuss in Chapter 17. For now we define **acids** as molecular compounds that release hydrogen ions (H^+) when dissolved in water. Acids are composed of hydrogen, usually written first in their formula, and one or more nonmetals, written second. For example, HCl is a molecular compound that, when dissolved in water, forms $H^+(aq)$ and $Cl^-(aq)$ ions, where *aqueous* (*aq*) means *dissolved in water*. Therefore, HCl is an acid when dissolved in water. To distinguish between gaseous HCl (which is named hydrogen monochloride because it is a molecular compound) and HCl in solution (which is named hydrochloric acid because it is an acid), we write the former as HCl(*g*) and the latter as HCl(*aq*).

▲ Many fruits are acidic and have the characteristically sour taste of acids.

Acids are characterized by their sour taste and their ability to dissolve many metals. For example, hydrochloric acid is present in stomach fluids, and its sour taste becomes painfully obvious during vomiting. Hydrochloric acid also dissolves some metals. For example, if we put a strip of zinc into a test tube of hydrochloric acid, it slowly dissolves as the $H^+(aq)$ ions convert the zinc metal into $Zn^{2+}(aq)$ cations (Figure 3.10▶).

Acids are present in foods such as lemons and limes and are used in household products such as toilet bowl cleanser and Lime-A-Way. In this section, we discuss how to name them; in Chapter 17 you will learn more about their properties. We categorize acids into two types: binary acids and oxyacids.

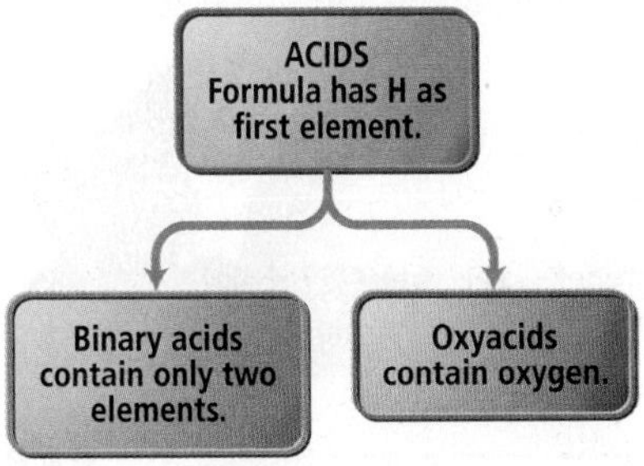

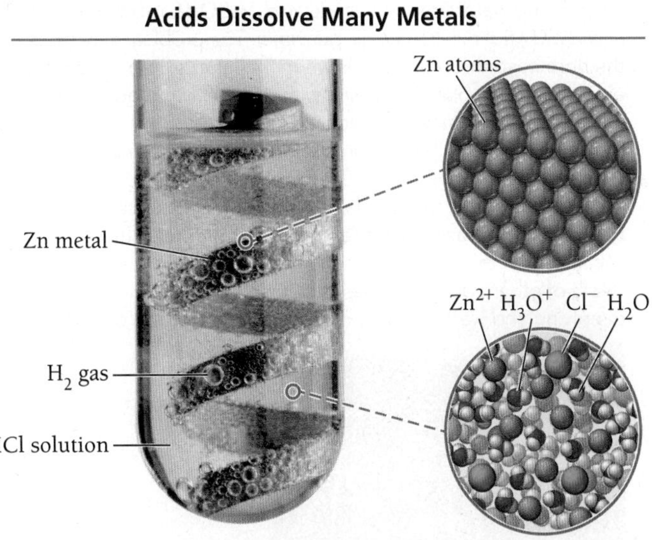

▲ **FIGURE 3.10 Hydrochloric Acid Dissolving Zinc Metal** The zinc atoms are ionized to zinc ions, which dissolve in the water. The HCl forms H_2 gas, which is responsible for the bubbles you can see in the test tube.

Naming Binary Acids

Binary acids are composed of hydrogen and a nonmetal. Names for binary acids have the form:

hydro	base name of nonmetal + *-ic*	acid

For example, HCl(*aq*) is hydro*chlor*ic acid and HBr(*aq*) is hydro*brom*ic acid.

HCl(*aq*) hydrochloric acid HBr(*aq*) hydrobromic acid

EXAMPLE 3.9 Naming Binary Acids

Name the acid HI(*aq*).

SOLUTION

The base name of I is *iod*, so HI(*aq*) is hydroiodic acid.

HI(*aq*) hydroiodic acid

FOR PRACTICE 3.9 Name the acid HF(*aq*).

Naming Oxyacids

Oxyacids contain hydrogen and an oxyanion (an anion containing a nonmetal and oxygen). The common oxyanions are listed in the table of polyatomic ions (Table 3.4). For example, HNO_3(*aq*) contains the nitrate (NO_3^-) ion, H_2SO_3(*aq*) contains the sulfite (SO_3^{2-}) ion, and H_2SO_4(*aq*) contains the sulfate (SO_4^{2-}) ion. Oxyacids are a combination of one or more H^+ ions with an oxyanion. The number of H^+ ions depends on the

CHEMISTRY IN THE ENVIRONMENT | Acid Rain

Certain pollutants—such as NO, NO_2, and SO_2—form acids when mixed with water. NO and NO_2, primarily emitted in vehicular exhaust, combine with atmospheric oxygen and water to form nitric acid, HNO_3(*aq*). SO_2, emitted primarily from coal-powered electricity generation, combines with atmospheric oxygen and water to form sulfuric acid, H_2SO_4(*aq*). Both HNO_3(*aq*) and H_2SO_4(*aq*) result in acidic rainwater. The problem is greatest in the northeastern United States where pollutants from midwestern electrical power plants combine with rainwater to produce rain that is up to ten times more acidic than normal.

Acid rain can fall or flow into lakes and streams, making these bodies of water more acidic. Some species of aquatic animals—such as trout, bass, snails, salamanders, and clams—cannot tolerate the increased acidity and die. This in turn disturbs the ecosystem of the lake, resulting in imbalances that may lead to the death of other aquatic species. Acid rain also weakens trees by dissolving and washing away nutrients in the soil and by damaging leaves. Appalachian red spruce trees have been the hardest hit, with many forests showing significant acid rain damage.

In addition, acid rain degrades building materials because acids dissolve iron, the main component of steel, and $CaCO_3$ (limestone), a main component of marble and concrete. Consequently, acid rain has damaged many statues, buildings, and bridges in the northeastern United States.

Acid rain has been a problem for many years, but legislation passed toward the end of the last century has begun to address this issue. In 1990, Congress passed several amendments to the Clean Air Act that included provisions requiring electrical utilities to lower SO_2 emissions. Since then, SO_2 emissions have decreased and rain in the northeastern United States has become less acidic. With time, and with continued enforcement of the acid rain regulation, lakes, streams, and forests damaged by acid rain should recover.

QUESTION

Name each compound: NO, NO_2, SO_2, H_2SO_4, HNO_3, $CaCO_3$.

◀ A forest damaged by acid rain.

▶ Acid rain damages building materials, including the limestone that composes many statues.

charge of the oxyanion; the formula is always charge-neutral. The names of oxyacids depend on the ending of the oxyanion and take the following forms:

oxyanions ending with *-ate*: **base name of oxyanion + *-ic*** **acid**

oxyanions ending with *-ite*: **base name of oxyanion + *-ous*** **acid**

For example, $HNO_3(aq)$ is nitric acid (oxyanion is nitrate), and $H_2SO_3(aq)$ is sulfurous acid (oxyanion is sulfite).

$HNO_3(aq)$ nitric acid $\quad H_2SO_3(aq)$ sulfurous acid

EXAMPLE 3.10 Naming Oxyacids

Name the acid $HC_2H_3O_2(aq)$.

SOLUTION

The oxyanion is acetate, which ends in *-ate*; therefore, the name of the acid is *acetic acid.*

$HC_2H_3O_2(aq)$ acetic acid

FOR PRACTICE 3.10 Name the acid $HNO_2(aq)$.

FOR MORE PRACTICE 3.10 Write the formula for perchloric acid.

3.7 Summary of Inorganic Nomenclature

In Sections 3.5 and 3.6, we discussed naming inorganic compounds, specifically ionic compounds, molecular compounds, and acids. However, we often have to name a compound without initially knowing the category into which it falls. In other words, real-life nomenclature is a bit messier than the categorized nomenclature we just worked through. Figure 3.11▼ summarizes inorganic nomenclature in a flowchart that will help you to tackle nomenclature from beginning to end.

▼ FIGURE 3.11 Inorganic Nomenclature Flowchart The chart summarizes how to name inorganic compounds. Begin by determining if the compound is ionic, molecular, or an acid. Then follow the flowchart for that category from top to bottom until you arrive at a name for the compound.

Inorganic Nomenclature Flowchart

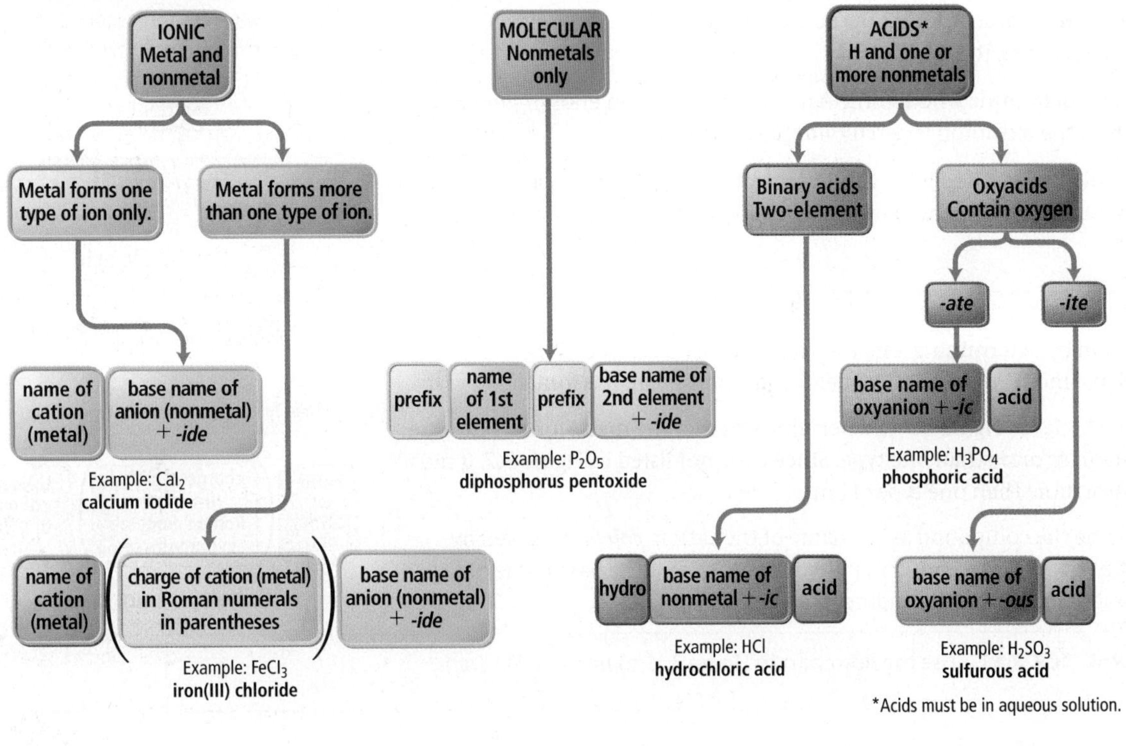

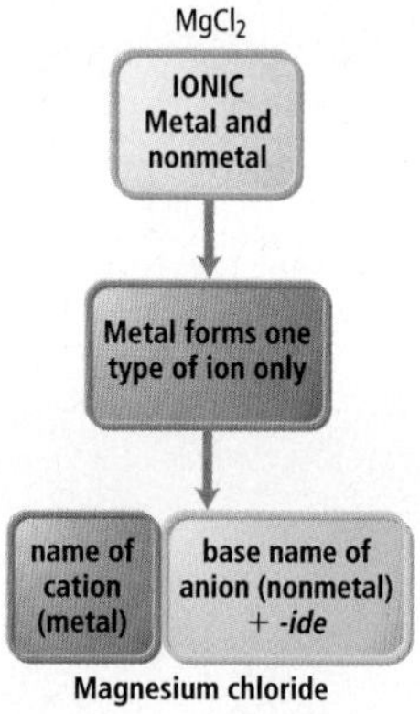

▲ **FIGURE 3.12 Flowchart Path for $MgCl_2$**

To use the flowchart, begin by determining what type of compound you are trying to name. For example, to name the compound $MgCl_2$, you need to decide if the compound is ionic, molecular, or an acid. In this case, since $MgCl_2$ is composed of a metal and nonmetal, it is ionic. Therefore, you begin at the box labeled "IONIC" at the far left side of the flowchart.

Next, decide whether the metal in the compound forms only one type of ion or more than one type. You can determine this by looking for the metal (in this case magnesium) in Figure 3.7. Since magnesium is listed in the figure, it forms only one type of ion; therefore, you take the left branch in the flowchart as shown in Figure 3.12◄.

Finally, name the compound according to the blocks at the end of the path in the flowchart. In this case, write the name of the cation (the metal) followed by the base name of the anion (the nonmetal) appended with the ending *-ide*. Its full name is magnesium chloride.

WATCH **NOW!**
INTERACTIVE WORKED EXAMPLE 3.11

EXAMPLE 3.11 Using the Nomenclature Flowchart to Name Compounds

Use the flowchart in Figure 3.11 to name each compound.

(a) SO_2 **(b)** $HClO_4(aq)$ **(c)** CoF_2

SOLUTION

(a) SO_2

Begin by determining whether the compound is ionic, molecular, or an acid. SO_2 contains only nonmetals; therefore it is molecular.

Name the compound as the name of the first element, *sulfur* (no prefix since the prefix is dropped for mono), followed by the base name of the second element, *ox*, prefixed by *di-* to indicate two, and given the suffix *-ide*.

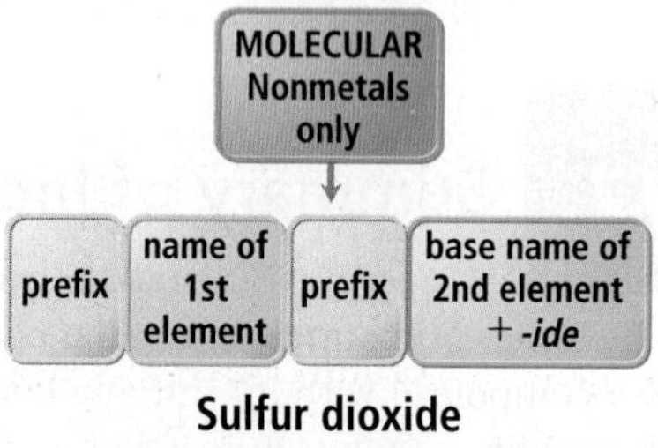

(b) $HClO_4(aq)$

Begin by determining whether the compound is ionic, molecular, or an acid. Since $HClO_4(aq)$ contains H and one more nonmetal and is designated as aqueous, it is an acid.

Next determine whether the acid contains oxygen. Since $HClO_4$ contains oxygen, it is an oxyacid.

Then determine whether the name of the oxyanion ends in *-ate* or *-ite*. Since the oxyanion is perchlor*ate*, it ends in *-ate*.

Finally, name the acid as the base name of the oxyanion, *perchlor*, with the ending *-ic*, followed by the word *acid*.

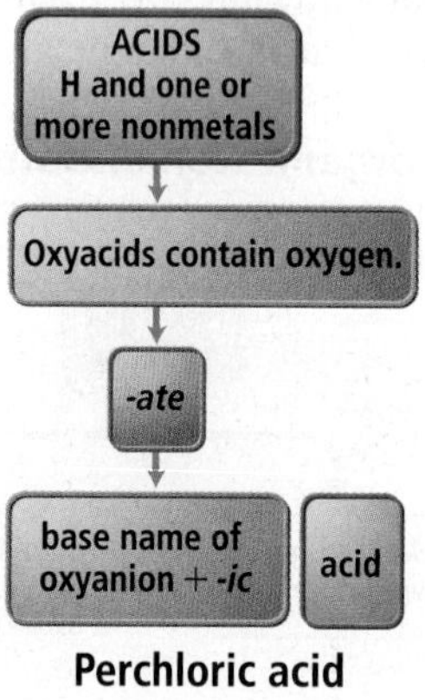

(c) CoF_2

Begin by determining whether the compound is ionic, molecular, or an acid. Since CoF_2 contains a metal and a nonmetal, it is ionic.

Next refer to Figure 3.7 to determine whether the metal forms one type of ion or more than one type. Since Co is not listed in Figure 3.7, it must form more than one type of ion.

Name the compound as the name of the cation, *cobalt*, followed by the charge of the cation in parentheses (*II*), and the base name of the anion, *fluor*, with the ending *-ide*.

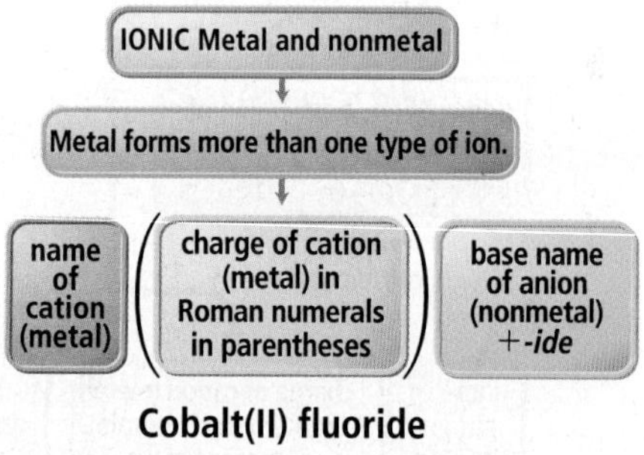

FOR PRACTICE 3.11 Use the flowchart in Figure 3.11 to name $H_2SO_3(aq)$.

3.8 Formula Mass and the Mole Concept for Compounds

In Chapter 2, we defined the average mass of an atom of an element as its *atomic mass*. Similarly, we now define the average mass of a molecule (or a formula unit) of a compound as its **formula mass**. (The common terms *molecular mass* and *molecular weight* are synonymous with formula mass.) For any compound, the formula mass is the sum of the atomic masses of all the atoms in its chemical formula.

Remember, ionic compounds do not contain individual molecules. In casual language, the smallest electrically neutral collection of ions is sometimes called a molecule but is more correctly called a formula unit.

$$\text{Formula mass} = \left(\begin{array}{c}\text{Number of atoms}\\ \text{of 1st element in}\\ \text{chemical formula}\end{array} \times \begin{array}{c}\text{Atomic mass}\\ \text{of}\\ \text{1st element}\end{array}\right) + \left(\begin{array}{c}\text{Number of atoms}\\ \text{of 2nd element in}\\ \text{chemical formula}\end{array} \times \begin{array}{c}\text{Atomic mass}\\ \text{of}\\ \text{2nd element}\end{array}\right) + \ldots$$

For example, the formula mass of carbon dioxide, CO_2, is:

Multiply by 2 because formula has two oxygen atoms.

$$\begin{aligned}\text{Formula mass} &= 12.01\ \text{amu} + 2(16.00\ \text{amu})\\ &= 44.01\ \text{amu}\end{aligned}$$

and that of sodium oxide, Na_2O, is:

Multiply by 2 because formula has two sodium atoms.

$$\begin{aligned}\text{Formula mass} &= 2(22.99\ \text{amu}) + 16.00\ \text{amu}\\ &= 61.98\ \text{amu}\end{aligned}$$

EXAMPLE 3.12 Calculating Formula Mass

Calculate the formula mass of glucose, $C_6H_{12}O_6$.

SOLUTION

To find the formula mass, add the atomic masses of each atom in the chemical formula.

$$\begin{aligned}\text{Formula mass} &= 6 \times (\text{atomic mass C}) + 12 \times (\text{atomic mass H}) + 6 \times (\text{atomic mass O})\\ &= 6(12.01\ \text{amu}) \quad + 12(1.008\ \text{amu}) \quad + 6(16.00\ \text{amu})\\ &= 180.16\ \text{amu}\end{aligned}$$

FOR PRACTICE 3.12 Calculate the formula mass of calcium nitrate.

Molar Mass of a Compound

In Chapter 2 (Section 2.9), we saw that an element's molar mass—the mass in grams of one mole of its atoms—is numerically equivalent to its atomic mass. We then used the molar mass in combination with Avogadro's number to determine the number of atoms in a given mass of the element. We can apply the same concept to compounds. The *molar mass of a compound*—the mass in grams of 1 mol of its molecules or formula units—is numerically equivalent to its formula mass. For example, we just calculated the formula mass of CO_2 to be 44.01 amu. The molar mass is, therefore:

$$CO_2\ \text{molar mass} = 44.01\ \text{g/mol}$$

Using Molar Mass to Count Molecules by Weighing

The molar mass of CO_2 is a conversion factor between mass (in grams) and amount (in moles) of CO_2. Suppose we want to find the number of CO_2 molecules in a sample of dry ice (solid CO_2) with a mass of 10.8 g. This calculation is analogous to Example 2.8, where we found the number of atoms in a sample of copper of a given mass. We begin with the mass of 10.8 g and use the molar mass to convert to the amount in moles. Then we use Avogadro's number to convert to number of molecules. The conceptual plan is as follows:

Conceptual Plan

g CO_2 → mol CO_2 → CO_2 molecules

$$\frac{1 \text{ mol } CO_2}{44.01 \text{ g } CO_2} \qquad \frac{6.022 \times 10^{23} \text{ } CO_2 \text{ molecules}}{1 \text{ mol } CO_2}$$

To solve the problem, we follow the conceptual plan, beginning with 10.8 g CO_2, converting to moles, and then to molecules.

Solution

$$10.8 \text{ g } CO_2 \times \frac{1 \text{ mol } CO_2}{44.01 \text{ g } CO_2} \times \frac{6.022 \times 10^{23} \text{ } CO_2 \text{ molecules}}{1 \text{ mol } CO_2}$$

$$= 1.48 \times 10^{23} \text{ } CO_2 \text{ molecules}$$

WATCH **NOW!**
INTERACTIVE WORKED EXAMPLE 3.13

EXAMPLE 3.13 The Mole Concept—Converting between Mass and Number of Molecules

An aspirin tablet contains 325 mg of acetylsalicylic acid ($C_9H_8O_4$). How many acetylsalicylic acid molecules does it contain?

SORT You are given the mass of acetylsalicylic acid and asked to find the number of molecules.

GIVEN: 325 mg $C_9H_8O_4$

FIND: number of $C_9H_8O_4$ molecules

STRATEGIZE First convert to moles (using the molar mass of the compound) and then to number of molecules (using Avogadro's number). You need both the molar mass of acetylsalicylic acid and Avogadro's number as conversion factors. You also need the conversion factor between g and mg.

CONCEPTUAL PLAN

mg $C_9H_8O_4$ → g $C_9H_8O_4$ →

$$\frac{10^{-3} \text{ g}}{1 \text{ mg}} \qquad \frac{1 \text{ mol } C_9H_8O_4}{180.15 \text{ g } C_9H_8O_4}$$

mol $C_9H_8O_4$ → number of $C_9H_8O_4$ molecules

$$\frac{6.022 \times 10^{23} \text{ } C_9H_8O_4 \text{ molecules}}{1 \text{ mol } C_9H_8O_4}$$

RELATIONSHIPS USED

$$C_9H_8O_4 \text{ molar mass} = 9(12.01) + 8(1.008) + 4(16.00) = 180.15 \text{ g/mol}$$

$$6.022 \times 10^{23} = 1 \text{ mol}$$
$$1 \text{ mg} = 10^{-3} \text{ g}$$

SOLVE Follow the conceptual plan to solve the problem.

SOLUTION

$$325 \text{ mg } C_9H_8O_4 \times \frac{10^{-3} \text{ g}}{1 \text{ mg}} \times \frac{1 \text{ mol } C_9H_8O_4}{180.15 \text{ g } C_9H_8O_4} \times \frac{6.022 \times 10^{23} \text{ } C_9H_8O_4 \text{ molecules}}{1 \text{ mol } C_9H_8O_4} = 1.09 \times 10^{21} \text{ } C_9H_8O_4 \text{ molecules}$$

CHECK The units of the answer, $C_9H_8O_4$ molecules, are correct. The magnitude is smaller than Avogadro's number, as expected, since you have less than 1 molar mass of acetylsalicylic acid.

FOR PRACTICE 3.13 Find the number of ibuprofen molecules in a tablet containing 200.0 mg of ibuprofen ($C_{13}H_{18}O_2$).

FOR MORE PRACTICE 3.13 Determine the mass of a sample of water containing 3.55×10^{22} H_2O molecules.

MOLECULAR MODELS AND THE SIZE OF MOLECULES

3.9 Cc Conceptual Connection — ANSWER NOW!

Throughout this book, you will find space-filling molecular models to represent molecules. Which number is the best estimate for the scaling factor used in these models? In other words, by approximately what number would you have to multiply the radius of an actual oxygen atom to get the radius of the sphere used to represent the oxygen atom in the water molecule shown here?

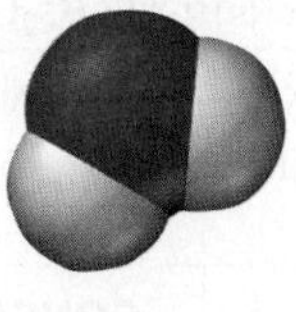

(a) 10 **(b)** 10^4 **(c)** 10^8 **(d)** 10^{16}

3.9 Composition of Compounds

A chemical formula, in combination with the molar masses of its constituent elements, indicates the relative quantities of each element in a compound, which is extremely useful information. For example, about 40 years ago, scientists began to suspect that synthetic compounds known as chlorofluorocarbons (or CFCs) were destroying ozone (O_3) in Earth's upper atmosphere. Upper atmospheric ozone is important because it acts as a shield, protecting life on Earth from the sun's harmful ultraviolet light.

CFCs are chemically inert compounds used primarily as refrigerants and industrial solvents. Over time, CFCs accumulated in the atmosphere. In the upper atmosphere, sunlight breaks bonds within CFCs, releasing chlorine atoms. The chlorine atoms react with ozone, converting it into O_2. So the harmful part of CFCs is the chlorine atoms that they carry. How can we determine the mass of chlorine in a given mass of a CFC?

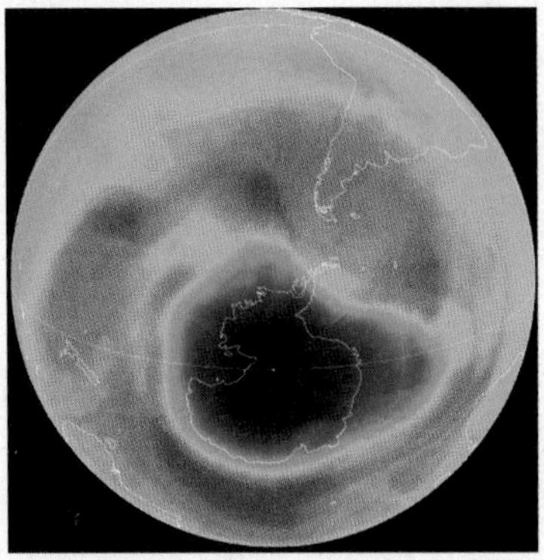

▲ The chlorine in chlorofluorocarbons caused the ozone hole over Antarctica. The dark blue color indicates depressed ozone levels.

One way to express how much of an element is in a given compound is to use the element's mass percent composition for that compound. The **mass percent composition** or **mass percent** of an element is that element's percentage of the compound's total mass. We calculate the mass percent of element X in a compound from the chemical formula as follows:

$$\text{Mass percent of element X} = \frac{\text{mass of element X in 1 mol of compound}}{\text{mass of 1 mol of the compound}} \times 100\%$$

Suppose, for example, that we want to calculate the mass percent composition of Cl in the chlorofluorocarbon CCl_2F_2. The mass percent Cl is given by:

CCl_2F_2

$$\text{Mass percent Cl} = \frac{2 \times \text{molar mass Cl}}{\text{molar mass } CCl_2F_2} \times 100\%$$

We multiply the molar mass of Cl by 2 because the chemical formula has a subscript of 2 for Cl, indicating that 1 mol of CCl_2F_2 contains 2 mol of Cl atoms. We calculate the molar mass of CCl_2F_2 as follows:

$$\begin{aligned}\text{Molar mass} &= 12.01\text{ g/mol} + 2(35.45\text{ g/mol}) + 2(19.00\text{ g/mol})\\ &= 120.91\text{ g/mol}\end{aligned}$$

So the mass percent of Cl in CCl_2F_2 is:

$$\begin{aligned}\text{Mass percent Cl} &= \frac{2 \times \text{molar mass Cl}}{\text{molar mass } CCl_2F_2} \times 100\%\\ &= \frac{2 \times 35.45 \cancel{\text{g/mol}}}{120.91 \cancel{\text{g/mol}}} \times 100\%\\ &= 58.64\%\end{aligned}$$

EXAMPLE 3.14 Mass Percent Composition

Calculate the mass percent of Cl in Freon-112 ($C_2Cl_4F_2$), a CFC refrigerant.

SORT You are given the molecular formula of Freon-112 and asked to find the mass percent of Cl.

GIVEN: $C_2Cl_4F_2$

FIND: mass percent Cl

STRATEGIZE The molecular formula tells you that there are 4 mol of Cl in each mole of Freon-112. Find the mass percent composition from the chemical formula by using the equation that defines mass percent. The conceptual plan shows you how to use the mass of Cl in 1 mol of $C_2Cl_4F_2$ and the molar mass of $C_2Cl_4F_2$ to find the mass percent of Cl.

CONCEPTUAL PLAN

$$\text{Mass \% Cl} = \frac{4 \times \text{molar mass Cl}}{\text{molar mass } C_2Cl_4F_2} \times 100\%$$

RELATIONSHIPS USED

$$\text{Mass percent of element X} = \frac{\text{mass of element X in 1 mol of compound}}{\text{mass of 1 mol of compound}} \times 100\%$$

SOLVE Calculate the necessary parts of the equation and substitute the values into the equation to find mass percent Cl.

SOLUTION

$$4 \times \text{molar mass Cl} = 4(35.45 \text{ g/mol}) = 141.8 \text{ g/mol}$$

$$\text{Molar mass } C_2Cl_4F_2 = 2(12.01 \text{ g/mol}) + 4(35.45 \text{ g/mol}) + 2(19.00 \text{ g/mol})$$
$$= 24.02 \text{ g/mol} + 141.8 \text{ g/mol} + 38.00 \text{ g/mol} = 203.8 \text{ g/mol}$$

$$\text{Mass \% Cl} = \frac{4 \times \text{molar mass Cl}}{\text{molar mass } C_2Cl_4F_2} \times 100\%$$
$$= \frac{141.8 \text{ g/}\cancel{\text{mol}}}{203.8 \text{ g/}\cancel{\text{mol}}} \times 100\%$$
$$= 69.58\%$$

CHECK The units of the answer (%) are correct. The magnitude is reasonable because it is between 0 and 100% and chlorine is the heaviest atom in the molecule and there are four atoms of it.

FOR PRACTICE 3.14 Acetic acid ($HC_2H_3O_2$) is the active ingredient in vinegar. Calculate the mass percent composition of oxygen in acetic acid.

FOR MORE PRACTICE 3.14 Calculate the mass percent composition of sodium in sodium oxide.

ANSWER **NOW!**

3.10 **Cc** Conceptual Connection

CHEMICAL FORMULA AND MASS PERCENT COMPOSITION Without doing any calculations, list the elements in C_6H_6O in order of decreasing mass percent composition.

(a) C>O>H **(b)** O>C>H **(c)** H>O>C **(d)** C>H>O

Mass Percent Composition as a Conversion Factor

The mass percent composition of an element in a compound is a conversion factor between mass of the element and mass of the compound. For example, we saw that the mass percent composition of Cl in CCl_2F_2 is 58.64%. Since percent means *per hundred*, there are 58.64 g Cl *per hundred* grams CCl_2F_2, which can be expressed as the ratio:

$$58.64 \text{ g Cl} : 100 \text{ g } CCl_2F_2$$

or, in fractional form:

$$\frac{58.64 \text{ g Cl}}{100 \text{ g } CCl_2F_2} \quad \text{or} \quad \frac{100 \text{ g } CCl_2F_2}{58.64 \text{ g Cl}}$$

These ratios can function as conversion factors between grams of Cl and grams of CCl_2F_2. For example, to calculate the mass of Cl in 1.00 kg CCl_2F_2, we use the following conceptual plan:

Conceptual Plan

$$\text{kg } CCl_2F_2 \xrightarrow{\frac{1000\text{ g}}{1\text{ kg}}} \text{g } CCl_2F_2 \xrightarrow{\frac{58.64\text{ g Cl}}{100\text{ g } CCl_2F_2}} \text{g Cl}$$

Notice that the mass percent composition acts as a conversion factor between grams of the compound and grams of the constituent element. To calculate grams Cl, we follow the conceptual plan.

Solution

$$1.00\ \cancel{\text{kg}}\ \cancel{CCl_2F_2} \times \frac{1000\ \cancel{\text{g}}}{1\ \cancel{\text{kg}}} \times \frac{58.64\text{ g Cl}}{100\ \cancel{\text{g}}\ \cancel{CCl_2F_2}} = 5.86 \times 10^2\text{ g Cl}$$

WATCH **NOW!**

INTERACTIVE WORKED EXAMPLE 3.15

EXAMPLE 3.15 Using Mass Percent Composition as a Conversion Factor

The U.S. Food and Drug Administration (FDA) recommends that an adult consume less than 2.4 g of sodium per day. What mass of sodium chloride (in grams) can you consume and still be within the FDA guidelines? Sodium chloride is 39% sodium by mass.

SORT You are given a mass of sodium and the mass percent of sodium in sodium chloride. You are asked to find the mass of NaCl that contains the given mass of sodium.

GIVEN: 2.4 g Na
FIND: g NaCl

STRATEGIZE Convert between mass of a constituent element and mass of a compound by using mass percent composition as a conversion factor.

CONCEPTUAL PLAN

$$\text{g Na} \xrightarrow{\frac{100\text{ g NaCl}}{39\text{ g Na}}} \text{g NaCl}$$

RELATIONSHIPS USED

39 g Na : 100 g NaCl

SOLVE Follow the conceptual plan to solve the problem.

SOLUTION

$$2.4\ \cancel{\text{g Na}} \times \frac{100\text{ g NaCl}}{39\ \cancel{\text{g Na}}} = 6.2\text{ g NaCl}$$

You can consume 6.2 g NaCl and still be within the FDA guidelines.

CHECK The units of the answer are correct. The magnitude seems reasonable because it is larger than the amount of sodium, as expected, because sodium is only one of the elements in NaCl.

FOR PRACTICE 3.15 What mass (in grams) of iron(III) oxide contains 58.7 g of iron? Iron(III) oxide is 69.94% iron by mass.

FOR MORE PRACTICE 3.15 If someone consumes 22 g of sodium chloride per day, what mass (in grams) of sodium does that person consume? Sodium chloride is 39% sodium by mass.

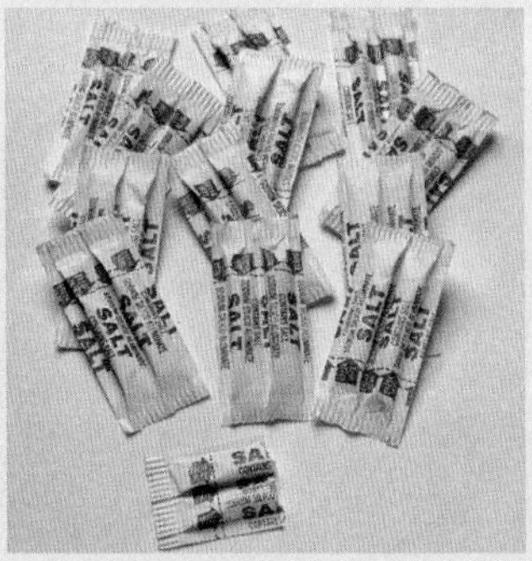

◀12.5 packets of salt contain 6.2 g of NaCl.

Conversion Factors from Chemical Formulas

Mass percent composition is one way to understand how much chlorine is in a particular chlorofluorocarbon or, more generally, how much of a constituent element is present in a given mass of any compound. However, we can also approach this type of problem in a different way. Chemical formulas contain within them inherent relationships between atoms (or moles of atoms) and molecules (or moles of molecules). For example, the formula for CCl_2F_2 tells us that 1 mol of CCl_2F_2 contains 2 mol of Cl atoms. We write the ratio as:

$$1 \text{ mol } CCl_2F_2 : 2 \text{ mol Cl}$$

With ratios such as these—which come from the chemical formula—we can directly determine the amounts of the constituent elements present in a given amount of a compound without having to calculate mass percent composition. For example, we calculate the number of moles of Cl in 38.5 mol of CCl_2F_2 as follows:

Conceptual Plan

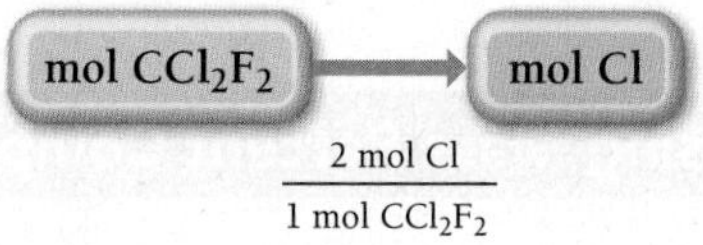

Solution

$$38.5 \cancel{\text{mol } CCl_2F_2} \times \frac{2 \text{ mol Cl}}{1 \cancel{\text{mol } CCl_2F_2}} = 77.0 \text{ mol Cl}$$

As we have seen, however, we often want to know, not the *amount in moles* of an element in a certain number of moles of compound, but the *mass in grams* (or other units) of a constituent element in a given *mass* of the compound. Suppose we want to know the mass (in grams) of Cl in 25.0 g CCl_2F_2. The relationship inherent in the chemical formula (2 mol Cl : 1 mol CCl_2F_2) applies to the amount in moles, not to mass. Therefore, we first convert the mass of CCl_2F_2 to moles CCl_2F_2. *Then* we use the conversion factor from the chemical formula to convert to moles Cl. Finally, we use the molar mass of Cl to convert to grams Cl.

Conceptual Plan

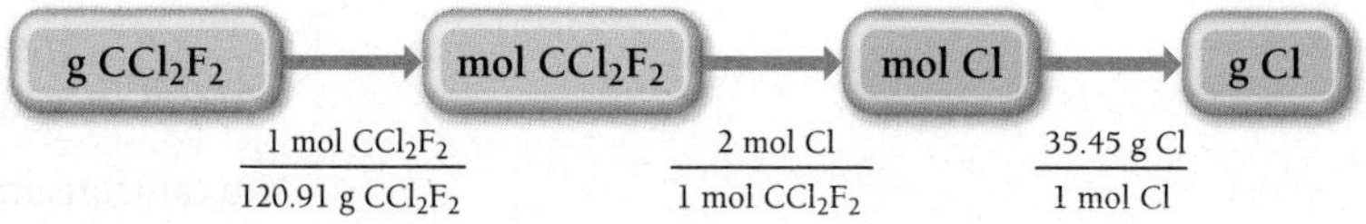

Solution

$$25.0 \cancel{\text{g } CCl_2F_2} \times \frac{1 \cancel{\text{mol } CCl_2F_2}}{120.91 \cancel{\text{g } CCl_2F_2}} \times \frac{2 \cancel{\text{mol Cl}}}{1 \cancel{\text{mol } CCl_2F_2}} \times \frac{35.45 \text{ g Cl}}{1 \cancel{\text{mol Cl}}} = 14.7 \text{ g Cl}$$

Notice that we must convert from g CCl_2F_2 to mol CCl_2F_2 *before* we can use the chemical formula as a conversion factor. *Always remember that the chemical formula indicates the relationship between the amounts (in moles) of substances, not between the masses (in grams) of them.*

The general form for solving problems in which we need to find the mass of an element present in a given mass of a compound is:

$$\text{Mass compound} \longrightarrow \text{moles compound} \longrightarrow \text{moles element} \longrightarrow \text{mass element}$$

We use the atomic or molar mass to convert between mass and moles, and we use relationships inherent in the chemical to convert between moles and moles.

WATCH **NOW!**

INTERACTIVE WORKED EXAMPLE 3.16

EXAMPLE 3.16 Chemical Formulas as Conversion Factors

Hydrogen may be used in the future to replace gasoline as a fuel. Most major automobile companies are developing vehicles that run on hydrogen. These cars have the potential to be less environmentally harmful than our current vehicles because their only emission is water vapor. One way to obtain hydrogen for fuel is to use an emission-free energy source such as wind power to form elemental hydrogen from water. What mass of hydrogen (in grams) is contained in 1.00 gallon of water? (The density of water is 1.00 g/mL.)

SORT You are given a volume of water and asked to find the mass of hydrogen it contains. You are also given the density of water.

GIVEN: 1.00 gal H_2O

$d_{H_2O} = 1.00 \text{ g/mL}$

FIND: g H

STRATEGIZE The first part of the conceptual plan shows how to convert the units of volume from gallons to liters and then to mL. It also shows how to use the density to convert mL to g.

CONCEPTUAL PLAN

$$\text{gal } H_2O \xrightarrow{\frac{3.785 \text{ L}}{1 \text{ gal}}} \text{L } H_2O \xrightarrow{\frac{1000 \text{ mL}}{1 \text{ L}}} \text{mL } H_2O \xrightarrow{\frac{1.00 \text{ g}}{1 \text{ mL}}} \text{g } H_2O$$

The second part of the conceptual plan is the basic sequence: mass → moles → moles → mass. Convert between moles and mass using the appropriate molar masses, and convert from mol H_2O to mol H using the conversion factor derived from the molecular formula.

$$\text{g } H_2O \xrightarrow{\frac{1 \text{ mol } H_2O}{18.02 \text{ g } H_2O}} \text{mol } H_2O \xrightarrow{\frac{2 \text{ mol H}}{1 \text{ mol } H_2O}} \text{mol H} \xrightarrow{\frac{1.008 \text{ g H}}{1 \text{ mol H}}} \text{g H}$$

RELATIONSHIPS USED

3.785 L = 1 gal

1000 mL = 1 L

1.00 g H_2O = 1 mL H_2O (density of H_2O)

Molar mass H_2O = 2(1.008) + 16.00 = 18.02 g/mol

2 mol H : 1 mol H_2O

1.008 g H = 1 mol H

SOLVE Follow the conceptual plan to solve the problem.

SOLUTION

$$1.00 \text{ gal } H_2O \times \frac{3.785 \text{ L}}{1 \text{ gal}} \times \frac{1000 \text{ mL}}{1 \text{ L}} \times \frac{1.00 \text{ g}}{\text{mL}} = 3.7\underline{8}5 \times 10^3 \text{ g } H_2O$$

$$3.7\underline{8}5 \times 10^3 \text{ g } H_2O \times \frac{1 \text{ mol } H_2O}{18.02 \text{ g } H_2O} \times \frac{2 \text{ mol H}}{1 \text{ mol } H_2O} \times \frac{1.008 \text{ g H}}{1 \text{ mol H}} = 4.23 \times 10^2 \text{ g H}$$

CHECK The units of the answer (g H) are correct. Since a gallon of water is about 3.8 L, its mass is about 3.8 kg. H is a light atom, so its mass should be significantly less than 3.8 kg, which it is in the answer.

FOR PRACTICE 3.16 Determine the mass of oxygen in a 7.2-g sample of $Al_2(SO_4)_3$.

FOR MORE PRACTICE 3.16 Butane (C_4H_{10}) is the liquid fuel in lighters. How many grams of carbon are present within a lighter containing 7.25 mL of butane? (The density of liquid butane is 0.601 g/mL.)

CHEMICAL FORMULAS AND ELEMENTAL COMPOSITION

3.11 Cc Conceptual Connection ANSWER **NOW!**

The molecular formula for water is H_2O. Which ratio can be correctly derived from this formula? Explain.

(a) 2 g H : 1 g H_2O **(b)** 2 mL H : 1 mL H_2O **(c)** 2 mol H : 1 mol H_2O

CHEMISTRY AND MEDICINE | Methylmercury in Fish

In the last decade, the U.S. Environmental Protection Agency (EPA) has grown increasingly concerned about mercury levels in fish. Mercury—which is present in fish as methylmercury—affects the central nervous system of humans who eat the fish, especially children and developing fetuses. In a developing fetus, excessive mercury exposure can result in slowed mental development and even retardation. Some lakes now have warnings about eating too much fish caught in the lakes.

Recent regulations force fish vendors to alert customers about the dangers of eating too much of certain kinds of commercial fish, including shark, tuna, and mackerel. These fish tend to contain high levels of methylmercury and therefore should be eaten in moderation, especially by children and pregnant women. The U.S. Food and Drug Administration (FDA) *action level*—the level below which the FDA claims the food has no adverse health effects—for methylmercury in fish is 1.0 ppm or 1.0 g of methylmercury per million grams of fish. However, a number of environmental advocacy groups, including the EPA, have suggested that, while this level may be safe for adults, it is too high for children and pregnant women. Consequently, the FDA suggests that pregnant women limit their intake of fish to 12 ounces per week.

▲ Lakes containing mercury—either from natural sources or from pollution—often have posted limits for the number of fish from the lake that can be eaten safely.

QUESTION *The levels of methylmercury in fish are normally tested by laboratory techniques that measure only the mercury (Hg). Suppose a lab analyzes a 14.5 g sample of fish and finds that it contains 1.03×10^{-5} g of mercury. How much methylmercury ($HgCH_3Cl$) is in the fish in parts per million (ppm)? Is this above the FDA action level?*

3.10 Determining a Chemical Formula from Experimental Data

In Section 3.8, we calculated mass percent composition from a chemical formula. Can we also do the reverse? Can we calculate a chemical formula from mass percent composition? This question is important because many laboratory analyses of compounds list the relative masses of each element present in the compound. For example, if we decompose water into hydrogen and oxygen in the laboratory, we can measure the masses of hydrogen and oxygen produced. Can we determine a chemical formula from these data? The answer is a qualified yes. We can determine a chemical formula, but it is an empirical formula (not a molecular formula). To get a molecular formula, we need additional information, such as the molar mass of the compound.

Suppose we decompose a sample of water in the laboratory and find that it produces 0.857 g of hydrogen and 6.86 g of oxygen. How do we determine an empirical formula from these data? We know that an empirical formula represents a ratio of atoms or a ratio of moles of atoms, *not a ratio of masses*. So the first thing we must do is convert our data from mass (in grams) to amount (in moles). How many moles of each element are present in the sample? To convert to moles, we divide each mass by the molar mass of that element:

$$\text{Moles H} = 0.857\,\cancel{\text{g H}} \times \frac{1\ \text{mol H}}{1.01\,\cancel{\text{g H}}} = 0.849\ \text{mol H}$$

$$\text{Moles O} = 6.86\,\cancel{\text{g O}} \times \frac{1\ \text{mol O}}{16.00\,\cancel{\text{g O}}} = 0.429\ \text{mol O}$$

From these data, we know there are 0.849 mol H for every 0.429 mol O. We can now write a *pseudoformula* for water:

$$H_{0.849}O_{0.429}$$

To get the smallest whole-number subscripts in our formula, we divide all the subscripts by the smallest one, in this case 0.429:

$$H_{\frac{0.849}{0.429}}O_{\frac{0.429}{0.429}} = H_{1.98}O = H_2O$$

Our empirical formula for water, which also happens to be the molecular formula, is H_2O. You can use the procedure shown here to obtain the empirical formula of any compound from experimental data giving the relative masses of the constituent elements. The left column outlines the procedure, and the center and right columns contain two examples of how to apply the procedure.

WATCH **NOW!**
INTERACTIVE WORKED EXAMPLE VIDEO 3.18

HOW TO: *Obtain an Empirical Formula from Experimental Data*	**EXAMPLE 3.17** Obtaining an Empirical Formula from Experimental Data	**EXAMPLE 3.18** Obtaining an Empirical Formula from Experimental Data
	A compound containing nitrogen and oxygen is decomposed in the laboratory. It produces 24.5 g nitrogen and 70.0 g oxygen. Calculate the empirical formula of the compound.	A laboratory analysis of aspirin determines the following mass percent composition: C 60.00%; H 4.48%; O 35.52% Find the empirical formula.
1. Write down (or calculate) as *given* the masses of each element present in a sample of the compound. If you are given mass percent composition, assume a 100-g sample and calculate the masses of each element from the given percentages.	**GIVEN:** 24.5 g N, 70.0 g O **FIND:** empirical formula	**GIVEN:** In a 100-g sample: 60.00 g C, 4.48 g H, 35.52 g O **FIND:** empirical formula
2. Convert each of the masses in step 1 to moles by using the appropriate molar mass for each element as a conversion factor.	$24.5\ \cancel{g\,N} \times \frac{1\ mol\ N}{14.01\ \cancel{g\,N}} = 1.75\ mol\ N$ $70.0\ \cancel{g\,O} \times \frac{1\ mol\ O}{16.00\ \cancel{g\,O}} = 4.38\ mol\ O$	$60.00\ \cancel{g\,C} \times \frac{1\ mol\ C}{12.01\ \cancel{g\,C}} = 4.996\ mol\ C$ $4.48\ \cancel{g\,H} \times \frac{1\ mol\ H}{1.008\ \cancel{g\,H}} = 4.44\ mol\ H$ $35.52\ \cancel{g\,O} \times \frac{1\ mol\ O}{16.00\ \cancel{g\,O}} = 2.220\ mol\ O$
3. Write down a pseudoformula for the compound using the number of moles of each element (from step 2) as subscripts.	$N_{1.75}O_{4.38}$	$C_{4.996}H_{4.44}O_{2.220}$
4. Divide all the subscripts in the formula by the smallest subscript.	$N_{\frac{1.75}{1.75}}O_{\frac{4.38}{1.75}} \longrightarrow N_1O_{2.5}$	$C_{\frac{4.996}{2.220}}H_{\frac{4.44}{2.220}}O_{\frac{2.220}{2.220}} \longrightarrow C_{2.25}H_2O_1$
5. If the subscripts are not whole numbers, multiply all the subscripts by a small whole number (see table) to get whole-number subscripts.	$N_1O_{2.5} \times 2 \longrightarrow N_2O_5$ The correct empirical formula is N_2O_5.	$C_{2.25}H_2O_1 \times 4 \longrightarrow C_9H_8O_4$ The correct empirical formula is $C_9H_8O_4$.

Fractional Subscript	Multiply by This
0.20	5
0.25	4
0.33	3
0.40	5
0.50	2
0.66	3
0.75	4
0.80	5

FOR PRACTICE 3.17
A sample of a compound is decomposed in the laboratory and produces 165 g carbon, 27.8 g hydrogen, and 220.2 g oxygen. Calculate the empirical formula of the compound.

FOR PRACTICE 3.18
Ibuprofen has the following mass percent composition:
C 75.69%, H 8.80%, O 15.51%.
What is the empirical formula of ibuprofen?

Determining Molecular Formulas for Compounds

We can find the molecular formula of a compound from the empirical formula if we also know the molar mass of the compound. Recall from Section 3.3 that the molecular formula is always a whole-number multiple of the empirical formula:

$$\text{Molecular formula} = \text{empirical formula} \times n, \text{ where } n = 1, 2, 3, \ldots$$

Suppose we want to find the molecular formula for fructose (a sugar found in fruit) from its empirical formula, CH_2O, and its molar mass, 180.2 g/mol. We know that the molecular formula is a whole-number multiple of CH_2O:

$$\begin{aligned}\text{Molecular formula} &= (CH_2O) \times n \\ &= C_nH_{2n}O_n\end{aligned}$$

We also know that the molar mass is a whole-number multiple of the **empirical formula molar mass**, the sum of the masses of all the atoms in the empirical formula.

$$\text{Molar mass} = \text{empirical formula molar mass} \times n$$

For a particular compound, the value of n in both cases is the same. Therefore, we can find n by calculating the ratio of the molar mass to the empirical formula molar mass:

$$n = \frac{\text{molar mass}}{\text{empirical formula molar mass}}$$

For fructose, the empirical formula molar mass is:

$$\begin{aligned}&\text{Empirical formula molar mass} \\ &\quad = 12.01 \text{ g/mol} + 2(1.01 \text{ g/mol}) + 16.00 \text{ g/mol} = 30.03 \text{ g/mol}\end{aligned}$$

Therefore, n is:

$$n = \frac{180.2 \cancel{\text{g/mol}}}{30.03 \cancel{\text{g/mol}}} = 6$$

We can then use this value of n to find the molecular formula:

$$\text{Molecular formula} = (CH_2O) \times 6 = C_6H_{12}O_6$$

EXAMPLE 3.19 Determining a Molecular Formula from an Empirical Formula and Molar Mass

Butanedione—the component responsible for the smell and taste of butter and cheese—contains the elements carbon, hydrogen, and oxygen. The empirical formula of butanedione is C_2H_3O, and its molar mass is 86.09 g/mol. Determine its molecular formula.

SORT You are given the empirical formula and molar mass of butanedione and asked to find the molecular formula.	**GIVEN:** Empirical formula $= C_2H_3O$ molar mass $= 86.09$ g/mol **FIND:** Molecular formula
STRATEGIZE A molecular formula is always a whole-number multiple of the empirical formula. Divide the molar mass by the empirical formula molar mass to find the whole number.	Molecular formula = empirical formula $\times n$ $n = \frac{\text{molar mass}}{\text{empirical formula molar mass}}$
SOLVE Calculate the empirical formula mass.	Empirical formula molar mass $= 2(12.01 \text{ g/mol}) + 3(1.008 \text{ g/mol}) + 16.00 \text{ g/mol} = 43.04 \text{ g/mol}$
Divide the molar mass by the empirical formula mass to find n.	$n = \frac{\text{molar mass}}{\text{empirical formula molar mass}} = \frac{86.09 \cancel{\text{g/mol}}}{43.04 \cancel{\text{g/mol}}} = 2$
Multiply the empirical formula by n to obtain the molecular formula.	Molecular formula $= C_2H_3O \times 2$ $= C_4H_6O_2$

CHECK Check the answer by calculating the molar mass of the formula as follows:

$4(12.01\ g/mol) + 6(1.008\ g/mol) + 2(16.00\ g/mol) = 86.09\ g/mol$

The calculated molar mass is in agreement with the given molar mass.

FOR PRACTICE 3.19 A compound has the empirical formula CH and a molar mass of 78.11 g/mol. What is its molecular formula?

FOR MORE PRACTICE 3.19 Determine the molecular formula for the compound with a molar mass of 60.10 g/mol and the following percent composition:

C, 39.97%
H, 13.41%
N, 46.62%

Combustion Analysis

In the previous section, we discussed how to determine the empirical formula of a compound from the relative masses of its constituent elements. Another common (and related) way to obtain empirical formulas for unknown compounds, especially those containing carbon and hydrogen, is **combustion analysis**. In combustion analysis, the unknown compound undergoes combustion (or burning) in the presence of pure oxygen, as shown in Figure 3.13▼. When the sample burns, all of the carbon converts to CO_2, and all of the hydrogen converts to H_2O. The CO_2 and H_2O are weighed. With these masses, we can use the numerical relationships between moles inherent in the formulas for CO_2 and H_2O (1 mol CO_2 : 1 mol C and 1 mol H_2O : 2 mol H) to determine the amounts of C and H in the original sample. We can determine the amounts of any other elemental constituents, such as O, Cl, or N, by subtracting the sum of the masses of C and H from the original mass of the sample. Examples 3.20 and 3.21 illustrate how to perform these calculations for a sample containing only C and H and for a sample containing C, H, and O.

Combustion is a type of *chemical reaction*. We discuss chemical reactions and their representation in Section 4.2.

Combustion Analysis

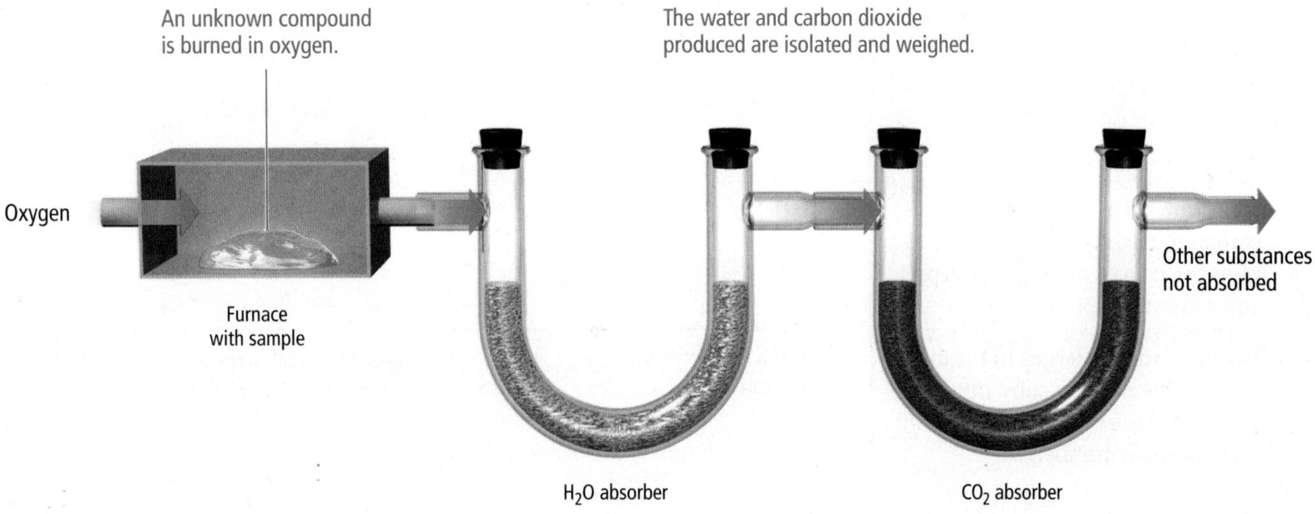

▲ **FIGURE 3.13 Combustion Analysis Apparatus**

WATCH **NOW!**
INTERACTIVE WORKED EXAMPLE VIDEO 3.21

HOW TO: *Determine an Empirical Formula from Combustion Analysis*	**EXAMPLE 3.20** Determining an Empirical Formula from Combustion Analysis	**EXAMPLE 3.21** Determining an Empirical Formula from Combustion Analysis
	Upon combustion, a compound containing only carbon and hydrogen produces 1.83 g CO_2 and 0.901 g H_2O. Find the empirical formula of the compound.	Upon combustion, a 0.8233-g sample of a compound containing only carbon, hydrogen, and oxygen produces 2.445 g CO_2 and 0.6003 g H_2O. Find the empirical formula of the compound.
1. Write down as *given* the masses of each combustion product and the mass of the sample (if given).	**GIVEN:** 1.83 g CO_2, 0.901 g H_2O **FIND:** empirical formula	**GIVEN:** 0.8233-g sample, 2.445 g CO_2, 0.6003 g H_2O **FIND:** empirical formula
2. Convert the masses of CO_2 and H_2O from step 1 to moles by using the appropriate molar mass for each compound as a conversion factor.	$1.83\ \text{g}\ \cancel{CO_2} \times \frac{1\ \text{mol}\ CO_2}{44.01\ \text{g}\ \cancel{CO_2}} = 0.0416\ \text{mol}\ CO_2$ $0.901\ \text{g}\ \cancel{H_2O} \times \frac{1\ \text{mol}\ H_2O}{18.02\ \text{g}\ \cancel{H_2O}} = 0.0500\ \text{mol}\ H_2O$	$2.445\ \text{g}\ \cancel{CO_2} \times \frac{1\ \text{mol}\ CO_2}{44.01\ \text{g}\ \cancel{CO_2}} = 0.05556\ \text{mol}\ CO_2$ $0.6003\ \text{g}\ \cancel{H_2O} \times \frac{1\ \text{mol}\ H_2O}{18.02\ \text{g}\ \cancel{H_2O}} = 0.03331\ \text{mol}\ H_2O$
3. Convert the moles of CO_2 and moles of H_2O from step 2 to moles of C and moles of H using the conversion factors inherent in the chemical formulas of CO_2 and H_2O.	$0.0416\ \cancel{\text{mol}\ CO_2} \times \frac{1\ \text{mol C}}{1\ \cancel{\text{mol}\ CO_2}} = 0.0416\ \text{mol C}$ $0.0500\ \cancel{\text{mol}\ H_2O} \times \frac{2\ \text{mol H}}{1\ \cancel{\text{mol}\ H_2O}} = 0.100\ \text{mol H}$	$0.05556\ \cancel{\text{mol}\ CO_2} \times \frac{1\ \text{mol C}}{1\ \cancel{\text{mol}\ CO_2}} = 0.05556\ \text{mol C}$ $0.03331\ \cancel{\text{mol}\ H_2O} \times \frac{2\ \text{mol H}}{1\ \cancel{\text{mol}\ H_2O}} = 0.06662\ \text{mol H}$
4. If the compound contains an element other than C and H, find the mass of the other element by subtracting the sum of the masses of C and H from the mass of the sample. Finally, convert the mass of the other element to moles.	The sample contains no elements other than C and H, so proceed to the next step.	$\text{Mass C} = 0.05556\ \cancel{\text{mol C}} \times \frac{12.01\ \text{g C}}{\cancel{\text{mol C}}} = 0.6673\ \text{g C}$ $\text{Mass H} = 0.06662\ \cancel{\text{mol H}} \times \frac{1.008\ \text{g H}}{\cancel{\text{mol H}}} = 0.06715\ \text{g H}$ $\text{Mass O} = 0.8233\ \text{g} - (0.6673\ \text{g} + 0.06715\ \text{g}) = 0.0889\ \text{g}$ $\text{Mol O} = 0.0889\ \cancel{\text{g O}} \times \frac{\text{mol O}}{16.00\ \cancel{\text{g O}}} = 0.00556\ \text{mol O}$
5. Write down a pseudoformula for the compound using the number of moles of each element (from steps 3 and 4) as subscripts.	$C_{0.0416}H_{0.100}$	$C_{0.05556}H_{0.06662}O_{0.00556}$
6. Divide all the subscripts in the formula by the smallest subscript. (Round all subscripts that are within 0.1 of a whole number.)	$C_{\frac{0.0416}{0.0416}}H_{\frac{0.100}{0.0416}} \longrightarrow C_1H_{2.4}$	$C_{\frac{0.05556}{0.00556}}H_{\frac{0.0662}{0.00556}}O_{\frac{0.00556}{0.00556}} \longrightarrow C_{10}H_{12}O_1$

7. If the subscripts are not whole numbers, multiply all the subscripts by a small whole number to get whole-number subscripts.	$C_1H_{2.4} \times 5 \longrightarrow C_5H_{12}$ The correct empirical formula is C_5H_{12}.	The subscripts are whole numbers; no additional multiplication is needed. The correct empirical formula is $C_{10}H_{12}O$.
	FOR PRACTICE 3.20 Upon combustion, a compound containing only carbon and hydrogen produces 1.60 g CO_2 and 0.819 g H_2O. Find the empirical formula of the compound.	**FOR PRACTICE 3.21** Upon combustion, a 0.8009-g sample of a compound containing only carbon, hydrogen, and oxygen produces 1.6004 g CO_2 and 0.6551 g H_2O. Find the empirical formula of the compound.

3.11 Organic Compounds

Early chemists divided compounds into two types: organic and inorganic. They designated organic compounds as those that originate from living things. Sugar—from sugar-cane or the sugar beet—is a common example of an organic compound. Inorganic compounds, on the other hand, originate from the earth. Salt—mined from the ground or from the ocean—is a common example of an inorganic compound.

Not only did early chemists view organic and inorganic compounds as different in their origin, but also they recognized organic and inorganic compounds to be different in their properties. Organic compounds are easily decomposed. Inorganic compounds, however, are typically more difficult to decompose. Eighteenth-century chemists could synthesize inorganic compounds in the laboratory, but they could not synthesize organic compounds. This was considered to be another great difference between the two different types of compounds. Today, chemists can synthesize both organic and inorganic compounds, and even though organic chemistry is a subfield of chemistry, the differences between organic and inorganic compounds are now viewed as primarily organizational (not fundamental).

▲ The organic compound cinnamaldehyde is largely responsible for the taste and smell of cinnamon.

Organic compounds are common in everyday substances. Many smells—such as those in perfumes, spices, and foods—are caused by organic compounds. When you sprinkle cinnamon onto your French toast, some cinnamaldehyde—an organic compound present in cinnamon—evaporates into the air. As you inhale cinnamaldehyde molecules, you experience the unique smell of cinnamon. Organic compounds are the major components of living organisms. They are also the main components of most fuels, such as gasoline, oil, and natural gas, and they are the active ingredients in most pharmaceuticals, such as aspirin and ibuprofen.

Organic compounds are composed of carbon and hydrogen and a few other elements, including nitrogen, oxygen, and sulfur. The key element in organic chemistry, however, is carbon. In its compounds, carbon always forms four bonds. The simplest organic compound is methane, or CH_4.

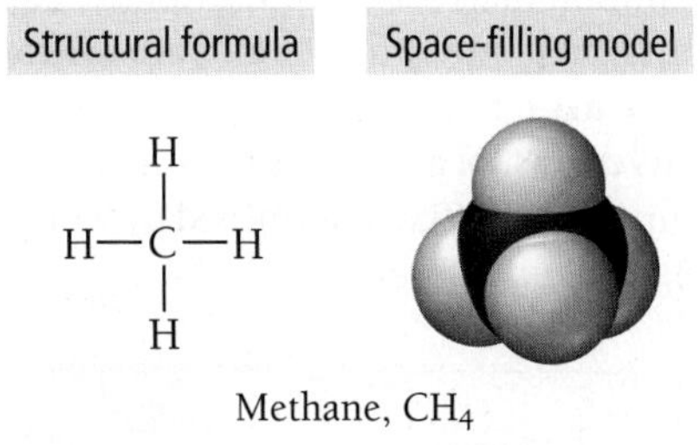

Methane, CH_4

The chemistry of carbon is unique and complex because carbon frequently bonds to itself to form chain, branched, and ring structures.

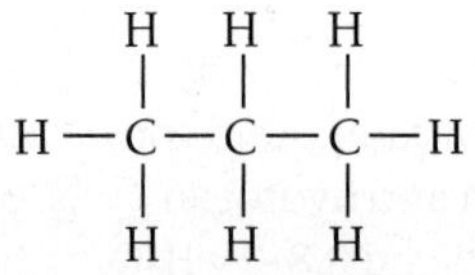

Propane (C_3H_8)

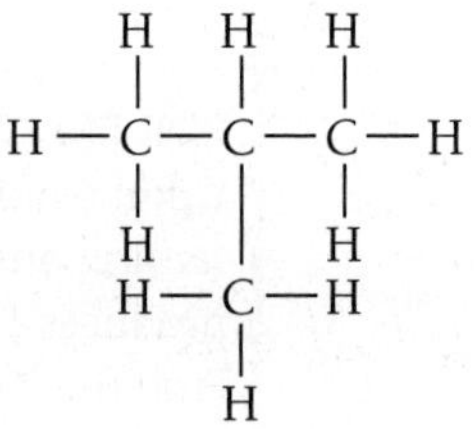

Isobutane (C_4H_{10})

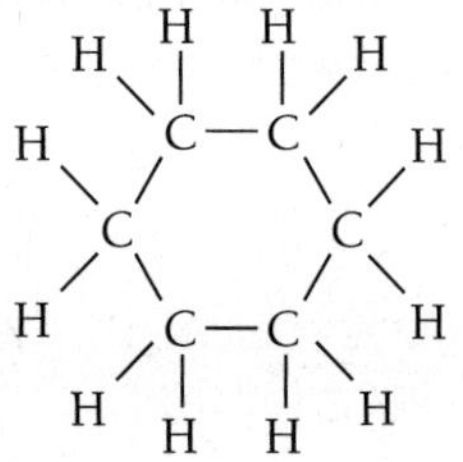

Cyclohexane (C_6H_{12})

Carbon can also form double bonds and triple bonds with itself and with other elements.

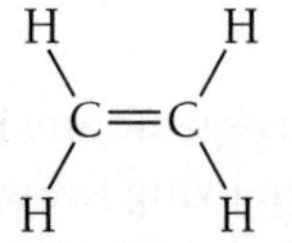

Ethene (C_2H_4)

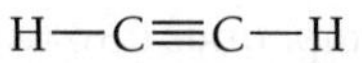

Ethyne (C_2H_2)

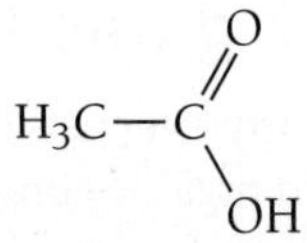

Acetic acid (CH_3COOH)

This versatility allows carbon to serve as the backbone of millions of different chemical compounds, which is why a general survey of organic chemistry is a year-long course.

Hydrocarbons

We can begin to scratch the surface of organic chemistry by categorizing organic compounds into types: hydrocarbons and functionalized hydrocarbons.

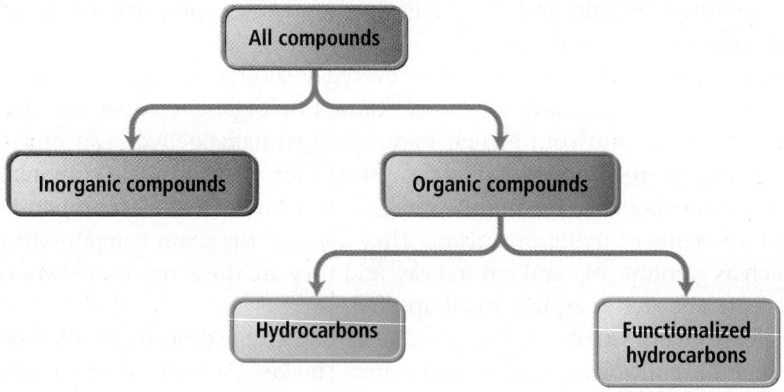

▲ Gasoline is composed mostly of hydrocarbons.

Hydrocarbons are organic compounds that contain only carbon and hydrogen. Hydrocarbons compose common fuels such as oil, gasoline, liquid propane gas, and natural gas. Hydrocarbons containing only single bonds are **alkanes**, while those containing double or triple bonds are **alkenes** and **alkynes**, respectively. The names of simple, straight-chain hydrocarbons consist of a base name, which is determined by the number of carbon atoms in the chain, and a suffix, determined by whether the hydrocarbon is an alkane (*-ane*), alkene (*-ene*), or alkyne (*-yne*).

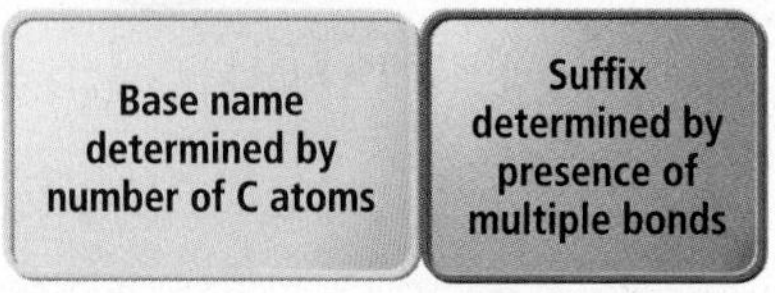

The base names for a number of hydrocarbons are listed here:

meth = 1	hex = 6
eth = 2	hept = 7
prop = 3	oct = 8
but = 4	non = 9
pent = 5	dec = 10

Table 3.5 lists some common hydrocarbons, their names, and their uses.

TABLE 3.5 ■ Common Hydrocarbons

Name	Molecular Formula	Structural Formula	Space-filling Model	Common Uses
Methane	CH_4	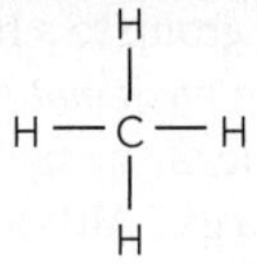		Primary component of natural gas
Propane	C_3H_8	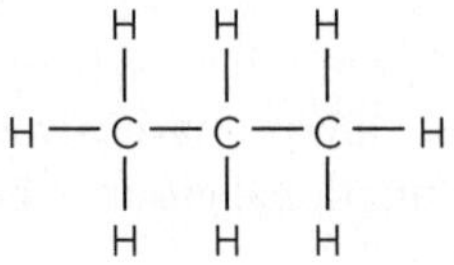	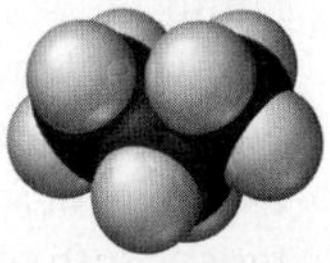	LP gas for grills and outdoor stoves
n-Butane*	C_4H_{10}	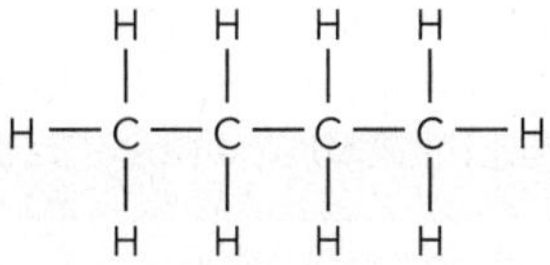	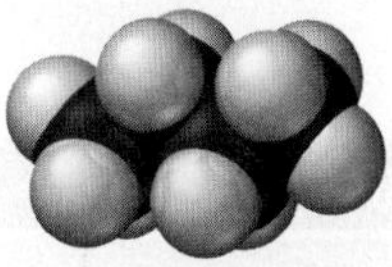	Common fuel for lighters
n-Pentane*	C_5H_{12}	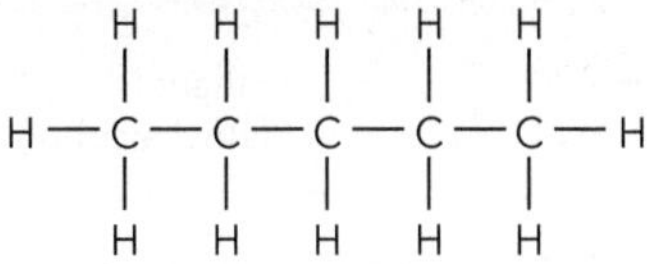	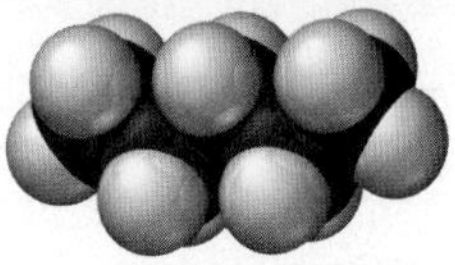	Component of gasoline
Ethene	C_2H_4	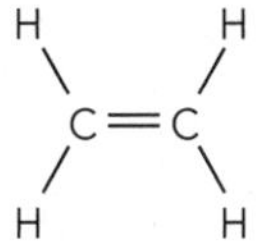	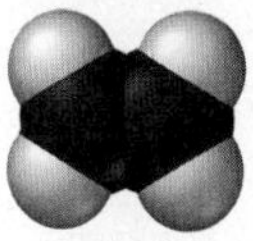	Ripening agent in fruit
Ethyne	C_2H_2			Fuel for welding torches

*The "*n*" in the names of these hydrocarbons stands for "normal," which means straight chain.

Functionalized Hydrocarbons

Functionalized hydrocarbons are hydrocarbons in which a **functional group**—a characteristic atom or group of atoms—is incorporated into the hydrocarbon. For example, **alcohols** are organic compounds that have an —OH functional group. We designate the hydrocarbon portion of a molecule as "R," and we write the general formula for an alcohol as R—OH. Some examples of alcohols include methanol (also

The term *functional group* derives from the functionality or chemical character that a specific atom or group of atoms imparts to an organic compound. Even a carbon–carbon double bond can justifiably be called a "functional group."

known as methyl alcohol or wood alcohol) and isopropanol (also known as isopropyl alcohol or rubbing alcohol).

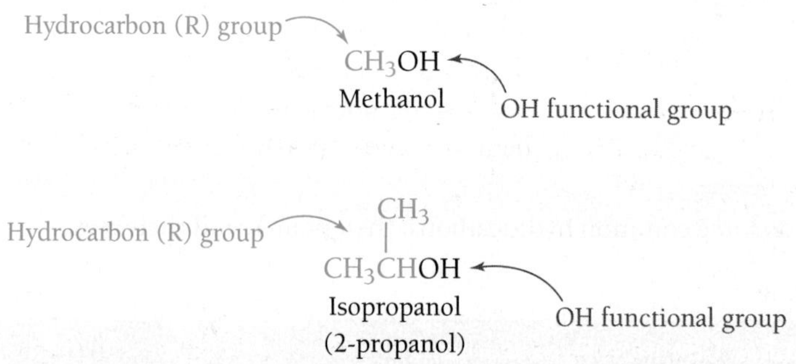

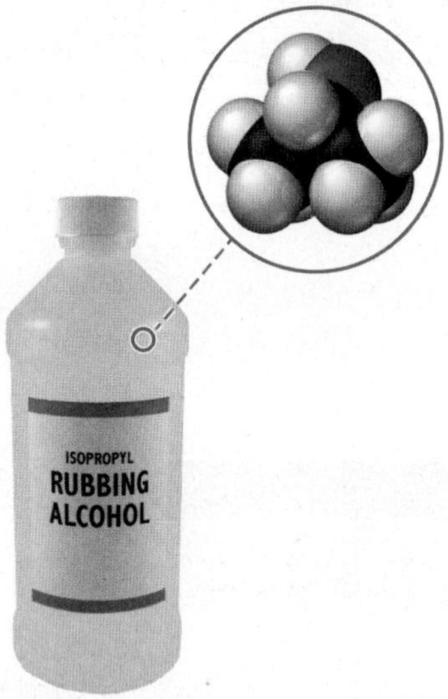

▲ Rubbing alcohol is isopropyl alcohol.

A group of organic compounds with the same functional group forms a **family**. Methanol and isopropyl alcohol are both members of the alcohol family of compounds.

The addition of a functional group to a hydrocarbon usually alters the properties of the compound significantly. Take *methanol*, which can be thought of as methane with an —OH group substituted for one of the hydrogen atoms. Methanol is a liquid at room temperature, whereas *methane* is a gas. Although each member of a family is unique, the common functional group bestows some chemical similarities on members of the same family.

The names of functional groups have suffixes or endings unique to that functional group. Alcohols, for example, always have names that end in *-ol*. Table 3.6 provides examples of some common functional groups, their general formulas, and their characteristic suffixes or endings.

TABLE 3.6 ■ Families of Organic Compounds

Family	Name Ending	General Formula	Example	Name	Occurrence/Use
Alcohols	-ol	R—OH	CH_3CH_2—OH	Ethanol (ethyl alcohol)	Alcohol in fermented beverages
Ethers	ether	R—O—R′	CH_3CH_2—O—CH_2CH_3	Diethyl ether	Anesthetic; laboratory solvent
Aldehydes	-al	R—C(=O)—H	H_3C—C(=O)—H	Ethanal (acetaldehyde)	Perfumes; flavors
Ketones	-one	R—C(=O)—R′	H_3C—C(=O)—CH_3	Propanone (acetone)	Fingernail polish remover
Carboxylic acids	acid	R—C(=O)—OH	H_3C—C(=O)—OH	Acetic acid	Vinegar
Esters	-ate	R—C(=O)—OR′	H_3C—C(=O)—OCH_3	Methyl acetate	Laboratory solvent
Amines	amine	RNH_2	CH_3CH_2—N(H)—H	Ethyl amine	Smell of rotten fish

Self-Assessment Quiz

Q1. What is the empirical formula of a compound with the molecular formula $C_{10}H_8$? **MISSED THIS?** *Read Section 3.3*

a) C_5H_3
b) C_2H_4
c) C_5H_4
d) CH

Q2. Which substance is an ionic compound?

MISSED THIS? *Read Section 3.2*

a) SrI_2
b) N_2O_4
c) He
d) CCl_4

Q3. What is the correct formula for the compound formed between calcium and sulfur?

MISSED THIS? *Read Section 3.5; Watch KCV 3.5, IWE 3.3*

a) CaS
b) Ca_2S
c) CaS_2
d) CaS_3

Q4. Name the compound SrI_2.

MISSED THIS? *Read Section 3.5; Watch KCV 3.5, IWE 3.11*

a) strontium iodide
b) strontium diiodide
c) strontium(II) iodide
d) strontium(II) diiodide

Q5. What is the formula for manganese(IV) oxide?

MISSED THIS? *Read Section 3.5; Watch KCV 3.5*

a) Mn_4O
b) MnO_4
c) Mn_2O
d) MnO_2

Q6. Name the compound $Pb(C_2H_3O_2)_2$.

MISSED THIS? *Read Section 3.5; Watch KCV 3.5, IWE 3.11*

a) lead(II) carbonate
b) lead(II) acetate
c) lead bicarbonate
d) lead diacetate

Q7. Name the compound P_2I_4.

MISSED THIS? *Read Section 3.6; Watch KCV 3.6, IWE 3.11*

a) phosphorus iodide
b) phosphorus diiodide
c) phosphorus(II) iodide
d) diphosphorus tetraiodide

Q8. Name the compound $HNO_2(aq)$.

MISSED THIS? *Read Section 3.6; Watch KCV 3.6, IWE 3.11*

a) hydrogen nitrogen dioxide
b) hydrogen nitrate
c) nitric acid
d) nitrous acid

Q9. Determine the number of CH_2Cl_2 molecules in 25.0 g CH_2Cl_2.

MISSED THIS? *Read Section 3.8; Watch IWE 3.13*

a) 0.294 molecules
b) 1.77×10^{23} molecules
c) 1.28×10^{27} molecules
d) 1.51×10^{25} molecules

Q10. List the elements in the compound CF_2Cl_2 in order of decreasing mass percent composition.

MISSED THIS? *Read Section 3.9*

a) C > F > Cl
b) F > Cl > C
c) Cl > C > F
d) Cl > F > C

Q11. Determine the mass of potassium in 35.5 g of KBr.

MISSED THIS? *Read Section 3.9; Watch IWE 3.16*

a) 17.4 g
b) 0.298 g
c) 11.7 g
d) 32.9 g

Q12. A compound is 52.14% C, 13.13% H, and 34.73% O by mass. What is the empirical formula of the compound?

MISSED THIS? *Read Section 3.10; Watch IWE 3.18*

a) $C_2H_8O_3$
b) C_2H_6O
c) C_4HO_3
d) C_3HO_6

Q13. A compound has the empirical formula CH_2O and a formula mass of 120.10 amu. What is the molecular formula of the compound? **MISSED THIS?** *Read Section 3.10*

a) CH_2O
b) $C_2H_4O_2$
c) $C_3H_6O_3$
d) $C_4H_8O_4$

Q14. Combustion of 30.42 g of a compound containing only carbon, hydrogen, and oxygen produces 35.21 g CO_2 and 14.42 g H_2O. What is the empirical formula of the compound? **MISSED THIS?** *Read Section 3.10; Watch IWE 3.21*

a) $C_4H_8O_6$
b) $C_2H_4O_3$
c) $C_2H_2O_3$
d) C_6HO_{12}

Answers: 1. (c) **2.** (a) **3.** (a) **4.** (a) **5.** (d) **6.** (b) **7.** (d) **8.** (d) **9.** (b) **10.** (d) **11.** (c) **12.** (b) **13.** (d) **14.** (b)

CHAPTER 3 IN REVIEW

TERMS

Section 3.2
ionic bond (93)
ionic compound (93)
covalent bond (94)
molecular compound (94)

Section 3.3
chemical formula (94)
empirical formula (94)
molecular formula (94)
structural formula (95)
ball-and-stick molecular model (96)
space-filling molecular model (96)

Section 3.4
atomic element (96)
molecular element (96)
formula unit (98)
polyatomic ion (99)

Section 3.5
common name (101)
systematic name (101)
binary compound (102)
oxyanion (104)
hydrate (105)

Section 3.6
acid (107)
binary acid (108)
oxyacid (108)

Section 3.8
formula mass (111)

Section 3.9
mass percent composition (mass percent) (113)

Section 3.10
empirical formula molar mass (120)
combustion analysis (121)

Section 3.11
organic compound (123)
hydrocarbon (124)
alkane (124)
alkene (124)
alkyne (124)
functional group (125)
alcohol (125)
family (126)

CONCEPTS

Chemical Bonds (3.2)

- Chemical bonds, the forces that hold atoms together in compounds, arise from the interactions between nuclei and electrons in atoms.
- In an ionic bond, one or more electrons are *transferred* from one atom to another, forming a cation (positively charged) and an anion (negatively charged). The two ions are drawn together by the attraction between the opposite charges.
- In a covalent bond, one or more electrons are *shared* between two atoms. The atoms are held together by the attraction between their nuclei and the shared electrons.

Representing Molecules and Compounds (3.3, 3.4)

- A compound is represented with a chemical formula, which indicates the elements present and the number of atoms of each.
- An empirical formula gives only the *relative* number of atoms, while a molecular formula gives the *actual* number of atoms present in the molecule.
- Structural formulas show how atoms are bonded together, while molecular models portray the geometry of the molecule.
- Compounds can be divided into two types: molecular compounds, formed between two or more covalently bonded nonmetals, and ionic compounds, usually formed between a metal ionically bonded to one or more nonmetals. The smallest identifiable unit of a molecular compound is a molecule, and the smallest identifiable unit of an ionic compound is a formula unit: the smallest electrically neutral collection of ions.
- Elements can also be divided into two types: molecular elements, which occur as (mostly diatomic) molecules, and atomic elements, which occur as individual atoms.

Naming Inorganic Ionic and Molecular Compounds and Acids (3.5–3.7)

- A flowchart for naming simple inorganic compounds is provided in Section 3.7.

Formula Mass and Mole Concept for Compounds (3.8)

- The formula mass of a compound is the sum of the atomic masses of all the atoms in the chemical formula. Like the atomic masses of elements, the formula mass characterizes the average mass of a molecule (or a formula unit).
- The mass of one mole of a compound is the molar mass of that compound and equals its formula mass (in grams).

Chemical Composition (3.9, 3.10)

- The mass percent composition of a compound indicates each element's percentage of the total compound's mass. We can determine the mass percent composition from the compound's chemical formula and the molar masses of its elements.
- The chemical formula of a compound provides the relative number of atoms (or moles) of each element in a compound, and we can therefore use it to determine numerical relationships between moles of the compound and moles of its constituent elements. We can extend this relationship to mass by using the molar masses of the compound and its constituent elements.
- If the mass percent composition and molar mass of a compound are known, we can determine its empirical and molecular formulas.

Organic Compounds (3.11)

- Organic compounds are composed of carbon, hydrogen, and a few other elements such as nitrogen, oxygen, and sulfur.

- The simplest organic compounds are hydrocarbons, compounds composed of only carbon and hydrogen.
- Hydrocarbons are categorized into three types based on the bonds they contain: alkanes contain single bonds, alkenes contain double bonds, and alkynes contain triple bonds.
- All other organic compounds can be thought of as hydrocarbons with one or more functional groups—characteristic atoms or groups of atoms.
- Common functionalized hydrocarbons include alcohols, ethers, aldehydes, ketones, carboxylic acids, esters, and amines.

EQUATIONS AND RELATIONSHIPS

Formula Mass (**3.8**)

$$\left(\begin{array}{c}\text{No. of atoms of 1st element}\\ \text{in chemical formula}\end{array} \times \begin{array}{c}\text{atomic mass}\\ \text{of 1st element}\end{array}\right) + \left(\begin{array}{c}\text{No. of atoms of 2nd element}\\ \text{in chemical formula}\end{array} \times \begin{array}{c}\text{atomic mass}\\ \text{of 2nd element}\end{array}\right) + \cdots$$

Mass Percent Composition (**3.9**)

$$\text{Mass \% of element X} = \frac{\text{mass of X in 1 mol compound}}{\text{mass of 1 mol compound}} \times 100\%$$

Empirical Formula Molar Mass (**3.10**)

$$\text{Molecular formula} = n \times (\text{empirical formula})$$

$$n = \frac{\text{molar mass}}{\text{empirical formula molar mass}}$$

LEARNING OUTCOMES

Chapter Objectives	Assessment
Analyze substances by bond type (covalent or ionic), compound type (molecular or ionic), and formula (chemical, molecular, and structural) (**3.2–3.4**)	Examples 3.1, 3.2 **For Practice** 3.1, 3.2 **Exercises** 27–32
Write formulas and names for ionic compounds (**3.5**)	Examples 3.3, 3.4, 3.5, 3.6, 3.7 **For Practice** 3.3, 3.4, 3.5, 3.6, 3.7 **For More Practice** 3.5, 3.6, 3.7 **Exercises** 33–44, 55–58
Write formulas and names for hydrated ionic compounds (**3.5**)	Exercises 45–46
Write formulas and names for molecular compounds (**3.6**)	Example 3.8 **For Practice** 3.8 **For More Practice** 3.8 **Exercises** 47–50, 55–58
Write formulas and names for acids and oxyacids (**3.6**)	Examples 3.9, 3.10 **For Practice** 3.9, 3.10, 3.11 **For More Practice** 3.10 **Exercises** 51–54, 55–58
Analyze the composition of compounds in terms of formula mass, mass percent, and moles (**3.8–3.9**)	Examples 3.12, 3.13, 3.14, 3.15, 3.16 **For Practice** 3.12, 3.13, 3.14, 3.15, 3.16 **For More Practice** 3.13, 3.14, 3.15 **Exercises** 59–86
Write chemical formulas from experimental data (**3.10**)	Examples 3.17, 3.18, 3.19, 3.20, 3.21 **For Practice** 3.17, 3.18, 3.19, 3.20, 3.21 **Exercises** 87–100
Write formulas and names for organic compounds (**3.11**)	**Exercises** 101–108

EXERCISES

Mastering Chemistry provides end-of-chapter exercises, feedback-enriched tutorial problems, animations, and interactive activities to encourage problem-solving practice and deeper understanding of key concepts and topics.

REVIEW QUESTIONS

1. How do the properties of compounds compare to the properties of the elements from which the compounds are composed?

2. What is a chemical bond? Explain the difference between an ionic bond and a covalent bond.

3. Explain the different ways to represent compounds. Why are there so many?

4. What is the difference between an empirical formula and a molecular formula?

5. Define and provide an example for each of the following: atomic element, molecular element, ionic compound, molecular compound.

6. Explain how to write a formula for an ionic compound given the names of the metal and nonmetal (or polyatomic ion) in the compound.

7. Explain how to name binary ionic compounds. How do you name an ionic compound if it contains a polyatomic ion?

8. Why do the names of some ionic compounds include the charge of the metal ion while others do not?

9. Explain how to name molecular inorganic compounds.

10. How many atoms are specified by each of these prefixes: *mono-*, *di-*, *tri-*, *tetra-*, *penta-*, *hexa-*?

11. Explain how to name binary acids and oxyacids.

12. What is the formula mass for a compound? Why is it useful?

13. Explain how you can use the information in a chemical formula to determine how much of a particular element is present in a given amount of a compound. Provide some examples of why this might be important.

14. What is mass percent composition? Why is it useful?

15. What kinds of conversion factors are inherent in chemical formulas? Provide an example.

16. What kind of chemical formula can be obtained from experimental data showing the relative masses of the elements in a compound?

17. How can a molecular formula be obtained from an empirical formula? What additional information is required?

18. What is combustion analysis? What is it used for?

19. Which elements are normally present in organic compounds?

20. What is the difference between an alkane, an alkene, and an alkyne?

21. What are functionalized hydrocarbons? Cite an example of a functionalized hydrocarbon.

22. Write a generic formula for each of the families of organic compounds.

a. alcohols
b. ethers
c. aldehydes
d. ketones
e. carboxylic acids
f. esters
g. amines

PROBLEMS BY TOPIC

Note: Answers to all odd-numbered Problems, numbered in blue, can be found in Appendix III. Exercises in the Problems by Topic section are paired, with each odd-numbered problem followed by a similar even-numbered problem. Exercises in the Cumulative Problems section are also paired, but somewhat more loosely. (Challenge Problems and Conceptual Problems, because of their nature, are unpaired.)

Chemical Formulas and Molecular View of Elements and Compounds

23. Determine the number of each type of atom in each formula. **MISSED THIS?** *Read Section 3.3*

a. $Mg_3(PO_4)_2$
b. $BaCl_2$
c. $Fe(NO_2)_2$
d. $Ca(OH)_2$

24. Determine the number of each type of atom in each formula.

a. $Ca(NO_2)_2$
b. $CuSO_4$
c. $Al(NO_3)_3$
d. $Mg(HCO_3)_2$

25. Write a chemical formula for each molecular model. (See Appendix IIA for color codes.) **MISSED THIS?** *Read Section 3.3*

a.

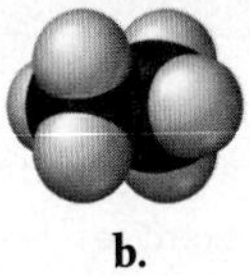
b.

c.

26. Write a chemical formula for each molecular model. (See Appendix IIA for color codes.)

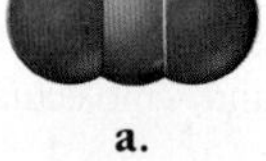
a.

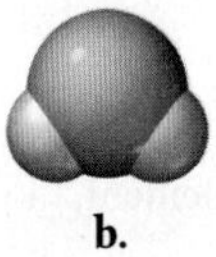
b.

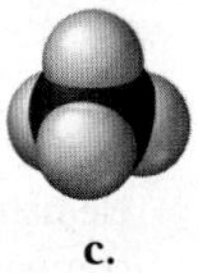
c.

27. Classify each element as atomic or molecular. **MISSED THIS?** *Read Section 3.4*

a. neon
b. fluorine
c. potassium
d. nitrogen

28. Identify the elements that have molecules as their basic units.

a. hydrogen
b. iodine
c. lead
d. oxygen

29. Classify each compound as ionic or molecular. **MISSED THIS?** *Read Section 3.2*

a. CO_2
b. $NiCl_2$
c. NaI
d. PCl_3

30. Classify each compound as ionic or molecular.

a. CF_2Cl_2
b. CCl_4
c. PtO_2
d. SO_3

31. Based on the molecular views, classify each substance as an atomic element, a molecular element, an ionic compound, or a molecular compound. **MISSED THIS?** *Read Section 3.4*

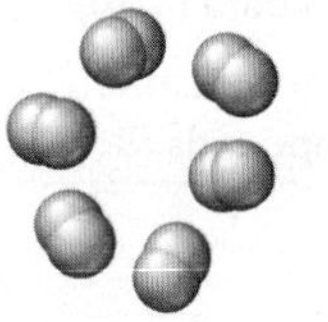
a.

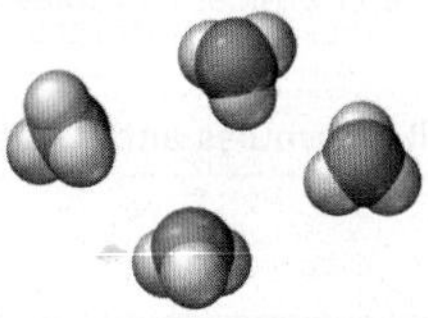
b.

c.

32. Based on the molecular views, classify each substance as an atomic element, a molecular element, an ionic compound, or a molecular compound.

a.

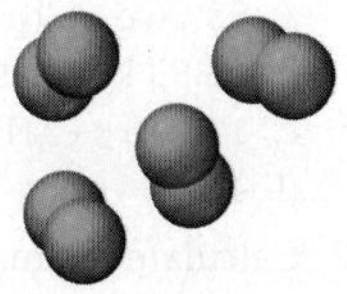

b.

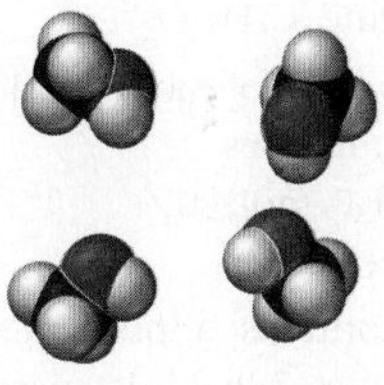

c.

Formulas and Names for Ionic Compounds

33. Write a formula for the ionic compound that forms between each pair of elements.
MISSED THIS? *Read Section 3.5; Watch KCV 3.5, IWE 3.3*
a. calcium and oxygen
b. zinc and sulfur
c. rubidium and bromine
d. aluminum and oxygen

34. Write a formula for the ionic compound that forms between each pair of elements.
a. silver and chlorine
b. sodium and sulfur
c. aluminum and sulfur
d. potassium and chlorine

35. Write a formula for the compound that forms between calcium and each polyatomic ion.
MISSED THIS? *Read Section 3.5; Watch KCV 3.5, IWE 3.3*
a. hydroxide
b. chromate
c. phosphate
d. cyanide

36. Write a formula for the compound that forms between potassium and each polyatomic ion.
a. carbonate
b. phosphate
c. hydrogen phosphate
d. acetate

37. Name each ionic compound.
MISSED THIS? *Read Section 3.5; Watch KCV 3.5, IWE 3.11*
a. Mg_3N_2 b. KF c. Na_2O
d. Li_2S e. CsF f. KI

38. Name each ionic compound.
a. $SnCl_4$ b. PbI_2 c. Fe_2O_3
d. CuI_2 e. $HgBr_2$ f. $CrCl_2$

39. Give each ionic compound an appropriate name.
MISSED THIS? *Read Section 3.5; Watch KCV 3.5, IWE 3.11*
a. SnO b. Cr_2S_3 c. RbI d. $BaBr_2$

40. Give each ionic compound an appropriate name.
a. BaS b. $FeCl_3$ c. PbI_4 d. $SrBr_2$

41. Name each ionic compound containing a polyatomic ion.
MISSED THIS? *Read Section 3.5; Watch KCV 3.5, IWE 3.11*
a. $CuNO_2$ b. $Mg(C_2H_3O_2)_2$
c. $Ba(NO_3)_2$ d. $Pb(C_2H_3O_2)_2$

42. Name each ionic compound containing a polyatomic ion.
a. $Ba(OH)_2$ b. NH_4I c. $NaBrO_4$ d. $Fe(OH)_3$

43. Write the formula for each ionic compound.
MISSED THIS? *Read Section 3.5; Watch KCV 3.5, IWE 3.11*
a. sodium hydrogen sulfite
b. lithium permanganate
c. silver nitrate
d. potassium sulfate
e. rubidium hydrogen sulfate
f. potassium hydrogen carbonate

44. Write the formula for each ionic compound.
a. copper(II) chloride
b. copper(I) iodate
c. lead(II) chromate
d. calcium fluoride
e. potassium hydroxide
f. iron(II) phosphate

45. Write the name from the formula or the formula from the name for each hydrated ionic compound.
MISSED THIS? *Read Section 3.5; Watch KCV 3.5, IWE 3.11*
a. $CoSO_4 \cdot 7\,H_2O$
b. iridium(III) bromide tetrahydrate
c. $Mg(BrO_3)_2 \cdot 6\,H_2O$
d. potassium carbonate dihydrate

46. Write the name from the formula or the formula from the name for each hydrated ionic compound.
a. cobalt(II) phosphate octahydrate
b. $BeCl_2 \cdot 2\,H_2O$
c. chromium(III) phosphate trihydrate
d. $LiNO_2 \cdot H_2O$

Formulas and Names for Molecular Compounds and Acids

47. Name each molecular compound.
MISSED THIS? *Read Section 3.6; Watch KCV 3.6, IWE 3.11*
a. CO b. NI_3 c. $SiCl_4$ d. N_4Se_4

48. Name each molecular compound.
a. SO_3 b. SO_2 c. BrF_5 d. NO

49. Write the formula for each molecular compound.
MISSED THIS? *Read Section 3.6; Watch KCV 3.6, IWE 3.11*
a. phosphorus trichloride
b. chlorine monoxide
c. disulfur tetrafluoride
d. phosphorus pentafluoride

50. Write the formula for each molecular compound.
a. boron tribromide
b. dichlorine monoxide
c. xenon tetrafluoride
d. carbon tetrabromide

51. Name each acid.
MISSED THIS? *Read Section 3.6; Watch IWE 3.11*
a. $HI(aq)$
b. $HNO_3(aq)$
c. $H_2CO_3(aq)$

52. Name each acid.
a. $HCl(aq)$ b. $HClO_2(aq)$ c. $H_2SO_4(aq)$

53. Write the formula for each acid.
MISSED THIS? *Read Section 3.6; Watch IWE 3.11*
a. hydrofluoric acid
b. hydrobromic acid
c. sulfurous acid

54. Write the formula for each acid.
a. phosphoric acid
b. hydrocyanic acid
c. chlorous acid

Using the Nomenclature Flowchart

55. Refer to the nomenclature flowchart (Figure 3.11) to name each compound.
MISSED THIS? *Read Section 3.7; Watch IWE 3.11*
a. $SrCl_2$ b. SnO_2
c. P_2S_5 d. $HC_2H_3O_2(aq)$

56. Refer to the nomenclature flowchart (Figure 3.11) to name each compound.
a. $HNO_2(aq)$ b. B_2Cl_2
c. $BaCl_2$ d. $CrCl_3$

57. Refer to the nomenclature flowchart (Figure 3.11) to name each compound.
MISSED THIS? *Read Section 3.7; Watch IWE 3.11*
a. $KClO_3$ b. I_2O_5 c. $PbSO_4$

58. Refer to the nomenclature flowchart (Figure 3.11) to name each compound.
a. XeO_3 b. $KClO$ c. $CoSO_4$

Formula Mass and the Mole Concept for Compounds

59. Calculate the formula mass for each compound.
MISSED THIS? *Read Section 3.8*
a. NO_2 b. C_4H_{10}
c. $C_6H_{12}O_6$ d. $Cr(NO_3)_3$

60. Calculate the formula mass for each compound.
a. $MgBr_2$ b. HNO_2
c. CBr_4 d. $Ca(NO_3)_2$

61. Calculate the number of moles in each sample.
MISSED THIS? *Read Section 3.8; Watch IWE 3.13*
a. 72.5 g CCl_4
b. 12.4 g $C_{12}H_{22}O_{11}$
c. 25.2 kg C_2H_2
d. 12.3 g dinitrogen monoxide

62. Calculate the mass of each sample.
a. 15.7 mol HNO_3
b. 1.04×10^{-3} mol H_2O_2
c. 72.1 mmol SO_2
d. 1.23 mol xenon difluoride

63. Determine the number of moles (of molecules or formula units) in each sample.
MISSED THIS? *Read Section 3.8; Watch IWE 3.13*
a. 25.5 g NO_2
b. 1.25 kg CO_2
c. 38.2 g KNO_3
d. 155.2 kg Na_2SO_4

64. Determine the number of moles (of molecules or formula units) in each sample.
a. 55.98 g CF_2Cl_2
b. 23.6 kg $Fe(NO_3)_2$
c. 0.1187 g C_8H_{18}
d. 195 kg CaO

65. How many molecules are in each sample?
MISSED THIS? *Read Section 3.8; Watch IWE 3.13*
a. 6.5 g H_2O
b. 389 g CBr_4
c. 22.1 g O_2
d. 19.3 g C_8H_{10}

66. How many molecules (or formula units) are in each sample?
a. 85.26 g CCl_4
b. 55.93 kg $NaHCO_3$
c. 119.78 g C_4H_{10}
d. 4.59×10^5 g Na_3PO_4

67. Calculate the mass (in g) of each sample.
MISSED THIS? *Read Section 3.8; Watch IWE 3.13*
a. 5.94×10^{20} SO_3 molecules
b. 2.8×10^{22} H_2O molecules
c. 1 glucose molecule ($C_6H_{12}O_6$)

68. Calculate the mass (in g) of each sample.
a. 4.5×10^{25} O_3 molecules
b. 9.85×10^{19} CCl_2F_2 molecules
c. 1 water molecule

69. A sugar crystal contains approximately 1.8×10^{17} sucrose ($C_{12}H_{22}O_{11}$) molecules. What is its mass in mg?
MISSED THIS? *Read Section 3.8; Watch IWE 3.13*

70. A salt crystal has a mass of 0.12 mg. How many NaCl formula units does it contain?

Composition of Compounds

71. Calculate the mass percent composition of carbon in each carbon-containing compound.
MISSED THIS? *Read Section 3.9*
a. CH_4 b. C_2H_6 c. C_2H_2 d. C_2H_5Cl

72. Calculate the mass percent composition of nitrogen in each nitrogen-containing compound.
a. N_2O b. NO c. NO_2 d. HNO_3

73. Most fertilizers consist of nitrogen-containing compounds such as NH_3, $CO(NH_2)_2$, NH_4NO_3, and $(NH_4)_2SO_4$. Plants use the nitrogen content in these compounds for protein synthesis. Calculate the mass percent composition of nitrogen in each of the fertilizers listed. Which fertilizer has the highest nitrogen content?
MISSED THIS? *Read Section 3.9*

74. Iron in the earth is in the form of iron ore. Common ores include Fe_2O_3 (hematite), Fe_3O_4 (magnetite), and $FeCO_3$ (siderite). Calculate the mass percent composition of iron for each of these iron ores. Which ore has the highest iron content?

75. Copper(II) fluoride contains 37.42% F by mass. Calculate the mass of fluorine (in g) in 55.5 g of copper(II) fluoride.
MISSED THIS? *Read Section 3.9; Watch IWE 3.15*

76. Silver chloride, often used in silver plating, contains 75.27% Ag by mass. Calculate the mass of silver chloride required to plate 155 mg of pure silver.

77. The iodide ion is a dietary mineral essential to good nutrition. In countries where potassium iodide is added to salt, iodine deficiency (or goiter) has been almost completely eliminated. The recommended daily allowance (RDA) for iodine is 150 μg/day. How much potassium iodide (76.45% I) should you consume if you want to meet the RDA?
MISSED THIS? *Read Section 3.9; Watch IWE 3.15*

78. The American Dental Association recommends that an adult female should consume 3.0 mg of fluoride (F^-) per day to prevent tooth decay. If the fluoride is consumed in the form of sodium fluoride (45.24% F), what amount of sodium fluoride contains the recommended amount of fluoride?

79. Write a ratio showing the relationship between the molar amounts of each element for each compound. (See Appendix IIA for color codes.) **MISSED THIS?** *Read Section 3.9*

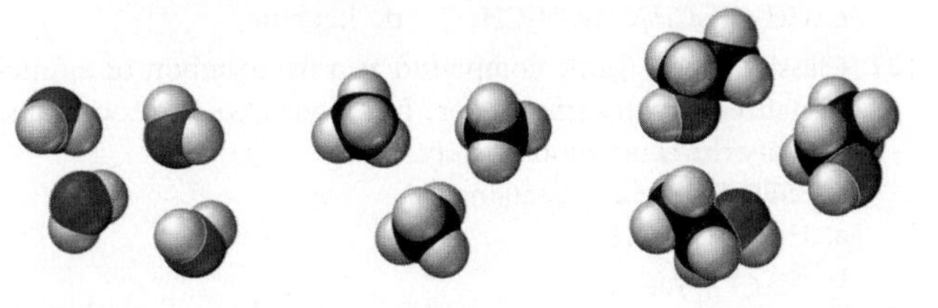

a. b. c.

80. Write a ratio showing the relationship between the molar amounts of each element for each compound. (See Appendix IIA for color codes.)

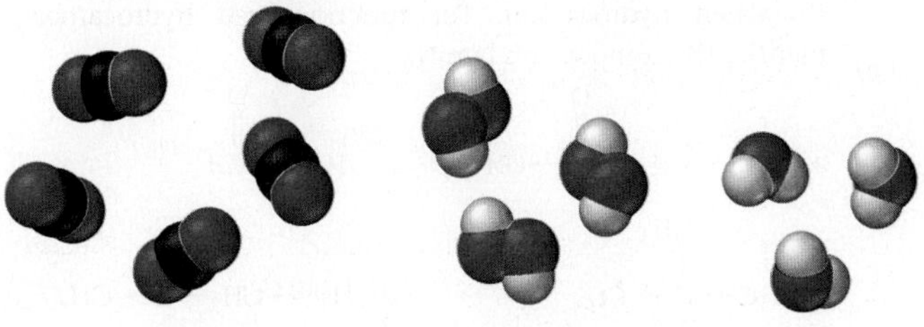

a. b. c.

81. Determine the number of moles of hydrogen atoms in each sample. **MISSED THIS?** *Read Section 3.9; Watch IWE 3.16*

a. 0.0885 mol C_4H_{10} b. 1.3 mol CH_4
c. 2.4 mol C_6H_{12} d. 1.87 mol C_8H_{18}

82. Determine the number of moles of oxygen atoms in each sample.

a. 4.88 mol H_2O_2 b. 2.15 mol N_2O
c. 0.0237 mol H_2CO_3 d. 24.1 mol CO_2

83. Calculate the mass (in grams) of sodium in 8.5 g of each sodium-containing food additive.
MISSED THIS? *Read Section 3.9; Watch IWE 3.16*

a. NaCl (table salt)
b. Na_3PO_4 (sodium phosphate)
c. $NaC_7H_5O_2$ (sodium benzoate)
d. $Na_2C_6H_6O_7$ (sodium hydrogen citrate)

84. Calculate the mass (in kilograms) of chlorine in 25 kg of each chlorofluorocarbon (CFC).

a. CF_2Cl_2 b. $CFCl_3$ c. $C_2F_3Cl_3$ d. CF_3Cl

85. How many fluorine atoms are present in 5.85 g of C_2F_4?
MISSED THIS? *Read Section 3.9; Watch IWE 3.16*

86. How many bromine atoms are present in 35.2 g of CH_2Br_2?

Chemical Formulas from Experimental Data

87. A chemist decomposes samples of several compounds; the masses of their constituent elements are listed. Calculate the empirical formula for each compound.
MISSED THIS? *Read Section 3.10; Watch IWE 3.18*

a. 1.651 g Ag, 0.1224 g O
b. 0.672 g Co, 0.569 g As, 0.486 g O
c. 1.443 g Se, 5.841 g Br

88. A chemist decomposes samples of several compounds; the masses of their constituent elements are listed. Calculate the empirical formula for each compound.

a. 1.245 g Ni, 5.381 g I
b. 2.677 g Ba, 3.115 g Br
c. 2.128 g Be, 7.557 g S, 15.107 g O

89. Calculate the empirical formula for each stimulant based on its elemental mass percent composition.
MISSED THIS? *Read Section 3.10; Watch IWE 3.18*

a. nicotine (found in tobacco leaves): C 74.03%, H 8.70%, N 17.27%
b. caffeine (found in coffee beans): C 49.48%, H 5.19%, N 28.85%, O 16.48%

90. Calculate the empirical formula for each natural flavor based on its elemental mass percent composition.

a. methyl butyrate (component of apple taste and smell): C 58.80%, H 9.87%, O 31.33%
b. vanillin (responsible for the taste and smell of vanilla): C 63.15%, H 5.30%, O 31.55%

91. The elemental mass percent composition of ibuprofen (a nonsteroidal anti-inflammatory drug [NSAID]) is 75.69% C, 8.80% H, and 15.51% O. Determine the empirical formula of ibuprofen. **MISSED THIS?** *Read Section 3.10; Watch IWE 3.18*

92. The elemental mass percent composition of ascorbic acid (vitamin C) is 40.92% C, 4.58% H, and 54.50% O. Determine the empirical formula of ascorbic acid.

93. A 0.77-mg sample of nitrogen reacts with chlorine to form 6.61 mg of the chloride. Determine the empirical formula of nitrogen chloride.
MISSED THIS? *Read Section 3.10; Watch IWE 3.18*

94. A 45.2-mg sample of phosphorus reacts with selenium to form 131.6 mg of the selenide. Determine the empirical formula of phosphorus selenide.

95. From the given empirical formula and molar mass, find the molecular formula of each compound.
MISSED THIS? *Read Section 3.10*

a. C_6H_7N, 186.24 g/mol   b. C_2HCl, 181.44 g/mol
c. $C_5H_{10}NS_2$, 296.54 g/mol

96. From the given molar mass and empirical formula of several compounds, find the molecular formula of each compound.

a. C_4H_9, 114.22 g/mol   b. CCl, 284.77 g/mol
c. C_3H_2N, 312.29 g/mol

97. Combustion analysis of a hydrocarbon produces 33.01 g CO_2 and 13.51 g H_2O. Calculate the empirical formula of the hydrocarbon. **MISSED THIS?** *Read Section 3.10; Watch IWE 3.21*

98. Combustion analysis of naphthalene, a hydrocarbon used in mothballs, produces 8.80 g CO_2 and 1.44 g H_2O. Calculate the empirical formula of naphthalene.

99. The foul odor of rancid butter is due largely to butyric acid, a compound containing carbon, hydrogen, and oxygen. Combustion analysis of a 4.30-g sample of butyric acid produces 8.59 g CO_2 and 3.52 g H_2O. Determine the empirical formula of butyric acid. **MISSED THIS?** *Read Section 3.10; Watch IWE 3.21*

100. Tartaric acid is the white, powdery substance that coats tart candies such as Sour Patch Kids. Combustion analysis of a 12.01-g sample of tartaric acid—which contains only carbon, hydrogen, and oxygen—produces 14.08 g CO_2 and 4.32 g H_2O. Determine the empirical formula of tartaric acid.

Organic Compounds

101. Classify each compound as organic or inorganic.
MISSED THIS? *Read Section 3.11*

a. $CaCO_3$
b. C_4H_8
c. $C_4H_6O_6$
d. LiF

102. Classify each compound as organic or inorganic.
a. C_8H_{18}
b. CH_3NH_2
c. CaO
d. $FeCO_3$

103. Classify each hydrocarbon as an alkane, alkene, or alkyne.
MISSED THIS? *Read Section 3.11*
a. $H_2C{=}CH{-}CH_3$
b. $H_3C{-}CH_2{-}CH_3$
c. $HC{\equiv}C{-}CH_3$
d. $H_3C{-}CH_2{-}CH_2{-}CH_3$

104. Classify each hydrocarbon as an alkane, alkene, or alkyne.
a. $HC{\equiv}CH$
b. $H_3C{-}CH{=}CH{-}CH_3$
c. 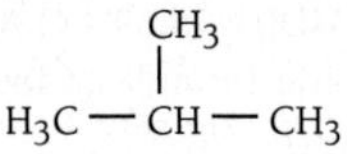
d. $H_3C{-}C{\equiv}C{-}CH_3$

105. Write the formula based on the name, or the name based on the formula, for each hydrocarbon.
MISSED THIS? *Read Section 3.11*
a. propane
b. $CH_3CH_2CH_3$
c. octane
d. $CH_3CH_2CH_2CH_2CH_3$

106. Write the formula based on the name, or the name based on the formula, for each hydrocarbon.
a. CH_3CH_3
b. pentane
c. $CH_3CH_2CH_2CH_2CH_2CH_3$
d. heptane

107. Classify each organic compound as a hydrocarbon or a functionalized hydrocarbon. For functionalized hydrocarbons, identify the compound's family.
MISSED THIS? *Read Section 3.11*
a. $H_3C{-}CH_2OH$
b. $H_3C{-}CH_3$
c. 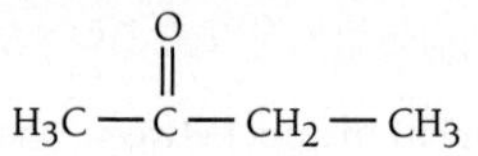
d. $H_3C{-}NH_2$

108. Classify each organic compound as a hydrocarbon or a functionalized hydrocarbon. For functionalized hydrocarbons, identify the compound's family.
a. 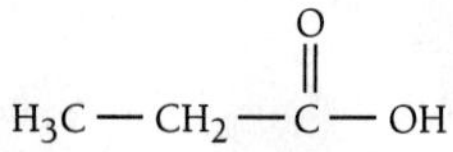
b. 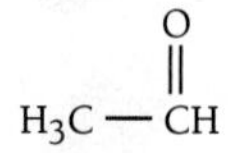
c. 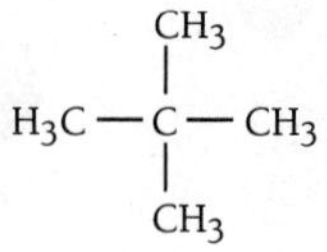
d. $H_3C{-}CH_2{-}O{-}CH_3$

CUMULATIVE PROBLEMS

109. How many molecules of ethanol (C_2H_5OH) (the alcohol in alcoholic beverages) are present in 145 mL of ethanol? The density of ethanol is $0.789\,g/cm^3$.

110. A drop of water has a volume of approximately 0.05 mL. How many water molecules does it contain? The density of water is $1.0\ g/cm^3$.

111. Determine the chemical formula of each compound and then use it to calculate the mass percent composition of each constituent element.
a. potassium chromate
b. lead(II) phosphate
c. sulfurous acid
d. cobalt(II) bromide

112. Determine the chemical formula of each compound and then use it to calculate the mass percent composition of each constituent element.
a. perchloric acid
b. phosphorus pentachloride
c. nitrogen triiodide
d. carbon dioxide

113. A Freon leak in the air-conditioning system of an old car releases 25 g of CF_2Cl_2 per month. What mass of chlorine does this car emit into the atmosphere each year?

114. A Freon leak in the air-conditioning system of a large building releases 12 kg of CHF_2Cl per month. If the leak is allowed to continue, how many kilograms of Cl will be emitted into the atmosphere each year?

115. A metal (M) forms a compound with the formula MCl_3. If the compound contains 65.57% Cl by mass, what is the identity of the metal?

116. A metal (M) forms an oxide with the formula M_2O. If the oxide contains 16.99% O by mass, what is the identity of the metal?

117. Estradiol is a female sexual hormone that is responsible for the maturation and maintenance of the female reproductive system. Elemental analysis of estradiol gives the following mass percent composition: C 79.37%, H 8.88%, O 11.75%. The molar mass of estradiol is 272.37 g/mol. Find the molecular formula of estradiol.

118. Fructose is a common sugar found in fruit. Elemental analysis of fructose gives the following mass percent composition: C 40.00%, H 6.72%, O 53.28%. The molar mass of fructose is 180.16 g/mol. Find the molecular formula of fructose.

119. Combustion analysis of a 13.42-g sample of equilin (which contains only carbon, hydrogen, and oxygen) produces 39.61 g CO_2 and 9.01 g H_2O. The molar mass of equilin is 268.34 g/mol. Find its molecular formula.

120. Estrone, which contains only carbon, hydrogen, and oxygen, is a female sexual hormone in the urine of pregnant women. Combustion analysis of a 1.893-g sample of estrone produces 5.545 g of CO_2 and 1.388 g H_2O. The molar mass of estrone is 270.36 g/mol. Find its molecular formula.

121. Epsom salts is a hydrated ionic compound with the following formula: $MgSO_4 \cdot x\,H_2O$. A 4.93-g sample of Epsom salts is heated to drive off the water of hydration. The mass of the sample after complete dehydration is 2.41 g. Find the number of waters of hydration (x) in Epsom salts.

122. A hydrate of copper(II) chloride has the following formula: $CuCl_2 \cdot x\,H_2O$. The water in a 3.41-g sample of the hydrate is driven off by heating. The remaining sample has a mass of 2.69 g. Find the number of waters of hydration (x) in the hydrate.

123. A compound of molar mass 177 g/mol contains only carbon, hydrogen, bromine, and oxygen. Analysis reveals that the compound contains eight times as much carbon as hydrogen by mass. Find the molecular formula.

124. Researchers obtained the following data from experiments to find the molecular formula of benzocaine, a local anesthetic, which contains only carbon, hydrogen, nitrogen, and oxygen. Complete combustion of a 3.54-g sample of benzocaine with excess O_2 forms 8.49 g of CO_2 and 2.14 g H_2O. Another 2.35-g sample contains 0.199 g of N. The molar mass of benzocaine is 165 g/mol. Find the molar formula of benzocaine.

125. Find the total number of atoms in a sample of cocaine hydrochloride, $C_{17}H_{22}ClNO_4$, of mass 23.5 mg.

126. Vanadium forms four different oxides in which the percent by mass of vanadium is, respectively, (a) 76%, (b) 68%, (c) 61%, and (d) 56%. Determine the formula and the name of each oxide.

127. The chloride of an unknown metal is believed to have the formula MCl_3. A 2.395-g sample of the compound contains 3.606×10^{-2} mol Cl. Find the atomic mass of M.

128. Write the structural formulas of three different compounds that each have the molecular formula C_5H_{12}.

129. A chromium-containing compound has the formula $Fe_xCr_yO_4$ and is 28.59% oxygen by mass. Find x and y.

130. A phosphorus compound that contains 34.00% phosphorus by mass has the formula X_3P_2. Identify the element X.

131. A particular brand of beef jerky contains 0.0552% sodium nitrite by mass and is sold in an 8.00-oz bag. What mass of sodium does the sodium nitrite contribute to the sodium content of the bag of beef jerky?

132. Phosphorus is obtained primarily from ores containing calcium phosphate. If a particular ore contains 57.8% calcium phosphate, what minimum mass of the ore must be processed to obtain 1.00 kg of phosphorus?

CHALLENGE PROBLEMS

133. A mixture of NaCl and NaBr has a mass of 2.00 g and contains 0.75 g of Na. What is the mass of NaBr in the mixture?

134. Three pure compounds form when 1.00-g samples of element X combine with, respectively, 0.472 g, 0.630 g, and 0.789 g of element Z. The first compound has the formula X_2Z_3. Find the empirical formulas of the other two compounds.

135. A mixture of $CaCO_3$ and $(NH_4)_2CO_3$ is 61.9% CO_3 by mass. Find the mass percent of $CaCO_3$ in the mixture.

136. A mixture of 50.0 g of S and 1.00×10^2 g of Cl_2 reacts completely to form S_2Cl_2 and SCl_2. Find the mass of S_2Cl_2 formed.

137. Because of increasing evidence of damage to the ozone layer, chlorofluorocarbon (CFC) production was banned in 1996. However, many older cars still have air conditioners that use CFC-12 (CF_2Cl_2). These air conditioners are recharged from stockpiled supplies of CFC-12. Suppose that 100 million automobiles each contain 1.1 kg of CFC-12 and leak 25% of their CFC-12 into the atmosphere per year. How much chlorine, in kg, is added to the atmosphere each year due to these air conditioners? (Assume two significant figures in your calculations.)

138. A particular coal contains 2.55% sulfur by mass. When the coal is burned, it produces SO_2 emissions, which combine with rainwater to produce sulfuric acid. Use the formula of sulfuric acid to calculate the mass percent of S in sulfuric acid. Then determine how much sulfuric acid (in metric tons) is produced by the combustion of 1.0 metric ton of this coal. (A metric ton is 1000 kg.)

139. Lead is found in Earth's crust as several different lead ores. Suppose a certain rock is 38.0% PbS (galena), 25.0% $PbCO_3$ (cerussite), and 17.4% $PbSO_4$ (anglesite). The remainder of the rock is composed of substances containing no lead. How much of this rock (in kg) must be processed to obtain 5.0 metric tons of lead? (A metric ton is 1000 kg.)

140. A 2.52-g sample of a compound containing only carbon, hydrogen, nitrogen, oxygen, and sulfur is burned in excess oxygen to yield 4.23 g of CO_2 and 1.01 g of H_2O. Another sample of the same compound, of mass 4.14 g, yields 2.11 g of SO_3. A third sample, of mass 5.66 g, yields 2.27 g of HNO_3. Calculate the empirical formula of the compound.

141. A compound of molar mass 229 g/mol contains only carbon, hydrogen, iodine, and sulfur. Analysis shows that a sample of the compound contains six times as much carbon as hydrogen, by mass. Calculate the molecular formula of the compound.

142. The elements X and Y form a compound that is 40% X and 60% Y by mass. The atomic mass of X is twice that of Y. What is the empirical formula of the compound?

143. A compound of X and Y is $\frac{1}{3}$ X by mass. The atomic mass of element X is $\frac{1}{3}$ the atomic mass of element Y. Find the empirical formula of the compound.

144. A mixture of carbon and sulfur has a mass of 9.0 g. Complete combustion with excess O_2 gives 23.3 g of a mixture of CO_2 and SO_2. Find the mass of sulfur in the original mixture.

CONCEPTUAL PROBLEMS

145. When molecules are represented by molecular models, what does each sphere represent? How big is the nucleus of an atom in comparison to the sphere used to represent an atom in a molecular model?

146. Without doing any calculations, determine which element in each compound has the highest mass percent composition.

a. CO
b. N_2O
c. $C_6H_{12}O_6$
d. NH_3

147. Explain the problem with the following statement and correct it: "The chemical formula for ammonia (NH_3) indicates that ammonia contains three grams of hydrogen for each gram of nitrogen."

148. Element A is an atomic element, and element B is a diatomic molecular element. Using circles to represent atoms of A and squares to represent atoms of B, draw molecular-level views of each element.

149. Without doing any calculations, arrange the elements in H_2SO_4 in order of decreasing mass percent composition.

QUESTIONS FOR GROUP WORK

Active Classroom Learning

Discuss these questions with the group and record your consensus answer.

150. With group members playing the roles of nuclei and electrons, demonstrate the formation of an ionic bond between Na and Cl. Demonstrate the formation of the covalent bonds in H_2O.

151. Create a flowchart with a series of simple questions that can be used to determine whether a chemical formula is that of an atomic element, a molecular element, a molecular compound, or an ionic compound. Use your flowchart to identify the correct category for P_4, KCl, CH_4, Ne, and NH_4NO_3.

152. Have each member of your group list one similarity or difference between the naming conventions for ionic and molecular compounds.

153. A compound isolated from the rind of lemons is found to be 88.14% carbon and 11.86% hydrogen by mass. How many grams of C and H are there in a 100.0-g sample of this substance? How many moles of C and H? What is the empirical formula? The molar mass is determined to be 136.26 g/mol. What is the molecular formula? Which step of the process just described does your group understand the least? Which step will be hardest for the members of your group to remember?

DATA INTERPRETATION AND ANALYSIS

Sulfur Dioxide Air Pollution

154. Sulfur dioxide is a pollutant emitted primarily by coal-burning power plants and industrial smelters. Sulfur dioxide in air affects the respiratory system in humans and is the main cause of acid rain. Thanks to the Clean Air Act and its amendments, sulfur dioxide levels in the United States have dramatically fallen over the last 30 years. The graph below shows the mean sulfur dioxide levels from 136 measuring sites in the United States for the period 1990 to 2016. Examine the graph and answer the questions that follow.

Sulfur Dioxide Mean Concentration

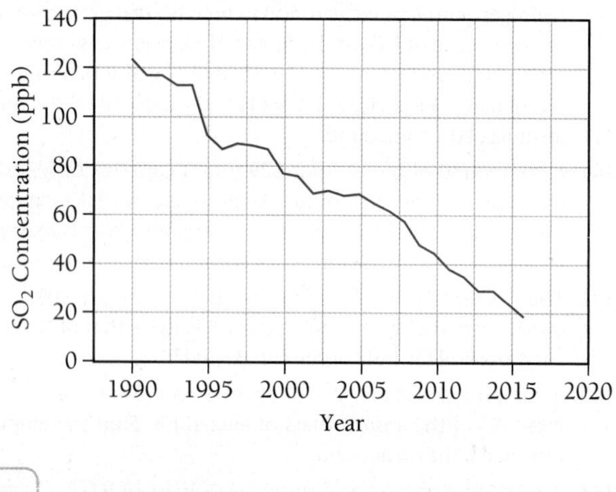

a. On its website, the EPA claims that sulfur dioxide levels have fallen by 85% between 1990 and 2016. Is this claim accurate?

b. The EPA air quality standard for SO_2 is 75 ppm. In what year did the average U.S. SO_2 concentration begin to meet this standard?

c. What is the percent by mass of S in SO_2?

d. A 100 m^3 room with an SO_2 concentration of 75 ppb contains about 0.021 g SO_2. How many sulfur atoms does it contain?

Cc ANSWERS TO CONCEPTUAL CONNECTIONS

Types of Chemical Bonds

3.1 **(b)** The bond is covalent because it is forming between two nonmetals.

Structural Formulas

3.2 **(c)** H—O—H

Representing Molecules

3.3 **(b)** The spheres represent the electron cloud of the atom. It would be nearly impossible to draw a nucleus to scale on any of the space-filling molecular models in this book—the nucleus would be too small to see.

A Molecular View of Elements and Compounds

3.4 **(b)** A molecular element has molecules made of the same atoms as its basic unit.

Ionic and Molecular Compounds

3.5 **(a)** Only molecular compounds contain discrete molecules. Ionic compounds result in extended networks of alternating cations and anions.

Types of Metals

3.6 **(d)** Sr is a group II metal and forms a cation with a 2+ charge in all its compounds.

Polyatomic Ions

3.7 **(a)** Only this choice contains the polyatomic ions in the formulas.

Nomenclature

3.8 **(b)** This conceptual connection addresses one of the main errors you can make in nomenclature: the failure to correctly categorize the compound. Remember that you must first determine whether the compound is an ionic compound, a molecular compound, or an acid, and then you must name it accordingly. NCl_3 is a molecular compound (two or more nonmetals), and therefore in its name prefixes indicate the number of each type of atom—so NCl_3 is nitrogen trichloride. The compound $AlCl_3$, however, is an ionic compound (metal and nonmetal), and therefore does not require prefixes—so $AlCl_3$ is aluminum chloride.

Molecular Models and the Size of Molecules

3.9 **(c)** Atomic radii range in the hundreds of picometers, while the spheres in these models have radii of about a centimeter. The scaling factor is therefore about 10^8 (100 million).

Chemical Formula and Mass Percent Composition

3.10 **(a)** $C > O > H$ Since carbon and oxygen differ in atomic mass by only 4 amu, and since there are six carbon atoms in the formula, we can conclude that carbon constitutes the greatest fraction of the mass. Oxygen is next because its mass is 16 times that of hydrogen and there are only six hydrogen atoms for every one oxygen atom.

Chemical Formulas and Elemental Composition

3.11 **(c)** The chemical formula for a compound gives relationships between *atoms* or *moles of atoms*. The chemical formula for water states that water molecules contain two H atoms to every one O atom or 2 mol H to every 1 mol H_2O. This *does not* imply a two-to-one relationship between *masses* of hydrogen and oxygen because these atoms have different masses. It also does not imply a two-to-one relationship between volumes.

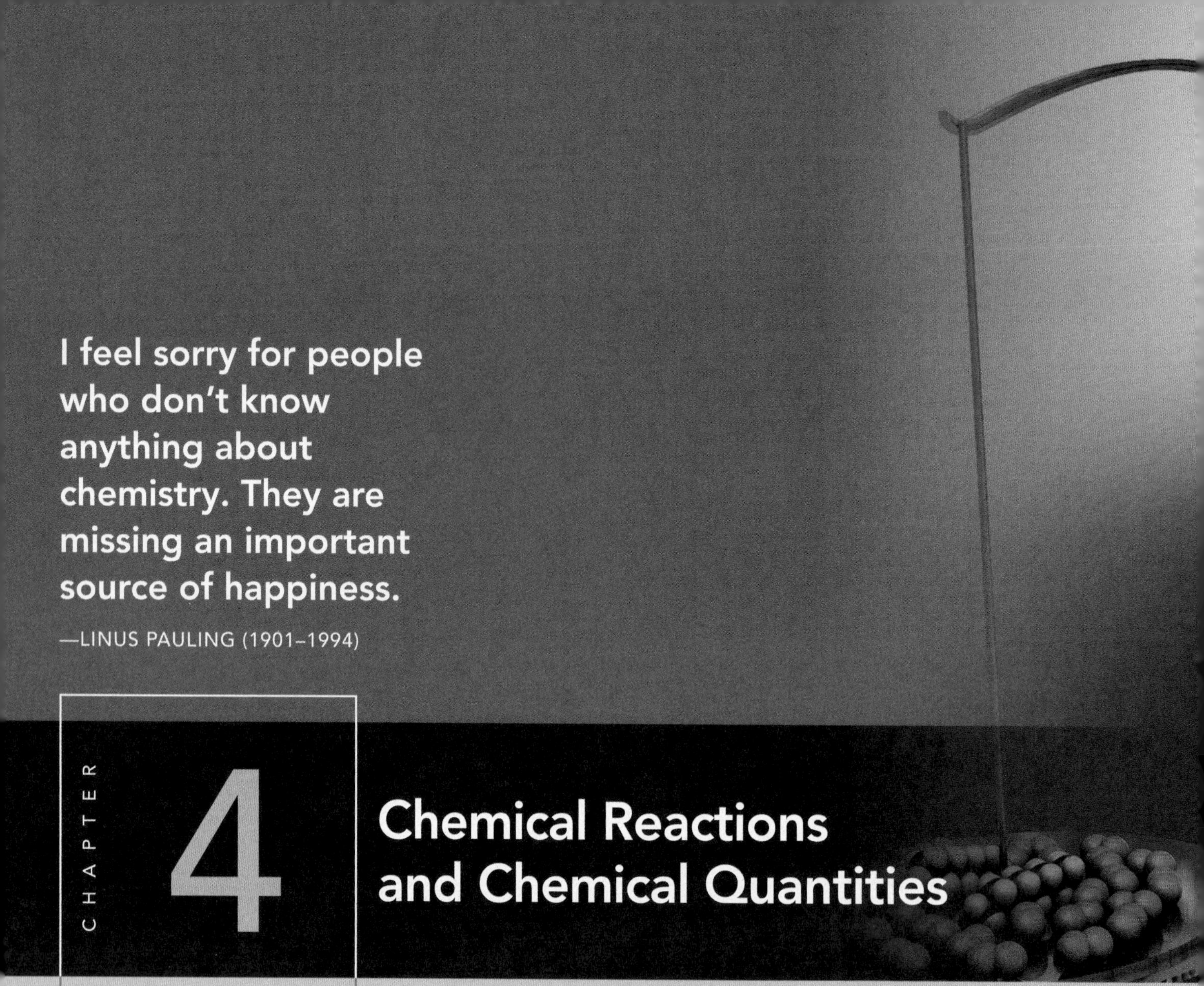

I feel sorry for people who don't know anything about chemistry. They are missing an important source of happiness.

—LINUS PAULING (1901–1994)

CHAPTER

4 Chemical Reactions and Chemical Quantities

In Chapter 3, we examined chemical compounds. We now turn to the process that can create and transform compounds: *chemical reactions*. We have seen that matter is composed of particles (atoms and molecules). When we mix certain types of particles with others, the electrons from one set of particles are attracted to the nuclei in the other set. If the conditions are right, a chemical reaction occurs and the particles are transformed. In this chapter, we learn to write chemical equations that represent these transformations. We also examine *chemical stoichiometry*—the numerical relationships between the amounts of reactants and products in chemical reactions.

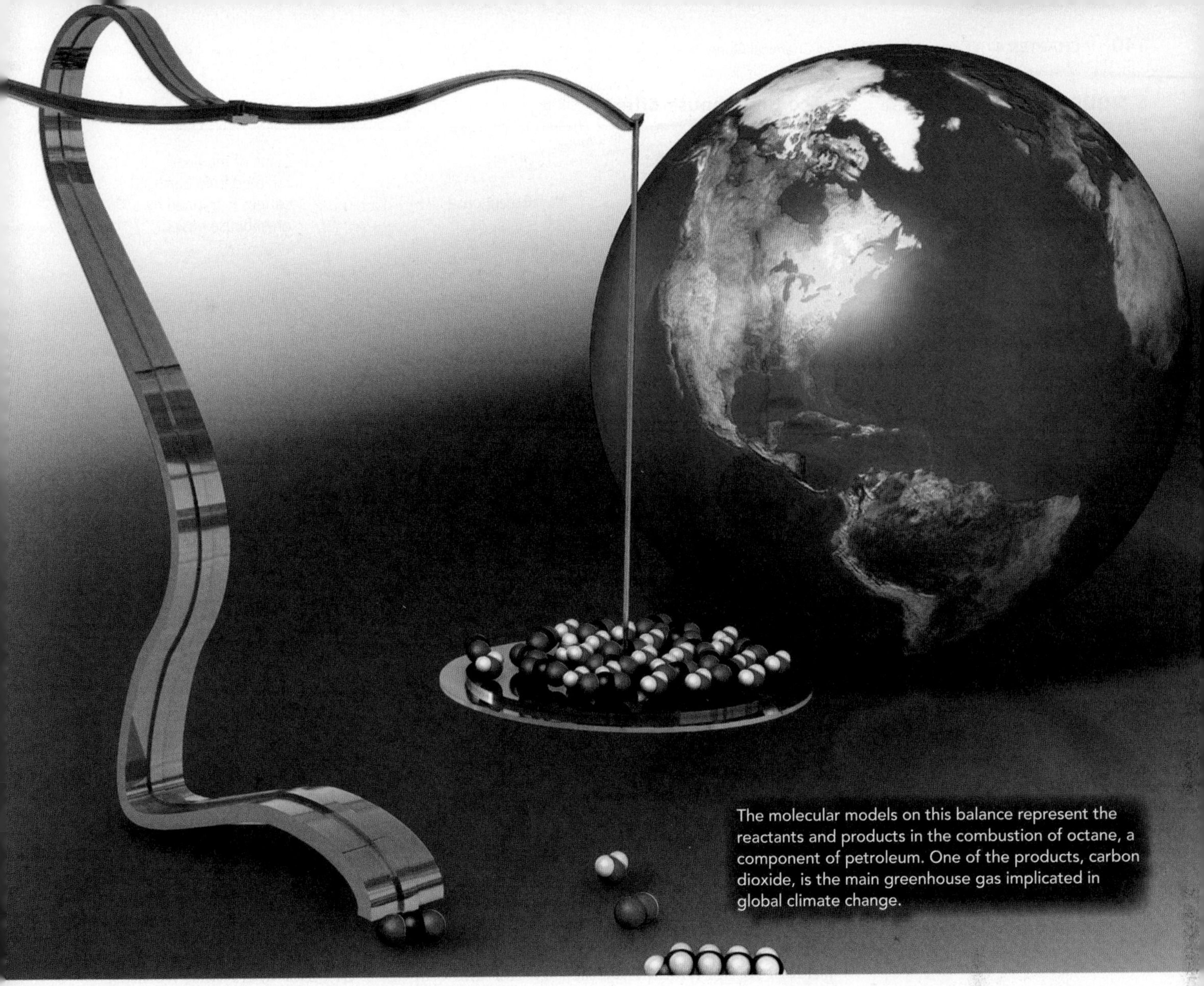

The molecular models on this balance represent the reactants and products in the combustion of octane, a component of petroleum. One of the products, carbon dioxide, is the main greenhouse gas implicated in global climate change.

4.1 Climate Change and the Combustion of Fossil Fuels 139

4.2 Writing and Balancing Chemical Equations 141

4.3 Reaction Stoichiometry: How Much Carbon Dioxide? 145

4.4 Stoichiometric Relationships: Limiting Reactant, Theoretical Yield, Percent Yield, and Reactant in Excess 149

4.5 Three Examples of Chemical Reactions: Combustion, Alkali Metals, and Halogens 155

LEARNING OUTCOMES 159

4.1 Climate Change and the Combustion of Fossil Fuels

The temperature outside my office today is a cool 48 °F, lower than normal for this time of year on the California coast. However, today's "chill" pales in comparison with how cold it would be without the presence of *greenhouse gases* in the atmosphere.

Greenhouse gases in the atmosphere act as a one-way filter. They allow visible light to pass through and warm Earth's surface, but they prevent heat energy from radiating back out into space.

These gases act like the glass of a greenhouse, allowing sunlight to enter the atmosphere and warm Earth's surface but preventing some of the heat generated by the

▶ **FIGURE 4.1 The Greenhouse Effect**

sunlight from escaping, as shown in Figure 4.1▲. The balance between incoming and outgoing energy from the sun determines Earth's average temperature.

If the greenhouse gases in the atmosphere were not present, more heat energy would escape, and Earth's average temperature would be about 60 °F colder than it currently is. The temperature outside of my office today would be below 0 °F, and even the sunniest U.S. cities would most likely be covered with snow. However, if the concentration of greenhouse gases in the atmosphere were to increase, Earth's average temperature would rise.

The extremely cold temperatures of Mars are as much a result of its lack of atmosphere as its greater distance from the sun than Earth. Conversely, Venus is an inferno partly because its thick atmosphere is rich in greenhouse gases.

In recent decades, scientists have become increasingly concerned because the quantity of atmospheric carbon dioxide (CO_2)—a significant greenhouse gas—is rising. More CO_2 enhances the atmosphere's ability to hold heat and leads to *global warming*, an increase in Earth's average temperature. Since 1860, atmospheric CO_2 levels have risen by 38% (Figure 4.2▼), and Earth's average temperature has risen by about 1.6 °F (0.9 °C) (as shown in Figure 4.3▼).

Most scientists believe that the primary cause of rising atmospheric CO_2 concentration is the burning of fossil fuels (natural gas, petroleum, and coal), which provides about 90% of our society's energy. Some people, however, have suggested that fossil fuel combustion does not significantly contribute to global warming and climate change. They argue that the amount of carbon dioxide emitted into the atmosphere by natural sources, such as volcanic eruptions, far exceeds that from fossil fuel combustion. Which group is right? One way to judge the validity of the naysayers' argument is by calculating how much carbon dioxide is emitted by fossil fuel combustion and comparing that amount to the amount released by volcanic eruptions. In order to do this, we must understand the chemical equations that govern fossil fuel combustion and how those equations relate the amounts of reactants to the amounts of products.

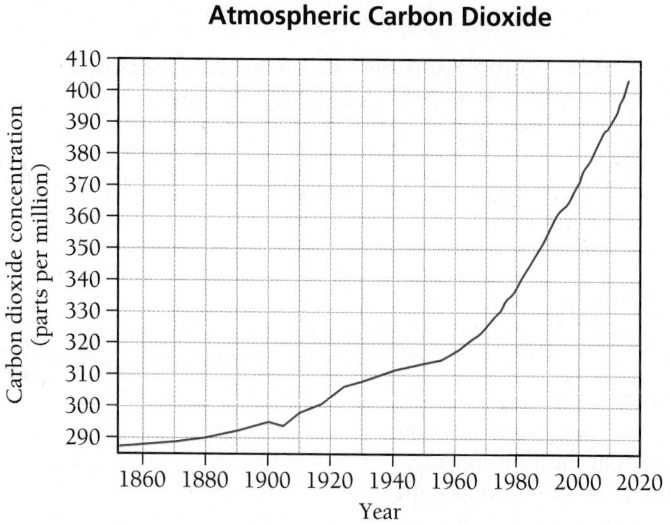

▲ **FIGURE 4.2 Carbon Dioxide Concentrations in the Atmosphere** The rise in carbon dioxide levels is due largely to fossil fuel combustion.

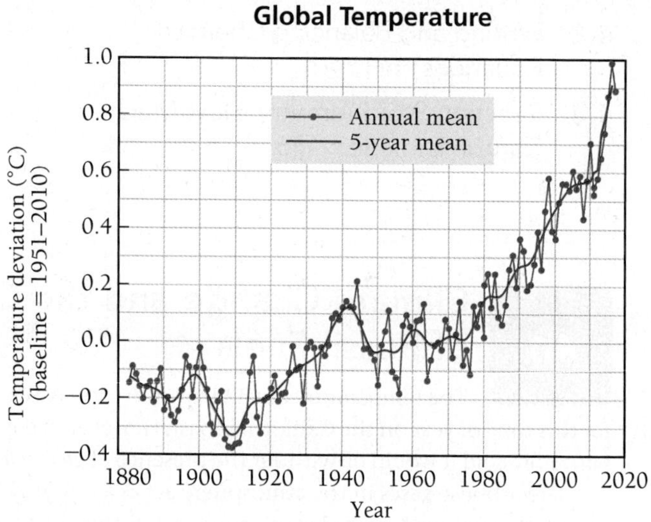

▲ **FIGURE 4.3 Global Temperature** Average temperatures worldwide have risen by about 0.9 °C since 1880. Each point on the graph is the deviation from the 1951–2010 average temperature.

4.2 Writing and Balancing Chemical Equations

Combustion analysis (which we examined in Section 3.10) employs a **chemical reaction**, a process in which one or more substances are converted into one or more different ones. Compounds form and change through chemical reactions. For example, water is formed by the reaction of hydrogen with oxygen. A **combustion reaction** is a particular type of chemical reaction in which a substance combines with oxygen to form one or more oxygen-containing compounds. Combustion reactions also emit heat. The heat produced in a number of combustion reactions is critical to supplying our society's energy needs. For example, the heat from the combustion of gasoline expands the gaseous combustion products in a car engine's cylinders, which push the pistons and propel the car. We use the heat released by the combustion of *natural gas* to cook food and to heat our homes.

WATCH **NOW!**

KEY CONCEPT VIDEO 4.2
Writing and Balancing Chemical Equations

We represent a chemical reaction with a **chemical equation**. For example, we represent the combustion of natural gas with the equation:

$$\underbrace{CH_4 + O_2}_{\text{reactants}} \longrightarrow \underbrace{CO_2 + H_2O}_{\text{products}}$$

The substances on the left side of the equation are the **reactants**, and the substances on the right side are the **products**. We often specify the states of each reactant or product in parentheses next to the formula as follows:

$$CH_4(g) + O_2(g) \longrightarrow CO_2(g) + H_2O(g)$$

The (*g*) indicates that these substances are gases in the reaction. Table 4.1 summarizes the common states of reactants and products and their symbols used in chemical equations.

TABLE 4.1 ■ States of Reactants and Products in Chemical Equations

Abbreviation	State
(*g*)	Gas
(*l*)	Liquid
(*s*)	Solid
(*aq*)	Aqueous (water solution)

The equation just presented for the combustion of natural gas is not complete, however. If we look closely, we can immediately spot a problem.

$$CH_4(g) + O_2(g) \longrightarrow CO_2(g) + H_2O(g)$$

2 O atoms (in O_2) — 2 O atoms + 1 O atom = 3 O atoms (in CO_2 and H_2O)

The left side of the equation has two oxygen atoms, while the right side has three. The reaction as written, therefore, violates the law of conservation of mass because an oxygen atom formed out of nothing. Notice also that the left side has four hydrogen atoms, while the right side has only two.

$$CH_4(g) + O_2(g) \longrightarrow CO_2(g) + H_2O(g)$$

4 H atoms (in CH_4) — 2 H atoms (in H_2O)

Two hydrogen atoms have vanished, again violating mass conservation. To correct these problems—that is, to write an equation that more closely represents *what actually happens*—we must **balance** the equation. We need to change the coefficients (the numbers *in front of* the chemical formulas), not the subscripts (the numbers within the chemical formulas), to ensure that the number of each type of atom on the left side of the equation is equal to the number on the right side. New atoms do not form during a reaction, nor do atoms vanish—matter must be conserved.

We cannot change the subscripts when balancing a chemical equation because changing the subscripts changes the substance itself, while changing the coefficients changes the number of molecules of the substance. For example, 2 H_2O is simply two water molecules, but H_2O_2 is hydrogen peroxide, a drastically different compound.

When we add coefficients to the reactants and products to balance an equation, we change the number of molecules in the equation but not the *kind of* molecules. To balance the equation for the combustion of methane, we put the coefficient 2 before O_2 in the reactants, and the coefficient 2 before H_2O in the products.

$$CH_4(g) + 2\,O_2(g) \longrightarrow CO_2(g) + 2\,H_2O(g)$$

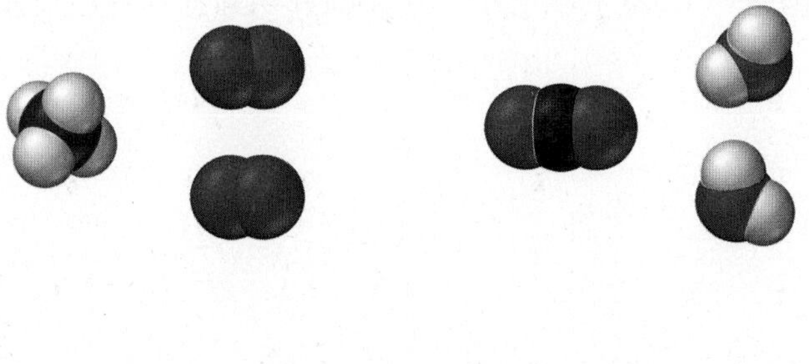

The equation is now balanced because the numbers of each type of atom on either side of the equation are equal. The balanced equation tells us that one CH_4 molecule reacts with two O_2 molecules to form one CO_2 molecule and two H_2O molecules. We verify that the equation is balanced by summing the number of each type of atom on each side of the equation.

$$CH_4(g) + 2\,O_2(g) \longrightarrow CO_2(g) + 2\,H_2O(g)$$

Reactants	Products
1 C atom (1 × CH_4)	1 C atom (1 × CO_2)
4 H atoms (1 × CH_4)	4 H atoms (2 × H_2O)
4 O atoms (2 × O_2)	4 O atoms (1 × CO_2 + 2 × H_2O)

The number of each type of atom on both sides of the equation is now equal—the equation is balanced.

ANSWER **NOW!**

4.1 Cc Conceptual Connection

COUNTING ATOMS IN A CHEMICAL EQUATION How many oxygen atoms are on the right-hand side of the following chemical equation?

$$4\,FeCO_3(s) + O_2(g) \longrightarrow 2\,Fe_2O_3(s) + 4\,CO_2(g)$$

(a) 4 **(b)** 5 **(c)** 6 **(d)** 14

We can balance many chemical equations simply by trial and error. However, some guidelines are useful. For example, balancing the atoms in the most complex substances first and the atoms in the simplest substances (such as pure elements) last often makes the process shorter. The following examples of how to balance chemical equations are presented in a two- or three-column format. The general procedure is shown on the left, with the application of the procedure on the right. This procedure is meant only as a flexible guide, not a rigid set of steps.

WATCH **NOW!** INTERACTIVE WORKED EXAMPLE 4.2

HOW TO: *Balance Chemical Equations*	EXAMPLE 4.1 Balancing Chemical Equations	EXAMPLE 4.2 Balancing Chemical Equations
	Write a balanced equation for the reaction between solid cobalt(III) oxide and solid carbon to produce solid cobalt and carbon dioxide gas.	Write a balanced equation for the combustion of gaseous butane (C_4H_{10}), a fuel used in portable stoves and grills, in which it combines with gaseous oxygen to form gaseous carbon dioxide and gaseous water.
1. Write a skeletal equation by writing chemical formulas for each of the reactants and products. Review Sections 3.5 and 3.6 for nomenclature rules. (If a skeletal equation is provided, go to step 2.)	$Co_2O_3(s) + C(s) \longrightarrow Co(s) + CO_2(g)$	$C_4H_{10}(g) + O_2(g) \longrightarrow CO_2(g) + H_2O(g)$

Procedure	Example 4.1	Example 4.2
2. Balance atoms that occur in more complex substances first. Always balance atoms in compounds before atoms in pure elements.	**Begin with O:** $Co_2O_3(s) + C(s) \longrightarrow Co(s) + CO_2(g)$ 3 O atoms $\longrightarrow$ 2 O atoms To balance O, put a 2 before $Co_2O_3(s)$ and a 3 before $CO_2(g)$. $2\,Co_2O_3(s) + C(s) \longrightarrow Co(s) + 3\,CO_2(g)$ 6 O atoms $\longrightarrow$ 6 O atoms	**Begin with C:** $C_4H_{10}(g) + O_2(g) \longrightarrow CO_2(g) + H_2O(g)$ 4 C atoms $\longrightarrow$ 1 C atom To balance C, put a 4 before $CO_2(g)$. $C_4H_{10}(g) + O_2(g) \longrightarrow 4\,CO_2(g) + H_2O(g)$ 4 C atoms $\longrightarrow$ 4 C atoms **Balance H:** $C_4H_{10}(g) + O_2(g) \longrightarrow 4\,CO_2(g) + H_2O(g)$ 10 H atoms $\longrightarrow$ 2 H atoms To balance H, put a 5 before $H_2O(g)$: $C_4H_{10}(g) + O_2(g) \longrightarrow 4\,CO_2(g) + 5\,H_2O(g)$ 10 H atoms $\longrightarrow$ 10 H atoms
3. Balance atoms that occur as free elements on either side of the equation last. Balance free elements by adjusting their coefficients.	**Balance Co:** $2\,Co_2O_3(s) + C(s) \longrightarrow Co(s) + 3\,CO_2(g)$ 4 Co atoms $\longrightarrow$ 1 Co atom To balance Co, put a 4 before Co(*s*). $2\,Co_2O_3(s) + C(s) \longrightarrow 4\,Co(s) + 3\,CO_2(g)$ 4 Co atoms $\longrightarrow$ 4 Co atoms **Balance C:** $2\,Co_2O_3(s) + C(s) \longrightarrow 4\,Co(s) + 3\,CO_2(g)$ 1 C atom $\longrightarrow$ 3 C atoms To balance C, put a 3 before C(*s*). $2\,Co_2O_3(s) + 3\,C(s) \longrightarrow 4\,Co(s) + 3\,CO_2(g)$	**Balance O:** $C_4H_{10}(g) + O_2(g) \longrightarrow 4\,CO_2(g) + 5\,H_2O(g)$ 2 O atoms $\longrightarrow$ 8 O + 5 O = 13 O atoms To balance O, put a 13/2 before $O_2(g)$. $C_4H_{10}(g) + 13/2\,O_2(g) \longrightarrow 4\,CO_2(g) + 5\,H_2O(g)$ 13 O atoms $\longrightarrow$ 13 O atoms
4. If the balanced equation contains coefficient fractions, clear these by multiplying each of the coefficients in the entire equation by the denominator of the fraction.	This step is not necessary in this example. Proceed to step 5.	$[C_4H_{10}(g) + 13/2\,O_2(g) \longrightarrow 4\,CO_2(g) + 5\,H_2O(g)] \times 2$ $2\,C_4H_{10}(g) + 13\,O_2(g) \longrightarrow 8\,CO_2(g) + 10\,H_2O(g)$
5. Check to make certain the equation is balanced by summing the total number of each type of atom on both sides of the equation.	$2\,Co_2O_3(s) + 3\,C(s) \longrightarrow 4\,Co(s) + 3\,CO_2(g)$	$2\,C_4H_{10}(g) + 13\,O_2(g) \longrightarrow 8\,CO_2(g) + 10\,H_2O(g)$

Left	Right
4 Co atoms	4 Co atoms
6 O atoms	6 O atoms
3 C atoms	3 C atoms

The equation is balanced.

Left	Right
8 C atoms	8 C atoms
20 H atoms	20 H atoms
26 O atoms	26 O atoms

The equation is balanced.

FOR PRACTICE 4.1
Write a balanced equation for the reaction between solid silicon dioxide and solid carbon to produce solid silicon carbide and carbon monoxide gas.

FOR PRACTICE 4.2
Write a balanced equation for the combustion of gaseous ethane (C_2H_6), a minority component of natural gas, in which it combines with gaseous oxygen to form gaseous carbon dioxide and gaseous water.

ANSWER **NOW!**

4.2 Cc Conceptual Connection

BALANCED CHEMICAL EQUATIONS Which quantity or quantities must always be the same on both sides of a chemical equation?

(a) the number of atoms of each kind
(b) the number of molecules of each kind
(c) the number of moles of each kind of molecule

WATCH **NOW!**
INTERACTIVE WORKED EXAMPLE 4.3

EXAMPLE 4.3 Balancing Chemical Equations Containing Polyatomic Ions

Write a balanced equation for the reaction between aqueous strontium chloride and aqueous lithium phosphate to form solid strontium phosphate and aqueous lithium chloride.

SOLUTION

1. Write a skeletal equation by writing chemical formulas for each of the reactants and products. Review Sections 3.5 and 3.6 for naming rules. (If a skeletal equation is provided, go to step 2.)

$SrCl_2(aq) + Li_3PO_4(aq) \longrightarrow Sr_3(PO_4)_2(s) + LiCl(aq)$

2. Balance metal ions (cations) first. If a polyatomic cation exists on both sides of the equation, balance it as a unit.

Begin with Sr^{2+}:

$SrCl_2(aq) + Li_3PO_4(aq) \longrightarrow Sr_3(PO_4)_2(s) + LiCl(aq)$

1 Sr^{2+} ion ⟶ 3 Sr^{2+} ions

To balance Sr^{2+}, put a 3 before $SrCl_2(aq)$.

$3\,SrCl_2(aq) + Li_3PO_4(aq) \longrightarrow Sr_3(PO_4)_2(s) + LiCl(aq)$

3 Sr^{2+} ions ⟶ 3 Sr^{2+} ions

Balance Li^+:

$3\,SrCl_2(aq) + Li_3PO_4(aq) \longrightarrow Sr_3(PO_4)_2(s) + LiCl(aq)$

3 Li^+ ions ⟶ 1 Li^+ ion

To balance Li^+, put a 3 before $LiCl(aq)$.

$3\,SrCl_2(aq) + Li_3PO_4(aq) \longrightarrow Sr_3(PO_4)_2(s) + 3\,LiCl(aq)$

3 Li^+ ions ⟶ 3 Li^+ ions

3. Balance nonmetal ions (anions) second. If a polyatomic anion exists on both sides of the equation, balance it as a unit.

Balance PO_4^{3-}:

$3\,SrCl_2(aq) + Li_3PO_4(aq) \longrightarrow Sr_3(PO_4)_2(s) + 3\,LiCl(aq)$

1 PO_4^{3-} ion ⟶ 2 PO_4^{3-} ions

To balance PO_4^{3-}, put a 2 before $Li_3PO_4(aq)$.

$3\,SrCl_2(aq) + 2\,Li_3PO_4(aq) \longrightarrow Sr_3(PO_4)_2(s) + 3\,LiCl(aq)$

2 PO_4^{3-} ions ⟶ 2 PO_4^{3-} ions

Balance Cl^-:

$3\,SrCl_2(aq) + 2\,Li_3PO_4(aq) \longrightarrow Sr_3(PO_4)_2(s) + 3\,LiCl(aq)$

6 Cl^- ions ⟶ 3 Cl^- ions

To balance Cl^-, replace the 3 before $LiCl(aq)$ with a 6. This also corrects the balance for Li^+, which was thrown off in the previous step.

$3\,SrCl_2(aq) + 2\,Li_3PO_4(aq) \longrightarrow Sr_3(PO_4)_2(s) + 6\,LiCl(aq)$

6 Cl^- ions ⟶ 6 Cl^- ions

4. Check to make certain the equation is balanced by summing the total number of each type of ion on both sides of the equation.

$3\,SrCl_2(aq) + 2\,Li_3PO_4(aq) \longrightarrow Sr_3(PO_4)_2(s) + 6\,LiCl(aq)$

Left	Right
3 Sr^{2+} ions	3 Sr^{2+} ions
6 Li^{+} ions	6 Li^{+} ions
2 PO_4^{3-} ions	2 PO_4^{3-} ions
6 Cl^{-} ions	6 Cl^{-} ions

The equation is balanced.

FOR PRACTICE 4.3 Write a balanced equation for the reaction between aqueous lead(II) nitrate and aqueous potassium chloride to form solid lead(II) chloride and aqueous potassium nitrate.

4.3 Reaction Stoichiometry: How Much Carbon Dioxide?

WATCH **NOW!**

KEY CONCEPT VIDEO 4.3
Reaction Stoichiometry

The balanced chemical equations for fossil fuel combustion reactions provide the exact relationships between the amount of fossil fuel burned and the amount of carbon dioxide emitted. In this discussion, we use octane (a component of gasoline) as a representative fossil fuel. The balanced equation for the combustion of octane is:

$$2\,C_8H_{18}(l) + 25\,O_2(g) \longrightarrow 16\,CO_2(g) + 18\,H_2O(g)$$

The balanced equation shows that 16 CO_2 molecules are produced for every 2 molecules of octane burned. We can extend this numerical relationship between molecules to the amounts in moles as follows:

The coefficients in a chemical equation specify the relative amounts in moles of each of the substances involved in the reaction.

In other words, from the equation, we know that 16 *moles* of CO_2 are produced for every 2 *moles* of octane burned. The numerical relationships between chemical amounts in a balanced chemical equation are called reaction **stoichiometry**. Stoichiometry allows us to predict the amounts of products that will form in a chemical reaction based on the amounts of reactants that react. Stoichiometry also allows us to determine the amounts of reactants necessary to form a given amount of product. These calculations are central to chemistry, allowing chemists to plan and carry out chemical reactions to obtain products in the desired quantities.

Stoichiometry is pronounced stoy-kee-AHM-e-tree.

Making Pizza: The Relationships among Ingredients

The concepts of stoichiometry are similar to a cooking recipe. Calculating the amount of carbon dioxide produced by the combustion of a given amount of a fossil fuel is analogous to calculating the number of pizzas that can be made from a given amount of cheese. For example, suppose we use the following pizza recipe:

$$1 \text{ crust} + 5 \text{ ounces tomato sauce} + 2 \text{ cups cheese} \longrightarrow 1 \text{ pizza}$$

The recipe contains the numerical relationships between the pizza ingredients. It says that if we have two cups of cheese—and enough of everything else—we can make one pizza. We can write this relationship as a ratio between the cheese and the pizza:

$$2 \text{ cups cheese} : 1 \text{ pizza}$$

What if we have six cups of cheese? Assuming that we have enough of everything else, we can use the ratio as a conversion factor to calculate the number of pizzas:

$$6 \text{ cups cheese} \times \frac{1 \text{ pizza}}{2 \text{ cups cheese}} = 3 \text{ pizzas}$$

Six cups of cheese are sufficient to make three pizzas. The pizza recipe contains numerical ratios between other ingredients as well, including the crust and the tomato sauce:

1 crust : 1 pizza

5 ounces tomato sauce : 1 pizza

Making Molecules: Mole-to-Mole Conversions

In a balanced chemical equation, we have a "recipe" for how reactants combine to form products. From our balanced equation for the combustion of octane, for example, we can write the following stoichiometric ratio:

$$2 \text{ mol } C_8H_{18} : 16 \text{ mol } CO_2$$

We can use this ratio to determine how many moles of CO_2 form when a given number of moles of C_8H_{18} burns. Suppose that we burn 22.0 moles of C_8H_{18}; how many moles of CO_2 form? We use the ratio from the balanced chemical equation in the same way that we used the ratio from the pizza recipe. The ratio acts as a conversion factor between the amount in moles of the reactant (C_8H_{18}) and the amount in moles of the product (CO_2):

$$22.0 \text{ mol } C_8H_{18} \times \frac{16 \text{ mol } CO_2}{2 \text{ mol } C_8H_{18}} = 176 \text{ mol } CO_2$$

The combustion of 22.0 moles of C_8H_{18} adds 176 moles of CO_2 to the atmosphere.

ANSWER **NOW!**

4.3 Cc Conceptual Connection

STOICHIOMETRY I Use the balanced equation for the combustion of octane to determine how many moles of H_2O are produced by the combustion of 22.0 moles of C_8H_{18}.

$$2\,C_8H_{18}(l) + 25\,O_2(g) \longrightarrow 16\,CO_2(g) + 18\,H_2O(g)$$

(a) 18 moles H_2O **(b)** 22 moles H_2O

(c) 176 moles H_2O **(d)** 198 moles H_2O

Making Molecules: Mass-to-Mass Conversions

According to the U.S. Department of Energy, the world burned 3.6×10^{10} barrels of petroleum in 2017, the equivalent of approximately 4.0×10^{15} g of gasoline. We can estimate the mass of CO_2 emitted into the atmosphere from burning this much gasoline using the combustion of 4.0×10^{15} g octane as the representative reaction. This calculation is similar to the one we just did, except that we are now given the *mass* of octane instead of the *amount* of octane in moles. Consequently, we must first convert the mass (in grams) to the amount (in moles). The general conceptual plan for calculations in which we are given the mass of a reactant or product in a chemical reaction and asked to find the mass of a different reactant or product takes the form:

Mass A → Amount A (in moles) → Amount B (in moles) → Mass B

where A and B are two different substances involved in the reaction.

We use the molar mass of A to convert from the mass of A to the amount of A (in moles). We use the appropriate ratio from the balanced chemical equation to convert from the amount of A (in moles) to the amount of B (in moles). And finally, we use the molar mass of B to convert from the amount of B (in moles) to the mass of B. To calculate the mass of CO_2 emitted upon the combustion of 4.0×10^{15} g of octane, we use the following conceptual plan:

Conceptual Plan

g C_8H_{18} → mol C_8H_{18} → mol CO_2 → g CO_2

$$\frac{1 \text{ mol } C_8H_{18}}{114.22 \text{ g } C_8H_{18}} \qquad \frac{16 \text{ mol } CO_2}{2 \text{ mol } C_8H_{18}} \qquad \frac{44.01 \text{ g } CO_2}{1 \text{ mol } CO_2}$$

Relationships used

$2\ \text{mol}\ C_8H_{18} : 16\ \text{mol}\ CO_2$ (from the chemical equation)

molar mass $C_8H_{18} = 114.22\ \text{g/mol}$

molar mass $CO_2 = 44.01\ \text{g/mol}$

Solution

We follow the conceptual plan to solve the problem, beginning with $\text{g}\ C_8H_{18}$ and canceling units to arrive at $\text{g}\ CO_2$:

$$4.0 \times 10^{15}\ \text{g}\ C_8H_{18} \times \frac{1\ \text{mol}\ C_8H_{18}}{114.22\ \text{g}\ C_8H_{18}} \times \frac{16\ \text{mol}\ CO_2}{2\ \text{mol}\ C_8H_{18}} \times \frac{44.01\ \text{g}\ CO_2}{1\ \text{mol}\ CO_2} = 1.2 \times 10^{16}\ \text{g}\ CO_2$$

The world's petroleum combustion produces $1.2 \times 10^{16}\ \text{g}\ CO_2$ (1.2×10^{13} kg) per year. In comparison, volcanoes produce about $2 \times 10^{11}\ \text{kg}\ CO_2$ per year.* In other words, volcanoes emit only $\frac{2 \times 10^{11}\ \text{kg}}{1.2 \times 10^{13}\ \text{kg}} \times 100\% = 1.7\%$ as much CO_2 per year as petroleum combustion. The argument that volcanoes emit more carbon dioxide than fossil fuel combustion is clearly mistaken. Examples 4.4 and 4.5 provide additional practice with stoichiometric calculations.

The percentage of CO_2 emitted by volcanoes relative to all fossil fuels is even less than 1.7% because the combustion of coal and natural gas also emits CO_2.

WATCH **NOW!**

INTERACTIVE WORKED EXAMPLE 4.4

EXAMPLE 4.4 Stoichiometry

During photosynthesis, plants convert carbon dioxide and water into glucose ($C_6H_{12}O_6$) according to the reaction:

$$6\ CO_2(g) + 6\ H_2O(l) \xrightarrow{\text{sunlight}} 6\ O_2(g) + C_6H_{12}O_6(aq)$$

Suppose that a particular plant consumes 37.8 g of CO_2 in one week. Assuming that there is more than enough water present to react with all of the CO_2, what mass of glucose (in grams) can the plant synthesize from the CO_2?

SORT The problem provides the mass of carbon dioxide and asks you to find the mass of glucose that can be produced.

GIVEN: $37.8\ \text{g}\ CO_2$

FIND: $\text{g}\ C_6H_{12}O_6$

STRATEGIZE The conceptual plan follows the general pattern of mass A → amount A (in moles) → amount B (in moles) → mass B. From the chemical equation, deduce the relationship between moles of carbon dioxide and moles of glucose. Use the molar masses to convert between grams and moles.

CONCEPTUAL PLAN

$\text{g}\ CO_2 \rightarrow \text{mol}\ CO_2 \rightarrow \text{mol}\ C_6H_{12}O_6 \rightarrow \text{g}\ C_6H_{12}O_6$

$\frac{1\ \text{mol}\ CO_2}{44.01\ \text{g}\ CO_2}$; $\frac{1\ \text{mol}\ C_6H_{12}O_6}{6\ \text{mol}\ CO_2}$; $\frac{180.2\ \text{g}\ C_6H_{12}O_6}{1\ \text{mol}\ C_6H_{12}O_6}$

RELATIONSHIPS USED

molar mass $CO_2 = 44.01\ \text{g/mol}$

$6\ \text{mol}\ CO_2 : 1\ \text{mol}\ C_6H_{12}O_6$

molar mass $C_6H_{12}O_6 = 180.2\ \text{g/mol}$

SOLVE Follow the conceptual plan to solve the problem. Begin with $\text{g}\ CO_2$ and use the conversion factors to arrive at $\text{g}\ C_6H_{12}O_6$.

SOLUTION

$$37.8\ \text{g}\ CO_2 \times \frac{1\ \text{mol}\ CO_2}{44.01\ \text{g}\ CO_2} \times \frac{1\ \text{mol}\ C_6H_{12}O_6}{6\ \text{mol}\ CO_2} \times \frac{180.2\ \text{g}\ C_6H_{12}O_6}{1\ \text{mol}\ C_6H_{12}O_6} = 25.8\ \text{g}\ C_6H_{12}O_6$$

—*Continued on the next page*

*Gerlach, T. M., Present-day CO_2 emissions from volcanoes. *Eos, Transactions, American Geophysical Union* 72(1991): 249, 254–255.

Continued—

CHECK The units of the answer are correct. The magnitude of the answer (25.8 g) is less than the initial mass of CO_2 (37.8 g). This is reasonable because each carbon in CO_2 has two oxygen atoms associated with it, while in $C_6H_{12}O_6$ each carbon has only one oxygen atom associated with it and two hydrogen atoms, which are much lighter than oxygen. Therefore, the mass of glucose produced should be less than the mass of carbon dioxide for this reaction.

FOR PRACTICE 4.4 Magnesium hydroxide, the active ingredient in milk of magnesia, neutralizes stomach acid, primarily HCl, according to the reaction:

$$Mg(OH)_2(s) + 2\,HCl(aq) \longrightarrow 2\,H_2O(l) + MgCl_2(aq)$$

What mass of HCl, in grams, is neutralized by a dose of milk of magnesia containing 3.26 g $Mg(OH)_2$?

EXAMPLE 4.5 Stoichiometry

Sulfuric acid (H_2SO_4) is a component of acid rain that forms when SO_2, a pollutant, reacts with oxygen and water according to the simplified reaction:

$$2\,SO_2(g) + O_2(g) + 2\,H_2O(l) \longrightarrow 2\,H_2SO_4(aq)$$

The generation of the electricity used by a medium-sized home produces about 25 kg of SO_2 per year. Assuming that there is more than enough O_2 and H_2O, what mass of H_2SO_4, in kg, can form from this much SO_2?

SORT The problem gives the mass of sulfur dioxide and asks you to find the mass of sulfuric acid.

GIVEN: 25 kg SO_2

FIND: kg H_2SO_4

STRATEGIZE The conceptual plan follows the standard format of mass → amount (in moles) → amount (in moles) → mass. Since the original quantity of SO_2 is given in kilograms, you must first convert to grams. You can deduce the relationship between moles of sulfur dioxide and moles of sulfuric acid from the chemical equation. Since the final quantity is requested in kilograms, convert to kilograms at the end.

CONCEPTUAL PLAN

$$\text{kg } SO_2 \xrightarrow{\frac{1000\text{ g}}{1\text{ kg}}} \text{g } SO_2 \xrightarrow{\frac{1\text{ mol } SO_2}{64.07\text{ g } SO_2}} \text{mol } SO_2 \xrightarrow{\frac{2\text{ mol } H_2SO_4}{2\text{ mol } SO_2}}$$

$$\text{mol } H_2SO_4 \xrightarrow{\frac{98.09\text{ g } H_2SO_4}{1\text{ mol } H_2SO_4}} \text{g } H_2SO_4 \xrightarrow{\frac{1\text{ kg}}{1000\text{ g}}} \text{kg } H_2SO_4$$

RELATIONSHIPS USED

1 kg = 1000 g

2 mol SO_2 : 2 mol H_2SO_4

molar mass SO_2 = 64.07 g/mol

molar mass H_2SO_4 = 98.09 g/mol

SOLVE Follow the conceptual plan to solve the problem. Begin with the given amount of SO_2 in kilograms and use the conversion factors to arrive at kg H_2SO_4.

SOLUTION

$$25\,\cancel{\text{kg}}\,\cancel{SO_2} \times \frac{1000\,\cancel{\text{g}}}{1\,\cancel{\text{kg}}} \times \frac{1\,\cancel{\text{mol } SO_2}}{64.07\,\cancel{\text{g } SO_2}} \times \frac{2\,\cancel{\text{mol } H_2SO_4}}{2\,\cancel{\text{mol } SO_2}}$$

$$\times \frac{98.09\,\cancel{\text{g}}\,H_2SO_4}{1\,\cancel{\text{mol } H_2SO_4}} \times \frac{1\text{ kg}}{1000\,\cancel{\text{g}}} = 38\text{ kg } H_2SO_4$$

CHECK The units of the final answer are correct. The magnitude of the final answer (38 kg H_2SO_4) is larger than the amount of SO_2 given (25 kg). This is reasonable because in the reaction each SO_2 molecule "gains weight" by reacting with O_2 and H_2O.

FOR PRACTICE 4.5 Another component of acid rain is nitric acid, which forms when NO_2, also a pollutant, reacts with oxygen and water according to the simplified equation:

$$4\,NO_2(g) + O_2(g) + 2\,H_2O(l) \longrightarrow 4\,HNO_3(aq)$$

The generation of the electricity used by a medium-sized home produces about 16 kg of NO_2 per year. Assuming that there is adequate O_2 and H_2O, what mass of HNO_3, in kg, can form from this amount of NO_2 pollutant?

STOICHIOMETRY II Under certain conditions, sodium reacts with oxygen to form sodium oxide according to the reaction:

$$4\,\text{Na}(s) + \text{O}_2(g) \longrightarrow 2\,\text{Na}_2\text{O}(s)$$

A flask contains the amount of oxygen represented by the diagram shown at far right.

Which of the following images best represents the amount of sodium required to completely react with all of the oxygen in the flask according to the equation?

4.4 Cc Conceptual Connection — ANSWER **NOW!**

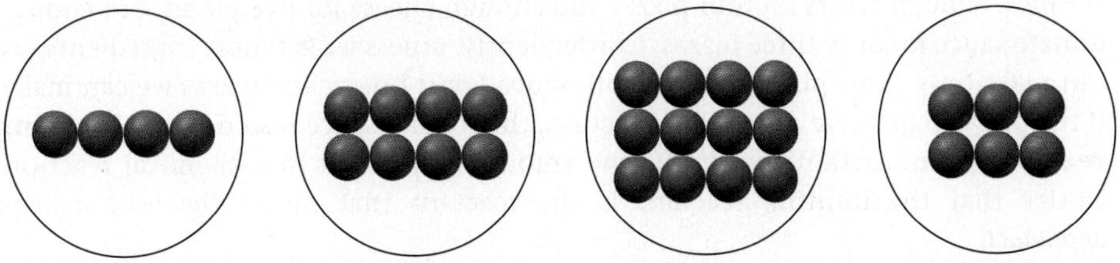

(a) (b) (c) (d)

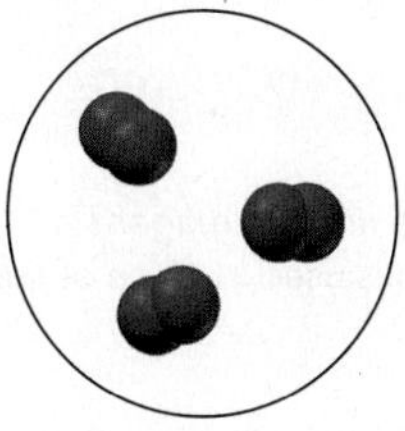

STOICHIOMETRY III Consider the generic chemical equation A + 3B → 2C. Let circles represent molecules of A and squares represent molecules of B. The diagram shown at the far right represents the amount of B available for reaction. Which diagram in the answer options accurately represents the amount of A necessary to completely react with B?

4.5 Cc Conceptual Connection — ANSWER **NOW!**

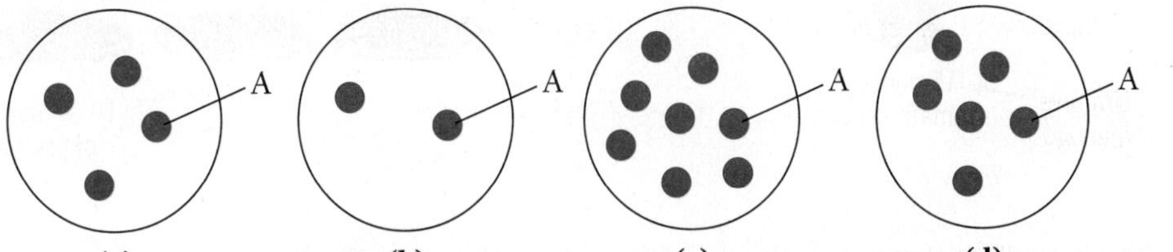

(a) (b) (c) (d)

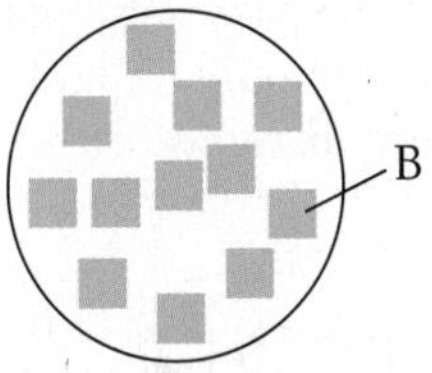

4.4 Stoichiometric Relationships: Limiting Reactant, Theoretical Yield, Percent Yield, and Reactant in Excess

WATCH **NOW!**

KEY CONCEPT VIDEO 4.4 *Limiting Reactant, Theoretical Yield, and Percent Yield*

Let's return to our pizza analogy to understand three more important concepts in reaction stoichiometry: *limiting reactant*, *theoretical yield*, and *percent yield*. Recall our pizza recipe from Section 4.3:

$$1\text{ crust} + 5\text{ ounces tomato sauce} + 2\text{ cups cheese} \longrightarrow 1\text{ pizza}$$

Suppose that we have four crusts, ten cups of cheese, and 15 ounces of tomato sauce. How many pizzas can we make?

We have enough crusts to make:

$$4\ \cancel{\text{crusts}} \times \frac{1\text{ pizza}}{1\ \cancel{\text{crust}}} = 4\text{ pizzas}$$

We have enough cheese to make:

$$10\ \cancel{\text{cups cheese}} \times \frac{1\text{ pizza}}{2\ \cancel{\text{cups cheese}}} = 5\text{ pizzas}$$

We have enough tomato sauce to make:

$$15\ \text{ounces tomato sauce} \times \frac{1\ \text{pizza}}{5\ \text{ounces tomato sauce}} = 3\ \text{pizzas}$$

Limiting reactant — Smallest number of pizzas

The term *limiting reagent* is sometimes used in place of *limiting reactant.*

We have enough crusts for four pizzas and enough cheese for five pizzas, but enough tomato sauce for only three pizzas. Consequently, unless we get more ingredients, we can make only three pizzas. The tomato sauce *limits* how many pizzas we can make. If the pizza recipe were a chemical reaction, the tomato sauce would be the **limiting reactant**, the reactant that limits the amount of product in a chemical reaction. Notice that the limiting reactant is the reactant that makes *the least amount of product.*

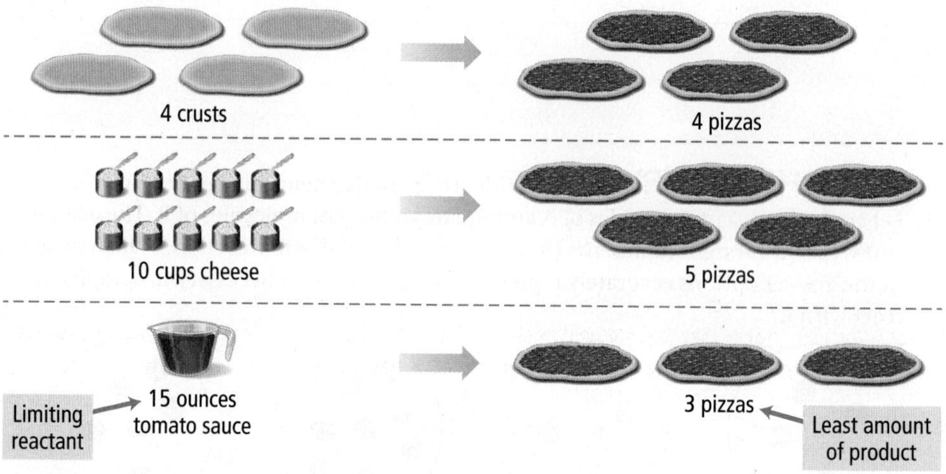

The ingredient that makes the least amount of pizza determines how many pizzas you can make.

The reactants that *do not* limit the amount of product—such as the crusts and the cheese in this example—are said to be **in excess**. If this were a chemical reaction, three pizzas would be the **theoretical yield**, the maximum amount of product that can be made in a chemical reaction based on the amount of limiting reactant.

Let us carry this analogy one step further. Suppose we go on to cook our pizzas and accidentally burn one of them. Even though we theoretically have enough ingredients for three pizzas, we end up with only two. If this were a chemical reaction, the two pizzas would be our **actual yield**, the amount of product actually produced by a chemical reaction. (The actual yield is always equal to or less than the theoretical yield because a small amount of product is usually lost to other reactions or does not form during a reaction.) Finally, our **percent yield**, the percentage of the theoretical yield that was actually attained, is calculated as the ratio of the actual yield to the theoretical yield:

Actual yield

$$\%\ \text{yield} = \frac{2\ \text{pizzas}}{3\ \text{pizzas}} \times 100\% = 67\%$$

Theoretical yield

Since one of our pizzas burned, our percent yield for pizzas is 67%.

Summarizing Limiting Reactant and Yield

- **The limiting reactant** (or **limiting reagent**) is the reactant that is completely consumed in a chemical reaction and limits the amount of product.
- **The reactant in excess** is any reactant that occurs in a quantity greater than is required to completely react with the limiting reactant.
- **The theoretical yield** is the amount of product that can be made in a chemical reaction based on the amount of limiting reactant.
- **The actual yield** is the amount of product actually produced by a chemical reaction.
- **The percent yield** is calculated as $\frac{\text{actual yield}}{\text{theoretical yield}} \times 100\%$.

Calculating Limiting Reactant, Theoretical Yield, and Percent Yield

We can apply these concepts to a chemical reaction. Recall from Section 4.2 our balanced equation for the combustion of methane:

$$CH_4(g) + 2\,O_2(g) \longrightarrow CO_2(g) + 2\,H_2O(l)$$

If we start out with five CH_4 molecules and eight O_2 molecules, what is our limiting reactant? What is our theoretical yield of carbon dioxide molecules? First, we calculate the number of CO_2 molecules that can be made from five CH_4 molecules:

$$5\,\cancel{CH_4} \times \frac{1\,CO_2}{1\,\cancel{CH_4}} = 5\,CO_2$$

We then calculate the number of CO_2 molecules that can be made from eight O_2 molecules:

$$8\,\cancel{O_2} \times \frac{1\,CO_2}{2\,\cancel{O_2}} = 4\,CO_2$$

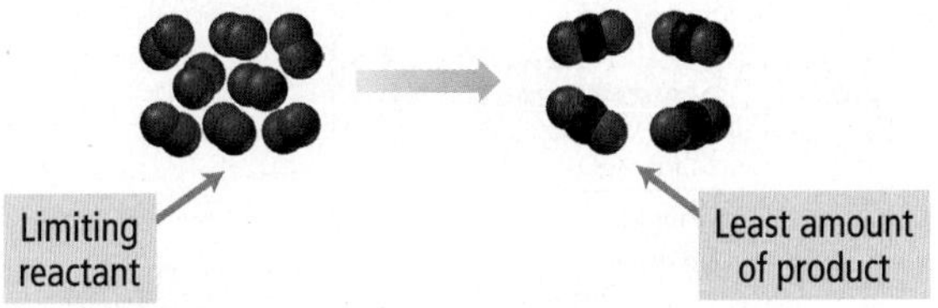

We have enough CH_4 to make five CO_2 molecules and enough O_2 to make four CO_2 molecules; therefore, O_2 is the limiting reactant, and four CO_2 molecules is the theoretical yield. The CH_4 is in excess.

An alternative way to calculate the limiting reactant (which we describe here but do not use again in this book) is to pick any reactant and determine how much of the *other reactant* is necessary to completely react with it. For the reaction we just examined, we have five CH_4 molecules and eight O_2 molecules. Let's pick the five CH_4 molecules and determine how many O_2 molecules are necessary to completely react with them:

$$5\,\cancel{CH_4} \times \frac{2\,O_2}{1\,\cancel{CH_4}} = 10\,O_2$$

Since we need ten O_2 molecules to completely react with the five CH_4 molecules, and since we have only eight O_2 molecules, we know that the O_2 is the limiting reactant. The same method can be applied by comparing the amounts of reactants in moles.

ANSWER NOW!

4.6 Cc Conceptual Connection

LIMITING REACTANT AND THEORETICAL YIELD Nitrogen and hydrogen gas react to form ammonia according to the reaction:

$$N_2(g) + 3\,H_2(g) \longrightarrow 2\,NH_3(g)$$

A flask contains a mixture of reactants represented by the image shown at the left.

Which of the following images best represents the mixture in the flask after the reactants have reacted as completely as possible? What is the limiting reactant? Which reactant is in excess?

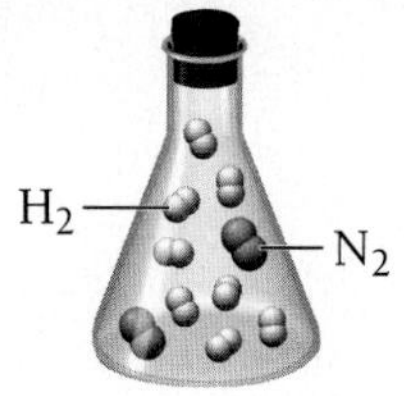

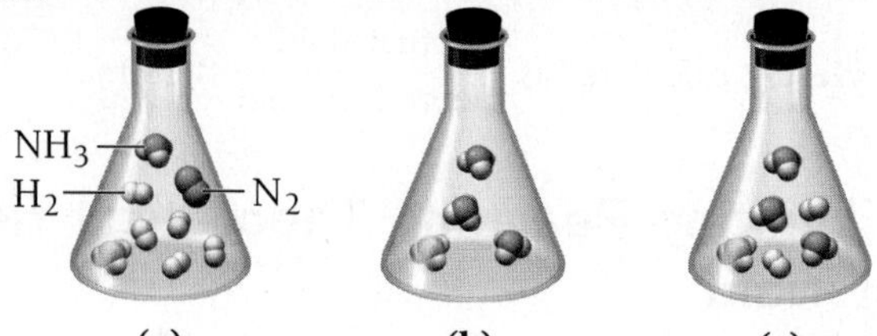

(a) (b) (c)

Calculating Limiting Reactant, Theoretical Yield, and Percent Yield from Initial Reactant Masses

When working in the laboratory, we normally measure the initial quantities of reactants in grams, not in number of molecules. To find the limiting reactant and theoretical yield from initial masses, we must first convert the masses to amounts in moles. Consider the reaction:

$$2\,Mg(s) + O_2(g) \longrightarrow 2\,MgO(s)$$

A reaction mixture contains 42.5 g Mg and 33.8 g O_2; what is the limiting reactant and theoretical yield?

To solve this problem, we must determine which of the reactants makes the least amount of product.

Conceptual Plan

We can find the limiting reactant by calculating how much product can be made from each reactant. However, we are given the initial quantities in grams, and stoichiometric relationships are between moles, so we must first convert to moles. We then convert from moles of the reactant to moles of product. The reactant that makes the *least amount of product* is the limiting reactant. The conceptual plan is:

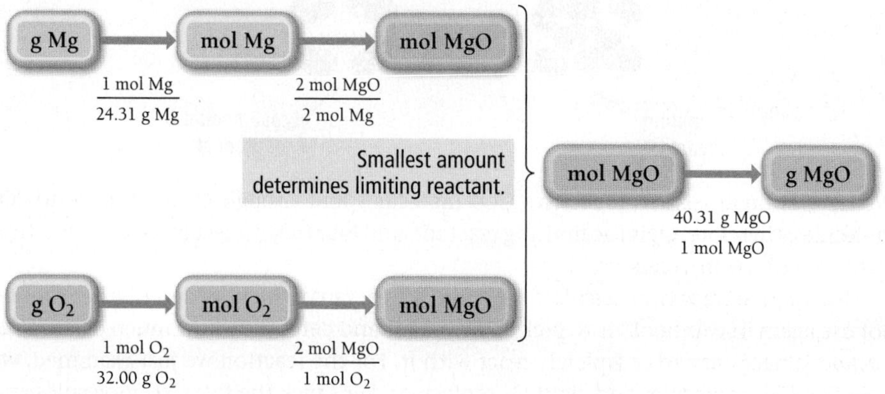

In this conceptual plan, we compare the number of moles of MgO made by each reactant and convert only the smaller amount to grams. (Alternatively, we can convert both quantities to grams and determine the limiting reactant based on the mass of the product.)

Relationships Used

molar mass Mg = 24.31 g/mol

molar mass O_2 = 32.00 g/mol

2 mol Mg : 2 mol MgO

1 mol O_2 : 2 mol MgO

molar mass MgO = 40.31 g/mol

Solution

Beginning with the masses of each reactant, we follow the conceptual plan to calculate how much product can be made from each:

$$42.5\ \text{g Mg} \times \frac{1\ \text{mol Mg}}{24.31\ \text{g Mg}} \times \frac{2\ \text{mol MgO}}{2\ \text{mol Mg}} = 1.7\underline{4}83\ \text{mol MgO}$$

Limiting reactant (42.5 g Mg) — Least amount of product (1.7483 mol MgO)

$$33.8\ \text{g } O_2 \times \frac{1\ \text{mol } O_2}{32.00\ \text{g } O_2} \times \frac{2\ \text{mol MgO}}{1\ \text{mol } O_2} = 2.1\underline{1}25\ \text{mol MgO}$$

$$1.7\underline{4}83\ \text{mol MgO} \times \frac{40.31\ \text{g MgO}}{1\ \text{mol MgO}} = 70.5\ \text{g MgO}$$

Since Mg makes the least amount of product, it is the limiting reactant, and O_2 is in excess. Notice that the limiting reactant is not necessarily the reactant with the least mass. In this case, the mass of O_2 is less than the mass of Mg, yet Mg is the limiting reactant because it makes the least amount of MgO. The theoretical yield is 70.5 g of MgO, the mass of product possible based on the limiting reactant.

Suppose that after the synthesis, the actual yield of MgO is 55.9 g. What is the percent yield? We calculate the percent yield as follows:

$$\%\ \text{yield} = \frac{\text{actual yield}}{\text{theoretical yield}} \times 100\% = \frac{55.9\ \text{g}}{70.5\ \text{g}} \times 100\% = 79.3\%$$

WATCH **NOW!**

INTERACTIVE WORKED EXAMPLE 4.6

EXAMPLE 4.6 Limiting Reactant and Theoretical Yield

Ammonia, NH_3, can be synthesized by the reaction:

$$2\,NO(g) + 5\,H_2(g) \longrightarrow 2\,NH_3(g) + 2\,H_2O(g)$$

Starting with 86.3 g NO and 25.6 g H_2, find the theoretical yield of ammonia in grams.

SORT You are given the mass of each reactant in grams and asked to find the theoretical yield of a product.

GIVEN: 86.3 g NO, 25.6 g H_2

FIND: theoretical yield of $NH_3(g)$

STRATEGIZE Determine which reactant makes the least amount of product by converting from grams of each reactant to moles of the reactant to moles of the product. Use molar masses to convert between grams and moles and use the stoichiometric relationships (from the chemical equation) to convert between moles of reactant and moles of product. Remember that the reactant that makes *the least amount of product* is the limiting reactant. Convert the number of moles of product obtained using the limiting reactant to grams of product.

CONCEPTUAL PLAN

g NO → mol NO → mol NH_3

$\frac{1\ \text{mol NO}}{30.01\ \text{g NO}}$ $\frac{2\ \text{mol } NH_3}{2\ \text{mol NO}}$

g H_2 → mol H_2 → mol NH_3

$\frac{1\ \text{mol } H_2}{2.02\ \text{g } H_2}$ $\frac{2\ \text{mol } NH_3}{5\ \text{mol } H_2}$

Smallest amount determines limiting reactant.

mol NH_3 → g NH_3

$\frac{17.03\ \text{g } NH_3}{1\ \text{mol } NH_3}$

RELATIONSHIPS USED

molar mass NO = 30.01 g/mol

molar mass H_2 = 2.02 g/mol

2 mol NO : 2 mol NH_3 (from chemical equation)

5 mol H_2 : 2 mol NH_3 (from chemical equation)

molar mass NH_3 = 17.03 g/mol

—Continued on the next page

Continued—

SOLVE Beginning with the given mass of each reactant, calculate the amount of product that can be made in moles. Convert the amount of product made by the limiting reactant to grams—this is the theoretical yield.

SOLUTION

$$86.3\ \text{g NO} \times \frac{1\ \text{mol NO}}{30.01\ \text{g NO}} \times \frac{2\ \text{mol NH}_3}{2\ \text{mol NO}} = 2.8\underline{7}57\ \text{mol NH}_3$$

Limiting reactant — Least amount of product

$$25.6\ \text{g H}_2 \times \frac{1\ \text{mol H}_2}{2.02\ \text{g H}_2} \times \frac{2\ \text{mol NH}_3}{5\ \text{mol H}_2} = 5.0\underline{6}93\ \text{mol NH}_3$$

$$2.8\underline{7}57\ \text{mol NH}_3 \times \frac{17.03\ \text{g NH}_3}{\text{mol NH}_3} = 49.0\ \text{g NH}_3$$

Since NO makes the least amount of product, it is the limiting reactant, and the theoretical yield of ammonia is 49.0 g.

CHECK The units of the answer (g NH_3) are correct. The magnitude (49.0 g) seems reasonable given that 86.3 g NO is the limiting reactant. NO contains one oxygen atom per nitrogen atom, and NH_3 contains three hydrogen atoms per nitrogen atom. Since three hydrogen atoms have less mass than one oxygen atom, it is reasonable that the mass of NH_3 obtained is less than the mass of NO.

FOR PRACTICE 4.6 Ammonia can also be synthesized by the reaction:

$$3\ H_2(g) + N_2(g) \longrightarrow 2\ NH_3(g)$$

What is the theoretical yield of ammonia, in kg, that we can synthesize from 5.22 kg of H_2 and 31.5 kg of N_2?

EXAMPLE 4.7 Limiting Reactant and Theoretical Yield

We can obtain titanium metal from its oxide according to the following balanced equation:

$$TiO_2(s) + 2\ C(s) \longrightarrow Ti(s) + 2\ CO(g)$$

When 28.6 kg of C reacts with 88.2 kg of TiO_2, 42.8 kg of Ti is produced. Find the limiting reactant, theoretical yield (in kg), and percent yield.

SORT You are given the mass of each reactant and the mass of product formed. You are asked to find the limiting reactant, theoretical yield, and percent yield.

GIVEN: 28.6 kg C, 88.2 kg TiO_2, 42.8 kg Ti produced
FIND: limiting reactant, theoretical yield, % yield

STRATEGIZE Determine which of the reactants makes the least amount of product by converting from kilograms of each reactant to moles of product. Convert between grams and moles using molar mass. Convert between moles of reactant and moles of product using the stoichiometric relationships derived from the chemical equation. Remember that the reactant that makes the *least amount of product* is the limiting reactant.

CONCEPTUAL PLAN

$$\text{kg C} \xrightarrow{\frac{1000\ \text{g}}{1\ \text{kg}}} \text{g C} \xrightarrow{\frac{1\ \text{mol C}}{12.01\ \text{g C}}} \text{mol C} \xrightarrow{\frac{1\ \text{mol Ti}}{2\ \text{mol C}}} \text{mol Ti}$$

$$\text{kg TiO}_2 \xrightarrow{\frac{1000\ \text{g}}{1\ \text{kg}}} \text{g TiO}_2 \xrightarrow{\frac{1\ \text{mol TiO}_2}{79.87\ \text{g TiO}_2}} \text{mol TiO}_2 \xrightarrow{\frac{1\ \text{mol Ti}}{1\ \text{mol TiO}_2}} \text{mol Ti}$$

Smallest amount determines limiting reactant.

$$\text{mol Ti} \xrightarrow{\frac{47.87\ \text{g Ti}}{\text{mol Ti}}} \text{g Ti} \xrightarrow{\frac{1\ \text{kg}}{1000\ \text{g}}} \text{kg Ti}$$

Determine the theoretical yield (in kilograms) by converting the number of moles of product obtained with the limiting reactant to kilograms of product.

RELATIONSHIPS USED

$1000\ \text{g} = 1\ \text{kg}$

molar mass of C $= 12.01$ g/mol

molar mass of $TiO_2 = 79.87$ g/mol

1 mol TiO_2 : 1 mol Ti

2 mol C : 1 mol Ti

molar mass of Ti $= 47.87$ g/mol

SOLVE Beginning with the actual amount of each reactant, calculate the amount of product that can be made in moles. Convert the amount of product made by the limiting reactant to kilograms—this is the theoretical yield.

SOLUTION

$$28.6\ \cancel{\text{kg C}} \times \frac{1000\ \cancel{\text{g}}}{1\ \cancel{\text{kg}}} \times \frac{1\ \cancel{\text{mol C}}}{12.01\ \cancel{\text{g C}}} \times \frac{1\ \text{mol Ti}}{2\ \cancel{\text{mol C}}} = 1.1\underline{9}07 \times 10^3\ \text{mol Ti}$$

Limiting reactant

Least amount of product

$$88.2\ \cancel{\text{kg TiO}_2} \times \frac{1000\ \cancel{\text{g}}}{1\ \cancel{\text{kg}}} \times \frac{1\ \cancel{\text{mol TiO}_2}}{79.87\ \cancel{\text{g TiO}_2}} \times \frac{1\ \text{mol Ti}}{1\ \cancel{\text{mol TiO}_2}} = 1.1\underline{0}43 \times 10^3\ \text{mol Ti}$$

$$1.10\underline{4}3 \times 10^3\ \cancel{\text{mol Ti}} \times \frac{47.87\ \cancel{\text{g Ti}}}{1\ \cancel{\text{mol Ti}}} \times \frac{1\ \text{kg}}{1000\ \cancel{\text{g}}} = 52.9\ \text{kg Ti}$$

Calculate the percent yield by dividing the actual yield (42.8 kg Ti) by the theoretical yield.

Since TiO_2 makes the least amount of product, it is the limiting reactant, and 52.9 kg Ti is the theoretical yield.

$$\%\ \text{yield} = \frac{\text{actual yield}}{\text{theoretical yield}} \times 100\% = \frac{42.8\ \text{kg}}{52.9\ \text{kg}} \times 100\% = 80.9\%$$

CHECK The theoretical yield has the correct units (kg Ti) and has a reasonable magnitude compared to the mass of TiO_2. Since Ti has a lower molar mass than TiO_2, the amount of Ti made from TiO_2 should have a lower mass. The percent yield is reasonable (under 100% as it should be).

FOR PRACTICE 4.7 Mining companies use this reaction to obtain iron from iron ore:

$$Fe_2O_3(s) + 3\ CO(g) \longrightarrow 2\ Fe(s) + 3\ CO_2(g)$$

The reaction of 167 g Fe_2O_3 with 85.8 g CO produces 72.3 g Fe. Determine the limiting reactant, theoretical yield, and percent yield.

REACTANT IN EXCESS

4.7 Cc Conceptual Connection ANSWER **NOW!**

Nitrogen dioxide reacts with water to form nitric acid and nitrogen monoxide according to the equation:

$$3\ NO_2(g) + H_2O(l) \longrightarrow 2\ HNO_3(l) + NO(g)$$

Suppose that 5 mol NO_2 and 1 mol H_2O combine and react completely. How many moles of the reactant in excess are present after the reaction has completed?

(a) 1 mol NO_2 **(b)** 1 mol H_2O **(c)** 2 mol NO_2 **(d)** 2 mol H_2O

4.5 Three Examples of Chemical Reactions: Combustion, Alkali Metals, and Halogens

In this section, we examine three types of reactions. The first is combustion reactions, which we encountered in Section 4.2. The second is the reactions of the alkali metals. As we discussed in Section 2.7, alkali metals are among the most active metals. Alkali metal reactions are good examples of the types of reactions that many metals undergo. The third type of reactions involves the halogens. Halogens are among the most active nonmetals.

Combustion Reactions

A *combustion reaction* involves the reaction of a substance with O_2 to form one or more oxygen-containing compounds, often including water. Combustion reactions also emit heat. For example, as you saw earlier in this chapter, natural gas (CH_4) reacts with oxygen to form carbon dioxide and water:

$$CH_4(g) + 2\ O_2(g) \longrightarrow CO_2(g) + 2\ H_2O(g)$$

Ethanol, the alcohol in alcoholic beverages, also reacts with oxygen in a combustion reaction to form carbon dioxide and water:

$$C_2H_5OH(l) + 3\,O_2(g) \longrightarrow 2\,CO_2(g) + 3\,H_2O(g)$$

Compounds containing carbon and hydrogen—or carbon, hydrogen, and oxygen—always form carbon dioxide and water upon complete combustion. Other combustion reactions include the reaction of carbon with oxygen to form carbon dioxide:

$$C(s) + O_2(g) \longrightarrow CO_2(g)$$

and the reaction of hydrogen with oxygen to form water:

$$2\,H_2(g) + O_2(g) \longrightarrow 2\,H_2O(g)$$

We can write chemical equations for most combustion reactions by noticing the pattern of reactivity. Any carbon in a combustion reaction reacts with oxygen to produce carbon dioxide, and any hydrogen reacts with oxygen to form water.

EXAMPLE 4.8 Writing Equations for Combustion Reactions

Write a balanced equation for the combustion of liquid methyl alcohol (CH_3OH).

SOLUTION

Begin by writing an unbalanced equation showing the reaction of CH_3OH with O_2 to form CO_2 and H_2O.	$CH_3OH(l) + O_2(g) \longrightarrow CO_2(g) + H_2O(g)$
Balance the equation using the guidelines from Section 4.2.	$2\,CH_3OH(l) + 3\,O_2(g) \longrightarrow 2\,CO_2(g) + 4\,H_2O(g)$

FOR PRACTICE 4.8 Write a balanced equation for the complete combustion of liquid C_2H_5SH. *Hint:* The sulfur in this compound reacts to form SO_2.

Alkali Metal Reactions

The reactions of the alkali metals (group 1A in the periodic table) with nonmetals are vigorous. For example, the alkali metals (M) react with halogens (X) according to the reaction:

$$2\,M + X_2 \longrightarrow 2\,MX$$

The reaction of sodium and chlorine to form sodium chloride is typical:

$$2\,Na(s) + Cl_2(g) \longrightarrow 2\,NaCl(s)$$

This reaction emits heat and sparks as it occurs (Figure 4.4◀). Each successive alkali metal reacts even more vigorously with chlorine.

The alkali metals also react with water to form the dissolved alkali metal ion, the hydroxide ion, and hydrogen gas:

$$2\,M(s) + 2\,H_2O(l) \longrightarrow 2\,M^+(aq) + 2\,OH^-(aq) + H_2(g)$$

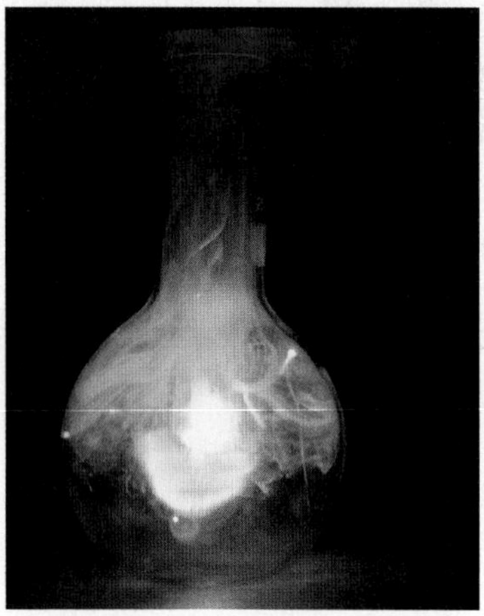

▲ **FIGURE 4.4 Reaction of Sodium and Chlorine to Form Sodium Chloride**

The reaction is highly exothermic and can be explosive because the heat from the reaction can ignite the hydrogen gas. The reaction becomes more explosive as we move down the column from one metal to the next, as shown in Figure 4.5▶.*

Halogen Reactions

The halogens (group 7A) are among the most active nonmetals in the periodic table. The halogens all react with many metals to form *metal halides* according to the equation:

$$2\,M + n\,X_2 \longrightarrow 2\,MX_n$$

*The rate of the alkali metal reaction with water, and therefore its vigor, is enhanced by the successively lower melting points of the alkali metals as we move down the column. The low melting points of the heavier metals allow the emitted heat to actually melt the metal, increasing the reaction rate.

Reactions of the Alkali Metals with Water

◀ **FIGURE 4.5 Reactions of the Alkali Metals with Water** The reactions become progressively more vigorous as we move down the group.

where M is the metal, X is the halogen, and MX_n is the metal halide. For example, chlorine reacts with iron according to the equation:

$$2\,Fe(s) + 3\,Cl_2(g) \longrightarrow 2\,FeCl_3(s)$$

Since metals tend to lose electrons and the halogens tend to gain them, the metal halides—like all compounds that form between metals and nonmetals—contain ionic bonds.

The halogens also react with hydrogen to form *hydrogen halides* according to the equation:

$$H_2(g) + X_2 \longrightarrow 2\,HX(g)$$

The hydrogen halides—like all compounds that form between two nonmetals—contain covalent bonds. All of the hydrogen halides form acids when combined with water.

The halogens also react with each other to form *interhalogen compounds*. For example, bromine reacts with fluorine according to the equation:

$$Br_2(l) + F_2(g) \longrightarrow 2\,BrF(g)$$

Again, like all compounds that form between two nonmetals, the interhalogen compounds contain covalent bonds.

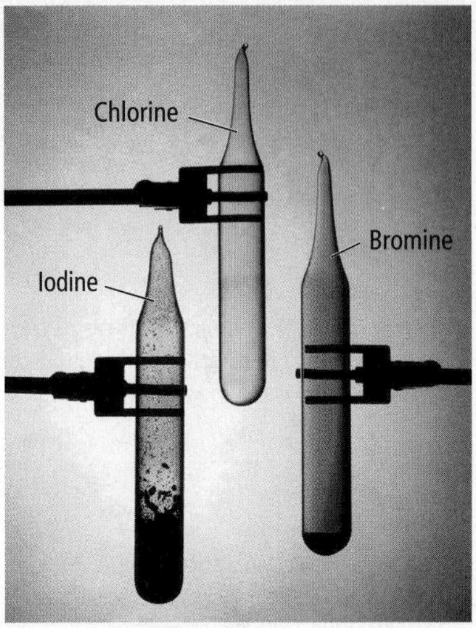

▲ Three Halogens

EXAMPLE 4.9 Alkali Metal and Halogen Reactions

Write a balanced chemical equation for each reaction.

(a) the reaction between potassium metal and bromine gas

(b) the reaction between rubidium metal and liquid water

(c) the reaction between gaseous chlorine and solid iodine

SOLUTION

(a) Alkali metals react with halogens to form metal halides. Write the formulas for the reactants and the metal halide product (making sure to write the correct ionic chemical formula for the metal halide, as outlined in Section 3.5), and then balance the equation.	$2\,K(s) + Br_2(g) \longrightarrow 2\,KBr(s)$
(b) Alkali metals react with water to form the dissolved metal ion, the hydroxide ion, and hydrogen gas. Write the skeletal equation including these and then balance it.	$2\,Rb(s) + 2\,H_2O(l) \longrightarrow 2\,Rb^+(aq) + 2\,OH^-(aq) + H_2(g)$

—*Continued on the next page*

Continued—

(c) Halogens react with each other to form interhalogen compounds. Write the skeletal equation with the halogens as the reactants and the interhalogen compound as the product and balance the equation.	$Cl_2(g) + I_2(s) \longrightarrow 2\,ICl(g)$

FOR PRACTICE 4.9 Write a balanced chemical equation for each reaction.

(a) the reaction between aluminum metal and chlorine gas

(b) the reaction between lithium metal and liquid water

(c) the reaction between gaseous hydrogen and liquid bromine

QUIZ YOURSELF **NOW!**

Self-Assessment Quiz

Q1. What is the coefficient of H_2O when the reaction is balanced?
MISSED THIS? *Read Section 4.2; Watch KCV 4.2, IWE 4.2*

$$K(s) + H_2O(l) \rightarrow KOH(aq) + H_2(g)$$

a) 1 b) 2
c) 3 d) 4

Q2. What are the correct coefficients (reading from left to right) when the chemical equation is balanced?
MISSED THIS? *Read Section 4.2; Watch KCV 4.2, IWE 4.2*

$$\_PCl_3(l) + \_H_2O(l) \longrightarrow \_H_3PO_3(aq) + \_HCl(aq)$$

a) 1, 3, 1, 3 b) 1, 2, 1, 1
c) 1, 3, 2, 1 d) 3, 6, 1, 9

Q3. For the reaction shown here, 3.5 mol A is mixed with 5.9 mol B and 2.2 mol C. What is the limiting reactant?
MISSED THIS? *Read Section 4.4; Watch KCV 4.4, IWE 4.6*

$$3\,A + 2\,B + C \rightarrow 2\,D$$

a) A b) B c) C d) D

Q4. Manganese(IV) oxide reacts with aluminum to form elemental manganese and aluminum oxide:

$$3\,MnO_2 + 4\,Al \longrightarrow 3\,Mn + 2\,Al_2O_3$$

What mass of Al is required to completely react with 25.0 g MnO_2? **MISSED THIS?** *Read Section 4.3; Watch KCV 4.3, IWE 4.4*

a) 7.76 g Al b) 5.82 g Al
c) 33.3 g Al d) 10.3 g Al

Q5. Sodium and chlorine react to form sodium chloride:

$$2\,Na(s) + Cl_2(g) \longrightarrow 2\,NaCl(s)$$

What is the theoretical yield of sodium chloride for the reaction of 55.0 g Na with 67.2 g Cl_2?
MISSED THIS? *Read Section 4.4; Watch KCV 4.4, IWE 4.6*

a) 1.40×10^2 g NaCl b) 111 g NaCl
c) 55.4 g NaCl d) 222 g NaCl

Q6. Sulfur and fluorine react to form sulfur hexafluoride:

$$S(s) + 3\,F_2(g) \longrightarrow SF_6(g)$$

If 50.0 g S is allowed to react as completely as possible with 105.0 g F_2, what mass of the excess reactant is left?
MISSED THIS? *Read Section 4.4; Watch KCV 4.4, IWE 4.6*

a) 20.5 g S b) 45.7 g F_2
c) 15.0 g S d) 36.3 g F_2

Q7. A reaction has a theoretical yield of 45.8 g. When the reaction is carried out, 37.2 g of the product is obtained. What is the percent yield?
MISSED THIS? *Read Section 4.4; Watch KCV 4.4, IWE 4.6*

a) 55.1% b) 44.8%
c) 123% d) 81.2%

Q8. Identify the correct balanced equation for the combustion of propane (C_3H_8). **MISSED THIS?** *Read Section 4.5*

a) $C_3H_8(g) \longrightarrow 4\,H_2(g) + 3\,C(s)$
b) $C_3H_8(g) + 5\,O_2(g) \longrightarrow 4\,H_2O(g) + 3\,CO_2(g)$
c) $C_3H_8(g) + 3\,O_2(g) \longrightarrow 4\,H_2O(g) + 3\,CO_2(g)$
d) $2\,C_3H_8(g) + 9\,O_2(g) \longrightarrow 6\,H_2CO_3(g) + 2\,H_2(g)$

Q9. Solid potassium chlorate ($KClO_3$) decomposes into potassium chloride and oxygen gas when heated. How many moles of oxygen form when 55.8 g $KClO_3$ completely decompose?
MISSED THIS? *Read Section 4.3; Watch KCV 4.3, IWE 4.4*

a) 0.455 mol O_2
b) 0.304 mol O_2
c) 83.7 mol O_2
d) 0.683 mol O_2

Q10. Identify the product of the reaction between hydrogen gas and bromine. **MISSED THIS?** *Read Section 4.5*

a) HBr b) H_2Br
c) HBr_2 d) H_2Br_3

Answers: 1. (b) **2.** (a) **3.** (a) **4.** (d) **5.** (b) **6.** (a) **7.** (d) **8.** (b) **9.** (d) **10.** (a)

CHAPTER 4 IN REVIEW

TERMS

Section 4.2
chemical reaction (141)
combustion reaction (141)
chemical equation (141)
reactants (141)
products (141)
balanced chemical equation (141)

Section 4.3
stoichiometry (145)

Section 4.4
limiting reactant (150)
reactant in excess (150)
theoretical yield (150)
actual yield (150)
percent yield (150)

CONCEPTS

Climate Change and the Combustion of Fossil Fuels (4.1)

- Greenhouse gases warm Earth by trapping some of the sunlight that penetrates Earth's atmosphere. Global warming, resulting from rising atmospheric carbon dioxide levels, is potentially harmful.
- The largest atmospheric carbon dioxide source is the burning of fossil fuels. This can be verified by reaction stoichiometry.

Writing and Balancing Chemical Equations (4.2)

- In chemistry, we represent chemical reactions with chemical equations. The substances on the left-hand side of a chemical equation are the reactants, and the substances on the right-hand side are the products.
- Chemical equations are balanced when the number of each type of atom on the left side of the equation is equal to the number on the right side.

Reaction Stoichiometry (4.3)

- Reaction stoichiometry refers to the numerical relationships between the reactants and products in a balanced chemical equation.
- Reaction stoichiometry allows us to predict, for example, the amount of product that can be formed for a given amount of reactant, or how much of one reactant is required to react with a given amount of another.

Limiting Reactant, Theoretical Yield, and Percent Yield (4.4)

- When a chemical reaction actually occurs, the reactants are usually not present in the exact stoichiometric ratios specified by the balanced chemical equation. The limiting reactant is the one that is available in the smallest stoichiometric quantity—it will be completely consumed in the reaction, and it limits the amount of product that can be made.
- Any reactant that does not limit the amount of product is in excess.
- The amount of product that can be made from the limiting reactant is the theoretical yield.
- The actual yield—always equal to or less than the theoretical yield—is the amount of product that is actually made when the reaction is carried out.
- The percentage of the theoretical yield that is actually produced when the reaction is carried out is the percent yield.

Combustion, Alkali Metals, and Halogens (4.5)

- In a combustion reaction, a substance reacts with oxygen—emitting heat and forming one or more oxygen-containing products. The alkali metals react with nonmetals, losing electrons in the process.
- The halogens react with many metals to form metal halides. They also react with hydrogen to form hydrogen halides and with one another to form interhalogen compounds.

EQUATIONS AND RELATIONSHIPS

Mass-to-Mass Conversion: Stoichiometry (4.2)

mass A ⟶ amount A (in moles) ⟶ amount B (in moles) ⟶ mass B

Percent Yield (4.3)

$$\%\text{ yield} = \frac{\text{actual yield}}{\text{theoretical yield}} \times 100\%$$

LEARNING OUTCOMES

Chapter Objectives	Assessment
Balance chemical equations (4.2)	Examples 4.1, 4.2, 4.3 **For Practice** 4.1, 4.2, 4.3 **Exercises** 13–24
Perform calculations involving the stoichiometry of a reaction (4.3)	Examples 4.4, 4.5 **For Practice** 4.4, 4.5 **Exercises** 25–34
Analyze chemical reactions involving a limiting reactant (4.4)	Examples 4.6, 4.7 **For Practice** 4.6, 4.7 **Exercises** 35–50
Write chemical equations for combustion reactions (4.5)	Example 4.8 **For Practice** 4.8 **Exercises** 51–52
Write chemical equations for reactions involving alkali metals and halogens (4.5)	Example 4.9 **For Practice** 4.9 **Exercises** 53–58

EXERCISES

Mastering Chemistry provides end-of-chapter exercises, feedback-enriched tutorial problems, animations, and interactive activities to encourage problem-solving practice and deeper understanding of key concepts and topics.

REVIEW QUESTIONS

1. What is the greenhouse effect?
2. Why are scientists concerned about increases in atmospheric carbon dioxide? What is the source of the increase?
3. What is a balanced chemical equation?
4. Identify the reactants and products in this chemical equation.
   $4\ NH_3(g) + 5\ O_2(g) \longrightarrow 4\ NO(g) + 6\ H_2O(g)$
5. Why must chemical equations be balanced?
6. What is reaction stoichiometry? What is the significance of the coefficients in a balanced chemical equation?
7. In a chemical reaction, what is the limiting reactant? What do we mean when we say a reactant is in excess?
8. In a chemical reaction, what is the theoretical yield and the percent yield?
9. We typically calculate the percent yield using the actual yield and theoretical yield in units of mass (grams or kilograms). Would the percent yield be different if the actual yield and theoretical yield were in units of amount (moles)?
10. What is a combustion reaction? Why are combustion reactions important? Give an example.
11. Write a general equation for the reaction of an alkali metal with:
    a. a halogen
    b. water
12. Write a general equation for the reaction of a halogen with:
    a. a metal b. hydrogen
    c. another halogen

PROBLEMS BY TOPIC

Writing and Balancing Chemical Equations

13. Sulfuric acid is a component of acid rain formed when gaseous sulfur dioxide pollutant reacts with gaseous oxygen and liquid water to form aqueous sulfuric acid. Write the balanced chemical equation for this reaction. (*Note:* This is a simplified representation of this reaction.)
    MISSED THIS? *Read Section 4.2; Watch KCV 4.2, IWE 4.2*
14. Nitric acid is a component of acid rain that forms when gaseous nitrogen dioxide pollutant reacts with gaseous oxygen and liquid water to form aqueous nitric acid. Write the balanced chemical equation for this reaction. (*Note:* This is a simplified representation of this reaction.)
15. In a popular classroom demonstration, solid sodium is added to liquid water and reacts to produce hydrogen gas and aqueous sodium hydroxide. Write the balanced chemical equation for this reaction.
    MISSED THIS? *Read Sections 4.2, 4.5; Watch KCV 4.2, IWE 4.2*
16. When iron rusts, solid iron reacts with gaseous oxygen to form solid iron(III) oxide. Write the balanced chemical equation for this reaction.
17. Write the balanced chemical equation for the fermentation of sucrose ($C_{12}H_{22}O_{11}$) by yeasts in which the aqueous sugar reacts with water to form aqueous ethanol (C_2H_5OH) and carbon dioxide gas.
    MISSED THIS? *Read Section 4.2; Watch KCV 4.2, IWE 4.2*
18. Write the balanced equation for the photosynthesis reaction in which gaseous carbon dioxide and liquid water react in the presence of chlorophyll to produce aqueous glucose ($C_6H_{12}O_6$) and oxygen gas.
19. Write the balanced chemical equation for each reaction.
    MISSED THIS? *Read Section 4.2; Watch KCV 4.2, IWE 4.2*
    a. Solid lead(II) sulfide reacts with aqueous hydrobromic acid to form solid lead(II) bromide and dihydrogen monosulfide gas.
    b. Gaseous carbon monoxide reacts with hydrogen gas to form gaseous methane (CH_4) and liquid water.
    c. Aqueous hydrochloric acid reacts with solid manganese(IV) oxide to form aqueous manganese(II) chloride, liquid water, and chlorine gas.
    d. Liquid pentane (C_5H_{12}) reacts with gaseous oxygen to form carbon dioxide and liquid water.
20. Write the balanced chemical equation for each reaction.
    a. Solid copper reacts with solid sulfur to form solid copper(I) sulfide.
    b. Solid iron(III) oxide reacts with hydrogen gas to form solid iron and liquid water.
    c. Sulfur dioxide gas reacts with oxygen gas to form sulfur trioxide gas.
    d. Gaseous ammonia (NH_3) reacts with gaseous oxygen to form gaseous nitrogen monoxide and gaseous water.
21. Write the balanced chemical equation for the reaction of aqueous sodium carbonate with aqueous copper(II) chloride to form solid copper(II) carbonate and aqueous sodium chloride.
    MISSED THIS? *Read Section 4.2; Watch KCV 4.2, IWE 4.3*
22. Write the balanced chemical equation for the reaction of aqueous potassium hydroxide with aqueous iron(III) chloride to form solid iron(III) hydroxide and aqueous potassium chloride.
23. Balance each chemical equation.
    MISSED THIS? *Read Section 4.2; Watch KCV 4.2, IWE 4.2, 4.3*
    a. $CO_2(g) + CaSiO_3(s) + H_2O(l) \longrightarrow SiO_2(s) + Ca(HCO_3)_2(aq)$
    b. $Co(NO_3)_3(aq) + (NH_4)_2S(aq) \longrightarrow Co_2S_3(s) + NH_4NO_3(aq)$
    c. $Cu_2O(s) + C(s) \longrightarrow Cu(s) + CO(g)$
    d. $H_2(g) + Cl_2(g) \longrightarrow HCl(g)$
24. Balance each chemical equation.
    a. $Na_2S(aq) + Cu(NO_3)_2(aq) \longrightarrow NaNO_3(aq) + CuS(s)$
    b. $N_2H_4(l) \longrightarrow NH_3(g) + N_2(g)$
    c. $HCl(aq) + O_2(g) \longrightarrow H_2O(l) + Cl_2(g)$
    d. $FeS(s) + HCl(aq) \longrightarrow FeCl_2(aq) + H_2S(g)$

Reaction Stoichiometry

25. Consider the unbalanced equation for the combustion of hexane:

$$C_6H_{14}(g) + O_2(g) \longrightarrow CO_2(g) + H_2O(g)$$

Balance the equation and determine how many moles of O_2 are required to react completely with 7.2 moles of C_6H_{14}.

MISSED THIS? *Read Section 4.3; Watch KCV 4.3, IWE 4.4*

26. Consider the unbalanced equation for the neutralization of acetic acid:

$$HC_2H_3O_2(aq) + Ba(OH)_2(aq) \longrightarrow H_2O(l) + Ba(C_2H_3O_2)_2(aq)$$

Balance the equation and determine how many moles of $Ba(OH)_2$ are required to completely neutralize 0.461 mole of $HC_2H_3O_2$.

27. Calculate how many moles of NO_2 form when each quantity of reactant completely reacts.

MISSED THIS? *Read Section 4.3; Watch KCV 4.3, IWE 4.4*

$$2\,N_2O_5(g) \longrightarrow 4\,NO_2(g) + O_2(g)$$

a. 2.5 mol N_2O_5
b. 6.8 mol N_2O_5
c. 15.2 g N_2O_5
d. 2.87 kg N_2O_5

28. Calculate how many moles of NH_3 form when each quantity of reactant completely reacts.

$$3\,N_2H_4(l) \longrightarrow 4\,NH_3(g) + N_2(g)$$

a. 2.6 mol N_2H_4
b. 3.55 mol N_2H_4
c. 65.3 g N_2H_4
d. 4.88 kg N_2H_4

29. Consider the balanced equation:

$$SiO_2(s) + 3\,C(s) \longrightarrow SiC(s) + 2\,CO(g)$$

Complete the table showing the appropriate number of moles of reactants and products. If the number of moles of a *reactant* is provided, fill in the required amount of the other reactant, as well as the moles of each product that forms. If the number of moles of a *product* is provided, fill in the required amount of each reactant to make that amount of product, as well as the amount of the other product that forms.

MISSED THIS? *Read Section 4.3; Watch KCV 4.3, IWE 4.4*

Mol SiO_2	Mol C	Mol SiC	Mol CO
3	____	____	____
____	6	____	____
____	____	____	10
2.8	____	____	____
____	1.55	____	____

30. Consider the balanced equation:

$$2\,N_2H_4(g) + N_2O_4(g) \longrightarrow 3\,N_2(g) + 4\,H_2O(g)$$

Complete the table showing the appropriate number of moles of reactants and products. If the number of moles of a *reactant* is provided, fill in the required amount of the other reactant, as well as the moles of each product that forms. If the number of moles of a *product* is provided, fill in the required amount of each reactant to make that amount of product, as well as the amount of the other product that forms.

Mol N_2H_4	Mol N_2O_4	Mol N_2	Mol H_2O
2	____	____	____
____	5	____	____
____	____	____	10
2.5	____	____	____
____	4.2	____	____
____	____	11.8	____

31. Hydrobromic acid dissolves solid iron according to the reaction:

$$Fe(s) + 2\,HBr(aq) \longrightarrow FeBr_2(aq) + H_2(g)$$

What mass of HBr (in g) do you need to dissolve a 3.2-g pure iron bar on a padlock? What mass of H_2 would the complete reaction of the iron bar produce?

MISSED THIS? *Read Section 4.3; Watch KCV 4.3, IWE 4.4*

32. Sulfuric acid dissolves aluminum metal according to the reaction:

$$2\,Al(s) + 3\,H_2SO_4(aq) \longrightarrow Al_2(SO_4)_3(aq) + 3\,H_2(g)$$

Suppose you want to dissolve an aluminum block with a mass of 15.2 g. What minimum mass of H_2SO_4 (in g) do you need? What mass of H_2 gas (in g) does the complete reaction of the aluminum block produce?

33. For each of the reactions, calculate the mass (in grams) of the product that forms when 3.67 g of the underlined reactant completely reacts. Assume that there is more than enough of the other reactant.

MISSED THIS? *Read Section 4.3; Watch KCV 4.3, IWE 4.4*

a. $\underline{Ba(s)} + Cl_2(g) \longrightarrow BaCl_2(s)$
b. $\underline{CaO(s)} + CO_2(g) \longrightarrow CaCO_3(s)$
c. $2\,\underline{Mg(s)} + O_2(g) \longrightarrow 2\,MgO(s)$
d. $4\,\underline{Al(s)} + 3\,O_2(g) \longrightarrow 2\,Al_2O_3(s)$

34. For each of the reactions, calculate the mass (in grams) of the product that forms when 15.39 g of the underlined reactant completely reacts. Assume that there is more than enough of the other reactant.

a. $2\,K(s) + \underline{Cl_2(g)} \longrightarrow 2\,KCl(s)$
b. $2\,K(s) + \underline{Br_2(l)} \longrightarrow 2\,KBr(s)$
c. $4\,Cr(s) + 3\,\underline{O_2(g)} \longrightarrow 2\,Cr_2O_3(s)$
d. $2\,\underline{Sr(s)} + O_2(g) \longrightarrow 2\,SrO(s)$

Limiting Reactant, Theoretical Yield, and Percent Yield

35. Find the limiting reactant for each initial amount of reactants.

MISSED THIS? *Read Section 4.4; Watch KCV 4.4, IWE 4.6*

$$2\,Na(s) + Br_2(g) \longrightarrow 2\,NaBr(s)$$

a. 2 mol Na, 2 mol Br_2
b. 1.8 mol Na, 1.4 mol Br_2
c. 2.5 mol Na, 1 mol Br_2
d. 12.6 mol Na, 6.9 mol Br_2

36. Find the limiting reactant for each initial amount of reactants.

$$4\,Al(s) + 3\,O_2(g) \longrightarrow 2\,Al_2O_3(s)$$

a. 1 mol Al, 1 mol O_2
b. 4 mol Al, 2.6 mol O_2
c. 16 mol Al, 13 mol O_2
d. 7.4 mol Al, 6.5 mol O_2

37. Consider the reaction:

$$4\,HCl(g) + O_2(g) \longrightarrow 2\,H_2O(g) + 2\,Cl_2(g)$$

Each molecular diagram represents an initial mixture of reactants. Which mixture produces the greatest amount of products? How many molecules of Cl_2 form from the reaction mixture that produces the greatest amount of products?

MISSED THIS? *Read Section 4.4; Watch KCV 4.4, IWE 4.6*

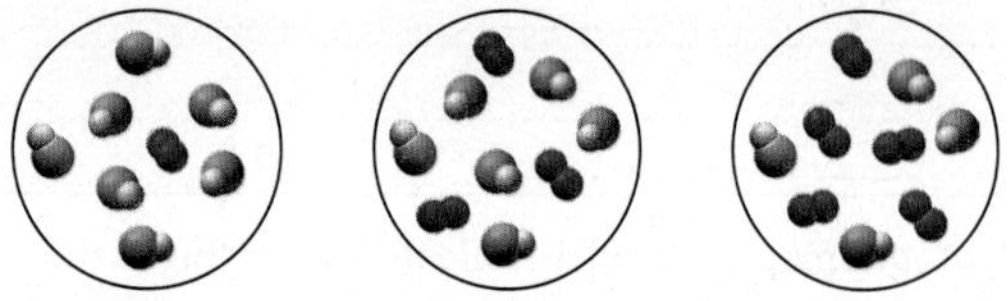

a. b. c.

38. Consider the reaction:

$$2\,CH_3OH(g) + 3\,O_2(g) \longrightarrow 2\,CO_2(g) + 4\,H_2O(g)$$

Each of the molecular diagrams represents an initial mixture of the reactants. Which reaction mixture produces the greatest amount of products? How many CO_2 molecules form from the reaction mixture that produces the greatest amount of products?

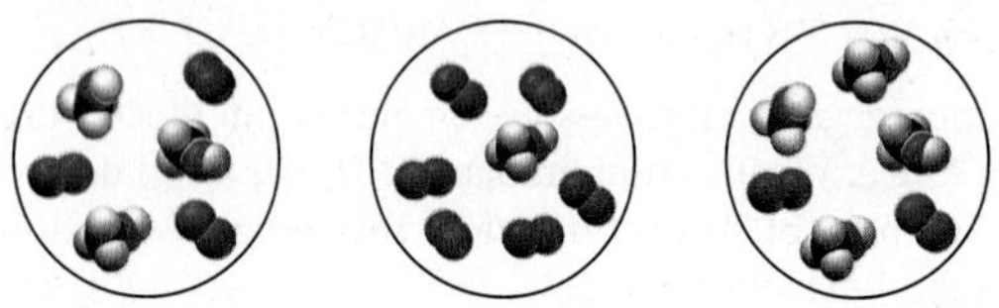

a. b. c.

39. Calculate the theoretical yield of the product (in moles) for each initial amount of reactants.

MISSED THIS? *Read Section 4.4; Watch KCV 4.4, IWE 4.6*

$$Ti(s) + 2\,Cl_2(g) \longrightarrow TiCl_4(l)$$

a. 4 mol Ti, 4 mol Cl_2 b. 7 mol Ti, 17 mol Cl_2
c. 12.4 mol Ti, 18.8 mol Cl_2

40. Calculate the theoretical yield of product (in moles) for each initial amount of reactants.

$$3\,Mn(s) + 2\,O_2(g) \longrightarrow Mn_3O_4(s)$$

a. 3 mol Mn, 3 mol O_2 b. 4 mol Mn, 7 mol O_2
c. 27.5 mol Mn, 43.8 mol O_2

41. Zinc sulfide reacts with oxygen according to the reaction:

$$2\,ZnS(s) + 3\,O_2(g) \longrightarrow 2\,ZnO(s) + 2\,SO_2(g)$$

A reaction mixture initially contains 4.2 mol ZnS and 6.8 mol O_2. Once the reaction has occurred as completely as possible, what amount (in moles) of the excess reactant remains?

MISSED THIS? *Read Section 4.4; Watch KCV 4.4, IWE 4.6*

42. Iron(II) sulfide reacts with hydrochloric acid according to the reaction:

$$FeS(s) + 2\,HCl(aq) \longrightarrow FeCl_2(s) + H_2S(g)$$

A reaction mixture initially contains 0.223 mol FeS and 0.652 mol HCl. Once the reaction has occurred as completely as possible, what amount (in moles) of the excess reactant remains?

43. For the reaction shown, calculate the theoretical yield of product (in grams) for each initial amount of reactants.

MISSED THIS? *Read Section 4.4; Watch KCV 4.4, IWE 4.6*

$$2\,Al(s) + 3\,Cl_2(g) \longrightarrow 2\,AlCl_3(s)$$

a. 2.0 g Al, 2.0 g Cl_2
b. 7.5 g Al, 24.8 g Cl_2
c. 0.235 g Al, 1.15 g Cl_2

44. For the reaction shown, calculate the theoretical yield of the product (in grams) for each initial amount of reactants.

$$Ti(s) + 2\,F_2(g) \longrightarrow TiF_4(s)$$

a. 5.0 g Ti, 5.0 g F_2 b. 2.4 g Ti, 1.6 g F_2
c. 0.233 g Ti, 0.288 g F_2

45. Iron(III) oxide reacts with carbon monoxide according to the equation:

$$Fe_2O_3(s) + 3\,CO(g) \longrightarrow 2\,Fe(s) + 3\,CO_2(g)$$

A reaction mixture initially contains 22.55 g Fe_2O_3 and 14.78 g CO. Once the reaction has occurred as completely as possible, what mass (in g) of the excess reactant remains?

MISSED THIS? *Read Section 4.4; Watch KCV 4.4, IWE 4.6*

46. Elemental phosphorus reacts with chlorine gas according to the equation:

$$P_4(s) + 6\,Cl_2(g) \longrightarrow 4\,PCl_3(l)$$

A reaction mixture initially contains 45.69 g P_4 and 131.3 g Cl_2. Once the reaction has occurred as completely as possible, what mass (in g) of the excess reactant remains?

47. Lead ions can be precipitated from solution with KCl according to the reaction:

$$Pb^{2+}(aq) + 2\,KCl(aq) \longrightarrow PbCl_2(s) + 2\,K^+(aq)$$

When 28.5 g KCl is added to a solution containing 25.7 g Pb^{2+}, a $PbCl_2$ precipitate forms. The precipitate is filtered and dried and found to have a mass of 29.4 g. Determine the limiting reactant, theoretical yield of $PbCl_2$, and percent yield for the reaction.

MISSED THIS? *Read Section 4.4; Watch KCV 4.4, IWE 4.6*

48. Magnesium oxide can be made by heating magnesium metal in the presence of oxygen. The balanced equation for the reaction is:

$$2\,Mg(s) + O_2(g) \longrightarrow 2\,MgO(s)$$

When 10.1 g of Mg reacts with 10.5 g O_2, 11.9 g MgO is collected. Determine the limiting reactant, theoretical yield, and percent yield for the reaction.

49. Urea (CH_4N_2O) is a common fertilizer that is synthesized by the reaction of ammonia (NH_3) with carbon dioxide:

$$2\,NH_3(aq) + CO_2(aq) \longrightarrow CH_4N_2O(aq) + H_2O(l)$$

In an industrial synthesis of urea, a chemist combines 136.4 kg of ammonia with 211.4 kg of carbon dioxide and obtains 168.4 kg of urea. Determine the limiting reactant, theoretical yield of urea, and percent yield for the reaction.

MISSED THIS? *Read Section 4.4; Watch KCV 4.4, IWE 4.6*

50. Many computer chips are manufactured from silicon, which occurs in nature as SiO_2. When SiO_2 is heated to melting, it reacts with solid carbon to form liquid silicon and carbon monoxide gas. In an industrial preparation of silicon, 155.8 kg of SiO_2 reacts with 78.3 kg of carbon to produce 66.1 kg of silicon. Determine the limiting reactant, theoretical yield, and percent yield for the reaction.

Combustion, Alkali Metal, and Halogen Reactions

51. Complete and balance each combustion reaction equation.

MISSED THIS? *Read Section 4.5*

a. $S(s) + O_2(g) \longrightarrow$ b. $C_3H_6(g) + O_2(g) \longrightarrow$
c. $Ca(s) + O_2(g) \longrightarrow$ d. $C_5H_{12}S(l) + O_2(g) \longrightarrow$

52. Complete and balance each combustion reaction equation:

a. $C_4H_6(g) + O_2(g) \longrightarrow$ b. $C(s) + O_2(g) \longrightarrow$
c. $CS_2(s) + O_2(g) \longrightarrow$ d. $C_3H_8O(l) + O_2(g) \longrightarrow$

53. Write a balanced chemical equation for the reaction of solid strontium with iodine gas.

MISSED THIS? *Read Section 4.5*

54. Write a balanced chemical equation for the reaction between lithium metal and chlorine gas.

55. Write a balanced chemical equation for the reaction of solid lithium with liquid water. **MISSED THIS?** *Read Section 4.5*

56. Write a balanced chemical equation for the reaction of solid potassium with liquid water.

57. Write a balanced equation for the reaction of hydrogen gas with bromine gas. **MISSED THIS?** *Read Section 4.5*

58. Write a balanced equation for the reaction of chlorine gas with fluorine gas.

CUMULATIVE PROBLEMS

59. The combustion of gasoline produces carbon dioxide and water. Assume gasoline to be pure octane (C_8H_{18}) and calculate the mass (in kg) of carbon dioxide that is added to the atmosphere per 1.0 kg of octane burned. (*Hint:* Begin by writing a balanced equation for the combustion reaction.)

60. Many home barbeques are fueled with propane gas (C_3H_8). What mass of carbon dioxide (in kg) is produced upon the complete combustion of 18.9 L of propane (approximate contents of one 5-gallon tank)? Assume that the density of the liquid propane in the tank is 0.621 g/mL. (*Hint:* Begin by writing a balanced equation for the combustion reaction.)

61. Aspirin can be made in the laboratory by reacting acetic anhydride ($C_4H_6O_3$) with salicylic acid ($C_7H_6O_3$) to form aspirin ($C_9H_8O_4$) and acetic acid ($C_2H_4O_2$). The balanced equation is:

$$C_4H_6O_3 + C_7H_6O_3 \longrightarrow C_9H_8O_4 + C_2H_4O_2$$

In a laboratory synthesis, a student begins with 3.00 mL of acetic anhydride (density = 1.08 g/mL) and 1.25 g of salicylic acid. Once the reaction is complete, the student collects 1.22 g of aspirin. Determine the limiting reactant, theoretical yield of aspirin, and percent yield for the reaction.

62. The combustion of liquid ethanol (C_2H_5OH) produces carbon dioxide and water. After 4.62 mL of ethanol (density = 0.789 g/mL) is allowed to burn in the presence of 15.55 g of oxygen gas, 3.72 mL of water (density = 1.00 g/mL) is collected. Determine the limiting reactant, theoretical yield of H_2O, and percent yield for the reaction. (*Hint:* Write a balanced equation for the combustion of ethanol.)

63. A loud classroom demonstration involves igniting a hydrogen-filled balloon. The hydrogen within the balloon reacts explosively with oxygen in the air to form water. If the balloon is filled with a mixture of hydrogen and oxygen, the explosion is even louder than if the balloon is filled only with hydrogen—the intensity of the explosion depends on the relative amounts of oxygen and hydrogen within the balloon. Look at the molecular views representing different amounts of hydrogen and oxygen in four different balloons. Based on the balanced chemical equation, which balloon will make the loudest explosion?

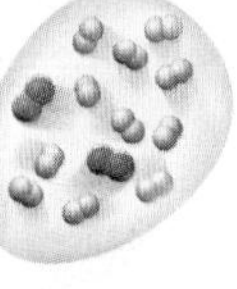
a.

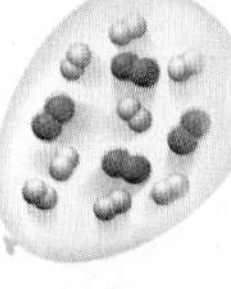
b.

c.

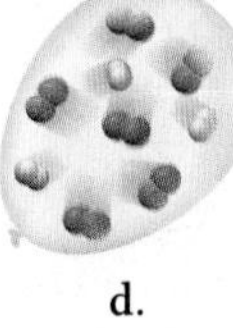
d.

64. Gaseous methane reacts with oxygen to form carbon dioxide and water vapor. Write a balanced equation for the combustion reaction and determine which mixture has neither reactant in excess.

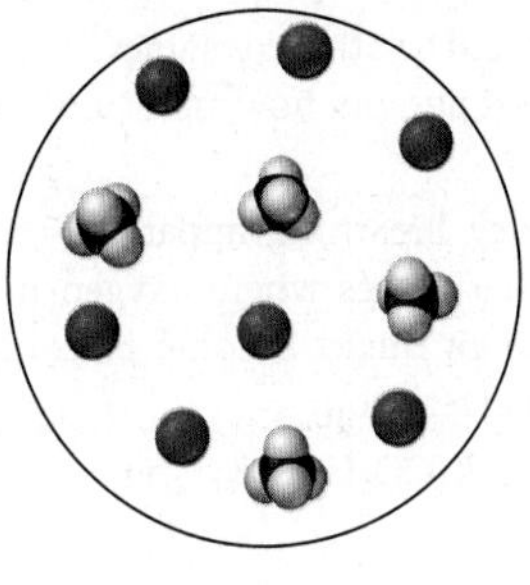
a.

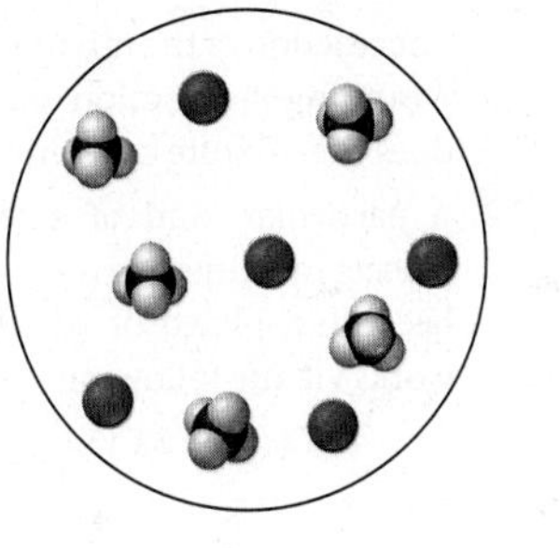
b.

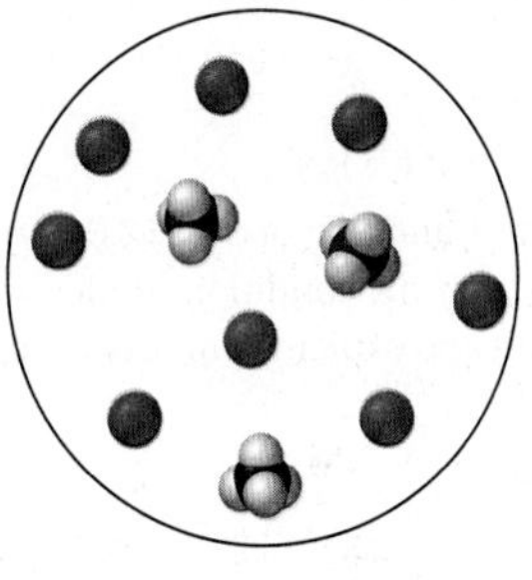
c.

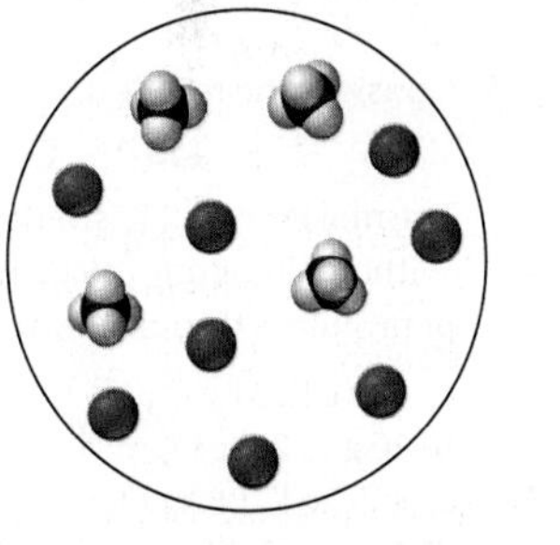
d.

65. The reaction of NH_3 and O_2 forms NO and water. The NO can be used to convert P_4 to P_4O_6, forming N_2 in the process. The P_4O_6 can be treated with water to form H_3PO_3, which forms PH_3 and H_3PO_4 when heated. Find the mass of PH_3 that forms from the reaction of 1.00 g of NH_3.

66. An important reaction that takes place in a blast furnace during the production of iron is the formation of iron metal and CO_2 from Fe_2O_3 and CO. Determine the mass of Fe_2O_3 required to form 910 kg of iron. Determine the amount of CO_2 that forms in this process.

67. A liquid fuel mixture contains 30.35% hexane (C_6H_{14}), 15.85% heptane (C_7H_{16}), and the rest octane (C_8H_{18}). What maximum mass of carbon dioxide is produced by the complete combustion of 10.0 kg of this fuel mixture?

68. Titanium occurs in the magnetic mineral ilmenite ($FeTiO_3$), which is often found mixed with sand. The ilmenite can be separated from the sand with magnets. The titanium can then be extracted from the ilmenite by the following set of reactions:

$$FeTiO_3(s) + 3\,Cl_2(g) + 3\,C(s) \longrightarrow 3\,CO(g) + FeCl_2(s) + TiCl_4(g)$$
$$TiCl_4(g) + 2\,Mg(s) \longrightarrow 2\,MgCl_2(l) + Ti(s)$$

Suppose that an ilmenite–sand mixture contains 22.8% ilmenite by mass and that the first reaction is carried out with a 90.8% yield. If the second reaction is carried out with an 85.9% yield, what mass of titanium can be obtained from 1.00 kg of the ilmenite–sand mixture?

CHALLENGE PROBLEMS

69. A mixture of C_3H_8 and C_2H_2 has a mass of 2.0 g. It is burned in excess O_2 to form a mixture of water and carbon dioxide that contains 1.5 times as many moles of CO_2 as of water. Find the mass of C_2H_2 in the original mixture.

70. A mixture of 20.6 g of P and 79.4 g of Cl_2 reacts completely to form PCl_3 and PCl_5 as the only products. Find the mass of PCl_3 that forms.

71. A mixture of A and B contains a total of 5.3 mols. Both A and B react with Z according to the following equations:

$$A + Z \longrightarrow AZ$$
$$B + 2\,Z \longrightarrow BZ_2$$

The reaction of the mixture of A and B with Z consumes 7.8 mol Z. Assuming the reactions go to completion, how many moles of A does the mixture contain?

72. A particular kind of emergency breathing apparatus—often placed in mines, caves, or other places where oxygen might become depleted or where the air might become poisoned—works via the following chemical reaction:

$$4\,KO_2(s) + 2\,CO_2(g) \longrightarrow 2\,K_2CO_3(s) + 3\,O_2(g)$$

Notice that the reaction produces O_2, which can be breathed, and absorbs CO_2, a product of respiration. Suppose you work for a company interested in producing a self-rescue breathing apparatus (based on the given reaction) that would allow the user to survive for 10 minutes in an emergency situation. What are the important chemical considerations in designing such a unit? Estimate how much KO_2 would be required for the apparatus. (Find any necessary additional information—such as human breathing rates—from appropriate sources. Assume that normal air is 20% oxygen.)

73. Metallic aluminum reacts with MnO_2 at elevated temperatures to form manganese metal and aluminum oxide. A mixture of the two reactants is 67.2% mole percent Al. Find the theoretical yield (in grams) of manganese from the reaction of 250 g of this mixture.

74. Hydrolysis of the compound B_5H_9 forms boric acid, H_3BO_3. Fusion of boric acid with sodium oxide forms a borate salt, $Na_2B_4O_7$. Without writing complete equations, find the mass (in grams) of B_5H_9 required to form 151 g of the borate salt by this reaction sequence.

CONCEPTUAL PROBLEMS

75. Consider the reaction:

$$4\,K(s) + O_2(g) \longrightarrow 2\,K_2O(s)$$

The molar mass of K is 39.10 g/mol, and that of O_2 is 32.00 g/mol. Without doing any calculations, pick the conditions under which potassium is the limiting reactant and explain your reasoning.

a. 170 g K, 31 g O_2
b. 16 g K, 2.5 g O_2
c. 165 kg K, 28 kg O_2
d. 1.5 g K, 0.38 g O_2

76. Consider the reaction:

$$2\,NO(g) + 5\,H_2(g) \longrightarrow 2\,NH_3(g) + 2\,H_2O(g)$$

A reaction mixture initially contains 5 moles of NO and 10 moles of H_2. Without doing any calculations, determine which set of amounts best represents the mixture after the reactants have reacted as completely as possible. Explain your reasoning.

a. 1 mol NO, 0 mol H_2, 4 mol NH_3, 4 mol H_2O
b. 0 mol NO, 1 mol H_2, 5 mol NH_3, 5 mol H_2O
c. 3 mol NO, 5 mol H_2, 2 mol NH_3, 2 mol H_2O
d. 0 mol NO, 0 mol H_2, 4 mol NH_3, 4 mol H_2O

77. Consider the reaction:

$$2\,N_2H_4(g) + N_2O_4(g) \longrightarrow 3\,N_2(g) + 4\,H_2O(g)$$

Consider also this representation of an initial mixture of N_2H_4 and N_2O_4:

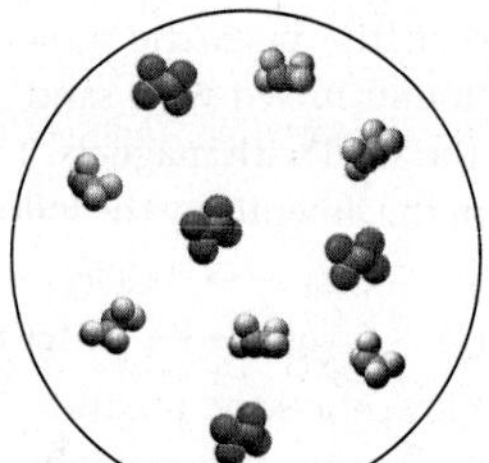

Which diagram best represents the reaction mixture after the reactants have reacted as completely as possible?

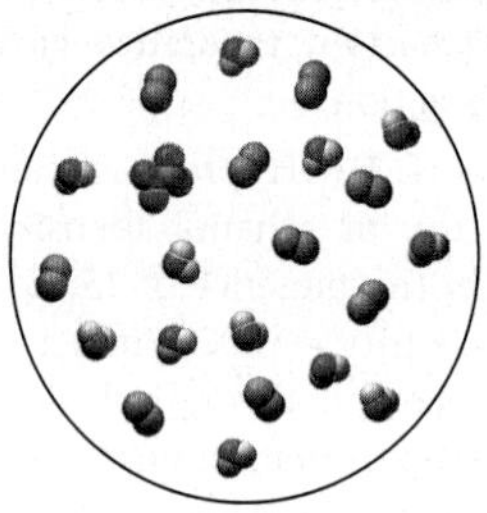

a.

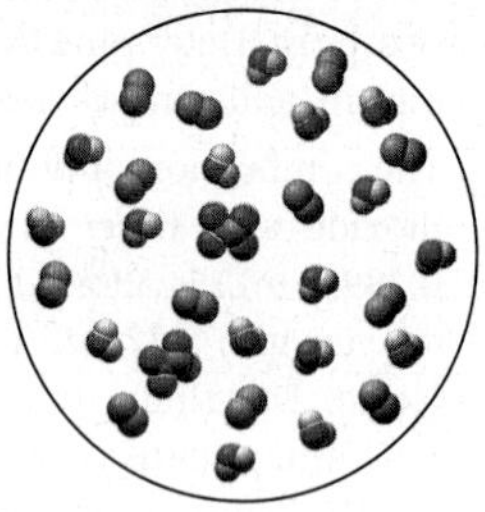

b.

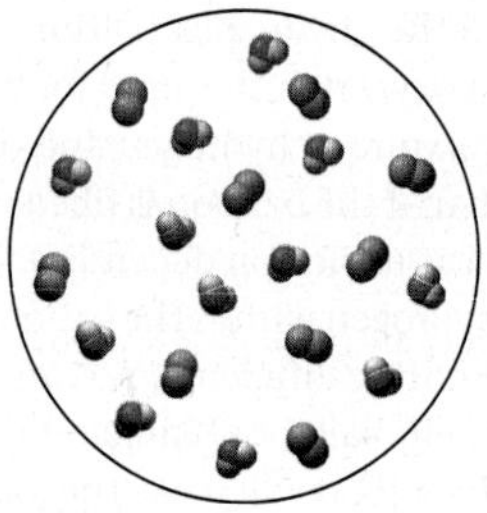

c.

QUESTIONS FOR GROUP WORK

Active Classroom Learning

Discuss these questions with the group and record your consensus answer.

78. Octane (C_8H_{18}), a component of gasoline, reacts with oxygen to form carbon dioxide and water. Write the balanced chemical reaction for this process by passing a single piece of paper around your group and asking each group member to complete the next logical step. As each member completes his or her step, explain your reasoning to the group.

79. Imagine you mix 16.05 g of methane (CH_4) gas and 96.00 g of oxygen (O_2) gas and then ignite the mixture. After a bright flash and a loud bang, some water vapor forms.

a. Write the balanced chemical reaction for the combustion of methane.

b. Depict the process that occurred using circles to represent atoms. Represent carbon with black circles, hydrogen with white circles, and oxygen with gray circles. Let one circle (or one molecule made of circles bonded together) represent exactly one mole.

c. How many moles of water can you make? How many moles of carbon dioxide?

d. Will anything be left over? If so, how much?

e. Identify the following: limiting reagent, excess reagent, and theoretical yield.

80. Explain the problem with the following statement to your group and correct it. "When a chemical equation is balanced, the number of molecules of each type on both sides of the equation is equal."

DATA INTERPRETATION AND ANALYSIS

Limiting Reactant and Percent Yield

81. A chemical reaction in which reactants A and B form the product C is studied in the laboratory. The researcher carries out the reaction with differing relative amounts of reactants and measures the amount of product produced. Examine the given tabulated data from the experiment and answer the questions.

Experiment #	Mass A (g)	Mass B (g)	Mass C Obtained (g)
1	2.51	7.54	3.76
2	5.03	7.51	7.43
3	7.55	7.52	11.13
4	12.53	7.49	14.84
5	15.04	7.47	14.94
6	19.98	7.51	15.17
7	20.04	9.95	19.31
8	20.02	12.55	24.69

a. For which experiments is A the limiting reactant?

b. For which experiments is B the limiting reactant?

c. The molar mass of A is 50.0 g/mol, and the molar mass of B is 75.0 g/mol. What are the coeffecients of A and B in the balanced chemical equation?

d. For each of the experiments in which A is the limiting reactant, calculate the mass of B remaining after the reaction has gone to completion. Use the molar masses and coeffecients from part c.

e. The molar mass of C is 88.0 g/mol. What is the coefficient of C in the balanced chemical equation?

f. Calculate an average percent yield for the reaction.

Cc ANSWERS TO CONCEPTUAL CONNECTIONS

Counting Atoms in a Chemical Equation

4.1 **(d)** The number of oxygen atoms in 2 Fe_2O_3 is 6, and the number in 4 CO_2 is 8, for a total of 14.

Balanced Chemical Equations

4.2 **(a)** When the equation is balanced, the number of atoms of each type is the same on both sides of the equation. Since molecules change during a chemical reaction, the number of molecules is not the same on both sides, nor is the number of moles of each molecule necessarily the same.

Stoichiometry I

4.3 **(d)** $22.0\ \cancel{\text{mol } C_8H_{18}} \times \dfrac{18\ \text{mol } H_2O}{2\ \cancel{\text{mol } C_8H_{18}}} = 198\ \text{mol } H_2O$

Stoichiometry II

4.4 **(c)** Since each O_2 molecule reacts with 4 Na atoms, 12 Na atoms are required to react with 3 O_2 molecules.

Stoichiometry III

4.5 **(a)** Since the balanced equation indicates that one A reacts with three B, and since the diagram in the question includes 12 B available to react, the amount of A necessary is four A.

Limiting Reactant and Theoretical Yield

4.6 **(c)** Nitrogen is the limiting reactant, and there is enough nitrogen to make four NH_3 molecules. Hydrogen is in excess, and two hydrogen molecules remain after the reactants have reacted as completely as possible.

Reactant in Excess

4.7 **(c)** The limiting reactant is the 1 mol H_2O, which is completely consumed. The 1 mol of H_2O requires 3 mol of NO_2 to completely react; therefore, 2 mol NO_2 remain after the reaction is complete.

Science may be described as the art of systemic oversimplification—the art of discerning what we may with advantage omit.

—KARL POPPER (1902–1994)

CHAPTER

5 Introduction to Solutions and Aqueous Reactions

In this chapter, we turn to describing chemical reactions that occur in water. You have probably witnessed many of these types of reactions in your daily life because they are so common. Have you ever mixed baking soda with vinegar and observed the subsequent bubbling? Have you noticed the hard water deposits that form on plumbing fixtures? These reactions—and many others, including those that occur within the watery environment of living cells—are aqueous chemical reactions, the subject of this chapter.

The spherified cherry, a product of a cooking technique known as molecular gastronomy.

5.1 Molecular Gastronomy and the Spherified Cherry 167

5.2 Solution Concentration 168

5.3 Solution Stoichiometry 173

5.4 Types of Aqueous Solutions and Solubility 175

5.5 Precipitation Reactions 179

5.6 Representing Aqueous Reactions: Molecular, Ionic, and Net Ionic Equations 183

5.7 Acid–Base Reactions 185

5.8 Gas-Evolution Reactions 191

5.9 Oxidation–Reduction Reactions 193

LEARNING OUTCOMES 203

5.1 Molecular Gastronomy and the Spherified Cherry

One of my favorite chefs is the Spaniard José Andrés, who owns and operates restaurants all over the world including *The Bazaar* in Los Angeles and Miami, and *Jaleo* in Washington, D.C. Andrés was born in the province of Austurias, Spain, the same province as my grandfather (no wonder I like him so much). Andrés is not only an amazing chef, who is credited with bringing small plates (or *tapas*) to America, but he also dabbles in *molecular gastronomy*, a way of preparing food that involves chemistry.

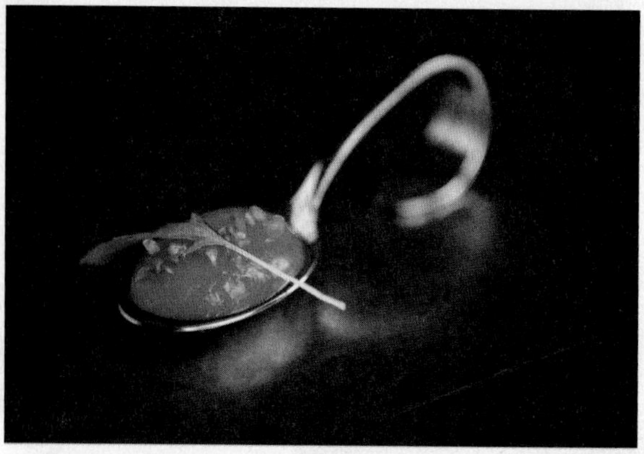

▶ **FIGURE 5.1 The Spherified Cherry** The spherified cherry is made by precipitating an encapsulating layer around cherry juice.

A common chemical reaction in molecular gastronomy is precipitation. In a *precipitation reaction*, two *solutions*—homogeneous mixtures often containing a solid dissolved in a liquid—are mixed. Upon mixing, a solid (or *precipitate*) forms. For example, when we mix solutions of lead(II) nitrate and potassium iodide, a brilliant yellow solid forms. The solid is lead(II) iodide.

In molecular gastronomy, chefs use a similar precipitation reaction—called spherification—to encapsulate liquids. Among the most popular molecular gastronomy creations is the spherified cherry (Figure 5.1▲). To make a spherified cherry, chefs take juice from real cherries and mix it with a calcium salt (such as calcium chloride), which dissolves in the cherry juice. They then carefully pour the cherry juice into a bath of sodium alginate. Sodium alginate is a sodium salt that dissolves into water, resulting in the presence of alginate ions. When the calcium ions in the cherry juice encounter the alginate ions in the bath, a precipitation reaction occurs. In this case, the precipitation reaction forms in the area immediately surrounding the cherry juice, forming an encapsulating sphere around the juice. The result is a spherical, edible "cherry" that ruptures in the mouth and releases its juice.

In this chapter, we explore solutions, focusing especially on *aqueous* solutions (solutions in which one component is water). The cherry juice and calcium chloride mixture just discussed is an example of an aqueous solution. Other common aqueous solutions include seawater, vinegar, and the watery environment within biological cells. We will also explore the chemical reactions that occur within solutions, such as precipitation reactions, which have many common applications.

WATCH **NOW!**

KEY CONCEPT VIDEO 5.2
Solution Concentration

5.2 Solution Concentration

The reactions that occur in lakes, streams, and oceans, as well as the reactions that occur in every cell within our bodies, take place in water. Chemical reactions involving reactants dissolved in water are among the most common and important. A homogeneous mixture of two substances—such as salt and water—is a **solution**. The majority component of the mixture is the **solvent**, and the minority component is the **solute**. An **aqueous solution** is one in which water acts as the solvent. In this section, we examine how to quantify the concentration of a solution (the amount of solute relative to solvent).

Solution Concentration

The amount of solute in a solution is variable. For example, we can add just a little salt to water to make a **dilute solution**, one that contains a small amount of solute relative to the solvent, or we can add a lot of salt to water to make a **concentrated solution**, one that contains a large amount of solute relative to the solvent (Figure 5.2▶). A common way to express solution concentration is **molarity (M)**, the amount of solute (in moles) divided by the volume of solution (in liters):

$$\text{Molarity (M)} = \frac{\text{amount of solute (in mol)}}{\text{volume of solution (in L)}}$$

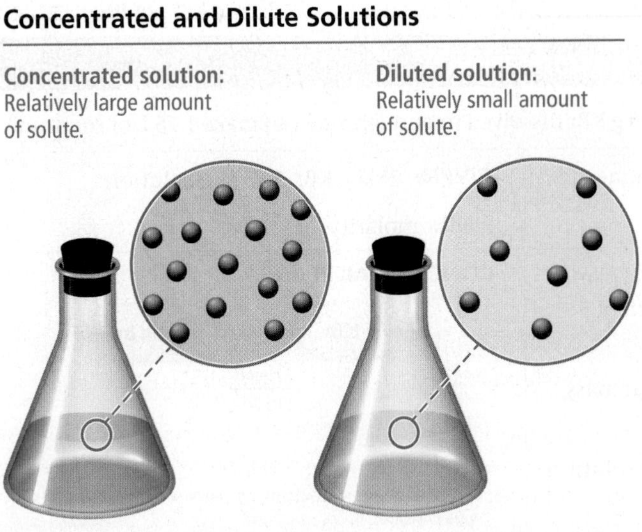

◀ **FIGURE 5.2 Concentrated and Dilute Solutions**

Notice that molarity is a ratio of the amount of solute per liter of *solution*, not per liter of solvent. To make an aqueous solution of a specified molarity, we usually put the solute into a flask and then add water to reach the desired volume of solution. For example, to make 1 L of a 1 M NaCl solution, we add 1 mol of NaCl to a flask and then add enough water to make 1 L of solution (Figure 5.3▼). We *do not* combine 1 mol of NaCl with 1 L of water because the resulting solution would have a total volume different from 1 L and therefore a molarity different than 1 M. To calculate molarity, divide the amount of the solute in moles by the volume of the solution (solute *and* solvent) in liters, as shown in Example 5.1.

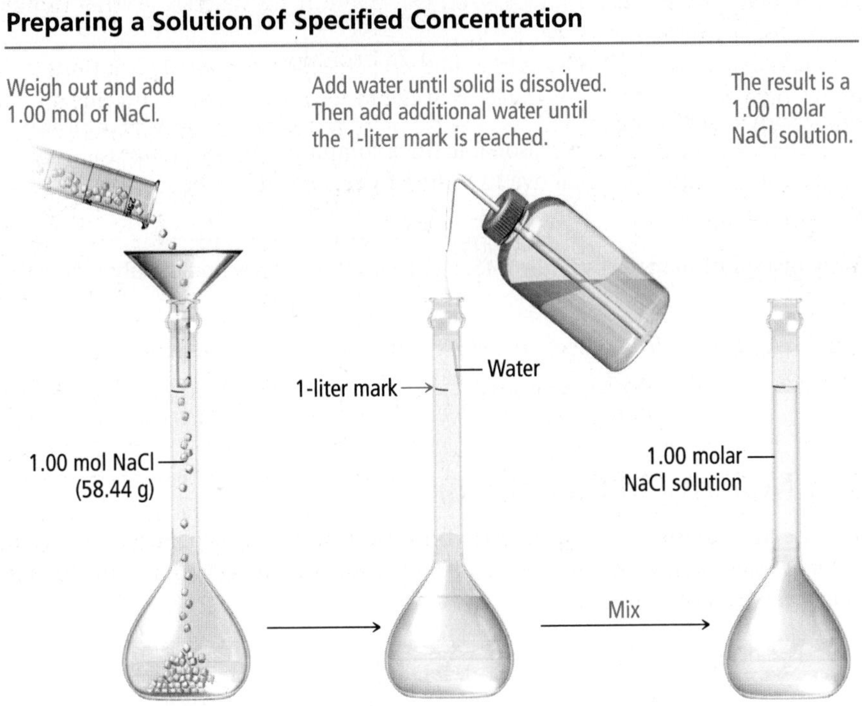

◀ **FIGURE 5.3 Preparing a 1 Molar NaCl Solution**

MOLARITY How many moles of solute are required to make 3.0 L of a 2.0 M solution?

(a) 2.0 mol solute
(b) 3.0 mol solute
(c) 4.0 mol solute
(d) 6.0 mol solute

5.1 Cc Conceptual Connection

ANSWER **NOW!**

WATCH **NOW!**

INTERACTIVE WORKED EXAMPLE 5.1

EXAMPLE 5.1 Calculating Solution Concentration

What is the molarity of a solution containing 25.5 g KBr dissolved in enough water to make 1.75 L of solution?

SORT You are given the mass of KBr and the volume of a solution and asked to find its molarity.

GIVEN: 25.5 g KBr, 1.75 L of solution

FIND: molarity (M)

STRATEGIZE When formulating the conceptual plan, think about the definition of molarity, the amount of solute *in moles* per liter of solution.

You are given the mass of KBr, so first use the molar mass of KBr to convert from g KBr to mol KBr.

Then use the number of moles of KBr and liters of solution to find the molarity.

CONCEPTUAL PLAN

g KBr → mol KBr

$$\frac{1 \text{ mol}}{119.00 \text{ g}}$$

mol KBr, L solution → Molarity

$$\text{Molarity (M)} = \frac{\text{amount of solute (in mol)}}{\text{volume of solution (in L)}}$$

RELATIONSHIPS USED

molar mass of KBr = 119.00 g/mol

SOLVE Follow the conceptual plan. Begin with g KBr and convert to mol KBr; then use mol KBr and L solution to calculate molarity.

SOLUTION

$$25.5 \text{ g KBr} \times \frac{1 \text{ mol KBr}}{119.00 \text{ g KBr}} = 0.21\underline{4}29 \text{ mol KBr}$$

$$\text{molarity (M)} = \frac{\text{amount of solute (in mol)}}{\text{volume of solution (in L)}}$$

$$= \frac{0.21\underline{4}29 \text{ mol KBr}}{1.75 \text{ L solution}}$$

$$= 0.122 \text{ M}$$

CHECK The units of the answer (M) are correct. The magnitude is reasonable since common solutions range in concentration from 0 to about 18 M. Concentrations significantly above 18 M are suspect and should be double-checked.

FOR PRACTICE 5.1 Calculate the molarity of a solution made by adding 45.4 g of $NaNO_3$ to a flask and dissolving it with water to create a total volume of 2.50 L.

FOR MORE PRACTICE 5.1 What mass of KBr (in grams) do you need to make 250.0 mL of a 1.50 M KBr solution?

Using Molarity in Calculations

We can use the molarity of a solution as a conversion factor between moles of the solute and liters of the solution. For example, a 0.500 M NaCl solution contains 0.500 moles NaCl for every liter of solution:

$$\frac{0.500 \text{ mol NaCl}}{\text{L solution}}$$ *converts* L solution → mol NaCl

This conversion factor converts from liters solution to mole NaCl. If we want to convert in the other direction, we invert the conversion factor:

$$\frac{\text{L solution}}{0.500 \text{ mol NaCl}}$$ *converts* mol NaCl → L solution

Example 5.2 illustrates how to use molarity in this way.

WATCH **NOW!**

INTERACTIVE WORKED EXAMPLE 5.2

EXAMPLE 5.2 Using Molarity in Calculations

How many liters of a 0.125 M NaOH solution contain 0.255 mol of NaOH?

SORT You are given the concentration of a NaOH solution. You are asked to find the volume of the solution that contains a given amount (in moles) of NaOH.

GIVEN: 0.125 M NaOH solution, 0.255 mol NaOH

FIND: volume of NaOH solution (in L)

STRATEGIZE The conceptual plan begins with mol NaOH and shows the conversion to L of solution using molarity as a conversion factor.

CONCEPTUAL PLAN

mol NaOH → L solution

$$\frac{1\text{ L solution}}{0.125\text{ mol NaOH}}$$

RELATIONSHIPS USED

$$0.125\text{ M NaOH} = \frac{0.125\text{ mol NaOH}}{1\text{ L solution}}$$

SOLVE Follow the conceptual plan. Begin with mol NaOH and convert to L solution.

SOLUTION

$$0.255\ \cancel{\text{mol NaOH}} \times \frac{1\text{ L solution}}{0.125\ \cancel{\text{mol NaOH}}} = 2.04\text{ L solution}$$

CHECK The units of the answer (L) are correct. The magnitude is reasonable because the solution contains 0.125 mol per liter. Therefore, roughly 2 L contains the given amount of moles (0.255 mol).

FOR PRACTICE 5.2 How many grams of sucrose ($C_{12}H_{22}O_{11}$) are in 1.55 L of a 0.758 M sucrose solution?

FOR MORE PRACTICE 5.2 How many mL of a 0.155 M KCl solution contain 2.55 g KCl?

SOLUTIONS If we dissolve 25 g of salt in 251 g of water, what is the mass of the resulting solution?

(a) 251 g

(b) 276 g

(c) 226 g

5.2 Cc Conceptual Connection

ANSWER **NOW!**

Solution Dilution

To save space in storerooms, laboratories often store solutions in concentrated forms called **stock solutions**. For example, hydrochloric acid is frequently stored as a 12 M stock solution. However, many lab procedures call for much less concentrated hydrochloric acid solutions, so we must dilute the stock solution to the required concentration. How do we know how much of the stock solution to use? The easiest way to solve dilution problems is to use the following dilution equation:

$$M_1V_1 = M_2V_2 \qquad [5.1]$$

where M_1 and V_1 are the molarity and volume of the initial concentrated solution, and M_2 and V_2 are the molarity and volume of the final diluted solution. This equation works because the molarity multiplied by the volume gives the number of moles of solute, which is the same in both solutions.

$$M_1V_1 = M_2V_2$$
$$\text{mol}_1 = \text{mol}_2$$

In other words, the number of moles of solute does not change when we dilute a solution.

For example, suppose a laboratory procedure calls for 3.00 L of a 0.500 M $CaCl_2$ solution. How should we prepare this solution from a 10.0 M stock solution? We solve

When diluting acids, always add the concentrated acid to the water. Never add water to concentrated acid solutions, as the heat generated may cause the concentrated acid to splatter and burn your skin.

Equation 5.1 for V_1, the volume of the stock solution required for the dilution, and then substitute in the correct values to calculate it.

$$M_1V_1 = M_2V_2$$

$$V_1 = \frac{M_2V_2}{M_1}$$

$$= \frac{0.500\ \cancel{\text{mol/L}} \times 3.00\ \text{L}}{10.0\ \cancel{\text{mol/L}}}$$

$$= 0.150\ \text{L}$$

Consequently, we make the solution by diluting 0.150 L of the stock solution to a total volume of 3.00 L (V_2). The resulting solution will be 0.500 M in $CaCl_2$ (Figure 5.4▼).

Diluting a Solution

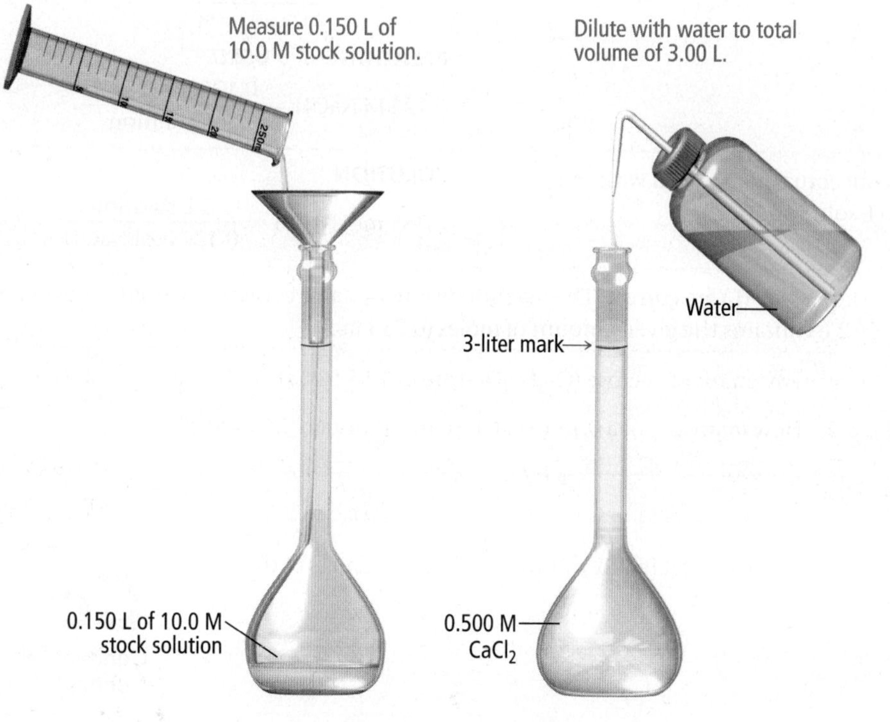

$$M_1V_1 = M_2V_2$$

$$\frac{10.0\ \text{mol}}{\cancel{\text{L}}} \times 0.150\ \cancel{\text{L}} = \frac{0.500\ \text{mol}}{\cancel{\text{L}}} \times 3.00\ \cancel{\text{L}}$$

$$1.50\ \text{mol} = 1.50\ \text{mol}$$

▶ **FIGURE 5.4 Preparing 3.00 L of 0.500 M $CaCl_2$ from a 10.0 M Stock Solution**

WATCH **NOW!**

INTERACTIVE WORKED EXAMPLE 5.3

EXAMPLE 5.3 Solution Dilution

To what volume should you dilute 0.200 L of a 15.0 M NaOH solution to obtain a 3.00 M NaOH solution?

SORT You are given the initial volume, initial concentration, and final concentration of a solution. You need to determine the final volume.

GIVEN: $V_1 = 0.200\ \text{L}$

$M_1 = 15.0\ \text{M}$

$M_2 = 3.00\ \text{M}$

FIND: V_2

STRATEGIZE Equation 5.1 relates the initial and final volumes and concentrations for solution dilution problems. You are asked to find V_2. The other quantities (V_1, M_1, and M_2) are all given in the problem.

CONCEPTUAL PLAN

V_1, M_1, M_2 → V_2

$M_1V_1 = M_2V_2$

RELATIONSHIPS USED

$M_1V_1 = M_2V_2$

SOLVE Begin with the solution dilution equation and solve it for V_2.

Substitute in the required quantities and calculate V_2.

Make the solution by diluting 0.200 L of the stock solution to a total volume of 1.00 L (V_2). The resulting solution will have a concentration of 3.00 M.

SOLUTION $M_1V_1 = M_2V_2$

$$V_2 = \frac{M_1V_1}{M_2}$$

$$= \frac{15.0\ \cancel{\text{mol/L}} \times 0.200\ \text{L}}{3.00\ \cancel{\text{mol/L}}}$$

$$= 1.00\ \text{L}$$

CHECK The final units (L) are correct. The magnitude of the answer is reasonable because the solution is diluted from 15.0 M to 3.00 M, a factor of five. Therefore, the volume should increase by a factor of five.

FOR PRACTICE 5.3 To what volume (in mL) should you dilute 100.0 mL of a 5.00 M $CaCl_2$ solution to obtain a 0.750 M $CaCl_2$ solution?

FOR MORE PRACTICE 5.3 What volume of a 6.00 M $NaNO_3$ solution should you use to make 0.525 L of a 1.20 M $NaNO_3$ solution?

SOLUTION DILUTION The image shown at the far right represents a small volume within 500 mL of aqueous ethanol (CH_3CH_2OH) solution. (The water molecules have been omitted for clarity.)

Which of the following images best represents the same volume of the solution after we add an additional 500 mL of water?

5.3 Cc Conceptual Connection

ANSWER **NOW!**

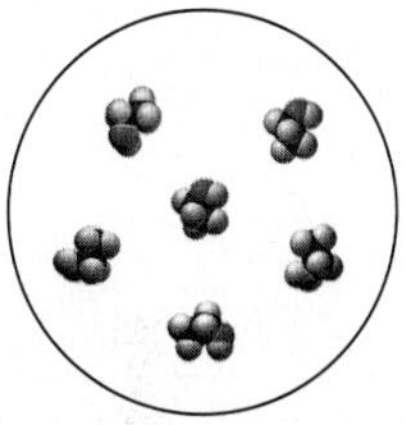

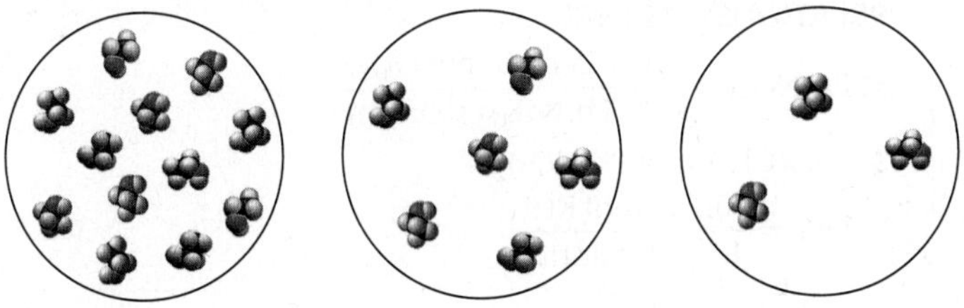

(a) (b) (c)

5.3 Solution Stoichiometry

In Section 4.3, we discussed how we can use the coefficients in chemical equations as conversion factors between the amounts of reactants (in moles) and the amounts of products (in moles). In aqueous reactions, quantities of reactants and products are often specified in terms of volumes and concentrations. We can use the volume and concentration of a reactant or product to calculate its amount in moles. We can then use the stoichiometric coefficients in the chemical equation to convert to the amount of another reactant or product in moles. The general conceptual plan for these kinds of calculations begins with the volume of a reactant or product:

Volume A → Amount A (in moles) → Amount B (in moles) → Volume B

We make the conversions between solution volumes and amounts of solute in moles using the molarities of the solutions. We make the conversions between amounts in moles of A and B using the stoichiometric coefficients from the balanced chemical equation. Example 5.4 demonstrates solution stoichiometry.

WATCH **NOW!**

INTERACTIVE WORKED EXAMPLE 5.4

EXAMPLE 5.4 Solution Stoichiometry

What volume (in L) of a 0.150 M KCl solution will completely react with 0.150 L of a 0.175 M $Pb(NO_3)_2$ solution according to the following balanced chemical equation?

$$2\,KCl(aq) + Pb(NO_3)_2(aq) \longrightarrow PbCl_2(s) + 2\,KNO_3(aq)$$

SORT You are given the volume and concentration of a $Pb(NO_3)_2$ solution. You are asked to find the volume of KCl solution (of a given concentration) required to react with it.

GIVEN: 0.150 L of $Pb(NO_3)_2$ solution, 0.175 M $Pb(NO_3)_2$ solution, 0.150 M KCl solution

FIND: volume KCl solution (in L)

STRATEGIZE The conceptual plan has the form: volume A → amount A (in moles) → amount B (in moles) → volume B. Use the molar concentrations of the KCl and $Pb(NO_3)_2$ solutions as conversion factors between the number of moles of reactants in these solutions and their volumes. Use the stoichiometric coefficients from the balanced equation to convert between number of moles of $Pb(NO_3)_2$ and number of moles of KCl.

CONCEPTUAL PLAN

$$\text{L } Pb(NO_3)_2 \text{ solution} \xrightarrow{\frac{0.175 \text{ mol } Pb(NO_3)_2}{1 \text{ L } Pb(NO_3)_2 \text{ solution}}} \text{mol } Pb(NO_3)_2 \xrightarrow{\frac{2 \text{ mol KCl}}{1 \text{ mol } Pb(NO_3)_2}}$$

$$\text{mol KCl} \xrightarrow{\frac{1 \text{ L KCl solution}}{0.150 \text{ mol KCl}}} \text{L KCl solution}$$

RELATIONSHIPS USED

$$M\,Pb(NO_3)_2 = \frac{0.175 \text{ mol } Pb(NO_3)_2}{1 \text{ L } Pb(NO_3)_2 \text{ solution}}$$

$$2 \text{ mol KCl} : 1 \text{ mol } Pb(NO_3)_2$$

$$M\,KCl = \frac{0.150 \text{ mol KCl}}{1 \text{ L KCl solution}}$$

SOLVE Begin with L $Pb(NO_3)_2$ solution and follow the conceptual plan to arrive at L KCl solution.

SOLUTION

$$0.150 \text{ L } \cancel{Pb(NO_3)_2 \text{ solution}} \times \frac{0.175 \text{ } \cancel{\text{mol } Pb(NO_3)_2}}{1 \text{ L } \cancel{Pb(NO_3)_2 \text{ solution}}}$$

$$\times \frac{2 \text{ } \cancel{\text{mol KCl}}}{1 \text{ } \cancel{\text{mol } Pb(NO_3)_2}} \times \frac{1 \text{ L KCl solution}}{0.150 \text{ } \cancel{\text{mol KCl}}} = 0.350 \text{ L KCl solution}$$

CHECK The final units (L KCl solution) are correct. The magnitude (0.350 L) is reasonable because the reaction stoichiometry requires 2 mol of KCl per mole of $Pb(NO_3)_2$. Since the concentrations of the two solutions are not very different (0.150 M compared to 0.175 M), the volume of KCl required is roughly two times the 0.150 L of $Pb(NO_3)_2$ given in the problem.

FOR PRACTICE 5.4 What volume (in mL) of a 0.150 M HNO_3 solution will completely react with 35.7 mL of a 0.108 M Na_2CO_3 solution according to the following balanced chemical equation?

$$Na_2CO_3(aq) + 2\,HNO_3(aq) \longrightarrow 2\,NaNO_3(aq) + CO_2(g) + H_2O(l)$$

FOR MORE PRACTICE 5.4 In the previous reaction, what mass (in grams) of carbon dioxide forms?

ANSWER **NOW!**

5.4 Cc Conceptual Connection

SOLUTION STOICHIOMETRY Consider the reaction:

$$2\,A(aq) + B(aq) \longrightarrow C(aq)$$

What is the limiting reactant if you mix equal volumes of a 1 M solution of A and a 1 M solution of B?

(a) A **(b)** B

5.4 Types of Aqueous Solutions and Solubility

Consider two familiar aqueous solutions: salt water and sugar water. Salt water is a homogeneous mixture of NaCl and H_2O, and sugar water is a homogeneous mixture of $C_{12}H_{22}O_{11}$ and H_2O. You may have made these solutions yourself by adding table salt or sugar to water. As you stir either of these two substances into the water, the substance seems to disappear. However, you know that the original substance is still present because the mixture tastes salty or sweet. How do solids such as salt and sugar dissolve in water?

When a solid is put into a liquid solvent, the attractive forces that hold the solid together (the solute–solute interactions) compete with the attractive forces between the solvent molecules and the particles that compose the solid (the solvent–solute interactions), as shown in Figure 5.5▶. For example, when sodium chloride is put into water, there is a competition between the attraction of Na^+ cations and Cl^- anions to each other (due to their opposite charges) and the attraction of Na^+ and Cl^- to water molecules. The attraction of Na^+ and Cl^- to water is based on the *polar nature* of the water molecule. For reasons we discuss later in this book (Section 10.6), the oxygen atom in water is electron-rich, giving it a partial negative charge (δ^-), as shown in Figure 5.6▶. The hydrogen atoms, in contrast, are electron-poor, giving them a partial positive charge (δ^+). As a result, the positively charged sodium ions are strongly attracted to the oxygen side of the water molecule (which has a partial negative charge), and the negatively charged chloride ions are attracted to the hydrogen side of the water molecule (which has a partial positive charge), as shown in Figure 5.7▼. In the case of NaCl, the attraction between the separated ions and the water molecules overcomes the attraction of sodium and chloride ions to each other, and the sodium chloride dissolves in the water (Figure 5.8▼).

Solute and Solvent Interactions

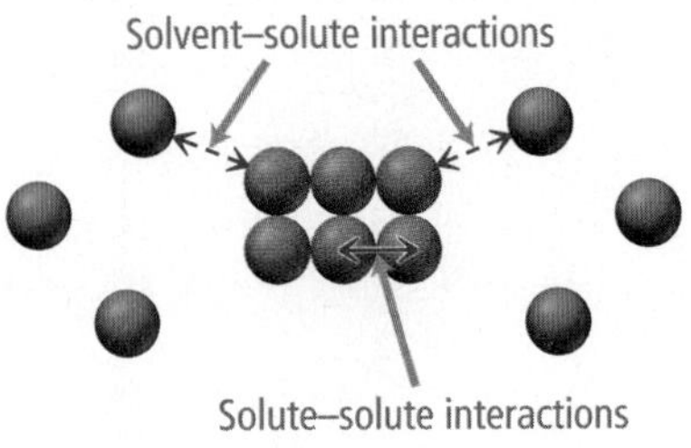

▲ **FIGURE 5.5 Solute and Solvent Interactions**

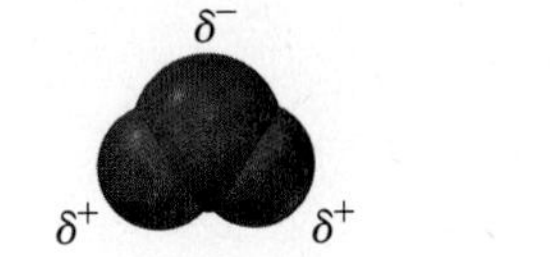

▲ **FIGURE 5.6 Charge Distribution in Water** An uneven distribution of electrons causes the oxygen side of the water molecule to have a partial negative charge and the hydrogen side to have a partial positive charge.

Electrolyte and Nonelectrolyte Solutions

As Figure 5.9▶ illustrates, a salt solution conducts electricity while a sugar solution does not. The difference between the ways that salt (an ionic compound) and sugar (a molecular compound) dissolve in water illustrates a fundamental difference between types of solutions. Ionic compounds such as the sodium chloride in the previous example dissociate into their component ions when they dissolve in water. An NaCl solution, represented as NaCl(*aq*), does not contain any NaCl units, but rather dissolved Na^+ ions and Cl^- ions. The dissolved ions act as charge carriers, allowing the solution to conduct electricity. Substances that dissolve in water to form solutions that conduct electricity are **electrolytes**. Substances such

Interactions in a Sodium Chloride Solution

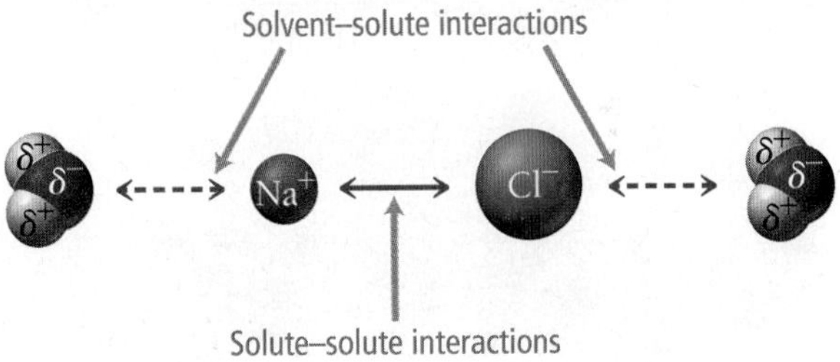

▲ **FIGURE 5.7 Solute and Solvent Interactions in a Sodium Chloride Solution** When sodium chloride is put into water, the attraction of Na^+ and Cl^- ions to water molecules competes with the attraction between the oppositely charged ions themselves.

Dissolution of an Ionic Compound

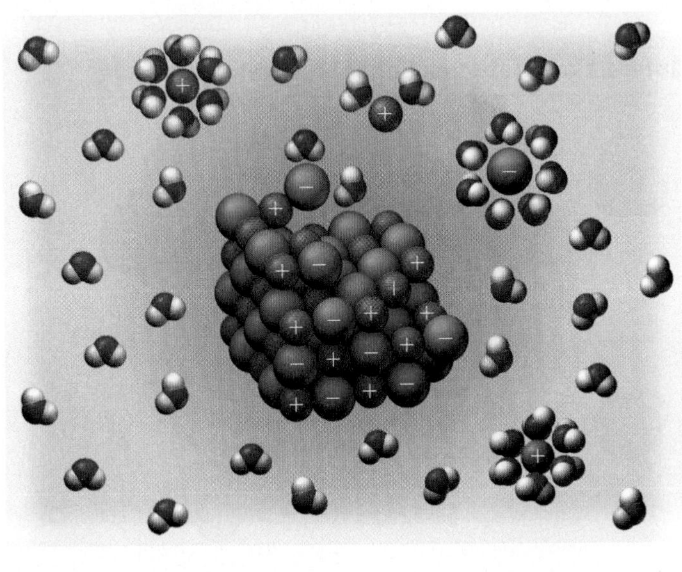

▲ **FIGURE 5.8 Sodium Chloride Dissolving in Water** The attraction between water molecules and the ions of sodium chloride causes NaCl to dissolve in the water.

▶ **FIGURE 5.9 Electrolyte and Nonelectrolyte Solutions**

Electrolyte and Nonelectrolyte Solutions

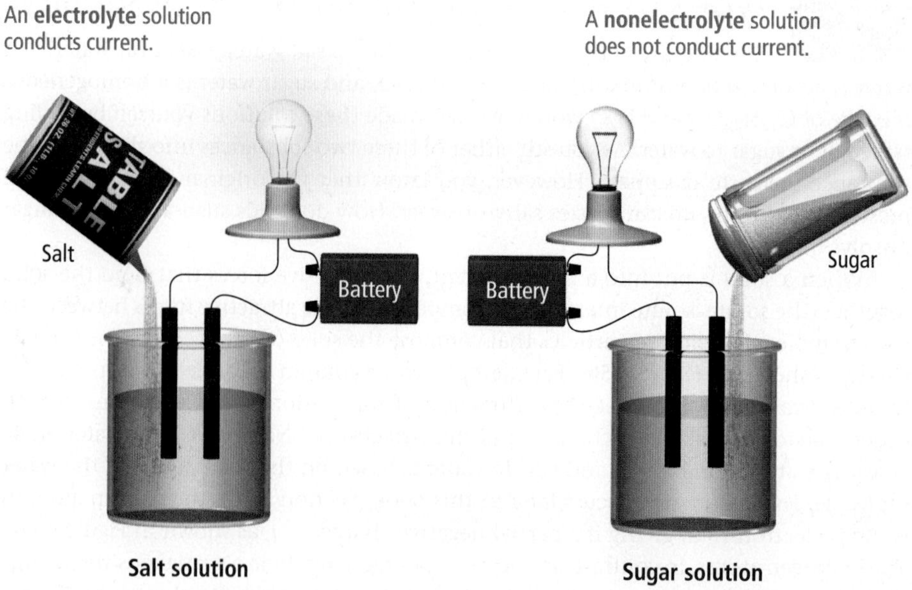

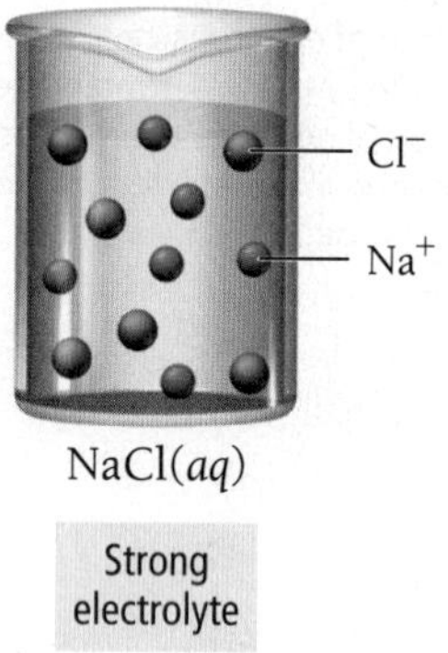

as sodium chloride that completely dissociate into ions when they dissolve in water are **strong electrolytes**, and the resulting solutions are *strong electrolyte solutions*.

In contrast to sodium chloride, sugar is a molecular compound. Most molecular compounds—with the important exception of acids, which we discuss shortly—dissolve in water as intact molecules. Sugar dissolves because the attraction between sugar molecules and water molecules (shown in Figure 5.10▼) overcomes the attraction of sugar molecules to each other (Figure 5.11▼). So unlike a sodium chloride solution (which is composed of dissociated ions), a sugar solution is composed of intact $C_{12}H_{22}O_{11}$ molecules homogeneously mixed with the water molecules. Compounds such as sugar that do not dissociate into ions when dissolved in water are called **nonelectrolytes**, and the resulting solutions—called *nonelectrolyte solutions*—do not conduct electricity.

Acids, which we introduced in Section 3.6, are molecular compounds, but they ionize—form ions—when they dissolve in water. Hydrochloric acid (HCl) is a molecular compound that ionizes into H^+ and Cl^- when it dissolves in water. HCl is an example of a **strong acid**, one that completely ionizes in solution. Since strong acids completely

Interactions between Sugar and Water Molecules

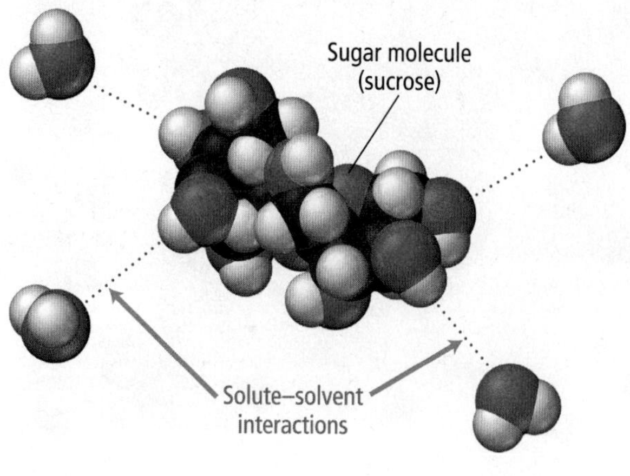

▲ **FIGURE 5.10 Sugar and Water Interactions** Partial charges on sugar molecules and water molecules (which we will discuss more fully in Chapter 12) result in attractions between the sugar molecules and water molecules.

Sugar Solution

▲ **FIGURE 5.11 A Sugar Solution** Sugar dissolves because the attractions between sugar molecules and water molecules, which both contain a distribution of electrons that results in partial positive and partial negative charges, overcome the attractions between sugar molecules to each other.

ionize in solution, they are also strong electrolytes. We represent the complete ionization of a strong acid with a single reaction arrow between the acid and its ionized form:

$$HCl(aq) \longrightarrow H^+(aq) + Cl^-(aq)$$

Unlike soluble ionic compounds, which contain ions and therefore *dissociate* in water, acids are molecular compounds that *ionize* in water.

Many acids are **weak acids**; they do not completely ionize in water. For example, acetic acid ($HC_2H_3O_2$), the acid in vinegar, is a weak acid. A solution of a weak acid is composed mostly of the nonionized acid—only a small percentage of the acid molecules ionize. We represent the partial ionization of a weak acid with opposing half arrows between the reactants and products:

$$HC_2H_3O_2(aq) \rightleftharpoons H^+(aq) + C_2H_3O_2^-(aq)$$

Weak acids are **weak electrolytes**, and the resulting solutions—called *weak electrolyte solutions*—conduct electricity only weakly. Figure 5.12▼ summarizes the electrolytic properties of solutions.

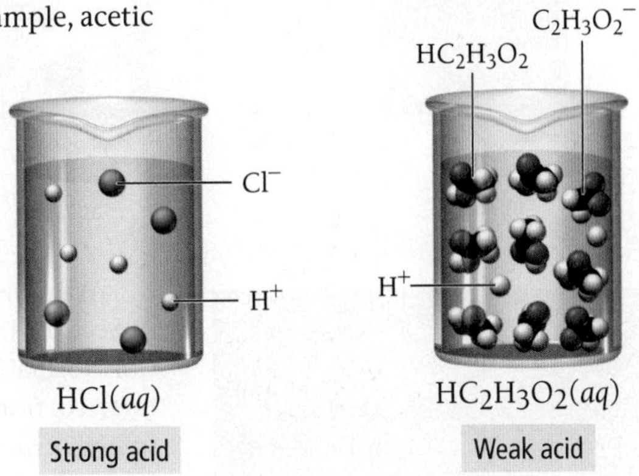

Electrolytic Properties of Solutions

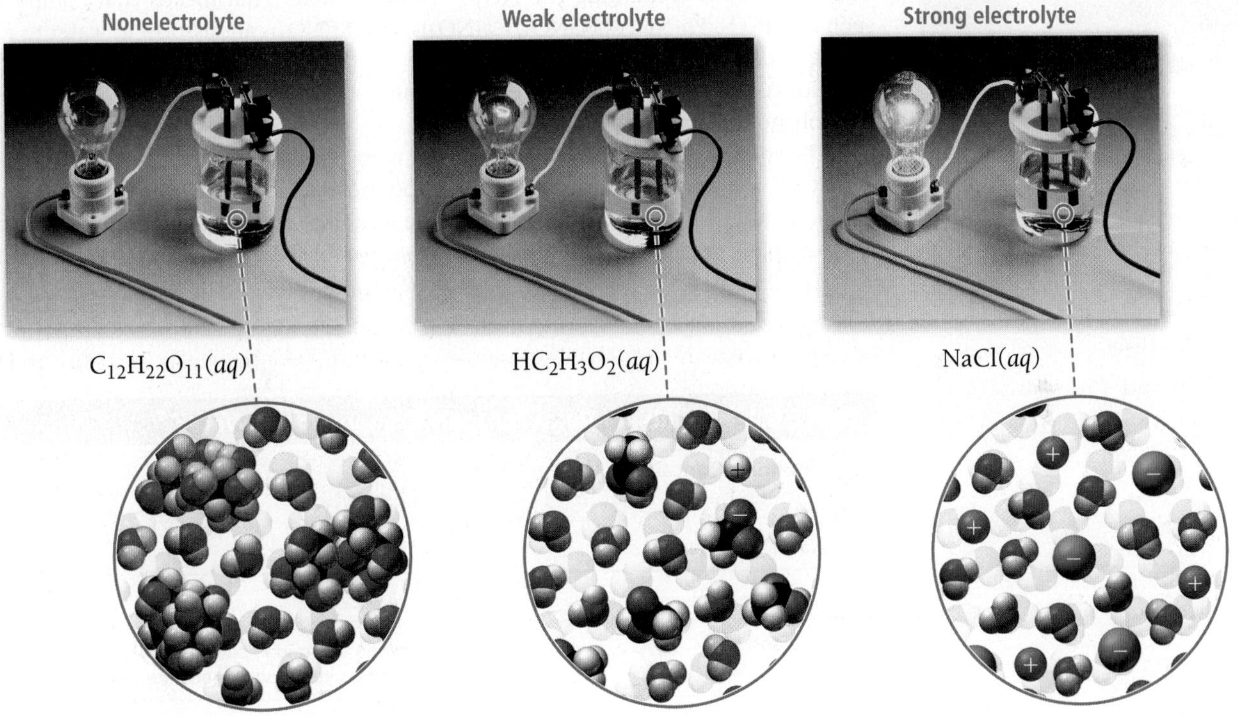

▲ **FIGURE 5.12 Electrolytic Properties of Solutions**

ELECTROLYTE SOLUTIONS Which aqueous solution conducts electricity?

(a) 1.0 M KBr **(b)** 1.0 M $C_6H_{12}O_6$ **(c)** 1.0 M CH_3OH

5.5 Cc Conceptual Connection

ANSWER **NOW!**

The Solubility of Ionic Compounds

As we have just discussed, when an ionic compound dissolves in water, the resulting solution contains not the intact ionic compound itself, but its component ions dissolved in water. However, not all ionic compounds dissolve in water. If we add AgCl to water, for example, it remains solid and appears as a white powder at the bottom of the water.

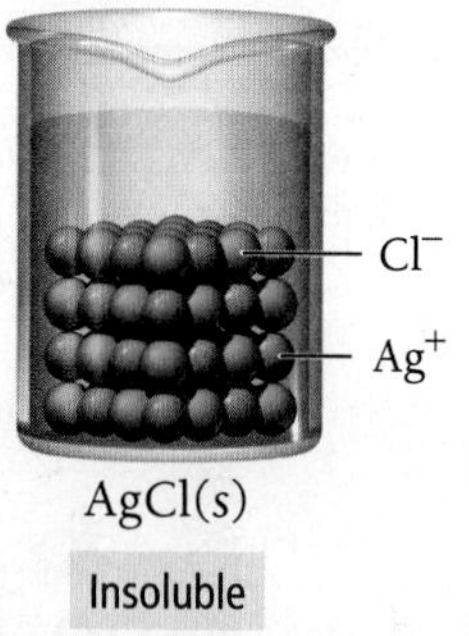

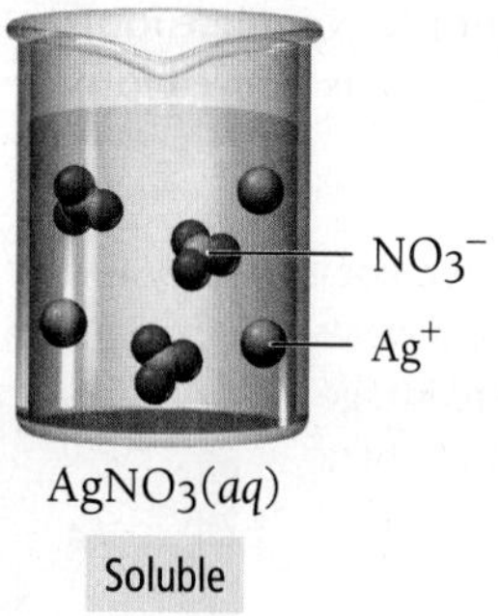

In general, a compound is termed **soluble** if it dissolves in water and **insoluble** if it does not. However, these classifications are a bit of an oversimplification. (In reality, solubility is a continuum and even "insoluble" compounds dissolve to some extent, though usually orders of magnitude less than soluble compounds.) For example, silver nitrate is soluble. If we mix solid $AgNO_3$ with water, it dissolves and forms a strong electrolyte solution. Silver chloride, as we just saw, is almost completely insoluble. If we mix solid AgCl with water, virtually all of it remains as a solid within the liquid water.

Whether a particular compound is soluble or insoluble depends on several factors. In Section 13.3, we will examine more closely the energy changes associated with solution formation. For now, we can follow a set of empirical rules that chemists have inferred from observations on many ionic compounds. Table 5.1 summarizes these *solubility rules*.

The solubility rules state that compounds containing the sodium ion are soluble. That means that compounds such as NaBr, $NaNO_3$, Na_2SO_4, NaOH, and Na_2CO_3 all dissolve in water to form strong electrolyte solutions. Similarly, the solubility rules state that compounds containing the NO_3^- ion are soluble. That means that compounds such as $AgNO_3$, $Pb(NO_3)_2$, $NaNO_3$, $Ca(NO_3)_2$, and $Sr(NO_3)_2$ all dissolve in water to form strong electrolyte solutions.

▲ AgCl does not dissolve in water; it remains as a white powder at the bottom of the beaker.

Notice that when compounds containing polyatomic ions such as NO_3^- dissolve, the polyatomic ions dissolve as intact units.

The solubility rules also state that, with some exceptions, compounds containing the CO_3^{2-} ion are insoluble. Therefore, compounds such as $CuCO_3$, $CaCO_3$, $SrCO_3$, and $FeCO_3$ do not dissolve in water. Note that the solubility rules contain many exceptions. For example, compounds containing CO_3^{2-} *are* soluble when paired with Li^+, Na^+, K^+, or NH_4^+. Thus Li_2CO_3, Na_2CO_3, K_2CO_3, and $(NH_4)_2CO_3$ are all soluble.

TABLE 5.1 ■ Solubility Rules for Ionic Compounds in Water

Compounds Containing the Following Ions Are Generally Soluble	Exceptions
Li^+, Na^+, K^+, and NH_4^+	None
NO_3^- and $C_2H_3O_2^-$	None
Cl^-, Br^-, and I^-	When these ions pair with Ag^+, Hg_2^{2+}, or Pb^{2+}, the resulting compounds are insoluble.
SO_4^{2-}	When SO_4^{2-} pairs with Sr^{2+}, Ba^{2+}, Pb^{2+}, Ag^+, or Ca^{2+}, the resulting compound is insoluble.
Compounds Containing the Following Ions Are Generally Insoluble	**Exceptions**
OH^- and S^{2-}	When these ions pair with Li^+, Na^+, K^+, or NH_4^+, the resulting compounds are soluble. When S^{2-} pairs with Ca^{2+}, Sr^{2+}, or Ba^{2+}, the resulting compound is soluble. When OH^- pairs with Ca^{2+}, Sr^{2+}, or Ba^{2+}, the resulting compound is slightly soluble.
CO_3^{2-} and PO_4^{3-}	When these ions pair with Li^+, Na^+, K^+, or NH_4^+, the resulting compounds are soluble.

WATCH **NOW!**

INTERACTIVE WORKED EXAMPLE 5.5

EXAMPLE 5.5 Predicting Whether an Ionic Compound Is Soluble

Predict whether each compound is soluble or insoluble.

(a) $PbCl_2$ **(b)** $CuCl_2$ **(c)** $Ca(NO_3)_2$ **(d)** $BaSO_4$

SOLUTION

(a) Insoluble. Compounds containing Cl^- are normally soluble, but Pb^{2+} is an exception.

(b) Soluble. Compounds containing Cl^- are normally soluble, and Cu^{2+} is not an exception.

(c) Soluble. Compounds containing NO_3^- are always soluble.

(d) Insoluble. Compounds containing SO_4^{2-} are normally soluble, but Ba^{2+} is an exception.

FOR PRACTICE 5.5 Predict whether each compound is soluble or insoluble.

(a) NiS **(b)** $Mg_3(PO_4)_2$ **(c)** Li_2CO_3 **(d)** NH_4Cl

SOLUBILITY OF IONIC COMPOUNDS The presence of one of the following ions within a compound indicates that a compound is soluble with no exceptions. Which ion?

(a) OH^- **(b)** SO_4^{2-} **(c)** NO_3^-

5.6 Cc Conceptual Connection

ANSWER **NOW!**

5.5 Precipitation Reactions

WATCH **NOW!**

KEY CONCEPT VIDEO 5.5 *Reactions in Solution*

Have you ever taken a bath in hard water? Hard water contains dissolved ions such as Ca^{2+} and Mg^{2+} that diminish the effectiveness of soap. These ions react with soap to form a gray soap scum that may appear as a "bathtub ring" after you drain the tub. Hard water is particularly troublesome when washing clothes. Consider how your white shirt would look covered with the soap scum from the bathtub and you can understand the problem. Consequently, most laundry detergents include substances designed to remove Ca^{2+} and Mg^{2+} from the laundry mixture. The most common substance used for this purpose is sodium carbonate, which dissolves in water to form sodium cations (Na^+) and carbonate (CO_3^{2-}) anions:

$$Na_2CO_3(aq) \longrightarrow 2\,Na^+(aq) + CO_3^{2-}(aq)$$

Sodium carbonate is soluble, but calcium carbonate and magnesium carbonate are not (see the solubility rules in Table 5.1). Consequently, the carbonate anions react with dissolved Mg^{2+} and Ca^{2+} ions in hard water to form solids that *precipitate* from (or come out of) solution:

$$Mg^{2+}(aq) + CO_3^{2-}(aq) \longrightarrow MgCO_3(s)$$

$$Ca^{2+}(aq) + CO_3^{2-}(aq) \longrightarrow CaCO_3(s)$$

▲ The reaction of ions in hard water with soap produces a gray soap scum that is visible after you drain the bathwater.

The precipitation of these ions prevents their reaction with the soap, eliminating curd and preventing white shirts from turning gray.

The reactions between CO_3^{2-} and Mg^{2+} and Ca^{2+} are examples of **precipitation reactions**, reactions in which a solid or **precipitate** forms when we mix two solutions. Precipitation reactions are common in chemistry. As another example, consider potassium iodide and lead(II) nitrate, which form colorless, strong electrolyte solutions when dissolved in water separately. When the two solutions are combined, however, a brilliant yellow precipitate forms (Figure 5.13▶). We describe this precipitation reaction with the following chemical equation:

$$2\,KI(aq) + Pb(NO_3)_2(aq) \longrightarrow PbI_2(s) + 2\,KNO_3(aq)$$

Precipitation Reaction

$2\ KI(aq) + Pb(NO_3)_2(aq) \longrightarrow PbI_2(s) + 2\ KNO_3(aq)$
(soluble) (soluble) (insoluble) (soluble)

◀ **FIGURE 5.13 Precipitation of Lead(II) Iodide**

$2\ KI(aq)$ (soluble) + $Pb(NO_3)_2(aq)$ (soluble) $\longrightarrow$ $PbI_2(s)$ (insoluble) + $2\ KNO_3(aq)$ (soluble)

Precipitation reactions do not always occur when two aqueous solutions are mixed. For example, if we combine solutions of $KI(aq)$ and $NaCl(aq)$, nothing happens (Figure 5.14▶):

$$KI(aq) + NaCl(aq) \not\longrightarrow \text{NO REACTION}$$

The key to predicting precipitation reactions is to understand that *only insoluble compounds form precipitates*. In a precipitation reaction, two solutions containing soluble compounds combine and an insoluble compound precipitates. Consider the precipitation reaction described previously:

$$\underset{\text{soluble}}{2\ KI(aq)} + \underset{\text{soluble}}{Pb(NO_3)_2(aq)} \longrightarrow \underset{\text{insoluble}}{PbI_2(s)} + \underset{\text{soluble}}{2\ KNO_3(aq)}$$

KI and $Pb(NO_3)_2$ are both soluble, but the precipitate, PbI_2, is insoluble. Before mixing, $KI(aq)$ and $Pb(NO_3)_2(aq)$ are both dissociated in their respective solutions:

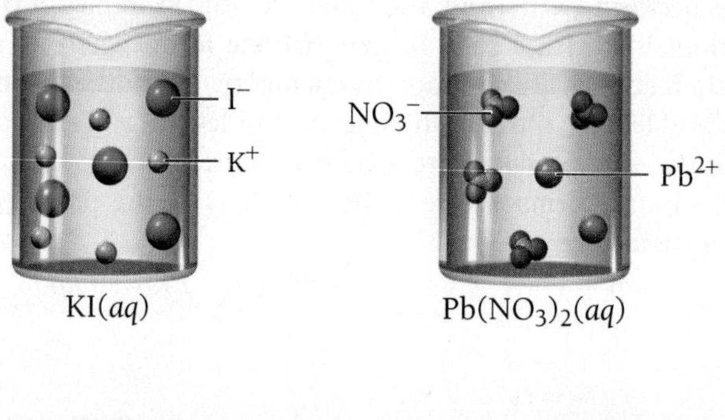

The instant that the solutions come into contact, all four ions are present:

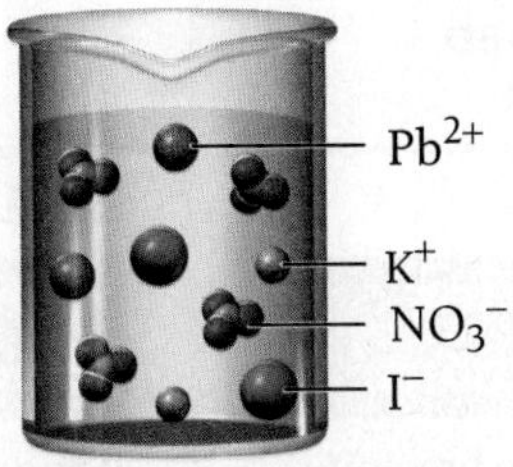

$KI(aq)$ and $Pb(NO_3)_2(aq)$

Now, new compounds—one or both of which might be insoluble—are possible. Specifically, the cation from either compound can pair with the anion from the other to form possibly insoluble products:

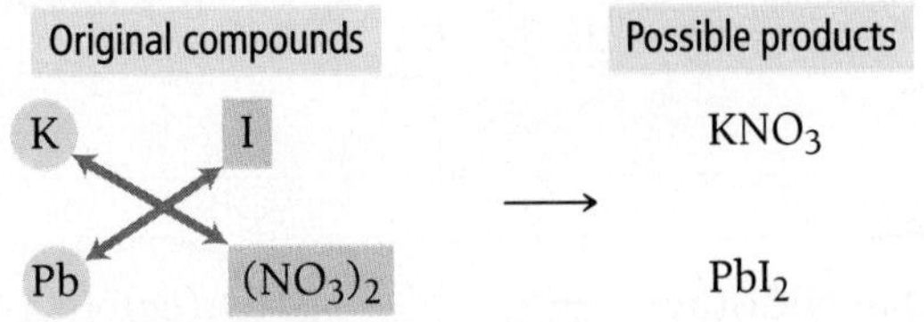

If the possible products are both soluble, no reaction occurs and no precipitate forms. If one or both of the possible products are insoluble, a precipitation reaction occurs. In this case, KNO_3 is soluble, but PbI_2 is insoluble. Consequently, PbI_2 precipitates.

To predict whether a precipitation reaction will occur when two solutions are mixed and to write an equation for the reaction, we use the procedure that follows. The steps are outlined in the left column, and two examples illustrating how to apply the procedure are shown in the center and right columns.

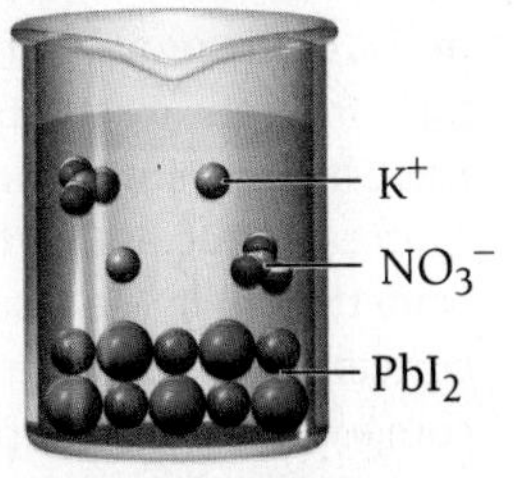

$PbI_2(s)$ and $KNO_3(aq)$

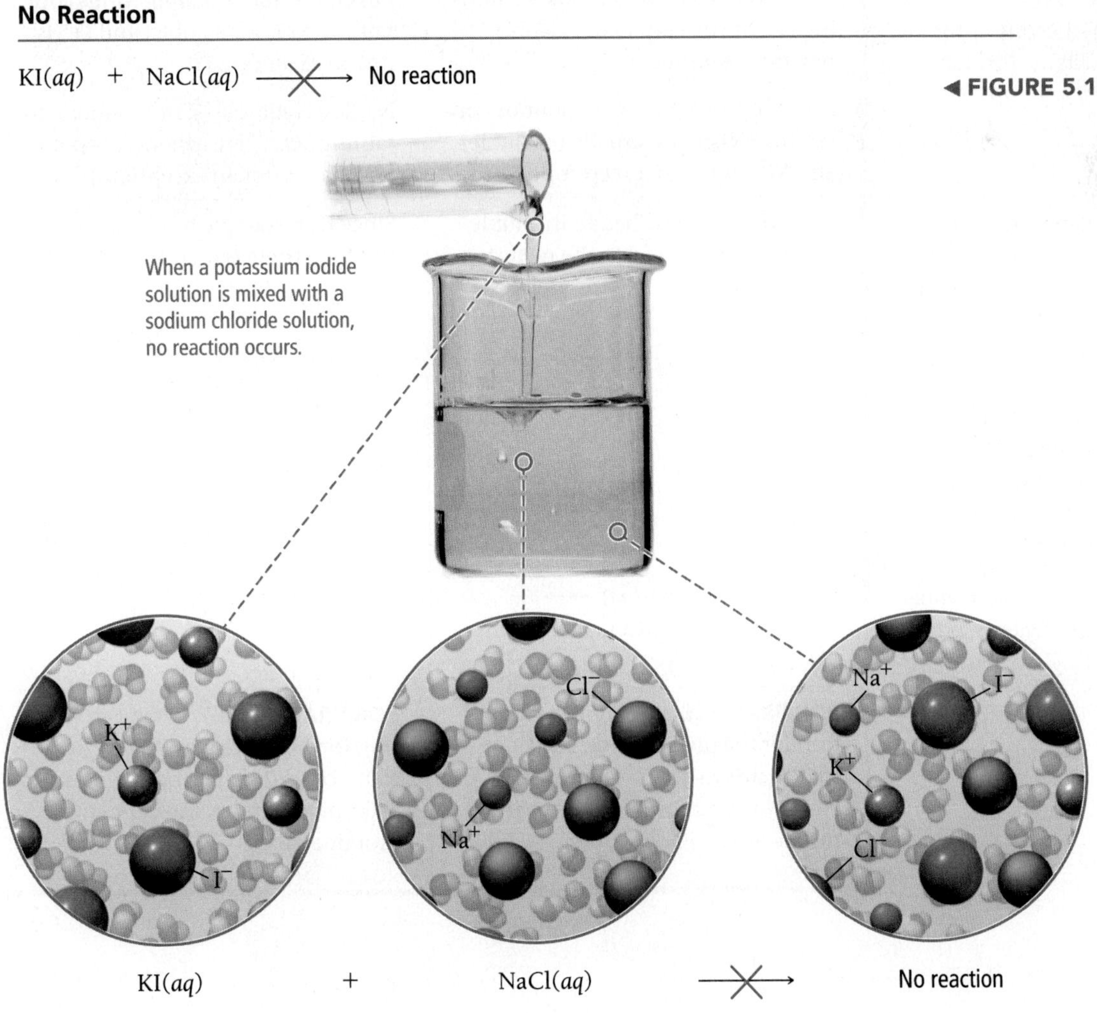

◀ **FIGURE 5.14 No Precipitation**

WATCH **NOW!**

INTERACTIVE WORKED EXAMPLE VIDEO 5.6

HOW TO: *Write Equations for Precipitation Reactions*	**EXAMPLE 5.6** **Writing Equations for Precipitation Reactions** Write an equation for the precipitation reaction that occurs (if any) when solutions of potassium carbonate and nickel(II) chloride are mixed.	**EXAMPLE 5.7** **Writing Equations for Precipitation Reactions** Write an equation for the precipitation reaction that occurs (if any) when solutions of sodium nitrate and lithium sulfate are mixed.
1. Write the formulas of the two compounds being mixed as reactants in a chemical equation.	$K_2CO_3(aq) + NiCl_2(aq) \longrightarrow$	$NaNO_3(aq) + Li_2SO_4(aq) \longrightarrow$
2. Below the equation, write the formulas of the products that could form from the reactants. Obtain these by combining the cation from each reactant with the anion from the other. Make sure to write correct formulas for these ionic compounds using the procedure demonstrated in Section 3.5.	$K_2CO_3(aq) + NiCl_2(aq) \longrightarrow$ Possible products KCl $NiCO_3$	$NaNO_3(aq) + Li_2SO_4(aq) \longrightarrow$ Possible products $LiNO_3$ Na_2SO_4
3. Refer to the solubility rules to determine whether any of the possible products are insoluble.	KCl is soluble. (Compounds containing Cl^- are usually soluble, and K^+ is not an exception.) $NiCO_3$ is insoluble. (Compounds containing CO_3^{2-} are usually insoluble, and Ni^{2+} is not an exception.)	$LiNO_3$ is soluble. (Compounds containing NO_3^- are soluble, and Li^+ is not an exception.) Na_2SO_4 is soluble. (Compounds containing SO_4^{2-} are generally soluble, and Na^+ is not an exception.)
4. If all of the possible products are soluble, there is no precipitate. Write "NO REACTION" after the arrow.	Since this example has an insoluble product, we proceed to the next step.	Since this example has no insoluble product, there is no reaction. $NaNO_3(aq) + Li_2SO_4(aq) \not\longrightarrow$ NO REACTION
5. If any of the possible products are insoluble, write their formulas as the products of the reaction, using (*s*) to indicate solid. Include an (*aq*) to indicate aqueous after any soluble products.	$K_2CO_3(aq) + NiCl_2(aq) \longrightarrow NiCO_3(s) + KCl(aq)$	
6. Balance the equation. Remember to adjust only coefficients, not subscripts.	$K_2CO_3(aq) + NiCl_2(aq) \longrightarrow NiCO_3(s) + 2\,KCl(aq)$	
	FOR PRACTICE 5.6 Write an equation for the precipitation reaction that occurs (if any) when solutions of ammonium chloride and iron(III) nitrate mix.	**FOR PRACTICE 5.7** Write an equation for the precipitation reaction that occurs (if any) when solutions of sodium hydroxide and copper(II) bromide mix.

5.7 Cc Conceptual Connection

ANSWER **NOW!**

PRECIPITATION REACTIONS Consider the generic ionic compounds with the formulas AX and BY and the following solubility rules:

AX soluble; BY soluble; AY soluble; BX insoluble

Let circles represent A^+ ions; squares represent B^+ ions; triangles represent X^- ions; and diamonds represent Y^- ions. We represent solutions of the two compounds (AX and BY) as follows:

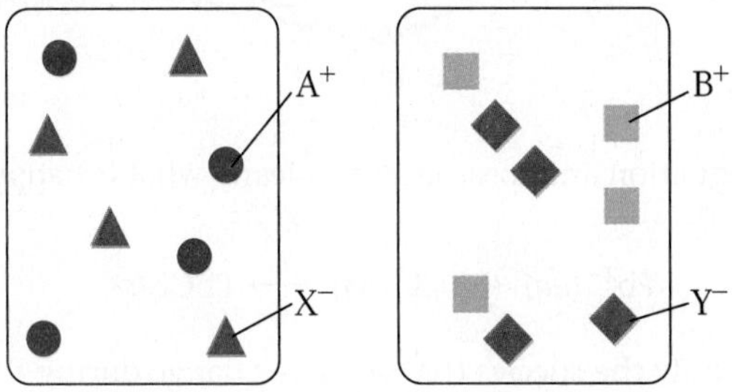

AX(*aq*) BY(*aq*)

From the answer options, choose the representation that correctly shows the result of mixing the two solutions (AX and BY) and the correct equation to represent the reaction.

(a) $AX(aq) + BY(aq) \longrightarrow AY(s) + BX(aq)$

(b) NO REACTION

(c) $AX(aq) + BY(aq) \longrightarrow BX(s) + AY(aq)$

5.6 Representing Aqueous Reactions: Molecular, Ionic, and Net Ionic Equations

Consider the following equation for a precipitation reaction:

$$Pb(NO_3)_2(aq) + 2\,KCl(aq) \longrightarrow PbCl_2(s) + 2\,KNO_3(aq)$$

This equation is a **molecular equation**, an equation showing the complete neutral formulas for each compound in the reaction as if they existed as molecules. In actual solutions of soluble ionic compounds, dissolved substances are present as ions. We can write equations for reactions occurring in aqueous solution in a way that better shows the dissociated nature of dissolved ionic compounds. For example, we can rewrite the previous equation as:

$$Pb^{2+}(aq) + 2\,NO_3^-(aq) + 2\,K^+(aq) + 2\,Cl^-(aq) \longrightarrow PbCl_2(s) + 2\,K^+(aq) + 2\,NO_3^-(aq)$$

Equations such as this, which list all of the ions present as either reactants or products in a chemical reaction, are **complete ionic equations**. Strong electrolytes are always represented as their component ions in ionic equations—weak electrolytes are not.

Notice that in the complete ionic equation, some of the ions in solution appear unchanged on both sides of the equation. These ions are called **spectator ions** because they do not participate in the reaction.

$$Pb^{2+}(aq) + 2\,NO_3^-(aq) + 2\,K^+(aq) + 2\,Cl^-(aq) \longrightarrow PbCl_2(s) + 2\,K^+(aq) + 2\,NO_3^-(aq)$$

Spectator ions

To simplify the equation and to show more clearly what is happening, we can omit spectator ions:

$$Pb^{2+}(aq) + 2\,Cl^-(aq) \longrightarrow PbCl_2(s)$$

Equations that show only the species that actually change during the reaction are **net ionic equations.**

As another example, consider the reaction between $HCl(aq)$ and $KOH(aq)$:

$$HCl(aq) + KOH(aq) \longrightarrow H_2O(l) + KCl(aq)$$

Since HCl, KOH, and KCl all exist in solution primarily as independent ions, the complete ionic equation is:

$$H^+(aq) + Cl^-(aq) + K^+(aq) + OH^-(aq) \longrightarrow H_2O(l) + K^+(aq) + Cl^-(aq)$$

To write the net ionic equation, we remove the spectator ions, those that are unchanged on both sides of the equation:

$$H^+(aq) + \cancel{Cl^-}(aq) + \cancel{K^+}(aq) + OH^-(aq) \longrightarrow H_2O(l) + \cancel{K^+}(aq) + \cancel{Cl^-}(aq)$$

Spectator ions

The net ionic equation is $H^+(aq) + OH^-(aq) \longrightarrow H_2O(l)$.

Summarizing Aqueous Equations

- A **molecular equation** is a chemical equation showing the complete, neutral formulas for every compound in a reaction.
- A **complete ionic equation** is a chemical equation showing all of the species as they are actually present in solution: strong electrolytes are therefore represented as their component ions.
- A **net ionic equation** is an equation showing only the species that actually change during the reaction.

ANSWER NOW!

5.8 Cc Conceptual Connection

SPECTATOR IONS Which of the ions listed below is a spectator ion in the complete ionic equation shown here?

$$Ag^+(aq) + NO_3^-(aq) + Na^+(aq) + I^-(aq) \longrightarrow AgI(s) + NO_3^-(aq) + Na^+(aq)$$

(a) $Ag^+(aq)$ **(b)** $NO_3^-(aq)$ **(c)** $I^-(aq)$

EXAMPLE 5.8 Writing Complete Ionic and Net Ionic Equations

Write complete ionic and net ionic equations for each reaction.

(a) $3\,SrCl_2(aq) + 2\,Li_3PO_4(aq) \longrightarrow Sr_3(PO_4)_2(s) + 6\,LiCl(aq)$

(b) $HC_2H_3O_2(aq) + KOH(aq) \longrightarrow H_2O(l) + KC_2H_3O_2(aq)$

SOLUTION

(a) Write the complete ionic equation by separating strong electrolytes into their constituent ions. The $Sr_3(PO_4)_2(s)$, precipitating as a solid, remains as one unit.

Complete ionic equation:

$$3\,Sr^{2+}(aq) + 6\,Cl^-(aq) + 6\,Li^+(aq) + 2\,PO_4^{3-}(aq) \longrightarrow Sr_3(PO_4)_2(s) + 6\,Li^+(aq) + 6\,Cl^-(aq)$$

Write the net ionic equation by eliminating the spectator ions, those that do not change from one side of the reaction to the other.

Net ionic equation:

$$3\,Sr^{2+}(aq) + 2\,PO_4^{3-}(aq) \longrightarrow Sr_3(PO_4)_2(s)$$

(b) Write the complete ionic equation by separating strong electrolytes into their constituent ions. Do not separate $HC_2H_3O_2(aq)$ because it is a weak electrolyte.

Complete ionic equation:

$$HC_2H_3O_2(aq) + K^+(aq) + OH^-(aq) \longrightarrow H_2O(l) + K^+(aq) + C_2H_3O_2^-(aq)$$

Write the net ionic equation by eliminating the spectator ions.

Net ionic equation:

$$HC_2H_3O_2(aq) + OH^-(aq) \longrightarrow H_2O(l) + C_2H_3O_2^-(aq)$$

FOR PRACTICE 5.8 Write the complete ionic equation and net ionic equation for the following reaction:

$$2\,HI(aq) + Ba(OH)_2(aq) \longrightarrow 2\,H_2O(l) + BaI_2(aq)$$

5.7 Acid–Base Reactions

Two other important classes of reactions that occur in aqueous solution are acid–base reactions and gas-evolution reactions. In an **acid–base reaction** (also called a **neutralization reaction**), an acid reacts with a base and the two neutralize each other, producing water (or in some cases a weak electrolyte). In a **gas-evolution reaction**, a gas forms, resulting in bubbling. In both cases, as in precipitation reactions, the reactions occur when the anion from one reactant combines with the cation of the other. Many gas-evolution reactions are also acid–base reactions.

Acid–Base Reactions

Our stomachs contain hydrochloric acid (HCl), which acts in the digestion of food. Certain foods or stress, however, can increase the stomach's acidity to uncomfortable levels, causing acid stomach or heartburn. Antacids are over-the-counter medicines that work by reacting with and neutralizing stomach acid. Antacids employ different *bases*—substances that produce hydroxide (OH^-) ions in water—as neutralizing agents. Milk of magnesia, for example, contains $Mg(OH)_2$ and Mylanta contains $Al(OH)_3$. All antacids, regardless of the base they employ, have the same effect of neutralizing stomach acid and relieving heartburn through *acid–base reactions*.

Recall from Chapter 3 that an acid forms H^+ ions in solution, and we just saw that a base is a substance that produces OH^- ions in solution. More formally:

- Acid: Substance that produces H^+ ions in aqueous solution
- Base: Substance that produces OH^- ions in aqueous solution

▲ Gas-evolution reactions, such as the reaction of hydrochloric acid (HCl) with limestone ($CaCO_3$), typically produce CO_2; bubbling occurs as the gas is released.

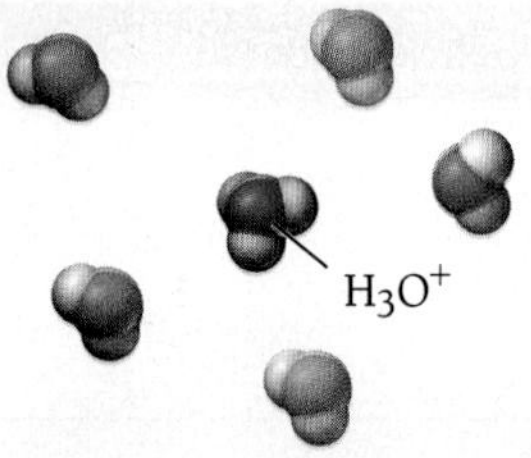

▲ FIGURE 5.15 The Hydronium Ion Protons normally associate with water molecules in solution to form H_3O^+ ions, which in turn interact with other water molecules.

These definitions of acids and bases, called the **Arrhenius definitions**, are named after Swedish chemist Svante Arrhenius (1859–1927). In Chapter 16, we will learn more general definitions of acids and bases, but these definitions are sufficient to describe neutralization reactions.

According to the Arrhenius definition, HCl is an acid because it produces H^+ ions in solution:

$$HCl(aq) \longrightarrow H^+(aq) + Cl^-(aq)$$

An H^+ ion is a bare proton. In solution, bare protons normally associate with water molecules to form **hydronium ions** (Figure 5.15◀):

$$H^+(aq) + H_2O(l) \longrightarrow H_3O^+(aq)$$

Chemists use $H^+(aq)$ and $H_3O^+(aq)$ interchangeably to mean the same thing—a hydronium ion. The chemical equation for the ionization of HCl and other acids is often written to show the association of the proton with a water molecule to form the hydronium ion:

$$HCl(aq) + H_2O(l) \longrightarrow H_3O^+(aq) + Cl^-(aq)$$

As we discussed in Section 5.4, some acids are weak acids—they do not completely ionize in solution. We represent the partial ionization of a weak acid with opposing half arrows.

$$HC_2H_3O_2(aq) \rightleftharpoons H^+(aq) + C_2H_3O_2^-(aq)$$

Some acids—called **polyprotic acids**—contain more than one ionizable proton and release them sequentially. For example, sulfuric acid, H_2SO_4, is a **diprotic acid**. It is strong in its first ionizable proton, but weak in its second:

$$H_2SO_4(aq) \longrightarrow H^+(aq) + HSO_4^-(aq)$$

$$HSO_4^-(aq) \rightleftharpoons H^+(aq) + SO_4^{2-}(aq)$$

According to the Arrhenius definition, NaOH is a base because it produces OH^- ions in solution:

$$NaOH(aq) \longrightarrow Na^+(aq) + OH^-(aq)$$

In analogy to diprotic acids, some bases such as $Sr(OH)_2$ produce two moles of OH^- per mole of the base:

$$Sr(OH)_2(aq) \longrightarrow Sr^{2+}(aq) + 2\,OH^-(aq)$$

▲ These household substances all contain acids.

Table 5.2 lists common acids and bases. You can find acids and bases in many everyday substances. Foods such as citrus fruits and vinegar contain acids. Soap, baking soda, and milk of magnesia all contain bases.

When we mix an acid and a base, the $H^+(aq)$ from the acid—whether it is weak or strong—combines with the $OH^-(aq)$ from the base to form $H_2O(l)$ (Figure 5.16▶). Consider the reaction between hydrochloric acid and sodium hydroxide:

$$\underset{\text{Acid}}{HCl(aq)} + \underset{\text{Base}}{NaOH(aq)} \longrightarrow \underset{\text{Water}}{H_2O(l)} + \underset{\text{Salt}}{NaCl(aq)}$$

Acid–base reactions generally form water and an ionic compound—called a **salt**—that usually remains dissolved in the solution. The net ionic equation for acid–base reactions involving a strong acid is:

$$H^+(aq) + OH^-(aq) \longrightarrow H_2O(l)$$

TABLE 5.2 ■ Some Common Acids and Bases

Name of Acid	Formula	Name of Base	Formula
Hydrochloric acid	HCl	Sodium hydroxide	$NaOH$
Hydrobromic acid	HBr	Lithium hydroxide	$LiOH$
Hydroiodic acid	HI	Potassium hydroxide	KOH
Nitric acid	HNO_3	Calcium hydroxide	$Ca(OH)_2$
Sulfuric acid	H_2SO_4	Barium hydroxide	$Ba(OH)_2$
Perchloric acid	$HClO_4$	Ammonia*	NH_3 (weak base)
Formic acid	$HCHO_2$ (weak acid)		
Acetic acid	$HC_2H_3O_2$ (weak acid)		
Hydrofluoric acid	HF (weak acid)		

*Ammonia does not contain OH^-, but it produces OH^- in a reaction with water that occurs only to a small extent: $NH_3(aq) + H_2O(l) \rightleftharpoons NH_4^+(aq) + OH^-(aq)$.

▲ Many common household products contain bases.

Acid–Base Reaction

$$HCl(aq) + NaOH(aq) \longrightarrow H_2O(l) + NaCl(aq)$$

The reaction between hydrochloric acid and sodium hydroxide forms water and a salt, sodium chloride, which remains dissolved in the solution.

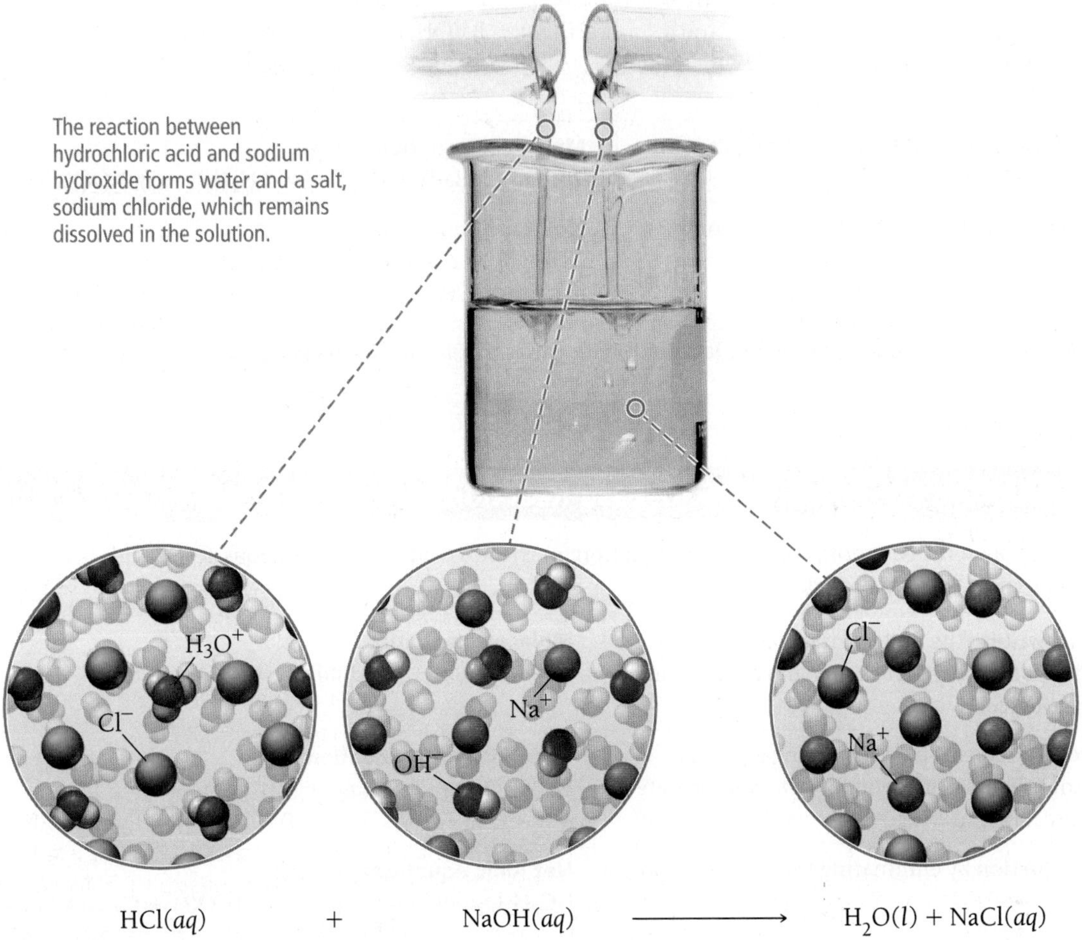

▲ FIGURE 5.16 Acid–Base Reaction

The word *salt* in this sense applies to any ionic compound and is therefore more general than the common usage, which refers only to table salt (NaCl).

However, if the acid is a weak acid, the net ionic equation is slightly different. For example, consider the acid–base equation between hydrofluoric acid and sodium hydroxide:

$$\underset{\text{acid}}{HF(aq)} + \underset{\text{base}}{NaOH(aq)} \longrightarrow \underset{\text{water}}{H_2O(l)} + \underset{\text{salt}}{NaF(aq)}$$

The complete ionic equation and the net ionic equation for this reaction are:

$$HF(aq) + Na^+(aq) + OH^-(aq) \longrightarrow H_2O(l) + Na^+(aq) + F^-(aq) \quad \text{(Complete ionic equation)}$$

$$HF(aq) + OH^-(aq) \longrightarrow H_2O(l) + F^-(aq) \quad \text{(Net ionic equation)}$$

Notice that, since HF is a weak acid, we do not show it as ionized in the ionic equations.

Another example of an acid–base reaction is the reaction between sulfuric acid and potassium hydroxide:

$$\underset{\text{acid}}{H_2SO_4(aq)} + \underset{\text{base}}{2\,KOH(aq)} \longrightarrow \underset{\text{water}}{2\,H_2O(l)} + \underset{\text{salt}}{K_2SO_4(aq)}$$

Again, notice the pattern of acid and base reacting to form water and a salt.

$$\textbf{Acid} + \textbf{Base} \longrightarrow \textbf{Water} + \textbf{Salt} \quad \text{(acid–base reactions)}$$

When writing equations for acid–base reactions, write the formula of the salt using the procedure for writing formulas of ionic compounds demonstrated in Section 3.5.

WATCH **NOW!**

INTERACTIVE WORKED EXAMPLE 5.9

EXAMPLE 5.9 Writing Equations for Acid–Base Reactions Involving a Strong Acid

Write a molecular and net ionic equation for the reaction between aqueous HI and aqueous $Ba(OH)_2$.

SOLUTION First identify these substances as an acid and a base. Begin by writing the unbalanced equation in which the acid and the base combine to form water and a salt.	$\underset{\text{acid}}{HI(aq)} + \underset{\text{base}}{Ba(OH)_2(aq)} \longrightarrow \underset{\text{water}}{H_2O(l)} + \underset{\text{salt}}{BaI_2(aq)}$
Next, balance the equation; this is the molecular equation.	**Molecular equation:** $2\,HI(aq) + Ba(OH)_2(aq) \longrightarrow 2\,H_2O(l) + BaI_2(aq)$
Write the net ionic equation by removing the spectator ions.	**Net ionic equation:** $2\,H^+(aq) + 2\,OH^-(aq) \longrightarrow 2\,H_2O(l)$ or simply $H^+(aq) + OH^-(aq) \longrightarrow H_2O(l)$

FOR PRACTICE 5.9 Write a molecular and a net ionic equation for the reaction that occurs between aqueous HBr and aqueous LiOH.

EXAMPLE 5.10 Writing Equations for Acid–Base Reactions Involving a Weak Acid

Write a molecular equation, ionic equation, and net ionic equation for the reaction between aqueous acetic acid ($HC_2H_3O_2$) and aqueous potassium hydroxide (KOH).

SOLUTION Begin by writing the molecular equation in which the acid and the base combine to form water and a salt. (The equation is already balanced.)	**Molecular equation:** $HC_2H_3O_2(aq) + KOH(aq) \longrightarrow H_2O(l) + KC_2H_3O_2(aq)$
Write the complete ionic equation by separating aqueous ionic compounds into their constituent ions. Do not separate $HC_2H_3O_2(aq)$ because it is a weak acid (and a weak electrolyte).	**Complete ionic equation:** $HC_2H_3O_2(aq) + K^+(aq) + OH^-(aq) \longrightarrow H_2O(l) + K^+(aq) + C_2H_3O_2^-(aq)$
Write the net ionic equation by eliminating the spectator ions.	**Net ionic equation:** $HC_2H_3O_2(aq) + OH^-(aq) \longrightarrow H_2O(l) + C_2H_3O_2^-(aq)$

FOR PRACTICE 5.10 Write the net ionic equation for the reaction between $HCHO_2$ (a weak acid) and NaOH.

Acid–Base Titrations

We can apply the principles of acid–base neutralization and stoichiometry to a common laboratory procedure called a *titration*. In a **titration**, a substance in a solution of known concentration is reacted with another substance in a solution of unknown concentration. For example, consider the following acid–base reaction:

$$HCl(aq) + NaOH(aq) \longrightarrow H_2O(l) + NaCl(aq)$$

The net ionic equation for this reaction eliminates the spectator ions:

$$H^+(aq) + OH^-(aq) \longrightarrow H_2O(l)$$

Suppose we have an HCl solution represented by the molecular diagram shown here (for purposes of clarity, we have omitted the Cl^- ions and the H_2O molecules not involved in the reaction from this representation).

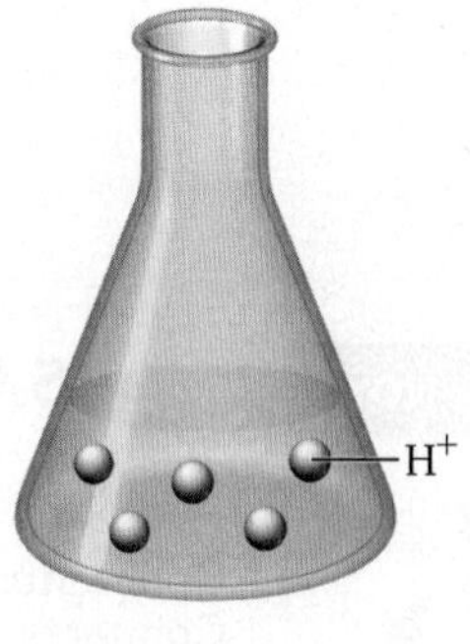

In titrating this sample, we slowly add a solution of known OH^- concentration, as shown in the molecular diagrams in Figure 5.17▼. As we add the OH^-, it reacts with and neutralizes the H^+, forming water. At the **equivalence point**—the point in the titration when the number of moles of OH^- added equals the number of moles of H^+ initially in solution—the titration is complete. The equivalence point is typically signaled by an **indicator**, a dye whose color depends on the acidity or basicity of the solution (Figure 5.18▶).

We cover acid–base titrations and indicators in more detail in Chapter 18. In most laboratory titrations, the concentration of one of the reactant solutions is unknown, and the concentration of the other is precisely known. By carefully measuring the volume of each solution required to reach the equivalence point, we can determine the concentration of the unknown solution, as demonstrated in Example 5.11.

Acid–Base Titration

$$H^+(aq) + OH^-(aq) \longrightarrow H_2O(l)$$

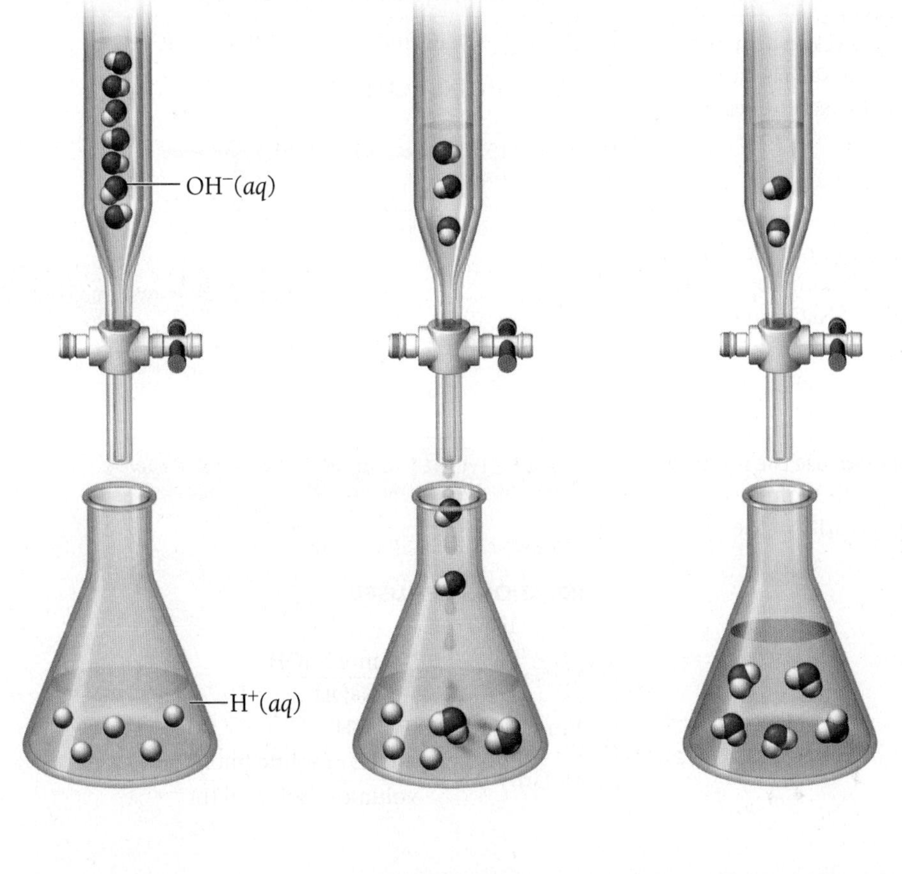

◀ **FIGURE 5.17 Acid–Base Titration**

Indicator in Titration

▶ **FIGURE 5.18 Titration** In this titration, NaOH is added to a dilute HCl solution. When the NaOH and HCl reach stoichiometric proportions (the equivalence point), the phenolphthalein indicator changes color to pink.

ANSWER **NOW!**

5.9 Cc Conceptual Connection

ACID–BASE TITRATION A 10.0 mL sample of 0.20 M HBr solution is titrated with 0.10 M NaOH. What volume of NaOH is required to reach the equivalence point?

(a) 10.0 mL **(b)** 20.0 mL **(c)** 40.0 mL

WATCH **NOW!**

INTERACTIVE WORKED EXAMPLE 5.11

EXAMPLE 5.11 Acid–Base Titration

The titration of 10.00 mL of HCl solution of unknown concentration requires 12.54 mL of a 0.100 M NaOH solution to reach the equivalence point. What is the concentration of the unknown HCl solution in M?

SORT You are given the volume and concentration of NaOH solution required to titrate a given volume of HCl solution. You are asked to find the concentration of the HCl solution.

GIVEN: 12.54 mL of NaOH solution, 0.100 M NaOH solution, 10.00 mL of HCl solution

FIND: concentration of HCl solution

STRATEGIZE Since this problem involves an acid–base neutralization reaction between HCl and NaOH, start by writing the balanced equation, using the techniques covered earlier in this section.

$$HCl(aq) + NaOH(aq) \longrightarrow H_2O(l) + NaCl(aq)$$

The first part of the conceptual plan has the form volume A ⟶ moles A ⟶ moles B. The concentration of the NaOH solution is a conversion factor between moles and volume of NaOH. The balanced equation provides the relationship between number of moles of NaOH and number of moles of HCl.

CONCEPTUAL PLAN

mL NaOH ⟶ L NaOH ⟶

$$\frac{1\ \text{L}}{1000\ \text{mL}} \qquad \frac{0.100\ \text{mol NaOH}}{\text{L NaOH}}$$

mol NaOH ⟶ mol HCl

$$\frac{1\ \text{mol HCl}}{1\ \text{mol NaOH}}$$

In the second part of the conceptual plan, use the number of moles of HCl (from the first part) and the volume of HCl solution (given) to calculate the molarity of the HCl solution.

mol HCl, L HCl solution ⟶ Molarity

$$M = \frac{\text{mol}}{\text{L}}$$

RELATIONSHIPS USED

$1\ \text{L} = 1000\ \text{mL}$

$$\text{M (NaOH)} = \frac{0.100\ \text{mol NaOH}}{\text{L NaOH}}$$

1 mol HCl : 1 mol NaOH

$$\text{Molarity (M)} = \frac{\text{moles of solute (mol)}}{\text{volume of solution (L)}}$$

SOLVE In the first part of the solution, determine the number of moles of HCl in the unknown solution.

SOLUTION

$$12.54\ \cancel{\text{mL NaOH}} \times \frac{1\ \cancel{\text{L}}}{1000\ \cancel{\text{mL}}} \times \frac{0.100\ \cancel{\text{mol NaOH}}}{\cancel{\text{L}}\ \cancel{\text{NaOH}}} \times \frac{1\ \text{mol HCl}}{1\ \cancel{\text{mol NaOH}}} = 1.25 \times 10^{-3}\ \text{mol HCl}$$

In the second part of the solution, divide the number of moles of HCl by the volume of the HCl solution in L. 10.00 mL is equivalent to 0.01000 L.

$$\text{Molarity} = \frac{1.25 \times 10^{-3}\ \text{mol HCl}}{0.01000\ \text{L}} = 0.125\ \text{M HCl}$$

CHECK The units of the answer (M HCl) are correct. The magnitude of the answer (0.125 M) is reasonable because it is similar to the molarity of the NaOH solution, as expected from the reaction stoichiometry (1 mol HCl reacts with 1 mol NaOH) and the similar volumes of NaOH and HCl.

FOR PRACTICE 5.11 The titration of a 20.0-mL sample of an H_2SO_4 solution of unknown concentration requires 22.87 mL of a 0.158 M KOH solution to reach the equivalence point. What is the concentration of the unknown H_2SO_4 solution?

FOR MORE PRACTICE 5.11 What volume (in mL) of 0.200 M NaOH do we need to titrate 35.00 mL of 0.140 M HBr to the equivalence point?

5.8 Gas-Evolution Reactions

In a *gas-evolution reaction*, two aqueous solutions mix to form a gaseous product that bubbles out of solution. Some gas-evolution reactions form a gaseous product directly when the cation of one reactant combines with the anion of the other. For example, when sulfuric acid reacts with lithium sulfide, dihydrogen sulfide gas forms:

$$H_2SO_4(aq) + Li_2S(aq) \longrightarrow \underset{\text{gas}}{H_2S(g)} + Li_2SO_4(aq)$$

Other gas-evolution reactions often form an intermediate product that then decomposes (breaks down into simpler substances) to form a gas. For example, when aqueous hydrochloric acid is mixed with aqueous sodium bicarbonate, the following reaction occurs (Figure 5.19►):

Many gas-evolution reactions such as this one are also acid–base reactions. In Chapter 17 we will learn how ions such as CO_3^{2-} act as bases in aqueous solution.

$$HCl(aq) + NaHCO_3(aq) \longrightarrow \underset{\text{intermediate product}}{H_2CO_3(aq)} + NaCl(aq) \longrightarrow H_2O(l) + \underset{\text{gas}}{CO_2(g)} + NaCl(aq)$$

The intermediate product, H_2CO_3, is not stable and decomposes into H_2O and gaseous CO_2. Other important gas-evolution reactions form either H_2SO_3 or NH_4OH as intermediate products:

$$HCl(aq) + NaHSO_3(aq) \longrightarrow \underset{\text{intermediate product}}{H_2SO_3(aq)} + NaCl(aq) \longrightarrow H_2O(l) + \underset{\text{gas}}{SO_2(g)} + NaCl(aq)$$

$$NH_4Cl(aq) + NaOH(aq) \longrightarrow \underset{\text{intermediate product}}{NH_4OH(aq)} + NaCl(aq) \longrightarrow H_2O(l) + \underset{\text{gas}}{NH_3(g)} + NaCl(aq)$$

The intermediate product NH_4OH provides a convenient way to think about this reaction, but the extent to which it actually forms is debatable.

Table 5.3 lists the main types of compounds that form gases in aqueous reactions, as well as the gases formed.

TABLE 5.3 ■ Types of Compounds That Undergo Gas-Evolution Reactions

Reactant Type	Intermediate Product	Gas Evolved	Example
Sulfides	None	H_2S	$2\ HCl(aq) + K_2S(aq) \longrightarrow H_2S(g) + 2\ KCl(aq)$
Carbonates and bicarbonates	H_2CO_3	CO_2	$2\ HCl(aq) + K_2CO_3(aq) \longrightarrow H_2O(l) + CO_2(g) + 2\ KCl(aq)$
Sulfites and bisulfites	H_2SO_3	SO_2	$2\ HCl(aq) + K_2SO_3(aq) \longrightarrow H_2O(l) + SO_2(g) + 2\ KCl(aq)$
Ammonium	NH_4OH	NH_3	$NH_4Cl(aq) + KOH(aq) \longrightarrow H_2O(l) + NH_3(g) + KCl(aq)$

Gas-Evolution Reaction

$$NaHCO_3(aq) + HCl(aq) \longrightarrow H_2O(l) + NaCl(aq) + CO_2(g)$$

When aqueous sodium bicarbonate is mixed with aqueous hydrochloric acid, gaseous CO_2 bubbles are the result of the reaction.

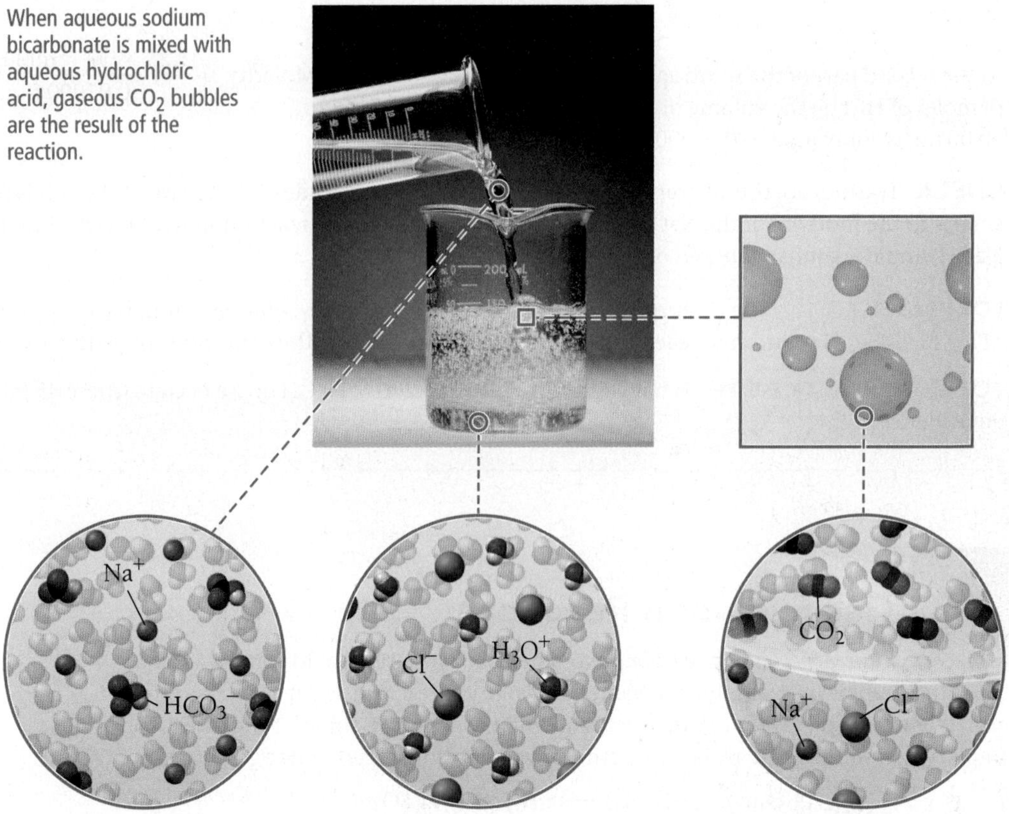

$$NaHCO_3(aq) \quad + \quad HCl(aq) \longrightarrow H_2O(l) + NaCl(aq) + CO_2(g)$$

▲ **FIGURE 5.19** Gas-Evolution Reaction

EXAMPLE 5.12 Writing Equations for Gas-Evolution Reactions

Write a molecular equation for the gas-evolution reaction that occurs when you mix aqueous nitric acid and aqueous sodium carbonate.

Begin by writing an unbalanced equation in which the cation of each reactant combines with the anion of the other.	$HNO_3(aq) + Na_2CO_3(aq) \longrightarrow H_2CO_3(aq) + NaNO_3(aq)$
You must then recognize that $H_2CO_3(aq)$ decomposes into $H_2O(l)$ and $CO_2(g)$ and write these products into the equation.	$HNO_3(aq) + Na_2CO_3(aq) \longrightarrow H_2O(l) + CO_2(g) + NaNO_3(aq)$
Finally, balance the equation.	$2\,HNO_3(aq) + Na_2CO_3(aq) \longrightarrow H_2O(l) + CO_2(g) + 2\,NaNO_3(aq)$

FOR PRACTICE 5.12 Write a molecular equation for the gas-evolution reaction that occurs when you mix aqueous hydrobromic acid and aqueous potassium sulfite.

FOR MORE PRACTICE 5.12 Write a net ionic equation for the reaction that occurs when you mix hydroiodic acid with calcium sulfide.

5.9 Oxidation–Reduction Reactions

Oxidation–reduction reactions or **redox reactions** are reactions in which electrons transfer from one reactant to the other. The rusting of iron, the bleaching of hair, and the production of electricity in batteries involve redox reactions. Many redox reactions involve the reaction of a substance with oxygen (Figure 5.20▼).

Oxidation–reduction reactions are covered in more detail in Chapter 20.

$$4\,Fe(s) + 3\,O_2(g) \longrightarrow 2\,Fe_2O_3(s) \quad \text{(rusting of iron)}$$

$$2\,C_8H_{18}(l) + 25\,O_2(g) \longrightarrow 16\,CO_2(g) + 18\,H_2O(g) \quad \text{(combustion of octane)}$$

$$2\,H_2(g) + O_2(g) \longrightarrow 2\,H_2O(g) \quad \text{(combustion of hydrogen)}$$

Oxidation–Reduction Reaction

$$2\,H_2(g) + O_2(g) \longrightarrow 2\,H_2O(g)$$

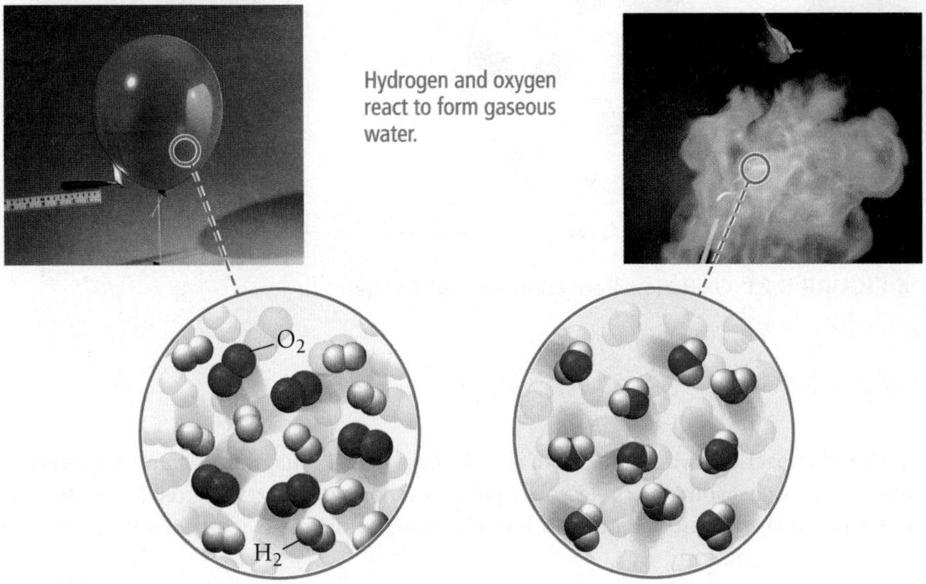

$$2\,H_2(g) + O_2(g) \longrightarrow 2\,H_2O(g)$$

▲ **FIGURE 5.20 Oxidation–Reduction Reaction**

However, redox reactions need not involve oxygen. Consider, for example, the reaction between sodium and chlorine to form sodium chloride (NaCl), depicted in Figure 5.21▶:

$$2\,Na(s) + Cl_2(g) \longrightarrow 2\,NaCl(s)$$

This reaction is similar to the reaction between sodium and oxygen, which forms sodium oxide:

$$4\,Na(s) + O_2(g) \longrightarrow 2\,Na_2O(s)$$

The reaction between sodium and oxygen forms other oxides as well.

In both cases, a metal (which has a tendency to lose electrons) reacts with a nonmetal (which has a tendency to gain electrons). And in both cases, metal atoms lose electrons to nonmetal atoms. A fundamental definition of **oxidation** is the loss of electrons, and a fundamental definition of **reduction** is the gain of electrons.

Helpful Mnemonic: O I L R I G **O**xidation **I**s **L**oss; **R**eduction **I**s **G**ain.

The transfer of electrons does not need to be a *complete* transfer (as occurs in the formation of an ionic compound) for the reaction to qualify as oxidation–reduction. For example, consider the reaction between hydrogen gas and chlorine gas:

$$H_2(g) + Cl_2(g) \longrightarrow 2\,HCl(g)$$

The ability of an element to attract electrons in a chemical bond is called electronegativity. We cover electronegativity in more detail in Section 10.6.

Even though hydrogen chloride is a molecular compound with a covalent bond, and even though the hydrogen has not completely transferred its electron to chlorine

Oxidation–Reduction Reaction without Oxygen

$2\,Na(s) + Cl_2(g) \longrightarrow 2\,NaCl(s)$

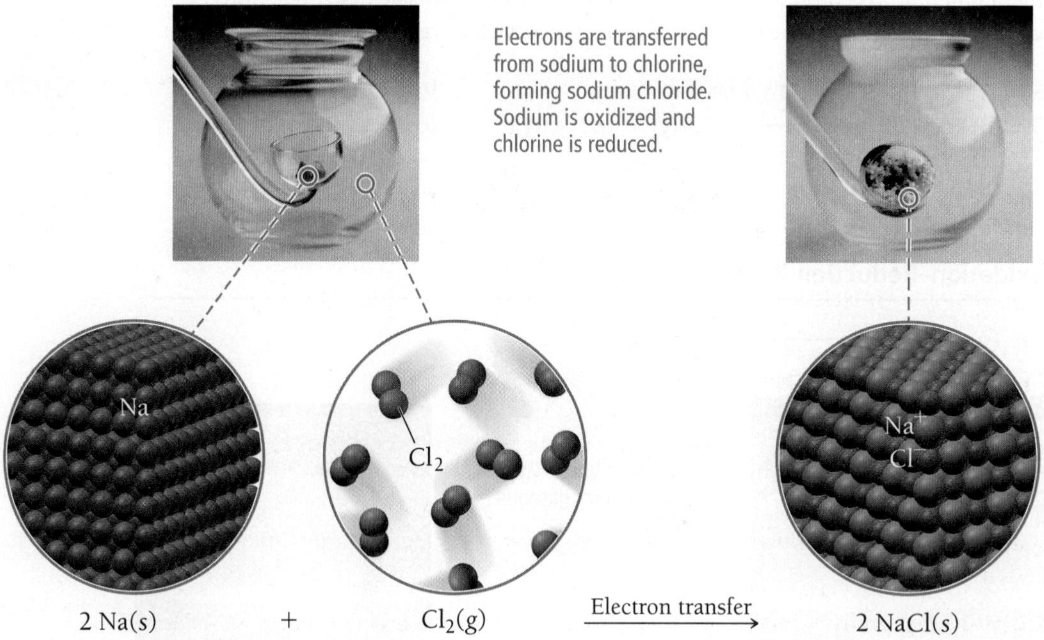

▲ **FIGURE 5.21 Oxidation–Reduction without Oxygen**

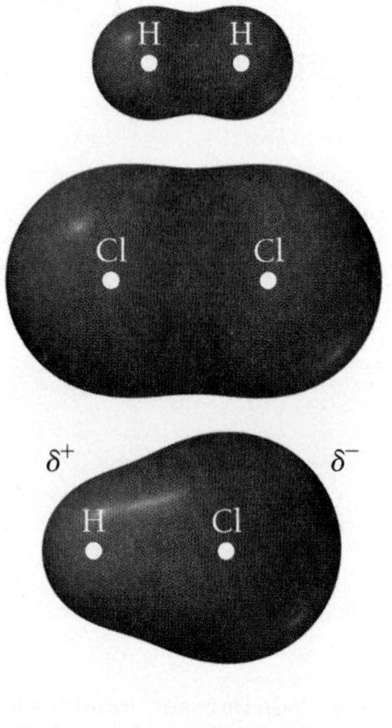

▲ **FIGURE 5.22 Redox with Partial Electron Transfer** When hydrogen bonds to chlorine, the electrons are unevenly shared, resulting in an increase of electron density (reduction) for chlorine and a decrease in electron density (oxidation) for hydrogen.

during the reaction, we can see from the electron density diagrams (Figure 5.22◀) that hydrogen has lost some of its electron density—it has *partially* transferred its electron to chlorine. In the reaction, hydrogen is oxidized and chlorine is reduced and, therefore, this is a redox reaction.

Oxidation States

Identifying whether or not a reaction between a metal and a nonmetal is a redox reaction is fairly straightforward because of ion formation. But how do we identify redox reactions that occur between nonmetals? Chemists have devised a scheme to track electrons before and after a chemical reaction. In this scheme—which is like bookkeeping for electrons—each shared electron is assigned to the atom that attracts the electrons most strongly. Then a number, called the **oxidation state** or **oxidation number**, is given to each atom based on the electron assignments. In other words, the oxidation number of an atom in a compound is the "charge" it would have if all shared electrons were assigned to the atom with the greatest attraction for those electrons.

For example, consider HCl. Since chlorine attracts electrons more strongly than hydrogen, we assign the two shared electrons in the bond to chlorine; then H (which has lost an electron in our assignment) has an oxidation state of +1, and Cl (which has gained one electron in our assignment) has an oxidation state of −1. Notice that in contrast to ionic charges, which are usually written with the sign of the charge *after* the magnitude (1+ and 1−, for example), oxidation states are written with the sign of the charge *before* the magnitude (+1 and −1, for example). We use the following rules to assign oxidation states to atoms in elements, ions, and compounds.

Rules for Assigning Oxidation States | **Examples**

(These rules are hierarchical. If any two rules conflict, follow the rule that is higher on the list.)

1. The oxidation state of an atom in a free element is 0.

Cu (0 ox state) Cl_2 (0 ox state)

2. The oxidation state of a monoatomic ion is equal to its charge.

Ca^{2+} (+2 ox state) Cl^- (−1 ox state)

3. The sum of the oxidation states of all atoms in:

- A neutral molecule or formula unit is 0.

  H_2O 2(H ox state) + 1(O ox state) = 0

- An ion is equal to the charge of the ion.

  NO_3^- 1(N ox state) + 3(O ox state) = −1

4. In their compounds, metals have positive oxidation states.

- Group 1A metals *always* have an oxidation state of +1.

  NaCl +1 ox state

- Group 2A metals *always* have an oxidation state of +2.

  CaF_2 +2 ox state

5. In their compounds, nonmetals are assigned oxidation states according to the table shown here. Entries at the top of the table take precedence over entries at the bottom of the table.

When assigning oxidation states, keep these points in mind:

- The oxidation state of any given element generally depends on what other elements are present in the compound. (The exceptions are the group 1A and 2A metals, which are *always* +1 and +2, respectively.)
- Rule 3 must always be followed. Therefore, when following the hierarchy shown in rule 5, give priority to the element(s) highest on the list and then assign the oxidation state of the element lowest on the list using rule 3.
- When assigning oxidation states to elements that are not covered by rules 4 and 5 (such as carbon), use rule 3 to deduce their oxidation state once all other oxidation states have been assigned.

Do not confuse oxidation state with ionic charge. Unlike ionic charge—which is a real property of an ion—the oxidation state of an atom is merely a theoretical (but useful) construct.

Nonmetal	Oxidation State	Example
Fluorine	−1	MgF_2 −1 ox state
Hydrogen	+1	H_2O +1 ox state
Oxygen	−2	CO_2 −2 ox state
Group 7A	−1	CCl_4 −1 ox state
Group 6A	−2	H_2S −2 ox state
Group 5A	−3	NH_3 −3 ox state

WATCH **NOW!**

INTERACTIVE WORKED EXAMPLE 5.13

EXAMPLE 5.13 Assigning Oxidation States

Assign an oxidation state to each atom in each element, ion, or compound.

(a) Cl_2 **(b)** Na^+ **(c)** KF **(d)** CO_2 **(e)** SO_4^{2-} **(f)** K_2O_2

SOLUTION

Since Cl_2 is a free element, the oxidation state of both Cl atoms is 0 (rule 1).	**(a)** Cl_2 ClCl 0 0
Since Na^+ is a monoatomic ion, the oxidation state of the Na^+ ion is +1 (rule 2).	**(b)** Na^+ Na^+ +1
The oxidation state of K is +1 (rule 4). The oxidation state of F is −1 (rule 5). Since this is a neutral compound, the sum of the oxidation states is 0.	**(c)** KF KF +1 −1 sum: +1 −1 = 0

The oxidation state of oxygen is −2 (rule 5). The oxidation state of carbon must be deduced using rule 3, which says that the sum of the oxidation states of all the atoms must be 0.	**(d)** CO_2 (C ox state) + 2(O ox state) = 0 (C ox state) + 2(−2) = 0 (C ox state) = +4 CO_2 +4−2 sum: +4+2(−2) = 0
The oxidation state of oxygen is −2 (rule 5). You would ordinarily expect the oxidation state of S to be −2 (rule 5). However, if that were the case, the sum of the oxidation states would not equal the charge of the ion. Since O is higher on the list than S, it takes priority, and you calculate the oxidation state of sulfur by setting the *sum* of all of the oxidation states equal to −2 (the charge of the ion).	**(e)** SO_4^{2-} (S ox state) + 4(O ox state) = −2 (S ox state) + 4(−2) = −2 S ox state = +6 SO_4^{2-} +6−2 sum: +6 + 4(−2) = −2
The oxidation state of potassium is +1 (rule 4). You would ordinarily expect the oxidation state of O to be −2 (rule 5), but rule 4 takes priority, and you deduce the oxidation state of O by setting the sum of all of the oxidation states equal to 0.	**(f)** K_2O_2 2(K ox state) + 2(O ox state) = 0 2(+1) + 2(O ox state) = 0 O ox state = −1 K_2O_2 +1 −1 sum: 2(+1)+2(−1) = 0

FOR PRACTICE 5.13 Assign an oxidation state to each atom in each element, ion, or compound.

(a) Cr **(b)** Cr^{3+} **(c)** CCl_4 **(d)** $SrBr_2$ **(e)** SO_3 **(f)** NO_3^-

In most cases, oxidation states are positive or negative integers; however, on occasion an atom within a compound can have a fractional oxidation state. Consider KO_2. The oxidation states are assigned as follows:

$$\underset{+1\ -\frac{1}{2}}{KO_2}$$

$$\text{sum: } +1+2\left(-\frac{1}{2}\right) = 0$$

In KO_2, oxygen has a $-\frac{1}{2}$ oxidation state. Although this seems unusual, it is accepted because oxidation states are merely an imposed electron bookkeeping scheme, not an actual physical quantity.

ANSWER **NOW!**

5.10 Cc Conceptual Connection

OXIDATION NUMBERS IN POLYATOMIC IONS Which statement best describes the *difference* between the *charge* of a polyatomic ion and the *oxidation states* of its constituent atoms? (For example, the charge of NO_3^- is 1−, and the oxidation states of its atoms are +5 for the nitrogen atom and −2 for each oxygen atom.)

(a) The charge of a polyatomic ion is a property of the entire ion, while the oxidation states are assigned to each individual atom.
(b) The oxidation state of the ion is the same as its charge.
(c) The charge of a polyatomic ion is not a real physical property, while the oxidation states of atoms are actual physical properties.

Identifying Redox Reactions

We can use oxidation states to identify redox reactions, even between nonmetals. For example, is the following reaction between carbon and sulfur a redox reaction?

$$C + 2\,S \longrightarrow CS_2$$

If so, what element is oxidized? What element is reduced? We can use the oxidation state rules to assign oxidation states to all elements on both sides of the equation.

$$C + 2\,S \longrightarrow CS_2$$

Oxidation states: C: 0; S: 0; CS_2: +4 −2

(S: 0 → −2, Reduction; C: 0 → +4, Oxidation)

Carbon changes from an oxidation state of 0 to an oxidation state of +4. In terms of our electron bookkeeping scheme (the assigned oxidation state), carbon *loses electrons* and is *oxidized*. Sulfur changes from an oxidation state of 0 to an oxidation state of −2. In terms of our electron bookkeeping scheme, sulfur *gains electrons* and is *reduced*. In terms of oxidation states, oxidation and reduction are defined as follows:

- Oxidation: An increase in oxidation state
- Reduction: A decrease in oxidation state

Remember that a reduction is a *reduction* in oxidation state.

EXAMPLE 5.14 Using Oxidation States to Identify Oxidation and Reduction

Use oxidation states to identify the element that is oxidized and the element that is reduced in the following redox reaction:

$$Mg(s) + 2\,H_2O(l) \longrightarrow Mg(OH)_2(aq) + H_2(g)$$

SOLUTION

Begin by assigning oxidation states to each atom in the reaction.

$$Mg(s) + 2\,H_2O(l) \longrightarrow Mg(OH)_2(aq) + H_2(g)$$

Oxidation states: Mg: 0; H_2O: +1 −2; $Mg(OH)_2$: +2 −2 +1; H_2: 0

(H: +1 → 0, Reduction; Mg: 0 → +2, Oxidation)

Since Mg increased in oxidation state, it was oxidized. Since H decreased in oxidation state, it was reduced.

FOR PRACTICE 5.14 Use oxidation states to identify the element that is oxidized and the element that is reduced in the following redox reaction:

$$Sn(s) + 4\,HNO_3(aq) \longrightarrow SnO_2(s) + 4\,NO_2(g) + 2\,H_2O(g)$$

FOR MORE PRACTICE 5.14 Determine whether or not each reaction is a redox reaction. If the reaction is a redox reaction, identify which element is oxidized and which is reduced.

(a) $Hg_2(NO_3)_2(aq) + 2\,KBr(aq) \longrightarrow Hg_2Br_2(s) + 2\,KNO_3(aq)$

(b) $4\,Al(s) + 3\,O_2(g) \longrightarrow 2\,Al_2O_3(s)$

(c) $CaO(s) + CO_2(g) \longrightarrow CaCO_3(s)$

Notice that *oxidation and reduction must occur together*. If one substance loses electrons (oxidation), then another substance must gain electrons (reduction). A substance that causes the oxidation of another substance is an **oxidizing agent**. Oxygen, for example, is an excellent oxidizing agent. In a redox reaction, *the oxidizing agent is always reduced*. A substance that causes the reduction of another substance is a **reducing agent**. Hydrogen, for example, and group 1A and group 2A metals (because of their tendency to lose electrons) are excellent reducing agents. In a redox reaction, *the reducing agent is always oxidized*.

In Section 20.2, you will learn more about redox reactions, including how to balance them. For now, be able to identify redox reactions, as well as oxidizing and reducing agents, according to the following guidelines.

Redox reactions:

- Any reaction in which there is a change in the oxidation states of atoms in going from reactants to products.

In a redox reaction:

- The oxidizing agent oxidizes another substance (and is itself reduced).
- The reducing agent reduces another substance (and is itself oxidized).

EXAMPLE 5.15 Identifying Redox Reactions, Oxidizing Agents, and Reducing Agents

Determine whether each reaction is an oxidation–reduction reaction. For each oxidation–reduction reaction, identify the oxidizing agent and the reducing agent.

(a) $2\,Mg(s) + O_2(g) \longrightarrow 2\,MgO(s)$

(b) $2\,HBr(aq) + Ca(OH)_2(aq) \longrightarrow 2\,H_2O(l) + CaBr_2(aq)$

(c) $Zn(s) + Fe^{2+}(aq) \longrightarrow Zn^{2+}(aq) + Fe(s)$

SOLUTION

This is a redox reaction because magnesium increases in oxidation number (oxidation) and oxygen decreases in oxidation number (reduction).

(a) $2\,Mg(s) + O_2(g) \longrightarrow 2\,MgO(s)$

Oxidation numbers: Mg 0, O_2 0; MgO +2 −2

Reduction (O: 0 → −2); Oxidation (Mg: 0 → +2)

Oxidizing agent: O_2
Reducing agent: Mg

This is not a redox reaction because none of the atoms undergo a change in oxidation number.

(b) $2\,HBr(aq) + Ca(OH)_2(aq) \rightarrow 2\,H_2O(l) + CaBr_2(aq)$

Oxidation numbers: HBr +1 −1; $Ca(OH)_2$ +2 −2 +1; H_2O +1 −2; $CaBr_2$ +2 −1

This is a redox reaction because zinc increases in oxidation number (oxidation) and iron decreases in oxidation number (reduction).

(c) $Zn(s) + Fe^{2+}(aq) \longrightarrow Zn^{2+}(aq) + Fe(s)$

Oxidation numbers: Zn 0, Fe^{2+} +2; Zn^{2+} +2, Fe 0

Reduction (Fe: +2 → 0); Oxidation (Zn: 0 → +2)

Oxidizing agent: Fe^{2+}
Reducing agent: Zn

FOR PRACTICE 5.15 Determine whether or not each reaction is a redox reaction. For each redox reaction, identify the oxidizing agent and the reducing agent.

(a) $2\,Li(s) + Cl_2(g) \longrightarrow 2\,LiCl(s)$

(b) $2\,Al(s) + 3\,Sn^{2+}(aq) \longrightarrow 2\,Al^{3+}(aq) + 3\,Sn(s)$

(c) $Pb(NO_3)_2(aq) + 2\,LiCl(aq) \longrightarrow PbCl_2(s) + 2\,LiNO_3(aq)$

(d) $C(s) + O_2(g) \longrightarrow CO_2(g)$

ANSWER NOW!

5.11 Cc Conceptual Connection

OXIDATION AND REDUCTION Which statement is true?

(a) A redox reaction involves *either* the transfer of an electron *or* a change in the oxidation state of an element.

(b) If any of the reactants or products in a reaction contain oxygen, the reaction is a redox reaction.

(c) In a reaction, oxidation can occur independently of reduction.

(d) In a redox reaction, any increase in the oxidation state of a reactant must be accompanied by a decrease in the oxidation state of another reactant.

The Activity Series: Predicting Whether a Redox Reaction Is Spontaneous

Is there a way to predict whether a particular redox reaction will spontaneously occur? Suppose we knew that substance A has a greater tendency to lose electrons than substance B. (In other words, A is more easily oxidized than B.) Knowing this, we could predict that mixing A with cations of B would result in a redox reaction in which A loses its electrons (A is oxidized) to the cations of B (B is reduced). For example, Mg has a greater tendency to lose electrons than Cu. Consequently, if we put solid Mg into a solution containing Cu^{2+} ions, Mg is oxidized and Cu^{2+} is reduced.

$$Mg(s) + Cu^{2+}(aq) \longrightarrow Mg^{2+}(aq) + Cu(s)$$

CHEMISTRY IN YOUR DAY | Bleached Blonde

Have you ever bleached your hair? Most home kits for hair bleaching contain hydrogen peroxide (H_2O_2), an excellent oxidizing agent. When applied to hair, hydrogen peroxide oxidizes melanin, the dark pigment that gives hair its color. Once melanin is oxidized, it no longer imparts a dark color, leaving the hair with the familiar bleached look. Hydrogen peroxide also oxidizes other components of hair. For example, protein molecules in hair contain —SH groups called thiols. Hydrogen peroxide oxidizes these thiol groups to sulfonic acid groups, $—SO_3H$. The oxidation of thiol groups to sulfonic acid groups causes changes in the proteins that compose hair, making the hair more brittle and more likely to tangle. Consequently, people with heavily bleached hair generally use conditioners, which contain compounds that form thin, lubricating coatings on individual hair shafts. These coatings prevent tangling and make hair softer and more manageable.

▲ The bleaching of hair involves a redox reaction in which melanin—the main pigment in hair—is oxidized.

QUESTION *The following is a reaction of hydrogen peroxide with an alkene:*

$$H_2O_2 + C_2H_4 \longrightarrow C_2H_4O + H_2O$$

Can you see why this reaction is a redox reaction? Can you identify the oxidizing and reducing agents?

We see this as the fading of blue (the color of the Cu^{2+} ions in solution), the dissolving of the solid magnesium, and the appearance of solid copper on the remaining magnesium surface (Figure 5.23▼). This reaction is spontaneous—it occurs on its own when Mg(*s*) and $Cu^{2+}(aq)$ come into contact. If, however, we put Cu(*s*) in a solution containing $Mg^{2+}(aq)$ ions, no reaction occurs (Figure 5.24▼).

$$Cu(s) + Mg^{2+}(aq) \not\longrightarrow \text{NO REACTION}$$

No reaction occurs because, as noted previously, Mg atoms have a greater tendency to lose electrons than do Cu atoms; Cu atoms will therefore not lose electrons to Mg^{2+} ions.

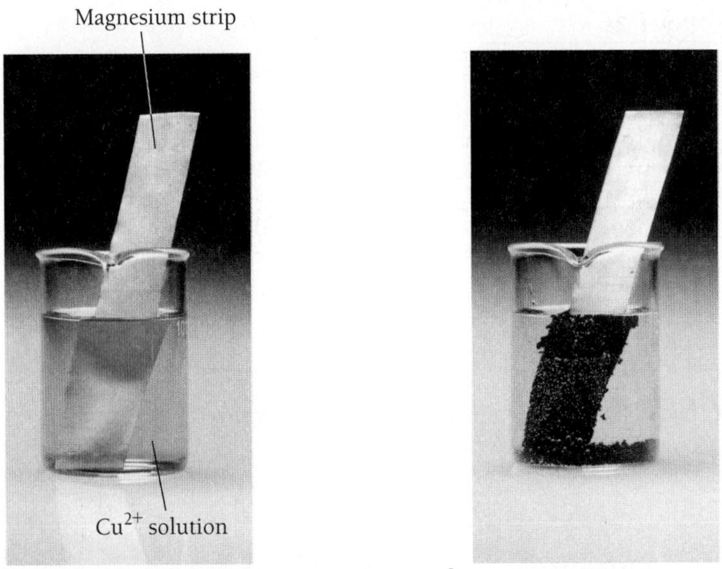

$$Mg(s) + Cu^{2+}(aq) \longrightarrow Mg^{2+}(aq) + Cu(s)$$

▲ FIGURE 5.23 Cu^{2+} Oxidizes Magnesium When we put a magnesium strip into a Cu^{2+} solution, the magnesium is oxidized to Mg^{2+} and the copper ion is reduced to Cu(s). Notice the fading of the blue color (due to Cu^{2+} ions) in solution and the appearance of solid copper on the magnesium strip.

▲ FIGURE 5.24 Mg^{2+} Does Not Oxidize Copper When we place solid copper in a solution containing Mg^{2+} ions, no reaction occurs.

Table 5.4 presents the **activity series of metals**. This table lists metals in order of decreasing tendency to lose electrons. The metals at the top of the list have the greatest tendency to lose electrons—they are most easily oxidized and therefore the most reactive. The metals at the bottom of the list have the lowest tendency to lose electrons—they are the most difficult to oxidize and therefore the least reactive. It is not a coincidence that the metals used for jewelry, such as silver and gold, are near the bottom of the list. They are among the least reactive metals and therefore do not form compounds easily. Instead, they tend to remain as solid silver and solid gold rather than being oxidized to silver and gold cations by elements in the environment (such as the oxygen in the air).

Each reaction in the activity series is an oxidation *half-reaction*. The half-reactions at the top are most likely to occur in the *forward* direction, and the half-reactions at the bottom are most likely to occur in the *reverse* direction. Consequently, if we pair a half-reaction from the top of the list with the reverse of a half-reaction from the bottom of the list, we get a spontaneous reaction.

More specifically,

Any half-reaction on the list is spontaneous when paired with the reverse of any half-reaction below it on the list.

▲ Gold is very low on the activity series. Because it is so difficult to oxidize, it resists the tarnishing and corrosion that more active metals undergo.

TABLE 5.4 ■ Activity Series of Metals

Half-reaction	
$Li(s) \longrightarrow Li^+(aq) + e^-$	Most reactive
$K(s) \longrightarrow K^+(aq) + e^-$	Most easily oxidized
$Ca(s) \longrightarrow Ca^{2+}(aq) + 2e^-$	Strongest tendency to lose electrons
$Na(s) \longrightarrow Na^+(aq) + e^-$	
$Mg(s) \longrightarrow Mg^{2+}(aq) + 2e^-$	↓
$Al(s) \longrightarrow Al^{3+}(aq) + 3e^-$	
$Mn(s) \longrightarrow Mn^{2+}(aq) + 2e^-$	
$Zn(s) \longrightarrow Zn^{2+}(aq) + 2e^-$	
$Cr(s) \longrightarrow Cr^{3+}(aq) + 3e^-$	
$Fe(s) \longrightarrow Fe^{2+}(aq) + 2e^-$	
$Ni(s) \longrightarrow Ni^{2+}(aq) + 2e^-$	
$Sn(s) \longrightarrow Sn^{2+}(aq) + 2e^-$	
$Pb(s) \longrightarrow Pb^{2+}(aq) + 2e^-$	
$\mathbf{H_2(g) \longrightarrow 2H^+(aq) + 2e^-}$	Least reactive
$Cu(s) \longrightarrow Cu^{2+}(aq) + 2e^-$	Most difficult to oxidize
$Ag(s) \longrightarrow Ag^+(aq) + e^-$	
$Au(s) \longrightarrow Au^{3+}(aq) + 3e^-$	Least tendency to lose electrons

ANSWER **NOW!**

5.12 Cc Conceptual Connection

ACTIVITY SERIES Which metal is most easily oxidized?

(a) Na
(b) Cr
(c) Au

EXAMPLE 5.16 Predicting Spontaneous Redox Reactions

Determine whether each redox reaction is spontaneous.

(a) $Fe(s) + Mg^{2+}(aq) \longrightarrow Fe^{2+}(aq) + Mg(s)$

(b) $Fe(s) + Pb^{2+}(aq) \longrightarrow Fe^{2+}(aq) + Pb(s)$

SOLUTION

(a) $Fe(s) + Mg^{2+}(aq) \longrightarrow Fe^{2+}(aq) + Mg(s)$

This reaction involves the oxidation of Fe:

$$Fe(s) \longrightarrow Fe^{2+}(aq) + 2e^-$$

with the reverse of a half-reaction *above it* in the activity series:

$$Mg^{2+}(aq) + 2e^- \longrightarrow Mg(s)$$

Therefore, the reaction *is not* spontaneous.

(b) $Fe(s) + Pb^{2+}(aq) \longrightarrow Fe^{2+}(aq) + Pb(s)$

This reaction involves the oxidation of Fe:

$$Fe(s) \longrightarrow Fe^{2+}(aq) + 2e^-$$

with the reverse of a half-reaction *below it* in the activity series:

$$Pb^{2+}(aq) + 2e^- \longrightarrow Pb(s)$$

Therefore, the reaction *is* spontaneous.

FOR PRACTICE 5.16 Predicting Spontaneous Redox Reactions

Determine whether each redox reaction is spontaneous.

(a) $Zn(s) + Ni^{2+}(aq) \longrightarrow Zn^{2+}(aq) + Ni(s)$

(b) $Zn(s) + Ca^{2+}(aq) \longrightarrow Zn^{2+}(aq) + Ca(s)$

QUIZ YOURSELF **NOW!**

Self-Assessment Quiz

Q1. What is the molarity of a solution containing 55.8 g of $MgCl_2$ dissolved in 1.00 L of solution?
MISSED THIS? *Read Section 5.2; Watch KCV 5.2, IWE 5.1*

a) 55.8 M b) 1.71 M c) 0.586 M d) 0.558 M

Q2. What mass (in grams) of $Mg(NO_3)_2$ is present in 145 mL of a 0.150 M solution of $Mg(NO_3)_2$?
MISSED THIS? *Read Section 5.2; Watch KCV 5.2, IWE 5.2*

a) 3.23 g b) 0.022 g c) 1.88 g d) 143 g

Q3. What volume of a 1.50 M HCl solution should you use to prepare 2.00 L of a 0.100 M HCl solution?
MISSED THIS? *Read Section 5.2; Watch KCV 5.2, IWE 5.3*

a) 0.300 L b) 0.133 L c) 30.0 L d) 2.00 L

Q4. Potassium iodide reacts with lead(II) nitrate in the following precipitation reaction:

$$2\,KI(aq) + Pb(NO_3)_2(aq) \longrightarrow 2\,KNO_3(aq) + PbI_2(s)$$

What minimum volume of 0.200 M potassium iodide solution is required to completely precipitate all of the lead in 155.0 mL of a 0.112 M lead(II) nitrate solution?
MISSED THIS? *Read Section 5.3; Watch IWE 5.4*

a) 348 mL b) 86.8 mL c) 174 mL d) 43.4 mL

Q5. Which solution forms a precipitate when mixed with a solution of aqueous Na_2CO_3?
MISSED THIS? *Read Section 5.5; Watch KCV 5.5, IWE 5.6*

a) $KNO_3(aq)$ b) $NaBr(aq)$
c) $NH_4Cl(aq)$ d) $CuCl_2(aq)$

Q6. What is the net ionic equation for the reaction that occurs when aqueous solutions of KOH and $SrCl_2$ are mixed?
MISSED THIS? *Read Section 5.6*

a) $K^+(aq) + Cl^-(aq) \longrightarrow KCl(s)$
b) $Sr^{2+}(aq) + 2\,OH^-(aq) \longrightarrow Sr(OH)_2(s)$
c) $H^+(aq) + OH^-(aq) \longrightarrow H_2O(l)$
d) None of the above because no reaction occurs.

Q7. What is the net ionic equation for the reaction that occurs when aqueous solutions of KOH and HNO_3 are mixed?
MISSED THIS? *Read Section 5.7; Watch IWE 5.9*

a) $K^+(aq) + NO_3^-(aq) \longrightarrow KNO_3(s)$
b) $NO_3^-(aq) + OH^-(aq) \longrightarrow NO_3OH(s)$
c) $H^+(aq) + OH^-(aq) \longrightarrow H_2O(l)$
d) None of the above because no reaction occurs.

Q8. The titration of 15.00 mL of HBr solution of unknown concentration requires 18.44 mL of a 0.100 M KOH solution to reach the equivalence point. What is the concentration of the unknown HBr solution in M?
MISSED THIS? *Read Section 5.7; Watch IWE 5.11*

a) 0.001844 M b) 0.813 M c) 44 M d) 0.123 M

—Continued on the next page

Continued—

Q9. What is the net ionic equation for the reaction that occurs when aqueous solutions of $KHCO_3$ and HBr are mixed?
MISSED THIS? *Read Sections 5.6, 5.8*

a) $K^+(aq) + C_2H_3O_2^-(aq) \longrightarrow KC_2H_3O_2(s)$
b) $H^+(aq) + HCO_3^-(aq) \longrightarrow CO_2(g) + H_2O(l)$
c) $H^+(aq) + OH^-(aq) \longrightarrow H_2O(l)$
d) None of the above because no reaction occurs.

Q10. What is the oxidation state of carbon in CO_3^{2-}?
MISSED THIS? *Read Section 5.9; Watch KCV 5.13*

a) +4 b) +3 c) −3 d) −2

Q11. Sodium reacts with water according to the reaction:

$$2\,Na(s) + 2\,H_2O(l) \longrightarrow 2\,NaOH(aq) + H_2(g)$$

Identify the oxidizing agent.
MISSED THIS? *Read Section 5.9; Watch KCV 5.13*

a) $Na(s)$ b) $H_2O(l)$c) $NaOH(aq)$ d) $H_2(aq)$

Q12. Which of these ions will spontaneously react with Ni(*s*) in solution? **MISSED THIS?** *Read Section 5.9*

a) $Cu^{2+}(aq)$ b) $Zn^{2+}(aq)$
c) $Mg^{2+}(aq)$ d) $K^+(aq)$

Answers: 1. (c) **2.** (a) **3.** (b) **4.** (c) **5.** (d) **6.** (b) **7.** (c) **8.** (d) **9.** (b) **10.** (a) **11.** (b) **12.** (a)

CHAPTER 5 IN REVIEW

TERMS

Section 5.2
solution (168)
solvent (168)
solute (168)
aqueous solution (168)
dilute solution (168)
concentrated solution (168)
molarity (M) (168)
stock solution (171)

Section 5.4
electrolyte (175)
strong electrolyte (176)
nonelectrolyte (176)
strong acid (176)
weak acid (177)
weak electrolyte (177)
soluble (178)
insoluble (178)

Section 5.5
precipitation reaction (179)
precipitate (179)

Section 5.6
molecular equation (183)
complete ionic equation (183)
spectator ion (184)
net ionic equation (184)

Section 5.7
acid–base reaction (neutralization reaction) (185)
gas-evolution reaction (185)
Arrhenius definitions (186)
hydronium ion (186)
polyprotic acid (186)
diprotic acid (186)
salt (186)
titration (189)
equivalence point (189)
indicator (189)

Section 5.9
oxidation–reduction (redox) reaction (193)
oxidation (193)
reduction (193)
oxidation state (oxidation number) (194)
oxidizing agent (197)
reducing agent (197)
activity series of metals (200)

CONCEPTS

Solution Concentration and Stoichiometry (5.2, 5.3)

- An aqueous solution is a homogeneous mixture of water (the solvent) with another substance (the solute).
- We express the concentration of a solution in molarity, the number of moles of solute per liter of solution.
- We can use the molarities and volumes of reactant solutions to predict the amount of product that forms in an aqueous reaction.

Aqueous Solutions and Precipitation Reactions (5.4, 5.5)

- Solutes that completely dissociate (or completely ionize in the case of the strong acids) to ions in solution are strong electrolytes, and their solutions are good conductors of electricity.
- Solutes that only partially dissociate (or partially ionize) are weak electrolytes.
- Solutes that do not dissociate (or ionize) are nonelectrolytes.
- A substance that dissolves in water to form a solution is soluble.
- In a precipitation reaction, we mix two aqueous solutions and a solid (precipitate) forms.
- The solubility rules are an empirical set of guidelines that help predict the solubilities of ionic compounds; these rules are especially useful when determining whether or not a precipitate will form.

Equations for Aqueous Reactions (5.6)

- We can represent an aqueous reaction with a molecular equation, which shows the complete neutral formula for each compound in the reaction.
- We can also represent an aqueous reaction with a complete ionic equation, which shows the dissociated nature of strong electrolytes.
- A third representation of an aqueous reaction is the net ionic equation, in which the spectator ions—those that do not change in the course of the reaction—are left out of the equation.

Acid–Base and Gas-Evolution Reactions (5.7, 5.8)

- In an acid–base reaction, an acid, a substance that produces H^+ in solution, reacts with a base, a substance that produces OH^- in solution, and the two neutralize each other, producing water (or in some cases a weak electrolyte).

- An acid–base titration is a laboratory procedure in which a reaction is carried to its equivalence point—the point at which the reactants are in exact stoichiometric proportions; titrations are useful in determining the concentrations of unknown solutions.
- In gas-evolution reactions, two aqueous solutions combine, and a gas is produced.

Oxidation–Reduction Reactions (5.9)

- In oxidation–reduction reactions, one substance transfers electrons to another substance.
- In oxidation–reduction reactions, the substance that loses electrons is oxidized, and the substance that gains them is reduced.
- An oxidation state is a fictitious charge given to each atom in an oxidation–reduction reaction by assigning all shared electrons to the atom with the greater attraction for those electrons. An oxidation state is an imposed electronic bookkeeping scheme, not an actual physical state.
- The oxidation state of an atom increases upon oxidation and decreases upon reduction.
- The activity series of metals can be used to predict spontaneous redox reaction. Any half-reaction in the series is spontaneous when paired with any reverse half-reaction below it.

EQUATIONS AND RELATIONSHIPS

Molarity (M): Solution Concentration (5.2)

$$M = \frac{\text{amount of solute (in mol)}}{\text{volume of solution (in L)}}$$

Solution Dilution (5.2)

$$M_1V_1 = M_2V_2$$

Solution Stoichiometry (5.3)

$$\text{volume A} \longrightarrow \text{amount A (in moles)} \longrightarrow \text{amount B (in moles)} \longrightarrow \text{volume B}$$

LEARNING OUTCOMES

Chapter Objectives	Assessment
Calculate molarity and apply it to conversion and dilution problems (5.2)	Examples 5.1, 5.2, 5.3 **For Practice** 5.1, 5.2, 5.3 **For More Practice** 5.1, 5.2, 5.3 **Exercises** 21–32
Calculate the amounts of reactants and products involved in aqueous reactions (5.3)	Example 5.4 **For Practice** 5.4 **For More Practice** 5.4 **Exercises** 33–38
Classify compounds as soluble or insoluble, electrolyte or nonelectrolyte (5.4)	Example 5.5 **For Practice** 5.5 **Exercises** 39–42
Write chemical equations for precipitation reactions between two or more aqueous solutions (5.5)	Examples 5.6, 5.7 **For Practice** 5.6, 5.7 **Exercises** 43–46
Express molecular equations as complete ionic and net ionic equations (5.6)	Example 5.8 **For Practice** 5.8 **Exercises** 47–50
Write molecular, complete ionic, and net ionic equations for neutralization reactions (5.7)	Examples 5.9, 5.10 **For Practice** 5.9, 5.10 **Exercises** 51–56
Perform calculations involving titration reactions (5.7)	Example 5.11 **For Practice** 5.11 **For More Practice** 5.11 **Exercises** 57–58
Write equations for gas-evolution reactions (5.8)	Example 5.12 **For Practice** 5.12 **For More Practice** 5.12 **Exercises** 59–60
Determine the oxidation state of elements in compounds (5.9)	Example 5.13 **For Practice** 5.13 **Exercises** 61–64
Determine if a reaction is a redox reaction and if so, identify the oxidizing and reducing agents (5.9)	Examples 5.14, 5.15 **For Practice** 5.14, 5.15 **For More Practice** 5.14 **Exercises** 65–68
Predict the spontaneity of redox reactions (5.9)	Example 5.16 **For Practice** 5.16 **Exercises** 69–72

EXERCISES

Mastering Chemistry provides end-of-chapter exercises, feedback-enriched tutorial problems, animations, and interactive activities to encourage problem-solving practice and deeper understanding of key concepts and topics.

REVIEW QUESTIONS

1. What is an aqueous solution? What is the difference between the solute and the solvent?
2. What is molarity? How is it useful?
3. Explain how a strong electrolyte, a weak electrolyte, and a nonelectrolyte differ.
4. Explain the difference between a strong acid and a weak acid.
5. What does it mean for a compound to be soluble? Insoluble?
6. What are the solubility rules? How are they useful?
7. What are the cations and anions whose compounds are usually soluble? What are the exceptions? What are the anions whose compounds are mostly insoluble? What are the exceptions?
8. What is a precipitation reaction? Give an example.
9. How can you predict whether a precipitation reaction will occur upon mixing two aqueous solutions?
10. Explain how a molecular equation, a complete ionic equation, and a net ionic equation differ.
11. What is the Arrhenius definition of an acid? A base?
12. What is an acid–base reaction? Give an example.
13. Explain the principles behind an acid–base titration. What is an indicator?
14. What is a gas-evolution reaction? Give an example.
15. What reactant types give rise to gas-evolution reactions?
16. What is an oxidation–reduction reaction? Give an example.
17. What are oxidation states?
18. How can oxidation states be used to identify redox reactions?
19. What happens to a substance when it becomes oxidized? Reduced?
20. In a redox reaction, which reactant is the oxidizing agent? The reducing agent?

PROBLEMS BY TOPIC

Solution Concentration and Solution Stoichiometry

21. Calculate the molarity of each solution.
MISSED THIS? *Read Section 5.2; Watch KCV 5.2, IWE 5.1*
    a. 3.25 mol of LiCl in 2.78 L solution
    b. 28.33 g $C_6H_{12}O_6$ in 1.28 L of solution
    c. 32.4 mg NaCl in 122.4 mL of solution
22. Calculate the molarity of each solution.
    a. 0.38 mol of $LiNO_3$ in 6.14 L of solution
    b. 72.8 g C_2H_6O in 2.34 L of solution
    c. 12.87 mg KI in 112.4 mL of solution
23. What is the molarity of NO_3^- in each solution?
MISSED THIS? *Read Sections 5.2, 5.4; Watch KCV 5.2, IWE 5.1*
    a. 0.150 M KNO_3
    b. 0.150 M $Ca(NO_3)_2$
    c. 0.150 M $Al(NO_3)_3$
24. What is the molarity of Cl^- in each solution?
    a. 0.200 M NaCl
    b. 0.150 M $SrCl_2$
    c. 0.100 M $AlCl_3$
25. How many moles of KCl are contained in each solution?
MISSED THIS? *Read Section 5.2; Watch KCV 5.2, IWE 5.2*
    a. 0.556 L of a 2.3 M KCl solution
    b. 1.8 L of a 0.85 M KCl solution
    c. 114 mL of a 1.85 M KCl solution
26. What volume of 0.200 M ethanol solution contains each amount in moles of ethanol?
    a. 0.45 mol ethanol
    b. 1.22 mol ethanol
    c. 1.2×10^{-2} mol ethanol
27. A laboratory procedure calls for making 400.0 mL of a 1.1 M $NaNO_3$ solution. What mass of $NaNO_3$ (in g) is needed?
MISSED THIS? *Read Section 5.2; Watch KCV 5.2, IWE 5.2*
28. A chemist wants to make 5.5 L of a 0.300 M $CaCl_2$ solution. What mass of $CaCl_2$ (in g) should the chemist use?
29. If 123 mL of a 1.1 M glucose solution is diluted to 500.0 mL, what is the molarity of the diluted solution?
MISSED THIS? *Read Section 5.2; Watch KCV 5.2, IWE 5.3*
30. If 3.5 L of a 4.8 M $SrCl_2$ solution is diluted to 45 L, what is the molarity of the diluted solution?
31. To what volume should you dilute 50.0 mL of a 12 M stock HNO_3 solution to obtain a 0.100 M HNO_3 solution?
MISSED THIS? *Read Section 5.2; Watch KCV 5.2, IWE 5.3*
32. To what volume should you dilute 25 mL of a 10.0 M H_2SO_4 solution to obtain a 0.150 M H_2SO_4 solution?
33. Consider the precipitation reaction:
MISSED THIS? *Read Section 5.3; Watch IWE 5.4*
$$2\,Na_3PO_4(aq) + 3\,CuCl_2(aq) \longrightarrow Cu_3(PO_4)_2(s) + 6\,NaCl(aq)$$
What volume of 0.175 M Na_3PO_4 solution is necessary to completely react with 95.4 mL of 0.102 M $CuCl_2$?
34. Consider the reaction:
$$Li_2S(aq) + Co(NO_3)_2(aq) \longrightarrow 2\,LiNO_3(aq) + CoS(s)$$
What volume of 0.150 M Li_2S solution is required to completely react with 125 mL of 0.150 M $Co(NO_3)_2$?
35. What is the minimum amount of 6.0 M H_2SO_4 necessary to produce 25.0 g of $H_2(g)$ according to the reaction between aluminum and sulfuric acid?
MISSED THIS? *Read Section 5.3; Watch IWE 5.4*
$$2\,Al(s) + 3\,H_2SO_4(aq) \longrightarrow Al_2(SO_4)_3(aq) + 3\,H_2(g)$$
36. What is the molarity of $ZnCl_2$ that forms when 25.0 g of zinc completely reacts with $CuCl_2$ according to the following reaction? Assume a final volume of 275 mL.
$$Zn(s) + CuCl_2(aq) \longrightarrow ZnCl_2(aq) + Cu(s)$$

37. A 25.0-mL sample of a 1.20 M potassium chloride solution is mixed with 15.0 mL of a 0.900 M lead(II) nitrate solution, and this precipitation reaction occurs:
MISSED THIS? *Read Section 4.3, 5.3; Watch KCV 4.3, IWE 4.6, 5.4*

$$2\,KCl(aq) + Pb(NO_3)_2(aq) \longrightarrow PbCl_2(s) + 2\,KNO_3(aq)$$

The solid $PbCl_2$ is collected, dried, and found to have a mass of 2.45 g. Determine the limiting reactant, the theoretical yield, and the percent yield.

38. A 55.0-mL sample of a 0.102 M potassium sulfate solution is mixed with 35.0 mL of a 0.114 M lead(II) acetate solution and this precipitation reaction occurs:

$$K_2SO_4(aq) + Pb(C_2H_3O_2)_2(aq) \longrightarrow 2\,KC_2H_3O_2(aq) + PbSO_4(s)$$

The solid $PbSO_4$ is collected, dried, and found to have a mass of 1.01 g. Determine the limiting reactant, the theoretical yield, and the percent yield.

Types of Aqueous Solutions and Solubility

39. For each compound (all water soluble), would you expect the resulting aqueous solution to conduct electrical current?
MISSED THIS? *Read Section 5.4*
a. $CsCl$ **b.** CH_3OH **c.** $Ca(NO_2)_2$ **d.** $C_6H_{12}O_6$

40. Classify each compound as a strong electrolyte or nonelectrolyte.
a. $MgBr_2$ **b.** $C_{12}H_{22}O_{11}$ **c.** Na_2CO_3 **d.** KOH

41. Determine whether each compound is soluble or insoluble. If the compound is soluble, list the ions present in solution.
MISSED THIS? *Read Section 5.4; Watch IWE 5.5*
a. $AgNO_3$ **b.** $Pb(C_2H_3O_2)_2$
c. KNO_3 **d.** $(NH_4)_2S$

42. Determine whether each compound is soluble or insoluble. If the compound is soluble, list the ions present in solution.
a. AgI **b.** $Cu_3(PO_4)_2$
c. $CoCO_3$ **d.** K_3PO_4

Precipitation Reactions

43. Complete and balance each equation. If no reaction occurs, write "NO REACTION."
MISSED THIS? *Read Section 5.5; Watch KCV 5.5, IWE 5.6*
a. $LiI(aq) + BaS(aq) \longrightarrow$
b. $KCl(aq) + CaS(aq) \longrightarrow$
c. $CrBr_2(aq) + Na_2CO_3(aq) \longrightarrow$
d. $NaOH(aq) + FeCl_3(aq) \longrightarrow$

44. Complete and balance each equation. If no reaction occurs, write "NO REACTION."
a. $NaNO_3(aq) + KCl(aq) \longrightarrow$
b. $NaCl(aq) + Hg_2(C_2H_3O_2)_2(aq) \longrightarrow$
c. $(NH_4)_2SO_4(aq) + SrCl_2(aq) \longrightarrow$
d. $NH_4Cl(aq) + AgNO_3(aq) \longrightarrow$

45. Write a molecular equation for the precipitation reaction that occurs (if any) when each pair of aqueous solutions is mixed. If no reaction occurs, write "NO REACTION."
MISSED THIS? *Read Section 5.5; Watch KCV 5.5, IWE 5.6*
a. potassium carbonate and lead(II) nitrate
b. lithium sulfate and lead(II) acetate
c. copper(II) nitrate and magnesium sulfide
d. strontium nitrate and potassium iodide

46. Write a molecular equation for the precipitation reaction that occurs (if any) when each pair of aqueous solutions is mixed. If no reaction occurs, write "NO REACTION."
a. sodium chloride and lead(II) acetate
b. potassium sulfate and strontium iodide
c. cesium chloride and calcium sulfide
d. chromium(III) nitrate and sodium phosphate

Ionic and Net Ionic Equations

47. Write balanced complete ionic and net ionic equations for each reaction. **MISSED THIS?** *Read Section 5.6*
a. $HCl(aq) + LiOH(aq) \longrightarrow H_2O(l) + LiCl(aq)$
b. $CaS(aq) + CuCl_2(aq) \longrightarrow CuS(s) + CaCl_2(aq)$
c. $NaOH(aq) + HC_2H_3O_2(aq) \longrightarrow H_2O(l) + NaC_2H_3O_2(aq)$
d. $Na_3PO_4(aq) + NiCl_2(aq) \longrightarrow Ni_3(PO_4)_2(s) + NaCl(aq)$

48. Write balanced complete ionic and net ionic equations for each reaction.
a. $K_2SO_4(aq) + CaI_2(aq) \longrightarrow CaSO_4(s) + KI(aq)$
b. $NH_4Cl(aq) + NaOH(aq) \longrightarrow H_2O(l) + NH_3(g) + NaCl(aq)$
c. $AgNO_3(aq) + NaCl(aq) \longrightarrow AgCl(s) + NaNO_3(aq)$
d. $HC_2H_3O_2(aq) + K_2CO_3(aq) \longrightarrow H_2O(l) + CO_2(g) + KC_2H_3O_2(aq)$

49. Mercury(I) ions (Hg_2^{2+}) can be removed from solution by precipitation with Cl^-. Suppose that a solution contains aqueous $Hg_2(NO_3)_2$. Write complete ionic and net ionic equations for the reaction of aqueous $Hg_2(NO_3)_2$ with aqueous sodium chloride to form solid Hg_2Cl_2 and aqueous sodium nitrate.
MISSED THIS? *Read Section 5.6*

50. Lead(II) ions can be removed from solution by precipitation with sulfate ions. Suppose that a solution contains lead(II) nitrate. Write complete ionic and net ionic equations for the reaction of aqueous lead(II) nitrate with aqueous potassium sulfate to form solid lead(II) sulfate and aqueous potassium nitrate.

Acid–Base and Gas-Evolution Reactions

51. Write balanced molecular and net ionic equations for the reaction between hydrobromic acid and potassium hydroxide.
MISSED THIS? *Read Section 5.7; Watch KCV 5.5, IWE 5.9*

52. Write balanced molecular and net ionic equations for the reaction between nitric acid and calcium hydroxide.

53. Complete and balance each acid–base equation.
MISSED THIS? *Read Section 5.7; Watch IWE 5.9*
a. $H_2SO_4(aq) + Ca(OH)_2(aq) \longrightarrow$
b. $HClO_4(aq) + KOH(aq) \longrightarrow$
c. $H_2SO_4(aq) + NaOH(aq) \longrightarrow$

54. Complete and balance each acid–base equation.
a. $HI(aq) + LiOH(aq) \longrightarrow$
b. $HC_2H_3O_2(aq) + Ca(OH)_2(aq) \longrightarrow$
c. $HCl(aq) + Ba(OH)_2(aq) \longrightarrow$

55. Write balanced complete ionic and net ionic equations for each acid–base reaction.
MISSED THIS? *Read Section 5.7; Watch KCV 5.5, IWE 5.9*
a. $HBr(aq) + NaOH(aq) \longrightarrow$
b. $HF(aq) + NaOH(aq) \longrightarrow$
c. $HC_2H_3O_2(aq) + RbOH(aq) \longrightarrow$

56. Write balanced complete ionic and net ionic equations for each acid–base reaction.
a. $HI(aq) + RbOH(aq) \longrightarrow$
b. $HCHO_2(aq) + NaOH(aq) \longrightarrow$
c. $HC_2H_3O_2(aq) + LiOH(aq) \longrightarrow$

57. A 25.00-mL sample of an unknown $HClO_4$ solution requires titration with 22.62 mL of 0.2000 M NaOH to reach the equivalence point. What is the concentration of the unknown $HClO_4$ solution? The neutralization reaction is
MISSED THIS? *Read Section 5.7; Watch IWE 5.11*

$$HClO_4(aq) + NaOH(aq) \longrightarrow H_2O(l) + NaClO_4(aq)$$

58. A 30.00-mL sample of an unknown H_3PO_4 solution is titrated with a 0.100 M NaOH solution. The equivalence point is reached when 26.38 mL of NaOH solution is added. What is the concentration of the unknown H_3PO_4 solution? The neutralization reaction is

$$H_3PO_4(aq) + 3\,NaOH(aq) \longrightarrow 3\,H_2O(l) + Na_3PO_4(aq)$$

59. Complete and balance each gas-evolution equation. **MISSED THIS?** *Read Section 5.8; Watch KCV 5.5*

a. $HBr(aq) + NiS(s) \longrightarrow$

b. $NH_4I(aq) + NaOH(aq) \longrightarrow$

c. $HBr(aq) + Na_2S(aq) \longrightarrow$

d. $HClO_4(aq) + Li_2CO_3(aq) \longrightarrow$

60. Complete and balance each gas-evolution equation.

a. $HNO_3(aq) + Na_2SO_3(aq) \longrightarrow$

b. $HCl(aq) + KHCO_3(aq) \longrightarrow$

c. $HC_2H_3O_2(aq) + NaHSO_3(aq) \longrightarrow$

d. $(NH_4)_2SO_4(aq) + Ca(OH)_2(aq) \longrightarrow$

Oxidation–Reduction

61. Assign oxidation states to each atom in each element, ion, or compound. **MISSED THIS?** *Read Section 5.9; Watch IWE 5.13*

a. Ag **b.** Ag^+ **c.** CaF_2

d. H_2S **e.** CO_3^{2-} **f.** CrO_4^{2-}

62. Assign oxidation states to each atom in each element, ion, or compound.

a. Cl_2 **b.** Fe^{3+} **c.** $CuCl_2$

d. CH_4 **e.** $Cr_2O_7^{2-}$ **f.** HSO_4^-

63. What is the oxidation state of Cr in each compound? **MISSED THIS?** *Read Section 5.9; Watch IWE 5.13*

a. CrO **b.** CrO_3 **c.** Cr_2O_3

64. What is the oxidation state of Cl in each ion?

a. ClO^- **b.** ClO_2^- **c.** ClO_3^- **d.** ClO_4^-

65. Determine whether each reaction is a redox reaction. For each redox reaction, identify the oxidizing agent and the reducing agent. **MISSED THIS?** *Read Section 5.9*

a. $4\,Li(s) + O_2(g) \longrightarrow 2\,Li_2O(s)$

b. $Mg(s) + Fe^{2+}(aq) \longrightarrow Mg^{2+}(aq) + Fe(s)$

c. $Pb(NO_3)_2(aq) + Na_2SO_4(aq) \longrightarrow PbSO_4(s) + 2\,NaNO_3(aq)$

d. $HBr(aq) + KOH(aq) \longrightarrow H_2O(l) + KBr(aq)$

66. Determine whether each reaction is a redox reaction. For each redox reaction, identify the oxidizing agent and the reducing agent.

a. $Al(s) + 3\,Ag^+(aq) \longrightarrow Al^{3+}(aq) + 3\,Ag(s)$

b. $SO_3(g) + H_2O(l) \longrightarrow H_2SO_4(aq)$

c. $Ba(s) + Cl_2(g) \longrightarrow BaCl_2(s)$

d. $Mg(s) + Br_2(l) \longrightarrow MgBr_2(s)$

67. Determine whether each redox reaction occurs spontaneously in the forward direction. **MISSED THIS?** *Read Section 5.9*

a. $Ni(s) + Zn^{2+}(aq) \longrightarrow Ni^{2+}(aq) + Zn(s)$

b. $Ni(s) + Pb^{2+}(aq) \longrightarrow Ni^{2+}(aq) + Pb(s)$

c. $Al(s) + 3\,Ag^+(aq) \longrightarrow Al^{3+}(aq) + 3\,Ag(s)$

d. $Pb(s) + Mn^{2+}(aq) \longrightarrow Pb^{2+}(aq) + Mn(s)$

68. Determine whether each redox reaction occurs spontaneously in the forward direction.

a. $Ca^{2+}(aq) + Zn(s) \longrightarrow Ca(s) + Zn^{2+}(aq)$

b. $2\,Ag^+(aq) + Ni(s) \longrightarrow 2\,Ag(s) + Ni^{2+}(aq)$

c. $Fe(s) + Mn^{2+}(aq) \longrightarrow Fe^{2+}(aq) + Mn(s)$

d. $2\,Al(s) + 3\,Pb^{2+}(aq) \longrightarrow 2\,Al^{3+}(aq) + 3\,Pb(s)$

69. Suppose you wanted to cause Ni^{2+} ions to come out of solution as solid Ni. Which metal could you use to accomplish this? **MISSED THIS?** *Read Section 5.9*

70. Suppose you wanted to cause Pb^{2+} ions to come out of solution as solid Pb. Which metal could you use to accomplish this?

71. Which metal in the activity series reduces Al^{3+} ions but not Na^+ ions? **MISSED THIS?** *Read Section 5.9*

72. Which metal in the activity series is oxidized with a Ni^{2+} solution but not with a Cr^{3+} solution?

CUMULATIVE PROBLEMS

73. The density of a 20.0% by mass ethylene glycol ($C_2H_6O_2$) solution in water is 1.03 g/mL. Find the molarity of the solution.

74. Find the percent by mass of sodium chloride in a 1.35 M NaCl solution. The density of the solution is 1.05 g/mL.

75. People sometimes use sodium bicarbonate as an antacid to neutralize excess hydrochloric acid in an upset stomach. What mass of hydrochloric acid (in grams) can 2.5 g of sodium bicarbonate neutralize? (*Hint*: Begin by writing a balanced equation for the reaction between aqueous sodium bicarbonate and aqueous hydrochloric acid.)

76. Toilet bowl cleaners often contain hydrochloric acid, which dissolves the calcium carbonate deposits that accumulate within a toilet bowl. What mass of calcium carbonate (in grams) can 3.8 g of HCl dissolve? (*Hint*: Begin by writing a balanced equation for the reaction between hydrochloric acid and calcium carbonate.)

77. Predict the products and write a balanced molecular equation for each reaction. If no reaction occurs, write "NO REACTION."

a. $HCl(aq) + Hg_2(NO_3)_2(aq) \longrightarrow$

b. $KHSO_3(aq) + HNO_3(aq) \longrightarrow$

c. aqueous ammonium chloride and aqueous lead(II) nitrate

d. aqueous ammonium chloride and aqueous calcium hydroxide

78. Predict the products and write a balanced molecular equation for each reaction. If no reaction occurs, write "NO REACTION."

a. $H_2SO_4(aq) + HNO_3(aq) \longrightarrow$

b. $Cr(NO_3)_3(aq) + LiOH(aq) \longrightarrow$

c. aqueous strontium sulfide and aqueous copper(II) sulfate

79. Hard water often contains dissolved Ca^{2+} and Mg^{2+} ions. One way to soften water is to add phosphates. The phosphate ion forms insoluble precipitates with calcium and magnesium ions, removing them from solution. A solution is 0.050 M in calcium chloride and 0.085 M in magnesium nitrate. What mass of sodium phosphate would you add to 1.5 L of this solution to completely eliminate the hard water ions? Assume complete reaction.

80. An acid solution is 0.100 M in HCl and 0.200 M in H_2SO_4. What volume of a 0.150 M KOH solution would completely neutralize all the acid in 500.0 mL of this solution?

81. Find the mass of barium metal (in grams) that must react with O_2 to produce enough barium oxide to prepare 1.0 L of a 0.10 M solution of OH^-. (*Hint*: Barium metal reacts with oxygen to form BaO; BaO reacts with water to form $Ba(OH)_2$.)

82. A solution contains Cr^{3+} ions and Mg^{2+} ions. The addition of 1.00 L of 1.51 M NaF solution causes the complete precipitation of these ions as $CrF_3(s)$ and $MgF_2(s)$. The total mass of the precipitate is 49.6 g. Find the mass of Cr^{3+} in the original solution.

83. Treatment of gold metal with BrF_3 and KF produces Br_2 and $KAuF_4$, a salt of gold. Identify the oxidizing agent and the reducing agent in this reaction. Find the mass of the gold salt that forms when a 73.5-g mixture of equal masses of all three reactants is prepared.

84. We prepare a solution by mixing 0.10 L of 0.12 M sodium chloride with 0.23 L of a 0.18 M $MgCl_2$ solution. What volume of a 0.20 M silver nitrate solution do we need to precipitate all the Cl^- ion in the solution as AgCl?

85. A solution contains one or more of the following ions: Ag^+, Ca^{2+}, and Cu^{2+}. When you add sodium chloride to the solution, no precipitate forms. When you add sodium sulfate to the solution, a white precipitate forms. You filter off the precipitate and add sodium carbonate to the remaining solution, producing another precipitate. Which ions were present in the original solution? Write net ionic equations for the formation of each of the precipitates observed.

86. A solution contains one or more of the following ions: Hg_2^{2+}, Ba^{2+}, and Fe^{2+}. When you add potassium chloride to the solution, a precipitate forms. The precipitate is filtered off, and you add potassium sulfate to the remaining solution, producing no precipitate. When you add potassium carbonate to the remaining solution, a precipitate forms. Which ions were present in the original solution? Write net ionic equations for the formation of each of the precipitates observed.

CHALLENGE PROBLEMS

87. A solution contains Ag^+ and Hg^{2+} ions. The addition of 0.100 L of 1.22 M NaI solution is just enough to precipitate all the ions as AgI and HgI_2. The total mass of the precipitate is 28.1 g. Find the mass of AgI in the precipitate.

88. The water in lakes that have been acidified by acid rain (HNO_3 and H_2SO_4) can be neutralized by a process called liming, in which limestone ($CaCO_3$) is added to the acidified water. What mass of limestone (in kg) would completely neutralize a 15.2 billion-liter lake that is 1.8×10^{-5} M in H_2SO_4 and 8.7×10^{-6} M in HNO_3?

89. Sodium carbonate is often added to laundry detergents to soften hard water and make the detergent more effective. Suppose that a particular detergent mixture is designed to soften hard water that is 3.5×10^{-3} M in Ca^{2+} and 1.1×10^{-3} M in Mg^{2+} and that the average capacity of a washing machine is 19.5 gallons of water. If the detergent requires using 0.65 kg detergent per load of laundry, what percentage (by mass) of the detergent should be sodium carbonate in order to completely precipitate all of the calcium and magnesium ions in an average load of laundry water?

90. Lead poisoning is a serious condition resulting from the ingestion of lead in food, water, or other environmental sources. It affects the central nervous system, leading to a variety of symptoms such as distractibility, lethargy, and loss of motor coordination. Lead poisoning is treated with chelating agents, substances that bind to metal ions, allowing them to be eliminated in the urine. A modern chelating agent used for this purpose is succimer ($C_4H_6O_4S_2$). Suppose you are trying to determine the appropriate dose for succimer treatment of lead poisoning. What minimum mass of succimer (in mg) is needed to bind all of the lead in a patient's bloodstream? Assume that patient blood lead levels are 45 μg/dL, that total blood volume is 5.0 L, and that 1 mol of succimer binds 1 mol of lead.

CONCEPTUAL PROBLEMS

91. The following circle represents 1.0 liter of a solution with a solute concentration of 1 M:

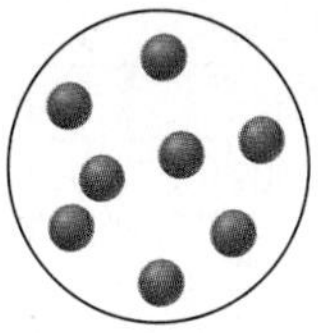

Explain what you would add (the amount of solute or volume of solvent) to the solution to obtain a solution represented by each diagram:

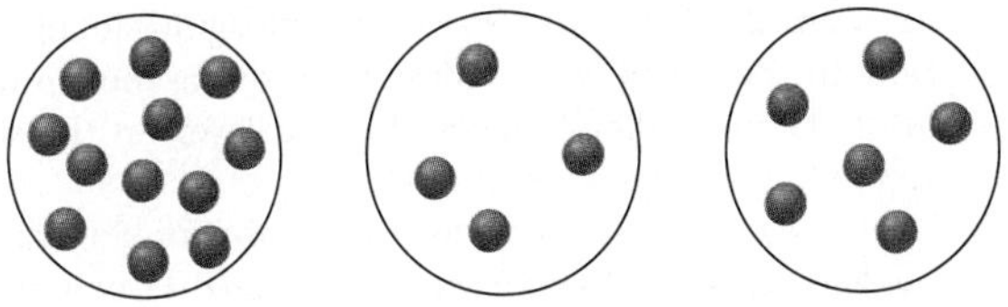

a. b. c.

92. Consider the generic ionic compounds with the formulas A_2X and BY_2 and the following solubility rules:

A_2X soluble; BY_2 soluble; AY insoluble; BX soluble.

Assume A^+ ions are circles, B^{2+} ions are squares, X^{2-} ions are triangles, and Y^- ions are diamonds. Solutions of the two compounds (A_2X and BY_2) are represented as follows:

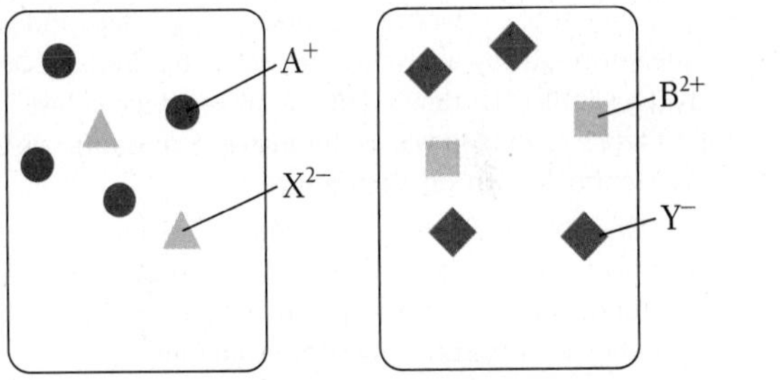

Draw a molecular-level representation showing the result of mixing the two given solutions and write an equation to represent the reaction.

93. A hydrochloric acid solution will neutralize a sodium hydroxide solution. Look at the molecular views showing one beaker of HCl and four beakers of NaOH. Which NaOH beaker will just neutralize the HCl beaker? Begin by writing a balanced chemical equation for the neutralization reaction.

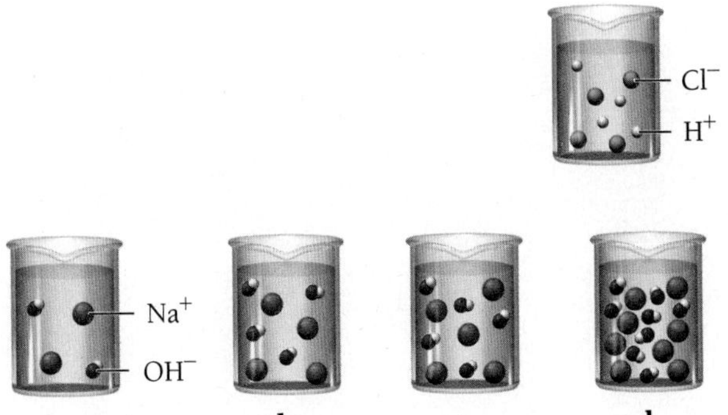

a. b. c. d.

QUESTIONS FOR GROUP WORK

Active Classroom Learning

94. Write a detailed set of instructions for making two solutions: (1) 100 mL of 12 M NaOH from solid sodium hydroxide and (2) 1.00 L of 0.1 M NaOH from your first solution. You have in your lab: volumetric flasks marked to contain 100.0 mL and 1.000 L, a graduated cylinder, and a balance.

95. Review the solubility rules. Without referring back to the rules, have each group member list two ionic compounds that are expected to be soluble and two that are expected to be insoluble. Include at least one exception. Check the work of the other members of your group.

96. Define and give an example of each of the following classes of reactions: precipitation, acid–base, gas-evolution, and redox. Each group member can do one, and then present his or her reaction to the group.

97. Using group members to represent atoms, ions, or electrons, act out the reaction $Zn(s) + Fe^{2+}(aq) \longrightarrow Zn^{2+}(aq) + Fe(s)$. Which group member is oxidized? Which is reduced? Which is the oxidizing agent? Which is the reducing agent?

DATA INTERPRETATION AND ANALYSIS

The Flint, Michigan Water Crisis

98. In April of 2014, in an effort to save money, officials in Flint, Michigan, changed their water source from Lake Huron to the Flint River. In subsequent months, residents began complaining about the quality of the water, and General Motors stopped using the water in manufacturing processes because of its corrosiveness. That corrosiveness was causing problems that would soon fuel a national outrage. The water flowed through pipes to taps in homes, and as it flowed through the pipes—many of which contained lead—the corrosive water became contaminated with lead. Routine monitoring of the tap water in select homes did not reveal the magnitude of the problem because samples were collected only after preflushing the tap (allowing the water to run for a time). A Virginia Tech professor and his students began an independent test of the water coming from Flint's taps and got much different results by analyzing the water that initially came from the taps (called 1st draw). Their results—which showed elevated lead levels in the tap water—ultimately forced officials to switch back to the Lake Huron water source.

The table below shows a set of data collected by the Virginia Tech team. The lead levels in water are expressed in units of part per billion (ppb). 1 ppb = 1 g Pb/10^9 parts solution. Examine the data and answer the questions that follow.

Sample #	Lead Level 1st draw (ppb)	Lead Level 45 sec flush (ppb)	Lead Level 2 min flush (ppb)
1	0.344	0.226	0.145
2	8.133	10.77	2.761
3	1.111	0.11	0.123
4	8.007	7.446	3.384
5	1.951	0.048	0.035
6	7.2	1.4	0.2
7	40.63	9.726	6.132
8	1.1	2.5	0.1
9	10.6	1.038	1.294
10	6.2	4.2	2.3
11	4.358	0.822	0.147
12	24.37	8.796	4.347
13	6.609	5.752	1.433
14	4.062	1.099	1.085
15	29.59	3.258	1.843

Source: FlintWaterStudy.org (2015) "Lead Results from Tap Water Sampling in Flint, MI during the Flint Water Crisis"

a. Determine the average value of lead for 1st draw, 45-second flush, and 2-minute flush (round to three significant figures).

b. Does the data support the idea that running the tap water before taking a sample made the lead levels in the water appear lower? Why might this occur?

c. The EPA requires water providers to monitor drinking water at customer taps. If lead concentrations exceed 15 ppb in 10% or more of the taps sampled, the water provider must notify the customer and take steps to control the corrosiveness of the water. If the water provider in Flint had used 1st-draw samples to monitor lead levels, would they have been required to take action by EPA requirements? If the Flint water provider used 2-min flush samples, would they have had to take action? Which drawing technique do you think more closely mimics the way residents actually use their water?

d. Using the highest value of lead from the 1st-draw data set, and assuming a resident drinks 2 L of water per day, calculate the mass of lead that the resident would consume over the course of 1 year. (Assume the water has a density of 1.0 g/mL.)

Cc ANSWERS TO CONCEPTUAL CONNECTIONS

Molarity

5.1 **(d)** $3.0\cancel{L} \times \frac{2.0\text{ mol}}{\cancel{L}} = 6.0\text{ mol}$

Solutions

5.2 **(b)** The mass of a solution is equal to the mass of the solute plus the mass of the solvent. Although the solute seems to disappear, it really does not, and its mass becomes part of the mass of the solution, in accordance with the law of mass conservation.

Solution Dilution

5.3 **(c)** Since the volume has doubled, the concentration is halved, so the same volume should contain half as many solute molecules.

Solution Stoichiometry

5.4 **(a)** A is the limiting reactant. You have equal amounts of both reactants, but the reaction requires twice as much of A as B.

Electrolyte Solutions

5.5 **(a)** KBr is an ionic compound and a strong electrolyte.

Solubility of Ionic Compounds

5.6 **(c)** Compounds containing the NO_3^- ion are soluble with no exceptions.

Precipitation Reactions

5.7 **(c)**

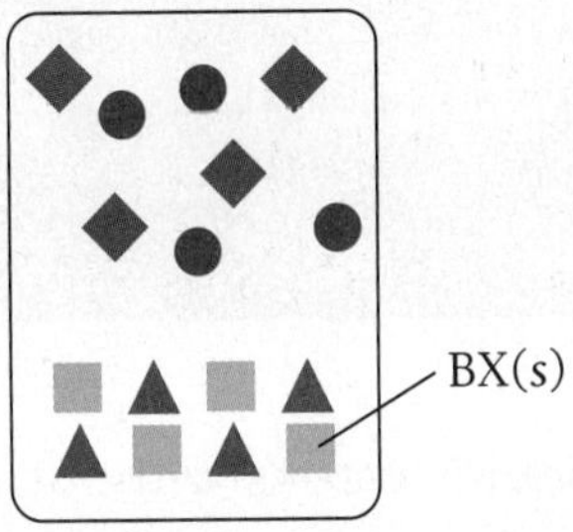

$$AX(aq) + BY(aq) \longrightarrow BX(s) + AY(aq)$$

Spectator Ions

5.8 **(b)** NO_3^- does not participate in the reaction and is therefore a spectator ion.

Acid–Base Titration

5.9 **(b)** The endpoint occurs when moles of added OH^- equals moles of H^+ in the solution. The solution contains 0.0020 mol H^+, and 20.0 mL of 0.10 M NaOH only contains 0.0020 mol OH^-.

Oxidation Numbers in Polyatomic Ions

5.10 **(a)** The charge of a polyatomic ion is the charge associated with the ion *as a whole*. The oxidation states of the individual atoms must sum to the charge of the ion, but they are assigned to *the individual atoms themselves*. Answer **(b)** is incorrect because oxidation state and charge *are not identical*, even though the charge of a *monoatomic* ion is equal to its oxidation state. Answer **(c)** is incorrect because charge *is* a physical property of ions. Conversely, the oxidation states of atoms are *not* real physical properties but an imposed electron bookkeeping scheme.

Oxidation and Reduction

5.11 **(d)** Since oxidation and reduction must occur together, an increase in the oxidation state of a reactant is always accompanied by a decrease in the oxidation state of another reactant.

Activity Series

5.12 **(a)** Sodium is highest on the activity series and therefore most easily oxidized.

So many of the properties of matter, especially when in the gaseous form, can be deduced from the hypothesis that their minute parts are in rapid motion, the velocity increasing with the temperature, that the precise nature of this motion becomes a subject of rational curiosity.

—JAMES CLERK MAXWELL (1831–1879)

CHAPTER 6

Gases

Human beings can survive for weeks without food, days without water, but only minutes without air. Fortunately, we live at the bottom of a vast ocean of air, held to Earth by gravity. We inhale a lungful of this air every few seconds, keep some of the molecules for our own uses, add some molecules that our bodies no longer need, and exhale the mixture back into the surrounding air. The air around us is matter in the gaseous state. What are the fundamental properties of these gases? What laws describe their behavior? What theory explains these properties and laws? Recall that the scientific approach (see Section 1.2) proceeds in this way—from observations to laws to theories—exactly the way we will proceed in this chapter. The gaseous state is the simplest and best-understood state of matter. In this chapter, we examine that state.

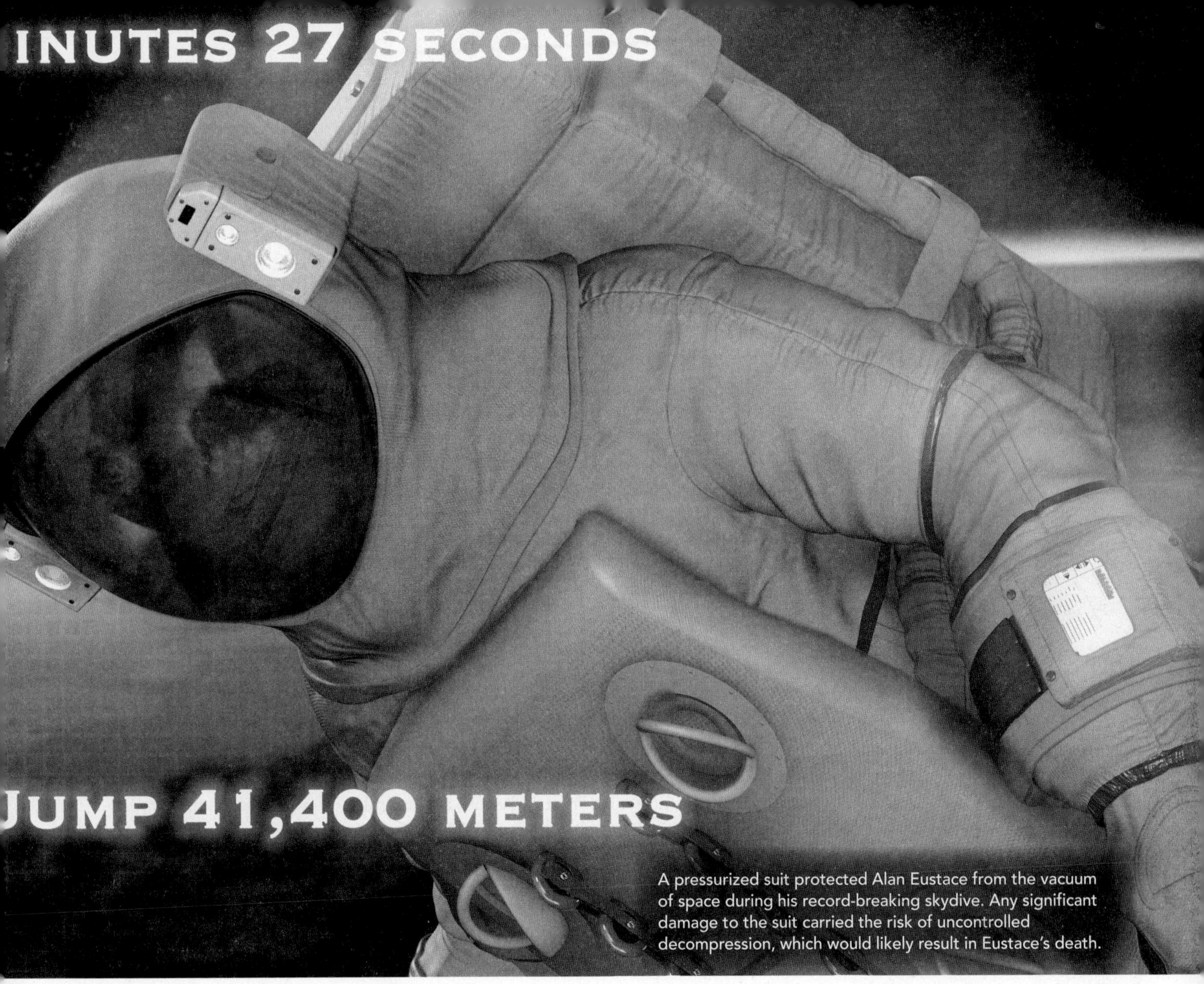

A pressurized suit protected Alan Eustace from the vacuum of space during his record-breaking skydive. Any significant damage to the suit carried the risk of uncontrolled decompression, which would likely result in Eustace's death.

6.1 Supersonic Skydiving and the Risk of Decompression 211

6.2 Pressure: The Result of Molecular Collisions 212

6.3 The Simple Gas Laws: Boyle's Law, Charles's Law, and Avogadro's Law 215

6.4 The Ideal Gas Law 222

6.5 Applications of the Ideal Gas Law: Molar Volume, Density, and Molar Mass of a Gas 225

6.6 Mixtures of Gases and Partial Pressures 228

6.7 Gases in Chemical Reactions: Stoichiometry Revisited 235

6.8 Kinetic Molecular Theory: A Model for Gases 238

6.9 Mean Free Path, Diffusion, and Effusion of Gases 245

6.10 Real Gases: The Effects of Size and Intermolecular Forces 246

LEARNING OUTCOMES 252

6.1 Supersonic Skydiving and the Risk of Decompression

On October 24, 2014, Google executive Alan Eustace released himself into the dark void of space 25.7 miles (41.4 km) above Earth's surface. Eustace's 15-minute journey back to Earth's surface broke the sound barrier and broke the previous skydiving record of 24 miles (38.6 km) set just two years before by Felix Baumgartner.

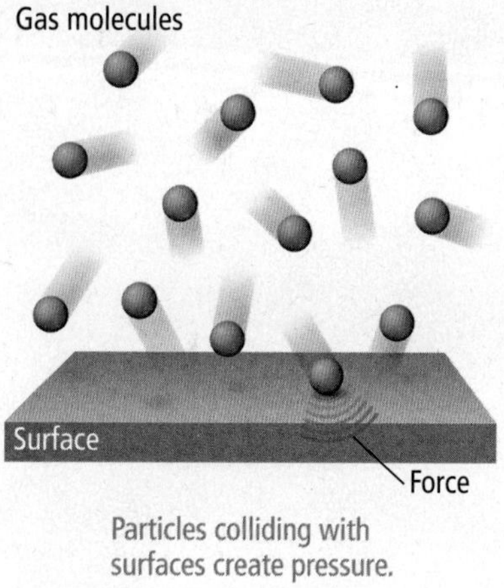

▲ **FIGURE 6.1 Gas Pressure** For a gas, pressure is the force per unit area exerted by gas molecules colliding with the surfaces around them.

While Eustace was in space, he was protected from the surrounding vacuum by a pressurized suit. The suit contained air at a pressure similar to that found on the surface of Earth. **Pressure** is the amount of force per unit area, so the pressure exerted by a gas equals the force exerted by its particles divided by the surface area they strike (Figure 6.1◀). Just as a ball exerts a force when it bounces against a wall, a gaseous atom or molecule exerts a force when it collides with a surface. The average of these countless collisions over time results in pressure. The total pressure exerted by a gas depends on several factors, including the concentration of gas particles in the sample; the lower the concentration, the lower the pressure. At 25.7 miles (41.4 km) above Earth's surface, the concentration of gas particles is much lower than it is at sea level; consequently, the pressure at that high altitude is very low. Without the pressurized suit, Eustace could not have survived the space-like conditions.

One of the primary risks that Eustace faced while in space was uncontrolled decompression. Any significant damage to his suit could have caused the air within the suit to escape, resulting in a large pressure drop. While the effects of a large pressure drop are sometimes exaggerated—one urban myth claims that a person can explode—they are nonetheless lethal. A sudden pressure drop would have produced a large pressure difference between the air in Eustace's lungs and the surrounding vacuum. The pressure difference would have caused his lungs to expand too much, resulting in severe lung damage. Fortunately, Eustace's suit worked just as it was designed to do, and he plunged safely back to Earth.

▲ **FIGURE 6.2 Pressure and Particle Density** A low density of gas particles results in low pressure; a high density of gas particles results in high pressure.

6.2 Pressure: The Result of Molecular Collisions

Air can hold up a jumbo jet or knock down a building. How? As we discussed in Section 6.1, air contains gaseous atoms and molecules in constant motion. The particles collide with each other and with the surfaces around them creating pressure. Because of pressure, we can drink from straws, inflate basketballs, and breathe. Variation in pressure in Earth's atmosphere creates wind, and changes in pressure help us to predict weather. Pressure is all around us and inside of us.

The pressure that a gas sample exerts is the *force* that results from the collisions of gas particles divided by the *area* of the surface with which they collide:

$$\text{Pressure} = \frac{\text{force}}{\text{area}} = \frac{F}{A} \qquad [6.1]$$

The pressure exerted by a gas sample, therefore, depends on the number of gas particles in a given volume—the fewer the gas particles, the lower the force per unit area and the lower the pressure (Figure 6.2◀). Since the number of gas particles in a given volume

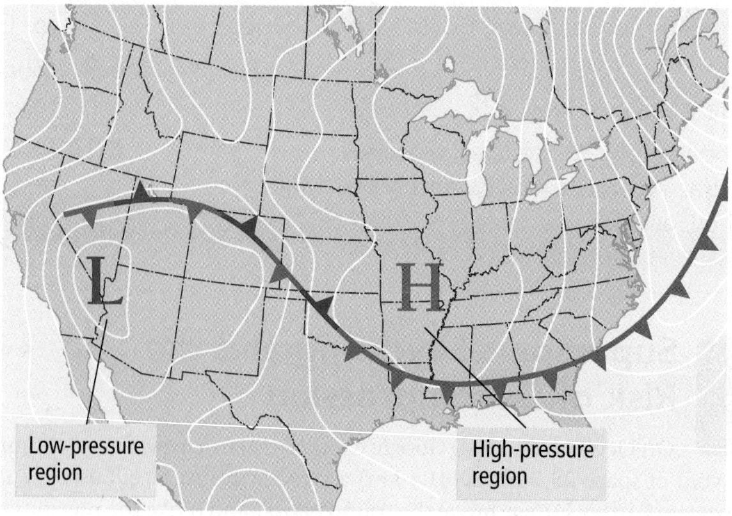

▶ Pressure variations in Earth's atmosphere create wind and weather. The H on this map indicates a region of high pressure, usually associated with clear weather. The L indicates a region of low pressure, usually associated with unstable weather.

generally decreases with increasing altitude, *pressure decreases with increasing altitude*. Above 30,000 ft, for example, where most commercial airplanes fly, the pressure is so low that a person could pass out due to a lack of oxygen. For this reason, most airplane cabins are artificially pressurized.

You may sometimes feel the effect of a drop in pressure as a brief pain in your ears. This pain arises within the air-containing cavities in your ear (Figure 6.3▶). When you ascend to a higher altitude, the external pressure (the pressure that surrounds you) drops, while the pressure within your ear cavities (the internal pressure) remains the same. This creates an imbalance—the greater internal pressure forces your eardrum to bulge outward, causing pain. With time, and with the help of a yawn or two, the excess air within your ear's cavities escapes, equalizing the internal and external pressure and relieving the pain.

Pressure Imbalance

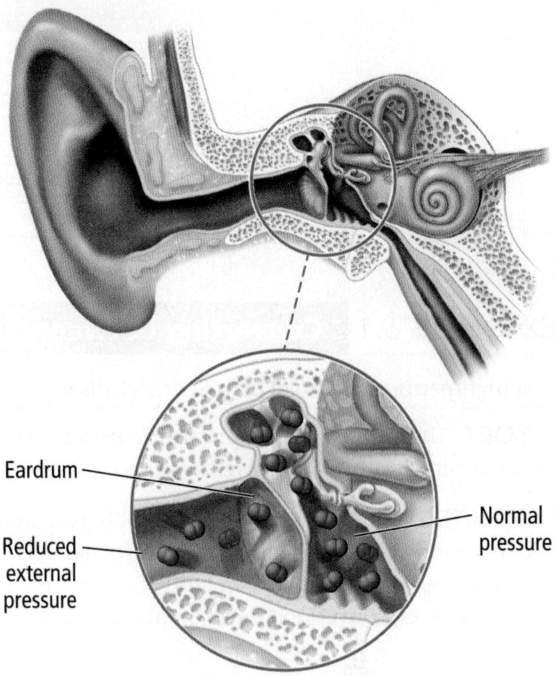

▲ **FIGURE 6.3 Pressure Imbalance** The discomfort you may feel in your ears upon ascending a mountain is caused by a pressure imbalance between the cavities in your ears and the outside air.

Pressure Units

We measure pressure in several different units. A common unit of pressure, the **millimeter of mercury (mmHg)**, originates from how pressure is measured with a **barometer** (Figure 6.4▼). A barometer is an evacuated glass tube, the tip of which is submerged in a pool of mercury (Hg). Atmospheric pressure on the liquid mercury's surface forces the mercury upward into the evacuated tube. Because mercury is so dense (13.5 times more dense than water), atmospheric pressure can support a column of Hg that is only about 0.760 m or 760 mm (about 30 in) tall. By contrast, atmospheric pressure can support a column of water that is about 10.3 m tall. This makes a column of mercury a convenient way to measure pressure.

In a barometer, when the atmospheric pressure rises, the height of the mercury column rises as well. Similarly, when atmospheric pressure falls, the height of the column falls. The unit *millimeter of mercury* is often called a **torr**, after the Italian physicist Evangelista Torricelli (1608–1647) who invented the barometer:

$$1 \text{ mmHg} = 1 \text{ torr}$$

A second unit of pressure is the **atmosphere (atm)**, the average pressure at sea level. Since one atmosphere of pressure pushes a column of mercury to a height of 760 mm, 1 atm and 760 mmHg are equal:

$$1 \text{ atm} = 760 \text{ mmHg}$$

A fully inflated bike tire has a pressure of about 6 atm, and the pressure at the top of Mount Everest is about 0.31 atm.

The SI unit of pressure is the **pascal (Pa)**, defined as 1 newton (N) per square meter:

$$1 \text{ Pa} = 1 \text{ N/m}^2$$

The pascal is a much smaller unit of pressure than the atmosphere:

$$1 \text{ atm} = 101{,}325 \text{ Pa}$$

Other common units of pressure include inches of mercury (in Hg) and pounds per square inch (psi):

$$1 \text{ atm} = 29.92 \text{ in Hg} \qquad 1 \text{ atm} = 14.7 \text{ psi}$$

Table 6.1 summarizes common pressure units.

The Mercury Barometer

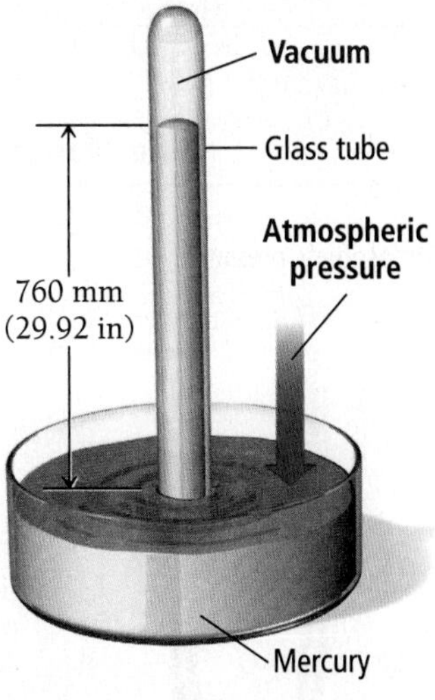

▲ **FIGURE 6.4 The Mercury Barometer** Average atmospheric pressure at sea level can support a column of mercury 760 mm in height.

TABLE 6.1 ■ Common Units of Pressure

Unit	Abbreviation	Average Air Pressure at Sea Level
Pascal (1 N/m^2)	Pa	101,325 Pa
Pounds per square inch	psi	14.7 psi
Torr (1 mmHg)	torr	760 torr (exact)
Inches of mercury	in Hg	29.92 in Hg
Atmosphere	atm	1 atm

EXAMPLE 6.1 Converting between Pressure Units

A high-performance road bicycle tire is inflated to a total pressure of 132 psi. What is this pressure in mmHg?

SORT The problem gives a pressure in psi and asks you to convert the units to mmHg.

GIVEN: 132 psi
FIND: mmHg

STRATEGIZE Since Table 6.1 does not have a direct conversion factor between psi and mmHg but does provide relationships between both of these units and atmospheres, convert to atm as an intermediate step.

CONCEPTUAL PLAN

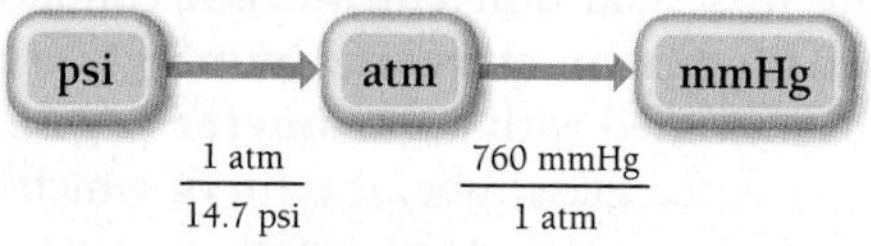

RELATIONSHIPS USED

1 atm = 14.7 psi
760 mmHg = 1 atm (both from Table 6.1)

SOLVE Follow the conceptual plan to solve the problem. Begin with 132 psi and use the conversion factors to arrive at the pressure in mmHg.

SOLUTION

$$132\ \text{psi} \times \frac{1\ \text{atm}}{14.7\ \text{psi}} \times \frac{760\ \text{mmHg}}{1\ \text{atm}} = 6.82 \times 10^3\ \text{mmHg}$$

CHECK The units of the answer are correct. The magnitude of the answer (6.82×10^3 mmHg) is greater than the given pressure in psi. This is reasonable since mmHg is a much smaller unit than psi.

FOR PRACTICE 6.1 Your local weather report announces that the barometric pressure is 30.44 in Hg. Convert this pressure to psi.

FOR MORE PRACTICE 6.1 Convert a pressure of 23.8 in Hg to kPa.

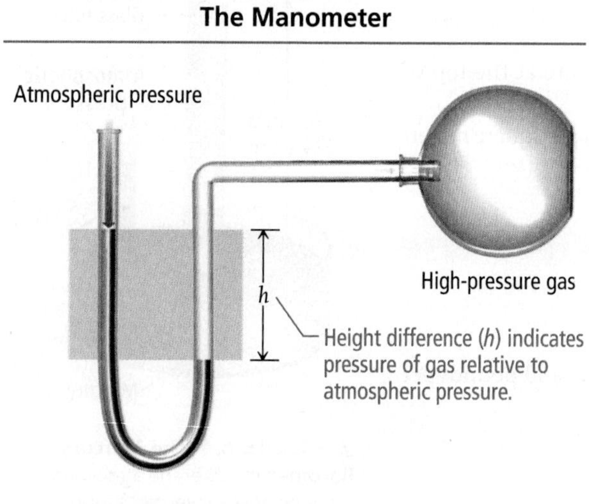

▲ **FIGURE 6.5 The Manometer** A manometer measures the pressure exerted by a sample of gas.

The Manometer: A Way to Measure Pressure in the Laboratory

We can measure the pressure of a gas sample in the laboratory with a **manometer**. A manometer is a U-shaped tube containing a dense liquid, usually mercury, as shown in Figure 6.5◄. In this manometer, one end of the tube is open to atmospheric pressure, and the other is attached to a flask containing the gas sample. If the pressure of the gas sample is exactly equal to atmospheric pressure, then the mercury levels on both sides of the tube are the same. If the pressure of the gas sample is *greater than* atmospheric pressure, the mercury level on the left side of the tube is *higher than* the level on the right. If the pressure of the sample is *less than* atmospheric pressure, the mercury level on the left side is *lower than* the level on the right. This type of manometer always measures the pressure of the gas sample relative to atmospheric pressure. The difference in height between the two levels is equal to the difference between the sample's pressure and atmospheric pressure. To accurately calculate the absolute pressure of the sample, we also need a barometer to measure atmospheric pressure (which can vary from day to day).

CHEMISTRY AND MEDICINE | Blood Pressure

Blood pressure is the force within our arteries that drives the circulation of blood throughout the body. Blood pressure in the body is analogous to water pressure in a plumbing system. Just as water pressure pushes water through the pipes to faucets and fixtures throughout a house, blood pressure pushes blood to muscles and other tissues throughout the body. However, unlike the water pressure in a plumbing system—which is typically nearly constant—blood pressure varies with each heartbeat. When the heart muscle contracts, blood pressure increases; between contractions it decreases. Systolic blood pressure is the peak pressure during a contraction, and diastolic blood pressure is the lowest pressure between contractions. Just as excessively high water pressure in a plumbing system can damage pipes, blood pressure that is too high in a circulatory system can damage the heart and arteries, resulting in increased risk of stroke and heart attack.

Medical professionals usually measure blood pressure with an instrument called a sphygmomanometer—an inflatable cuff equipped with a pressure gauge—and a stethoscope. The cuff is wrapped around the patient's arm and inflated with air. As air is pumped into the cuff, the pressure in the cuff increases. The cuff tightens around the arm and compresses the artery, momentarily stopping blood flow. The person measuring the blood pressure listens to the artery through the stethoscope while slowly releasing the air pressure in the cuff. When the air pressure in the cuff equals the systolic blood pressure (the peak pressure), a pulse is heard through the stethoscope. The pulse is the sound of blood getting through the compressed artery during a contraction of the heart. The pressure reading at that exact moment is the systolic blood pressure. As the pressure in the cuff continues to decrease, the blood can flow through the compressed artery even between contractions, so the pulsing sound stops. The pressure reading when the pulsing sound stops is the diastolic blood pressure (the lowest pressure).

A blood pressure measurement is usually reported as two pressures, in mmHg, separated by a slash. For example, a blood pressure measurement of 122/84 indicates that the systolic blood pressure is 122 mmHg and the diastolic blood pressure is 84 mmHg. Although the value of blood pressure can vary throughout the day, healthy (or normal) values are usually considered to be below 120 mmHg for systolic and below 80 mmHg for diastolic (Table 6.2). High blood pressure, also called hypertension, entails the health risks mentioned previously.

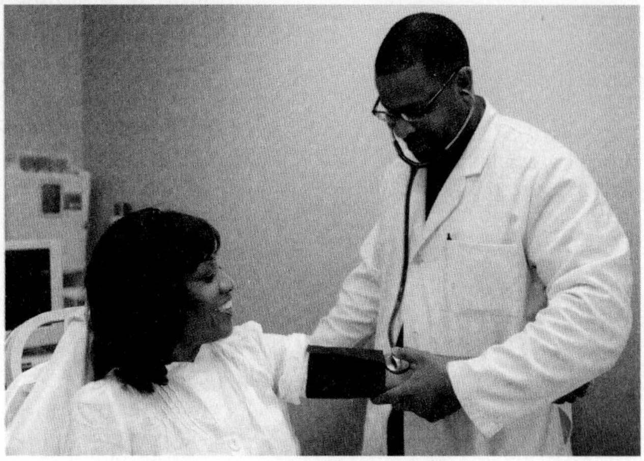

▲ A health care provider measures blood pressure with an inflatable cuff that compresses the main artery in the arm. A stethoscope is used to listen for blood flowing through the artery with each heartbeat.

Risk factors for hypertension include obesity, high salt (sodium) intake, high alcohol intake, lack of exercise, stress, a family history of high blood pressure, and age (blood pressure tends to increase as we get older). Mild hypertension can be managed with diet and exercise. Moderate to severe cases require doctor-prescribed medication.

TABLE 6.2 ■ Blood Pressure Ranges

Blood Pressure	Systolic (mmHg)	Diastolic (mmHg)
Hypotension	<100	<60
Normal	100–119	60–79
Prehypertension	120–139	80–89
Hypertension Stage 1	140–159	90–99
Hypertension Stage 2	>160	>100

6.3 The Simple Gas Laws: Boyle's Law, Charles's Law, and Avogadro's Law

WATCH **NOW!**

KEY CONCEPT VIDEO 6.3
Simple Gas Laws and Ideal Gas Law

We have learned about pressure and its characteristics in Section 6.2. We now broaden our discussion to include the four basic properties of a gas sample: pressure (P), volume (V), temperature (T), and amount in moles (n). These properties are interrelated—when one changes, it affects the others. The *simple gas laws* describe the relationships between pairs of these properties. For example, one simple gas law describes how *volume* varies with *pressure* at constant temperature and amount of gas; another law describes how *volume* varies with *temperature* at constant pressure and amount of gas. These laws were deduced from observations in which two of the four basic properties were held constant in order to elucidate the relationship between the other two.

Boyle's Law: Volume and Pressure

In the early 1660s, the pioneering English scientist Robert Boyle (1627–1691) and his assistant Robert Hooke (1635–1703) used a J-tube (Figure 6.6▼) to measure the volume of a sample of gas at different pressures. They trapped a sample of air in the J-tube and added mercury to increase the pressure on the gas. Boyle and Hooke observed an *inverse relationship* between volume and pressure—an increase in one causes a decrease in the other—as shown in Figure 6.7▼. This relationship is now known as **Boyle's law**.

Boyle's law assumes constant temperature and constant amount of gas.

$$\text{Boyle's law:} \quad V \propto \frac{1}{P} \quad (\text{constant } T \text{ and } n)$$

Boyle's law follows from the idea that pressure results from the collisions of the gas particles with the walls of their container. When the volume of a gas sample decreases, the same number of gas particles is crowded into a smaller volume, resulting in more collisions with the walls and therefore an increase in pressure (Figure 6.8▶).

Scuba divers learn about Boyle's law during certification because it explains why a diver should not ascend toward the surface without continuous breathing. For every 10 m of depth that a diver descends in water, she experiences an additional 1 atm of pressure due to the weight of the water above her (Figure 6.9▶). The pressure regulator used in scuba diving delivers air into the diver's lungs at a pressure that matches the external pressure; otherwise the diver could not inhale the air (see *Chemistry in Your Day: Extra-Long Snorkels* on page 219). For example, when a diver is 20 m below the surface, the regulator delivers air at a pressure of 3 atm to match the 3 atm of pressure around the diver (1 atm due to normal atmospheric pressure and 2 additional atmospheres due to the weight of the water at 20 m). Suppose that a diver inhaled a lungful of air at a pressure of 3 atm and swam quickly to the surface (where the pressure is 1 atm) while holding her breath. What would happen to the volume of air in her lungs?

The J-Tube

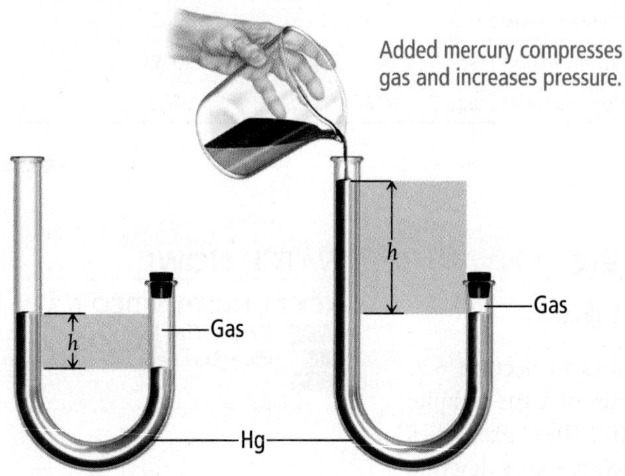

▲ **FIGURE 6.6 The J-Tube** In a J-tube, a column of mercury traps a sample of gas. The pressure on the gas can be increased by increasing the height (*h*) of mercury in the column.

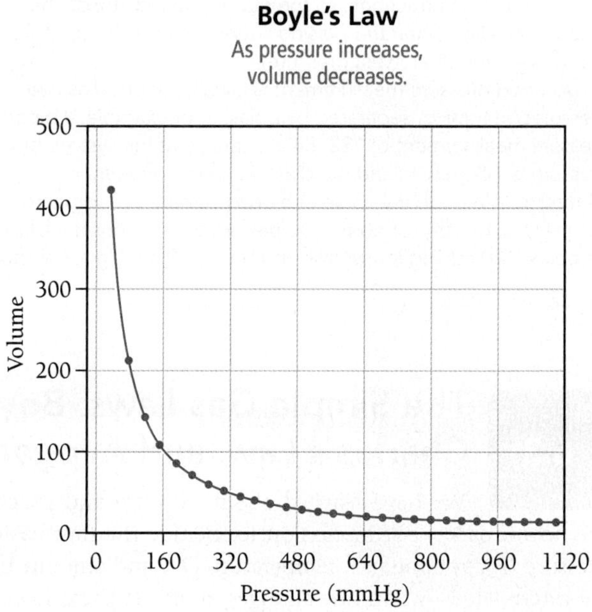

▲ **FIGURE 6.7 Volume versus Pressure** A plot of the volume of a gas sample versus pressure. The plot shows that volume and pressure are inversely related.

Volume versus Pressure: A Molecular View

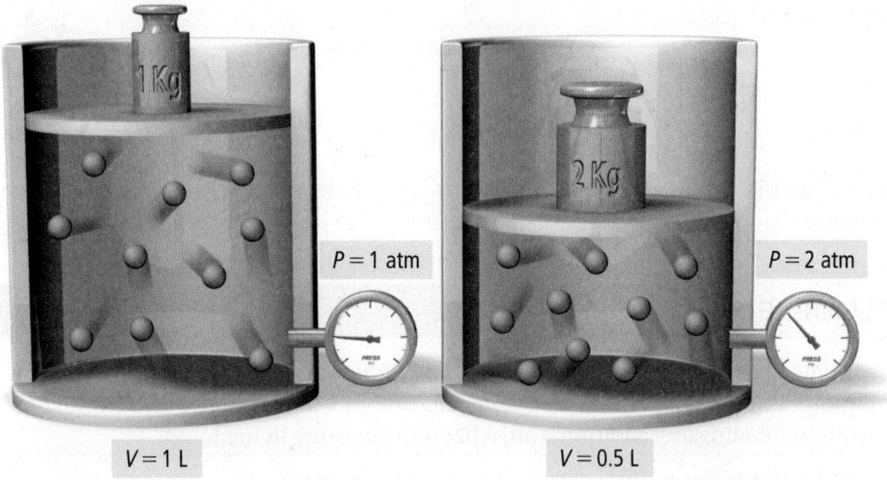

◀ **FIGURE 6.8 Molecular Interpretation of Boyle's Law** As the volume of a gas sample decreases, gas molecules collide with surrounding surfaces more frequently, resulting in greater pressure.

Since the pressure decreases by a factor of 3, the volume of the air in her lungs would increase by a factor of 3—a dangerous situation. The volume increase in the diver's lungs would be so great that she would not be able to hold her breath all the way to the surface—the air would force itself out of her mouth but probably not before the expanded air severely damaged her lungs, possibly killing her. Consequently, the most important rule in diving is *never hold your breath*. To avoid catastrophic results, divers must ascend slowly and breathe continuously, allowing the regulator to bring the air pressure in their lungs back to 1 atm by the time they reach the surface.

We can use Boyle's law to calculate the volume of a gas following a pressure change or the pressure of a gas following a volume change *as long as the temperature and the amount of gas remain constant*. For these types of calculations, we write Boyle's law in a slightly different way.

If two quantities are proportional, then one is equal to the other multiplied by a constant.

$$\text{Since } V \propto \frac{1}{P} \quad \text{then} \quad V = \text{constant} \times \frac{1}{P} \quad \text{or} \quad V = \frac{\text{constant}}{P}$$

If we multiply both sides by P, we find that the product of P and V is equal to a constant:

$$PV = \text{constant}$$

◀ **FIGURE 6.9 Increase in Pressure with Depth** For every 10 m of depth, a diver experiences approximately 1 additional atmosphere of pressure due to the weight of the surrounding water. At 20 m, for example, the diver experiences approximately 3 atm of pressure (1 atm of normal atmospheric pressure plus an additional 2 atm due to the weight of the water).

This relationship indicates that if the pressure increases, the volume decreases, but the product $P \times V$ always equals the same constant. For two different sets of conditions, we can say that:

$$P_1V_1 = \text{constant} = P_2V_2$$

or:

$$P_1V_1 = P_2V_2 \qquad [6.2]$$

where P_1 and V_1 are the initial pressure and volume of the gas and P_2 and V_2 are the final volume and pressure.

EXAMPLE 6.2 Boyle's Law

A woman has an initial lung volume of 2.75 L, which is filled with air at an atmospheric pressure of 1.02 atm. If she increases her lung volume to 3.25 L without inhaling any additional air, what is the pressure in her lungs?

To solve the problem, first solve Boyle's law (Equation 6.2) for P_2 and then substitute the given quantities to calculate P_2.	**SOLUTION** $P_1V_1 = P_2V_2$ $P_2 = \frac{V_1}{V_2}P_1$ $= \frac{2.75\ \cancel{L}}{3.25\ \cancel{L}}1.02\ \text{atm}$ $= 0.863\ \text{atm}$

FOR PRACTICE 6.2 A snorkeler takes a syringe filled with 16 mL of air from the surface, where the pressure is 1.0 atm, to an unknown depth. The volume of the air in the syringe at this depth is 7.5 mL. What is the pressure at the unknown depth? If the pressure increases by 1 atm for every additional 10 m of depth, how deep is the snorkeler?

Charles's Law: Volume and Temperature

Suppose we keep the pressure of a gas sample constant and measure its volume at a number of different temperatures. Figure 6.10 ▼ shows the results of several such measurements.

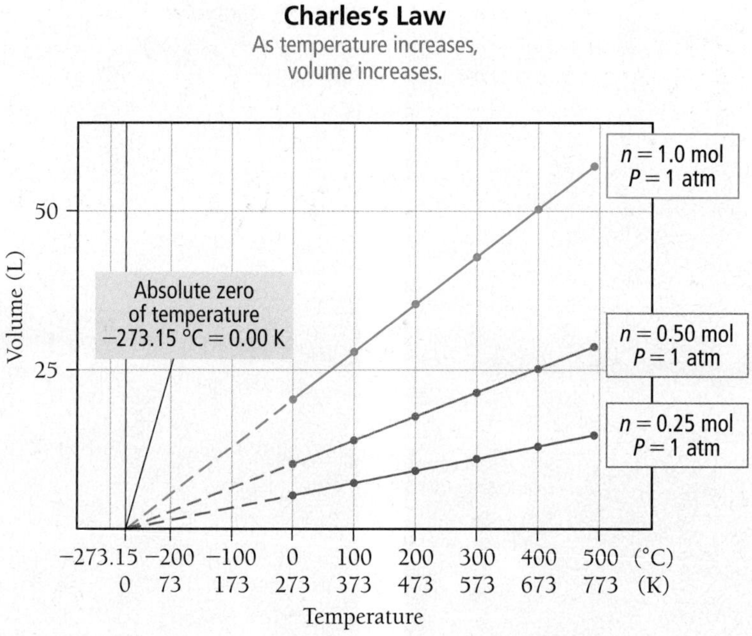

▶ **FIGURE 6.10 Volume versus Temperature** The volume of a fixed amount of gas at a constant pressure increases linearly with increasing temperature in kelvins. (The extrapolated lines cannot be measured experimentally because all gases condense into liquids before −273.15 °C is reached.)

CHEMISTRY IN YOUR DAY | Extra-Long Snorkels

Several episodes of *The Flintstones* cartoon featured Fred Flintstone and Barney Rubble snorkeling. Their snorkels, however, were not the modern kind, but long reeds that stretched from the surface of the water down to many meters of depth. Fred and Barney swam around in deep water while breathing air provided to them by these extra-long snorkels. Would this work? Why do people bother with scuba diving equipment if they could instead simply use 10-meter snorkels as Fred and Barney did?

When we breathe, we expand the volume of our chest cavity, reducing the pressure in our lungs to less than 1 atm (Boyle's law). Because of this pressure differential, air from outside our lungs flows into them. Extra-long snorkels do not work because the pressure exerted by water at depth is too great. A diver at 10 m experiences an external pressure of 2 atm. This is more than the muscles of the chest cavity can overcome. Instead, the chest cavity and lungs are compressed, resulting in an air pressure within them of more than 1 atm. If the diver had a snorkel that went to the surface—where the air pressure is 1 atm—air would flow out of the diver's lungs (*from* greater pressure *to* less pressure), not into them. It would be impossible for the diver to breathe.

QUESTION *A diver takes a balloon with a volume of 2.5 L from the surface, where the pressure is 1.0 atm, to a depth of 20 m, where the pressure is 3.0 atm. What happens to the volume of the balloon? What if the end of the submerged balloon is on a long pipe that goes to the surface and is attached to another balloon? Which way would air flow as the diver descended?*

▲ In the popular cartoon *The Flintstones*, cavemen used long reeds to breathe surface air while swimming at depth. This would not work because the increased pressure at depth would force air out of their lungs; the pressure would not allow them to inhale.

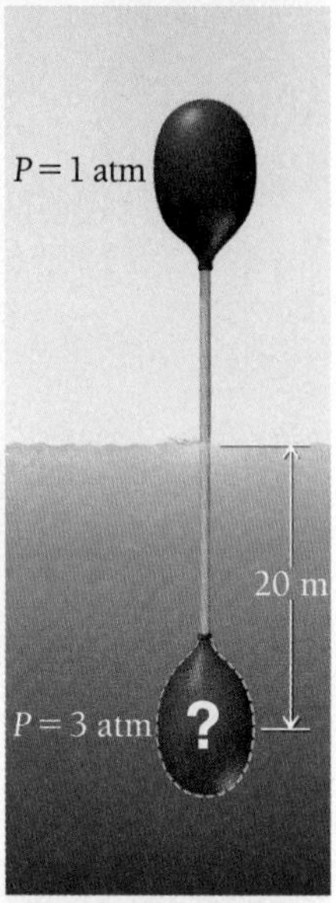

▲ If two balloons were joined by a long tube and one end was submerged in water, what would happen to the volumes of the two balloons?

From the plot we can see a relationship between volume and temperature: the volume of a gas increases with increasing temperature. Looking at the plot more closely reveals more—volume and temperature are *linearly related*. If two variables are linearly related, plotting one against the other produces a straight line.

Another interesting feature emerges if we extend or *extrapolate* each line in the plot in Figure 6.10 backward from the lowest measured temperature. The dotted extrapolated lines show that the gas should have a zero volume at −273.15 °C. Recall from Chapter 1 that −273.15 °C corresponds to 0 K (zero on the Kelvin scale), the coldest possible temperature. The extrapolated lines indicate that below −273.15 °C, the gas would have a negative volume, which is physically impossible. For this reason, we refer to 0 K as *absolute zero*—colder temperatures do not exist.

The first person to carefully quantify the relationship between the volume of a gas and its temperature was J. A. C. Charles (1746–1823), a French mathematician and physicist. Charles was interested in gases and was among the first people to ascend in a hydrogen-filled balloon. The direct proportionality between volume and temperature is named **Charles's law** after him.

$$\text{Charles's law:} \quad V \propto T \quad (\text{constant } P \text{ and } n)$$

Charles's law assumes constant pressure and constant amount of gas.

When the temperature of a gas sample increases, the gas particles move faster; collisions with the walls are more frequent, and the force exerted with each collision is greater. The only way for the pressure (the force per unit area) to remain constant is for the gas to occupy a larger volume so that collisions become less frequent and occur over a larger area (Figure 6.11▶).

▲ A hot-air balloon floats because the hot air within the balloon is less dense than the surrounding cold air.

▲ If we pour liquid nitrogen (which is at 77 K) onto a balloon, it shrivels up as the air within it cools and occupies less volume at the same external pressure.

Volume versus Temperature: A Molecular View

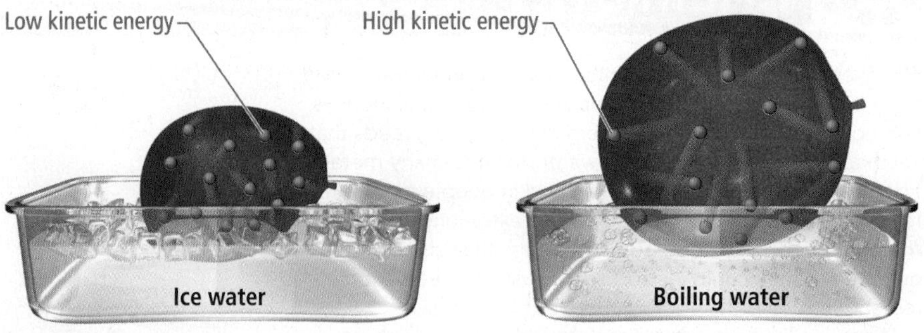

▲ **FIGURE 6.11 Molecular Interpretation of Charles's Law** If we move a balloon from an ice water bath to a boiling water bath, its volume expands as the gas particles within the balloon move faster (due to the increased temperature) and collectively occupy more space.

Charles's law explains why the second floor of a house is usually warmer than the ground floor. According to Charles's law, when air is heated, its volume increases, resulting in a lower density. The warm, less dense air tends to rise in a room filled with colder, denser air. Similarly, Charles's law explains why a hot-air balloon can take flight. The gas that fills a hot-air balloon is warmed with a burner, increasing its volume, lowering its density, and causing it to float in the colder, denser surrounding air.

You can experience Charles's law directly by holding a partially inflated balloon over a warm toaster. As the air in the balloon warms, you can feel the balloon expanding. Alternatively, you can put an inflated balloon into liquid nitrogen and watch it become smaller as it cools.

We can use Charles's law to calculate the volume of a gas following a temperature change or the temperature of a gas following a volume change *as long as the pressure and the amount of gas are constant*. For these calculations, we rearrange Charles's law as follows:

$$\text{Since } V \propto T, \quad \text{then } V = \text{constant} \times T$$

If we divide both sides by T, we find that V/T is equal to a constant:

$$V/T = \text{constant}$$

If the temperature increases, the volume increases in direct proportion so that the quotient, V/T, is always equal to the same constant. So, for two different measurements, we can say that:

$$V_1/T_1 = \text{constant} = V_2/T_2$$

or

$$\frac{V_1}{T_1} = \frac{V_2}{T_2} \qquad [6.3]$$

where V_1 and T_1 are the initial volume and temperature of the gas and V_2 and T_2 are the final volume and temperature. *The temperatures must always be expressed in kelvins (K)* because, as shown in Figure 6.10, the volume of a gas is directly proportional to its *absolute* temperature, not its temperature in °C. For example, doubling the temperature of a gas sample from 1 °C to 2 °C does not double its volume, but doubling the temperature from 200 K to 400 K does.

EXAMPLE 6.3 Charles's Law

A sample of gas has a volume of 2.80 L at an unknown temperature. When the sample is submerged in ice water at $T = 0.00\ °C$, its volume decreases to 2.57 L. What was its initial temperature (in K and in °C)?

	SOLUTION
To solve the problem, first solve Charles's law for T_1.	$\frac{V_1}{T_1} = \frac{V_2}{T_2}$ $T_1 = \frac{V_1}{V_2}T_2$
Before you substitute the numerical values to calculate T_1, convert the temperature to kelvins (K). *Remember, gas law problems must always be worked with Kelvin temperatures.*	$T_2(\text{K}) = 0.00 + 273.15 = 273.15\ \text{K}$
Substitute T_2 and the other given quantities to calculate T_1.	$T_1 = \frac{V_1}{V_2}T_2$ $= \frac{2.80\ \cancel{\text{L}}}{2.57\ \cancel{\text{L}}}273.15\ \text{K}$ $= 29\underline{7}.6\ \text{K}$
Calculate T_1 in °C by subtracting 273.15 from the value in kelvins.	$T_1(°\text{C}) = 29\underline{7}.6 - 273.15 = 24\ °\text{C}$

FOR PRACTICE 6.3 A gas in a cylinder with a moveable piston has an initial volume of 88.2 mL. If we heat the gas from 35 °C to 155 °C, what is its final volume (in mL)?

BOYLE'S LAW AND CHARLES'S LAW The pressure exerted on a sample of a fixed amount of gas is doubled at constant temperature, and then the temperature of the gas in kelvins is doubled at constant pressure. What is the final volume of the gas?

6.1 Cc Conceptual Connection — ANSWER **NOW!**

(a) The final volume is twice the initial volume.
(b) The final volume of the gas is four times the initial volume.
(c) The final volume of the gas is one-half the initial volume.
(d) The final volume of the gas is one-fourth the initial volume.
(e) The final volume of the gas is the same as the initial volume.

Avogadro's Law: Volume and Amount (in Moles)

So far, we have discussed the relationships between volume and pressure, and volume and temperature, but we have considered only a constant amount of a gas. What happens when the amount of gas changes? The volume of a gas sample (at constant temperature and pressure) as a function of the amount of gas (in moles) in the sample is shown in Figure 6.12▶. We can see that the relationship between volume and amount is linear. As we might expect, extrapolation to zero moles shows zero volume. This relationship, first stated formally by Amedeo Avogadro (1776–1856), is **Avogadro's law**.

$$\text{Avogadro's law:} \quad V \propto n \quad (\text{constant } T \text{ and } P)$$

When the amount of gas in a sample increases at constant temperature and pressure, its volume increases in direct proportion because the greater number of gas particles fills more space.

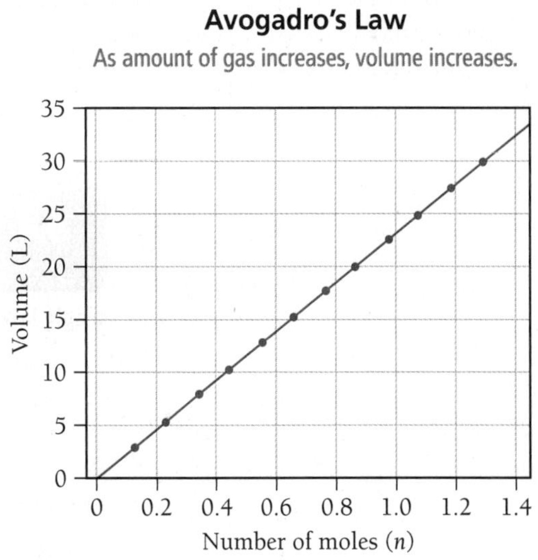

▶ **FIGURE 6.12 Volume versus Number of Moles** The volume of a gas sample increases linearly with the number of moles of gas in the sample.

You experience Avogadro's law when you inflate a balloon. With each exhaled breath, you add more gas particles to the inside of the balloon, increasing its volume. We can use Avogadro's law to calculate the volume of a gas following a change in the amount of the gas *as long as the pressure and temperature of the gas are constant.* For these types of calculations, we express Avogadro's law as:

Avogadro's law assumes constant temperature and constant pressure and is independent of the nature of the gas.

$$\frac{V_1}{n_1} = \frac{V_2}{n_2} \qquad [6.4]$$

where V_1 and n_1 are the initial volume and number of moles of the gas and V_2 and n_2 are the final volume and number of moles. In calculations, we use Avogadro's law in a manner similar to the other gas laws, as demonstrated in Example 6.4.

ANSWER **NOW!**

6.2 Cc Conceptual Connection

SIMPLE GAS LAWS Which action causes the volume of a gas sample to increase?

(a) Decreasing the pressure (at constant temperature and number of moles).
(b) Decreasing the temperature (at constant pressure and number of moles).
(c) Decreasing the number of moles of gas (at constant temperature and pressure).
(d) None of the above.

EXAMPLE 6.4 Avogadro's Law

A male athlete in a kinesiology research study has a lung volume of 6.15 L during a deep inhalation. At this volume, his lungs contain 0.254 mol of air. During exhalation, his lung volume decreases to 2.55 L. How many moles of gas did the athlete exhale? Assume constant temperature and pressure.

To solve the problem, first solve Avogadro's law for the number of moles of gas left in the athlete's lungs after exhalation, n_2. Then substitute the given quantities to calculate n_2.

SOLUTION

$$\frac{V_1}{n_1} = \frac{V_2}{n_2}$$

$$n_2 = \frac{V_2}{V_1} n_1$$

$$= \frac{2.55\ \cancel{L}}{6.15\ \cancel{L}} 0.254\ \text{mol}$$

$$= 0.105\ \text{mol}$$

Since the lungs initially contained 0.254 mol of air, calculate the amount of air exhaled by subtracting the result from 0.254 mol. (In Chapter 1, we introduced the practice of underlining the least [rightmost] significant digit of intermediate answers but not rounding the final answer until the very end of the calculation. We continue that practice throughout the book. However, in order to avoid unnecessary notation, we will not carry additional digits in cases, such as this one, where doing so does not affect the final answer.)

$$\text{moles exhaled} = 0.254\ \text{mol} - 0.105\ \text{mol}$$
$$= 0.149\ \text{mol}$$

FOR PRACTICE 6.4 A chemical reaction occurring in a cylinder equipped with a moveable piston produces 0.621 mol of a gaseous product. If the cylinder contained 0.120 mol of gas before the reaction and had an initial volume of 2.18 L, what is its volume after the reaction? (Assume constant pressure and temperature and that the initial amount of gas completely reacts.)

6.4 The Ideal Gas Law

The relationships that we have discussed so far can be combined into a single law that encompasses all of them. So far, we have shown that:

$$V \propto \frac{1}{P} \qquad \text{(Boyle's law)}$$

$$V \propto T \qquad \text{(Charles's law)}$$

$$V \propto n \qquad \text{(Avogadro's law)}$$

Combining these three expressions, we find that V is proportional to nT/P:

$$V \propto \frac{nT}{P}$$

The volume of a gas is directly proportional to the number of moles of gas and to the temperature of the gas but is inversely proportional to the pressure of the gas. We can replace the proportionality sign with an equals sign by incorporating R, a proportionality constant called the *ideal gas constant*:

$$V = \frac{RnT}{P}$$

Rearranging, we get the equation:

$$PV = nRT \qquad [6.5]$$

This equation is the **ideal gas law**, and a hypothetical gas that exactly follows this law is an **ideal gas**. The value of R, the **ideal gas constant**, is the same for all gases and has the value:

$$R = 0.08206 \frac{\text{L} \cdot \text{atm}}{\text{mol} \cdot \text{K}}$$

L = liters
atm = atmospheres
mol = moles
K = kelvins

The ideal gas law contains within it the simple gas laws that we have discussed. For example, recall that Boyle's law states that $V \propto 1/P$ when the amount of gas (n) and the temperature of the gas (T) are kept constant. We can rearrange the ideal gas law as follows:

$$PV = nRT$$

First, divide both sides by P:

$$V = \frac{nRT}{P}$$

Then put the variables that are constant, along with R, in parentheses:

$$V = (nRT)\frac{1}{P}$$

Since n and T are constant in this case and since R is always a constant, we can write:

$$V \propto \text{constant} \times \frac{1}{P}$$

which means that $V \propto 1/P$.

Ideal Gas Law

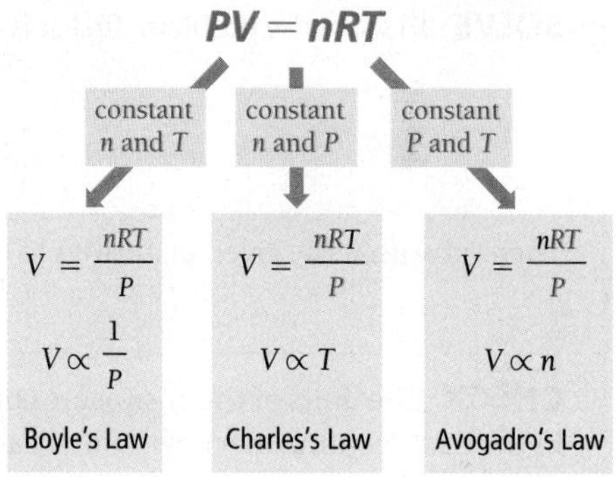

▲ The ideal gas law contains the simple gas laws within it.

The ideal gas law also shows how other pairs of variables are related. For example, from Charles's law we know that $V \propto T$ at constant pressure and constant number of moles. But what if we heat a sample of gas at constant *volume* and constant number of moles? This question applies to the warning labels on aerosol cans such as hair spray or deodorants. These labels warn against excessive heating or incineration of the can, even after the contents are used up. Why? An "empty" aerosol can is not really empty but contains a fixed amount of gas trapped in a fixed volume. What would happen if we were to heat the can? We can rearrange the ideal gas law to clearly see the relationship between pressure and temperature at constant volume and constant number of moles:

$$PV = nRT$$

Divide both sides by V.

$$P = \frac{nRT}{V} = \left(\frac{nR}{V}\right)T$$

Since n and V are constant and since R is always a constant:

$$P = \text{constant} \times T$$

This relationship between pressure and temperature is also known as *Gay-Lussac's law*. As the temperature of a fixed amount of gas in a fixed volume increases, the pressure increases. In an aerosol can, this pressure increase can blow the can apart, which is why aerosol cans should not be heated or incinerated. They might explode.

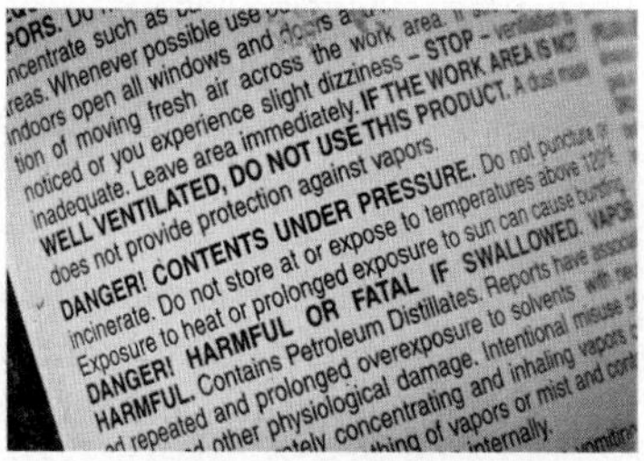

▲ The labels on most aerosol cans warn against incineration. Since the volume of the can is constant, an increase in temperature causes an increase in pressure and possibly an explosion.

We can use the ideal gas law to determine the value of any one of the four variables (P, V, n, or T) given the other three. To do so, we must express each of the quantities in the ideal gas law in the units within R:

- pressure (P) in atm
- volume (V) in L
- moles (n) in mol
- temperature (T) in K

WATCH NOW!
INTERACTIVE WORKED EXAMPLE 6.5

EXAMPLE 6.5 Ideal Gas Law I

Calculate the volume occupied by 0.845 mol of nitrogen gas at a pressure of 1.37 atm and a temperature of 315 K.

SORT The problem gives you the number of moles of nitrogen gas, the pressure, and the temperature. You are asked to find the volume.

GIVEN: $n = 0.845$ mol, $P = 1.37$ atm, $T = 315$ K

FIND: V

STRATEGIZE You are given three of the four variables (P, T, and n) in the ideal gas law and asked to find the fourth (V). The conceptual plan shows how the ideal gas law provides the relationship between the known quantities and the unknown quantity.

CONCEPTUAL PLAN

$n, P, T \rightarrow V$

$PV = nRT$

RELATIONSHIPS USED

$PV = nRT$ (ideal gas law)

SOLVE To solve the problem, first solve the ideal gas law for V.

SOLUTION

$$PV = nRT$$

$$V = \frac{nRT}{P}$$

Then substitute the given quantities to calculate V.

$$V = \frac{0.845 \text{ mol} \times 0.08206 \frac{\text{L} \cdot \text{atm}}{\text{mol} \cdot \text{K}} \times 315 \text{ K}}{1.37 \text{ atm}}$$

$$= 15.9 \text{ L}$$

CHECK The units of the answer are correct. The magnitude of the answer (15.9 L) makes sense because, as you will see in the next section, one mole of an ideal gas under standard temperature and pressure (273 K and 1 atm) occupies 22.4 L. Although this is not standard temperature and pressure, the conditions are close enough for a ballpark check of the answer. Since this gas sample contains 0.845 mol, a volume of 15.9 L is reasonable.

FOR PRACTICE 6.5 An 8.50-L tire contains 0.552 mol of gas at a temperature of 305 K. What is the pressure (in atm and psi) of the gas in the tire?

EXAMPLE 6.6 Ideal Gas Law II

Calculate the number of moles of gas in a 3.24-L basketball inflated to a *total pressure* of 24.3 psi at 25 °C. (Note: The *total pressure* is not the same as the pressure read on a pressure gauge such as the type used for checking a car or bicycle tire. That pressure, called the *gauge pressure*, is the *difference* between the total pressure and atmospheric pressure. In this case, if atmospheric pressure is 14.7 psi, the gauge pressure would be 9.6 psi. However, for calculations involving the ideal gas law, you must use the *total pressure* of 24.3 psi.)

SORT The problem gives you the pressure, the volume, and the temperature. You are asked to find the number of moles of gas.

GIVEN: $P = 24.3$ psi, $V = 3.24$ L, $T(°\text{C}) = 25$ °C

FIND: n

STRATEGIZE The conceptual plan shows how the ideal gas law provides the relationship between the given quantities and the quantity to be found.

CONCEPTUAL PLAN

$P, V, T \rightarrow n$

$PV = nRT$

RELATIONSHIPS USED $PV = nRT$ (ideal gas law)

SOLVE To solve the problem, first solve the ideal gas law for n.

SOLUTION

$$PV = nRT$$

$$n = \frac{PV}{RT}$$

Before substituting into the equation, convert P and T into the correct units.

$$P = 24.3\ \cancel{\text{psi}} \times \frac{1\ \text{atm}}{14.7\ \cancel{\text{psi}}} = 1.6\underline{5}31\ \text{atm}$$

(Since rounding the intermediate answer would result in a slightly different final answer, mark the least significant digit in the intermediate answer but don't round until the end.)

$$T(\text{K}) = 25 + 273 = 298\ \text{K}$$

Finally, substitute into the equation and calculate n.

$$n = \frac{1.6\underline{5}31\ \cancel{\text{atm}} \times 3.24\ \cancel{\text{L}}}{0.08206\ \frac{\cancel{\text{L}}\cdot\cancel{\text{atm}}}{\text{mol}\cdot\cancel{\text{K}}} \times 298\ \cancel{\text{K}}} = 0.219\ \text{mol}$$

CHECK The units of the answer are correct. The magnitude of the answer (0.219 mol) makes sense because, as you will see in the next section, one mole of an ideal gas under standard temperature and pressure (273 K and 1 atm) occupies 22.4 L. At a pressure that is 65% higher than standard pressure, the volume of 1 mol of gas is proportionally lower. Since this gas sample occupies 3.24 L, the answer of 0.219 mol is reasonable.

FOR PRACTICE 6.6 What volume does 0.556 mol of gas occupy at a pressure of 715 mmHg and a temperature of 58 °C?

FOR MORE PRACTICE 6.6 Determine the pressure in mmHg of a 0.133-g sample of helium gas in a 648-mL container at 32 °C.

6.5 Applications of the Ideal Gas Law: Molar Volume, Density, and Molar Mass of a Gas

The molar volume of 22.4 L only applies at STP.

We just examined how we can use the ideal gas law to calculate one of the variables (P, V, T, or n) given the other three. We now turn to three other applications of the ideal gas law: molar volume, density, and molar mass.

Molar Volume at Standard Temperature and Pressure

The volume occupied by one mole of a substance is its **molar volume**. For gases, we often specify the molar volume under conditions known as **standard temperature** ($T = 0\ ^\circ\text{C}$ or 273 K) **and pressure** ($P = 1.00$ atm), abbreviated as **STP**. Applying the ideal gas law, we can determine that the molar volume of an ideal gas at STP is:

$$V = \frac{nRT}{P}$$

$$= \frac{1.00\ \cancel{\text{mol}} \times 0.08206\ \frac{\text{L}\cdot\cancel{\text{atm}}}{\cancel{\text{mol}}\cdot\cancel{\text{K}}} \times 273\ \cancel{\text{K}}}{1.00\ \cancel{\text{atm}}}$$

$$= 22.4\ \text{L}$$

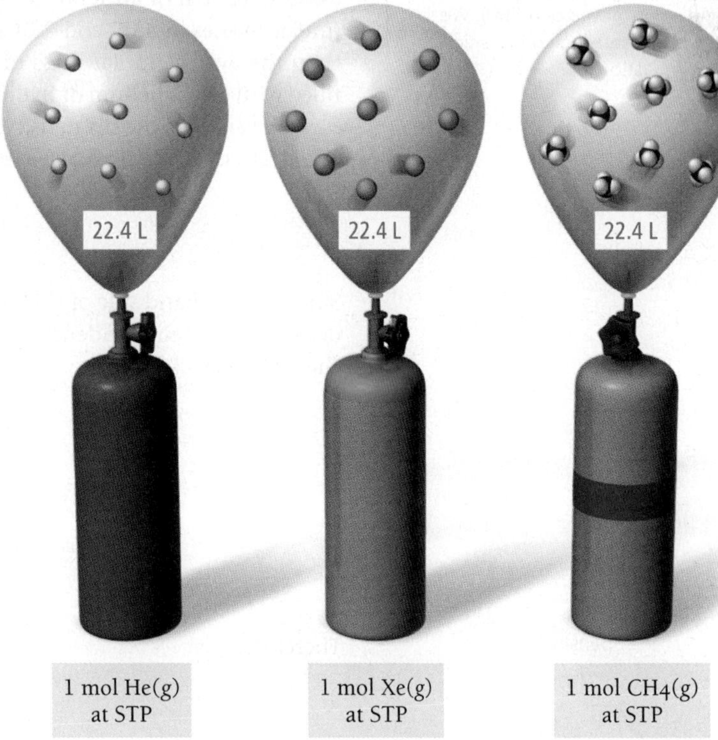

▲ One mole of any gas occupies approximately 22.4 L at standard temperature (273 K) and pressure (1.0 atm).

The molar volume of an ideal gas at STP is useful because—as we saw in the *Check* steps of Examples 6.5 and 6.6—it gives us a way to approximate the volume of an ideal gas under conditions that are close to STP.

ANSWER **NOW!**

6.3 Cc Conceptual Connection

MOLAR VOLUME Assuming ideal behavior, which of these gas samples has the greatest volume at STP?

(a) 1 g of H_2
(b) 1 g of O_2
(c) 1 g of Ar

Density of a Gas

Since one mole of an ideal gas occupies 22.4 L under standard temperature and pressure, we can readily calculate the density of an ideal gas under these conditions. Because density is mass/volume and because the mass of one mole of a gas is simply its molar mass, the *density of a gas* is its molar mass divided by its molar volume:

$$\text{Density} = \frac{\text{molar mass}}{\text{molar volume}}$$

We can calculate the density of a gas at STP by using 22.4 L as the molar volume. For example, the densities of helium and nitrogen gas at STP are:

$$d_{He} = \frac{4.00\ \text{g/mol}}{22.4\ \text{L/mol}} = 0.179\ \text{g/L} \qquad d_{N_2} = \frac{28.02\ \text{g/mol}}{22.4\ \text{L/mol}} = 1.25\ \text{g/L}$$

Notice that *the density of a gas is directly proportional to its molar mass*. The greater the molar mass of a gas, the more dense the gas. For this reason, a gas with a molar mass lower than that of air tends to rise in air. For example, both helium and hydrogen gas (molar masses of 4.00 and 2.01 g/mol, respectively) have molar masses that are lower than the average molar mass of air (approximately 28.8 g/mol). Therefore, a balloon filled with either helium or hydrogen gas floats in air.

The primary components of air are nitrogen (about four-fifths) and oxygen (about one-fifth). We discuss the detailed composition of air in Section 6.6.

We can calculate the density of a gas more generally (under any conditions) by using the ideal gas law. To do so, we can arrange the ideal gas law as:

$$PV = nRT$$

$$\frac{n}{V} = \frac{P}{RT}$$

Since the left-hand side of this equation has units of moles/liter, it represents the *molar* density. We obtain the density in grams/liter from the molar density by multiplying by the molar mass ($\mathcal{M}$):

$$\frac{\cancel{\text{moles}}}{\text{liter}} \times \frac{\text{grams}}{\cancel{\text{mole}}} = \frac{\text{grams}}{\text{liter}}$$

Molar density | Molar mass | Density in grams/liter

Therefore,

$$d = \frac{P\mathcal{M}}{RT} \qquad [6.6]$$

Density

$$\frac{n}{V}\mathcal{M} = \frac{P\mathcal{M}}{RT}$$

Molar density | Molar mass

$$d = \frac{P\mathcal{M}}{RT}$$

Notice that, as expected, density increases with increasing molar mass. Notice also that, as we discussed in Section 6.3, density decreases with increasing temperature.

WATCH NOW!
INTERACTIVE WORKED EXAMPLE 6.7

EXAMPLE 6.7 Density

Calculate the density of nitrogen gas at 125 °C and a pressure of 755 mmHg.

SORT The problem gives you the temperature and pressure of nitrogen gas and asks you to find its density.

GIVEN: $T(°C) = 125\ °C, P = 755\ mmHg$
FIND: d

STRATEGIZE Equation 6.6 provides the relationship between the density of a gas and its temperature, pressure, and molar mass. The temperature and pressure are given. You can calculate the molar mass from the formula of the gas, which you know is N_2.

CONCEPTUAL PLAN

$P, T, \mathcal{M} \rightarrow d$

$$d = \frac{P\mathcal{M}}{RT}$$

RELATIONSHIPS USED

$$d = \frac{P\mathcal{M}}{RT} \text{ (density of a gas)}$$

Molar mass $N_2 = 28.02\ g/mol$

SOLVE To solve the problem, gather each of the required quantities in the correct units. Convert the temperature to kelvins and the pressure to atmospheres.

SOLUTION

$T(K) = 125 + 273 = 398\ K$

$$P = 755\ \cancel{mmHg} \times \frac{1\ atm}{760\ \cancel{mmHg}} = 0.99\underline{3}42\ atm$$

Substitute the quantities into the equation to calculate density.

$$d = \frac{P\mathcal{M}}{RT}$$

$$= \frac{0.99\underline{3}42\ \cancel{atm}\left(28.02\frac{g}{\cancel{mol}}\right)}{0.08206\frac{L \cdot \cancel{atm}}{\cancel{mol} \cdot \cancel{K}}(398\ \cancel{K})}$$

$$= 0.852\ g/L$$

CHECK The units of the answer are correct. The magnitude of the answer (0.852 g/L) makes sense because earlier you calculated the density of nitrogen gas at STP as 1.25 g/L. Since the temperature is higher than standard temperature, it follows that the density is lower.

FOR PRACTICE 6.7 Calculate the density of xenon gas at a pressure of 742 mmHg and a temperature of 45 °C.

FOR MORE PRACTICE 6.7 The density of a gas is 1.43 g/L at a temperature of 23 °C and a pressure of 0.789 atm. Calculate the molar mass of the gas.

6.4 Cc Conceptual Connection ANSWER NOW!

DENSITY OF A GAS Arrange the following gases in order of increasing density at STP: Ne, Cl_2, F_2, and O_2.

(a) $Ne < O_2 < F_2 < Cl_2$
(b) $F_2 < Ne < O_2 < Cl_2$
(c) $Cl_2 < F_2 < O_2 < Ne$

Molar Mass of a Gas

We can use the ideal gas law in combination with mass measurements to calculate the molar mass of an unknown gas. First, we measure the mass and volume of an unknown gas under conditions of known pressure and temperature. Then, we determine the amount of the gas in moles from the ideal gas law. Finally, we calculate the molar mass by dividing the mass (in grams) by the amount (in moles) as demonstrated in Example 6.8.

WATCH NOW!
INTERACTIVE WORKED EXAMPLE 6.8

EXAMPLE 6.8 Molar Mass of a Gas

A sample of gas has a mass of 0.311 g. Its volume is 0.225 L at a temperature of 55 °C and a pressure of 886 mmHg. Find its molar mass.

SORT The problem gives you the mass of a gas sample, along with its volume, temperature, and pressure. You are asked to find the molar mass.

GIVEN: $m = 0.331 \text{ g}, V = 0.225 \text{ L},$
$T(°\text{C}) = 55 \text{ °C}, P = 886 \text{ mmHg}$
FIND: molar mass (g/mol)

STRATEGIZE The conceptual plan has two parts. In the first part, use the ideal gas law to find the number of moles of gas.

CONCEPTUAL PLAN

$P, V, T \rightarrow n$

$PV = nRT$

In the second part, use the definition of molar mass to determine the molar mass.

$n, m \rightarrow$ molar mass

$$\text{molar mass} = \frac{\text{mass } (m)}{\text{moles } (n)}$$

RELATIONSHIPS USED

$PV = nRT$

$$\text{Molar mass} = \frac{\text{mass } (m)}{\text{moles } (n)}$$

SOLVE To find the number of moles, first solve the ideal gas law for n.

SOLUTION

$$PV = nRT$$

$$n = \frac{PV}{RT}$$

Before substituting into the equation for n, convert the pressure to atm and the temperature to K.

$$P = 886 \cancel{\text{mmHg}} \times \frac{1 \text{ atm}}{760 \cancel{\text{mmHg}}} = 1.1\underline{6}58 \text{ atm}$$

$$T(\text{K}) = 55 + 273 = 328 \text{ K}$$

Then substitute into the equation and calculate n, the number of moles.

$$n = \frac{1.1\underline{6}58 \cancel{\text{atm}} \times 0.225 \cancel{\text{L}}}{0.08206 \frac{\cancel{\text{L}} \cdot \cancel{\text{atm}}}{\text{mol} \cdot \cancel{\text{K}}} \times 328 \cancel{\text{K}}}$$

$$= 9.7\underline{4}54 \times 10^{-3} \text{ mol}$$

Finally, use the number of moles (n) and the given mass (m) to calculate the molar mass.

$$\text{molar mass} = \frac{\text{mass } (m)}{\text{moles } (n)}$$

$$= \frac{0.311 \text{ g}}{9.7\underline{4}54 \times 10^{-3} \text{ mol}}$$

$$= 31.9 \text{ g/mol}$$

CHECK The units of the answer are correct. The magnitude of the answer (31.9 g/mol) is a reasonable number for a molar mass. If you calculated a very small number (such as any number smaller than 1) or a very large number, you solved the problem incorrectly. Most gases have molar masses between one and several hundred grams per mole.

FOR PRACTICE 6.8 The mass of a sample of gas is 827 mg. Its volume is 0.270 L at a temperature of 88 °C and a pressure of 975 mmHg. Find its molar mass.

WATCH **NOW!**
KEY CONCEPT VIDEO 6.6
Mixtures of Gases and Partial Pressures

6.6 Mixtures of Gases and Partial Pressures

Many gas samples are not pure but are mixtures of gases. Dry air, for example, is a mixture containing nitrogen, oxygen, argon, carbon dioxide, and a few other gases in trace amounts (Table 6.3).

Because the molecules in an ideal gas do not interact (as we will discuss further in Section 6.8), each of the components in an ideal gas mixture acts independently of the others. For example, the nitrogen molecules in air exert a certain pressure—78% of the total pressure—that is independent of the other gases in the mixture. Likewise, the oxygen molecules in air exert a certain pressure—21% of the total pressure—that is also independent of the other gases in the mixture. The pressure due to any individual component in a gas mixture is its **partial pressure** (P_n). We can calculate partial pressure from the ideal gas law by assuming that each gas component acts independently.

$$P_n = n_n \frac{RT}{V}$$

For a multicomponent gas mixture, we calculate the partial pressure of each component from the ideal gas law and the number of moles of that component (n_n) as follows:

$$P_a = n_a \frac{RT}{V};\ P_b = n_b \frac{RT}{V};\ P_c = n_c \frac{RT}{V};\ldots \qquad [6.7]$$

The sum of the partial pressures of the components in a gas mixture equals the total pressure:

$$P_{total} = P_a + P_b + P_c + \ldots \qquad [6.8]$$

where P_{total} is the total pressure and $P_a, P_b, P_c, \ldots$ are the partial pressures of the components. This relationship is known as **Dalton's law of partial pressures**.

Combining Equations 6.7 and 6.8, we get:

$$\begin{aligned} P_{total} &= P_a + P_b + P_c + \ldots \\ &= n_a \frac{RT}{V} + n_b \frac{RT}{V} + n_c \frac{RT}{V} + \ldots \\ &= (n_a + n_b + n_c + \ldots) \frac{RT}{V} \qquad [6.9] \\ &= (n_{total}) \frac{RT}{V} \end{aligned}$$

The total number of moles in the mixture, when substituted into the ideal gas law, indicates the total pressure of the sample.

If we divide Equation 6.7 by Equation 6.9, we get:

$$\frac{P_a}{P_{total}} = \frac{n_a(\cancel{RT/V})}{n_{total}(\cancel{RT/V})} = \frac{n_a}{n_{total}} \qquad [6.10]$$

The quantity n_a/n_{total}, the number of moles of a component in a mixture divided by the total number of moles in the mixture, is the **mole fraction** (χ_a):

$$\chi_a = \frac{n_a}{n_{total}} \qquad [6.11]$$

Rearranging Equation 6.10 and substituting the definition of mole fraction gives:

$$\frac{P_a}{P_{total}} = \frac{n_a}{n_{total}}$$

$$P_a = \frac{n_a}{n_{total}} P_{total} = \chi_a P_{total}$$

or simply

$$P_a = \chi_a P_{total} \qquad [6.12]$$

The partial pressure of a component in a gaseous mixture is its mole fraction multiplied by the total pressure. For gases, the mole fraction of a component is equivalent to its percent by volume divided by 100%. Therefore, based on Table 6.3, we calculate the partial pressure of nitrogen (P_{N_2}) in air at 1.00 atm as:

$$\begin{aligned} P_{N_2} &= 0.78 \times 1.00\ \text{atm} \\ &= 0.78\ \text{atm} \end{aligned}$$

TABLE 6.3 ■ Composition of Dry Air

Gas	Percent by Volume (%)
Nitrogen (N_2)	78
Oxygen (O_2)	21
Argon (Ar)	0.9
Carbon dioxide (CO_2)	0.04

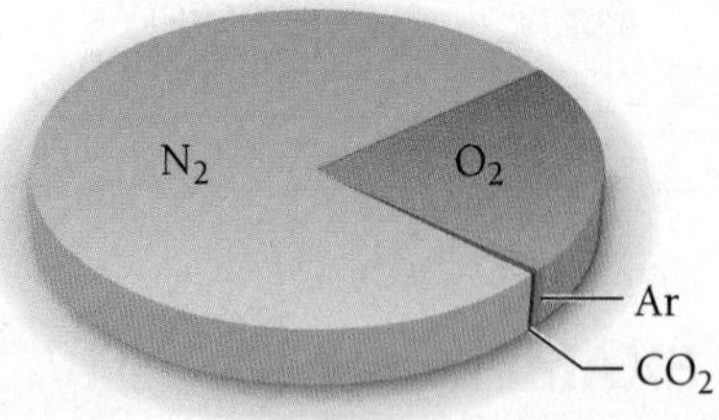

For these purposes, we can ignore the contribution of the CO_2 and other trace gases because they are so small.

Likewise, the partial pressure of oxygen in air at 1.00 atm is 0.21 atm, and the partial pressure of Ar in air is 0.009 atm. Applying Dalton's law of partial pressures to air at 1.00 atm, we can find the total pressure:

$$P_{total} = P_{N_2} + P_{O_2} + P_{Ar}$$
$$P_{total} = 0.78 \text{ atm} + 0.21 \text{ atm} + 0.009 \text{ atm}$$
$$= 1.00 \text{ atm}$$

ANSWER **NOW!**

6.5 **Cc** Conceptual Connection

PARTIAL PRESSURES A gas mixture contains an equal number of moles of He and Ne. The total pressure of the mixture is 3.0 atm. What are the partial pressures of He and Ne?

(a) $P_{He} = 2.0$ atm; $P_{Ne} = 1.0$ atm **(b)** $P_{He} = 1.0$ atm; $P_{Ne} = 2.0$ atm
(c) $P_{He} = 1.5$ atm; $P_{Ne} = 1.5$ atm

EXAMPLE 6.9 Total Pressure and Partial Pressures

A 1.00-L mixture of helium, neon, and argon has a total pressure of 662 mmHg at 298 K. If the partial pressure of helium is 341 mmHg and the partial pressure of neon is 112 mmHg, what mass of argon is present in the mixture?

SORT The problem gives you the partial pressures of two of the three components in a gas mixture, along with the total pressure, the volume, and the temperature, and asks you to find the mass of the third component.

GIVEN: $P_{He} = 341$ mmHg, $P_{Ne} = 112$ mmHg, $P_{total} = 662$ mmHg, $V = 1.00$ L, $T = 298$ K

FIND: m_{Ar}

STRATEGIZE You can find the mass of argon from the number of moles of argon, which you can calculate from the partial pressure of argon and the ideal gas law. Begin by using Dalton's law to determine the partial pressure of argon.

CONCEPTUAL PLAN

$P_{tot}, P_{He}, P_{Ne} \rightarrow P_{Ar}$

$P_{tot} = P_{He} + P_{Ne} + P_{Ar}$

Then use the partial pressure of argon together with the volume of the sample and the temperature to find the number of moles of argon.

$P_{Ar}, V, T \rightarrow n_{Ar}$

$PV = nRT$

Finally, use the molar mass of argon to calculate the mass of argon from the number of moles of argon.

$n_{Ar} \rightarrow m_{Ar}$

$\frac{39.95 \text{ g Ar}}{1 \text{ mol Ar}}$

RELATIONSHIPS USED

$P_{total} = P_{He} + P_{Ne} + P_{Ar}$ (Dalton's law)
$PV = nRT$ (ideal gas law)
molar mass Ar = 39.95 g/mol

SOLVE Follow the conceptual plan. To find the partial pressure of argon, solve the equation for P_{Ar} and substitute the values of the other partial pressures to calculate P_{Ar}.

SOLUTION

$$P_{total} = P_{He} + P_{Ne} + P_{Ar}$$
$$P_{Ar} = P_{total} - P_{He} - P_{Ne}$$
$$= 662 \text{ mmHg} - 341 \text{ mmHg} - 112 \text{ mmHg}$$
$$= 209 \text{ mmHg}$$

Convert the partial pressure from mmHg to atm and use it in the ideal gas law to calculate the amount of argon in moles.

$$209 \cancel{\text{mmHg}} \times \frac{1 \text{ atm}}{760 \cancel{\text{mmHg}}} = 0.275 \text{ atm}$$

$$n = \frac{PV}{RT} = \frac{0.275 \cancel{\text{atm}} (1.00 \cancel{\text{L}})}{0.08206 \frac{\cancel{\text{L}} \cdot \cancel{\text{atm}}}{\text{mol} \cdot \cancel{\text{K}}} (298 \cancel{\text{K}})} = 1.1\underline{2}5 \times 10^{-2} \text{ mol Ar}$$

Use the molar mass of argon to convert from amount of argon in moles to mass of argon.

$$1.1\underline{2}5 \times 10^{-2} \cancel{\text{mol Ar}} \times \frac{39.95 \text{ g Ar}}{1 \cancel{\text{mol Ar}}} = 0.449 \text{ g Ar}$$

CHECK The units of the answer are correct. The magnitude of the answer makes sense because the volume is 1.0 L, which at STP would contain about 1/22 mol. Since the partial pressure of argon in the mixture is about 1/3 of the total pressure, you can roughly estimate about 1/66 of one molar mass of argon, which is fairly close to your answer.

FOR PRACTICE 6.9 A sample of hydrogen gas is mixed with water vapor. The mixture has a total pressure of 755 torr, and the water vapor has a partial pressure of 24 torr. What amount (in moles) of hydrogen gas is contained in 1.55 L of this mixture at 298 K?

Deep-Sea Diving and Partial Pressures

Our lungs have evolved to breathe oxygen at a partial pressure of $P_{O_2} = 0.21$ atm. If the total pressure decreases—when we climb a mountain, for example—the partial pressure of oxygen also decreases. On top of Mount Everest, where the total pressure is 0.311 atm, the partial pressure of oxygen is only 0.065 atm. Low oxygen levels produce a physiological condition called **hypoxia** or oxygen starvation (Figure 6.13▶). Mild hypoxia causes dizziness, headache, and shortness of breath. Severe hypoxia, which occurs when P_{O_2} drops below 0.1 atm, may result in unconsciousness or even death. For this reason, climbers hoping to make the summit of Mount Everest usually carry oxygen to breathe.

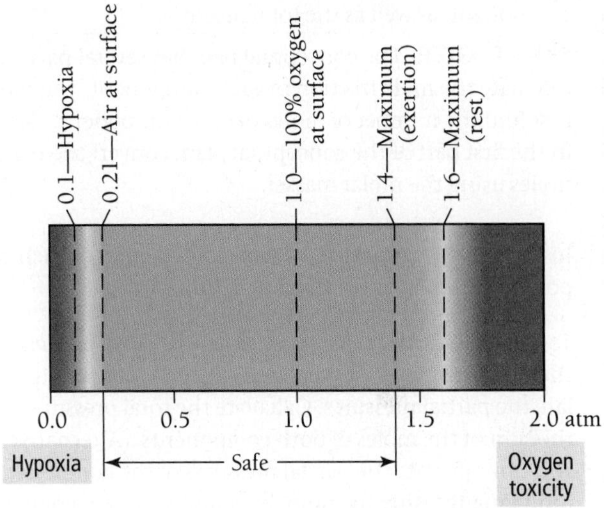

▲ **FIGURE 6.13 Oxygen Partial Pressure Limits** The partial pressure of oxygen in air at sea level is 0.21 atm. Partial pressures of oxygen below 0.1 atm and above 1.4 atm are dangerous to humans.

Though not as dangerous as a lack of oxygen, too much oxygen can also cause physiological problems. Recall from Section 6.3 that scuba divers breathe pressurized air. At 30 m, a scuba diver breathes air at a total pressure of 4.0 atm, making P_{O_2} about 0.84 atm. This elevated partial pressure of oxygen raises the density of oxygen molecules in the lungs, resulting in a higher concentration of oxygen in body tissues. When P_{O_2} increases beyond 1.4 atm, the increased oxygen concentration in body tissues causes a condition called **oxygen toxicity**, which results in muscle twitching, tunnel vision, and convulsions. Divers who venture too deep without proper precautions have drowned because of oxygen toxicity. A second problem associated with breathing pressurized air is the increase of nitrogen in the lungs. At 30 m, a scuba diver breathes nitrogen at $P_{N_2} = 3.12$ atm, which increases the nitrogen concentration in body tissues and fluids. When P_{N_2} increases beyond about 4 atm, a condition called **nitrogen narcosis** or *rapture of the deep* results. Divers describe this condition as feeling inebriated or drunk. A diver breathing compressed air at 60 m feels as if he has consumed too much wine.

To avoid oxygen toxicity and nitrogen narcosis, deep-sea divers—those who descend beyond 50 m—breathe specialized mixtures of gases. One common mixture is heliox, a mixture of helium and oxygen. These mixtures usually contain a smaller percentage of oxygen than would be found in air, thereby lowering the risk of oxygen toxicity. Heliox also contains helium instead of nitrogen, eliminating the risk of nitrogen narcosis.

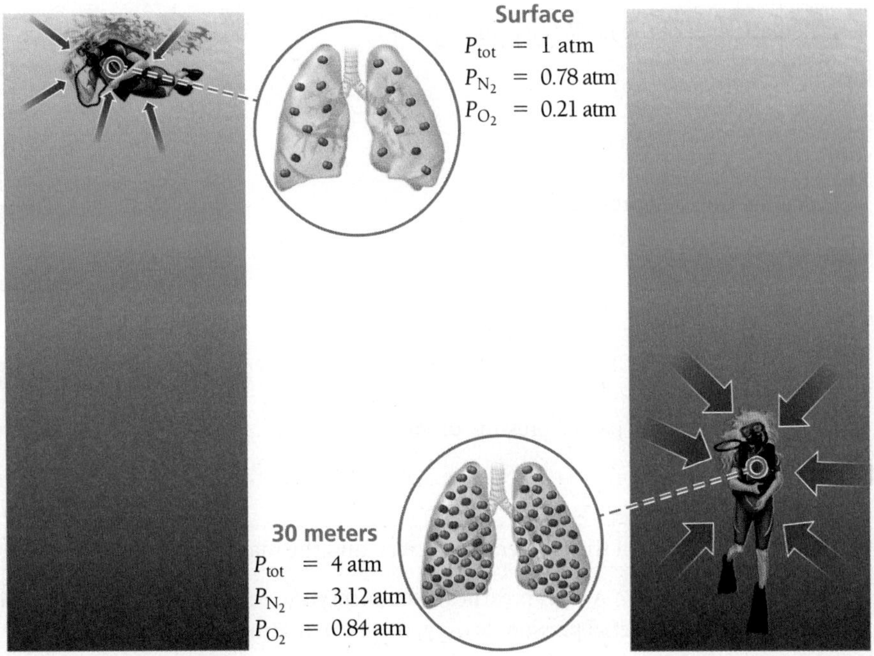

▶ When a diver breathes compressed air, the abnormally high partial pressure of oxygen in the lungs leads to an elevated concentration of oxygen in body tissues.

WATCH NOW!
INTERACTIVE WORKED EXAMPLE 6.10

EXAMPLE 6.10 Partial Pressures and Mole Fractions

A 12.5-L scuba diving tank contains a helium–oxygen (heliox) mixture made up of 24.2 g of He and 4.32 g of O_2 at 298 K. Calculate the mole fraction and partial pressure of each component in the mixture and the total pressure of the mixture.

SORT The problem gives the masses of two gases in a mixture and the volume and temperature of the mixture. You are to find the mole fraction and partial pressure of each component, as well as the total pressure.

GIVEN: $m_{He} = 24.2\ g, m_{O_2} = 4.32\ g,$
$V = 12.5\ L, T = 298\ K$

FIND: $\chi_{He}, \chi_{O_2}, P_{He}, P_{O_2}, P_{total}$

STRATEGIZE The conceptual plan has several parts. To calculate the mole fraction of each component, you must first find the number of moles of each component. Therefore, in the first part of the conceptual plan, convert the masses to moles using the molar masses.

CONCEPTUAL PLAN

$$m_{He} \xrightarrow{\frac{1\ mol\ He}{4.00\ g\ He}} n_{He} \qquad m_{O_2} \xrightarrow{\frac{1\ mol\ O_2}{32.00\ g\ O_2}} n_{O_2}$$

In the second part, calculate the mole fraction of each component using the mole fraction definition.

$$\chi_{He} = \frac{n_{He}}{n_{He} + n_{O_2}}; \quad \chi_{O_2} = \frac{n_{O_2}}{n_{He} + n_{O_2}}$$

To calculate *partial pressures*, calculate the *total pressure* and then use the mole fractions from the previous part to calculate the partial pressures. Calculate the total pressure from the sum of the moles of both components. (Alternatively, you can calculate the partial pressures of the components individually, using the number of moles of each component. Then you can sum them to obtain the total pressure.)

$$P_{total} = \frac{(n_{He} + n_{O_2})RT}{V}$$

$$P_{He} = \chi_{He}P_{total}; \quad P_{O_2} = \chi_{O_2}P_{total}$$

RELATIONSHIPS USED

$\chi_a = n_a/n_{total}$ (mole fraction definition)

$P_{total}V = n_{total}RT$

Last, use the mole fractions of each component and the total pressure to calculate the partial pressure of each component.

$P_a = \chi_a P_{total}$

SOLVE Follow the plan to solve the problem. Begin by converting each of the masses to amounts in moles.

SOLUTION

$$24.2\ \cancel{g\ He} \times \frac{1\ mol\ He}{4.00\ \cancel{g\ He}} = 6.05\ mol\ He$$

$$4.32\ \cancel{g\ O_2} \times \frac{1\ mol\ O_2}{32.00\ \cancel{g\ O_2}} = 0.135\ mol\ O_2$$

Calculate each of the mole fractions.

$$\chi_{He} = \frac{n_{He}}{n_{He} + n_{O_2}} = \frac{6.05}{6.05 + 0.135} = 0.97\underline{8}17$$

$$\chi_{O_2} = \frac{n_{O_2}}{n_{He} + n_{O_2}} = \frac{0.135}{6.05 + 0.135} = 0.021\underline{8}27$$

Calculate the total pressure.

$$P_{total} = \frac{(n_{He} + n_{O_2})RT}{V}$$

$$= \frac{(6.05\ \cancel{mol} + 0.135\ \cancel{mol})\left(0.08206\frac{\cancel{L}\cdot atm}{\cancel{mol}\cdot \cancel{K}}\right)(298\ \cancel{K})}{12.5\ \cancel{L}}$$

$$= 12.\underline{0}99\ atm$$

Finally, calculate the partial pressure of each component.

$$P_{He} = \chi_{He}P_{total} = 0.967\underline{8}17 \times 12.\underline{0}99\ atm = 11.8\ atm$$

$$P_{O_2} = \chi_{O_2}P_{total} = 0.021\underline{8}27 \times 12.\underline{0}99\ atm$$
$$= 0.264\ atm$$

CHECK The units of the answers are correct, and the magnitudes are reasonable.

FOR PRACTICE 6.10 A diver breathes a heliox mixture with an oxygen mole fraction of 0.050. What must the total pressure be for the partial pressure of oxygen to be 0.21 atm?

Collecting Gases over Water

When the desired product of a chemical reaction is a gas, the gas is often collected by the displacement of water. For example, suppose we use the reaction of zinc with hydrochloric acid as a source of hydrogen gas:

$$Zn(s) + 2\,HCl(aq) \longrightarrow ZnCl_2(aq) + H_2(g)$$

To collect the gas, we can set up an apparatus like the one shown in Figure 6.14▼. As the hydrogen gas forms, it bubbles through the water and gathers in the collection flask. The hydrogen gas collected in this way is not pure, however. It is mixed with water vapor because some water molecules evaporate and combine with the hydrogen molecules.

The partial pressure of water in the mixture, called its **vapor pressure**, depends on temperature (Table 6.4). Vapor pressure increases with increasing temperature because higher temperatures cause more water molecules to evaporate. We will discuss vapor pressure more thoroughly in Chapter 12.

Appendix IIE includes a more complete table of the vapor pressure of water versus temperature.

Suppose we collect hydrogen gas over water at a total pressure of 758.2 mmHg and a temperature of 25 °C. What is the partial pressure of the hydrogen gas? We know that the total pressure is 758.2 mmHg and that the partial pressure of water is 23.78 mmHg (its vapor pressure at 25 °C):

$$P_{total} = P_{H_2} + P_{H_2O}$$

$$758.2\text{ mmHg} = P_{H_2} + 23.78\text{ mmHg}$$

Therefore,

$$P_{H_2} = 758.2\text{ mmHg} - 23.78\text{ mmHg}$$

$$= 734.4\text{ mmHg}$$

The partial pressure of the hydrogen in the mixture is 734.4 mmHg.

TABLE 6.4 ■ Vapor Pressure of Water versus Temperature

Temperature (°C)	Pressure (mmHg)	Temperature (°C)	Pressure (mmHg)
0	4.58	55	118.2
5	6.54	60	149.6
10	9.21	65	187.5
15	12.79	70	233.7
20	17.55	75	289.1
25	23.78	80	355.1
30	31.86	85	433.6
35	42.23	90	525.8
40	55.40	95	633.9
45	71.97	100	760.0
50	92.6		

Collecting a Gas over Water

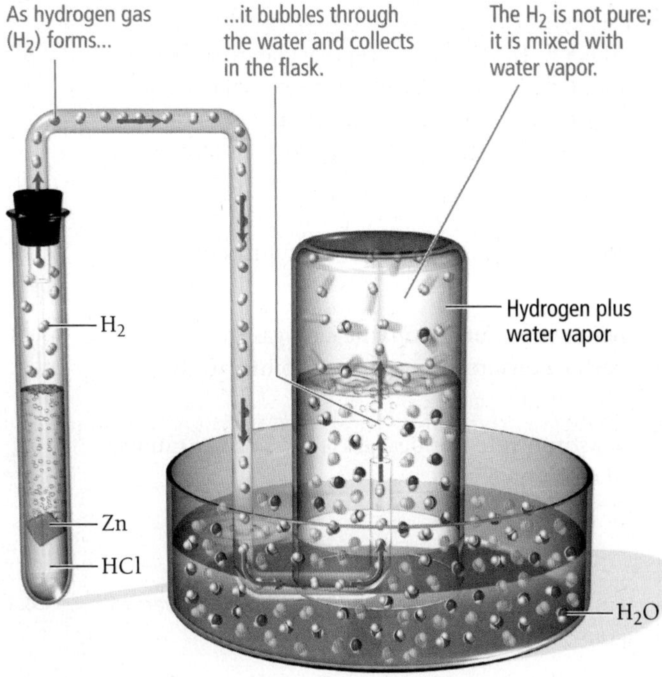

▶ **FIGURE 6.14 Collecting a Gas over Water** When the gaseous product of a chemical reaction is collected over water, the product molecules (in this case H_2) mix with water molecules. The pressure of water in the final mixture is equal to the vapor pressure of water at the temperature at which the gas is collected. The partial pressure of the product is the total pressure minus the partial pressure of water.

WATCH NOW!

INTERACTIVE WORKED EXAMPLE 6.11

EXAMPLE 6.11 Collecting Gases over Water

In order to determine the rate of photosynthesis (the conversion by plants of carbon dioxide and water into glucose and oxygen), the oxygen gas emitted by an aquatic plant is collected over water at a temperature of 293 K and a total pressure of 755.2 mmHg. Over a specific time period, a total of 1.02 L of gas is collected. What mass of oxygen gas (in grams) forms?

SORT The problem gives the volume of gas collected over water as well as the temperature and the pressure. You are to find the mass in grams of oxygen that forms.

GIVEN: $V = 1.02\text{ L}, P_{\text{total}} = 755.2\text{ mmHg}, T = 293\text{ K}$

FIND: $\text{g } O_2$

STRATEGIZE You can determine the mass of oxygen from the amount of oxygen in moles, which you can calculate from the ideal gas law if you know the partial pressure of oxygen. Since the oxygen is mixed with water vapor, you find the partial pressure of oxygen in the mixture by subtracting the partial pressure of water at 293 K (20 °C) from the total pressure.

CONCEPTUAL PLAN

$$P_{O_2} = P_{\text{total}} - P_{H_2O}(20\ °\text{C})$$

Next, use the ideal gas law to determine the number of moles of oxygen from its partial pressure, volume, and temperature.

$$P_{O_2}, V, T \longrightarrow n_{O_2}$$

$$P_{O_2}V = n_{O_2}RT$$

Finally, use the molar mass of oxygen to convert the number of moles to grams.

$$n_{O_2} \longrightarrow \text{g } O_2$$

$$\frac{32.00\text{ g } O_2}{\text{mol } O_2}$$

RELATIONSHIPS USED

$P_{\text{total}} = P_a + P_b + P_c + \ldots$ (Dalton's law)

$PV = nRT$ (ideal gas law)

SOLVE Follow the conceptual plan to solve the problem. Begin by calculating the partial pressure of oxygen in the oxygen/water mixture. You can find the partial pressure of water at 20 °C in Table 6.4.

SOLUTION

$$\begin{aligned} P_{O_2} &= P_{\text{total}} - P_{H_2O}(20\ °\text{C}) \\ &= 755.2\text{ mmHg} - 17.55\text{ mmHg} \\ &= 737.\underline{6}5\text{ mmHg} \end{aligned}$$

Next, solve the ideal gas law for number of moles.

$$n_{O_2} = \frac{P_{O_2}V}{RT}$$

Before substituting into the ideal gas law, convert the partial pressure of oxygen from mmHg to atm.

$$737.\underline{6}5\ \cancel{\text{mmHg}} \times \frac{1\text{ atm}}{760\ \cancel{\text{mmHg}}} = 0.970\underline{5}9\text{ atm}$$

Substitute into the ideal gas law to find the number of moles of oxygen.

$$n_{O_2} = \frac{P_{O_2}V}{RT} = \frac{0.970\underline{5}9\ \cancel{\text{atm}}(1.02\ \cancel{\text{L}})}{0.08206\frac{\cancel{\text{L}}\cdot\cancel{\text{atm}}}{\text{mol}\cdot\cancel{\text{K}}}(293\ \cancel{\text{K}})}$$

$$= 4.1\underline{1}75 \times 10^{-2}\text{ mol}$$

Finally, use the molar mass of oxygen to convert to grams of oxygen.

$$4.1\underline{1}75 \times 10^{-2}\ \cancel{\text{mol } O_2} \times \frac{32.00\text{ g } O_2}{1\ \cancel{\text{mol } O_2}} = 1.32\text{ g } O_2$$

CHECK The answer is in the correct units. You can quickly check the magnitude of the answer by using molar volume. Under STP, one liter is about 1/22 of one mole. Therefore, the answer should be about 1/22 the molar mass of oxygen ($1/22 \times 32 = 1.45$). The magnitude of the answer seems reasonable.

FOR PRACTICE 6.11 A common way to make hydrogen gas in the laboratory is to place a metal such as zinc in hydrochloric acid. The hydrochloric acid reacts with the metal to produce hydrogen gas, which is then collected over water. Suppose a student carries out this reaction and collects a total of 154.4 mL of gas at a pressure of 742 mmHg and a temperature of 25 °C. What mass of hydrogen gas (in mg) does the student collect?

6.7 Gases in Chemical Reactions: Stoichiometry Revisited

In Chapter 4, we discussed how to use the coefficients in chemical equations as conversion factors between number of moles of reactants and number of moles of products in a chemical reaction. We can use these conversion factors to determine, for example, the mass of product obtained in a chemical reaction based on a given mass of reactant, or the mass of one reactant needed to react completely with a given mass of another reactant. The general conceptual plan for these kinds of calculations is:

mass A → amount A (in moles) → amount B (in moles) → mass B

where A and B are two different substances involved in the reaction and the conversion factor between amounts (in moles) of each comes from the stoichiometric coefficients in the balanced chemical equation.

In reactions involving *gaseous* reactant or products, we often specify the quantity of a gas in terms of its volume at a given temperature and pressure. As we have seen, stoichiometry involves relationships between amounts in moles. For stoichiometric calculations involving gases, we can use the ideal gas law to determine the amounts in moles from the volumes, or to determine the volumes from the amounts in moles.

$$n = \frac{PV}{RT} \qquad V = \frac{nRT}{P}$$

The pressures here could also be partial pressures.

The general conceptual plan for these kinds of calculations is:

P, V, T of gas A → amount A (in moles) → amount B (in moles) → P, V, T of gas B

Examples 6.12 and 6.13 demonstrate this kind of calculation.

WATCH NOW!
INTERACTIVE WORKED EXAMPLE 6.12

EXAMPLE 6.12 Gases in Chemical Reactions

Methanol (CH_3OH) can be synthesized by the reaction:

$$CO(g) + 2\,H_2(g) \longrightarrow CH_3OH(g)$$

What volume (in liters) of hydrogen gas, at a temperature of 355 K and a pressure of 738 mmHg, is needed to synthesize 35.7 g of methanol?

SORT You are given the mass of methanol, the product of the chemical reaction. You are asked to find the required volume of one of the reactants (hydrogen gas) at a specified temperature and pressure.	**GIVEN:** 35.7 g CH_3OH, $T = 355$ K, $P = 738$ mmHg **FIND:** V_{H_2}

—*Continued on the next page*

Continued—

STRATEGIZE You can calculate the required volume of hydrogen gas from the number of moles of hydrogen gas, which you can obtain from the number of moles of methanol via the stoichiometry of the reaction.

CONCEPTUAL PLAN

First, find the number of moles of methanol from its mass by using the molar mass.

$$\text{g } CH_3OH \longrightarrow \text{mol } CH_3OH$$

$$\frac{1 \text{ mol } CH_3OH}{32.04 \text{ g } CH_3OH}$$

Then use the stoichiometric relationship from the balanced chemical equation to find the number of moles of hydrogen you need to form that quantity of methanol.

$$\text{mol } CH_3OH \longrightarrow \text{mol } H_2$$

$$\frac{2 \text{ mol } H_2}{1 \text{ mol } CH_3OH}$$

Finally, substitute the number of moles of hydrogen together with the pressure and temperature into the ideal gas law to find the volume of hydrogen.

$$n \text{ (mol } H_2\text{)}, P, T \longrightarrow V_{H_2}$$

$$PV = nRT$$

RELATIONSHIPS USED

$PV = nRT$ (ideal gas law)

2 mol H_2 : 1 mol CH_3OH (from balanced chemical equation)

molar mass CH_3OH = 32.04 g/mol

SOLVE Follow the conceptual plan to solve the problem. Begin by using the mass of methanol to determine the number of moles of methanol.

SOLUTION

$$35.7 \text{ g } CH_3OH \times \frac{1 \text{ mol } CH_3OH}{32.04 \text{ g } CH_3OH} = 1.1\underline{1}42 \text{ mol } CH_3OH$$

Next, convert the number of moles of methanol to moles of hydrogen.

$$1.1\underline{1}42 \text{ mol } CH_3OH \times \frac{2 \text{ mol } H_2}{1 \text{ mol } CH_3OH} = 2.2\underline{2}84 \text{ mol } H_2$$

Finally, use the ideal gas law to calculate the volume of hydrogen. Before substituting into the equation, you need to convert the pressure to atmospheres.

$$V_{H_2} = \frac{n_{H_2}RT}{P}$$

$$P = 738 \text{ mmHg} \times \frac{1 \text{ atm}}{760 \text{ mmHg}} = 0.97\underline{1}05 \text{ atm}$$

$$V_{H_2} = \frac{(2.2\underline{2}84 \text{ mol})\left(0.08206 \frac{\text{L} \cdot \text{atm}}{\text{mol} \cdot \text{K}}\right)(355 \text{ K})}{0.97\underline{1}05 \text{ atm}}$$

$$= 66.9 \text{ L}$$

CHECK The units of the answer are correct. The magnitude of the answer (66.9 L) seems reasonable. You are given slightly more than one molar mass of methanol, which is therefore slightly more than one mole of methanol. From the equation you can see that you need 2 mol hydrogen to make 1 mol methanol, so the answer must be slightly greater than 2 mol hydrogen. Under standard temperature and pressure, slightly more than 2 mol hydrogen occupies slightly more than $2 \times 22.4 \text{ L} = 44.8 \text{ L}$. At a temperature greater than standard temperature, the volume would be even greater; therefore, your answer is reasonable.

FOR PRACTICE 6.12 In the reaction shown here, 4.58 L of O_2 forms at $P = 745$ mmHg and $T = 308$ K. How many grams of Ag_2O decomposed?

$$2\,Ag_2O(s) \longrightarrow 4\,Ag(s) + O_2(g)$$

FOR MORE PRACTICE 6.12 In the previous reaction, what mass of $Ag_2O(s)$ (in grams) is required to form 388 mL of oxygen gas at $P = 734$ mmHg and 25.0 °C?

Molar Volume and Stoichiometry

In Section 6.5, we saw that under standard temperature and pressure, 1 mol of an ideal gas occupies 22.4 L. Consequently, if a reaction occurs at or near standard temperature and pressure, we can use 1 mol = 22.4 L as a conversion factor in stoichiometric calculations, as demonstrated in Example 6.13.

EXAMPLE 6.13 Using Molar Volume in Gas Stoichiometric Calculations

How many grams of water form when 1.24 L of H_2 gas at STP completely reacts with O_2?

$$2\,H_2(g) + O_2(g) \longrightarrow 2\,H_2O(g)$$

SORT You are given the volume of hydrogen gas (a reactant) at STP and asked to determine the mass of water that forms upon complete reaction.

GIVEN: 1.24 L H_2

FIND: g H_2O

STRATEGIZE Since the reaction occurs under standard temperature and pressure, you can convert directly from the volume (in liters) of hydrogen gas to the amount in moles. Then use the stoichiometric relationship from the balanced equation to find the number of moles of water formed. Finally, use the molar mass of water to obtain the mass of water formed.

CONCEPTUAL PLAN

L H_2 → mol H_2 → mol H_2O → g H_2O

$$\frac{1\text{ mol }H_2}{22.4\text{ L }H_2} \qquad \frac{2\text{ mol }H_2O}{2\text{ mol }H_2} \qquad \frac{18.02\text{ g }H_2O}{1\text{ mol }H_2O}$$

RELATIONSHIPS USED

1 mol = 22.4 L (at STP)

2 mol H_2 : 2 mol H_2O (from balanced equation)

molar mass H_2O = 18.02 g/mol

SOLVE Follow the conceptual plan to solve the problem.

$$1.24\text{ L }H_2 \times \frac{1\text{ mol }H_2}{22.4\text{ L }H_2} \times \frac{2\text{ mol }H_2O}{2\text{ mol }H_2} \times \frac{18.02\text{ g }H_2O}{1\text{ mol }H_2O} = 0.998\text{ g }H_2O$$

CHECK The units of the answer are correct. The magnitude of the answer (0.998 g) is about 1/18 of the molar mass of water, which is roughly equivalent to the approximately 1/22 of a mole of hydrogen gas given, as expected for the 1:1 stoichiometric relationship between number of moles of hydrogen and number of moles of water.

FOR PRACTICE 6.13 How many liters of oxygen (at STP) are required to form 10.5 g of H_2O?

$$2\,H_2(g) + O_2(g) \longrightarrow 2\,H_2O(g)$$

6.6 Cc Conceptual Connection ANSWER NOW!

PRESSURE AND NUMBER OF MOLES Nitrogen and hydrogen react to form ammonia according to the following equation:

$$N_2(g) + 3\,H_2(g) \rightleftharpoons 2\,NH_3(g)$$

Consider the following representations of the initial mixture of reactants and the resulting mixture after the reaction has been allowed to react for some time:

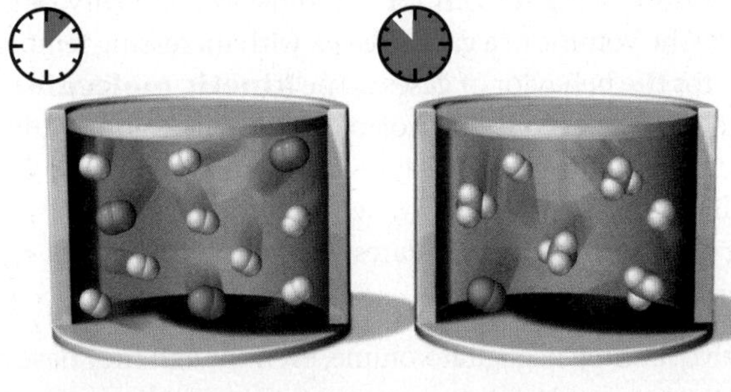

If the volume is kept constant, and nothing is added to the reaction mixture, what happens to the total pressure during the course of the reaction?

(a) The pressure increases.
(b) The pressure decreases.
(c) The pressure does not change.

ANALYZING AND INTERPRETING DATA

Good News about Our Nation's Air Quality

Air pollution has been a major problem in most U.S. cities. These gaseous pollutants are produced (either directly or indirectly) by chemical reactions, especially the combustion of fossil fuels such as petroleum and coal. The major pollutants include carbon monoxide, nitrogen dioxide, sulfur dioxide, and ozone. These pollutants have adverse effects on our health because they affect our respiratory and cardiovascular systems.

The good news is that the concentrations of these pollutants in U.S. cities is decreasing significantly. The U.S. Environmental Protection Agency (EPA) regularly monitors levels of these pollutants relative to standards called the National Ambient Air Quality Standards. The accompanying graph shows progress relative to those standards from 1990 to 2016.

Whenever you encounter data like this, the first thing you should examine are the *x*- and *y*-axes. You can't understand a graph if you don't understand its axes. In this case, the *x*-axis is straightforward: it represents time between 1990 and 2016. The *y*-axis is a bit more challenging because it represents the percent above or below the National Ambient Air Quality Standards (NAAQS; shown in the following table). By representing the levels this way, the EPA can show the changes in all four of these pollutants on the same graph. If they graphed the actual concentrations of the pollutants, the changes in the pollutants with low concentrations (O_3 and SO_2) would not be visible because they would appear as flat lines on the bottom of the graph.

The vast improvements in U.S. air quality have been realized even though the economy, the population, and overall energy use have grown substantially over the same period. The reasons for these improvements are good legislation (the Clean Air Act and its amendments) and vast improvements in technological innovation. We all breathe cleaner air today thanks to these developments.

National Air Pollutant Concentration Averages

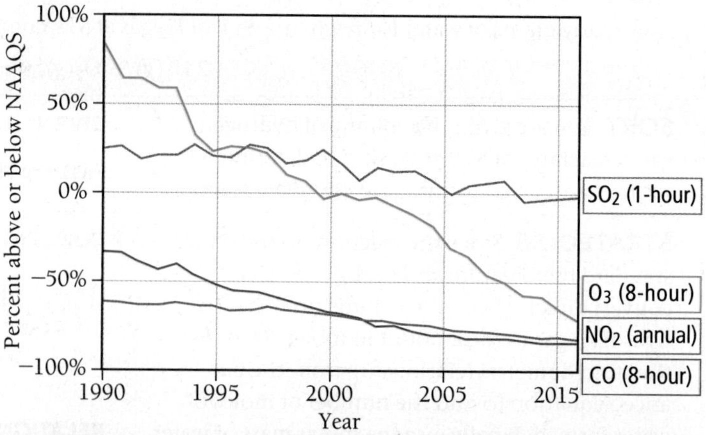

National Ambient Air Quality Standards

Pollutant	Standard
CO (8 hour)	9 ppm
NO_2 (annual)	53 ppm
O_3 (8 hour)	0.070 ppm
SO_2 (1 hour)	75 ppb

ppm = parts per million; ppb = parts per billion

WATCH **NOW!**

KEY CONCEPT VIDEO 6.8
Kinetic Molecular Theory

6.8 Kinetic Molecular Theory: A Model for Gases

In Chapter 1, we discussed how the scientific approach proceeds from observations to laws and eventually to theories. Remember that laws summarize behavior—for example, Charles's law summarizes *how* the volume of a gas depends on temperature—whereas theories give the underlying reasons for the behavior. A theory of gas behavior explains, for example, *why* the volume of a gas increases with increasing temperature.

The simplest model for the behavior of gases is the **kinetic molecular theory**. In this theory, a gas is modeled as a collection of particles (either molecules or atoms, depending on the gas) in constant motion (Figure 6.15▶). A single particle moves in a straight line until it collides with another particle (or with the wall of the container). Kinetic molecular theory has three basic postulates (or assumptions):

1. **The size of a particle is negligibly small.** Kinetic molecular theory assumes that the particles themselves occupy negligible volume, even though they have mass. This postulate is justified because, under normal pressures, the space between atoms or molecules in a gas is very large compared to the size of the atoms or molecules themselves. For example, in a sample of argon gas at STP, only about 0.01% of the volume is occupied by atoms, and the average distance from one argon atom to another is 3.3 nm. In comparison, the atomic radius of argon is 97 pm. If an argon atom were the size of a golf ball, its nearest neighbor would be, on average, over 4 ft (1.2 m) away at STP.

2. **The average kinetic energy of a particle is proportional to the temperature in kelvins.** The motion of atoms or molecules in a gas is due to thermal energy, which distributes itself among the particles in the gas. At any given moment, some particles are moving faster than others—there is a distribution of velocities—but the higher the temperature, the faster the overall motion and the greater the average kinetic energy. Notice that *kinetic energy* ($\frac{1}{2}mv^2$)—not *velocity*—is proportional to temperature. The atoms in a sample of helium and a sample of argon at the same temperature have the same average *kinetic energy* but not the same average *velocity*. Because the helium atoms are lighter, they must move faster to have the same kinetic energy as argon atoms.
3. **The collision of one particle with another (or with the walls of its container) is completely elastic.** When two particles collide, they may *exchange energy*, but there is no overall *loss of energy*. Any kinetic energy lost by one particle is completely gained by the other. In other words, the particles have no "stickiness," and they are not deformed by the collision. An encounter between two particles in kinetic molecular theory is more like the collision between two billiard balls than the collision between two lumps of clay (Figure 6.16▼). Between collisions, the particles do not exert any forces on one another.

If we start with the postulates of kinetic molecular theory, we can mathematically derive the ideal gas law (as we demonstrate later). Since the ideal gas law follows directly from kinetic molecular theory, we have confidence that the assumptions of the theory are valid, at least under conditions where the ideal gas law applies.

Kinetic Molecular Theory

▲ **FIGURE 6.15 A Model for Gas Behavior** In the kinetic molecular theory of gases, a gas sample is modeled as a collection of particles in constant straight-line motion. The size of each particle is negligibly small, and the particles' collisions are elastic.

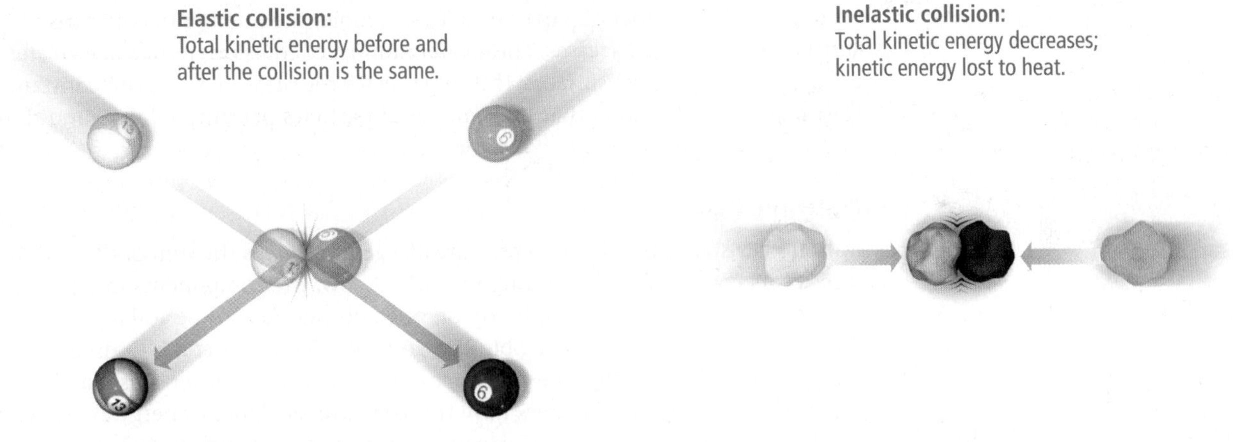

▲ **FIGURE 6.16 Elastic versus Inelastic Collisions** When two billiard balls collide, the collision is elastic—the total kinetic energy of the colliding bodies is the same before and after the collision. When two lumps of clay collide, the collision is inelastic—the kinetic energy of the colliding bodies dissipates in the form of heat during the collision.

How Kinetic Molecular Theory Explains Pressure and the Simple Gas Laws

Let's examine how the concept of pressure as well as each of the gas laws we have examined in this chapter follow conceptually from kinetic molecular theory.

The Nature of Pressure

In Section 6.2, we defined pressure as force divided by area:

$$P = \frac{F}{A}$$

From Newton's second law, the force (F) associated with an individual collision is given by $F = ma$, where m is the mass of the particle and a is its acceleration as it changes its direction of travel due to the collision.

According to kinetic molecular theory, a gas is a collection of particles in constant motion. The motion results in collisions between the particles and the surfaces around them. As each particle collides with a surface, it exerts a force upon that surface.

The result of many particles in a gas sample exerting forces on the surfaces around them is a constant pressure.

Boyle's Law

Boyle's law states that for a constant number of particles at constant temperature, the volume of a gas is inversely proportional to its pressure. According to kinetic molecular theory, if we decrease the volume of a gas, we force the gas particles to occupy a smaller space. As long as the temperature remains the same, the number of collisions with the surrounding surfaces (per unit surface area) must necessarily increase, resulting in a greater pressure.

Charles's Law

Charles's law states that for a constant number of particles at constant pressure, the volume of a gas is proportional to its temperature. According to kinetic molecular theory, when we increase the temperature of a gas, the average speed, and thus the average kinetic energy, of the particles increases. Since this greater kinetic energy results in more frequent collisions and more force per collision, the pressure of the gas increases if its volume is held constant (Gay-Lussac's law). The only way for the pressure to remain constant is for the volume to increase. The greater volume spreads the collisions out over a greater surface area so that the pressure (defined as force per unit area) is unchanged.

Avogadro's Law

Avogadro's law states that at constant temperature and pressure, the volume of a gas is proportional to the number of particles. According to kinetic molecular theory, when we increase the number of particles in a gas sample, the number of collisions with the surrounding surfaces increases. The greater number of collisions results in a greater overall force on surrounding surfaces; the only way for the pressure to remain constant is for the volume to increase so that the number of particles per unit volume (and thus the number of collisions) remains constant.

Dalton's Law

Dalton's law states that the total pressure of a gas mixture is the sum of the partial pressures of its components. According to Dalton's law, the components in a gas mixture act identically to, and independently of, one another. According to kinetic molecular theory, the particles have negligible size and they do not interact. Consequently, the only property that distinguishes one type of particle from another is its mass. However, even particles of different masses have the same average kinetic energy at a given temperature, so they exert the same force upon collision with a surface. Consequently, adding components to a gas mixture—even different *kinds* of gases—has the same effect as simply adding more particles. The partial pressures of all the components sum to the overall pressure.

Kinetic Molecular Theory and the Ideal Gas Law

We have just seen how each of the gas laws conceptually follows from kinetic molecular theory. We can also *derive* the ideal gas law from the postulates of kinetic molecular theory. In other words, the kinetic molecular theory is a quantitative model that *implies* $PV = nRT$. Let's explore this derivation.

The pressure on a wall of a container (Figure 6.17▶) occupied by particles in constant motion is the total force on the wall (due to the collisions) divided by the area of the wall.

$$P = \frac{F_{\text{total}}}{A} \qquad [6.13]$$

Recall that the force (F) associated with an individual collision is given by $F = ma$, where m is the mass of the particle and a is its acceleration as it changes its direction of travel

Calculating Gas Pressure: A Molecular View

Only particles within the volume defined by $A \times v\Delta t$ are capable of hitting the end wall within the time period Δt.

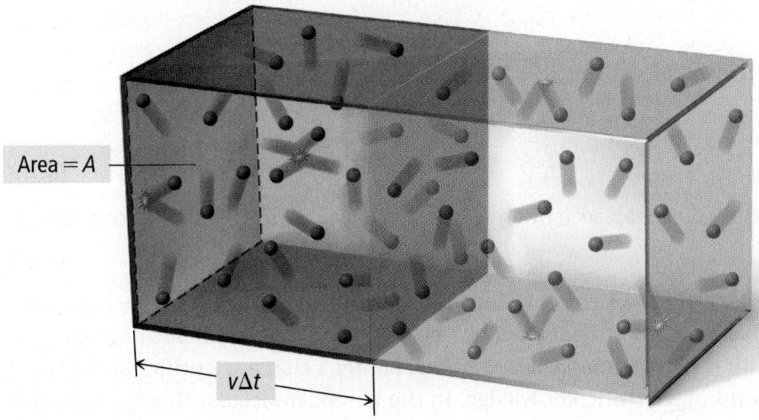

◀ FIGURE 6.17 The Pressure on the Wall of a Container The pressure on the wall of a container can be calculated by determining the total force due to collisions of the particles with the wall.

due to the collision. The acceleration for each collision is the change in velocity (Δv) divided by the time interval (Δt), so the force imparted for each collision is:

$$F_{\text{collision}} = m\frac{\Delta v}{\Delta t} \qquad [6.14]$$

If a particle collides elastically with the wall, it bounces off the wall with no loss of energy. For a straight-line collision, the change in velocity is $2v$ (the particle's velocity was v before the collision and $-v$ after the collision; therefore, the change is $2v$). The force per collision is given by:

$$F_{\text{collision}} = m\frac{2v}{\Delta t} \qquad [6.15]$$

The total number of collisions in the time interval Δt on a wall of surface area A is proportional to the number of particles that can reach the wall in this time interval—in other words, all particles within a distance of $v\Delta t$ of the wall. These particles occupy a volume given by $v\Delta t \times A$, and their total number is equal to this volume multiplied by the density of particles in the container (n/V):

$$\text{Number of collisions} \propto \text{number of particles within } v\Delta t$$

$$\propto \underbrace{v\Delta t \times A}_{\text{Volume}} \times \underbrace{\frac{n}{V}}_{\text{Density of particles}} \qquad [6.16]$$

The *total force* on the wall is equal to the force per collision multiplied by the number of collisions:

$$\begin{aligned} F_{\text{total}} &= F_{\text{collision}} \times \text{number of collisions} \\ &\propto m\frac{2v}{\cancel{\Delta t}} \times v\cancel{\Delta t} \times A \times \frac{n}{V} \\ &\propto mv^2 \times A \times \frac{n}{V} \end{aligned} \qquad [6.17]$$

The pressure on the wall is equal to the total force divided by the surface area of the wall:

$$\begin{aligned} P &= \frac{F_{\text{total}}}{A} \\ &\propto \frac{mv^2 \times \cancel{A} \times \frac{n}{V}}{\cancel{A}} \\ P &\propto mv^2 \times \frac{n}{V} \end{aligned} \qquad [6.18]$$

Notice that Equation 6.18 contains within it Boyle's law ($P \propto 1/V$) and Avogadro's law ($V \propto n$). We can get the complete ideal gas law from postulate 2 of the kinetic molecular theory, which states that the average kinetic energy ($\frac{1}{2}mv^2$) is proportional to the temperature in kelvins (T):

$$mv^2 \propto T \qquad [6.19]$$

By combining Equations 6.18 and 6.19, we get:

$$P \propto \frac{T \times n}{V}$$

$$PV \propto nT \qquad [6.20]$$

The proportionality can be replaced by an equals sign if we provide the correct constant, R:

$$PV = nRT \qquad [6.21]$$

In other words, the kinetic molecular theory (a model for how gases behave) predicts behavior that is consistent with our observations and measurements of gases—the theory agrees with the experiment. Recall from Chapter 1 that a scientific theory is the most powerful kind of scientific knowledge. In the kinetic molecular theory, we have a model for what a gas is like. Although the model is not perfect—indeed, it breaks down under certain conditions, as we shall see later in this chapter—it predicts a great deal about the behavior of gases. Therefore, the model is a good approximation of what a gas is actually like. A careful examination of the conditions under which the model breaks down (see Section 6.10) gives us even more insight into the behavior of gases.

Temperature and Molecular Velocities

According to kinetic molecular theory, particles of different masses have the same average kinetic energy at a given temperature. The kinetic energy of a particle depends on its mass and velocity according to the equation:

$$\text{KE} = \tfrac{1}{2}mv^2$$

The only way for particles of different masses to have the same kinetic energy is for them to have different velocities. *In a gas mixture at a given temperature, lighter particles travel faster (on average) than heavier ones.*

In kinetic molecular theory, we define the root mean square velocity (u_{rms}) of a particle as:

$$u_{\text{rms}} = \sqrt{\overline{u^2}} \qquad [6.22]$$

where $\overline{u^2}$ is the average of the squares of the particle velocities. Even though the root mean square velocity of a collection of particles is not identical to the average velocity, the two are close in value and conceptually similar. Root mean square velocity is a special *type* of average. The average kinetic energy of one mole of gas particles is given by the equation:

$$\text{KE}_{\text{avg}} = \tfrac{1}{2}N_A m\overline{u^2} \qquad [6.23]$$

where N_A is Avogadro's number and m is the mass of the particle.

Postulate 2 of the kinetic molecular theory states that the average kinetic energy is proportional to the temperature in kelvins. The constant of proportionality in this relationship is $(3/2)R$:

The $(3/2)R$ proportionality constant comes from a derivation that is beyond the scope of this book.

$$\text{KE}_{\text{avg}} = (3/2)RT \qquad [6.24]$$

where R is the gas constant but in different units ($R = 8.314\ \text{J/mol}\cdot\text{K}$) than those we use in the ideal gas law. If we combine Equations 6.23 and 6.24, and solve for $\overline{u^2}$, we get:

The joule (J) is a unit of energy that we will discuss in more detail in Section 7.2. $\left(1\ \text{J} = 1\ \text{kg}\frac{\text{m}^2}{\text{s}^2}\right)$

$$(1/2)N_A m\overline{u^2} = (3/2)RT$$

$$\overline{u^2} = \frac{(3/2)RT}{(1/2)N_A m} = \frac{3RT}{N_A m}$$

Taking the square root of both sides, we get:

$$\sqrt{\overline{u^2}} = u_{\text{rms}} = \sqrt{\frac{3RT}{N_A m}} \qquad [6.25]$$

In Equation 6.25, m is the mass of a particle in kg and N_A is Avogadro's number. The product $N_A m$, then, is the molar mass in kg/mol. If we call this quantity $\mathcal{M}$, then the expression for mean square velocity as a function of temperature becomes the following important result:

$$u_{rms} = \sqrt{\frac{3RT}{\mathcal{M}}} \qquad [6.26]$$

The root mean square velocity of a collection of gas particles is proportional to the square root of the temperature in kelvins and inversely proportional to the square root of the molar mass of the particles (which because of the units of R must be in kilograms per mole). The root mean square velocity of nitrogen molecules at 25 °C, for example, is 515 m/s (1152 mi/hr). The root mean square velocity of hydrogen molecules at room temperature is 1920 m/s (4295 mi/hr). Notice that the lighter molecules move much faster at a given temperature.

6.7 Cc Conceptual Connection ANSWER **NOW!**

ROOT MEAN SQUARE VELOCITY How does the approximate root mean square velocity of neon compare to that of krypton at the same temperature?

(a) The root mean square velocity of Ne is approximately four times that of Kr.
(b) The root mean square velocity of Ne is approximately two times that of Kr.
(c) The root mean square velocity of Ne is approximately one-half that of Kr.
(d) The root mean square velocity of Ne is approximately one-fourth that of Kr.

The root mean square velocity, as we have seen, is a kind of average velocity. Some particles move faster, and some move more slowly than this average. The velocities of all the particles in a gas sample form distributions like those shown in Figure 6.18▼. We can see from these distributions that some particles indeed travel at the root mean square velocity. However, many particles travel faster, and many travel more slowly than the root mean square velocity. For lighter particles, such as helium and hydrogen, the velocity distribution is shifted toward higher velocities and the curve becomes broader, indicating a wider range of velocities. Figure 6.19▶ illustrates the velocity distribution for nitrogen at different temperatures. As the temperature increases, the root mean square velocity increases and the distribution becomes broader.

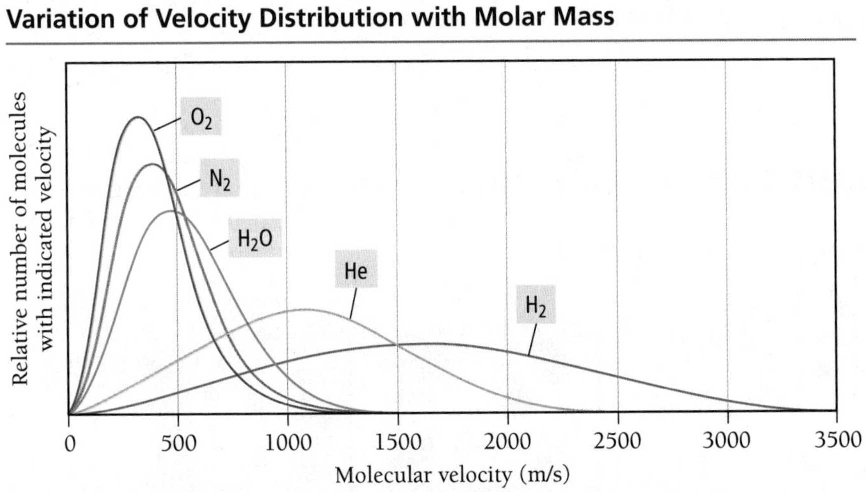

▲ **FIGURE 6.18 Velocity Distribution for Several Gases at 25 °C** At a given temperature, there is a distribution of velocities among the particles in a sample of gas. The exact shape and peak of the distribution vary with the molar mass of the gas.

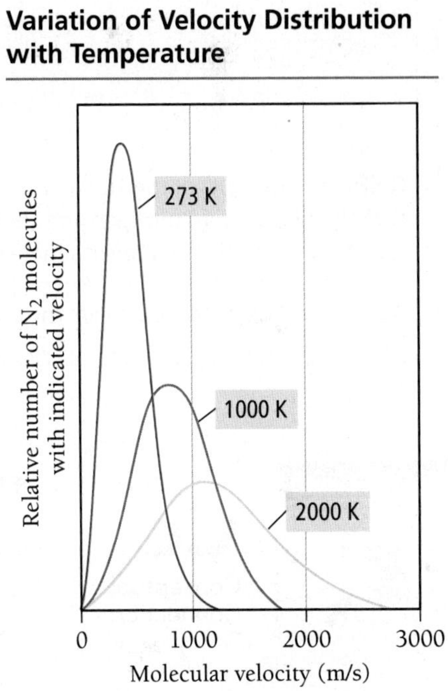

▲ **FIGURE 6.19 Velocity Distribution for Nitrogen at Several Temperatures** As the temperature of a gas sample increases, the velocity distribution of the molecules shifts toward higher velocity and becomes less sharply peaked.

EXAMPLE 6.14 Root Mean Square Velocity

Calculate the root mean square velocity of oxygen molecules at 25 °C.

SORT You are given the kind of molecule and the temperature and asked to find the root mean square velocity.

GIVEN: O_2, $t = 25\ °C$

FIND: u_{rms}

STRATEGIZE The conceptual plan for this problem shows how you can use the molar mass of oxygen and the temperature (in kelvins) with the equation that defines the root mean square velocity to calculate root mean square velocity.

CONCEPTUAL PLAN

$\mathcal{M}, T \rightarrow u_{rms}$

$$u_{rms} = \sqrt{\frac{3RT}{\mathcal{M}}}$$

RELATIONSHIP USED

$$u_{rms} = \sqrt{\frac{3RT}{\mathcal{M}}} \quad \text{(Equation 6.26)}$$

SOLVE First, gather the required quantities in the correct units. Note that molar mass must be in kg/mol.

Substitute the quantities into the equation to calculate root mean square velocity. Note that $1\ J = 1\ kg \cdot m^2/s^2$.

SOLUTION

$T = 25 + 273 = 298\ K$

$$\mathcal{M} = \frac{32.00\ \cancel{g}\ O_2}{1\ mol\ O_2} \times \frac{1\ kg}{1000\ \cancel{g}} = \frac{32.00 \times 10^{-3}\ kg\ O_2}{1\ mol\ O_2}$$

$$u_{rms} = \sqrt{\frac{3RT}{\mathcal{M}}}$$

$$= \sqrt{\frac{3\left(8.314\frac{J}{\cancel{mol} \cdot \cancel{K}}\right)(298\ \cancel{K})}{\frac{32.00 \times 10^{-3}\ kg\ \cancel{O_2}}{1\ \cancel{mol}\ \cancel{O_2}}}}$$

$$= \sqrt{2.32 \times 10^5 \frac{J}{kg}}$$

$$= \sqrt{2.32 \times 10^5 \frac{\frac{\cancel{kg} \cdot m^2}{s^2}}{\cancel{kg}}} = 482\ m/s$$

CHECK The units of the answer (m/s) are correct. The magnitude of the answer seems reasonable because oxygen is slightly heavier than nitrogen and should therefore have a slightly lower root mean square velocity at the same temperature. Recall that the root mean square velocity of nitrogen is 515 m/s at 25 °C.

FOR PRACTICE 6.14 Calculate the root mean square velocity of gaseous xenon atoms at 25 °C.

ANSWER **NOW!**

6.8 Cc Conceptual Connection

KINETIC MOLECULAR THEORY Which sample of an ideal gas has the greatest pressure? Assume that the mass of each particle is proportional to its size and that all the gas samples are at the same temperature.

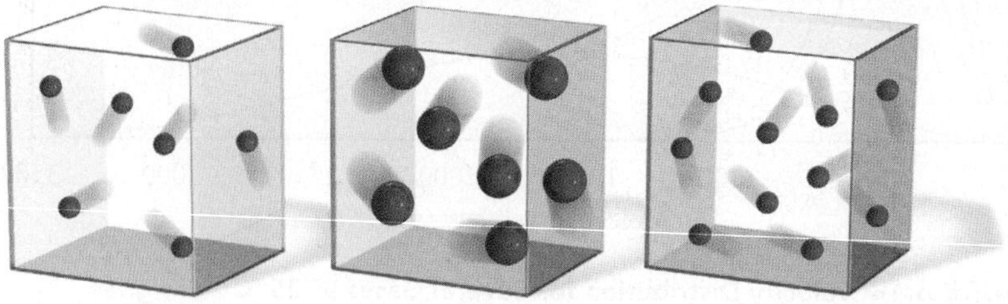

(a) (b) (c)

6.9 Mean Free Path, Diffusion, and Effusion of Gases

We have just seen that the root mean square velocity of gas molecules at room temperature is in the range of hundreds of meters per second. However, suppose that your roommate just put on too much perfume in the bathroom only 6 ft (1.8 m) away. Why does it take a minute or two before you can smell the fragrance? Although most molecules in a perfume bottle have higher molar masses than nitrogen, their velocities are still hundreds of meters per second, so why the delay? The answer is that even though gaseous particles travel at tremendous speeds, they also travel in haphazard paths (Figure 6.20 ▶). To a perfume molecule, the path from the perfume bottle in the bathroom to your nose 6 ft away is much like a bargain hunter's path through a busy shopping mall during a clearance sale. The molecule travels only a short distance before it collides with another molecule and changes direction, only to collide again, and so on. In fact, at room temperature and atmospheric pressure, a molecule in the air experiences several billion collisions per second. The average distance that a molecule travels between collisions is its **mean free path**. At room temperature and atmospheric pressure, the mean free path of a nitrogen molecule with a molecular diameter of 300 pm (four times the covalent radius) is 93 nm, or about 310 molecular diameters. If the nitrogen molecule were the size of a golf ball, it would travel about 40 ft between collisions. Mean free path increases with *decreasing* pressure. Under conditions of ultrahigh vacuum (10^{-10} torr), the mean free path of a nitrogen molecule is hundreds of kilometers.

Typical Gas Molecule Path

The average distance between collisions is the mean free path.

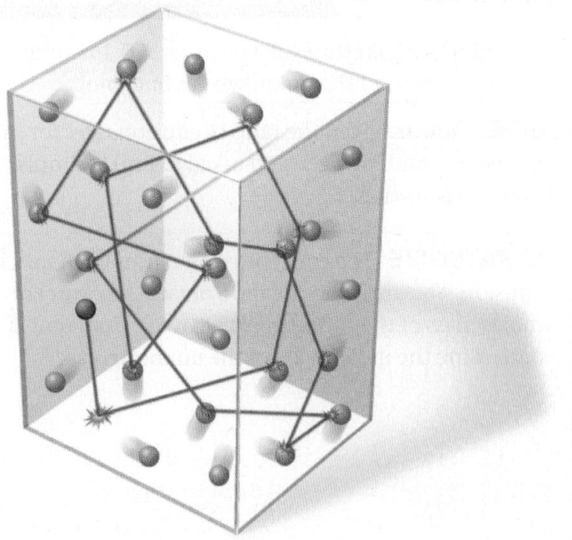

▲ **FIGURE 6.20 Mean Free Path** A molecule in a volume of gas follows a haphazard path, involving many collisions with other molecules.

The process by which gas molecules spread out in response to a concentration gradient is **diffusion**, and even though the particles undergo many collisions, the root mean square velocity still influences the rate of diffusion. Heavier molecules diffuse more slowly than lighter ones, so the first molecules you smell from a perfume mixture (in a room with no air currents) are the lighter ones.

In a ventilated room, air currents also enhance the transport of gas molecules.

A process related to diffusion is **effusion**, the process by which a gas escapes from a container into a vacuum through a small hole (Figure 6.21 ▶). The rate of effusion is also related to root mean square velocity—heavier molecules effuse more slowly than lighter ones. The rate of effusion—the amount of gas that effuses in a given time—is inversely proportional to the square root of the molar mass of the gas as follows:

$$\text{rate} \propto \frac{1}{\sqrt{\mathcal{M}}}$$

The ratio of effusion rates of two different gases is given by **Graham's law of effusion**, named after Thomas Graham (1805–1869):

$$\frac{\text{rate}_A}{\text{rate}_B} = \sqrt{\frac{\mathcal{M}_B}{\mathcal{M}_A}} \qquad [6.27]$$

Effusion

Gas escapes from container into a vacuum through a small hole.

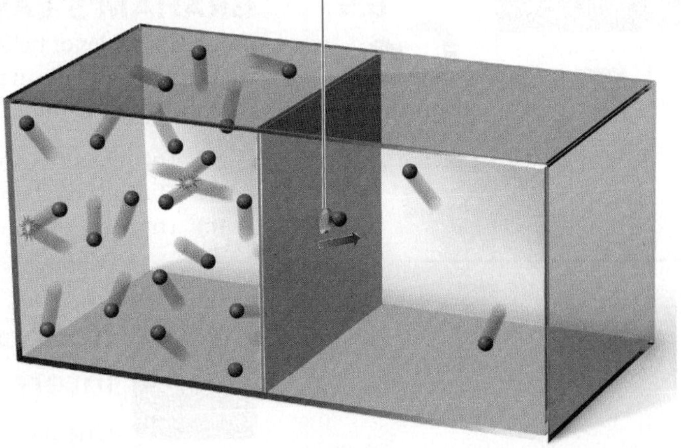

▲ **FIGURE 6.21 Effusion** Effusion is the escape of a gas from a container into a vacuum through a small hole.

In this expression, rate_A and rate_B are the effusion rates of gases A and B, and $\mathcal{M}_A$ and $\mathcal{M}_B$ are their molar masses.

Graham's law explains, in part, why helium balloons only float for a day or so. Because helium has such a low molar mass, it escapes from the balloon quite quickly. A balloon filled with air, by contrast, remains inflated longer.

WATCH NOW!

INTERACTIVE WORKED EXAMPLE 6.15

EXAMPLE 6.15 Graham's Law of Effusion

An unknown gas effuses at a rate that is 0.462 times that of nitrogen gas (at the same temperature). Calculate the molar mass of the unknown gas in g/mol.

SORT You are given the ratio of effusion rates for the unknown gas and nitrogen and asked to find the molar mass of the unknown gas.

GIVEN: $\frac{\text{rate}_{\text{unk}}}{\text{rate}_{N_2}} = 0.462$

FIND: $\mathcal{M}_{\text{unk}}$

STRATEGIZE The conceptual plan uses Graham's law of effusion. You are given the ratio of rates and you know the molar mass of the nitrogen. You can use Graham's law to determine the molar mass of the unknown gas.

CONCEPTUAL PLAN

$$\frac{\text{Rate}_{\text{unk}}}{\text{Rate}_{N_2}}, \mathcal{M}_{N_2} \longrightarrow \mathcal{M}_{\text{unk}}$$

$$\frac{\text{Rate}_{\text{unk}}}{\text{Rate}_{N_2}} = \sqrt{\frac{\mathcal{M}_{N_2}}{\mathcal{M}_{\text{unk}}}}$$

RELATIONSHIPS USED

$$\frac{\text{rate}_A}{\text{rate}_B} = \sqrt{\frac{\mathcal{M}_B}{\mathcal{M}_A}} \quad \text{(Graham's law)}$$

SOLVE Solve the equation for $\mathcal{M}_{\text{unk}}$ and substitute the correct values and calculate.

SOLUTION

$$\frac{\text{rate}_{\text{unk}}}{\text{rate}_{N_2}} = \sqrt{\frac{\mathcal{M}_{N_2}}{\mathcal{M}_{\text{unk}}}}$$

$$\mathcal{M}_{\text{unk}} = \frac{\mathcal{M}_{N_2}}{\left(\frac{\text{rate}_{\text{unk}}}{\text{rate}_{N_2}}\right)^2}$$

$$= \frac{28.02\ \text{g/mol}}{(0.462)^2}$$

$$= 131\ \text{g/mol}$$

CHECK The units of the answer are correct. The magnitude of the answer seems reasonable for the molar mass of a gas. From the answer you can even conclude that the gas is probably xenon, which has a molar mass of 131.29 g/mol.

FOR PRACTICE 6.15 Find the ratio of effusion rates of hydrogen gas and krypton gas.

ANSWER **NOW!**

6.9 Cc Conceptual Connection

GRAHAM'S LAW OF EFFUSION A glass tube contains an equal number of moles of helium and argon. After five minutes, half of the particles escape through a small hole in the glass. What are the *relative* amounts of helium and argon in the tube at five minutes?

(a) The tube still contains an equal number of moles of helium and argon.
(b) The tube contains a greater number of moles of helium than argon.
(c) The tube contains a greater number of moles of argon than helium.

6.10 Real Gases: The Effects of Size and Intermolecular Forces

One mole of an ideal gas has a volume of 22.41 L at STP. Figure 6.22▶ shows the molar volume of several real gases at STP. Note that most of these gases have a volume that is very close to 22.41 L, meaning that they act very nearly as ideal gases. Gases behave ideally when both of the following are true: (a) the volume of the gas particles is small compared to the space between them, and (b) the forces between the gas

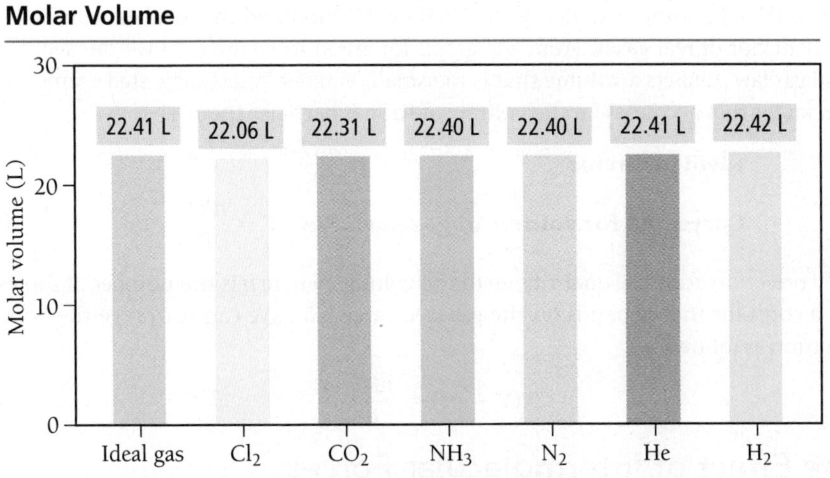

▲ **FIGURE 6.22 Molar Volumes of Real Gases** The molar volumes of several gases at STP are all close to 22.41 L, indicating that their departures from ideal behavior are small.

particles are not significant. At STP, these assumptions are valid for most common gases. However, these assumptions break down at higher pressures or lower temperatures.

The Effect of the Finite Volume of Gas Particles

The finite volume of gas particles—that is, their actual *sizes*—becomes important at high pressure because the volume of the particles themselves occupies a significant portion of the total gas volume (Figure 6.23▶). We can see the effect of particle volume by comparing the molar volume of argon to the molar volume of an ideal gas as a function of pressure at 500 K as shown in Figure 6.24▼. At low pressures, the molar volume of argon is nearly identical to that of an ideal gas. But as the pressure increases, the molar volume of argon becomes *greater than* that of an ideal gas. At the higher pressures, the argon atoms themselves occupy a significant portion of the gas volume, making the actual volume greater than that predicted by the ideal gas law.

▲ **FIGURE 6.23 Particle Volume and Ideal Behavior** As a gas is compressed, the gas particles themselves begin to occupy a significant portion of the total gas volume, leading to deviations from ideal behavior.

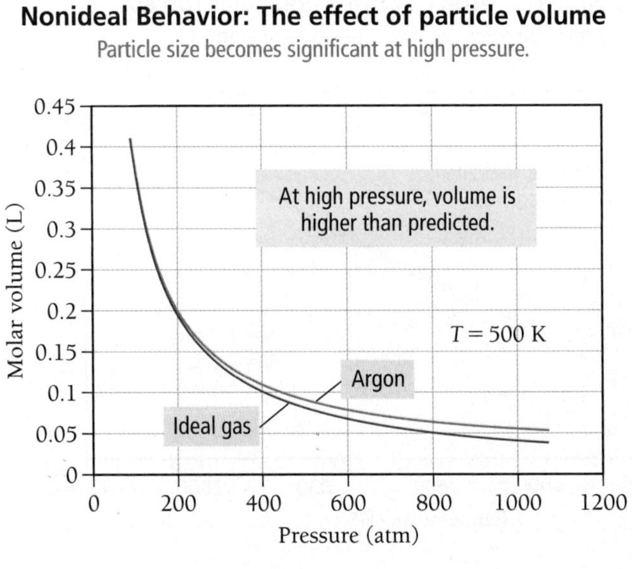

◀ **FIGURE 6.24 The Effect of Particle Volume** At high pressures, 1 mol of argon occupies a larger volume than 1 mol of an ideal gas because of the volume of the argon atoms themselves. (This example was chosen to minimize the effects of intermolecular forces, which are very small in argon at 500 K, thereby isolating the effect of particle volume.)

TABLE 6.5 ■ Van der Waals Constants for Common Gases

Gas	*a* ($L^2 \cdot atm/mol^2$)	*b* (L/mol)
He	0.0342	0.02370
Ne	0.211	0.0171
Ar	1.35	0.0322
Kr	2.32	0.0398
Xe	4.19	0.0511
H_2	0.244	0.0266
N_2	1.39	0.0391
O_2	1.36	0.0318
Cl_2	6.49	0.0562
H_2O	5.46	0.0305
CH_4	2.25	0.0428
CO_2	3.59	0.0427
CCl_4	20.4	0.1383

In 1873, Johannes van der Waals (1837–1923) modified the ideal gas equation to fit the behavior of real gases. From the graph for argon in Figure 6.24 we can see that the ideal gas law predicts a volume that is too small. Van der Waals suggested a small correction factor that accounts for the volume of the gas particles themselves:

Ideal behavior $$V = \frac{nRT}{P}$$

Corrected for volume of gas particles $$V = \frac{nRT}{P} + nb \qquad [6.28]$$

The correction adds the quantity nb to the volume, where n is the number of moles and b is a constant that depends on the gas (see Table 6.5). We can rearrange the corrected equation as follows:

$$(V - nb) = \frac{nRT}{P} \qquad [6.29]$$

The Effect of Intermolecular Forces

Intermolecular forces, which we will discuss in more detail in Chapter 12, are attractions between the atoms or molecules that compose any substance. These attractions are typically small in gases and therefore do not matter much at low pressure because the molecules are too far apart to "feel" the attractions. They also do not matter much at high temperatures because the molecules have a lot of kinetic energy. Therefore a weak attraction between them does not affect the collision much. At lower temperatures, however, the collisions occur with less kinetic energy, and weak attractions can affect the collisions. We can understand this difference with an analogy to billiard balls. Imagine two billiard balls coated with a substance that makes them slightly sticky. If they collide when moving at high velocities, the stickiness will not have much of an effect—the balls bounce off one another as if the sticky substance was not even there. However, if the two billiard balls collide when moving very slowly (say barely rolling), the sticky substance would have an effect. The billiard balls might even stick together and not bounce off one another.

The effect of these weak attractions between particles is a decrease in the number of collisions with the surfaces of the container and a corresponding decrease in the pressure compared to that of an ideal gas. We can see the effect of intermolecular forces when we compare the pressure of 1.0 mol of xenon gas to the pressure of 1.0 mol of an ideal gas as a function of temperature and at a fixed volume of 1.0 L, as shown in Figure 6.25▼. At high temperature, the pressure of the xenon gas is nearly identical to that of an ideal gas. But at lower temperatures, the pressure of xenon is *less than* that of an ideal gas. At the lower temperatures, the xenon atoms spend more time interacting with each other and less time colliding with the walls, making the actual pressure less than that predicted by the ideal gas law.

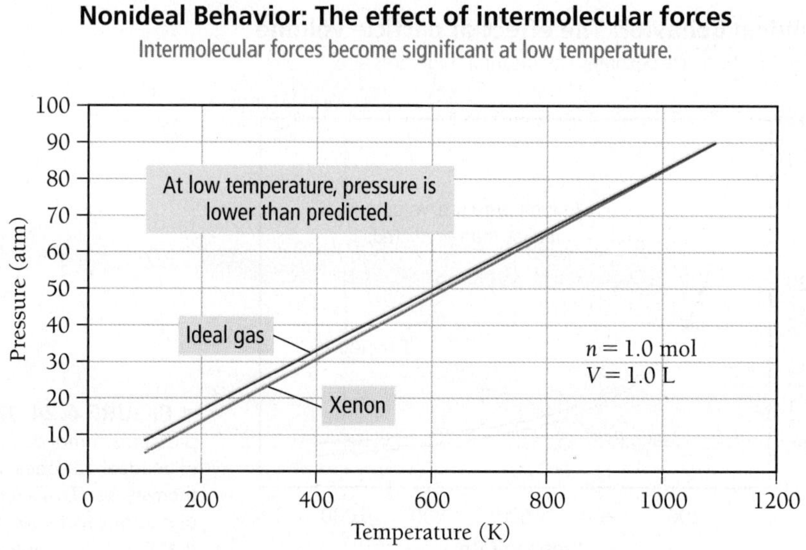

▶ **FIGURE 6.25 The Effect of Intermolecular Forces** At low temperatures, the pressure of xenon is less than an ideal gas exerts because interactions among xenon molecules reduce the number of collisions with the walls of the container.

From the graph for xenon shown in Figure 6.25 we can see that the ideal gas law predicts a pressure that is too large at low temperatures. Van der Waals suggested a small correction factor that accounts for the intermolecular forces between gas particles:

Ideal behavior $$P = \frac{nRT}{V}$$

Corrected for intermolecular forces $$P = \frac{nRT}{V} - a\left(\frac{n}{V}\right)^2 \qquad [6.30]$$

The correction subtracts the quantity $a(n/V)^2$ from the pressure, where n is the number of moles, V is the volume, and a is a constant that depends on the gas (see Table 6.5). Notice that the correction factor increases as n/V (the number of moles of particles per unit volume) increases because a greater concentration of particles makes it more likely that the particles will interact with one another. We can rearrange the corrected equation as:

$$P + a\left(\frac{n}{V}\right)^2 = \frac{nRT}{V} \qquad [6.31]$$

Van der Waals Equation

We can combine the effects of particle volume (Equation 6.29) and particle intermolecular forces (Equation 6.31) into one equation that describes nonideal gas behavior:

$$[P + a(\tfrac{n}{V})^2] \times [V - nb] = nRT$$

Correction for intermolecular forces — Correction for particle volume

This equation is the **van der Waals equation**, and we can use it to calculate the properties of a gas under nonideal conditions.

Real Gases

We can see the combined effects of particle volume and intermolecular forces by examining a plot of PV/RT versus P for 1 mol of a number of real gases (Figure 6.26▶). For an ideal gas, $PV/RT = n$, the number of moles of gas. Therefore, for 1 mol of an ideal gas, PV/RT is equal to 1, as shown in the plot. For real gases, PV/RT deviates from 1, but the deviations are not uniform. For example, water displays a large negative deviation from PV/RT because, for water, the effect of intermolecular forces on lowering the pressure (relative to an ideal gas) is far greater than the effect of particle size on increasing the volume. Notice from Table 6.5 that water has a high value of a, the constant that corrects for intermolecular forces, but a moderate value of b, the constant that corrects for particle size. Therefore, PV/RT for water is lower than predicted from the ideal gas law.

By contrast, consider the behavior of helium, which displays a positive deviation from the ideal behavior. This is because helium has very weak intermolecular forces and the effect of these forces on lowering the pressure (relative to ideal gas) is small compared to the effect of particle size on increasing the volume. Therefore PV/RT for helium is greater than predicted from the ideal gas law.

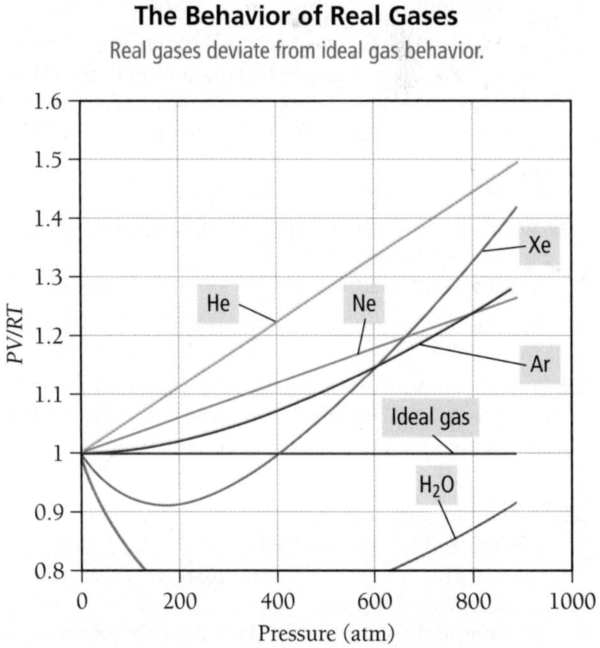

▲ **FIGURE 6.26 Real versus Ideal Behavior** For 1 mol of an ideal gas, PV/RT is equal to 1. The combined effects of the volume of gas particles and the interactions among them cause each real gas to deviate from ideal behavior in a slightly different way. These curves were calculated at a temperature of 500 K.

ANSWER **NOW!**

6.10
Cc
Conceptual Connection

REAL GASES The graph shows PV/RT for carbon dioxide at three different temperatures. Rank the curves in order of increasing temperature.

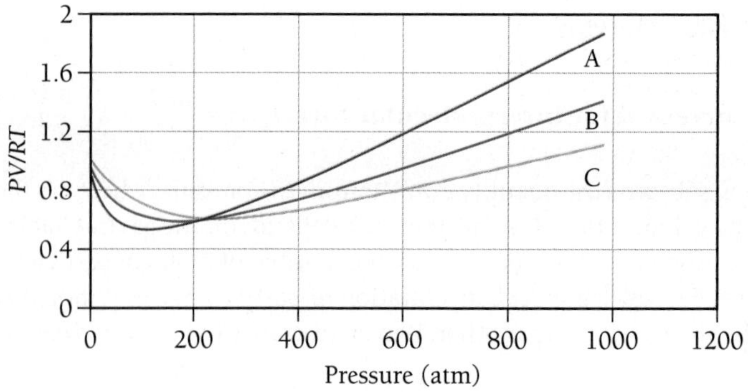

(a) C<A<B **(b)** A<B<C **(c)** B<C<A **(d)** C<B<A

QUIZ YOURSELF **NOW!**

Self-Assessment Quiz

Q1. A gas sample has an initial pressure of 547 mmHg and an initial volume of 0.500 L. What is the pressure (in atm) when the volume of the sample is decreased to 225 mL? (Assume constant temperature and constant number of moles of gas.) **MISSED THIS?** *Read Section 6.3; Watch KCV 6.3*

a) 1.60×10^{-3} atm b) 1.60 atm
c) 0.324 atm d) 1.22 atm

Q2. A gas sample has a volume of 178 mL at 0.00 °C. The temperature is raised (at constant pressure) until the volume is 211 mL. What is the temperature of the gas sample in °C at this volume? **MISSED THIS?** *Read Section 6.3; Watch KCV 6.3*

a) 0.00 °C b) 324 °C
c) −43 °C d) 51 °C

Q3. What is the pressure of 1.78 g of nitrogen gas confined to a volume of 0.118 L at 25 °C?
MISSED THIS? *Read Section 6.4; Watch KCV 6.3, IWE 6.5*

a) 13.2 atm b) 369 atm
c) 1.10 atm d) 26.3 atm

Q4. What is the density of a sample of argon gas at 55 °C and 765 mmHg? **MISSED THIS?** *Read Section 6.5; Watch IWE 6.7*

a) 2.99 g/L b) 1.13×10^3 g/L
c) 1.49 g/L d) 8.91 g/L

Q5. Which gas sample has the greatest volume at STP?
MISSED THIS? *Read Section 6.5*

a) 10.0 g Ar b) 10.0 g Kr
c) 10.0 g Xe
d) None of the above (They all have the same volume.)

Q6. A 1.25-g gas sample occupies 663 mL at 25 °C and 1.00 atm. What is the molar mass of the gas?
MISSED THIS? *Read Section 6.5; Watch IWE 6.8*

a) 0.258 g/mol b) 0.0461 g/mol
c) 3.87 g/mol d) 46.1 g/mol

Q7. A 255-mL gas sample contains argon and nitrogen at a temperature of 65 °C. The total pressure of the sample is 725 mmHg, and the partial pressure of argon is 231 mmHg. What mass of nitrogen is present in the sample? **MISSED THIS?** *Read Section 6.6; Watch KCV 6.6*

a) 0.324 g nitrogen b) 0.167 g nitrogen
c) 0.0837 g nitrogen d) 0.870 g nitrogen

Q8. A gas mixture in a 1.55-L container at 298 K contains 10.0 g of Ne and 10.0 g of Ar. Calculate the partial pressure (in atm) of Ne and Ar in the container.
MISSED THIS? *Read Section 6.6; Watch KCV 6.6, IWE 6.10*

a) $P_{Ne} = 10.5$ atm, $P_{Ar} = 5.29$ atm
b) $P_{Ne} = 5.83$ atm, $P_{Ar} = 2.95$ atm
c) $P_{Ne} = 5.88$ atm, $P_{Ar} = 5.88$ atm
d) $P_{Ne} = 7.82$ atm, $P_{Ar} = 3.95$ atm

Q9. A gas sample at STP contains 1.15 g oxygen and 1.55 g nitrogen. What is the volume of the gas sample?
MISSED THIS? *Read Sections 6.5, 6.6*

a) 1.26 L b) 2.04 L
c) 4.08 L d) 61.0 L

Q10. Aluminum reacts with chlorine gas to form aluminum chloride.

$$2\,Al(s) + 3\,Cl_2(g) \longrightarrow 2\,AlCl_3(s)$$

What minimum volume of chlorine gas (at 298 K and 225 mmHg) is required to completely react with 7.85 g of aluminum?
MISSED THIS? *Read Section 6.7; Watch IWE 6.12*

a) 36.0 L b) 24.0 L c) 0.0474 L d) 16.0 L

Q11. Calculate the root mean square velocity of $I_2(g)$ at 373 K.
MISSED THIS? *Read Section 6.8; Watch KCV 6.8*

a) 19.0 m/s b) 191 m/s
c) 6.05 m/s d) 99.1 m/s

Q12. Which gas has the greatest kinetic energy at STP?
MISSED THIS? *Read Section 6.8; Watch KCV 6.8*

a) He b) Ne c) Ar
d) None of the above (All have the same kinetic energy.)

Q13. A sample of Xe takes 75 seconds to effuse out of a container. An unknown gas takes 37 seconds to effuse out of the identical container under identical conditions. What is the most likely identity of the unknown gas?
MISSED THIS? *Read Section 6.9; Watch IWE 6.15*

a) He b) O_2 c) Br_2 d) Kr

Q14. Consider the generic reaction: $2\,A(g) + B(g) \longrightarrow 2\,C(g)$. If a flask initially contains 1.0 atm of A and 1.0 atm of B, what will be the pressure in the flask if the reaction proceeds to completion? (Assume constant volume and temperature.)
MISSED THIS? *Read Section 6.7*

a) 1.0 atm b) 1.5 atm c) 2.0 atm d) 3.0 atm

Q15. Rank the gases Ar, N_2, CH_4, and C_2H_6 in order of increasing density at STP. **MISSED THIS?** *Read Section 6.5; Watch IWE 6.7*

a) $CH_4 < C_2H_6 < N_2 < Ar$ b) $CH_4 < N_2 < Ar < C_2H_6$
c) $Ar < C_2H_6 < N_2 < CH_4$ d) $CH_4 < N_2 < C_2H_6 < Ar$

Answers: **1.** (b) **2.** (d) **3.** (a) **4.** (c) **5.** (a) **6.** (d) **7.** (b) **8.** (d) **9.** (b) **10.** (a) **11.** (b) **12.** (d) **13.** (b) **14.** (b) **15.** (d)

CHAPTER 6 IN REVIEW

TERMS

Section 6.1
pressure (212)

Section 6.2
millimeter of mercury (mmHg) (213)
barometer (213)
torr (213)
atmosphere (atm) (213)
pascal (Pa) (213)
manometer (214)

Section 6.3
Boyle's law (216)
Charles's law (219)
Avogadro's law (221)

Section 6.4
ideal gas law (223)
ideal gas (223)
ideal gas constant (223)

Section 6.5
molar volume (225)
standard temperature and pressure (STP) (225)

Section 6.6
partial pressure (229)
Dalton's law of partial pressures (229)
mole fraction (χ_a) (229)
hypoxia (231)
oxygen toxicity (231)
nitrogen narcosis (231)
vapor pressure (233)

Section 6.8
kinetic molecular theory (238)

Section 6.9
mean free path (245)
diffusion (245)
effusion (245)
Graham's law of effusion (245)

Section 6.10
van der Waals equation (249)

CONCEPTS

Pressure (6.1, 6.2)

- Gas pressure is the force per unit area that results from gas particles colliding with the surfaces around them. We use various units to measure pressure, including mmHg, torr, Pa, psi, in Hg, and atm.

The Simple Gas Laws (6.3)

- The simple gas laws express relationships between pairs of variables when other variables are constant.
- Boyle's law states that the volume of a gas is inversely proportional to its pressure.
- Charles's law states that the volume of a gas is directly proportional to its temperature.
- Avogadro's law states that the volume of a gas is directly proportional to the amount (in moles).

The Ideal Gas Law and Its Applications (6.4, 6.5)

- The ideal gas law, $PV = nRT$, describes the relationship among all four gas variables and contains the simple gas laws within it.
- We can use the ideal gas law to find one of the four variables given the other three. We can use it to calculate the molar volume of an ideal gas, which is 22.4 L at STP, and to calculate the density and molar mass of a gas.

Mixtures of Gases and Partial Pressures (6.6)

- In a mixture of gases, each gas acts independently of the others so that any overall property of the mixture is the sum of the properties of the individual components.
- The pressure of any individual component is its partial pressure.

Gas Stoichiometry (6.7)

- In reactions involving gaseous reactants and products, we often report quantities in volumes at specified pressures and temperatures. We can convert these quantities to amounts (in moles) using the ideal gas law. Then we can use the stoichiometric coefficients from the balanced equation to determine the stoichiometric amounts of other reactants or products.
- The general form for these types of calculations is: volume A $\rightarrow$ amount A (in moles) $\rightarrow$ amount B (in moles) $\rightarrow$ quantity of B (in desired units).
- In cases where the reaction is carried out at STP, we can use the molar volume at STP (22.4 L = 1 mol) to convert between volume in liters and amount in moles.

Kinetic Molecular Theory and Its Applications (6.8, 6.9)

- Kinetic molecular theory is a quantitative model for gases. The theory has three main assumptions: (1) gas particles are negligibly small, (2) the average kinetic energy of a gas particle is proportional to the temperature in kelvins, and (3) the collision of one gas particle with another is completely elastic (the particles do not stick together). The gas laws all follow from the kinetic molecular theory.
- We can use kinetic molecular theory to derive the expression for the root mean square velocity of gas particles. This velocity is inversely proportional to the molar mass of the gas, and therefore—at a given temperature—smaller gas particles are (on average) moving more quickly than larger ones.
- The kinetic molecular theory also allows us to predict the mean free path of a gas particle (the distance it travels between collisions) and relative rates of diffusion or effusion.

Real Gases (6.10)

- Real gases differ from ideal gases to the extent that they do not always fit the assumptions of kinetic molecular theory.
- These assumptions tend to break down at high pressures where the volume is higher than predicted for an ideal gas because the particles are no longer negligibly small compared to the space between them.
- The assumptions also break down at low temperatures where the pressure is lower than predicted because the attraction between molecules combined with low kinetic energies causes partially inelastic collisions.
- The van der Waals equation predicts gas properties under nonideal conditions.

EQUATIONS AND RELATIONSHIPS

Relationship between Pressure (P), Force (F), and Area (A) (**6.2**)

$$P = \frac{F}{A}$$

Boyle's Law: Relationship between Pressure (P) and Volume (V) (**6.3**)

$$V \propto \frac{1}{P}$$

$$P_1V_1 = P_2V_2$$

Charles's Law: Relationship between Volume (V) and Temperature (T) (**6.3**)

$$V \propto T \text{ (in K)}$$

$$\frac{V_1}{T_1} = \frac{V_2}{T_2}$$

Avogadro's Law: Relationship between Volume (V) and Amount in Moles (n) (**6.3**)

$$V \propto n$$

$$\frac{V_1}{n_1} = \frac{V_2}{n_2}$$

Ideal Gas Law: Relationship between Volume (V), Pressure (P), Temperature (T), and Amount (n) (**6.4**)

$$PV = nRT$$

Dalton's Law: Relationship between Partial Pressures P_n in Mixture of Gases and Total Pressure (P_{total}) (**6.6**)

$$P_{total} = P_a + P_b + P_c + \ldots$$

$$P_a = \frac{n_aRT}{V} \quad P_b = \frac{n_bRT}{V} \quad P_c = \frac{n_cRT}{V}$$

Mole Fraction (χ_a) (**6.6**)

$$\chi_a = \frac{n_a}{n_{total}}$$

$$P_a = \chi_a P_{total}$$

Average Kinetic Energy (KE_{avg}) (**6.8**)

$$KE_{avg} = \frac{3}{2}RT$$

Relationship between Root Mean Square Velocity (u_{rms}) and Temperature (T) (**6.8**)

$$u_{rms} = \sqrt{\frac{3RT}{\mathcal{M}}}$$

Relationship of Effusion Rates of Two Different Gases (**6.9**)

$$\frac{\text{rate A}}{\text{rate B}} = \sqrt{\frac{\mathcal{M}_B}{\mathcal{M}_A}}$$

Van der Waals Equation: The Effects of Volume and Intermolecular Forces on Nonideal Gas Behavior (**6.10**)

$$\left[P + a\left(\frac{n}{V}\right)^2\right] \times (V - nb) = nRT$$

LEARNING OUTCOMES

Chapter Objectives	Assessment
Convert between units of pressure (**6.2**)	Example 6.1 **For Practice** 6.1 **For More Practice** 6.1 **Exercises** 25–30
Calculate properties of gases using the simple gas laws (**6.3**)	Examples 6.2, 6.3, 6.4 **For Practice** 6.2, 6.3, 6.4 **Exercises** 31–36
Calculate properties of gases using the ideal gas law (**6.4**)	Examples 6.5, 6.6, 6.7, 6.8 **For Practice** 6.5, 6.6, 6.7, 6.8 **For More Practice** 6.6, 6.7 **Exercises** 37–60

Analyze gas mixtures using Dalton's law of partial pressures (**6.5**)	Examples 6.9, 6.10, 6.11 **For Practice** 6.9, 6.10, 6.11 **Exercises** 61–70
Perform stoichiometric calculations involving gas reactions (**6.6**)	Examples 6.12, 6.13 **For Practice** 6.12, 6.13 **For More Practice** 6.12 **Exercises** 71–80
Calculate the root mean square velocity of a gas (**6.8**)	Example 6.14 **For Practice** 6.14 **Exercises** 81–84
Calculate the effusion rate of a gas or the ratio of effusion rates of two different gases (**6.9**)	Example 6.15 **For Practice** 6.15 **Exercises** 85–89
Calculate gas properties of real gases (**6.10**)	**Exercises** 91–94

EXERCISES

Mastering Chemistry provides end-of-chapter exercises, feedback-enriched tutorial problems, animations, and interactive activities to encourage problem-solving practice and deeper understanding of key concepts and topics.

REVIEW QUESTIONS

1. What is pressure? What causes pressure?

2. Explain what happens when a person inhales. What forces air into the lungs?

3. Explain what happens when a person exhales. What forces air out of the lungs?

4. What are the common units of pressure? List them in order of smallest to largest unit.

5. What is a manometer? How does it measure the pressure of a sample of gas?

6. Summarize each of the simple gas laws (Boyle's law, Charles's law, and Avogadro's law). For each, explain the relationship between the two variables and also state which variables must be kept constant.

7. Explain why people may experience ear pain after a rapid change in altitude.

8. Explain why scuba divers should never hold their breath when they ascend to the surface.

9. Why is it impossible to breathe air through an extra-long snorkel (longer than a couple of meters) while swimming under water?

10. Explain why hot-air balloons float above the ground and why the second story of a two-story home is often warmer than the ground story.

11. What is the ideal gas law? Why is it useful?

12. Explain how the ideal gas law contains within it the simple gas laws (show an example).

13. Define molar volume and list its value for a gas at STP.

14. How does the density of a gas depend on temperature? Pressure? How does it depend on the molar mass of the gas?

15. What is partial pressure? What is the relationship between the partial pressures of each gas in a sample and the total pressure of gas in the sample?

16. Why do deep-sea divers breathe a mixture of helium and oxygen?

17. When a gas is collected over water, is the gas pure? Why or why not? How can the partial pressure of the collected gas be determined?

18. If a reaction occurs in the gas phase at STP, we can determine the mass of a product from the volumes of reactants. Explain.

19. What are the basic postulates of kinetic molecular theory? How does the concept of pressure follow from kinetic molecular theory?

20. Explain how Boyle's law, Charles's law, Avogadro's law, and Dalton's law all follow from kinetic molecular theory.

21. How is the kinetic energy of a gas related to temperature? How is the root mean square velocity of a gas related to its molar mass?

22. Describe how the molecules in a perfume bottle travel from the bottle to your nose. What is mean free path?

23. Explain the difference between diffusion and effusion. How is the effusion rate of a gas related to its molar mass?

24. Deviations from the ideal gas law are observed at high pressure and low temperature. Explain this in light of kinetic molecular theory.

PROBLEMS BY TOPIC

Converting between Pressure Units

25. The pressure in Denver, Colorado (elevation 5280 ft), averages about 24.9 in Hg. Convert this pressure to each indicated unit. **MISSED THIS?** *Read Section 6.2*

a. atm b. mmHg c. psi d. Pa

26. The pressure on top of Mount Everest (29,029 ft) averages about 235 mmHg. Convert this pressure to each indicated unit.

a. torr
b. psi
c. in Hg
d. atm

27. The North American record for highest recorded barometric pressure is 31.85 in Hg, set in 1989 in Northway, Alaska. Convert this pressure to each indicated unit.
MISSED THIS? *Read Section 6.2*
a. mmHg
b. atm
c. torr
d. kPa (kilopascals)

28. The world record for lowest pressure (at sea level) was 652.5 mmHg recorded inside Typhoon Tip on October 12, 1979, in the western Pacific Ocean. Convert this pressure to each indicated unit.
a. torr b. atm c. in Hg d. psi

29. Given a barometric pressure of 762.4 mmHg, calculate the pressure of each gas sample as indicated by the manometer.
MISSED THIS? *Read Section 6.2*

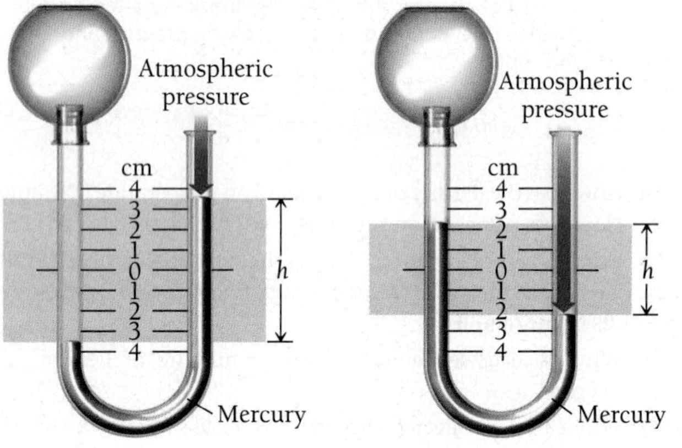

(a) (b)

30. Given a barometric pressure of 751.5 mmHg, calculate the pressure of each gas sample as indicated by the manometer.

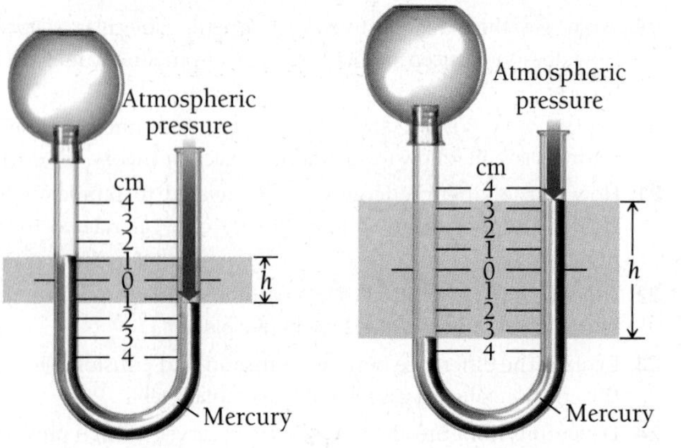

(a) (b)

Simple Gas Laws

31. A sample of gas has an initial volume of 5.6 L at a pressure of 735 mmHg. If the volume of the gas is increased to 9.4 L, what is its pressure?
MISSED THIS? *Read Section 6.3; Watch KCV 6.3*

32. A sample of gas has an initial volume of 13.9 L at a pressure of 1.22 atm. If the sample is compressed to a volume of 10.3 L, what is its pressure?

33. A 48.3-mL sample of gas in a cylinder is warmed from 22 °C to 87 °C. What is its volume at the final temperature?
MISSED THIS? *Read Section 6.3; Watch KCV 6.3*

34. A syringe containing 1.55 mL of oxygen gas is cooled from 95.3 °C to 0.0 °C. What is the final volume of oxygen gas?

35. A balloon contains 0.158 mol of gas and has a volume of 2.46 L. If an additional 0.113 mol of gas is added to the balloon (at the same temperature and pressure), what is its final volume?
MISSED THIS? *Read Section 6.3; Watch KCV 6.3*

36. A cylinder with a moveable piston contains 0.553 mol of gas and has a volume of 253 mL. What is its volume if an additional 0.365 mol of gas is added to the cylinder? (Assume constant temperature and pressure.)

Ideal Gas Law

37. What volume is occupied by 0.118 mol of helium gas at a pressure of 0.97 atm and a temperature of 305 K? Would the volume be different if the gas was argon (under the same conditions)?
MISSED THIS? *Read Section 6.4; Watch KCV 6.3, IWE 6.5*

38. What volume is occupied by 12.5 g of argon gas at a pressure of 1.05 atm and a temperature of 322 K? Would the volume be different if the sample were 12.5 g of helium (under identical conditions)?

39. What is the pressure in a 10.0-L cylinder filled with 0.448 mol of nitrogen gas at a temperature of 315 K?
MISSED THIS? *Read Section 6.4; Watch KCV 6.3, IWE 6.5*

40. What is the pressure in a 15.0-L cylinder filled with 32.7 g of oxygen gas at a temperature of 302 K?

41. A cylinder contains 28.5 L of oxygen gas at a pressure of 1.8 atm and a temperature of 298 K. How much gas (in moles) is in the cylinder?
MISSED THIS? *Read Section 6.4; Watch KCV 6.3, IWE 6.5*

42. What is the temperature of 0.52 mol of gas at a pressure of 1.3 atm and a volume of 11.8 L?

43. An automobile tire has a maximum rating of 38.0 psi (gauge pressure). The tire is inflated (while cold) to a volume of 11.8 L and a gauge pressure of 36.0 psi at a temperature of 12.0 °C. On a hot day, the tire warms to 65.0 °C, and its volume expands to 12.2 L. Does the pressure in the tire exceed its maximum rating? (Note: The *gauge pressure* is the *difference* between the total pressure and atmospheric pressure. In this case, assume that atmospheric pressure is 14.7 psi.)
MISSED THIS? *Read Section 6.4; Watch KCV 6.3, IWE 6.5*

44. A weather balloon is inflated to a volume of 28.5 L at a pressure of 748 mmHg and a temperature of 28.0 °C. The balloon rises in the atmosphere to an altitude of approximately 25,000 ft, where the pressure is 385 mmHg and the temperature is −15.0 °C. Assuming the balloon can freely expand, calculate the volume of the balloon at this altitude.

45. A piece of dry ice (solid carbon dioxide) with a mass of 28.8 g sublimes (converts from solid to gas) into a large balloon. Assuming that all of the carbon dioxide ends up in the balloon, what is the volume of the balloon at 22 °C and a pressure of 742 mmHg?
MISSED THIS? *Read Section 6.4; Watch KCV 6.3, IWE 6.5*

46. A 1.0-L container of liquid nitrogen is kept in a closet measuring 1.0 m by 1.0 m by 2.0 m. Assuming that the container is completely full, that the temperature is 25.0 °C, and that the atmospheric pressure is 1.0 atm, calculate the percent (by volume) of air that is displaced if all of the liquid nitrogen evaporates. (Liquid nitrogen has a density of 0.807 g/mL.)

47. A wine-dispensing system uses argon canisters to pressurize and preserve wine in the bottle. An argon canister for the system has a volume of 55.0 mL and contains 26.0 g of argon. Assuming ideal gas behavior, what is the pressure in the canister at 295 K? When the argon is released from the canister, it expands to fill the wine bottle. How many 750.0-mL wine bottles can be purged with the argon in the canister at a pressure of 1.20 atm and a temperature of 295 K?
MISSED THIS? *Read Section 6.4; Watch KCV 6.3, IWE 6.5*

48. Cyclists sometimes use pressurized carbon dioxide inflators to inflate a bicycle tire in the event of a flat. These inflators use metal cartridges that contain 16.0 g of carbon dioxide. At 298 K, to what pressure (in psi) can the carbon dioxide in the cartridge inflate a 3.45-L mountain bike tire? (Note: The *gauge pressure* is the *difference* between the total pressure and atmospheric pressure. In this case, assume that atmospheric pressure is 14.7 psi.)

49. Which gas sample has the greatest pressure? Assume that all the samples are at the same temperature. Explain.
MISSED THIS? *Read Section 6.4; Watch KCV 6.3*

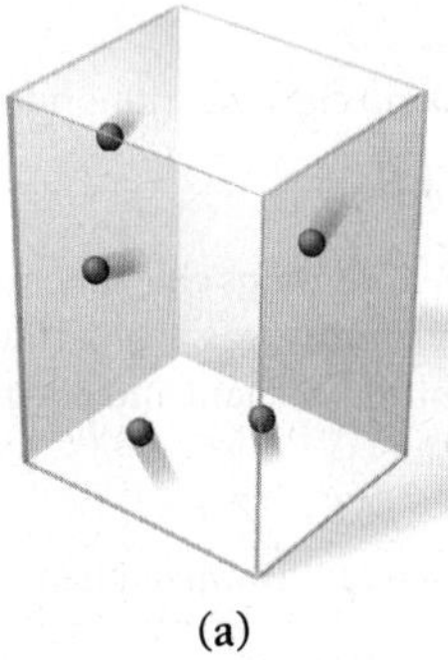
(a)

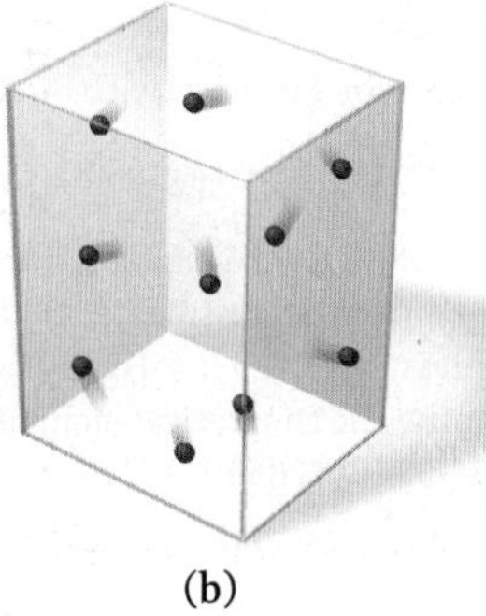
(b)

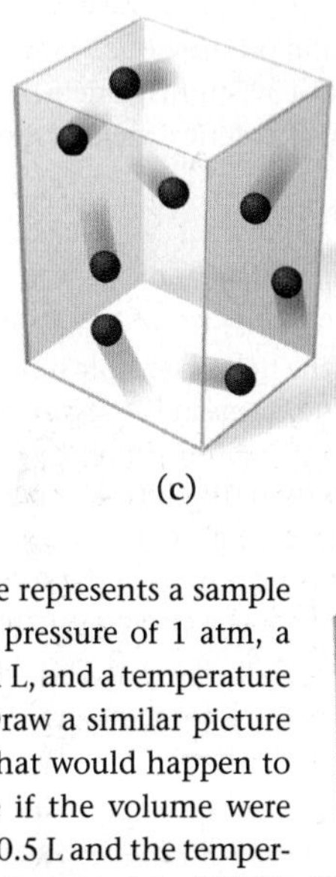
(c)

50. This picture represents a sample of gas at a pressure of 1 atm, a volume of 1 L, and a temperature of 25 °C. Draw a similar picture showing what would happen to the sample if the volume were reduced to 0.5 L and the temperature were increased to 250 °C. What would happen to the pressure?

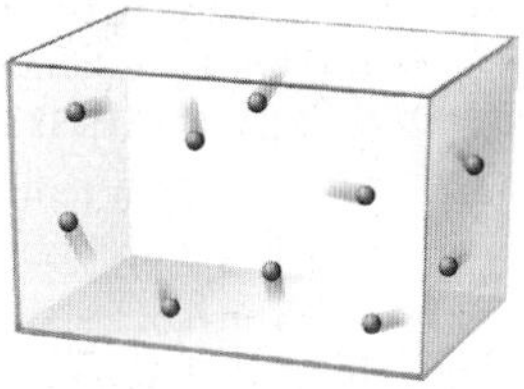

51. Aerosol cans carry clear warnings against incineration because of the high pressures that can develop upon heating. Suppose that a can contains a residual amount of gas at a pressure of 755 mmHg and a temperature of 25 °C. What would the pressure be if the can were heated to 1155 °C? **MISSED THIS?** *Read Section 6.4*

52. A sample of nitrogen gas in a 1.75-L container exerts a pressure of 1.35 atm at 25 °C. What is the pressure if the volume of the container is maintained constant and the temperature is raised to 355 °C?

Molar Volume, Density, and Molar Mass of a Gas

53. Use the molar volume of a gas at STP to determine the volume (in L) occupied by 33.6 g of neon at STP.
MISSED THIS? *Read Section 6.5*

54. Use the molar volume of a gas at STP to calculate the density (in g/L) of nitrogen gas at STP.

55. What is the density (in g/L) of hydrogen gas at 20.0 °C and a pressure of 1655 psi?
MISSED THIS? *Read Section 6.5; Watch IWE 6.7*

56. A sample of N_2O gas has a density of 2.85 g/L at 298 K. What is the pressure of the gas (in mmHg)?

57. A 248-mL gas sample has a mass of 0.433 g at a pressure of 745 mmHg and a temperature of 28 °C. What is the molar mass of the gas? **MISSED THIS?** *Read Section 6.5; Watch IWE 6.8*

58. A 113-mL gas sample has a mass of 0.171 g at a pressure of 721 mmHg and a temperature of 32 °C. What is the molar mass of the gas?

59. A sample of gas has a mass of 38.8 mg. Its volume is 224 mL at a temperature of 55 °C and a pressure of 886 torr. Find the molar mass of the gas. **MISSED THIS?** *Read Section 6.5; Watch IWE 6.8*

60. A sample of gas has a mass of 0.555 g. Its volume is 117 mL at a temperature of 85 °C and a pressure of 753 mmHg. Find the molar mass of the gas.

Partial Pressure

61. A gas mixture contains each of the following gases at the indicated partial pressures: N_2, 215 torr; O_2, 102 torr; and He, 117 torr. What is the total pressure of the mixture? What mass of each gas is present in a 1.35-L sample of this mixture at 25.0 °C?
MISSED THIS? *Read Section 6.6; Watch KCV 6.6*

62. A gas mixture with a total pressure of 745 mmHg contains each of the following gases at the indicated partial pressures: CO_2, 125 mmHg; Ar, 214 mmHg; and O_2, 187 mmHg. The mixture also contains helium gas. What is the partial pressure of the helium gas? What mass of helium gas is present in a 12.0-L sample of this mixture at 273 K?

63. A 1.20-g sample of dry ice is added to a 755 mL flask containing nitrogen gas at a temperature of 25.0 °C and a pressure of 725 mmHg. The dry ice sublimes (converts from solid to gas), and the mixture returns to 25.0 °C. What is the total pressure in the flask? **MISSED THIS?** *Read Section 6.6; Watch KCV 6.6*

64. A 275-mL flask contains pure helium at a pressure of 752 torr. A second flask with a volume of 475 mL contains pure argon at a pressure of 722 torr. If we connect the two flasks through a stopcock and we open the stopcock, what is the partial pressure of each gas and the total pressure?

65. A gas mixture contains 1.25 g N_2 and 0.85 g O_2 in a 1.55 L container at 18 °C. Calculate the mole fraction and partial pressure of each component in the gas mixture.
MISSED THIS? *Read Section 6.6; Watch KCV 6.6, IWE 6.10*

66. What is the mole fraction of oxygen gas in air (see Table 6.3)? What volume of air contains 10.0 g of oxygen gas at 273 K and 1.00 atm?

67. The hydrogen gas formed in a chemical reaction is collected over water at 30.0 °C at a total pressure of 732 mmHg. What is the partial pressure of the hydrogen gas collected in this way? If the total volume of gas collected is 722 mL, what mass of hydrogen gas is collected?
MISSED THIS? *Read Section 6.6; Watch KCV 6.6, IWE 6.11*

68. The air in a bicycle tire is bubbled through water and collected at 25 °C. If the total volume of gas collected is 5.45 L at a temperature of 25 °C and a pressure of 745 torr, how many moles of gas were in the bicycle tire?

69. The zinc in a copper-plated penny will dissolve in hydrochloric acid if the copper coating is filed down in several spots (so that the hydrochloric acid can get to the zinc). The reaction between the acid and the zinc is $2\,H^+(aq) + Zn(s) \longrightarrow H_2(g) + Zn^{2+}(aq)$. When the zinc in a certain penny dissolves, the total volume of gas collected over water at 25 °C is 0.951 L at a total pressure of 748 mmHg. What mass of hydrogen gas is collected?
MISSED THIS? *Read Section 6.6; Watch KCV 6.6, IWE 6.11*

70. A heliox deep-sea diving mixture contains 2.0 g of oxygen to every 98.0 g of helium. What is the partial pressure of oxygen when this mixture is delivered at a total pressure of 8.5 atm?

Reaction Stoichiometry Involving Gases

71. Consider the chemical reaction:

$$C(s) + H_2O(g) \longrightarrow CO(g) + H_2(g)$$

How many liters of hydrogen gas are formed from the complete reaction of 15.7 g C? Assume that the hydrogen gas is collected at a pressure of 1.0 atm and a temperature of 355 K.
MISSED THIS? *Read Section 6.7; Watch IWE 6.12*

72. Consider the chemical reaction:

$$2\,H_2O(l) \longrightarrow 2\,H_2(g) + O_2(g)$$

What mass of H_2O is required to form 1.4 L of O_2 at a temperature of 315 K and a pressure of 0.957 atm?

73. CH_3OH can be synthesized by the reaction:

$$CO(g) + 2\,H_2(g) \longrightarrow CH_3OH(g)$$

What volume of H_2 gas (in L), at 748 mmHg and 86 °C, is required to synthesize 25.8 g CH_3OH? How many liters of CO gas, measured under the same conditions, are required?
MISSED THIS? *Read Section 6.7; Watch IWE 6.12*

74. Oxygen gas reacts with powdered aluminum according to the reaction:

$$4\,Al(s) + 3\,O_2(g) \longrightarrow 2\,Al_2O_3(s)$$

What volume of O_2 gas (in L), measured at 782 mmHg and 25 °C, completely reacts with 53.2 g Al?

75. Automobile air bags inflate following a serious impact. The impact triggers the chemical reaction:

$$2\,NaN_3(s) \longrightarrow 2\,Na(s) + 3\,N_2(g)$$

If an automobile airbag has a volume of 11.8 L, what mass of NaN_3 (in g) is required to fully inflate the airbag upon impact? Assume STP conditions.
MISSED THIS? *Read Section 6.7; Watch IWE 6.12*

76. Lithium reacts with nitrogen gas according to the reaction:

$$6\,Li(s) + N_2(g) \longrightarrow 2\,Li_3N(s)$$

What mass of lithium (in g) reacts completely with 58.5 mL of N_2 gas at STP?

77. Hydrogen gas (a potential future fuel) can be formed by the reaction of methane with water according to the equation:

$$CH_4(g) + H_2O(g) \longrightarrow CO(g) + 3\,H_2(g)$$

In a particular reaction, 25.5 L of methane gas (measured at a pressure of 732 torr and a temperature of 25 °C) mixes with 22.8 L of water vapor (measured at a pressure of 702 torr and a temperature of 125 °C). The reaction produces 26.2 L of hydrogen gas at STP. What is the percent yield of the reaction?
MISSED THIS? *Read Section 6.7; Watch IWE 6.12*

78. Ozone is depleted in the stratosphere by chlorine from CF_3Cl according to this set of equations:

$$CF_3Cl + \text{UV light} \longrightarrow CF_3 + Cl$$
$$Cl + O_3 \longrightarrow ClO + O_2$$
$$O_3 + \text{UV light} \longrightarrow O_2 + O$$
$$ClO + O \longrightarrow Cl + O_2$$

What total volume of ozone at a pressure of 25.0 mmHg and a temperature of 225 K is destroyed when all of the chlorine from 15.0 g of CF_3Cl goes through 10 cycles of the given reactions?

79. Chlorine gas reacts with fluorine gas to form chlorine trifluoride.

$$Cl_2(g) + 3\,F_2(g) \longrightarrow 2\,ClF_3(g)$$

A 2.00-L reaction vessel, initially at 298 K, contains chlorine gas at a partial pressure of 337 mmHg and fluorine gas at a partial pressure of 729 mmHg. Identify the limiting reactant and determine the theoretical yield of ClF_3 in grams.
MISSED THIS? *Read Section 6.7; Watch IWE 6.12*

80. Carbon monoxide gas reacts with hydrogen gas to form methanol.

$$CO(g) + 2\,H_2(g) \longrightarrow CH_3OH(g)$$

A 1.50-L reaction vessel, initially at 305 K, contains carbon monoxide gas at a partial pressure of 232 mmHg and hydrogen gas at a partial pressure of 397 mmHg. Identify the limiting reactant and determine the theoretical yield of methanol in grams.

Kinetic Molecular Theory

81. Consider a 1.0-L sample of helium gas and a 1.0-L sample of argon gas, both at room temperature and atmospheric pressure.
  a. Do the atoms in the helium sample have the same *average kinetic energy* as the atoms in the argon sample?
  b. Do the atoms in the helium sample have the same *average velocity* as the atoms in the argon sample?
  c. Do the argon atoms, because they are more massive, exert a greater pressure on the walls of the container? Explain.
  d. Which gas sample has the faster rate of effusion?
  MISSED THIS? *Read Section 6.8; Watch KCV 6.8*

82. A flask at room temperature contains exactly equal amounts (in moles) of nitrogen and xenon.
  a. Which of the two gases exerts the greater partial pressure?
  b. The molecules or atoms of which gas have the greater average velocity?
  c. The molecules or atoms of which gas have the greater average kinetic energy?
  d. If a small hole were opened in the flask, which gas effuses more quickly?

83. Calculate the root mean square velocity and kinetic energy of F_2, Cl_2, and Br_2 at 298 K. Rank these three halogens with respect to their rate of effusion.
MISSED THIS? *Read Section 6.8; Watch KCV 6.8*

84. Calculate the root mean square velocity and kinetic energy of CO, CO_2, and SO_3 at 298 K. Which gas has the greatest velocity? The greatest kinetic energy? The greatest effusion rate?

85. We separate U-235 from U-238 by fluorinating a sample of uranium to form UF_6 (which is a gas) and then taking advantage of the different rates of effusion and diffusion for compounds containing the two isotopes. Calculate the ratio of effusion rates for $^{238}UF_6$ and $^{235}UF_6$. The atomic mass of U-235 is 235.054 amu and that of U-238 is 238.051 amu.
MISSED THIS? *Read Section 6.9; Watch IWE 6.15*

86. Calculate the ratio of effusion rates for Ar and Kr.

87. A sample of neon effuses from a container in 76 seconds. The same amount of an unknown noble gas requires 155 seconds. Identify the second gas.
MISSED THIS? *Read Section 6.9; Watch IWE 6.15*

88. A sample of N_2O effuses from a container in 42 seconds. How long will it take the same amount of gaseous I_2 to effuse from the same container under identical conditions?

89. The graph shows the distribution of molecular velocities for two different molecules (A and B) at the same temperature. Which molecule has the higher molar mass? Which molecule has the higher rate of effusion?
MISSED THIS? *Read Section 6.8; Watch KCV 6.8*

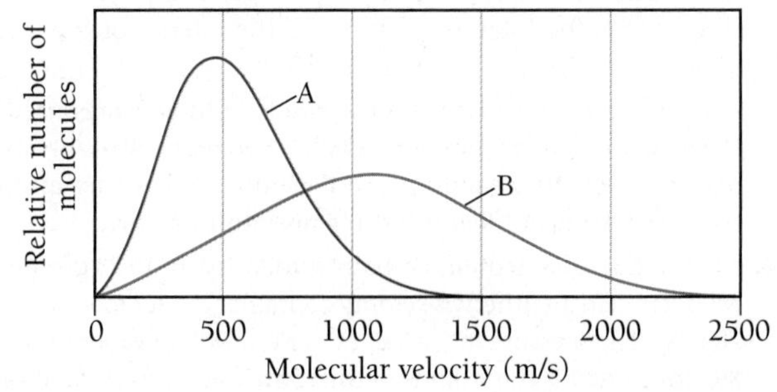

90. The graph shows the distribution of molecular velocities for the same molecule at two different temperatures (T_1 and T_2). Which temperature is greater? Explain.

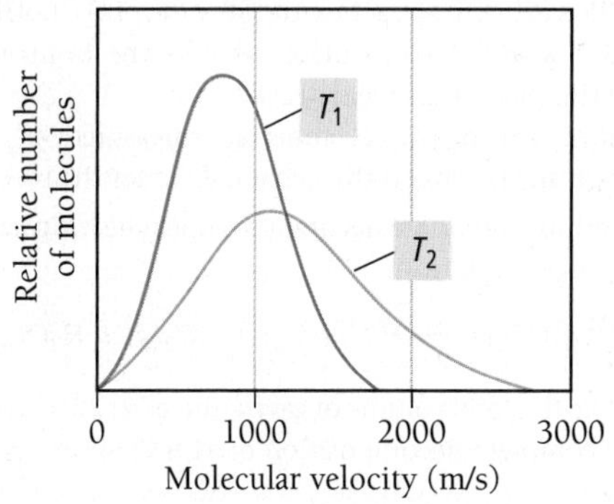

Real Gases

91. Which postulate of the kinetic molecular theory breaks down under conditions of high pressure? Explain.
MISSED THIS? *Read Section 6.10*

92. Which postulate of the kinetic molecular theory breaks down under conditions of low temperature? Explain.

93. Use the van der Waals equation and the ideal gas equation to calculate the volume of 1.000 mol of neon at a pressure of 500.0 atm and a temperature of 355.0 K. Explain why the two values are different. (*Hint:* One way to solve the van der Waals equation for *V* is to use successive approximations. Use the ideal gas law to get a preliminary estimate for *V*.)
MISSED THIS? *Read Section 6.10*

94. Use the van der Waals equation and the ideal gas equation to calculate the pressure exerted by 1.000 mol of Cl_2 in a volume of 5.000 L at a temperature of 273.0 K. Explain why the two values are different.

CUMULATIVE PROBLEMS

95. Modern pennies are composed of zinc coated with copper. A student determines the mass of a penny to be 2.482 g and then makes several scratches in the copper coating (to expose the underlying zinc). The student puts the scratched penny in hydrochloric acid, where the following reaction occurs between the zinc and the HCl (the copper remains undissolved):

$$Zn(s) + 2\,HCl(aq) \longrightarrow H_2(g) + ZnCl_2(aq)$$

The student collects the hydrogen produced over water at 25 °C. The collected gas occupies a volume of 0.899 L at a total pressure of 791 mmHg. Calculate the percent zinc (by mass) in the penny. (Assume that all the Zn in the penny dissolves.)

96. A 2.85-g sample of an unknown chlorofluorocarbon decomposes and produces 564 mL of chlorine gas at a pressure of 752 mmHg and a temperature of 298 K. What is the percent chlorine (by mass) in the unknown chlorofluorocarbon?

97. The mass of an evacuated 255 mL flask is 143.187 g. The mass of the flask filled with 267 torr of an unknown gas at 25 °C is 143.289 g. Calculate the molar mass of the unknown gas.

98. A 118-mL flask is evacuated and found to have a mass of 97.129 g. When the flask is filled with 768 torr of helium gas at 35 °C, it has a mass of 97.171 g. Was the helium gas pure?

99. A gaseous hydrogen- and carbon-containing compound is decomposed and found to contain 82.66% carbon and 17.34% hydrogen by mass. The mass of 158 mL of the gas, measured at 556 mmHg and 25 °C, was 0.275 g. What is the molecular formula of the compound?

100. A gaseous hydrogen- and carbon-containing compound is decomposed and found to contain 85.63% C and 14.37% H by mass. The mass of 258 mL of the gas, measured at STP, was 0.646 g. What is the molecular formula of the compound?

101. Consider the reaction:

$$2\,NiO(s) \longrightarrow 2\,Ni(s) + O_2(g)$$

If O_2 is collected over water at 40.0 °C and a total pressure of 745 mmHg, what volume of gas is collected for the complete reaction of 24.78 g of NiO?

102. Consider the reaction:

$$2\,Ag_2O(s) \longrightarrow 4\,Ag(s) + O_2(g)$$

If this reaction produces 15.8 g of Ag(*s*), what total volume of gas can be collected over water at a temperature of 25 °C and a total pressure of 752 mmHg?

103. When hydrochloric acid is poured over potassium sulfide, 42.9 mL of hydrogen sulfide gas is produced at a pressure of 752 torr and 25.8 °C. Write an equation for the gas-evolution reaction and determine how much potassium sulfide (in grams) reacted.

104. Consider the reaction:

$$2\,SO_2(g) + O_2(g) \longrightarrow 2\,SO_3(g)$$

a. If 285.5 mL of SO_2 reacts with 158.9 mL of O_2 (both measured at 315 K and 50.0 mmHg), what is the limiting reactant and the theoretical yield of SO_3?

b. If 187.2 mL of SO_3 is collected (measured at 315 K and 50.0 mmHg), what is the percent yield for the reaction?

105. Ammonium carbonate decomposes upon heating according to the balanced equation:

$$(NH_4)_2CO_3(s) \longrightarrow 2\,NH_3(g) + CO_2(g) + H_2O(g)$$

Calculate the total volume of gas produced at 22 °C and 1.02 atm by the complete decomposition of 11.83 g of ammonium carbonate.

106. Ammonium nitrate decomposes explosively upon heating according to the balanced equation:

$$2\,NH_4NO_3(s) \longrightarrow 2\,N_2(g) + O_2(g) + 4\,H_2O(g)$$

Calculate the total volume of gas (at 125 °C and 748 mmHg) produced by the complete decomposition of 1.55 kg of ammonium nitrate.

107. Olympic cyclists fill their tires with helium to make them lighter. Calculate the mass of air in an air-filled tire and the mass of helium in a helium-filled tire. What is the mass difference between the two? Assume that the volume of the tire is 855 mL, that it is filled to a total pressure of 125 psi, and that the temperature is 25 °C. Also assume an average molar mass for air of 28.8 g/mol.

108. In a common classroom demonstration, a balloon is filled with air and drenched with liquid nitrogen. The balloon contracts as the gases within the balloon cool. Suppose a balloon initially contains 2.95 L of air at a temperature of 25.0 °C and a pressure of 0.998 atm. Calculate the expected volume of the balloon upon cooling to −196 °C (the boiling point of liquid nitrogen). When the demonstration is carried out, the actual volume of the balloon decreases to 0.61 L. How does the observed volume of the balloon compare to your calculated value? Explain the difference.

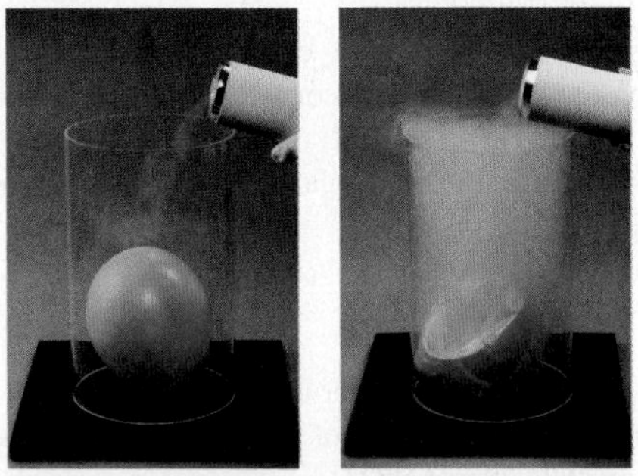

109. Gaseous ammonia is injected into the exhaust stream of a coal-burning power plant to reduce the pollutant NO to N_2 according to the reaction:

$$4\,NH_3(g) + 4\,NO(g) + O_2(g) \longrightarrow 4\,N_2(g) + 6\,H_2O(g)$$

Suppose that the exhaust stream of a power plant has a flow rate of 335 L/s at a temperature of 955 K and that the exhaust contains a partial pressure of NO of 22.4 torr. What should be the flow rate of ammonia delivered at 755 torr and 298 K into the stream to react completely with the NO if the ammonia is 65.2% pure (by volume)?

110. The emission of NO_2 by fossil fuel combustion can be prevented by injecting gaseous urea into the combustion mixture. The urea reduces NO (which oxidizes in air to form NO_2) according to the reaction:

$$2\,CO(NH_2)_2(g) + 4\,NO(g) + O_2(g) \longrightarrow 4\,N_2(g) + 2\,CO_2(g) + 4\,H_2O(g)$$

Suppose that the exhaust stream of an automobile has a flow rate of 2.55 L/s at 655 K and contains a partial pressure of NO of 12.4 torr. What total mass of urea is necessary to react completely with the NO formed during 8.0 hours of driving?

111. An ordinary gasoline can measuring 30.0 cm by 20.0 cm by 15.0 cm is evacuated with a vacuum pump. Assuming that virtually all of the air can be removed from inside the can and that atmospheric pressure is 14.7 psi, what is the total force (in pounds) on the surface of the can? Do you think that the can could withstand the force?

112. Twenty-five milliliters of liquid nitrogen (density = 0.807 g/mL) is poured into a cylindrical container with a radius of 10.0 cm and a length of 20.0 cm. The container initially contains only air at a pressure of 760.0 mmHg (atmospheric pressure) and a temperature of 298 K. If the liquid nitrogen completely vaporizes, what is the total force (in lb) on the interior of the container at 298 K?

113. A 160.0-L helium tank contains pure helium at a pressure of 1855 psi and a temperature of 298 K. How many 3.5-L helium balloons will the helium in the tank fill? (Assume an atmospheric pressure of 1.0 atm and a temperature of 298 K.)

114. An 11.5-mL sample of liquid butane (density = 0.573 g/mL) is evaporated in an otherwise empty container at a temperature of 28.5 °C. The pressure in the container following evaporation is 892 torr. What is the volume of the container?

115. A scuba diver creates a spherical bubble with a radius of 2.5 cm at a depth of 30.0 m where the total pressure (including atmospheric pressure) is 4.00 atm. What is the radius of the bubble when it reaches the surface of the water? (Assume that the atmospheric pressure is 1.00 atm and the temperature is 298 K.)

116. A particular balloon can be stretched to a maximum surface area of 1257 cm^2. The balloon is filled with 3.0 L of helium gas at a pressure of 755 torr and a temperature of 298 K. The balloon is then allowed to rise in the atmosphere. If the atmospheric temperature is 273 K, at what pressure will the balloon burst? (Assume the balloon is the shape of a sphere.)

117. A catalytic converter in an automobile uses a palladium or platinum catalyst (a substance that increases the rate of a reaction without being consumed by the reaction) to convert carbon monoxide gas to carbon dioxide according to the reaction:

$$2\,CO(g) + O_2(g) \longrightarrow 2\,CO_2(g)$$

A chemist researching the effectiveness of a new catalyst combines a 2.0:1.0 mole ratio mixture of carbon monoxide and oxygen gas, respectively, over the catalyst in a 2.45-L flask at a total pressure of 745 torr and a temperature of 552 °C. When the reaction is complete, the pressure in the flask has dropped to 552 torr. What percentage of the carbon monoxide was converted to carbon dioxide?

118. A quantity of N_2 occupies a volume of 1.0 L at 300 K and 1.0 atm. The gas expands to a volume of 3.0 L as the result of a change in both temperature and pressure. Find the density of the gas at these new conditions.

119. A mixture of $CO(g)$ and $O_2(g)$ in a 1.0-L container at 1.0×10^3 K has a total pressure of 2.2 atm. After some time, the total pressure falls to 1.9 atm as the result of the formation of CO_2. Determine the mass (in grams) of CO_2 that forms.

120. The radius of a xenon atom is 1.3×10^{-8} cm. A 100-mL flask is filled with Xe at a pressure of 1.0 atm and a temperature of 273 K. Calculate the fraction of the volume that is occupied by Xe atoms. (*Hint:* The atoms are spheres.)

121. A natural gas storage tank is a cylinder with a moveable top. Its volume can change only as its height changes, and its radius remains fixed. The height of the cylinder is 22.6 m on a day when the temperature is 22 °C. The next day the height of the cylinder increases to 23.8 m when the gas expands because of a heat wave. Determine the temperature on the second day, assuming that the pressure and amount of gas in the storage tank have not changed.

122. A mixture of 8.0 g CH_4 and 8.0 g Xe is placed in a container, and the total pressure is found to be 0.44 atm. Determine the partial pressure of CH_4.

123. A steel container of volume 0.35 L can withstand pressures up to 88 atm before exploding. What mass of helium can be stored in this container at 299 K?

124. Binary compounds of alkali metals and hydrogen react with water to liberate $H_2(g)$. The H_2 from the reaction of a sample of NaH with an excess of water fills a volume of 0.490 L above the water. The temperature of the gas is 35 °C, and the total pressure is 758 mmHg. Determine the mass of H_2 liberated and the mass of NaH that reacted.

125. In a given diffusion apparatus, 15.0 mL of HBr gas diffuses in 1.0 min. In the same apparatus and under the same conditions, 20.3 mL of an unknown gas diffuses in 1.0 min. The unknown gas is a hydrocarbon. Find its molecular formula.

126. A sample of $N_2O_3(g)$ has a pressure of 0.017 atm. The temperature (in K) is doubled, and the N_2O_3 undergoes complete decomposition to $NO_2(g)$ and $NO(g)$. Find the total pressure of the mixture of gases assuming constant volume and no additional temperature change.

127. When 0.583 g of neon is added to an 800-cm^3 bulb containing a sample of argon, the total pressure of the gases is 1.17 atm at a temperature of 295 K. Find the mass of the argon in the bulb.

128. A gas mixture composed of helium and argon has a density of 0.670 g/L at 755 mmHg and 298 K. What is the composition of the mixture by volume?

129. A gas mixture contains 75.2% nitrogen and 24.8% krypton by mass. What is the partial pressure of krypton in the mixture if the total pressure is 745 mmHg?

CHALLENGE PROBLEMS

130. A 10-L container is filled with 0.10 mol of $H_2(g)$ and heated to 3000 K, causing some of the $H_2(g)$ to decompose into $H(g)$. The pressure is found to be 3.0 atm. Find the partial pressure of the $H(g)$ that forms from H_2 at this temperature. (Assume two significant figures for the temperature.)

131. A mixture of $NH_3(g)$ and $N_2H_4(g)$ is placed in a sealed container at 300 K. The total pressure is 0.50 atm. The container is heated to 1200 K, at which time both substances decompose completely according to the equations $2\,NH_3(g) \longrightarrow N_2(g) + 3\,H_2(g)$; $N_2H_4(g) \longrightarrow N_2(g) + 2\,H_2(g)$. After decomposition is complete, the total pressure at 1200 K is found to be 4.5 atm. Find the percent of $N_2H_4(g)$ in the original mixture. (Assume two significant figures for the temperature.)

132. A quantity of CO gas occupies a volume of 0.48 L at 1.0 atm and 275 K. The pressure of the gas is lowered, and its temperature is raised until its volume is 1.3 L. Determine the density of the CO under the new conditions.

133. When $CO_2(g)$ is put in a sealed container at 701 K and a pressure of 10.0 atm and is heated to 1401 K, the pressure rises to 22.5 atm. Some of the CO_2 decomposes to CO and O_2. Calculate the mole percent of CO_2 that decomposes.

134. The world burns approximately 3.7×10^{12} kg of fossil fuel per year. Use the combustion of octane as the representative reaction and determine the mass of carbon dioxide (the most significant greenhouse gas) formed per year. The current concentration of carbon dioxide in the atmosphere is approximately 399 ppm (by volume). By what percentage does the concentration increase each year due to fossil fuel combustion? Approximate the average properties of the entire atmosphere by assuming that the atmosphere extends from sea level to 15 km and that it has an average pressure of 381 torr and average temperature of 275 K. Assume Earth is a perfect sphere with a radius of 6371 km.

135. The atmosphere slowly oxidizes hydrocarbons in a number of steps that eventually convert the hydrocarbon into carbon dioxide and water. Part of the process for methane gas is

$$CH_4(g) + 5\,O_2(g) + 5\,NO(g) \longrightarrow CO_2(g) + H_2O(g) + 5\,NO(g) + 2\,OH(g)$$

Suppose that an atmospheric chemist combines 155 mL of methane at STP, 885 mL of oxygen at STP, and 55.5 mL of NO at STP in a 2.0 L flask. The flask is allowed to stand for several weeks at 275 K. If the reaction reaches 90.0% of completion (90.0% of the limiting reactant is consumed), what is the partial pressure of each of the reactants and products in the flask at 275 K? What is the total pressure in the flask?

136. Two identical balloons are filled to the same volume, one with air and one with helium. The next day, the volume of the air-filled balloon has decreased by 5.0%. By what percent has the volume of the helium-filled balloon decreased? (Assume that the air is four-fifths nitrogen and one-fifth oxygen and that the temperature did not change.)

137. A mixture of $CH_4(g)$ and $C_2H_6(g)$ has a total pressure of 0.53 atm. Just enough $O_2(g)$ is added to the mixture to bring about its complete combustion to $CO_2(g)$ and $H_2O(g)$. The total pressure of the two product gases is 2.2 atm. Assuming constant volume and temperature, find the mole fraction of CH_4 in the mixture.

138. A sample of $C_2H_2(g)$ has a pressure of 7.8 kPa. After some time a portion of it reacts to form $C_6H_6(g)$. The total pressure of the mixture of gases is then 3.9 kPa. Assume the volume and the temperature do not change. What fraction of $C_2H_2(g)$ has undergone reaction?

CONCEPTUAL PROBLEMS

139. When the driver of an automobile applies the brakes, the passengers are pushed toward the front of the car, but a helium balloon is pushed toward the back of the car. Upon forward acceleration, the passengers are pushed toward the back of the car, but the helium balloon is pushed toward the front of the car. Why?

140. Suppose that a liquid is 10 times denser than water. If you were to sip this liquid at sea level using a straw, what is the maximum length your straw would be?

141. This reaction occurs in a closed container:

$$A(g) + 2\,B(g) \longrightarrow 2\,C(g)$$

A reaction mixture initially contains 1.5 L of A and 2.0 L of B. Assuming that the volume and temperature of the reaction mixture remain constant, what is the percent change in pressure if the reaction goes to completion?

142. One mole of nitrogen and one mole of neon are combined in a closed container at STP. How big is the container?

143. Exactly equal amounts (in moles) of gas A and gas B are combined in a 1-L container at room temperature. Gas B has a molar mass that is twice that of gas A. Which statement is true for the mixture of gases and why?

a. The molecules of gas B have greater kinetic energy than those of gas A.
b. Gas B has a greater partial pressure than gas A.
c. The molecules of gas B have a greater average velocity than those of gas A.
d. Gas B makes a greater contribution to the average density of the mixture than gas A.

144. Which gas would you expect to deviate most from ideal behavior under conditions of low temperature: F_2, Cl_2, or Br_2? Explain.

145. The volume of a sample of a fixed amount of gas is decreased from 2.0 L to 1.0 L. The temperature of the gas in kelvins is then doubled. What is the final pressure of the gas in terms of the initial pressure?

146. Which gas sample has the greatest volume at STP?
a. 10.0 g Kr b. 10.0 g Xe c. 10.0 g He

147. Draw a depiction of a gas sample, as described by kinetic molecular theory, containing equal molar amounts of helium, neon, and krypton. Use different color dots to represent each element. Give each atom a "tail" to represent its velocity relative to the others in the mixture.

QUESTIONS FOR GROUP WORK

Active Classroom Learning

Discuss these questions with the group and record your consensus answer.

148. Assign one of the three simple gas laws to each member of your group. For the assigned gas law, have each member write two equations, draw a graph, and describe it in a complete sentence. Have each group member present his or her law to the group.

149. Review the ideal gas law. Without referring back to the text, use algebra to write the ideal gas law and solve for each of the individual variables it contains. Have each group member solve for a different variable and present answers to the group.

150. Hydrogen peroxide (H_2O_2) decomposes in the presence of a catalyst to form water and oxygen. The catalyst is added to 5.00 mL of a hydrogen peroxide solution at 25.0 °C, and 49.5 mL of gas is collected over water at a total pressure of 763.8 mmHg.

a. Write and balance the chemical reaction (Note: catalysts do not appear in balanced chemical equations).
b. Look up the vapor pressure of water under these conditions.
c. What is the partial pressure of oxygen collected over the water?
d. How many moles of oxygen are collected?
e. How many grams of hydrogen peroxide were in the original sample?
f. What is the concentration (in mol/L) of the hydrogen peroxide solution?
g. Which part of this process is conceptually most difficult for your group?

151. A box contains equal amounts of helium, argon, and krypton (all gases) at 25 °C. Using complete sentences, describe the temperatures, masses, average velocities, and average kinetic energy of the three kinds of gas in the mixture. What do they have in common? What are the differences? How are these properties related?

152. Calculate the pressure exerted by 1 mol of an ideal gas in a box that is 0.500 L and 298 K. Have each group member calculate the pressure of 1 mol of the following gases in the same box at the same temperature: He, Ne, H_2, CH_4, and CO_2. Compare group members' answers as well as all answers with the pressure of an ideal gas. Assuming that the van der Waals equation predictions are accurate, account for why the pressure of each gas is higher or lower than that predicted for an ideal gas.

DATA INTERPRETATION AND ANALYSIS

Nitrogen Oxide from Automobiles

153. When fuels are burned in air, such as in an automobile engine, some of the nitrogen in the air oxidizes to form nitrogen oxide gases such as NO and NO_2 (known collectively as NO_x). The U.S. Environmental Protection Agency (EPA) sets standards for air quality of several pollutants including NO_2. According to the EPA, NO_2 levels in U.S. cities are not to exceed a yearly average of 53 ppb or a 1-hour average of 100 ppb. Another pollutant associated with automobile exhaust is ozone (O_3). The EPA standard for ozone is an 8-hour average of 70 ppb. Breathing air with elevated levels of NO_2 or O_3 can cause asthma and other respiratory problems. The graph shown here shows the average concentration of nitrogen dioxide (NO_2) and ozone (O_3) gases in units of parts per billion by volume (ppbv) over seven days in a city.

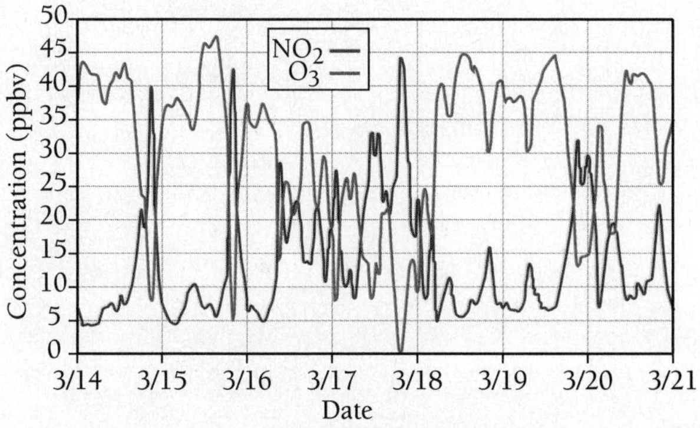

▲ Concentration of NO_2 and O_3 over Seven Days

Source: http://www.cas.manchester.ac.uk/resprojects/holmemoss/results/fig2/

Study the graph and answer the following questions:

a. What type of relationship exists between nitrogen dioxide and ozone between March 14 and March 16?

b. Calculate the number of moles of NO_2 in 1.00 m^3 produced on March 14. Assume an average temperature of 25.0 °C and a pressure of 1 atm. Note that the number of moles of NO_2 produced is the difference between the existing amount at the start of the day and the peak amount.

c. Calculate the number of moles of O_3 in 1.00 m^3 consumed on March 14. Assume an average temperature of 25.0 °C and a pressure of 1 atm. Note that the number of moles of O_3 consumed is the difference between the existing amount at the start of the day and the minimum amount.

d. What is the mole-to-mole ratio of O_3 consumed to NO_2 produced?

e. The following chemical equations model the interactions of nitrogen dioxide gas and ozone gas. Can this set of equations account for the trends observed in the graph? Explain your answer.

$$N_2 + O_2 \longrightarrow 2\,NO$$
$$NO + O_3 \longrightarrow NO_2 + O_2 + \text{light}$$

f. Do the concentrations of NO_2 or O_3 exceed the standards set by the EPA?

Cc ANSWERS TO CONCEPTUAL CONNECTIONS

Boyle's Law and Charles's Law

6.1 **(e)** The final volume of the gas is the same as the initial volume because doubling the pressure *decreases* the volume by a factor of 2, but doubling the temperature *increases* the volume by a factor of 2. The two changes in volume are equal in magnitude but opposite in sign, resulting in a final volume that is equal to the initial volume.

Simple Gas Laws

6.2 **(a)** According to Boyle's law, decreasing the pressure increases the volume (at constant temperature and number of moles.)

Molar Volume

6.3 **(a)** Since one gram of H_2 contains the greatest number of moles (due to H_2 having the lowest molar mass of the listed gases) and since one mole of *any* ideal gas occupies the same volume, the H_2 occupies the greatest volume.

Density of a Gas

6.4 **(a)** $Ne < O_2 < F_2 < Cl_2$

Partial Pressures

6.5 **(c)** $P_{He} = 1.5$ atm; $P_{Ne} = 1.5$ atm. Since the number of moles of each gas is equal, the mole fraction of each gas is 0.50 and the partial pressure of each gas is $0.50 \times P_{tot}$.

Pressure and Number of Moles

6.6 **(b)** Since the total number of gas molecules decreases, the total pressure—the sum of all the partial pressures—must also decrease.

Root Mean Square Velocity

6.7 **(b)** The molar mass of neon (20.18 g/mol) is approximately one-quarter the molar mass of krypton (83.80 g/mol), so the root mean square velocity of neon is $\sqrt{\frac{1}{1/4}}$ times that of krypton.

Kinetic Molecular Theory

6.8 **(c)** Since the temperature and the volume are both constant, the ideal gas law tells us that the pressure depends solely on the number of particles. Sample (c) has the greatest number of particles per unit volume and therefore has the greatest pressure. The pressures of samples (a) and (b) at a given temperature are identical. Even though the particles in (b) are more massive than those in (a), they have the same average kinetic energy at a given temperature. The particles in (b) move more slowly than those in (a) and so exert the same pressure as the particles in (a).

Graham's Law of Effusion

6.9 **(c)** Since the molar mass of helium is less than that of argon, helium effuses faster than argon, resulting in an increase in the relative amount of argon relative to helium left in the tube.

Real Gases

6.10 **(b)** A < B < C. Curve A is the lowest temperature curve because it deviates the most from ideality. The tendency for the intermolecular forces in carbon dioxide to lower the pressure (relative to that of an ideal gas) is greatest at low temperature (because the molecules are moving more slowly and are therefore less able to overcome the intermolecular forces). As a result, the curve that dips the lowest must correspond to the lowest temperature.

There is a fact, or if you wish, a law, governing all natural phenomena that are known to date. There is no known exception to this law—it is exact as far as we know. The law is called the conservation of energy. It states that there is a certain quantity, which we call energy, that does not change in the manifold changes which nature undergoes.

—RICHARD P. FEYNMAN (1918–1988)

CHAPTER 7 Thermochemistry

We have spent the first few chapters of this book examining one of the two major components of our universe—matter. We now turn our attention to the other major component—energy. As far as we know, matter and energy—which can be interchanged but not destroyed—make up the physical universe. Unlike matter, energy is not something we can touch or hold in our hand, but we experience it in many ways. The warmth of sunlight, the feel of wind on our faces, and the force that presses us back when a car accelerates are all manifestations of energy and its interconversions. And of course energy is critical to society and to the world. The standard of living around the globe is strongly correlated with the access to and use of energy resources. Most of those resources, as we shall see, are chemical ones, and we can understand their advantages as well as their drawbacks in terms of chemistry.

A chemical hand warmer contains substances that react to emit heat.

7.1 Chemical Hand Warmers 263
7.2 The Nature of Energy: Key Definitions 264
7.3 The First Law of Thermodynamics: There Is No Free Lunch 267
7.4 Quantifying Heat and Work 272
7.5 Measuring ΔE for Chemical Reactions: Constant-Volume Calorimetry 278
7.6 Enthalpy: The Heat Evolved in a Chemical Reaction at Constant Pressure 281
7.7 Constant-Pressure Calorimetry: Measuring ΔH_{rxn} 285
7.8 Relationships Involving ΔH_{rxn} 286
7.9 Determining Enthalpies of Reaction from Standard Enthalpies of Formation 289
7.10 Energy Use and the Environment 294
LEARNING OUTCOMES 301

7.1 Chemical Hand Warmers

My family loves to snowboard. However, my wife hates being cold (with a passion), especially in her hands and toes. Her solution is the chemical hand warmer, a small pouch that comes sealed in a plastic package. She opens the package and places the pouch in her glove or boot. The pouch slowly warms up and keeps her hand (or foot) warm all day long.

Warming your hands with chemical hand warmers involves many of the principles of **thermochemistry**, the study of the relationships between chemistry and energy. When you open the package that contains the hand warmer, the contents are exposed to air, and an *exothermic reaction* occurs. Most hand warmers use the oxidation of iron as the exothermic reaction:

$$4\,Fe(s) + 3\,O_2(g) \longrightarrow 2\,Fe_2O_3(s) + \text{heat}$$

The useful product of this reaction is not a substance—it is *heat*. We'll define heat more carefully later, but heat is what you feel when you touch something that is warmer than your hand (in this case, the hand warmer). Although some of the heat is lost through the minute openings in your gloves (which is why my wife prefers mittens, which have fewer openings), most of it is transferred to your hands and to the pocket of air surrounding your hands, resulting in a temperature increase. The magnitude of the temperature increase depends on the size of the hand warmer and the size of your glove (as well as some other details). But in general, the size of the temperature increase is proportional to the amount of heat released by the reaction.

In this chapter, we examine the relationship between chemical reactions and energy. Specifically, we look at how chemical reactions can *exchange* energy with their surroundings and how we can quantify the magnitude of those exchanges. These kinds of calculations are important, not only for chemical hand warmers, but also for many other important processes such as the production of energy.

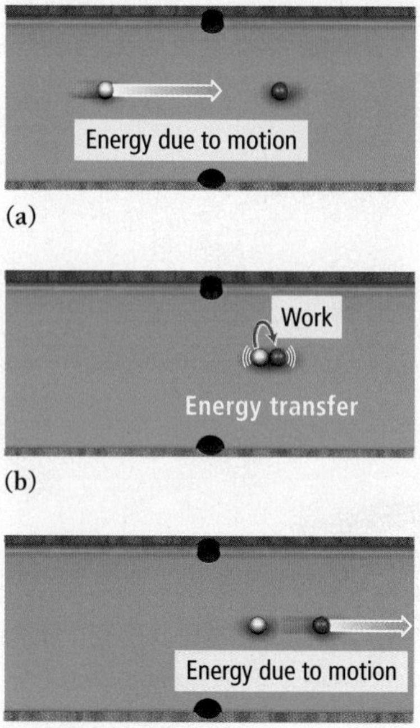

▲ **(a)** A rolling billiard ball has energy due to its motion. **(b)** When the ball collides with a second ball, it does work, transferring energy to the second ball. **(c)** The second ball has energy as it rolls away from the collision.

7.2 The Nature of Energy: Key Definitions

Recall that we briefly examined energy in Section 1.5. We defined **energy** as the capacity to do work and defined **work** as the result of a force acting through a distance. When you push a box across the floor, you have done work. Consider another example of work: a billiard ball rolling across a billiard table and colliding straight on with a second, stationary billiard ball. The rolling ball has *energy* due to its motion. When it collides with another stationary ball, it does *work* on it, resulting in the *transfer* of energy from one ball to the other. The second billiard ball absorbs the energy and begins to roll across the table.

As we just saw with chemical hand warmers, energy can also be transferred through **heat**, the flow of energy caused by a temperature difference. For example, if you hold a cup of coffee in your hand, energy is transferred, in the form of heat, from the hot coffee to your cooler hand. Think of *energy* as something that an object or set of objects possesses. Think of *heat* and *work* as ways that objects or sets of objects *exchange* energy.

Breaking chemical bonds always takes energy. The reactions that produce energy involve breaking weak bonds and forming stronger bonds.

Types of Energy

The energy contained in a rolling billiard ball is an example of **kinetic energy**, the energy associated with the *motion* of an object. The energy contained in a hot cup of coffee is **thermal energy**, the energy associated with the *temperature* of an object. Thermal energy is actually a type of kinetic energy because it arises from the motions of atoms or molecules within a substance. If you raise a billiard ball off the table, you increase its **potential energy**, the energy associated with the *position* or *composition* of an object. The potential energy of the billiard ball, for example, is a result of its position in Earth's gravitational field. Raising the ball off the table, against Earth's gravitational pull, gives the ball more potential energy. Another example of potential energy is the energy contained in a compressed spring. When you compress a spring, you push against the forces that tend to maintain the spring's uncompressed shape, storing energy as potential energy. **Chemical energy**, the energy associated with the relative positions of electrons and nuclei in atoms and molecules, is also a form of potential energy. Some chemical compounds, such as the methane in natural gas or the iron in a chemical hand warmer, are like compressed springs—they contain potential energy, and a chemical reaction can release that potential energy. Figure 7.1◀ summarizes these different kinds of energy.

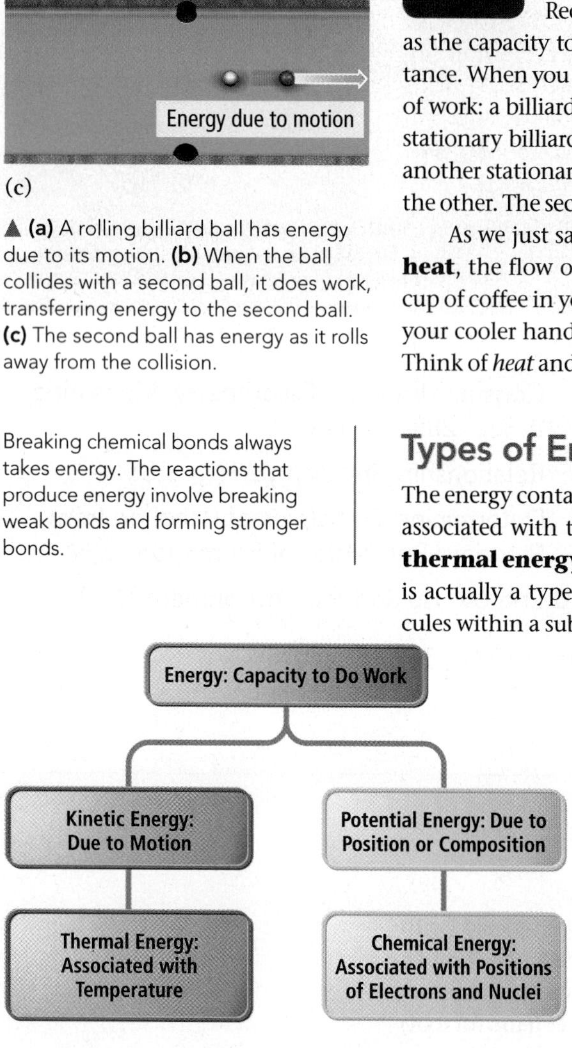

▲ **FIGURE 7.1 The Different Manifestations of Energy**

Energy Transformation I

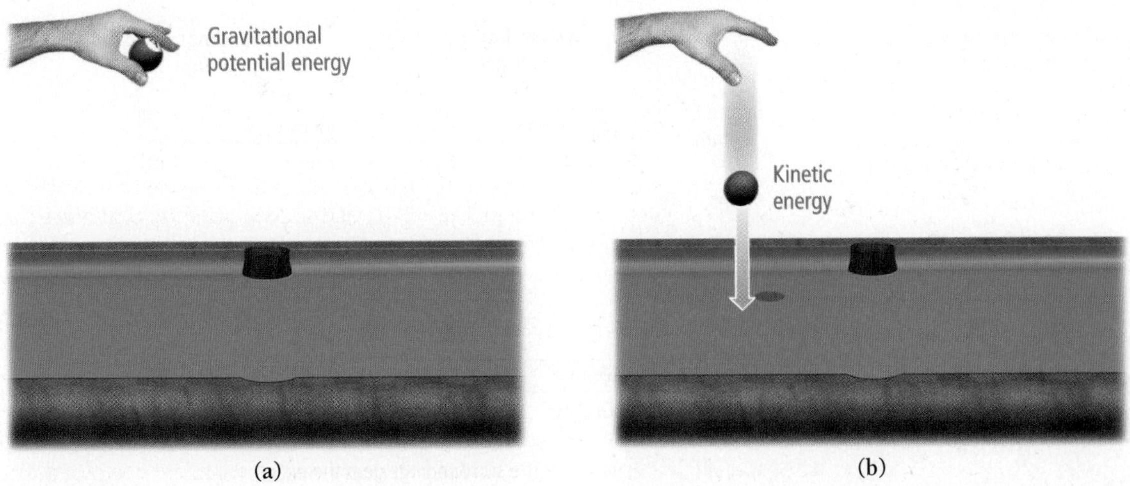

▲ **FIGURE 7.2 Energy Transformation: Potential and Kinetic Energy I** **(a)** A billiard ball held above the table has gravitational potential energy. **(b)** When the ball is released, the potential energy is transformed into kinetic energy, the energy of motion.

Energy Conservation and Energy Transfer

The **law of conservation of energy** states that *energy can be neither created nor destroyed*. However, energy can be transferred from one object to another, and it can assume different forms. For example, if you drop a raised billiard ball, some of its potential energy becomes kinetic energy as the ball falls toward the table, as shown in Figure 7.2▲. If you release a compressed spring, the potential energy becomes kinetic energy as the spring expands outward, as shown in Figure 7.3▼. When iron reacts with oxygen within a chemical hand warmer, the chemical energy of the iron and oxygen becomes thermal energy that increases the temperature of your hand and glove.

Einstein showed that it is mass–energy that is conserved; one can be converted into the other. This equivalence becomes important in nuclear reactions, discussed in Chapter 21. In ordinary chemical reactions, however, the interconversion of mass and energy is not a significant factor, and we can regard mass and energy as independently conserved.

A good way to understand and track energy changes is to define the **system** under investigation. For example, the system may be the chemicals in a beaker, or it may be the iron reacting in a hand warmer. The system's **surroundings** are everything with which the system can exchange energy. If we define the chemicals in a beaker as the system, the surroundings may include the water in which the chemicals are dissolved (for aqueous solutions), the beaker itself, the lab bench on which the beaker sits, the air in the room, and so on. For the iron in the hand warmer, the surroundings include your hand, your glove, the air in the glove, and even the air outside of the glove.

In an energy exchange, energy transfers between the system and the surroundings, as shown in Figure 7.4▶. If the system loses energy, the surroundings gain the same exact amount of energy, and vice versa. When the iron within the chemical hand warmer reacts, the system loses energy to the surroundings, producing the desired temperature increase within your gloves.

Energy Transformation II

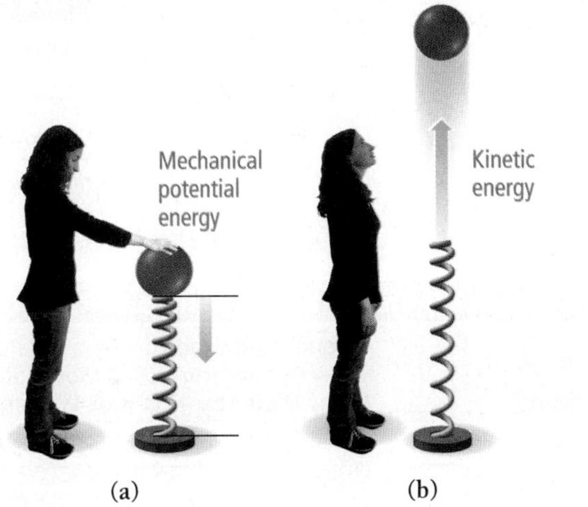

▲ **FIGURE 7.3 Energy Transformation: Potential and Kinetic Energy II** **(a)** A compressed spring has potential energy. **(b)** When the spring is released, the potential energy is transformed into kinetic energy.

Units of Energy

We can deduce the units of energy from the definition of kinetic energy. An object of mass m, moving at velocity v, has a kinetic energy KE given by the equation:

$$\mathrm{KE} = \frac{1}{2}mv^2 \qquad [7.1]$$

kg m/s

▶ **FIGURE 7.4 Energy Transfer** If a system and surroundings had energy gauges (which measure energy content in the way a fuel gauge measures fuel content), an energy transfer in which the system transfers energy to the surroundings would result in a decrease in the energy content of the system and an increase in the energy content of the surroundings. The total amount of energy, however, must be conserved.

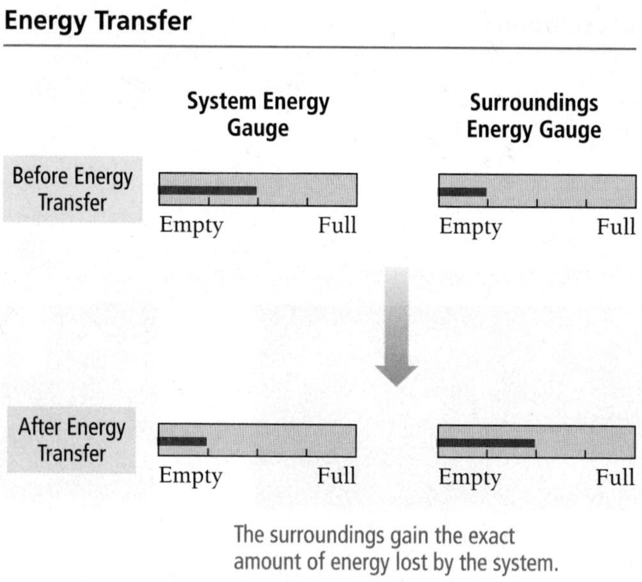

▲ A watt (W) is 1 J/s, so a 10-W lightbulb uses 10 J every second or 3.6×10^4 J every hour.

The SI unit of mass is the kg, and the unit of velocity is m/s. The SI unit of energy is therefore $\text{kg} \cdot \text{m}^2/\text{s}^2$, defined as the **joule (J)**, named after the English scientist James Joule (1818–1889).

$$1 \text{ kg} \frac{\text{m}^2}{\text{s}^2} = 1 \text{ J}$$

One joule is a relatively small amount of energy—for example, a 10-watt lightbulb uses 3.6×10^4 J in 1 hour. Therefore, we often use the kilojoule (kJ) in our energy discussions and calculations $(1 \text{ kJ} = 1000 \text{ J})$. A second commonly used unit of energy is the **calorie (cal)**, originally defined as the amount of energy required to raise the temperature of 1 g of water by 1 °C. The current definition is 1 cal = 4.184 J (exact); a calorie is a larger unit than a joule. A related energy unit is the nutritional, or uppercase "C" **Calorie (Cal)**, equivalent to 1000 lowercase "c" calories. The Calorie is the same as a kilocalorie (kcal): 1 Cal = 1 kcal = 1000 cal. Electricity bills typically are based on another, even larger, energy unit, the **kilowatt-hour (kWh)**: 1 kWh = 3.60×10^6 J. Electricity costs \$0.08–\$0.18 per kWh. Table 7.1 lists various energy units and their conversion factors. Table 7.2 shows the amount of energy required for various processes.

The "calorie" referred to on all nutritional labels (regardless of the capitalization) is always the capital C Calorie.

TABLE 7.1 ■ Energy Conversion Factors*

1 calorie (cal)	= 4.184 joules (J)
1 Calorie (Cal) or kilocalorie (kcal)	= 1000 cal = 4184 J
1 kilowatt-hour (kWh)	= 3.60×10^6 J

*All conversion factors in this table are exact.

TABLE 7.2 ■ Energy Uses in Various Units

Unit	Amount Required to Raise Temperature of 1 g of Water by 1 °C	Amount Required to Light 10-W Bulb for 1 Hour	Amount Used by Human Body in Running 1 Mile (Approximate)	Amount Used by Average U.S. Citizen in 1 Day
joule (J)	4.18	3.60×10^4	4.2×10^5	9.0×10^8
calorie (cal)	1.00	8.60×10^3	1.0×10^5	2.2×10^8
Calorie (Cal)	0.00100	8.60	100	2.2×10^5
kilowatt-hour (kWh)	1.16×10^{-6}	0.0100	0.12	2.5×10^2

7.3 The First Law of Thermodynamics: There Is No Free Lunch

WATCH **NOW!**

KEY CONCEPT VIDEO 7.3
The First Law of Thermodynamics

Thermodynamics is the general study of energy and its interconversions. The laws of thermodynamics are among the most fundamental in all of science, governing virtually every process that involves change. The **first law of thermodynamics** is the law of energy conservation, which we state as follows:

The total energy of the universe is constant.

In other words, since energy is neither created nor destroyed, and since the universe does not exchange energy with anything else, its energy content does not change.

The first law has many implications: the most important one is that with energy, you cannot get something for nothing. The best you can do with energy is break even—there is no free lunch. According to the first law, a device that would continually produce energy with no energy input, sometimes known as a *perpetual motion machine*, cannot exist. Occasionally, the media report or speculate on the discovery of a machine that can produce energy without the need for energy input. For example, you may have heard someone propose an electric car that recharges itself while driving, or a new motor that can create additional usable electricity as well as the electricity to power itself. Although some hybrid (electric and gasoline-powered) vehicles can capture energy from braking and use that energy to recharge their batteries, they could never run indefinitely without additional fuel. As for the motor that powers an external load as well as itself—no such thing exists. Our society has a continual need for energy, and as our current energy resources dwindle, new energy sources will be required. But those sources, whatever they may be, must follow the first law of thermodynamics—energy is always conserved.

Internal Energy

The **internal energy (E)** of a system is *the sum of the kinetic and potential energies of all of the particles that compose the system.* Internal energy is a **state function**, which means that its value depends *only on the state of the system*, not on how the system arrived at that state.

CHEMISTRY IN YOUR DAY | Redheffer's Perpetual Motion Machine

In 1812, a man named Charles Redheffer appeared in Philadelphia with a machine that he claimed could run forever without any energy input—a perpetual motion machine. He set up the machine on the edge of town and charged admission to view it. He also appealed to the city for money to build a larger version of the machine. When city commissioners came out to inspect the machine, Redheffer did his best to keep them from viewing it too closely. Nonetheless, one of the commissioners noticed something suspicious: the gears that supposedly ran to an external driveshaft were cut in the wrong direction. The driveshaft that the machine was allegedly powering was instead powering the machine. The city commissioners hired a local engineer and clockmaker named Isaiah Lukens to make a similar machine to expose Redheffer's deception. Lukens's machine was even more ingenious than Redheffer's, and Redheffer left Philadelphia exposed as a fraud.

Redheffer was persistent, however, and took his machine to New York. In 1813, during a public display of the machine, the famous mechanical engineer Robert Fulton (1765–1815)—who had demonstrated the first successful steamboat six years earlier—noticed a rhythm to the machine's motion. It seemed to speed up and slow down at regular intervals. Fulton knew that such rhythmic motion is indicative of motion generated by a manual crank. He knocked away some boards in a wall next to the machine and discovered a long belt that led to an enclosed room where, indeed, an old man sat turning a crank. Redheffer's machine—like many other perpetual motion machines throughout history—was again exposed as a hoax.

QUESTION *Can you think of any recent claims of perpetual motion or limitless free energy?*

▶ **FIGURE 7.5 Altitude as a State Function**

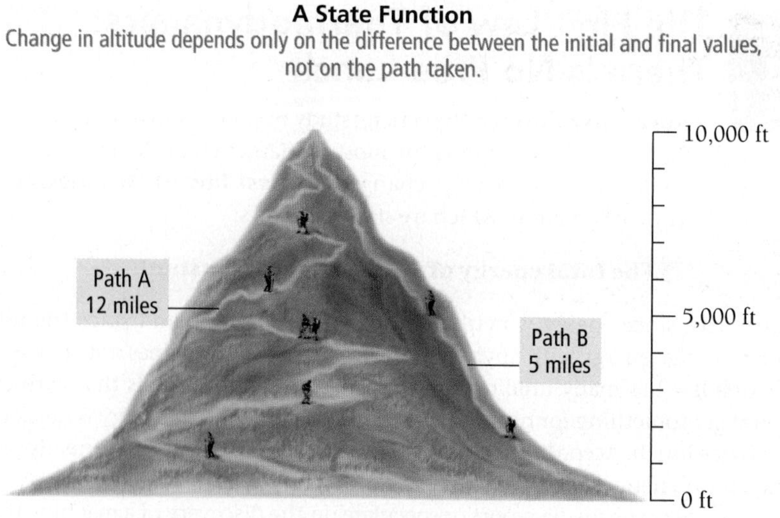

The state of a chemical system is specified by parameters such as temperature, pressure, concentration, and physical state (solid, liquid, or gas). Consider the mountain-climbing analogy depicted in Figure 7.5▲. The elevation at any point during a mountain climb is analogous to a state function. For example, when we reach 10,000 ft, our elevation is 10,000 ft, no matter how we got there. The distance we traveled to get there, by contrast, is not a state function; we could have climbed the mountain by any number of routes, each requiring us to cover a different distance.

Since state functions depend only on the state of the system, the value of a *change* in a state function is always the difference between its final and initial values. If we start climbing a mountain at an elevation of 3000 ft and reach the summit at 10,000 ft, then our elevation change is 7000 ft (10,000 ft − 3000 ft), regardless of what path we traveled.

Like an altitude change, an internal energy change (ΔE) is determined by the difference in internal energy between the final and initial states:

$$\Delta E = E_{\text{final}} - E_{\text{initial}}$$

In a chemical system, the reactants constitute the initial state and the products constitute the final state. So ΔE is the difference in internal energy between the products and the reactants:

$$\Delta E = E_{\text{products}} - E_{\text{reactants}} \quad [7.2]$$

For example, consider the reaction between carbon and oxygen to form carbon dioxide:

$$\text{C}(s) + \text{O}_2(g) \longrightarrow \text{CO}_2(g)$$

Just as we can portray the changes that occur when climbing a mountain with an *altitude* diagram that depicts the *altitude* before and after the climb (see Figure 7.5), we can portray the energy changes that occur during a reaction with an *energy* diagram, which compares the *internal energy* of the reactants and the products:

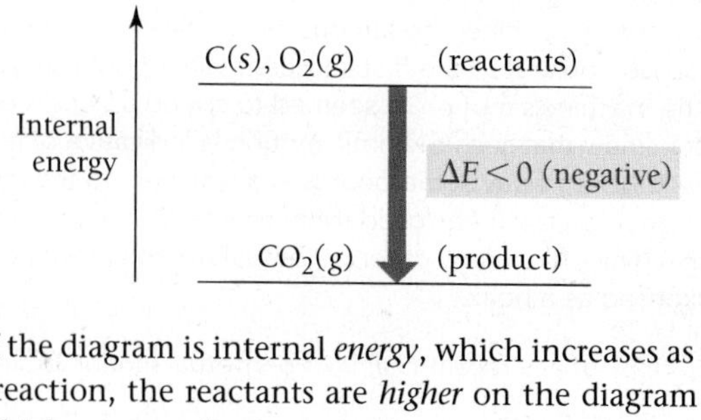

The vertical axis of the diagram is internal *energy*, which increases as we move up on the diagram. For this reaction, the reactants are *higher* on the diagram than the products because they have higher internal energy. As the reaction occurs, the reactants become products, which have lower internal energy. Therefore, energy is given off by the reaction and ΔE (that is, $E_{\text{products}} - E_{\text{reactants}}$) is *negative*.

Where does the energy lost by the reactants (as they transform to products) go? If we define the thermodynamic *system* as the reactants and products of the reaction, then energy flows *out of the system* and *into the surroundings*.

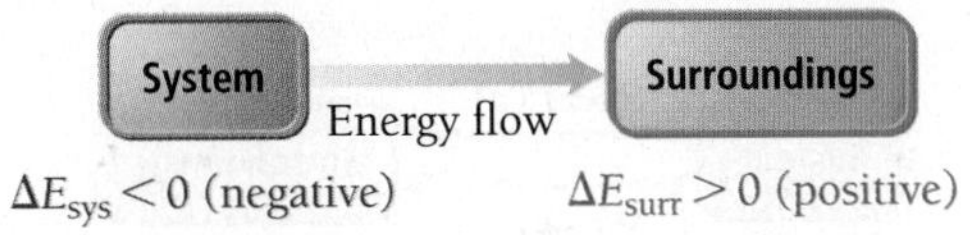

According to the first law, energy must be conserved. Therefore, the amount of energy lost by the system must exactly equal the amount gained by the surroundings:

$$\Delta E_{sys} = -\Delta E_{surr} \qquad [7.3]$$

Now, suppose the reaction is reversed:

$$CO_2(g) \longrightarrow C(s) + O_2(g)$$

The energy-level diagram is nearly identical, with one important difference: $CO_2(g)$ is now the reactant and $C(s)$ and $O_2(g)$ are the products. Instead of decreasing in energy as the reaction occurs, the system increases in energy as shown at right. In this reversed reaction, ΔE is *positive*, and energy flows *into the system* and *out of the surroundings*:

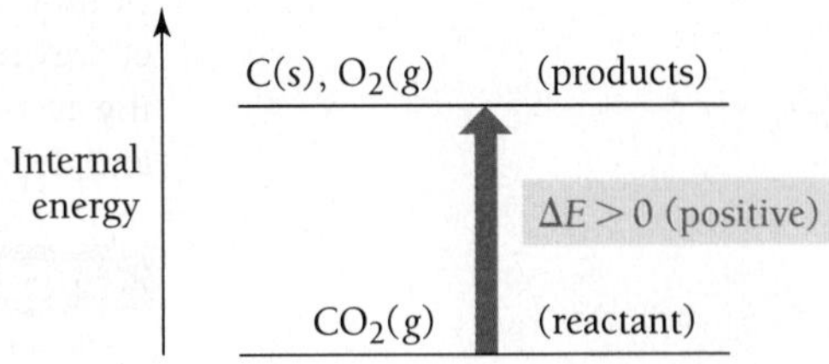

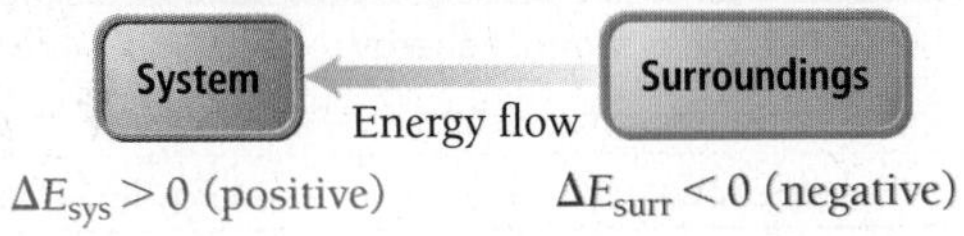

Summarizing Energy Flow:

- If the reactants have a higher internal energy than the products, ΔE_{sys} is negative and energy flows out of the system into the surroundings.
- If the reactants have a lower internal energy than the products, ΔE_{sys} is positive and energy flows into the system from the surroundings.

We can think of the internal energy of the system in the same way we think about the balance in a checking account. Energy flowing *out of* the system is like a withdrawal and therefore carries a negative sign. Energy flowing *into* the system is like a deposit and carries a positive sign.

7.1 Cc Conceptual Connection

ANSWER **NOW!**

SYSTEM AND SURROUNDINGS Consider these fictitious internal energy gauges that describe the initial conditions for a chemical system and its surroundings:

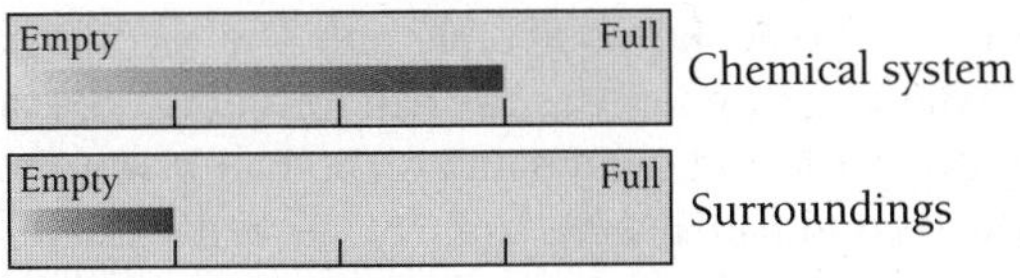

Which energy gauges correspond to the final conditions following an energy exchange in which ΔE_{sys} is negative?

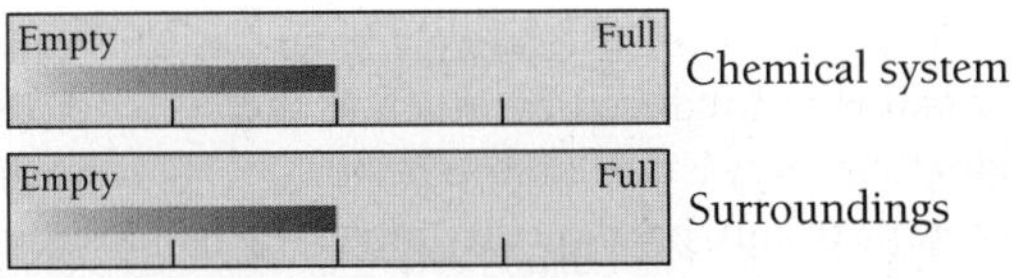

(a)

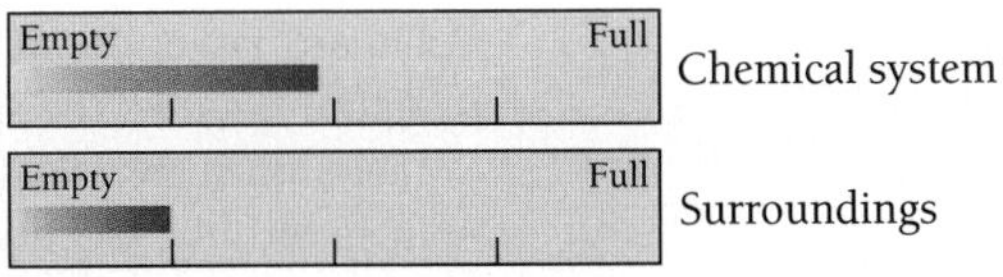

(b)

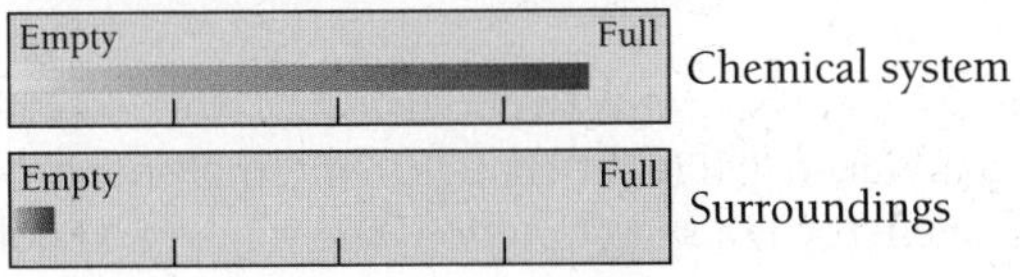

(c)

Heat and Work

As we discussed in Section 7.2, a system can exchange energy with its surroundings through *heat* and *work*:

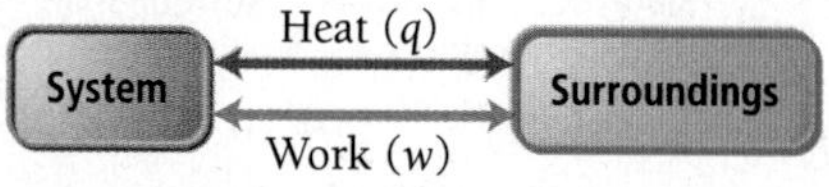

According to the first law of thermodynamics, the change in the internal energy of the system (ΔE) is the sum of the heat transferred (q) and the work done (w):

$$\Delta E = q + w \qquad [7.4]$$

In Equation 7.4, and from this point forward, we follow the standard convention that ΔE (with no subscript) refers to the internal energy change of the *system*. As shown in Table 7.3, energy entering the system through heat or work carries a positive sign, and energy leaving the system through heat or work carries a negative sign. Recall our checking account analogy. The system is like the checking account—withdrawals are negative and deposits are positive.

TABLE 7.3 ■ Sign Conventions for q, w, and ΔE

q (heat)	+ system *gains* thermal energy	− system *loses* thermal energy
w (work)	+ work done *on* the system	− work done *by* the system
ΔE (change in internal energy)	+ energy flows *into* the system	− energy flows *out* of the system

We can define our system as the previously discussed billiard ball rolling across a pool table. The rolling ball has a certain initial amount of kinetic energy. When it reaches the other end of the table, the rolling ball collides head-on with a second ball. Assume that the first ball loses all of its kinetic energy so that it remains completely still (it has no kinetic energy) at the point of collision. The total change in internal energy (ΔE) for the first ball is the difference between its initial kinetic energy and its final kinetic energy (which is zero); the first billiard ball lost all of its energy. What happened to that energy? According to the first law, it must have been transferred to the surroundings. In fact, the energy lost by the system must *exactly equal* the amount gained by the surroundings:

$$\Delta E_{sys} = -\Delta E_{surr}$$

Energy lost by first ball (points to ΔE_{sys})

Energy gained by surroundings (points to $-\Delta E_{surr}$)

The surroundings include both the pool table and the second ball. The pool table absorbs some of the ball's kinetic energy as the ball rolls down the table. Minute bumps on the table surface cause friction, which slows the ball down by converting kinetic energy to heat (q). The second ball absorbs some of the ball's kinetic energy in the form of work (w) upon collision.

Although it is always the case that $\Delta E_{sys} = -\Delta E_{surr}$, the exact amount of *work* done on the second ball depends on the quality of the billiard table. On a smooth, high-quality billiard table, the amount of energy lost to friction is relatively small, as illustrated in Figure 7.6(a)▶. The speed of the first ball is not reduced by much as it travels across the table, and a great deal of its original kinetic energy is available to perform work when it collides with the second ball. In contrast, on a rough, poor-quality table, the ball loses much of its initial kinetic energy as heat, leaving only a relatively small amount available for work, as illustrated in Figure 7.6(b)▶.

Notice that the respective amounts of energy converted to heat and work depend on the details of the pool table and the path taken, while the change in internal energy of the rolling ball does not. Because internal energy is a state function, the value of ΔE for the process in which the ball moves across the table and collides with another ball depends

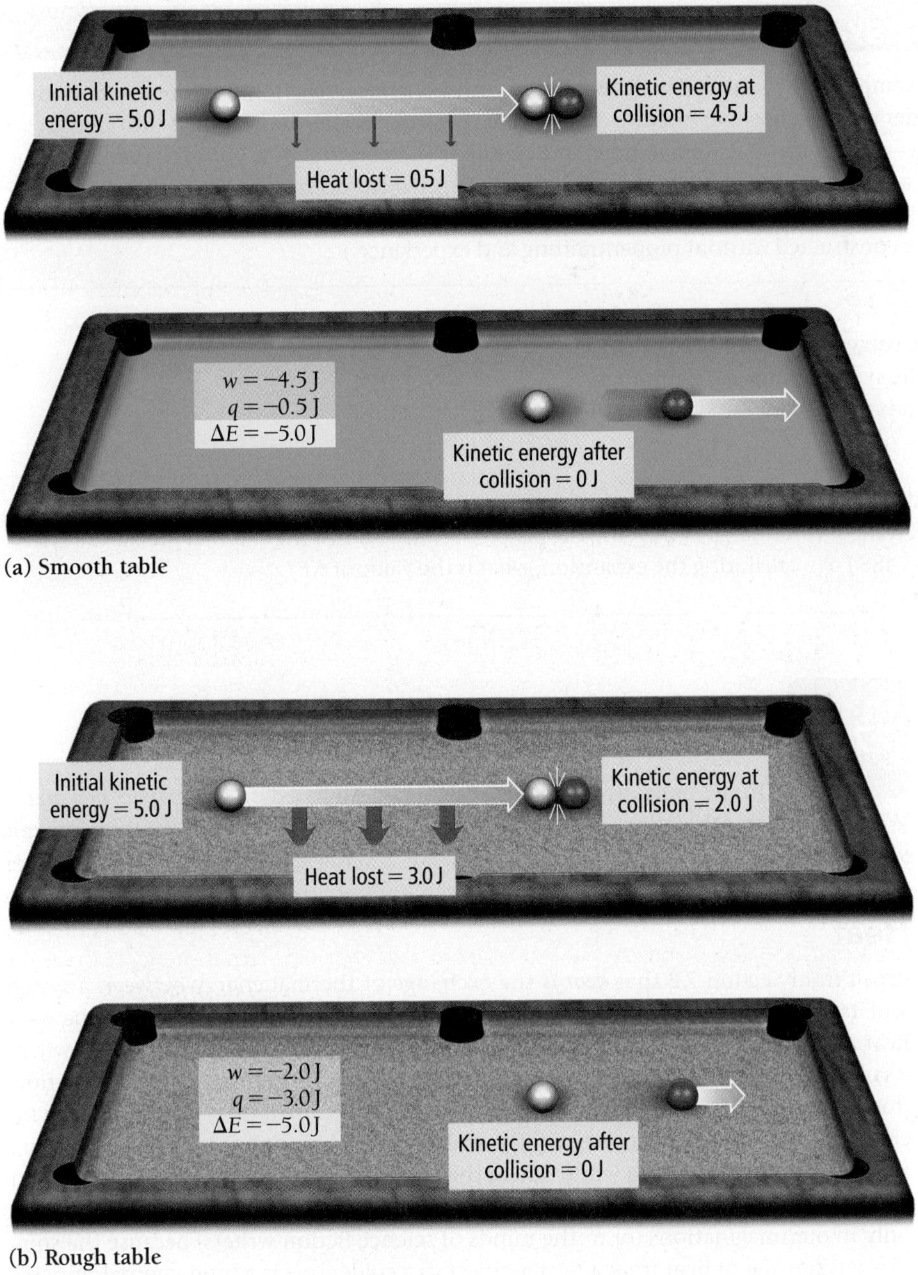

▲ **FIGURE 7.6 Energy, Work, and Heat** **(a)** On a smooth table, most of the first billiard ball's initial kinetic energy is transferred to the second ball as work. Only a small amount is lost to heat. **(b)** On a rough table, most of the first billiard ball's initial kinetic energy is lost to heat. Only a small amount is left to do work on the second billiard ball.

only on the ball's initial and final kinetic energy. Work and heat, however, are *not* state functions; therefore, the values of q and w depend on the details of the ball's journey across the table. On the smooth table, w is greater in magnitude than q; on the rough table, q is greater in magnitude than w. However, ΔE (the sum of q and w) is constant.

HEAT AND WORK Which heat exchange is best classified as work?

(a) An ice cube melts and cools the surrounding beverage.
(b) A metal cylinder is rolled up a ramp.
(c) Steam condenses on skin, causing a burn.

7.2 Cc Conceptual Connection

ANSWER **NOW!**

EXAMPLE 7.1 Internal Energy, Heat, and Work

A potato cannon provides a good example of the heat and work associated with a chemical reaction. In a potato cannon, a potato is stuffed into a long cylinder that is capped on one end and open at the other. Some kind of fuel is introduced under the potato at the capped end—usually through a small hole—and ignited. The potato shoots out of the cannon, sometimes flying hundreds of feet, and the cannon emits heat to the surroundings. If the burning of the fuel performs 855 J of work on the potato and produces 1422 J of heat, what is ΔE for the burning of the fuel? (Note: A potato cannon can be dangerous and should not be constructed without proper training and experience.)

SOLUTION

To solve the problem, substitute the values of q and w into the equation for ΔE. Since work is done by the system on the surroundings, w is negative. Similarly, because heat is released by the system to the surroundings, q is also negative.

$$\begin{aligned} \Delta E &= q + w \\ &= -1422\ \text{J} - 855\ \text{J} \\ &= -2277\ \text{J} \end{aligned}$$

FOR PRACTICE 7.1 A cylinder and piston assembly (defined as the system) is warmed by an external flame. The contents of the cylinder expand, doing work on the surroundings by pushing the piston outward against the external pressure. If the system absorbs 559 J of heat and does 488 J of work during the expansion, what is the value of ΔE?

WATCH **NOW!**

KEY CONCEPT VIDEO 7.4

Heat Capacity

7.4 Quantifying Heat and Work

In the previous section, we calculated ΔE based on *given values of q and w*. We now turn to *calculating q (heat) and w (work)* based on changes in temperature and volume.

Heat

Recall from Section 7.2 that *heat* is the exchange of thermal energy between a system and its surroundings caused by a temperature difference. Notice the distinction between heat and temperature. Temperature is a *measure* of the average thermal energy within a sample of matter. Heat is the *transfer* of thermal energy. Thermal energy always flows from matter at higher temperatures to matter at lower temperatures. For example, a hot cup of coffee transfers thermal energy—as heat—to the lower-temperature surroundings as it cools down. Imagine a world where the cooler surroundings actually got colder as they transferred thermal energy to the hot coffee, which got hotter. Such a world exists only in our imaginations (or in the minds of science fiction writers) because the spontaneous transfer of heat from a hotter object to a colder one is a fundamental principle of our universe—no exception has ever been observed. The thermal energy in the molecules that compose the hot coffee distributes itself to the molecules in the surroundings. The heat transfer from the coffee to the surroundings stops when the two reach the same temperature, a condition called **thermal equilibrium**. At thermal equilibrium, there is no additional net transfer of heat.

The reason for this one-way transfer is related to the second law of thermodynamics, which we discuss in Chapter 19.

Temperature Changes and Heat Capacity

When a system absorbs heat (q), its temperature changes by ΔT:

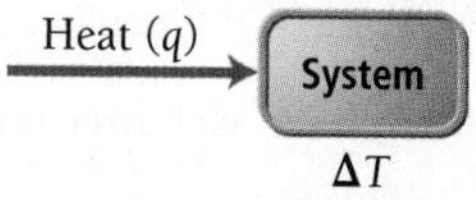

Experiments show that the heat absorbed by a system and its corresponding temperature change are directly proportional: $q \propto \Delta T$. The constant of proportionality between q and ΔT is the system's *heat capacity* (C), a measure of the system's ability to absorb thermal energy without undergoing a large change in temperature.

$$q = C \times \Delta T \quad [7.5]$$

Heat capacity

Notice that the higher the heat capacity of a system, the smaller the change in temperature for a given amount of absorbed heat. We define the **heat capacity (*C*)** of a system as the quantity of heat required to change its temperature by 1 °C. As we can see by solving Equation 7.5 for heat capacity, the units of heat capacity are those of heat (typically J) divided by those of temperature (typically °C):

$$C = \frac{q}{\Delta T} = \frac{\text{J}}{°\text{C}}$$

In order to understand two important concepts related to heat capacity, imagine putting a steel saucepan on a kitchen flame. The saucepan's temperature rises rapidly as it absorbs heat from the flame. However, if you add some water to the saucepan, the temperature rises more slowly. Why? The first reason is that when you add the water, the same amount of heat must now warm more matter, so the temperature rises more slowly. In other words, heat capacity is an extensive property—*it depends on the amount of matter being heated* (see Section 1.6). The second (and more fundamental) reason is that *water is more resistant to temperature change than steel*—water has an intrinsically higher capacity to absorb heat without undergoing a large temperature change. The measure of the *intrinsic capacity* of a substance to absorb heat is its **specific heat capacity (C_s)**, the amount of heat required to raise the temperature of *1 gram* of the substance by 1 °C. The units of specific heat capacity (also called *specific heat*) are J/g · °C. Table 7.4 lists the values of the specific heat capacity for several substances. Heat capacity is sometimes reported as **molar heat capacity**, the amount of heat required to raise the temperature of *1 mole* of a substance by 1 °C. The units of molar heat capacity are J/mol · °C. We can see from these definitions that *specific* heat capacity and *molar* heat capacity are intensive properties—they depend on the *kind* of substance being heated, not on the amount.

TABLE 7.4 ■ Specific Heat Capacities of Some Common Substances

Substance	Specific Heat Capacity, C_s (J/g · °C)*
Elements	
Lead	0.128
Gold	0.128
Silver	0.235
Copper	0.385
Iron	0.449
Aluminum	0.903
Compounds	
Ethanol	2.42
Water	4.18
Materials	
Glass (Pyrex)	0.75
Granite	0.79
Sand	0.84

*At 298 K.

Notice that water has the highest specific heat capacity of all the substances in Table 7.4—changing the temperature of water requires a lot of heat. If you have ever experienced the drop in temperature that occurs when traveling from an inland region to the coast during the summer, you have experienced the effects of water's high specific heat capacity. On a summer's day in California, for example, the temperature difference between Sacramento (an inland city) and San Francisco (a coastal city) may be as large as 18 °C (30 °F)—San Francisco enjoys a cool 20 °C (68 °F), while Sacramento bakes at nearly 38 °C (100 °F). Yet the intensity of sunlight falling on these two cities is the same. Why the large temperature difference? San Francisco sits on a peninsula, surrounded by the water of the Pacific Ocean. Water, with its high heat capacity, absorbs much of the sun's heat without undergoing a large increase in temperature, keeping San Francisco cool. Sacramento, by contrast, is about 160 km (100 mi) inland. The land surrounding Sacramento, with its low heat capacity, undergoes a large increase in temperature as it absorbs a similar amount of heat.

▲ The high heat capacity of the water surrounding San Francisco results in relatively cool summer temperatures.

Similarly, only two U.S. states have never recorded a temperature above 100 °F. One of them is obvious: Alaska. It is too far north to get that hot. The other one, however, may come as a surprise. It is Hawaii. The high heat capacity of the water that surrounds the only island state moderates the temperature, preventing Hawaii from ever getting too hot.

We can use the specific heat capacity of a substance to quantify the relationship between the amount of heat added to a given amount of the substance and the corresponding temperature increase. The following equation relates these quantities:

$$q = m \times C_s \times \Delta T \quad [7.6]$$

Heat (J) → q; Mass (g) → m; Specific heat capacity J/g · °C → C_s; Temperature change (°C) → ΔT

where q is the amount of heat in J, m is the mass of the substance in g, C_s is the specific heat capacity in J/g · °C, and ΔT is the temperature change in °C. Example 7.2 demonstrates the use of this equation.

ΔT in °C is equal to ΔT in K, but not equal to ΔT in °F (Section 1.6).

WATCH **NOW!**

INTERACTIVE WORKED EXAMPLE 7.2

EXAMPLE 7.2 Temperature Changes and Heat Capacity

Suppose you find a penny (minted before 1982, when pennies were almost entirely copper) in the snow. How much heat is absorbed by the penny as it warms from the temperature of the snow, which is −8.0 °C, to the temperature of your body, 37.0 °C? Assume the penny is pure copper and has a mass of 3.10 g.

SORT You are given the mass of copper as well as its initial and final temperature. You are asked to find the heat required for the given temperature change.	**GIVEN:** $m = 3.10\ \text{g copper}$ $T_i = -8.0\ °\text{C}$ $T_f = 37.0\ °\text{C}$ **FIND:** q
STRATEGIZE The equation $q = m \times C_s \times \Delta T$ gives the relationship between the amount of heat (q) and the temperature change (ΔT).	**CONCEPTUAL PLAN** $C_s, m, \Delta T \rightarrow q$ $q = m \times C_s \times \Delta T$ **RELATIONSHIPS USED** $q = m \times C_s \times \Delta T$ (Equation 7.6) $C_s = 0.385\ \text{J/g}\cdot°\text{C}$ (Table 7.4)
SOLVE Gather the necessary quantities for the equation in the correct units and substitute into the equation to calculate q.	**SOLUTION** $\Delta T = T_f - T_i = 37.0\ °\text{C} - (-8.0\ °\text{C}) = 45.0\ °\text{C}$ $q = m \times C_s \times \Delta T$ $= 3.10\ \text{g} \times 0.385 \frac{\text{J}}{\text{g}\cdot°\text{C}} \times 45.0\ °\text{C} = 53.7\ \text{J}$

CHECK The units (J) are correct for heat. The sign of q is *positive*, as it should be because the penny *absorbed* heat from the surroundings.

FOR PRACTICE 7.2 To determine whether a shiny gold-colored rock is actually gold, a chemistry student decides to measure its heat capacity. She first weighs the rock and finds it has a mass of 4.7 g. She then finds that upon absorption of 57.2 J of heat, the temperature of the rock rises from 25 °C to 57 °C. Find the specific heat capacity of the substance composing the rock and determine whether the value is consistent with the rock being pure gold.

FOR MORE PRACTICE 7.2 A 55.0-g aluminum block initially at 27.5 °C absorbs 725 J of heat. What is the final temperature of the aluminum?

ANSWER **NOW!**

7.3 Cc Conceptual Connection

THE HEAT CAPACITY OF WATER Suppose you are cold-weather camping and decide to heat some objects to bring into your sleeping bag for added warmth. You place a large water jug and a rock of equal mass near the fire. Over time, both the rock and the water jug warm to about 38 °C (100 °F). If you can bring only one into your sleeping bag, which one should you choose to keep you warmer? Why?

(a) The water, because it will release more heat as it cools.
(b) The rock, because it will absorb more heat as it cools.
(c) The rock, because it will release more heat as it cools.
(d) The water, because it will absorb more heat as it cools.

Thermal Energy Transfer

As we noted earlier, when two substances of different temperature are combined, thermal energy flows as heat from the hotter substance to the cooler one. If we assume that the two substances are thermally isolated from everything else, then the heat lost by one substance exactly equals the heat gained by the other (according to the law of energy conservation). If we define one substance as the system and the other as the surroundings, we can quantify the heat exchange as:

$$q_{sys} = -q_{surr}$$

Suppose a block of metal initially at 55 °C is submerged into water initially at 25 °C. Thermal energy transfers as heat from the metal to the water:

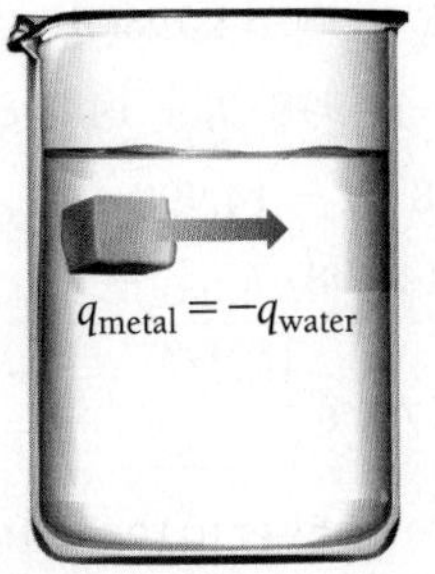

The metal becomes colder and the water becomes warmer until the two substances reach the same temperature (thermal equilibrium). The exact temperature change that occurs depends on the masses of the metal and the water and on their specific heat capacities. Since $q = m \times C_s \times \Delta T$, we can arrive at the following relationship:

$$q_{metal} = -q_{water}$$

$$m_{metal} \times C_{s,\,metal} \times \Delta T_{metal} = -m_{water} \times C_{s,\,water} \times \Delta T_{water}$$

Example 7.3 shows how to work with thermal energy transfer.

WATCH **NOW!**

INTERACTIVE WORKED EXAMPLE 7.3

EXAMPLE 7.3 Thermal Energy Transfer

A 32.5 g cube of aluminum initially at 45.8 °C is submerged into 105.3 g of water at 15.4 °C. What is the final temperature of both substances at thermal equilibrium? (Assume that the aluminum and the water are thermally isolated from everything else.)

SORT You are given the masses of aluminum and water and their initial temperatures. You are asked to find the final temperature.

GIVEN: $m_{Al} = 32.5\text{ g}$ $m_{H_2O} = 105.3\text{ g}$

$T_{i,\,Al} = 45.8\text{ °C}$; $T_{i,\,H_2O} = 15.4\text{ °C}$

FIND: T_f

STRATEGIZE The heat lost by the aluminum (q_{Al}) equals the heat gained by the water (q_{H_2O}).

CONCEPTUAL PLAN $q_{Al} = -q_{H_2O}$

Use the relationship between q and ΔT and the given variables to find a relationship between ΔT_{Al} and ΔT_{H_2O}.

$m_{Al}, C_{s,\,Al}, m_{H_2O}, C_{s,\,H_2O}$ → $\Delta T_{Al} = \text{constant} \times \Delta T_{H_2O}$

$m_{Al} \times C_{s,\,Al} \times \Delta T_{Al} = -m_{H_2O} \times C_{s,\,H_2O} \times \Delta T_{H_2O}$

Use the relationship between ΔT_{Al} and ΔT_{H_2O} (that you just found) along with the initial temperatures of the aluminum and the water to determine the final temperature. Note that at thermal equilibrium, the final temperature of the aluminum and the water is the same, that is, $T_{f,\,Al} = T_{f,\,H_2O} = T_f$.

$T_{i,\,Al}; T_{i,\,H_2O}$ → T_f

$\Delta T_{Al} = \text{constant} \times \Delta T_{H_2O}$

RELATIONSHIPS USED

$C_{s,\,H_2O} = 4.18\text{ J/g}\cdot\text{°C}$; $C_{s,\,Al} = 0.903\text{ J/g}\cdot\text{°C}$ (Table 7.4)

$q = m \times C_s \times \Delta T$ (Equation 7.6)

SOLVE

Write the equation for the relationship between the heat lost by the aluminum (q_{Al}) and the heat gained by the water $q_{Al} = -q_{H_2O}$ and substitute $q = m \times C_s \times \Delta T$ for each substance.

SOLUTION

$q_{Al} = -q_{H_2O}$

$m_{Al} \times C_{s,\,Al} \times \Delta T_{Al} = -m_{H_2O} \times C_{s,\,H_2O} \times \Delta T_{H_2O}$

—Continued on the next page

Continued—

Substitute the values of m (given) and C_s (from Table 7.4) for each substance and solve the equation for ΔT_{Al}. (Alternatively, you can solve the equation for ΔT_{H_2O}.)

$$32.5\ \text{g} \times \frac{0.903\ \text{J}}{\text{g}\cdot{}^\circ\text{C}} \cdot \Delta T_{Al} = -105.3\ \text{g} \times \frac{4.18\ \text{J}}{\text{J}\cdot{}^\circ\text{C}} \cdot \Delta T_{H_2O}$$

$$29.3\underline{4}8 \cdot \Delta T_{Al} = -44\underline{0}.15 \cdot \Delta T_{H_2O}$$

$$\Delta T_{Al} = -14.\underline{9}98 \cdot \Delta T_{H_2O}$$

Substitute the initial temperatures of aluminum and water into the relationship from the previous step and solve the expression for the final temperature (T_f). Remember that the final temperature for both substances will be the same.

$$T_f - T_{i,\,Al} = -14.\underline{9}98(T_f - T_{i,\,H_2O})$$

$$T_f = -14.\underline{9}98 \cdot T_f + 14.\underline{9}98 \cdot T_{i,\,H_2O} + T_{i,\,Al}$$

$$15.\underline{9}98 \cdot T_f = 14.\underline{9}98 \cdot T_{i,\,H_2O} + T_{i,\,Al}$$

$$T_f = \frac{14.\underline{9}98 \cdot T_{i,\,H_2O} + T_{i,\,Al}}{15.\underline{9}98} = \frac{14.\underline{9}98 \cdot 15.4\ {}^\circ\text{C} + 45.8\ {}^\circ\text{C}}{15.\underline{9}98}$$

$$= 17.3\,{}^\circ\text{C}$$

CHECK The units °C are correct. The final temperature of the mixture is closer to the initial temperature of the *water* than the *aluminum*. This makes sense for two reasons: (1) water has a higher specific heat capacity than aluminum, and (2) there is more water than aluminum. Because the aluminum loses the same amount of heat that is gained by the water, the greater mass and specific heat capacity of the water make the temperature change in the water *less than* the temperature change in the aluminum.

FOR PRACTICE 7.3 A block of copper of unknown mass has an initial temperature of 65.4 °C. The copper is immersed in a beaker containing 95.7 g of water at 22.7 °C. When the two substances reach thermal equilibrium, the final temperature is 24.2 °C. What is the mass of the copper block?

ANSWER **NOW!**

7.4 Cc Conceptual Connection

THERMAL ENERGY TRANSFER Substances A and B, initially at different temperatures, come in contact with each other and reach thermal equilibrium. The mass of substance A is twice the mass of substance B. The specific heat capacity of substance B is twice the specific heat capacity of substance A. Which statement is true about the final temperature of the two substances once thermal equilibrium is reached?

(a) The final temperature is closer to the initial temperature of substance A than it is to the initial temperature of substance B.
(b) The final temperature is closer to the initial temperature of substance B than it is to the initial temperature of substance A.
(c) The final temperature is exactly midway between the initial temperatures of substances A and B.

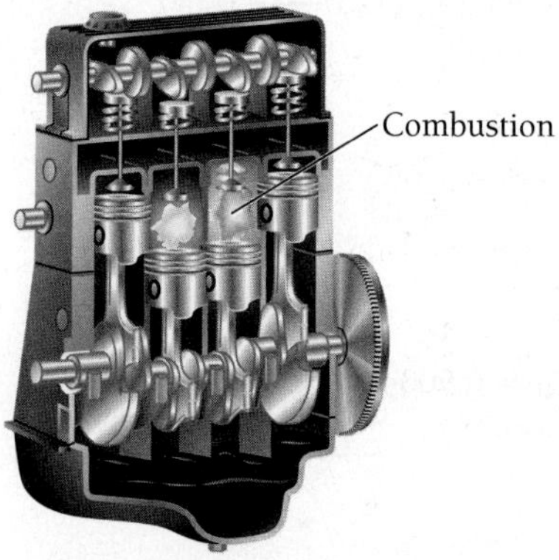

▲ The combustion of gasoline within an engine's cylinders does pressure–volume work that ultimately results in the motion of the car.

Work: Pressure–Volume Work

We know that energy transfer can occur via heat (q) or work (w). In Example 7.3, we calculated the *heat* associated with an observed *temperature* change. We now turn to calculating the *work* associated with an observed *volume* change.

Although a chemical reaction can do several different types of work, for now we limit our discussion to **pressure–volume work**. We have already defined work as a force acting through a distance. Pressure–volume work occurs when a force (caused by a change in volume) acts through a distance against an external pressure. For example, pressure–volume work occurs in the cylinder of an automobile engine. The combustion of gasoline causes gases within the cylinders to expand, pushing the piston and ultimately moving the wheels of the car.

We can derive an equation for the value of pressure–volume work from the definition of work as a force (F) acting through a distance (D):

$$w = F \times D \qquad [7.7]$$

When the volume of a cylinder increases (Figure 7.7▼), it pushes against an external force. That external force equals the product of the external pressure (P_{ext}) and area the pressure acts on (A):

$$F = P_{ext} \times A$$

If we substitute this expression for force into the definition of work given in Equation 7.7, we arrive at the expression:

$$\begin{aligned} w &= F \times D \\ &= P_{ext} \times A \times D \end{aligned}$$

The distance through which the force acts is the change in the height of the piston as it moves during the expansion (Δh). Substituting Δh for D, we get:

$$w = P_{ext} \times A \times \Delta h$$

The volume of a cylinder is the area of its base times its height, so $A \times \Delta h$ is actually the change in volume (ΔV) that occurs during the expansion. Thus, the expression for work becomes the *product of* the pressure *times* the change in volume:

$$w = P_{ext}\,\Delta V$$

Still missing from the equation is the *sign* of the work done by the expanding gases. As the volume of the cylinder increases, work is done *on* the surroundings *by* the system, so w should be negative. However, upon expansion, V_2 (the final volume) is greater than V_1 (the initial volume), so ΔV is positive. In order for w to be negative for a positive expansion, we need to add a negative sign to our equation. In other words, w and ΔV must be opposite in sign:

$$w = -P_{ext}\,\Delta V \qquad [7.8]$$

So the work caused by an expansion of volume is the negative of the pressure that the volume expands against multiplied by the change in volume that occurs during the expansion. The units of the work obtained by using this equation are those of pressure (usually atm) multiplied by those of volume (usually L). To convert between L · atm and J, we use the conversion factor 101.3 J = 1 L · atm.

The force in this equation must be a constant force.

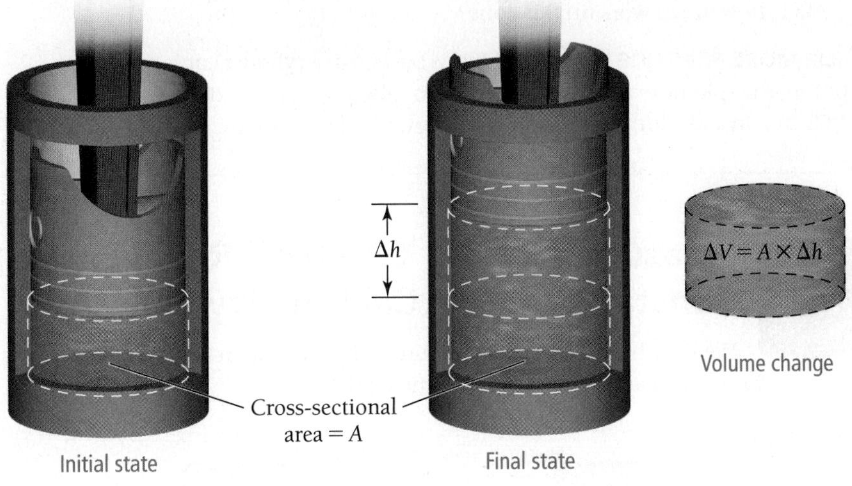

▲ **FIGURE 7.7 Piston Moving within a Cylinder against an External Pressure**

PRESSURE–VOLUME WORK A cylinder within a piston expands from a volume of 1.00 L to a volume of 2.00 L against an external pressure of 1.00 atm. How much work (in J) was done by the expansion?

(a) 1.00 J **(b)** −1.00 J **(c)** 101 J **(d)** −101 J

7.5 Cc Conceptual Connection — ANSWER **NOW!**

EXAMPLE 7.4 Pressure–Volume Work

To inflate a balloon, you must do pressure–volume work on the surroundings. If you inflate a balloon from a volume of 0.100 L to 1.85 L against an external pressure of 1.00 atm, how much work is done (in joules)?

SORT You know the initial and final volumes of the balloon and the pressure against which it expands. The balloon and its contents are the system.

GIVEN: $V_1 = 0.100\,\text{L}$
$V_2 = 1.85\,\text{L}$
$P = 1.00\,\text{atm}$

FIND: w

STRATEGIZE The equation $w = -P_{ext}\,\Delta V$ specifies the amount of work done during a volume change against an external pressure.

CONCEPTUAL PLAN

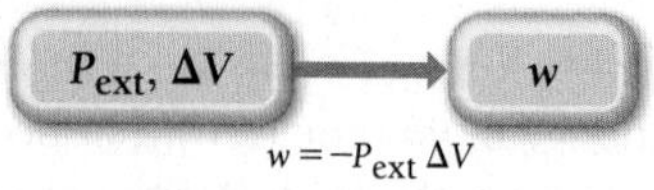

SOLVE To solve the problem, calculate the value of ΔV and substitute it, together with P_{ext}, into the equation.

SOLUTION

$$\Delta V = V_2 - V_1 = 1.85\,\text{L} - 0.100\,\text{L} = 1.75\,\text{L}$$

$$w = -P_{ext}\,\Delta V = -1.00\,\text{atm} \times 1.75\,\text{L} = -1.75\,\text{L}\cdot\text{atm}$$

Convert the units of the answer (L · atm) to joules using 101.3 J = 1 L · atm.

$$-1.75\,\cancel{\text{L}\cdot\text{atm}} \times \frac{101.3\,\text{J}}{1\,\cancel{\text{L}\cdot\text{atm}}} = -177\,\text{J}$$

CHECK The units (J) are correct for work. The sign of the work is negative, as it should be for an expansion: work is done on the surroundings by the expanding balloon.

FOR PRACTICE 7.4 A cylinder equipped with a piston expands against an external pressure of 1.58 atm. If the initial volume is 0.485 L and the final volume is 1.245 L, how much work (in J) is done?

FOR MORE PRACTICE 7.4 When fuel is burned in a cylinder equipped with a piston, the volume expands from 0.255 L to 1.45 L against an external pressure of 1.02 atm. In addition, 875 J is emitted as heat. What is ΔE for the burning of the fuel?

7.5 Measuring ΔE for Chemical Reactions: Constant-Volume Calorimetry

We now have a complete picture of how a system exchanges energy with its surroundings via heat and pressure–volume work:

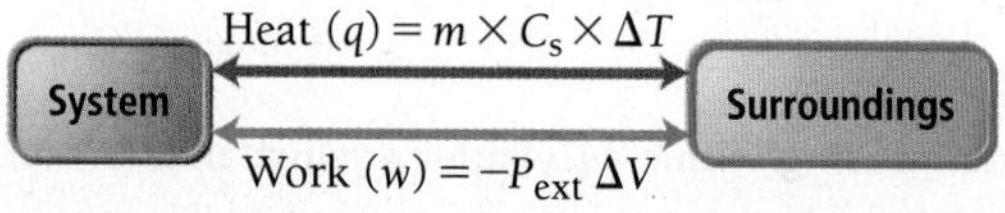

Recall from Section 7.3 that the change in internal energy that occurs during a chemical reaction (ΔE) is a measure of *all of the energy* (heat and work) exchanged with the surroundings ($\Delta E = q + w$). Therefore, we can measure the changes in temperature (to calculate heat) and the changes in volume (to calculate work) that occur during a chemical reaction, and then sum them together to calculate ΔE. However, an easier way to obtain the value of ΔE for a chemical reaction is to force all of the energy change associated with a reaction to manifest itself as heat rather than work. We can then measure the temperature change caused by the heat flow.

Recall that $\Delta E = q + w$ and that $w = -P_{ext}\,\Delta V$. If a reaction is carried out at constant volume, then $\Delta V = 0$ and $w = 0$. The heat evolved (or given off), called the *heat at constant volume* (q_v), is then equal to ΔE_{rxn}:

Equals zero at constant volume (points to w)

$$\Delta E_{rxn} = q_v + w$$

$$\Delta E_{rxn} = q_v \qquad [7.9]$$

We can measure the heat evolved in a chemical reaction using *calorimetry*. In **calorimetry**, we measure the thermal energy exchanged between the reaction (defined as the system) and the surroundings by observing the change in temperature of the surroundings:

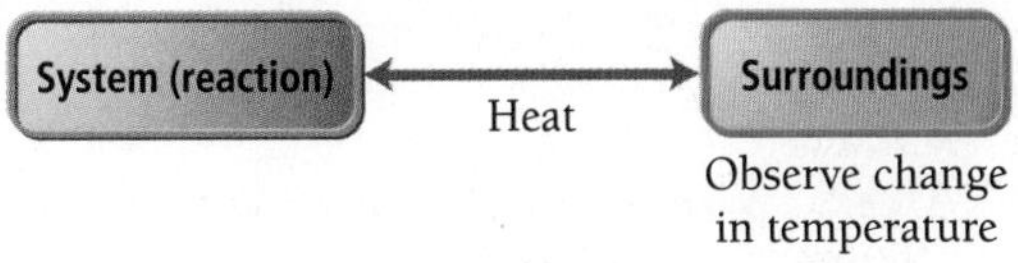

The magnitude of the temperature change in the surroundings depends on the magnitude of ΔE for the reaction and on the heat capacity of the surroundings.

Figure 7.8► shows a **bomb calorimeter**, a piece of equipment that measures ΔE for combustion reactions. In a bomb calorimeter, the reaction occurs in a sealed container called a *bomb*, which ensures that the reaction occurs at constant volume. To use a bomb calorimeter, we put the sample to be burned (of known mass) into a cup equipped with an ignition wire. We then seal the cup into the bomb, which is filled with oxygen gas, and place the bomb in a water-filled, insulated container. The container is equipped with a stirrer and a thermometer. Finally, we ignite the sample with a wire coil and monitor the temperature with the thermometer. The temperature change (ΔT) is related to the heat absorbed by the entire calorimeter assembly (q_{cal}) by the equation:

The Bomb Calorimeter

A bomb calorimeter measures changes in internal energy for combustion reactions.

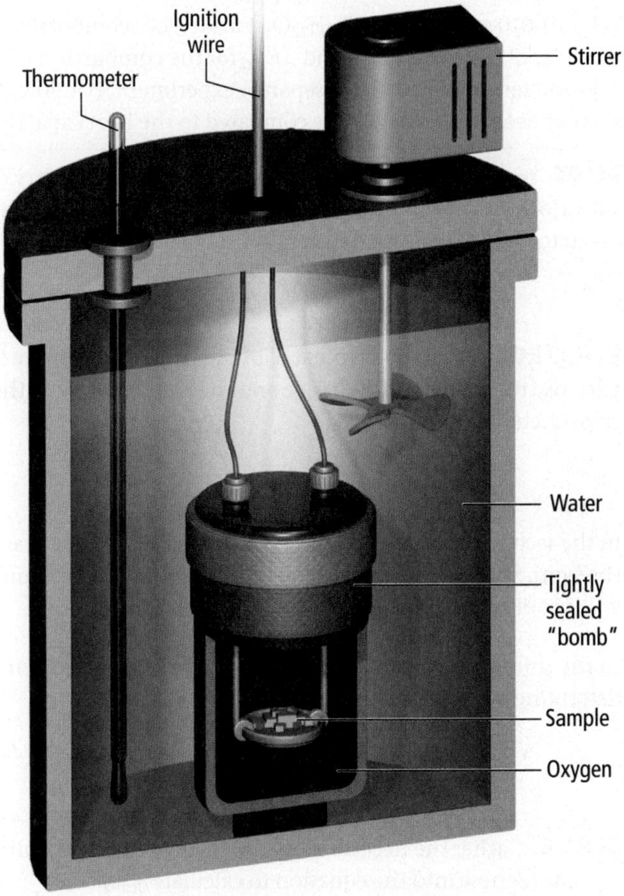

▲ **FIGURE 7.8 The Bomb Calorimeter**

$$q_{cal} = C_{cal} \times \Delta T \qquad [7.10]$$

where C_{cal} is the heat capacity of the entire calorimeter assembly (which is usually determined in a separate measurement involving the burning of a substance that gives off a known amount of heat). If no heat escapes from the calorimeter, the amount of heat *gained by* the calorimeter exactly equals that *released by* the reaction (the two are equal in magnitude but opposite in sign):

The heat capacity of the calorimeter, C_{cal}, has units of energy over temperature; its value accounts for all of the heat absorbed by all of the components within the calorimeter (including the water).

$$q_{cal} = -q_{rxn} \qquad [7.11]$$

Since the reaction occurs under conditions of constant volume, $q_{rxn} = q_v = \Delta E_{rxn}$. This measured quantity is the change in the internal energy of the reaction for the specific amount of reactant burned. To get ΔE_{rxn} per mole of a particular reactant—a more general quantity—we divide by the number of moles that actually reacted, as demonstrated in Example 7.5.

WATCH **NOW!**

INTERACTIVE WORKED EXAMPLE 7.5

EXAMPLE 7.5 Measuring ΔE_{rxn} in a Bomb Calorimeter

When 1.010 g of sucrose ($C_{12}H_{22}O_{11}$) undergoes combustion in a bomb calorimeter, the temperature rises from 24.92 °C to 28.33 °C. Find ΔE_{rxn} for the combustion of sucrose in kJ/mol sucrose. The heat capacity of the bomb calorimeter, determined in a separate experiment, is 4.90 kJ/°C. (You can ignore the heat capacity of the small sample of sucrose because it is negligible compared to the heat capacity of the calorimeter.)

SORT You are given the mass of sucrose, the heat capacity of the calorimeter, and the initial and final temperatures. You are asked to find the change in internal energy for the reaction.

GIVEN: 1.010 g $C_{12}H_{22}O_{11}$

$T_i = 24.92\ °C$

$T_f = 28.33\ °C$

$C_{cal} = 4.90\ kJ/°C$

FIND: ΔE_{rxn}

STRATEGIZE The conceptual plan has three parts. In the first part, use the temperature change and the heat capacity of the calorimeter to find q_{cal}.

CONCEPTUAL PLAN

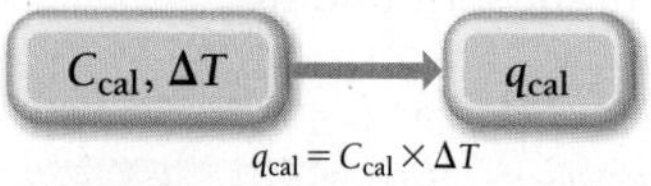

In the second part, use q_{cal} to get q_{rxn} (which just involves changing the sign). Since the bomb calorimeter ensures constant volume, q_{rxn} is equivalent to ΔE_{rxn} for the amount of sucrose burned.

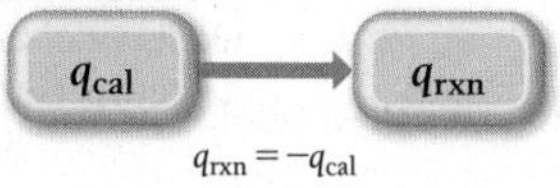

In the third part, divide q_{rxn} by the number of moles of sucrose to determine ΔE_{rxn} per mole of sucrose.

$$\Delta E_{rxn} = \frac{q_{rxn}}{\text{mol } C_{12}H_{22}O_{11}}$$

RELATIONSHIPS USED

$q_{cal} = C_{cal} \times \Delta T = -q_{rxn}$

molar mass $C_{12}H_{22}O_{11} = 342.3\ g/mol$

SOLVE Gather the necessary quantities in the correct units and substitute these into the equation to calculate q_{cal}.

SOLUTION

$$\Delta T = T_f - T_i$$
$$= 28.33\ °C - 24.92\ °C = 3.41\ °C$$
$$q_{cal} = C_{cal} \times \Delta T$$
$$q_{cal} = 4.90 \frac{kJ}{\cancel{°C}} \times 3.41\ \cancel{°C} = 16.7\ kJ$$

Find q_{rxn} by taking the negative of q_{cal}.

$$q_{rxn} = -q_{cal} = -16.7\ kJ$$

Find ΔE_{rxn} per mole of sucrose by dividing q_{rxn} by the number of moles of sucrose (calculated from the given mass of sucrose and its molar mass).

$$\Delta E_{rxn} = \frac{q_{rxn}}{\text{mol } C_{12}H_{22}O_{11}}$$
$$= \frac{-16.7\ kJ}{1.010\ \cancel{g\ C_{12}H_{22}O_{11}} \times \frac{1\ mol\ C_{12}H_{22}O_{11}}{342.3\ \cancel{g\ C_{12}H_{22}O_{11}}}}$$
$$= -5.66 \times 10^3\ kJ/mol\ C_{12}H_{22}O_{11}$$

CHECK The units of the answer (kJ) are correct for a change in internal energy. The sign of ΔE_{rxn} is negative, as it should be for a combustion reaction that gives off energy.

FOR PRACTICE 7.5 When 1.550 g of liquid hexane (C_6H_{14}) undergoes combustion in a bomb calorimeter, the temperature rises from 25.87 °C to 38.13 °C. Find ΔE_{rxn} for the reaction in kJ/mol hexane. The heat capacity of the bomb calorimeter, determined in a separate experiment, is 5.73 kJ/°C.

FOR MORE PRACTICE 7.5 The combustion of toluene has a ΔE_{rxn} of -3.91×10^3 kJ/mol. When 1.55 g of toluene (C_7H_8) undergoes combustion in a bomb calorimeter, the temperature rises from 23.12 °C to 37.57 °C. Find the heat capacity of the bomb calorimeter.

7.6 Enthalpy: The Heat Evolved in a Chemical Reaction at Constant Pressure

WATCH **NOW!**

KEY CONCEPT VIDEO 7.6

The Change in Enthalpy for a Chemical Reaction

We have just seen that when a chemical reaction occurs in a sealed container under conditions of constant volume, the energy evolves only as heat. However, when a chemical reaction occurs open to the atmosphere under conditions of constant pressure—such as a reaction occurring in an open beaker or the burning of natural gas on a stove—the energy can evolve as both heat and work. As we have also seen, ΔE_{rxn} is a measure of the *total energy change* (both heat and work) that occurs during the reaction. However, in many cases, we are interested only in the heat exchanged, not the work done. For example, when we burn natural gas on a stove to cook food, we do not really care how much work the combustion reaction does on the atmosphere by expanding against it—we just want to know how much heat is given off to cook the food. Under conditions of constant pressure, a thermodynamic quantity called *enthalpy* represents exactly this.

We define the **enthalpy (*H*)** of a system as the sum of its internal energy and the product of its pressure and volume:

$$H = E + PV \qquad [7.12]$$

Since internal energy, pressure, and volume are all state functions, enthalpy is also a state function. The *change in enthalpy* (ΔH) for any process occurring under constant pressure is given by the expression:

$$\Delta H = \Delta E + P\Delta V \qquad [7.13]$$

To better understand this expression, we can interpret the two terms on the right with the help of relationships already familiar to us. We saw previously that $\Delta E = q + w$. If we represent the heat at constant pressure as q_p, then the change in internal energy at constant pressure is $\Delta E = q_p + w$. In addition, from our definition of pressure–volume work, we know that $P_{ext}\,\Delta V = -w$. Substituting these expressions into the expression for ΔH gives us the following expression:

$$\begin{aligned} \Delta H &= \Delta E + P\Delta V \\ &= (q_p + w) + P\Delta V \qquad [7.14] \\ &= q_p + w - w \\ \Delta H &= q_p \end{aligned}$$

We can see that ΔH is equal to q_p, the heat at constant pressure.

Conceptually (and often numerically), ΔH and ΔE are similar: they both represent changes in a state function for the system. However, ΔE is a measure of *all of the energy* (heat and work) exchanged with the surroundings, while ΔH is a measure of only the heat exchanged under conditions of constant pressure. For chemical reactions that do not exchange much work with the surroundings—that is, those that do not cause a large change in reaction volume as they occur—ΔH and ΔE are nearly identical in value. For chemical reactions that produce or consume large amounts of gas, and therefore result in large volume changes, ΔH and ΔE may differ slightly in value.

7.6 Cc Conceptual Connection — ANSWER **NOW!**

THE DIFFERENCE BETWEEN ΔH AND ΔE Lighters are usually fueled by butane (C_4H_{10}). When 1 mol of butane burns at constant pressure, it produces 2658 kJ of heat and does 3 kJ of work. What are the values of ΔH and ΔE for the combustion of one mole of butane?

(a) $\Delta H = -2658$ kJ; $\Delta E = -2655$ kJ
(b) $\Delta H = -2658$ kJ; $\Delta E = -3$ kJ
(c) $\Delta H = -2658$ kJ; $\Delta E = -2661$ kJ
(d) $\Delta H = 2658$ kJ; $\Delta E = 2661$ kJ

The signs of ΔH and ΔE follow the same conventions. A positive ΔH indicates that heat flows into the system as the reaction occurs. A chemical reaction with a positive ΔH, called an **endothermic reaction**, absorbs heat from its surroundings.

▶ The reaction that occurs in a chemical cold pack is endothermic—it absorbs energy from the surroundings. The combustion of natural gas is an exothermic reaction—it releases energy to the surroundings.

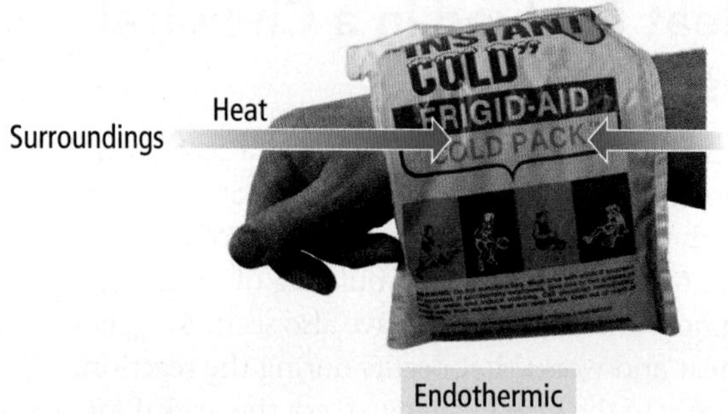

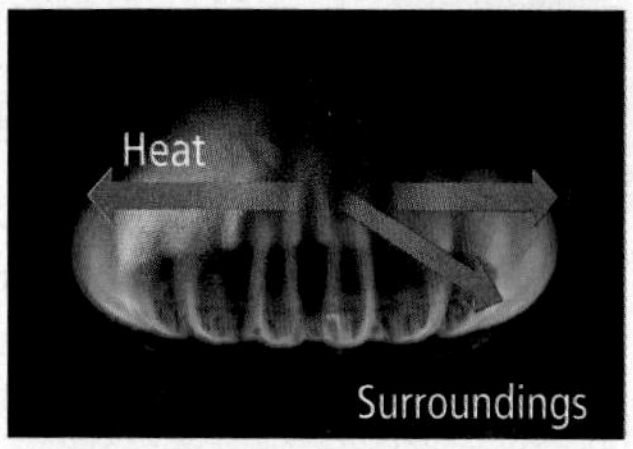

The reaction that occurs in a chemical cold pack, often used to ice athletic injuries, is a good example of an endothermic reaction. When you break the barrier separating the reactants in a chemical cold pack, the substances mix, react, and absorb heat from the surroundings. The surroundings—including, say, your bruised wrist—get *colder* because they *lose* energy as the cold pack absorbs it.

A chemical reaction with a negative ΔH, called an **exothermic reaction**, gives off heat to its surroundings. The reaction that occurs in the chemical hand warmer discussed in Section 7.1 is a good example of an exothermic reaction. When the reaction takes place, heat is given off into the surroundings (including your hand and glove), making them warmer. The burning of natural gas is another exothermic reaction. As the gas burns, it gives off energy, raising the temperature of its surroundings.

Summarizing Enthalpy:

- The value of ΔH for a chemical reaction is the amount of heat absorbed or evolved in the reaction under conditions of constant pressure.
- An endothermic reaction has a *positive* ΔH and absorbs heat from the surroundings. An endothermic reaction feels cold to the touch.
- An exothermic reaction has a *negative* ΔH and gives off heat to the surroundings. An exothermic reaction feels warm to the touch.

EXAMPLE 7.6 Exothermic and Endothermic Processes

Identify each process as endothermic or exothermic and indicate the sign of ΔH.

(a) sweat evaporating from skin

(b) water freezing in a freezer

(c) wood burning in a fire

SOLUTION

(a) Sweat evaporating from skin cools the skin and is therefore endothermic, with a positive ΔH. The skin must supply heat to the perspiration in order for it to continue to evaporate.

(b) Water freezing in a freezer releases heat and is therefore exothermic, with a negative ΔH. The refrigeration system in the freezer must remove this heat for the water to continue to freeze.

(c) Wood burning in a fire releases heat and is therefore exothermic, with a negative ΔH.

FOR PRACTICE 7.6 Identify each process as endothermic or exothermic and indicate the sign of ΔH.

(a) an ice cube melting

(b) nail polish remover quickly evaporating after it is accidentally spilled on the skin

(c) gasoline burning within the cylinder of an automobile engine

Exothermic and Endothermic Processes: A Molecular View

When a chemical system undergoes a change in enthalpy, where does the energy come from or go to? For example, we just saw that an exothermic chemical reaction gives off *thermal energy*—what is the source of that energy?

First, we know that the emitted thermal energy *does not* come from the original thermal energy of the system. Recall from Section 7.2 that the thermal energy of a system is the total kinetic energy of the atoms and molecules that compose the system. This kinetic energy *cannot* be the source of the energy given off in an exothermic reaction because if the atoms and molecules that compose the system were to lose kinetic energy, their temperature would necessarily fall—the system would get colder. Yet we know that in exothermic reactions, the temperature of the system and the surroundings rises. So there must be some other source of energy.

Recall also from Section 7.2 that the internal energy of a chemical system is the sum of its kinetic energy and its *potential energy*. This potential energy is the source in an exothermic chemical reaction. Under normal circumstances, chemical potential energy (or simply chemical energy) arises primarily from the electrostatic forces between the protons and electrons that compose the atoms and molecules within the system. In an exothermic reaction, some bonds break and new ones form, and the nuclei and electrons reorganize into an arrangement with lower potential energy. As the atoms rearrange, their potential energy converts into thermal energy, the heat emitted in the reaction. Note that breaking bonds always *absorbs* energy. In an exothermic reaction, weak bonds break and stronger bonds form. It only takes a small amount of energy to break the weak bonds, and a greater amount is given off when the stronger bonds form, resulting in net energy production. In an endothermic reaction, the opposite happens: strong bonds break and weak ones form. The nuclei and electrons reorganize into an arrangement with higher potential energy, absorbing thermal energy in the process.

EXOTHERMIC AND ENDOTHERMIC REACTIONS An endothermic reaction occurs in a flask. What happens to the temperature of the flask?

(a) The temperature rises.
(b) The temperature falls.
(c) The temperature remains unchanged.

7.7 Cc Conceptual Connection

ANSWER **NOW!**

Stoichiometry Involving ΔH: Thermochemical Equations

The enthalpy change for a chemical reaction, abbreviated ΔH_{rxn}, is also called the **enthalpy of reaction** or **heat of reaction** and depends on the amount of material undergoing the reaction. In other words, the amount of heat generated or absorbed when a chemical reaction occurs depends on the *amounts* of reactants that actually react. We usually specify ΔH_{rxn} in combination with the balanced chemical equation for the reaction. *The magnitude of ΔH_{rxn} reflects the stoichiometric amounts of reactants and products for the reaction as written.* For example, consider the balanced equation and ΔH_{rxn} for the combustion of propane, the main component of LP gas:

$$C_3H_8(g) + 5\,O_2(g) \longrightarrow 3\,CO_2(g) + 4\,H_2O(g) \quad \Delta H_{rxn} = -2044\text{ kJ}$$

The equation tells us that when 1 mol of C_3H_8 reacts with 5 mol of O_2 to form 3 mol of CO_2 and 4 mol of H_2O, 2044 kJ of heat is emitted. We can write these relationships in the same way that we expressed stoichiometric relationships in Chapter 4, as ratios between two quantities. For example, for the reactants, we write the following ratios:

$$1\text{ mol } C_3H_8 : -2044\text{ kJ} \quad \text{or} \quad 5\text{ mol } O_2 : -2044\text{ kJ}$$

The ratios indicate that 2044 kJ of heat evolve when 1 mol of C_3H_8 and 5 mol of O_2 completely react. We can use these ratios to construct conversion factors between amounts of reactants or products and the quantity of heat emitted (for exothermic reactions) or absorbed (for endothermic reactions). To find out how much heat is emitted upon the combustion of a certain mass in grams of C_3H_8, we work with the following conceptual plan:

$$\text{g } C_3H_8 \longrightarrow \text{mol } C_3H_8 \longrightarrow \text{kJ}$$

$$\frac{1 \text{ mol } C_3H_8}{44.09 \text{ g } C_3H_8} \qquad \frac{-2044 \text{ kJ}}{1 \text{ mol } C_3H_8}$$

We use the molar mass to convert between grams and moles, and the stoichiometric relationship between moles of C_3H_8 and the heat of reaction to convert between moles and kilojoules, as demonstrated in Example 7.7.

ANSWER **NOW!**

7.8 Cc Conceptual Connection

THERMOCHEMICAL EQUATIONS Consider the following thermochemical equation:

$$2\text{ A} \rightarrow \text{AA} \quad \Delta H_{rxn} = -51.0 \text{ J}$$

What is the heat associated with the reaction of 6 moles of A?

(a) −51.0 J **(b)** −306 J **(c)** −153 J **(d)** 153 J

WATCH **NOW!**

INTERACTIVE WORKED EXAMPLE 7.7

EXAMPLE 7.7 Stoichiometry Involving ΔH

An LP gas tank in a home barbeque contains 13.2 kg of propane, C_3H_8. Calculate the heat (in kJ) associated with the complete combustion of all of the propane in the tank.

$$C_3H_8(g) + 5\,O_2(g) \longrightarrow 3\,CO_2(g) + 4\,H_2O(g) \qquad \Delta H_{rxn} = -2044 \text{ kJ}$$

SORT You are given the mass of propane and asked to find the heat evolved in its combustion.

GIVEN: 13.2 kg C_3H_8
FIND: q

STRATEGIZE Starting with kg C_3H_8, convert to g C_3H_8 and then use the molar mass of C_3H_8 to find the number of moles. Next, use the stoichiometric relationship between mol C_3H_8 and kJ to determine the heat evolved.

CONCEPTUAL PLAN

$$\text{kg } C_3H_8 \longrightarrow \text{g } C_3H_8 \longrightarrow \text{mol } C_3H_8 \longrightarrow \text{kJ}$$

$$\frac{1000 \text{ g}}{1 \text{ kg}} \qquad \frac{1 \text{ mol } C_3H_8}{44.09 \text{ g } C_3H_8} \qquad \frac{-2044 \text{ kJ}}{1 \text{ mol } C_3H_8}$$

RELATIONSHIPS USED

1000 g = 1 kg
molar mass C_3H_8 = 44.09 g/mol
1 mol C_3H_8 : −2044 kJ (from balanced equation)

SOLVE Follow the conceptual plan to solve the problem. Begin with 13.2 kg C_3H_8 and multiply by the appropriate conversion factors to arrive at kJ.

SOLUTION

$$13.2 \text{ kg } C_3H_8 \times \frac{1000 \text{ g}}{1 \text{ kg}} \times \frac{1 \text{ mol } C_3H_8}{44.09 \text{ g } C_3H_8} \times \frac{-2044 \text{ kJ}}{1 \text{ mol } C_3H_8}$$

$$= -6.12 \times 10^5 \text{ kJ}$$

CHECK The units of the answer (kJ) are correct for energy. The answer is negative, as it should be for heat evolved by the reaction.

FOR PRACTICE 7.7 Ammonia reacts with oxygen according to the equation:

$$4\,NH_3(g) + 5\,O_2(g) \longrightarrow 4\,NO(g) + 6\,H_2O(g) \qquad \Delta H_{rxn} = -906 \text{ kJ}$$

Calculate the heat (in kJ) associated with the complete reaction of 155 g of NH_3.

FOR MORE PRACTICE 7.7 What mass of butane in grams is necessary to produce 1.5×10^3 kJ of heat? What mass of CO_2 is produced?

$$C_4H_{10}(g) + 13/2\,O_2(g) \longrightarrow 4\,CO_2(g) + 5\,H_2O(g) \qquad \Delta H_{rxn} = -2658 \text{ kJ}$$

7.7 Constant-Pressure Calorimetry: Measuring ΔH_{rxn}

For many aqueous reactions, we can measure ΔH_{rxn} fairly simply using the **coffee-cup calorimeter** shown in Figure 7.9▶. The calorimeter consists of two Styrofoam coffee cups, one inserted into the other, to provide insulation from the laboratory environment. The calorimeter is equipped with a thermometer and a stirrer. The reaction occurs in a specifically measured quantity of solution within the calorimeter, so that the mass of the solution is known. During the reaction, the heat evolved (or absorbed) causes a temperature change in the solution, which the thermometer measures. If we know the specific heat capacity of the solution, normally assumed to be that of water, we can calculate q_{soln}, the heat absorbed by or lost from the solution (which is acting as the surroundings) using the equation:

$$q_{soln} = m_{soln} \times C_{s,\,soln} \times \Delta T$$

The insulated calorimeter prevents heat from escaping, so we assume that the heat gained by the solution equals that lost by the reaction (or vice versa):

$$q_{rxn} = -q_{soln}$$

Because the reaction happens under conditions of constant pressure (open to the atmosphere), $q_{rxn} = q_p = \Delta H_{rxn}$. This measured quantity is the heat of reaction for the specific amount (which is measured ahead of time) of reactants that react. To find ΔH_{rxn} per mole of a particular reactant—a more general quantity—we divide by the number of moles that actually reacted, as demonstrated in Example 7.8.

Summarizing Calorimetry:

- Bomb calorimetry occurs at constant *volume* and measures ΔE for a reaction.
- Coffee-cup calorimetry occurs at constant *pressure* and measures ΔH for a reaction.

The Coffee-Cup Calorimeter

A coffee cup calorimeter measures enthalpy changes for chemical reactions in solution.

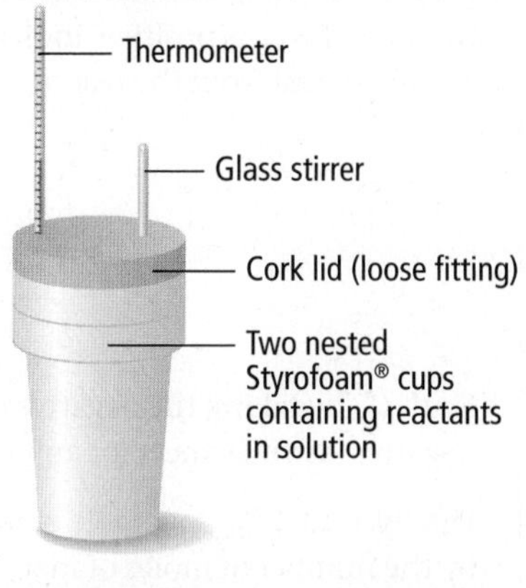

▲ **FIGURE 7.9 The Coffee-Cup Calorimeter**

The equation $q_{rxn} = -q_{soln}$ assumes that no heat is lost to the calorimeter itself. If heat absorbed by the calorimeter is accounted for, the equation becomes $q_{rxn} = -(q_{soln} + q_{cal})$.

WATCH **NOW!**

INTERACTIVE WORKED EXAMPLE 7.8

EXAMPLE 7.8 Measuring ΔH_{rxn} in a Coffee-Cup Calorimeter

Magnesium metal reacts with hydrochloric acid according to the balanced equation:

$$Mg(s) + 2\,HCl(aq) \longrightarrow MgCl_2(aq) + H_2(g)$$

In an experiment to determine the enthalpy change for this reaction, 0.158 g of Mg metal is combined with enough HCl to make 100.0 mL of solution in a coffee-cup calorimeter. The HCl is sufficiently concentrated so that the Mg completely reacts. The temperature of the solution rises from 25.6 °C to 32.8 °C as a result of the reaction. Find ΔH_{rxn} for the reaction as written. Use 1.00 g/mL as the density of the solution and $C_{s,\,soln} = 4.18\ J/g\cdot°C$ as the specific heat capacity of the solution.

SORT You are given the mass of magnesium, the volume of solution, the initial and final temperatures, the density of the solution, and the heat capacity of the solution. You are asked to find the change in enthalpy for the reaction.

GIVEN: 0.158 g Mg
100.0 mL soln
$T_i = 25.6\ °C$ $T_f = 32.8\ °C$
$d = 1.00\ g/mL$ $C_{s,\,soln} = 4.18\ J/g\cdot°C$

FIND: ΔH_{rxn}

STRATEGIZE The conceptual plan has three parts. In the first part, use the temperature change and the other given quantities, together with the equation $q = m \times C_s \times \Delta T$, to find q_{soln}.

CONCEPTUAL PLAN

$C_{s,\,soln}, m_{soln}, \Delta T \longrightarrow q_{soln}$

$q = m \times C_s \times \Delta T$

In the second part, use q_{soln} to get q_{rxn} (which simply involves changing the sign). Because the pressure is constant, q_{rxn} is equivalent to ΔH_{rxn} for the amount of magnesium that reacts.

$q_{soln} \longrightarrow q_{rxn}$

$q_{rxn} = -q_{soln}$

In the third part, divide q_{rxn} by the number of moles of magnesium to determine ΔH_{rxn} per mole of magnesium.

$$\Delta H_{rxn} = \frac{q_{rxn}}{\text{mol Mg}}$$

RELATIONSHIPS USED

$q = m \times C_s \times \Delta T$

$q_{rxn} = -q_{soln}$

—*Continued on the next page*

Continued—

SOLVE Gather the necessary quantities in the correct units for the equation $q = m \times C_s \times \Delta T$ and substitute these into the equation to calculate q_{soln}. Notice that the sign of q_{soln} is positive, indicating that the solution absorbed heat from the reaction.

SOLUTION

$$C_{s,\,soln} = 4.18\ \text{J/g}\cdot{}^\circ\text{C}$$

$$m_{soln} = 100.0\ \cancel{\text{mL soln}} \times \frac{1.00\ \text{g}}{1\ \cancel{\text{mL soln}}} = 1.00 \times 10^2\ \text{g}$$

$$\Delta T = T_f - T_i$$
$$= 32.8\ {}^\circ\text{C} - 25.6\ {}^\circ\text{C} = 7.2\ {}^\circ\text{C}$$

$$q_{soln} = m_{soln} \times C_{s,\,soln} \times \Delta T$$
$$= 1.00 \times 10^2\ \cancel{\text{g}} \times 4.18 \frac{\text{J}}{\cancel{\text{g}}\cdot\cancel{{}^\circ\text{C}}} \times 7.2\ \cancel{{}^\circ\text{C}} = 3.0 \times 10^3\ \text{J}$$

Find q_{rxn} by taking the negative of q_{soln}. Notice that q_{rxn} is negative, as you expect for an exothermic reaction.

$$q_{rxn} = -q_{soln} = -3.0 \times 10^3\ \text{J}$$

Finally, find ΔH_{rxn} per mole of magnesium by dividing q_{rxn} by the number of moles of magnesium that reacts. Find the number of moles of magnesium from the given mass of magnesium and its molar mass.

$$\Delta H_{rxn} = \frac{q_{rxn}}{\text{mol Mg}}$$
$$= \frac{-3.0 \times 10^3\ \text{J}}{0.158\ \cancel{\text{g Mg}} \times \dfrac{1\ \text{mol Mg}}{24.31\ \cancel{\text{g Mg}}}}$$
$$= -4.6 \times 10^5\ \text{J/mol Mg}$$

Since the stoichiometric coefficient for magnesium in the balanced chemical equation is 1, the calculated value represents ΔH_{rxn} for the reaction as written.

$$Mg(s) + 2\,HCl(aq) \longrightarrow MgCl_2(aq) + H_2(g) \qquad \Delta H_{rxn} = -4.6 \times 10^5\ \text{J}$$

CHECK The units of the answer (J) are correct for the change in enthalpy of a reaction. The sign is negative, as you expect for an exothermic reaction.

FOR PRACTICE 7.8 The addition of hydrochloric acid to a silver nitrate solution precipitates silver chloride according to the reaction:

$$AgNO_3(aq) + HCl(aq) \longrightarrow AgCl(s) + HNO_3(aq)$$

When 50.0 mL of 0.100 M $AgNO_3$ is combined with 50.0 mL of 0.100 M HCl in a coffee-cup calorimeter, the temperature changes from 23.40 °C to 24.21 °C. Calculate ΔH_{rxn} for the reaction as written. Use 1.00 g/mL as the density of the solution and $C = 4.18\ \text{J/g}\cdot{}^\circ\text{C}$ as the specific heat capacity.

ANSWER **NOW!**

7.9 Cc Conceptual Connection

CONSTANT-PRESSURE VERSUS CONSTANT-VOLUME CALORIMETRY The same reaction, with exactly the same amount of reactant, is conducted in a bomb calorimeter and in a coffee-cup calorimeter. In one of the calorimeters, $q_{rxn} = -12.5$ kJ and in the other $q_{rxn} = -11.8$ kJ. Which value was obtained in the bomb calorimeter? (Assume that the reaction has a positive ΔV in the coffee-cup calorimeter.)

(a) $q_{rxn} = -12.5$ kJ **(b)** $q_{rxn} = -11.8$ kJ

7.8 Relationships Involving ΔH_{rxn}

The change in enthalpy for a reaction is always associated with a *particular* reaction. If we change the reaction in well-defined ways, then ΔH_{rxn} also changes in well-defined ways. We now turn our attention to three quantitative relationships between a chemical equation and ΔH_{rxn}.

1. **If a chemical equation is multiplied by some factor, then ΔH_{rxn} is also multiplied by the same factor.**

Recall from Section 7.6 that ΔH_{rxn} is an extensive property; it depends on the quantity of reactants undergoing reaction. Recall also that ΔH_{rxn} is usually reported for a reaction involving stoichiometric amounts of reactants. For example, for a reaction $A + 2\,B \longrightarrow C$, ΔH_{rxn} is typically reported as the amount of heat emitted or absorbed when 1 mol A reacts with 2 mol B to form 1 mol C. Therefore, if a chemical equation is multiplied by a factor, then ΔH_{rxn} is also multiplied by the same factor. For example,

$$A + 2\,B \longrightarrow C \qquad \Delta H_1$$
$$2\,A + 4\,B \longrightarrow 2\,C \qquad \Delta H_2 = 2 \times \Delta H_1$$

2. **If a chemical equation is reversed, then ΔH_{rxn} changes sign.**

Recall from Section 7.6 that ΔH_{rxn} is a state function, which means that its value depends only on the initial and final states of the system.

$$\Delta H = H_{final} - H_{initial}$$

When a reaction is reversed, the final state becomes the initial state and vice versa. Consequently, ΔH_{rxn} changes sign:

$$A + 2\,B \longrightarrow C \qquad \Delta H_1$$
$$C \longrightarrow A + 2\,B \qquad \Delta H_2 = -\Delta H_1$$

3. **If a chemical equation can be expressed as the sum of a series of steps, then ΔH_{rxn} for the overall equation is the sum of the heats of reaction for each step.**

This last relationship, known as **Hess's law**, also follows from the enthalpy of reaction being a state function. Since ΔH_{rxn} is dependent only on the initial and final states, and not on the pathway the reaction follows, ΔH obtained from summing the individual steps that lead to an overall reaction must be the same as ΔH for that overall reaction. For example,

$$A + 2\,B \longrightarrow \cancel{C} \qquad \Delta H_1$$
$$\cancel{C} \longrightarrow 2\,D \qquad \Delta H_2$$
$$\overline{A + 2\,B \longrightarrow 2\,D \qquad \Delta H_3 = \Delta H_1 + \Delta H_2}$$

We illustrate Hess's law with the energy-level diagram in Figure 7.10▶.

Hess's Law

The change in enthalpy for a stepwise process is the sum of the enthalpy changes of the steps.

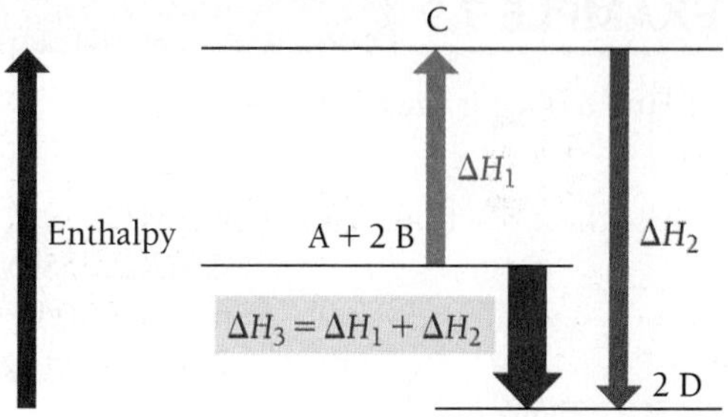

▲ **FIGURE 7.10 Hess's Law**

RELATIONSHIPS INVOLVING ΔH_{rxn} Consider the following chemical equation:

$$2\,A + B \longrightarrow C \qquad \Delta H_{rxn} = 122\,J$$

What is ΔH_{rxn} for the reaction $2\,C \longrightarrow 4\,A + 2\,B$?

(a) 122 J **(b)** −122 J **(c)** 244 J **(d)** −244 J

7.10 Cc Conceptual Connection ANSWER **NOW!**

These three quantitative relationships make it possible to determine ΔH for a reaction without directly measuring it in the laboratory. (For some reactions, direct measurement can be difficult.) If we can find related reactions (with known ΔH's) that sum to the reaction of interest, we can find ΔH for the reaction of interest. For example, the following reaction between $C(s)$ and $H_2O(g)$ is an industrially important method of generating hydrogen gas:

$$C(s) + H_2O(g) \longrightarrow CO(g) + H_2(g) \qquad \Delta H_{rxn} = ?$$

We can find ΔH_{rxn} from the following reactions that have known ΔH's:

$$C(s) + O_2(g) \longrightarrow CO_2(g) \qquad \Delta H = -393.5\text{ kJ}$$
$$2\,CO(g) + O_2(g) \longrightarrow 2\,CO_2(g) \qquad \Delta H = -566.0\text{ kJ}$$
$$2\,H_2(g) + O_2(g) \longrightarrow 2\,H_2O(g) \qquad \Delta H = -483.6\text{ kJ}$$

To get the overall reaction of interest, we just have to determine how to sum these reactions. We do this by manipulating the reactions with known ΔH's in such a way as to get the reactants of interest on the left, the products of interest on the right, and other species to cancel.

Since the first reaction has C(s) as a reactant, and the reaction of interest also has C(s) as a reactant, we write the first reaction unchanged.

$$C(s) + O_2(g) \longrightarrow CO_2(g) \quad \Delta H = -393.5\ \text{kJ}$$

The second reaction has 2 mol of CO(g) as a reactant. However, the reaction of interest has 1 mol of CO(g) as a product. Therefore, we reverse the second reaction, change the sign of ΔH, and multiply the reaction and ΔH by $\frac{1}{2}$.

$$\tfrac{1}{2} \times [2\,CO_2(g) \longrightarrow 2\,CO(g) + O_2(g)] \quad \Delta H = \tfrac{1}{2} \times (+566.0\ \text{kJ})$$

In the third reaction $H_2(g)$ is a reactant. In the reaction of interest, however, $H_2(g)$ is a product. Therefore, we reverse the equation and change the sign of ΔH. In addition, to obtain coefficients that match the reaction of interest, and to cancel O_2, we must multiply the reaction and ΔH, by $\frac{1}{2}$.

$$\tfrac{1}{2} \times [2\,H_2O(g) \longrightarrow 2\,H_2(g) + O_2(g)] \quad \Delta H = \tfrac{1}{2} \times (+483.6\ \text{kJ})$$

Lastly, we rewrite the three reactions after multiplying through by the indicated factors and show how they sum to the reaction of interest. ΔH for the reaction of interest is the sum of the ΔH's for the steps.

$$\begin{aligned}
C(s) + \cancel{O_2(g)} &\longrightarrow \cancel{CO_2(g)} & \Delta H &= -393.5\ \text{kJ} \\
\cancel{CO_2(g)} &\longrightarrow CO(g) + \cancel{\tfrac{1}{2}O_2(g)} & \Delta H &= +283.0\ \text{kJ} \\
H_2O(g) &\longrightarrow H_2(g) + \cancel{\tfrac{1}{2}O_2(g)} & \Delta H &= +241.8\ \text{kJ} \\
\hline
C(s) + H_2O(g) &\longrightarrow CO(g) + H_2(g) & \Delta H_{rxn} &= +131.3\ \text{kJ}
\end{aligned}$$

WATCH **NOW!**

INTERACTIVE WORKED EXAMPLE 7.9

EXAMPLE 7.9 Hess's Law

Find ΔH_{rxn} for the reaction:

$$3\,C(s) + 4\,H_2(g) \longrightarrow C_3H_8(g)$$

Use these reactions with known ΔH's:

$$\begin{aligned}
C_3H_8(g) + 5\,O_2(g) &\longrightarrow 3\,CO_2(g) + 4\,H_2O(g) & \Delta H &= -2043\ \text{kJ} \\
C(s) + O_2(g) &\longrightarrow CO_2(g) & \Delta H &= -393.5\ \text{kJ} \\
2\,H_2(g) + O_2(g) &\longrightarrow 2\,H_2O(g) & \Delta H &= -483.6\ \text{kJ}
\end{aligned}$$

SOLUTION

To work this and other Hess's law problems, manipulate the reactions with known ΔH's in such a way as to get the reactants of interest on the left, the products of interest on the right, and other species to cancel.

The first reaction has C_3H_8 as a reactant, and the reaction of interest has C_3H_8 as a product, so reverse the first reaction and change the sign of ΔH.

$$3\,CO_2(g) + 4\,H_2O(g) \longrightarrow C_3H_8(g) + 5\,O_2(g) \quad \Delta H = +2043\ \text{kJ}$$

The second reaction has C as a reactant and CO_2 as a product, just as required in the reaction of interest. However, the coefficient for C is 1, and in the reaction of interest, the coefficient for C is 3. You need to multiply this equation and its ΔH by 3.

$$3 \times [C(s) + O_2(g) \longrightarrow CO_2(g)] \quad \Delta H = 3 \times (-393.5\ \text{kJ})$$

The third reaction has $H_2(g)$ as a reactant, as required. However, the coefficient for H_2 is 2, and in the reaction of interest, the coefficient for H_2 is 4. Multiply this reaction and its ΔH by 2.

$$2 \times [2\,H_2(g) + O_2(g) \longrightarrow 2\,H_2O(g)] \quad \Delta H = 2 \times (-483.6\ \text{kJ})$$

Rewrite the three reactions after multiplying through by the indicated factors and show how they sum to the reaction of interest. ΔH for the reaction of interest is the sum of the ΔH's for the steps.

$$\begin{aligned}
\cancel{3\,CO_2(g)} + \cancel{4\,H_2O(g)} &\longrightarrow C_3H_8(g) + \cancel{5\,O_2(g)} & \Delta H &= +2043\ \text{kJ} \\
3\,C(s) + \cancel{3\,O_2(g)} &\longrightarrow \cancel{3\,CO_2(g)} & \Delta H &= -1181\ \text{kJ} \\
4\,H_2(g) + \cancel{2\,O_2(g)} &\longrightarrow \cancel{4\,H_2O(g)} & \Delta H &= -967.2\ \text{kJ} \\
\hline
3\,C(s) + 4\,H_2(g) &\longrightarrow C_3H_8(g) & \Delta H_{rxn} &= -105\ \text{kJ}
\end{aligned}$$

FOR PRACTICE 7.9 Find ΔH_{rxn} for the reaction:

$$N_2O(g) + NO_2(g) \longrightarrow 3\,NO(g)$$

Use these reactions with known ΔH's:

$$\begin{aligned}
2\,NO(g) + O_2(g) &\longrightarrow 2\,NO_2(g) & \Delta H &= -113.1\ \text{kJ} \\
N_2(g) + O_2(g) &\longrightarrow 2\,NO(g) & \Delta H &= +182.6\ \text{kJ} \\
2\,N_2O(g) &\longrightarrow 2\,N_2(g) + O_2(g) & \Delta H &= -163.2\ \text{kJ}
\end{aligned}$$

FOR MORE PRACTICE 7.9 Find ΔH_{rxn} for the reaction:

$$3\,H_2(g) + O_3(g) \longrightarrow 3\,H_2O(g)$$

Use these reactions with known ΔH's:

$$2\,H_2(g) + O_2(g) \longrightarrow 2\,H_2O(g) \quad \Delta H = -483.6\text{ kJ}$$
$$3\,O_2(g) \longrightarrow 2\,O_3(g) \quad \Delta H = +285.4\text{ kJ}$$

7.9 Determining Enthalpies of Reaction from Standard Enthalpies of Formation

WATCH **NOW!**

KEY CONCEPT VIDEO 7.9
Determining the Enthalpy of Reaction from Standard Enthalpies of Formation

We have examined two ways to determine ΔH for a chemical reaction: experimentally through calorimetry and inferentially through Hess's law. We now turn to a third and more convenient way to determine ΔH for a large number of chemical reactions: from tabulated *standard enthalpies of formation*.

Standard States and Standard Enthalpy Changes

Recall that ΔH is the *change* in enthalpy for a chemical reaction—the difference in enthalpy between the products and the reactants. Because we are interested in changes in enthalpy (and not in absolute values of enthalpy itself), we are free to define the *zero* of enthalpy as conveniently as possible. Returning to our mountain-climbing analogy, a change in altitude (like a change in enthalpy) is an absolute quantity. Altitude itself (like enthalpy), however, is a relative quantity, defined relative to some standard (such as sea level in the case of altitude). We define a similar, albeit slightly more complex, standard for enthalpy. This standard has three parts: the **standard state**, the **standard enthalpy change ($\Delta H°$)**, and the **standard enthalpy of formation ($\Delta H_f°$)**.

1. **Standard State**
   - *For a Gas:* The standard state for a gas is the pure gas at a pressure of exactly 1 atm.
   - *For a Liquid or Solid:* The standard state for a liquid or solid is the pure substance in its most stable form at a pressure of 1 atm and at the temperature of interest (often taken to be 25 °C).
   - *For a Substance in Solution:* The standard state for a substance in solution is a concentration of exactly 1 M.
2. **Standard Enthalpy Change ($\Delta H°$)**
   - The change in enthalpy for a process when all reactants and products are in their standard states. The degree sign indicates standard states.
3. **Standard Enthalpy of Formation ($\Delta H_f°$)**
   - *For a Pure Compound:* The change in enthalpy when 1 mol of the compound forms from its constituent elements in their standard states.
   - *For a Pure Element in Its Standard State:* $\Delta H_f° = 0$.

The standard state was changed in 1997 to a pressure of 1 bar, which is very close to 1 atm (1 atm = 1.013 bar). Both standards are now in common use.

The standard enthalpy of formation is also called the **standard heat of formation.**

Assigning the value of zero to the standard enthalpy of formation for an element in its standard state is the equivalent of assigning an altitude of zero to sea level. Once we assume sea level is zero, we can then measure all subsequent changes in altitude relative to sea level. Similarly, we can measure all changes in enthalpy relative to those of pure elements in their standard states. For example, consider the standard enthalpy of formation of methane gas at 25 °C:

$$C(s, \text{graphite}) + 2\,H_2(g) \longrightarrow CH_4(g) \quad \Delta H_f° = -74.6\text{ kJ/mol}$$

The carbon in this equation must be graphite (the most stable form of carbon at 1 atm and 25 °C).

For methane, as with most compounds, $\Delta H_f°$ is negative. Continuing our analogy, if we think of pure elements in their standard states as being at *sea level*, then most compounds lie *below sea level*. The chemical equation for the enthalpy of formation of a compound is always written to form 1 mol of the compound, so $\Delta H_f°$ has the units of kJ/mol. Table 7.5 lists $\Delta H_f°$ values for some selected compounds. A more complete list is presented in Appendix IIB.

TABLE 7.5 ■ Standard Enthalpies (or Heats) of Formation, ΔH_f°, at 298 K

Formula	ΔH_f°(kJ/mol)	Formula	ΔH_f°(kJ/mol)	Formula	ΔH_f°(kJ/mol)
Bromine		C_3H_8O(*l*, isopropanol)	−318.1	**Oxygen**	
Br(*g*)	111.9	C_6H_6(*l*)	49.1	O_2(*g*)	0
Br_2(*l*)	0	$C_6H_{12}O_6$(*s*, glucose)	−1273.3	O_3(*g*)	142.7
HBr(*g*)	−36.3	$C_{12}H_{22}O_{11}$(*s*, sucrose)	−2226.1	H_2O(*g*)	−241.8
Calcium		**Chlorine**		H_2O(*l*)	−285.8
Ca(*s*)	0	Cl(*g*)	121.3	**Silver**	
CaO(*s*)	−634.9	Cl_2(*g*)	0	Ag(*s*)	0
$CaCO_3$(*s*)	−1207.6	HCl(*g*)	−92.3	AgCl(*s*)	−127.0
Carbon		**Fluorine**		**Sodium**	
C(*s*, graphite)	0	F(*g*)	79.38	Na(*s*)	0
C(*s*, diamond)	1.88	F_2(*g*)	0	Na(*g*)	107.5
CO(*g*)	−110.5	HF(*g*)	−273.3	NaCl(*s*)	−411.2
CO_2(*g*)	−393.5	**Hydrogen**		Na_2CO_3(*s*)	−1130.7
CH_4(*g*)	−74.6	H(*g*)	218.0	$NaHCO_3$(*s*)	−950.8
CH_3OH(*l*)	−238.6	H_2(*g*)	0	**Sulfur**	
C_2H_2(*g*)	227.4	**Nitrogen**		S_8(*s*, rhombic)	0
C_2H_4(*g*)	52.4	N_2(*g*)	0	S_8(*s*, monoclinic)	0.3
C_2H_6(*g*)	−84.68	NH_3(*g*)	−45.9	SO_2(*g*)	−296.8
C_2H_5OH(*l*)	−277.6	NH_4NO_3(*s*)	−365.6	SO_3(*g*)	−395.7
C_3H_8(*g*)	−103.85	NO(*g*)	91.3	H_2SO_4(*l*)	−814.0
C_3H_6O(*l*, acetone)	−248.4	N_2O(*g*)	81.6		

EXAMPLE 7.10 Standard Enthalpies of Formation

Write equations for the formation of (a) $MgCO_3(s)$ and (b) $C_6H_{12}O_6(s)$ from their respective elements in their standard states. Include the value of ΔH_f° for each equation.

SOLUTION

(a) $MgCO_3(s)$

Write the equation with the elements in $MgCO_3$ in their standard states as the reactants and 1 mol of $MgCO_3$ as the product.

$$Mg(s) + C(s, \text{graphite}) + O_2(g) \longrightarrow MgCO_3(s)$$

Balance the equation and look up ΔH_f° in Appendix II B. (Use fractional coefficients so that the product of the reaction is 1 mol of $MgCO_3$.)

$$Mg(s) + C(s, \text{graphite}) + \frac{3}{2} O_2(g) \longrightarrow MgCO_3(s)$$

$$\Delta H_f^\circ = -1095.8 \text{ kJ/mol}$$

(b) $C_6H_{12}O_6(s)$

Write the equation with the elements in $C_6H_{12}O_6$ in their standard states as the reactants and 1 mol of $C_6H_{12}O_6$ as the product.

$$C(s, \text{graphite}) + H_2(g) + O_2(g) \longrightarrow C_6H_{12}O_6(s)$$

Balance the equation and look up ΔH_f° in Appendix IIB.

$$6\,C(s, \text{graphite}) + 6\,H_2(g) + 3\,O_2(g) \longrightarrow C_6H_{12}O_6(s)$$

$$\Delta H_f^\circ = -1273.3 \text{ kJ/mol}$$

FOR PRACTICE 7.10 Write equations for the formation of (a) NaCl(*s*) and (b) $Pb(NO_3)_2(s)$ from their respective elements in their standard states. Include the value of ΔH_f° for each equation.

Calculating the Standard Enthalpy Change for a Reaction

We have just seen that the standard enthalpy of formation corresponds to the *formation* of a compound from its constituent elements in their standard states:

$$\text{elements} \longrightarrow \text{compound} \qquad \Delta H_f^\circ$$

Therefore, the *negative* of the standard enthalpy of formation corresponds to the *decomposition* of a compound into its constituent elements in their standard states:

$$\text{compound} \longrightarrow \text{elements} \qquad -\Delta H_f^\circ$$

We can use these two concepts—the decomposition of a compound into its elements and the formation of a compound from its elements—to calculate the enthalpy change of any reaction by mentally taking the reactants through two steps. In the first step, we *decompose the reactants* into their constituent elements in their standard states; in the second step, we *form the products* from the constituent elements in their standard states:

$$\begin{array}{lll} \text{reactants} \longrightarrow \text{elements} & \Delta H_1 = -\Sigma\Delta H_f^\circ(\text{reactants}) \\ \text{elements} \longrightarrow \text{products} & \Delta H_2 = +\Sigma\Delta H_f^\circ(\text{products}) \\ \hline \text{reactants} \longrightarrow \text{products} & \Delta H_{rxn}^\circ = \Delta H_1 + \Delta H_2 \end{array}$$

In these equations, Σ means sum so that ΔH_1 is the sum of the negatives of the heats of formation of the reactants and ΔH_2 is the sum of the heats of formation of the products.

We can demonstrate this procedure by calculating the standard enthalpy change (ΔH_{rxn}°) for the combustion of methane:

$$CH_4(g) + 2\,O_2(g) \longrightarrow CO_2(g) + 2\,H_2O(g) \qquad \Delta H_{rxn}^\circ = ?$$

The energy changes associated with the decomposition of the reactants and the formation of the products are shown in Figure 7.11▼. The first step (1) is the decomposition of 1 mol of methane into its constituent elements in their standard states. We can obtain the change in enthalpy for this step by reversing the enthalpy of formation equation for methane and changing the sign of ΔH_f°:

$$(1)\ CH_4(g) \longrightarrow C(s, \text{graphite}) + 2\,H_2(g) \qquad -\Delta H_f^\circ = +74.6\ \text{kJ/mol}$$

The second step, the formation of the products from their constituent elements, has two parts: (a) the formation of 1 mol CO_2 and (b) the formation of 2 mol H_2O. Because part b forms 2 mol H_2O, we multiply the ΔH_f° for that step by 2:

$$(2a)\ C(s, \text{graphite}) + O_2(g) \longrightarrow CO_2(g) \qquad \Delta H_f^\circ = -393.5\ \text{kJ/mol}$$

$$(2b)\ 2 \times [H_2(g) + {}^1\!/_2\,O_2(g) \longrightarrow H_2O(g)] \quad 2 \times \Delta H_f^\circ = 2 \times (-241.8\ \text{kJ/mol})$$

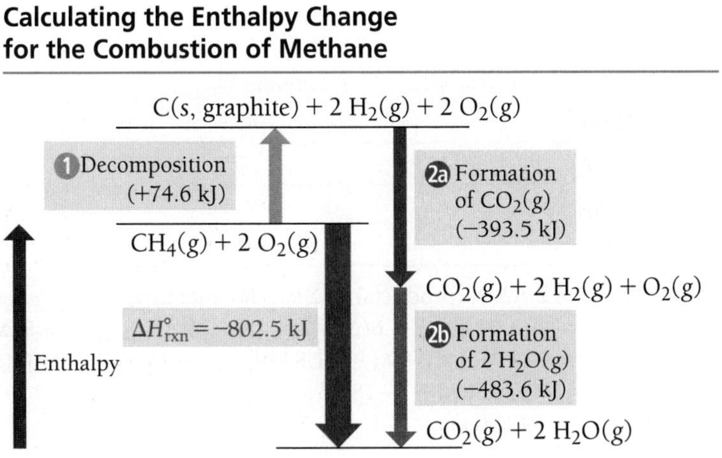

◀ **FIGURE 7.11 Enthalpy Change for the Combustion of Methane**

As we know from Hess's law, the enthalpy of reaction for the overall reaction is the sum of the enthalpies of reaction of the individual steps:

$$
\begin{array}{lr}
(1)\ CH_4(g) \longrightarrow \cancel{C(s,\text{graphite})} + \cancel{2\,H_2(g)} & -\Delta H_f^\circ = +74.6\ \text{kJ/mol} \\
(2a)\ \cancel{C(s,\text{graphite})} + O_2(g) \longrightarrow CO_2(g) & \Delta H_f^\circ = -393.5\ \text{kJ/mol} \\
(2b)\ \cancel{2\,H_2(g)} + O_2(g) \longrightarrow 2\,H_2O(g) & 2 \times \Delta H_f^\circ = -483.6\ \text{kJ/mol} \\
\hline
CH_4(g) + 2\,O_2(g) \longrightarrow CO_2(g) + 2\,H_2O(g) & \Delta H_{rxn}^\circ = -802.5\ \text{kJ/mol}
\end{array}
$$

We can streamline and generalize this process as follows:

To calculate ΔH_{rxn}°, subtract the enthalpies of formation of the reactants multiplied by their stoichiometric coefficients from the enthalpies of formation of the products multiplied by their stoichiometric coefficients.

In the form of an equation:

$$\Delta H_{rxn}^\circ = \sum n_p \Delta H_f^\circ(\text{products}) - \sum n_r \Delta H_f^\circ(\text{reactants}) \qquad [7.15]$$

In this equation, n_p represents the stoichiometric coefficients of the products, n_r represents the stoichiometric coefficients of the reactants, and ΔH_f° represents the standard enthalpies of formation. Keep in mind when using this equation that elements in their standard states have $\Delta H_f^\circ = 0$. Examples 7.11 and 7.12 demonstrate this process.

WATCH **NOW!**
INTERACTIVE WORKED EXAMPLE 7.11

EXAMPLE 7.11 ΔH_{rxn}° and Standard Enthalpies of Formation

Use the standard enthalpies of formation to determine ΔH_{rxn}° for the reaction:

$$4\,NH_3(g) + 5\,O_2(g) \longrightarrow 4\,NO(g) + 6\,H_2O(g)$$

SORT You are given the balanced equation and asked to find the enthalpy of reaction.

GIVEN: $4\,NH_3(g) + 5\,O_2(g) \longrightarrow 4\,NO(g) + 6\,H_2O(g)$

FIND: ΔH_{rxn}°

STRATEGIZE To calculate ΔH_{rxn}° from standard enthalpies of formation, subtract the heats of formation of the reactants multiplied by their stoichiometric coefficients from the heats of formation of the products multiplied by their stoichiometric coefficients.

CONCEPTUAL PLAN

$\Delta H_{rxn}^\circ = \Sigma n_p \Delta H_f^\circ(\text{products}) - \Sigma n_r \Delta H_f^\circ(\text{reactants})$

SOLVE Begin by looking up (in Appendix IIB) the standard enthalpy of formation for each reactant and product. Remember that the standard enthalpy of formation of pure elements in their standard state is zero. Calculate ΔH_{rxn}° by substituting into the equation.

SOLUTION

Reactant or product	ΔH_f° (kJ/mol, from Appendix IIB)
$NH_3(g)$	−45.9
$O_2(g)$	0.0
$NO(g)$	+91.3
$H_2O(g)$	−241.8

$$
\begin{aligned}
\Delta H_{rxn}^\circ &= \Sigma n_p \Delta H_f^\circ(\text{products}) - \Sigma n_r \Delta H_f^\circ(\text{reactants}) \\
&= [4(\Delta H_{f,\,NO(g)}^\circ) + 6(\Delta H_{f,\,H_2O(g)}^\circ)] - [4(\Delta H_{f,\,NH_3(g)}^\circ) + 5(\Delta H_{f,\,O_2(g)}^\circ)] \\
&= [4(+91.3\ \text{kJ}) + 6(-241.8\ \text{kJ})] - [4(-45.9\ \text{kJ}) + 5(0.0\ \text{kJ})] \\
&= -1085.6\ \text{kJ} - (-183.6\ \text{kJ}) \\
&= -902.0\ \text{kJ}
\end{aligned}
$$

CHECK The units of the answer (kJ) are correct. The answer is negative, which means that the reaction is exothermic.

FOR PRACTICE 7.11 The thermite reaction, in which powdered aluminum reacts with iron oxide, is highly exothermic.

$$2\,Al(s) + Fe_2O_3(s) \longrightarrow Al_2O_3(s) + 2\,Fe(s)$$

Use standard enthalpies of formation to determine ΔH°_{rxn} for the thermite reaction.

▶ The reaction of powdered aluminum with iron oxide, known as the thermite reaction, releases a large amount of heat.

EXAMPLE 7.12 ΔH°_{rxn} and Standard Enthalpies of Formation

A city of 100,000 people uses approximately 1.0×10^{11} kJ of energy per day. Suppose all of that energy comes from the combustion of liquid octane (C_8H_{18}) to form gaseous water and gaseous carbon dioxide. Use standard enthalpies of formation to calculate ΔH°_{rxn} for the combustion of octane and then determine the number of kilograms of octane necessary to provide this amount of energy.

SORT You are given the amount of energy used and asked to find the mass of octane required to produce the energy.

GIVEN: 1.0×10^{11} kJ

FIND: kg C_8H_{18}

STRATEGIZE The conceptual plan has three parts. In the first part, write a balanced equation for the combustion of octane.

CONCEPTUAL PLAN

(1) Write the balanced equation.

In the second part, calculate ΔH°_{rxn} from the ΔH°_f's of the reactants and products.

(2) ΔH°_f's → ΔH°_{rxn}

$\Delta H^\circ_{rxn} = \Sigma\, n_p \Delta H^\circ_f\,(\text{products}) - \Sigma\, n_r \Delta H^\circ_f\,(\text{reactants})$

In the third part, convert from kilojoules of energy to moles of octane using the conversion factor found in step 2, and then convert from moles of octane to mass of octane using the molar mass.

(3) kJ → mol C_8H_{18} → g C_8H_{18} → kg C_8H_{18}

Conversion factor to be determined from steps 1 and 2; $\dfrac{114.22\text{ g } C_8H_{18}}{\text{mol } C_8H_{18}}$; $\dfrac{1\text{ kg}}{1000\text{ g}}$

RELATIONSHIPS USED

molar mass C_8H_{18} = 114.22 g/mol

1 kg = 1000 g

SOLVE Begin by writing the balanced equation for the combustion of octane. For convenience, do not clear the 25/2 fraction in order to keep the coefficient on octane as 1.

SOLUTION STEP 1

$$C_8H_{18}(l) + \frac{25}{2}O_2(g) \longrightarrow 8\,CO_2(g) + 9\,H_2O(g)$$

Look up (in Appendix IIB) the standard enthalpy of formation for each reactant and product and then calculate ΔH°_{rxn}.

SOLUTION STEP 2

Reactant or product	ΔH°_f (kJ/mol, from Appendix IIB)
$C_8H_{18}(l)$	−250.1
$O_2(g)$	0.0
$CO_2(g)$	−393.5
$H_2O(g)$	−241.8

—Continued on the next page

Continued—

$$\begin{aligned}\Delta H^\circ_{rxn} &= \Sigma n_p \Delta H^\circ_f(\text{products}) - \Sigma n_r \Delta H^\circ_f(\text{reactants}) \\ &= [8(\Delta H^\circ_{f,\,CO_2(g)}) + 9(\Delta H^\circ_{f,\,H_2O(g)})] \\ &\quad - \left[1(\Delta H^\circ_{f,\,C_8H_{18}(l)}) + \frac{25}{2}(\Delta H^\circ_{f,\,O_2(g)})\right] \\ &= [8(-393.5\text{ kJ}) + 9(-241.8\text{ kJ})] - \left[1(-250.1\text{ kJ}) + \frac{25}{2}(0.0\text{ kJ})\right] \\ &= -5324.2\text{ kJ} - (-250.1\text{ kJ}) \\ &= -5074.1\text{ kJ}\end{aligned}$$

From steps 1 and 2 build a conversion factor between mol C_8H_{18} and kJ.

SOLUTION STEP 3

1 mol C_8H_{18} : −5074.1 kJ

Follow step 3 of the conceptual plan. Begin with -1.0×10^{11} kJ (since the city uses this much energy, the reaction must emit it, and therefore the sign is negative) and follow the steps to determine kilograms of octane.

$$-1.0 \times 10^{11}\text{ kJ} \times \frac{1\text{ mol } C_8H_{18}}{-5074.1\text{ kJ}} \times \frac{114.22\text{ g } C_8H_{18}}{1\text{ mol } C_8H_{18}} \times \frac{1\text{ kg}}{1000\text{ g}} = 2.3 \times 10^6\text{ kg } C_8H_{18}$$

CHECK The units of the answer (kg C_8H_{18}) are correct. The answer is positive, as it should be for mass. The magnitude is fairly large, as you would expect since this amount of octane is supposed to provide the energy for an entire city.

FOR PRACTICE 7.12 The chemical hand warmers described in Section 7.1 produce heat when they are removed from their airtight plastic wrappers. Recall that they utilize the oxidation of iron to form iron oxide according to the reaction $4\,Fe(s) + 3\,O_2(g) \longrightarrow 2\,Fe_2O_3(s)$. Calculate ΔH°_{rxn} for this reaction and calculate how much heat is produced from a hand warmer containing 15.0 g of iron powder.

7.10 Energy Use and the Environment

In this chapter, we explored the relationship between chemical reactions and energy changes. As noted earlier, our society derives the majority of its energy from the energy changes associated with burning fossil fuels. Fossil fuels have traditionally been regarded as convenient sources of energy due to their abundance and portability and because they undergo combustion reactions that have large negative enthalpies of reaction (the reactions are highly exothermic). However, the burning of fossil fuels also has some serious environmental impacts.

Energy Consumption

According to the U.S. Department of Energy, the United States currently consumes close to 100 quads (1 quad = 1 quadrillion British thermal units = 1.06×10^{18} J) of energy per year in the categories shown in this chart.

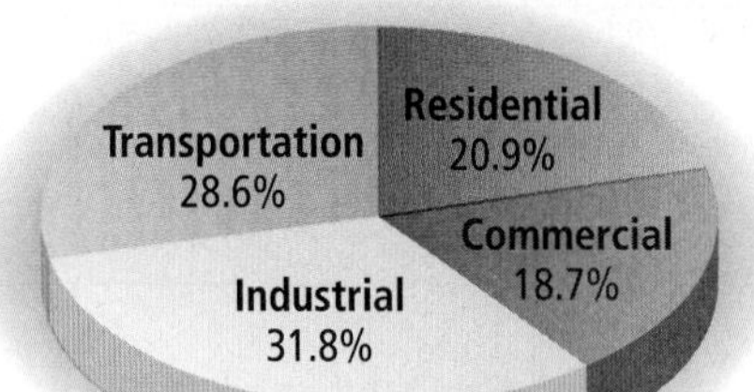

Source: U.S. Energy Information Administration. *Monthly Energy Review,* October 2017 (percentages for the 2016 calendar year).

This corresponds to over 100,000 kWh of energy use per person per year. If we used physical laborers to do the equivalent amount of work, each person would need about 120 people. In other words, the average American employs the work output of 120 people, day and night, all year long! For this reason, Americans enjoy one of the highest standards of living in the world. However, our consumption of energy has significant environmental consequences.

Most U.S. energy comes from the combustion of fossil fuels, as shown in Figure 7.12►. Fossil fuels include petroleum, natural gas, and coal, all of which have been considered convenient fuels because they are relatively abundant in Earth's crust (and therefore relatively inexpensive), they are easily transportable, and their combustion is highly exothermic.

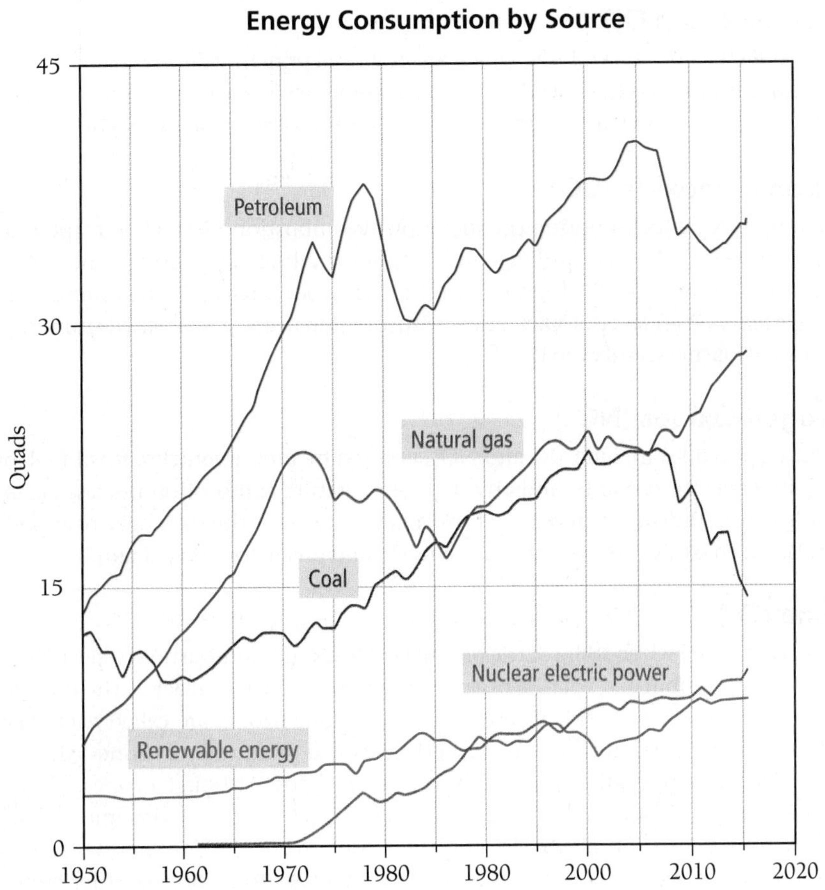

◀ FIGURE 7.12 Energy Consumption by Source
Source: U.S. Energy Information Administration. *Monthly Energy Review*, October 2017.

The reactions for the combustion of the main or representative components of several fossil fuels, and the associated enthalpies of reaction, are:

Coal: $C(s) + O_2(g) \longrightarrow CO_2(g)$ $\Delta H^\circ_{rxn} = -393.5\text{ kJ}$

Natural gas: $CH_4(g) + 2\,O_2(g) \longrightarrow CO_2(g) + 2\,H_2O(g)$ $\Delta H^\circ_{rxn} = -802.3\text{ kJ}$

Petroleum: $C_8H_{18}(l) + 25/2\,O_2(g) \longrightarrow 8\,CO_2(g) + 9\,H_2O(g)$ $\Delta H^\circ_{rxn} = -5074.1\text{ kJ}$

Environmental Problems Associated with Fossil Fuel Use

One of the main problems associated with the burning of fossil fuels is that even though they are abundant in Earth's crust, fossil fuels are also finite. Fossil fuels originate from ancient plant and animal life and are a nonrenewable energy source—once they are all burned, they cannot be replenished. At current rates of consumption, oil and natural gas supplies will be depleted in 50 to 100 years. Although there is enough coal to last much longer, it is a dirtier fuel (it produces more pollution), and, because it is a solid, it is less convenient (more difficult to transport and use) than petroleum and natural gas.

The other major problems associated with fossil fuel use stem from the products of combustion. The chemical equations we show in this section for fossil fuel combustion all produce carbon dioxide and water. However, these equations represent the reactions under ideal conditions and do not account for impurities in the fuel, side reactions, and incomplete combustion. When these are taken into account, we can identify three major environmental problems associated with the emissions of fossil fuel combustion: air pollution, acid rain, and global climate change. We discussed acid rain in Chapter 3 (see *Chemistry in the Environment: Acid Rain* in Section 3.6). Here we address air pollution and global climate change, which we first touched on in Section 4.1.

Air Pollution

The air in all major cities in the world is polluted. Pollution comes from a number of sources, including electricity generation, motor vehicle emissions, and industrial waste. There are many different kinds of air pollutants.

Sulfur Oxides (SO_x)

Sulfur oxides include SO_2 and SO_3, which are produced primarily during coal-fired electricity generation and industrial metal refining. The sulfur oxides are lung and eye irritants that affect the respiratory system and are the main precursors of acid rain (see Section 3.6).

Carbon Monoxide (CO)

Carbon monoxide forms during the incomplete combustion of fossil fuels (petroleum, natural gas, and coal). It is emitted mainly by motor vehicles. In humans and other animals, carbon monoxide displaces oxygen in the blood, forcing the heart and lungs to work harder. At high levels, CO can cause sensory impairment, decreased thinking ability, unconsciousness, and even death.

Nitrogen Oxides (NO_x)

The nitrogen oxides include NO and NO_2, emitted by motor vehicles, fossil fuel–based electricity generation plants, and any high-temperature combustion process occurring in air. Nitrogen dioxide is an orange-brown gas that causes the dark haze over polluted cities. Nitrogen oxides are eye and lung irritants and precursors of acid rain.

TABLE 7.6 ■ Changes in National Average Pollutant Levels, 1990–2016

Pollutant	Change (%) in Average Level
SO_2	−85
CO	−77
NO_2	−50
O_3	−22

Source: EPA's National Air Trends

Ozone (O_3)

Ozone is produced when some of the products of fossil fuel combustion, especially nitrogen oxides and unburned volatile organic compounds (VOCs), react in the presence of sunlight. The products of this reaction, which include ozone, are called *photochemical smog*. Ozone produced in this way—sometimes called ground-level ozone—should not be confused with upper atmospheric or *stratospheric* ozone. Although ozone is always the same molecule (O_3), stratospheric ozone is a natural part of our environment that protects Earth from harmful ultraviolet light. Stratospheric ozone does not harm humans because we are not directly exposed to it. Ground-level ozone, on the other hand, is a pollutant to which we are directly exposed; it is an eye and lung irritant, and prolonged exposure can cause permanent lung damage.

In the United States, the U.S. Environmental Protection Agency (EPA) has established limits on these pollutants. Beginning in the 1970s, the U.S. Congress passed the Clean Air Act and its amendments, requiring U.S. cities to reduce their pollution and maintain levels below the standards set by the EPA. As a result of this legislation, pollutant levels in U.S. cities have decreased over the last 30 years, even as the number of vehicles has increased. According to the EPA, the levels of the major pollutants in the air of U.S. cities decreased significantly during the period 1990–2016, as shown in Table 7.6.

Although the levels of pollutants (especially ozone) in some cities are still above what the EPA considers safe, real progress has been made. These trends demonstrate that legislation can improve our environment.

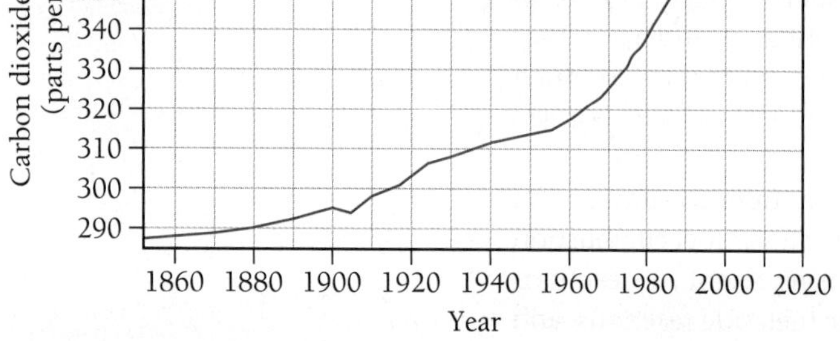

▲ **FIGURE 7.13 The Rise in Atmospheric Carbon Dioxide** Atmospheric carbon dioxide levels have been steadily increasing as a result of fossil fuel combustion. Source: Dr. Pieter Tans, NOAA/ESRL (www.esrl.noaa.gov/gmd/ccgg/trends/) and Dr. Ralph Keeling, Scripps Institution of Oceanography (www.scrippsco2.ucsd.edu/)

Global Climate Change

One of the main products of fossil fuel combustion is carbon dioxide. Carbon dioxide is a greenhouse gas; it allows visible light from the sun to enter Earth's atmosphere, but it prevents heat (in the form of infrared light) from escaping. In doing so, carbon dioxide acts as a blanket, keeping Earth warm, which, in moderation, is a very good thing and allows life as we know it to exist on our planet. However, because of fossil fuel combustion, carbon dioxide levels in the atmosphere have been steadily increasing, as shown in Figure 7.13◀. This increase is expected to change the global climate and further raise Earth's average temperature. Current observations suggest that Earth has already warmed by about 0.9 °C in the last century due to an approximately 38% increase in atmospheric carbon dioxide. Computer models suggest that the warming could worsen if carbon dioxide emissions are not curbed.

The possible effects of this warming include heightened storm severity, increasing numbers of floods and droughts, major shifts in agricultural zones, rising sea levels and coastal flooding, and profound changes in habitats that could result in the extinction of some plant and animal species.

EXAMPLE 7.13 Fossil Fuels and Climate Change

One way to evaluate fuels with respect to global warming is to determine how much heat they release during combustion relative to how much CO_2 they produce. The greater the heat relative to the amount of CO_2, the better the fuel. Use the combustion reactions of carbon, natural gas, and octane, in combination with the enthalpy of combustion for each reaction (all given earlier), to calculate the heat (in kJ) released by each fuel per 1.00 kg of CO_2 produced.

SORT You are given the mass of CO_2 emitted and asked to find the energy output for three different fuels.

GIVEN: 1.00 kg CO_2

FIND: kJ

STRATEGIZE First write the thermochemical equations for the combustion of each fuel given in Section 7.10.

$$C(s) + O_2(g) \longrightarrow CO_2(g) \qquad \Delta H^\circ_{rxn} = -393.5\ \text{kJ}$$

$$CH_4(g) + 2\,O_2(g) \longrightarrow CO_2(g) + 2\,H_2O(g) \qquad \Delta H^\circ_{rxn} = -802.3\ \text{kJ}$$

$$C_8H_{18}(l) + 25/2\,O_2(g) \longrightarrow 8\,CO_2(g) + 9\,H_2O(g) \qquad \Delta H^\circ_{rxn} = -5074.1\ \text{kJ}$$

The conceptual plan has two parts. In the first part, use the molar mass of CO_2 to convert from mass of CO_2 to moles of CO_2. This step is the same for each fuel.

CONCEPTUAL PLAN

In the second part, use the stoichiometric relationship between moles of CO_2 produced and kilojoules of energy released to calculate the energy output. Repeat the second part for each fuel using the appropriate stoichiometric relationship from the balanced equations.

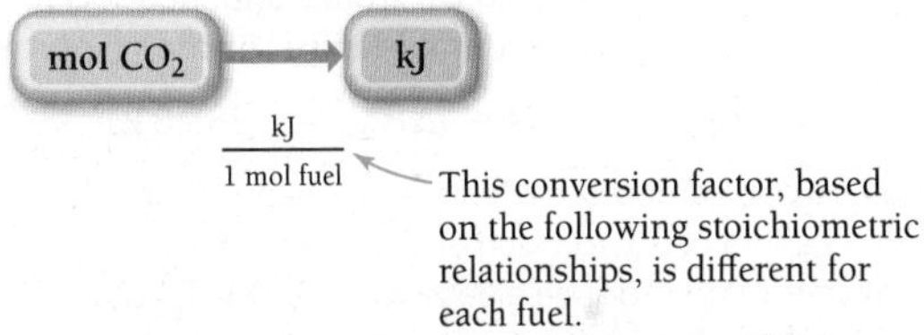

STOICHIOMETRIC RELATIONSHIPS

For C: 1 mol CO_2 : -393.5 kJ

For CH_4: 1 mol CO_2 : -802.3 kJ

For C_8H_{18}: 8 mol CO_2 : -5074.1 kJ

OTHER RELATIONSHIPS USED

1 kg = 1000 g

molar mass CO_2 = 44.01 g/mol

SOLVE Begin by converting kg CO_2 to mol CO_2.

SOLUTION

$$1.00\ \text{kg}\ CO_2 \times \frac{1000\ \text{g}}{1\ \text{kg}} \times \frac{1\ \text{mol}\ CO_2}{44.01\ \text{g}\ CO_2} = 22.\underline{7}2\ \text{mol}\ CO_2$$

Then, for each fuel, convert mol CO_2 to kJ.

$$\text{For C:}\quad 22.\underline{7}2\ \text{mol}\ CO_2 \times \frac{-393.5\ \text{kJ}}{1\ \text{mol}\ CO_2} = -8.94 \times 10^3\ \text{kJ}$$

$$\text{For } CH_4\text{:}\quad 22.\underline{7}2\ \text{mol}\ CO_2 \times \frac{-802.3\ \text{kJ}}{1\ \text{mol}\ CO_2} = -1.82 \times 10^4\ \text{kJ}$$

$$\text{For } C_8H_{18}\text{:}\quad 22.\underline{7}2\ \text{mol}\ CO_2 \times \frac{-5074.1\ \text{kJ}}{8\ \text{mol}\ CO_2} = -1.44 \times 10^4\ \text{kJ}$$

As you can see from the heat released in the production of 1 kg CO_2, natural gas, CH_4, provides the most energy per kg CO_2; therefore, it is the best fuel with respect to climate change.

CHECK Each answer is in kJ, as it should be for heat produced. Each answer is negative, as expected for exothermic combustion reactions.

FOR PRACTICE 7.13 What mass of CO_2 (in kilograms) does the combustion of a 15-gallon tank of gasoline release into the atmosphere? Assume the gasoline is pure octane (C_8H_{18}) and that it has a density of 0.70 g/mL.

CHEMISTRY IN THE ENVIRONMENT | Renewable Energy

Because of their finite supply and environmental impacts, fossil fuels will not be our major source of energy in the future. What will replace them? Although the answer is not clear, several alternative energy technologies are beginning to emerge. Unlike fossil fuels, these technologies are renewable, and we can use them indefinitely.

Our planet's greatest source of renewable energy is the sun. If we could capture and harness just a small fraction of the total sunlight falling on Earth, we could meet our energy needs several times over. The main problem with solar energy, however, is diffuseness—the sun's energy falls over an enormous area. How do we concentrate and store it? In California, some of the state's electricity is generated by parabolic troughs, solar power towers, and dish/engines.

These devices use reflective surfaces to focus the sun's energy and produce enough heat to generate electricity. Although the direct cost of generating electricity this way is higher than using fossil fuels, the benefits to the environment are obvious. In addition, with time, the costs are expected to fall.

Another way to capture the sun's energy is in chemical bonds. For example, solar energy could be used to drive the decomposition of water:

$$H_2O(l) \longrightarrow H_2(g) + \tfrac{1}{2}O_2(g) \quad \Delta H^\circ_{rxn} = +285.8 \text{ kJ}$$

The hydrogen gas produced could be stored until needed to provide energy by re-forming water in the reverse reaction:

$$H_2(g) + \tfrac{1}{2}O_2(g) \longrightarrow H_2O(l) \quad \Delta H^\circ_{rxn} = -285.8 \text{ kJ}$$

This reaction can be carried out in an electrochemical device called a fuel cell. In a fuel cell, hydrogen and oxygen gases combine to form water and produce electricity. In 2015, Toyota introduced the Mirai (which means *future* in Japanese), the first mass-produced fuel cell vehicle. The Mirai has a 300-mile range and produces 153 horsepower. Unlike most electric vehicles (such as the Tesla Model S), a fuel cell vehicle can be refueled instead of recharged. The refueling process only takes a few minutes (compared to recharging, which can take several hours). California has earmarked $200 million to build a "hydrogen highway," a series of 100 hydrogen refueling stations to be operational by 2020.

Other renewable energy sources are hydroelectric power and wind power. Hydroelectric power plants—which generate approximately 7% of U.S. electricity—harness the gravitational potential energy of water held behind a dam. Water is released at a controlled rate. As the released water falls, it acquires kinetic energy that is used to spin turbines, generating electricity. Wind power plants—which produce nearly 5% of U.S. electricity—consist of hundreds of turbines that are spun by the wind to generate electricity. Both of these technologies are cost competitive with fossil fuels, have no emissions, and are completely renewable.

Our energy future will probably involve a combination of these technologies and some new ones, combined with a focus on greater efficiency and conservation. One thing, however, is clear—the future of fossil fuels is limited.

▲ The Toyota Mirai, a fuel cell vehicle that runs on hydrogen gas and produces only water as exhaust.

▲ Wind turbines such as these generate nearly 5% of U.S. electricity.

Parabolic troughs

Solar power tower

Dish/engine

▲ The sun's energy, concentrated by reflective surfaces in various arrangements, can produce enough heat to generate electricity.

Self-Assessment Quiz

Q1. A chemical system produces 155 kJ of heat and does 22 kJ of work. What is ΔE for the *surroundings*?
MISSED THIS? *Read Section 7.2*

a) 177 kJ b) −177 kJ c) 133 kJ d) −133 kJ

Q2. Which sample is most likely to undergo the smallest change in temperature upon the absorption of 100 kJ of heat?
MISSED THIS? *Read Section 7.4; Watch KCV 7.4*

a) 15 g water b) 15 g lead c) 50 g water d) 50 g lead

Q3. How much heat must be absorbed by a 15.0-g sample of water to raise its temperature from 25.0 °C to 55.0 °C? (For water, $C_s = 4.18\ J/g \cdot °C$.)
MISSED THIS? *Read Section 7.4; Watch KCV 7.4, IWE 7.2*

a) 1.57 kJ b) 1.88 kJ c) 3.45 kJ d) 107 J

Q4. A 12.5-g sample of granite initially at 82.0 °C is immersed into 25.0 g of water initially at 22.0 °C. What is the final temperature of both substances when they reach thermal equilibrium? (For water, $C_s = 4.18\ J/g \cdot °C$ and for granite, $C_s = 0.790\ J/g \cdot °C$.)
MISSED THIS? *Read Section 7.4; Watch KCV 7.4, IWE 7.3*

a) 52.0 °C b) 1.55×10^3 °C c) 15.7 °C d) 27.2 °C

Q5. A cylinder with a moving piston expands from an initial volume of 0.250 L against an external pressure of 2.00 atm. The expansion does 288 J of work on the surroundings. What is the final volume of the cylinder?
MISSED THIS? *Read Section 7.4*

a) 1.42 L b) 1.17 L c) 144 L d) 1.67 L

Q6. When a 3.80-g sample of liquid octane (C_8H_{18}) is burned in a bomb calorimeter, the temperature of the calorimeter rises by 27.3 °C. The heat capacity of the calorimeter, measured in a separate experiment, is 7.18 kJ/°C. Determine the ΔE for octane combustion in units of kJ/mol octane.
MISSED THIS? *Read Section 7.5; Watch IWE 7.5*

a) -5.07×10^3 kJ/mol b) 5.07×10^3 kJ/mol
c) -44.4×10^3 kJ/mol d) -16.7×10^3 kJ/mol

Q7. Hydrogen gas reacts with oxygen to form water:

$$2\,H_2(g) + O_2(g) \longrightarrow 2\,H_2O(g) \qquad \Delta H = -483.5\ kJ$$

Determine the minimum mass of hydrogen gas required to produce 226 kJ of heat.
MISSED THIS? *Read Section 7.6; Watch KCV 7.6, IWE 7.7*

a) 8.63 g b) 1.88 g c) 0.942 g d) 0.935 g

Q8. Manganese reacts with hydrochloric acid to produce manganese(II) chloride and hydrogen gas:

$$Mn(s) + 2\,HCl(aq) \longrightarrow MnCl_2(aq) + H_2(g)$$

When 0.625 g Mn is combined with enough hydrochloric acid to make 100.0 mL of solution in a coffee-cup calorimeter, all of the Mn reacts, raising the temperature of the solution from 23.5 °C to 28.8 °C. Find ΔH_{rxn} for the reaction as written. (Assume that the specific heat capacity of the solution is 4.18 J/g·°C and the density is 1.00 g/mL.)
MISSED THIS? *Read Section 7.7; Watch IWE 7.8*

a) −195 kJ b) −3.54 kJ c) −1.22 kJ d) −2.21 kJ

Q9. Consider the reactions:

$$A \longrightarrow 2\,B \qquad \Delta H_1$$
$$A \longrightarrow 3\,C \qquad \Delta H_2$$

What is ΔH for the reaction $2\,B \longrightarrow 3\,C$?
MISSED THIS? *Read Section 7.8; Watch IWE 7.9*

a) $\Delta H_1 + \Delta H_2$ b) $\Delta H_1 - \Delta H_2$
c) $\Delta H_2 - \Delta H_1$ d) $2 \times (\Delta H_1 + \Delta H_2)$

Q10. Use standard enthalpies of formation to determine ΔH°_{rxn} for the reaction:

$$Fe_2O_3(s) + 3\,CO(g) \longrightarrow 2\,Fe(s) + 3\,CO(g)$$

MISSED THIS? *Read Section 7.9; Watch KCV 7.9, IWE 7.11*

a) −541.2 kJ b) −2336 kJ c) 541.2 kJ d) −24.8 kJ

Q11. Two substances, A and B, of equal mass but at different temperatures come into thermal contact. The specific heat capacity of substance A is twice the specific heat capacity of substance B. Which statement is true of the temperature of the two substances when they reach thermal equilibrium? (Assume no heat loss other than the thermal transfer between the substances.)
MISSED THIS? *Read Section 7.4; Watch KCV 7.4, IWE 7.3*

a) The final temperature of both substances is closer to the initial temperature of substance A than the initial temperature of substance B.
b) The final temperature of both substances is closer to the initial temperature of substance B than the initial temperature of substance A.
c) The final temperature of both substances is exactly midway between the initial temperatures of substance A and substance B.
d) The final temperature of substance B is greater than the final temperature of substance A.

Q12. Which process is endothermic?
MISSED THIS? *Read Section 7.6; Watch KCV 7.6*

a) the evaporation of water from the skin
b) the burning of candle wax
c) the oxidation of iron in a chemical hand warmer
d) the combustion of natural gas in a stove

Q13. Which fuel is not a fossil fuel?
MISSED THIS? *Read Section 7.10*

a) coal b) hydrogen
c) natural gas d) petroleum

Q14. The standard enthalpy of formation for glucose $[C_6H_{12}O_6(s)]$ is −1273.3 kJ/mol. What is the correct formation equation corresponding to this ΔH°_f?
MISSED THIS? *Read Section 7.9; Watch IWE 7.9*

a) $6\,C(s, \text{graphite}) + 6\,H_2O(g) \longrightarrow C_6H_{12}O_6(s, \text{glucose})$
b) $6\,C(s, \text{graphite}) + 6\,H_2O(l) \longrightarrow C_6H_{12}O_6(s, \text{glucose})$
c) $6\,C(s, \text{graphite}) + 6\,H_2(l) + 3\,O_2(l) \longrightarrow C_6H_{12}O_6(s, \text{glucose})$
d) $6\,C(s, \text{graphite}) + 6\,H_2(g) + 3\,O_2(g) \longrightarrow C_6H_{12}O_6(s, \text{glucose})$

Q15. Natural gas burns in air to form carbon dioxide and water, releasing heat.

$$CH_4(g) + O_2(g) \longrightarrow CO_2(g) + H_2O(g) \qquad \Delta H^\circ_{rxn} = -802.3\ kJ$$

What minimum mass of CH_4 is required to heat 55 g of water by 25 °C? (Assume 100% heating efficiency.)
MISSED THIS? *Read Sections 7.4, 7.6; KCV 7.4, 7.6, IWE 7.2, 7.7*

a) 0.115 g b) 2.25×10^3 g
c) 115 g d) 8.70 g

Answers: 1. (a) **2.** (c) **3.** (b) **4.** (d) **5.** (d) **6.** (a) **7.** (b) **8.** (a) **9.** (c) **10.** (d) **11.** (a) **12.** (a) **13.** (b) **14.** (d) **15.** (a)

CHAPTER 7 IN REVIEW

TERMS

Section 7.1
thermochemistry (264)

Section 7.2
energy (264)
work (264)
heat (264)
kinetic energy (264)
thermal energy (264)
potential energy (264)
chemical energy (264)
law of conservation of energy (265)
system (265)
surroundings (265)
joule (J) (266)
calorie (cal) (266)
Calorie (Cal) (266)
kilowatt-hour (kWh) (266)

Section 7.3
thermodynamics (267)
first law of thermodynamics (267)
internal energy (E) (267)
state function (267)

Section 7.4
thermal equilibrium (272)
heat capacity (C) (273)
specific heat capacity (C_s) (273)
molar heat capacity (273)
pressure–volume work (276)

Section 7.5
calorimetry (279)
bomb calorimeter (279)

Section 7.6
enthalpy (H) (281)
endothermic reaction (281)
exothermic reaction (282)
enthalpy (heat) of reaction (ΔH_{rxn}) (283)

Section 7.7
coffee-cup calorimeter (285)

Section 7.8
Hess's law (287)

Section 7.9
standard state (289)
standard enthalpy change ($\Delta H°$) (289)
standard enthalpy of formation ($\Delta H_f°$) (289)
standard heat of formation (289)

CONCEPTS

The Nature of Energy and Thermodynamics (7.2, 7.3)

- Energy, which is measured in the SI unit of joules (J), is the capacity to do work.
- Work is the result of a force acting through a distance.
- Many different kinds of energy exist, including kinetic energy, thermal energy, potential energy, and chemical energy, a type of potential energy associated with the relative positions of electrons and nuclei in atoms and molecules.
- The first law of thermodynamics states that energy can be converted from one form to another, but the total amount of energy is always conserved.
- The internal energy (E) of a system is the sum of all of its kinetic and potential energy. Internal energy is a state function, which means that it depends only on the state of the system and not on the pathway by which it got to that state.
- A chemical system exchanges energy with its surroundings through heat (the transfer of thermal energy caused by a temperature difference) or work. The total change in internal energy is the sum of these two quantities.

Heat and Work (7.4)

- We quantify heat with the equation $q = m \times C_s \times \Delta T$. In this expression, C_s is the specific heat capacity, the amount of heat required to change the temperature of 1 g of the substance by 1 °C. Compared to most substances, water has a very high heat capacity—it takes a lot of heat to change its temperature.
- The type of work most characteristic of chemical reactions is pressure–volume work, which occurs when a gas expands against an external pressure. Pressure–volume work can be quantified with the equation $w = -P_{ext}\Delta V$.
- The change in internal energy (ΔE) that occurs during a chemical reaction is the sum of the heat (q) exchanged and the work (w) done: $\Delta E = q + w$.

Enthalpy (7.6)

- The heat evolved in a chemical reaction occurring at constant pressure is the change in enthalpy (ΔH) for the reaction. Like internal energy, enthalpy is a state function.
- An endothermic reaction has a positive enthalpy of reaction; an exothermic reaction has a negative enthalpy of reaction.
- We can use the enthalpy of reaction to stoichiometrically determine the heat evolved when a specific amount of reactant reacts.

Calorimetry (7.5, 7.7)

- Calorimetry is a method of measuring ΔE or ΔH for a reaction.
- In bomb calorimetry, the reaction is carried out under conditions of constant volume, so $\Delta E = q_V$. We can therefore use the temperature change of the calorimeter to calculate ΔE for the reaction.
- When a reaction takes place at constant pressure, energy may be released both as heat and as work.
- In coffee-cup calorimetry, a reaction is carried out under atmospheric pressure in a solution, so $q = \Delta H$. We use the temperature change of the solution to calculate ΔH for the reaction.

Calculating ΔH_{rxn} (7.8, 7.9)

- We can calculate the enthalpy of reaction (ΔH_{rxn}) from known thermochemical data using the following relationships: (a) when a reaction is multiplied by a factor, ΔH_{rxn} is multiplied by the same factor; (b) when a reaction is reversed, ΔH_{rxn} changes sign; and (c) if a chemical reaction can be expressed as a sum of two or more steps, ΔH_{rxn} is the sum of the ΔH's for the individual steps (Hess's law). We can use these relationships to determine the enthalpy change of an unknown reaction from reactions with known enthalpy changes.
- A second method to calculate ΔH_{rxn} from known thermochemical data involves using tabulated standard enthalpies of formation for the reactants and products of the reaction. These are usually tabulated for substances in their standard states, and the enthalpy of reaction is called the standard enthalpy of reaction ($\Delta H°_{rxn}$). For any reaction, we obtain $\Delta H°_{rxn}$ by subtracting the sum of the enthalpies of formation of the reactants multiplied by their stoichiometric coefficients from the sum of the enthalpies of formation of the products multiplied by their stoichiometric coefficients.

Environmental Problems Associated with Fossil Fuel Use (7.10)

- Fossil fuels are nonrenewable fuels; once humans consume them, they cannot be replaced.
- At current rates of consumption, natural gas and petroleum reserves will be depleted in 50–100 years.
- In addition to their limited supply, the products of the combustion of fossil fuels—directly or indirectly formed—contribute to environmental problems including air pollution, acid rain, and global climate change, which involves an increase in Earth's average temperature caused by CO_2 emission.

EQUATIONS AND RELATIONSHIPS

Kinetic Energy (**7.2**)

$$KE = \frac{1}{2}mv^2$$

Change in Internal Energy (ΔE) of a Chemical System (**7.3**)

$$\Delta E = E_{products} - E_{reactants}$$

Energy Flow between System and Surroundings (**7.3**)

$$\Delta E_{system} = -\Delta E_{surroundings}$$

Relationship between Internal Energy (ΔE), Heat (q), and Work (w) (**7.3**)

$$\Delta E = q + w$$

Relationship between Heat (q), Temperature (T), and Heat Capacity (C) (**7.4**)

$$q = C \times \Delta T$$

Relationship between Heat (q), Mass (m), Temperature (T), and Specific Heat Capacity of a Substance (C_s) (**7.4**)

$$q = m \times C_s \times \Delta T$$

Relationship between Work (w), Force (F), and Distance (D) (**7.4**)

$$w = F \times D$$

Relationship between Work (w), Pressure (P), and Change in Volume (ΔV) (**7.4**)

$$w = -P_{ext}\,\Delta V$$

Change in Internal Energy (ΔE) of System at Constant Volume (**7.5**)

$$\Delta E = q_v$$

Heat of a Bomb Calorimeter (q_{cal}) (**7.5**)

$$q_{cal} = C_{cal} \times \Delta T$$

Heat Exchange between a Calorimeter and a Reaction (**7.5**)

$$q_{cal} = -q_{rxn}$$

Relationship between Enthalpy (ΔH), Internal Energy (ΔE), Pressure (P), and Volume (V) (**7.6**)

$$\Delta H = \Delta E + P\Delta V$$

$$\Delta H = q_p$$

Relationship between Enthalpy of a Reaction (ΔH°_{rxn}) and the Heats of Formation (ΔH°_f) (**7.9**)

$$\Delta H^\circ_{rxn} = \sum n_p \Delta H^\circ_f(\text{products}) - \sum n_r \Delta H^\circ_f(\text{reactants})$$

LEARNING OUTCOMES

Chapter Objectives	Assessment
Analyze types of energy and convert between energy units (**7.2**)	**Exercises** 33–36
Analyze changes in internal energy in terms of heat and work (**7.3**)	Example 7.1 **For Practice** 7.1 **Exercises** 37–44
Determine heat from temperature changes (**7.4**)	Example 7.2 **For Practice** 7.2 **For More Practice** 7.2 **Exercises** 45–50
Calculate quantities in thermal energy transfer (**7.4**)	Example 7.3 **For Practice** 7.3 **Exercises** 65–70
Analyze processes involving pressure–volume work (**7.4**)	Example 7.4 **For Practice** 7.4 **For More Practice** 7.4 **Exercises** 51–54
Analyze energy changes for combustion reactions inside a bomb calorimeter (**7.5**)	Example 7.5 **For Practice** 7.5 **For More Practice** 7.5 **Exercises** 73–74
Predict endothermic and exothermic processes (**7.6**)	Example 7.6 **For Practice** 7.6 **Exercises** 55–58
Perform stoichiometric calculations involving the enthalpy of reaction (**7.6**)	Example 7.7 **For Practice** 7.7 **For More Practice** 7.7 **Exercises** 59–64
Analyze enthalpy changes for reactions in a coffee-cup calorimeter (**7.7**)	Example 7.8 **For Practice** 7.8 **Exercises** 71–72, 75–76
Analyze how changes in chemical reactions affect the enthalpy of reaction (**7.8**)	Example 7.9 **For Practice** 7.9 **For More Practice** 7.9 **Exercises** 77–82
Determine the standard enthalpy change for a reaction using standard enthalpies of formation (**7.9**)	Examples 7.10, 7.11, 7.12 **For Practice** 7.10, 7.11, 7.12 **Exercises** 83–92
Analyze the effects of energy use on the environment (**7.10**)	Example 7.13 **For Practice** 7.13 **Exercises** 93–96

EXERCISES

Mastering Chemistry provides end-of-chapter exercises, feedback-enriched tutorial problems, animations, and interactive activities to encourage problem-solving practice and deeper understanding of key concepts and topics.

REVIEW QUESTIONS

1. What is thermochemistry? Why is it important?
2. What is energy? What is work? List some examples of each.
3. What is kinetic energy? What is potential energy? List some examples of each.
4. State the law of conservation of energy. How does it relate to energy exchanges between a thermodynamic system and its surroundings?
5. What is the SI unit of energy? List some other common units of energy.
6. State the first law of thermodynamics. What are its implications?
7. A friend claims to have constructed a machine that creates electricity but requires no energy input. Explain why you should be suspicious of your friend's claim.
8. What is a state function? List some examples of state functions.
9. What is internal energy? Is internal energy a state function?
10. If energy flows out of a chemical system and into the surroundings, what is the sign of ΔE_{system}?
11. If the internal energy of the products of a reaction is higher than the internal energy of the reactants, what is the sign of ΔE for the reaction? In which direction does energy flow?
12. What is heat? Explain the difference between heat and temperature.
13. How is the change in internal energy of a system related to heat and work?
14. Explain how the sum of heat and work can be a state function, even though heat and work are themselves not state functions.
15. What is heat capacity? Explain the difference between heat capacity and specific heat capacity.
16. Explain how the high specific heat capacity of water can affect the weather in coastal regions.
17. If two objects, A and B, of different temperature come into direct contact, what is the relationship between the heat lost by one object and the heat gained by the other? What is the relationship between the temperature changes of the two objects? (Assume that the two objects do not lose any heat to anything else.)
18. What is pressure–volume work? How is it calculated?
19. What is calorimetry? Explain the difference between a coffee-cup calorimeter and a bomb calorimeter. What is each designed to measure?
20. What is the change in enthalpy (ΔH) for a chemical reaction? How is ΔH different from ΔE?
21. Explain the difference between an exothermic and an endothermic reaction. Give the sign of ΔH for each type of reaction.
22. From a molecular viewpoint, where does the energy emitted in an exothermic chemical reaction come from? Why does the reaction mixture undergo an increase in temperature even though energy is emitted?
23. From a molecular viewpoint, where does the energy absorbed in an endothermic chemical reaction go? Why does the reaction mixture undergo a decrease in temperature even though energy is absorbed?
24. Is the change in enthalpy for a reaction an extensive property? Explain the relationship between ΔH for a reaction and the amounts of reactants and products that undergo reaction.
25. Explain how the value of ΔH for a reaction changes upon each operation.
    a. multiplying the reaction by a factor
    b. reversing the reaction

    Why do these relationships hold?
26. What is Hess's law? Why is it useful?
27. What is a standard state? What is the standard enthalpy change for a reaction?
28. What is the standard enthalpy of formation for a compound? For a pure element in its standard state?
29. How do you calculate ΔH°_{rxn} from tabulated standard enthalpies of formation?
30. What are the main sources of the energy consumed in the United States?
31. What are the main environmental problems associated with fossil fuel use?
32. Explain global climate change. What causes global warming? What is the evidence that global warming is occurring?

PROBLEMS BY TOPIC

Energy Units

33. Convert between energy units.
    MISSED THIS? *Read Section 7.2*
    a. 534 kWh to J
    b. 215 kJ to Cal
    c. 567 Cal to J
    d. 2.85×10^3 J to cal
34. Convert between energy units.
    a. 231 cal to kJ
    b. 132×10^4 kJ to kcal
    c. 4.99×10^3 kJ to kWh
    d. 2.88×10^4 J to Cal
35. Suppose that a person eats 2387 Calories per day. Convert this amount of energy into each unit.
    MISSED THIS? *Read Section 7.2*
    a. J
    b. kJ
    c. kWh
36. A particular frost-free refrigerator uses about 745 kWh of electrical energy per year. Express this amount of energy in each unit.
    a. J
    b. kJ
    c. Cal

Internal Energy, Heat, and Work

37. Which statement is true of the internal energy of a system and its surroundings during an energy exchange with a negative ΔE_{sys}?
MISSED THIS? *Read Section 7.3; Watch KCV 7.3*
a. The internal energy of the system increases and the internal energy of the surroundings decreases.
b. The internal energy of both the system and the surroundings increases.
c. The internal energy of both the system and the surroundings decreases.
d. The internal energy of the system decreases and the internal energy of the surroundings increases.

38. During an energy exchange, a chemical system absorbs energy from its surroundings. What is the sign of ΔE_{sys} for this process? Explain.

39. Identify each energy exchange as primarily heat or work and determine whether the sign of ΔE is positive or negative for the system.
MISSED THIS? *Read Section 7.3; Watch KCV 7.3*
a. Sweat evaporates from skin, cooling the skin. (The evaporating sweat is the system.)
b. A balloon expands against an external pressure. (The contents of the balloon is the system.)
c. An aqueous chemical reaction mixture is warmed with an external flame. (The reaction mixture is the system.)

40. Identify each energy exchange as primarily heat or work and determine whether the sign of ΔE is positive or negative for the system.
a. A rolling billiard ball collides with another billiard ball. The first billiard ball (defined as the system) stops rolling after the collision.
b. A book falls to the floor. (The book is the system.)
c. A father pushes his daughter on a swing. (The daughter and the swing are the system.)

41. A system releases 622 kJ of heat and does 105 kJ of work on the surroundings. What is the change in internal energy of the system?
MISSED THIS? *Read Section 7.3*

42. A system absorbs 196 kJ of heat, and the surroundings do 117 kJ of work on the system. What is the change in internal energy of the system?

43. The gas in a piston (defined as the system) warms and absorbs 655 J of heat. The expansion performs 344 J of work on the surroundings. What is the change in internal energy for the system? **MISSED THIS?** *Read Section 7.3*

44. The air in an inflated balloon (defined as the system) warms over a toaster and absorbs 115 J of heat. As it expands, it does 77 kJ of work. What is the change in internal energy for the system?

Heat, Heat Capacity, and Work

45. We pack two identical coolers for a picnic, placing 24 12-ounce soft drinks and five pounds of ice in each. However, the drinks that we put into cooler A were refrigerated for several hours before they were packed in the cooler, while the drinks that we put into cooler B were at room temperature. When we open the two coolers three hours later, most of the ice in cooler A is still present, while nearly all of the ice in cooler B has melted. Explain this difference.
MISSED THIS? *Read Section 7.4; Watch KCV 7.4*

46. A kilogram of aluminum metal and a kilogram of water are each warmed to 75 °C and placed in two identical insulated containers. One hour later, the two containers are opened, and the temperature of each substance is measured. The aluminum has cooled to 35 °C, while the water has cooled only to 66 °C. Explain this difference.

47. How much heat is required to warm 1.50 L of water from 25.0 °C to 100.0 °C? (Assume a density of 1.0 g/mL for the water.)
MISSED THIS? *Read Section 7.3; Watch KCV 7.3, IWE 7.2*

48. How much heat is required to warm 1.50 kg of sand from 25.0 °C to 100.0 °C?

49. Suppose that 25 g of each substance is initially at 27.0 °C. What is the final temperature of each substance upon absorbing 2.35 kJ of heat?
MISSED THIS? *Read Section 7.3; Watch KCV 7.3, IWE 7.2*
a. gold b. silver c. aluminum d. water

50. An unknown mass of each substance, initially at 23.0 °C, absorbs 1.95×10^3 J of heat. The final temperature is recorded. Find the mass of each substance.
a. Pyrex glass ($T_f = 55.4$ °C)
b. sand ($T_f = 62.1$ °C)
c. ethanol ($T_f = 44.2$ °C)
d. water ($T_f = 32.4$ °C)

51. How much work (in J) is required to expand the volume of a pump from 0.0 L to 2.5 L against an external pressure of 1.1 atm?
MISSED THIS? *Read Section 7.4*

52. The average human lung expands by about 0.50 L during each breath. If this expansion occurs against an external pressure of 1.0 atm, how much work (in J) is done during the expansion?

53. The air within a piston equipped with a cylinder absorbs 565 J of heat and expands from an initial volume of 0.10 L to a final volume of 0.85 L against an external pressure of 1.0 atm. What is the change in internal energy of the air within the piston?
MISSED THIS? *Read Section 7.4*

54. A gas is compressed from an initial volume of 5.55 L to a final volume of 1.22 L by an external pressure of 1.00 atm. During the compression the gas releases 124 J of heat. What is the change in internal energy of the gas?

Enthalpy and Thermochemical Stoichiometry

55. When 1 mol of a fuel burns at constant pressure, it produces 3452 kJ of heat and does 11 kJ of work. What are ΔE and ΔH for the combustion of the fuel? **MISSED THIS?** *Read Section 7.6*

56. The change in internal energy for the combustion of 1.0 mol of octane at a pressure of 1.0 atm is 5084.3 kJ. If the change in enthalpy is 5074.1 kJ, how much work is done during the combustion?

57. Determine whether each process is exothermic or endothermic and indicate the sign of ΔH.
MISSED THIS? *Read Section 7.6; Watch KCV 7.6*
a. natural gas burning on a stove
b. isopropyl alcohol evaporating from skin
c. water condensing from steam

58. Determine whether each process is exothermic or endothermic and indicate the sign of ΔH.
a. dry ice evaporating
b. a sparkler burning
c. the reaction that occurs in a chemical cold pack used to ice athletic injuries

59. Consider the thermochemical equation for the combustion of acetone (C_3H_6O), the main ingredient in nail polish remover:

$$C_3H_6O(l) + 4\,O_2(g) \longrightarrow 3\,CO_2(g) + 3\,H_2O(g) \qquad \Delta H^\circ_{rxn} = -1790\text{ kJ}$$

If a bottle of nail polish remover contains 177 mL of acetone, how much heat is released by its complete combustion? The density of acetone is 0.788 g/mL.
MISSED THIS? *Read Section 7.6; Watch IWE 7.7*

60. What mass of natural gas (CH_4) must burn to emit 267 kJ of heat?

$$CH_4(g) + 2\,O_2(g) \longrightarrow CO_2(g) + 2\,H_2O(g) \qquad \Delta H^\circ_{rxn} = -802.3\text{ kJ}$$

61. Nitromethane (CH_3NO_2) burns in air to produce significant amounts of heat.

$$2\,CH_3NO_2(l) + {}^3/_2\,O_2(g) \longrightarrow 2\,CO_2(g) + 3\,H_2O(l) + N_2(g) \qquad \Delta H^\circ_{rxn} = -1418\text{ kJ}$$

How much heat is produced by the complete reaction of 5.56 kg of nitromethane?
MISSED THIS? *Read Section 7.6; Watch IWE 7.7*

62. Titanium reacts with iodine to form titanium(III) iodide, emitting heat.

$$2\,Ti(s) + 3\,I_2(g) \longrightarrow 2\,TiI_3(s) \qquad \Delta H^\circ_{rxn} = -839\text{ kJ}$$

Determine the masses of titanium and iodine that react if 1.55×10^3 kJ of heat is emitted by the reaction.

63. The propane fuel (C_3H_8) used in gas barbeques burns according to the thermochemical equation:

$$C_3H_8(g) + 5\,O_2(g) \longrightarrow 3\,CO_2(g) + 4\,H_2O(g) \qquad \Delta H^\circ_{rxn} = -2044\text{ kJ}$$

If a pork roast must absorb 1.6×10^3 kJ to fully cook, and if only 10% of the heat produced by the barbeque is actually absorbed by the roast, what mass of CO_2 is emitted into the atmosphere during the grilling of the pork roast?
MISSED THIS? *Read Section 7.6; Watch IWE 7.7*

64. Charcoal is primarily carbon. Determine the mass of CO_2 produced by burning enough carbon (in the form of charcoal) to produce 5.00×10^2 kJ of heat.

$$C(s) + O_2(g) \longrightarrow CO_2(g) \qquad \Delta H^\circ_{rxn} = -393.5\text{ kJ}$$

Thermal Energy Transfer

65. A silver block, initially at 58.5 °C, is submerged into 100.0 g of water at 24.8 °C, in an insulated container. The final temperature of the mixture upon reaching thermal equilibrium is 26.2 °C. What is the mass of the silver block?
MISSED THIS? *Read Section 7.4; Watch KCV 7.4, IWE 7.3*

66. A 32.5-g iron rod, initially at 22.7 °C, is submerged into an unknown mass of water at 63.2 °C, in an insulated container. The final temperature of the mixture upon reaching thermal equilibrium is 59.5 °C. What is the mass of the water?

67. A 31.1-g wafer of pure gold, initially at 69.3 °C, is submerged into 64.2 g of water at 27.8 °C in an insulated container. What is the final temperature of both substances at thermal equilibrium?
MISSED THIS? *Read Section 7.4; Watch KCV 7.4, IWE 7.3*

68. A 2.85-g lead weight, initially at 10.3 °C, is submerged in 7.55 g of water at 52.3 °C in an insulated container. What is the final temperature of both substances at thermal equilibrium?

69. Two substances, A and B, initially at different temperatures, come into contact and reach thermal equilibrium. The mass of substance A is 6.15 g and its initial temperature is 20.5 °C. The mass of substance B is 25.2 g and its initial temperature is 52.7 °C. The final temperature of both substances at thermal equilibrium is 46.7 °C. If the specific heat capacity of substance B is 1.17 J/g·°C, what is the specific heat capacity of substance A?
MISSED THIS? *Read Section 7.4; Watch KCV 7.4, IWE 7.3*

70. A 2.74-g sample of a substance suspected of being pure gold is warmed to 72.1 °C and submerged into 15.2 g of water initially at 24.7 °C. The final temperature of the mixture is 26.3 °C. What is the heat capacity of the unknown substance? Could the substance be pure gold?

Calorimetry

71. Exactly 1.5 g of a fuel burns under conditions of constant pressure and then again under conditions of constant volume. In measurement A the reaction produces 25.9 kJ of heat, and in measurement B the reaction produces 23.3 kJ of heat. Which measurement (A or B) corresponds to conditions of constant pressure? Which one corresponds to conditions of constant volume? Explain.
MISSED THIS? *Read Section 7.6*

72. In order to obtain the largest possible amount of heat from a chemical reaction in which there is a large increase in the number of moles of gas, should you carry out the reaction under conditions of constant volume or constant pressure? Explain.

73. When 0.514 g of biphenyl ($C_{12}H_{10}$) undergoes combustion in a bomb calorimeter, the temperature rises from 25.8 °C to 29.4 °C. Find ΔE_{rxn} for the combustion of biphenyl in kJ/mol biphenyl. The heat capacity of the bomb calorimeter, determined in a separate experiment, is 5.86 kJ/°C.
MISSED THIS? *Read Section 7.5; Watch IWE 7.5*

74. Mothballs are composed primarily of the hydrocarbon naphthalene ($C_{10}H_8$). When 1.025 g of naphthalene burns in a bomb calorimeter, the temperature rises from 24.25 °C to 32.33 °C. Find ΔE_{rxn} for the combustion of naphthalene. The heat capacity of the bomb calorimeter, determined in a separate experiment, is 5.11 kJ/°C.

75. Zinc metal reacts with hydrochloric acid according to the balanced equation:

$$Zn(s) + 2\,HCl(aq) \longrightarrow ZnCl_2(aq) + H_2(g)$$

When 0.103 g of Zn(s) is combined with enough HCl to make 50.0 mL of solution in a coffee-cup calorimeter, all of the zinc reacts, raising the temperature of the solution from 22.5 °C to 23.7 °C. Find ΔH_{rxn} for this reaction as written. (Use 1.0 g/mL for the density of the solution and 4.18 J/g·°C as the specific heat capacity.)
MISSED THIS? *Read Section 7.7; Watch IWE 7.8*

76. Instant cold packs used to ice athletic injuries on the field contain ammonium nitrate and water separated by a thin plastic divider. When the divider is broken, the ammonium nitrate dissolves according to the endothermic reaction:

$$NH_4NO_3(s) \longrightarrow NH_4^+(aq) + NO_3^-(aq)$$

In order to measure the enthalpy change for this reaction, 1.25 g of NH_4NO_3 is dissolved in enough water to make 25.0 mL of solution. The initial temperature is 25.8 °C and the final temperature (after the solid dissolves) is 21.9 °C. Calculate the change in enthalpy for the reaction in kJ. (Use 1.0 g/mL as the density of the solution and 4.18 J/g·°C as the specific heat capacity.)

Quantitative Relationships Involving ΔH and Hess's Law

77. For each generic reaction, determine the value of ΔH_2 in terms of ΔH_1. **MISSED THIS?** *Read Section 7.8*

a. $A + B \longrightarrow 2\,C \qquad \Delta H_1$
$2\,C \longrightarrow A + B \qquad \Delta H_2 = ?$

b. $A + {}^1/_2\,B \longrightarrow C \qquad \Delta H_1$
$2\,A + B \longrightarrow 2\,C \qquad \Delta H_2 = ?$

c. $A \longrightarrow B + 2\,C \qquad \Delta H_1$
${}^1/_2\,B + C \longrightarrow {}^1/_2\,A \qquad \Delta H_2 = ?$

78. Consider the generic reaction:

$$A + 2\,B \longrightarrow C + 3\,D \qquad \Delta H = 155\ \text{kJ}$$

Determine the value of ΔH for each related reaction.

a. $3\,A + 6\,B \longrightarrow 3\,C + 9\,D$ b. $C + 3\,D \longrightarrow A + 2\,B$

c. $\frac{1}{2}C + \frac{3}{2}D \longrightarrow \frac{1}{2}A + B$

79. Calculate ΔH_{rxn} for the reaction:

$$Fe_2O_3(s) + 3\,CO(g) \longrightarrow 2\,Fe(s) + 3\,CO_2(g)$$

Use the following reactions and given ΔH's:

$2\,Fe(s) + \frac{3}{2}O_2(g) \longrightarrow Fe_2O_3(s) \quad \Delta H = -824.2\ \text{kJ}$

$CO(g) + \frac{1}{2}O_2(g) \longrightarrow CO_2(g) \quad \Delta H = -282.7\ \text{kJ}$

MISSED THIS? *Read Section 7.8; Watch IWE 7.9*

80. Calculate ΔH_{rxn} for the reaction:

$$CaO(s) + CO_2(g) \longrightarrow CaCO_3(s)$$

Use the following reactions and given ΔH's:

$Ca(s) + CO_2(g) + \frac{1}{2}O_2(g) \longrightarrow CaCO_3(s) \quad \Delta H = -812.8\ \text{kJ}$

$2\,Ca(s) + O_2(g) \longrightarrow 2\,CaO(s) \quad \Delta H = -1269.8\ \text{kJ}$

81. Calculate ΔH_{rxn} for the reaction:

$$5\,C(s) + 6\,H_2(g) \longrightarrow C_5H_{12}(l)$$

Use the following reactions and given ΔH's:

$C_5H_{12}(l) + 8\,O_2(g) \longrightarrow 5\,CO_2(g) + 6\,H_2O(g) \quad \Delta H = -3244.8\ \text{kJ}$

$C(s) + O_2(g) \longrightarrow CO_2(g) \quad \Delta H = -393.5\ \text{kJ}$

$2\,H_2(g) + O_2(g) \longrightarrow 2\,H_2O(g) \quad \Delta H = -483.5\ \text{kJ}$

MISSED THIS? *Read Section 7.8; Watch IWE 7.9*

82. Calculate ΔH_{rxn} for the reaction:

$$CH_4(g) + 4\,Cl_2(g) \longrightarrow CCl_4(g) + 4\,HCl(g)$$

Use the following reactions and given ΔH's:

$C(s) + 2\,H_2(g) \longrightarrow CH_4(g) \quad \Delta H = -74.4\ \text{kJ}$

$C(s) + 2\,Cl_2(g) \longrightarrow CCl_4(g) \quad \Delta H = -95.7\ \text{kJ}$

$H_2(g) + Cl_2(g) \longrightarrow 2\,HCl(g) \quad \Delta H = -92.3\ \text{kJ}$

Enthalpies of Formation and ΔH

83. Write an equation for the formation of each compound from its elements in their standard states, and find ΔH_f° for each in Appendix IIB. **MISSED THIS?** *Read Section 7.9*

a. $NH_3(g)$ b. $CO_2(g)$ c. $Fe_2O_3(s)$ d. $CH_4(g)$

84. Write an equation for the formation of each compound from its elements in their standard states, and find ΔH°_{rxn} for each in Appendix IIB.

a. $NO_2(g)$ b. $MgCO_3(s)$ c. $C_2H_4(g)$ d. $CH_3OH(l)$

85. Hydrazine (N_2H_4) is a fuel used by some spacecraft. It is normally oxidized by N_2O_4 according to the equation:

$$N_2H_4(l) + N_2O_4(g) \longrightarrow 2\,N_2O(g) + 2\,H_2O(g)$$

Calculate ΔH°_{rxn} for this reaction using standard enthalpies of formation.

MISSED THIS? *Read Section 7.9; Watch KCV 7.9, IWE 7.11*

86. Pentane (C_5H_{12}) is a component of gasoline that burns according to the following balanced equation:

$$C_5H_{12}(l) + 8\,O_2(g) \longrightarrow 5\,CO_2(g) + 6\,H_2O(g)$$

Calculate ΔH°_{rxn} for this reaction using standard enthalpies of formation. (The standard enthalpy of formation of liquid pentane is -146.8 kJ/mol.)

87. Use standard enthalpies of formation to calculate ΔH°_{rxn} for each reaction.

MISSED THIS? *Read Section 7.9; Watch KCV 7.9, IWE 7.11*

a. $C_2H_4(g) + H_2(g) \longrightarrow C_2H_6(g)$

b. $CO(g) + H_2O(g) \longrightarrow H_2(g) + CO_2(g)$

c. $3\,NO_2(g) + H_2O(l) \longrightarrow 2\,HNO_3(aq) + NO(g)$

d. $Cr_2O_3(s) + 3\,CO(g) \longrightarrow 2\,Cr(s) + 3\,CO_2(g)$

88. Use standard enthalpies of formation to calculate ΔH°_{rxn} for each reaction.

a. $2\,H_2S(g) + 3\,O_2(g) \longrightarrow 2\,H_2O(l) + 2\,SO_2(g)$

b. $SO_2(g) + \frac{1}{2}O_2(g) \longrightarrow SO_3(g)$

c. $C(s) + H_2O(g) \longrightarrow CO(g) + H_2(g)$

d. $N_2O_4(g) + 4\,H_2(g) \longrightarrow N_2(g) + 4\,H_2O(g)$

89. During photosynthesis, plants use energy from sunlight to form glucose ($C_6H_{12}O_6$) and oxygen from carbon dioxide and water. Write a balanced equation for photosynthesis and calculate ΔH°_{rxn}.

MISSED THIS? *Read Section 7.9; Watch KCV 7.9, IWE 7.11*

90. Ethanol (C_2H_5OH) can be made from the fermentation of crops and has been used as a fuel additive to gasoline. Write a balanced equation for the combustion of ethanol and calculate ΔH°_{rxn}.

91. Top fuel dragsters and funny cars burn nitromethane as fuel according to the balanced combustion equation:

$$2\,CH_3NO_2(l) + \tfrac{3}{2}O_2(g) \longrightarrow 2\,CO_2(g) + 3\,H_2O(l) + N_2(g)$$

$$\Delta H^\circ_{rxn} = -1418\ \text{kJ}$$

Calculate the standard enthalpy of formation (ΔH_f°) for nitromethane.

MISSED THIS? *Read Section 7.9; Watch KCV 7.9, IWE 7.11*

92. The explosive nitroglycerin ($C_3H_5N_3O_9$) decomposes rapidly upon ignition or sudden impact according to the balanced equation:

$$4\,C_3H_5N_3O_9(l) \longrightarrow 12\,CO_2(g) + 10\,H_2O(g) + 6\,N_2(g) + O_2(g)$$

$$\Delta H^\circ_{rxn} = -5678\ \text{kJ}$$

Calculate the standard enthalpy of formation (ΔH_f°) for nitroglycerin.

Energy Use and the Environment

93. Determine the mass of CO_2 produced by burning enough of each fuel to produce 1.00×10^2 kJ of heat. Which fuel contributes least to global warming per kJ of heat produced?

MISSED THIS? *Read Sections 7.4, 7.6; KCV 7.4, 7.6, IWE 7.2, 7.7*

a. $CH_4(g) + 2\,O_2(g) \longrightarrow CO_2(g) + 2\,H_2O(g) \quad \Delta H^\circ_{rxn} = -802.3\ \text{kJ}$

b. $C_3H_8(g) + 5\,O_2(g) \longrightarrow 3\,CO_2(g) + 4\,H_2O(g) \quad \Delta H^\circ_{rxn} = -2043\ \text{kJ}$

c. $C_8H_{18}(l) + \frac{25}{2}O_2(g) \longrightarrow 8\,CO_2(g) + 9\,H_2O(g) \quad \Delta H^\circ_{rxn} = -5074.1\ \text{kJ}$

94. Methanol (CH_3OH) has been suggested as a fuel to replace gasoline. Write a balanced equation for the combustion of methanol, find ΔH°_{rxn}, and determine the mass of carbon dioxide emitted per kJ of heat produced. Use the information from the previous exercise to calculate the same quantity for octane, C_8H_{18}. How does methanol compare to octane with respect to global warming?

95. The citizens of the world burn the fossil fuel equivalent of 7×10^{12} kg of petroleum per year. Assume that all of this petroleum is in the form of octane (C_8H_{18}) and calculate how much CO_2 (in kg) the world produces from fossil fuel combustion per year. (*Hint:* Begin by writing a balanced equation for the combustion of octane.) If the atmosphere currently contains approximately 3×10^{15} kg of CO_2, how long will it take for the world's fossil fuel combustion to double the amount of atmospheric carbon dioxide?

MISSED THIS? *Read Sections 7.4, 7.6; KCV 7.4, 7.6, IWE 7.2, 7.7*

96. In a sunny location, sunlight has a power density of about 1 kW/m^2. Photovoltaic solar cells can convert this power into electricity with 15% efficiency. If a typical home uses 385 kWh of electricity per month, how many square meters of solar cells are required to meet its energy requirements? Assume that electricity can be generated from the sunlight for 8 hours per day.

▲ What area of solar cells do you need to power a home?

CUMULATIVE PROBLEMS

97. The kinetic energy of a rolling billiard ball is given by $KE = \frac{1}{2}mv^2$. Suppose a 0.17-kg billiard ball is rolling down a pool table with an initial speed of 4.5 m/s. As it travels, it loses some of its energy as heat. The ball slows down to 3.8 m/s and then collides head-on with a second billiard ball of equal mass. The first billiard ball completely stops, and the second one rolls away with a velocity of 3.8 m/s. Assume the first billiard ball is the system. Calculate w, q, and ΔE for the process.

98. A 100-W lightbulb is placed in a cylinder equipped with a moveable piston. The lightbulb is turned on for 0.015 hour, and the assembly expands from an initial volume of 0.85 L to a final volume of 5.88 L against an external pressure of 1.0 atm. Use the wattage of the lightbulb and the time it is on to calculate ΔE in joules (assume that the cylinder and lightbulb assembly is the system and assume two significant figures). Calculate w and q.

99. Evaporating sweat cools the body because evaporation is an endothermic process:

$$H_2O(l) \longrightarrow H_2O(g) \qquad \Delta H^\circ_{rxn} = +44.01 \text{ kJ}$$

Estimate the mass of water that must evaporate from the skin to cool the body by 0.50 °C. Assume a body mass of 95 kg and assume that the specific heat capacity of the body is 4.0 J/g·°C.

100. LP gas burns according to the exothermic reaction:

$$C_3H_8(g) + 5\,O_2(g) \longrightarrow 3\,CO_2(g) + 4\,H_2O(g) \qquad \Delta H^\circ_{rxn} = -2044 \text{ kJ}$$

What mass of LP gas is necessary to heat 1.5 L of water from room temperature (25.0 °C) to boiling (100.0 °C)? Assume that during heating, 15% of the heat emitted by the LP gas combustion goes to heat the water. The rest is lost as heat to the surroundings.

101. Use standard enthalpies of formation to calculate the standard change in enthalpy for the melting of ice. (The ΔH°_f for $H_2O(s)$ is −291.8 kJ/mol.) Use this value to calculate the mass of ice required to cool 355 mL of a beverage from room temperature (25.0 °C) to 0.0 °C. Assume that the specific heat capacity and density of the beverage are the same as those of water.

102. Dry ice is solid carbon dioxide. Instead of melting, solid carbon dioxide sublimes according to the equation:

$$CO_2(s) \longrightarrow CO_2(g)$$

When dry ice is added to warm water, heat from the water causes the dry ice to sublime more quickly. The evaporating carbon dioxide produces a dense fog often used to create special effects. In a simple dry ice fog machine, dry ice is added to warm water in a Styrofoam cooler. The dry ice produces fog until it evaporates away, or until the water gets too cold to sublime the dry ice quickly enough. Suppose that a small Styrofoam cooler holds 15.0 L of water heated to 85 °C. Use standard enthalpies of formation to calculate the change in enthalpy for dry ice sublimation, and calculate the mass of dry ice that should be added to the water so that the dry ice completely sublimes away when the water reaches 25 °C. Assume no heat loss to the surroundings. (The ΔH°_f for $CO_2(s)$ is −427.4 kJ/mol.)

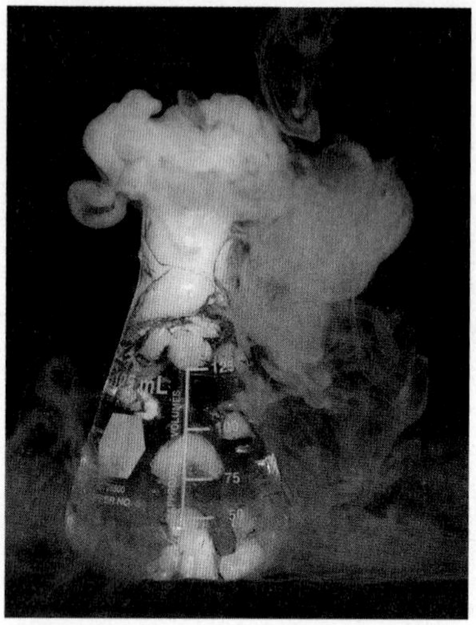

▲ When carbon dioxide sublimes, the gaseous CO_2 is cold enough to cause water vapor in the air to condense, forming fog.

103. A 25.5-g aluminum block is warmed to 65.4 °C and plunged into an insulated beaker containing 55.2 g water initially at 22.2 °C. The aluminum and the water are allowed to come to thermal equilibrium. Assuming that no heat is lost, what is the final temperature of the water and aluminum?

104. If 50.0 mL of ethanol (density = 0.789 g/mL) initially at 7.0 °C is mixed with 50.0 mL of water (density = 1.0 g/mL) initially at 28.4 °C in an insulated beaker, and assuming that no heat is lost, what is the final temperature of the mixture?

105. Palmitic acid ($C_{16}H_{32}O_2$) is a dietary fat found in beef and butter. The caloric content of palmitic acid is typical of fats in general. Write a balanced equation for the complete combustion of palmitic acid and calculate the standard enthalpy of combustion. What is the caloric content of palmitic acid in Cal/g? Do the same calculation for table sugar (sucrose, $C_{12}H_{22}O_{11}$). Which dietary substance (sugar or fat) contains more Calories per gram? The standard enthalpy of formation of palmitic acid is −208 kJ/mol and that of sucrose is −2226.1 kJ/mol. [Use $H_2O(l)$ in the balanced chemical equations because the metabolism of these compounds produces liquid water.]

106. Hydrogen and methanol have both been proposed as alternatives to hydrocarbon fuels. Write balanced reactions for the complete combustion of hydrogen and methanol and use standard enthalpies of formation to calculate the amount of heat released per kilogram of the fuel. Which fuel contains the most energy in the least mass? How does the energy of these fuels compare to that of octane (C_8H_{18})?

107. Derive a relationship between ΔH and ΔE for a process in which the temperature of a fixed amount of an ideal gas changes.

108. Under certain nonstandard conditions, oxidation by $O_2(g)$ of 1 mol of $SO_2(g)$ to $SO_3(g)$ absorbs 89.5 kJ. The enthalpy of formation of $SO_3(g)$ is −204.2 kJ under these conditions. Find the enthalpy of formation of $SO_2(g)$.

109. One tablespoon of peanut butter has a mass of 16 g. It is combusted in a calorimeter whose heat capacity is 120.0 kJ/°C. The temperature of the calorimeter rises from 22.2 °C to 25.4 °C. Find the food caloric content of peanut butter.

110. A mixture of 2.0 mol of $H_2(g)$ and 1.0 mol of $O_2(g)$ is placed in a sealed evacuated container made of a perfect insulating material at 25 °C. The mixture is ignited with a spark and reacts to form liquid water. Determine the temperature of the water.

111. A 20.0-L volume of an ideal gas in a cylinder with a piston is at a pressure of 3.0 atm. Enough weight is suddenly removed from the piston to lower the external pressure to 1.5 atm. The gas then expands at constant temperature until its pressure is 1.5 atm. Find ΔE, ΔH, q, and w for this change in state.

112. When 10.00 g of phosphorus is burned in $O_2(g)$ to form $P_4O_{10}(s)$, enough heat is generated to raise the temperature of 2950 g of water from 18.0 °C to 38.0 °C. Calculate the enthalpy of formation of $P_4O_{10}(s)$ under these conditions.

113. The ΔH for the oxidation of sulfur in the gas phase to SO_3 is −204 kJ/mol and for the oxidation of SO_2 to SO_3 is 89.5 kJ/mol. Find the enthalpy of formation of SO_2 under these conditions.

114. The ΔH_f° of $TiI_3(s)$ is −328 kJ/mol and the ΔH° for the reaction $2\,Ti(s) + 3\,I_2(g) \longrightarrow 2\,TiI_3(s)$ is −839 kJ. Calculate the ΔH of sublimation of $I_2(s)$, which is a solid at 25 °C.

115. A gaseous fuel mixture contains 25.3% methane (CH_4), 38.2% ethane (C_2H_6), and the rest propane (C_3H_8) by volume. When the fuel mixture contained in a 1.55 L tank, stored at 755 mmHg and 298 K, undergoes complete combustion, how much heat is emitted? (Assume that the water produced by the combustion is in the gaseous state.)

116. A gaseous fuel mixture stored at 745 mmHg and 298 K contains only methane (CH_4) and propane (C_3H_8). When 11.7 L of this fuel mixture is burned, it produces 769 kJ of heat. What is the mole fraction of methane in the mixture? (Assume that the water produced by the combustion is in the gaseous state.)

117. A copper cube with an edge measuring 1.55 cm and an aluminum cube with an edge measuring 1.62 cm are both heated to 55.0 °C and submerged in 100.0 mL of water at 22.2 °C. What is the final temperature of the water when equilibrium is reached? (Assume a density of 0.998 g/mL for water.)

118. A pure gold ring and a pure silver ring have a total mass of 14.9 g. The two rings are heated to 62.0 °C and dropped into 15.0 mL of water at 23.5 °C. When equilibrium is reached, the temperature of the water is 25.0 °C. What is the mass of each ring? (Assume a density of 0.998 g/mL for water.)

CHALLENGE PROBLEMS

119. A typical frostless refrigerator uses 655 kWh of energy per year in the form of electricity. Suppose that all of this electricity is generated at a power plant that burns coal containing 3.2% sulfur by mass and that all of the sulfur is emitted as SO_2 when the coal is burned. If all of the SO_2 goes on to react with rainwater to form H_2SO_4, what mass of H_2SO_4 does the annual operation of the refrigerator produce? (*Hint:* Assume that the remaining percentage of the coal is carbon and begin by calculating ΔH°_{rxn} for the combustion of carbon.)

120. A large sport utility vehicle has a mass of 2.5×10^3 kg. Calculate the mass of CO_2 emitted into the atmosphere upon accelerating the SUV from 0.0 mph to 65.0 mph. Assume that the required energy comes from the combustion of octane with 30% efficiency. (*Hint:* Use $KE = \frac{1}{2}mv^2$ to calculate the kinetic energy required for the acceleration.)

121. Combustion of natural gas (primarily methane) occurs in most household heaters. The heat given off in this reaction is used to raise the temperature of the air in the house. Assuming that all the energy given off in the reaction goes to heating up only the air in the house, determine the mass of methane required to heat the air in a house by 10.0 °C. Assume that the house dimensions are 30.0 m × 30.0 m × 3.0 m, specific heat capacity of air is 30 J/K·mol, and 1.00 mol of air occupies 22.4 L for all temperatures concerned.

122. When backpacking in the wilderness, hikers often boil water to sterilize it for drinking. Suppose that you are planning a backpacking trip and will need to boil 35 L of water for your group. What volume of fuel should you bring? Assume that the fuel has an average formula of C_7H_{16}, 15% of the heat generated from combustion goes to heat the water (the rest is lost to the surroundings), the density of the fuel is 0.78 g/mL, the initial temperature of the water is 25.0 °C, and the standard enthalpy of formation of C_7H_{16} is −224.4 kJ/mol.

123. An ice cube of mass 9.0 g is added to a cup of coffee. The coffee's initial temperature is 90.0 °C and the cup contains 120.0 g of liquid. Assume the specific heat capacity of the coffee is the same as that of water. The heat of fusion of ice (the heat associated with ice melting) is 6.0 kJ/mol. Find the temperature of the coffee after the ice melts.

124. Find ΔH, ΔE, q, and w for the freezing of water at −10.0 °C. The specific heat capacity of ice is 2.04 J/g·°C and its heat of fusion (the quantity of heat associated with melting) is −332 J/g.

125. Starting from the relationship between temperature and kinetic energy for an ideal gas, find the value of the molar heat capacity of an ideal gas when its temperature is changed at constant volume. Find its molar heat capacity when its temperature is changed at constant pressure.

126. An amount of an ideal gas expands from 12.0 L to 24.0 L at a constant pressure of 1.0 atm. Then the gas is cooled at a constant volume of 24.0 L back to its original temperature. Then it contracts back to its original volume. Find the total heat flow for the entire process.

127. The heat of vaporization of water at 373 K is 40.7 kJ/mol. Find q, w, ΔE, and ΔH for the evaporation of 454 g of water at this temperature at 1 atm.

128. Find ΔE, ΔH, q, and w for the change in state of 1.0 mol $H_2O(l)$ at 80 °C to $H_2O(g)$ at 110 °C. The heat capacity of $H_2O(l)$ = 75.3 J/mol K, the heat capacity of $H_2O(g)$ = 25.0 J/mol K, and the heat of vaporization of H_2O is 40.7×10^3 J/mol at 100 °C.

129. The heat of combustion of liquid octane (C_8H_{18}) to carbon dioxide and liquid water at 298 K is −1303 kJ/mol. Find ΔE for this reaction.

130. Find ΔH for the combustion of ethanol (C_2H_6O) to carbon dioxide and liquid water from the following data. The heat capacity of the bomb calorimeter is 34.65 kJ/K, and the combustion of 1.765 g of ethanol raises the temperature of the calorimeter from 294.33 K to 295.84 K.

CONCEPTUAL PROBLEMS

131. Which statement is true of the internal energy of the system and its surroundings following a process in which $\Delta E_{sys} = +65$ kJ? Explain.

a. The system and the surroundings both lose 65 kJ of energy.
b. The system and the surroundings both gain 65 kJ of energy.
c. The system loses 65 kJ of energy and the surroundings gain 65 kJ of energy.
d. The system gains 65 kJ of energy and the surroundings lose 65 kJ of energy.

132. The internal energy of an ideal gas depends only on its temperature. Which statement is true of an isothermal (constant-temperature) expansion of an ideal gas against a constant external pressure? Explain.

a. ΔE is positive.
b. w is positive.
c. q is positive.
d. ΔE is negative.

133. Which expression describes the heat evolved in a chemical reaction when the reaction is carried out at constant pressure? Explain.

a. $\Delta E - w$
b. ΔE
c. $\Delta E - q$

134. Two identical new refrigerators are plugged in for the first time. Refrigerator A is empty (except for air) and refrigerator B is filled with jugs of water. The compressors of both refrigerators immediately turn on and begin cooling the interiors of the refrigerators. After two hours, the compressor of refrigerator A turns off, while the compressor of refrigerator B continues to run. The next day, the compressor of refrigerator A can be heard turning on and off every few minutes, while the compressor of refrigerator B turns off and on every hour or so (and stays on longer each time). Explain these observations.

135. A 1-kg cylinder of aluminum and 1-kg jug of water, both at room temperature, are put into a refrigerator. After 1 hour, the temperature of each object is measured. One of the objects is much cooler than the other. Which one is cooler and why?

136. Two substances A and B, initially at different temperatures, are thermally isolated from their surroundings and allowed to come into thermal contact. The mass of substance A is twice the mass of substance B, but the specific heat capacity of substance B is four times the specific heat capacity of substance A. Which substance will undergo a larger change in temperature?

137. When 1 mol of a gas burns at constant pressure, it produces 2418 J of heat and does 5 J of work. Determine ΔE, ΔH, q, and w for the process.

138. In an exothermic reaction, the reactants lose energy, and the reaction feels hot to the touch. Explain why the reaction feels hot even though the reactants are losing energy. Where does the energy come from?

139. Which statement is true of a reaction in which ΔV is positive? Explain.

a. $\Delta H = \Delta E$
b. $\Delta H > \Delta E$
c. $\Delta H < \Delta E$

QUESTIONS FOR GROUP WORK

Active Classroom Learning

Discuss these questions with the group and record your consensus answer.

140. Have each group member write a problem involving the transfer of heat from one material in Table 7.4 to another material in the table. Working as a group, solve each problem. The group member who wrote each problem may act as the group facilitator when the group is working on his or her problem. What do all of your problems have in common? How do they differ?

141. Classify each process as endothermic or exothermic. What is the sign of ΔH for each process? Explain your answers.

a. gasoline burning in an engine
b. steam condensing on a mirror
c. water boiling in a pot

Provide at least two additional examples of exothermic processes and two additional examples of endothermic processes. Have each member of your group provide an example.

142. A propane tank on a home barbeque contains 10.4×10^3 g of propane.

a. Write the balanced chemical reaction for the combustion of gaseous propane (C_3H_8) to form water vapor and gaseous carbon dioxide.
b. Use the value for ΔH_{rxn} provided in the text to calculate the total amount of heat produced when the entire contents of the tank of propane is burned.
c. What mass of water could be warmed from 25 °C to 100 °C with this much heat?

143. Consider the decomposition of liquid hydrogen peroxide (H_2O_2) to form water and oxygen.

a. What is the heat of formation for hydrogen peroxide?
b. What is the heat of formation for liquid water?
c. What is the heat of formation for gaseous oxygen? Why?
d. Write the balanced chemical equations that correspond to the ΔH values you looked up for parts a, b, and c.
e. Write the balanced chemical equation for the decomposition of hydrogen peroxide to form water and oxygen. (Write the equation such that the coefficient on oxygen is 1.)
f. What is the heat of reaction for the process in part e?
g. Draw a scale diagram of this reaction (1 cm = 100 kJ) that shows the relative energies of reactants (on the left), products (on the right), and the elements in their most stable states (in the middle). Label all the energies you know.

DATA INTERPRETATION AND ANALYSIS

Heat Content of Fuels

144. The heating value of combustible fuels is evaluated based on the quantities known as the higher heating value (HHV) and the lower heating value (LHV). The HHV has a higher absolute value and assumes that the water produced in the combustion reaction is formed in the liquid state. The LHV has a lower absolute value and assumes that the water produced in the combustion reaction is formed in the gaseous state. The LHV is therefore the sum of the HHV (which is negative) and the heat of vaporization of water for the number of moles of water formed in the reaction (which is positive). The table lists the enthalpy of combustion—which is equivalent to the HHV—for several closely related hydrocarbons.

Hydrocarbon	ΔH_{comb} (kJ/mol)
$CH_4(g)$	−890
$C_2H_6(g)$	−1560
$C_3H_8(g)$	−2219
$C_4H_{10}(g)$	−2877
$C_5H_{12}(l)$	−3509
$C_6H_{14}(l)$	−4163
$C_7H_{16}(l)$	−4817
$C_8H_{18}(l)$	−5470

Use the information in the table to answer the following questions.

a. Write two balanced equations for the combustion of C_3H_8; one assuming the formation of liquid water and the other assuming the formation of gaseous water.

b. Given that the heat of vaporization of water is 44.0 kJ/mol, what is ΔH_{rxn} for each reaction in part a? Which quantity is the HHV? The LHV?

c. When propane is used to cook in an outdoor grill, is the amount of heat released the HHV or the LHV? What amount of heat is released upon combustion of 1.00 kg of propane in an outdoor grill?

d. For each CH_2 unit added to a hydrocarbon, what is the average increase in the absolute value of ΔH_{comb}?

Cc ANSWERS TO CONCEPTUAL CONNECTIONS

System and Surroundings

7.1 **(a)** When ΔE_{sys} is negative, energy flows out of the system and into the surroundings. The energy increase in the surroundings must exactly match the decrease in the system.

Heat and Work

7.2 **(b)** Rolling a metal cylinder up a ramp requires that a force be applied to the cylinder over a distance and is therefore work.

The Heat Capacity of Water

7.3 **(a)** Bring the water into your sleeping bag; it has the higher heat capacity and will therefore release more heat as it cools.

Thermal Energy Transfer

7.4 **(c)** The specific heat capacity of substance B is twice that of A, but since the mass of B is half that of A, the quantity $m \times C_s$ is identical for both substances so that the final temperature is exactly midway between the two initial temperatures.

Pressure–Volume Work

7.5 **(d)** The work done is given by $w = -P_{ext} \cdot \Delta V$, which is equal to $-1.00\text{ atm}\,(2.00\text{ L} - 1.00\text{ L}) = -1.00\text{ L} \cdot \text{atm}$. Since $1\text{ L} \cdot \text{atm} = 101.3\text{ J}$, the work done (rounded to the correct number of significant figures) is −101 J.

The Difference between ΔH and ΔE

7.6 **(c)** ΔH represents only the heat exchanged; therefore, $\Delta H = -2658$ kJ. ΔE represents the heat *and work* exchanged; therefore, $\Delta E = -2661$ kJ. The signs of both ΔH and ΔE are negative because heat and work are flowing out of the system and into the surroundings. Notice that the values of ΔH and ΔE are similar in magnitude, as is the case in many chemical reactions.

Exothermic and Endothermic Reactions

7.7 **(b)** The temperature falls. An endothermic reaction absorbs heat from the surroundings. Since the flask is part of the immediate surroundings, the temperature of the flask falls.

Thermochemical Equations

7.8 **(c)** From the thermochemical equation, you can get the ratio

$$2\text{ mol A} : -51.0\text{ J} \qquad 6\,\cancel{\text{mol A}}\left(\frac{-51.0\text{ J}}{2\,\cancel{\text{mol A}}}\right) = -153\text{ J}$$

Constant-Pressure versus Constant-Volume Calorimetry

7.9 **(a)** The value of q_{rxn} with the greater magnitude (−12.5 kJ) must have come from the bomb calorimeter. Recall that $\Delta E_{rxn} = q_{rxn} + w_{rxn}$. In a bomb calorimeter, the energy change that occurs in the course of the reaction all takes the form of heat (q). In a coffee-cup calorimeter, the amount of energy released as heat may be smaller because some of the energy may be used to do work (w).

Relationships Involving ΔH_{rxn}

7.10 **(d)** When a chemical equation is multiplied by some factor, ΔH_{rxn} must be multiplied by the same factor and when a chemical equation is reversed, ΔH_{rxn} changes sign. So $\Delta H_{rxn} = -2(122\text{ J}) = -144\text{ J}$.

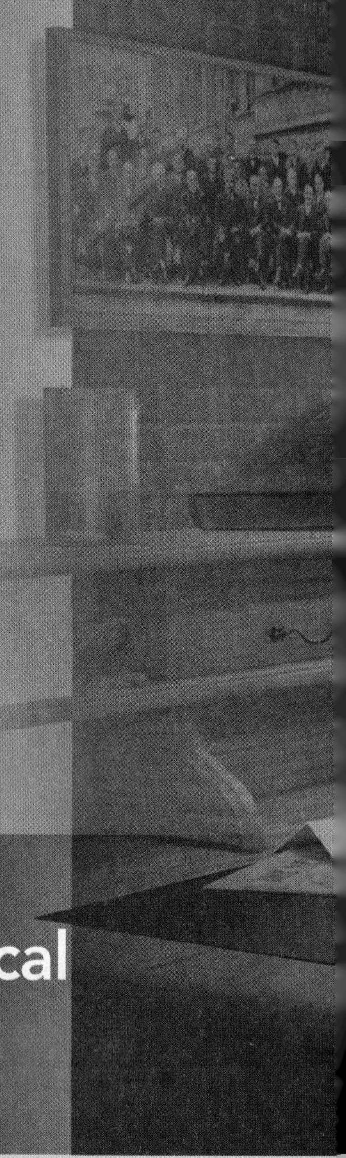

Anyone who is not shocked by quantum mechanics has not understood it.

—NIELS BOHR (1885–1962)

CHAPTER 8

The Quantum-Mechanical Model of the Atom

The early part of the twentieth century revolutionized how we think about physical reality. Before then, all descriptions of the behavior of matter were deterministic—the present conditions completely determining the future. The new theory of quantum mechanics suggested that for subatomic particles—electrons, neutrons, and protons—the present does NOT completely determine the future. For example, if you shoot one electron down a path and measure where it lands, a second electron shot down the same path under the same conditions will most likely land in a different place! Several gifted scientists, including Albert Einstein, Niels Bohr, Louis de Broglie, Max Planck, Werner Heisenberg, P. A. M. Dirac, and Erwin Schrödinger, developed quantum-mechanical theory; they also realized its strangeness. Bohr said, "Anyone who is not shocked by quantum mechanics has not understood it." Schrödinger wrote, "I don't like it, and I'm sorry I ever had anything to do with it." Albert Einstein disbelieved the very theory he helped develop, stating, "God does not play dice with the universe." In fact, Einstein attempted to disprove quantum mechanics—without success—until he died. Today, quantum mechanics forms the foundation of chemistry—explaining the periodic table and chemical bonding—as well as providing the practical basis for lasers, computers, and countless other applications.

The thought experiment known as Schrödinger's cat is intended to show that the strangeness of the quantum world does not transfer to the macroscopic world.

8.1 Schrödinger's Cat 311
8.2 The Nature of Light 312
8.3 Atomic Spectroscopy and the Bohr Model 322
8.4 The Wave Nature of Matter: The de Broglie Wavelength, the Uncertainty Principle, and Indeterminacy 325
8.5 Quantum Mechanics and the Atom 331
8.6 The Shapes of Atomic Orbitals 337
LEARNING OUTCOMES 344

8.1 Schrödinger's Cat

Atoms and the particles that compose them are unimaginably small. Electrons have a mass of less than a trillionth of a trillionth of a gram, and a size so small that it is immeasurable. A single speck of dust contains more electrons than the number of people who have existed on Earth over all the centuries of time. Electrons are *small* in the absolute sense of the word—they are among the smallest particles that compose matter. And yet, as we have seen in the preceding chapters, an atom's electrons determine many of its chemical and physical properties. If we are to understand these properties, we must try to understand electrons.

In the early twentieth century, scientists discovered that the *absolutely small* (or *quantum*) world of the electron behaves differently than the *large* (or *macroscopic*) world that we are used to observing. Chief among these differences is the idea that, when unobserved, *absolutely small particles like electrons can be in two different states at the same time.* For example, through a process called radioactive decay (see Chapter 21) an atom can emit small (that is, *absolutely* small) energetic particles from its nucleus. In the macroscopic world, something either emits an energetic particle or it doesn't. In the quantum world, however, the unobserved atom can be in a state in which it is doing both—emitting the particle and not emitting the particle—simultaneously. At first, this seems absurd. The absurdity resolves itself, however, upon observation. When we set out to measure the emitted particle, the act of measurement actually forces the atom into one state or the other.

Early twentieth-century physicists struggled with this idea. Austrian physicist Erwin Schrödinger (1887–1961), in an attempt to demonstrate that this quantum strangeness could never transfer itself to the macroscopic world, published a paper in 1935 that contained a thought experiment about a cat, now known as Schrödinger's cat. In the thought experiment, the imaginary cat is put into a steel chamber that contains radioactive atoms such as the atom described in the previous paragraph. The chamber is equipped with a mechanism that, upon the emission of an energetic particle by one of the radioactive atoms, causes a hammer to break a flask of hydrocyanic acid, a poison. If the flask breaks, the poison is released and the cat dies.

Now here comes the absurdity: if the steel chamber is closed, the whole system remains unobserved, and the radioactive atom is in a state in which it has both emitted the particle and not emitted the particle (with equal probability). Therefore, the cat is both dead and undead. Schrödinger put it this way: "[the steel chamber would have] *in it the living and dead cat (pardon the expression) mixed or smeared out in equal parts.*" When the chamber is opened, the act of observation forces the entire system into one state or the other: the cat is either dead or alive, not both. However, while unobserved, the cat is both dead and alive. The absurdity of the both dead and undead cat in Schrödinger's thought experiment was meant to demonstrate how quantum strangeness does not transfer to the macroscopic world.

In this chapter, we examine the **quantum-mechanical model** of the atom, a model that explains the strange behavior of electrons. In particular, we focus on how the model describes electrons as they exist within atoms, and how those electrons determine the chemical and physical properties of elements. You have already learned much about those properties. You know, for example, that some elements are metals and that others are nonmetals. You know that the noble gases are chemically inert and that the alkali metals are chemically reactive. You know that sodium tends to form 1+ ions and that fluorine tends to form 1− ions. But we have not explored *why*. The quantum-mechanical model explains why. In doing so, it explains the modern periodic table and provides the basis for our understanding of chemical bonding.

WATCH **NOW!**

KEY CONCEPT VIDEO 8.2
The Nature of Light

8.2 The Nature of Light

Before we explore electrons and their behavior within the atom, we must understand some of the properties of light. As quantum mechanics developed, light was (surprisingly) found to have many characteristics in common with electrons. Chief among these is the *wave–particle duality* of light. Certain properties of light are best described by thinking of it as a wave, while other properties are best described by thinking of it as a particle. In this section, we first explore light's dual nature (its wave behavior and its particle behavior), and then turn to electrons to see that they too display the same wave–particle duality.

The Wave Nature of Light

Light is **electromagnetic radiation**, a type of energy embodied in oscillating electric and magnetic fields. A *magnetic field* is a region of space where a magnetic particle experiences a force (think of the space around a magnet). An *electric field* is a region of space where an electrically charged particle experiences a force. A proton, for example, has an electric field around it. If you bring another charged particle into that field, that particle will experience a force.

We can describe electromagnetic radiation as a wave composed of oscillating, mutually perpendicular electric and magnetic fields propagating through space, as shown in Figure 8.1▼. In a vacuum, these waves move at a constant speed of 3.00×10^8 m/s (186,000 mi/s)—fast enough to circle Earth in one-seventh of a second. This great speed is the reason for the delay between the moment when you see a firework in the sky and the moment when you hear the sound of its explosion. The light from the exploding firework reaches your eye almost instantaneously. The sound, traveling much more slowly (340 m/s), takes longer. The same thing happens in a thunderstorm—you see the flash of lightning immediately, but the sound of thunder takes a few seconds to reach you. (The sound of thunder is delayed by five seconds for each mile between you and its origin.)

◀ Because light travels nearly a million times faster than sound, the flash of lightning reaches your eyes before the roll of thunder reaches your ears.

Electromagnetic Radiation

Electromagnetic radiation can be described as a wave composed of electric and magnetic fields that oscillate in perpendicular planes.

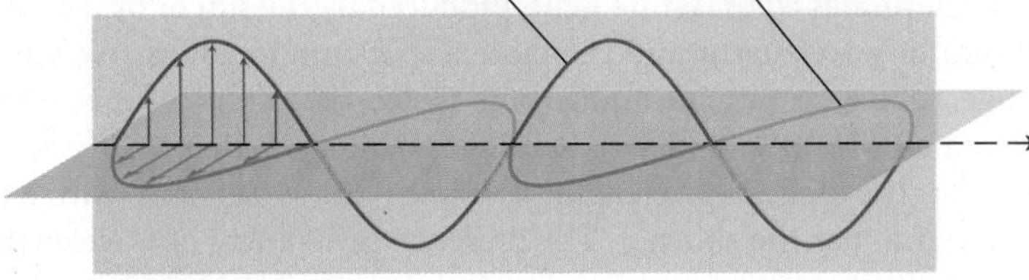

◀ **FIGURE 8.1 Electromagnetic Radiation**

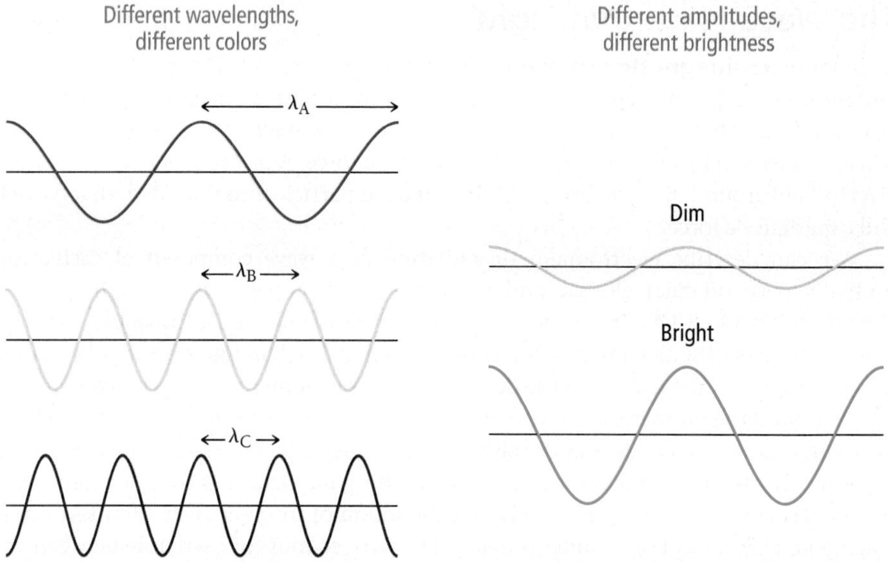

▶ **FIGURE 8.2 Wavelength and Amplitude** Wavelength and amplitude are independent properties. The wavelength of light determines its color. The amplitude, or intensity, determines its brightness.

The symbol λ is the Greek letter lambda, pronounced "lamb-duh."

We characterize a wave by its *amplitude* and its *wavelength.* In the graphical representation shown here, the **amplitude** of the wave is the vertical height of a crest (or depth of a trough). The amplitude of the electric and magnetic field waves in light determines the light's *intensity* or brightness—the greater the amplitude, the greater the intensity. The **wavelength (λ)** of the wave is the distance between adjacent crests (or any two analogous points) and is measured in units such as meters, micrometers, or nanometers. Amplitude and wavelength can vary independently of one another, as shown in Figure 8.2▲.

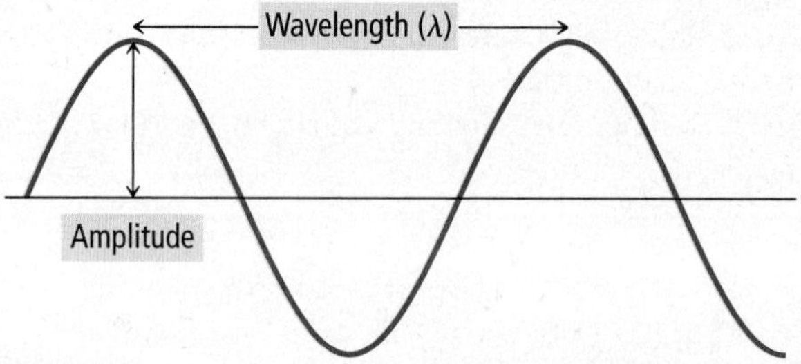

The symbol ν is the Greek letter nu, pronounced "noo."

Like all waves, light is also characterized by its **frequency (ν)**, the number of cycles (or wave crests) that pass through a stationary point in a given period of time. The units of frequency are cycles per second (cycle/s) or simply s^{-1}. An equivalent unit of frequency is the hertz (Hz), defined as 1 cycle/s. The frequency of a wave is directly proportional to the speed at which the wave is traveling—the faster the wave, the greater the number of crests that pass a fixed location per unit time. Frequency is also *inversely* proportional to the wavelength (λ)—the farther apart the crests, the lower the number of crests that pass a fixed location per unit time. For light, therefore, we can write the equation:

$$\nu = \frac{c}{\lambda} \qquad [8.1]$$

where the speed of light, *c*, and the wavelength, λ, are both expressed in the same unit of distance. Wavelength and frequency represent different ways of specifying the same information—if we know one, we can readily calculate the other.

For *visible light*—light that can be seen by the human eye—wavelength (or, alternatively, frequency) determines color. White light, produced by the sun or by a lightbulb, contains a spectrum of wavelengths and therefore a spectrum of colors. We see these colors—red, orange, yellow, green, blue, indigo, and violet—in a rainbow or when white light passes through a prism (Figure 8.3▶). Red light, with a wavelength of about 750 nanometers (nm), has the longest wavelength of visible light; violet light, with a wavelength of about 400 nm, has the shortest. The presence of a variety of wavelengths in white light is responsible for the way we perceive colors in objects. When a substance absorbs some colors while reflecting others, it appears colored. For example, a red shirt

nano = 10^{-9}

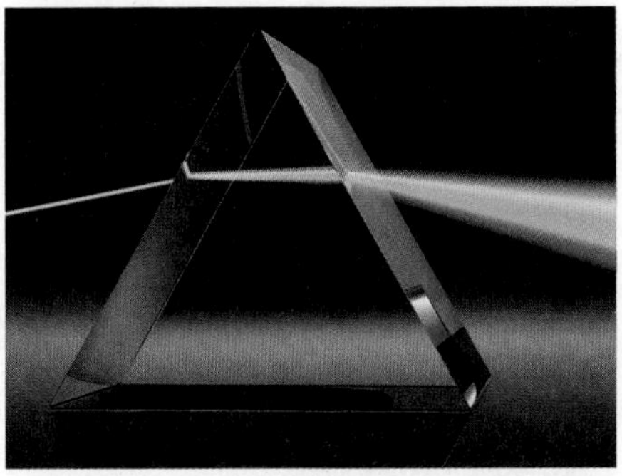

▲ **FIGURE 8.3 Components of White Light** We can pass white light through a prism and decompose it into its constituent colors, each with a different wavelength. The array of colors makes up the spectrum of visible light.

▲ **FIGURE 8.4 The Color of an Object** A red shirt is red because it reflects predominantly red light while absorbing most other colors.

appears red because it reflects predominantly red light while absorbing most other colors (Figure 8.4▲). Our eyes see only the reflected light, making the shirt appear red.

8.1 Cc Conceptual Connection ANSWER **NOW!**

WAVE NATURE OF LIGHT Which statement best describes the differences between a bright green laser and a dim red laser?

(a) The two lasers emit light of the same frequency, and the light from the green laser has a greater amplitude.
(b) The two lasers emit light of different frequencies, and the light from the green laser has a smaller amplitude.
(c) The two lasers emit light of different frequencies, and the light from the green laser has a greater amplitude.

EXAMPLE 8.1 Wavelength and Frequency

Calculate the wavelength (in nm) of the red light emitted by a barcode scanner that has a frequency of $4.62 \times 10^{14}\ s^{-1}$.

SOLUTION

You are given the frequency of the light and asked to find its wavelength. Use Equation 8.1, which relates frequency to wavelength. You can convert the wavelength from meters to nanometers by using the conversion factor between the two ($1\ nm = 10^{-9}\ m$).	$\nu = \frac{c}{\lambda}$ $\lambda = \frac{c}{\nu} = \frac{3.00 \times 10^{8}\ m/\cancel{s}}{4.62 \times 10^{14}/\cancel{s}}$ $= 6.49 \times 10^{-7}\ m$ $= 6.49 \times 10^{-7}\ \cancel{m} \times \frac{1\ nm}{10^{-9}\ \cancel{m}} = 649\ nm$

FOR PRACTICE 8.1 A laser dazzles the audience in a rock concert by emitting green light with a wavelength of 515 nm. Calculate the frequency of the light.

The Electromagnetic Spectrum

Visible light makes up only a tiny portion of the entire **electromagnetic spectrum**, which includes all wavelengths of electromagnetic radiation. Figure 8.5▶ shows the main regions of the electromagnetic spectrum, ranging in wavelength from 10^{-15} m (gamma rays) to 10^{5} m (radio waves). In Figure 8.5, short-wavelength, high-frequency radiation is on the right, and long-wavelength, low-frequency radiation is on the left.

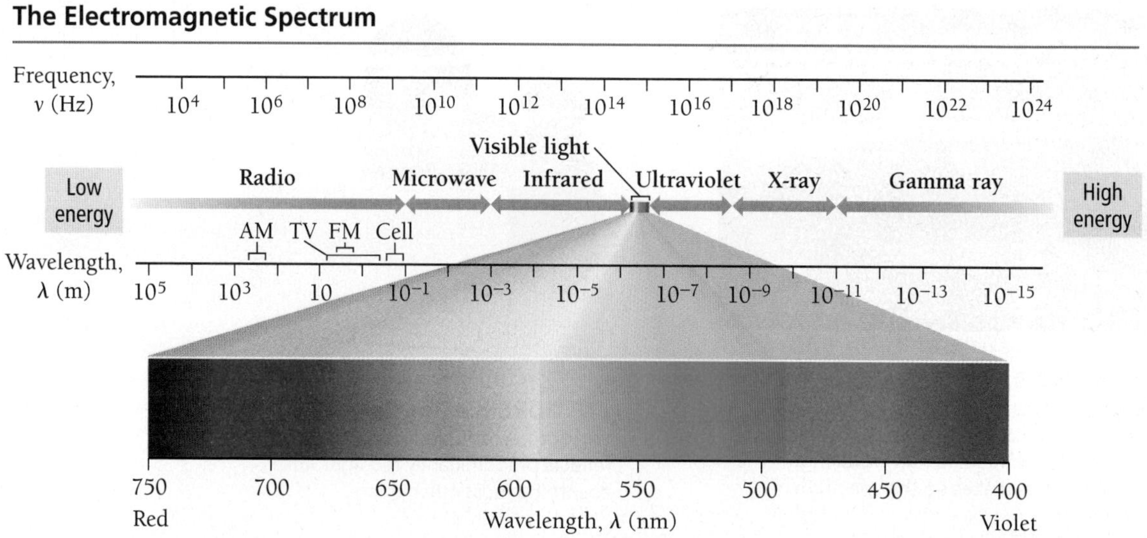

▲ **FIGURE 8.5 The Electromagnetic Spectrum** The right side of the spectrum consists of high-energy, high-frequency, short-wavelength radiation. The left side consists of low-energy, low-frequency, long-wavelength radiation. Visible light constitutes a small segment in the middle.

We will discuss gamma rays in more detail in Chapter 21.

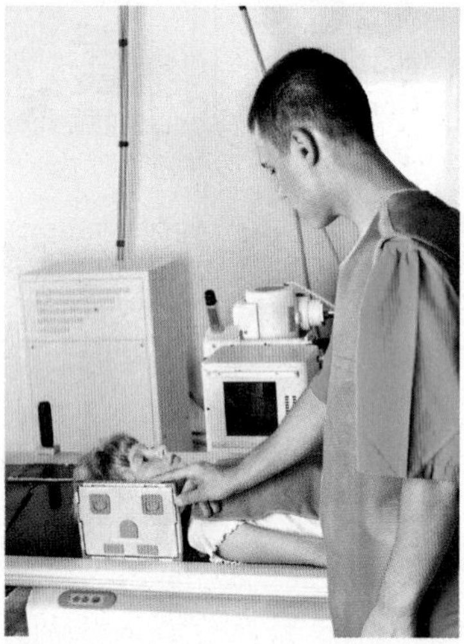

▲ To produce a medical X-ray, short-wavelength electromagnetic radiation passes through the skin and creates an image of bones and internal organs.

▲ Warm objects emit infrared light, which is invisible to the eye but can be captured on film or by detectors to produce an infrared photograph.

We will see later in this section that short-wavelength light inherently has greater energy than long-wavelength light (because of the particle nature of light). The most energetic forms of electromagnetic radiation have the shortest wavelengths. The form of electromagnetic radiation with the shortest wavelength is the **gamma (γ) ray**. Gamma rays are produced by the sun, other stars, and certain unstable atomic nuclei on Earth. Excessive exposure to gamma rays is dangerous to humans because the high energy of gamma rays can damage biological molecules.

Next on the electromagnetic spectrum, with longer wavelengths than gamma rays, are **X-rays**, familiar to us from their medical use. X-rays pass through many substances that block visible light and are therefore used to image bones and internal organs. Like gamma rays, X-rays are sufficiently energetic to damage biological molecules. Although several annual medical X-rays are relatively harmless, too much exposure to X-rays increases cancer risk.

Sandwiched between X-rays and visible light in the electromagnetic spectrum is **ultraviolet (UV) radiation**, most familiar to us as the component of sunlight that produces a sunburn or suntan. Though not as energetic as gamma rays or X-rays, ultraviolet light still carries enough energy to damage biological molecules. Excessive exposure to ultraviolet light increases the risk of skin cancer and cataracts and causes premature wrinkling of the skin.

Next on the spectrum is **visible light**, ranging from violet (shorter wavelength, higher energy) to red (longer wavelength, lower energy). Visible light—at low to moderate intensity—does not carry enough energy to damage biological molecules. It does, however, cause certain molecules in our eyes to change their shape, sending a signal to our brains that results in our ability to see.

Beyond visible light lies **infrared (IR) radiation**. The heat you feel when you place your hand near a hot object is infrared radiation. All warm objects, including human bodies, emit infrared light. Although infrared light is invisible to our eyes, infrared sensors can detect it and are often employed in night vision technology to help people "see" in the dark.

Beyond infrared light, at longer wavelengths still, are **microwaves**, used for radar and in microwave ovens. Although microwave radiation has longer wavelengths and therefore lower energies than visible or infrared light, it is efficiently absorbed by water and can therefore heat substances that contain water. The longest wavelengths on the electromagnetic spectrum are those of **radio waves**, which are used to transmit the signals responsible for AM and FM radio, cellular telephone, television, and other forms of communication.

ELECTROMAGNETIC RADIATION Arrange the following types of electromagnetic radiation in order of increasing wavelength: visible, X-ray, infrared.

(a) X-ray < visible < infrared
(b) X-ray < infrared < visible
(c) visible < infrared < X-ray
(d) infrared < X-ray < visible

8.2 Cc Conceptual Connection

ANSWER NOW!

CHEMISTRY AND MEDICINE | Radiation Treatment for Cancer

X-rays and gamma rays are sometimes called *ionizing radiation* because their short wavelengths correspond to high energies that can ionize atoms and molecules. When ionizing radiation interacts with biological molecules, it can permanently change or even destroy them. Consequently, we normally try to limit our exposure to ionizing radiation. However, doctors use ionizing radiation to destroy molecules within unwanted cells such as cancer cells.

In radiation therapy (also called radiotherapy) doctors aim X-ray or gamma-ray beams at cancerous tumors (groups of cells that divide uncontrollably and invade surrounding healthy tissue). The ionizing radiation damages the molecules within the tumor's cells that carry genetic information—information necessary for the cell to grow and divide. Consequently, the cell dies or stops dividing. Ionizing radiation also damages molecules in healthy cells, but cancerous cells divide more quickly than normal cells, making them more susceptible to genetic damage. Nonetheless, harm to healthy tissues during radiation therapy treatments can result in side effects such as fatigue, skin lesions, hair loss, and organ damage. Medical workers try to reduce such effects by appropriate shielding (of healthy tissue) and by targeting the tumor from multiple directions, minimizing the exposure of healthy cells while maximizing the exposure of cancerous cells.

Another side effect of exposing healthy cells to radiation is that the healthy cells may become cancerous. If a treatment for cancer may cause cancer, why do we continue to use it? In radiation therapy, as in most other disease therapies, there is an associated risk. We take risks all the time, many of them for lesser reasons. For example, every time we fly in an airplane or drive in a car, we risk injury or even death. Why? Because we perceive the benefit—the convenience of being able to travel a significant distance in a short time—to be worth the relatively small risk. The situation is similar in cancer therapy, or any other medical therapy for that matter. The benefit of cancer therapy (possibly curing a cancer that might otherwise kill you) is worth the risk (a slight increase in the chance of developing a future cancer).

QUESTION *Why is visible light (by itself) not used to destroy cancerous tumors?*

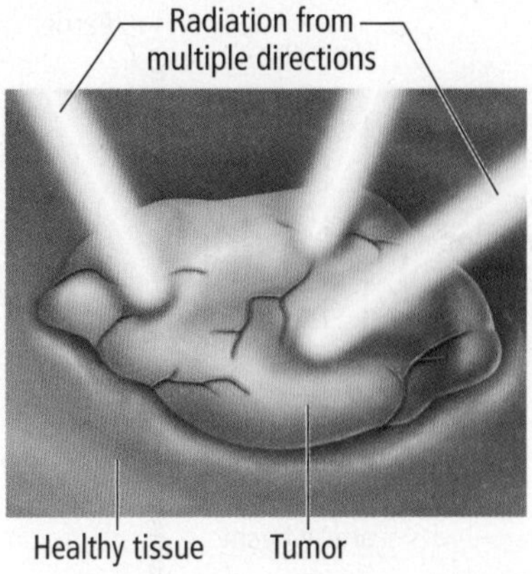

▲ During radiation therapy, a tumor is targeted from multiple directions in order to minimize the exposure of healthy cells while maximizing the exposure of cancerous cells.

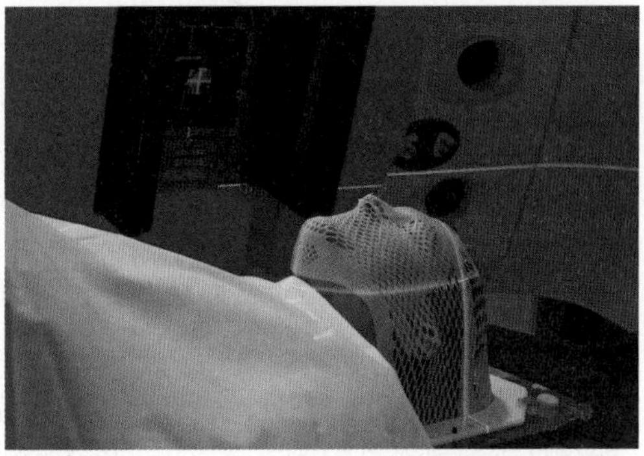

▲ In radiation therapy, highly energetic gamma rays are aimed at cancerous tumors.

Interference and Diffraction

Waves, including electromagnetic waves, interact with each other in a characteristic way called **interference:** they cancel each other out or build each other up, depending on their alignment upon interaction. For example, if two waves of equal amplitude are *in phase* when they interact—that is, they align with overlapping crests—a wave with twice the amplitude results. This is called **constructive interference**.

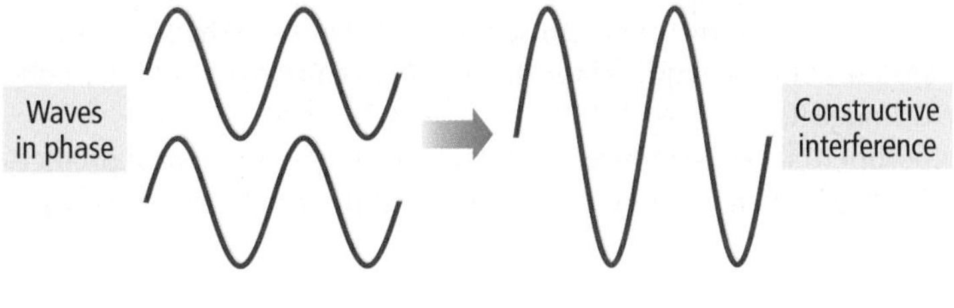

▲ When a reflected wave meets an incoming wave near the shore, the two waves interfere constructively for an instant, producing a large-amplitude spike.

On the other hand, if two waves are completely *out of phase* when they interact—that is, they align so that the crest from one source overlaps with the trough from the other source—the waves cancel by **destructive interference**.

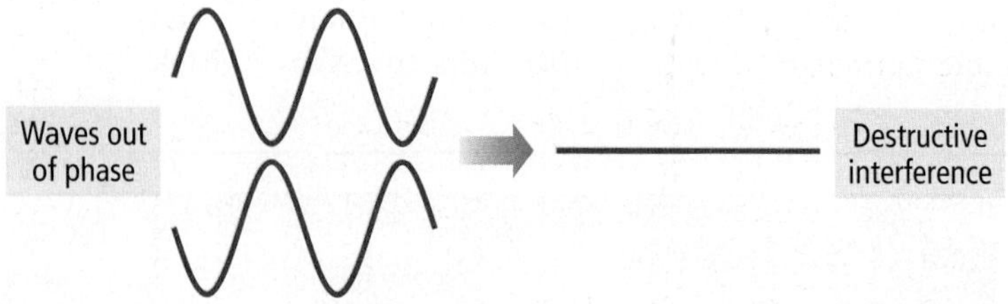

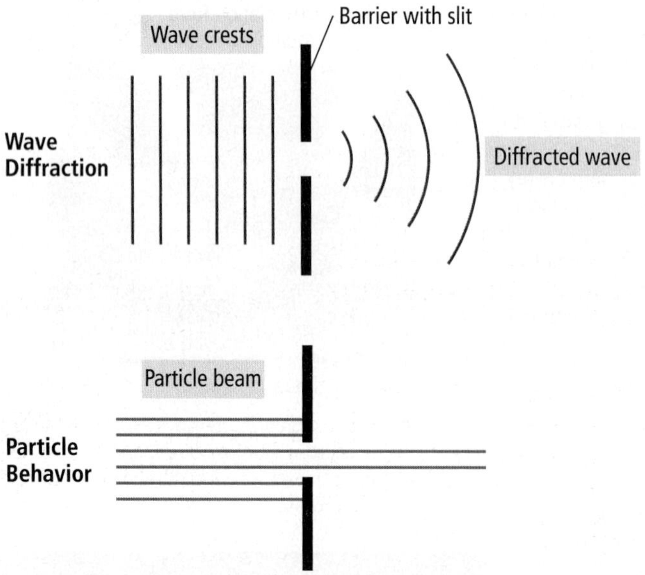

▲ **FIGURE 8.6 Diffraction** In this view from above, we can see how a wave bends, or diffracts, when it encounters an obstacle or slit with a size comparable to its wavelength. When a wave passes through a small opening, it spreads out. Particles, by contrast, do not diffract; they simply pass through the opening.

Waves also exhibit a characteristic behavior called **diffraction** (Figure 8.6◀). When a wave encounters an obstacle or a slit that is comparable in size to its wavelength, it bends (or *diffracts*) around it. The diffraction of light through two slits separated by a distance comparable to the wavelength of the light, coupled with interference, results in an *interference pattern*, illustrated in Figure 8.7▶. Each slit acts as a new wave source, and the two new waves interfere with each other. The resulting pattern is a series of bright and dark lines that can be viewed on a screen (or recorded on a film) placed a short distance behind the slits. At the center of the screen, the two waves travel equal distances and interfere constructively to produce a bright line. A small distance away from the center in either direction, the two waves travel slightly different distances, so they are out of phase. At the point where the difference in distance is one-half of one wavelength, the interference is destructive and a dark line appears on the screen. A bit farther away from the center we see constructive interference again because the difference between the paths is one whole wavelength. The end result is the interference pattern shown by the light and dark bars in Figure 8.7. Notice that interference results from the ability of a wave to diffract through two slits—an inherent property of waves.

The Particle Nature of Light

The term *classical*, as in classical electromagnetic theory or classical mechanics, refers to descriptions of matter and energy before the advent of quantum mechanics.

Prior to the early 1900s, and especially after the discovery of the diffraction of light, light was thought to be purely a wave phenomenon. Its behavior was described adequately by classical electromagnetic theory, which treated the electric and magnetic fields that constitute light as waves propagating through space. However, a number of discoveries brought the classical view into question. Chief among these discoveries was the *photoelectric effect.*

The **photoelectric effect** is the observation that many metals emit electrons when light shines upon them, as shown in Figure 8.8▶. Classical electromagnetic theory attributed this effect to the transfer of energy from the light to an electron in the metal, which resulted in the dislodgment of the electron. According to this explanation, only the amplitude (intensity) of the light affects the emission of electrons, not the wavelength. In other words, according to the classical description, the rate at which electrons leave the metal due to the photoelectric effect increases with increasing intensity of the light. A dim light was expected to result in a *lag time* between the initial shining of the light and the subsequent emission of an electron. The lag time would be the minimum amount of time required for the dim light to transfer sufficient energy to the electron to dislodge it.

The experimental results, however, did not support the classical prediction. Scientists found that a high-frequency, low-intensity light produces electrons *without* the

Interference from Two Slits

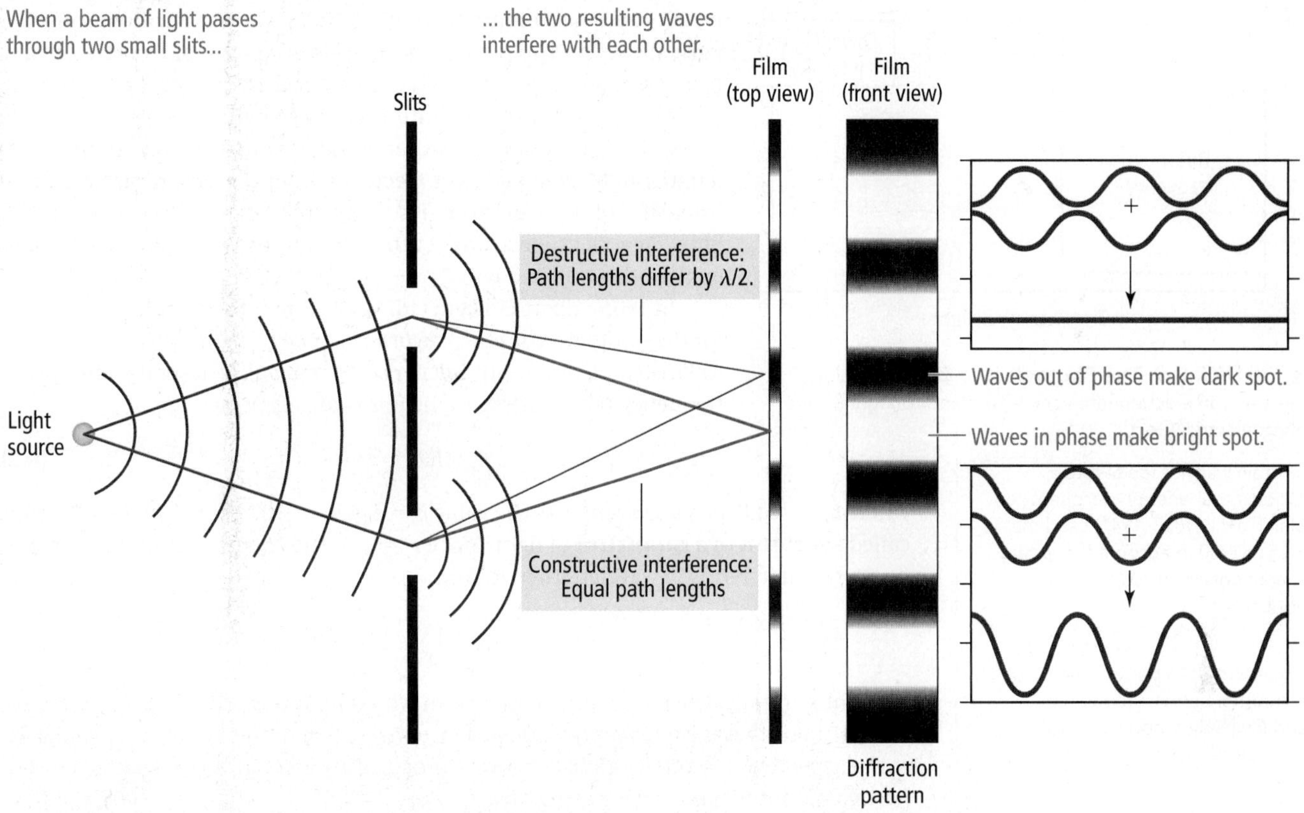

▲ **FIGURE 8.7 Interference from Two Slits** Whether the interference is constructive or destructive at any given point depends on the difference in the path lengths traveled by the waves.

The Photoelectric Effect

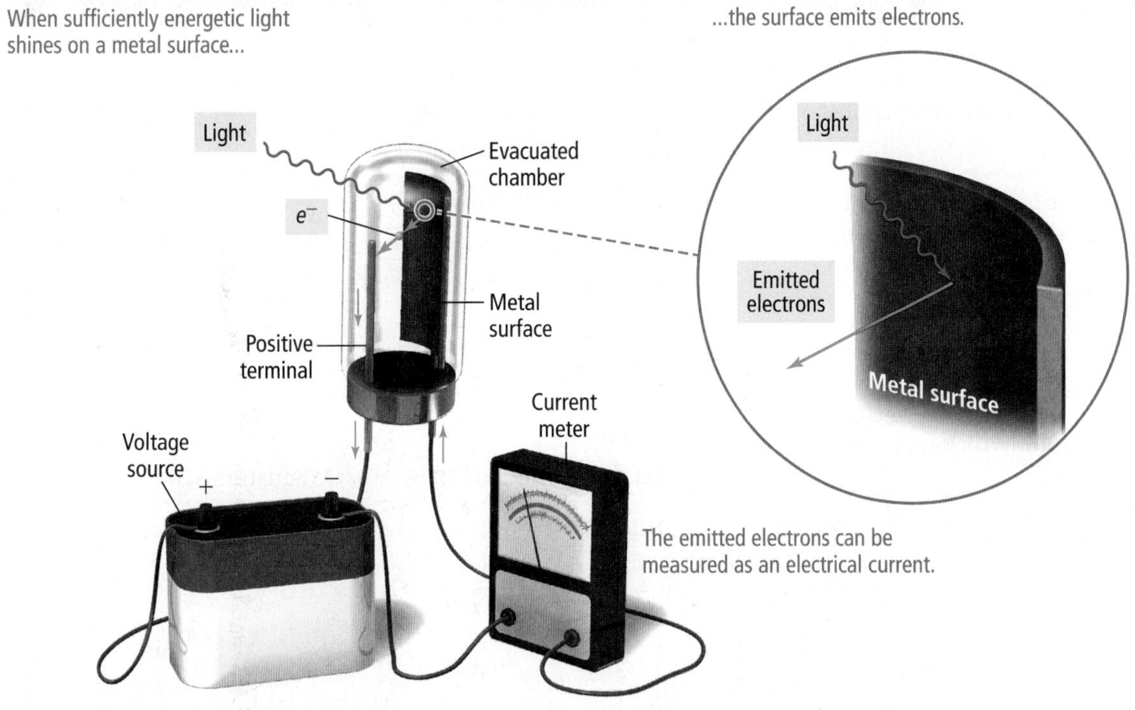

▲ **FIGURE 8.8 The Photoelectric Effect**

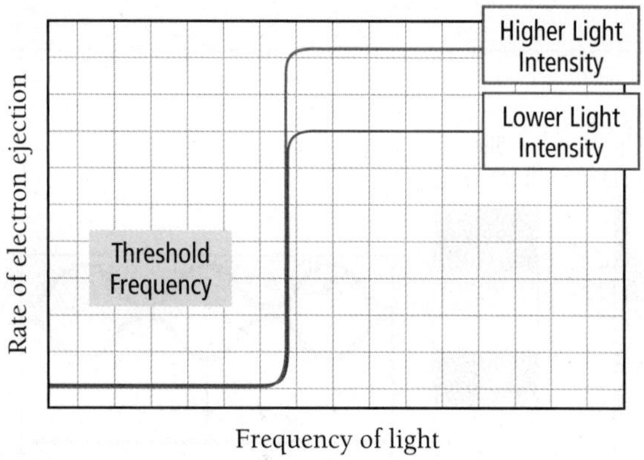

▲ **FIGURE 8.9 The Photoelectric Effect** A plot of the electron ejection rate versus frequency of light for the photoelectric effect.

predicted lag time. Furthermore, the light used to dislodge electrons in the photoelectric effect exhibits a *threshold frequency,* below which no electrons are emitted from the metal, no matter how long the light shines on the metal. Figure 8.9◀ is a graph of the rate of electron ejection from the metal versus the frequency of light used. Notice that increasing the intensity of the light does not change the threshold frequency. In other words, low-frequency (long-wavelength) light *does not* eject electrons from a metal regardless of its intensity or its duration. But high-frequency (short-wavelength) light *does* eject electrons, even if its intensity is low. What could explain this odd behavior?

In 1905, Albert Einstein (1879–1955) proposed a bold explanation for the photoelectric effect: *light energy must come in packets.* According to Einstein, the amount of energy (E) in a light packet depends on its frequency (ν) according to the following equation:

Einstein was not the first to suggest that energy was quantized. Max Planck (1858–1947) used the idea in 1900 to account for certain characteristics of radiation from hot bodies.

$$E = h\nu \qquad [8.2]$$

where h, called *Planck's constant,* has the value $h = 6.626 \times 10^{-34}\,\text{J}\cdot\text{s}$. A *packet* of light is called a **photon** or a **quantum** of light. Since $\nu = c/\lambda$, the energy of a photon can also be expressed in terms of wavelength as follows:

The energy of a photon is directly proportional to its frequency and inversely proportional to its wavelength.

$$E = \frac{hc}{\lambda} \qquad [8.3]$$

Unlike classical electromagnetic theory, in which light was viewed purely as a wave whose intensity was *continuously variable,* Einstein suggested that light was *lumpy.* From this perspective, a beam of light is *not* a wave propagating through space, but a shower of particles (photons), each with energy $h\nu$.

WATCH **NOW!**

INTERACTIVE WORKED EXAMPLE 8.2

EXAMPLE 8.2 Photon Energy

A nitrogen gas laser pulse with a wavelength of 337 nm contains 3.83 mJ of energy. How many photons does it contain?

SORT You are given the wavelength and total energy of a light pulse and asked to find the number of photons it contains.

GIVEN: $E_{\text{pulse}} = 3.83\ \text{mJ}$

$\lambda = 337\ \text{nm}$

FIND: number of photons

STRATEGIZE In the first part of the conceptual plan, calculate the energy of an individual photon from its wavelength.

CONCEPTUAL PLAN

$\lambda \rightarrow E_{\text{photon}}$

$E = \dfrac{hc}{\lambda}$

In the second part, divide the total energy of the pulse by the energy of a photon to determine the number of photons in the pulse.

$$\frac{E_{\text{pulse}}}{E_{\text{photon}}} = \text{number of photons}$$

RELATIONSHIPS USED $E = hc/\lambda$ (Equation 8.3)

SOLVE To execute the first part of the conceptual plan, convert the wavelength to meters and substitute it into the equation to calculate the energy of a 337-nm photon.

SOLUTION

$$\lambda = 337\ \cancel{\text{nm}} \times \frac{10^{-9}\ \text{m}}{1\ \cancel{\text{nm}}} = 3.37 \times 10^{-7}\ \text{m}$$

$$E_{\text{photon}} = \frac{hc}{\lambda} = \frac{(6.626 \times 10^{-34}\ \text{J}\cdot\cancel{\text{s}})\left(3.00 \times 10^{8}\ \frac{\cancel{\text{m}}}{\cancel{\text{s}}}\right)}{3.37 \times 10^{-7}\ \cancel{\text{m}}}$$

$$= 5.8\underline{9}85 \times 10^{-19}\ \text{J}$$

To execute the second part of the conceptual plan, convert the energy of the pulse from mJ to J. Then divide the energy of the pulse by the energy of a photon to obtain the number of photons.	$3.83 \text{ mJ} \times \frac{10^{-3}\text{ J}}{1 \text{ mJ}} = 3.83 \times 10^{-3}\text{ J}$ $\text{number of photons} = \frac{E_{\text{pulse}}}{E_{\text{photon}}} = \frac{3.83 \times 10^{-3}\text{ J}}{5.8985 \times 10^{-19}\text{ J}}$ $= 6.49 \times 10^{15}$ photons

CHECK The units of the answer, photons, are correct. The magnitude of the answer (10^{15}) is reasonable. Photons are small particles, and any macroscopic collection must contain a large number of them.

FOR PRACTICE 8.2 A 100-watt lightbulb radiates energy at a rate of 100 J/s. (The watt, a unit of power, or energy over time, is defined as 1 J/s.) If all of the light emitted has a wavelength of 525 nm, how many photons are emitted per second? (Assume three significant figures in this calculation.)

FOR MORE PRACTICE 8.2 The energy required to dislodge electrons from sodium metal via the photoelectric effect is 275 kJ/mol. What wavelength in nm of light has sufficient energy per photon to dislodge an electron from the surface of sodium?

WATCH **NOW!**

INTERACTIVE WORKED EXAMPLE 8.3

EXAMPLE 8.3 Wavelength, Energy, and Frequency

Arrange these three types of electromagnetic radiation—visible light, X-rays, and microwaves—in order of increasing

(a) wavelength. **(b)** frequency. **(c)** energy per photon.

SOLUTION

Examine Figure 8.5 and note that X-rays have the shortest wavelength, followed by visible light and then microwaves.	**(a)** wavelength X-rays < visible < microwaves
Since frequency and wavelength are inversely proportional—the longer the wavelength, the shorter the frequency—the ordering with respect to frequency is the reverse of the ordering with respect to wavelength.	**(b)** frequency microwaves < visible < X-rays
Energy per photon decreases with increasing wavelength but increases with increasing frequency; therefore, the ordering with respect to energy per photon is the same as for frequency.	**(c)** energy per photon microwaves < visible < X-rays

FOR PRACTICE 8.3 Arrange these three colors of visible light—green, red, and blue—in order of increasing

(a) wavelength. **(b)** frequency. **(c)** energy per photon.

Einstein's idea that light is quantized elegantly explains the photoelectric effect. The emission of electrons from the metal depends on whether or not a single photon has sufficient energy (as given by $h\nu$) to dislodge a single electron. For an electron bound to the metal with binding energy ϕ, the threshold frequency is reached when the energy of the photon is equal to ϕ.

The symbol ϕ is the Greek letter phi, pronounced "fi."

Threshold frequency condition

$$h\nu = \phi$$

Energy of photon ($h\nu$); Binding energy of emitted electron (ϕ)

Low-frequency light does not eject electrons because no single photon has the minimum energy necessary to dislodge the electron. We can draw an analogy between a photon ejecting an electron from a metal surface and a ball breaking a glass window. In this analogy, low-frequency photons are like ping-pong balls—a ping-pong ball thrown at a glass window does not break it (just as a low-frequency photon does not eject an electron). Increasing the *intensity* of low-frequency light is like increasing the number of ping-pong balls thrown at the window—doing so simply increases the number of low-energy photons but does not produce any single photon with sufficient energy. In contrast, increasing the *frequency* of the light, even at low intensity, *increases the energy of each photon.* In our analogy, a high-frequency photon is like a baseball—a baseball thrown at a glass window breaks it (just as a high-frequency photon dislodges an electron with no lag time).

As the frequency of the light increases past the threshold frequency, the excess energy of the photon (beyond what is needed to dislodge the electron) transfers to the electron in the form of kinetic energy. The kinetic energy (KE) of the ejected electron, therefore, is the difference between the energy of the photon ($h\nu$) and the binding energy of the electron, as given by the equation:

$$\text{KE} = h\nu - \phi$$

Although the quantization of light explained the photoelectric effect, the wave explanation of light continued to have explanatory power as well, depending on the circumstances of the particular observation. So the principle that slowly emerged (albeit with some measure of resistance) is what we now call the *wave–particle duality of light.* Sometimes light appears to behave like a wave, at other times like a particle. Which behavior we observe depends on the particular experiment.

ANSWER **NOW!**

8.3 Cc Conceptual Connection

THE PHOTOELECTRIC EFFECT We shine light of three different wavelengths—325 nm, 455 nm, and 632 nm—on a metal surface and record the following observations for each wavelength, labeled A, B, and C:

Observation A: No photoelectrons were observed.

Observation B: Photoelectrons with a kinetic energy of 155 kJ/mol were observed.

Observation C: Photoelectrons with a kinetic energy of 51 kJ/mol were observed.

Which observation corresponds to the 325 nm light?

(a) Observation A **(b)** Observation B **(c)** Observation C

8.3 Atomic Spectroscopy and the Bohr Model

The discovery of the particle nature of light began to break down the division that existed in nineteenth-century physics between electromagnetic radiation, which was thought of as a wave phenomenon, and the small particles (protons, neutrons, and electrons) that compose atoms, which were thought to follow Newton's laws of motion. Just as the photoelectric effect suggested the particle nature of light, so certain observations about atoms began to suggest a wave nature for particles. The most important of these observations came from *atomic spectroscopy,* the study of the electromagnetic radiation absorbed and emitted by atoms.

▲ The familiar red light from a neon sign is emitted by neon atoms that have absorbed electrical energy, which the atoms reemit as visible radiation.

When an atom absorbs energy—in the form of heat, light, or electricity—it often reemits that energy as light. For example, a neon sign is composed of one or more glass tubes filled with neon gas. When an electric current is passed through the tube, the neon atoms absorb some of the electrical energy and reemit it as the familiar red light of a neon sign. If the atoms in the tube are different (that is, not neon), they emit light of a different color. In other words, atoms of each element emit light of a characteristic color. Mercury atoms, for example, emit light that appears blue, helium atoms emit light that appears violet, and hydrogen atoms emit light that appears reddish (Figure 8.10▶).

Remember that the color of visible light is determined by its wavelength. Closer inspection of the light emitted by various atoms reveals that it contains several distinct wavelengths. We can separate the light emitted by a single element in a glass tube into its constituent wavelengths by passing it through a prism (just like we separate the white light from a lightbulb), as shown in Figure 8.11▼. The result is a series of bright lines called an **emission spectrum**. The emission spectrum of a particular element is always the same—it consists of the same bright lines at the same characteristic wavelengths. We can use the emission spectrum to identify the element. For example, light arriving from a distant star contains the emission spectra of the elements that compose the star. Analysis of the light allows us to identify the elements present in the star.

Notice the differences between a white light spectrum and the emission spectra of hydrogen, helium, and barium (shown in Figure 8.11). The white light spectrum is *continuous,* meaning that there are no sudden interruptions in the intensity of the light as a function of wavelength—the spectrum consists of light of all wavelengths. The emission spectra of hydrogen, helium, and barium, however, are not continuous—they consist of bright lines at specific wavelengths, with complete darkness in between. That is, only certain discrete wavelengths of light are present. Classical physics could not explain why these spectra consisted of discrete lines. In fact, according to classical physics, an atom composed of an electron orbiting a nucleus should emit a continuous white light spectrum. Even more problematic, the electron should lose energy as it emits the light and spirals into the nucleus. According to classical physics, an atom should not even be stable.

Johannes Rydberg (1854–1919), a Swedish mathematician, analyzed many atomic spectra and developed an equation that predicts the wavelengths of the hydrogen emission spectrum. However, his equation (shown in the margin) gives little insight into *why* atomic spectra are discrete, *why* atoms are stable, or *why* his equation works.

The Danish physicist Niels Bohr (1885–1962) attempted to develop a model for the hydrogen atom that explained its atomic spectrum. In his model, the electron travels

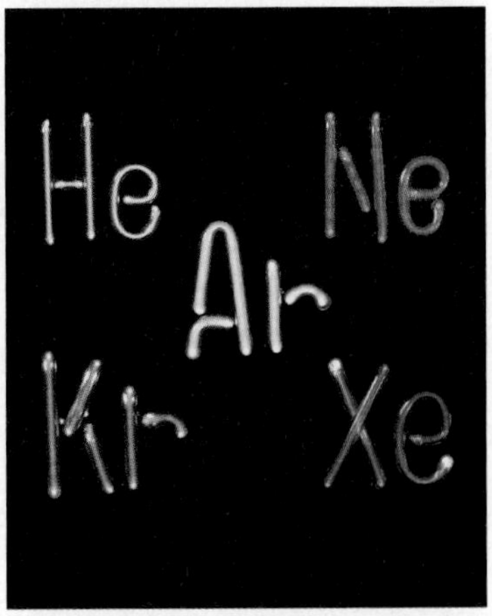

▲ **FIGURE 8.10 Light emitted from various elements.** Each element emits a characteristic color.

The Rydberg equation is $1/\lambda = R(1/m^2 - 1/n^2)$, where R is the Rydberg constant ($1.097 \times 10^7\ m^{-1}$) and m and n are integers.

Emission Spectra

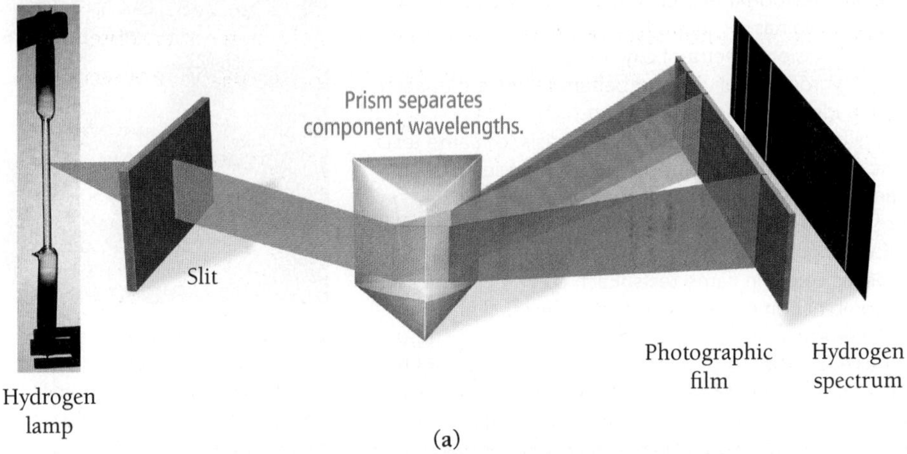

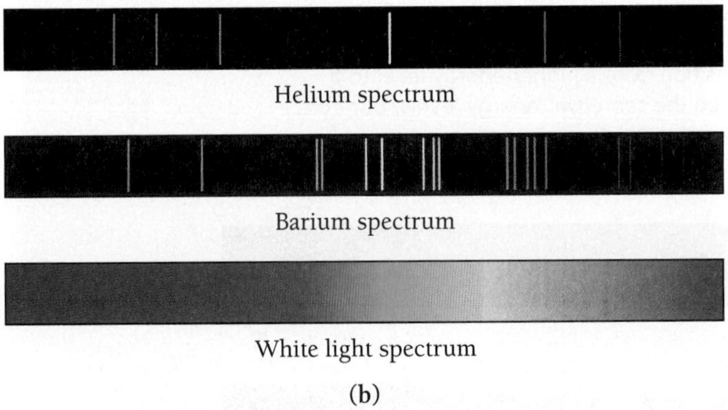

▲ **FIGURE 8.11 Emission Spectra** **(a)** The light emitted from a hydrogen, helium, or barium lamp consists of specific wavelengths that can be separated by passing the light through a prism. **(b)** The resulting bright lines constitute an emission spectrum characteristic of the element that produced it.

The Bohr Model and Emission Spectra

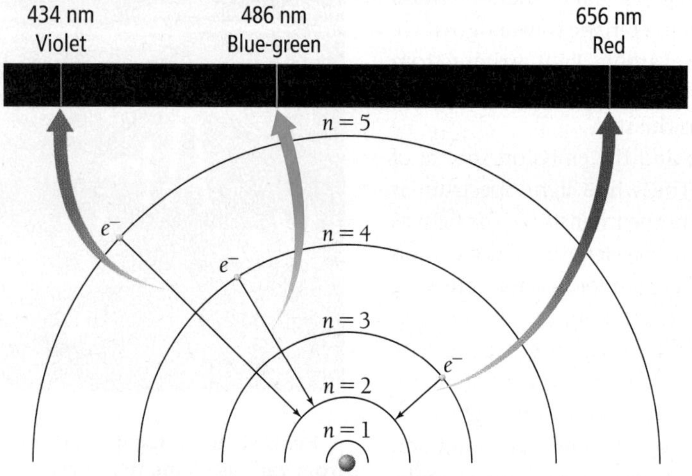

▲ **FIGURE 8.12 The Bohr Model for the Hydrogen Atom** According to the Bohr model, each spectral line is produced when an electron falls from one stable orbit, or stationary state, to another of lower energy.

around the nucleus in circular orbit (analogous to those of the planets around the sun). However, in contrast to planetary orbits—which theoretically can exist at any distance from the sun—Bohr's orbits exist only at specific, fixed distances from the nucleus. The energy of each Bohr orbit is also fixed, or *quantized.* Bohr called these orbits *stationary states* and suggested that, although they obey the laws of classical mechanics, they also possess "a peculiar, mechanically unexplainable, stability." Scientists now know that the stationary states were really manifestations of the wave nature of the electron, which we will expand upon shortly. Bohr further proposed that, in contradiction to classical electromagnetic theory, an electron orbiting the nucleus in a stationary state emits no radiation. It is only when an electron jumps, or makes a *transition*, from one stationary state to another that radiation is emitted or absorbed (Figure 8.12◀).

CHEMISTRY IN YOUR DAY | Atomic Spectroscopy, a Bar Code for Atoms

When you check out of the grocery store, a laser scanner reads the bar code on the items that you buy. Each item has a unique code that identifies the item and its price. Similarly, each element in the periodic table has a spectrum unlike that of any other element. For example, Figure 8.13▼ shows the emission spectra of oxygen and neon. (In Figure 8.11, we saw the emission spectra of hydrogen, helium, and barium.) Notice that each spectrum is unique and, as such, can be used to identify the substance.

The presence of intense lines in the spectra of a number of metals is the basis for *flame tests*, simple tests used to identify elements in ionic compounds in the absence of a precise analysis of a compound's spectrum. For example, the emission spectrum of sodium features two closely spaced, bright yellow lines. When a crystal of a sodium salt (or a drop of a solution containing a sodium salt) is put into a flame, the flame glows bright yellow (Figure 8.14▶). As Figure 8.14 shows, other metals exhibit similarly characteristic colors in flame tests. Each color represents an especially bright spectral emission line (or a combination of two or more such lines). Similar emissions form the basis of the colors seen in fireworks.

Although the *emission* of light from elements is easier to detect, the *absorption* of light by elements is even more commonly used for purposes of identification. Whereas emission spectra consist of bright lines on a dim background, absorption spectra consist of dark lines (absorbed light) on a bright background (Figure 8.15▶). An absorption spectrum is measured by passing white light through a sample and observing what wavelengths are *missing* due to absorption by the sample. Notice that, in the spectrum of mercury shown in Figure 8.15, the absorption lines are at the same wavelengths as the emission lines. This is because the processes that produce them are mirror images. In emission, an electron makes a transition from a higher-energy level to a lower-energy one. In absorption, the transition is between the same two energy levels, but from the lower level to the higher one.

▲ Fireworks typically contain the salts of such metals as sodium, calcium, strontium, barium, and copper. Emissions from these elements produce the brilliant colors of pyrotechnic displays.

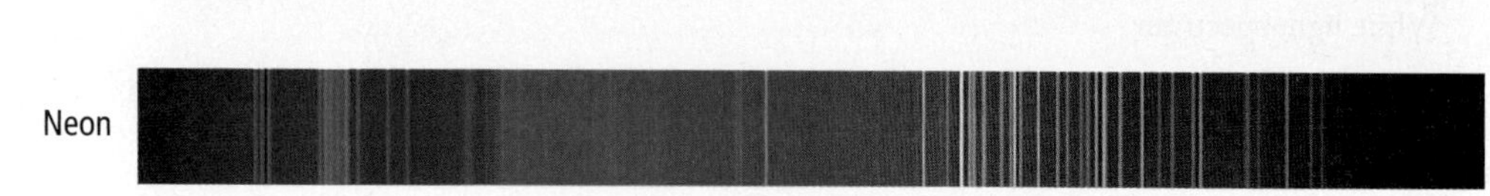

▲ **FIGURE 8.13 Emission Spectra of Oxygen and Neon** The emission spectrum of each element is unique, and we can use it to identify the element.

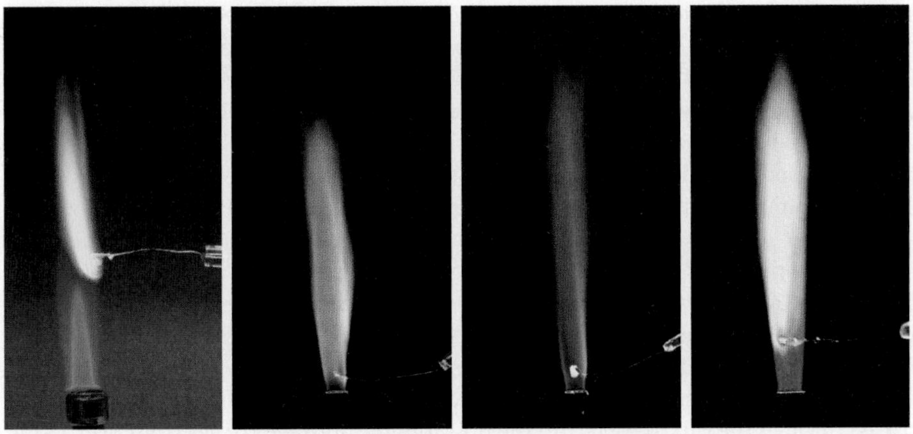

◀ **FIGURE 8.14 Flame Tests (from left to right) for Sodium, Potassium, Lithium, and Barium** We can identify elements by the characteristic color of the light they produce when heated. The colors derive from especially bright lines in their emission spectra.

Absorption spectrometers, found in most chemistry laboratories, typically plot the intensity of absorption as a function of wavelength. Such plots are useful both for identifying substances (qualitative analysis) and for determining the concentration of substances (quantitative analysis). Quantitative analysis is possible because the amount of light absorbed by a sample depends on the concentration of the absorbing substance within the sample. For example, we can determine the concentration of Ca^{2+} in a hard water sample by measuring the quantity of light absorbed by the calcium ion at its characteristic wavelength.

In spite of its initial success in explaining the line spectrum of hydrogen, the Bohr model left many unanswered questions. It did, however, serve as an intermediate model between a classical view of the electron and a fully quantum-mechanical view, and therefore has great historical and conceptual importance. Nonetheless, it was ultimately replaced by a more complete quantum-mechanical theory that fully incorporated the wave nature of the electron.

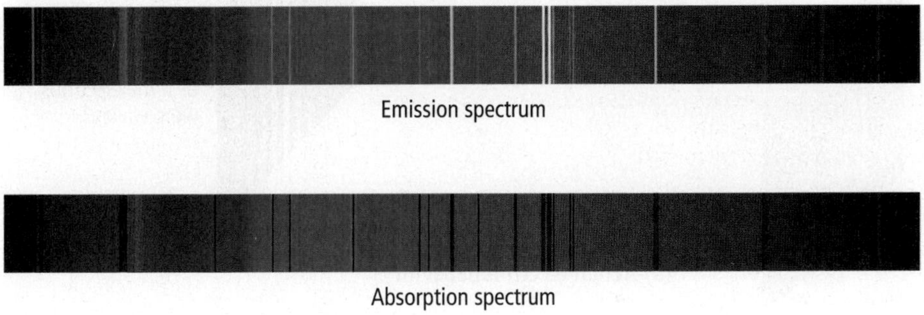

◀ **FIGURE 8.15 Emission and Absorption Spectrum of Mercury** Elements absorb light of the same wavelengths that they radiate when heated. When these wavelengths are subtracted from a beam of white light, the result is a pattern of dark lines corresponding to an absorption spectrum.

The transitions between stationary states in a hydrogen atom are quite unlike transitions in the macroscopic world. The electron is *never* observed *between states*; it is observed only in one state or another. The emission spectrum of an atom consists of discrete lines because the stationary states exist only at specific, fixed energies. The energy of the photon emitted when an electron makes a transition from one stationary state to another is the energy difference between the two stationary states. Transitions between stationary states that are closer together, therefore, produce light of lower energy (longer wavelength) than transitions between stationary states that are farther apart.

8.4 The Wave Nature of Matter: The de Broglie Wavelength, the Uncertainty Principle, and Indeterminacy

WATCH **NOW!**

KEY CONCEPT VIDEO 8.4
The Wave Nature of Matter

The heart of quantum-mechanical theory is the wave nature of the electron, first proposed by Louis de Broglie (1892–1987) in 1924 and confirmed by experiments in 1927. It seemed incredible at the time, but electrons—which were then thought of only as particles and known to have mass—also have a wave nature. The wave nature of the electron is seen most clearly in its diffraction. If an electron beam is aimed at two closely

The Davisson–Germer experiment of 1927 provided the first evidence of electron wave properties. In this experiment, electrons were observed to undergo diffraction by a metal crystal.

spaced slits, and a series (or array) of detectors is arranged to detect the electrons after they pass through the slits, an interference pattern similar to that observed for light (see Figure 8.6) is recorded behind the slits (Figure 8.16(a)▼). The detectors at the center of the array (midway between the two slits) detect a large number of electrons—exactly the opposite of what you would expect for particles (Figure 8.16(b)▼). Moving outward from this center spot, the detectors alternately detect small numbers of electrons and then large numbers again and so on, forming an interference pattern characteristic of waves.

For interference to occur, the spacing of the slits has to be on the order of atomic dimensions.

Counter to what might be our initial intuition about electron interference, the interference pattern is *not caused by pairs of electrons interfering with each other, but rather by single electrons interfering with themselves*. If the electron source is turned down to a very low level, so that electrons come out only one at a time, *the interference pattern remains*. In other words, we can design an experiment in which electrons come out of the source singly. We can then record where each electron strikes the detector after it has passed through the slits. If we record the positions of thousands of electrons over a long period of time, we find the same interference pattern shown in Figure 8.16(a).

This observation leads us to an important conclusion: *the wave nature of the electron is an inherent property of individual electrons*. Recall from Section 8.1 that unobserved electrons can simultaneously occupy two different states. In this case, the unobserved electron goes through both slits—it exists in two states simultaneously, just like Schrödinger's cat—and interferes with itself. This wave nature explains the existence of stationary states (in the Bohr model) and prevents the electrons in an atom from crashing into the nucleus as predicted by

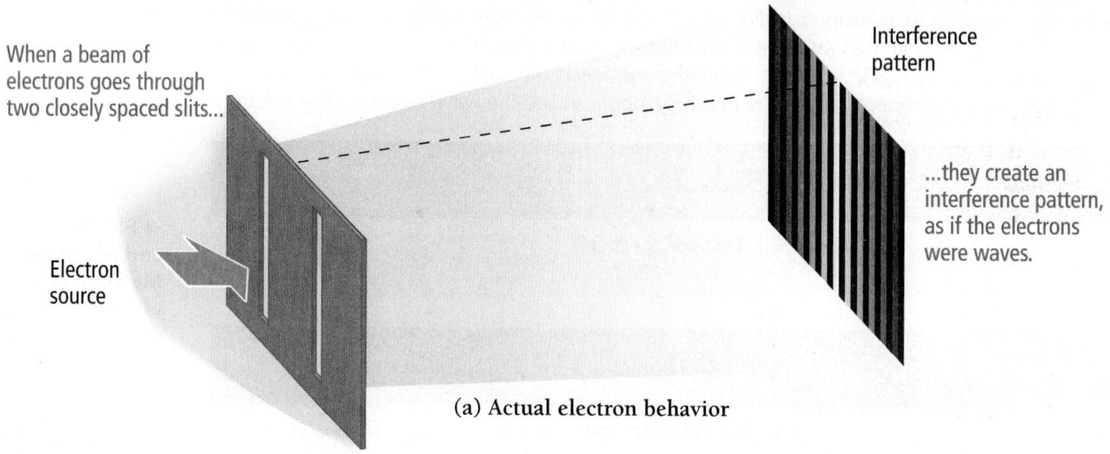

(a) Actual electron behavior

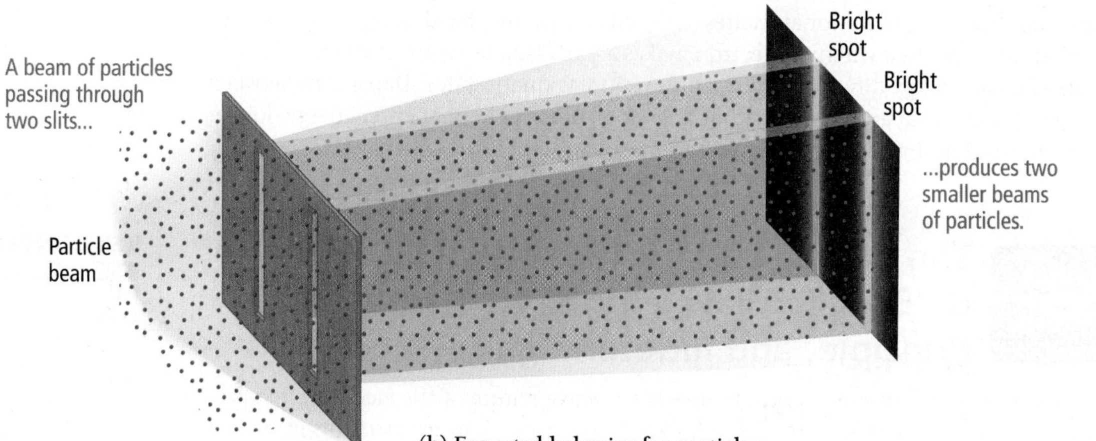

(b) Expected behavior for particles

▲ **FIGURE 8.16 Electron Diffraction** Notice that the wave source (electrons) produces a diffraction pattern that is brightest at the center, whereas the particle beam produces two bright stripes and a central dark band.

classical physics. We now turn to three important manifestations of the electron's wave nature: the de Broglie wavelength, the uncertainty principle, and indeterminacy.

The de Broglie Wavelength

As we have seen, a single electron traveling through space has a wave nature; its wavelength is related to its kinetic energy (the energy associated with its motion). The faster the electron is moving, the higher its kinetic energy and the shorter its wavelength. The wavelength (λ) of an electron of mass m moving at velocity v is given by the **de Broglie relation**:

$$\lambda = \frac{h}{mv} \quad \text{de Broglie relation} \qquad [8.4]$$

The mass of an object (m) times its velocity (v) is its momentum. Therefore, the wavelength of an electron is inversely proportional to its momentum.

where h is Planck's constant. *Notice that the velocity of a moving electron is related to its wavelength—knowing one is equivalent to knowing the other.*

EXAMPLE 8.4 De Broglie Wavelength

Calculate the wavelength of an electron traveling with a speed of 2.65×10^6 m/s.

SORT You are given the speed of an electron and asked to calculate its wavelength.

GIVEN: $v = 2.65 \times 10^6$ m/s

FIND: λ

STRATEGIZE The conceptual plan shows how the de Broglie relation relates the wavelength of an electron to its mass and velocity.

CONCEPTUAL PLAN

$v \rightarrow \lambda$

$$\lambda = \frac{h}{mv}$$

RELATIONSHIPS USED

$\lambda = h/mv$ (de Broglie relation, Equation 8.4)

SOLVE Substitute the velocity, Planck's constant, and the mass of an electron into Equation 8.4 to calculate the electron's wavelength. To correctly cancel the units, break down the J in Planck's constant into its SI base units ($1\text{ J} = 1\text{ kg}\cdot\text{m}^2/\text{s}^2$).

SOLUTION

$$\lambda = \frac{h}{mv} = \frac{6.626 \times 10^{-34} \frac{\text{kg}\cdot\text{m}^2}{\text{s}^2}\text{s}}{(9.11 \times 10^{-31}\text{ kg})\left(2.65 \times 10^6 \frac{\text{m}}{\text{s}}\right)}$$

$$= 2.74 \times 10^{-10}\text{ m}$$

CHECK The units of the answer (m) are correct. The magnitude of the answer is very small, as expected for the wavelength of an electron.

FOR PRACTICE 8.4 What is the velocity of an electron that has a de Broglie wavelength approximately the length of a chemical bond? Assume the length of a chemical bond is 1.2×10^{-10} m.

THE DE BROGLIE WAVELENGTH OF MACROSCOPIC OBJECTS Since quantum-mechanical theory is universal, it applies to all objects, regardless of size. Therefore, according to the de Broglie relation, a thrown baseball should also exhibit wave properties. Why don't we observe such properties at the ballpark?

8.4 Cc Conceptual Connection ANSWER **NOW!**

(a) Because of the baseball's large mass, its de Broglie wavelength is minuscule and insignificant compared to the baseball's size.

(b) Since baseballs do not have any charge, quantum mechanics does not apply to them.

(c) Quantum mechanics does not apply to baseballs.

The Uncertainty Principle

The wave nature of the electron is difficult to reconcile with its particle nature. How can a single entity behave as both a wave and a particle? We can begin to address this question by returning to the single-electron diffraction experiment. How does a single electron aimed at a double slit produce an interference pattern? We saw previously that the electron travels through both slits and interferes with itself. This idea is testable. We simply have to observe the single electron as it travels through both of the slits. If it travels through both slits simultaneously, our hypothesis is correct. But here is where nature gets tricky.

Any experiment designed to observe the electron as it travels through the slits results in the detection of an electron "particle" traveling through a single slit and no interference pattern. Recall from Section 8.1 that an *unobserved* electron can occupy two different states; however, the act of observation forces it into one state or the other. Similarly, the act of observing the electron as it travels through both slits forces it to go through only one slit. The electron diffraction experiment illustrated here is designed to observe which slit the electron travels through by using a laser beam placed directly behind the slits:

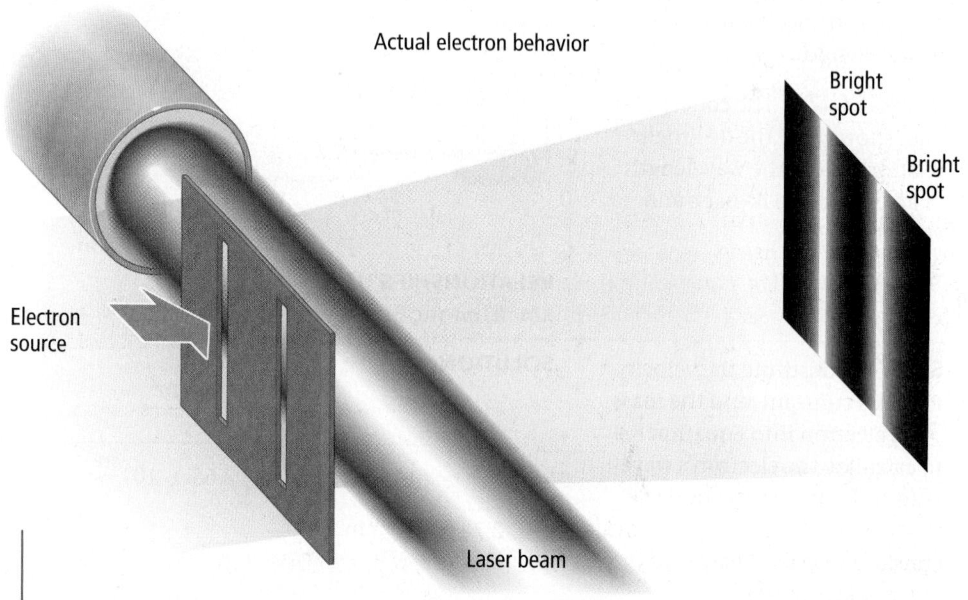

The laser experiment described here is not an actual experiment because it would be difficult to carry out for practical reasons; however, the results are consistent with similar experiments designed to measure the same thing.

An electron that crosses the laser beam produces a tiny "flash" when a single photon is scattered at the point of crossing. If a flash shows up behind a particular slit, that indicates an electron is passing through that slit. However, as the electrons are detected, the flash always originates either from one slit *or* the other, but *never* from both at once. Furthermore, the interference pattern, which was present without the laser, is absent when the electrons are observed going through the slits. With the laser on, the electrons hit positions directly behind each slit, as if they were ordinary particles; their wavelike behavior is no longer observed.

As it turns out, no matter how hard we try or whatever method we set up, *we can never both see the interference pattern and simultaneously determine which hole the electron goes through.* It has never been done, and most scientists agree that it never will. In the words of theoretical physicist P. A. M. Dirac (1902–1984),

> There is a limit to the fineness of our powers of observation and the smallness of the accompanying disturbance—a limit which is inherent in the nature of things and can never be surpassed by improved technique or increased skill on the part of the observer.

The single electron diffraction experiment demonstrates that we cannot simultaneously observe both the wave nature and the particle nature of the electron. When we try to observe which hole the electron goes through (associated with the particle nature of the electron), we lose the interference pattern (associated with the wave nature of the electron). When we try to observe the interference pattern, we cannot determine which hole the electron goes through. The wave nature and particle nature of the electron are said to be **complementary properties**. Complementary properties exclude one another—the more we know about one, the less we know about the other. Which of two complementary properties we observe depends on the experiment we perform—in quantum mechanics, the observation of an event affects its outcome.

As we just saw in the de Broglie relation, the *velocity* of an electron is related to its *wave nature.* The *position* of an electron, however, is related to its *particle nature.* (Particles have well-defined position, but waves do not.) Consequently, our inability to observe the electron simultaneously as both a particle and a wave means that *we cannot simultaneously measure its position and its velocity.* Werner Heisenberg (1901–1976) formalized this idea with the equation:

▲ Werner Heisenberg, a pioneer of quantum mechanics

$$\Delta x \times m\Delta v \geq \frac{h}{4\pi} \quad \text{Heisenberg's uncertainty principle} \quad [8.5]$$

where Δx is the uncertainty in the position, Δv is the uncertainty in the velocity, m is the mass of the particle, and h is Planck's constant. **Heisenberg's uncertainty principle** states that the product of Δx and $m\Delta v$ must be greater than or equal to a finite number ($h/4\pi$). In other words, the more accurately we know the position of an electron (the smaller Δx), the less accurately we can know its velocity (the bigger Δv) and vice versa. The complementarity of the wave nature and particle nature of the electron results in the complementarity of velocity and position.

Although Heisenberg's uncertainty principle may seem puzzling, it actually solves a great puzzle. Without the uncertainty principle, we are left with a paradox: how can something be *both* a particle and a wave? Saying that an object is both a particle and a wave is like saying that an object is both a circle and a square, a contradiction. Heisenberg solved the contradiction by introducing complementarity—an electron is observed as *either* a particle or a wave but never both at once. This idea was captured by Schrödinger's thought experiment about the cat, which we discussed in Section 8.1: when observed, the cat is either dead or alive, not both.

8.5 Cc Conceptual Connection

ANSWER NOW!

THE UNCERTAINTY PRINCIPLE Which statement best summarizes the uncertainty principle?

(a) Both the position and the velocity of an electron can be accurately known at the same instant.

(b) Either the position or the velocity of an electron can be accurately known at the same instant.

(c) Neither the position nor the velocity of an electron can be accurately known at the same instant.

Indeterminacy and Probability Distribution Maps

According to classical physics, and in particular Newton's laws of motion, particles move in a *trajectory* (or path) that is determined by the particle's velocity (the speed and direction of travel), its position, and the forces acting on it. Even if you are not familiar with Newton's laws, you probably have an intuitive sense of them. For example, when you chase a baseball in the outfield, you visually predict where the ball will land by observing its path. You do this by noting its initial position and velocity, watching how these are affected by the forces acting on it (gravity, air resistance, wind), and then inferring its trajectory, as shown in Figure 8.17▶. If you knew only the ball's velocity, or only its position (imagine a still photo of the baseball in the air), you could not predict its landing spot. In classical mechanics, both position and velocity are required to predict a trajectory.

The Classical Concept of Trajectory

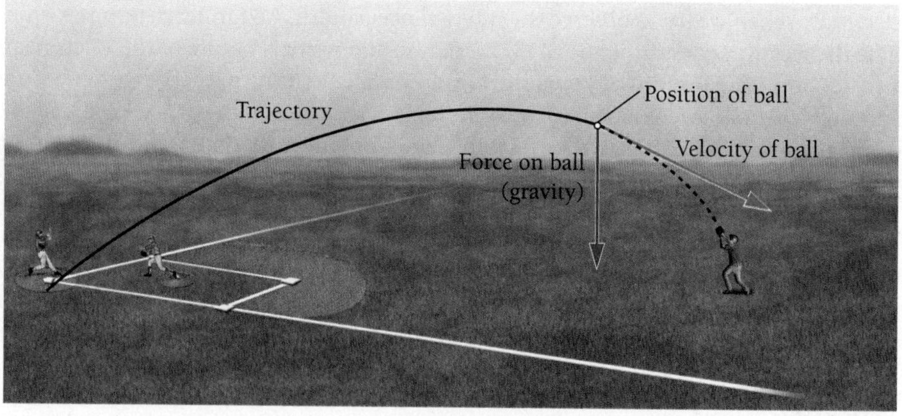

▶ **FIGURE 8.17 The Concept of Trajectory** In classical mechanics, the position and velocity of a particle determine its future trajectory, or path. Thus, an outfielder can catch a baseball by observing its position and velocity, allowing for the effects of forces acting on it, such as gravity, and estimating its trajectory. (For simplicity, air resistance and wind are not shown.)

Remember that velocity includes speed as well as direction of travel.

Newton's laws of motion are **deterministic**—the present *determines* the future. This means that if two baseballs are hit consecutively with the same velocity from the same position under identical conditions, they will land in exactly the same place. The same is not true of electrons. We have just seen that we cannot simultaneously know the position and velocity of an electron; therefore, we cannot know its trajectory. In quantum mechanics, trajectories are replaced with *probability distribution maps* (Figure 8.18▼). A probability distribution map is a statistical map that shows where an electron is likely to be found under a given set of conditions.

▲ **FIGURE 8.18 Trajectory versus Probability** In quantum mechanics, we cannot calculate deterministic trajectories. Instead, it is necessary to think in terms of probability maps: statistical pictures of where a quantum-mechanical particle, such as an electron, is most likely to be found. In this hypothetical map, darker shading indicates greater probability.

▲ **FIGURE 8.19 Trajectory of a Macroscopic Object** A baseball follows a well-defined trajectory from the hand of the pitcher to the mitt of the catcher.

To understand the concept of a probability distribution map, let us return to baseball. Imagine a baseball thrown from the pitcher's mound to a catcher behind home plate (Figure 8.19◀). The catcher can watch the baseball's path, predict exactly where it will cross home plate, and place his mitt in the correct place to catch it. As we have seen, the same predictions cannot be made for an electron. If an electron were thrown from the pitcher's mound to home plate, it would land in a different place every time, even if it were thrown in exactly the same way. This behavior is called **indeterminacy**. A baseball's future path is *determined* by its position and velocity when it leaves the pitcher's hand. In contrast, the future path of an electron is indeterminate and can only be described statistically.

In the quantum-mechanical world of the electron, the catcher cannot know where the electron will cross the plate for any given throw. However, if he were to record hundreds of identical electron throws, the catcher would observe a reproducible, *statistical pattern* of where the electron crosses the plate. He could even draw a map of the strike zone showing the probability of an electron crossing a certain area, as shown in Figure 8.20▶. This is a probability distribution map. In the sections that follow, we discuss quantum-mechanical electron *orbitals*, which are essentially probability distribution maps for electrons as they exist within atoms.

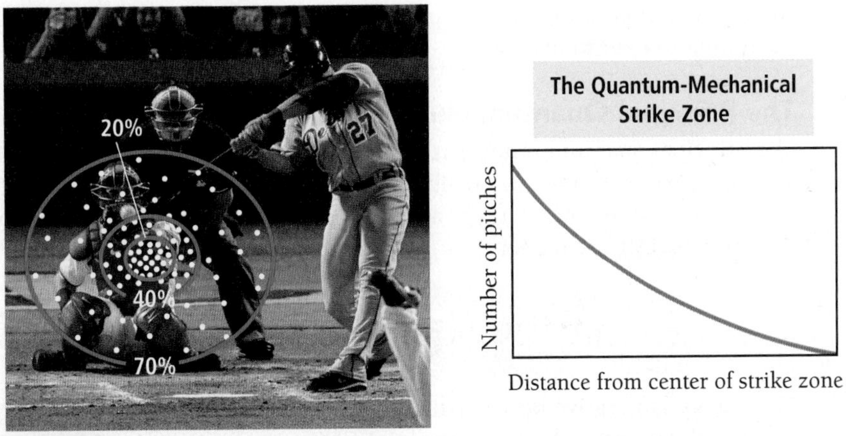

◀ **FIGURE 8.20 The Quantum-Mechanical Strike Zone** An electron does not have a well-defined trajectory. However, we can construct a probability distribution map to show the relative probability of it crossing home plate at different points.

8.5 Quantum Mechanics and the Atom

WATCH **NOW!**

KEY CONCEPT VIDEO 8.5A
Quantum Mechanics and the Atom: Orbitals and Quantum Numbers

As we have seen, the position and velocity of the electron are complementary properties—if we know one accurately, the other becomes indeterminate. Since velocity is directly related to energy (recall that kinetic energy equals $\frac{1}{2}mv^2$), position and *energy* are also complementary properties—the more we know about one, the less we know about the other. Many of the properties of an element, however, depend on the energies of its electrons. For example, whether an electron is transferred from one atom to another to form an ionic bond depends in part on the relative energies of the electron in the two atoms.

In the following paragraphs, we describe the probability distribution maps for electron states in which the electron has well-defined energy but not well-defined position. In other words, for each of these states, we can specify the *energy* of the electron precisely, but not its location at a given instant. Instead, the electron's position is described in terms of an **orbital**, a probability distribution map showing where the electron is likely to be found. Since chemical bonding often involves the sharing of electrons between atoms to form covalent bonds, the spatial distribution of atomic electrons is important to bonding.

These states are known as energy *eigenstates*.

The mathematical derivation of energies and orbitals for electrons in atoms comes from solving the Schrödinger equation for the atom of interest. The general form of the Schrödinger equation is:

$$\mathcal{H}\psi = E\psi \qquad [8.6]$$

The symbol $\mathcal{H}$ is the Hamiltonian operator, a set of mathematical operations that represents the total energy (kinetic and potential) of the electron within the atom. The symbol E is the actual energy of the electron. The symbol ψ is the **wave function**, a mathematical function that describes the wavelike nature of the electron. A plot of the wave function squared (ψ^2) represents an orbital, a position probability distribution map of the electron.

An operator is different from a normal algebraic entity. In general, an operator transforms a mathematical function into another mathematical function. For example, d/dx is an operator that means "take the derivative of." When d/dx operates on a function (such as x^2), it returns another function ($2x$).

The symbol ψ is the Greek letter psi, pronounced "sigh."

Solutions to the Schrödinger Equation for the Hydrogen Atom

When the Schrödinger equation is solved, it yields many solutions—many possible wave functions. The wave functions themselves are fairly complicated mathematical functions, and we do not examine them in detail in this book. Instead, we introduce graphical representations (or plots) of the orbitals that correspond to the wave functions. Each orbital is specified by three interrelated **quantum numbers:**

- n, the **principal quantum number**
- l, the **angular momentum quantum number** (sometimes called the *azimuthal quantum number*)
- m_l, the **magnetic quantum number**

These quantum numbers all have integer values, as had been hinted at by both the Rydberg equation and Bohr's model. A fourth quantum number, m_s, the **spin quantum number**,

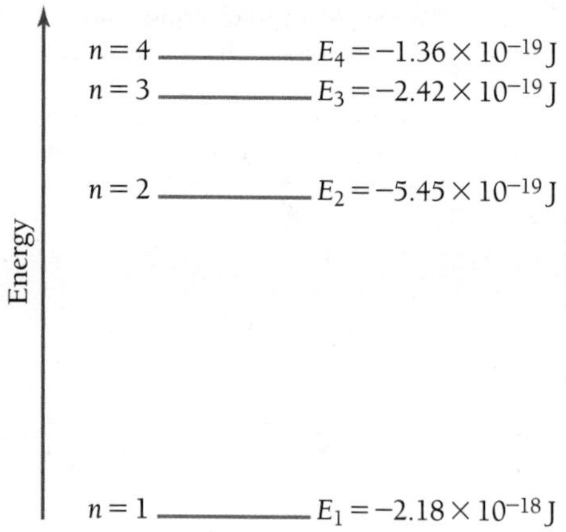

specifies the orientation of the spin of the electron. We examine each of these quantum numbers individually.

The Principal Quantum Number (*n*)

The principal quantum number is an integer that determines the overall size and energy of an orbital. Its possible values are $n = 1, 2, 3, \ldots$ and so on. For the hydrogen atom, the energy of an electron in an orbital with quantum number *n* is given by the equation:

$$E_n = -2.18 \times 10^{-18}\,\text{J}\left(\frac{1}{n^2}\right) \qquad (n = 1, 2, 3, \ldots) \qquad [8.7]$$

The energy is negative because the electron's energy is lowered (made more negative) by its interaction with the nucleus (see the description of Coulomb's law in Section 9.3). The constant, 2.18×10^{-18} J, is known as the Rydberg constant for hydrogen (R_H). Notice that orbitals with higher values of *n* have greater (less negative) energies, as shown in the energy-level diagram at left. Notice also that, as *n* increases, the spacing between the energy levels decreases.

The Angular Momentum Quantum Number (*l*)

The angular momentum quantum number is an integer that determines the shape of the orbital. We will consider these shapes in Section 8.6. The possible values of *l* are $0, 1, 2, \ldots, (n - 1)$. In other words, for a given value of *n*, *l* can be any integer (including 0) up to $n - 1$. For example, if $n = 1$, then the only possible value of *l* is 0; if $n = 2$, the possible values of *l* are 0 and 1. To avoid confusion between *n* and *l*, values of *l* are often assigned letters as follows:

The values of *l* beyond 3 are designated with letters in alphabetical order so that $l = 4$ is designated *g*, $l = 5$ is designated *h*, and so on.

Value of *l*	Letter Designation
$l = 0$	s
$l = 1$	p
$l = 2$	d
$l = 3$	f

ANSWER **NOW!**

8.6 Cc Conceptual Connection

THE RELATIONSHIP BETWEEN *n* AND *l* What values of *l* are possible for $n = 3$?

(a) 0 (or *s*)
(b) 0 and 1 (or *s* and *p*)
(c) 0, 1, and 2 (or *s*, *p*, and *d*)
(d) 0, 1, 2, and 3 (or *s*, *p*, *d*, and *f*)

The Magnetic Quantum Number (m_l)

The magnetic quantum number is an integer that specifies the orientation of the orbital. We will consider these orientations in Section 8.6. The possible values of m_l are the integer values (including zero) ranging from $-l$ to $+l$. For example, if $l = 0$, then the only possible value of m_l is 0; if $l = 1$, the possible values of m_l are -1, 0, and $+1$.

ANSWER **NOW!**

8.7 Cc Conceptual Connection

THE RELATIONSHIP BETWEEN *l* AND m_l What values of m_l are possible for $l = 2$?

(a) 0, 1, and 2
(b) 0
(c) -1, 0, and $+1$
(d) $-2, -1, 0, +1$, and $+2$

The Spin Quantum Number (m_s)

The idea of a "spinning" electron is something of a metaphor. A more correct way to express the same idea is to say that an electron has inherent angular momentum.

The spin quantum number specifies the orientation of the *spin* of the electron. Electron spin is a fundamental property of an electron (like its negative charge). One electron does not have more or less spin than another—all electrons have the same amount of spin. The orientation of the electron's spin is quantized, with only two possibilities: that we can call spin up ($m_s = +1/2$) and spin down ($m_s = -1/2$). The spin quantum number becomes important in Section 9.3 when we begin to consider how electrons occupy orbitals. Here, we focus only on the first three quantum numbers.

Each specific combination of the first three quantum numbers (n, l, and m_l) specifies one atomic orbital. For example, the orbital with $n = 1, l = 0$, and $m_l = 0$ is known as the 1*s* orbital. The 1 in 1*s* is the value of n, and the *s* specifies that $l = 0$. There is only one 1*s* orbital in an atom, and its m_l value is zero. Orbitals with the same value of n are said to be in the same **principal level (or principal shell)**. Orbitals with the same value of n and l are said to be in the same **sublevel (or subshell)**. The following diagram shows all of the orbitals (each represented by a small square) in the first three principal levels:

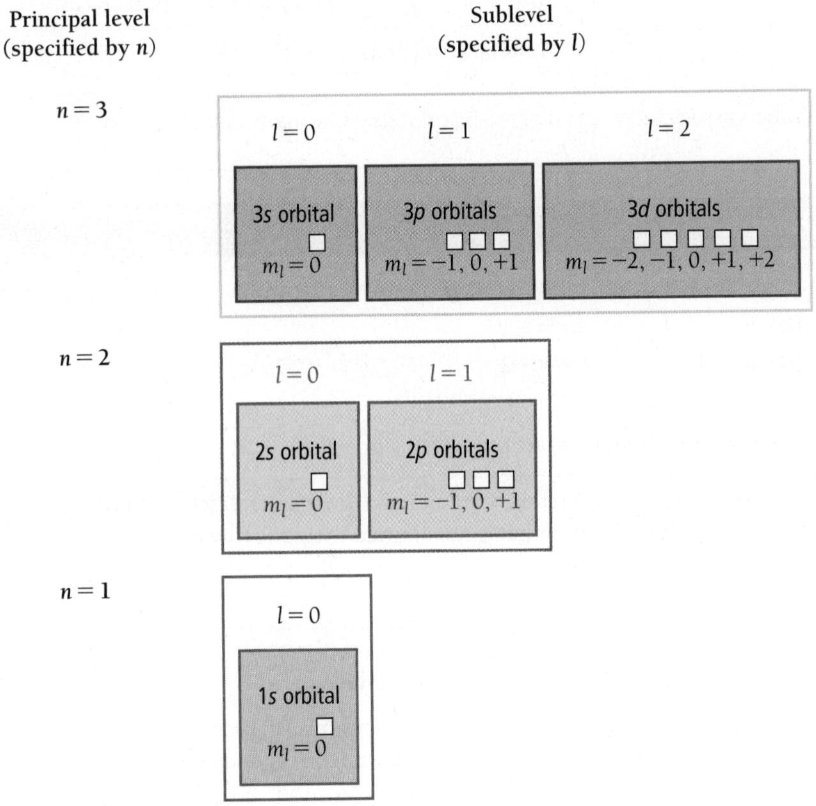

For example, the $n = 2$ level contains the $l = 0$ and $l = 1$ sublevels. Within the $n = 2$ level, the $l = 0$ sublevel—called the 2*s* sublevel—contains only one orbital (the 2*s* orbital), with $m_l = 0$. The $l = 1$ sublevel—called the 2*p* sublevel—contains three 2*p* orbitals, with $m_l = -1, 0, +1$.

Summarizing Orbitals

- The number of sublevels in any level is equal to n, the principal quantum number. Therefore, the $n = 1$ level has one sublevel, the $n = 2$ level has two sublevels, and so on.
- The number of orbitals in any sublevel is equal to $2l + 1$. Therefore, the *s* sublevel ($l = 0$) has one orbital, the *p* sublevel ($l = 1$) has three orbitals, the *d* sublevel ($l = 2$) has five orbitals, and so on.
- The number of orbitals in a level is equal to n^2. Therefore, the $n = 1$ level has one orbital, the $n = 2$ level has four orbitals, the $n = 3$ level has nine orbitals, and so on.

WATCH **NOW!**

INTERACTIVE WORKED EXAMPLE 8.5

EXAMPLE 8.5 Quantum Numbers I

What are the quantum numbers and names (for example, 2*s*, 2*p*) of the orbitals in the $n = 4$ principal level? How many $n = 4$ orbitals exist?

SOLUTION

First, determine the possible values of l (from the given value of n). For a given value of n, the possible values of l are $0, 1, 2, \ldots, (n - 1)$.

$n = 4$; therefore, $l = 0, 1, 2,$ and 3

Next, determine the possible values of m_l for each value of l. For a given value of l, the possible values of m_l are the integer values, including zero, ranging from $-l$ to $+l$. The name of an orbital is its principal quantum number (n) followed by the letter corresponding to the value l. The total number of orbitals is given by n^2.

l	Possible m_l Values	Orbital Name
0	0	4*s* (1 orbital)
1	−1, 0, +1	4*p* (3 orbitals)
2	−2, −1, 0, +1, +2	4*d* (5 orbitals)
3	−3, −2, −1, 0, +1, +2, +3	4*f* (7 orbitals)
Total number of orbitals $= 4^2 = 16$		

FOR PRACTICE 8.5 List the quantum numbers associated with all of the 5*d* orbitals. How many 5*d* orbitals exist?

EXAMPLE 8.6 Quantum Numbers II

These sets of quantum numbers are each supposed to specify an orbital. One set, however, is erroneous. Which one and why?

(a) $n = 3;\ l = 0;\ m_l = 0$ **(b)** $n = 2;\ l = 1;\ m_l = -1$

(c) $n = 1;\ l = 0;\ m_l = 0$ **(d)** $n = 4;\ l = 1;\ m_l = -2$

SOLUTION

Choice **(d)** is erroneous because for $l = 1$, the possible values of m_l are only -1, 0, and $+1$.

FOR PRACTICE 8.6 Each set of quantum numbers is supposed to specify an orbital. However, each set contains one quantum number that is not allowed. Replace the quantum number that is not allowed with one that is allowed.

(a) $n = 3;\ l = 3;\ m_l = +2$ **(b)** $n = 2;\ l = 1;\ m_l = -2$ **(c)** $n = 1;\ l = 1;\ m_l = 0$

WATCH **NOW!**

KEY CONCEPT VIDEO 8.5B
Atomic Spectroscopy

Atomic Spectroscopy Explained

Quantum theory explains the atomic spectra of atoms we discussed in Section 8.3. Each wavelength in the emission spectrum of an atom corresponds to an electron *transition* between quantum-mechanical orbitals. When an atom absorbs energy, an electron in a lower-energy orbital is *excited* or promoted to a higher-energy orbital, as shown in Figure 8.21▼. In this new configuration, however, the atom is unstable, and the

Excitation and Radiation

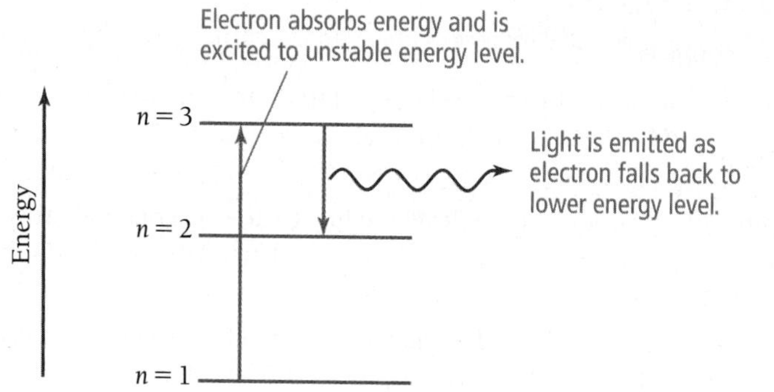

▶ **FIGURE 8.21 Excitation and Radiation** When an atom absorbs energy, an electron can be excited from an orbital in a lower-energy level to an orbital in a higher-energy level. The electron in this "excited state" is unstable, however, and relaxes to a lower-energy level, releasing energy in the form of electromagnetic radiation.

electron quickly falls back or *relaxes* to a lower-energy orbital. As it does so, it releases a photon of light containing an amount of energy precisely equal to the energy difference between the two energy levels. We saw previously (see Equation 8.7) that the energy of an orbital in a hydrogen atom with principal quantum number n is given by $E_n = -2.18 \times 10^{-18}\,\text{J}(1/n^2)$, where $n = 1, 2, 3, \ldots$ The *difference* in energy between two levels n_{initial} and n_{final} is given by $\Delta E = E_{\text{final}} - E_{\text{initial}}$. If we substitute the expression for E_n into the expression for ΔE, we get the following important expression for the change in energy that occurs in a hydrogen atom when an electron changes energy levels:

$$\begin{aligned}\Delta E &= E_{\text{final}} - E_{\text{initial}}\\ &= -2.18 \times 10^{-18}\,\text{J}\left(\frac{1}{n_f^2}\right) - \left[-2.18 \times 10^{-18}\,\text{J}\left(\frac{1}{n_i^2}\right)\right]\end{aligned}$$

$$\Delta E = -2.18 \times 10^{-18}\,\text{J}\left(\frac{1}{n_f^2} - \frac{1}{n_i^2}\right) \quad [8.8]$$

For example, suppose that an electron in a hydrogen atom relaxes from an orbital in the $n = 3$ level to an orbital in the $n = 2$ level. We determine ΔE, the energy difference corresponding to the transition from $n = 3$ to $n = 2$, as follows:

The Rydberg equation, $1/\lambda = R(1/m^2 - 1/n^2)$, can be derived from the relationships just covered. We leave this derivation to an exercise (see Problem 8.98).

$$\begin{aligned}\Delta E_{\text{atom}} &= E_2 - E_3\\ &= -2.18 \times 10^{-18}\,\text{J}\left(\frac{1}{2^2}\right) - \left[-2.18 \times 10^{-18}\,\text{J}\left(\frac{1}{3^2}\right)\right]\\ &= -2.18 \times 10^{-18}\,\text{J}\left(\frac{1}{2^2} - \frac{1}{3^2}\right)\\ &= -3.03 \times 10^{-19}\,\text{J}\end{aligned}$$

The energy carries a negative sign because the atom *emits* the energy as it relaxes from $n = 3$ to $n = 2$. Since energy must be conserved, the exact amount of energy emitted by the atom is carried away by the photon:

The energy of a photon is always positive.

$$\Delta E_{\text{atom}} = -E_{\text{photon}}$$

This energy determines the frequency and wavelength of the photon. Since the wavelength of the photon is related to its energy as $E = hc/\lambda$, we calculate the wavelength of the photon as:

$$\begin{aligned}\lambda &= \frac{hc}{E}\\ &= \frac{(6.626 \times 10^{-34}\,\cancel{\text{J}}\cdot\cancel{\text{s}})(3.00 \times 10^{8}\,\text{m}/\cancel{\text{s}})}{3.03 \times 10^{-19}\,\cancel{\text{J}}}\\ &= 6.56 \times 10^{-7}\,\text{m} \quad \text{or} \quad 656\,\text{nm}\end{aligned}$$

Consequently, the light emitted by an excited hydrogen atom as it relaxes from an orbital in the $n = 3$ level to an orbital in the $n = 2$ level has a wavelength of 656 nm (red). Similarly, we can calculate the light emitted due to a transition from $n = 4$ to $n = 2$, which is 486 nm (green). Notice that transitions between orbitals that are further apart in energy produce light that is higher in energy, and therefore shorter in wavelength, than transitions between orbitals that are closer together. Figure 8.22▶ shows several of the transitions in the hydrogen atom and their corresponding wavelengths.

EMISSION SPECTRA Which transition emits light with the shortest wavelength?

(a) $n = 5 \longrightarrow n = 4$ **(b)** $n = 4 \longrightarrow n = 3$

(c) $n = 3 \longrightarrow n = 2$

8.8 Cc Conceptual Connection

ANSWER **NOW!**

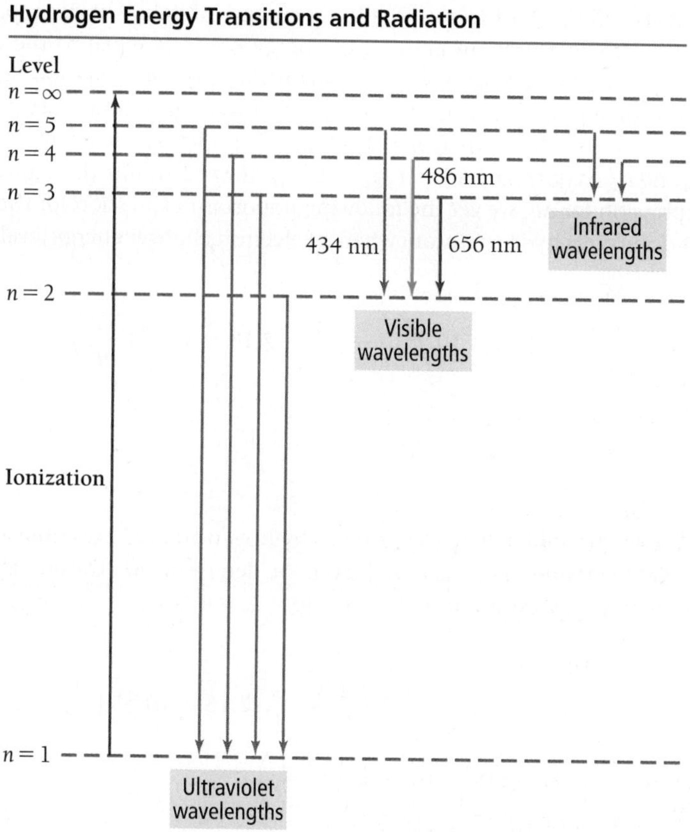

▶ **FIGURE 8.22 Hydrogen Energy Transitions and Radiation** An atomic energy level diagram for hydrogen, showing some possible electron transitions between levels and the corresponding wavelengths of emitted light.

WATCH **NOW!**
INTERACTIVE WORKED EXAMPLE 8.7

EXAMPLE 8.7 Wavelength of Light for a Transition in the Hydrogen Atom

Determine the wavelength of light emitted when an electron in a hydrogen atom makes a transition from an orbital in $n = 6$ to an orbital in $n = 5$.

SORT You are given the energy levels of an atomic transition and asked to find the wavelength of emitted light.

GIVEN: $n = 6 \longrightarrow n = 5$

FIND: λ

STRATEGIZE In the first part of the conceptual plan, calculate the energy of the electron in the $n = 6$ and $n = 5$ orbitals using Equation 8.7 and subtract to find ΔE_{atom}.

CONCEPTUAL PLAN

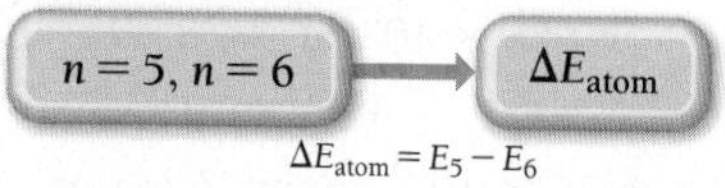

In the second part, find E_{photon} by taking the negative of ΔE_{atom} and then calculate the wavelength corresponding to a photon of this energy using Equation 8.3. (The difference in sign between E_{photon} and ΔE_{atom} applies only to emission. *The energy of a photon must always be positive.*)

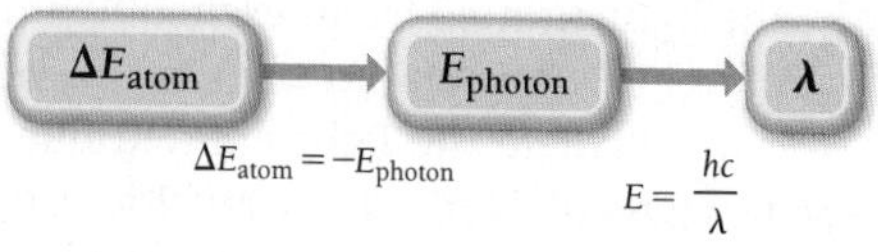

RELATIONSHIPS USED

$E_n = -2.18 \times 10^{-18}\,\text{J}(1/n^2)$
$E = hc/\lambda$

SOLVE Follow the conceptual plan. Begin by calculating ΔE_{atom}.

SOLUTION

$$\begin{aligned}\Delta E_{atom} &= E_5 - E_6\\ &= -2.18 \times 10^{-18}\,\text{J}\left(\frac{1}{5^2}\right) - \left[-2.18 \times 10^{-18}\,\text{J}\left(\frac{1}{6^2}\right)\right]\\ &= -2.18 \times 10^{-18}\,\text{J}\left(\frac{1}{5^2} - \frac{1}{6^2}\right)\\ &= -2.6\underline{6}44 \times 10^{-20}\,\text{J}\end{aligned}$$

Calculate E_{photon} by changing the sign of ΔE_{atom}.	$E_{photon} = -\Delta E_{atom} = +2.6644 \times 10^{-20}$ J
Solve the equation relating the energy of a photon to its wavelength for λ. Substitute the energy of the photon and calculate λ.	$E = \dfrac{hc}{\lambda}$ $\lambda = \dfrac{hc}{E}$ $= \dfrac{(6.626 \times 10^{-34}\,\text{J}\cdot\text{s})(3.00 \times 10^{8}\,\text{m/s})}{2.6644 \times 10^{-20}\,\text{J}}$ $= 7.46 \times 10^{-6}$ m or 7460 nm

CHECK The units of the answer (m) are correct for wavelength. The magnitude is reasonable because 10^{-6} m is in the infrared region of the electromagnetic spectrum. You know that transitions from $n = 3$ or $n = 4$ to $n = 2$ lie in the visible region, so it makes sense that a transition between levels of higher n value (which are energetically closer to one another) results in light of longer wavelength.

FOR PRACTICE 8.7 Determine the wavelength of the light absorbed when an electron in a hydrogen atom makes a transition from an orbital in the $n = 2$ level to an orbital in the $n = 7$ level.

FOR MORE PRACTICE 8.7 An electron in the $n = 6$ level of the hydrogen atom relaxes to a lower energy level, emitting light of $\lambda = 93.8$ nm. Find the principal level to which the electron relaxed.

8.6 The Shapes of Atomic Orbitals

As we noted previously, the shapes of atomic orbitals are important because covalent chemical bonds depend on the sharing of the electrons that occupy these orbitals. In one model of chemical bonding, for example, a bond consists of the overlap of atomic orbitals on adjacent atoms. The shapes of the overlapping orbitals determine the shape of the molecule. Although we limit ourselves in this chapter to the orbitals of the hydrogen atom, we will see in Chapter 9 that the orbitals of all atoms can be approximated as being hydrogen-like and therefore having very similar shapes to those of hydrogen.

The shape of an atomic orbital is determined primarily by l, the angular momentum quantum number. Recall that each value of l is assigned a letter that corresponds to particular orbitals. For example, the orbitals with $l = 0$ are called *s* orbitals; those with $l = 1$, *p* orbitals; those with $l = 2$, *d* orbitals, and so on. We now examine the shape of each of these orbitals.

s Orbitals ($l = 0$)

The lowest energy orbital is the spherically symmetrical 1*s* orbital shown in Figure 8.23(a)▼. This image is actually a three-dimensional plot of the wave function squared (ψ^2), which represents **probability density**, the probability (per unit volume) of finding the electron at a point in space.

$$\psi^2 = \text{probability density} = \frac{\text{probability}}{\text{unit volume}}$$

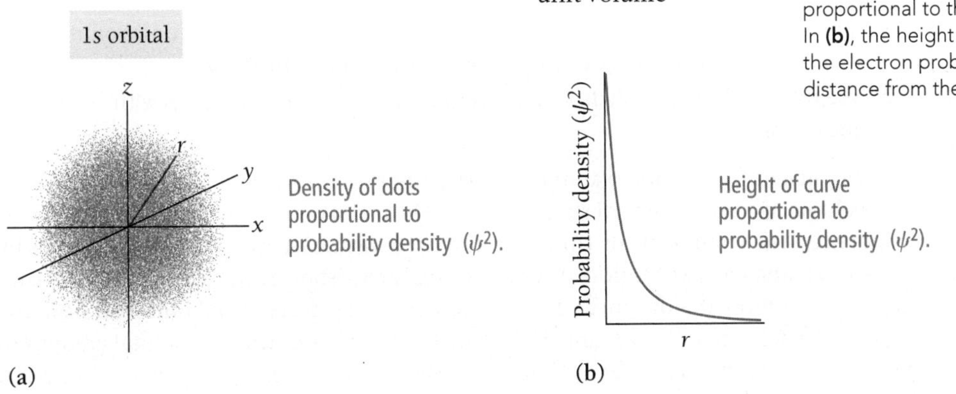

◀ **FIGURE 8.23 The 1*s* Orbital: Two Representations** In **(a)** the dot density is proportional to the electron probability density. In **(b)**, the height of the curve is proportional to the electron probability density. The *x*-axis is *r*, the distance from the nucleus.

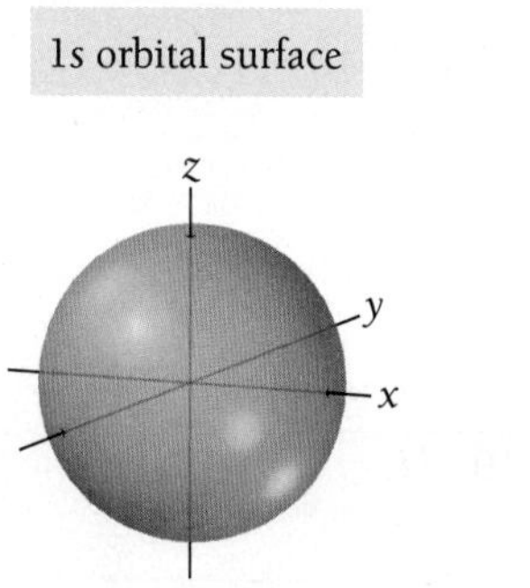

▲ FIGURE 8.24 The 1*s* Orbital Surface In this representation, the surface of the sphere encompasses the volume where the electron is found 90% of the time when the electron is in the 1*s* orbital.

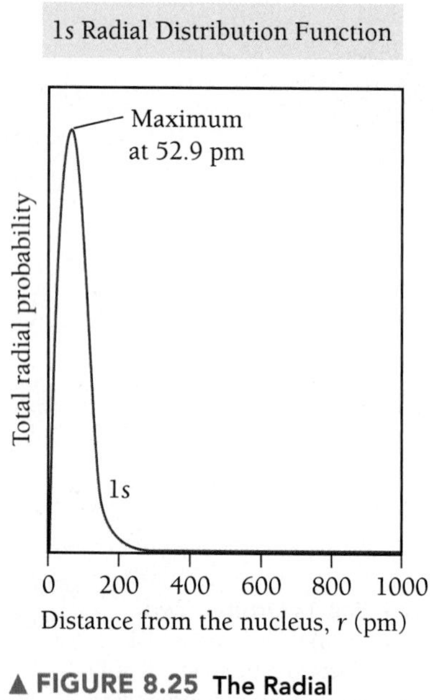

▲ FIGURE 8.25 The Radial Distribution Function for the 1*s* Orbital The curve shows the total probability of finding the electron within a thin shell at a distance *r* from the nucleus.

$1\,\text{pm} = 10^{-12}\,\text{m}$

The magnitude of ψ^2 in this plot is proportional to the density of the dots shown in the image. The high dot density near the nucleus (at the very center of the plot) indicates a higher probability density for the electron. As you move away from the nucleus, the probability density decreases. Figure 8.23(b) shows a plot of probability density (ψ^2) versus *r*, the distance from the nucleus. The plot represents a slice through the three-dimensional plot of ψ^2 and illustrates how the probability density decreases as *r* increases.

We can better understand probability density with the help of a thought experiment. Imagine an electron in the 1*s* orbital located within the volume surrounding the nucleus. Imagine also taking a photograph of the electron every second for 10 or 15 minutes. In one photograph, the electron is very close to the nucleus, in another it is farther away, and so on. Each photo has a dot showing the electron's position relative to the nucleus when the photo was taken. Remember that we can never predict where the electron will be for any one photo. However, if we took hundreds of photos and superimposed all of them, we would have a plot similar to Figure 8.23(a)—a statistical representation of how likely the electron is to be found at each point.

This thought experiment can result in a possible misunderstanding: that the electron is moving around (like a moth near a flame) between photographs. However, in the quantum-mechanical model, that is not the case. Between photographs, the location of the electron is uncertain—in a sense its location is spread out over the entire volume of the orbital. Only when the photograph is taken (that is, when a measurement of the electron's location is made) does the location of the electron become localized to one spot. Between measurements, the electron has no single location. Recall from Section 8.1 that the measurement affects the outcome of any quantum system.

We can also represent an atomic orbital as a geometrical shape that encompasses the volume where the electron is likely to be found most frequently—typically, 90% of the time. For example, we represent the 1*s* orbital as the three-dimensional sphere shown in Figure 8.24◀. If we were to superimpose the dot-density representation of the 1*s* orbital on the shape representation, 90% of the dots would be within the sphere, meaning that when the electron is in the 1*s* orbital it has a 90% chance of being found within the sphere.

The plots we have just seen in Figures 8.23 and 8.24 represent probability *density*. However, they are a bit misleading because they seem to imply that the electron is most likely to be found *at the nucleus*. To get a better idea of where the electron is most likely to be found, we use a plot called the **radial distribution function**, shown in Figure 8.25◀ for the 1*s* orbital. The radial distribution function represents the *total probability of finding the electron within a thin spherical shell at a distance r from the nucleus*:

$$\text{Total radial probability (at a given } r) = \frac{\text{probability}}{\text{unit volume}} \times \text{volume of shell at } r$$

The radial distribution function represents, not probability density *at a point r*, but total probability *at a radius r*. In contrast to probability density, which has a maximum at the nucleus, the radial distribution function has a value of *zero* at the nucleus. It increases to a maximum at 52.9 pm and then decreases again with increasing *r*.

The shape of the radial distribution function is the result of multiplying together two functions with opposite trends in *r*. The two functions are:

1. the probability density function (ψ^2), which is the probability per unit volume, has a maximum at the nucleus, and decreases with increasing *r*; and
2. the volume of the thin shell, which is zero at the nucleus and increases with increasing *r*.

At the nucleus ($r = 0$), for example, the probability *density* is at a maximum; however, the volume of a thin spherical shell is zero, so the radial distribution function is zero. As *r* increases, the volume of the thin spherical shell increases. We can understand this by making an analogy to an onion. A spherical shell at a distance *r* from the nucleus is like a layer in an onion at a distance *r* from its center. If the layers of the onion all have the same thickness, then the volume of any one layer—think of this as the total amount of onion in the layer—is greater as *r* increases. Similarly, the volume of any one spherical shell in the radial distribution function increases with increasing distance from the nucleus, resulting in a greater total probability of finding the electron within that shell. Close to the nucleus, this increase in volume with increasing *r* outpaces the decrease in probability density, reaching a maximum at 52.9 pm. Farther out, however, the density tapers off faster than the volume increases.

The maximum in the radial distribution function, 52.9 pm, turns out to be the very same radius that Bohr had predicted for the innermost orbit of the hydrogen atom. However, there is a significant conceptual difference between the two radii. In the Bohr model, every time you probe the atom (in its lowest energy state), you would find the electron at a radius of 52.9 pm. In the quantum-mechanical model, you would generally find the electron at various radii, with 52.9 pm having the greatest probability.

The probability densities and radial distribution functions for the 2*s* and 3*s* orbitals are shown in Figure 8.26▼. Like the 1*s* orbital, these orbitals are spherically symmetric.

▼ **FIGURE 8.26 Probability Densities and Radial Distribution Functions for the 2*s* and 3*s* Orbitals**

The 2*s* and 3*s* Orbitals

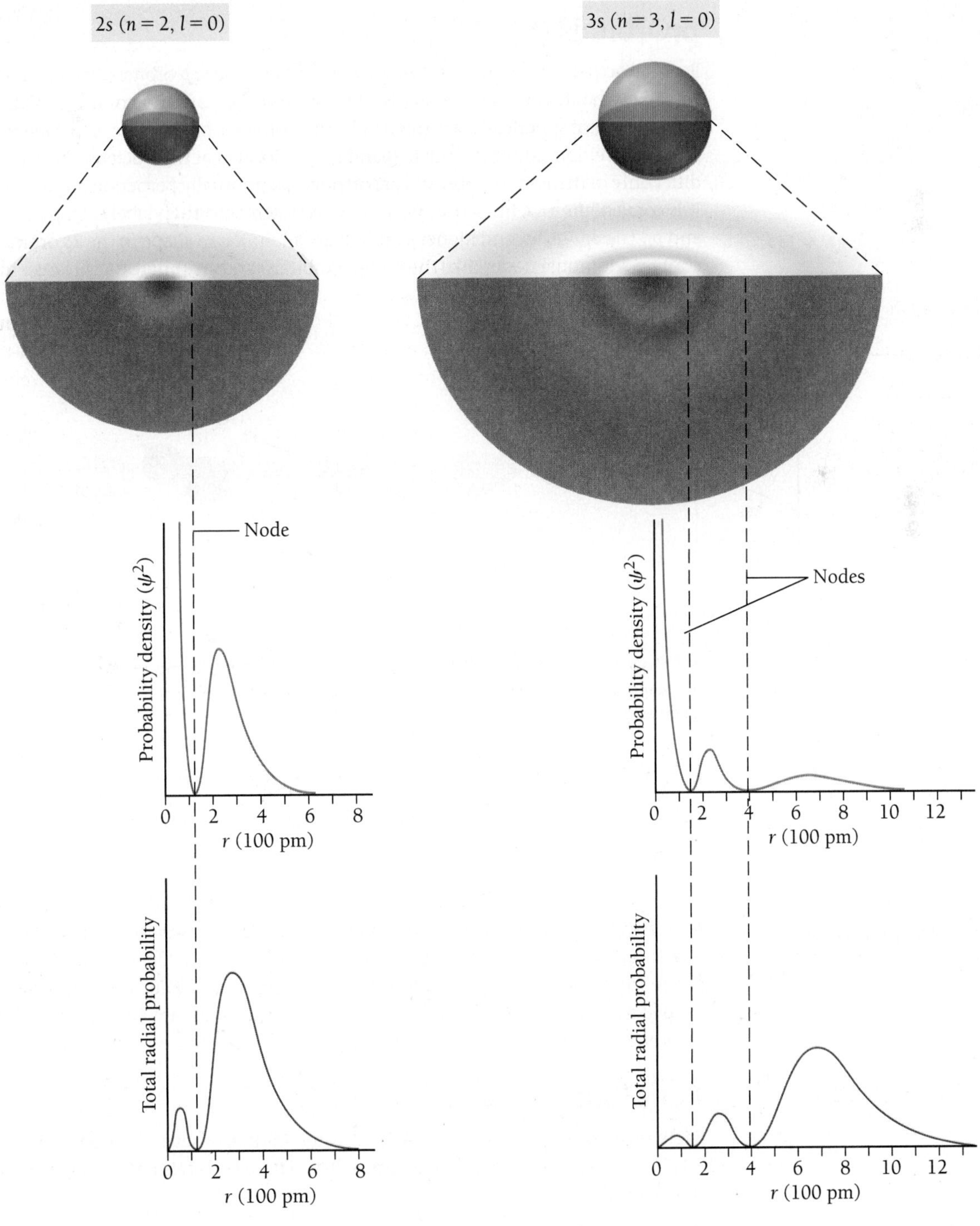

These orbitals are larger in size than the 1*s* orbital, and, unlike the 1*s* orbital, they contain at least one *node*. A **node** is a point where the wave function (ψ), and therefore the probability density (ψ^2) and radial distribution function, all pass through zero. A node in a wave function is much like a node in a standing wave on a vibrating string. We can see nodes in an orbital most clearly by looking at a slice through the orbital. Plots of probability density and the radial distribution function as a function of *r* both reveal the presence of nodes. The probability of finding the electron at a node is zero.

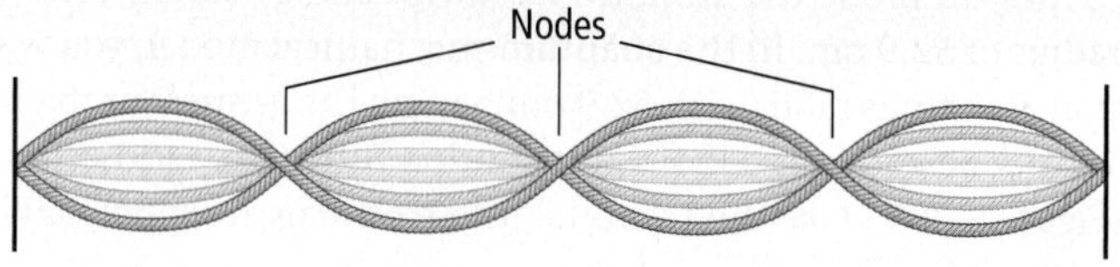

▲ The nodes in quantum-mechanical atomic orbitals are three-dimensional analogs of the nodes on a vibrating string.

p Orbitals ($l = 1$)

Each principal level with $n = 2$ or greater contains three *p* orbitals ($m_l = -1, 0, +1$). The three 2*p* orbitals and their radial distribution functions are shown in Figure 8.27▼. The *p* orbitals are not spherically symmetric like the *s* orbitals, but they have two *lobes* of electron density on either side of the nucleus and a node located at the nucleus. The three *p* orbitals differ only in their orientation and are orthogonal (mutually perpendicular) to one another. It is convenient to define an *x*-, *y*-, and *z*-axis system and then label each *p* orbital as p_x, p_y, and p_z. The 3*p*, 4*p*, 5*p*, and higher *p* orbitals are all similar in shape to the 2*p* orbitals, but they contain additional nodes (like the higher *s* orbitals) and are progressively larger in size.

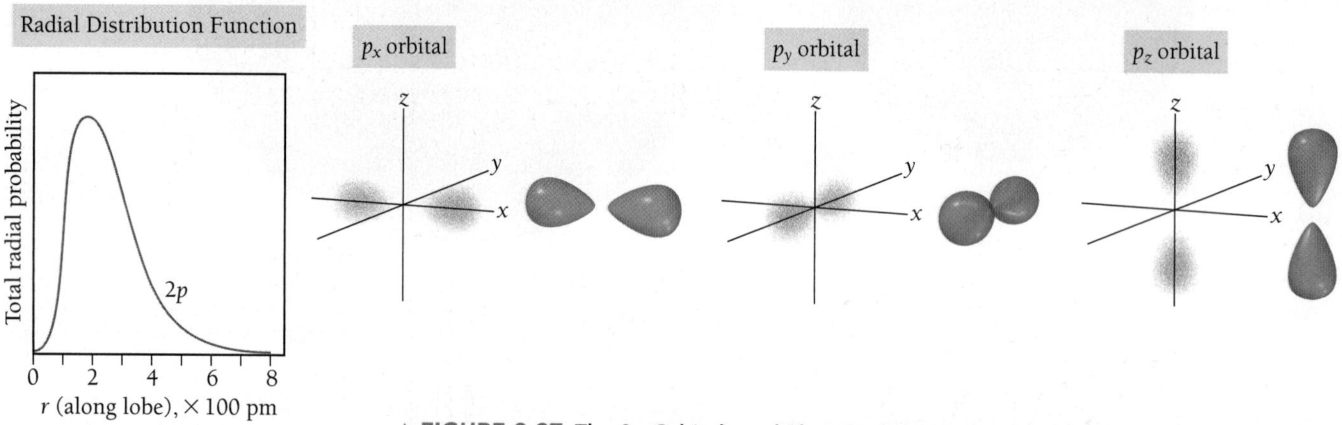

▲ **FIGURE 8.27 The 2*p* Orbitals and Their Radial Distribution Function** The radial distribution function is the same for each of the three 2*p* orbitals when the *x*-axis of the graph is taken as the axis containing the lobes of the orbital.

d Orbitals ($l = 2$)

Each principal level with $n = 3$ or greater contains five *d* orbitals ($m_l = -2, -1, 0, +1, +2$). The five 3*d* orbitals are shown in Figure 8.28▶. Four of these orbitals have a cloverleaf shape, with four lobes of electron density around the nucleus and two perpendicular nodal planes. The d_{xy}, d_{xz}, and d_{yz} orbitals are oriented along the *xy*, *xz*, and *yz* planes, respectively, and their lobes are oriented *between* the corresponding axes. The four lobes of the $d_{x^2-y^2}$ orbital are oriented along the *x*- and *y*-axes. The d_{z^2} orbital is different in shape from the other four, having two lobes oriented along the *z*-axis and a donut-shaped ring along the *xy* plane. The 4*d*, 5*d*, 6*d*,..., orbitals are all similar in shape to the 3*d* orbitals, but they contain additional nodes and are progressively larger in size.

A nodal plane is a plane where the electron probability density is zero. For example, in the d_{xy} orbitals, the nodal planes lie in the *xz* and *yz* planes.

f Orbitals ($l = 3$)

Each principal level with $n = 4$ or greater contains seven *f* orbitals ($m_l = -3, -2, -1, 0, +1, +2, +3$), as shown in Figure 8.29▶. These *f* orbitals have more lobes and nodes than *d* orbitals.

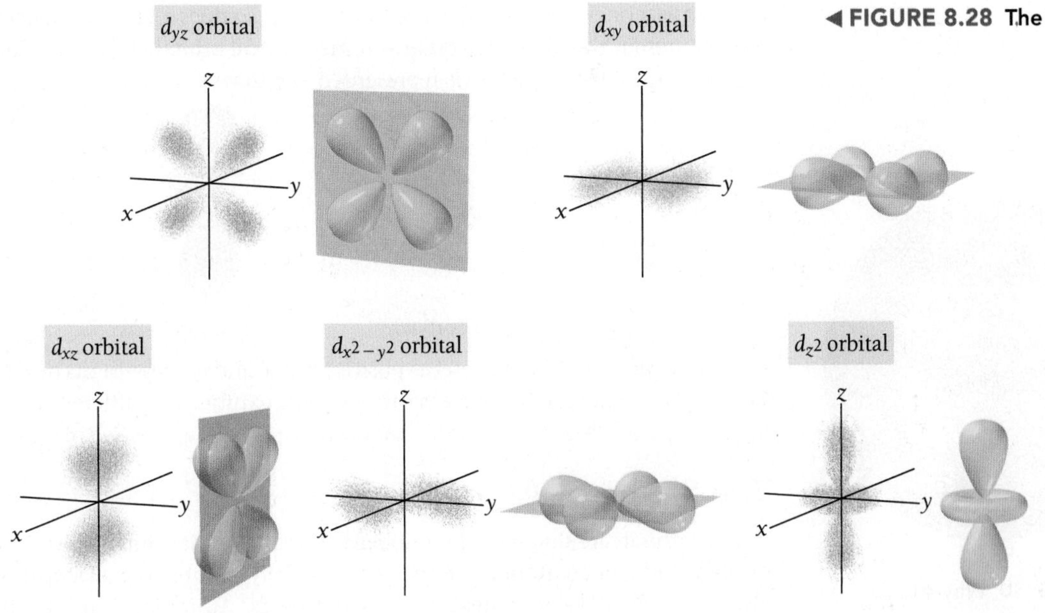

◀ **FIGURE 8.28 The 3*d* Orbitals**

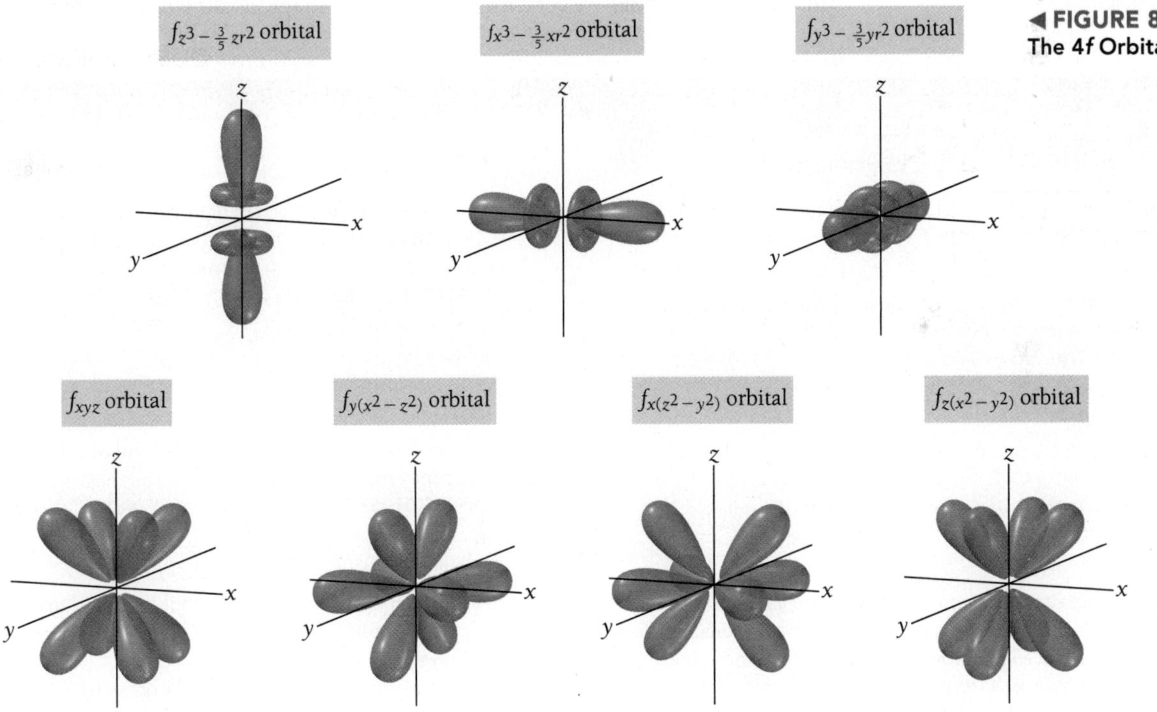

◀ **FIGURE 8.29 The 4*f* Orbitals**

The Phase of Orbitals

The orbitals we have just shown are three-dimensional waves. We can understand an important property of these orbitals by analogy to one-dimensional waves. Consider the following one-dimensional waves:

The wave on the left has a positive amplitude over its entire length, whereas the wave on the right has a positive amplitude over half of its length and a negative amplitude over the other half. The sign of the amplitude of a wave—positive or negative—is known as its **phase**. In these images, blue indicates positive phase and red indicates negative phase. The phase of a wave determines how it interferes with another wave as we saw in Section 8.2.

Just as a one-dimensional wave has a phase, so does a three-dimensional wave. We often represent the phase of a quantum-mechanical orbital with color. For example, the phases of a 1*s* and 2*p* orbital are represented as follows:

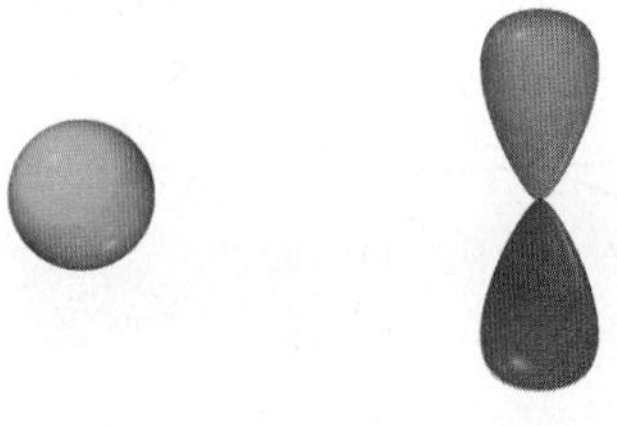

In these depictions, blue represents positive phase and red represents negative phase. The 1*s* orbital is all one phase, whereas the 2*p* orbital exhibits two different phases. The phase of quantum-mechanical orbitals is important in bonding, as we shall see in Chapter 11.

The Shape of Atoms

If some orbitals are shaped like dumbbells and three-dimensional cloverleafs, and if most of the volume of an atom is empty space diffusely occupied by electrons in these orbitals, then why do we often depict atoms as spheres? Atoms are drawn as spheres because most atoms contain many electrons occupying a number of different orbitals. Therefore, the shape of an atom is obtained by superimposing all of its orbitals. If we superimpose the *s*, *p*, and *d* orbitals, we get a roughly spherical shape, as shown in Figure 8.30◀.

▲ **FIGURE 8.30 Why Atoms Are Spherical** Atoms are depicted as roughly spherical because all the orbitals together make up a roughly spherical shape.

QUIZ YOURSELF **NOW!**

Self-Assessment Quiz

Q1. Which wavelength of light has the highest frequency?
MISSED THIS? *Read Section 8.2; Watch KCV 8.2, IWE 8.3*

a) 10 nm b) 10 mm c) 1 nm d) 1 mm

Q2. Which kind of electromagnetic radiation contains the greatest energy per photon?
MISSED THIS? *Read Section 8.2; Watch KCV 8.2, IWE 8.3*

a) microwaves b) gamma rays
c) X-rays d) visible light

Q3. How much energy (in J) is contained in 1.00 mole of 552-nm photons?
MISSED THIS? *Read Section 8.2; Watch KCV 8.2, IWE 8.2*

a) 3.60×10^{-19} J b) 2.17×10^{5} J
c) 3.60×10^{-28} J d) 5.98×10^{-43} J

Q4. Light from three different lasers (A, B, and C), each with a different wavelength, was shined onto the same metal surface. Laser A produced no photoelectrons. Lasers B and C both produced photoelectrons, but the photoelectrons produced by laser B had a greater velocity than those produced by laser C. Arrange the lasers in order of increasing wavelength.
MISSED THIS? *Read Section 8.2*

a) A < B < C b) B < C < A
c) C < B < A d) A < C < B

Q5. Calculate the wavelength of an electron traveling at 1.85×10^{7} m/s.
MISSED THIS? *Read Section 8.4; Watch KCV 8.4*

a) 2.54×10^{13} m b) 3.93×10^{-14} m
c) 2.54×10^{10} m d) 3.93×10^{-11} m

Q6. Which set of three quantum numbers *does not* specify an orbital in the hydrogen atom?
MISSED THIS? *Read Section 8.5; Watch KCV 8.5A, IWE 8.5*

a) $n = 2; l = 1; m_l = -1$ b) $n = 3; l = 3; m_l = -2$
c) $n = 2; l = 0; m_l = 0$ d) $n = 3; l = 2; m_l = 2$

Q7. Calculate the wavelength of light emitted when an electron in the hydrogen atom makes a transition from an orbital with $n = 5$ to an orbital with $n = 3$.
MISSED THIS? *Read Section 8.5; Watch KCV 8.5B, IWE 8.7*

a) 1.28×10^{-6} m
b) 6.04×10^{-7} m
c) 2.28×10^{-6} m
d) 1.55×10^{-19} m

Q8. Which electron transition produces light of the highest frequency in the hydrogen atom?
MISSED THIS? *Read Section 8.5; Watch KCV 8.5B, IWE 8.7*

a) $5p \longrightarrow 1s$ b) $4p \longrightarrow 1s$
c) $3p \longrightarrow 1s$ d) $2p \longrightarrow 1s$

Q9. How much time (in seconds) does it take light in a vacuum to travel 1.00 billion km? **MISSED THIS?** *Read Section 8.2*

a) 3.00×10^{17} s b) 3.33 s
c) 3.33×10^{3} s d) 3.00×10^{20} s

Q10. Which orbital is a *d* orbital?
MISSED THIS? *Read Section 8.6*

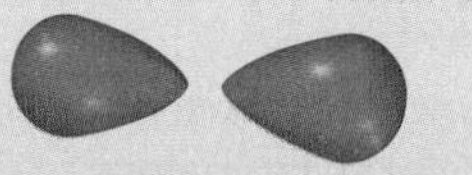

a)

b)

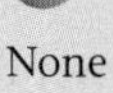

c)

d) None of the above

Answers: **1.** (c) **2.** (b) **3.** (b) **4.** (b) **5.** (d) **6.** (b) **7.** (a) **8.** (a) **9.** (c) **10.** (b)

CHAPTER 8 IN REVIEW

TERMS

Section 8.1
quantum-mechanical model (312)

Section 8.2
electromagnetic radiation (313)
amplitude (314)
wavelength (λ) (314)
frequency (ν) (314)
electromagnetic spectrum (315)
gamma (γ) rays (316)
X-rays (316)
ultraviolet (UV) radiation (316)
visible light (316)
infrared (IR) radiation (316)
microwaves (316)
radio waves (316)
interference (317)
constructive interference (317)
destructive interference (318)
diffraction (318)
photoelectric effect (318)
photon (quantum) (320)

Section 8.3
emission spectrum (323)

Section 8.4
de Broglie relation (327)
complementary properties (329)
Heisenberg's uncertainty principle (329)
deterministic (330)
indeterminacy (330)

Section 8.5
orbital (331)
wave function (331)
quantum number (331)
principal quantum number (n) (331)
angular momentum quantum number (l) (331)
magnetic quantum number (m_l) (331)
spin quantum number (m_s) (331)
principal level (shell) (333)
sublevel (subshell) (333)

Section 8.6
probability density (337)
radial distribution function (338)
node (340)
phase (341)

CONCEPTS

The Realm of Quantum Mechanics (8.1)

- The theory of quantum mechanics explains the behavior of particles, such as photons (particles of light) and electrons, in the atomic and subatomic realms.
- Since the electrons of an atom determine many of its chemical and physical properties, quantum mechanics is foundational to understanding chemistry.

The Nature of Light (8.2)

- Light is a type of electromagnetic radiation—a form of energy embodied in oscillating electric and magnetic fields that travels through space at 3.00×10^8 m/s.
- The wave nature of light is characterized by its wavelength—the distance between wave crests—and its ability to experience interference (constructive or destructive) and diffraction.
- The particle nature of light is characterized by the specific quantity of energy carried in each photon.
- The electromagnetic spectrum includes all wavelengths of electromagnetic radiation from gamma rays (high energy per photon, short wavelength) to radio waves (low energy per photon, long wavelength). Visible light is a tiny sliver in the middle of the electromagnetic spectrum.

Atomic Spectroscopy (8.3)

- Atomic spectroscopy is study of the light absorbed and emitted by atoms when an electron makes a transition from one energy level to another.
- The wavelengths absorbed or emitted in atomic spectra depend on the energy differences between the levels involved in the transition; large energy differences result in short wavelengths, and small energy differences result in long wavelengths.

The Wave Nature of Matter (8.4)

- Electrons have a wave nature with an associated wavelength; the de Broglie relation quantifies the wavelength of an electron.
- The wave nature and particle nature of matter are complementary—the more we know of one, the less we know of the other.
- The wave–particle duality of electrons is quantified in Heisenberg's uncertainty principle, which states that there is a limit to how well we can know both the position of an electron (associated with the electron's particle nature) and the velocity times the mass of an electron (associated with the electron's wave nature)—the more accurately one is measured, the greater the uncertainty in measurement of the other.
- The inability to simultaneously know both the position and velocity of an electron results in indeterminacy, the inability to predict a trajectory for an electron. Consequently, electron behavior is described differently than the behavior of everyday-sized particles.
- The trajectory we normally associate with macroscopic objects is replaced, for electrons, with statistical descriptions that show not the electron's path, but the region where it is most likely to be found.

The Quantum-Mechanical Model of the Atom (8.5, 8.6)

- The most common way to describe electrons in atoms according to quantum mechanics is to solve the Schrödinger equation for the energy states of the electrons within the atom. When the electron is in these states, its energy is well defined but its position is not. The position of an electron is described by a probability distribution map called an orbital.
- The solutions to the Schrödinger equation (including the energies and orbitals) are characterized by four quantum numbers: n, l, m_l, and m_s.
- The principal quantum number (n) determines the energy of the electron and the size of the orbital; the angular momentum quantum number (l) determines the shape of the orbital; the magnetic quantum number (m_l) determines the orientation of the orbital; and the spin quantum number (m_s) specifies the orientation of the spin of the electron.

EQUATIONS AND RELATIONSHIPS

Relationship between Frequency (ν), Wavelength (λ), and the Speed of Light (c) (**8.2**)

$$\nu = \frac{c}{\lambda}$$

Relationship between Energy (E), Frequency (ν), Wavelength (λ), and Planck's Constant (h) (**8.2**)

$$E = h\nu$$

$$E = \frac{hc}{\lambda}$$

De Broglie Relation: Relationship between Wavelength (λ), Mass (m), and Velocity (v) of a Particle (**8.4**)

$$\lambda = \frac{h}{mv}$$

Heisenberg's Uncertainty Principle: Relationship between a Particle's Uncertainty in Position (Δx) and Uncertainty in Velocity (Δv) (**8.4**)

$$\Delta x \times m\Delta v \geq \frac{h}{4\pi}$$

Energy of an Electron in an Orbital with Quantum Number n in a Hydrogen Atom (**8.5**)

$$E_n = -2.18 \times 10^{-18}\,\text{J}\left(\frac{1}{n^2}\right) \quad (n = 1, 2, 3, \ldots)$$

Change in Energy That Occurs in an Atom When It Undergoes a Transition between Levels n_{initial} and n_{final} (**8.5**)

$$\Delta E = -2.18 \times 10^{-18}\,\text{J}\left(\frac{1}{n_f^2} - \frac{1}{n_i^2}\right)$$

LEARNING OUTCOMES

Chapter Objectives	Assessment
Analyze the wave properties and wave behaviors associated with light (**8.2**)	Example 8.1 **For Practice** 8.1 **Exercises** 35–36, 39–40
Analyze the particle properties and particle behaviors associated with light (**8.2**)	Examples 8.2, 8.3 **For Practice** 8.2, 8.3 **For More Practice** 8.2 **Exercises** 37–38, 41–46
Analyze the wave properties of matter (**8.4**)	Example 8.4 **For Practice** 8.4 **Exercises** 47–56
Describe orbitals using quantum numbers (**8.5**)	Examples 8.5, 8.6 **For Practice** 8.5, 8.6 **Exercises** 57–64
Calculate the energy change of an electron transition according to the Bohr model (**8.5**)	Example 8.7 **For Practice** 8.7 **For More Practice** 8.7 **Exercises** 65–72

EXERCISES

Mastering Chemistry provides end-of-chapter exercises, feedback-enriched tutorial problems, animations, and interactive activities to encourage problem-solving practice and deeper understanding of key concepts and topics.

REVIEW QUESTIONS

1. Why is the quantum-mechanical model of the atom important for understanding chemistry?

2. What is light? How fast does it travel in a vacuum?

3. Define the wavelength and amplitude of a wave. How are these related to the energy of the wave?

4. Define the frequency of electromagnetic radiation. How is frequency related to wavelength?

5. What determines the color of light? Describe the difference between red light and blue light.

6. What determines the color of a colored object? Explain why grass appears green.

7. Give an approximate range of wavelengths for each type of electromagnetic radiation and summarize the characteristics and/or the uses of each.

a. gamma rays
b. X-rays
c. ultraviolet radiation
d. visible light
e. infrared radiation
f. microwave radiation
g. radio waves

8. Explain the wave behavior known as interference. Explain the difference between constructive and destructive interference.

9. Explain the wave behavior known as diffraction. Draw the diffraction pattern that occurs when light travels through two slits comparable in size and separation to the light's wavelength.

10. Describe the photoelectric effect. How did experimental observations of this phenomenon differ from the predictions of classical electromagnetic theory?

11. How did the photoelectric effect lead Einstein to propose that light is quantized?

12. What is a photon? How is the energy of a photon related to its wavelength? Its frequency?

13. What is an emission spectrum? How does an emission spectrum of a gas in a discharge tube differ from a white light spectrum?

14. Describe the Bohr model for the atom. How did the Bohr model account for the emission spectra of atoms?

15. Explain electron diffraction.

16. What is the de Broglie wavelength of an electron? What determines the value of the de Broglie wavelength for an electron?

17. What are complementary properties? How does electron diffraction demonstrate the complementarity of the wave nature and particle nature of the electron?

18. Explain Heisenberg's uncertainty principle. What paradox is at least partially solved by the uncertainty principle?

19. What is a trajectory? What kind of information do you need to predict the trajectory of a particle?

20. Why does the uncertainty principle make it impossible to predict a trajectory for the electron?

21. Newton's laws of motion are *deterministic*. Explain this statement.

22. An electron behaves in ways that are at least partially indeterminate. Explain this statement.

23. What is a probability distribution map?

24. For each solution to the Schrödinger equation, what can be precisely specified: the electron's energy or its position? Explain.

25. What is a quantum-mechanical orbital?

26. What is the Schrödinger equation? What is a wave function? How is a wave function related to an orbital?

27. What are the possible values of the principal quantum number n? What does the principal quantum number determine?

28. What are the possible values of the angular momentum quantum number l? What does the angular momentum quantum number determine?

29. What are the possible values of the magnetic quantum number m_l? What does the magnetic quantum number determine?

30. List all the orbitals in each principal level. Specify the three quantum numbers for each orbital.

a. $n = 1$ b. $n = 2$ c. $n = 3$ d. $n = 4$

31. Explain the difference between a plot showing the probability density for an orbital and one showing the radial distribution function.

32. Make sketches of the general shapes of the *s*, *p*, and *d* orbitals.

33. List the four different sublevels associated with $n = 4$. Given that only a maximum of two electrons can occupy an orbital, determine the maximum number of electrons that can exist in each sublevel.

34. Why are atoms usually portrayed as spheres when most orbitals are not spherically shaped?

PROBLEMS BY TOPIC

Electromagnetic Radiation

35. The distance from the sun to Earth is 1.496×10^8 km. How long does it take light to travel from the sun to Earth?
MISSED THIS? *Read Section 8.2*

36. The nearest star to our sun is Proxima Centauri, at a distance of 4.3 light-years from the sun. A light-year is the distance that light travels in one year (365 days). How far away, in km, is Proxima Centauri from the sun?

37. List these types of electromagnetic radiation in order of (i) increasing wavelength and (ii) increasing energy per photon.
MISSED THIS? *Read Section 8.2; Watch KCV 8.2, IWE 8.3*

a. radio waves
b. microwaves
c. infrared radiation
d. ultraviolet radiation

38. List these types of electromagnetic radiation in order of (i) increasing frequency and (ii) decreasing energy per photon.

a. gamma rays
b. radio waves
c. microwaves
d. visible light

39. Calculate the frequency of each wavelength of electromagnetic radiation. **MISSED THIS?** *Read Section 8.2*

a. 632.8 nm (wavelength of red light from helium–neon laser)
b. 503 nm (wavelength of maximum solar radiation)
c. 0.052 nm (a wavelength contained in medical X-rays)

40. Calculate the wavelength of each frequency of electromagnetic radiation.

a. 100.2 MHz (typical frequency for FM radio broadcasting)
b. 1070 kHz (typical frequency for AM radio broadcasting) (assume four significant figures)
c. 835.6 MHz (common frequency used for cell phone communication)

41. Calculate the energy of a photon of electromagnetic radiation at each of the wavelengths indicated in Problem 39.
MISSED THIS? *Read Section 8.2; Watch KCV 8.2, IWE 8.2*

42. Calculate the energy of a photon of electromagnetic radiation at each of the frequencies indicated in Problem 40.

43. A laser pulse with wavelength 532 nm contains 3.85 mJ of energy. How many photons are in the laser pulse?
MISSED THIS? *Read Section 8.2; Watch KCV 8.2, IWE 8.2*

44. A heat lamp produces 32.8 watts of power at a wavelength of 6.5 μm. How many photons are emitted per second? (1 watt = 1 J/s)

45. Determine the energy of 1 mol of photons for each kind of light. (Assume three significant figures.)
MISSED THIS? *Read Section 8.2; Watch KCV 8.2, IWE 8.2*

a. infrared radiation (1500 nm)
b. visible light (500 nm)
c. ultraviolet radiation (150 nm)

46. How much energy is contained in 1 mol of each?

a. X-ray photons with a wavelength of 0.135 nm
b. γ-ray photons with a wavelength of 2.15×10^{-5} nm

The Wave Nature of Matter and the Uncertainty Principle

47. Sketch the interference pattern that results from the diffraction of electrons passing through two closely spaced slits.
MISSED THIS? *Read Section 8.4; Watch KCV 8.4*

48. What happens to the interference pattern described in Problem 47 if the rate of electrons going through the slits is decreased to one electron per hour? What happens to the pattern if we try to determine which slit the electron goes through by using a laser placed directly behind the slits?

49. The resolution limit of a microscope is roughly equal to the wavelength of light used in producing the image. Electron microscopes use an electron beam (in place of photons) to produce much higher resolution images, about 0.20 nm in modern instruments. Assuming that the resolution of an electron microscope is equal to the de Broglie wavelength of the electrons used, to what speed must the electrons be accelerated to obtain a resolution of 0.20 nm?
MISSED THIS? *Read Section 8.4; Watch KCV 8.4*

50. The smallest atoms can themselves exhibit quantum-mechanical behavior. Calculate the de Broglie wavelength (in pm) of a hydrogen atom traveling at 475 m/s.

51. What is the de Broglie wavelength of an electron traveling at 1.35×10^5 m/s? **MISSED THIS?** *Read Section 8.4; Watch KCV 8.4*

52. A proton in a linear accelerator has a de Broglie wavelength of 122 pm. What is the speed of the proton?

53. Calculate the de Broglie wavelength of a 143-g baseball traveling at 95 mph. Why is the wave nature of matter not important for a baseball? **MISSED THIS?** *Read Section 8.4; Watch KCV 8.4*

54. A 0.22-caliber handgun fires a 1.9-g bullet at a velocity of 765 m/s. Calculate the de Broglie wavelength of the bullet. Is the wave nature of matter significant for bullets?

55. An electron has an uncertainty in its position of 552 pm. What is the minimum uncertainty in its velocity?
MISSED THIS? *Read Section 8.4*

56. An electron traveling at 3.7×10^5 m/s has an uncertainty in its velocity of 1.88×10^5 m/s. What is the minimum uncertainty in its position?

Orbitals and Quantum Numbers

57. Which electron is, on average, closer to the nucleus: an electron in a 2*s* orbital or an electron in a 3*s* orbital?
MISSED THIS? *Read Sections 8.5, 8.6; Watch KCV 8.5A*

58. Which electron is, on average, farther from the nucleus: an electron in a 3*p* orbital or an electron in a 4*p* orbital?

59. What are the possible values of l for each value of n?
MISSED THIS? *Read Section 8.5; Watch KCV 8.5A*

a. 1 b. 2 c. 3 d. 4

60. What are the possible values of m_l for each value of l?

a. 0 b. 1 c. 2 d. 3

61. Which set of quantum numbers *cannot* specify an orbital?
MISSED THIS? *Read Section 8.5; Watch KCV 8.5A, IWE 8.5*

a. $n = 2, l = 1, m_l = -1$
b. $n = 3, l = 2, m_l = 0$
c. $n = 3, l = 3, m_l = 2$
d. $n = 4, l = 3, m_l = 0$

62. Which combinations of n and l represent real orbitals, and which do not exist?

a. 1*s* b. 2*p* c. 4*s* d. 2*d*

63. Sketch the 1*s* and 2*p* orbitals. How do the 2*s* and 3*p* orbitals differ from the 1*s* and 2*p* orbitals? **MISSED THIS?** *Read Section 8.6*

64. Sketch the 3*d* orbitals. How do the 4*d* orbitals differ from the 3*d* orbitals?

Atomic Spectroscopy

65. An electron in a hydrogen atom is excited with electrical energy to an excited state with $n = 2$. The atom then emits a photon. What is the value of n for the electron following the emission?
MISSED THIS? *Read Section 8.5; Watch KCV 8.5B*

66. Determine whether each transition in the hydrogen atom corresponds to absorption or emission of energy.

a. $n = 3 \longrightarrow n = 1$
b. $n = 2 \longrightarrow n = 4$
c. $n = 4 \longrightarrow n = 3$

67. According to the quantum-mechanical model for the hydrogen atom, which electron transition produces light with the longer wavelength: 2*p* ⟶ 1*s* or 3*p* ⟶ 1*s*?
MISSED THIS? *Read Section 8.5; Watch KCV 8.5B*

68. According to the quantum-mechanical model for the hydrogen atom, which electron transition produces light with the longer wavelength: 3*p* ⟶ 2*s* or 4*p* ⟶ 3*p*?

69. Calculate the wavelength of the light emitted when an electron in a hydrogen atom makes each transition and indicate the region of the electromagnetic spectrum (infrared, visible, ultraviolet, etc.) where the light is found.
MISSED THIS? *Read Section 8.5; Watch KCV 8.5B, IWE 8.7*

a. $n = 2 \longrightarrow n = 1$
b. $n = 3 \longrightarrow n = 1$
c. $n = 4 \longrightarrow n = 2$
d. $n = 5 \longrightarrow n = 2$

70. Calculate the frequency of the light emitted when an electron in a hydrogen atom makes each transition.

a. $n = 4 \longrightarrow n = 3$
b. $n = 5 \longrightarrow n = 1$
c. $n = 5 \longrightarrow n = 4$
d. $n = 6 \longrightarrow n = 5$

71. An electron in the $n = 7$ level of the hydrogen atom relaxes to a lower energy level, emitting light of 397 nm. What is the value of n for the level to which the electron relaxed?
MISSED THIS? *Read Section 8.5; Watch KCV 8.5B, IWE 8.7*

72. An electron in a hydrogen atom relaxes to the $n = 4$ level, emitting light of 114 THz. What is the value of n for the level in which the electron originated?

CUMULATIVE PROBLEMS

73. Ultraviolet radiation and radiation of shorter wavelengths can damage biological molecules because these kinds of radiation carry enough energy to break bonds within the molecules. A typical carbon–carbon bond requires 348 kJ/mol to break. What is the longest wavelength of radiation with enough energy to break carbon–carbon bonds?

74. The human eye contains a molecule called 11-*cis*-retinal that changes shape when struck with light of sufficient energy. The change in shape triggers a series of events that result in an electrical signal being sent to the brain that results in vision. The minimum energy required to change the conformation of 11-*cis*-retinal within the eye is about 164 kJ/mol. Calculate the longest wavelength visible to the human eye.

75. An argon ion laser puts out 5.0 W of continuous power at a wavelength of 532 nm. The diameter of the laser beam is 5.5 mm. If the laser is pointed toward a pinhole with a diameter of 1.2 mm, how many photons travel through the pinhole per second? Assume that the light intensity is equally distributed throughout the entire cross-sectional area of the beam. (1 W = 1 J/s)

76. A green leaf has a surface area of 2.50 cm^2. If solar radiation is 1000 W/m^2, how many photons strike the leaf every second? Assume three significant figures and an average wavelength of 504 nm for solar radiation.

77. In a technique used for surface analysis called Auger electron spectroscopy (AES), electrons are accelerated toward a metal surface. These electrons cause the emissions of secondary electrons—called Auger electrons—from the metal surface. The kinetic energy of the Auger electrons depends on the composition of the surface. The presence of oxygen atoms on the surface results in Auger electrons with a kinetic energy of approximately 506 eV. What is the de Broglie wavelength of one of these electrons?

$$[\text{KE} = \tfrac{1}{2}mv^2; 1 \text{ electron volt(eV)} = 1.602 \times 10^{-19} \text{ J}]$$

78. An X-ray photon of wavelength 0.989 nm strikes a surface. The emitted electron has a kinetic energy of 969 eV. What is the binding energy of the electron in kJ/mol?

$$[1 \text{ electron volt(eV)} = 1.602 \times 10^{-19} \text{ J}]$$

79. Ionization involves completely removing an electron from an atom. How much energy is required to ionize a hydrogen atom in its ground (or lowest energy) state? What wavelength of light contains enough energy in a single photon to ionize a hydrogen atom?

80. The energy required to ionize sodium is 496 kJ/mol. What minimum frequency of light is required to ionize sodium?

81. Suppose that in an alternate universe, the possible values of l are the integer values from 0 to n (instead of 0 to $n - 1$). Assuming no other differences between this imaginary universe and ours, how many orbitals exist in each level in the alternate universe?

a. $n = 1$ b. $n = 2$ c. $n = 3$

82. Suppose that, in an alternate universe, the possible values of m_l are the integer values including 0 ranging from $-l - 1$ to $l + 1$ (instead of simply $-l$ to $+l$). How many orbitals exist in each sublevel in the alternate universe?

a. s sublevel b. p sublevel c. d sublevel

83. An atomic emission spectrum of hydrogen shows three wavelengths: 1875 nm, 1282 nm, and 1093 nm. Assign these wavelengths to transitions in the hydrogen atom.

84. An atomic emission spectrum of hydrogen shows three wavelengths: 121.5 nm, 102.6 nm, and 97.23 nm. Assign these wavelengths to transitions in the hydrogen atom.

85. The binding energy of electrons in a metal is 193 kJ/mol. Find the threshold frequency of the metal.

86. In order for a thermonuclear fusion reaction of two deuterons ($^2_1H^+$) to take place, the deuterons must collide and each must have a velocity of about 1×10^6 m/s. Find the wavelength of such a deuteron.

87. The speed of sound in air is 344 m/s at room temperature. The lowest frequency of a large organ pipe is 30 s^{-1} and the highest frequency of a piccolo is 1.5×10^4 s^{-1}. Find the difference in wavelength between these two sounds.

88. The distance from Earth to the sun is 1.5×10^8 km. Find the number of crests in a light wave of frequency 1.0×10^{14} s^{-1} traveling from the sun to Earth.

89. The iodine molecule can be photodissociated (broken apart with light) into iodine atoms in the gas phase with light of wavelengths shorter than about 792 nm. A 100.0-mL glass tube contains 55.7 mtorr of gaseous iodine at 25.0 °C. What minimum amount of light energy must be absorbed by the iodine in the tube to dissociate 15.0% of the molecules?

90. A 5.00-mL ampule of a 0.100-M solution of naphthalene in hexane is excited with a flash of light. The naphthalene emits 15.5 J of energy at an average wavelength of 349 nm. What percentage of the naphthalene molecules emitted a photon?

91. A laser produces 20.0 mW of red light. In 1.00 hr, the laser emits 2.29×10^{20} photons. What is the wavelength of the laser?

92. A particular laser consumes 150.0 watts of electrical power and produces a stream of 1.33×10^{19} 1064-nm photons per second. What is the percent efficiency of the laser in converting electrical power to light?

93. The quantum yield of light-induced chemical reactions (called photochemical reactions) measures the efficiency of the process. The quantum yield, ϕ, is defined as: $\phi = \dfrac{\text{number of reaction events}}{\text{number of photons absorbed}}$. Suppose the quantum yield for the reaction $CH_3X \longrightarrow CH_3 + X$ is $\phi = 0.24$. A cuvette containing a solution of CH_3X is irradiated with 280-nm light with a power of 885 mW for 10.0 minutes. Assuming total absorption of the light by the sample, what is the maximum amount (in moles) of CH_3X that breaks apart?

94. A student is studying the photodissociation (dissociation with light) of $I_2 \longrightarrow 2\,I$. When a sample of I_2 is irradiated with a power of 255 mW at 590 nm for 35 seconds, 0.0256 mmol of I forms. Assuming complete absorption of the incident radiation, what is the quantum yield, ϕ, of the reaction? (See Problem 93 for definition of quantum yield.)

CHALLENGE PROBLEMS

95. An electron confined to a one-dimensional box has energy levels given by the equation:

$$E_n = n^2h^2/8\,mL^2$$

where n is a quantum number with possible values of 1, 2, 3, . . . , m is the mass of the particle, and L is the length of the box.

a. Calculate the energies of the $n = 1, n = 2$, and $n = 3$ levels for an electron in a box with a length of 155 pm.

b. Calculate the wavelength of light required to make a transition from $n = 1 \longrightarrow n = 2$ from $n = 2 \longrightarrow n = 3$. In what region of the electromagnetic spectrum do these wavelengths lie?

96. The energy of a vibrating molecule is quantized much like the energy of an electron in the hydrogen atom. The energy levels of a vibrating molecule are given by the equation:

$$E_n = \left(n + \frac{1}{2}\right)h\nu$$

where n is a quantum number with possible values of 1, 2, . . . , and ν is the frequency of vibration. The vibration frequency of HCl is approximately 8.85×10^{13} s^{-1}. What minimum energy is required to excite a vibration in HCl? What wavelength of light is required to excite this vibration?

97. The wave functions for the 1s and 2s orbitals are as follows:

$$1s \quad \psi = (1/\pi)^{1/2}(1/a_0^{3/2})\exp(-r/a_0)$$

$$2s \quad \psi = (1/32\pi)^{1/2}(1/a_0^{3/2})(2 - r/a_0)\exp(-r/2a_0)$$

where a_0 is a constant ($a_0 = 53$ pm) and r is the distance from the nucleus. Use a spreadsheet to make a plot of each of these wave functions for values of r ranging from 0 pm to 200 pm. Describe the differences in the plots and identify the node in the 2s wave function.

98. Before quantum mechanics was developed, Johannes Rydberg developed an equation that predicted the wavelengths (λ) in the atomic spectrum of hydrogen:

$$1/\lambda = R(1/m^2 - 1/n^2)$$

In this equation, R is a constant and m and n are integers. Use the quantum-mechanical model for the hydrogen atom to derive the Rydberg equation.

99. Find the velocity of an electron emitted by a metal with a threshold frequency of $2.25 \times 10^{14}\ s^{-1}$ when it is exposed to visible light of wavelength 5.00×10^{-7} m.

100. Water is exposed to infrared radiation of wavelength 2.8×10^{-4} cm. Assume that all the radiation is absorbed and converted to heat. How many photons are required to raise the temperature of 2.0 g of water by 2.0 K?

101. The 2005 Nobel Prize in Physics was given, in part, to scientists who had made ultrashort pulses of light. These pulses are important in making measurements involving very short time periods. One challenge in making such pulses is the uncertainty principle, which can be stated with respect to energy and time as $\Delta E \cdot \Delta t \geq h/4\pi$. What is the energy uncertainty (ΔE) associated with a short pulse of laser light that lasts for only 5.0 femtoseconds (fs)? Suppose the low-energy end of the pulse had a wavelength of 722 nm. What is the wavelength of the high-energy end of the pulse that is limited only by the uncertainty principle?

102. A metal with a threshold frequency of $6.71 \times 10^{14}\ s^{-1}$ emits an electron with a velocity of 6.95×10^5 m/s when radiation of $1.01 \times 10^{15}\ s^{-1}$ strikes the metal. Calculate the mass of the electron.

103. Find the longest wavelength of a wave that can travel around in a circular orbit of radius 1.8 m.

104. The heat of fusion of ice is 6.00 kJ/mol. Find the number of photons of wavelength = 6.42×10^{-6} m that must be absorbed to melt 1.00 g of ice.

CONCEPTUAL PROBLEMS

105. Explain the difference between the Bohr model for the hydrogen atom and the quantum-mechanical model. Is the Bohr model consistent with Heisenberg's uncertainty principle?

106. The light emitted from one of the following electronic transitions ($n = 4 \longrightarrow n = 3$ or $n = 3 \longrightarrow n = 2$) in the hydrogen atom causes the photoelectric effect in a particular metal, while light from the other transition does not. Which transition causes the photoelectric effect and why?

107. Determine whether an interference pattern is observed on the other side of the slits in each experiment.

a. An electron beam is aimed at two closely spaced slits. The beam produces only one electron per minute.

b. An electron beam is aimed at two closely spaced slits. A light beam is placed at each slit to determine when an electron goes through the slit.

c. A high-intensity light beam is aimed at two closely spaced slits.

d. A gun is fired at a solid wall containing two closely spaced slits. (Will the bullets that pass through the slits form an interference pattern on the other side of the solid wall?)

108. Which transition in the hydrogen atom produces emitted light with the longest wavelength?

a. $n = 4 \longrightarrow n = 3$

b. $n = 2 \longrightarrow n = 1$

c. $n = 3 \longrightarrow n = 2$

QUESTIONS FOR GROUP WORK

Active Classroom Learning

Discuss these questions with the group and record your consensus answer.

109. Discuss the nature of light with your group. Ask each member of your group to transcribe one complete sentence about the physical nature of light.

110. How are electrons like baseballs? How are they unlike baseballs?

111. What are all the possible values of m_l if $l = 0$ (an s orbital)? If $l = 1$ (a p orbital)? If $l = 2$ (a d orbital)? How many possible values of m_l would there be if $l = 20$? Write an equation to determine the number of possible values of m_l from the value of l.

112. Have each group member choose a set of quantum numbers for an electron in a hydrogen atom. Calculate the wavelength of light produced if an electron moves from your state to each state of the other group members. Make a table comparing all possible combinations, and list all wavelengths in order of increasing energy.

113. How many nodes are there in the 1s, 2p, and 3d orbitals? How many nodes are in a 4f orbital?

DATA INTERPRETATION AND ANALYSIS

UV Radiation and Sunscreen

114. Sunscreen contains compounds that absorb ultraviolet light. When sunscreen is applied to skin, it prevents ultraviolet light from reaching the skin. The graph that follows shows the absorbance of light as a function of wavelength for two different compounds (2-EHMC and TDSA) common in sunscreen. Absorbance is a measure of the amount of light absorbed by the compound—the higher the absorbance, the more light is absorbed. Study the graph and answer the questions.

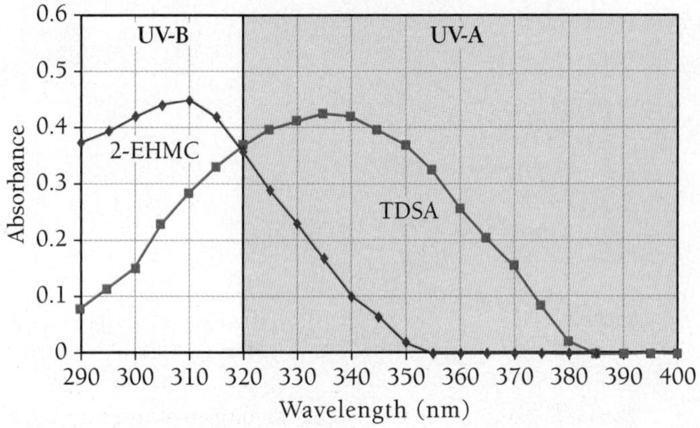

http://mycpss.com/critical-wavelength-broad-spectrum-uv-protection/

a. Calculate the energy of a photon at the maximum absorption of TDSA.

b. Calculate the energy of a photon at the maximum absorption of 2-EHMC.

c. Which compound absorbs more energy at its maximum absorption?

d. Why do you think sunscreens commonly contain both of these compounds and not just one of them?

e. Assuming that sunlight produces $3.066 \times 10^{22} \frac{\text{uv photons}}{\text{m}^2 \cdot \text{s}}$, and that the skin absorbs one-half of these photons (and reflects the other half) calculate the total uv energy absorbed over 0.42 m^2 of skin that is exposed to sunlight for one hour. Assume that the average wavelength of the uv photons is 330 nm.

Cc ANSWERS TO CONCEPTUAL CONNECTIONS

Wave Nature of Light

8.1 **(c)** Since the light emitted from the lasers have different colors, they must also have different frequencies. The brighter the light, the greater its amplitude, so the bright green laser emits light with a greater amplitude than the dim red one.

Frequency of Light

8.2 **(a)** As you can see in the electromagnetic spectrum, infrared has the longest wavelength of the three types of electromagnetic radiation listed and X-rays have the shortest.

The Photoelectric Effect

8.3 **(b)** The 325-nm light has the shortest wavelength of light (highest energy per photon) and corresponds to the photoelectrons with the greatest kinetic energy.

The de Broglie Wavelength of Macroscopic Objects

8.4 **(a)** Because of the baseball's large mass, its de Broglie wavelength is minuscule. (For a 150-g baseball, λ is on the order of 10^{-34} m.) This minuscule wavelength is insignificant compared to the size of the baseball itself, and therefore its effects are not observable.

The Uncertainty Principle

8.5 **(b)** The uncertainty principle states that the position and velocity of an electron cannot be simultaneously known. Position and velocity are complementary: the more precisely you know one quantity, the less precisely you know the other.

The Relationship between *n* and *l*

8.6 **(c)** Since l can have a maximum value of $n - 1$ and since $n = 3$, l can have a maximum value of 2.

The Relationship between *l* and m_l

8.7 **(d)** Since m_l can have the integer values (including 0) between $-l$ and $+l$ and since $l = 2$, the possible values of m_l are $-2, -1, 0, +1$, and $+2$.

Emission Spectra

8.8 **(c)** The energy difference between $n = 3$ and $n = 2$ is greatest because the energy differences become closer together with increasing n. The greater energy difference results in an emitted photon of greater energy and therefore shorter wavelength.

Beginning students of chemistry often think of the science as a mere collection of disconnected data to be memorized by brute force. Not at all! Just look at it properly and everything hangs together and makes sense.

—ISAAC ASIMOV (1920–1992)

CHAPTER

9 Periodic Properties of the Elements

Great advances in science occur not only when a scientist sees something new, but also when a scientist sees what everyone else has seen in a new way. In other words, great scientists often see patterns where others have seen only disjointed facts. Such was the case in 1869 when Dmitri Mendeleev (1834–1907), a Russian chemist, saw a pattern in the properties of elements. Mendeleev's insight led to the periodic table, arguably the single most important tool for chemists. Recall that scientists devise theories that explain the underlying reasons for observations. Mendeleev's periodic table is a compact way to summarize a large number of observations; quantum mechanics (covered in Chapter 8) is the theory that explains the underlying reasons for the periodic table. Quantum mechanics explains how electrons are arranged in atoms, which in turn determines the element's properties. Since the periodic table is organized according to those properties, quantum mechanics beautifully accounts for Mendeleev's periodic table. In this chapter, we see a continuation of the theme we have been developing since page one of this book—the properties of macroscopic substances (in this case, the elements in the periodic table) are explained by the properties of the particles that compose them (in this case, atoms and their electrons).

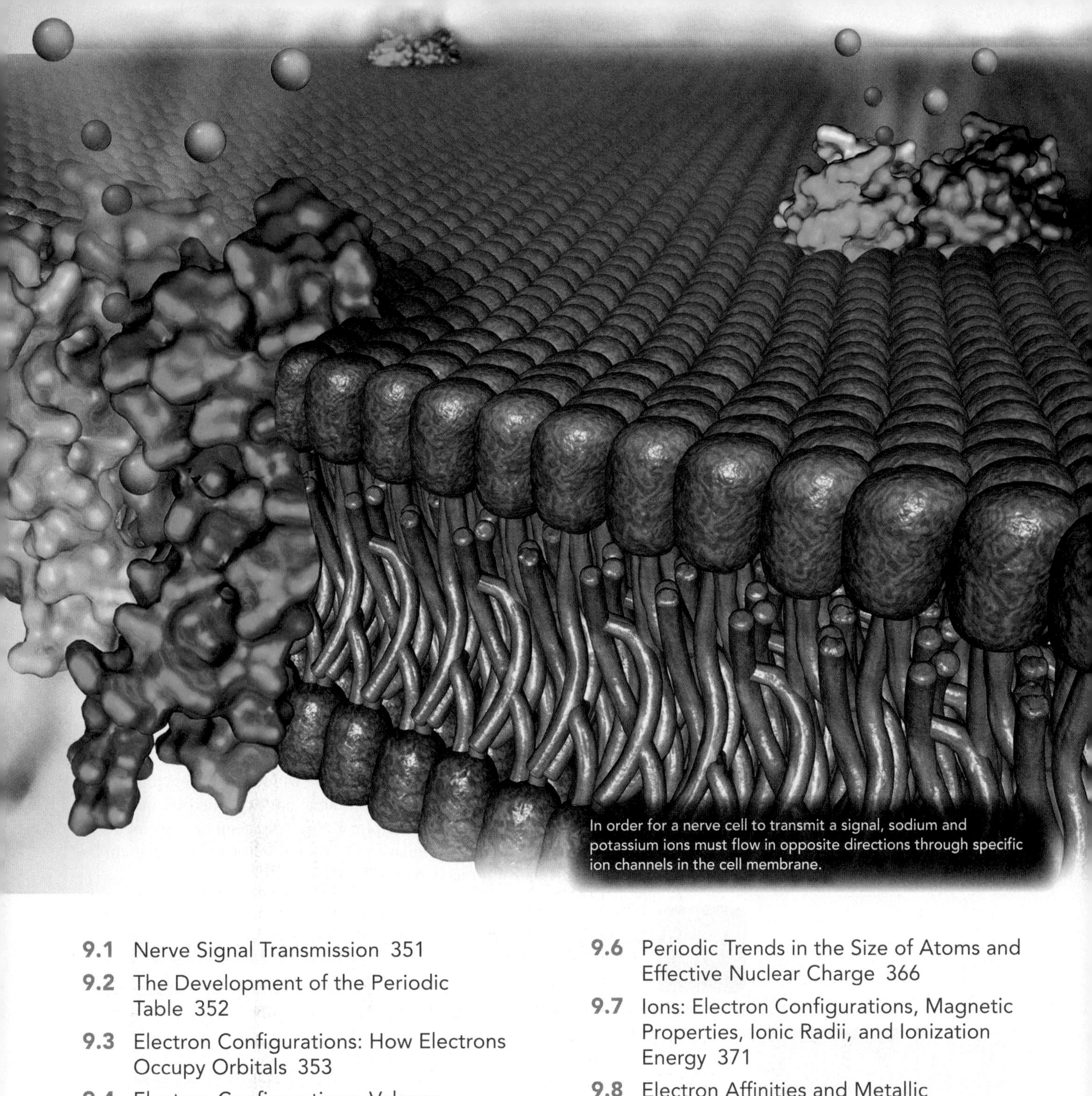

In order for a nerve cell to transmit a signal, sodium and potassium ions must flow in opposite directions through specific ion channels in the cell membrane.

9.1 Nerve Signal Transmission 351

9.2 The Development of the Periodic Table 352

9.3 Electron Configurations: How Electrons Occupy Orbitals 353

9.4 Electron Configurations, Valence Electrons, and the Periodic Table 361

9.5 The Explanatory Power of the Quantum-Mechanical Model 365

9.6 Periodic Trends in the Size of Atoms and Effective Nuclear Charge 366

9.7 Ions: Electron Configurations, Magnetic Properties, Ionic Radii, and Ionization Energy 371

9.8 Electron Affinities and Metallic Character 379

9.9 Periodic Trends Summary 383

LEARNING OUTCOMES 385

9.1 Nerve Signal Transmission

As you sit reading this book, tiny pumps in the membranes of your cells are working hard to transport ions—especially sodium (Na^+) and potassium (K^+)—through those membranes. Amazingly, the ions are pumped in opposite directions. Sodium ions are pumped *out of cells*, while potassium ions are pumped *into cells*. The result is a *chemical gradient* for each ion: the concentration of sodium is higher outside the cell than within, whereas just the opposite is true for potassium. These ion pumps are analogous to the water pumps in a high-rise building that pump water against the force of gravity to a tank on the roof. Other structures within the membrane, called ion channels, are like the building's faucets. When these open, sodium and potassium ions flow back down their gradients—sodium flowing in and potassium flowing out. This movement of ions is the basis for the transmission of nerve signals in the brain and throughout the body. Every move you make, every thought you have, and every sensation you experience is mediated by these ion movements.

How do the pumps and channels differentiate between sodium and potassium ions to selectively move one out of the cell and the other into the cell? To answer this question, we must examine the ions more closely. Both ions are cations of group 1A metals. All group 1A metals tend to lose one electron to form cations with a 1+ charge, so that cannot be the decisive factor. Potassium (atomic number 19) lies directly below sodium in the periodic table (atomic number 11), indicating that it has more protons, neutrons, and electrons than sodium. How do these additional subatomic particles affect the properties of potassium? As we will see in this chapter, although a higher atomic number does not always result in a larger ion (or atom), it does in the case of potassium (relative to sodium). The potassium ion has a radius of 133 pm, whereas the sodium ion has a radius of 95 pm. (Recall that $1\,\text{pm} = 10^{-12}\,\text{m}$.) The pumps and channels within cell membranes are so sensitive that they distinguish between the sizes of these two ions and selectively allow only one or the other to pass.

3	Li	6.94
11	Na	22.99
19	K	39.10
37	Rb	85.47
55	Cs	132.91
87	Fr	(223.02)

▲ The group 1A metals. Potassium is directly beneath sodium in the periodic table.

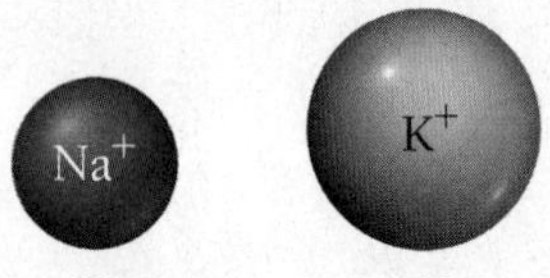

The relative size of sodium and potassium ions is an example of a **periodic property:** one that is predictable based on an element's position within the periodic table. In this chapter, we examine several periodic properties of elements, including atomic radius, ionization energy, and electron affinity. We will see that these properties, as well as the overall arrangement of the periodic table, are explained by quantum-mechanical theory, which we examined in Chapter 8. The arrangement of elements in the periodic table—originally based on similarities in the properties of the elements—reflects how electrons fill quantum-mechanical orbitals.

9.2 The Development of the Periodic Table

Prior to the 1700s, the number of known elements was relatively small, consisting mostly of the metals that had long been used for coinage, jewelry, and weapons. From the early 1700s to the mid-1800s, however, chemists discovered over 50 new elements. The first attempt to organize these elements according to similarities in their properties was made by the German chemist Johann Döbereiner (1780–1849), who grouped elements into *triads*: three elements with similar properties. For example, Döbereiner formed a triad out of barium, calcium, and strontium, three fairly reactive metals. About 50 years later, English chemist John Newlands (1837–1898) organized elements into *octaves*, in analogy to musical notes. When arranged this way, the properties of every eighth element were similar, much as every eighth note in the musical scale is similar. Newlands endured some ridicule for drawing an analogy between chemistry and music, including the derisive comments of one colleague who asked Newlands if he had ever tried ordering the elements according to the first letters of their names.

▲ Dmitri Mendeleev is credited with the arrangement of the periodic table.

The modern periodic table is credited primarily to the Russian chemist Dmitri Mendeleev, even though a similar organization had been suggested by the German chemist Julius Lothar Meyer (1830–1895). Recall from Chapter 2 that Mendeleev's table is based on the periodic law, which states that when elements are arranged in order of increasing mass, certain properties recur periodically. Mendeleev arranged the elements in a table in which mass increases from left to right and elements with similar properties fall in the same columns.

Gallium (eka-aluminum)

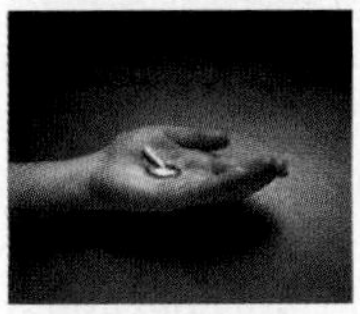

	Mendeleev's predicted properties	Actual properties
Atomic mass	About 68 amu	69.72 amu
Melting point	Low	29.8 °C
Density	5.9 g/cm^3	5.90 g/cm^3
Formula of oxide	X_2O_3	Ga_2O_3
Formula of chloride	XCl_3	$GaCl_3$

Germanium (eka-silicon)

	Mendeleev's predicted properties	Actual properties
Atomic mass	About 72 amu	72.64 amu
Density	5.5 g/cm^3	5.35 g/cm^3
Formula of oxide	XO_2	GeO_2
Formula of chloride	XCl_4	$GeCl_4$

▲ **FIGURE 9.1 Eka-aluminum and Eka-silicon** Mendeleev's arrangement of elements in the periodic table allowed him to predict the existence of these elements, now known as gallium and germanium, and anticipate their properties.

Mendeleev's arrangement was a huge success, allowing him to predict the existence and properties of yet undiscovered elements such as eka-aluminum (later discovered and named gallium) and eka-silicon (later discovered and named germanium). The properties of these two elements are summarized in Figure 9.1▲. (As noted in Chapter 2, *eka* means "the one beyond" or "the next one" in a family of elements.) However, Mendeleev did encounter some difficulties. For example, according to accepted values of atomic masses, tellurium (with higher mass) should come *after* iodine. But based on their properties, Mendeleev placed tellurium *before* iodine and suggested that the mass of tellurium was erroneous. The mass was correct; later work by the English physicist Henry Moseley (1887–1915) showed that listing elements according to *atomic number*, rather than atomic mass, resolves this problem and results in even better correlation with elemental properties.

Notice the scientific approach in practice in the history of the periodic table. A number of related observations led to a scientific law—the periodic law. Mendeleev's table, an expression of the periodic law, had predictive power as laws usually do. However, it did not explain *why* the properties of elements recurred or *why* certain elements had similar properties. Recall from Chapter 1 that laws *summarize* behavior while theories *explain* behavior. The theory that explains the reasons behind the periodic law is quantum-mechanical theory. In this chapter, we explore the connection between the periodic table and quantum-mechanical theory.

9.3 Electron Configurations: How Electrons Occupy Orbitals

WATCH **NOW!**
KEY CONCEPT VIDEO 9.3
Electron Configurations

Quantum-mechanical theory describes the behavior of electrons in atoms. Since chemical bonding involves the transfer or sharing of electrons, quantum-mechanical theory helps us understand and describe chemical behavior. As we saw in Chapter 8, electrons in atoms exist within orbitals. An **electron configuration** for an atom shows the particular orbitals that electrons occupy for that atom. For example, consider the **ground state**—or lowest energy state—electron configuration for a hydrogen atom:

$$\text{H} \quad 1s^1$$

1s = Orbital; superscript 1 = Number of electrons in orbital

The electron configuration indicates that hydrogen's one electron is in the 1*s* orbital. Electrons generally occupy the lowest energy orbitals available. Since the 1*s* orbital is the lowest energy orbital in hydrogen (see Section 8.5), hydrogen's electron occupies that orbital. If we could write electron configurations for all the elements, we could see how the arrangements of the electrons within their atoms correlate with the element's chemical properties. However, the Schrödinger equation solutions (the atomic orbitals and their energies) that we described in Chapter 8 are for the hydrogen atom. What do the atomic orbitals of *other atoms* look like? What are their relative energies?

The Schrödinger equation for multielectron atoms has terms to account for the interactions of the electrons with one another that make it too complicated to solve exactly. However, approximate solutions indicate that the orbitals in multielectron atoms are hydrogen-like—they are similar to the *s*, *p*, *d*, and *f* orbitals that we examined in Chapter 8. In order to see how the electrons in multielectron atoms occupy these hydrogen-like orbitals, we must examine two additional concepts: *the effects of electron spin*, a fundamental property of all electrons that affects the number of electrons allowed in any one orbital; and *sublevel energy splitting*, which determines the order of orbital filling within a level.

Electron Spin and the Pauli Exclusion Principle

We can represent the electron configuration of hydrogen ($1s^1$) in a slightly different way with an **orbital diagram**, which gives similar information but symbolizes the electron as an arrow and the orbital as a box. The orbital diagram for a hydrogen atom is:

H [↿]
1s

In an orbital diagram, the direction of the arrow (pointing up or pointing down) represents the orientation of the *electron's spin*. Recall from Section 8.5 that the orientation of the electron's spin is quantized, with only two possibilities—spin up ($m_s = +\frac{1}{2}$) and spin down ($m_s = -\frac{1}{2}$). In an orbital diagram, $m_s = +\frac{1}{2}$ is represented with a half-arrow pointing up (↿) and $m_s = -\frac{1}{2}$ is represented with a half-arrow pointing down (⇂). In a collection of hydrogen atoms, the electrons in about half of the atoms are spin up and the electrons in the other half are spin down. Since no additional electrons are present within the hydrogen atom, we conventionally represent the hydrogen atom electron configuration with its one electron as spin up.

Helium is the first element on the periodic table that contains two electrons. Its two electrons occupy the 1*s* orbital:

He $1s^2$

How do the spins of the two electrons in helium align relative to each other? The answer to this question is addressed by the **Pauli exclusion principle**, formulated by Wolfgang Pauli (1900–1958) in 1925:

Pauli exclusion principle: no two electrons in an atom can have the same four quantum numbers.

Since two electrons occupying the same orbital have three identical quantum numbers (n, l, and m_l), they must have different spin quantum numbers. Because there are only two possible spin quantum numbers ($+\frac{1}{2}$ and $-\frac{1}{2}$), the Pauli exclusion principle implies that *each orbital can have a maximum of only two electrons, with opposing spins*.

By applying the exclusion principle, we write an electron configuration and orbital diagram for helium as follows:

Electron configuration	Orbital diagram
He $1s^2$	[↿⇂] 1s

The following table shows the four quantum numbers for each of the two electrons in helium:

n	l	m_l	m_s
1	0	0	$+\frac{1}{2}$
1	0	0	$-\frac{1}{2}$

The two electrons have three quantum numbers in common (because they are in the same orbital) but have different spin quantum numbers (as indicated by the opposing half-arrows in the orbital diagram).

Sublevel Energy Splitting in Multielectron Atoms

Understanding the underlying reasons for sublevel energy splitting routinely causes my students confusion. This section of text, beginning here and extending to p. 367, is generally well-written and clear, but I have a few suggestions for improvement.

1. a key aspect that is somewhat glossed over is that electrons are particles and waves. And in looking at the three factors that influence sublevel energy splitting, two reflect the particle nature (Coulomb's Law and shielding, which is somewhat of an

extension of Coulomb's Law), and one reflects the wave nature of electrons (penetration). I would suggest making this more explicit.

2. The penetration concept is particularly difficult for students to grasp. And I think that this is partly due to the fact that when shielding is described, the text uses a fictitious scenario: that of an electron (particle) being physically moved closer to the nucleus. That to me seems an overly hypothetical scenario – I'm not aware that this is even experimentally feasible, but I could be ignorant of such things – and then students are presented with graphs that portray radial distribution functions without being reminded that these reflect/depict the wave nature of electrons. (I realize that this is a nuanced point that I am trying to make, and if necessary, I am happy to clarify further by phone.)
3. I suggest making the x-axis labels of Figures 9.3 and 9.4 more consistent with each other, for improved clarity, e.g., "r (pm), distance from nucleus" I have often found that students don't necessarily look at Fig. 9.3 and understand that "r" means distance from the nucleus.

A major difference in the (approximate) solutions to the Schrödinger equation for multielectron atoms compared to the solutions for the hydrogen atom is the energy ordering of the orbitals. In the hydrogen atom, the energy of an orbital depends only on n, the principal quantum number. For example, the 3s, 3p, and 3d orbitals (which are empty for hydrogen in its lowest energy state) all have the same energy—they are **degenerate**. The orbitals within a principal level of a *multielectron atom*, in contrast, are not degenerate—their energy depends on the value of l. We say that the energies of the sublevels are *split*. In general, the lower the value of l *within a principal level*, the lower the energy (E) of the corresponding orbital. Thus, for a given value of n:

$$E(s \text{ orbital}) < E(p \text{ orbital}) < E(d \text{ orbital}) < E(f \text{ orbital})$$

In order to understand why the sublevels split in this way, we must examine three key concepts associated with the energy of an electron in the vicinity of a nucleus: (1) Coulomb's law, which describes the interactions between charged particles; (2) shielding, which describes how one electron can shield another electron from the full charge of the nucleus; and (3) penetration, which describes how one atomic orbital can overlap spatially with another, thus penetrating into a region that is close to the nucleus (and therefore less shielded from nuclear charge). We then discuss how these concepts, together with the spatial distributions of electron probability for each orbital, result in the energy ordering that we just saw.

Coulomb's Law

The attractions and repulsions between charged particles, first introduced in Section 2.4, are described by **Coulomb's law**, which states that the potential energy (E) of two charged particles depends on their charges (q_1 and q_2) and on their separation (r):

$$E = \frac{1}{4\pi\varepsilon_0}\frac{q_1 q_2}{r} \qquad [9.1]$$

In this equation, ε_0 is a constant ($\varepsilon_0 = 8.85 \times 10^{-12}\ \text{C}^2/\text{J}\cdot\text{m}$). The potential energy is positive for charges of the same sign (plus × plus, or minus × minus) and negative for charges of opposite sign (plus × minus, or minus × plus). The *magnitude* of the potential energy depends inversely on the separation between the charged particles. We can draw three important conclusions from Coulomb's law:

- For like charges, the potential energy (E) is positive and decreases as the particles get *farther apart* (as r increases). Since systems tend toward lower potential energy, like charges repel each other (in much the same way that like poles of two magnets repel each other).
- For opposite charges, the potential energy is negative and becomes more negative as the particles get *closer together* (as r decreases). Therefore, opposite charges (like opposite poles on a magnet) *attract each other.*
- The *magnitude* of the interaction between charged particles increases as the charges of the particles increase. Consequently, an electron with a charge of 1− is more strongly attracted to a nucleus with a charge of 2+ than it is to a nucleus with a charge of 1+.

ANSWER **NOW!**

9.1 **Cc** Conceptual Connection

COULOMB'S LAW According to Coulomb's law, what happens to the potential energy of two oppositely charged particles as they get closer together?

(a) Their potential energy decreases.
(b) Their potential energy increases.
(c) Their potential energy does not change.

Shielding

In multielectron atoms, any one electron experiences both the positive charge of the nucleus (which is attractive) and the negative charges of the other electrons (which are repulsive). We can think of the repulsion of one electron by other electrons as *screening* or **shielding** that electron from the full effects of the nuclear charge. For example, consider a lithium ion (Li^+). The lithium ion contains two electrons, so its electron configuration is identical to that of helium:

$$Li^+ \quad 1s^2$$

Imagine bringing a third electron toward the lithium ion. When the third electron is far from the nucleus, it experiences the 3+ charge of the nucleus through the *screen* or *shield* of the 2− charge of the two 1*s* electrons, as shown in Figure 9.2(a)▼. We can think of the third electron as experiencing an **effective nuclear charge (Z_{eff})** of approximately 1+ (3+ from the nucleus and 2− from the electrons, for a net charge of 1+). The inner electrons in effect *shield* the outer electron from the full nuclear charge.

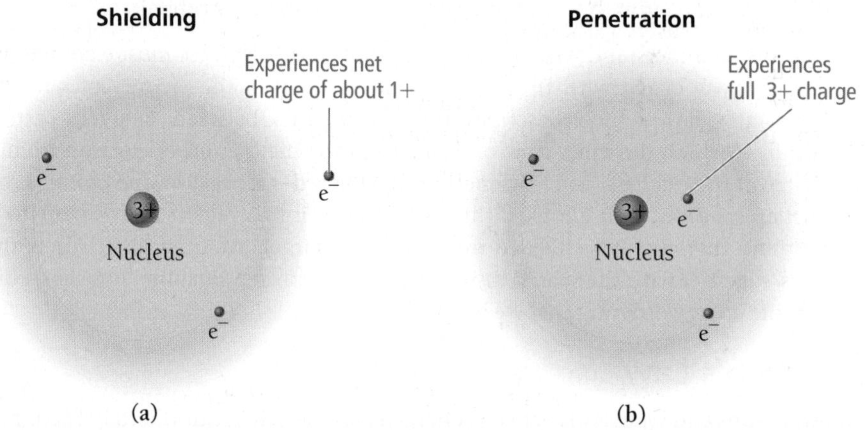

▲ **FIGURE 9.2 Shielding and Penetration** **(a)** An electron far from the nucleus is partly shielded by the electrons in the 1*s* orbital, reducing the effective net nuclear charge that it experiences. **(b)** An electron that penetrates the electron cloud of the 1*s* orbital experiences more of the nuclear charge.

Penetration

The probability of an electron penetrating into the region occupied by inner electrons is described by its radial distribution function (which reflects the wave nature of the electron).

Now imagine allowing this third electron to come closer to the nucleus. As the third electron *penetrates* the electron cloud of the 1*s* electrons, it begins to experience the 3+ charge of the nucleus more fully because it is less shielded by the intervening electrons. If the electron could somehow get closer to the nucleus than the 1*s* electrons, it would experience the full 3+ charge, as shown in Figure 9.2(b)▲. In other words, as the outer electron undergoes **penetration** into the region occupied by the inner electrons, it experiences a greater nuclear charge and therefore (according to Coulomb's law) a lower energy.

Electron Spatial Distributions and Sublevel Splitting

We now have examined the concepts we need to understand the energy splitting of the sublevels within a principal level. The splitting is a result of the spatial distributions of electrons within a sublevel. Recall from Section 8.6 that the radial distribution function for an atomic orbital shows the total probability of finding the electron within a thin spherical shell at a distance *r* from the nucleus.

Figure 9.3▶ shows the radial distribution functions of the 2*s* and 2*p* orbitals superimposed on one another (the radial distribution function of the 1*s* orbital is also shown). Notice that, in general, an electron in a 2*p* orbital has a greater probability of being found closer to the nucleus than an electron in a 2*s* orbital. We might initially expect, therefore, that the 2*p* orbital would be lower in energy. However, exactly the opposite is true—the 2*s* orbital is actually lower in energy, *but only when the 1s orbital is occupied.* (When the 1*s* orbital is empty, the 2*s* and 2*p* orbitals are degenerate.) Why? The reason is the bump near $r = 0$ (near the nucleus) for the 2*s* orbital. This bump represents a significant probability of the electron being found very close to the nucleus. Even more importantly, this area of the probability penetrates into the 1*s* orbital—it gets into the region where shielding by the 1*s* electrons is less effective. In contrast, most of the probability in the radial distribution function of the 2*p* orbital lies *outside* the radial distribution function of the 1*s* orbital. Consequently, almost all of the 2*p* orbital is shielded from nuclear charge by the 1*s* orbital. The end result is that the 2*s* orbital—since it experiences more of the nuclear charge due to its greater *penetration*—is lower in energy than the 2*p* orbital. The results are similar when we compare the 3*s*, 3*p*, and 3*d* orbitals. The *s* orbitals penetrate more fully than the *p* orbitals, which in turn penetrate more fully than the *d* orbitals, as shown in Figure 9.4▶.

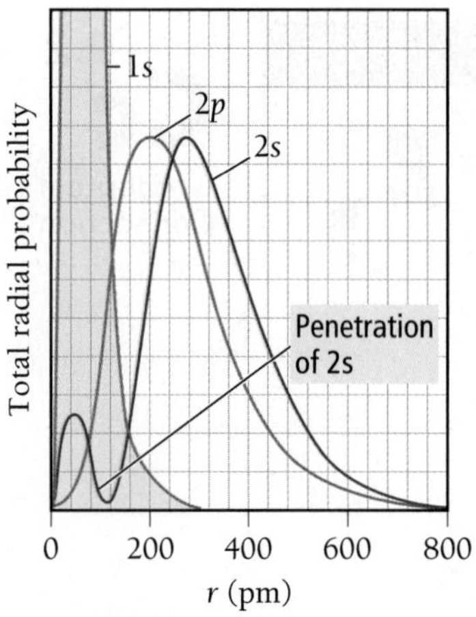

▲ **FIGURE 9.3 Radial Distribution Functions for the 1*s*, 2*s*, and 2*p* Orbitals**

Figure 9.5▼ shows the energy ordering of a number of orbitals in multielectron atoms. Notice these features of Figure 9.5:

- Because of penetration, the sublevels of each principal level are *not* degenerate for multielectron atoms.
- In the fourth and fifth principal levels, the effects of penetration become so important that the 4*s* orbital lies lower in energy than the 3*d* orbitals and the 5*s* orbital lies lower in energy than the 4*d* orbitals.
- The energy separations between one set of orbitals and the next become smaller for 4*s* orbitals and beyond, and the relative energy ordering of these orbitals can actually vary among elements. These variations result in irregularities in the electron configurations of the transition metals and their ions (as we shall see later).

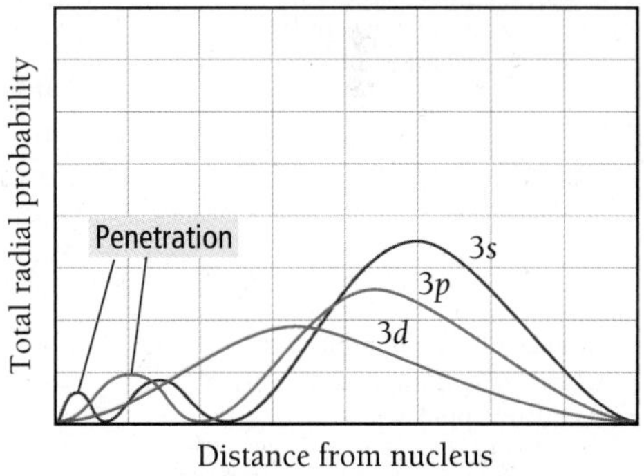

▲ **FIGURE 9.4 Radial Distribution Functions for the 3*s*, 3*p*, 3*d* Orbitals** The 3*s* electrons penetrate most deeply into the inner orbitals, are least shielded, and experience the "greatest" effective nuclear charge. The 3*d* electrons penetrate least. This accounts for the energy ordering of the sublevels: $s < p < d$.

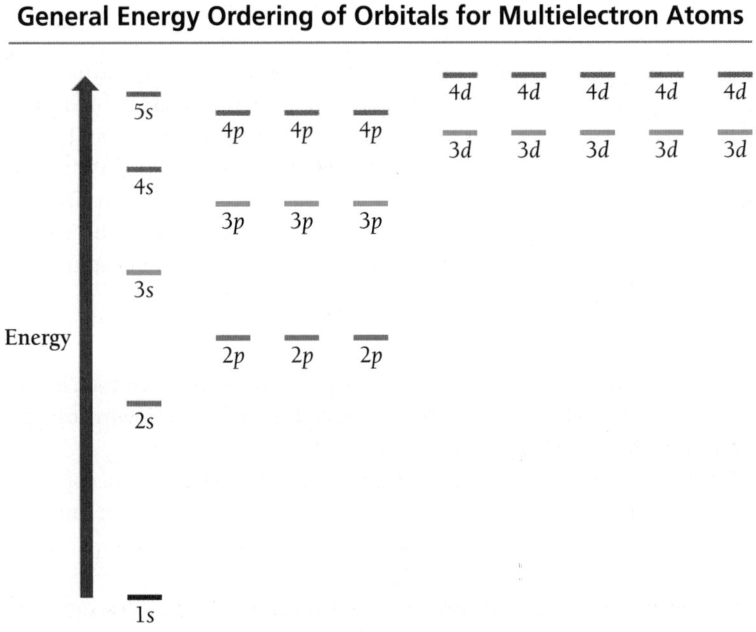

▲ **FIGURE 9.5 General Energy Ordering of Orbitals for Multielectron Atoms**

ANSWER **NOW!**

9.2 Cc Conceptual Connection

PENETRATION AND SHIELDING Which statement is true?

(a) An orbital that penetrates into the region occupied by core electrons is more shielded from nuclear charge than an orbital that does not penetrate and therefore has a higher energy.
(b) An orbital that penetrates into the region occupied by core electrons is less shielded from nuclear charge than an orbital that does not penetrate and therefore has a higher energy.
(c) An orbital that penetrates into the region occupied by core electrons is less shielded from nuclear charge than an orbital that does not penetrate and therefore has a lower energy.
(d) An orbital that penetrates into the region occupied by core electrons is more shielded from nuclear charge than an orbital that does not penetrate and therefore has a lower energy.

Electron Configurations for Multielectron Atoms

Unless otherwise specified, we use the term *electron configuration* to mean the ground state (or lowest energy) configuration.

Now that we know the energy ordering of orbitals in multielectron atoms, we can determine ground state electron configurations for the rest of the elements. Since we know that electrons occupy the lowest energy orbitals available when the atom is in its ground state and that only two electrons (with opposing spins) are allowed in each orbital, we can systematically build up the electron configurations for the elements. This pattern of orbital filling is known as the **aufbau principle** (the German word *aufbau* means "build up"). For lithium, with three electrons, the electron configuration and orbital diagram are:

Remember that the number of electrons in a neutral atom is equal to its atomic number.

Electron configuration — Orbital diagram

Li $1s^2 2s^1$

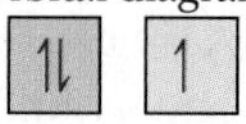

For carbon, which has six electrons, the electron configuration and orbital diagram are:

Electrons with parallel spins have correlated motion that minimizes their mutual repulsion.

Electron configuration — Orbital diagram

C $1s^2 2s^2 2p^2$

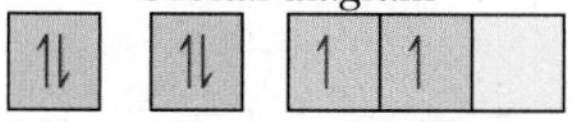

Notice that the $2p$ electrons occupy the p orbitals (of equal energy) singly, rather than pairing in one orbital. This way of filling orbitals is known as **Hund's rule**, which states that *when filling degenerate orbitals, electrons fill them singly first, with parallel spins*. Hund's rule is a result of an atom's tendency to find the lowest energy state possible. When two electrons occupy separate orbitals of equal energy, the repulsive interaction between them is lower than when they occupy the same orbital because the electrons are spread out over different regions of space. By convention, we denote these parallel spins with half-arrows pointing up.

Summarizing Orbital Filling

- Electrons occupy orbitals so as to minimize the energy of the atom; therefore, lower energy orbitals fill before higher energy orbitals. Orbitals fill in the following order: $1s\ 2s\ 2p\ 3s\ 3p\ 4s\ 3d\ 4p\ 5s\ 4d\ 5p\ 6s$.
- Orbitals can hold no more than two electrons each. When two electrons occupy the same orbital, their spins are opposite. This is another way of expressing the Pauli exclusion principle (no two electrons in one atom can have the same four quantum numbers).
- When orbitals of identical energy are available, electrons first occupy these orbitals singly with parallel spins rather than in pairs. Once the orbitals of equal energy are half full, the electrons start to pair (Hund's rule).

Consider the electron configurations and orbital diagrams for elements with atomic numbers 3–10:

Symbol	Number of electrons	Electron configuration	Orbital diagram
Li	3	$1s^22s^1$	1s [↑↓] 2s [↑]
Be	4	$1s^22s^2$	1s [↑↓] 2s [↑↓]
B	5	$1s^22s^22p^1$	1s [↑↓] 2s [↑↓] 2p [↑][ ][ ]
C	6	$1s^22s^22p^2$	1s [↑↓] 2s [↑↓] 2p [↑][↑][ ]

Notice that, as a result of Hund's rule, the *p* orbitals fill with single electrons before the electrons pair:

N	7	$1s^22s^22p^3$	1s [↑↓] 2s [↑↓] 2p [↑][↑][↑]
O	8	$1s^22s^22p^4$	1s [↑↓] 2s [↑↓] 2p [↑↓][↑][↑]
F	9	$1s^22s^22p^5$	1s [↑↓] 2s [↑↓] 2p [↑↓][↑↓][↑]
Ne	10	$1s^22s^22p^6$	1s [↑↓] 2s [↑↓] 2p [↑↓][↑↓][↑↓]

The electron configuration of neon represents the complete filling of the $n = 2$ principal level. When writing electron configurations for elements beyond neon, or beyond any other noble gas, we can abbreviate the electron configuration of the previous noble gas—sometimes called the *inner electron configuration*—by the symbol for the noble gas in square brackets. For example, the electron configuration of sodium is:

$$\text{Na} \quad 1s^22s^22p^63s^1$$

We can write this configuration more compactly by using [Ne] to represent the inner electrons:

$$\text{Na} \quad [\text{Ne}]\ 3s^1$$

[Ne] represents $1s^22s^22p^6$, the electron configuration for neon.

How to Write an Electron Configuration for an Element

1. Locate the element on the periodic table and determine its atomic number (this number equals the number of electrons).
2. Use the order of filling (Figure 9.5) to distribute the electrons in the appropriate orbitals. Remember that each orbital can hold a maximum of two electrons. Consequently,
   - the *s* sublevel has only one orbital and can therefore hold only 2 electrons.
   - the *p* sublevel has three orbitals and can hold 6 electrons.
   - the *d* sublevel has five orbitals and can hold 10 electrons.
   - the *f* sublevel has seven orbitals and can hold 14 electrons.

EXAMPLE 9.1 Electron Configurations

Write electron configurations for each element.

(a) Mg **(b)** P **(c)** Br **(d)** Al

SOLUTION

(a) Mg Magnesium has 12 electrons. Distribute 2 of these into the 1*s* orbital, 2 into the 2*s* orbital, 6 into the 2*p* orbitals, and 2 into the 3*s* orbital.	Mg $1s^22s^22p^63s^2$ or [Ne] $3s^2$
(b) P Phosphorus has 15 electrons. Distribute 2 of these into the 1*s* orbital, 2 into the 2*s* orbital, 6 into the 2*p* orbitals, 2 into the 3*s* orbital, and 3 into the 3*p* orbitals.	P $1s^22s^22p^63s^23p^3$ or [Ne] $3s^23p^3$
(c) Br Bromine has 35 electrons. Distribute 2 of these into the 1*s* orbital, 2 into the 2*s* orbital, 6 into the 2*p* orbitals, 2 into the 3*s* orbital, 6 into the 3*p* orbitals, 2 into the 4*s* orbital, 10 into the 3*d* orbitals, and 5 into the 4*p* orbitals.	Br $1s^22s^22p^63s^23p^64s^23d^{10}4p^5$ or [Ar] $4s^23d^{10}4p^5$
(d) Al Aluminum has 13 electrons. Distribute 2 of these into the 1*s* orbital, 2 into the 2*s* orbital, 6 into the 2*p* orbitals, 2 into the 3*s* orbital, and 1 into the 3*p* orbital.	Al $1s^22s^22p^63s^23p^1$ or [Ne] $3s^23p^1$

FOR PRACTICE 9.1 Write electron configurations for each element.

(a) Cl **(b)** Si **(c)** Sr **(d)** O

WATCH **NOW!**

INTERACTIVE WORKED EXAMPLE 9.2

EXAMPLE 9.2 Writing Orbital Diagrams

Write the orbital diagram for sulfur and determine the number of unpaired electrons.

SOLUTION

Sulfur's atomic number is 16; it therefore has 16 electrons, and the electron configuration $1s^22s^22p^63s^23p^4$. Draw a box for each orbital, putting the lowest energy orbital (1*s*) on the far left and proceeding to orbitals of higher energy to the right.

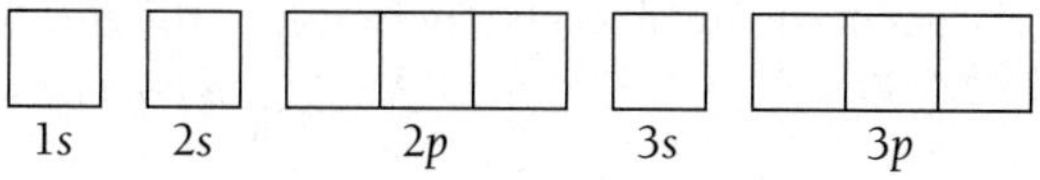

Distribute the 16 electrons into the boxes representing the orbitals, allowing a maximum of two electrons per orbital and remembering Hund's rule. You can see from the diagram that sulfur has two unpaired electrons.

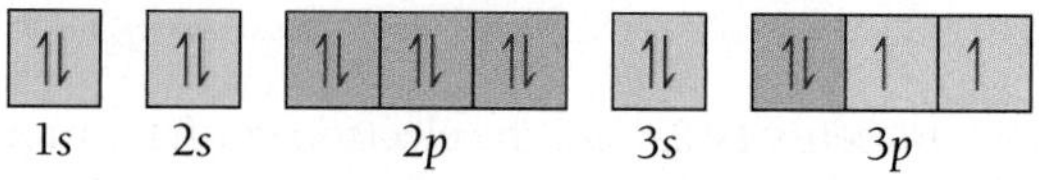

Two unpaired electrons

FOR PRACTICE 9.2 Write the orbital diagram for Ar and determine the number of unpaired electrons.

ANSWER **NOW!**

9.3 Cc Conceptual Connection

ELECTRON CONFIGURATIONS AND QUANTUM NUMBERS

What are the four quantum numbers for each of the two electrons in a 4*s* orbital?

(a) $n = 4, l = 0, m_l = 0, m_s = +½$; $n = 4, l = 0, m_l = 0, m_s = +½$

(b) $n = 4, l = 0, m_l = 0, m_s = +½$; $n = 4, l = 0, m_l = 0, m_s = -½$

(c) $n = 3, l = 0, m_l = 0, m_s = +½$; $n = 3, l = 0, m_l = 0, m_s = -½$

(d) $n = 4, l = 1, m_l = 0, m_s = +½$; $n = 4, l = 1, m_l = 0, m_s = -½$

9.4 Electron Configurations, Valence Electrons, and the Periodic Table

WATCH **NOW!**

KEY CONCEPT VIDEO 9.4
Writing an Electron Configuration based on an Element's Position on the Periodic Table

Recall that Mendeleev arranged the periodic table so that elements with similar chemical properties lie in the same column. We can begin to make the connection between an element's properties and its electron configuration by superimposing the electron configurations of the first 18 elements onto a partial periodic table, as shown in Figure 9.6▶. As we move to the right across a row, the orbitals fill in the correct order. With each subsequent row, the highest principal quantum number increases by one. Notice that as we move down a column, *the number of electrons in the outermost principal energy level (highest n value) remains the same.* The key connection between the macroscopic world (an element's chemical properties) and the atomic world (an atom's electronic structure) lies in these outermost electrons.

Outer Electron Configurations of Elements 1–18

1A	2A	3A	4A	5A	6A	7A	8A
1 H $1s^1$							2 He $1s^2$
3 Li $2s^1$	4 Be $2s^2$	5 B $2s^22p^1$	6 C $2s^22p^2$	7 N $2s^22p^3$	8 O $2s^22p^4$	9 F $2s^22p^5$	10 Ne $2s^22p^6$
11 Na $3s^1$	12 Mg $3s^2$	13 Al $3s^23p^1$	14 Si $3s^23p^2$	15 P $3s^23p^3$	16 S $3s^23p^4$	17 Cl $3s^23p^5$	18 Ar $3s^23p^6$

▲**FIGURE 9.6 Outer Electron Configurations of the First 18 Elements in the Periodic Table**

An atom's **valence electrons** are those that are important in chemical bonding. *For main-group elements, the valence electrons are those in the outermost principal energy level.* For transition elements, we also count the outermost *d* electrons among the valence electrons (even though they are not in an outermost principal energy level). The chemical properties of an element depend on its valence electrons, which are instrumental in bonding because they are held most loosely (and are therefore the easiest to lose or share). We can now see *why* the elements in a column of the periodic table have similar chemical properties: *they have the same number of valence electrons.*

We distinguish between valence electrons and all the other electrons in an atom, which are called **core electrons**. For example, silicon, with the electron configuration $1s^22s^22p^63s^23p^2$, has four valence electrons (those in the $n = 3$ principal level) and ten core electrons as shown in the margin.

Si $1s^22s^22p^63s^23p^2$

Core electrons ($1s^22s^22p^6$) — Valence electrons ($3s^23p^2$)

EXAMPLE 9.3 Valence Electrons and Core Electrons

Write the electron configuration for Ge. Identify the valence electrons and the core electrons.

SOLUTION

Determine the total number of electrons from germanium's atomic number (32). Distribute the electrons into the appropriate orbitals according to the information in *Summarizing Orbital Filling* on p. 358.

Ge $1s^22s^22p^63s^23p^64s^23d^{10}4p^2$

Since germanium is a main-group element, its valence electrons are those in the outermost principal energy level. For germanium the $n = 4$ principal level is outermost. Consequently, the $n = 4$ electrons are valence electrons and the rest are core electrons.

Note: In this book, we write electron configurations with the orbitals in the order of filling. However, electron configurations are sometimes written in order of increasing principal quantum number. The electron configuration of germanium written in order of increasing principal quantum number is Ge $1s^22s^22p^63s^23p^63d^{10}4s^24p^2$.

Ge $1s^22s^22p^63s^23p^64s^23d^{10}4p^2$

4 valence electrons ($4s^2$, $4p^2$)

28 core electrons

FOR PRACTICE 9.3 Write the electron configuration for phosphorus. Identify the valence electrons and core electrons.

Orbital Blocks in the Periodic Table

A pattern similar to what we just saw for the first 18 elements exists for the entire periodic table, as shown in Figure 9.7▼. Note that because of the filling order of orbitals, we can divide the periodic table into blocks representing the filling of particular sublevels.

s block The first two columns on the left side of the periodic table comprise the *s* block, with outer electron configurations of ns^1 (the alkali metals) and ns^2 (the alkaline earth metals).

p block The six columns on the right side of the periodic table comprise the *p* block, with outer electron configurations of ns^2np^1, ns^2np^2, ns^2np^3, ns^2np^4, ns^2np^5 (halogens), and ns^2np^6 (noble gases).

d block The transition elements comprise the *d* block.

f block The lanthanides and actinides (also called the inner transition elements) comprise the *f* block. (For compactness, the *f* block is normally printed below the *d* block instead of being embedded within it.)

You can see that *the number of columns in a block corresponds to the maximum number of electrons that can occupy the particular sublevel of that block.* The *s* block has two columns (corresponding to one *s* orbital holding a maximum of two electrons); the *p* block has six columns (corresponding to three *p* orbitals with two electrons each); the *d* block has 10 columns (corresponding to five *d* orbitals with two electrons each); and the *f* block has 14 columns (corresponding to seven *f* orbitals with two electrons each).

Notice also that, except for helium, *the number of valence electrons in any main-group element is equal to its lettered group number.* For example, we know that chlorine has seven valence electrons because it is in group 7A.

Lastly, note that, for main-group elements, *the row number in the periodic table is equal to the number (or n value) of the highest occupied principal level.* For example, because chlorine is in row 3, its highest principal level is the $n = 3$ level.

Helium is an exception. Even though it lies in the column with an outer electron configuration of ns^2np^6, its electron configuration is simply $1s^2$.

▼ FIGURE 9.7 The *s*, *p*, *d*, and *f* Blocks of the Periodic Table

Orbital Blocks of the Periodic Table

s-block elements | p-block elements | d-block elements | f-block elements

Periods / Groups	1 1A	2 2A	3 3B	4 4B	5 5B	6 6B	7 7B	8 8B	9 8B	10 8B	11 1B	12 2B	13 3A	14 4A	15 5A	16 6A	17 7A	18 8A
1	1 H $1s^1$																	2 He $1s^2$
2	3 Li $2s^1$	4 Be $2s^2$											5 B $2s^22p^1$	6 C $2s^22p^2$	7 N $2s^22p^3$	8 O $2s^22p^4$	9 F $2s^22p^5$	10 Ne $2s^22p^6$
3	11 Na $3s^1$	12 Mg $3s^2$											13 Al $3s^23p^1$	14 Si $3s^23p^2$	15 P $3s^23p^3$	16 S $3s^23p^4$	17 Cl $3s^23p^5$	18 Ar $3s^23p^6$
4	19 K $4s^1$	20 Ca $4s^2$	21 Sc $4s^23d^1$	22 Ti $4s^23d^2$	23 V $4s^23d^3$	24 Cr $4s^13d^5$	25 Mn $4s^23d^5$	26 Fe $4s^23d^6$	27 Co $4s^23d^7$	28 Ni $4s^23d^8$	29 Cu $4s^13d^{10}$	30 Zn $4s^23d^{10}$	31 Ga $4s^24p^1$	32 Ge $4s^24p^2$	33 As $4s^24p^3$	34 Se $4s^24p^4$	35 Br $4s^24p^5$	36 Kr $4s^24p^6$
5	37 Rb $5s^1$	38 Sr $5s^2$	39 Y $5s^24d^1$	40 Zr $5s^24d^2$	41 Nb $5s^14d^4$	42 Mo $5s^14d^5$	43 Tc $5s^24d^5$	44 Ru $5s^14d^7$	45 Rh $5s^14d^8$	46 Pd $4d^{10}$	47 Ag $5s^14d^{10}$	48 Cd $5s^24d^{10}$	49 In $5s^25p^1$	50 Sn $5s^25p^2$	51 Sb $5s^25p^3$	52 Te $5s^25p^4$	53 I $5s^25p^5$	54 Xe $5s^25p^6$
6	55 Cs $6s^1$	56 Ba $6s^2$	57 La $6s^25d^1$	72 Hf $6s^25d^2$	73 Ta $6s^25d^3$	74 W $6s^25d^4$	75 Re $6s^25d^5$	76 Os $6s^25d^6$	77 Ir $6s^25d^7$	78 Pt $6s^15d^9$	79 Au $6s^15d^{10}$	80 Hg $6s^25d^{10}$	81 Tl $6s^26p^1$	82 Pb $6s^26p^2$	83 Bi $6s^26p^3$	84 Po $6s^26p^4$	85 At $6s^26p^5$	86 Rn $6s^26p^6$
7	87 Fr $7s^1$	88 Ra $7s^2$	89 Ac $7s^26d^1$	104 Rf $7s^26d^2$	105 Db $7s^26d^3$	106 Sg $7s^26d^4$	107 Bh	108 Hs	109 Mt	110 Ds	111 Rg	112 Cn	113 Nh	114 Fl	115 Mc	116 Lv	117 Ts	118 Og

Lanthanides	58 Ce $6s^24f^15d^1$	59 Pr $6s^24f^3$	60 Nd $6s^24f^4$	61 Pm $6s^24f^5$	62 Sm $6s^24f^6$	63 Eu $6s^24f^7$	64 Gd $6s^24f^75d^1$	65 Tb $6s^24f^9$	66 Dy $6s^24f^{10}$	67 Ho $6s^24f^{11}$	68 Er $6s^24f^{12}$	69 Tm $6s^24f^{13}$	70 Yb $6s^24f^{14}$	71 Lu $6s^24f^{14}5d^1$
Actinides	90 Th $7s^26d^2$	91 Pa $7s^25f^26d^1$	92 U $7s^25f^36d^1$	93 Np $7s^25f^46d^1$	94 Pu $7s^25f^6$	95 Am $7s^25f^7$	96 Cm $7s^25f^76d^1$	97 Bk $7s^25f^9$	98 Cf $7s^25f^{10}$	99 Es $7s^25f^{11}$	100 Fm $7s^25f^{12}$	101 Md $7s^25f^{13}$	102 No $7s^25f^{14}$	103 Lr $7s^25f^{14}6d^1$

Recall from Chapter 2 that main-group elements are those in the two far left columns (groups 1A, 2A) and the six far right columns (groups 3A–8A) of the periodic table.

Summarizing Periodic Table Organization

- The periodic table is divisible into four blocks corresponding to the filling of the four quantum sublevels (*s*, *p*, *d*, and *f*).
- The lettered group number of a main-group element is equal to the number of valence electrons in that element.
- The row number of a main-group element is equal to the highest principal quantum number of that element.

VALENCE ELECTRONS AND GROUP NUMBER Without writing an electron configuration, determine the number of valence electrons in nitrogen.

(a) 3 **(b)** 4 **(c)** 5 **(d)** 6

9.4 Cc Conceptual Connection

ANSWER **NOW!**

Writing an Electron Configuration for an Element from Its Position in the Periodic Table

The organization of the periodic table allows us to write the electron configuration for an element based on its position in the periodic table.

How to Write an Electron Configuration for an Element from Its Position in the Periodic Table

1. Locate the element on the periodic table.
2. Locate the noble gas that precedes the element.
3. Represent the inner electron configuration by writing the symbol of the noble gas in brackets.
4. Determine the outer electron configuration by tracing the elements between the noble gas and the element of interest; assign electrons to the appropriate orbitals as you trace across the blocks on the periodic table.

For example, suppose we want to write an electron configuration for Cl. The *inner electron configuration* of Cl is that of the noble gas that precedes it in the periodic table, Ne. So we represent the inner electron configuration with [Ne]. We can determine the *outer electron configuration*—the configuration of the electrons beyond the previous noble gas—by tracing the elements between Ne and Cl and assigning electrons to the appropriate orbitals, as shown here. Remember that the highest *n* value is indicated by the row number (in this case, 3 for chlorine).

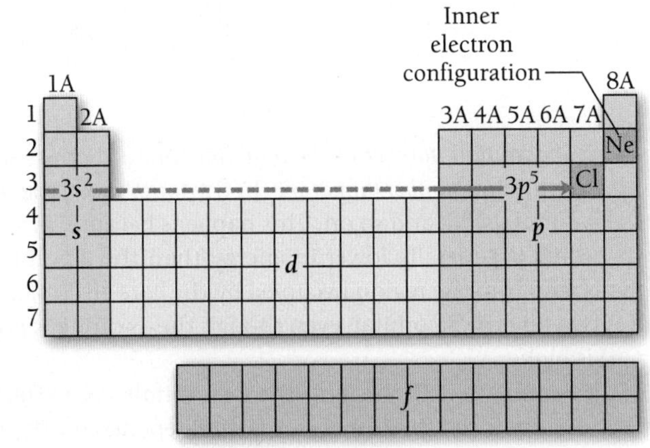

We begin with [Ne], then add in the two 3*s* electrons as we trace across the *s* block, followed by five 3*p* electrons as we trace across the *p* block to Cl, which is in the fifth column of the *p* block. The electron configuration is:

$$\text{Cl} \quad [\text{Ne}]3s^2 3p^5$$

Notice that Cl is in column 7A and therefore has seven valence electrons and an outer electron configuration of ns^2np^5.

WATCH **NOW!**
INTERACTIVE WORKED EXAMPLE 9.4

EXAMPLE 9.4 Writing Electron Configurations from the Periodic Table

Refer to the periodic table to write the electron configuration for selenium (Se).

SOLUTION

The atomic number of Se is 34. The noble gas that precedes Se in the periodic table is argon, so the inner electron configuration is [Ar]. Obtain the outer electron configuration by tracing the elements between Ar and Se and assigning electrons to the appropriate orbitals. Begin with [Ar]. Because Se is in row 4, add two 4*s* electrons as you trace across the *s* block (n = row number). Next, add ten 3*d* electrons as you trace across the *d* block (n = row number − 1). Lastly, add four 4*p* electrons as you trace across the *p* block to Se, which is in the fourth column of the *p* block (n = row number).

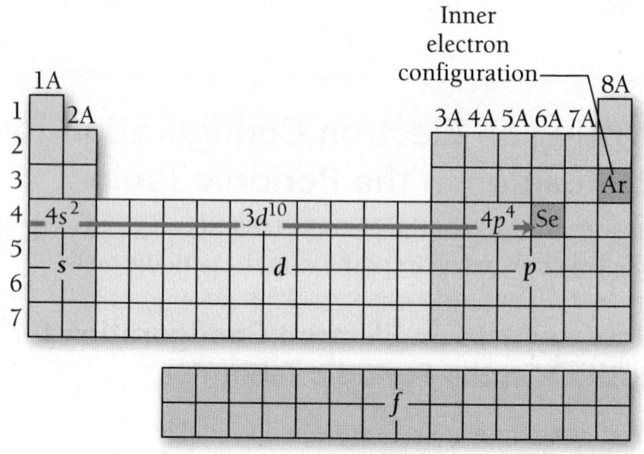

Se [Ar] $4s^2 3d^{10} 4p^4$

FOR PRACTICE 9.4 Refer to the periodic table to write the electron configuration of bismuth (Bi).

FOR MORE PRACTICE 9.4 Refer to the periodic table to write the electron configuration for iodine (I).

The Transition and Inner Transition Elements

The electron configurations of the transition elements (*d* block) and inner transition elements (*f* block) exhibit trends that differ somewhat from those of the main-group elements. As we move to the right across a row in the *d* block, the *d* orbitals fill as shown here:

21 Sc $4s^2 3d^1$	22 Ti $4s^2 3d^2$	23 V $4s^2 3d^3$	24 Cr $4s^1 3d^5$	25 Mn $4s^2 3d^5$	26 Fe $4s^2 3d^6$	27 Co $4s^2 3d^7$	28 Ni $4s^2 3d^8$	29 Cu $4s^1 3d^{10}$	30 Zn $4s^2 3d^{10}$
39 Y $5s^2 4d^1$	40 Zr $5s^2 4d^2$	41 Nb $5s^1 4d^4$	42 Mo $5s^1 4d^5$	43 Tc $5s^2 4d^5$	44 Ru $5s^1 4d^7$	45 Rh $5s^1 4d^8$	46 Pd $4d^{10}$	47 Ag $5s^1 4d^{10}$	48 Cd $5s^2 4d^{10}$

Notice that *the principal quantum number of the d orbitals that fill across each row in the transition series is equal to the row number minus one*. In the fourth row, the 3*d* orbitals fill; in the fifth row, the 4*d* orbitals fill; and so on. This happens because, as we discussed in Section 9.3, the 4*s* orbital is generally lower in energy than the 3*d* orbital (because it more efficiently penetrates into the region occupied by the core electrons). The result is that the 4*s* orbital fills before the 3*d* orbital, even though the 4*s* orbital's principal quantum number (n = 4) is higher.

Keep in mind, however, that the 4*s* and the 3*d* orbitals are extremely close to each other in energy, so their relative energy ordering depends on the exact species under consideration; this causes some irregular behavior in the transition metals. For example, in the first transition series of the *d* block, the outer configuration is $4s^2 3d^x$ with two exceptions: Cr is $4s^1 3d^5$ and Cu is $4s^1 3d^{10}$. This behavior is related to the closely spaced 3*d* and 4*s* energy levels and the stability associated with a half-filled (as in Cr) or completely filled (as in Cu) sublevel. Actual electron configurations are definitively determined experimentally (through spectroscopy) and do not always conform to the general pattern. Nonetheless, the patterns described here allow us to accurately predict electron configurations for most of the elements in the periodic table.

As we move across the *f* block (the inner transition series), the *f* orbitals fill. For these elements, the principal quantum number of the *f* orbitals that fill across each row is the row number *minus two*. (In the sixth row, the 4*f* orbitals fill, and in the seventh row, the 5*f* orbitals fill.) In addition, within the inner transition series, the close energy spacing of the 5*d* and 4*f* orbitals sometimes causes an electron to enter a 5*d* orbital instead of the expected 4*f* orbital. For example, the electron configuration of gadolinium is $[Xe]6s^2 4f^7 5d^1$ (instead of the expected $[Xe]6s^2 4f^8$).

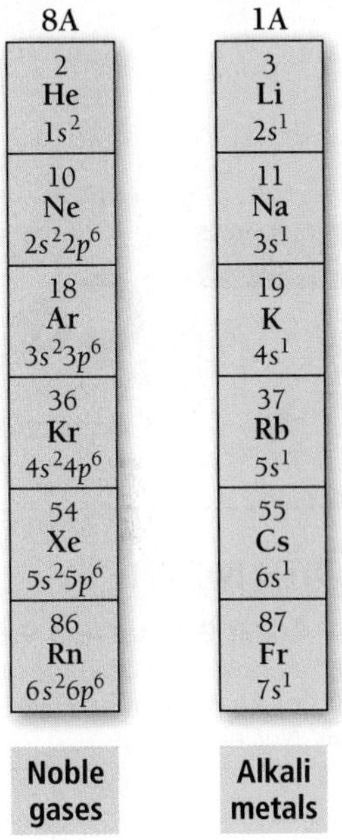

9.5 The Explanatory Power of the Quantum-Mechanical Model

We can now see how the quantum-mechanical model accounts for the chemical properties of the elements, such as the inertness of helium or the reactivity of hydrogen, and (more generally) how it accounts for the periodic law. *The chemical properties of elements are largely determined by the number of valence electrons they contain.* Their properties are periodic because the number of valence electrons is periodic.

Because elements within a column in the periodic table have the same number of valence electrons, they have similar chemical properties. The noble gases, for example, all have eight valence electrons, except for helium, which has two. Although we do not cover the quantitative (or numerical) aspects of the quantum-mechanical model in this book, calculations of the overall energy of the electrons within atoms with eight valence electrons (or two, in the case of helium) show that they are particularly stable. In other words, when *s* and *p* quantum sublevels are completely full, the overall energy of the electrons that occupy that level is particularly low. Therefore, those electrons *cannot* lower their energy by reacting with other atoms or molecules, so the corresponding atom is relatively unreactive or inert. The noble gases are the most chemically stable and relatively unreactive family in the periodic table.

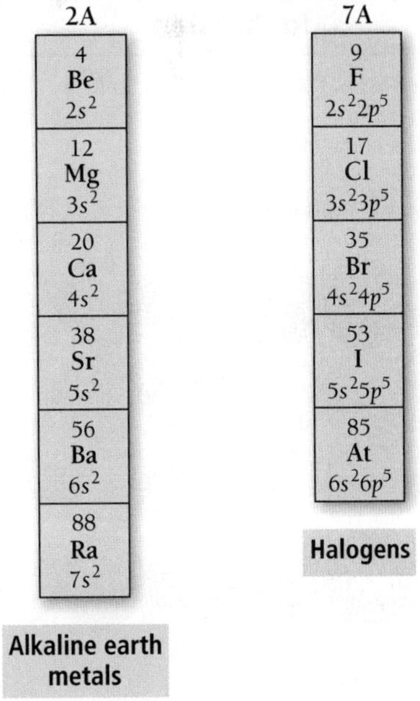

Elements with electron configurations *close* to those of the noble gases are the most reactive because they can attain noble gas electron configurations by losing or gaining a small number of electrons. For example, alkali metals (group 1A) are among the most reactive metals because their outer electron configuration (ns^1) is one electron beyond a noble gas configuration. They readily react to lose the ns^1 electron, obtaining a noble gas configuration. This explains why—as we saw in Chapter 2—the group 1A metals tend to form 1+ cations. Similarly, alkaline earth metals, with an outer electron configuration of ns^2, also tend to be reactive metals, losing their ns^2 electrons to form 2+ cations. This does not mean that forming an ion with a noble gas configuration is in itself energetically favorable. In fact, forming cations always *requires energy*. But when the cation formed has a noble gas configuration, the energy cost of forming the cation is often less than the energy payback that occurs when that cation forms ionic bonds with anions, as we shall see in Chapter 10.

On the right side of the periodic table, halogens are among the most reactive nonmetals because of their ns^2np^5 electron configurations. They are only one electron short of a noble gas configuration and tend to react to gain that one electron, forming 1− ions. Figure 9.8▶, which is similar to Figure 2.13 in Chapter 2, shows the elements that form predictable ions. The charges of these ions reflect their electron configurations—in their reactions, these elements form ions with noble gas electron configurations.

Elements That Form Ions with Predictable Charges

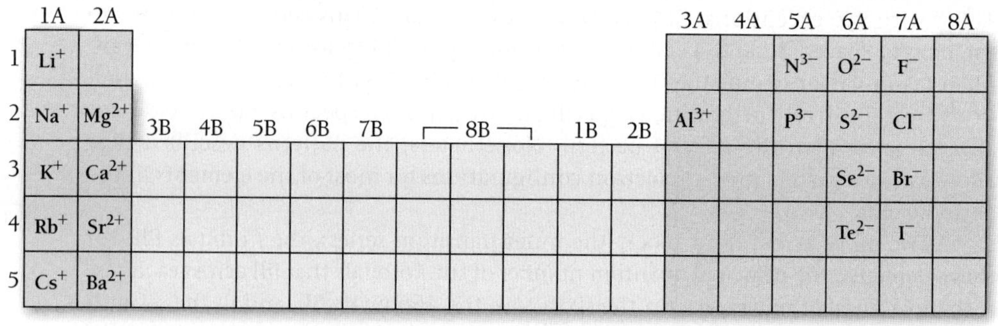

▲ **FIGURE 9.8 Elements That Form Ions with Predictable Charges** Notice that each ion has a noble gas electron configuration.

ANSWER **NOW!**

9.5 **Cc** Conceptual Connection

ELECTRON CONFIGURATIONS AND ION CHARGE

A main-group element has an outer electron configuration of ns^2np^4. What charge is likely for an ion of this element?

(a) 1− **(b)** 2− **(c)** 1+ **(d)** 2+

WATCH **NOW!**

KEY CONCEPT VIDEO 9.6
Periodic Trends in the Size of Atoms and Effective Nuclear Charge

9.6 Periodic Trends in the Size of Atoms and Effective Nuclear Charge

In previous chapters, we saw that the volume of an atom is taken up primarily by its electrons (Chapter 2) occupying quantum-mechanical orbitals (Chapter 8). We also discussed how these orbitals do not have a definite boundary but represent only a statistical probability distribution for where the electron is found. So how do we define the size of an atom? One way to define atomic radii is to consider the distance between *nonbonding* atoms that are in direct contact. For example, krypton can be frozen into a solid in which the krypton atoms are touching each other but are not bonded together. The distance between the centers of adjacent krypton atoms—which we can determine from the solid's density—is then twice the radius of a krypton atom. An atomic radius determined in this way is called the **nonbonding atomic radius** or the **van der Waals radius**. The van der Waals radius represents the radius of an atom when it is not bonded to another atom.

van der Waals Radius for Krypton

The van der Waals radius of an atom is one-half the distance between adjacent nuclei in the atomic solid.

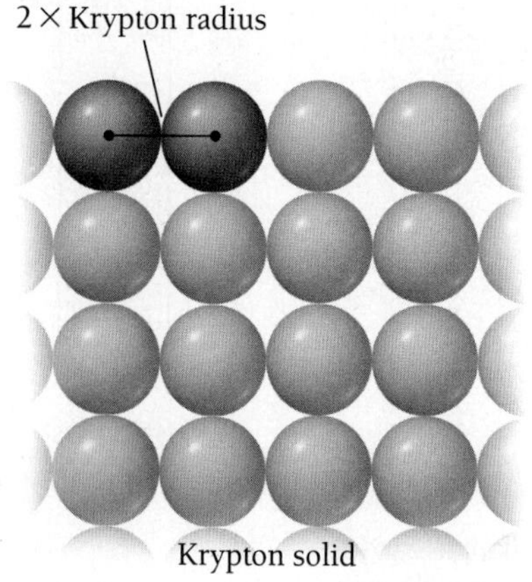

Another way to define the size of an atom—the **bonding atomic radius** or **covalent radius**—differs for nonmetals and metals, as follows:

Nonmetals: one-half the distance between two of the atoms bonded together

Metals: one-half the distance between two of the atoms next to each other in a crystal of the metal

For example, the distance between Br atoms in Br_2 is 228 pm; therefore, the Br covalent radius is one-half of 228 pm or 114 pm.

Using this method, we can assign radii to all elements in the periodic table that form chemical bonds or metallic crystals. A more general term, the **atomic radius**, refers to a set of average bonding radii determined from measurements on a large number of elements and compounds. The atomic radius represents the radius of an atom when it is bonded to another atom and is always smaller than the van der Waals radius. The approximate bond length of any two covalently bonded atoms is the sum of their atomic radii. For example, the approximate bond length for ICl is iodine's atomic radius (133 pm) plus chlorine's atomic radius (99 pm), a bond length of 232 pm. (The actual experimentally measured bond length in ICl is 232.07 pm.)

The bonding radii of some elements, such as helium and neon, must be approximated because they do not form chemical bonds or metallic crystals.

Figure 9.9▶ plots atomic radius as a function of atomic number for the first 57 elements in the periodic table. Notice the periodic trend in the radii. Atomic radii peak with each alkali metal. Figure 9.10▶ is a relief map of atomic radii for most of the elements in the periodic table. The general trends in the atomic radii of main-group elements, which are the same as trends observed in van der Waals radii, are:

1. As we move down a column (or family) in the periodic table, atomic radius increases.
2. As we move to the right across a period (or row) in the periodic table, atomic radius decreases.

We can understand the observed trend in radii as we move down a column based on the trends in the sizes of atomic orbitals. Atomic radius is largely determined by the valence electrons, the electrons farthest from the nucleus. As we move down a column in the periodic table, the highest principal quantum number (n) of the valence electrons increases. Consequently, the valence electrons occupy larger orbitals, resulting in larger atoms.

The observed trend in atomic radii as we move to the right across a row, however, is a bit more complex. To understand this trend, we must revisit some concepts from Section 9.3, including effective nuclear charge and shielding.

Covalent Radius for Bromine

The covalent radius is one-half the distance between two bonded atoms.

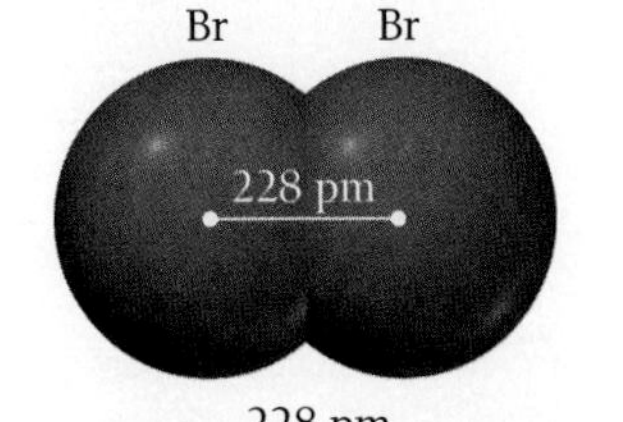

$$\text{Br radius} = \frac{228 \text{ pm}}{2} = 114 \text{ pm}$$

Atomic Radii

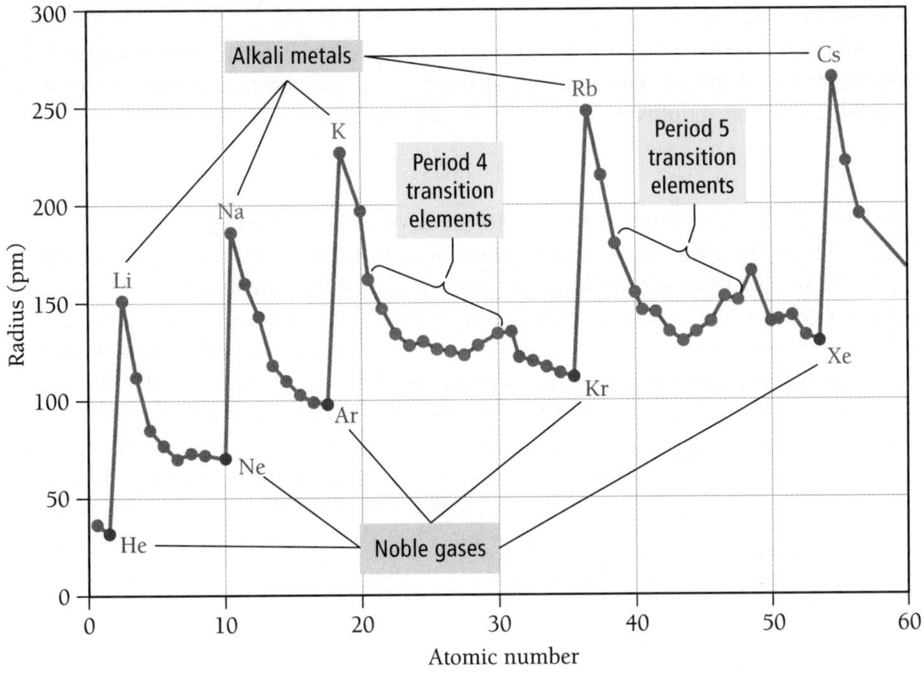

◀ **FIGURE 9.9 Atomic Radius versus Atomic Number** Notice the periodic trend in atomic radius, starting at a peak with each alkali metal and falling to a minimum with each noble gas.

Trends in Atomic Radius

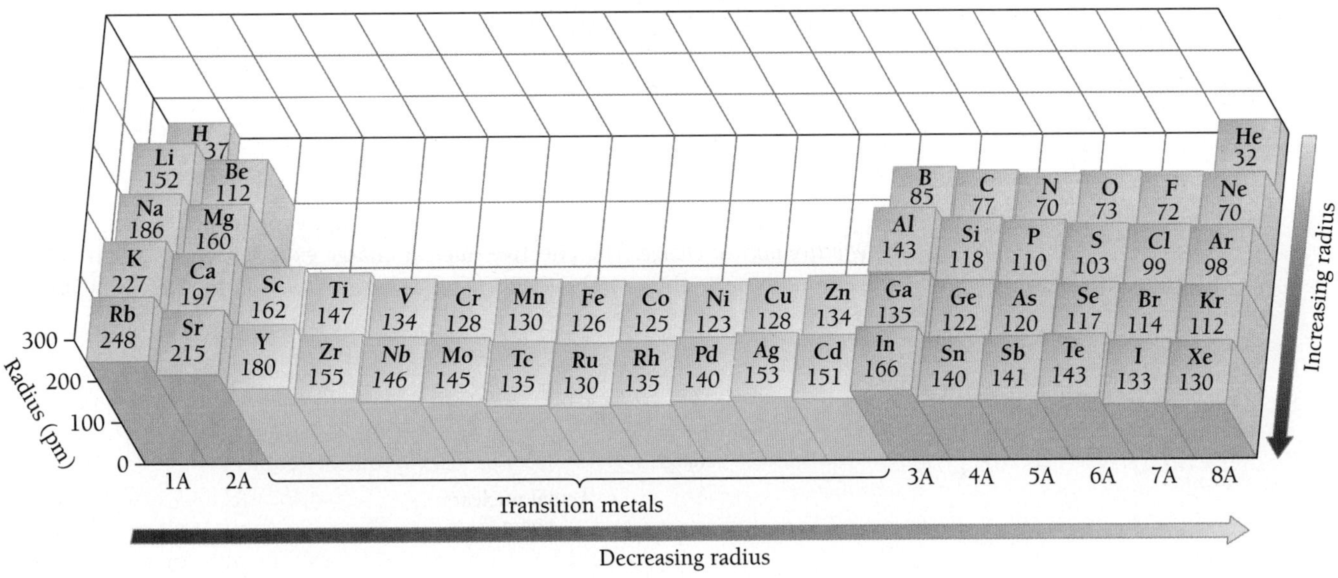

▼ **FIGURE 9.10 Trends in Atomic Radius** In general, atomic radii increase as we move down a column and decrease as we move to the right across a period in the periodic table.

Effective Nuclear Charge

The trend in atomic radius as we move to the right across a row in the periodic table is determined by the inward pull of the nucleus on the electrons in the outermost principal energy level (highest n value). According to Coulomb's law, the attraction between a nucleus and an electron increases with increasing magnitude of nuclear charge. For example, compare the H atom to the He^+ ion:

$$\text{H} \quad 1s^1$$

$$\text{He}^+ \quad 1s^1$$

It takes 1312 kJ/mol of energy to remove the 1s electron from hydrogen but 5251 kJ/mol of energy to remove it from He^+. Why? Although each electron is in a 1s orbital, the electron in the helium ion is attracted to the nucleus by a 2+ charge, while the electron in the hydrogen atom is attracted to the nucleus by only a 1+ charge. Therefore, the electron in the helium ion is held more tightly (it has lower potential energy according to Coulomb's law), making it more difficult to remove and making the helium ion smaller than the hydrogen atom.

As we saw in Section 9.3, any one electron in a multielectron atom experiences both the positive charge of the nucleus (which is attractive) and the negative charges of the other electrons (which are repulsive). Consider again the outermost electron in the lithium atom:

$$\text{Li} \quad 1s^2 2s^1$$

Even though the 2s orbital penetrates into the 1s orbital to some degree, the majority of the 2s orbital is outside of the 1s orbital. Therefore, the electron in the 2s orbital is partially *screened* or *shielded* from the 3+ charge of the nucleus by the 2− charge of the 1s (core) electrons. This reduces the net charge experienced by the 2s electron, as shown in Figure 9.11▼.

▶ FIGURE 9.11 Shielding and Effective Nuclear Charge The valence electron in lithium experiences the 3+ charge of the nucleus through the screen of the 2− charge of the core electrons. The effective nuclear charge acting on the valence electron is approximately 1+.

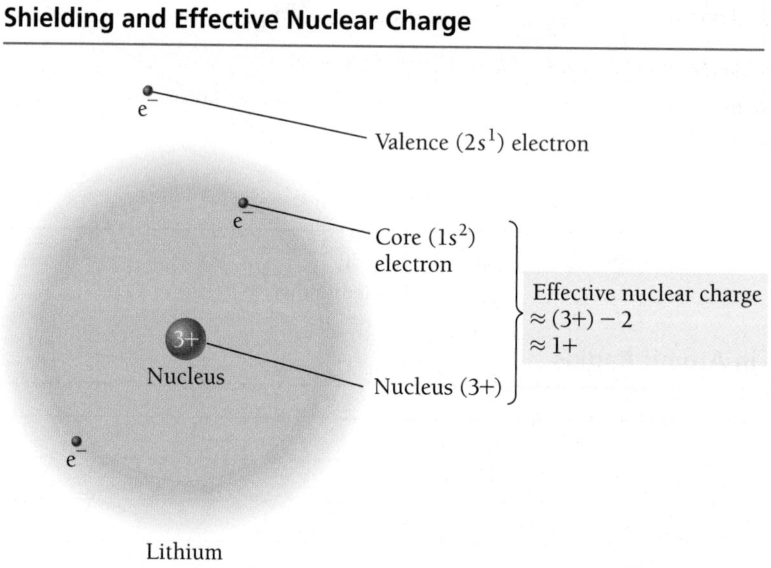

As we have seen, we can define the average or net charge experienced by an electron as the *effective nuclear charge*. The effective nuclear charge experienced by a particular electron in an atom is the *actual nuclear charge (Z)* minus *the charge shielded by other electrons (S)*:

$$Z_{eff} = Z - S$$

Effective nuclear charge (Z_{eff}); Actual nuclear charge (Z); Charge screened by other electrons (S)

For lithium, we estimate that the two core electrons shield the valence electron from the nuclear charge with high efficiency (s is nearly 2). The effective nuclear charge experienced by lithium's valence electron is therefore slightly greater than 1+.

Now consider the valence electrons in beryllium (Be), with atomic number 4. Its electron configuration is:

$$\text{Be} \quad 1s^2 2s^2$$

To estimate the effective nuclear charge experienced by the 2s electrons in beryllium, we must distinguish between two different types of shielding: (1) the shielding of the outermost electrons by the core electrons and (2) the shielding of the outermost electrons by *each other*. The key to understanding the trend in atomic radius is the difference between these two types of shielding:

Core electrons efficiently shield electrons in the outermost principal energy level from nuclear charge, but outermost electrons do not efficiently shield one another from nuclear charge.

For example, the two outermost electrons in beryllium experience the 4+ charge of the nucleus through the shield of the two 1s core electrons without shielding each other from that charge very much. We estimate that the shielding (S) experienced by any one of the outermost electrons due to the core electrons is nearly 2, but that the shielding due to the other outermost electron is nearly 0. The effective nuclear charge experienced by beryllium's outermost electrons is therefore slightly greater than 2+.

The effective nuclear charge experienced by *beryllium*'s outermost electrons is greater than that experienced by *lithium*'s outermost electron. Consequently, beryllium's outermost electrons are held more tightly than lithium's, resulting in a smaller atomic radius for beryllium. The effective nuclear charge experienced by an atom's outermost electrons continues to become more positive as we move to the right across the rest of the second row in the periodic table, resulting in successively smaller atomic radii. The same trend is generally observed in all main-group elements.

Summarizing Atomic Radii for Main-Group Elements

- As we move down a column in the periodic table, the principal quantum number (n) of the electrons in the outermost principal energy level increases, resulting in larger orbitals and therefore larger atomic radii.
- As we move to the right across a row in the periodic table, the effective nuclear charge (Z_{eff}) experienced by the electrons in the outermost principal energy level increases, resulting in a stronger attraction between the outermost electrons and the nucleus, and smaller atomic radii.

EFFECTIVE NUCLEAR CHARGE Which electrons experience the greatest effective nuclear charge?

(a) the valence electrons in Mg
(b) the valence electrons in Al
(c) the valence electrons in S

9.6 Cc Conceptual Connection

ANSWER **NOW!**

Atomic Radii and the Transition Elements

In Figure 9.10, we can see that as we move down the first two rows of a column within the transition metals, the elements follow the same general trend in atomic radii as the main-group elements (the radii get larger). However, with the exception of the first couple of elements in each transition series, the atomic radii of the transition elements *do not* follow the same trend as the main-group elements as we move to the right across a row. Instead of decreasing in size, *the radii of transition elements stay roughly constant across each row*. Why? The difference is that, across a row of transition elements, the number of electrons in the outermost principal energy level (highest n value) is nearly constant (recall from Section 9.3, for example, that the 4s orbital fills before the 3d). As another proton is added to the nucleus of each successive element, another electron is added as well, but the electron goes into an $n_{highest} - 1$ orbital. The number of outermost electrons stays constant, and they experience a roughly constant effective nuclear charge, keeping the radius approximately constant.

WATCH **NOW!**

INTERACTIVE WORKED EXAMPLE 9.5

EXAMPLE 9.5 Atomic Size

On the basis of periodic trends, choose the larger atom in each pair (if possible). Explain your choices.

(a) C or F

(b) C or Ge

(c) N or Al

(d) Al or Ge

SOLUTION

(a) C atoms are larger than F atoms because as you trace the path between C and F on the periodic table, you move to the right within the same period. As you move to the right across a period, the effective nuclear charge experienced by the outermost electrons increases, resulting in a smaller radius.

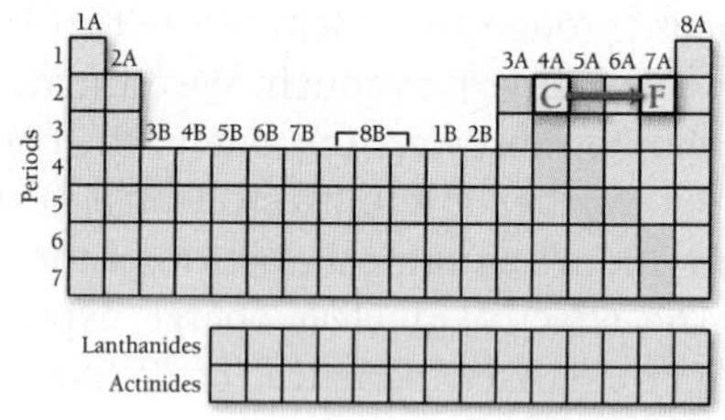

(b) Ge atoms are larger than C atoms because as you trace the path between C and Ge on the periodic table, you move down a column. Atomic size increases as you move down a column because the outermost electrons occupy orbitals with a higher principal quantum number that are therefore larger, resulting in a larger atom.

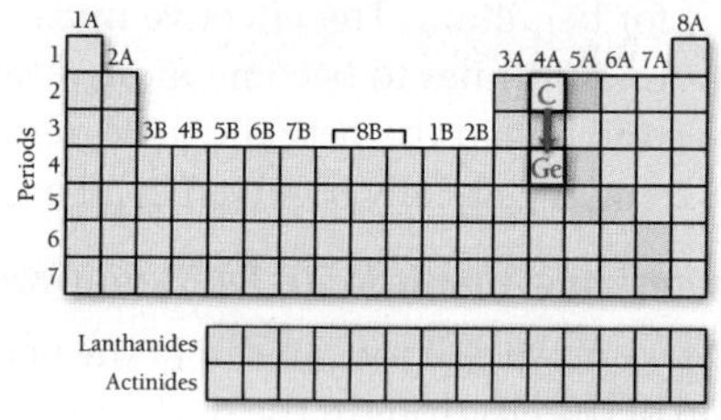

(c) Al atoms are larger than N atoms because as you trace the path between N and Al on the periodic table, you move down a column (atomic size increases) and then to the left across a period (atomic size increases). These effects add together for an overall increase.

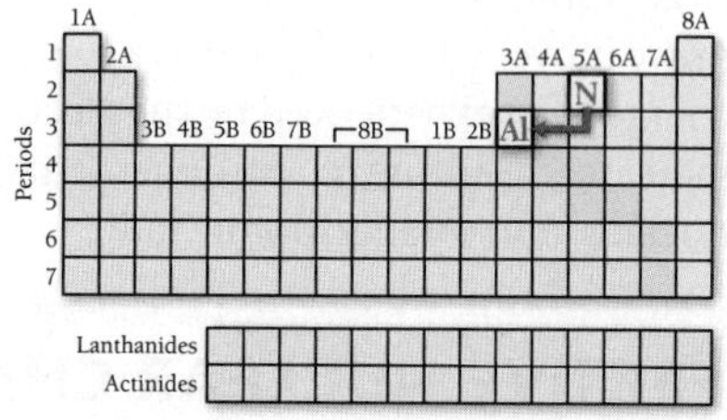

(d) Based on periodic trends alone, you cannot tell which atom is larger because as you trace the path between Al and Ge you move to the right across a period (atomic size decreases) and then down a column (atomic size increases). These effects tend to counter each other, and it is not easy to tell which will predominate.

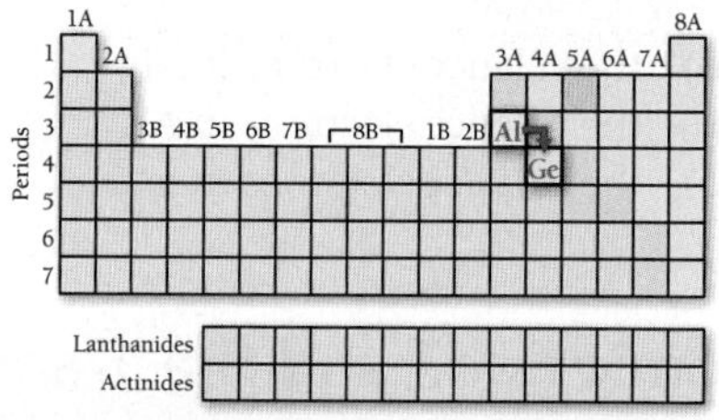

FOR PRACTICE 9.5 On the basis of periodic trends, choose the larger atom in each pair (if possible):

(a) Sn or I

(b) Ge or Po

(c) Cr or W

(d) F or Se

FOR MORE PRACTICE 9.5 Arrange the elements in order of decreasing radius: S, Ca, F, Rb, Si.

9.7 Ions: Electron Configurations, Magnetic Properties, Ionic Radii, and Ionization Energy

Recall that ions are atoms (or groups of atoms) that have lost or gained electrons. In this section, we examine periodic trends in ionic electron configurations, magnetic properties, ionic radii, and ionization energies.

Electron Configurations and Magnetic Properties of Ions

We can deduce the electron configuration of a main-group monoatomic ion from the electron configuration of the neutral atom and the charge of the ion. For anions, we *add* the number of electrons indicated by the magnitude of the charge of the anion. For example, the electron configuration of fluorine (F) is $1s^22s^22p^5$ and that of the fluoride ion (F^-) is $1s^22s^22p^6$.

We determine the electron configuration of cations by *subtracting* the number of electrons indicated by the magnitude of the charge. For example, the electron configuration of lithium (Li) is $1s^22s^1$ and that of the lithium ion (Li^+) is $1s^22s^0$ (or simply $1s^2$). For main-group cations, we remove the required number of electrons in the reverse order of filling. However, for transition metal cations, the trend is different. When writing the electron configuration of a transition metal cation, we *remove the electrons in the highest n-value orbitals first, even if this does not correspond to the reverse order of filling.* For example, the electron configuration of vanadium is:

$$\text{V} \quad [\text{Ar}]\ 4s^23d^3$$

The V^{2+} ion, however, has the following electron configuration:

$$\text{V}^{2+} \quad [\text{Ar}]\ 4s^03d^3$$

In other words, for transition metal cations, the order in which electrons are removed upon ionization is *not* the reverse of the filling order. During filling, the $4s$ orbital normally fills before the $3d$ orbital. When a fourth-period transition metal ionizes, however, it loses its $4s$ electrons before its $3d$ electrons. Why this unexpected behavior? The full answer to this question is beyond our scope, but the following two factors contribute to this phenomenon:

The order of removing electrons is not the reverse of the filling order because the energy levels in a cation shift relative to the neutral atom.

- As discussed previously, the ns and $(n-1)d$ orbitals are extremely close in energy and, depending on the exact configuration, can vary in relative energy ordering.
- As the $(n-1)d$ orbitals begin to fill in the first transition series, the increasing nuclear charge stabilizes the $(n-1)d$ orbitals relative to the ns orbitals. This happens because the $(n-1)d$ orbitals are not the outermost (or highest n) orbitals and are therefore not effectively shielded from the increasing nuclear charge by the ns orbitals.

The bottom-line experimental observation is that an $ns^0(n-1)d^x$ configuration is lower in energy than an $ns^2(n-1)d^{x-2}$ configuration for transition metal ions. Therefore, we remove the ns electrons before the $(n-1)d$ electrons when we write electron configurations for transition metal ions.

The magnetic properties of transition metal ions support these assignments. An unpaired electron generates a magnetic field due to its spin. Consequently, an atom or ion that contains unpaired electrons is attracted to an external magnetic field, and we say that the atom or ion is **paramagnetic**. For example, consider the electron configuration of silver:

Ag [Kr] $5s^14d^{10}$

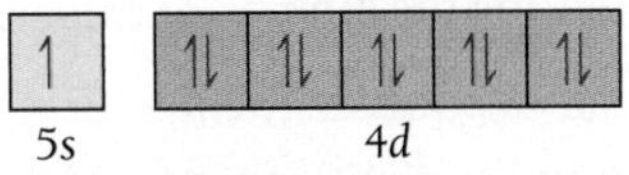

Silver's unpaired $5s$ electron causes silver to be paramagnetic. In fact, an early demonstration of electron spin—called the Stern–Gerlach experiment—involved the interaction of a beam of silver atoms with a magnetic field.

An atom or ion in which all electrons are paired is not attracted to an external magnetic field—it is instead slightly repelled—and we say that the atom or ion is **diamagnetic**. The zinc atom is diamagnetic:

Zn [Ar] $4s^2 3d^{10}$ 4s: [↑↓] 3d: [↑↓][↑↓][↑↓][↑↓][↑↓]

The magnetic properties of the zinc ion provide confirmation that the 4*s* electrons are indeed lost before 3*d* electrons in the ionization of zinc. If zinc lost two 3*d* electrons upon ionization, then the Zn^{2+} would be paramagnetic (because the two electrons would come out of two different filled *d* orbitals, leaving each of them with one unpaired electron). That does not happen and the zinc ion, like the zinc atom, is diamagnetic because the 4*s* electrons are lost instead:

Zn^{2+} [Ar] $4s^0 3d^{10}$ 4s: [ ] 3d: [↑↓][↑↓][↑↓][↑↓][↑↓]

Observations in other transition metals confirm that the *ns* electrons are lost before the $(n-1)d$ electrons upon ionization.

WATCH **NOW!**
INTERACTIVE WORKED EXAMPLE 9.6

EXAMPLE 9.6 Electron Configurations and Magnetic Properties for Ions

Write the electron configuration and orbital diagram for each ion and determine whether each is diamagnetic or paramagnetic.

(a) Al^{3+} **(b)** S^{2-} **(c)** Fe^{3+}

SOLUTION

(a) Al^{3+} Begin by writing the electron configuration of the neutral atom. This ion has a 3+ charge, so you remove three electrons to write the electron configuration of the ion. Write the orbital diagram by drawing half-arrows to represent each electron in boxes representing the orbitals. Because there are no unpaired electrons, Al^{3+} is diamagnetic.	Al [Ne]$3s^2 3p^1$ Al^{3+} [Ne] or [He]$2s^2 2p^6$ Al^{3+} [He] 2s: [↑↓] 2p: [↑↓][↑↓][↑↓] Diamagnetic
(b) S^{2-} Begin by writing the electron configuration of the neutral atom. Because this ion has a 2- charge, add two electrons to write the electron configuration of the ion. Write the orbital diagram by drawing half-arrows to represent each electron in boxes representing the orbitals. Because there are no unpaired electrons, S^{2-} is diamagnetic.	S [Ne]$3s^2 3p^4$ S^{2-} [Ne]$3s^2 3p^6$ S^{2-} [Ne] 3s: [↑↓] 3p: [↑↓][↑↓][↑↓] Diamagnetic
(c) Fe^{3+} Begin by writing the electron configuration of the neutral atom. Since this ion has a 3+ charge, remove three electrons to write the electron configuration of the ion. Because it is a transition metal, remove the electrons from the 4*s* orbital before removing electrons from the 3*d* orbitals. Write the orbital diagram by drawing half-arrows to represent each electron in boxes representing the orbitals. There are unpaired electrons, so Fe^{3+} is paramagnetic.	Fe [Ar]$4s^2 3d^6$ Fe^{3+} [Ar]$4s^0 3d^5$ Fe^{3+} [Ar] 4s: [ ] 3d: [↑][↑][↑][↑][↑] Paramagnetic

FOR PRACTICE 9.6 Write the electron configuration and orbital diagram for each ion and predict whether each is paramagnetic or diamagnetic.

(a) Co^{2+} **(b)** N^{3-} **(c)** Ca^{2+}

Ionic Radii

What happens to the radius of an atom when it becomes a cation? An anion? Consider, for example, the difference between the Na atom and the Na^+ ion. Their electron configurations are:

$$\text{Na} \quad [\text{Ne}]\, 3s^1$$

$$\text{Na}^+ \quad [\text{Ne}]\, 3s^0$$

The sodium atom has an outer 3*s* electron and a neon core. Because the 3*s* electron is the outermost electron and it is shielded from the nuclear charge by the core electrons, it contributes greatly to the size of the sodium atom. The sodium cation, having lost the outermost 3*s* electron, has only the neon core and carries a charge of 1+. Without the 3*s* electron, the sodium cation (ionic radius = 95 pm) is much smaller than the sodium atom (covalent radius = 186 pm). The trend is the same with all cations and their atoms, as shown in Figure 9.12▼:

Cations are much smaller than their corresponding atoms.

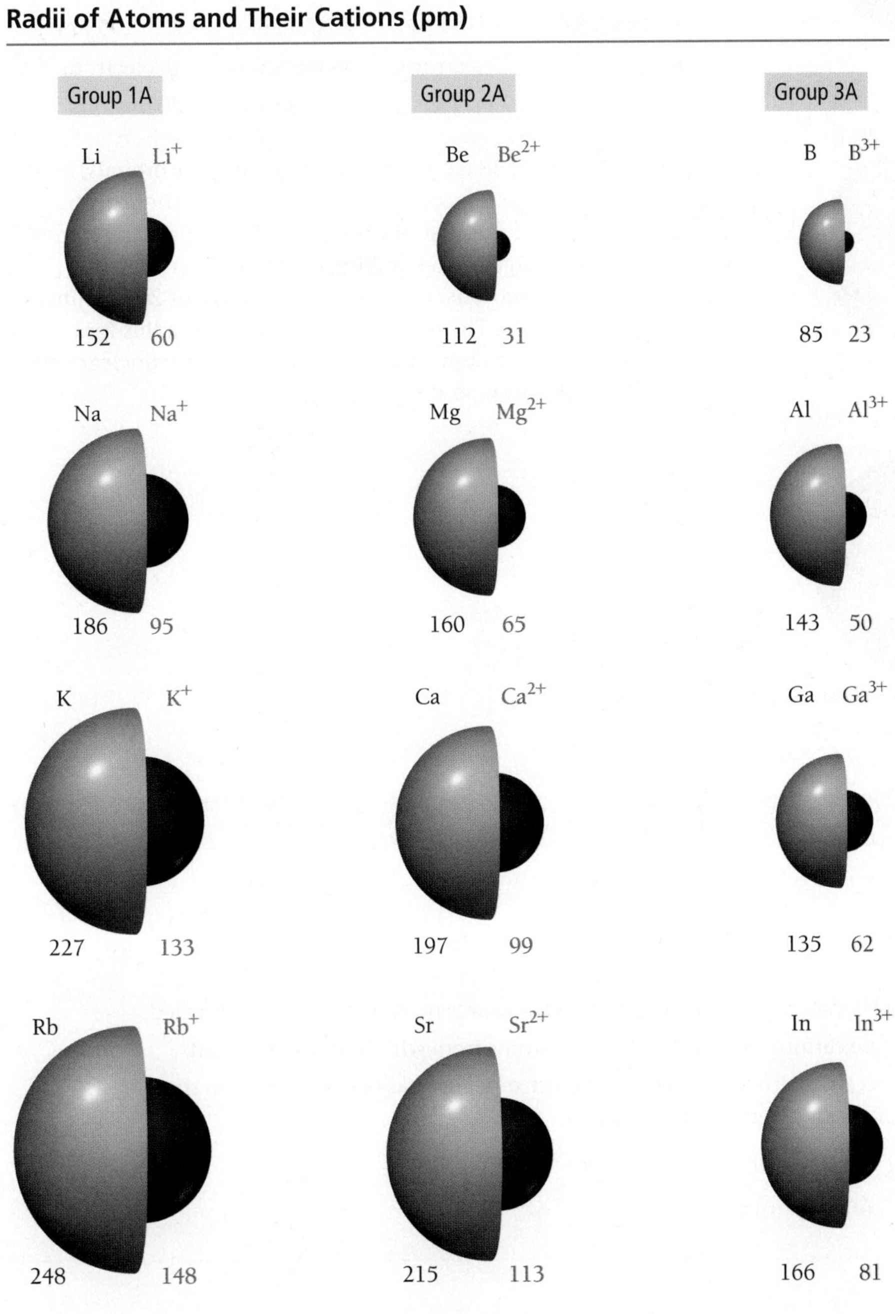

◀ **FIGURE 9.12 Sizes of Atoms and Their Cations** Atomic and ionic radii (pm) for the first three columns of main-group elements.

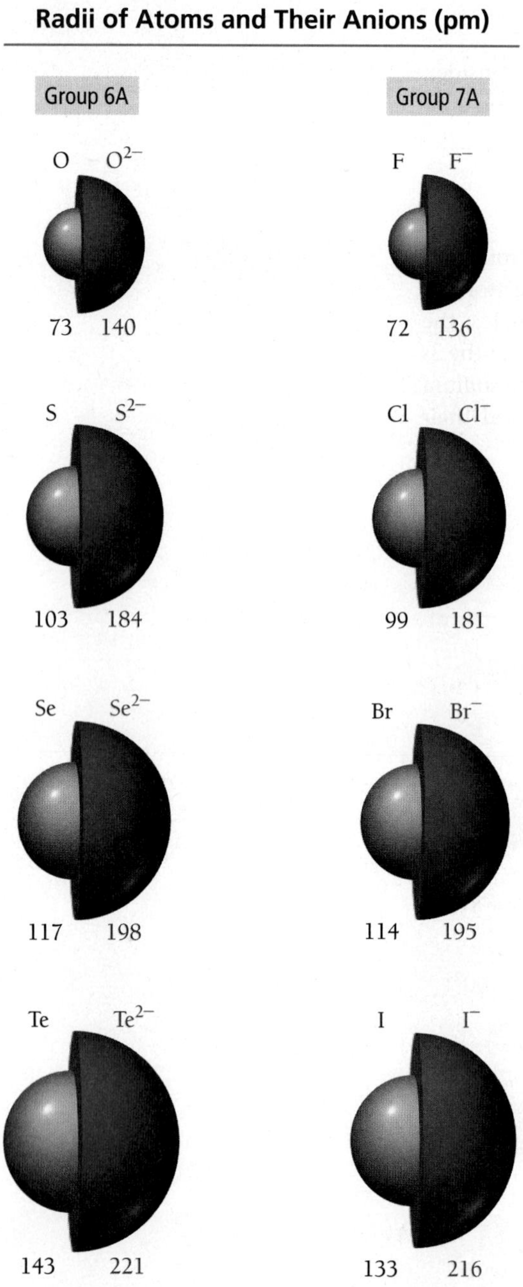

What about anions? Consider the difference between Cl and Cl^-. Their electron configurations are:

$$\text{Cl} \quad [\text{Ne}]\, 3s^2 3p^5$$

$$\text{Cl}^- \quad [\text{Ne}]\, 3s^2 3p^6$$

The chloride anion has one additional outermost electron but no additional proton to increase the nuclear charge. The extra electron increases the repulsions among the outermost electrons, resulting in a chloride anion that is larger than the chlorine atom. The trend is the same with all anions and their atoms, as shown in Figure 9.13◀.

Anions are much larger than their corresponding atoms.

We can observe an interesting trend in ionic size when we examine the radii of an *isoelectronic* series of ions—ions with the same number of electrons. Consider the following ions and their radii:

S^{2-} (184 pm)	Cl^- (181 pm)	K^+ (133 pm)	Ca^{2+} (99 pm)
18 electrons	18 electrons	18 electrons	18 electrons
16 protons	17 protons	19 protons	20 protons

All of these ions have 18 electrons in exactly the same orbitals, but the radius of each ion gets successively smaller. Why? The reason is the progressively greater number of protons. The S^{2-} ion has 16 protons and therefore a charge of 16+ pulling on 18 electrons. The Ca^{2+} ion, in contrast, has 20 protons, and therefore a charge of 20+ pulling on the same 18 electrons. The result is a much smaller radius for the calcium ion. For a given number of electrons, a greater nuclear charge results in a smaller atom or ion.

◀ **FIGURE 9.13 Sizes of Atoms and Their Anions** Atomic and ionic radii for groups 6A and 7A in the periodic table.

EXAMPLE 9.7 Ion Size

Choose the larger atom or ion from each pair.

(a) S or S^{2-} **(b)** Ca or Ca^{2+} **(c)** Br^- or Kr

SOLUTION

(a) The S^{2-} ion is larger than an S atom because anions are larger than the atoms from which they are formed.

(b) A Ca atom is larger than Ca^{2+} because cations are smaller than the atoms from which they are formed.

(c) A Br^- ion is larger than a Kr atom because, although they are isoelectronic, Br^- has one fewer proton than Kr, resulting in less pull on the electrons and therefore a larger radius.

FOR PRACTICE 9.7 Choose the larger atom or ion from each pair.

(a) K or K^+ **(b)** F or F^- **(c)** Ca^{2+} or Cl^-

IONS, ISOTOPES, AND ATOMIC SIZE In the previous sections, we have seen how the number of electrons and the number of protons affect the size of an atom or ion. However, we have not considered how the number of neutrons affects the size of an atom. Would you expect isotopes—for example, C-12 and C-13—to have different atomic radii?

(a) C-12 is larger than C-13.
(b) C-12 and C-13 are the same size.
(c) C-13 is larger than C-12.

9.7 Cc Conceptual Connection

ANSWER **NOW!**

Ionization Energy

The **ionization energy (IE)** of an atom or ion is the energy required to remove an electron from the atom or ion in the gaseous state. Ionization energy is always positive because removing an electron always takes energy. (The process is similar to an endothermic reaction, which absorbs heat and therefore has a positive ΔH.) The energy required to remove the first electron is the *first ionization energy* (IE_1). For example, we represent the first ionization of sodium with the equation:

$$Na(g) \longrightarrow Na^+(g) + 1\,e^- \qquad IE_1 = 496\ kJ/mol$$

The energy required to remove the second electron is the *second ionization energy* (IE_2), the energy required to remove the third electron is the *third ionization energy* (IE_3), and so on. We represent the second ionization energy of sodium as:

$$Na^+(g) \longrightarrow Na^{2+}(g) + 1\,e^- \qquad IE_2 = 4560\ kJ/mol$$

Notice that the second ionization energy is not the energy required to remove *two* electrons from sodium (that quantity is the sum of IE_1 and IE_2), but rather the energy required to remove one electron from Na^+. We look at trends in IE_1 and IE_2 separately.

Trends in First Ionization Energy

The first ionization energies of the elements through Xe are shown in Figure 9.14▼. Notice the periodic trend in ionization energy, peaking at each noble gas and bottoming at each alkali metal. Based on what we have learned about electron configurations and effective nuclear charge, how can we account for the observed trend? As we have seen,

First Ionization Energies

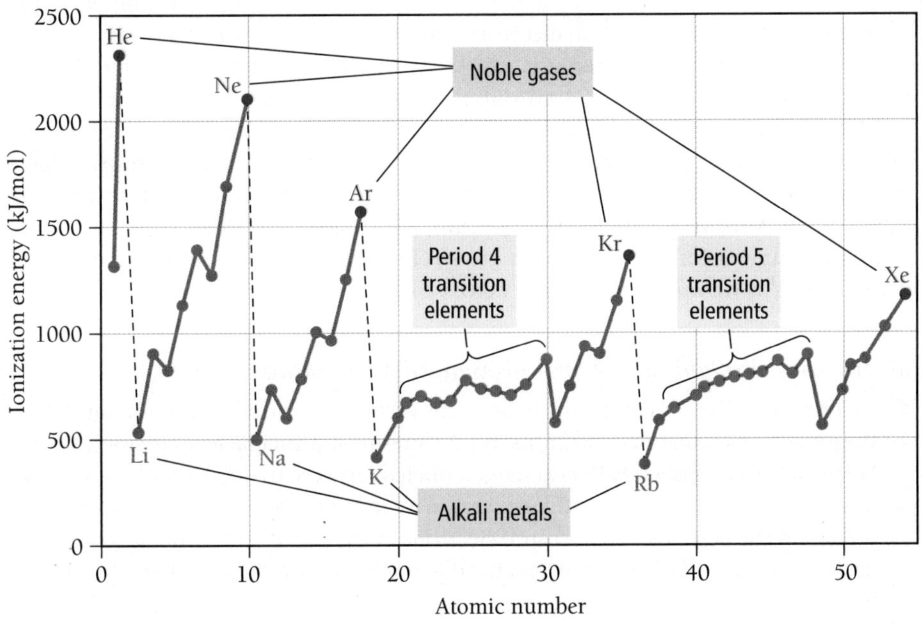

◀ **FIGURE 9.14 First Ionization Energy versus Atomic Number for the Elements through Xenon** First ionization energy starts at a minimum with each alkali metal and rises to a peak with each noble gas.

the principal quantum number, n, increases as we move down a column. Within a given sublevel, orbitals with higher principal quantum numbers are larger than orbitals with smaller principal quantum numbers. Consequently, electrons in the outermost principal level are farther away from the positively charged nucleus—and are therefore held less tightly—as we move down a column. This results in a lower ionization energy as we move down a column, as shown in Figure 9.15▼.

Trends in First Ionization Energy

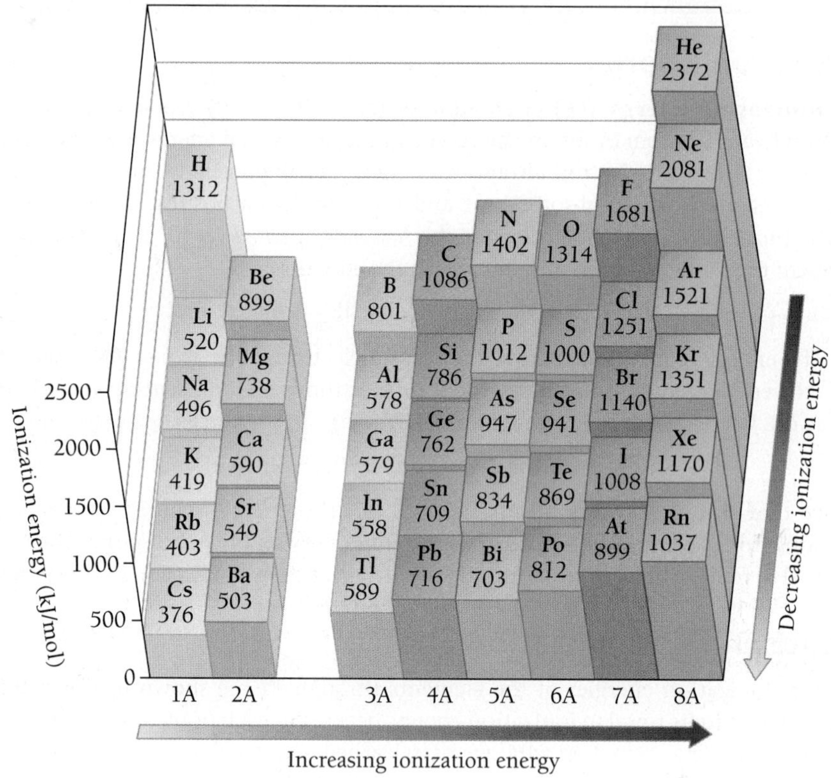

▲ **FIGURE 9.15 Trends in Ionization Energy** First ionization energy increases as we move to the right across a period and decreases as we move down a column in the periodic table.

What about the trend as we move to the right across a row? For example, would it take more energy to remove an electron from Na or from Cl, two elements on either end of the third row in the periodic table? We know that Na has an outer electron configuration of $3s^1$ and Cl has an outer electron configuration of $3s^2 3p^5$. As discussed previously, the outermost electrons in chlorine experience a higher effective nuclear charge than the outermost electrons in sodium (which is why chlorine has a smaller atomic radius than sodium). Consequently, we would expect chlorine to have a higher ionization energy than sodium, which is indeed the case. We can make a similar argument for the other main-group elements: first ionization energy generally increases as we move to the right across a row in the periodic table, as shown in Figure 9.15.

Summarizing First Ionization Energy for Main-Group Elements

- First ionization energy generally *decreases* as we move down a column (or family) in the periodic table because electrons in the outermost principal level are increasingly farther away from the positively charged nucleus and are therefore held less tightly.
- First ionization energy generally *increases* as we move to the right across a row (or period) in the periodic table because electrons in the outermost principal energy level generally experience a greater effective nuclear charge (Z_{eff}) and are therefore held more tightly.

WATCH **NOW!**

INTERACTIVE WORKED EXAMPLE 9.8

EXAMPLE 9.8 First Ionization Energy

On the basis of periodic trends, determine which element in each pair has the higher first ionization energy (if possible).

(a) Al or S **(b)** As or Sb **(c)** N or Si **(d)** O or Cl

SOLUTION

(a) Al or S

S has a higher ionization energy than Al because as you trace the path between Al and S on the periodic table, you move to the right within the same row. Ionization energy increases as you go to the right due to increasing effective nuclear charge.

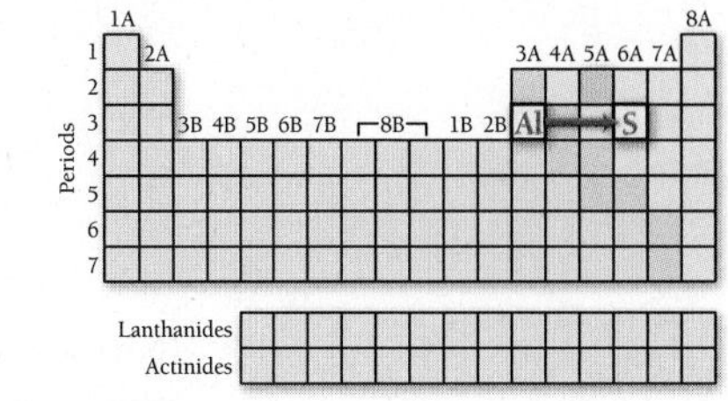

(b) As or Sb

As has a higher ionization energy than Sb because as you trace the path between As and Sb on the periodic table, you move down a column. Ionization energy decreases as you go down a column as a result of the increasing size of orbitals with increasing *n*.

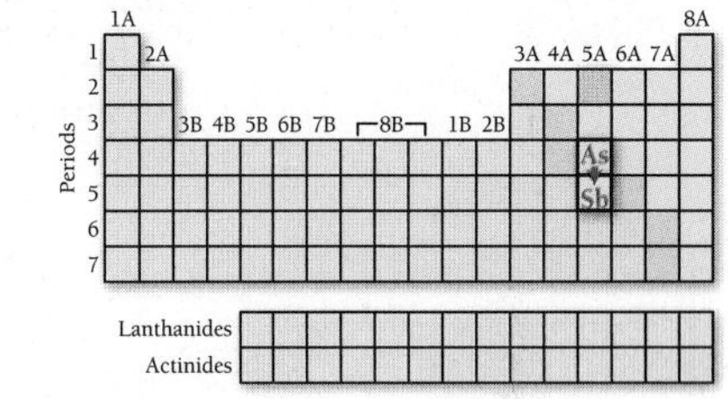

(c) N or Si

N has a higher ionization energy than Si because as you trace the path between N and Si on the periodic table, you move down a column (ionization energy decreases) and then to the left across a row (ionization energy decreases). These effects sum together for an overall decrease.

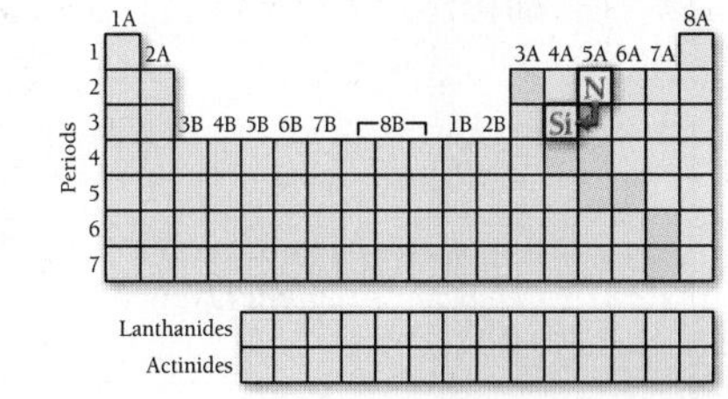

(d) O or Cl

Based on periodic trends alone, it is impossible to tell which has a higher ionization energy because, as you trace the path between O and Cl, you go to the right across a row (ionization energy increases) and then down a column (ionization energy decreases). These effects tend to counter each other, and it is not obvious which will dominate.

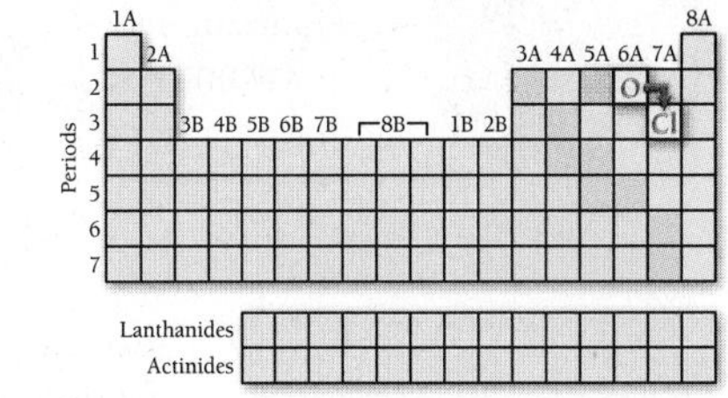

FOR PRACTICE 9.8 On the basis of periodic trends, determine the element in each pair with the higher first ionization energy (if possible).

(a) Sn or I **(b)** Ca or Sr **(c)** C or P **(d)** F or S

FOR MORE PRACTICE 9.8 Arrange the following elements in order of decreasing first ionization energy: S, Ca, F, Rb, Si.

Exceptions to Trends in First Ionization Energy

If we carefully examine Figure 9.15, we can see some exceptions to the trends in first ionization energies. For example, boron has a smaller ionization energy than beryllium, even though it lies to the right of beryllium in the same row. This exception is caused by the difference between the *s* block and the *p* block. Recall from Section 9.3 that the 2*p* orbital penetrates into the nuclear region *less than* the 2*s* orbital. Consequently, the 1*s* electrons shield the electron in the 2*p* orbital from nuclear charge more than they shield the electrons in the 2*s* orbital. The result, as we saw in Section 9.3, is that the

2*p* orbitals are higher in energy, and therefore the electron is easier to remove (it has a lower first ionization energy). Similar exceptions occur for aluminum and gallium, both directly below boron in group 3A.

Another exception occurs between nitrogen and oxygen. Although oxygen is to the right of nitrogen in the same row, it has a lower first ionization energy. This exception is caused by the repulsion between electrons when they occupy the same orbital. Examine the electron configurations and orbital diagrams of nitrogen and oxygen shown here:

N $1s^2 2s^2 2p^3$

O $1s^2 2s^2 2p^4$

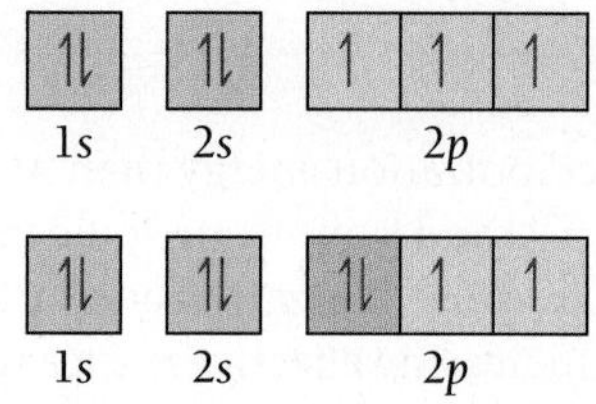

Nitrogen has three electrons in three *p* orbitals, whereas oxygen has four. In nitrogen, the 2*p* orbitals are half-filled (which makes the configuration particularly stable). One of oxygen's four 2*p* electrons must pair with another electron, making it easier to remove (and less stable). Exceptions for similar reasons occur for S and Se, directly below oxygen in group 6A.

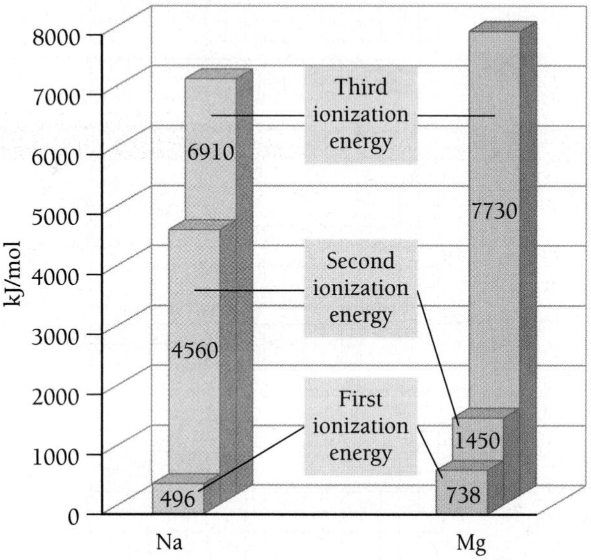

Trends in Second and Successive Ionization Energies

Notice the trends in the first, second, and third ionization energies of sodium (group 1A) and magnesium (group 2A), as shown at left.

For sodium, there is a huge jump between the first and second ionization energies. For magnesium, the ionization energy roughly doubles from the first to the second, but then a huge jump occurs between the second and third ionization energies. What is the reason for these jumps?

We can understand these trends by examining the electron configurations of sodium and magnesium:

Na [Ne] $3s^1$

Mg [Ne] $3s^2$

The first ionization of sodium involves removing the valence electron in the 3*s* orbital. Recall that these valence electrons are held more loosely than the core electrons and that the resulting ion has a noble gas configuration, which is particularly stable. Consequently, the first ionization energy is fairly low. The second ionization of sodium, however, involves removing a core electron from an ion with a noble gas configuration. This requires a tremendous amount of energy, making the value of IE_2 very high.

As with sodium, the first ionization of magnesium involves removing a valence electron in the 3*s* orbital. This requires a bit more energy than the corresponding ionization of sodium because of the trends in Z_{eff} that we discussed earlier (Z_{eff} increases as we move to the right across a row). The second ionization of magnesium also involves removing an outer electron in the 3*s* orbital, but this time from an ion with a 1+ charge (instead of from a neutral atom). This requires roughly twice the energy as removing the electron from the neutral atom. The third ionization of magnesium is analogous to the second ionization of sodium—it requires removing a core electron from an ion with a noble gas configuration. This requires a tremendous amount of energy, making the value of IE_3 very high.

As shown in Table 9.1, similar trends exist for the successive ionization energies of many elements. The ionization energy increases fairly uniformly with each successive removal of an outermost electron, but then takes a large jump with the removal of the first core electron.

TABLE 9.1 ■ Successive Ionization Energies for the Elements Sodium through Argon (kJ/mol)

Element	IE_1	IE_2	IE_3	IE_4	IE_5	IE_6	IE_7
Na	496	4560					
Mg	738	1450	7730				
Al	578	1820	2750	11,600			
Si	786	1580	3230	4360	16,100		
P	1012	1900	2910	4960	6270	22,200	
S	1000	2250	3360	4560	7010	8500	27,100
Cl	1251	2300	3820	5160	6540	9460	11,000
Ar	1521	2670	3930	5770	7240	8780	12,000

Core electrons

SUCCESSIVE IONIZATION ENERGIES A second row element has a large jump between its third and fourth ionization energies. What is the element?

(a) Li **(b)** Be **(c)** B **(d)** C

9.8 Cc Conceptual Connection

ANSWER **NOW!**

IONIZATION ENERGIES AND CHEMICAL BONDING Based on what you just learned about ionization energies, explain why valence electrons are more important than core electrons in determining the reactivity and bonding in atoms.

(a) Since bonding involves the transfer or sharing of electrons, valence electrons are most important because they are held most tightly.

(b) Since bonding involves the transfer or sharing of electrons, valence electrons are most important because they are held most loosely.

9.9 Cc Conceptual Connection

ANSWER **NOW!**

9.8 Electron Affinities and Metallic Character

Electron affinity and metallic character also exhibit periodic trends. Electron affinity is a measure of how easily an atom will accept an additional electron; it is crucial to chemical bonding because bonding involves the transfer or sharing of electrons. Metallic character is important because of the high proportion of metals in the periodic table and the large role they play in our lives. Of the 118 elements, 92 are metals. We examine each of these periodic properties individually in this section.

Electron Affinity

The **electron affinity (EA)** of an atom (or ion) is the energy change associated with the gaining of an electron by the atom in the gaseous state. Electron affinity is usually—though not always—negative because an atom or ion usually releases energy when it gains an electron. (The process is analogous to an exothermic reaction, which releases heat and therefore has a negative ΔH.) In other words, the coulombic attraction between the nucleus of an atom and the incoming electron usually results in the release of energy as the electron is gained. For example, we represent the electron affinity of chlorine with the equation:

$$\text{Cl}(g) + 1\,\text{e}^- \longrightarrow \text{Cl}^-(g) \quad \text{EA} = -349\ \text{kJ/mol}$$

Figure 9.16▶ displays the electron affinities for a number of main-group elements. As you can see from this figure, the trends in electron affinity are not as regular as trends in other properties we examined in Sections 9.6 and 9.7. For instance, we might expect

Electron Affinities (kJ/mol)

1A	2A	3A	4A	5A	6A	7A	8A
H −73							He >0
Li −60	Be >0	B −27	C −122	N >0	O −141	F −328	Ne >0
Na −53	Mg >0	Al −43	Si −134	P −72	S −200	Cl −349	Ar >0
K −48	Ca −2	Ga −30	Ge −119	As −78	Se −195	Br −325	Kr >0
Rb −47	Sr −5	In −30	Sn −107	Sb −103	Te −190	I −295	Xe >0

▲ **FIGURE 9.16 Electron Affinities of Selected Main-Group Elements**

electron affinities to become relatively more positive (so that the addition of an electron is less exothermic) as we move down a column because the electron is located in orbitals with successively higher principal quantum numbers and therefore is farther from the nucleus. This trend applies to the group 1A metals but does not hold for the other columns in the periodic table.

A more regular trend in electron affinity occurs across rows, however. For main-group elements, electron affinity generally becomes more negative (more exothermic) as we move to the right across a row in the periodic table. We can understand this trend by considering Na and Cl. Based on other periodic trends, would you expect Na or Cl to have the more negative (more exothermic) electron affinity? We know that Na has an outer electron configuration of $3s^1$ and Cl has an outer electron configuration of $3s^2 3p^5$. Since adding an electron to chlorine gives it a noble gas configuration and adding an electron to sodium does not, and since the outermost electrons in chlorine experience a higher Z_{eff} than the outermost electrons in sodium, we would expect chlorine to have a more negative electron affinity—the process should be more exothermic for chlorine. This is in fact the case. The halogens (group 7A) have the most negative electron affinities. But exceptions do occur. For example, notice that nitrogen and the other group 5A elements do not follow the general trend. These elements have ns^2np^3 outer electron configurations. When an electron is added to this configuration, it must pair with another electron in an already occupied *p* orbital. The repulsion between two electrons occupying the same orbital causes the electron affinity to be more positive than for elements in the previous column.

Summarizing Electron Affinity for Main-Group Elements

- Most groups (columns) of the periodic table do not exhibit any definite trend in electron affinity. Among the group 1A metals, however, electron affinity becomes more positive as we move down a column (adding an electron becomes less exothermic).
- Electron affinity generally becomes more negative (adding an electron becomes more exothermic) as we move to the right across a period (row) in the periodic table.

Metallic Character

As we discussed in Chapter 2, metals are good conductors of heat and electricity: they can be pounded into flat sheets (malleability), they can be drawn into wires (ductility), they are often shiny, and they tend to lose electrons in chemical reactions. Nonmetals, in contrast, have more varied physical properties; some are solids at room temperature, others are gases. However, in general, nonmetals are typically poor conductors of heat and electricity, and they all tend to gain electrons in chemical reactions.

As we move to the right across a row in the periodic table, ionization energy increases and electron affinity becomes more negative; therefore, elements on the left side of the periodic table are more likely to lose electrons than elements on the right side (which are more likely to gain them). The other properties associated with metals follow the same general trend (even though we do not quantify them here). Consequently, as shown in Figure 9.17▶:

As we move to the right across a row (or period) in the periodic table, metallic character decreases.

As we move down a column in the periodic table, ionization energy decreases, making electrons more likely to be lost in chemical reactions. Therefore,

As we move down a column (or family) in the periodic table, metallic character increases.

These trends, based on the quantum-mechanical model, explain the distribution of metals and nonmetals in the periodic table discussed in Chapter 2. Metals are found on the left side and toward the center and nonmetals on the upper right side. The change in chemical behavior from metallic to nonmetallic can be seen most clearly as we proceed to the right across period 3, or down along group 5A as we can see in Figure 9.18▶.

Trends in Metallic Character

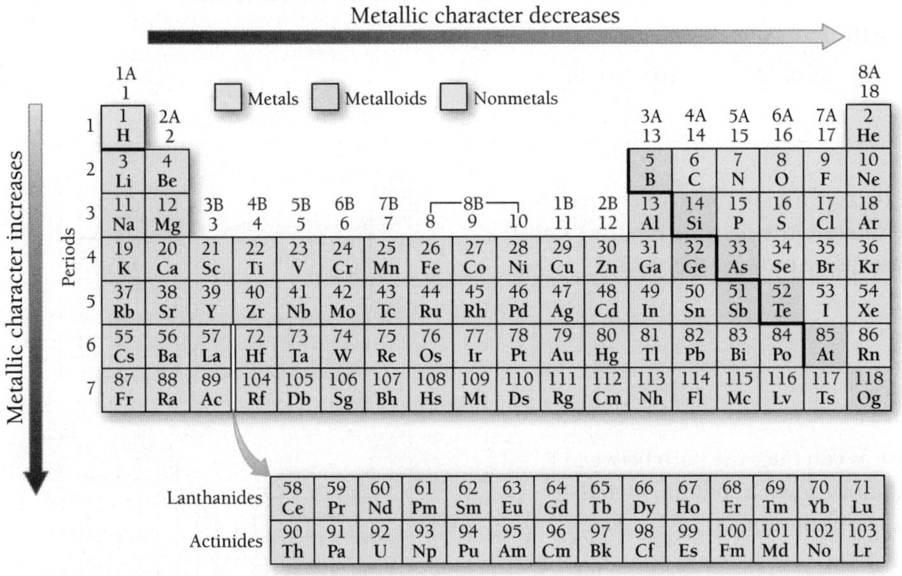

▲ **FIGURE 9.17 Trends in Metallic Character I** Metallic character decreases as we move to the right across a period and increases as we move down a column in the periodic table.

Trends in Metallic Character

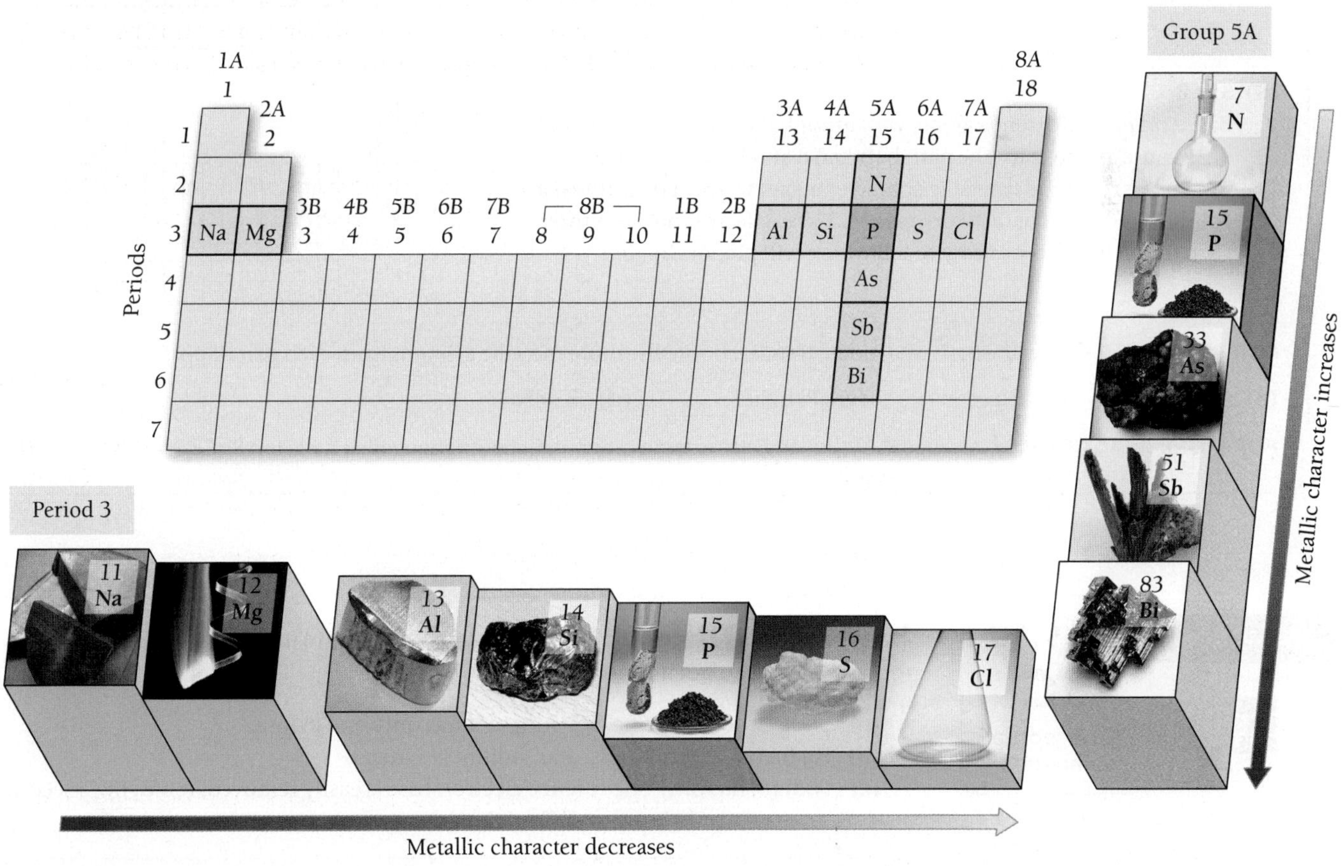

▲ **FIGURE 9.18 Trends in Metallic Character II** As we move down group 5A in the periodic table, metallic character increases. As we move across period 3, metallic character decreases.

EXAMPLE 9.9 Metallic Character

On the basis of periodic trends, choose the more metallic element from each pair (if possible).

(a) Sn or Te **(b)** P or Sb **(c)** Ge or In **(d)** S or Br

SOLUTION

(a) Sn or Te

Sn is more metallic than Te because as you trace the path between Sn and Te on the periodic table, you move to the right within the same period. Metallic character decreases as we move to the right.

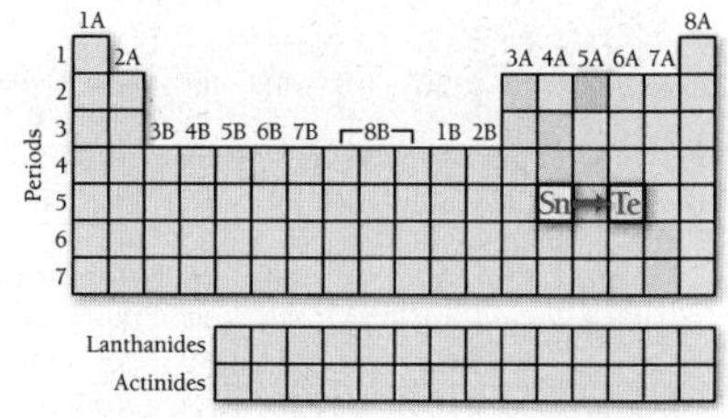

(b) P or Sb

Sb is more metallic than P because as you trace the path between P and Sb on the periodic table, you move down a column. Metallic character increases as we move down a column.

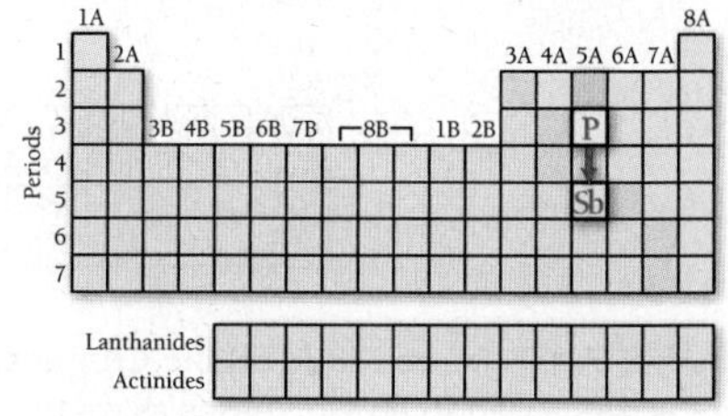

(c) Ge or In

In is more metallic than Ge because as you trace the path between Ge and In on the periodic table, you move down a column (metallic character increases) and then to the left across a period (metallic character increases). These effects add together for an overall increase.

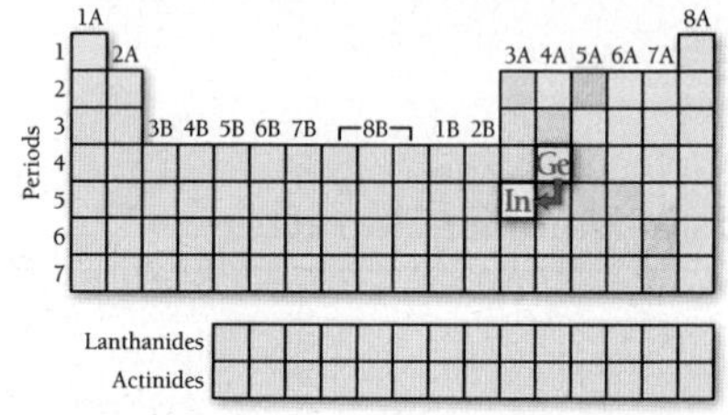

(d) S or Br

Based on periodic trends alone, we cannot tell which is more metallic because as you trace the path between S and Br, you move to the right across a period (metallic character decreases) and then down a column (metallic character increases). These effects tend to counter each other, and it is not easy to tell which will predominate.

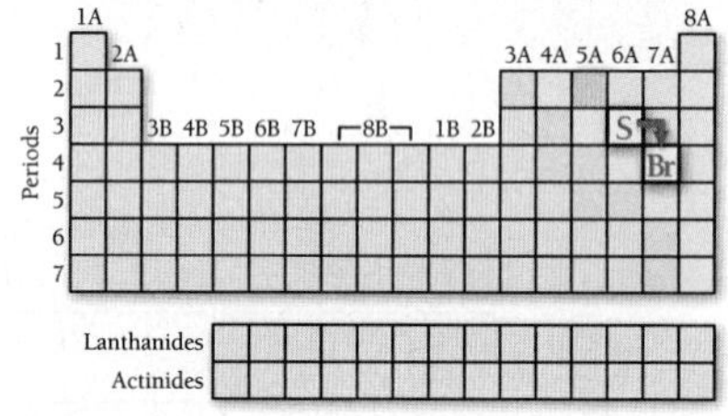

FOR PRACTICE 9.9 On the basis of periodic trends, choose the more metallic element from each pair (if possible).

(a) Ge or Sn **(b)** Ga or Sn **(c)** P or Bi **(d)** B or N

FOR MORE PRACTICE 9.9 Arrange the following elements in order of increasing metallic character: Si, Cl, Na, Rb.

ANSWER **NOW!**

9.10 Cc Conceptual Connection

PERIODIC TRENDS Which statement best explains why sodium commonly forms a 1+ ion and not a 2+ ion?

(a) Sodium only has one electron, so it has only one to lose.

(b) All metals form 1+ ions, and sodium is a metal.

(c) Sodium has only one valence electron that is easily removed; removing a second electron would be more difficult because it would be a core electron.

9.9 Periodic Trends Summary

In this chapter, we have examined various trends in properties that we can understand in terms of electron configurations. We have seen how electronic structure determines the size, ionization energy, electron affinity, and metallic character of atoms. We summarize these four important properties and their periodic trends in Table 9.2.

TABLE 9.2 ■ Summary of Periodic Properties

Property	Trend Moving Down a Column	Reason for Trend Moving Down	Trend Moving Across a Row	Reason for Trend Moving Across
Atomic Radii	Increasing	Size of outermost occupied orbital increases	Decreasing	Effective nuclear charge increases
First Ionization Energy	Decreasing	Outermost electrons further away from nucleus (and therefore easier to remove)	Increasing	Effective nuclear charge increases
Electron Affinity	No definite trend		Decreasing (more negative)	Effective nuclear charge increases
Metallic Character	Increasing	Ionization energy decreases	Decreasing	Ionization energy increases

QUIZ YOURSELF **NOW!**

Self-Assessment Quiz

Q1. According to Coulomb's law, if the separation between two particles of the same charge is doubled, what happens to the potential energy of the two particles?
MISSED THIS? *Read Section 9.3*

a) It is twice as high as it was before the distance separation.
b) It is one-half as high as it was before the separation.
c) It does not change.
d) It is one-fourth as high as it was before the separation.

Q2. Which electron in sulfur is most shielded from nuclear charge?
MISSED THIS? *Read Section 9.3*

a) an electron in the 1*s* orbital
b) an electron in a 2*p* orbital
c) an electron in a 3*p* orbital
d) none of the above (All of these electrons are equally shielded from nuclear charge.)

Q3. Choose the correct electron configuration for Se.
MISSED THIS? *Read Section 9.3; Watch KCV 9.3*

a) $1s^22s^22p^63s^23p^4$
b) $1s^22s^22p^63s^23p^64s^23d^{10}4p^4$
c) $1s^22s^22p^63s^23p^64s^24p^4$
d) $1s^22s^22p^63s^23p^64s^23d^4$

Q4. Choose the correct orbital diagram for vanadium.
MISSED THIS? *Read Section 9.3; Watch KCV 9.3, IWE 9.3*

a) [Ar] 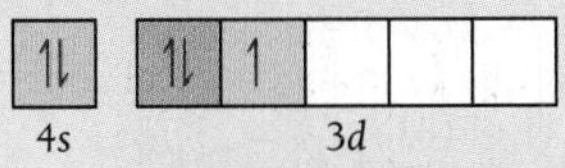

b) [Ar] 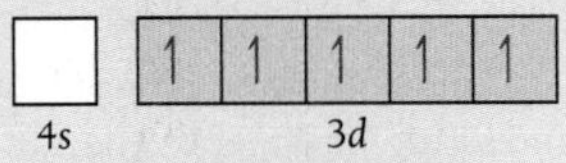

c) [Ar] 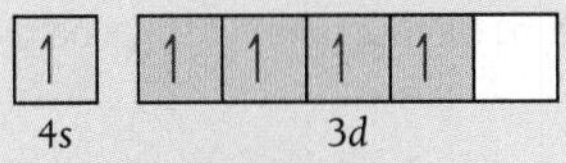

d) [Ar] 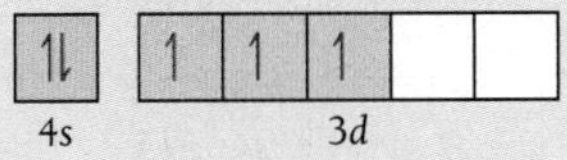

Q5. Which set of four quantum numbers corresponds to an electron in a 4*p* orbital?
MISSED THIS? *Read Section 9.3*

a) $n = 4, l = 1, m_l = 0, m_s = \frac{1}{2}$
b) $n = 4, l = 3, m_l = 3, m_s = -\frac{1}{2}$
c) $n = 4, l = 2, m_l = 0, m_s = \frac{1}{2}$
d) $n = 4, l = 4, m_l = 3, m_s = -\frac{1}{2}$

Q6. Which element has the smallest atomic radius?
MISSED THIS? *Read Section 9.6; Watch KCV 9.6, IWE 9.5*

a) C b) Si c) Be d) F

Q7. Which statement is true about electron shielding of nuclear charge? **MISSED THIS?** *Read Section 9.6; Watch KCV 9.6*

a) Outermost electrons efficiently shield one another from nuclear charge.
b) Core electrons efficiently shield one another from nuclear charge.
c) Outermost electrons efficiently shield core electrons from nuclear charge.
d) Core electrons efficiently shield outermost electrons from nuclear charge.

Q8. Which statement is true about effective nuclear charge?
MISSED THIS? *Read Section 9.6; Watch KCV 9.6*

a) Effective nuclear charge *decreases* as you move to the right across a row in the periodic table.
b) Effective nuclear charge *increases* as you move to the right across a row in the periodic table.
c) Effective nuclear charge *remains constant* as you move to the right across a row in the periodic table.
d) Effective nuclear charge *increases and decreases* at regular intervals as you move to the right across a row in the periodic table.

—Continued on the next page

Q9. Which is the correct electron configuration for Fe^{2+}?
MISSED THIS? *Read Section 9.7; Watch IWE 9.6*

a) $[Ar]4s^2 3d^6$ b) $[Ar]4s^2 3d^4$
c) $[Ar]4s^0 3d^6$ d) $[Ar]4s^2 3d^8$

Q10. Which species is diamagnetic?
MISSED THIS? *Read Section 9.7; Watch IWE 9.6*

a) Cr^{2+} b) Zn c) Mn d) C

Q11. Arrange these atoms and ions in order of increasing radius: Cs^+, Ba^{2+}, I^-. **MISSED THIS?** *Read Section 9.7*

a) $I^- < Ba^{2+} < Cs^+$ b) $Cs^+ < Ba^{2+} < I^-$
c) $Ba^{2+} < Cs^+ < I^-$ d) $I^- < Cs^+ < Ba^{2+}$

Q12. Arrange these elements in order of increasing first ionization energy: Cl, Sn, Si.
MISSED THIS? *Read Section 9.7; Watch IWE 9.8*

a) Cl < Si < Sn b) Sn < Si < Cl
c) Si < Cl < Sn d) Sn < Cl < Si

Q13. The ionization energies of an unknown third-period element are listed here. Identify the element. $IE_1 = 786$ kJ/mol; $IE_2 = 1580$ kJ/mol; $IE_3 = 3230$ kJ/mol; $IE_4 = 4360$ kJ/mol; $IE_5 = 16{,}100$ kJ/mol
MISSED THIS? *Read Section 9.7*

a) Mg b) Al c) Si d) P

Q14. Which statement is true about trends in metallic character?
MISSED THIS? *Read Section 9.8*

a) Metallic character *increases* as you move to the right across a row in the periodic table and *increases* as you move down a column.
b) Metallic character *decreases* as you move to the right across a row in the periodic table and *increases* as you move down a column.
c) Metallic character *decreases* as you move to the right across a row in the periodic table and *decreases* as you move down a column.
d) Metallic character *increases* as you move to the right across a row in the periodic table and *decreases* as you move down a column.

Q15. For which element is the gaining of an electron most exothermic? **MISSED THIS?** *Read Section 9.8*

a) Li b) N c) F d) B

Answers: 1. (b) **2.** (c) **3.** (b) **4.** (d) **5.** (a) **6.** (d) **7.** (d) **8.** (b) **9.** (c) **10.** (b) **11.** (c) **12.** (b) **13.** (c) **14.** (b) **15.** (c)

CHAPTER 9 IN REVIEW

TERMS

Section 9.1
periodic property (352)

Section 9.3
electron configuration (353)
ground state (353)
orbital diagram (354)
Pauli exclusion principle (354)
degenerate (355)
Coulomb's law (355)
shielding (356)
effective nuclear charge (Z_{eff}) (356)
penetration (356)
aufbau principle (358)
Hund's rule (358)

Section 9.4
valence electrons (361)
core electrons (361)

Section 9.6
van der Waals radius (nonbonding atomic radius) (366)
covalent radius (bonding atomic radius) (366)
atomic radius (366)

Section 9.7
paramagnetic (371)
diamagnetic (372)
ionization energy (IE) (375)

Section 9.8
electron affinity (EA) (379)

CONCEPTS

Periodic Properties and the Development of the Periodic Table (9.1, 9.2)

- In the nineteenth century, Dmitri Mendeleev arranged the elements in an early version of the periodic table so that atomic mass increased from left to right in a row and elements with similar properties fell in the same columns.
- Periodic properties are predictable based on an element's position within the periodic table. Periodic properties include atomic radius, ionization energy, electron affinity, density, and metallic character.
- Quantum mechanics explains the periodic table by describing how electrons fill the quantum-mechanical orbitals within the atoms that compose the elements.

Electron Configurations (9.3)

- An electron configuration for an atom shows which quantum-mechanical orbitals the atom's electrons occupy. For example, the electron configuration of helium ($1s^2$) indicates that helium's two electrons occupy the 1*s* orbital.
- The order of filling quantum-mechanical orbitals in multielectron atoms is 1*s* 2*s* 2*p* 3*s* 3*p* 4*s* 3*d* 4*p* 5*s* 4*d* 5*p* 6*s*.
- According to the Pauli exclusion principle, each orbital can hold a maximum of two electrons and those electrons have opposing spins.
- According to Hund's rule, orbitals of the same energy first fill singly with electrons having parallel spins before pairing.

Electron Configurations and the Periodic Table (9.4, 9.5)

- Because quantum-mechanical orbitals fill sequentially with increasing atomic number, we can infer the electron configuration of an element from its position in the periodic table.
- The most stable electron configurations are those with completely full *s* and *p* sublevels. Therefore, the most stable and unreactive elements—those with the lowest energy electron configurations—are the noble gases.
- Elements with one or two valence electrons are among the most active metals, readily losing their valence electrons to attain noble gas configurations.
- Elements with six or seven valence electrons are among the most active nonmetals, readily gaining enough electrons to attain a noble gas configuration.

Effective Nuclear Charge and Periodic Trends in Atomic Size (9.6)

- The size of an atom is largely determined by its outermost electrons. As we move down a column in the periodic table, the principal quantum number (n) of the outermost electrons increases, resulting in successively larger orbitals and therefore larger atomic radii.
- As we move across a row in the periodic table, atomic radii decrease because the effective nuclear charge—the net or average charge experienced by the atom's outermost electrons—increases.
- The atomic radii of the transition elements stay roughly constant as we move across each row because electrons are added to the $n_{\text{highest}} - 1$ orbitals, while the number of highest n electrons stays roughly constant.

Ion Properties (9.7)

- We determine the electron configuration of an ion by adding or subtracting the corresponding number of electrons to the electron configuration of the neutral atom.
- For main-group ions, the order in which electrons are removed is the same as the order in which they are added in building up the electron configuration.
- For transition metal atoms, the ns electrons are removed before the $(n - 1)d$ electrons.
- The radius of a cation is much *smaller* than that of the corresponding atom, and the radius of an anion is much *larger* than that of the corresponding atom.
- The first ionization energy—the energy required to remove the first electron from an atom in the gaseous state—generally decreases as we move down a column in the periodic table and increases when we move to the right across a row.
- Successive ionization energies increase smoothly from one valence electron to the next, but the ionization energy increases dramatically for the first core electron.

Electron Affinities and Metallic Character (9.8)

- Electron affinity—the energy associated with an atom in its gaseous state gaining an electron—does not show a general trend as we move down a column in the periodic table, but it generally becomes more negative (more exothermic) to the right across a row.
- Metallic character—the tendency to lose electrons in a chemical reaction—generally increases down a column in the periodic table and decreases to the right across a row.

EQUATIONS AND RELATIONSHIPS

Order of Filling Quantum-Mechanical Orbitals (**9.3**)

$$1s\ 2s\ 2p\ 3s\ 3p\ 4s\ 3d\ 4p\ 5s\ 4d\ 5p\ 6s$$

LEARNING OUTCOMES

Chapter Objectives	Assessment
Write electron configurations for elements (**9.3**)	Example 9.1 **For Practice** 9.1 **Exercises** 39–40
Draw orbital diagrams for elements (**9.3**)	Example 9.2 **For Practice** 9.2 **Exercises** 41–42
Write electron configurations based on periodic table location (**9.4**)	Examples 9.3, 9.4 **For Practice** 9.3, 9.4 **For More Practice** 9.4 **Exercises** 43–52
Predict relative atomic sizes of elements (**9.6**)	Example 9.5 **For Practice** 9.5 **For More Practice** 9.5 **Exercises** 53–62
Analyze ions in terms of magnetic properties (**9.7**)	Example 9.6 **For Practice** 9.6 **Exercises** 63–66
Predict the relative size of ions from periodic trends (**9.7**)	Example 9.7 **For Practice** 9.7 **Exercises** 67–70
Predict relative ionization energies for atoms and ions based on periodic trends (**9.7**)	Example 9.8 **For Practice** 9.8 **For More Practice** 9.8 **Exercises** 71–76
Predict the metallic character of atoms based on periodic trends (**9.8**)	Example 9.9 **For Practice** 9.9 **For More Practice** 9.9 **Exercises** 77–82

EXERCISES

Mastering Chemistry provides end-of-chapter exercises, feedback-enriched tutorial problems, animations, and interactive activities to encourage problem-solving practice and deeper understanding of key concepts and topics.

REVIEW QUESTIONS

1. What are periodic properties?

2. Which periodic property is particularly important to nerve signal transmission? Why?

3. Explain the contributions of Johann Döbereiner and John Newlands to the organization of elements according to their properties.

4. Who is credited with arranging the periodic table? How are the elements arranged in the modern periodic table?

5. Explain the contributions of Meyer and Moseley to the periodic table.

6. The periodic table is a result of the periodic law. What observations led to the periodic law? What theory explains the underlying reasons for the periodic law?

7. What is an electron configuration? Give an example.

8. What is Coulomb's law? Explain how the potential energy of two charged particles depends on the distance between the charged particles and on the magnitude and sign of their charges.

9. What is shielding? In an atom, which electrons tend to do the most shielding (core electrons or valence electrons)?

10. What is penetration? How does the penetration of an orbital into the region occupied by core electrons affect the energy of an electron in that orbital?

11. Why are the sublevels within a principal level split into different energies for multielectron atoms but not for the hydrogen atom?

12. What is an orbital diagram? Provide an example.

13. Why is electron spin important when writing electron configurations? Explain in terms of the Pauli exclusion principle.

14. What are degenerate orbitals? According to Hund's rule, how are degenerate orbitals occupied?

15. List all orbitals from 1*s* through 5*s* according to increasing energy for multielectron atoms.

16. What are valence electrons? Why are they important?

17. Copy this blank periodic table onto a sheet of paper and label each of the blocks within the table: *s* block, *p* block, *d* block, and *f* block.

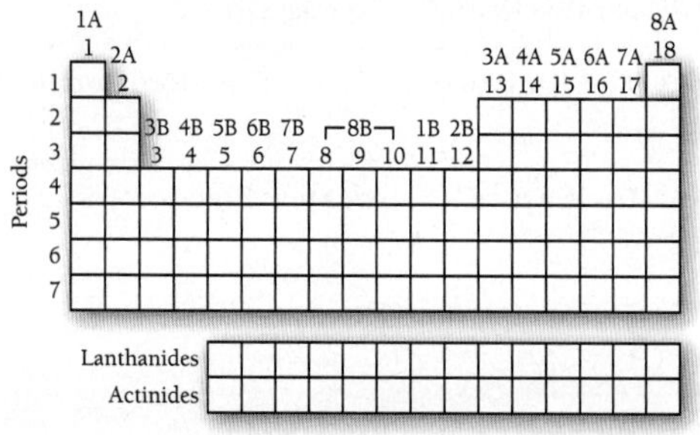

18. Explain why the *s* block in the periodic table has only two columns while the *p* block has six.

19. Why do the rows in the periodic table get progressively longer as you move down the table? For example, the first row contains 2 elements, the second and third rows each contain 8 elements, and the fourth and fifth rows each contain 18 elements. Explain.

20. Describe the relationship between a main-group element's lettered group number (the number of the element's column) and its valence electrons.

21. Describe the relationship between an element's row number in the periodic table and the highest principal quantum number in the element's electron configuration. How does this relationship differ for main-group elements, transition elements, and inner transition elements?

22. Which of the transition elements in the first transition series have anomalous electron configurations?

23. Describe how to write the electron configuration for an element based on its position in the periodic table.

24. Describe the relationship between the properties of an element and the number of valence electrons that it contains.

25. List the number of valence electrons for each family, and explain the relationship between the number of valence electrons and the resulting chemistry of the elements in the family.

a. alkali metals
b. alkaline earth metals
c. halogens
d. oxygen family

26. Define atomic radius. For main-group elements, describe the observed trends in atomic radius as you move:

a. across a period in the periodic table
b. down a column in the periodic table

27. What is effective nuclear charge? What is shielding?

28. Use the concepts of effective nuclear charge, shielding, and *n* value of the valence orbital to explain the trend in atomic radius as you move across a period in the periodic table.

29. For transition elements, describe and explain the observed trends in atomic radius as you move:

a. across a period in the periodic table
b. down a column in the periodic table

30. How is the electron configuration of an anion different from that of the corresponding neutral atom? How is the electron configuration of a cation different?

31. Describe how to write an electron configuration for a transition metal cation. Is the order of electron removal upon ionization simply the reverse of electron addition upon filling? Why or why not?

32. Describe the relationship between

a. the radius of a cation and that of the atom from which forms
b. the radius of an anion and that of the atom from which it forms

33. What is ionization energy? What is the difference between first ionization energy and second ionization energy?

34. What is the general trend in first ionization energy as you move down a column in the periodic table? As you move across a row?

35. What are the exceptions to the periodic trends in first ionization energy? Why do they occur?

36. Examination of the first few successive ionization energies for a given element usually reveals a large jump between two ionization energies. For example, the successive ionization energies of magnesium show a large jump between IE_2 and IE_3. The successive ionization energies of aluminum show a large jump between IE_3 and IE_4. Explain why these jumps occur and how you might predict them.

37. What is electron affinity? What are the observed periodic trends in electron affinity?

38. What is metallic character? What are the observed periodic trends in metallic character?

PROBLEMS BY TOPIC

Electron Configurations

39. Write the full electron configuration for each element.
MISSED THIS? *Read Section 9.3; Watch KCV 9.3*
a. Si b. O c. K d. Ne

40. Write the full electron configuration for each element.
a. C b. P c. Ar d. Na

41. Write the full orbital diagram for each element.
MISSED THIS? *Read Section 9.3; Watch KCV 9.3, IWE 9.2*
a. N b. F c. Mg d. Al

42. Write the full orbital diagram for each element.
a. S b. Ca c. Ne d. He

43. Use the periodic table to write an electron configuration for each element. Represent core electrons with the symbol of the previous noble gas in brackets.
MISSED THIS? *Read Section 9.4; Watch KCV 9.4, IWE 9.4*
a. P b. Ge c. Zr d. I

44. Use the periodic table to determine the element corresponding to each electron configuration.
a. $[Ar]\ 4s^2 3d^{10} 4p^6$ b. $[Ar]\ 4s^2 3d^2$
c. $[Kr]\ 5s^2 4d^{10} 5p^2$ d. $[Kr]\ 5s^2$

45. Use the periodic table to determine each quantity.
MISSED THIS? *Read Section 9.4; Watch KCV 9.4, IWE 9.4*
a. the number of 2*s* electrons in Li
b. the number of 3*d* electrons in Cu
c. the number of 4*p* electrons in Br
d. the number of 4*d* electrons in Zr

46. Use the periodic table to determine each quantity.
a. the number of 3*s* electrons in Mg
b. the number of 3*d* electrons in Cr
c. the number of 4*d* electrons in Y
d. the number of 6*p* electrons in Pb

47. Name an element in the fourth period (row) of the periodic table with the following:
MISSED THIS? *Read Section 9.4; Watch KCV 9.4, IWE 9.4*
a. five valence electrons
b. four 4*p* electrons
c. three 3*d* electrons
d. full *s* and *p* sublevels

48. Name an element in the third period (row) of the periodic table with the following:
a. three valence electrons
b. four 3*p* electrons
c. six 3*p* electrons
d. two 3*s* electrons and no 3*p* electrons

Valence Electrons and Simple Chemical Behavior from the Periodic Table

49. Determine the number of valence electrons in an atom of each element. **MISSED THIS?** *Read Section 9.4; Watch KCV 9.4*
a. Ba b. Cs c. Ni d. S

50. Determine the number of valence electrons in an atom of each element. Which elements do you expect to lose electrons in their chemical reactions? Which do you expect to gain electrons?
a. Al b. Sn c. Br d. Se

51. Which outer electron configuration would you expect to belong to a reactive metal? To a reactive nonmetal?
MISSED THIS? *Read Section 9.5*
a. ns^2 b. ns^2np^6 c. ns^2np^5 d. ns^2np^2

52. Which outer electron configurations would you expect to belong to a noble gas? To a metalloid?
a. ns^2 b. ns^2np^6 c. ns^2np^5 d. ns^2np^2

Coulomb's Law and Effective Nuclear Charge

53. According to Coulomb's law, which pair of charged particles has the lowest potential energy? **MISSED THIS?** *Read Section 9.3*
a. a particle with a 1− charge separated by 150 pm from a particle with a 2+ charge
b. a particle with a 1+ charge separated by 150 pm from a particle with a 1+ charge
c. a particle with a 1− charge separated by 100 pm from a particle with a 3+ charge

54. According to Coulomb's law, rank the interactions between charged particles from lowest potential energy to highest potential energy.
a. a 1+ charge and a 1− charge separated by 100 pm
b. a 2+ charge and a 1− charge separated by 100 pm
c. a 1+ charge and a 1+ charge separated by 100 pm
d. a 1+ charge and a 1− charge separated by 200 pm

55. Which experience a greater effective nuclear charge: the valence electrons in beryllium or the valence electrons in nitrogen? Why?
MISSED THIS? *Read Section 9.6; Watch KCV 9.6*

56. Arrange the atoms according to decreasing effective nuclear charge experienced by their valence electrons: S, Mg, Al, Si.

57. If core electrons completely shielded valence electrons from nuclear charge (i.e., if each core electron reduced nuclear charge by 1 unit) and if valence electrons did not shield one another from nuclear charge at all, what would be the effective nuclear charge experienced by the valence electrons of each atom?
MISSED THIS? *Read Section 9.6; Watch KCV 9.6*
a. K b. Ca c. O d. C

58. In Section 9.6, we estimated the effective nuclear charge on beryllium's valence electrons to be slightly greater than 2+. What would a similar process predict for the effective nuclear charge on boron's valence electrons? Would you expect the effective nuclear charge to be different for boron's 2*s* electrons compared to its 2*p* electron? In what way? (*Hint*: Consider the shape of the 2*p* orbital compared to that of the 2*s* orbital.)

Atomic Radius

59. Choose the larger atom from each pair.
MISSED THIS? *Read Section 9.6; Watch KCV 9.6, IWE 9.5*
a. Al or In b. Si or N
c. P or Pb d. C or F

60. Choose the larger atom from each pair, if possible.
a. Sn or Si b. Br or Ga
c. Sn or Bi d. Se or Sn

61. Arrange these elements in order of increasing atomic radius: Ca, Rb, S, Si, Ge, F.
MISSED THIS? *Read Section 9.6; Watch KCV 9.6, IWE 9.5*

62. Arrange these elements in order of decreasing atomic radius: Cs, Sb, S, Pb, Se.

Ionic Electron Configurations, Ionic Radii, Magnetic Properties, and Ionization Energy

63. Write the electron configuration for each ion.
MISSED THIS? *Read Section 9.7; Watch IWE 9.6*
a. O^{2-} b. Br^- c. Sr^{2+} d. Co^{3+} e. Cu^{2+}

64. Write the electron configuration for each ion.
a. Cl^- b. P^{3-} c. K^+ d. Mo^{3+} e. V^{3+}

65. Write orbital diagrams for each ion and indicate whether the ion is diamagnetic or paramagnetic.
MISSED THIS? *Read Section 9.7; Watch IWE 9.6*
a. V^{5+} b. Cr^{3+} c. Ni^{2+} d. Fe^{3+}

66. Write orbital diagrams for each ion and indicate whether the ion is diamagnetic or paramagnetic.
a. Cd^{2+} b. Au^+ c. Mo^{3+} d. Zr^{2+}

67. Which is the larger species in each pair?
MISSED THIS? *Read Section 9.7*
a. Li or Li^+ b. I^- or Cs^+
c. Cr or Cr^{3+} d. O or O^{2-}

68. Which is the larger species in each pair?
a. Sr or Sr^{2+} b. N or N^{3-}
c. Ni or Ni^{2+} d. S^{2-} or Ca^{2+}

69. Arrange this isoelectronic series in order of decreasing radius: F^-, O^{2-}, Mg^{2+}, Na^+. **MISSED THIS?** *Read Section 9.7*

70. Arrange this isoelectronic series in order of increasing atomic radius: Se^{2-}, Sr^{2+}, Rb^+, Br^-.

71. Choose the element with the higher first ionization energy from each pair. **MISSED THIS?** *Read Section 9.7; Watch IWE 9.8*
a. Br or Bi b. Na or Rb
c. As or At d. P or Sn

72. Choose the element with the higher first ionization energy from each pair.
a. P or I b. Si or Cl
c. P or Sb d. Ga or Ge

73. Arrange these elements in order of increasing first ionization energy: Si, F, In, N. **MISSED THIS?** *Read Section 9.7; Watch IWE 9.8*

74. Arrange these elements in order of decreasing first ionization energy: Cl, S, Sn, Pb.

75. For each element, predict where the "jump" occurs for successive ionization energies. (For example, does the jump occur between the first and second ionization energies, the second and third, or the third and fourth?) **MISSED THIS?** *Read Section 9.7*
a. Be b. N c. O d. Li

76. Consider this set of ionization energies.

$$IE_1 = 578 \text{ kJ/mol}$$
$$IE_2 = 1820 \text{ kJ/mol}$$
$$IE_3 = 2750 \text{ kJ/mol}$$
$$IE_4 = 11{,}600 \text{ kJ/mol}$$

To which third-period element do these ionization values belong?

Electron Affinities and Metallic Character

77. Choose the element with the more negative (more exothermic) electron affinity from each pair. **MISSED THIS?** *Read Section 9.8*
a. Na or Rb b. B or S
c. C or N d. Li or F

78. Choose the element with the more negative (more exothermic) electron affinity from each pair.
a. Mg or S b. K or Cs
c. Si or P d. Ga or Br

79. Choose the more metallic element from each pair.
MISSED THIS? *Read Section 9.8*
a. Sr or Sb b. As or Bi c. Cl or O d. S or As

80. Choose the more metallic element from each pair.
a. Sb or Pb b. K or Ge c. Ge or Sb d. As or Sn

81. Arrange these elements in order of increasing metallic character: Fr, Sb, In, S, Ba, Se. **MISSED THIS?** *Read Section 9.8*

82. Arrange these elements in order of decreasing metallic character: Sr, N, Si, P, Ga, Al.

CUMULATIVE PROBLEMS

83. Bromine is a highly reactive liquid while krypton is an inert gas. Explain this difference based on their electron configurations.

84. Potassium is a highly reactive metal while argon is an inert gas. Explain this difference based on their electron configurations.

85. Both vanadium and its 3+ ion are paramagnetic. Refer to their electron configurations to explain this statement.

86. Refer to their electron configurations to explain why copper is paramagnetic while its 1+ ion is not.

87. Suppose you were trying to find a substitute for K^+ in nerve signal transmission. Where would you begin your search? What ions would be most like K^+? For each ion you propose, explain the ways in which it would be similar to K^+ and the ways it would be different. Refer to periodic trends in your discussion.

88. Suppose you were trying to find a substitute for Na^+ in nerve signal transmission. Where would you begin your search? What ions would be most like Na^+? For each ion you propose, explain the ways in which it would be similar to Na^+ and the ways it would be different. Use periodic trends in your discussion.

89. Life on Earth evolved based on the element carbon. Based on periodic properties, what two or three elements would you expect to be most like carbon?

90. Which pair of elements would you expect to have the most similar atomic radii, and why?
a. Si and Ga
b. Si and Ge
c. Si and As

91. Consider these elements: N, Mg, O, F, Al.
a. Write the electron configuration for each element.
b. Arrange the elements in order of decreasing atomic radius.
c. Arrange the elements in order of increasing ionization energy.
d. Use the electron configurations in part a to explain the differences between your answers to parts b and c.

92. Consider these elements: P, Ca, Si, S, Ga.
a. Write the electron configuration for each element.
b. Arrange the elements in order of decreasing atomic radius.
c. Arrange the elements in order of increasing ionization energy.
d. Use the electron configurations in part a to explain the differences between your answers to parts b and c.

93. Explain why atomic radius decreases as you move to the right across a period for main-group elements but not for transition elements.

94. Explain why vanadium (radius = 134 pm) and copper (radius = 128 pm) have nearly identical atomic radii, even though the atomic number of copper is about 25% higher than that of vanadium. What would you predict about the relative densities of these two metals? Look up the densities in a reference book, periodic table, or on the Internet. Are your predictions correct?

95. The lightest noble gases, such as helium and neon, are completely inert—they do not form any chemical compounds whatsoever. The heavier noble gases, in contrast, do form a limited number of compounds. Explain this difference in terms of trends in fundamental periodic properties.

96. The lightest halogen is also the most chemically reactive, and reactivity generally decreases as you move down the column of halogens in the periodic table. Explain this trend in terms of periodic properties.

97. Write general outer electron configurations (ns^xnp^y) for groups 6A and 7A in the periodic table. The electron affinity of each group 7A element is more negative than that of each corresponding group 6A element. Use the electron configurations to explain why this is so.

98. The electron affinity of each group 5A element is more positive than that of each corresponding group 4A element. Use the outer electron configurations for these columns to suggest a reason for this observation.

99. The elements with atomic numbers 35 and 53 have similar chemical properties. Based on their electronic configurations, predict the atomic number of a heavier element that also should share these chemical properties.

100. Write the electron configurations of the six cations that form from sulfur by the loss of one to six electrons. For those cations that have unpaired electrons, write orbital diagrams.

101. You have cracked a secret code that uses elemental symbols to spell words. The code uses numbers to designate the elemental symbols. Each number is the sum of the atomic number and the highest principal quantum number of the highest occupied orbital of the element whose symbol is to be used. The message may be written forward or backward. Decode the following messages:

a. 10, 12, 58, 11, 7, 44, 63, 66
b. 9, 99, 30, 95, 19, 47, 79

102. The electron affinity of sodium is lower than that of lithium, while the electron affinity of chlorine is higher than that of fluorine. Suggest an explanation for this observation.

103. Use Coulomb's law to calculate the ionization energy in kJ/mol of an atom composed of a proton and an electron separated by 100.00 pm. What wavelength of light has sufficient energy to ionize the atom?

104. The first ionization energy of sodium is 496 kJ/mol. Use Coulomb's law to estimate the average distance between the sodium nucleus and the 3*s* electron. How does this distance compare to the atomic radius of sodium? Explain the difference.

105. Consider the elements: B, C, N, O, F.

a. Which element has the highest first ionization energy?
b. Which element has the largest atomic radius?
c. Which element is most metallic?
d. Which element has three unpaired electrons?

106. Consider the elements: Na, Mg, Al, Si, P.

a. Which element has the highest second ionization energy?
b. Which element has the smallest atomic radius?
c. Which element is least metallic?
d. Which element is diamagnetic?

CHALLENGE PROBLEMS

107. Consider the densities and atomic radii of the noble gases at 25 °C:

Element	Atomic Radius (pm)	Density (g/L)
He	32	0.18
Ne	70	0.90
Ar	98	-
Kr	112	3.75
Xe	130	-
Rn	-	9.73

a. Estimate the densities of argon and xenon by interpolation from the data.
b. Estimate the density of the element with atomic number 118 by extrapolation from the data.
c. Use the molar mass of neon to estimate the mass of a neon atom. Then use the atomic radius of neon to calculate the average density of a neon atom. How does this density compare to the density of neon gas? What does this comparison suggest about the nature of neon gas?
d. Use the densities and molar masses of krypton and neon to calculate the number of atoms of each element found in a volume of 1.0 L. Use these values to estimate the number of atoms present in 1.0 L of Ar. Now use the molar mass of argon to estimate the density of Ar. How does this estimate compare to that in part a?

108. As you have seen, the periodic table is a result of empirical observation (i.e., the periodic law), but quantum-mechanical theory explains *why* the table is so arranged. Suppose that, in another universe, quantum theory was such that there were one *s* orbital but only two *p* orbitals (instead of three) and only three *d* orbitals (instead of five). Draw out the first four periods of the periodic table in this alternative universe. Which elements would be the equivalent of the noble gases? Halogens? Alkali metals?

109. Consider the metals in the first transition series. Use periodic trends to predict a trend in density as you move to the right across the series.

110. Imagine a universe in which the value of m_s can be $+\frac{1}{2}$, 0, and $-\frac{1}{2}$. Assuming that all the other quantum numbers can take only the values possible in our world and that the Pauli exclusion principle applies, determine:

a. the new electronic configuration of neon
b. the atomic number of the element with a completed $n = 2$ shell
c. the number of unpaired electrons in fluorine

111. A carbon atom can absorb radiation of various wavelengths with resulting changes in its electron configuration. Write orbital diagrams for the electron configuration of carbon that results from absorption of the three longest wavelengths of radiation it can absorb.

112. Only trace amounts of the synthetic element darmstadtium, atomic number 110, have been obtained. The element is so highly unstable that no observations of its properties have been possible. Based on its position in the periodic table, propose three different reasonable valence electron configurations for this element.

113. What is the atomic number of the as yet undiscovered element in which the 8*s* and 8*p* electron energy levels fill? Predict the chemical behavior of this element.

114. The trend in second ionization energy for the elements from lithium to fluorine is not a regular one. Predict which of these elements has the highest second ionization energy and which has the lowest and explain. Of the elements N, O, and F, O has the highest and N the lowest second ionization energy. Explain.

115. Unlike the elements in groups 1A and 2A, those in group 3A do not show a regular decrease in first ionization energy as you move down the column. Explain the irregularities.

116. Using the data in Figures 9.15 and 9.16, calculate ΔE for the reaction $Na(g) + Cl(g) \longrightarrow Na^+(g) + Cl^-(g)$.

117. Even though adding two electrons to O or S forms an ion with a noble gas electron configuration, the second electron affinity of both of these elements is positive. Explain.

118. In Section 2.7 we discussed the metalloids, which form a diagonal band separating the metals from the nonmetals. There are other instances in which elements such as lithium and magnesium that are diagonal to each other have comparable metallic character. Suggest an explanation for this observation.

119. The heaviest known alkaline earth metal is radium, atomic number 88. Find the atomic numbers of the as yet undiscovered next two members of the series.

120. Predict the electronic configurations of the first two excited states (next higher-energy states beyond the ground state) of Pd.

121. Table 9.2 does not include francium because none of francium's isotopes are stable. Predict the values of the entries for Fr in Table 9.2. Predict the nature of the products of the reaction of Fr with: (a) water, (b) oxygen, and (c) chlorine.

122. From its electronic configuration, predict which of the first 10 elements would be most similar in chemical behavior to the as yet undiscovered element 165.

CONCEPTUAL PROBLEMS

123. Imagine that in another universe atoms and elements are identical to ours, except that atoms with six valence electrons have particular stability (in contrast to our universe where atoms with eight valence electrons have particular stability). Give an example of an element in the alternative universe that corresponds to each of the following:
   a. a noble gas
   b. a reactive nonmetal
   c. a reactive metal

124. The outermost valence electron in atom A experiences an effective nuclear charge of 2+ and is on average 225 pm from the nucleus. The outermost valence electron in atom B experiences an effective nuclear charge of 1+ and is on average 175 pm from the nucleus. Which atom (A or B) has the higher first ionization energy? Explain.

125. Determine whether each statement regarding penetration and shielding is true or false. (Assume that all lower energy orbitals are fully occupied.)
   a. An electron in a 3*s* orbital is more shielded than an electron in a 2*s* orbital.
   b. An electron in a 3*s* orbital penetrates into the region occupied by core electrons more than electrons in a 3*p* orbital penetrates into the region occupied by core electrons.
   c. An electron in an orbital that penetrates closer to the nucleus always experiences more shielding than an electron in an orbital that does not penetrate as far.
   d. An electron in an orbital that penetrates close to the nucleus tends to experience a higher effective nuclear charge than an electron in an orbital that does not penetrate close to the nucleus.

126. Give a combination of four quantum numbers that could be assigned to an electron occupying a 5*p* orbital. Do the same for an electron occupying a 6*d* orbital.

127. Use the trends in ionization energy and electron affinity to explain why calcium fluoride has the formula CaF_2 and not Ca_2F or CaF.

QUESTIONS FOR GROUP WORK

Active Classroom Learning

Discuss these questions with the group and record your consensus answer.

128. In a complete sentence describe the relationship between shielding and penetration.

129. Play a game to memorize the order in which orbitals fill. Have each group member in turn state the name of the next orbital to fill and the maximum number of electrons it can hold (for example, "1*s* two," "2*s* two," "2*p* six"). If a member gets stuck, other group members can help, consulting Figure 9.5 and the accompanying text summary if necessary. However, when a member gets stuck, the next player starts back at "1*s* two." Keep going until each group member can list all the orbitals in order up to "6*s* two."

130. Sketch a periodic table (without element symbols). Include the correct number of rows and columns in the *s*, *p*, *d*, and *f* blocks. Shade in the squares for elements that have irregular electron configurations.

131. In complete sentences, explain: (a) why Se^{2-} and Br^- are about the same size; (b) why Br^- is slightly smaller than Se^{2-}; and (c) which singly charged cation you would expect to be approximately the same size as Se^{2-} and Br^- and why.

132. Have each member of your group sketch a periodic table indicating a periodic trend (atomic size, first ionization energy, metallic character, etc.). Have each member present his or her table to the rest of the group and explain the trend based on concepts such as orbital size or effective nuclear charge.

DATA INTERPRETATION AND ANALYSIS

Periodic Properties of Period 3 Elements

133. The accompanying graphs show the first ionization energies and electron affinities of the period 3 elements. Refer to the graphs to answer the questions that follow.

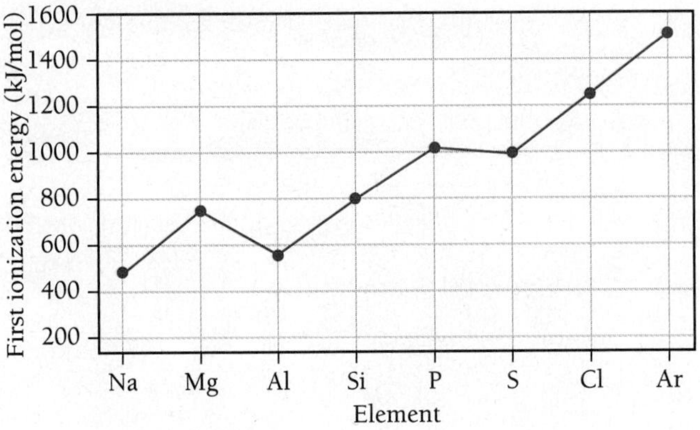

First Ionization Energies of Period 3 Elements

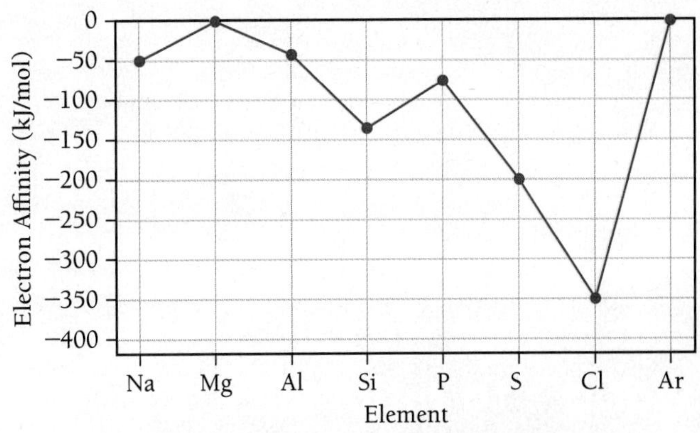

Electron Affinities of Period 3 Elements

a. Describe the general trend in period 3 first ionization energies as you move from left to right across the periodic table. Explain why this trend occurs.

b. The trend in first ionization energy has two exceptions: one at Al and another at S. Explain why the first ionization energy of Al is lower than that of Mg and why the first ionization of S is less than that of P.

c. Describe the general trend in period 3 electron affinities as you move from left to right across the periodic table. Explain why this trend occurs.

d. The trend in electron affinities has exceptions at Mg and P. Explain why the electron affinity of Mg is more positive (less exothermic) than that of Na and why the electron affinity of P is more positive (less exothermic) that that of Si.

e. Determine the overall energy change for removing one electron from Na and adding that electron to Cl. Is the exchange of the electron exothermic or endothermic?

Cc ANSWERS TO CONCEPTUAL CONNECTIONS

Coulomb's Law

9.1 **(a)** Since the charges are opposite, the potential energy of the interaction is negative. As the charges get closer together, r becomes smaller and the potential energy decreases (becomes more negative).

Penetration and Shielding

9.2 **(c)** Penetration results in less shielding from nuclear charge and therefore lower energy.

Electron Configurations and Quantum Numbers

9.3 **(b)** $n = 4,\ l = 0,\ m_l = 0,\ m_s = +\frac{1}{2};\ n = 4,\ l = 0,\ m_l = 0,\ m_s = -\frac{1}{2}$

Valence Electrons and Group Number

9.4 **(c)** Nitrogen has five valence electrons. Since nitrogen is a main-group element, it has the same number of valence electrons as its lettered group number in the periodic table.

Electron Configuration and Ion Charge

9.5 **(b)** Elements with electron configurations *close* to those of the noble gases gain or lose electrons to attain a noble gas configuration. The 2− charge implies that the element gained two electrons, which results in the configuration ns^2np^6, which is a noble gas configuration.

Effective Nuclear Charge

9.6 **(c)** Since Z_{eff} increases from left to right across a row in the periodic table, the valence electrons in S experience a greater effective nuclear charge than the valence electrons in Al or in Mg.

Ions, Isotopes, and Atomic Size

9.7 **(b)** The isotopes of an element all have the same radius for two reasons: (1) neutrons are negligibly small compared to the size of an atom and therefore extra neutrons do not increase atomic size, and (2) neutrons have no charge and therefore do not attract electrons in the way that protons do.

Successive Ionization Energies

9.8 **(c)** Since B has three valence electrons, it would have a huge jump between its third and fourth ionization energies. The third ionization energy corresponds to removing the third valence electron, while the fourth ionization energy corresponds to removing the first core electron.

Ionization Energies and Chemical Bonding

9.9 **(b)** As you can see from the successive ionization energies of any element, valence electrons are held most loosely and can therefore be transferred or shared most easily. Core electrons, however, are held tightly and are not easily transferred or shared. Consequently, valence electrons are most important to chemical bonding.

Periodic Trends

9.10 **(c)** The 3*s* electron in sodium has a relatively low ionization energy (496 kJ/mol) because it is a valence electron. The energetic cost for sodium to lose a second electron is extraordinarily high (4560 kJ/mol) because the next electron to be lost is a core electron (2*p*).

Theories are nets cast to catch what we call "the world": to rationalize, to explain, and to master it. We endeavor to make the mesh ever finer and finer.

—KARL POPPER (1902–1994)

CHAPTER 10

Chemical Bonding I: The Lewis Model

Chemical bonding is at the heart of chemistry. The bonding theories that we are about to examine are—as Karl Popper, a philosopher of science, eloquently states in the chapter-opening quote—nets cast to understand the world. In the next two chapters, we will examine three theories with successively finer "meshes." The first is the Lewis model, a simple model of chemical bonding, which can be sketched out on the back of an envelope. With just a few dots, dashes, and chemical symbols, the Lewis model can help us to understand and predict many chemical observations. The second is valence bond theory, which treats electrons in a more quantum-mechanical manner but stops short of viewing them as belonging to the entire molecule. The third is molecular orbital theory, essentially a full quantum-mechanical treatment of the molecule and its electrons as a whole. Molecular orbital theory has great predictive power, but at the expense of great complexity and intensive computational requirements. Which theory is "correct"? Remember that theories are models that help us understand and predict behavior. All three of these theories are extremely useful, depending on exactly what aspect of chemical bonding we want to predict or understand.

The AIDS drug Indinavir—shown here binding to the protein HIV-protease—was developed with the help of chemical bonding theories.

10.1 Bonding Models and AIDS Drugs 393
10.2 Types of Chemical Bonds 394
10.3 Representing Valence Electrons with Dots 396
10.4 Ionic Bonding: Lewis Symbols and Lattice Energies 397
10.5 Covalent Bonding: Lewis Structures 404
10.6 Electronegativity and Bond Polarity 406
10.7 Lewis Structures of Molecular Compounds and Polyatomic Ions 410
10.8 Resonance and Formal Charge 412
10.9 Exceptions to the Octet Rule: Odd-Electron Species, Incomplete Octets, and Expanded Octets 417
10.10 Bond Energies and Bond Lengths 422
10.11 Bonding in Metals: The Electron Sea Model 425
LEARNING OUTCOMES 429

10.1 Bonding Models and AIDS Drugs

In 1989, researchers using X-ray crystallography—a technique in which X-rays are scattered from crystals of the molecule of interest—determined the structure of a molecule called HIV-protease. HIV-protease is a protein (a class of large biological

We discuss X-ray crystallography in more detail in Section 13.2.

molecules) synthesized by the human immunodeficiency virus (HIV). This particular protein is crucial to the virus's ability to multiply and cause acquired immune deficiency syndrome, or AIDS. Without HIV-protease, HIV cannot spread in the human body because the virus cannot replicate. In other words, without HIV-protease, AIDS can't develop.

With knowledge of the HIV-protease structure, pharmaceutical companies set out to create a molecule that would disable HIV-protease by attaching to the working part of the molecule, called the active site. To design such a molecule, researchers used *bonding theories*—models that predict how atoms bond together to form molecules—to simulate the shape of potential drug molecules and determine how they would interact with the protease molecule. By the early 1990s, pharmaceutical companies had developed several drug molecules that seemed to work. Since these molecules inhibit the action of HIV-protease, they were named *protease inhibitors*. Protease inhibitors, when given in combination with other drugs, decrease the viral count in HIV-infected individuals to undetectable levels. Although protease inhibitors do not cure AIDS, many AIDS patients are still alive today because of these drugs.

We discuss proteins in more detail in Chapter 23.

▲ G. N. Lewis

Bonding theories are central to chemistry because they explain how atoms bond together to form molecules. They explain why some combinations of atoms are stable and others are not. For example, bonding theories explain why table salt is NaCl and not $NaCl_2$ and why water is H_2O and not H_3O. Bonding theories also predict the shapes of molecules—a topic in the next chapter—which in turn determine many of the physical and chemical properties of compounds.

The bonding model we examine in this chapter is the **Lewis model**, named after the American chemist G. N. Lewis (1875–1946). In the Lewis model, valence electrons are represented as dots, and we draw **Lewis electron-dot structures** (or simply **Lewis structures**) to depict molecules. These structures, which are fairly simple to draw, have tremendous predictive power. With minimal computation, the Lewis model can be used to predict whether a particular set of atoms will form a stable molecule and what that molecule might look like. Although we will also examine more advanced theories in the following chapter, the Lewis model remains the simplest model for making quick, everyday predictions about most molecules.

10.2 Types of Chemical Bonds

We begin our discussion of chemical bonding by asking why bonds form in the first place. This seemingly simple question is vitally important. Imagine our universe without chemical bonding. Such a universe would contain only 91 different kinds of substances (the 91 naturally occurring elements). With such a poor diversity of substances, life would be impossible, and we would not be around to wonder why. The *answer* to the question of why bonds form, however, is not simple and involves not only quantum mechanics but also some thermodynamics that we do not introduce until Chapter 19. Nonetheless, we can address an important *aspect* of the answer now: *Chemical bonds form because they lower the potential energy between the charged particles that compose atoms.*

As you already know, atoms are composed of particles with positive charges (the protons in the nucleus) and negative charges (the electrons). When two atoms approach each other, the electrons of one atom are attracted to the nucleus of the other according to Coulomb's law (see Section 9.3) and vice versa. However, at the same time, the electrons of each atom repel the electrons of the other, and the nucleus of each atom repels the nucleus of the other. The result is a complex set of interactions among a potentially large number of charged particles. If these interactions lead to an overall net reduction of energy between the charged particles, a chemical bond forms. Bonding theories help us to predict the circumstances under which bonds form and also the properties of the resultant molecules.

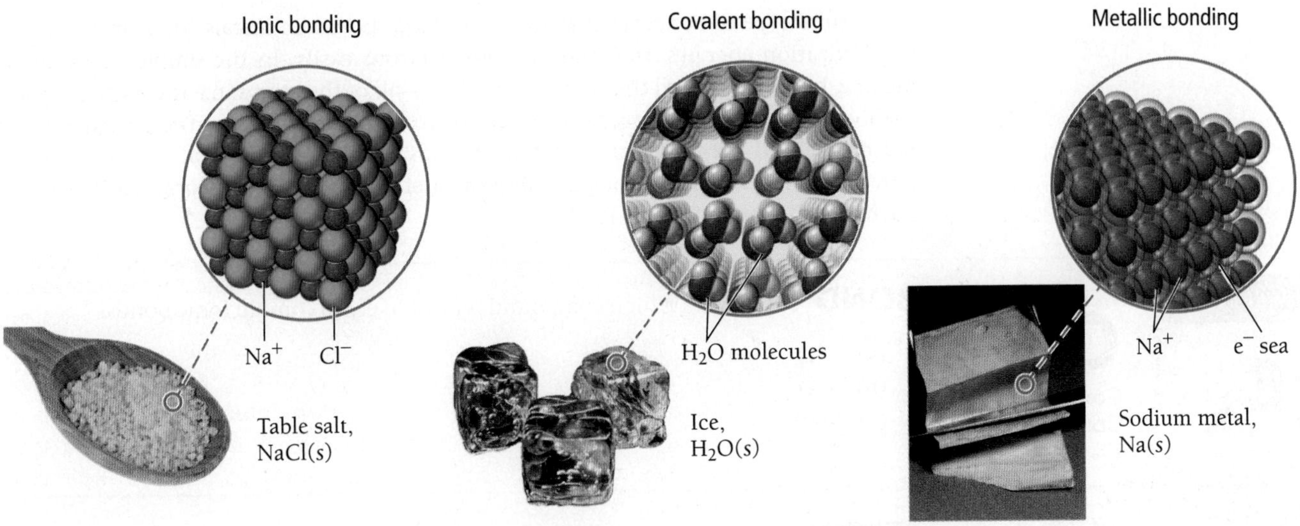

▲ **FIGURE 10.1 Ionic, Covalent, and Metallic Bonding**

We broadly classify chemical bonds into three types, depending on the kind of atoms involved in the bonding (Figure 10.1▲):

Types of Atoms	Type of Bond	Characteristic of Bond
Metal and nonmetal	Ionic	Electrons transferred
Nonmetal and nonmetal	Covalent	Electrons shared
Metal and metal	Metallic	Electrons pooled

Recall from Chapter 9 that metals tend to have low ionization energies (their electrons are relatively easy to remove) and that nonmetals tend to have negative electron affinities (they readily gain electrons). When a metal atom bonds with a nonmetal atom, it transfers one or more electrons to the nonmetal. The metal atom becomes a cation and the nonmetal atom an anion. These oppositely charged ions attract one another, lowering their overall potential energy as described by Coulomb's law. The resulting bond is an **ionic bond**.

We also discussed in Chapter 9 that nonmetals tend to have high ionization energies (their electrons are relatively difficult to remove). Therefore, when a nonmetal bonds with another nonmetal, neither atom transfers electrons to the other. Instead, the two atoms *share* some electrons. The shared electrons interact with the nuclei of both of the bonding atoms, lowering their potential energy in accordance with Coulomb's law. The resulting bond is a **covalent bond**.

Recall from Section 3.2 that we can understand the stability of a covalent bond by considering the most stable arrangement (the one with the lowest potential energy) of two positively charged particles separated by a small distance and a negatively charged particle. As we can see in Figure 10.2▼, the arrangement in which the negatively charged particle lies *between* the two positively charged ones has the lowest potential energy because in this arrangement, the negatively charged particle interacts most strongly with *both of the positively charged ones*. In a sense, the negatively charged particle holds the two positively charged ones together. Similarly, shared electrons in a covalent chemical bond *hold* the bonding atoms together by attracting the positive charges of their nuclei.

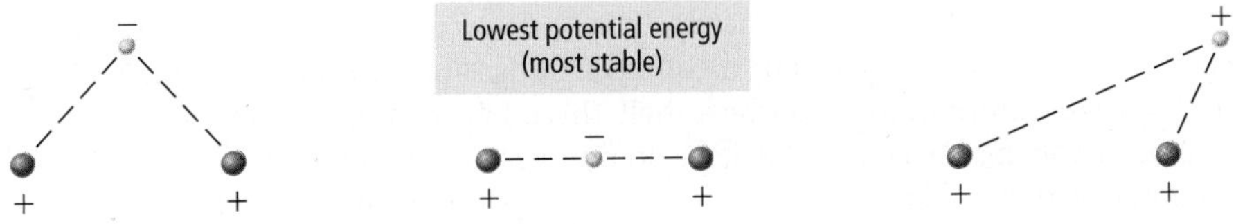

◀ **FIGURE 10.2 Possible Configurations of One Negatively Charged Particle and Two Positively Charged Ones**

A third type of bonding, **metallic bonding**, occurs in metals. Since metals have low ionization energies, they tend to lose electrons easily. In the simplest model for metallic bonding—called the *electron sea* model—all of the atoms in a metal lattice pool their valence electrons. These pooled electrons are no longer localized on a single atom, but delocalized over the entire metal. The positively charged metal atoms are then attracted to the sea of electrons, holding the metal together. We discuss metallic bonding in more detail in Section 10.11.

ANSWER **NOW!**

10.1 Cc Conceptual Connection

BOND TYPES Which compound is most likely to contain ionic bonds?

(a) CH_4
(b) N_2O
(c) MgF_2

10.3 Representing Valence Electrons with Dots

Remember, the number of valence electrons for any main group is equal to the group number of the element (except for helium, which is in group 8A but has only two valence electrons).

In Chapter 9, we saw that, for main-group elements, valence electrons are those electrons in the outermost principal energy level. Valence electrons are most important in bonding because they are held most loosely and chemical bonding involves the transfer or sharing of electrons between two or more atoms. Lewis models focus on valence electrons. In a **Lewis symbol**, we represent the valence electrons of main-group elements as dots surrounding the element symbol. For example, the electron configuration of O is:

$$1s^2\underline{2s^22p^4}$$ 6 valence electrons

The Lewis symbol for oxygen is:

$$\cdot\ddot{\underset{\cdot}{O}}:$$ 6 dots representing valence electrons

Although the exact location of dots is not critical, in this book we first place dots singly before pairing (except for helium, which always has two paired dots signifying its duet).

Each dot in a Lewis symbol represents a valence electron. The dots are placed around the element's symbol with a maximum of two dots per side. We draw the Lewis symbols for all of the period 2 elements similarly.

$$\text{Li}\cdot \quad \cdot\text{Be}\cdot \quad \cdot\dot{\text{B}}\cdot \quad \cdot\dot{\underset{\cdot}{\text{C}}}\cdot \quad \cdot\ddot{\underset{\cdot}{\text{N}}}: \quad \cdot\ddot{\underset{\cdot}{\text{O}}}: \quad :\ddot{\underset{\cdot}{\text{F}}}: \quad :\ddot{\underset{\cdot\cdot}{\text{Ne}}}:$$

Lewis symbols provide a simple way to visualize the number of valence electrons in a main-group atom. Notice that atoms with eight valence electrons—which are particularly stable because they have full *s* and *p* sublevels—are easily identified because they have eight dots, an **octet**.

Helium is somewhat of an exception. Its electron configuration and Lewis symbol are:

$$1s^2 \quad \text{He:}$$

The Lewis symbol of helium contains only two dots (a **duet**). For helium, a duet represents a stable electron configuration because the $n = 1$ quantum level fills with only two electrons.

In the Lewis model, a **chemical bond** is the sharing or transfer of electrons to attain stable electron configurations for the bonding atoms. If electrons are transferred, as occurs between a metal and a nonmetal, the bond is an *ionic bond*. If the electrons are shared, as occurs between two nonmetals, the bond is a *covalent bond*. In either case, the bonding atoms attain stable electron configurations; since the stable configuration is usually eight electrons in the outermost shell, this is known as the **octet rule**.

When applying the Lewis model, we do not try to calculate the energies associated with the attractions and repulsions between electrons and nuclei on neighboring atoms. The energy changes that occur because of these interactions are central to chemical bonding (as we saw in Section 10.2), yet the Lewis model ignores them because calculating these energy changes is extremely complicated. Instead the Lewis model uses the simple octet rule, a practical approach that accurately predicts what we see in nature for a large number of compounds—hence the success and longevity of the Lewis model.

LEWIS SYMBOLS What is the Lewis symbol for silicon?

10.2 Cc Conceptual Connection ANSWER NOW!

(a) $\cdot\mathrm{Si}\cdot$ (b) $:\dot{\underset{\cdot}{\mathrm{Si}}}\cdot$

(c) $:\ddot{\underset{\cdot\cdot}{\mathrm{Si}}}:$ (d) $\cdot\dot{\underset{\cdot}{\mathrm{Si}}}\cdot$

10.4 Ionic Bonding: Lewis Symbols and Lattice Energies

Although the Lewis model's strength is in modeling covalent bonding, it can also be applied to ionic bonding. To represent ionic bonding, we move electron dots from the Lewis symbol of the metal to the Lewis symbol of the nonmetal and allow the resultant ions to form a crystalline lattice composed of alternating cations and anions.

Ionic Bonding and Electron Transfer

Consider potassium and chlorine, which have the following Lewis symbols:

$$\mathrm{K}\cdot \quad :\ddot{\underset{\cdot}{\mathrm{Cl}}}:$$

When these atoms bond, potassium transfers its valence electron to chlorine:

$$\mathrm{K}\cdot + :\ddot{\underset{\cdot}{\mathrm{Cl}}}: \longrightarrow \mathrm{K}^+\left[:\ddot{\underset{\cdot\cdot}{\mathrm{Cl}}}:\right]^-$$

The transfer of the electron gives chlorine an octet (shown as eight dots around chlorine) and leaves potassium without any valence electrons but with an octet in the *previous* principal energy level (which is now the outermost level):

$$\mathrm{K} \quad 1s^22s^22p^63s^23p^64s^1$$
$$\mathrm{K}^+ \quad 1s^22s^22p^6\underbrace{3s^23p^6}_{\text{Octet in previous level}}4s^0$$

The potassium, having lost an electron, becomes positively charged (a cation), while the chlorine, which has gained an electron, becomes negatively charged (an anion). We typically write the Lewis symbol of an anion within brackets with the charge in the upper right-hand corner, outside the brackets. The positive and negative charges attract one another, resulting in the compound KCl.

Recall that solid ionic compounds do not contain distinct molecules; they are composed of alternating positive and negative ions in a three-dimensional crystalline array.

This example shows how we can use the Lewis model to predict the correct chemical formulas for ionic compounds. For the compound that forms between K and Cl, for example, the Lewis model predicts a ratio of one potassium cation to every one chloride anion, KCl. In nature, when we examine the compound formed between potassium and chlorine, we indeed find one potassium ion to every chloride ion.

As another example, consider the ionic compound formed between sodium and sulfur. The Lewis symbols for sodium and sulfur are:

$$\mathrm{Na}\cdot \quad \cdot\ddot{\underset{\cdot}{\mathrm{S}}}:$$

Sodium must lose its one valence electron in order to have an octet (in the previous principal shell), while sulfur must gain two electrons to attain an octet. Consequently, the compound that forms between sodium and sulfur requires a ratio of two sodium atoms to every one sulfur atom:

$$2\,\mathrm{Na}^+\left[:\ddot{\underset{\cdot\cdot}{\mathrm{S}}}:\right]^{2-}$$

The two sodium atoms each lose their one valence electron, while the sulfur atom gains two electrons and attains an octet. The Lewis model predicts that the correct chemical formula is Na_2S, which is exactly what we see in nature.

EXAMPLE 10.1 Using Lewis Symbols to Predict the Chemical Formula of an Ionic Compound

Use Lewis symbols to predict the formula for the compound that forms between calcium and chlorine.

SOLUTION

Draw Lewis symbols for calcium and chlorine based on their respective numbers of valence electrons, which you can determine from their group number in the periodic table.	·Ca· ·$\ddot{\underset{..}{Cl}}$:
Calcium must lose its two valence electrons (to end up with an octet in its previous principal shell), while chlorine only needs to gain one electron to attain an octet. Draw two chloride anions, each with an octet and a 1− charge, and one calcium cation with a 2+ charge. Place brackets around the chloride anions and indicate the charges on each ion.	$Ca^{2+}2[:\ddot{\underset{..}{Cl}}:]^-$
Finally, write the formula with subscripts to indicate the number of each ion.	$CaCl_2$

FOR PRACTICE 10.1 Use Lewis symbols to predict the formula for the compound that forms between magnesium and nitrogen.

Lattice Energy: The Rest of the Story

The formation of an ionic compound from its constituent elements is usually quite exothermic. For example, when sodium chloride (table salt) forms from elemental sodium and chlorine, 411 kJ of heat evolves in the following violent reaction:

$$Na(s) + \tfrac{1}{2}Cl_2(g) \longrightarrow NaCl(s) \qquad \Delta H_f^\circ = -411\ kJ/mol$$

Where does this energy come from? It might seem that it comes solely from the tendency of metals to lose electrons and nonmetals to gain electrons—but it does not. In fact, the transfer of an electron from sodium to chlorine—by itself—actually *absorbs* energy. The first ionization energy of sodium is +496 kJ/mol, and the electron affinity of Cl is only −349 kJ/mol. Based only on these energies, the reaction should be *endothermic* by +147 kJ/mol. So why is the reaction so *exothermic*?

The answer lies in the **lattice energy**—the energy associated with the formation of a crystalline lattice of alternating cations and anions from the gaseous ions. Because the sodium ions are positively charged and the chlorine ions are negatively charged, the potential energy decreases—as prescribed by Coulomb's law—when these ions come together to form a lattice. That energy is emitted as heat when the lattice forms, as shown in Figure 10.3▶. The exact value of the lattice energy, however, is not simple to determine because it involves a large number of interactions among many charged particles in a lattice. The most straightforward way to calculate lattice energy is with the *Born–Haber cycle.*

The Born–Haber Cycle

Recall that Hess's law states that the change in the overall enthalpy of a stepwise process is the sum of the enthalpy changes of the steps.

The **Born–Haber cycle** is a hypothetical series of steps that represents the formation of an ionic compound from its constituent elements. The steps are chosen so that the change in enthalpy of each step is known except for the last one, which is the lattice energy. The change in enthalpy for the overall process is also known. Using Hess's law (see Section 7.8), we can therefore determine the enthalpy change for the unknown last step, the lattice energy.

Consider the formation of NaCl from its constituent elements in their standard states. The enthalpy change for the overall reaction is simply the standard enthalpy of formation of NaCl(*s*):

$$Na(s) + \tfrac{1}{2}Cl_2(g) \longrightarrow NaCl(s) \qquad \Delta H_f^\circ = -411\ kJ/mol$$

Lattice Energy of an Ionic Compound

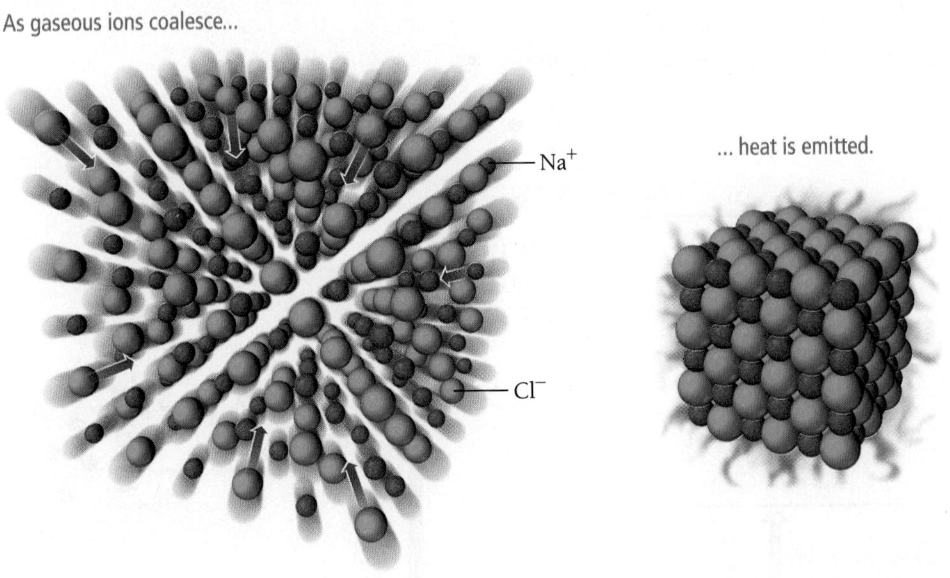

$Na^+(g) + Cl^-(g) \longrightarrow NaCl(s)$ ΔH° = lattice energy

▲ **FIGURE 10.3 Lattice Energy** The lattice energy of an ionic compound is the energy associated with the formation of a crystalline lattice of the compound from the gaseous ions.

Now consider the following set of steps—the Born–Haber cycle—from which $NaCl(s)$ can also be made from $Na(s)$ and $Cl_2(g)$:

- The first step is the formation of gaseous sodium from solid sodium.

$$Na(s) \longrightarrow Na(g) \quad \Delta H^\circ_{\text{step 1}} \text{(sublimation energy of Na)} = +108 \text{ kJ}$$

- The second step is the formation of a chlorine atom from a chlorine molecule.

$$\tfrac{1}{2}Cl_2(g) \longrightarrow Cl(g) \quad \Delta H^\circ_{\text{step 2}} \text{(bond energy of } Cl_2 \times \tfrac{1}{2}) = +122 \text{ kJ}$$

- The third step is the ionization of gaseous sodium. The enthalpy change for this step is the ionization energy of sodium.

$$Na(g) \longrightarrow Na^+(g) + e^- \quad \Delta H^\circ_{\text{step 3}} \text{(ionization energy of Na)} = +496 \text{ kJ}$$

- The fourth step is the addition of an electron to gaseous chlorine. The enthalpy change for this step is the electron affinity of chlorine.

$$Cl(g) + e^- \longrightarrow Cl^-(g) \quad \Delta H^\circ_{\text{step 4}} \text{(electron affinity of Cl)} = -349 \text{ kJ}$$

- The fifth and final step is the formation of the crystalline solid from the gaseous ions. The enthalpy change for this step is the lattice energy, the unknown quantity.

$$Na^+(g) + Cl^-(g) \longrightarrow NaCl(s) \quad \Delta H^\circ_{\text{step 5}} = \Delta H^\circ_{\text{lattice}} = ?$$

Figure 10.4▶ illustrates the entire Born–Haber cycle for NaCl.

Since the overall reaction obtained by summing the steps in the Born–Haber cycle is equivalent to the formation of NaCl from its constituent elements, we use Hess's law to set the overall enthalpy of formation for $NaCl(s)$ equal to the sum of the steps in the Born–Haber cycle:

Lattice energy ↓

$$\Delta H^\circ_f = \Delta H^\circ_{\text{step 1}} + \Delta H^\circ_{\text{step 2}} + \Delta H^\circ_{\text{step 3}} + \Delta H^\circ_{\text{step 4}} + \Delta H^\circ_{\text{step 5}}$$

Born–Haber Cycle for Production of NaCl from Na(*s*) and Cl₂(*g*)

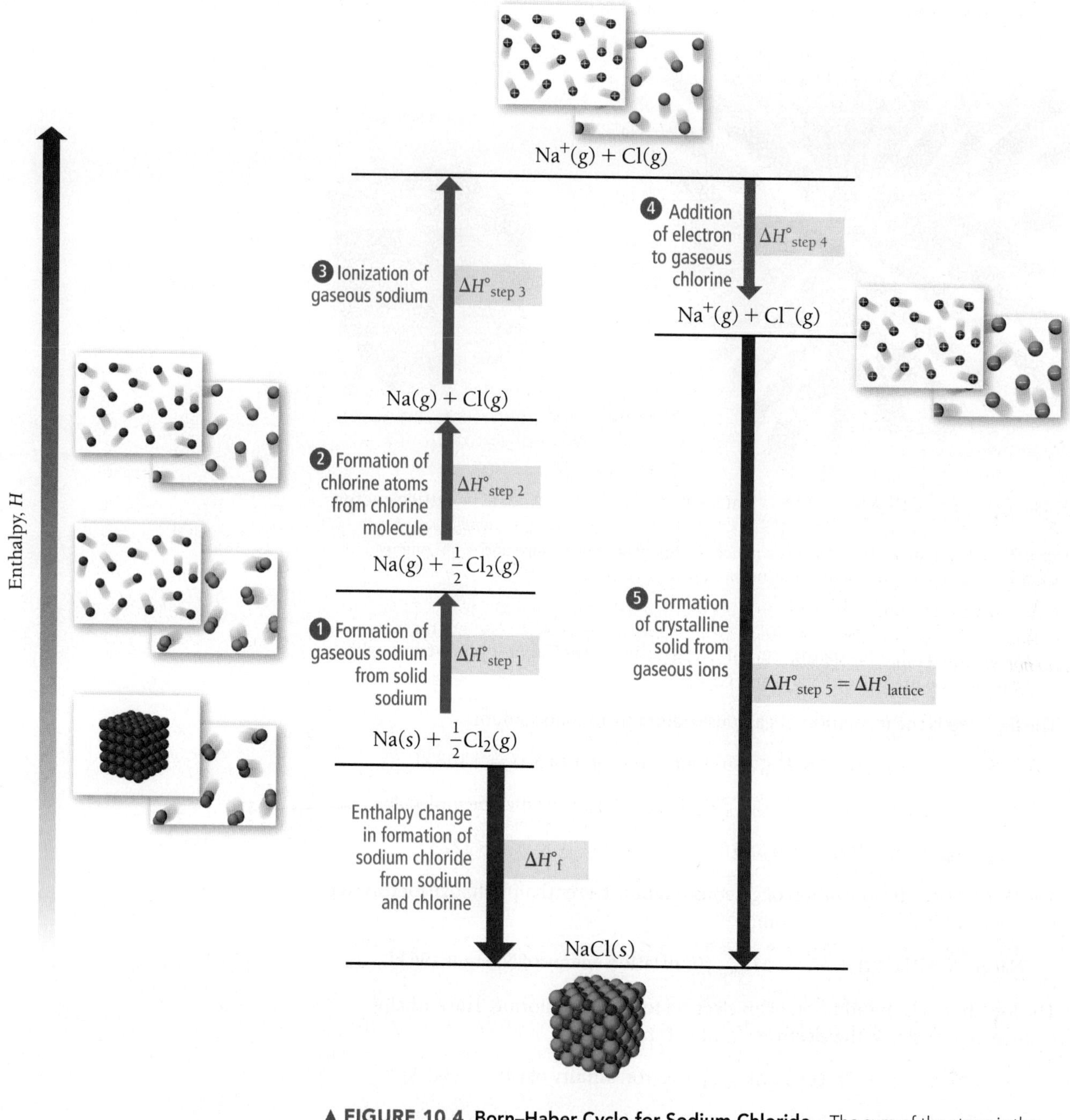

▲ **FIGURE 10.4 Born–Haber Cycle for Sodium Chloride** The sum of the steps is the formation of NaCl from elemental Na and Cl_2. The enthalpy change of the last step (step 5) is the lattice energy.

We then solve this equation for $\Delta H^\circ_{\text{step 5}}$, which is $\Delta H^\circ_{\text{lattice}}$, and substitute the appropriate values to calculate the lattice energy:

$$\begin{aligned}\Delta H^\circ_{\text{lattice}} &= \Delta H^\circ_{\text{step 5}} = \Delta H^\circ_{\text{f}} - (\Delta H^\circ_{\text{step 1}} + \Delta H^\circ_{\text{step 2}} + \Delta H^\circ_{\text{step 3}} + \Delta H^\circ_{\text{step 4}})\\ &= -411\text{ kJ} - (+108\text{ kJ} + 122\text{ kJ} + 496\text{ kJ} - 349\text{ kJ})\\ &= -788\text{ kJ}\end{aligned}$$

Some books define the lattice energy as the energy associated with separating one mole of an ionic lattice into its gaseous constituents, which makes the sign of the lattice energy positive instead of negative.

The value of the lattice energy is a large negative number. The formation of the crystalline NaCl lattice from sodium cations and chloride anions is highly exothermic and more than compensates for the endothermicity of the electron transfer process. In other words, the formation of ionic compounds is not exothermic because sodium "wants" to lose electrons and chlorine "wants" to gain them; rather, it is exothermic because of the large amount of heat released when sodium and chloride ions coalesce to form a crystalline lattice.

Trends in Lattice Energies: Ion Size

Consider the lattice energies of the following alkali metal chlorides:

Metal Chloride	Lattice Energy (kJ/mol)
LiCl	−834
NaCl	−788
KCl	−701
CsCl	−657

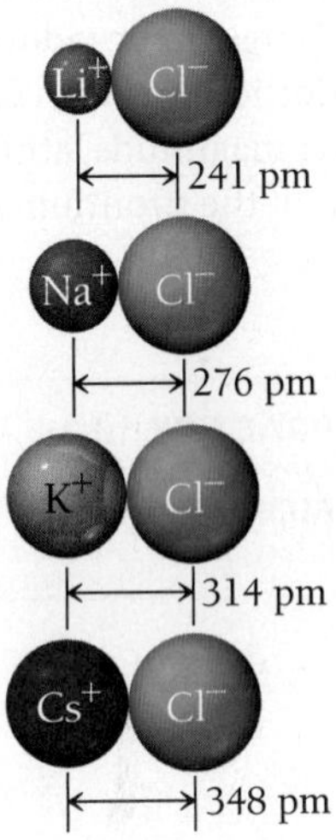

▲ Bond lengths of the group 1A metal chlorides.

Why does the magnitude of the lattice energy decrease as we move down the column? We know from the periodic trends discussed in Chapter 9 that ionic radius increases as we move down a column in the periodic table (see Section 9.7). We also know, from our discussion of Coulomb's law in Section 9.3, that the potential energy of oppositely charged ions becomes less negative (or more positive) as the distance between the ions increases. As the size of the alkali metal ions increases down the column, so does the distance between the metal cations and the chloride anions. The magnitude of each successive lattice energy of the chlorides decreases accordingly, making the formation of the chlorides less exothermic as you move down the column. In other words, *as the ionic radii increase as we move down the column, the ions cannot get as close to each other and therefore do not release as much energy when the lattice forms.*

Trends in Lattice Energies: Ion Charge

Consider the lattice energies of the following two compounds:

Compound	Lattice Energy (kJ/mol)
NaF	−910
CaO	−3414

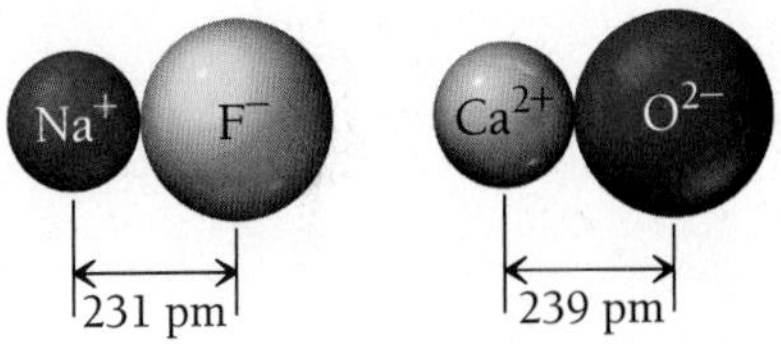

Why is the magnitude of the lattice energy of CaO so much greater than the lattice energy of NaF? Na^+ has a radius of 95 pm and F^- has a radius of 136 pm, resulting in a distance between ions of 231 pm. Ca^{2+} has a radius of 99 pm and O^{2-} has a radius of 140 pm, resulting in a distance between ions of 239 pm. Even though the separation between the calcium and oxygen is slightly greater (which would tend to lower the lattice energy), the lattice energy for CaO is almost four times *greater*.

The explanation lies in the charges of the ions. Recall from Coulomb's law that the magnitude of the potential energy of two interacting charges depends not only on the distance between the charges, but also on the product of the charges:

$$E = \frac{1}{4\pi\varepsilon_0}\frac{q_1 q_2}{r}$$

For NaF, E is proportional to $(1+)(1-) = 1-$, while for CaO, E is proportional to $(2+)(2-) = 4-$, so the relative stabilization for CaO relative to NaF is roughly four times greater, as observed in the lattice energy.

Summarizing Trends in Lattice Energies:

- Lattice energies become less exothermic (less negative) with increasing ionic radius.
- Lattice energies become more exothermic (more negative) with increasing magnitude of ionic charge.

EXAMPLE 10.2 Predicting Relative Lattice Energies

Arrange these ionic compounds in order of increasing *magnitude* of lattice energy: CaO, KBr, KCl, SrO.

SOLUTION

KBr and KCl have lattice energies of smaller magnitude than CaO and SrO because of their lower ionic charges (1+, 1− compared to 2+, 2−). When you compare KBr and KCl, you expect KBr to have a lattice energy of lower magnitude due to the larger ionic radius of the bromide ion relative to the chloride ion. Between CaO and SrO, you expect SrO to have a lower magnitude lattice energy due to the larger ionic radius of the strontium ion relative to the calcium ion.

Order of increasing *magnitude* of lattice energy:

KBr < KCl < SrO < CaO

Actual lattice energy values:

Compound	Lattice Energy (kJ/mol)
KBr	−671
KCl	−701
SrO	−3217
CaO	−3414

FOR PRACTICE 10.2 Arrange the following in order of increasing magnitude of lattice energy: LiBr, KI, and CaO.

FOR MORE PRACTICE 10.2 Which compound has a higher magnitude lattice energy: NaCl or $MgCl_2$?

Ionic Bonding: Models and Reality

In this section, we have developed a model for ionic bonding. The value of a model is in how well it accounts for what we see in nature (through experiments). Does our ionic bonding model explain the properties of ionic compounds, including their high melting and boiling points, their tendency *not to conduct* electricity as solids, and their tendency *to conduct* electricity when dissolved in water?

We modeled an ionic solid as a lattice of individual ions held together by coulombic forces that are *nondirectional* (which means that, as we move away from the center of an ion, the forces are equally strong in all directions). To melt the solid, these forces must be overcome, which requires a significant amount of heat. Therefore, our model accounts for the high melting points of ionic solids. In the model, electrons transfer from the metal to the nonmetal, but the transferred electrons remain localized on one atom. In other words, our model does not include any free electrons that might conduct electricity (the movement or flow of electrons or other charged particles in response to an electric potential, or voltage, is electrical current). In addition, the ions themselves are fixed in place; therefore, our model accounts for the nonconductivity of ionic solids. When our idealized ionic solid dissolves in water, however, the cations and anions dissociate, forming free ions in solution. These ions can move in response to electrical forces, creating an electrical current. Thus, our model predicts that solutions of ionic compounds conduct electricity (which in fact they do).

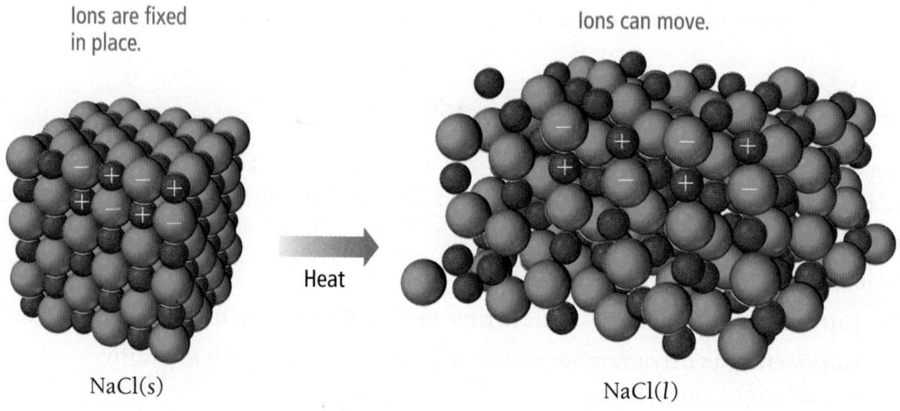

▶ The melting of solid ionic compounds such as sodium chloride requires enough heat to overcome the electrical forces holding the anions and cations together in a lattice. Thus, the melting points of ionic compounds are relatively high.

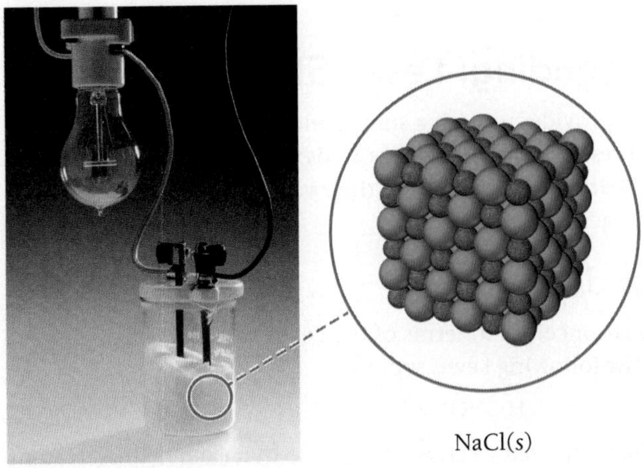

▲ Solid sodium chloride does not conduct electricity.

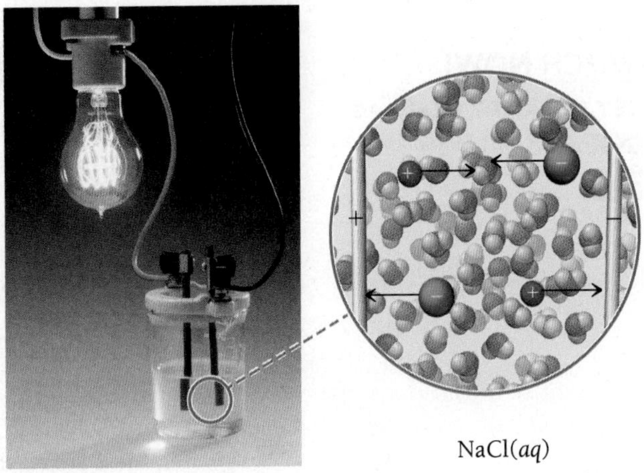

▲ Aqueous sodium chloride conducts electricity.

10.3 Cc Conceptual Connection — ANSWER NOW!

MELTING POINTS OF IONIC SOLIDS Use the ionic bonding model to determine which has the higher melting point: NaCl or MgO. Explain the relative ordering.

(a) MgO has a higher melting point because the ions have larger charges.
(b) MgO has a higher melting point because the ions have smaller charges.
(c) NaCl has a higher melting point because the ions have larger charges.
(d) NaCl has a higher melting point because the ions have smaller charges.

CHEMISTRY AND MEDICINE | Ionic Compounds in Medicine

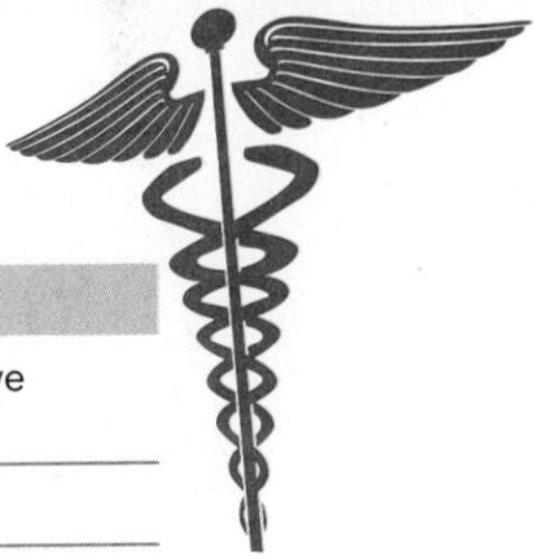

Although most drugs are molecular compounds, a number of ionic compounds have medical uses. Consider the following partial list of ionic compounds used in medicine. Notice that many of these compounds contain polyatomic ions. The bonding between a metal and a polyatomic ion is ionic. However, the bonding within a polyatomic ion is covalent, the topic of our next section.

Formula	Name	Medical Use
$AgNO_3$	Silver nitrate	Topical anti-infective agent; in solution, used to treat and prevent eye infection, especially in newborn infants
$BaSO_4$	Barium sulfate	Given as a contrast medium—or image enhancer—in X-rays
$CaSO_4$	Calcium sulfate	Used to make plaster casts
$KMnO_4$	Potassium permanganate	Topical anti-infective agent; often used to treat fungal infections on the feet
KI	Potassium iodide	Antiseptic and disinfectant; given orally to prevent radiation sickness
Li_2CO_3	Lithium carbonate	Used to treat bipolar (manic–depressive) disorders
$MgSO_4$	Magnesium sulfate	Used to treat eclampsia (a condition that can occur during pregnancy in which elevated blood pressure leads to convulsions)
$Mg(OH)_2$	Magnesium hydroxide	Antacid and mild laxative
$NaHCO_3$	Sodium bicarbonate	Oral antacid used to treat heartburn and acid stomach; injected into blood to treat severe acidosis (acidification of the blood)
NaF	Sodium fluoride	Used to strengthen teeth
ZnO	Zinc oxide	Used as protection from ultraviolet light in sun

WATCH **NOW!**

KEY CONCEPT VIDEO 10.5
The Lewis Model for Chemical Bonding

10.5 Covalent Bonding: Lewis Structures

The Lewis model provides us with a simple and useful model for covalent bonding. In this model, we represent molecular compounds with *Lewis structures*, which depict neighboring atoms as sharing some (or all) of their valence electrons in order to attain octets (or duets for hydrogen).

Single Covalent Bonds

To see how covalent bonding is conceived in terms of the Lewis model, consider hydrogen and oxygen, which have the following Lewis symbols:

H· ·Ö:

In water, these atoms share their unpaired valence electrons so that each hydrogen atom gets a duet and the oxygen atom gets an octet as represented with this Lewis structure:

H:Ö:H

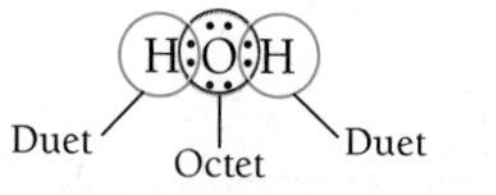

The shared electrons—those that appear in the space between the two atoms—count toward the octets (or duets) of *both of the atoms.*

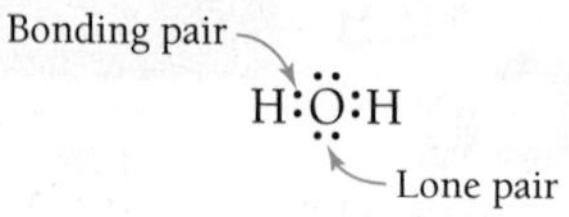

A shared pair of electrons is called a **bonding pair**, whereas a pair that is associated with only one atom—and therefore not involved in bonding—is a **lone pair** (shown at left). Lone pair electrons are also called **nonbonding electrons**.

We often represent a bonding pair of electrons by a dash to emphasize that it constitutes a chemical bond:

H—Ö—H

The Lewis model also shows why the halogens form diatomic molecules. Consider the Lewis symbol for chlorine:

:C̈l·

If two Cl atoms pair together, they can each have an octet:

:C̈l:C̈l: *or* :C̈l—C̈l:

Elemental chlorine does indeed exist as a diatomic molecule in nature, just as the Lewis model predicts. The same is true for the other halogens.

Similarly, the Lewis model predicts that hydrogen, which has the Lewis symbol:

H·

should exist as H_2. When two hydrogen atoms share their valence electrons, each gets a duet, a stable configuration for hydrogen:

H:H *or* H—H

Again, the Lewis model predicts correctly. In nature, elemental hydrogen exists as H_2 molecules.

Double and Triple Covalent Bonds

In the Lewis model, two atoms may share more than one electron pair to get octets. For example, two oxygen atoms share two electron pairs in order for each oxygen atom to have an octet:

Keep in mind that each dash always stands for *two* electrons (a single bonding pair).

·Ö: + ·Ö:

↓

:Ö::Ö: *or* :Ö=Ö:

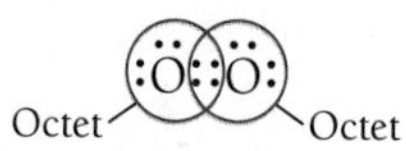

Each oxygen atom has an octet because *the additional bonding pair counts toward the octet of both oxygen atoms.* When two atoms share two electron pairs, the resulting bond is a **double bond**. In general, double bonds are shorter and stronger than single bonds. Atoms can also share three electron pairs. Consider the Lewis structure of N_2. Since each N atom has five valence electrons, the Lewis structure for N_2 has 10 electrons. Both nitrogen atoms attain octets by sharing three electron pairs:

:N:::N: *or* :N≡N:

The bond is a **triple bond**. Triple bonds are even shorter and stronger than double bonds. When we examine nitrogen in nature, we find that it exists as a diatomic molecule with a very strong bond between the two nitrogen atoms. The bond is so strong that it is difficult to break, making N_2 a relatively unreactive molecule.

We explore the characteristics of multiple bonds more fully in Section 10.10.

Covalent Bonding: Models and Reality

The Lewis model predicts the properties of molecular compounds in many ways. First, it accounts for why particular combinations of atoms form molecules and others do not. For example, why is water H_2O and not H_3O? We can write a good Lewis structure for H_2O, but not for H_3O.

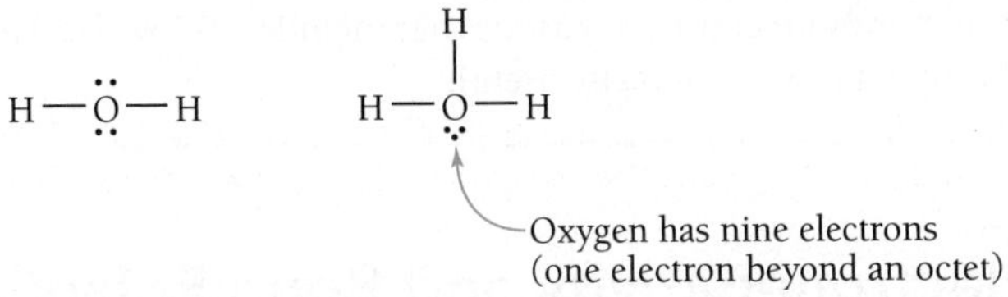

In this way, the Lewis model predicts that H_2O should be stable, while H_3O should not be, and that is in fact the case. However, if we remove an electron from H_3O, we get H_3O^+, which should be stable (according to the Lewis model) because, when we remove the extra electron, oxygen attains an octet:

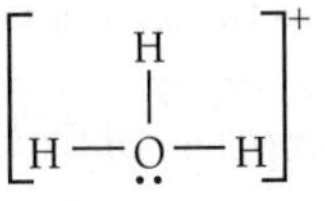

This ion, called the hydronium ion, is in fact stable in aqueous solutions (see Section 5.7).

The Lewis model predicts other possible combinations for hydrogen and oxygen as well. For example, we can write a Lewis structure for H_2O_2 as follows:

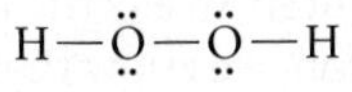

Indeed, H_2O_2, or hydrogen peroxide, exists and is often used as a disinfectant and a bleach.

The Lewis model also accounts for why covalent bonds are highly *directional*. The attraction between two covalently bonded atoms is due to the sharing of one or more electron pairs in the space between them. Thus, each bond links just one specific pair of atoms—*in contrast to ionic bonds, which are nondirectional and hold together an entire array of ions*. As a result, the fundamental units of covalently bonded compounds are individual molecules. These molecules can interact with one another in a number of different ways that we cover in Chapter 12. However, in covalently bonded molecular compounds the interactions *between* molecules (intermolecular forces) are generally much weaker than the bonding interactions within a molecule (intramolecular forces), as shown in Figure 10.5▼.

Molecular Compound

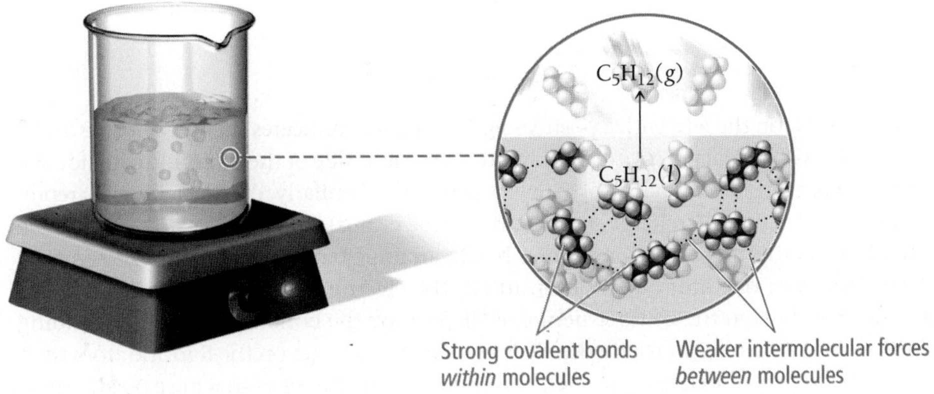

◀ **FIGURE 10.5 Intermolecular and Intramolecular Forces** The covalent bonds between atoms of a molecule are much stronger than the interactions between molecules. To boil a molecular substance, we simply have to overcome the relatively weak intermolecular forces, so molecular compounds generally have low boiling points.

When a molecular compound melts or boils, the molecules themselves remain intact—only the relatively weak interactions between molecules must be overcome. Consequently, molecular compounds tend to have lower melting and boiling points than ionic compounds.

ANSWER **NOW!**

10.4 Cc Conceptual Connection

ENERGY AND THE OCTET RULE What is wrong with the following statement? *Atoms form bonds in order to satisfy the octet rule.*

(a) Nothing. The statement is correct.
(b) Atoms form bonds for complex reasons that include the lowering of potential energy. The octet rule helps us predict in which cases bonds form.
(c) Atoms form bonds for complex reasons that include the lowering of potential energy. The octet rule is not really useful.

WATCH **NOW!**

KEY CONCEPT VIDEO 10.6
Electronegativity and Bond Polarity

10.6 Electronegativity and Bond Polarity

We know from Chapter 8 that representing electrons with dots, as we do in the Lewis model, is a drastic oversimplification. As we have already discussed, this does not invalidate the Lewis model—which is an extremely useful theory—but we must recognize and compensate for its inherent limitations. One limitation of representing electrons as dots, and covalent bonds as two dots shared between two atoms, is that the shared electrons always appear to be *equally* shared. Such is not the case.

For example, consider the Lewis structure of hydrogen fluoride:

$$\mathrm{H}:\ddot{\underset{\cdot\cdot}{\mathrm{F}}}:$$

The two shared electron dots sitting between the H and the F atoms appear to be equally shared between hydrogen and fluorine. However, based on laboratory measurements, we know they are not. When HF is put in an electric field, the molecules orient as shown in Figure 10.6▼. From this observation, we know that the hydrogen side of the molecule

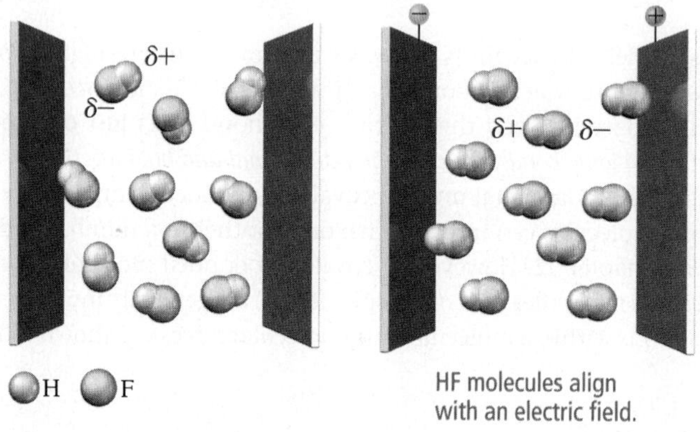

▶ **FIGURE 10.6 Orientation of Gaseous Hydrogen Fluoride in an Electric Field** Because one side of the HF molecule has a slight positive charge and the other side a slight negative charge, the molecules align themselves with an external electric field.

must have a slight positive charge and the fluorine side of the molecule must have a slight negative charge. We represent this partial separation of charge as follows:

$$\overset{+\!\!\longrightarrow}{\mathrm{H{-}F}} \quad or \quad \overset{\delta^+}{\mathrm{H}}{-}\overset{\delta^-}{\mathrm{F}}$$

The red arrow on the left, with a positive sign on the tail, indicates that the left side of the molecule has a partial positive charge and that the right side of the molecule (the side the arrow is pointing *toward*) has a partial negative charge. Similarly, the δ+ (delta plus) represents a partial positive charge and the δ− (delta minus) represents a partial negative charge. Does this make the bond ionic? No. In an ionic bond, the electron is essentially *transferred* from one atom to another. In HF, the electron is *unequally shared*. In other words, even though the Lewis structure of HF portrays the bonding electrons as residing *between* the two atoms, in reality the electron density is greater on the fluorine atom than on the hydrogen atom (Figure 10.7◀). The bond is said to be *polar*—having a positive pole

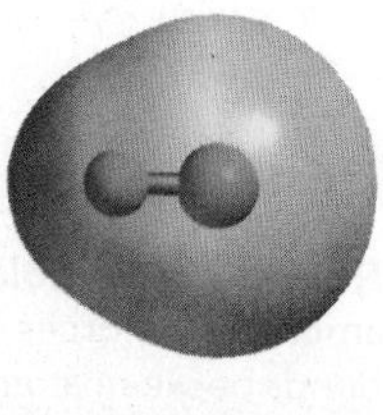

▲ **FIGURE 10.7 Electrostatic Potential Map for the HF Molecule** The F end of the molecule, with its partial negative charge, is yellow/pink; the H end, with its partial positive charge, is blue.

and a negative pole. A **polar covalent bond** is intermediate in nature between a pure covalent bond and an ionic bond. In fact, the categories of pure covalent and ionic are really two extremes within a broad continuum. Most covalent bonds between dissimilar atoms are actually *polar covalent*—somewhere between the two extremes.

Electronegativity

The ability of an atom to attract electrons to itself in a chemical bond (which results in polar and ionic bonds) is called **electronegativity**. We say that fluorine is more *electronegative* than hydrogen because it takes a greater share of the electron density in HF.

The American chemist Linus Pauling (1901–1994) quantified electronegativity in his classic book, *The Nature of the Chemical Bond.* Pauling compared the bond energy—the energy required to break a bond—of a heteronuclear diatomic molecule such as HF with the bond energies of its homonuclear counterparts, in this case H_2 and F_2. The bond energies of H_2 and F_2 are 436 kJ/mol and 155 kJ/mol, respectively. Pauling reasoned that if the HF bond were purely covalent—that is, if the electrons were shared exactly equally—the bond energy of HF should simply be an average of the bond energies of H_2 and F_2, which would be 296 kJ/mol. However, the bond energy of HF is experimentally measured to be 565 kJ/mol. Pauling suggested that the additional bond energy was due to the *ionic character* of the bond. Based on many such comparisons of bond energies, and by arbitrarily assigning an electronegativity of 4.0 to fluorine (the most electronegative element on the periodic table), Pauling developed the electronegativity values shown in Figure 10.8▼.

We cover the concept of bond energy in more detail in Section 10.10.

Pauling's "average" bond energy was actually calculated a little bit differently than the normal average shown here. He took the square root of the product of the bond energies of the homonuclear counterparts as the "average."

For main-group elements, notice the following periodic trends in electronegativity from Figure 10.8:

- Electronegativity generally increases across a period in the periodic table.
- Electronegativity generally decreases down a column in the periodic table.
- Fluorine is the most electronegative element.
- Francium is the least electronegative element (sometimes called the most *electropositive*).

▼ **FIGURE 10.8 Electronegativities of the Elements** Electronegativity generally increases as we move across a row in the periodic table and decreases as we move down a column.

Trends in Electronegativity

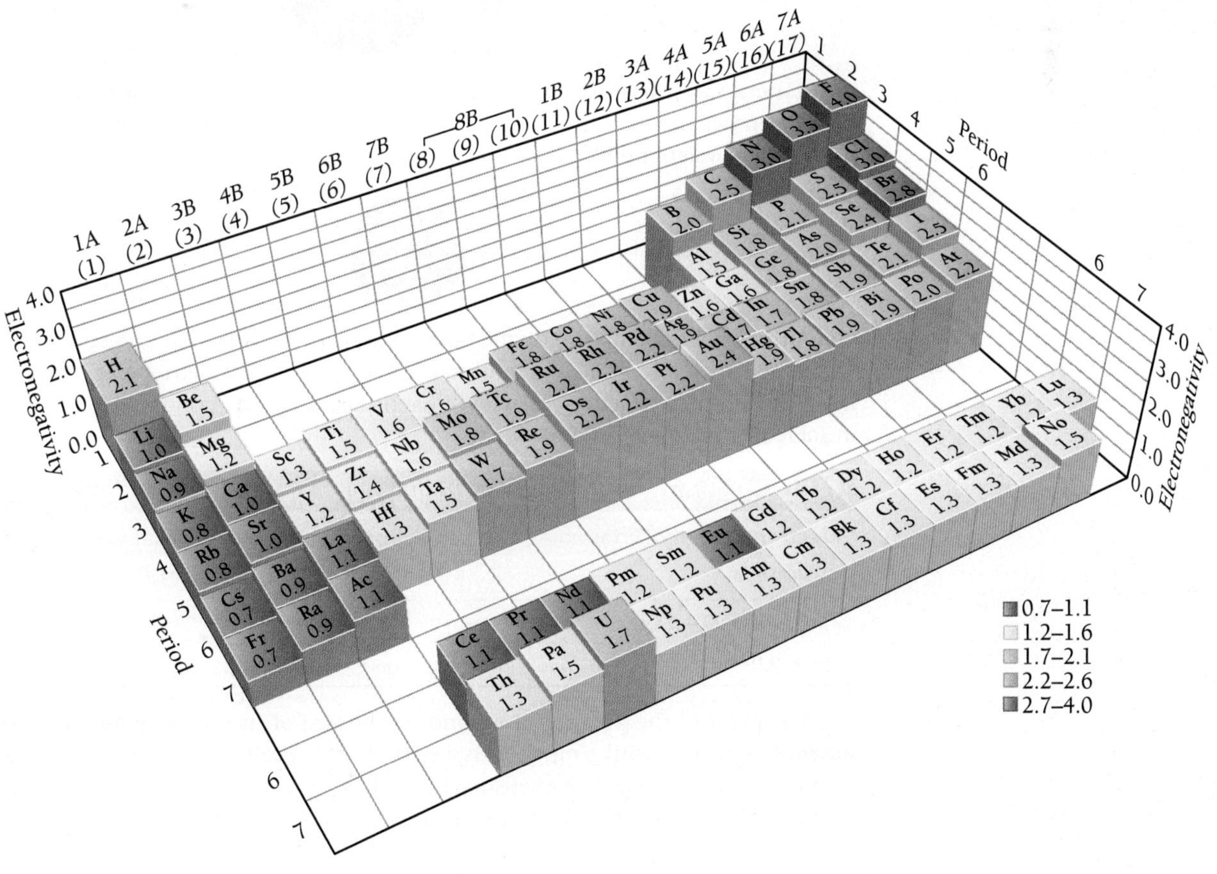

The periodic trends in electronegativity are consistent with other periodic trends we have seen. In general, electronegativity is inversely related to atomic size—the larger the atom, the less ability it has to attract electrons to itself in a chemical bond.

ANSWER NOW!

10.5 Cc Conceptual Connection

PERIODIC TRENDS IN ELECTRONEGATIVITY Arrange these elements in order of decreasing electronegativity: P, Na, N, Al.

(a) N > P > Al > Na
(b) P > Na > N > Al
(c) Na > Al > P > N
(d) Al > Na > N > P

Bond Polarity, Dipole Moment, and Percent Ionic Character

The degree of polarity in a chemical bond depends on the electronegativity difference (sometimes abbreviated ΔEN) between the two bonding atoms. The greater the electronegativity difference, the more polar the bond. If two atoms with identical electronegativities form a covalent bond, they share the electrons equally, and the bond is purely covalent or *nonpolar*. For example, the chlorine molecule, composed of two chlorine atoms (which necessarily have identical electronegativities), has a covalent bond in which electrons are evenly shared:

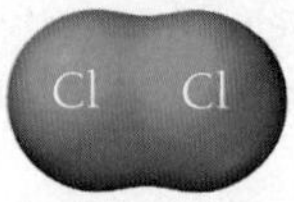

If there is a large electronegativity difference between the two atoms in a bond, such as normally occurs between a metal and a nonmetal, the electron from the metal is almost completely transferred to the nonmetal, and the bond is ionic. For example, sodium and chlorine form an ionic bond:

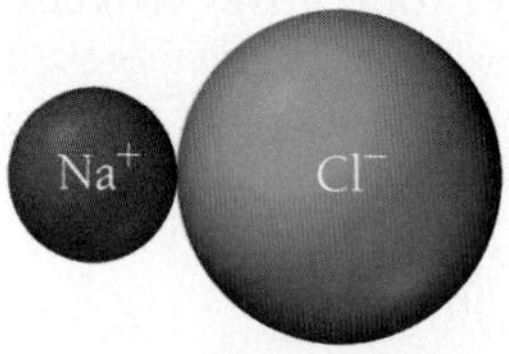

If there is an intermediate electronegativity difference between the two atoms, such as between two different nonmetals, then the bond is polar covalent. For example, HCl has a polar covalent bond:

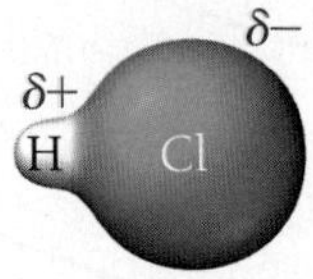

Although all attempts to divide the bond polarity continuum into specific regions are necessarily arbitrary, it is helpful to classify bonds as covalent, polar covalent, and ionic, based on the electronegativity difference between the bonding atoms, as shown in Table 10.1 and Figure 10.9▶.

TABLE 10.1 ■ The Effect of Electronegativity Difference on Bond Type

Electronegativity Difference (ΔEN)	Bond Type	Example
Small (0–0.4)	Covalent	Cl_2
Intermediate (0.4–2.0)	Polar covalent	HCl
Large (2.0+)	Ionic	NaCl

We quantify the polarity of a bond by the size of its dipole moment. A **dipole moment** (μ) occurs any time there is a separation of positive and negative charge. The magnitude of a dipole moment created by separating two particles of equal but opposite charges of magnitude q by a distance r is given by the equation:

$$\mu = qr \qquad [10.1]$$

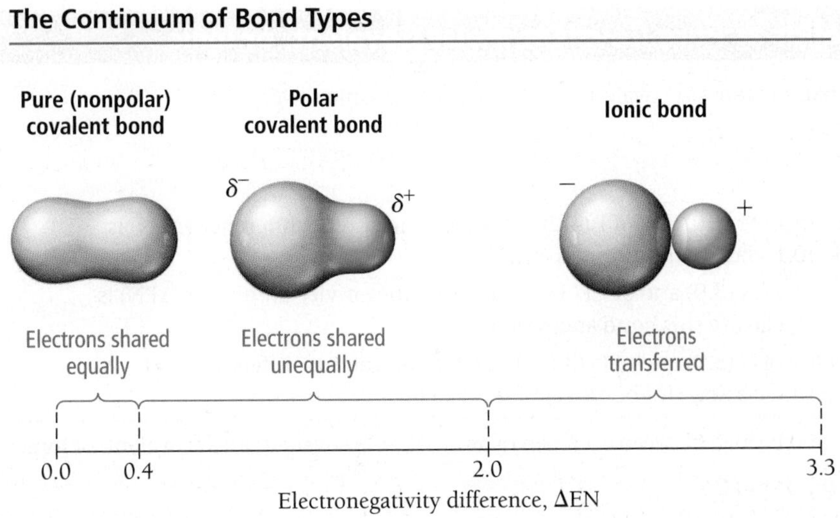

◀ **FIGURE 10.9 Electronegativity Difference (ΔEN) and Bond Type**

We can get a sense for the dipole moment of a completely ionic bond by calculating the dipole moment that results from separating a proton and an electron ($q = 1.6 \times 10^{-19}$ C) by a distance of $r = 130$ pm (the approximate length of a short chemical bond):

$$\begin{aligned} \mu &= qr \\ &= (1.6 \times 10^{-19}\,\text{C})(130 \times 10^{-12}\,\text{m}) \\ &= 2.1 \times 10^{-29}\,\text{C}\cdot\text{m} \\ &= 6.2\,\text{D} \end{aligned}$$

The debye (D) is the unit commonly used for reporting dipole moments ($1\,\text{D} = 3.34 \times 10^{-30}\,\text{C}\cdot\text{m}$). Based on this calculation, we would expect the dipole moment of completely ionic bonds with bond lengths close to 130 pm to be about 6 D. The smaller the magnitude of the charge separation, and the smaller the distance between the charges, the smaller the dipole moment. Table 10.2 lists the dipole moments of several molecules along with the electronegativity differences of their atoms.

TABLE 10.2 ■ Dipole Moments of Several Molecules in the Gas Phase

Molecule	ΔEN	Dipole Moment (D)
Cl_2	0	0
ClF	1.0	0.88
HF	1.9	1.82
LiF	3.0	6.33

By comparing the *actual* dipole moment of a bond to what the dipole moment would be if the electron were completely transferred from one atom to the other, we can get a sense of the degree to which the electron is transferred (or the degree to which the bond is ionic). The **percent ionic character** is the ratio of a bond's actual dipole moment to the dipole moment it would have if the electron were completely transferred from one atom to the other, multiplied by 100%:

$$\text{Percent ionic character} = \frac{\text{measured dipole moment of bond}}{\text{dipole moment if electron were completely transferred}} \times 100\%$$

For example, suppose a diatomic molecule with a bond length of 130 pm has a dipole moment of 3.5 D. We previously calculated that separating a proton and an electron by 130 pm results in a dipole moment of 6.2 D. Therefore, the percent ionic character of the bond is 56%:

$$\begin{aligned} \text{Percent ionic character} &= \frac{3.5\,\cancel{\text{D}}}{6.2\,\cancel{\text{D}}} \times 100\% \\ &= 56\% \end{aligned}$$

A bond in which an electron is completely transferred from one atom to another would have 100% ionic character (although even the most ionic bonds do not reach this ideal). Figure 10.10▶ shows the percent ionic character of a number of diatomic gas-phase molecules plotted against the electronegativity difference between the bonding atoms. As expected, the percent ionic character generally increases as the electronegativity difference increases. However, as we can see, no bond is 100% ionic. In general, bonds with greater than 50% ionic character are referred to as ionic bonds.

▼ **FIGURE 10.10 Percent Ionic Character versus Electronegativity Difference for Some Compounds**

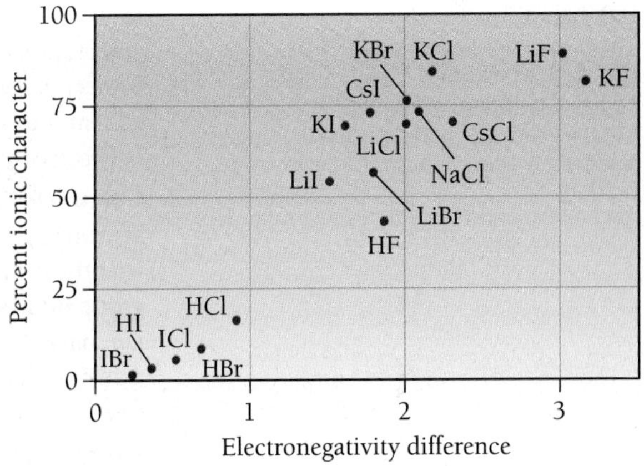

EXAMPLE 10.3 Classifying Bonds as Pure Covalent, Polar Covalent, or Ionic

Classify the bond formed between each pair of atoms as covalent, polar covalent, or ionic.

(a) Sr and F **(b)** N and Cl **(c)** N and O

SOLUTION

(a) In Figure 10.8, find the electronegativity of Sr (1.0) and of F (4.0). The electronegativity difference (ΔEN) is $\Delta EN = 4.0 - 1.0 = 3.0$. Using Table 10.1, classify this bond as ionic.

(b) In Figure 10.8, find the electronegativity of N (3.0) and of Cl (3.0). The electronegativity difference (ΔEN) is $\Delta EN = 3.0 - 3.0 = 0$. Using Table 10.1, classify this bond as covalent.

(c) In Figure 10.8, find the electronegativity of N (3.0) and of O (3.5). The electronegativity difference (ΔEN) is $\Delta EN = 3.5 - 3.0 = 0.5$. Using Table 10.1, classify this bond as polar covalent.

FOR PRACTICE 10.3 Determine if the bond formed between each pair of atoms is pure covalent, polar covalent, or ionic.

(a) I and I **(b)** Cs and Br **(c)** P and O

ANSWER **NOW!**

10.6 Cc Conceptual Connection

PERCENT IONIC CHARACTER The HCl(*g*) molecule has a bond length of 127 pm and a dipole moment of 1.08 D. Without doing detailed calculations, identify the best estimate for its percent ionic character.

(a) 5% **(b)** 15% **(c)** 50% **(d)** 80%

WATCH **NOW!**

KEY CONCEPT VIDEO 10.7
Writing Lewis Structures for Molecular Compounds

10.7 Lewis Structures of Molecular Compounds and Polyatomic Ions

We now turn to the basic sequence of steps involved in actually writing Lewis structures for given combinations of atoms.

Writing Lewis Structures for Molecular Compounds

To write a Lewis structure for a molecular compound, follow these steps:

Often, chemical formulas provide clues to how the atoms are bonded together. For example, CH_3OH indicates that three hydrogen atoms and the oxygen atom are bonded to the carbon atom, but the fourth hydrogen atom is bonded to the oxygen atom.

There are a few exceptions to this rule, such as diborane (B_2H_6), which contains *bridging hydrogens*, but these are rare and cannot be adequately addressed by the Lewis model.

1. **Write the correct skeletal structure for the molecule.** The Lewis structure of a molecule must have the atoms in the correct positions. For example, you could not write a Lewis structure for water if you started with the hydrogen atoms next to each other and the oxygen atom at the end (H H O). In nature, oxygen is the central atom and the hydrogen atoms are *terminal* (at the ends). The correct skeletal structure is H O H. The only way to determine the skeletal structure of a molecule with absolute certainty is to examine its structure experimentally. However, you can write likely skeletal structures by remembering two guidelines. First, *hydrogen atoms are always terminal.* Hydrogen does not ordinarily occur as a central atom because central atoms must form at least two bonds, and hydrogen, which has only a single valence electron to share and requires only a duet, can form just one bond. Second, *put the more electronegative elements in terminal positions* and the less electronegative elements (other than hydrogen) in the central position. Later in this section, you will learn how to distinguish between competing skeletal structures by applying the concept of formal charge.
2. **Calculate the total number of electrons for the Lewis structure by summing the valence electrons of each atom in the molecule.** Remember that the number of valence electrons for any main-group element is equal to its group number in the periodic table. *If you are writing a Lewis structure for a polyatomic ion, you must consider the charge of the ion when calculating the total number of electrons.* Add one electron for each negative charge and subtract one electron for each positive charge. Don't worry about which electron comes from which atom—only the total number is important.

3. **Distribute the electrons among the atoms, giving octets (or duets in the case of hydrogen) to as many atoms as possible.** Begin by placing two electrons between every two atoms. These represent the minimum number of bonding electrons. Then distribute the remaining electrons as lone pairs, first to terminal atoms and then to the central atom, giving octets (or duets for hydrogen) to as many atoms as possible.
4. **If any atoms lack an octet, form double or triple bonds as necessary to give them octets.** Do this by moving lone electron pairs from terminal atoms into the bonding region with the central atom.

Sometimes distributing all the remaining electrons to the central atom results in more than an octet. This is called an expanded octet, which we discuss in Section 10.9.

In the left column that follows, there is an abbreviated version of the procedure for writing Lewis structures; the center and right columns feature two examples of applying the procedure.

WATCH **NOW!**
INTERACTIVE WORKED EXAMPLE VIDEO 10.4

HOW TO: *Write Lewis Structures for Molecular Compounds*	**EXAMPLE 10.4** **Writing Lewis Structures** Write the Lewis structure for CO_2.	**EXAMPLE 10.5** **Writing Lewis Structures** Write the Lewis structure for NH_3.
1. Write the correct skeletal structure for the molecule.	**SOLUTION** Because carbon is the less electronegative atom, put it in the central position. O C O	**SOLUTION** Since hydrogen is always terminal, put nitrogen in the central position. H N H H
2. Calculate the total number of electrons for the Lewis structure by summing the valence electrons of each atom in the molecule.	Total number of electrons for Lewis structure = $\begin{pmatrix}\text{number of}\\ \text{valence}\\ e^- \text{ for C}\end{pmatrix} + 2\begin{pmatrix}\text{number of}\\ \text{valence}\\ e^- \text{ for O}\end{pmatrix}$ $= 4 + 2(6) = 16$	Total number of electrons for Lewis structure = $\begin{pmatrix}\text{number of}\\ \text{valence}\\ e^- \text{ for N}\end{pmatrix} + 3\begin{pmatrix}\text{number of}\\ \text{valence}\\ e^- \text{ for H}\end{pmatrix}$ $= 5 + 3(1) = 8$
3. Distribute the electrons among the atoms, giving octets (or duets for hydrogen) to as many atoms as possible. Begin with the bonding electrons, and then proceed to lone pairs on terminal atoms, and finally to lone pairs on the central atom.	Bonding electrons are first. O:C:O (4 of 16 electrons used) Lone pairs on terminal atoms are next. 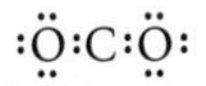 (16 of 16 electrons used)	Bonding electrons are first. 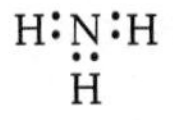 (6 of 8 electrons used) Lone pairs on terminal atoms are next, but none is needed on hydrogen. Lone pairs on the central atom are last. 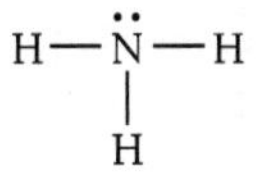 (8 of 8 electrons used)
4. If any atom lacks an octet, form double or triple bonds as necessary until all atoms have octets.	Since carbon lacks an octet, move lone pairs from the oxygen atoms to bonding regions to form double bonds. 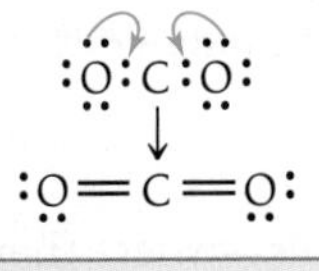	Since all of the atoms have octets (or duets for hydrogen), the Lewis structure for NH_3 is complete as shown in the previous step.
	FOR PRACTICE 10.4 Write the Lewis structure for CO.	**FOR PRACTICE 10.5** Write the Lewis structure for H_2CO.

Writing Lewis Structures for Polyatomic Ions

Write Lewis structures for polyatomic ions by following the same procedure, but pay special attention to the charge of the ion when calculating the number of electrons for the Lewis structure. Add one electron for each negative charge and subtract one electron for each positive charge. Write the Lewis structure for a polyatomic ion within brackets with the charge of the ion in the upper right-hand corner, outside the bracket.

WATCH **NOW!**

INTERACTIVE WORKED EXAMPLE 10.6

EXAMPLE 10.6 Writing Lewis Structures for Polyatomic Ions

Write the Lewis structure for the NH_4^+ ion.

SOLUTION

Begin by writing the skeletal structure. Since hydrogen is always terminal, put the nitrogen atom in the central position.	H H N H H
Calculate the total number of electrons for the Lewis structure by summing the number of valence electrons for each atom and subtracting 1 for the 1+ charge.	Total number of electrons for Lewis structure = (number of valence e^- in N) + 4 (number of valence e^- in H) − 1 = 5 + 4(1) − 1 = 8 Subtract 1 e^- to account for 1^+ charge of ion.
Place two bonding electrons between every two atoms. Since all of the atoms have complete octets, no double bonds are necessary.	H H:N:H H (8 of 8 electrons used)
Lastly, write the Lewis structure in brackets with the charge of the ion in the upper right-hand corner.	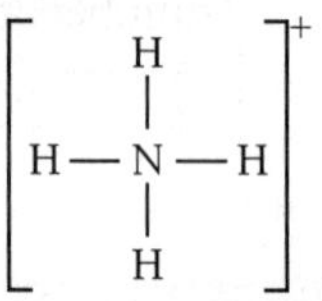

FOR PRACTICE 10.6 Write the Lewis structure for the hypochlorite ion, ClO^-.

WATCH **NOW!**

KEY CONCEPT VIDEO 10.8

Resonance and Formal Charge

10.8 Resonance and Formal Charge

We need two additional concepts to write the best possible Lewis structures for a large number of compounds. The concepts are *resonance,* which is relevant when two or more valid Lewis structures can be drawn for the same compound, and *formal charge,* an electron bookkeeping system that allows us to discriminate between alternative Lewis structures.

Resonance

For some molecules, we can write more than one valid Lewis structure. For example, consider writing a Lewis structure for O_3. The following two Lewis structures, with the double bond on alternate sides, are equally correct:

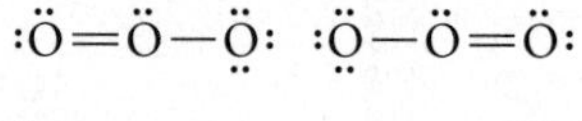

In cases such as this—where there are two or more valid Lewis structures for the same molecule—we find that, in nature, the molecule is an *average* of the two Lewis structures. Both of the two Lewis structures for O_3 predict that O_3 contains two different bonds (one double bond and one single bond). However, when we experimentally examine the structure of O_3, we find that the bonds in the O_3 molecule are equivalent and each is intermediate in strength and length between a double bond and single bond. We account for this by representing the molecule with both structures, called *resonance structures*, with a double-headed arrow between them:

$$:\ddot{O}=\ddot{O}-\underset{..}{\ddot{O}}: \longleftrightarrow :\underset{..}{\ddot{O}}-\ddot{O}=\ddot{O}:$$

A **resonance structure** is one of two or more Lewis structures that have the same skeletal formula (the atoms are in the same locations), but different electron arrangements. The actual structure of the molecule is intermediate between the two (or more) resonance structures and is called a **resonance hybrid**. The term *hybrid* comes from breeding and means the offspring of two animals or plants of different varieties or breeds. If we breed a Labrador retriever with a German shepherd, we get a *hybrid* that is intermediate between the two breeds (Figure 10.11(a)▼). Similarly, the actual structure of a resonance hybrid is intermediate between the two (or more) resonance structures (Figure 10.11(b)▼). The only structure that actually exists is the hybrid structure—the individual resonance structures do not exist and are merely a way to describe the actual structure. Notice that the actual structure of ozone has two equivalent bonds and a bent geometry (we discuss molecular geometries in Chapter 11).

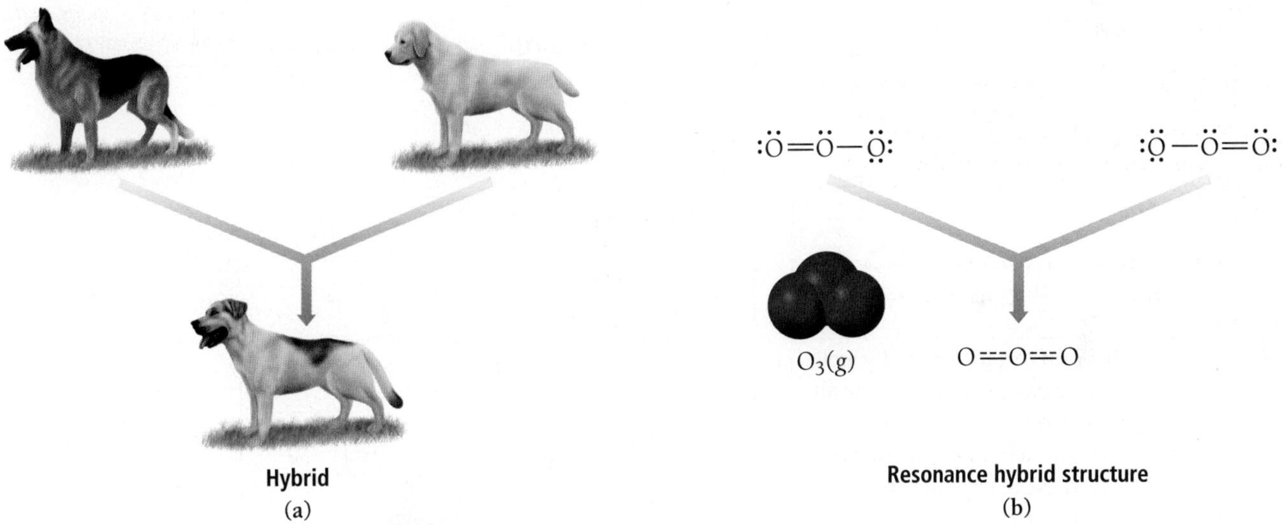

▲ **FIGURE 10.11 Hybridization** Just as the offspring of two different dog breeds is a hybrid that is intermediate between the two breeds (a), the structure of a resonance hybrid is intermediate between that of the contributing resonance structures (b).

The concept of resonance is an adaptation of the Lewis model that helps account for the complexity of actual molecules. In the Lewis model, electrons are *localized* either on one atom (lone pair) or between atoms (bonding pair). However, in nature, the electrons in molecules are often *delocalized* over several atoms or bonds. The delocalization of electrons lowers their energy; it stabilizes them (for reasons that are beyond the scope of this book). Resonance depicts two or more structures with the electrons in different places in an attempt to more accurately reflect the delocalization of electrons. In the real hybrid structure, an average between the resonance structures, the electrons are more spread out (or delocalized) than in any of the resonance structures. The resulting stabilization of the electrons (that is, the lowering of their potential energy due to delocalization) is sometimes called *resonance stabilization*. Resonance stabilization makes an important contribution to the stability of many molecules.

WATCH **NOW!**

INTERACTIVE WORKED EXAMPLE 10.7

EXAMPLE 10.7 Writing Resonance Structures

Write a Lewis structure for the NO_3^- ion. Include resonance structures.

SOLUTION

Begin by writing the skeletal structure. Since nitrogen is the least electronegative atom, put it in the central position.	O O N O
Calculate the total number of electrons for the Lewis structure by summing the number of valence electrons for each atom and adding 1 for the 1− charge.	Total number of electrons for Lewis structure = (number of valence e^- in N) + 3 (number of valence e^- in O) + 1 = 5 + 3(6) + 1 = 24 Add 1 e^- to account for 1− charge of ion.
Place two bonding electrons between each pair of atoms.	O O:N:O (6 of 24 electrons used)
Distribute the remaining electrons, first to terminal atoms. There are not enough electrons to complete the octet on the central atom.	:Ö: :Ö:N:Ö: (24 of 24 electrons used)
Form a double bond by moving a lone pair from one of the oxygen atoms into the bonding region with nitrogen. Enclose the structure in brackets and include the charge.	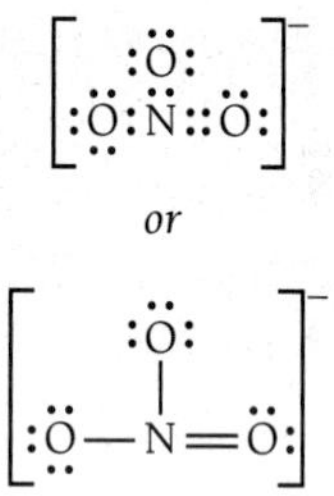
Since the double bond can form equally well with any of the three oxygen atoms, write all three structures as resonance structures. (The actual space-filling model of NO_3^- is shown here for comparison. Note that all three bonds are equal in length.)	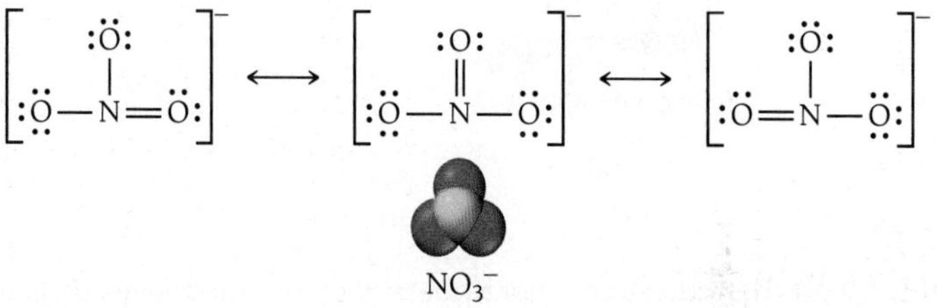 NO_3^-

FOR PRACTICE 10.7 Write a Lewis structure for the NO_2^- ion. Include resonance structures.

In the examples of resonance hybrids that we have examined so far, the contributing structures have been equivalent (or equally valid) Lewis structures. In these cases, the true structure is an equally weighted average of the resonance structures. In some cases, however, we can write resonance structures that are not equivalent. For reasons that we cover in the material that follows—such as formal charge—one resonance structure may be somewhat better than another. In such cases, the true structure is still an average of the resonance structures, but the better resonance structure contributes more to the true structure. In other words, multiple nonequivalent resonance structures may be weighted differently in their contributions to the true overall structure of a molecule (see Example 10.8).

Formal Charge

Formal charge is a fictitious charge assigned to each atom in a Lewis structure that helps us to distinguish among competing Lewis structures. The formal charge of an atom in a Lewis structure is *the charge it would have if all bonding electrons were shared equally between*

10.7 **Cc** Conceptual Connection

ANSWER **NOW!**

RESONANCE STRUCTURES Which structure is NOT a resonance structure of the ion shown here?

$[:\ddot{\underset{..}{S}}-C\equiv N:]^-$

(a) $[:\underset{..}{S}=C=\underset{..}{N}:]^-$ (b) $[:\ddot{\underset{..}{S}}-N\equiv C:]^-$ (c) $[:S\equiv C-\ddot{\underset{..}{N}}:]^-$

the bonded atoms. In other words, formal charge is the calculated charge for an atom if we completely ignore the effects of electronegativity. For example, we know that because fluorine is more electronegative than hydrogen, HF has a dipole moment—the hydrogen atom has a slight positive charge and the fluorine atom has a slight negative charge. However, the *formal charges* of hydrogen and fluorine in HF (the calculated charges if we ignore their differences in electronegativity) are both zero:

$H:\ddot{\underset{..}{F}}:$

Formal charge = 0 Formal charge = 0

We can calculate the formal charge on any atom as the difference between the number of valence electrons in the atom and the number of electrons that it "owns" in a Lewis structure. An atom in a Lewis structure can be thought of as "owning" all of its nonbonding electrons and one-half of its bonding electrons:

$$\text{Formal charge} = \text{number of valence electrons} - (\text{number of nonbonding electrons} + \tfrac{1}{2}\,\text{number of bonding electrons})$$

So the formal charge of hydrogen in HF is 0:

$$\text{Formal charge} = 1 - [0 + \tfrac{1}{2}(2)] = 0$$

Number of valence electrons for H; Number of electrons that H "owns" in the Lewis structure

Similarly, we calculate the formal charge of fluorine in HF as 0:

$$\text{Formal charge} = 7 - [6 + \tfrac{1}{2}(2)] = 0$$

Number of valence electrons for F; Number of electrons that F "owns" in the Lewis structure

The concept of formal charge is useful because it can help us distinguish between competing skeletal structures or competing resonance structures. In general, when we calculate formal charges, these four rules apply:

1. The sum of all formal charges in a neutral molecule must be zero.
2. The sum of all formal charges in an ion must equal the charge of the ion.
3. Small (or zero) formal charges on individual atoms are better than large ones.
4. When formal charge cannot be avoided, negative formal charge should reside on the most electronegative atom.

We can use formal charge to determine which of the competing skeletal structures for hydrogen cyanide shown here is best (or most stable). Notice that both skeletal structures satisfy the octet rule equally. The formal charge of each atom in the structure is calculated below it.

	Structure A			Structure B		
	H —	C ≡	N:	H —	N ≡	C:
number of valence e⁻	1	4	5	1	5	4
−number of nonbonding e⁻	−0	−0	−2	−0	−0	−2
$-\frac{1}{2}$(number of bonding e⁻)	$-\frac{1}{2}(2)$	$-\frac{1}{2}(8)$	$-\frac{1}{2}(6)$	$-\frac{1}{2}(2)$	$-\frac{1}{2}(8)$	$-\frac{1}{2}(6)$
Formal charge	**0**	**0**	**0**	**0**	**+1**	**−1**

As required, the sum of the formal charges for each of these structures is zero (as it always must be for neutral molecules). However, structure B has formal charges on both the N atom and the C atom, while structure A has no formal charges on any atom. Furthermore, in structure B, the negative formal charge is not on the most electronegative element (nitrogen is more electronegative than carbon). Consequently, structure A is the better skeletal structure. Since atoms in the middle of a molecule tend to have more bonding electrons and fewer nonbonding electrons, they also tend to have more positive formal charges. Consequently, the best skeletal structure usually has the least electronegative atom in the central position, as we learned in step 1 of our procedure for writing Lewis structures.

Both HCN and HNC exist, but—as predicted by formal charge—HCN is more stable than HNC.

WATCH **NOW!**

INTERACTIVE WORKED EXAMPLE 10.8

EXAMPLE 10.8 Assigning Formal Charges

Assign formal charges to each atom in the resonance structures of the cyanate ion (OCN^-). Which resonance structure is likely to contribute most to the correct structure of (OCN^-)?

A	B	C
[:Ö—C≡N:]⁻	[:Ö=C=N̈:]⁻	[:O≡C—N̈:]⁻

SOLUTION

Calculate the formal charge on each atom by finding the number of valence electrons and subtracting the number of nonbonding electrons and one-half the number of bonding electrons.

	A [:Ö—C≡N:]⁻			B [:Ö=C=N̈:]⁻			C [:O≡C—N̈:]⁻		
Number of valence e^-	6	4	5	6	4	5	6	4	5
−number of nonbonding e^-	−6	−0	−2	−4	−0	−4	−2	−0	−6
$-\frac{1}{2}$(number of bonding e^-)	−1	−4	−3	−2	−4	−2	−3	−4	−1
Formal charge	**−1**	**0**	**0**	**0**	**0**	**−1**	**+1**	**0**	**−2**

The sum of all formal charges for each structure is −1, as it should be for a 1− ion. Structures A and B have the fewest formal charges and are preferred over structure C. Structure A is preferable to B because it has the negative formal charge on the more electronegative atom. You therefore expect structure A to make the biggest contribution to the resonance forms of the cyanate ion.

FOR PRACTICE 10.8 Assign formal charges to each atom in the resonance structures of N_2O. Which resonance structure is likely to contribute most to the correct structure of N_2O?

A	B	C
:N̈=N=Ö:	:N≡N—Ö:	:N̈—N≡O:

FOR MORE PRACTICE 10.8 Assign formal charges to each of the atoms in the nitrate ion (NO_3^-). The Lewis structure for the nitrate ion is shown in Example 10.7.

WATCH **NOW!**

INTERACTIVE WORKED EXAMPLE 10.9

EXAMPLE 10.9 Drawing Resonance Structures and Assigning Formal Charge for Organic Compounds

Draw the Lewis structure (including resonance structures) for nitromethane (CH_3NO_2). For each resonance structure, assign formal charges to all atoms that have formal charge.

SOLUTION

Begin by writing the skeletal structure. For organic compounds, the condensed structural formula (in this case CH_3NO_2) indicates how the atoms are connected.

```
   H  O
H  C  N  O
   H
```

Calculate the total number of electrons for the Lewis structure by summing the number of valence electrons for each atom.	Total number of electrons for Lewis structure $= (\#\text{ valence e}^- \text{ in C}) + 3(\#\text{ valence e}^- \text{ in H}) + (\#\text{ valence e}^- \text{ in N}) + 2(\#\text{ valence e}^- \text{ in O})$ $= 4 + 3(1) + 5 + 2(6)$ $= 24$
Place a dash between each pair of atoms to indicate a bond. Each dash represents two electrons.	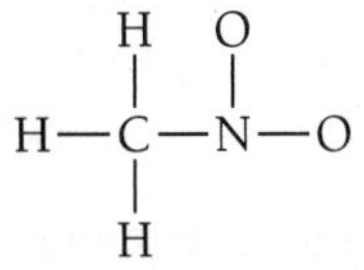 (12 of 24 electrons used)
Distribute the remaining electrons, first to terminal atoms, then to interior atoms.	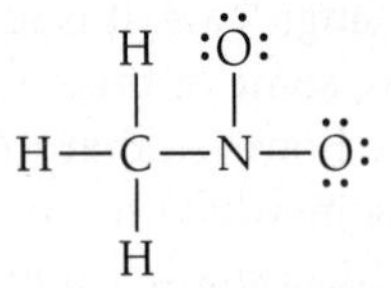 (24 of 24 electrons used)
If there are not enough electrons to complete the octets on the interior atoms, form double bonds by moving lone pair electrons from terminal atoms into the bonding region with interior atoms.	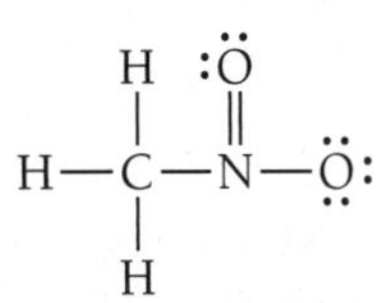
Draw any necessary resonance structures by moving only electron dots. (In this case, you can form a double bond between the nitrogen atom and the other oxygen atom.)	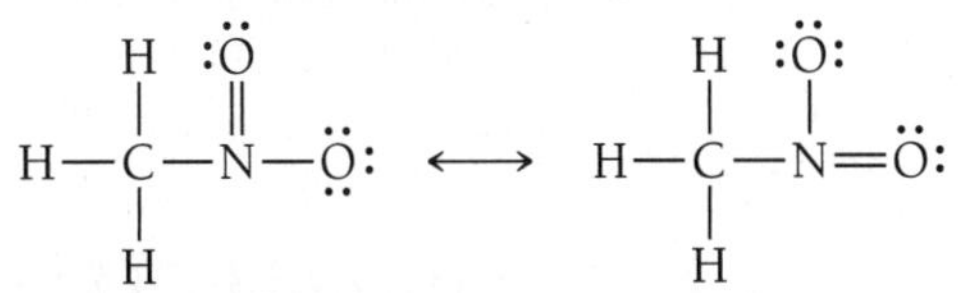
Assign formal charges (FC) to each atom. $\text{FC} = \#\text{ valence e}^- - (\#\text{ nonbonding e}^- + \frac{1}{2}\#\text{ bonding e}^-)$	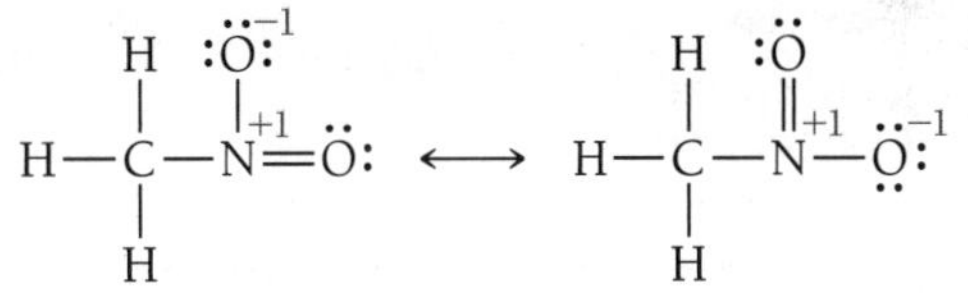 Carbon, hydrogen, and the double-bonded oxygen atoms have formal charges of zero. Nitrogen has a +1 formal charge $[5 - \frac{1}{2}(8)]$ and the singly bonded oxygen atom in each resonance structure has a −1 formal charge $[6 - (6 + \frac{1}{2}(2))]$.

FOR PRACTICE 10.9 Draw the Lewis structure (including resonance structures) for diazomethane (CH_2N_2). For each resonance structure, assign formal charges to all atoms that have formal charge.

10.9 Exceptions to the Octet Rule: Odd-Electron Species, Incomplete Octets, and Expanded Octets

WATCH **NOW!**

KEY CONCEPT VIDEO 10.9

Exceptions to the Octet Rule and Expanded Octets

The octet rule in the Lewis model has some exceptions, which we examine in this section of the chapter. They include (1) *odd-electron species,* molecules or ions with an odd number of electrons; (2) *incomplete octets,* molecules or ions with *fewer than eight electrons* around an atom; and (3) *expanded octets,* molecules or ions with *more than eight electrons* around an atom.

Odd-Electron Species

Molecules and ions with an odd number of electrons in their Lewis structures are **free radicals** (or simply *radicals*). For example, nitrogen monoxide—a pollutant found in motor vehicle exhaust—has 11 electrons. If we try to write a Lewis structure for nitrogen monoxide, we can't achieve octets for both atoms:

The unpaired electron in nitrogen monoxide is put on the nitrogen rather than the oxygen in order to minimize formal charges.

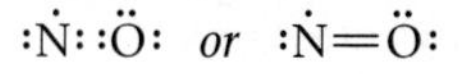

The nitrogen atom in nitrogen monoxide does not have an octet, so this Lewis structure does not satisfy the octet rule. Yet, nitrogen monoxide exists, especially in polluted air. Why? As with any simple theory, the Lewis model is not sophisticated enough to handle every single case. It is impossible to write good Lewis structures for free radicals; nevertheless, some of these molecules exist in nature. Perhaps it is a testament to the Lewis model, however, that *relatively few* such molecules exist and that, in general, they tend to be somewhat unstable and reactive. NO, for example, reacts with oxygen in the air to form NO_2, another odd-electron molecule represented with the following 17-electron resonance structures:

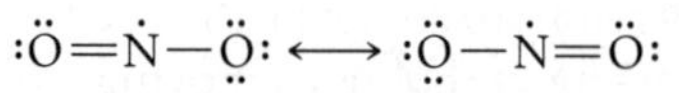

In turn, NO_2 reacts with water to form nitric acid (a component of acid rain) and also reacts with other atmospheric pollutants to form peroxyacetylnitrate (PAN), an active component of photochemical smog. For free radicals, such as NO and NO_2, we simply write the best Lewis structure that we can.

ANSWER **NOW!**

10.8 Cc Conceptual Connection

ODD-ELECTRON SPECIES Which molecule would you expect to be a free radical?

(a) CO **(b)** CO_2 **(c)** N_2O **(d)** ClO

Incomplete Octets

Another significant exception to the octet rule involves elements that tend to form *incomplete octets*. The most important of these is boron, which forms compounds with only six electrons around B, rather than eight. For example, BF_3 and BH_3 lack an octet for B.

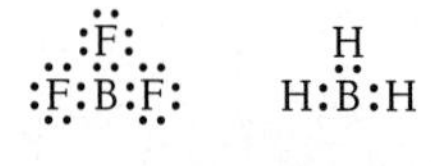

Beryllium compounds, such as BeH_2, also have incomplete octets.

You might be wondering why we don't just form double bonds to increase the number of electrons around B. For BH_3, we can't because there are no additional electrons to move into the bonding region. For BF_3, however, we could attempt to give B an octet by moving a lone pair from an F atom into the bonding region with B:

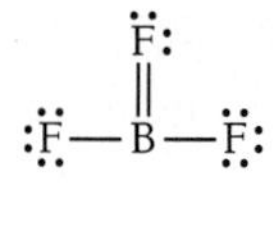

CHEMISTRY IN THE ENVIRONMENT | Free Radicals and the Atmospheric Vacuum Cleaner

Free radicals play a key role in much of the chemistry of the atmosphere. The free radical that is most important to atmospheric reactions is the hydroxyl radical:

$$:\dot{\underset{\cdot\cdot}{O}}-H$$

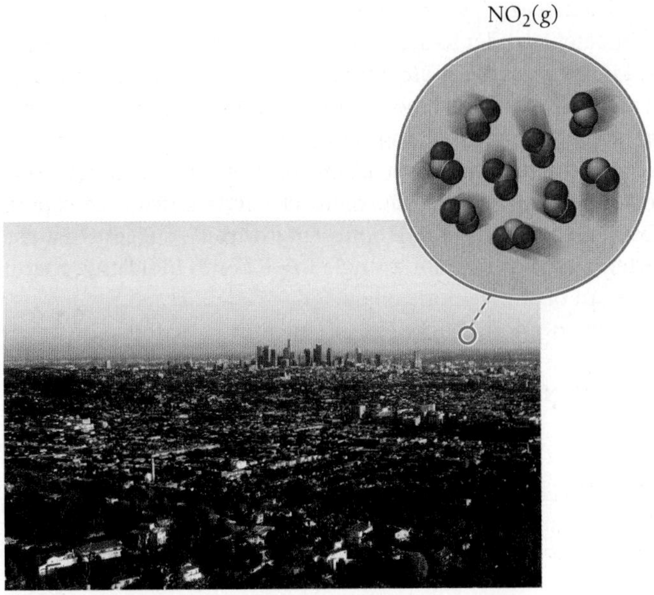

▲ $NO_2(g)$ is a pollutant found in urban air.

Many free radical structures are abbreviated by writing a single dot with the formula. Thus, the hydroxyl radical is often abbreviated as:

$$\cdot OH$$

In the atmosphere, the hydroxyl radical forms when excited oxygen atoms—formed from the photodecomposition of ozone—react with water vapor:

$$O_3 \xrightarrow{\text{UV light}} O_2 + O^*$$
$$O^* + H_2O \longrightarrow 2\cdot OH$$

The * next to the O indicates that the oxygen atom has excess energy.

The resulting hydroxyl radical reacts with a wide variety of molecules from both natural sources and from air pollution that are present in the atmosphere. For example, the hydroxyl radical reacts with carbon monoxide, an atmospheric pollutant that we first encountered in Chapter 1, in the following two-step process:

$$CO + \cdot OH \longrightarrow HOCO\cdot$$
$$HOCO\cdot + O_2 \longrightarrow CO_2 + HOO\cdot$$

We can see from this reaction that the hydroxyl radical converts toxic CO into relatively nontoxic CO_2.

The $HOO\cdot$ free radical generated by the second reaction is converted back into the hydroxyl radical when it reacts with other atmospheric substances, and the process repeats itself. Therefore, a single hydroxyl radical can convert a lot of CO into CO_2.

Do you ever wonder what happens to the hydrocarbons you accidentally spill when filling a car's gas tank or to the natural gas that is released into the atmosphere as you light a kitchen stove? Hydrocarbons released into the atmosphere are converted to CO_2 and H_2O in a series of steps initiated by the hydroxyl free radical. Consider the following representative reaction of methane, the main hydrocarbon in natural gas:

$$CH_4 + 5\,O_2 + NO\cdot + 2\cdot OH \xrightarrow{\text{UV light}} CO_2 + H_2O + NO_2\cdot + 4\,HOO\cdot$$

Notice the similarity between this reaction and the direct combustion (or burning) of methane:

$$CH_4 + 2\,O_2 \longrightarrow CO_2 + 2\,H_2O$$

As you can see, the free radical reaction initiates a slow "burning" of CH_4 in a series of steps that produces carbon dioxide and water and some additional free radicals. The hydroxyl radical initiates similar reactions with other pollutants as well as undesirable naturally occurring atmospheric gases. Without the hydroxyl free radical—sometimes called *the atmospheric vacuum cleaner*—our atmosphere would be a much dirtier place.

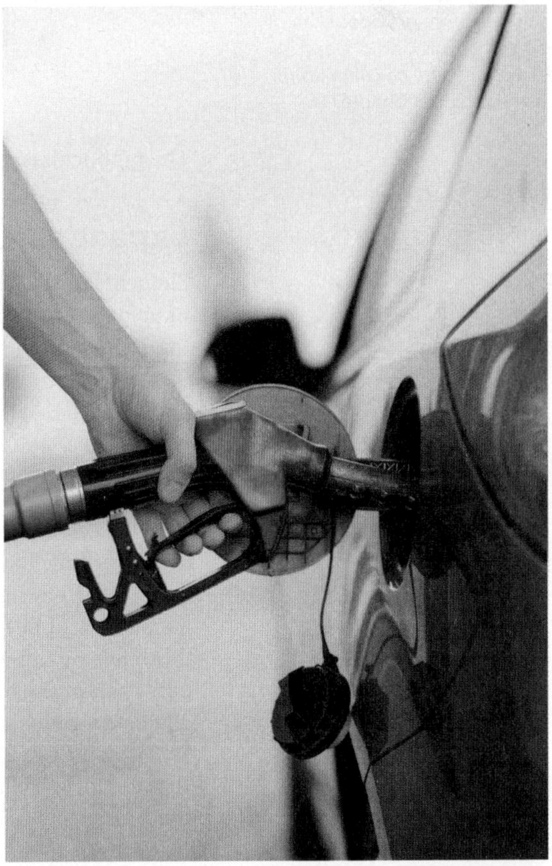

▲ Hydrocarbons such as octane evaporate into the atmosphere when a motor vehicle is fueled. What happens to them?

QUESTION *Draw the best possible Lewis structures for the free radicals important in atmospheric chemistry: NO, NO_2, HOO, OH, CH_3.*

This Lewis structure has octets for all atoms, including boron. However, when we assign formal charges to this structure, we get a negative formal charge on B and a positive formal charge on F:

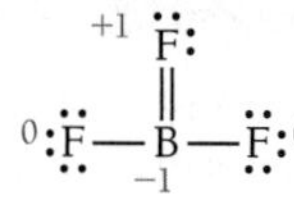

The positive formal charge on fluorine—the most electronegative element in the periodic table—makes this an unfavorable structure. This leaves us with some questions. Do we complete the octet on B at the expense of giving fluorine a positive formal charge? Or do we leave B without an octet in order to avoid the positive formal charge on fluorine? The answers to these kinds of questions are not always clear because we are pushing the limits of the Lewis model. In the case of boron, we usually accept the incomplete octet as the better Lewis structure. However, doing so does not rule out the possibility that the double-bonded Lewis structure might be a minor contributing resonance structure. The ultimate answers to these kinds of questions must be determined from experiments. Experimental measurements of the B—F bond length in BF_3 suggest that the bond may be slightly shorter than expected for a single B—F bond, indicating that it may indeed have a small amount of double-bond character.

BF_3 can complete its octet in another way—via a chemical reaction. The Lewis model predicts that BF_3 might react in ways that would complete its octet, and indeed it does. For example, BF_3 reacts with NH_3 as follows:

When nitrogen bonds to boron, the nitrogen atom provides both of the electrons. This kind of bond is called a *coordinate covalent bond*, which we discuss in Chapter 26.

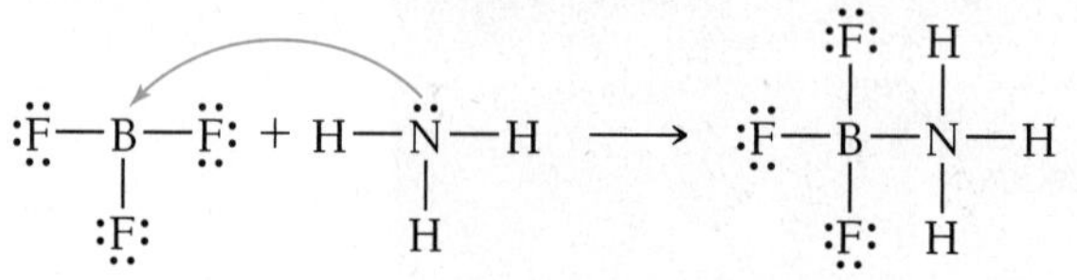

The product has complete octets for all atoms in the structure.

Expanded Octets

Elements in the third row of the periodic table and beyond often exhibit *expanded octets* of up to 12 (and occasionally 14) electrons. Consider the Lewis structures of arsenic pentafluoride and sulfur hexafluoride:

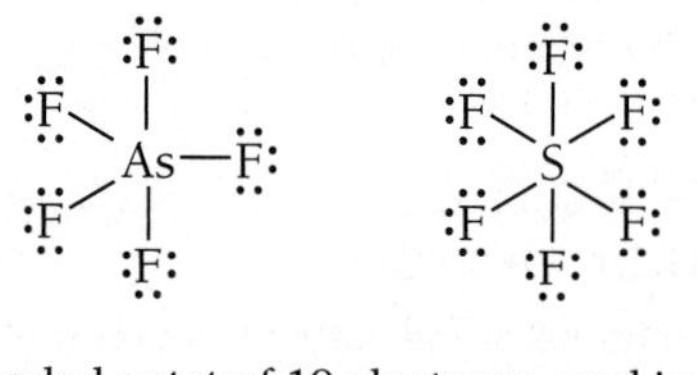

In AsF_5 arsenic has an expanded octet of 10 electrons, and in SF_6 sulfur has an expanded octet of 12 electrons. Both of these compounds exist and are stable. In third-period elements and beyond, 10- and 12-electron expanded octets are common because the *d* orbitals in these elements are energetically accessible (they are not much higher in energy than the orbitals occupied by the valence electrons) and can accommodate the extra electrons (see Section 9.3). Expanded octets *never* occur in second-period elements.

In some Lewis structures, we must decide whether or not to expand an octet in order to lower formal charge. For example, consider the Lewis structure of H_2SO_4:

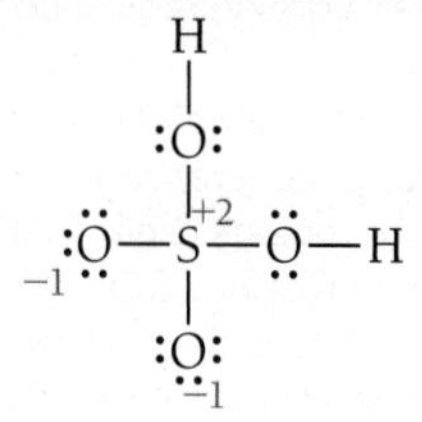

Notice that two of the oxygen atoms have a −1 formal charge and that sulfur has a +2 formal charge. While this amount of formal charge is acceptable, especially since the negative formal charge resides on the more electronegative atom, it is possible to eliminate the formal charge by expanding the octet on sulfur:

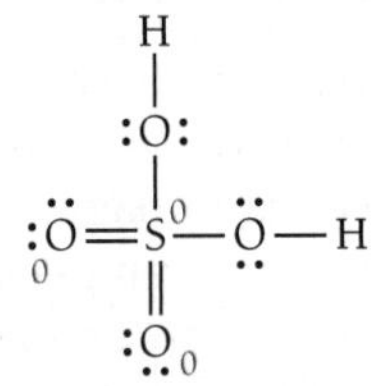

Which of these two Lewis structures for H_2SO_4 is better? Again, the answer is not straightforward. Experiments show that the sulfur–oxygen bond lengths in the two sulfur–oxygen bonds without the hydrogen atoms are shorter than expected for sulfur–oxygen single bonds, indicating that the double-bonded Lewis structure plays an important role in describing the bonding in H_2SO_4. In general, we expand octets in third-row (or beyond) elements in order to lower formal charge. However, we should *never* expand the octets of second-row elements. Second-row elements do not have energetically accessible *d* orbitals and therefore never exhibit expanded octets.

WATCH **NOW!**

INTERACTIVE WORKED EXAMPLE 10.10

EXAMPLE 10.10 Writing Lewis Structures for Compounds Having Expanded Octets

Write the Lewis structure for XeF_2.

SOLUTION

Begin by writing the skeletal structure. Since xenon is the less electronegative atom, put it in the central position.	F Xe F
Calculate the total number of electrons for the Lewis structure by summing the number of valence electrons for each atom.	Total number of electrons for Lewis structure = (number of valence e^- in Xe) + 2(number of valence e^- in F) = 8 + 2(7) = 22
Place two bonding electrons between the atoms of each pair of atoms.	F:Xe:F (4 of 22 electrons used)
Distribute the remaining electrons to give octets to as many atoms as possible, beginning with terminal atoms and finishing with the central atom. Arrange additional electrons around the central atom, giving it an expanded octet of up to 12 electrons.	:F̤̈: Xe :F̤̈: (16 of 22 electrons used) :F̤̈ :Ẍ̤e: F̤̈: or :F̤̈ — Ẍ̤e — F̤̈: (22 of 22 electrons used)

FOR PRACTICE 10.10 Write the Lewis structure for XeF_4.

FOR MORE PRACTICE 10.10 Write the Lewis structure for H_3PO_4. If necessary, expand the octet on any appropriate atoms to lower formal charge.

EXPANDED OCTETS Which molecule could have an expanded octet?

(a) H_2CO_3

(b) H_3PO_4

(c) HNO_2

10.9 Cc Conceptual Connection

ANSWER **NOW!**

10.10 Bond Energies and Bond Lengths

In Chapter 7, we discussed how to calculate the standard enthalpy change for a chemical reaction (ΔH°_{rxn}) from tabulated standard enthalpies of formation. However, sometimes we may not easily find standard enthalpies of formation for all of the reactants and products of a reaction. In such cases, we can use individual *bond energies* to estimate enthalpy changes of reaction. In this section, we examine the concept of bond energy and how we can use bond energies to calculate enthalpy changes of reaction. We also look at average bond lengths for a number of commonly encountered bonds.

Bond Energy

Bond energy is also called bond enthalpy or bond dissociation energy.

The **bond energy** of a chemical bond is the energy required to break 1 mole of the bonds in the gas phase. For example, the bond energy of the Cl—Cl bond in Cl_2 is 243 kJ/mol.

$$Cl_2(g) \longrightarrow 2\,Cl(g) \qquad \Delta H = 243\text{ kJ}$$

The bond energy of HCl is 431 kJ/mol.

$$HCl(g) \longrightarrow H(g) + Cl(g) \qquad \Delta H = 431\text{ kJ}$$

Bond energies are always positive because it always takes energy to break a bond. We say that the HCl bond is *stronger* than the Cl_2 bond because it requires more energy to break it. In general, compounds with stronger bonds tend to be more chemically stable, and therefore less chemically reactive, than compounds with weaker bonds. The triple bond in N_2 has a bond energy of 946 kJ/mol.

$$N_2(g) \longrightarrow N(g) + N(g) \qquad \Delta H = 946\text{ kJ}$$

It is a very strong and stable bond, which explains nitrogen's relative inertness.

The bond energy of a particular bond in a polyatomic molecule is a little more difficult to determine because a particular type of bond can have different bond energies in different molecules. For example, consider the C—H bond. In CH_4, the energy required to break one C—H bond is 438 kJ/mol.

$$H_3C{-}H(g) \longrightarrow H_3C(g) + H(g) \qquad \Delta H = 438\text{ kJ}$$

However, the energy required to break a C—H bond in other molecules varies slightly, as shown here:

$$F_3C{-}H(g) \longrightarrow F_3C(g) + H(g) \qquad \Delta H = 446\text{ kJ}$$
$$Br_3C{-}H(g) \longrightarrow Br_3C(g) + H(g) \qquad \Delta H = 402\text{ kJ}$$
$$Cl_3C{-}H(g) \longrightarrow Cl_3C(g) + H(g) \qquad \Delta H = 401\text{ kJ}$$

We can calculate an *average bond energy* for a chemical bond, which is an average of the bond energies for that bond in a large number of compounds. For the four compounds just discussed, we calculate an average C—H bond energy of 422 kJ/mol. Table 10.3 lists average bond energies for a number of common chemical bonds averaged over a large number of compounds. Notice that the C—H bond energy listed is 414 kJ/mol, which is not too different from the value we calculated from our limited number of compounds. Notice also that bond energies depend, not only on the kind of atoms involved in the bond, but also on the type of bond: single, double, or triple. In general, for a given pair of atoms, triple bonds are stronger than double bonds, which are, in turn, stronger than single bonds. For example, consider the bond energies of carbon–carbon triple, double, and single bonds listed in Table 10.3.

TABLE 10.3 ■ Average Bond Energies

Bond	Bond Energy (kJ/mol)	Bond	Bond Energy (kJ/mol)	Bond	Bond Energy (kJ/mol)
H—H	436	N—N	163	Br—F	237
H—C	414	N=N	418	Br—Cl	218
H—N	389	N≡N	946	Br—Br	193
H—O	464	N—O	222	I—Cl	208
H—S	368	N=O	590	I—Br	175
H—F	565	N—F	272	I—I	151
H—Cl	431	N—Cl	200	Si—H	323
H—Br	364	N—Br	243	Si—Si	226
H—I	297	N—I	159	Si—C	301
C—C	347	O—O	142	S—O	265
C=C	611	O=O	498	Si=O	368
C≡C	837	O—F	190	S=O	523
C—N	305	O—Cl	203	Si—Cl	464
C=N	615	O—I	234	S=S	418
C≡N	891	F—F	159	S—F	327
C—O	360	Cl—F	253	S—Cl	253
C=O	736*	Cl—Cl	243	S—Br	218
C≡O	1072			S—S	266
C—Cl	339				

*799 in CO_2

Using Average Bond Energies to Estimate Enthalpy Changes for Reactions

We can use average bond energies to *estimate* the enthalpy change of a reaction. For example, consider the reaction between methane and chlorine:

$$H_3C{-}H(g) + Cl{-}Cl(g) \longrightarrow H_3C{-}Cl(g) + H{-}Cl(g)$$

We can imagine this reaction occurring by the breaking of a C—H bond and a Cl—Cl bond and the forming of a C—Cl bond and an H—Cl bond. We know that when bonds break, the process is endothermic (positive bond energy) and when bonds form, the process is exothermic (negative bond energy). So we can calculate the overall enthalpy change as a sum of the enthalpy changes associated with breaking the required bonds in the reactants and forming the required bonds in the products, as shown in Figure 10.12▼.

$$H_3C{-}H(g) + Cl{-}Cl(g) \longrightarrow H_3C{-}Cl(g) + H{-}Cl(g)$$

Bonds Broken		**Bonds Formed**	
C—H break	+414 kJ	C—Cl form	−339 kJ
Cl—Cl break	+243 kJ	H—Cl form	−431 kJ
Sum (Σ)*ΔH's bonds broken:* +657 kJ		*Sum* (Σ)*ΔH's bonds formed:* −770 kJ	

$$\begin{aligned}\Delta H_{rxn} &= \Sigma(\Delta H\text{'s bonds broken}) + \Sigma(\Delta H\text{'s bonds formed})\\ &= +657\text{ kJ} - 770\text{ kJ}\\ &= -113\text{ kJ}\end{aligned}$$

We find that $\Delta H_{rxn} = -113$ kJ. Calculating ΔH°_{rxn} from tabulated enthalpies of formation—the method we learned in Chapter 7—gives $\Delta H^\circ_{rxn} = -101$ kJ, fairly close to the value we obtained from average bond energies.

In general, we can calculate ΔH_{rxn} from average bond energies by summing the changes in enthalpy for all of the bonds that are broken and adding the sum of the enthalpy changes for all of the bonds that are formed. Remember that ΔH is positive for breaking bonds and negative for forming them:

$$\Delta H_{rxn} = \underbrace{\Sigma(\Delta H\text{'s bonds broken})}_{\text{Positive}} + \underbrace{\Sigma(\Delta H\text{'s bonds formed})}_{\text{Negative}}$$

As we can see from the equation:

- A reaction is *exothermic* when weak bonds break and strong bonds form.
- A reaction is *endothermic* when strong bonds break and weak bonds form.

Scientists sometimes say that "energy is stored in chemical bonds or in a chemical compound," which may make it sound as if breaking the bonds in the compound releases energy. For example, in biology we often hear that energy is stored in glucose or in ATP. However, *breaking a chemical bond always requires energy*. When we say that energy is stored in a compound, or that a compound is energy rich, we mean that the compound can undergo a reaction in which weak bonds break and strong bonds form, thereby releasing energy in the overall process. However, *it is always the forming of chemical bonds that releases energy*.

▼ **FIGURE 10.12 Estimating ΔH_{rxn} from Bond Energies** We can approximate the enthalpy change of a reaction by summing up the enthalpy changes involved in breaking old bonds and forming new ones.

Estimating the Enthalpy Change of a Reaction from Bond Energies

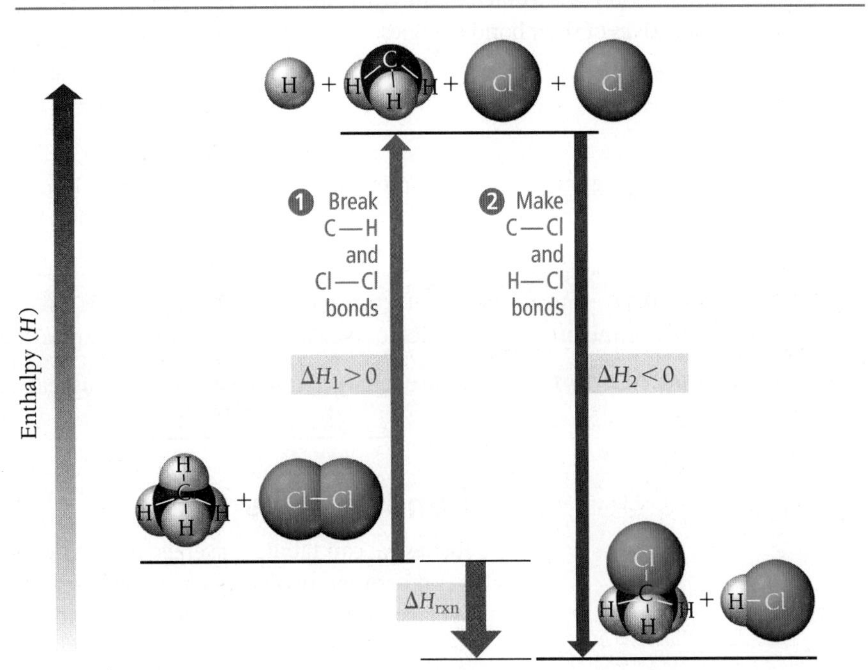

ANSWER **NOW!**

10.10 Cc Conceptual Connection

BOND ENERGIES AND ΔH_{rxn} The reaction between hydrogen and oxygen to form water is highly exothermic. Which statement is true of the energies of the bonds that break and form during the reaction?

(a) The energy needed to break the required bonds is greater than the energy released when the new bonds form.

(b) The energy needed to break the required bonds is less than the energy released when the new bonds form.

(c) The energy needed to break the required bonds is about the same as the energy released when the new bonds form.

WATCH **NOW!**

INTERACTIVE WORKED EXAMPLE 10.11

EXAMPLE 10.11 Calculating ΔH_{rxn} from Bond Energies

Hydrogen gas, a potential fuel, can be made by the reaction of methane gas and steam.

$$CH_4(g) + 2\,H_2O(g) \longrightarrow 4\,H_2(g) + CO_2(g)$$

Use bond energies to calculate ΔH_{rxn} for this reaction.

SOLUTION

Begin by rewriting the reaction using the Lewis structures of the molecules involved.	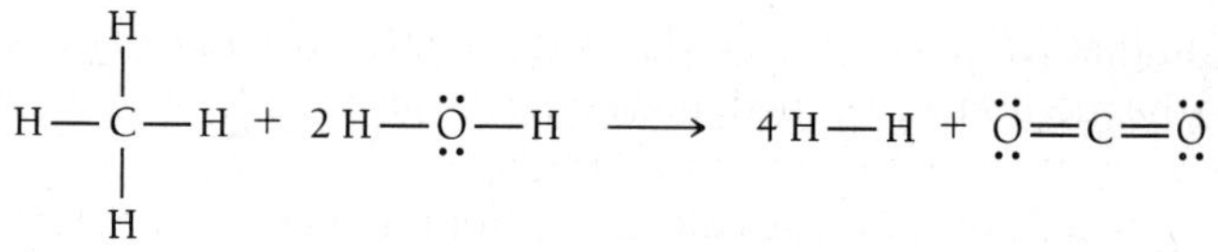
Determine which bonds are broken in the reaction and sum the bond energies of these.	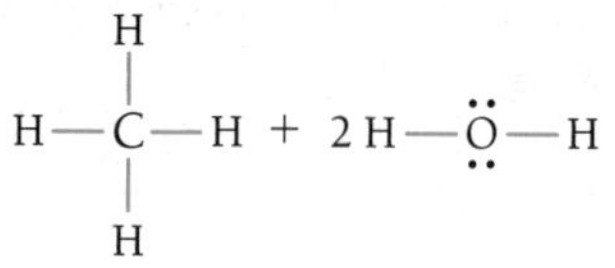 $\Sigma(\Delta H\text{'s bonds broken})$ $= 4(\text{C—H}) + 4(\text{O—H})$ $= 4(414\text{ kJ}) + 4(464\text{ kJ})$ $= 3512\text{ kJ}$
Determine which bonds are formed in the reaction and add the negatives of their bond energies.	$4\,\text{H—H} + \ddot{\text{O}}\text{=C=}\ddot{\text{O}}$ $\Sigma(\Delta H\text{'s bonds formed})$ $= -4(\text{H—H}) - 2(\text{C=O})$ $= -4(436\text{ kJ}) - 2(799\text{ kJ})$ $= -3342\text{ kJ}$
Find ΔH_{rxn} by summing the results of the previous two steps.	$\Delta H_{rxn} = \Sigma(\Delta H\text{'s bonds broken}) + \Sigma(\Delta H\text{'s bonds formed})$ $= 3512\text{ kJ} - 3342\text{ kJ}$ $= 1.70 \times 10^2\text{ kJ}$

FOR PRACTICE 10.11 Another potential future fuel is methanol (CH_3OH). Write a balanced equation for the combustion of gaseous methanol and use bond energies to calculate the enthalpy of combustion of methanol in kJ/mol.

FOR MORE PRACTICE 10.11 Use bond energies to calculate ΔH_{rxn} for this reaction: $N_2(g) + 3\,H_2(g) \longrightarrow 2\,NH_3(g)$.

Bond Lengths

Just as we can tabulate average bond energies, which represent the average energy of a bond between two particular atoms in a large number of compounds, we can tabulate average bond lengths (Table 10.4). The average **bond length** represents the average

TABLE 10.4 ■ Average Bond Lengths

Bond	Bond Length (pm)	Bond	Bond Length (pm)	Bond	Bond Length (pm)
H—H	74	C—C	154	N—N	145
H—C	110	C=C	134	N=N	123
H—N	100	C≡C	120	N≡N	110
H—O	97	C—N	147	N—O	136
H—S	132	C=N	128	N=O	120
H—F	92	C≡N	116	O—O	145
H—Cl	127	C—O	143	O=O	121
H—Br	141	C=O	120	F—F	143
H—I	161	C—Cl	178	Cl—Cl	199
				Br—Br	228
				I—I	266

Bond Lengths

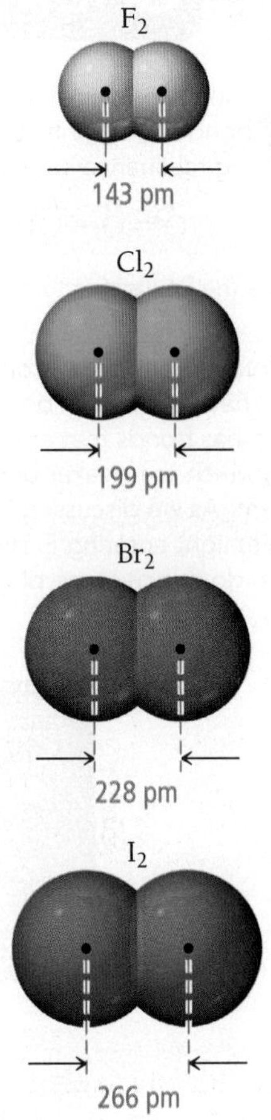

▲ Bond lengths in the diatomic halogen molecules.

length of a bond between two particular atoms in a large number of compounds. Like bond energies, bond lengths depend not only on the kind of atoms involved in the bond, but also on the type of bond: single, double, or triple. In general, for a particular pair of atoms, triple bonds are shorter than double bonds, which are in turn shorter than single bonds. For example, consider the bond lengths (shown here with bond strengths) of carbon–carbon triple, double, and single bonds:

Bond	Bond Length (pm)	Bond Strength (kJ/mol)
C≡C	120	837
C=C	134	611
C—C	154	347

Notice that, as the bond gets longer, it also becomes weaker. This relationship between the length of a bond and the strength of a bond does not necessarily hold true for all bonds. Consider the following series of nitrogen–halogen single bonds:

Bond	Bond Length (pm)	Bond Strength (kJ/mol)
N—F	139	272
N—Cl	191	200
N—Br	214	243
N—I	222	159

Although the bonds generally get weaker as they get longer, the trend is not a smooth one.

10.11 Bonding in Metals: The Electron Sea Model

So far, we have explored simple models for bonding between a metal and a nonmetal (ionic bonding) and for bonding between two nonmetals (covalent bonding). We have seen how these models account for and predict the properties of ionic and molecular compounds. The last type of bonding that we examine in this chapter is metallic bonding, which occurs between metals.

As we have already discussed, metals have a tendency to lose electrons, which means that they have relatively low ionization energies. When metal atoms bond together to form a solid lattice, each metal atom donates one or more electrons to an *electron sea*. For example, we can think of sodium metal as an array of positively charged Na^+ ions immersed in a sea of negatively charged electrons (e^-), as shown in Figure 10.13▶.

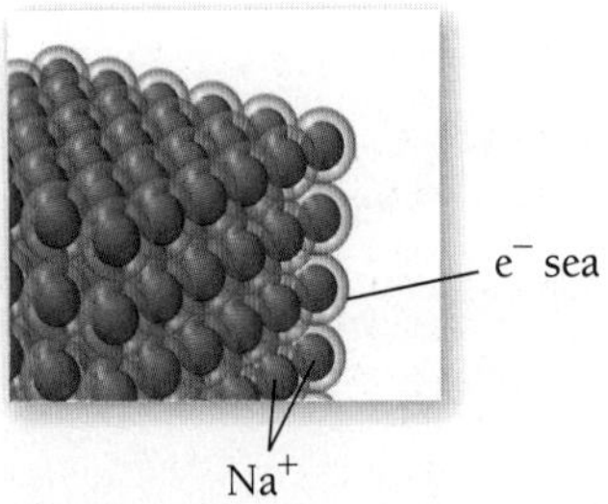

▲ **FIGURE 10.13 The Electron Sea Model for Sodium** In this model of metallic bonding, Na^+ ions are immersed in a "sea" of electrons.

CHEMISTRY IN THE ENVIRONMENT | The Lewis Structure of Ozone

Ozone is a form of oxygen in which three oxygen atoms bond together. Its Lewis structure consists of the following resonance structures:

$$:\ddot{O}=\ddot{O}-\underset{..}{\ddot{O}}: \longleftrightarrow :\underset{..}{\ddot{O}}-\ddot{O}=\ddot{O}:$$

Compare the Lewis structure of ozone to the Lewis structure of O_2:

$$:\ddot{O}=\ddot{O}:$$

Since double bonds are stronger and shorter than single bonds, O_2 must have a stronger bond because it is a double bond. O_3, however, has bonds that are intermediate between single and double, which are weaker bonds. The effects of this are significant. As we discussed in Section 7.10, O_3 absorbs harmful ultraviolet light entering Earth's atmosphere. Ozone is ideally suited to do this because photons at wavelengths of 280–320 nm (the most harmful components of sunlight) are just strong enough to break the bonds in the O_3 molecule:

$$:\ddot{O}=\ddot{O}-\underset{..}{\ddot{O}}: + \text{UV light} \longrightarrow :\ddot{O}=\ddot{O}: + \cdot\underset{\cdot}{\ddot{O}}:$$

In this process, the photon is absorbed. O_2 and O then recombine to re-form O_3, which can in turn absorb more UV light. The same wavelengths of UV light, however, do not have sufficient energy to break the stronger double bond of O_2. No other molecules in our atmosphere can do the job that ozone does. Consequently, we should continue, and even strengthen, the ban on ozone-depleting compounds.

QUESTION *Calculate the average bond energy of one O_3 bond. What wavelength of light has just the right amount of energy to break this bond?*

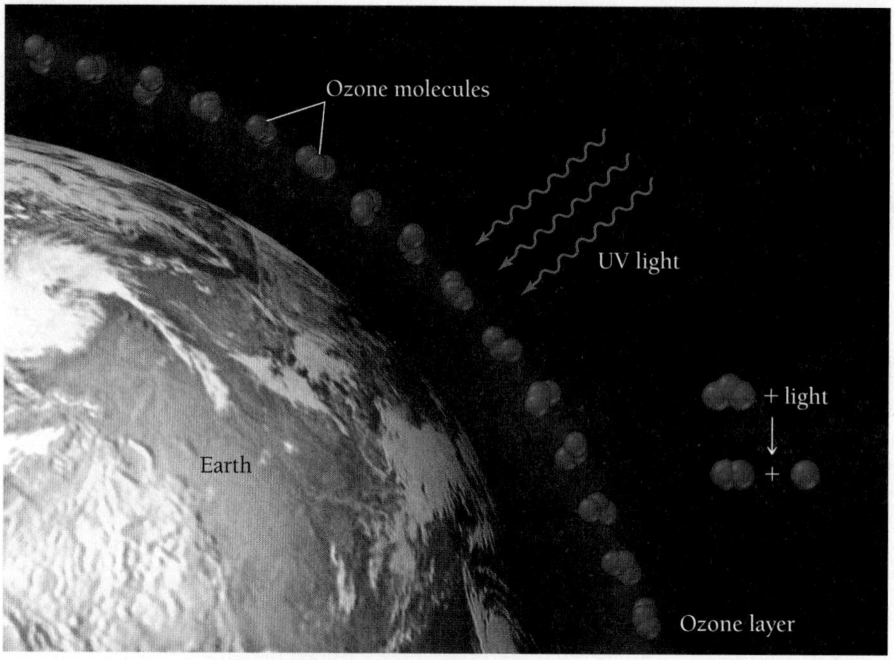

▲ Ozone protects life on Earth from harmful ultraviolet light.

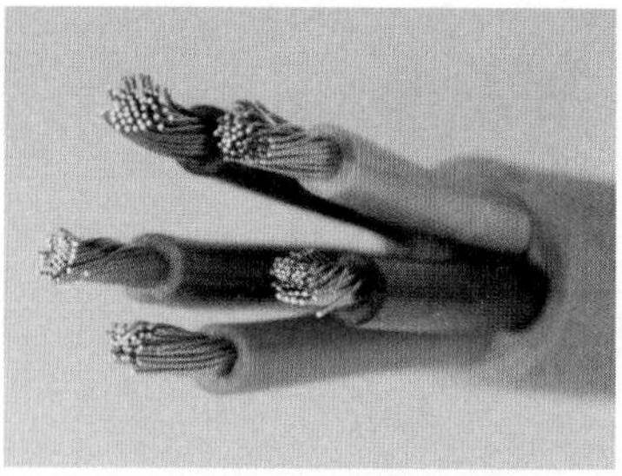

▲ Copper can easily be drawn into fine strands like those used in household electrical cords.

Each sodium atom donates its one valence electron to the "sea" and becomes a sodium ion. The sodium cations are held together by their attraction to the sea of electrons.

Although the electron sea model is simple, it accounts for many properties of metals. For example, metals conduct electricity because—in contrast to ionic solids, in which electrons are localized on an ion—the electrons in a metal are free to move. The movement or flow of electrons in response to an electric potential (or voltage) is an electric current. Metals are also excellent conductors of heat, again because of the highly mobile electrons, which help to disperse thermal energy throughout the metal.

The electron sea model also accounts for the *malleability* of metals (their capacity to be pounded into sheets) and the *ductility* of metals (their capacity to be drawn into wires). Since there are no localized or specific "bonds" in a metal, we can deform it relatively easily by forcing the metal ions to slide past one another. The electron sea easily accommodates deformations by flowing into the new shape.

Self-Assessment Quiz

Q1. Which pair of elements is most likely to form an ionic bond?
MISSED THIS? *Read Section 10.2*

a) nitrogen and oxygen
b) carbon and hydrogen
c) sulfur and oxygen
d) calcium and oxygen

Q2. Which set of elements is arranged in order of increasing electronegativity?
MISSED THIS? *Read Section 10.6; Watch KCV 10.6*

a) O < S < As < Ge
b) Ge < As < S < O
c) S < O < As < Ge
d) As < O < Ge < S

Q3. Which is the correct Lewis structure for magnesium bromide?
MISSED THIS? *Read Section 10.4*

Q4. Which compound is likely to have an incomplete octet?
MISSED THIS? *Read Section 10.9; Watch KCV 10.9*

a) NH_3 b) SO_3 c) N_2O d) BH_3

Q5. Which compound has the lattice energy with the greatest magnitude? **MISSED THIS?** *Read Section 10.4*

a) MgS b) CaS c) SrS d) BaS

Q6. Which set of compounds is arranged in order of increasing magnitude of lattice energy?
MISSED THIS? *Read Section 10.4*

a) CsI < NaCl < MgS
b) NaCl < CsI < MgS
c) MgS < NaCl < CsI
d) CsI < MgS < NaCl

Q7. Which pair of atoms forms the most polar bond?
MISSED THIS? *Read Section 10.6; Watch KCV 10.6*

a) N and O b) C and O c) C and F d) N and F

Q8. Which pair of atoms forms a nonpolar covalent bond?
MISSED THIS? *Read Section 10.6; Watch KCV 10.6*

a) C and S b) C and O c) B and O d) Na and Cl

Q9. Which is the correct Lewis structure for nitrogen trifluoride?
MISSED THIS? *Read Section 10.7; Watch KCV 10.7, IWE 10.4*

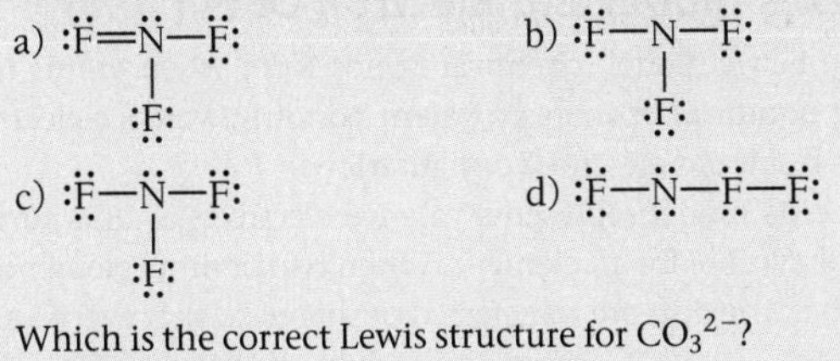

Q10. Which is the correct Lewis structure for CO_3^{2-}?
MISSED THIS? *Read Section 10.7; Watch KCV 10.7, IWE 10.6*

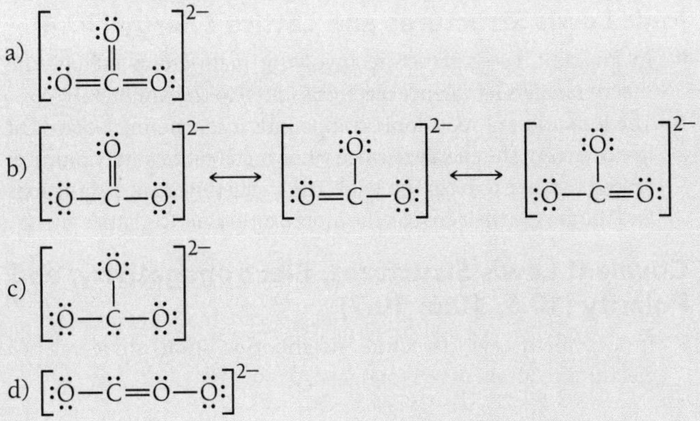

Q11. Determine the formal charge of nitrogen in the structure shown here:
MISSED THIS? *Read Section 10.8; Watch KCV 10.8, IWE 10.8*

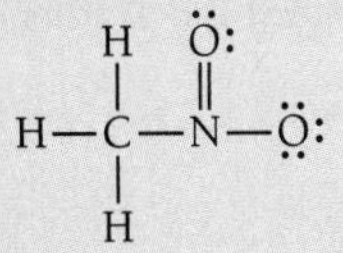

a) +1 b) +2 c) −1 d) −2

Q12. A Lewis structure for the acetate ion is shown here:
MISSED THIS? *Read Section 10.8; Watch KCV 10.8, IWE 10.7*

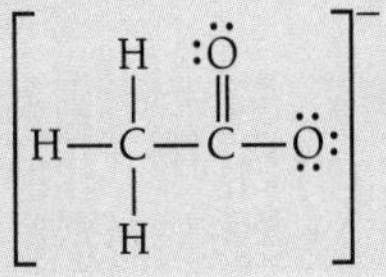

Which structure is the best resonance structure for the acetate ion?

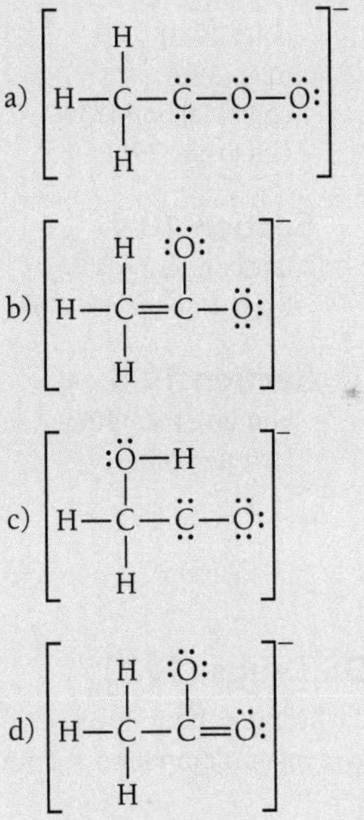

Q13. Use formal charge to choose the best Lewis structure for CH_3SOCH_3.
MISSED THIS? *Read Section 10.8; Watch KCV 10.8, IWE 10.8*

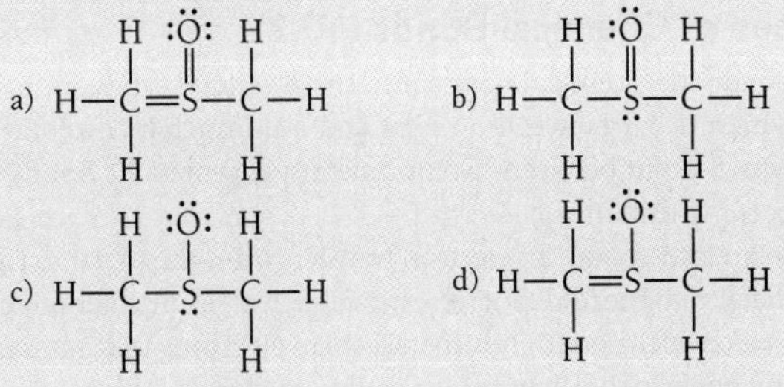

—Continued on the next page

Continued—

Q14. Use bond energies from Table 10.3 to determine ΔH_{rxn} for the reaction between ethanol and hydrogen chloride.
MISSED THIS? *Read Section 10.10; Watch IWE 10.11*

$$CH_3CH_2OH(g) + HCl(g) \longrightarrow CH_3CH_2Cl(g) + H_2O(g)$$

a) −1549 kJ b) 1549 kJ c) −12 kJ d) 12 kJ

Q15. Consider the halogenation of ethene, where X is a generic halogen:

$$H_2C{=}CH_2(g) + X_2(g) \longrightarrow H_2XC{-}CH_2X(g)$$

Use bond energies to determine which halogen produces the most exothermic halogenation reaction with ethene. The C—F, C—Br, and C—I bond energies are 552 kJ/mol, 280 kJ/mol, and 209 kJ/mol, respectively. Look up all other necessary bond energies in Table 10.3.
MISSED THIS? *Read Section 10.10; Watch IWE 10.11*

a) fluorine b) chlorine
c) bromine d) iodine

Answers: 1. (d) **2.** (b) **3.** (c) **4.** (d) **5.** (a) **6.** (a) **7.** (c) **8.** (a) **9.** (c) **10.** (b) **11.** (a) **12.** (d) **13.** (b) **14.** (c) **15.** (a)

CHAPTER 10 IN REVIEW

TERMS

Section 10.1
Lewis model (394)
Lewis electron-dot structures (Lewis structures) (394)
octet (396)
duet (396)
chemical bond (396)
octet rule (396)

Section 10.2
ionic bond (395)
covalent bond (395)
metallic bonding (396)

Section 10.3
Lewis symbol (396)

Section 10.4
lattice energy (398)
Born–Haber cycle (398)

Section 10.5
bonding pair (404)
lone pair (404)
nonbonding electrons (404)
double bond (404)
triple bond (405)

Section 10.6
polar covalent bond (407)
electronegativity (407)
dipole moment (μ) (408)
percent ionic character (409)

Section 10.8
resonance structures (413)
resonance hybrid (413)
formal charge (414)

Section 10.9
free radical (418)

Section 10.10
bond energy (422)
bond length (424)

CONCEPTS

Bonding Models and AIDS Drugs (10.1)

- Theories that predict how and why atoms bond together are central to chemistry because they explain compound stability and molecule shape.
- Bonding theories have been useful in combating HIV because they help in the design of molecules that bind to the active site of a protein crucial for the development of AIDS.

Types of Chemical Bonds (10.2)

- We divide chemical bonds into three general types: ionic bonds, which occur between a metal and a nonmetal; covalent bonds, which occur between two nonmetals; and metallic bonds, which occur within metals.
- In an ionic bond, an electron transfers from the metal to the nonmetal, and the resultant ions attract each other by coulombic forces.
- In a covalent bond, nonmetals share electrons that interact with the nuclei of both atoms via coulombic forces, holding the atoms together.
- In a metallic bond, the atoms form a lattice in which each metal loses electrons to an "electron sea." The attraction of the positively charged metal ions to the electron sea holds the metal together.

The Lewis Model and Electron Dots (10.3)

- In the Lewis model, chemical bonds form when atoms transfer (ionic bonding) or share (covalent bonding) valence electrons to attain noble gas electron configurations.
- The Lewis model represents valence electrons as dots surrounding the symbol for an element. When two or more elements bond together, the dots are transferred or shared so that every atom has eight dots, an octet (or two dots, a duet, in the case of hydrogen).

Ionic Lewis Structures and Lattice Energy (10.4)

- In an ionic Lewis structure involving main-group metals, the metal transfers its valence electrons (dots) to the nonmetal.
- The formation of most ionic compounds is exothermic because of lattice energy, the energy released when metal cations and nonmetal anions coalesce to form the solid. The smaller the radius of the ions and the greater their charge, the more exothermic the lattice energy.

Covalent Lewis Structures, Electronegativity, and Polarity (10.5, 10.6, 10.7)

- In a covalent Lewis structure, neighboring atoms share valence electrons to attain octets (or duets).

- A single shared electron pair constitutes a single bond, while two or three shared pairs constitute double or triple bonds, respectively.
- The shared electrons in a covalent bond are not always *equally* shared; when two dissimilar nonmetals form a covalent bond, the electron density is greater on the more electronegative element. The result is a polar bond, in which one element has a partial positive charge and the other a partial negative charge.
- Electronegativity—the ability of an atom to attract electrons to itself in chemical bonding—increases as we move to the right across a period in the periodic table and decreases as we move down a column.
- Elements with very dissimilar electronegativities form ionic bonds, those with very similar electronegativities form nonpolar covalent bonds, and those with intermediate electronegativity differences form polar covalent bonds.

Resonance and Formal Charge (10.8)

- We can best represent some molecules not by a single Lewis structure, but by two or more resonance structures. The actual structure of these molecules is a resonance hybrid: a combination or average of the contributing structures.
- The formal charge of an atom in a Lewis structure is the charge the atom would have if all bonding electrons were shared equally between bonding atoms.
- In general, the best Lewis structures have the fewest atoms with formal charge, and any negative formal charges are on the most electronegative atom.

Exceptions to the Octet Rule (10.9)

- Although the octet rule normally applies when we draw Lewis structures, some exceptions occur.
- These exceptions include odd-electron species, which necessarily have Lewis structures with only seven electrons around an atom. Such molecules, called free radicals, tend to be unstable and chemically reactive.
- Other exceptions to the octet rule include molecules with incomplete octets—usually totaling six electrons (especially important in compounds containing boron)—and molecules with expanded octets—usually 10 or 12 electrons (which can occur in compounds containing elements from the third row of the periodic table and below). Expanded octets never occur in second-period elements.

Bond Energies and Bond Lengths (10.10)

- The bond energy of a chemical bond is the energy required to break one mole of the bonds in the gas phase.
- Average bond energies for a number of different bonds are tabulated, and we can use them to calculate enthalpies of reaction.
- Average bond lengths are also tabulated.
- In general, triple bonds are shorter and stronger than double bonds, which are in turn shorter and stronger than single bonds.

Bonding in Metals (10.11)

- When metal atoms bond together to form a solid, each metal atom donates one or more electrons to an *electron sea*. The metal cations are held together by their attraction to the sea of electrons.
- The *electron sea* model accounts for the electrical conductivity, thermal conductivity, malleability, and ductility of metals.

EQUATIONS AND RELATIONSHIPS

Dipole Moment (μ): Separation of Two Particles of Equal but Opposite Charge of Magnitude q by a Distance r (**10.6**)

$$\mu = qr$$

Percent Ionic Character (**10.6**)

Percent ionic character =

$$\frac{\text{measured dipole moment of bond}}{\text{dipole moment if electron were completely transferred}} \times 100\%$$

Formal Charge (**10.8**)

Formal charge = number of valence electrons −

(number of nonbonding electrons + $\frac{1}{2}$ number of shared electrons)

Enthalpy Change of a Reaction (ΔH_{rxn}): Relationship of Bond Energies (**10.10**)

$$\Delta H_{rxn} = \Sigma(\Delta H\text{'s bonds broken}) + \Sigma(\Delta H\text{'s bonds formed})$$

LEARNING OUTCOMES

Chapter Objectives	Assessment
Write Lewis symbols for main group elements (**10.3**)	**Exercises** 35–38
Write and use Lewis symbols to describe and analyze ionic compounds (**10.4**)	Example 10.1 **For Practice** 10.1 **Exercise** 39–42
Compare the relative lattice energies of different compounds (**10.4**)	Example 10.2 **For Practice** 10.2 **For More Practice** 10.2 **Exercises** 43–46
Calculate lattice energies of ionic solids (**10.4**)	**Exercises** 47–48
Classify bonds as pure covalent, polar covalent, or ionic (**10.5–10.6**)	Example 10.3 **For Practice** 10.3 **Exercises** 55–58
Write and use Lewis structures to describe and analyze molecular compounds and polyatomic ions (**10.7**)	Examples 10.4–10.7 **For Practice** 10.4–10.7 **Exercises** 49–54, 59–62

—Continued on the next page

Continued—

Write the best possible Lewis structure using formal charge (**10.8**)	Examples 10.8, 10.9 **For Practice** 10.8, 10.9 **For More Practice** 10.8 **Exercises** 63–72
Write Lewis structures for molecules and ions that are exceptions to the octet rule (**10.9**)	Example 10.10 **For Practice** 10.10 **For More Practice** 10.10 **Exercises** 73–78
Analyze bonds in terms of bond energy and bond length (**10.10**)	Example 10.11 **For Practice** 10.11 **For More Practice** 10.11 **Exercises** 79–84

EXERCISES

Mastering Chemistry provides end-of-chapter exercises, feedback-enriched tutorial problems, animations, and interactive activities to encourage problem-solving practice and deeper understanding of key concepts and topics.

REVIEW QUESTIONS

1. Why are bonding theories important? Provide some examples of what bonding theories can predict.

2. Why do chemical bonds form? What basic forces are involved in bonding?

3. What are the three basic types of chemical bonds? What happens to electrons in the bonding atoms in each type?

4. How do you determine how many dots to put around the Lewis symbol of an element?

5. Describe the octet rule in the Lewis model.

6. According to the Lewis model, what is a chemical bond?

7. How do you draw an ionic Lewis structure?

8. How can Lewis structures be used to determine the formula of ionic compounds? Give an example.

9. What is lattice energy?

10. Why is the formation of solid sodium chloride from solid sodium and gaseous chlorine exothermic, even though it takes more energy to form the Na^+ ion than the amount of energy released upon formation of Cl^-?

11. What is the Born–Haber cycle? List each step in the cycle and show how the cycle is used to calculate lattice energy.

12. How does lattice energy relate to ionic radii? To ion charge?

13. How does the ionic bonding model explain the relatively high melting points of ionic compounds?

14. How does the ionic bonding model explain the nonconductivity of ionic solids, and at the same time the conductivity of ionic solutions?

15. In a covalent Lewis structure, what is the difference between lone pair and bonding pair electrons?

16. In what ways are double and triple covalent bonds different from single covalent bonds?

17. How does the Lewis model for covalent bonding account for why certain combinations of atoms are stable while others are not?

18. How does the Lewis model for covalent bonding account for the relatively low melting and boiling points of molecular compounds (compared to ionic compounds)?

19. What is electronegativity? What are the periodic trends in electronegativity?

20. How do a pure covalent bond, a polar covalent bond, and an ionic bond differ?

21. Explain percent ionic character of a bond. Do any bonds have 100% ionic character?

22. What is a dipole moment?

23. What is the magnitude of the dipole moment formed by separating a proton and an electron by 100 pm? 200 pm?

24. What is the basic procedure for writing a covalent Lewis structure?

25. How do you determine the number of electrons in the Lewis structure of a molecule? A polyatomic ion?

26. What are resonance structures? What is a resonance hybrid?

27. Do resonance structures always contribute equally to the overall structure of a molecule? Explain.

28. What is formal charge? How is formal charge calculated? How is it helpful?

29. Why does the octet rule have exceptions? List the three major categories of exceptions and an example of each.

30. Which elements can have expanded octets? Which elements should never have expanded octets?

31. What is bond energy? How can you use average bond energies to calculate enthalpies of reaction?

32. Explain the difference between endothermic reactions and exothermic reactions with respect to the bond energies of the bonds broken and formed.

33. What is the electron sea model for bonding in metals?

34. How does the electron sea model explain the conductivity of metals? The malleability and ductility of metals?

PROBLEMS BY TOPIC

Valence Electrons and Dot Structures

35. Write the electron configuration for N. Then write the Lewis symbol for N and show which electrons from the electron configuration are included in the Lewis symbol.
MISSED THIS? *Read Section 10.3*

36. Write the electron configuration for Ne. Then write the Lewis symbol for Ne and show which electrons from the electron configuration are included in the Lewis symbol.

37. Write the Lewis symbol for each atom or ion.
MISSED THIS? *Read Section 10.3*
a. Al **b.** Na^+ **c.** Cl **d.** Cl^-

38. Write the Lewis symbol for each atom or ion.
a. S^{2-} **b.** Mg **c.** Mg^{2+} **d.** P

Ionic Lewis Symbols and Lattice Energy

39. Write the Lewis symbols for the ions in each ionic compound.
MISSED THIS? *Read Section 10.4*
a. NaF b. CaO c. $SrBr_2$ d. K_2O

40. Write the Lewis symbols for the ions in each ionic compound.
a. SrO b. Li_2S c. CaI_2 d. RbF

41. Use Lewis symbols to determine the formula for the compound that forms between each pair of elements.
MISSED THIS? *Read Section 10.4*
a. Sr and Se b. Ba and Cl c. Na and S d. Al and O

42. Use Lewis symbols to determine the formula for the compound that forms between each pair of elements:
a. Ca and N b. Mg and I c. Ca and S d. Cs and F

43. Explain the trend in the lattice energies of the alkaline earth metal oxides. **MISSED THIS?** *Read Section 10.4*

Metal Oxide	Lattice Energy (kJ/mol)
MgO	−3795
CaO	−3414
SrO	−3217
BaO	−3029

44. Rubidium iodide has a lattice energy of −617 kJ/mol, while potassium bromide has a lattice energy of −671 kJ/mol. Why is the lattice energy of potassium bromide more exothermic than the lattice energy of rubidium iodide?

45. The lattice energy of CsF is −744 kJ/mol, whereas that of BaO is −3029 kJ/mol. Explain this large difference in lattice energy.
MISSED THIS? *Read Section 10.4*

46. Arrange these compounds in order of increasing magnitude of lattice energy: KCl, SrO, RbBr, CaO.

47. Use the Born–Haber cycle and data from Appendix IIB, Chapter 9, and this chapter to calculate the lattice energy of KCl. (ΔH_{sub} for potassium is 89.0 kJ/mol.) **MISSED THIS?** *Read Section 10.4*

48. Use the Born–Haber cycle and data from Appendix IIB and Table 10.3 to calculate the lattice energy of CaO. (ΔH_{sub} for calcium is 178 kJ/mol; IE_1 and IE_2 for calcium are 590 kJ/mol and 1145 kJ/mol, respectively; EA_1 and EA_2 for O are −141 kJ/mol and 744 kJ/mol, respectively.)

Simple Covalent Lewis Structures, Electronegativity, and Bond Polarity

49. Use covalent Lewis structures to explain why each element (or family of elements) occurs as diatomic molecules.
MISSED THIS? *Read Section 10.5; Watch KCV 10.5*
a. hydrogen
b. the halogens
c. oxygen
d. nitrogen

50. Use covalent Lewis structures to explain why the compound that forms between nitrogen and hydrogen has the formula NH_3. Show why NH_2 and NH_4 are not stable.

51. Write the Lewis structure for each molecule.
MISSED THIS? *Read Section 10.7; Watch KCV 10.7, IWE 10.4*
a. PH_3 b. SCl_2 c. HI d. CH_4

52. Write the Lewis structure for each molecule.
a. NF_3 b. HBr c. SBr_2 d. CCl_4

53. Write the Lewis structure for each molecule.
MISSED THIS? *Read Section 10.7; Watch KCV 10.7, IWE 10.4*
a. SF_2 b. SiH_4
c. HCOOH (both O bonded to C) d. CH_3SH (C and S central)

54. Write the Lewis structure for each molecule.
a. CH_2O b. C_2Cl_4
c. CH_3NH_2 d. $CFCl_3$ (C central)

55. Determine if a bond between each pair of atoms would be pure covalent, polar covalent, or ionic.
MISSED THIS? *Read Section 10.6; Watch KCV 10.6*
a. Br and Br b. C and Cl c. C and S d. Sr and O

56. Determine if a bond between each pair of atoms would be pure covalent, polar covalent, or ionic.
a. C and N b. N and S c. K and F d. N and N

57. Draw the Lewis structure for CO with an arrow representing the dipole moment. Refer to Figure 10.10 to estimate the percent ionic character of the CO bond.
MISSED THIS? *Read Section 10.6; Watch KCV 10.6*

58. Draw the Lewis structure for BrF with an arrow representing the dipole moment. Refer to Figure 10.10 to estimate the percent ionic character of the BrF bond.

Covalent Lewis Structures, Resonance, and Formal Charge

59. Write the Lewis structure for each molecule or ion.
MISSED THIS? *Read Section 10.7; Watch KCV 10.7, IWE 10.4*
a. CI_4 b. N_2O c. SiH_4 d. Cl_2CO

60. Write the Lewis structure for each molecule or ion.
a. H_3COH b. OH^- c. BrO^- d. O_2^{2-}

61. Write the Lewis structure for each molecule or ion.
MISSED THIS? *Read Section 10.7; Watch KCV 10.7, IWE 10.4*
a. N_2H_2 b. N_2H_4 c. C_2H_2 d. C_2H_4

62. Write the Lewis structure for each molecule or ion.
a. H_3COCH_3 b. CN^- c. NO_2^- d. ClO^-

63. Write a Lewis structure that obeys the octet rule for each molecule or ion. Include resonance structures if necessary and assign formal charges to each atom.
MISSED THIS? *Read Section 10.8; Watch KCV 10.8, IWE 10.7*
a. SeO_2 b. CO_3^{2-} c. ClO^- d. NO_2^-

64. Write a Lewis structure that obeys the octet rule for each ion. Include resonance structures if necessary and assign formal charges to each atom.
a. ClO_3^- b. ClO_4^- c. NO_3^- d. NH_4^+

65. Use formal charge to identify the better Lewis structure.
MISSED THIS? *Read Section 10.8; Watch KCV 10.8, IWE 10.8*

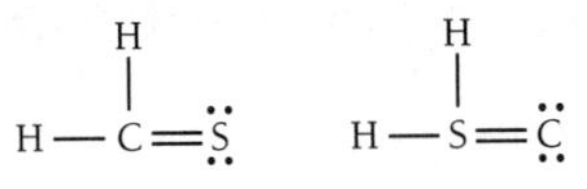

66. Use formal charges to identify the better Lewis structure.

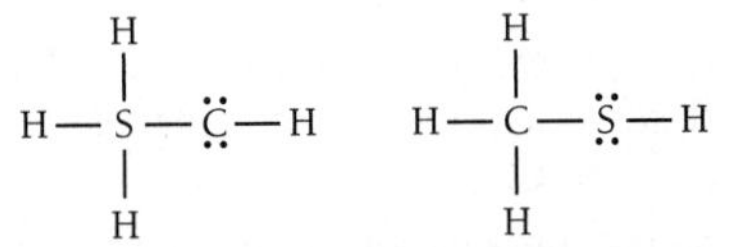

67. How important is the resonance structure shown here to the overall structure of carbon dioxide? Explain.
MISSED THIS? *Read Section 10.8; Watch KCV 10.8, IWE 10.8*

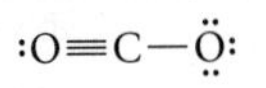

68. In N_2O, nitrogen is the central atom, and the oxygen atom is terminal. In OF_2, however, oxygen is the central atom. Use formal charges to explain why.

69. Draw the Lewis structure (including resonance structures) for the acetate ion (CH_3COO^-). For each resonance structure, assign formal charges to all atoms that have formal charge. **MISSED THIS?** *Read Section 10.8; Watch KCV 10.8, IWE 10.9*

70. Draw the Lewis structure (including resonance structures) for methyl azide (CH_3N_3). For each resonance structure, assign formal charges to all atoms that have formal charge.

71. What are the formal charges of the atoms shown in red? **MISSED THIS?** *Read Section 10.8; Watch KCV 10.8, IWE 10.9*

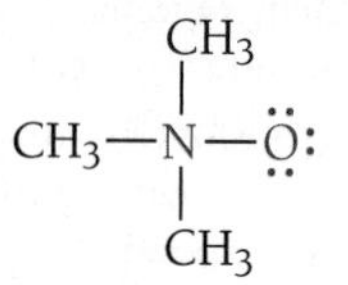

72. What are the formal charges of the atoms shown in red?

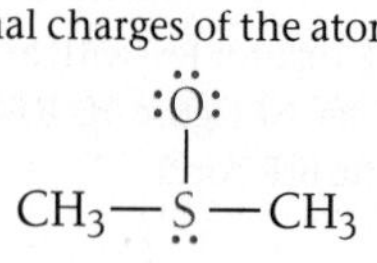

Odd-Electron Species, Incomplete Octets, and Expanded Octets

73. Write the Lewis structure for each molecule (octet rule not followed). **MISSED THIS?** *Read Section 10.9; Watch KCV 10.9*
a. BCl_3 b. NO_2 c. BH_3

74. Write the Lewis structure for each molecule (octet rule not followed).
a. BBr_3
b. NO
c. ClO_2

75. Write the Lewis structure for each ion. Include resonance structures if necessary and assign formal charges to all atoms. If necessary, expand the octet on the central atom to lower formal charge. **MISSED THIS?** *Read Section 10.9; Watch KCV 10.9, IWE 10.10*
a. PO_4^{3-} b. CN^- c. SO_3^{2-} d. ClO_2^-

76. Write Lewis structures for each molecule or ion. Include resonance structures if necessary and assign formal charges to all atoms. If necessary, expand the octet on the central atom to lower formal charge.
a. SO_4^{2-} b. HSO_4^- c. SO_3 d. BrO_2^-

77. Write Lewis structures for each molecule or ion. Use expanded octets as necessary.
MISSED THIS? *Read Section 10.9; Watch KCV 10.9, IWE 10.10*
a. PF_5 b. I_3^-
c. SF_4 d. GeF_4

78. Write Lewis structures for each molecule or ion. Use expanded octets as necessary.
a. ClF_5 b. AsF_6^-
c. Cl_3PO d. IF_5

Bond Energies and Bond Lengths

79. List these compounds in order of increasing carbon–carbon bond strength and in order of decreasing carbon–carbon bond length: HCCH, H_2CCH_2, H_3CCH_3. **MISSED THIS?** *Read Section 10.10*

80. Which compound shown here has the stronger nitrogen–nitrogen bond? The shorter nitrogen–nitrogen bond?

$$H_2NNH_2, \ HNNH$$

81. Hydrogenation reactions are used to add hydrogen across double bonds in hydrocarbons and other organic compounds. Use average bond energies to calculate ΔH_{rxn} for the hydrogenation reaction. **MISSED THIS?** *Read Section 10.10; Watch IWE 10.11*

$$H_2C = CH_2(g) + H_2(g) \longrightarrow H_3C-CH_3(g)$$

82. Ethanol is a possible fuel. Use average bond energies to calculate ΔH_{rxn} for the combustion of ethanol.

$$CH_3CH_2OH(g) + 3\,O_2(g) \longrightarrow 2\,CO_2(g) + 3\,H_2O(g)$$

83. Ethane burns in air to form carbon dixode and water vapor. **MISSED THIS?** *Read Section 10.10; Watch IWE 10.11*

$$2\,H_3C-CH_3(g) + 7\,O_2(g) \longrightarrow 4\,CO_2(g) + 6\,H_2O(g)$$

Use average bond energies to calculate ΔH_{rxn} for the reaction.

84. In the *Chemistry and the Environment* box on free radicals in this chapter, we discussed the importance of the hydroxyl radical in reacting with and eliminating many atmospheric pollutants. However, the hydroxyl radical does not clean up everything. For example, chlorofluorocarbons—which destroy stratospheric ozone—are not attacked by the hydroxyl radical. Consider the hypothetical reaction by which the hydroxyl radical might react with a chlorofluorocarbon:

$$OH(g) + CF_2Cl_2(g) \longrightarrow HOF(g) + CFCl_2(g)$$

Use bond energies to explain why this reaction is improbable. (The C—F bond energy is 552 kJ/mol.)

CUMULATIVE PROBLEMS

85. Write an appropriate Lewis structure for each compound. Make certain to distinguish between ionic and molecular compounds.
a. BI_3 b. K_2S c. HCFO d. PBr_3

86. Write an appropriate Lewis structure for each compound. Make certain to distinguish between ionic and molecular compounds.
a. Al_2O_3 b. ClF_5 c. MgI_2 d. XeO_4

87. Each compound contains both ionic and covalent bonds. Write ionic Lewis structures for each of them, including the covalent structure for the ion in brackets. Write resonance structures if necessary.
a. $BaCO_3$ b. $Ca(OH)_2$
c. KNO_3 d. LiIO

88. Each compound contains both ionic and covalent bonds. Write ionic Lewis structures for each of them, including the covalent structure for the ion in brackets. Write resonance structures if necessary.
a. $RbIO_2$ b. NH_4Cl c. KOH d. $Sr(CN)_2$

89. Carbon ring structures are common in organic chemistry. Draw a Lewis structure for each carbon ring structure, including any necessary resonance structures.
a. C_4H_8 b. C_4H_4 c. C_6H_{12} d. C_6H_6

90. Amino acids are the building blocks of proteins. The simplest amino acid is glycine (H_2NCH_2COOH). Draw a Lewis structure for glycine. (*Hint:* The central atoms in the skeletal structure are nitrogen and the two carbon atoms. Each oxygen atom is bonded directly to the right-most carbon atom.)

91. Formic acid is responsible for the sting of ant bites. By mass, formic acid is 26.10% C, 4.38% H, and 69.52% O. The molar mass of formic acid is 46.02 g/mol. Determine the molecular formula of formic acid and draw its Lewis structure.

92. Diazomethane is a highly poisonous, explosive compound because it readily evolves N_2. Diazomethane has the following composition by mass: 28.57% C; 4.80% H; and 66.64% N. The molar mass of diazomethane is 42.04 g/mol. Find the molecular formula of diazomethane, draw its Lewis structure, and assign formal charges to each atom. Why is diazomethane not very stable? Explain.

93. The reaction of $Fe_2O_3(s)$ with $Al(s)$ to form $Al_2O_3(s)$ and $Fe(s)$ is called the thermite reaction and is highly exothermic. What role does lattice energy play in the exothermicity of the reaction?

94. NaCl has a lattice energy of −787 kJ/mol. Consider a hypothetical salt XY. X^{3+} has the same radius as Na^+ and Y^{3-} has the same radius as Cl^-. Estimate the lattice energy of XY.

95. Draw the Lewis structure for nitric acid (the hydrogen atom is attached to one of the oxygen atoms). Include all three resonance structures by alternating the double bond among the three oxygen atoms. Use formal charge to determine which of the resonance structures is most important to the structure of nitric acid.

96. Phosgene (Cl_2CO) is a poisonous gas used as a chemical weapon during World War I. It is a potential agent for chemical terrorism today. Draw the Lewis structure of phosgene. Include all three resonance forms by alternating the double bond among the three terminal atoms. Which resonance structure is the best?

97. The cyanate ion (OCN^-) and the fulminate ion (CNO^-) share the same three atoms but have vastly different properties. The cyanate ion is stable, while the fulminate ion is unstable and forms explosive compounds. The resonance structures of the cyanate ion are explored in Example 10.8. Draw Lewis structures for the fulminate ion—including possible resonance forms—and use formal charge to explain why the fulminate ion is less stable (and therefore more reactive) than the cyanate ion.

98. Draw the Lewis structure for each organic compound from its condensed structural formula.
a. C_3H_8 b. CH_3OCH_3 c. CH_3COCH_3
d. CH_3COOH e. CH_3CHO

99. Draw the Lewis structure for each organic compound from its condensed structural formula.
a. C_2H_4 b. CH_3NH_2 c. HCHO
d. CH_3CH_2OH e. HCOOH

100. Use Lewis structures to explain why Br_3^- and I_3^- are stable, while F_3^- is not.

101. Draw the Lewis structure for $HCSNH_2$. (The carbon and nitrogen atoms are bonded together, and the sulfur atom is bonded to the carbon atom.) Label each bond in the molecule as polar or nonpolar.

102. Draw the Lewis structure for urea, H_2NCONH_2, one of the compounds responsible for the smell of urine. (The central carbon atom is bonded to both nitrogen atoms and to the oxygen atom.) Does urea contain polar bonds? Which bond in urea is most polar?

103. Some theories of aging suggest that free radicals cause certain diseases and perhaps aging in general. As you know from the Lewis model, such molecules are not chemically stable and will quickly react with other molecules. According to certain theories, free radicals may attack molecules within the cell, such as DNA, changing them and causing cancer or other diseases. Free radicals may also attack molecules on the surfaces of cells, making them appear foreign to the body's immune system. The immune system then attacks the cells and destroys them, weakening the body. Draw Lewis structures for each free radical implicated in this theory of aging.
a. O_2^- b. O^- c. OH
d. CH_3OO (unpaired electron on terminal oxygen)

104. Free radicals are important in many environmentally significant reactions (see the *Chemistry in the Environment* box on free radicals in this chapter). For example, photochemical smog—smog that results from the action of sunlight on air pollutants—forms in part by these two steps:

$$NO_2 \xrightarrow{\text{UV light}} NO + O$$
$$O + O_2 \longrightarrow O_3$$

The product of this reaction, ozone, is a pollutant in the lower atmosphere. (Upper atmospheric ozone is a natural part of the atmosphere that protects life on Earth from ultraviolet light.) Ozone is an eye and lung irritant and also accelerates the weathering of rubber products. Rewrite the given reactions using the Lewis structure of each reactant and product. Identify the free radicals.

105. If hydrogen were used as a fuel, it could be burned according to this reaction:

$$H_2(g) + \frac{1}{2}O_2(g) \longrightarrow H_2O(g)$$

Use average bond energies to calculate ΔH_{rxn} for this reaction and also for the combustion of methane (CH_4). Which fuel yields more energy per mole? Per gram?

106. Calculate ΔH_{rxn} for the combustion of octane (C_8H_{18}), a component of gasoline, by using average bond energies and then calculate it using enthalpies of formation from Appendix IIB. What is the percent difference between your results? Which result would you expect to be more accurate?

107. Draw the Lewis structure for each compound.
a. Cl_2O_7 (no Cl—Cl bond)
b. H_3PO_3 (two OH bonds)
c. H_3AsO_4

108. The azide ion, N_3^-, is a symmetrical ion, all of whose contributing resonance structures have formal charges. Draw three important contributing structures for this ion.

109. List the following gas-phase ion pairs in order of the quantity of energy released when they form from separated gas-phase ions. List the pair that releases the least energy first. Na^+F^-, $Mg^{2+}F^-$, Na^+O^{2-}, $Mg^{2+}O^{2-}$, $Al^{3+}O^{2-}$.

110. Calculate $\Delta H°$ for the reaction $H_2(g) + Br_2(g) \longrightarrow 2\,HBr(g)$ using the bond energy values. The $\Delta H_f°$ of HBr(g) is not equal to one-half of the value calculated. Account for the difference.

111. The heat of atomization is the heat required to convert a molecule in the gas phase into its constituent atoms in the gas phase. The heat of atomization is used to calculate average bond energies. Without using any tabulated bond energies, calculate the average C—Cl bond energy from the following data: the heat of atomization of CH_4 is 1660 kJ/mol, and the heat of atomization of CH_2Cl_2 is 1495 kJ/mol.

112. Calculate the heat of atomization (see previous problem) of C_2H_3Cl, using the average bond energies in Table 10.3.

113. A compound composed of only carbon and hydrogen is 7.743% hydrogen by mass. Propose a Lewis structure for the compound.

114. A compound composed of only carbon and chlorine is 85.5% chlorine by mass. Propose a Lewis structure for the compound.

CHALLENGE PROBLEMS

115. The main component of acid rain (H_2SO_4) forms from the SO_2 pollutant in the atmosphere via these steps:

$$SO_2 + OH\cdot \longrightarrow HSO_3\cdot$$

$$HSO_3\cdot + O_2 \longrightarrow SO_3 + HOO\cdot$$

$$SO_3 + H_2O \longrightarrow H_2SO_4$$

Draw the Lewis structure for each of the species in these steps and use bond energies and Hess's law to estimate ΔH_{rxn} for the overall process. (Use 265 kJ/mol for the S—O single bond energy.)

116. A 0.167-g sample of an unknown acid requires 27.8 mL of 0.100 M NaOH to titrate to the equivalence point. Elemental analysis of the acid gives the following percentages by mass: 40.00% C, 6.71% H, 53.29% O. Determine the molecular formula, molar mass, and Lewis structure of the unknown acid.

117. Use the dipole moments of HF and HCl (given at the end of the problem) together with the percent ionic character of each bond (Figure 10.10) to estimate the bond length in each molecule. How well does your estimated bond length agree with the bond length in Table 10.4?

$$\text{HCl } \mu = 1.08 \text{ D}$$

$$\text{HF } \mu = 1.82 \text{ D}$$

118. Use average bond energies together with the standard enthalpy of formation of C(*g*) (718.4 kJ/mol) to estimate the standard enthalpy of formation of gaseous benzene, $C_6H_6(g)$. (Remember that average bond energies apply to the gas phase only.) Compare the value you obtain using average bond energies to the actual standard enthalpy of formation of gaseous benzene, 82.9 kJ/mol. What does the difference between these two values tell you about the stability of benzene?

119. The standard state of phosphorus at 25 °C is P_4. This molecule has four equivalent P atoms, no double or triple bonds, and no expanded octets. Draw its Lewis structure.

120. The standard heat of formation of $CaBr_2$ is −675 kJ/mol. The first ionization energy of Ca is 590 kJ/mol, and its second ionization energy is 1145 kJ/mol. The heat of sublimation of Ca[Ca(*s*) ⟶ Ca(*g*)] is 178 kJ/mol. The bond energy of Br_2 is 193 kJ/mol, the heat of vaporization of $Br_2(l)$ is 31 kJ/mol, and the electron affinity of Br is −325 kJ/mol. Calculate the lattice energy of $CaBr_2$.

121. The standard heat of formation of $PI_3(s)$ is −24.7 kJ/mol, and the PI bond energy in this molecule is 184 kJ/mol. The standard heat of formation of P(*g*) is 334 kJ/mol, and that of $I_2(g)$ is 62 kJ/mol. The I_2 bond energy is 151 kJ/mol. Calculate the heat of sublimation of PI_3[$PI_3(s) \longrightarrow PI_3(g)$].

122. A compound has the formula C_8H_8 and does not contain any double or triple bonds. All the carbon atoms are chemically identical, and all the hydrogen atoms are chemically identical. Draw the Lewis structure for this molecule.

123. Find the oxidation number of each sulfur in the molecule H_2S_4, which has a linear arrangement of its atoms.

124. Ionic solids of the O^- and O^{3-} anions do not exist, while ionic solids of the O^{2-} anion are common. Explain.

125. The standard state of sulfur is solid rhombic sulfur. Use the appropriate standard heats of formation given in Appendix II to find the average bond energy of the S=O in SO_2.

CONCEPTUAL PROBLEMS

126. Which statement is true of an endothermic reaction?

a. Strong bonds break and weak bonds form.
b. Weak bonds break and strong bonds form.
c. The bonds that break and those that form are of approximately the same strength.

127. When a firecracker explodes, energy is obviously released. The compounds in the firecracker can be viewed as being "energy rich." What does this mean? Explain the source of the energy in terms of chemical bonds.

128. A fundamental difference between compounds containing ionic bonds and those containing covalent bonds is the existence of molecules. Explain why molecules exist in solid covalent compounds but not in solid ionic compounds.

129. In the very first chapter of this book, we described the scientific approach and put a special emphasis on scientific models or theories. In this chapter, we looked carefully at a model for chemical bonding (the Lewis model). Why is this theory successful? What are some of the limitations of the theory?

QUESTIONS FOR GROUP WORK

Active Classroom Learning

Discuss these questions with the group and record your consensus answer.

130. Have each member of your group represent an atom of a metal or an atom of a nonmetal. Each group member holds a coin to represent an electron. Which group members are most reluctant to give up their electrons? Which group members are most willing to give up their electrons? Determine which kind of bond could form between each pair of group members. Tabulate your results.

131. Spend a few minutes reviewing the Lewis dot symbols for the atoms H through Ne. Form a circle and have each group member ask the group member on his or her right to draw the Lewis symbol for a specific atom. Keep going around until each group member can write all the Lewis dot symbols for the atoms H through Ne. Determine the formal charge for each symbol. In a complete sentence or two, describe why they are all the same.

132. Draw the Lewis dot symbols for the atoms Al and O. Use the Lewis model to determine the formula for the compound formed from these two atoms.

133. Draft a list of step-by-step instructions for writing the correct Lewis dot structure for any molecule or polyatomic ion.

134. Pass a piece of paper around the group and ask each group member in turn to perform the next step in the process of determining a correct Lewis structure (including formal charges on all atoms and resonance structures, if appropriate) for the following molecules and ions: N_2H_4, CCl_4, CO_3^{2-}, and NH_4^+.

DATA INTERPRETATION AND ANALYSIS

Lattice Energy

135. Evidence for the additional stabilization of certain electron configurations comes from the experimental lattice energies of the metal fluorides, MF_2. The first figure below plots lattice energy for the 2+ metal cations for period 4 elements. The figure that follows plots the ionic radii of the 2+ metal cations of period 4 elements versus atomic number.

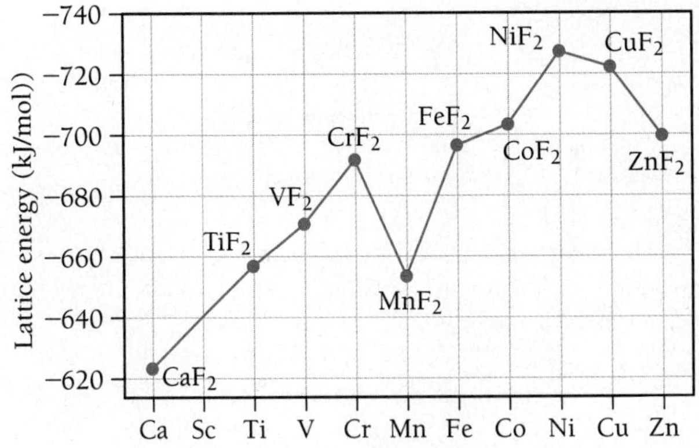

▲ **Lattice Energy of Period 4 Metal Fluorides**
Source: After C.S.G. Phillips, R. J. P Williams, Inorganic Chemistry, Volume 1, p. 179.

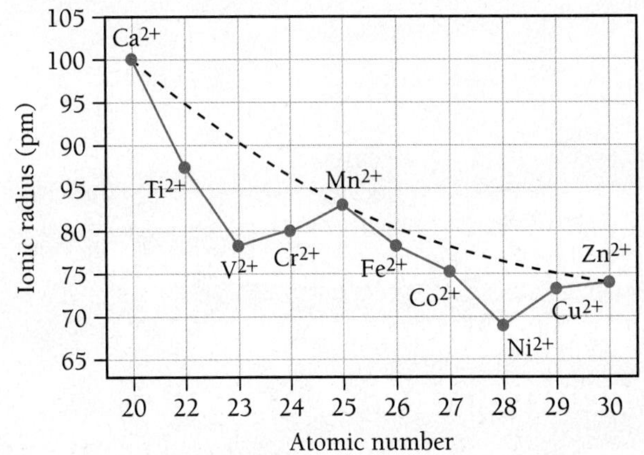

▲ **Ionic Radius Versus Atomic Number of 2+ Metal Cations for Period 4 Elements**

Use the information provided in the figures to answer the following questions:

a. Explain the general trend in lattice energy.

b. Is there a correlation between ionic radius and lattice energy? Explain.

c. What could account for the decrease in lattice energy between CrF_2 and MnF_2?

d. Which has the higher lattice energy: VF_2 or VCl_2? Explain.

Cc ANSWERS TO CONCEPTUAL CONNECTIONS

Bond Types

10.1 **(c)** MgF_2 contains a metal (Mg) bonded to a nonmetal (F), so the bonding is ionic.

Lewis Symbols

10.2 **(d)** This Lewis symbol has four dots, corresponding to silicon's four valence electrons.

Melting Points of Ionic Solids

10.3 **(a)** You would expect MgO to have the higher melting point because, in our bonding model, the magnesium and oxygen ions are held together in a crystalline lattice by charges of 2+ for magnesium and 2− for oxygen. In contrast, the NaCl lattice is held together by charges of 1+ for sodium and 1− for chlorine. The experimentally measured melting points of these compounds are 801 °C for NaCl and 2852 °C for MgO, in accordance with our model.

Energy and the Octet Rule

10.4 **(b)** The reasons that atoms form bonds are complex. One contributing factor is the lowering of their potential energy. The octet rule is just a handy way to predict the combinations of atoms that have a lower potential energy when they bond.

Periodic Trends in Electronegativity

10.5 **(a)** N > P > Al > Na

Percent Ionic Character

10.6 **(b)** You are given that the dipole moment of the HCl bond is about 1 D and that the bond length is 127 pm. Previously, we calculated the dipole moment for a 130-pm bond that is 100% ionic to be about 6.2 D. You can therefore estimate the bond's ionic character as $1/6 \times 100$, which is closest to 15%.

Resonance Structures

10.7 **(b)** This structure is not a resonance structure of the ion because it has a different skeletal structure.

Odd-Electron Species

10.8 **(d)** ClO because the sum of the valence electrons of its atoms is an odd number

Expanded Octets

10.9 **(b)** The only molecule in this group that could have an expanded octet is H_3PO_4 because phosphorus is a third-period element. Expanded octets *never* occur in second-period elements such as carbon and nitrogen.

Bond Energies and ΔH_{rxn}

10.10 **(b)** In a highly exothermic reaction, the energy needed to break bonds is less than the energy released when the new bonds form, resulting in a net release of energy.

No theory ever solves all the puzzles with which it is confronted at a given time; nor are the solutions already achieved often perfect.

—THOMAS KUHN (1922–1996)

CHAPTER 11

Chemical Bonding II: Molecular Shapes, Valence Bond Theory, and Molecular Orbital Theory

In Chapter 10, we examined a simple model for chemical bonding called the Lewis model. We saw how this model helps us to explain and predict the combinations of atoms that form stable molecules. When we combine the Lewis model with the idea that valence electron groups repel one another—the basis of an approach known as valence shell electron pair repulsion theory—we can predict the general shape of a molecule from its Lewis structure. We address molecular shape and its importance in the first part of this chapter. We then move on to explore two additional bonding theories—called valence bond theory and molecular orbital theory—that are progressively more sophisticated, but at the cost of being more complex, than the Lewis model. As you work through this chapter, our second on chemical bonding, keep in mind the importance of this topic. In our universe, atoms join together to form molecules, and that makes many things possible, including our own existence.

Morphinan (a morphine analog) binding to an opioid receptor (based on research don by Brian Kobilka and cowokers at Stanford university.)

11.1 Morphine: A Molecular Imposter 437

11.2 VSEPR Theory: The Five Basic Shapes 438

11.3 VSEPR Theory: The Effect of Lone Pairs 442

11.4 VSEPR Theory: Predicting Molecular Geometries 447

11.5 Molecular Shape and Polarity 450

11.6 Valence Bond Theory: Orbital Overlap as a Chemical Bond 455

11.7 Valence Bond Theory: Hybridization of Atomic Orbitals 457

11.8 Molecular Orbital Theory: Electron Delocalization 470

LEARNING OUTCOMES 485

11.1 Morphine: A Molecular Imposter

Morphine—a drug named after Morpheus, the Greek god of dreams—is the silver bullet in the human arsenal against pain. Morphine is often prescribed after surgery to aid recovery or to alleviate the severe pain associated with illnesses such as cancer. It is also prescribed to patients who have chronic pain toward the end of their lives. For these patients, prescribed morphine provides relief from an otherwise tortuous

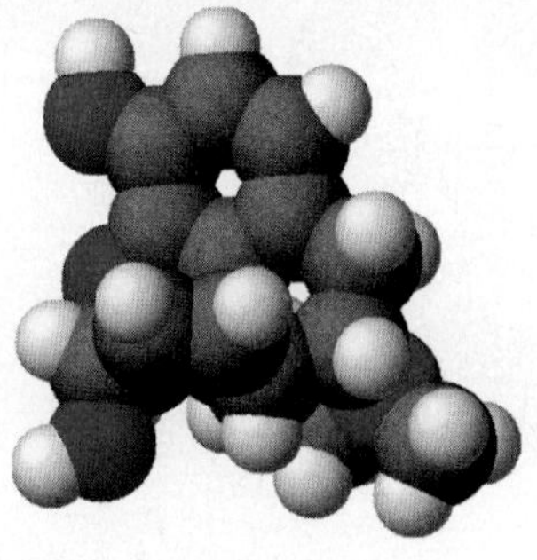

Morphine

existence. Morphine is a natural product derived from the sap of the opium poppy. The effects of opium sap have been known for thousands of years, but morphine itself was not isolated from opium until the early 1800s. Morphine acts by binding to receptors (called opioid receptors) that exist within nerve cells. When morphine binds to an opioid receptor, the transmission of nerve signals is altered, resulting in sedation, less pain, and feelings of euphoria and tranquility.

Why do humans (and other mammals) have receptors within their nerve cells that bind to molecules derived from the sap of a plant? Researchers long suspected that these receptors must also bind other molecules as well; otherwise, why would the receptors exist? In the 1970s, researchers discovered some of these molecules, known as endorphins (short for **endo**genous mo**rphine**; endogenous means produced within the organism). Endorphins are the body's natural painkillers. Our bodies naturally produce endorphins during periods of pain such as childbirth or intense exercise. Endorphins are at least partially responsible for the so-called runner's high, a feeling of well-being that often follows an athlete's intense workout.

Morphine binds to opioid receptors because it fits into a special pocket (called the active site) on the opioid receptor protein (just as a key fits into a lock) that normally binds endorphins. Certain parts of the morphine molecule have a similar enough shape to endorphins that they fit the lock (even though they are not the original key). In other words, morphine is a *molecular imposter*, mimicking the action of endorphins because of similarities in shape.

Proteins are among the most important biological molecules and serve many functions in living organisms.

The lock-and-key fit between the active site of a protein and a particular molecule is important not only to our perception of pain, but to many other biological functions as well. Immune response, the sense of smell, the sense of taste, and many types of drug actions depend on shape-specific interactions between molecules and proteins. In fact, our ability to determine the shapes of key biological molecules is largely responsible for the revolution that has occurred in biology over the last 50 years.

In this chapter, we look at ways to predict and account for the shapes of molecules. The molecules we examine are much smaller than the protein molecules we just discussed, but the same principles apply to both. The simple model we examine to account for molecular shape is *valence shell electron pair repulsion* theory, and in this chapter, we use it in conjunction with the Lewis model to make important predictions about the shapes of molecules. We then proceed to explore two additional bonding theories: *valence bond theory* and *molecular orbital theory*. They predict and account for molecular shape as well as other properties of molecules.

WATCH **NOW!**

KEY CONCEPT VIDEO 11.2
VSEPR Theory

11.2 VSEPR Theory: The Five Basic Shapes

Valence shell electron pair repulsion (VSEPR) theory is based on the simple idea that **electron groups**—which we define as lone pairs, single bonds, multiple bonds, and even single electrons—repel one another through coulombic forces. The electron groups are also attracted to the nucleus (otherwise the molecule would fall apart), but VSEPR theory focuses on the repulsions.

According to VSEPR theory, the repulsions between electron groups on *interior atoms* of a molecule determine the geometry of the molecule (Figure 11.1◀). The preferred geometry of a molecule is the one in which the electron groups have maximum separation (and therefore minimum repulsion energy). For molecules having just one interior atom (the central atom), molecular geometry depends on two factors:

- the number of electron groups around the central atom;
- how many of those electron groups are bonding groups and how many are lone pairs.

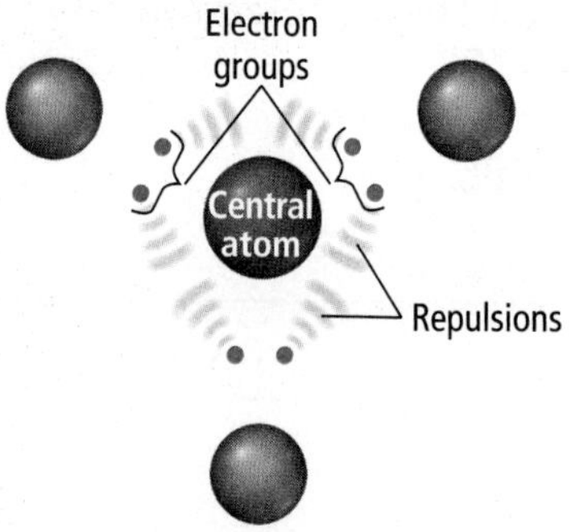

▲ **FIGURE 11.1 Repulsion between Electron Groups** The basic idea of VSEPR theory is that repulsions between electron groups determine molecular geometry.

We first look at the molecular geometries associated with having two to six electron bonding groups (single or multiple bonds) around the central atom. The resulting geometries constitute the five basic shapes of molecules. We then consider how these basic shapes are modified if one or more of the electron groups are lone pairs.

Two Electron Groups: Linear Geometry

Consider the Lewis structure of $BeCl_2$, which has two electron groups (two single bonds) about the central atom:

Beryllium often forms incomplete octets, as it does in this structure.

$$:\ddot{\underset{..}{Cl}}:Be:\ddot{\underset{..}{Cl}}:$$

According to VSEPR theory, the geometry of $BeCl_2$ is determined by the repulsion between these two electron groups, which maximize their separation by assuming a 180° bond angle or a **linear geometry**. Experimental measurements of the geometry of $BeCl_2$ indicate that the molecule is indeed linear, as predicted by the theory.

Linear geometry

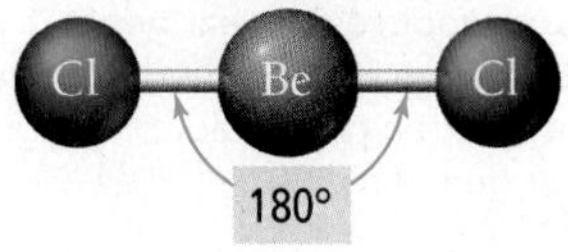

Molecules that form only two single bonds, with no lone pairs, are rare because they do not follow the octet rule. However, the same geometry is observed in all molecules that have two electron groups (and no lone pairs). Consider the Lewis structure of CO_2, which has two electron groups (the double bonds) around the central carbon atom:

A double bond counts as one electron group.

$$:\ddot{O}=C=\ddot{O}:$$

According to VSEPR theory, the two double bonds repel each other (just as the two single bonds in $BeCl_2$ repel each other), resulting in a linear geometry for CO_2. Experimental observations confirm that CO_2 is indeed a linear molecule.

Linear geometry

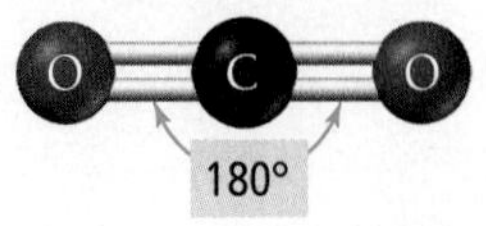

Three Electron Groups: Trigonal Planar Geometry

The Lewis structure of BF_3 (another molecule with an incomplete octet) has three electron groups around the central atom:

$$\begin{array}{c} :\ddot{F}: \\ :\ddot{\underset{..}{F}}:B:\ddot{\underset{..}{F}}: \end{array}$$

Trigonal planar geometry

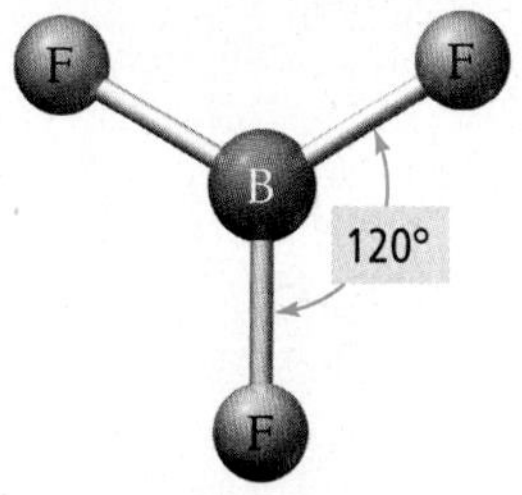

These three electron groups can maximize their separation by assuming 120° bond angles in a plane—a **trigonal planar geometry**. Experimental observations of the structure of BF_3 again confirm the predictions of VSEPR theory.

Another molecule with three electron groups, formaldehyde (HCHO), has one double bond and two single bonds around the central atom:

$$\begin{array}{c} :\ddot{O}: \\ \| \\ H—C—H \end{array}$$

Because formaldehyde has three electron groups around the central atom, we initially predict that the bond angles should also be 120°. However, experimental observations show that the HCO bond angles are 121.9° and the HCH bond angle is 116.2°. These bond angles are close to the idealized 120° that we originally predicted, but the HCO bond angles are slightly greater than the HCH bond angle because the double bond contains more electron density than the single bond and therefore exerts a slightly greater repulsion on the single bonds. In general, *different types of electron groups exert slightly different repulsions*—the resulting bond angles reflect these differences.

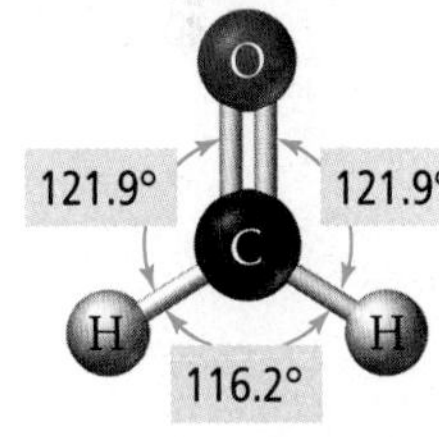

ELECTRON GROUPS AND MOLECULAR GEOMETRY

11.1 Cc Conceptual Connection — ANSWER NOW!

A central atom in a three-atom molecule forms two double bonds (and has no lone pairs). What is the geometry of the molecule?

(a) trigonal planar **(b)** linear

(c) Not enough information is given to determine the geometry of the molecule. To solve the problem, it is necessary to know how many electron pairs are on the other two atoms.

Four Electron Groups: Tetrahedral Geometry

VSEPR geometries for molecules with two or three electron groups around the central atom are two-dimensional and easy to represent on paper. Molecules with four or more electron groups around a central atom, however, have three-dimensional geometries that are more difficult to imagine and draw. Fortunately, we can understand these basic shapes by analogy to balloons tied together.

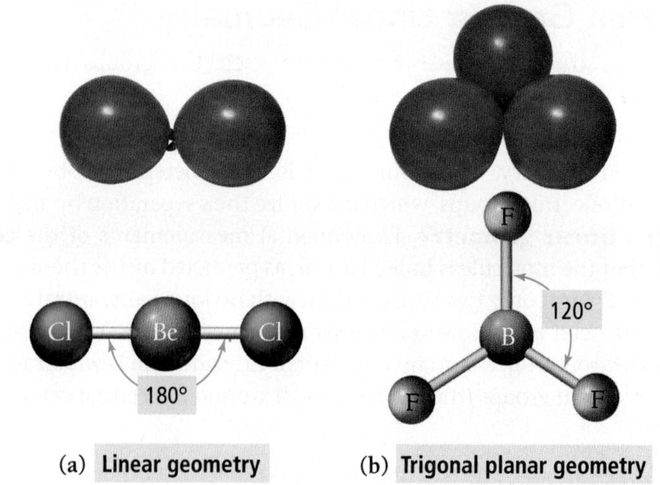

▶ **FIGURE 11.2 Representing Electron Geometry with Balloons** **(a)** The bulkiness of balloons causes them to assume a linear arrangement when two of them are tied together. Similarly, the repulsion between two electron groups produces a linear geometry. **(b)** Like three balloons tied together, three electron groups adopt a trigonal planar geometry.

In this analogy, each electron group around a central atom is like a balloon tied to a central point. The bulkiness of the balloons causes them to spread out as much as possible, much as the repulsion between electron groups causes them to position themselves as far apart as possible.

For example, if you tie two balloons together, they assume a roughly linear arrangement, as shown in Figure 11.2(a)▲, analogous to the linear geometry of $BeCl_2$ that we just examined. Notice that the balloons do not represent atoms, but *electron groups*. Similarly, if you tie three balloons together—in analogy to three electron groups—they assume a trigonal planar geometry, as shown in Figure 11.2(b)▲, much like the BF_3 molecule. If you tie *four* balloons together, however, they assume a three-dimensional **tetrahedral geometry** with 109.5° angles between the balloons. That is, the balloons point toward the vertices of a *tetrahedron*—a geometrical shape with four identical faces, each an equilateral triangle, as shown here:

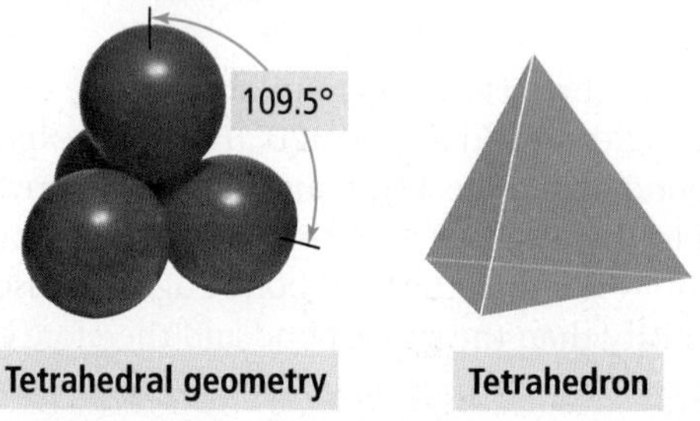

Methane is an example of a molecule with four electron groups around the central atom:

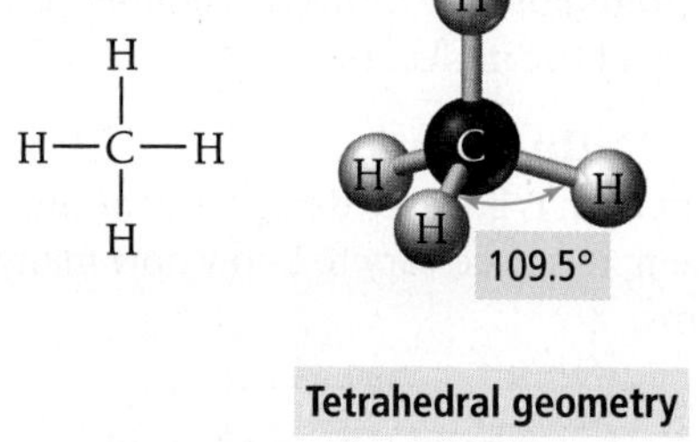

For four electron groups, the tetrahedron is the three-dimensional shape that allows the maximum separation among the groups. The repulsions among the four electron groups in the C—H bonds cause the molecule to assume the tetrahedral shape. When we write the Lewis structure of CH_4 on paper, it may seem that the molecule should be square planar, with bond angles of 90°. However, in three dimensions, the electron groups can get farther away from each other by forming the tetrahedral geometry, as illustrated by our balloon analogy.

MOLECULAR GEOMETRY What is the geometry of the HCN molecule? The Lewis structure of HCN is H—C≡N: .

(a) linear
(b) trigonal planar
(c) tetrahedral

11.2 Cc Conceptual Connection

ANSWER **NOW!**

Five Electron Groups: Trigonal Bipyramidal Geometry

Five electron groups around a central atom assume a **trigonal bipyramidal geometry**, like five balloons tied together. In this structure, three of the groups lie in a single plane, as in the trigonal planar configuration, whereas the other two are positioned above and below this plane. The angles in the trigonal bipyramidal structure are not all the same. The angles between the *equatorial positions* (the three bonds in the trigonal plane) are 120°, whereas the angle between the *axial positions* (the two bonds on either side of the trigonal plane) and the trigonal plane is 90°. PCl_5 is an example of a molecule with five electron groups around the central atom:

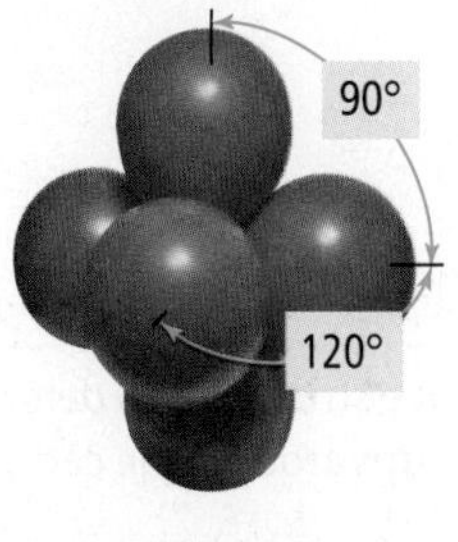

Trigonal bipyramidal geometry

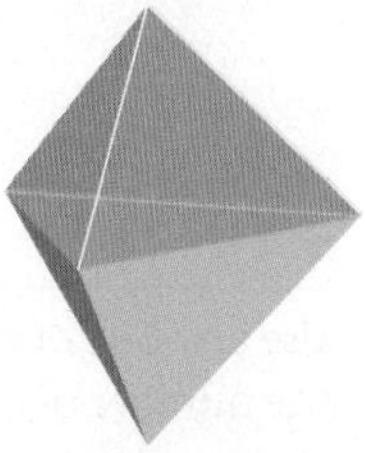
Trigonal bipyramid

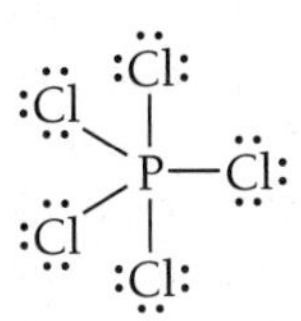

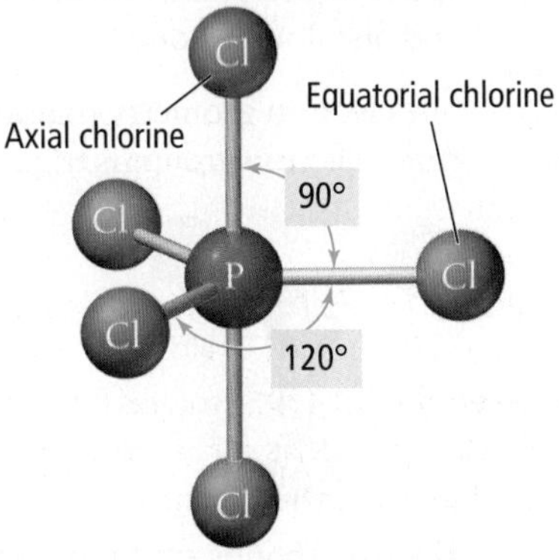

Trigonal bipyramidal geometry

The three equatorial chlorine atoms are separated by 120° bond angles, and the two axial chlorine atoms are separated from the equatorial atoms by 90° bond angles.

Six Electron Groups: Octahedral Geometry

Six electron groups around a central atom assume an **octahedral geometry**, like six balloons tied together. In this structure—named after the eight-sided geometrical shape called the octahedron—four of the groups lie in a single plane, with a fifth group above the plane and the sixth below it. The angles in this geometry are all 90°. SF_6 is a molecule with six electron groups around the central atom:

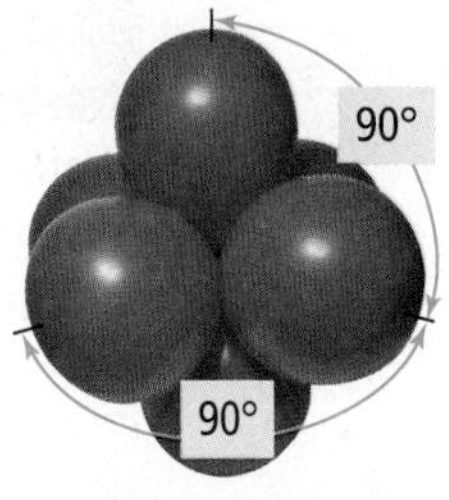

Octahedral geometry

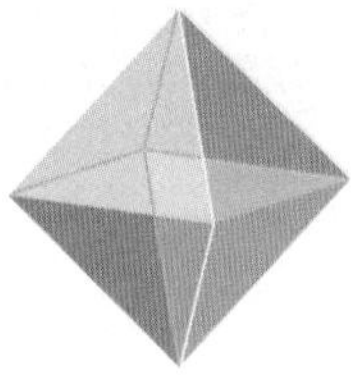
Octahedron

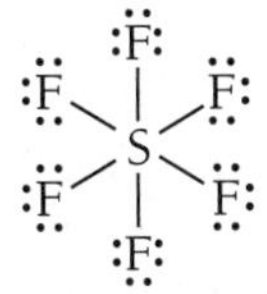

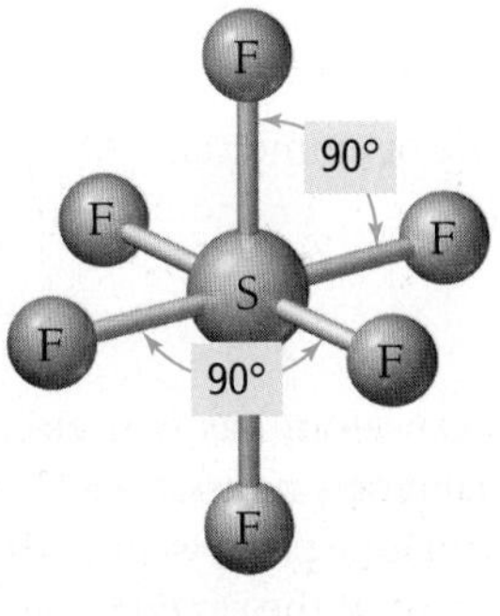

Octahedral geometry

The structure of this molecule is highly symmetrical; all six bonds are equivalent.

WATCH **NOW!**

INTERACTIVE WORKED EXAMPLE 11.1

EXAMPLE 11.1 VSEPR Theory and the Basic Shapes

Determine the molecular geometry of NO_3^-.

SOLUTION

Determine the molecular geometry of NO_3^- by counting the number of electron groups around the central atom (N). Begin by drawing a Lewis structure for NO_3^-.	NO_3^- has 5 + 3(6) + 1 = 24 valence electrons. The Lewis structure has three resonance structures: 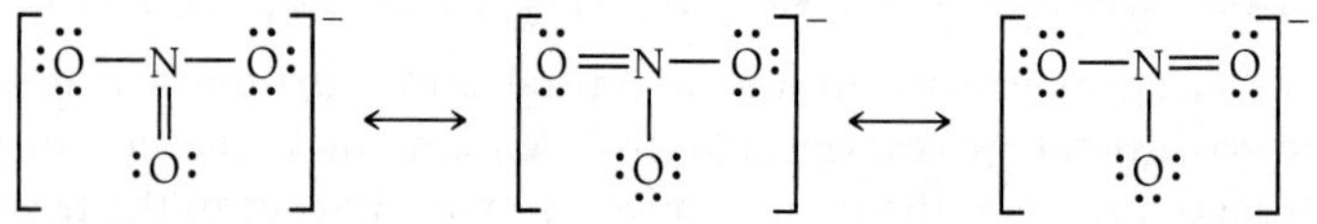 The hybrid structure is intermediate between these three and has three equivalent bonds.
Use any one of the resonance structures to determine the number of electron groups around the central atom.	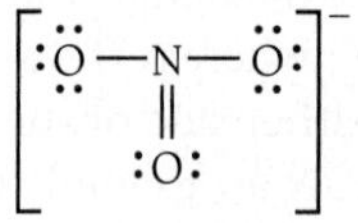 The nitrogen atom has three electron groups: two single bonds and one double bond.
Based on the number of electron groups, determine the geometry that minimizes the repulsions between the groups.	The electron geometry that minimizes the repulsions between three electron groups is trigonal planar. 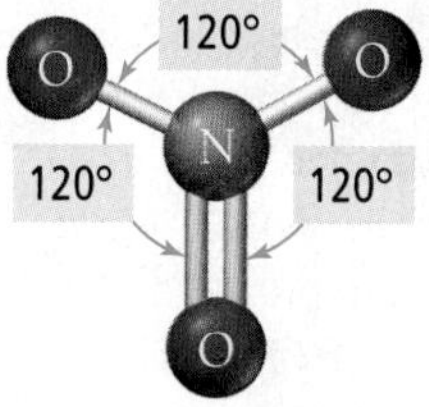 The three bonds are equivalent (because of the resonance structures), so they each exert the same repulsion on the other two and the molecule has three equal bond angles of 120°.

FOR PRACTICE 11.1 Determine the molecular geometry of CCl_4.

WATCH **NOW!**

KEY CONCEPT VIDEO 11.3
VSEPR Theory: The Effect of Lone Pairs

11.3 VSEPR Theory: The Effect of Lone Pairs

Each of the examples we have just seen has only bonding electron groups around the central atom. What happens in molecules that have lone pairs around the central atom as well? The lone pairs also repel other electron groups, as we see in the examples that follow.

Four Electron Groups with Lone Pairs

Consider the Lewis structure of ammonia:

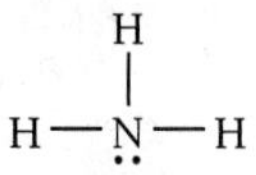

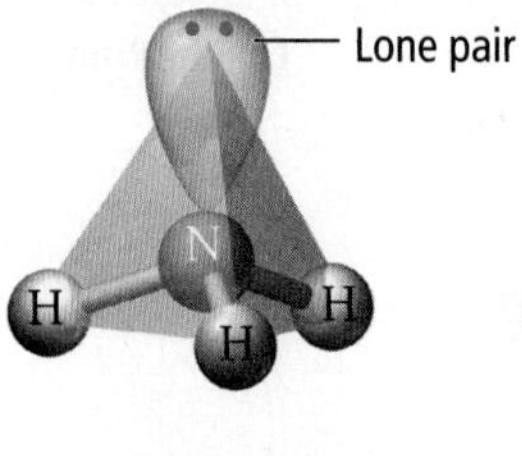

Electron geometry: tetrahedral

Molecular geometry: trigonal pyramidal

The central nitrogen atom has four electron groups (one lone pair and three bonding pairs) that repel one another. If we do not distinguish between bonding electron groups and lone pairs, we find that the **electron geometry**—the geometrical arrangement of the *electron groups*—is still tetrahedral, as we expect for four electron groups. However, the **molecular geometry**—the geometrical arrangement of the atoms—is **trigonal pyramidal geometry**, as shown here.

Notice that although the electron geometry and the molecular geometry are different, *the electron geometry is relevant to the molecular geometry*. The lone pair exerts its influence on the bonding pairs.

As we noted previously, different kinds of electron groups generally result in different amounts of repulsion. Lone pair electrons typically exert slightly greater repulsions than bonding electrons. If all four electron groups in NH_3 exerted equal repulsions on one another, the bond angles in the molecule would all be the ideal tetrahedral angle, 109.5°. However, the actual angle between N—H bonds in ammonia is slightly smaller, 107°. A lone electron pair is more spread out in space than a bonding electron pair because a lone pair is attracted to only one nucleus while a bonding pair is attracted to two (Figure 11.3▼). The lone pair occupies more of the angular space around a nucleus, exerting a greater repulsive force on neighboring electrons and compressing the N—H bond angles.

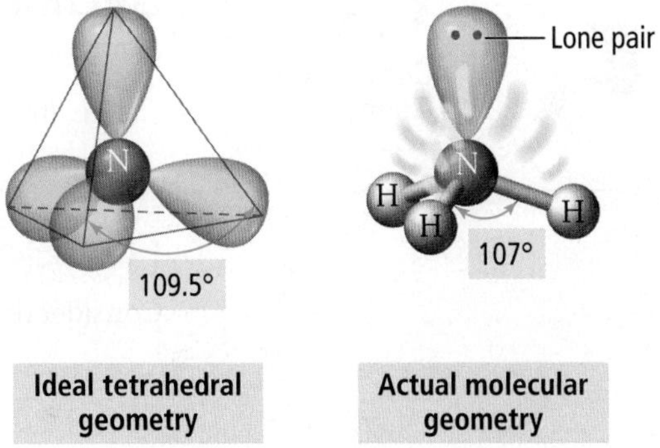

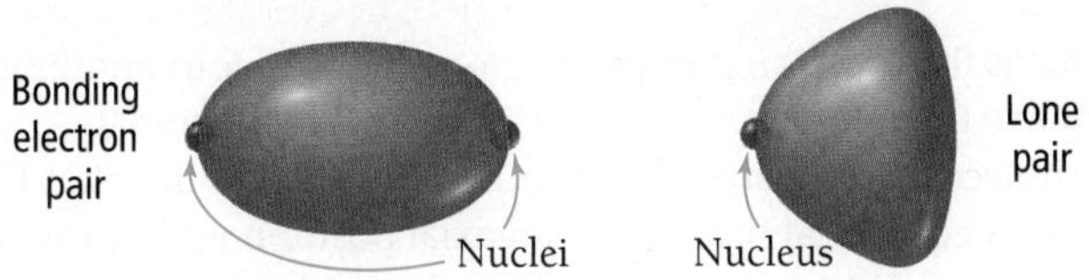

◀ **FIGURE 11.3 Lone Pair versus Bonding Electron Pairs** A lone electron pair occupies more space than a bonding pair.

A water molecule's Lewis structure is:

$$H-\underset{\cdot\cdot}{\ddot{O}}-H$$

Because water has four electron groups (two bonding pairs and two lone pairs), its *electron geometry* is also tetrahedral, but its *molecular geometry* is **bent geometry**, as shown here.

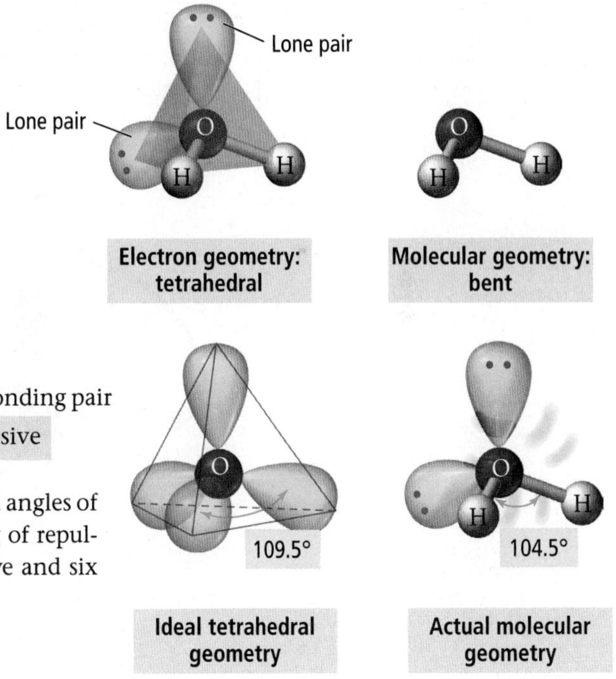

As in NH_3, the bond angles in H_2O are smaller (104.5°) than the ideal tetrahedral bond angles because of the greater repulsion exerted by the lone pair electrons. The bond angle in H_2O is even smaller than that in NH_3 because H_2O has *two* lone pairs of electrons on the central oxygen atom. These lone pairs compress the H_2O bond angle to a greater extent than in NH_3.

In general, electron group repulsions compare as follows:

Lone pair–lone pair > Lone pair–bonding pair > Bonding pair–bonding pair

Most repulsive ... Least repulsive

We see the effects of this ordering in the progressively smaller bond angles of CH_4, NH_3, and H_2O, shown in Figure 11.4▼. The relative ordering of repulsions also helps to determine the geometry of molecules with five and six electron groups when one or more of those groups are lone pairs.

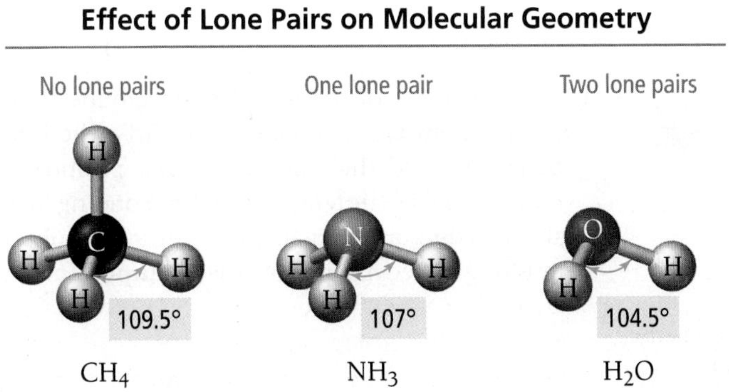

◀ **FIGURE 11.4 The Effect of Lone Pairs on Molecular Geometry** The bond angles get progressively smaller as the number of lone pairs on the central atom increases from zero in CH_4 to one in NH_3 to two in H_2O.

ANSWER **NOW!**

11.3 Cc Conceptual Connection

LONE PAIR ELECTRONS AND MOLECULAR GEOMETRY I

What is the molecular geometry of a molecule whose central atom has three bonding groups and one lone pair?

(a) linear **(b)** trigonal planar **(c)** tetrahedral **(d)** trigonal pyramidal

Five Electron Groups with Lone Pairs

Consider the Lewis structure of SF_4:

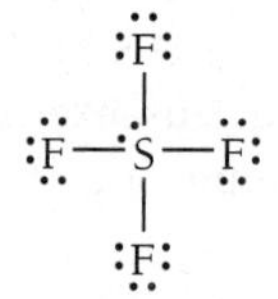

The central sulfur atom has five electron groups (one lone pair and four bonding pairs). The *electron geometry*, due to the five electron groups, is trigonal bipyramidal.

To determine the molecular geometry for sulfur tetrafluoride, notice that the lone pair could occupy either an equatorial position or an axial position within the trigonal bipyramidal electron geometry. Which position is more favorable? To answer this question, recall that, as we have just seen, lone pair–bonding pair repulsions are greater than bonding pair–bonding pair repulsions. Therefore, the lone pair occupies the position that minimizes its interaction with the bonding pairs. If the lone pair were in an axial position, it would have three 90° interactions with bonding pairs. In an equatorial position, however, it has only two 90° interactions. Consequently, the lone pair occupies an equatorial position. The resulting molecular geometry is called **seesaw geometry** because it resembles a seesaw (or teeter-totter).

The seesaw molecular geometry is sometimes called an *irregular tetrahedron.*

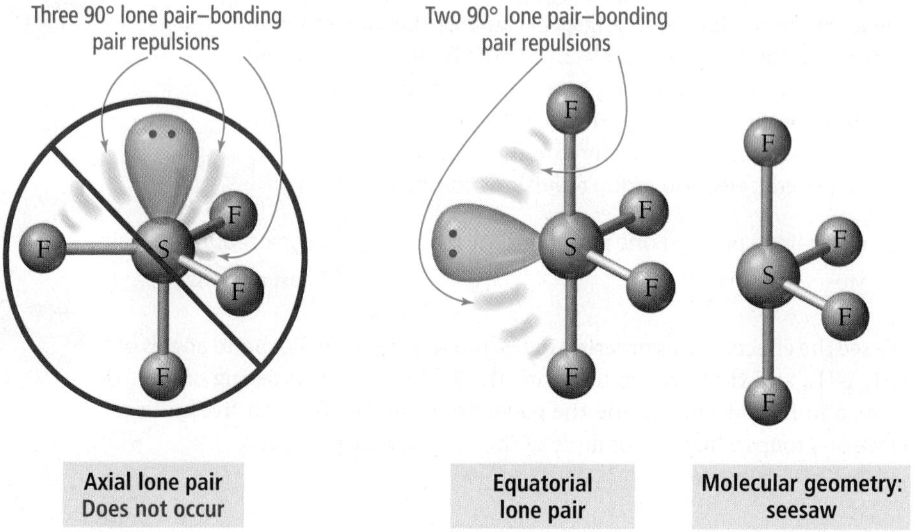

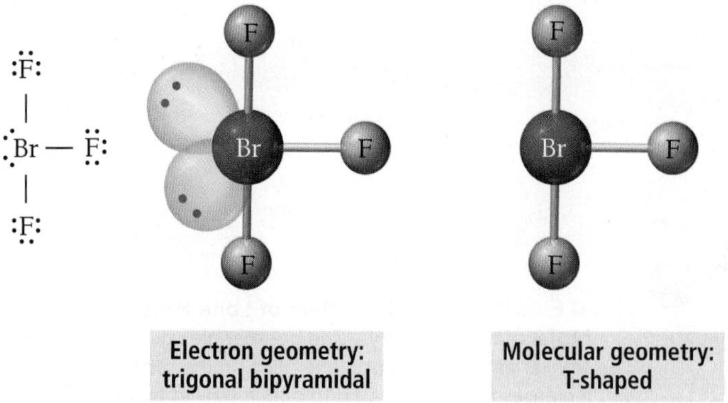

When two of the five electron groups around the central atom are lone pairs, as in BrF_3, the lone pairs occupy two of the three equatorial positions—again minimizing 90° interactions with bonding pairs and also avoiding a lone pair–lone pair 90° repulsion. The resulting molecular geometry is **T-shaped**.

When three of the five electron groups around the central atom are lone pairs, as in XeF_2, the lone pairs occupy all three of the equatorial positions, and the resulting molecular geometry is linear.

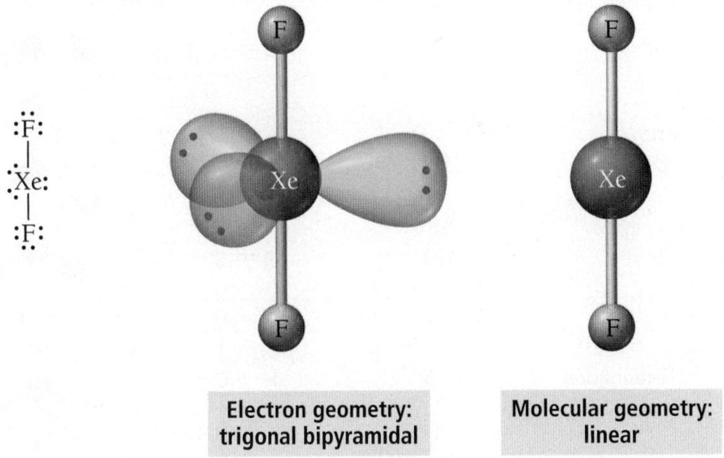

Six Electron Groups with Lone Pairs

Consider the Lewis structure of BrF_5 shown here. The central bromine atom has six electron groups (one lone pair and five bonding pairs). The electron geometry, due to the six electron groups, is octahedral. Since all six positions in the octahedral geometry are equivalent, the lone pair can be situated in any one of these positions. The resulting molecular geometry is **square pyramidal geometry**.

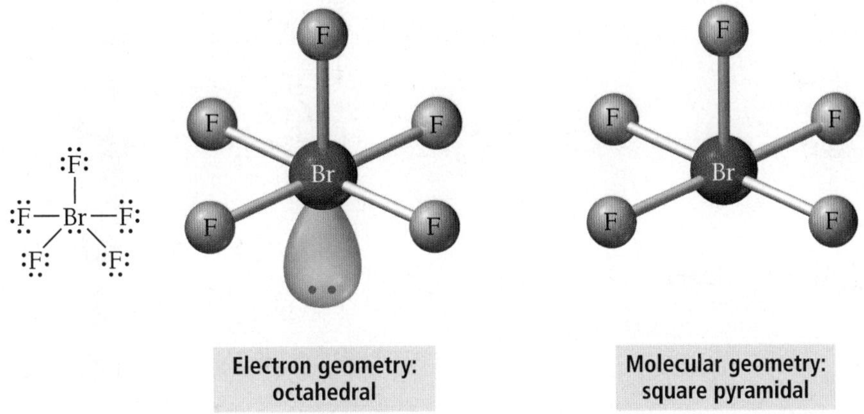

When two of the six electron groups around the central atom are lone pairs, as in XeF_4, the lone pairs occupy positions across from one another (to minimize lone pair–lone pair repulsions), and the resulting molecular geometry is **square planar geometry**.

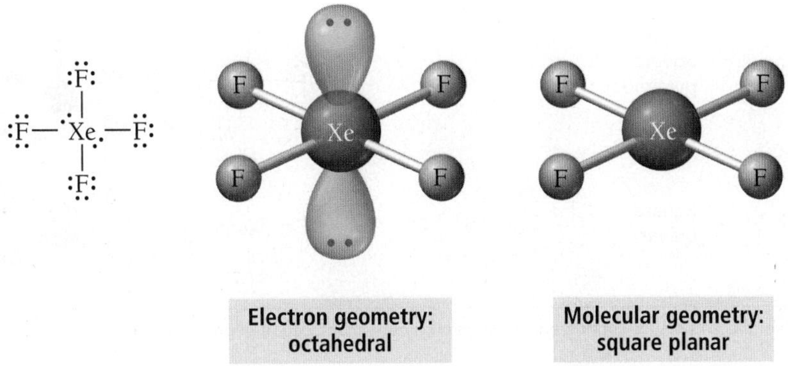

TABLE 11.1 ■ Electron and Molecular Geometries

Electron Groups*	Bonding Groups	Lone Pairs	Electron Geometry	Molecular Geometry	Approximate Bond Angles	Example
2	2	0	Linear	Linear	180°	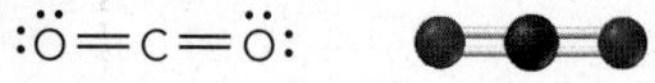
3	3	0	Trigonal planar	Trigonal planar	120°	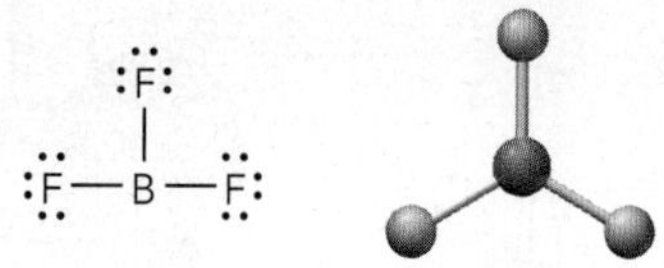
3	2	1	Trigonal planar	Bent	<120°	
4	4	0	Tetrahedral	Tetrahedral	109.5°	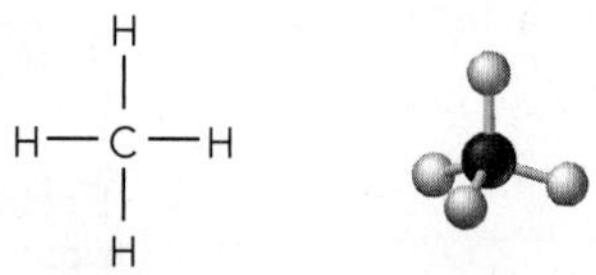
4	3	1	Tetrahedral	Trigonal pyramidal	<109.5°	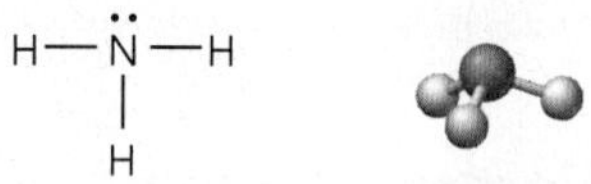
4	2	2	Tetrahedral	Bent	<109.5°	
5	5	0	Trigonal bipyramidal	Trigonal bipyramidal	120° (equatorial) 90° (axial)	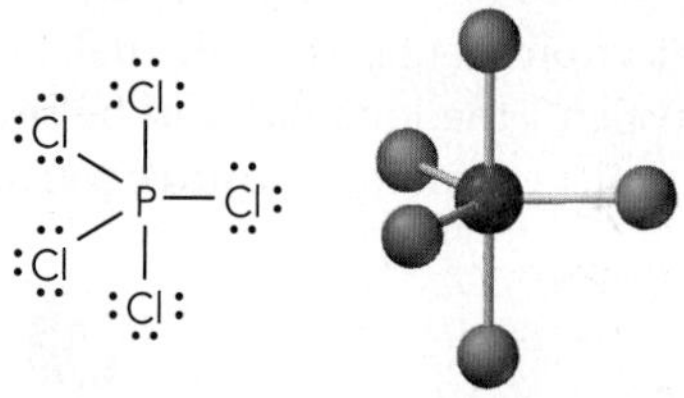
5	4	1	Trigonal bipyramidal	Seesaw	<120° (equatorial) <90° (axial)	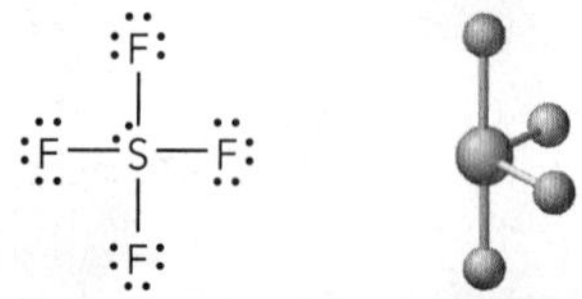
5	3	2	Trigonal bipyramidal	T-shaped	<90°	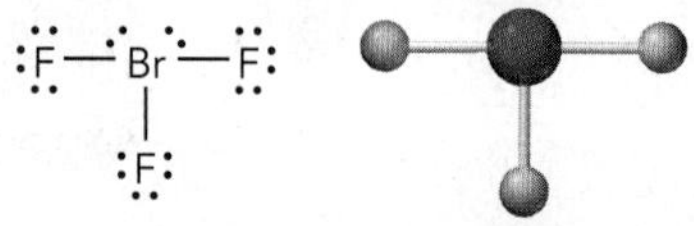
5	2	3	Trigonal bipyramidal	Linear	180°	
6	6	0	Octahedral	Octahedral	90°	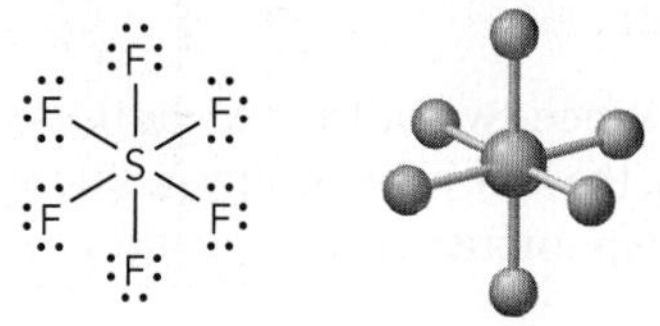
6	5	1	Octahedral	Square pyramidal	<90°	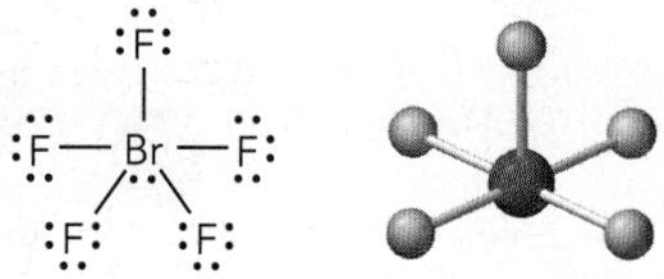
6	4	2	Octahedral	Square planar	90°	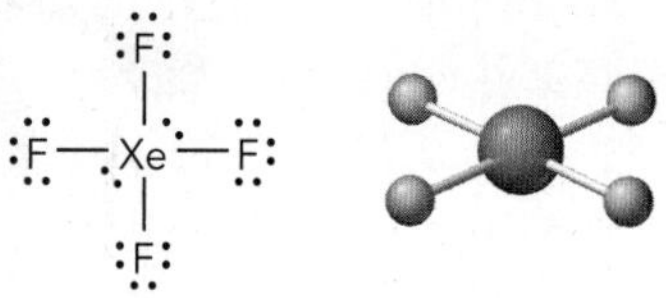

*Count only electron groups around the central atom. Each of the following is considered one electron group: a lone pair, a single bond, a double bond, a triple bond, or a single electron.

11.4 Cc Conceptual Connection ANSWER **NOW!**

LONE PAIR REPULSIONS Imagine that a molecule with six electron groups is confined to two dimensions and therefore has a hexagonal planar electron geometry. If two of the six groups are lone pairs, where are they located?

(a) positions 1 and 2
(b) positions 1 and 3
(c) positions 1 and 4

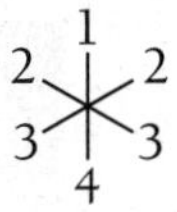

Summarizing VSEPR Theory:

- The geometry of a molecule is determined by the number of electron groups on the central atom (or on all interior atoms, if there is more than one).
- The number of electron groups is determined from the Lewis structure of the molecule. If the Lewis structure contains resonance structures, use any one of the resonance structures to determine the number of electron groups.
- Each of the following counts as a single electron group: a lone pair, a single bond, a double bond, a triple bond, or a single electron (as in a free radical).
- The geometry of the electron groups is determined by their repulsions as summarized in Table 11.1. In general, electron group repulsions vary as follows:

Lone pair–lone pair $<$ lone pair–bonding pair $<$ bonding pair–bonding pair

- Bond angles can vary from the idealized angles because double and triple bonds occupy more space than single bonds (they are bulkier even though they are shorter), and lone pairs occupy more space than bonding groups. The presence of lone pairs usually makes bond angles smaller than the ideal angles for the particular geometry.

11.5 Cc Conceptual Connection ANSWER **NOW!**

MOLECULAR GEOMETRY AND ELECTRON GROUP REPULSIONS Which statement is *always* true according to VSEPR theory?

(a) The shape of a molecule is determined only by repulsions among bonding electron groups.
(b) The shape of a molecule is determined only by repulsions among nonbonding electron groups.
(c) The shape of a molecule is determined by the polarity of its bonds.
(d) The shape of a molecule is determined by repulsions among all electron groups on the central atom (or interior atoms, if there is more than one).

11.4 VSEPR Theory: Predicting Molecular Geometries

To determine the geometry of a molecule, follow the procedure presented on the following page. As in other examples, we provide the steps in the left column and two examples of applying the steps in the center and right columns.

WATCH **NOW!**

INTERACTIVE WORKED EXAMPLE VIDEO 11.2

HOW TO: *Predict Molecular Geometries*

EXAMPLE 11.2 Predicting Molecular Geometries

Predict the geometry and bond angles of PCl_3.

EXAMPLE 11.3 Predicting Molecular Geometries

Predict the geometry and bond angles of ICl_4^-.

1. Draw the Lewis structure for the molecule.

Example 11.2: PCl_3 has 26 valence electrons.

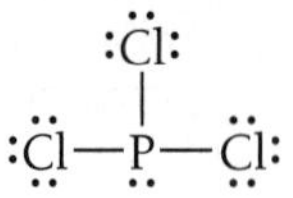

Example 11.3: ICl_4^- has 36 valence electrons.

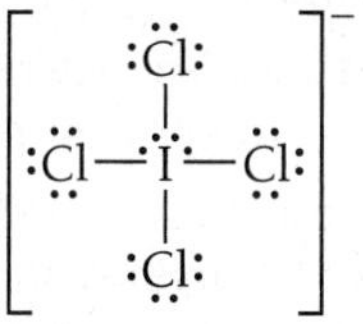

2. Determine the total number of electron groups around the central atom. Lone pairs, single bonds, double bonds, triple bonds, and single electrons each count as one group.

Example 11.2: The central atom (P) has four electron groups.

Example 11.3: The central atom (I) has six electron groups.

3. Determine the number of bonding groups and the number of lone pairs around the central atom. These should sum to your result from step 2. Bonding groups include single bonds, double bonds, and triple bonds.

Example 11.2:

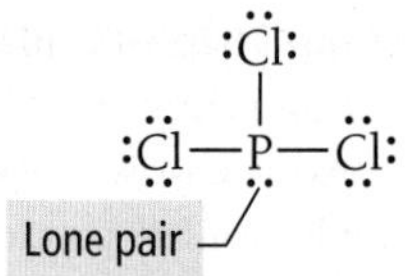

Three of the four electron groups around P are bonding groups, and one is a lone pair.

Example 11.3:

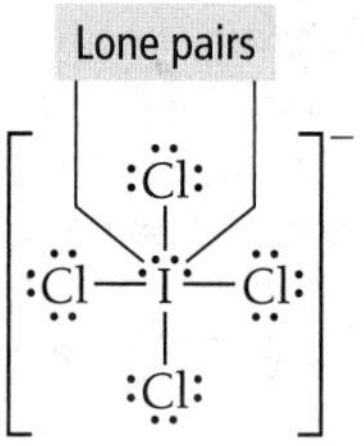

Four of the six electron groups around I are bonding groups, and two are lone pairs.

4. Refer to Table 11.1 to determine the electron geometry and molecular geometry. If no lone pairs are present around the central atom, the bond angles will be that of the ideal geometry. If lone pairs are present, the bond angles may be smaller than the ideal geometry.

Example 11.2: The electron geometry is tetrahedral (four electron groups), and the molecular geometry—the shape of the molecule—is *trigonal pyramidal* (three bonding groups and one lone pair). Because of the presence of a lone pair, the bond angles are less than 109.5°.

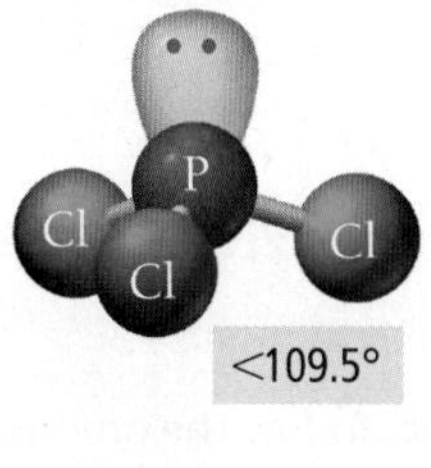

Trigonal pyramidal

Example 11.3: The electron geometry is octahedral (six electron groups), and the molecular geometry—the shape of the molecule—is *square planar* (four bonding groups and two lone pairs). Even though lone pairs are present, the bond angles are 90° because the lone pairs are symmetrically arranged and do not compress the I—Cl bond angles.

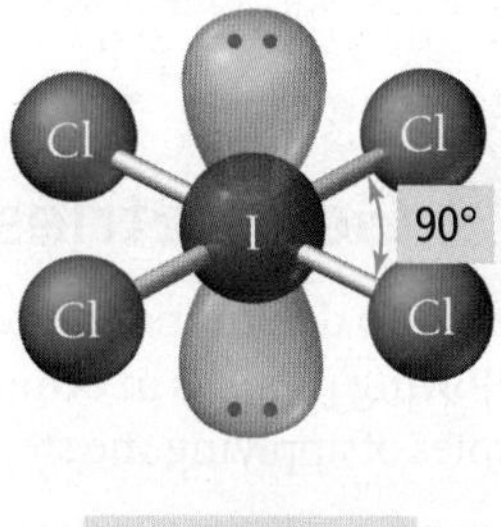

Square planar

FOR PRACTICE 11.2 Predict the molecular geometry and bond angle of ClNO.

FOR PRACTICE 11.3 Predict the molecular geometry of I_3^-.

Representing Molecular Geometries on Paper

Since molecular geometries are three-dimensional, they are often difficult to represent on two-dimensional paper. Many chemists use the notation shown here for bonds to indicate three-dimensional structures on two-dimensional paper.

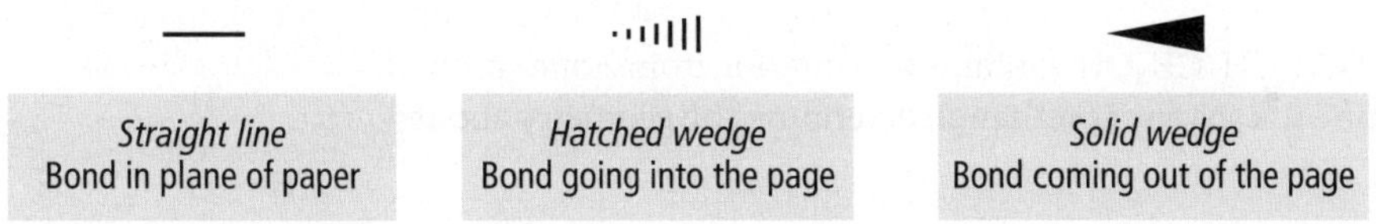

Some examples of the molecular geometries used in this book are shown below using this notation.

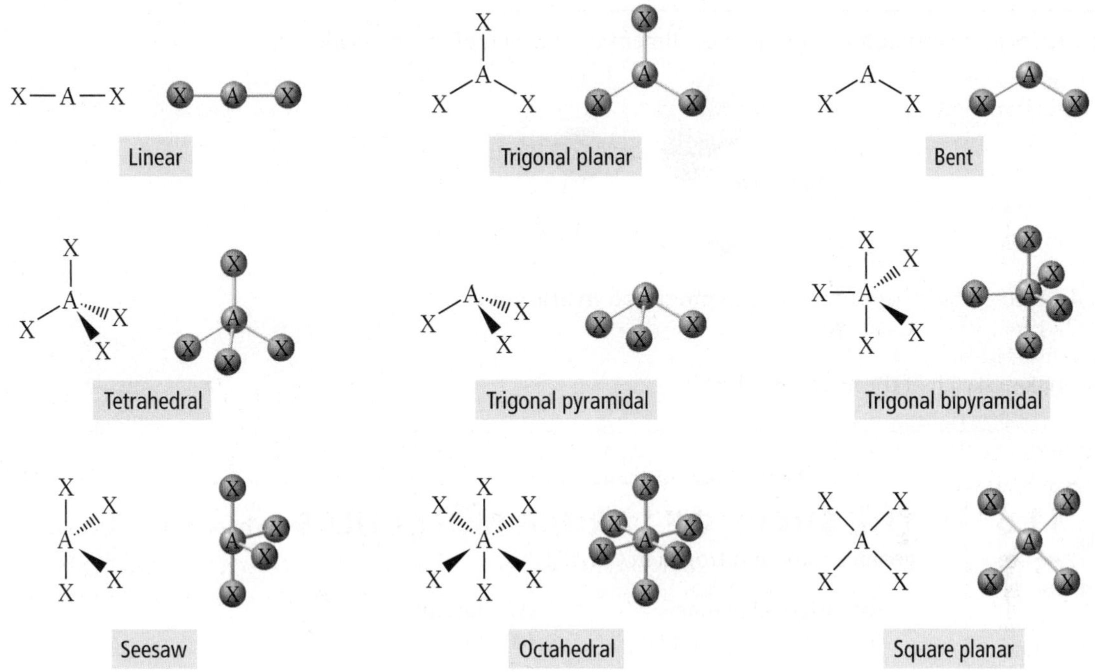

Predicting the Shapes of Larger Molecules

Larger molecules may have two or more *interior* atoms. When predicting the shapes of these molecules, we apply the principles we just covered to each interior atom. Consider glycine, an amino acid found in many proteins (such as those that act as opioid receptors, discussed in Section 11.1). Glycine, shown in the margin, contains four interior atoms: one nitrogen atom, two carbon atoms, and an oxygen atom. To determine the shape of glycine, we determine the geometry about each interior atom as follows:

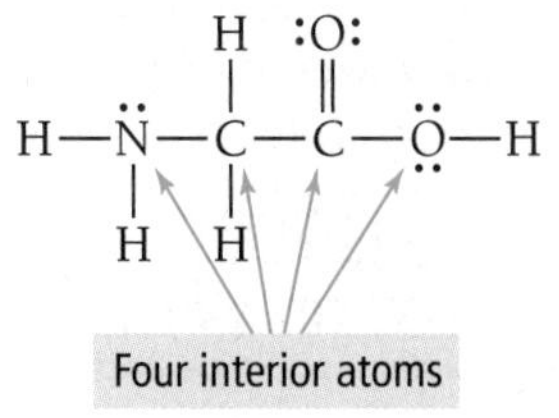

Glycine

Atom	Number of Electron Groups	Number of Lone Pairs	Molecular Geometry
Nitrogen	4	1	Trigonal pyramidal
Leftmost carbon	4	0	Tetrahedral
Rightmost carbon	3	0	Trigonal planar
Oxygen	4	2	Bent

Considering the geometries of each of these, we can determine the entire three-dimensional shape of the molecule as shown here.

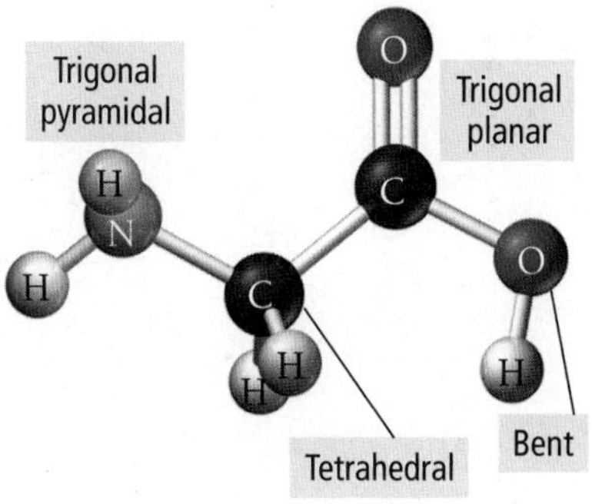

WATCH **NOW!**
INTERACTIVE WORKED EXAMPLE 11.4

EXAMPLE 11.4 Predicting the Shape of Larger Molecules

Predict the geometry about each interior atom in methanol (CH_3OH) and make a sketch of the molecule.

SOLUTION

Begin by drawing the Lewis structure of CH_3OH. CH_3OH contains two interior atoms: one carbon atom and one oxygen atom. To determine the shape of methanol, determine the geometry about each interior atom as follows:

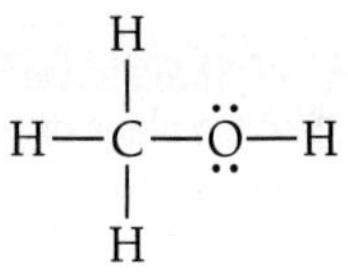

Atom	Number of Electron Groups	Number of Lone Pairs	Molecular Geometry
Carbon	4	0	Tetrahedral
Oxygen	4	2	Bent

Considering these interior atom geometries, draw a three-dimensional sketch of the molecule:

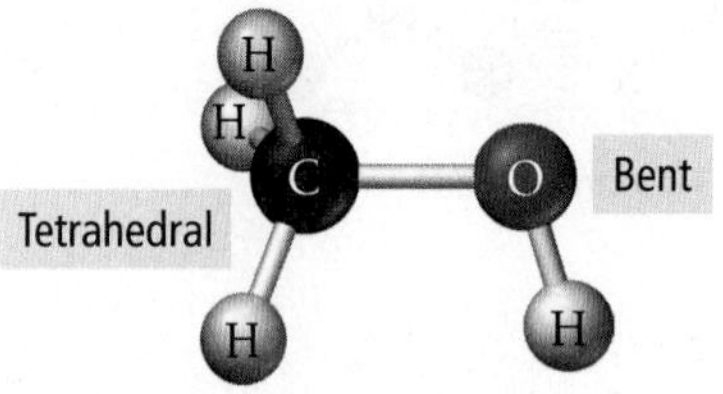

FOR PRACTICE 11.4 Predict the geometry about each interior atom in acetic acid $\left(H_3C{-}\overset{\overset{\displaystyle O}{\|}}{C}{-}H\right)$ and make a sketch of the molecule.

ANSWER **NOW!**

11.6 Cc Conceptual Connection

THE SHAPE OF LARGER MOLECULES What is the molecular geometry about nitrogen in CH_3NH_2?

(a) trigonal planar **(b)** tetrahedral
(c) trigonal pyramidal **(d)** bent

WATCH **NOW!**
KEY CONCEPT VIDEO 11.5
Molecular Shape and Polarity

11.5 Molecular Shape and Polarity

In Chapter 10, we discussed polar bonds. Entire molecules can also be polar, depending on their shape and the nature of their bonds. For example, if a diatomic molecule has a polar bond, the molecule as a whole is polar:

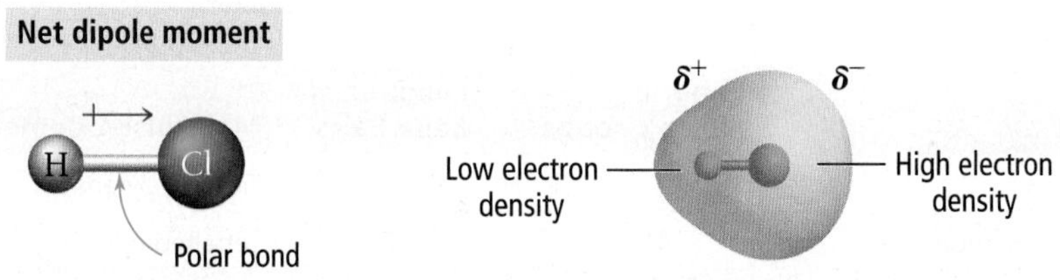

The figure on the right is an electrostatic potential map of HCl. In these maps, red areas indicate electron-rich regions in the molecule and the blue areas indicate electron-poor regions. Yellow indicates moderate electron density. Notice that the region around the more electronegative atom (chlorine) is more electron-rich than the region around the hydrogen atom. Thus the molecule itself is polar. If the bond in a diatomic molecule is *nonpolar*, the molecule as a whole is *nonpolar*.

In polyatomic molecules, the presence of polar bonds may or may not result in a polar molecule, depending on the molecular geometry. If the molecular geometry is such that the dipole moments of individual polar bonds sum together to a net dipole moment, then the molecule is polar. But if the molecular geometry is such that the dipole moments of the individual polar bonds cancel each other (that is, sum to zero), then the molecule is nonpolar. It all depends on the geometry of the molecule. Consider carbon dioxide:

$$:\ddot{O}=C=\ddot{O}:$$

Each C=O bond in CO_2 is polar because oxygen and carbon have significantly different electronegativities (3.5 and 2.5, respectively). However, since CO_2 is a linear molecule, the polar bonds directly oppose one another and the dipole moment of one bond exactly opposes the dipole moment of the other—the two dipole moments sum to zero and the *molecule* is nonpolar.

Dipole moments can cancel each other because they are *vector quantities*; they have both a magnitude and a direction. Think of each polar bond as a vector, pointing in the direction of the more electronegative atom. The length of the vector is proportional to the electronegativity difference between the bonding atoms. In CO_2, we have two identical vectors pointing in exactly opposite directions—the vectors sum to zero, much as +1 and −1 sum to zero:

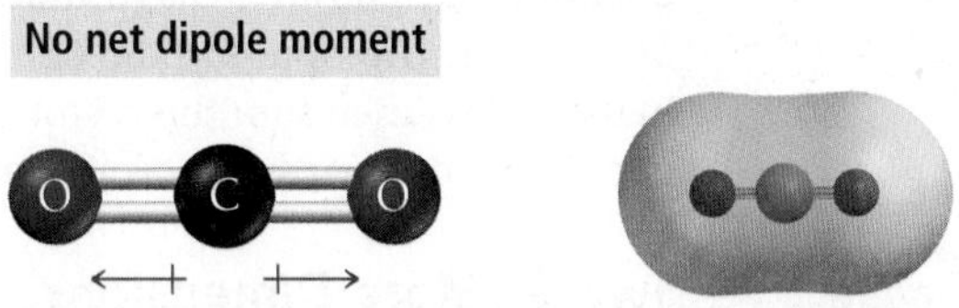

Notice that the electrostatic potential map shows regions of moderately high electron density (yellow with slight red) positioned symmetrically on either end of the molecule with a region of low electron density (blue) located in the middle.

In contrast, consider water:

$$H-\ddot{\underset{..}{O}}-H$$

The O—H bonds in water are also polar; oxygen and hydrogen have electronegativities of 3.5 and 2.1, respectively. However, the water molecule is not linear but bent, so the two dipole moments do not sum to zero as they do in carbon dioxide. If we imagine each bond in water as a vector pointing toward oxygen (the more electronegative atom), we see that, because of the angle between the vectors, they do not cancel but sum to an overall vector or a net dipole moment (shown by the dashed arrow):

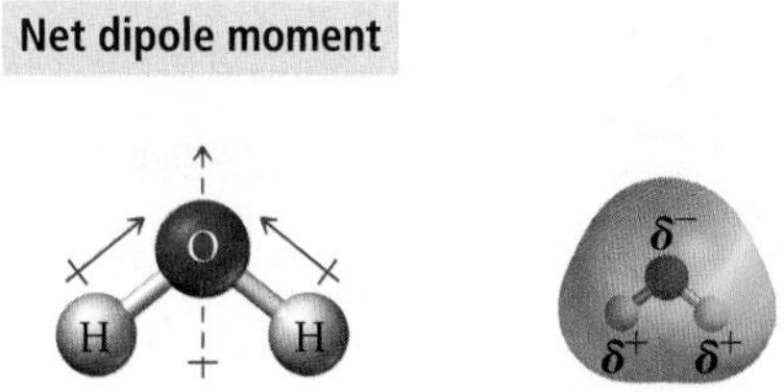

Table 11.2 (on page 453) summarizes common geometries and molecular polarity while the How To... feature summarizes how to determine if a molecule is polar.

HOW TO: *Determine Molecular Shape and Polarity*

- **Draw the Lewis structure for the molecule and determine its molecular geometry.**
- **Determine whether the molecule contains polar bonds.** A bond is polar if the two bonding atoms have sufficiently different electronegativities (see Figure 10.8). If the molecule contains polar bonds, superimpose a vector, pointing toward the more electronegative atom, on each bond. Draw the length of the vector proportional to the electronegativity difference between the bonding atoms.
- **Determine whether the polar bonds add together to form a net dipole moment.** Sum the vectors corresponding to the polar bonds together. If the vectors sum to zero, the molecule is nonpolar. If the vectors sum to a net vector, the molecule is polar.

ANSWER **NOW!**

11.7 Cc Conceptual Connection

POLARITY OF MOLECULES A molecule contains three identical polar bonds in a trigonal planar molecular geometry. Is the molecule polar?

(a) yes
(b) no
(c) unable to determine whether the molecule is polar without more information

Vector Addition

We determine whether a molecule is polar by summing the vectors associated with the dipole moments of all the polar bonds in the molecule. If the vectors sum to zero, the molecule is nonpolar. If they sum to a net vector, the molecule is polar. In this section, we demonstrate how to add vectors together in one dimension and in two or more dimensions.

One Dimension

To add two vectors that lie on the same line, assign one direction as positive. Vectors pointing in that direction have positive magnitudes. Consider vectors pointing in the opposite direction to have negative magnitudes. Then sum the vectors (always remembering to include their signs), as shown in Examples 1–3.

Example 1

Example 2

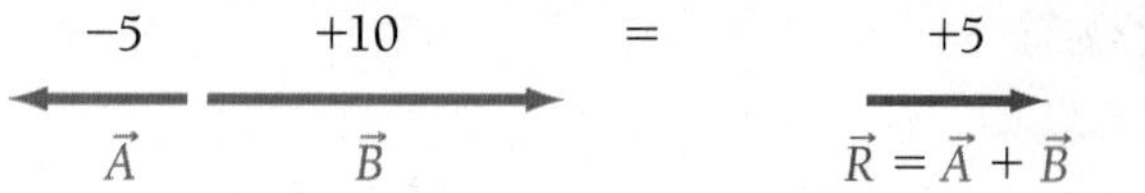

Example 3

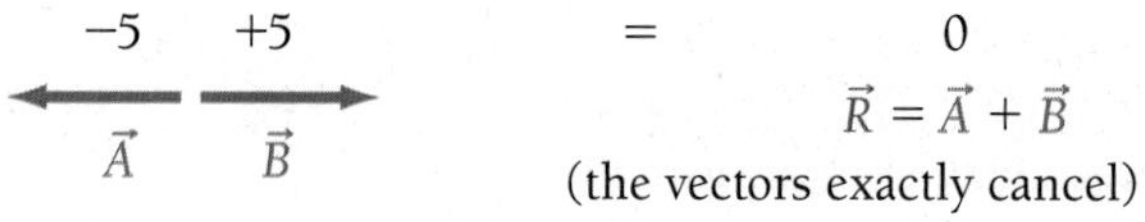

Two or More Dimensions

To add two vectors in two or more dimensions, draw a parallelogram in which the two vectors form two adjacent sides. Draw the other two sides of the parallelogram parallel to and the same length as the two original vectors. Draw the resultant vector beginning at the origin and extending to the far corner of the parallelogram, as shown in Examples 4 and 5.

To add three or more vectors in two or more dimensions, add two of them together first, and then add the third vector to the result as shown in Examples 6 and 7.

Example 4

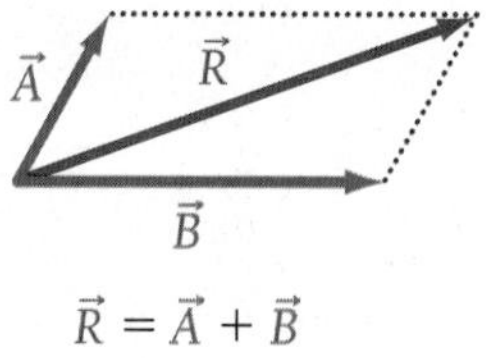

Example 5

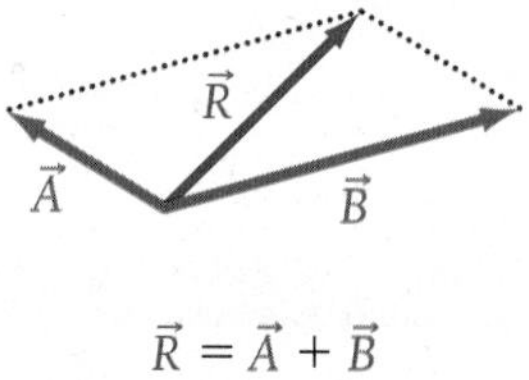

Example 6

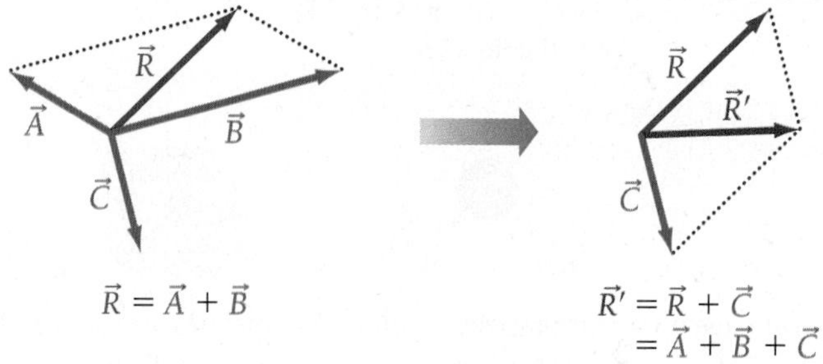

Example 7

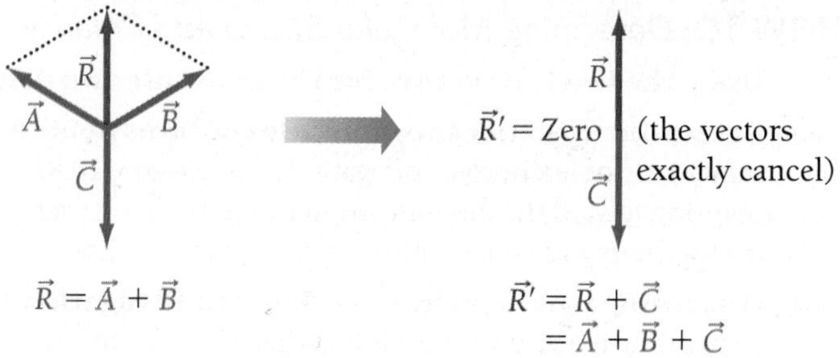

TABLE 11.2 ■ Common Cases of Adding Dipole Moments to Determine Whether a Molecule Is Polar

Linear

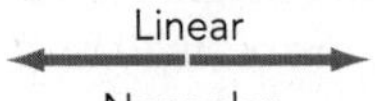

Nonpolar

The dipole moments of two identical polar bonds pointing in opposite directions cancel. The molecule is nonpolar.

Bent

Polar

The dipole moments of two polar bonds with an angle of less than 180° between them do not cancel. The resultant dipole moment vector is shown in red. The molecule is polar.

Trigonal planar

Nonpolar

The dipole moments of three identical polar bonds at 120° from each other cancel. The molecule is nonpolar.

Tetrahedral

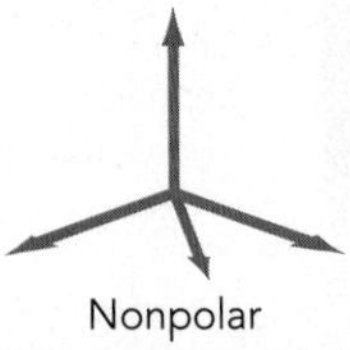

Nonpolar

The dipole moments of four identical polar bonds in a tetrahedral arrangement (109.5° from each other) cancel. The molecule is nonpolar.

Trigonal pyramidal

Polar

The dipole moments of three polar bonds in a trigonal pyramidal arrangement do not cancel. The resultant dipole moment vector is shown in red. The molecule is polar.

Note: In all cases in which the dipoles of two or more polar bonds cancel, the bonds are assumed to be identical. If one or more of the bonds are different from the other(s), the dipoles will not cancel and the molecule will be polar.

WATCH **NOW!**

INTERACTIVE WORKED EXAMPLE 11.5

EXAMPLE 11.5 Determining Whether a Molecule Is Polar

Determine whether NH_3 is polar.

SOLUTION

Draw the Lewis structure for the molecule and determine its molecular geometry.

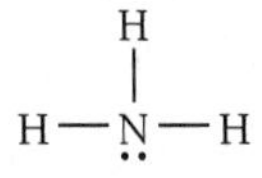

The Lewis structure has three bonding groups and one lone pair about the central atom. Therefore, the molecular geometry is trigonal pyramidal.

Determine whether the molecule contains polar bonds. Sketch the molecule and superimpose a vector for each polar bond. The relative length of each vector is proportional to the electronegativity difference between the atoms forming each bond. The vectors point in the direction of the more electronegative atom.

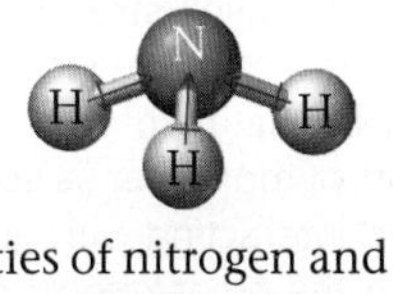

The electronegativities of nitrogen and hydrogen are 3.0 and 2.1, respectively. Therefore, the bonds are polar.

Determine whether the polar bonds add together to form a net dipole moment. Examine the symmetry of the vectors (representing dipole moments) and determine whether they cancel each other or sum to a net dipole moment.

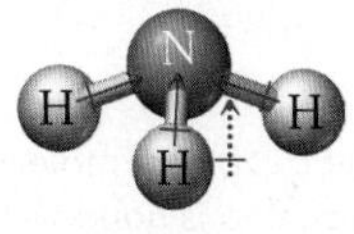

The three dipole moments sum to a net dipole moment. The molecule is polar.

FOR PRACTICE 11.5 Determine whether CF_4 is polar.

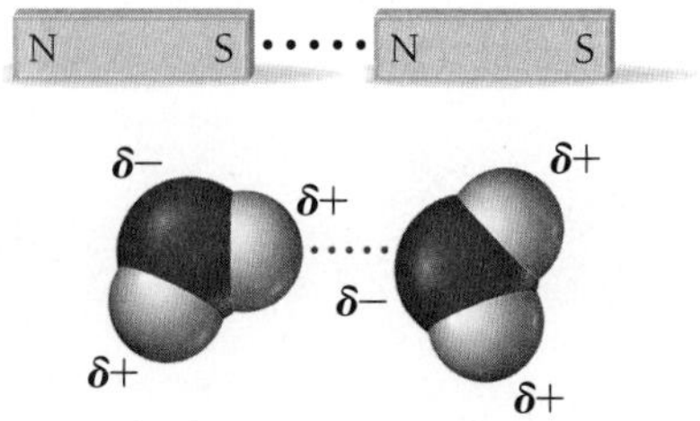

▲ **FIGURE 11.5 Interaction of Polar Molecules** The north pole of one magnet attracts the south pole of another magnet. In an analogous way, the positively charged end of one molecule attracts the negatively charged end of another (although the forces involved are different). As a result of this electrical attraction, polar molecules interact strongly with one another.

Polar and nonpolar molecules have different properties. Water and oil do not mix, for example, because water molecules are polar and the molecules that compose oil are generally nonpolar. Polar molecules interact strongly with other polar molecules because the positive end of one molecule is attracted to the negative end of another, just as the south pole of a magnet is attracted to the north pole of another magnet (Figure 11.5◀). A mixture of polar and nonpolar molecules is similar to a mixture of small magnetic particles and nonmagnetic ones. The magnetic particles (which are like polar molecules) clump together, excluding the nonmagnetic particles (which are like nonpolar molecules) and separating into distinct regions.

▲ Oil and water do not mix because water molecules are polar and the molecules that compose oil are nonpolar.

▲ A mixture of polar and nonpolar molecules is analogous to a mixture of magnetic marbles (opaque) and nonmagnetic marbles (transparent). As with the magnetic marbles, mutual attraction causes polar molecules to clump together, excluding the nonpolar molecules.

CHEMISTRY IN YOUR DAY | How Soap Works

Imagine eating a greasy cheeseburger with both hands without a napkin. By the end of the meal, grease and oil coat your hands. If you try to wash them with only water, they remain greasy. However, if you add a little soap, the grease washes away. Why? As we just learned, water molecules are polar and the molecules that compose grease and oil are nonpolar. As a result, water and grease do not mix.

The molecules that compose soap, however, have a special structure that allows them to interact strongly with both water and grease. One end of a soap molecule is polar and the other end is nonpolar.

The nonpolar end is a long hydrocarbon chain. Hydrocarbons are always nonpolar because the electronegativity difference between carbon and hydrogen is small and because the tetrahedral arrangement about each carbon atom tends to cancel any small dipole moments of individual bonds. The polar head of a soap molecule—usually, though not always, ionic—strongly attracts water molecules, while the nonpolar tail interacts more strongly with grease and oil molecules (we examine the nature of these interactions in Chapter 12). Thus, soap acts as a sort of molecular liaison, one end interacting with water and the other end interacting with grease. Soap allows water and grease to mix, removing the grease from your hands and washing it down the drain.

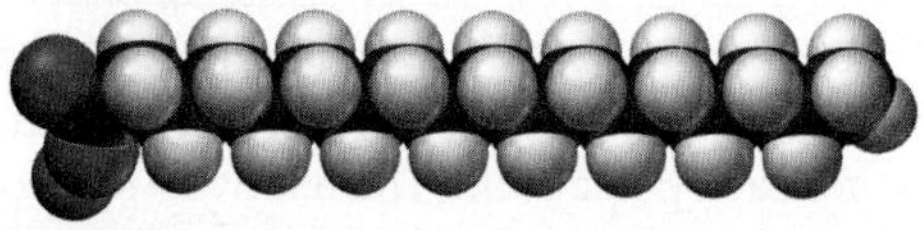

$CH_3(CH_2)_{11}OCH_2CH_2OH$

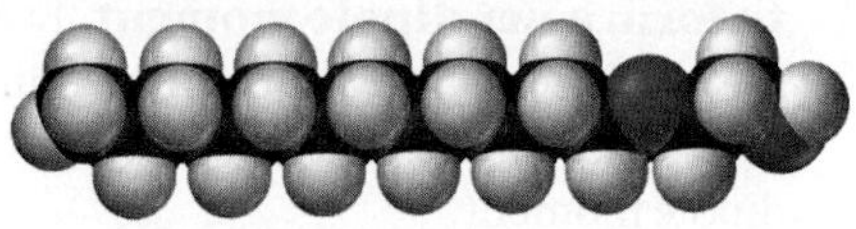

QUESTION *Consider the detergent molecule shown at right. Which end do you think is polar? Which end is nonpolar?*

11.6 Valence Bond Theory: Orbital Overlap as a Chemical Bond

WATCH **NOW!**

KEY CONCEPT VIDEO 11.6
Valence Bond Theory

In the Lewis model, we use dots to represent electrons. We know from quantum-mechanical theory, however, that such a treatment is an oversimplification. More advanced bonding theories treat electrons in a quantum-mechanical manner. These theories are actually extensions of quantum mechanics, applied to molecules. Although a detailed quantitative treatment of these theories is beyond the scope of this book, we introduce them in a *qualitative* manner in the sections that follow. Keep in mind, however, that modern *quantitative* approaches to chemical bonding using these theories accurately predict many of the properties of molecules—such as bond lengths, bond strengths, molecular geometries, and dipole moments—that we discuss in this book.

The simpler of the two more advanced bonding theories is **valence bond theory**. According to valence bond theory, electrons reside in quantum-mechanical orbitals localized on individual atoms. In many cases, these orbitals are simply the standard *s*, *p*, *d*, and *f* atomic orbitals that we learned about in Chapter 8 . In other cases, these orbitals are *hybridized atomic orbitals*, a kind of blend or combination of two or more standard atomic orbitals.

Valence bond theory is an application of a general quantum-mechanical approximation method called *perturbation theory.* In perturbation theory, a complex system (such as a molecule) is viewed as a simpler system (such as two atoms) that is slightly altered or perturbed by some additional force or interaction (such as the interaction between the two atoms).

When two atoms approach each other, the electrons and nucleus of one atom interact with the electrons and nucleus of the other atom. In valence bond theory, we calculate how these interactions affect the energies of the electrons in the atomic orbitals. If the energy of the system is lowered because of the interactions, then a chemical bond forms. If the energy of the system is raised by the interactions, then a chemical bond does not form.

The interaction energy is usually calculated as a function of the internuclear distance between the two bonding atoms. For example, Figure 11.6▼ shows the calculated interaction energy between two hydrogen atoms as a function of the distance between them. The *y*-axis of the graph is the potential energy of the interaction between the electron and nucleus of one hydrogen atom and the electron and nucleus of the other hydrogen atom. The *x*-axis is the separation (or internuclear distance) between the two atoms. As we can see from the graph, when the atoms are far apart (right side of the graph, labeled 1), the interaction energy is nearly zero because the two atoms do not interact to any significant extent. As the atoms get closer (labeled 2 and 3 on the graph), the interaction energy becomes negative. The lowering of the interaction energy is a net stabilization that attracts one hydrogen atom to the other. If the atoms get too close

Interaction Energy of Two Hydrogen Atoms

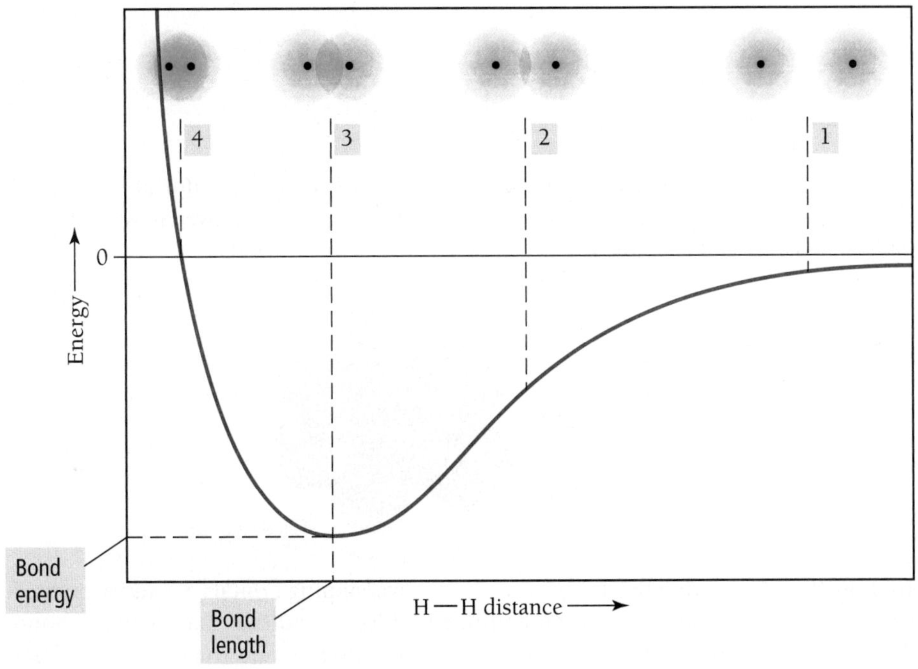

◀ **FIGURE 11.6 Interaction Energy Diagram for H_2** The potential energy of two hydrogen atoms is lowest when they are separated by a distance that allows their 1*s* orbitals a substantial degree of overlap without too much repulsion between their nuclei. This distance, at which the system is most stable, is the bond length of the H_2 molecule (labeled 3 on this graph).

(labeled 4 on the graph), however, the interaction energy begins to rise, primarily because of the mutual repulsion of the two positively charged nuclei. The most stable point on the curve occurs at the minimum of the interaction energy—this is the equilibrium bond length (labeled 3 on the graph). At this distance, the two atomic 1*s* orbitals have a significant amount of overlap, and the electrons spend time in the internuclear region where they can interact with both nuclei. The value of the interaction energy at the equilibrium bond distance is the bond energy.

When we apply valence bond theory to a number of atoms and their corresponding molecules, we arrive at the following general observation: *the interaction energy is usually negative (or stabilizing) when the interacting atomic orbitals contain a total of two electrons that can spin-pair (orient with opposing spins).* Most commonly, the two electrons come from two half-filled orbitals, but in some cases, the two electrons come from one filled orbital overlapping with a completely empty orbital (this is called a coordinate covalent bond, and we will cover it in more detail in Chapter 26). In other words, when two atoms with half-filled orbitals approach each other, the half-filled orbitals *overlap*—parts of the orbitals occupy the same space—and the electrons occupying them align with opposite spins. This results in a net energy stabilization that constitutes a covalent chemical bond. The resulting geometry of the molecule emerges from the geometry of the overlapping orbitals.

When *completely filled* orbitals overlap, the interaction energy is positive (or destabilizing) and no bond forms.

Summarizing Valence Bond Theory:

- The valence electrons of the atoms in a molecule reside in quantum-mechanical atomic orbitals. The orbitals can be the standard *s*, *p*, *d*, and *f* orbitals, or they may be hybrid combinations of these.
- A chemical bond results from the overlap of two half-filled orbitals with spin-pairing of the two valence electrons (or less commonly the overlap of a completely filled orbital with an empty orbital).
- The geometry of the overlapping orbitals determines the shape of the molecule.

We can apply the general concepts of valence bond theory to explain bonding in hydrogen sulfide, H_2S. The valence electron configurations of the atoms in the molecule are as follows:

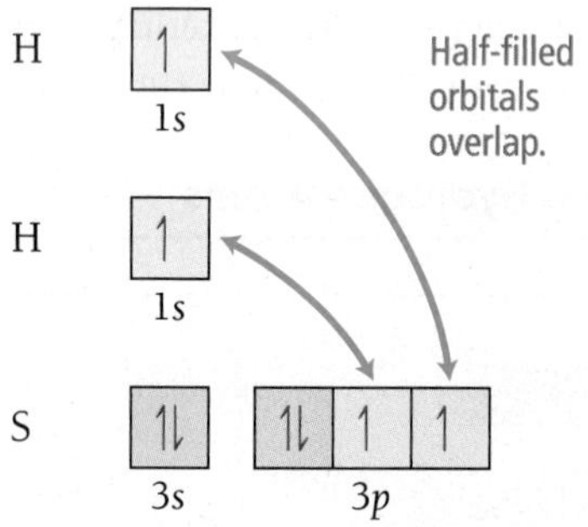

The hydrogen atoms each have one half-filled orbital, and the sulfur atom has two half-filled orbitals. The half-filled orbitals on each hydrogen atom overlap with the two half-filled orbitals on the sulfur atom, forming two chemical bonds:

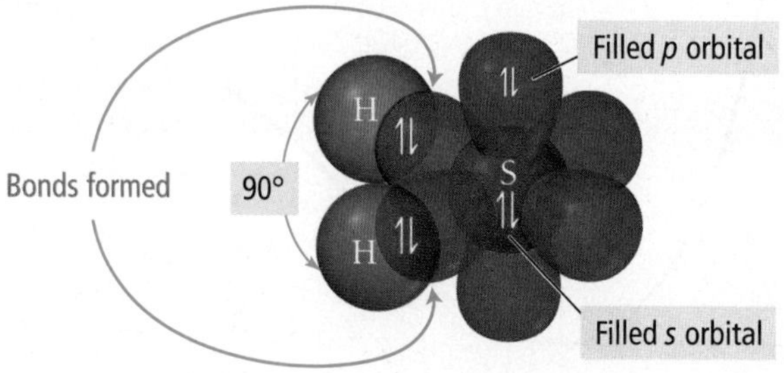

To show the spin-pairing of the electrons in the overlapping orbitals, we superimpose a half-arrow for each electron in each half-filled orbital to indicate that, within a bond, the electrons are spin-paired (one half-arrow is pointing up and the other is pointing down). We also superimpose paired half-arrows in the filled sulfur *s* and *p* orbitals to represent the lone pair electrons in those orbitals. (Since those orbitals are full, they are not involved in bonding.)

A quantitative calculation of H_2S using valence bond theory yields bond energies, bond lengths, and bond angles. In our qualitative treatment, we simply show how orbital overlap leads to bonding and make a rough sketch of the molecule based on the overlapping orbitals. Notice that, because the overlapping orbitals on the central atom (sulfur) are *p* orbitals and because *p* orbitals are oriented at 90° to one another, the predicted bond angle is 90°. The actual bond angle in H_2S is 92°. In the case of H_2S, a simple valence bond treatment matches well with the experimentally measured bond angle (in contrast to VSEPR theory, which predicts a bond angle of less than 109.5°).

WHAT IS A CHEMICAL BOND? PART I The answer to the question "What is a chemical bond?" depends on the bonding model. What is a chemical bond according to valence bond theory?

11.8 Cc Conceptual Connection

ANSWER **NOW!**

(a) lone electron pair
(b) the overlap between half-filled atomic orbitals on two atoms
(c) the overlap between filled atomic orbitals on two atoms
(d) a shared electron pair between two atoms

11.7 Valence Bond Theory: Hybridization of Atomic Orbitals

WATCH **NOW!**

KEY CONCEPT VIDEO 11.7
Valence Bond Theory: Hybridization

Although the overlap of half-filled *standard* atomic orbitals adequately explains the bonding in H_2S, it cannot adequately explain the bonding in many other molecules. For example, suppose we try to explain the bonding between hydrogen and carbon using the same approach. The valence electron configurations of H and C are as follows:

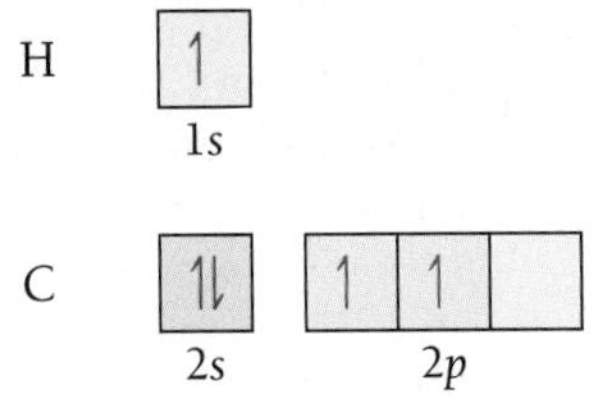

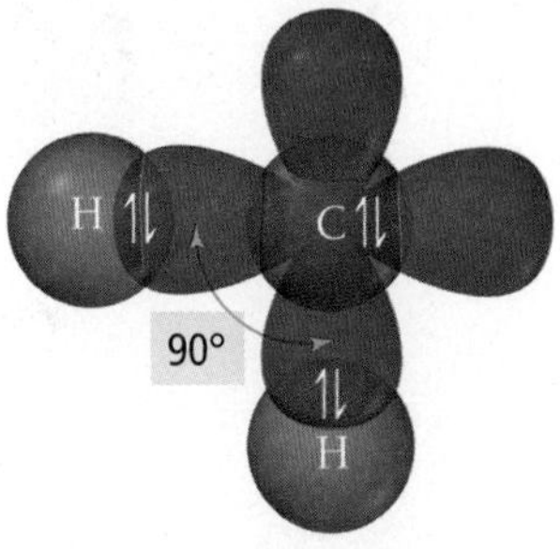

Theoretical prediction

Carbon has only two half-filled orbitals and should therefore form only two bonds with two hydrogen atoms. We would therefore predict that carbon and hydrogen should form a molecule with the formula CH_2 and with a bond angle of 90° (corresponding to the angle between any two *p* orbitals).

However, from experiments, we know that the stable compound formed from carbon and hydrogen is CH_4 (methane), which has bond angles of 109.5°. The experimental reality is different from our simple prediction in two ways. First, carbon forms bonds to four hydrogen atoms, not two. Second, the bond angles are much larger than the angle between two *p* orbitals. Valence bond theory accounts for the bonding in CH_4 and many other polyatomic molecules by incorporating an additional concept called *orbital hybridization*.

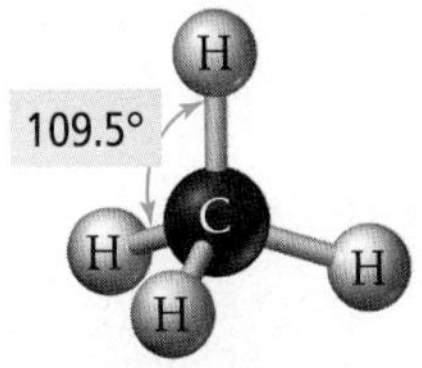

Observed reality

So far, we have assumed that the overlapping orbitals that form chemical bonds are simply the standard *s, p,* or *d* atomic orbitals. Valence bond theory treats the electrons in a molecule as if they occupied these standard atomic orbitals, but this is a major oversimplification. The concept of hybridization in valence bond theory is essentially a step toward recognizing that *the orbitals in a molecule are not necessarily the same as the orbitals in an atom.* **Hybridization** is a mathematical procedure in which the standard atomic orbitals are combined to form new atomic orbitals called **hybrid orbitals** that

In Section 11.8, we examine another theory called *molecular orbital theory,* which treats electrons in a molecule as occupying orbitals that belong to the molecule as a whole.

As we saw in Chapter 10, the word *hybrid* comes from breeding. A *hybrid* is an offspring of two animals or plants of different standard races or breeds. Similarly, a hybrid orbital is a product of mixing two or more standard atomic orbitals.

correspond more closely to the actual distribution of electrons in chemically bonded atoms. Hybrid orbitals are still localized on individual atoms, but their shapes and energies differ from those of standard atomic orbitals.

Why do we hypothesize that electrons in some molecules occupy hybrid orbitals? In valence bond theory, a chemical bond is the overlap of two orbitals that together contain two electrons. The greater the overlap, the stronger the bond and the lower the energy. In hybrid orbitals, the electron probability density is more concentrated in a single directional lobe, allowing greater overlap with the orbitals of other atoms. Hybrid orbitals *minimize* the energy of the molecule by *maximizing* the orbital overlap in a bond.

Hybridization, however, is not a free lunch—in most cases it actually costs some energy. So hybridization occurs only to the degree that the energy payback through bond formation is large. In general, therefore, the more bonds that an atom forms, the greater the tendency of its orbitals to hybridize. Central or interior atoms, which form the most bonds, have the greatest tendency to hybridize. Terminal atoms, which form the fewest bonds, have the least tendency to hybridize. *In this book, we focus on the hybridization of interior atoms and assume that all terminal atoms—those bonding to only one other atom—are unhybridized.* Hybridization is particularly important in carbon, which tends to form four bonds in its compounds and therefore always hybridizes.

In a more nuanced treatment, hybridization is not an all-or-nothing process—it can occur to varying degrees that are not always easy to predict. We saw earlier, for example, that sulfur does not hybridize very much in forming H_2S.

Although we cannot examine the procedure for obtaining hybrid orbitals in mathematical detail here, we can make the following general statements regarding hybridization:

- The *number of standard atomic orbitals* added together always equals the *number of hybrid orbitals* formed. The total number of orbitals is conserved.
- The *particular combination* of standard atomic orbitals added together determines the *shapes and energies* of the hybrid orbitals formed.
- The *particular type of hybridization that occurs* is the one that yields the *lowest overall energy for the molecule*. Since actual energy calculations are beyond the scope of this book, we use electron geometries as determined by VSEPR theory to predict the type of hybridization.

sp^3 Hybridization

We can account for the tetrahedral geometry in CH_4 by the hybridization of the one 2*s* orbital and the three 2*p* orbitals on the carbon atom. The four new orbitals that result, called sp^3 hybrids, are shown in the following energy diagram:

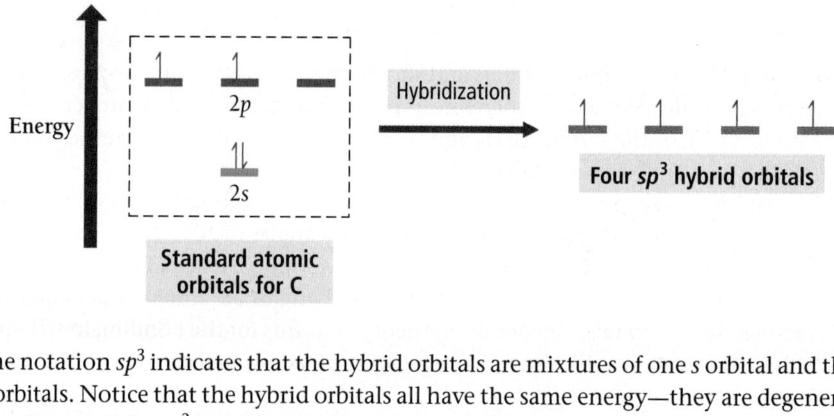

The notation sp^3 indicates that the hybrid orbitals are mixtures of one *s* orbital and three *p* orbitals. Notice that the hybrid orbitals all have the same energy—they are degenerate. The shapes of the sp^3 hybrid orbitals are shown in Figure 11.7▶. The four hybrid orbitals are arranged in a tetrahedral geometry with 109.5° angles between them.

We can write an orbital diagram for carbon using these hybrid orbitals:

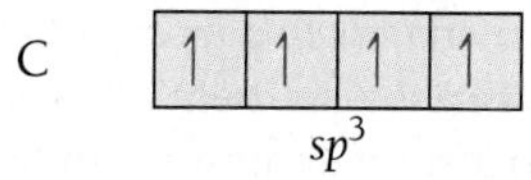

Formation of sp^3 Hybrid Orbitals

One *s* orbital and three *p* orbitals combine to form four sp^3 orbitals.

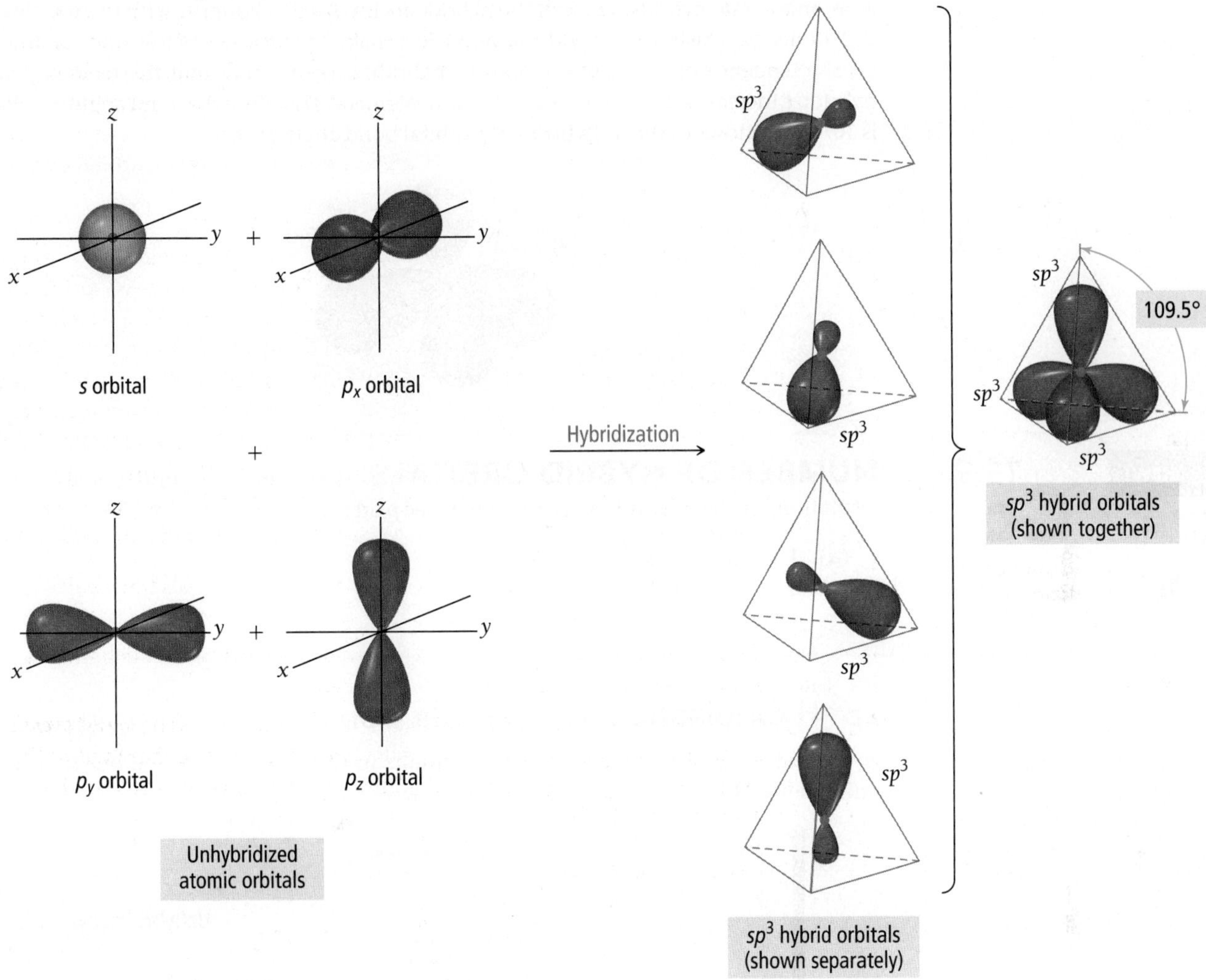

▲ **FIGURE 11.7** sp^3 **Hybridization**

Carbon's four valence electrons occupy the orbitals singly with parallel spins as dictated by Hund's rule. With this electron configuration, carbon has four half-filled orbitals and can form four bonds with four hydrogen atoms:

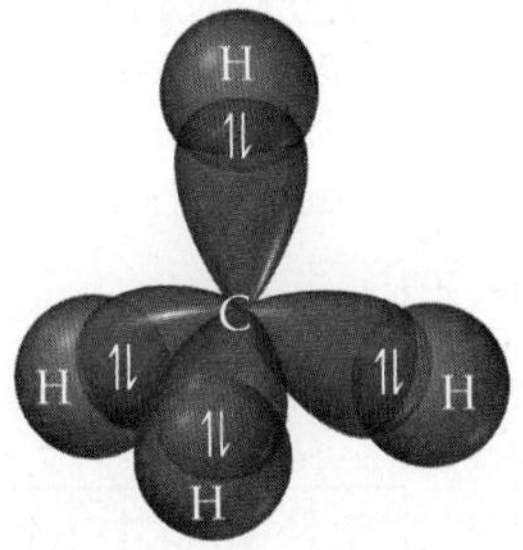

The geometry of the *overlapping orbitals* (the hybrids) is tetrahedral, with angles of 109.5° between the orbitals, so the *resulting geometry of the molecule* is tetrahedral, with 109.5° bond angles. This agrees with the experimentally measured geometry of CH_4 and with the predicted VSEPR geometry.

Hybridized orbitals readily form chemical bonds because they tend to maximize overlap with other orbitals. However, if the central atom of a molecule contains lone pairs, hybrid orbitals can also accommodate them. For example, the nitrogen orbitals in ammonia are sp^3 hybrids. Three of the hybrids are involved in bonding with three hydrogen atoms, but the fourth hybrid contains a lone pair. The presence of the lone pair lowers the tendency of nitrogen's orbitals to hybridize. (Remember that the tendency to hybridize increases with the number of bonds formed.) Therefore the bond angle in NH_3 is 107°, a bit closer to the unhybridized p orbital bond angle of 90°.

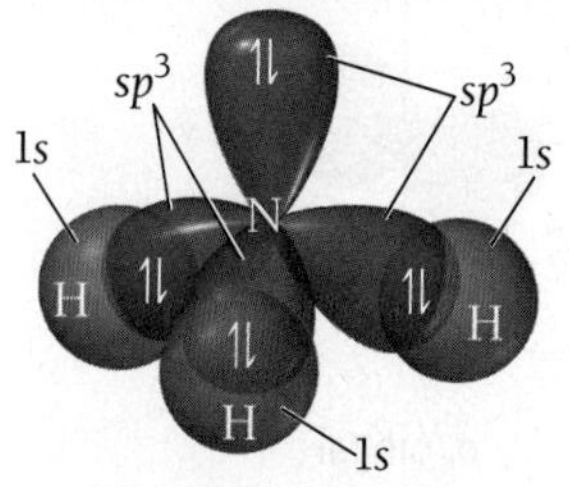

ANSWER **NOW!**

11.9 **Cc** Conceptual Connection

NUMBER OF HYBRID ORBITALS How many sp^3 hybrid orbitals result from the hybridization of one s and three p orbitals?

(a) 1 **(b)** 2
(c) 3 **(d)** 4

sp^2 Hybridization and Double Bonds

In valence bond theory, the particular hybridization scheme to follow sp^2 versus sp^3, for example, for a given molecule is determined computationally, which is beyond the scope of this text. In this book, we determine the particular hybridization scheme from the VSEPR geometry of the molecule, as shown later in this section.

Hybridization of one s and two p orbitals results in three sp^2 hybrids and one leftover unhybridized p orbital:

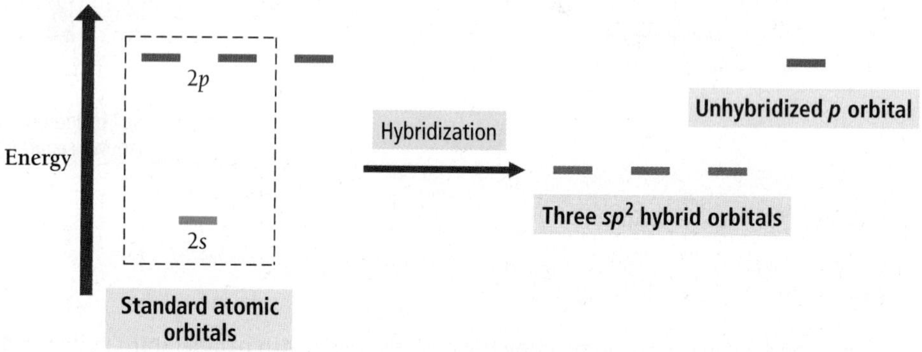

The notation sp^2 indicates that the hybrids are mixtures of one s orbital and two p orbitals. Figure 11.8▶ illustrates the shapes of the sp^2 hybrid orbitals. Notice that the three hybrid orbitals have a trigonal planar geometry with 120° angles between them. The unhybridized p orbital is perpendicular to the three hybridized orbitals.

As an example of a molecule with sp^2 hybrid orbitals, consider H_2CO. The unhybridized valence electron configurations of each of the atoms are as follows:

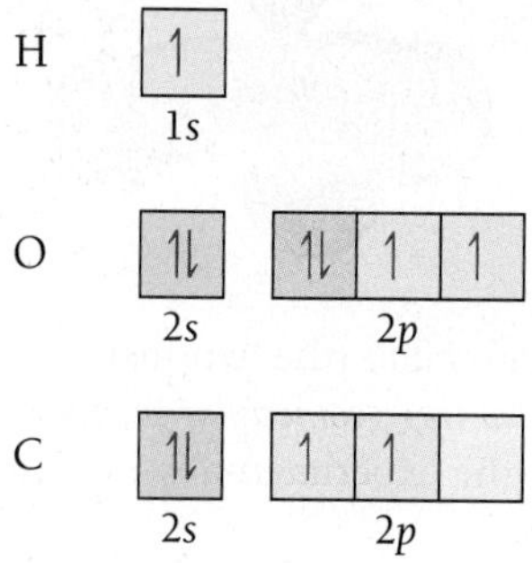

Formation of sp^2 Hybrid Orbitals

One s orbital and two p orbitals combine to form three sp^2 orbitals.

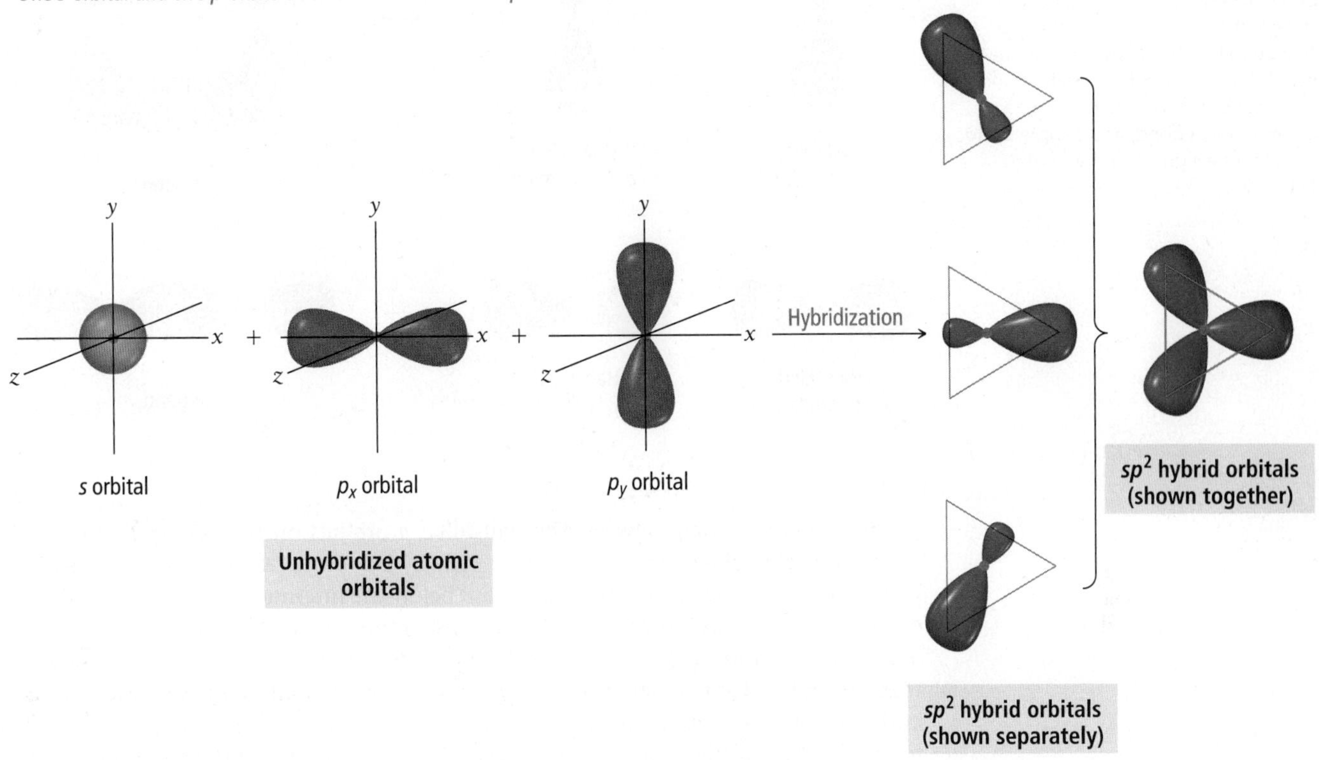

▲ **FIGURE 11.8 sp^2 Hybridization** When sp^2 hybrid orbitals form, one p orbital (not shown) remains unhybridized.

Carbon is the central atom, and the hybridization of its orbitals is sp^2:

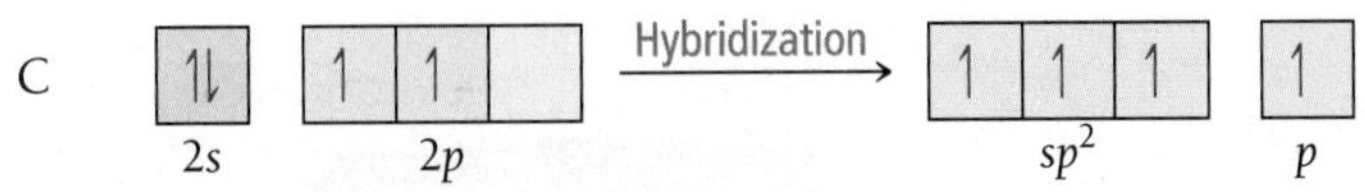

Each of the sp^2 orbitals is half filled. The remaining electron occupies the leftover p orbital, even though it is slightly higher in energy. We can now see that the carbon atom has four half-filled orbitals and can therefore form four bonds: two with two hydrogen atoms and two (a double bond) with the oxygen atom. We draw the molecule and the overlapping orbitals as follows:

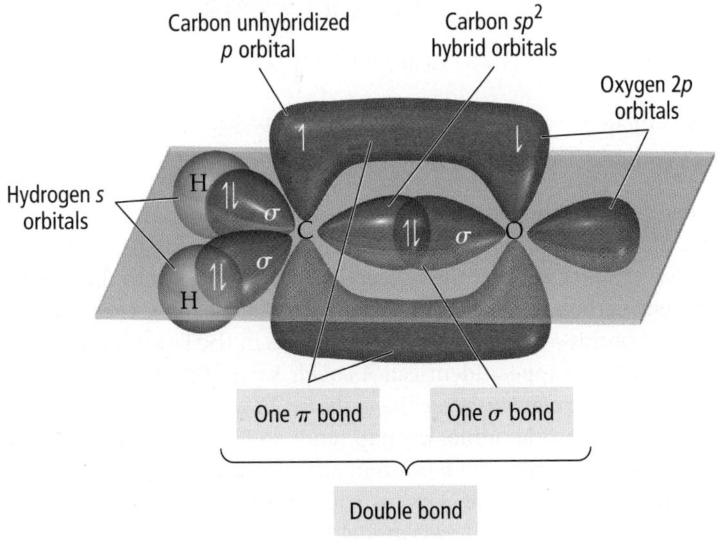

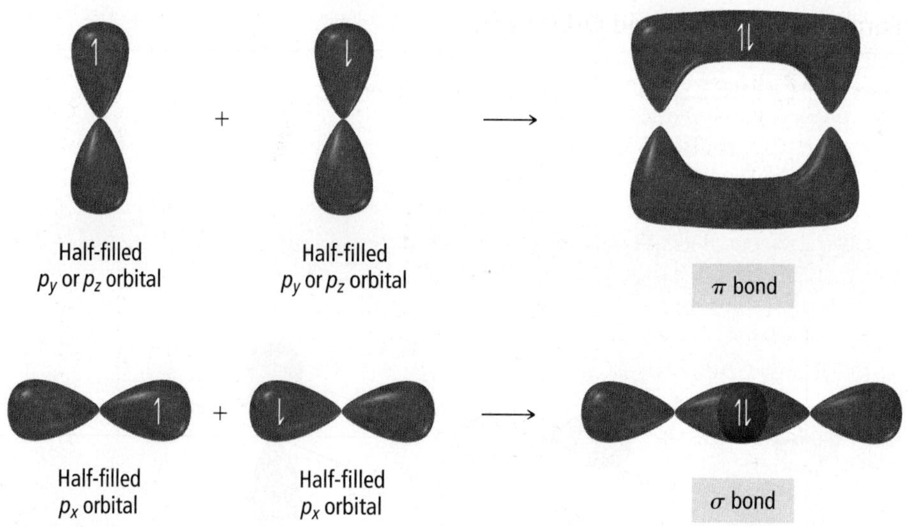

▶ **FIGURE 11.9 Sigma and Pi Bonding** When orbitals overlap side by side, the result is a pi (π) bond. When orbitals overlap end to end, they form a sigma (σ) bond. Two atoms can form only one sigma bond. A single bond is a sigma bond, a double bond consists of a sigma bond and a pi bond, and a triple bond consists of a sigma bond and two pi bonds.

Notice the overlap between the half-filled *p* orbitals on the carbon and oxygen atoms. When *p* orbitals overlap this way (side by side), the resulting bond is a **pi (π) bond**, and the electron density is above and below the internuclear axis. When orbitals overlap end to end, as is the case in all of the rest of the bonds in the molecule, the resulting bond is a **sigma (σ) bond** (Figure 11.9▲). Even though we represent the two electrons in a π bond as two half-arrows in the upper lobe, they are actually spread out over both the upper and lower lobes (this is one of the limitations we encounter when we try to represent electrons with arrows). We can label all the bonds in the molecule using a notation that specifies the type of bond (σ or π) as well as the type of overlapping orbitals. We have included this notation, as well as the Lewis structure of H_2CO for comparison, in the bonding diagram for H_2CO:

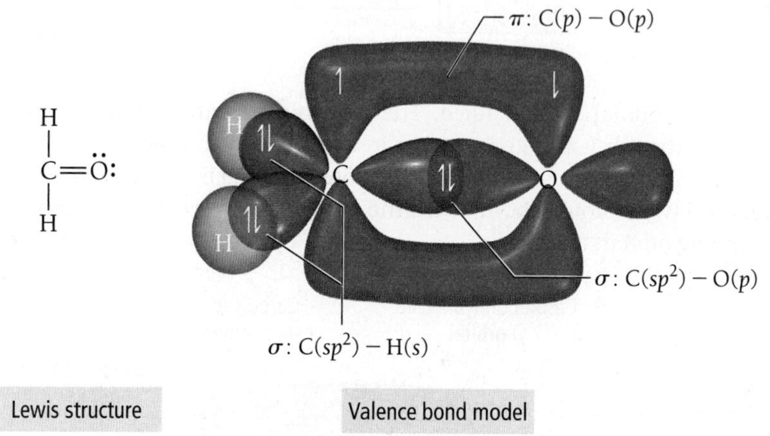

Notice the correspondence between valence bond theory and the Lewis model. In both models, the central carbon atom forms four bonds: two single bonds and one double bond. However, valence bond theory gives us more insight into the bonds. The double bond between carbon and oxygen according to valence bond theory consists of two different kinds of bonds—one σ and one π—whereas in the Lewis model the two bonds within the double bond appear identical. *A double bond in the Lewis model always corresponds to one σ and one π bond in valence bond theory.* In general, π bonds are weaker than σ bonds because side-to-side orbital overlap tends to be less efficient than end-to-end orbital overlap. Consequently, the π bond in a double bond is generally easier to break than the σ bond. Valence bond theory, as you can see, gives us more insight into the nature of a double bond than the Lewis model.

One—and only one—σ bond forms between any two atoms. Additional bonds must be π bonds.

Valence bond theory shows us the types of orbitals involved in the bonding and their shapes. For example, in H_2CO, the sp^2 hybrid orbitals on the central atom are trigonal planar with 120° angles between them, so the resulting predicted geometry of the molecule is trigonal planar with 120° bond angles. The experimentally measured bond angles in H_2CO, as discussed previously, are 121.9° for the HCO bond and 116.2° for the HCH bond angle, close to the predicted values.

Valence bond theory allows us to see why the rotation about a double bond is severely restricted. Because of the side-by-side overlap of the *p* orbitals, the π bond must essentially break for rotation to occur (see *Chemistry in Your Day: The Chemistry of Vision*).

Although rotation about a double bond is highly restricted, rotation about a single bond is relatively unrestricted. Consider, for example, the structures of two chlorinated hydrocarbons, 1,2-dichloroethane and 1,2-dichloroethene:

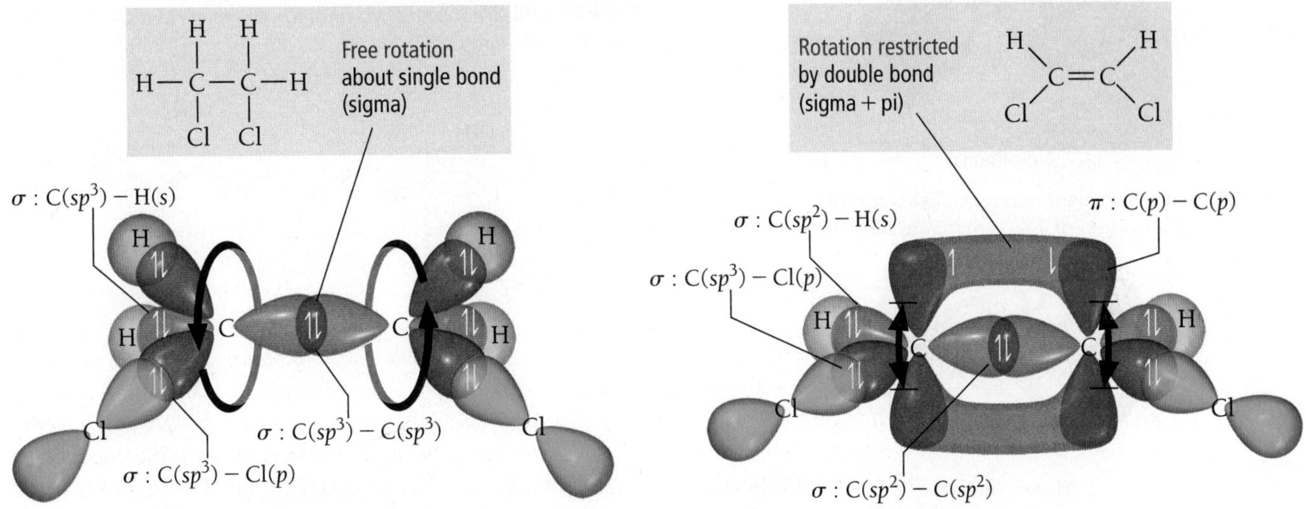

1,2-Dichloroethane

1,2-Dichloroethene

The hybridization of the carbon atoms in 1,2-dichloroethane is sp^3, resulting in relatively free rotation about the sigma single bond. Consequently, there is no difference between the following two structures at room temperature because they quickly interconvert:

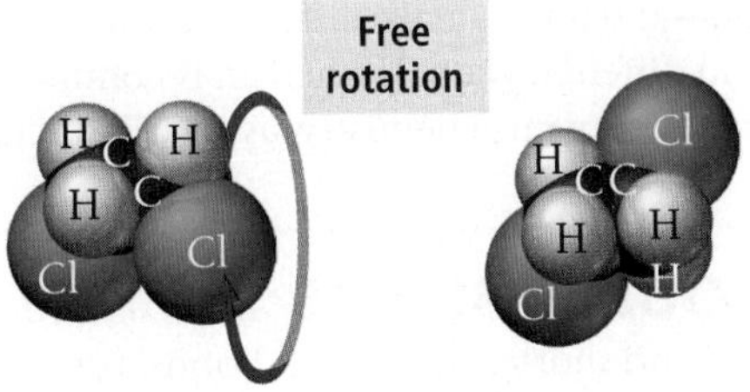

In contrast, rotation about the double bond (one σ and one π bond) in 1,2-dichloroethene is restricted; therefore at room temperature, 1,2-dichloroethene exists in two forms:

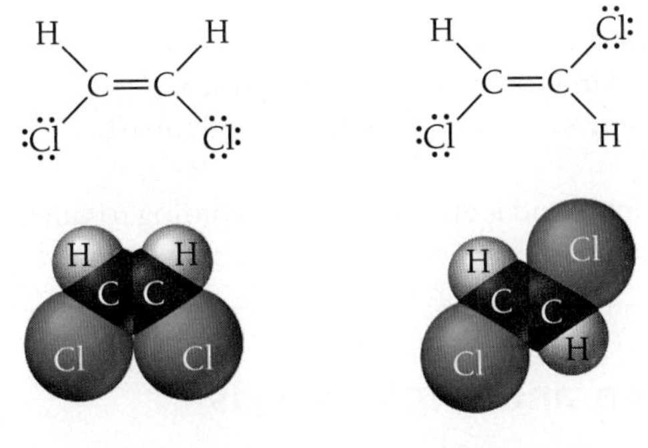

cis-1,2-Dichloroethene

trans-1,2-Dichloroethene

CHEMISTRY IN YOUR DAY | The Chemistry of Vision

In the human eye, light is detected by a chemical switch involving the breaking and re-forming of a π bond. The back portion of the eye, the retina, is coated with millions of light-sensitive cells called rods and cones. Each of these cells contains proteins that bind a compound called 11-*cis*-retinal, which has the following structure:

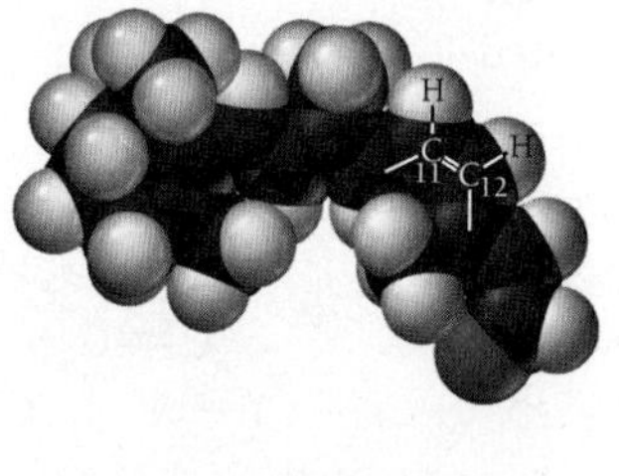

1-*cis*-Retinal

When a photon of sufficient energy strikes a rod or cone, it causes the isomerization of 11-*cis*-retinal to all-*trans*-retinal:

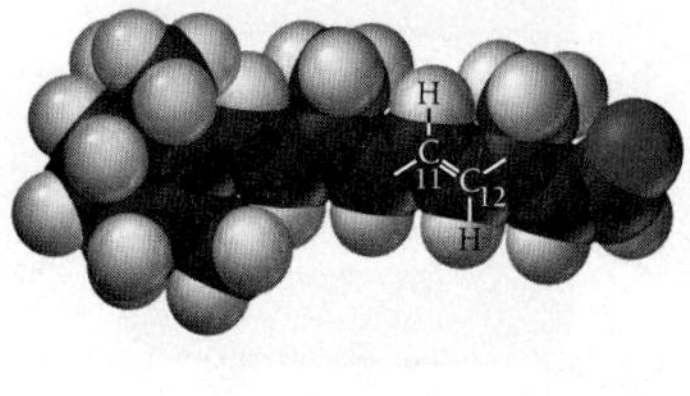

all-*trans*-Retinal

The isomerization occurs because visible light contains enough energy to break the π bond between the eleventh and twelfth carbon atom in 11-*cis*-retinal. The σ bond, which is stronger, does not break, allowing the molecule to freely rotate about that bond. The π bond then re-forms with the molecule in the *trans* conformation. The different shape of the resultant all-*trans*-retinal causes conformational changes in the protein to which it is bound. These changes cause an electrical signal to be transmitted to the brain.

QUESTION *What is the hybridization of the eleventh and twelfth carbon atoms in retinal?*

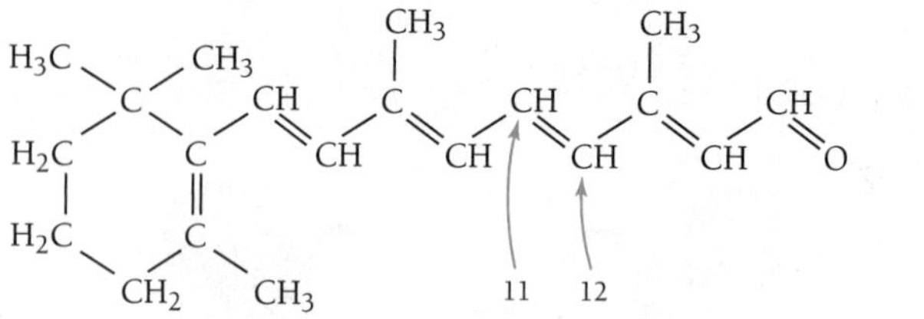

These two forms of 1,2-dichloroethene are different compounds with different properties. We distinguish between them with the designations *cis* (meaning "same side") and *trans* (meaning "opposite sides"). Compounds such as these, with the same molecular formula but different structures or different spatial arrangement of atoms, are called *isomers*. Nature can—and does—make different compounds out of the same atoms by arranging the atoms in different ways. Isomerism is common throughout chemistry and is especially important in organic chemistry, as we will discuss in Chapter 22.

ANSWER **NOW!**

11.10 Cc Conceptual Connection

SINGLE AND DOUBLE BONDS In Section 10.10, we learned that double bonds are stronger and shorter than single bonds. For example, a C—C single bond has an average bond energy of 347 kJ/mole, whereas a C=C double bond has an average bond energy of 611 kJ/mole. According to valence bond theory, why is a double bond *not* simply twice as strong as a single bond?

(a) Because according to valence bond theory, a double bond is actually composed of two different kinds of bonds, one σ and one π.

(b) Because according to valence bond theory, a double bond is the sharing of two electron pairs.

(c) The C=C double bond is an exception. According to valence bond theory, a double bond is generally twice as strong as a single bond.

sp Hybridization and Triple Bonds

Hybridization of one *s* and one *p* orbital results in two *sp* hybrid orbitals and two leftover unhybridized *p* orbitals:

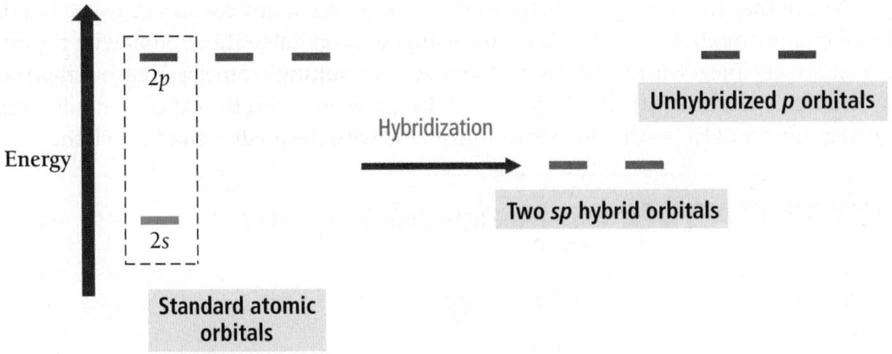

Figure 11.10▼ shows the shapes of the *sp* hybrid orbitals. Notice that the two *sp* hybrid orbitals are arranged in a linear geometry with a 180° angle between them. The unhybridized *p* orbitals are oriented in the plane that is perpendicular to the hybridized *sp* orbitals.

Formation of *sp* Hybrid Orbitals

One *s* orbital and one *p* orbital combine to form two *sp* orbitals.

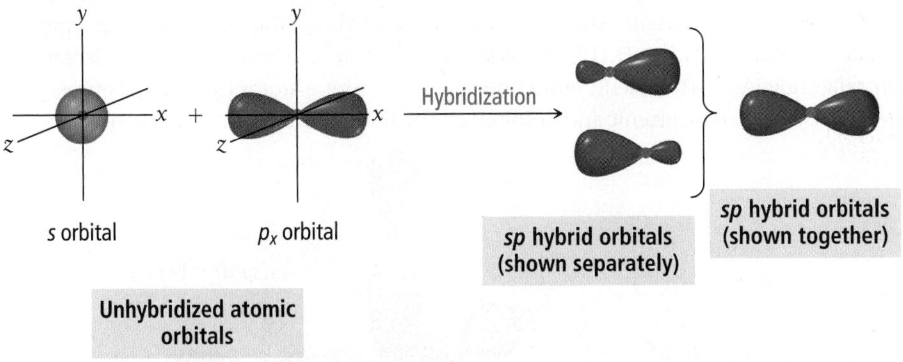

◀ **FIGURE 11.10**
***sp* Hybridization** When *sp* hybrid orbitals form, two *p* orbital (not shown) remain unhybridized.

The acetylene molecule, HC≡CH, has *sp* hybrid orbitals. The four valence electrons of carbon distribute themselves among the two *sp* hybrid orbitals and the two *p* orbitals:

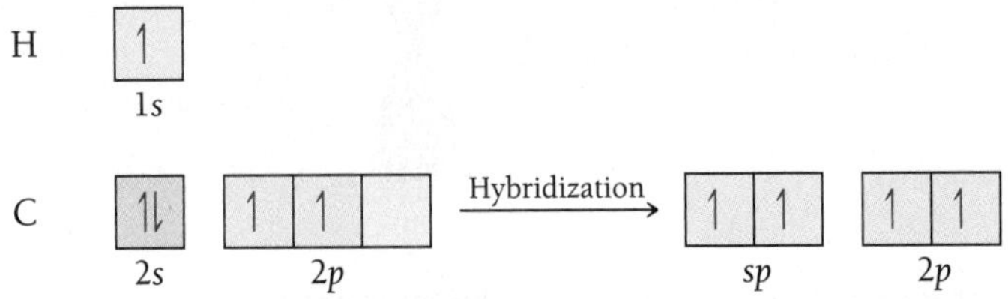

Each carbon atom then has four half-filled orbitals and can form four bonds: one with a hydrogen atom and three (a triple bond) with the other carbon atom. We draw the molecule and the overlapping orbitals as follows:

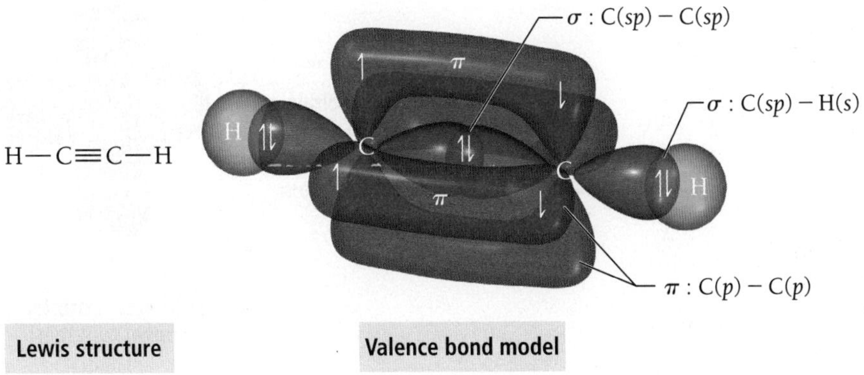

Notice that the triple bond between the two carbon atoms consists of two π bonds (overlapping *p* orbitals) and one σ bond (overlapping *sp* orbitals). The *sp* orbitals on the carbon atoms are linear with 180° between them, so the resulting geometry of each carbon on the molecule is linear with 180° bond angles, in agreement with the experimentally measured geometry of HC≡CH, and also in agreement with the prediction of VSEPR theory.

ANSWER **NOW!**

11.11 Cc Conceptual Connection

HYBRIDIZATION What is the hybridization of C in CO_2?

(a) *sp*
(b) sp^2
(c) sp^3

sp^3d and sp^3d^2 Hybridization

Recall that, according to the Lewis model, elements occurring in the third row of the periodic table (or below) can exhibit expanded octets (see Section 10.9). The equivalent concept in valence bond theory is hybridization involving the *d* orbitals. For third-period elements, the 3*d* orbitals are involved in hybridization because their energies are close to the energies of the 3*s* and 3*p* orbitals. The hybridization of one *s* orbital, three *p* orbitals, and one *d* orbital results in sp^3d hybrid orbitals (Figure 11.11(a)▼). The five sp^3d hybrid orbitals have a trigonal bipyramidal arrangement (Figure 11.11(b)▼). As an example of sp^3d hybridization, consider arsenic pentafluoride, AsF_5. The arsenic atom bonds to five fluorine atoms by overlap between the sp^3d hybrid orbitals on arsenic and *p* orbitals on the fluorine atoms, as shown here:

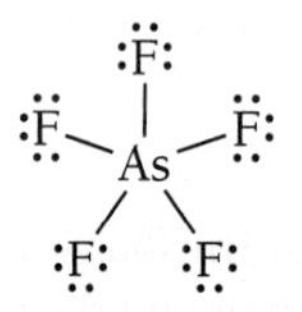

Lewis structure

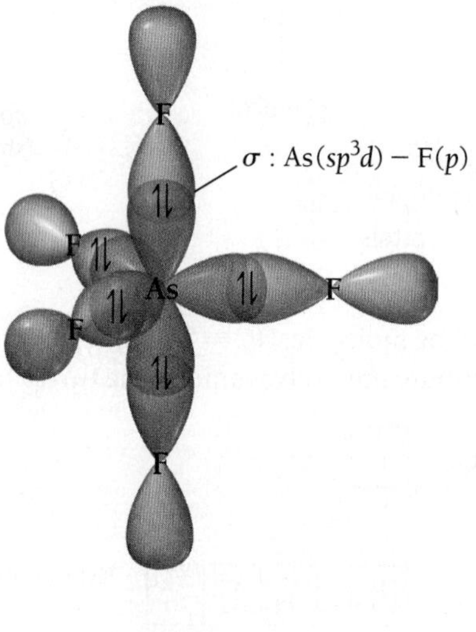

Valence bond model

The sp^3d orbitals on the arsenic atom are trigonal bipyramidal, so the molecular geometry is trigonal bipyramidal.

▼ FIGURE 11.11 sp^3d Hybridization One *s* orbital, three *p* orbitals, and one *d* orbital combine to form five sp^3d hybrid orbitals.

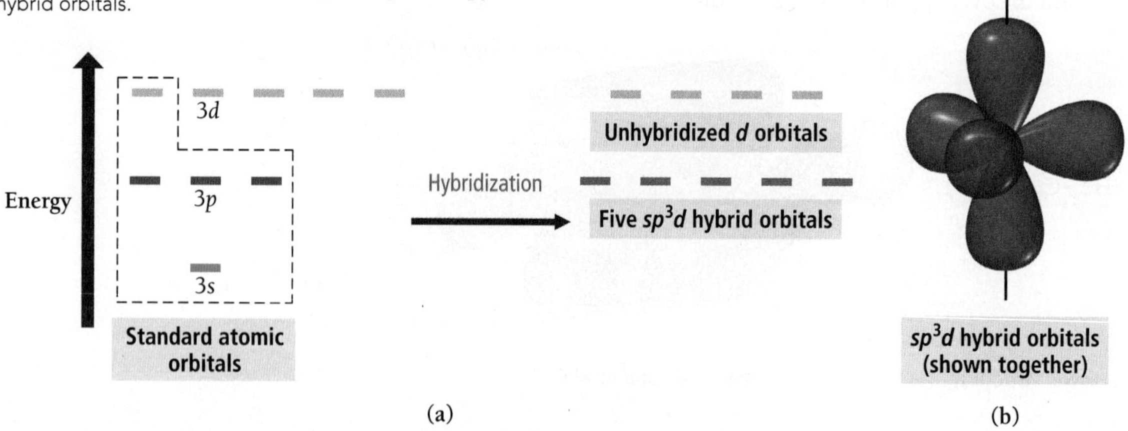

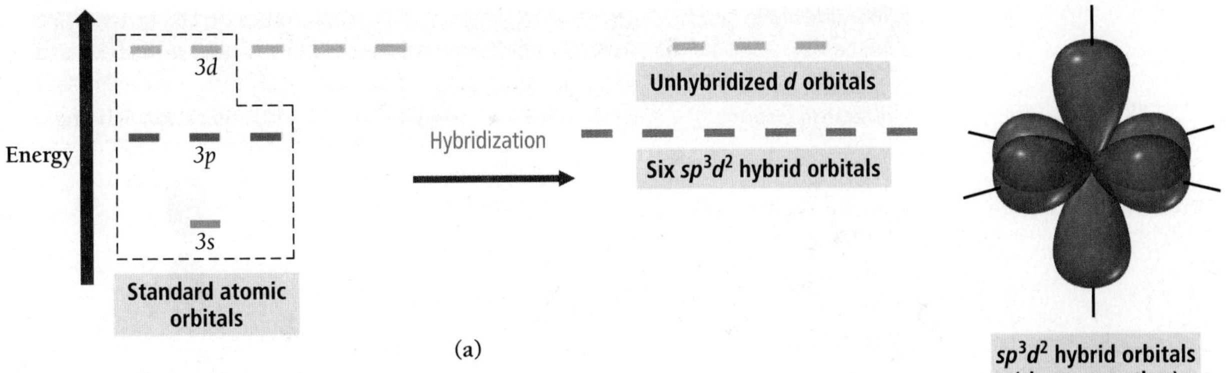

▲ **FIGURE 11.12** sp^3d^2 **Hybridization** One s orbital, three p orbitals, and two d orbitals combine to form six sp^3d^2 hybrid orbitals.

The hybridization of one *s* orbital, three *p* orbitals, and *two d* orbitals results in sp^3d^2 hybrid orbitals (Figure 11.12(a)▲). The six sp^3d^2 hybrid orbitals have an octahedral geometry (Figure 11.12(b)▲). As an example of sp^3d^2 hybridization, consider sulfur hexafluoride, SF_6. The sulfur atom bonds to six fluorine atoms by overlap between the sp^3d^2 hybrid orbitals on sulfur and *p* orbitals on the fluorine atoms:

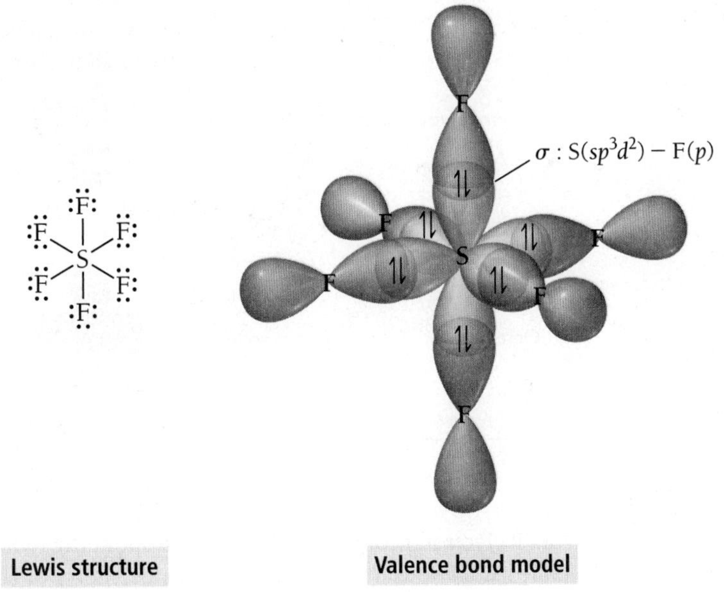

The sp^3d^2 orbitals on the sulfur atom are octahedral, so the molecular geometry is octahedral, again in agreement with VSEPR theory and with the experimentally observed geometry.

Writing Hybridization and Bonding Schemes

We have now studied examples of the five main types of atomic orbital hybridization. *But how do we know which hybridization scheme best describes the orbitals of a specific atom in a specific molecule?* In computational valence bond theory, the energy of the molecule is calculated using a computer; the degree of hybridization as well as the type of hybridization are varied to find the combination that gives the molecule the lowest overall energy. For our purposes, we can assign a hybridization scheme from the electron geometry—determined using VSEPR theory—of the central atom (or interior atoms) of

TABLE 11.3 ■ Hybridization Scheme from Electron Geometry

Number of Electron Groups	Electron Geometry (from VSEPR Theory)	Hybridization Scheme	
2	Linear	*sp*	
3	Trigonal planar	sp^2	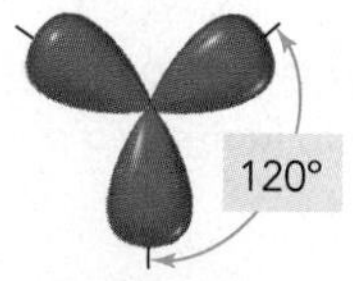
4	Tetrahedral	sp^3	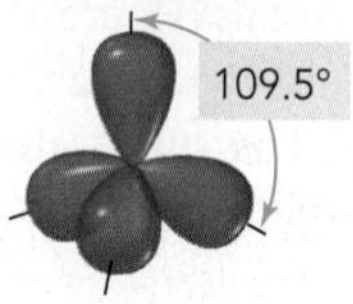
5	Trigonal bipyramidal	sp^3d	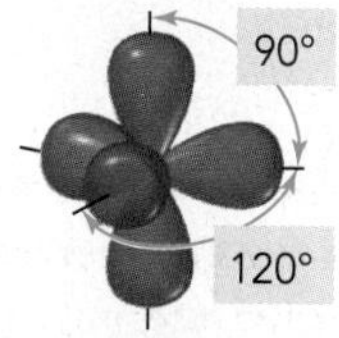
6	Octahedral	sp^3d^2	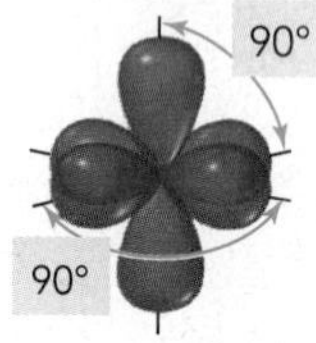

the molecule. The five VSEPR electron geometries and the corresponding hybridization schemes are shown in Table 11.3. For example, if the electron geometry of the central atom is tetrahedral, then the hybridization is sp^3, and if the electron geometry is octahedral, then the hybridization is sp^3d^2, and so on. Although this method of determining the hybridization scheme is not 100% accurate (for example, it predicts that H_2S should be sp^3 when in fact H_2S is largely unhybridized), it is the best we can do without more complex computer-based calculations.

We are now ready to put the Lewis model and valence bond theory together to describe bonding in molecules. In the procedure and examples that follow, you will learn how to write a *hybridization and bonding scheme* for a molecule. This involves drawing the Lewis structure for the molecule, determining its geometry using VSEPR theory, determining the hybridization of the interior atoms, drawing the molecule with its overlapping orbitals, and labeling each bond with the σ and π notation followed by the type of overlapping orbitals. As you can see, this procedure involves virtually everything you have learned about bonding in this chapter and Chapter 10. The procedure for writing a hybridization and bonding scheme is shown in the left column, with two examples of how to apply the procedure in the columns to the right.

HOW TO: *Determine Hybridization and Bonding Schemes*

EXAMPLE 11.6

Hybridization and Bonding Scheme

Write a hybridization and bonding scheme for bromine trifluoride, BrF_3.

EXAMPLE 11.7

Hybridization and Bonding Scheme

Write a hybridization and bonding scheme for acetaldehyde,

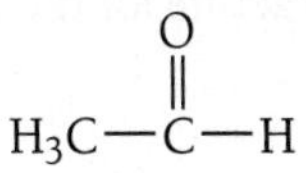

1. Write the Lewis structure for the molecule.

SOLUTION (Example 11.6)

BrF_3 has 28 valence electrons and the following Lewis structure:

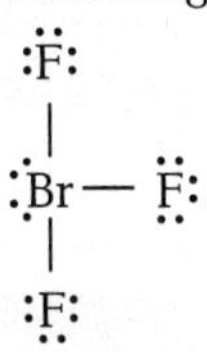

SOLUTION (Example 11.7)

Acetaldehyde has 18 valence electrons and the following Lewis structure:

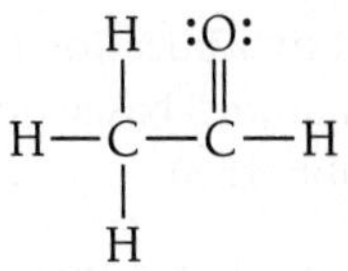

2. Use VSEPR theory to predict the electron geometry about the central atom (or interior atoms).

The bromine atom has five electron groups and therefore has a trigonal bipyramidal electron geometry.

The leftmost carbon atom has four electron groups and a tetrahedral electron geometry. The rightmost carbon atom has three electron groups and a trigonal planar geometry.

3. Select the correct hybridization for the central atom (or interior atoms) based on the electron geometry (see Table 11.3).

A trigonal bipyramidal electron geometry corresponds to sp^3d hybridization.

The leftmost carbon atom is sp^3 hybridized, and the rightmost carbon atom is sp^2 hybridized.

4. Sketch the molecule, beginning with the central atom and its orbitals. Show overlap with the appropriate orbitals on the terminal atoms.

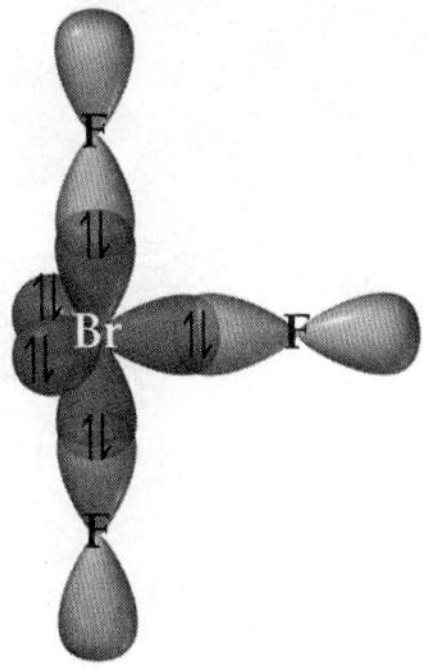

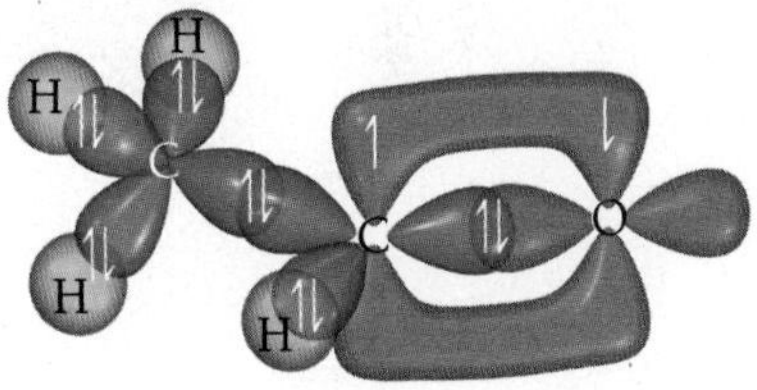

5. Label all bonds using σ or π notation followed by the type of overlapping orbitals.

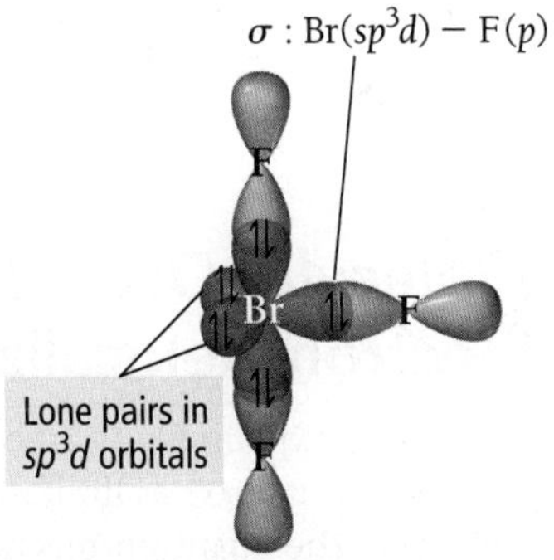

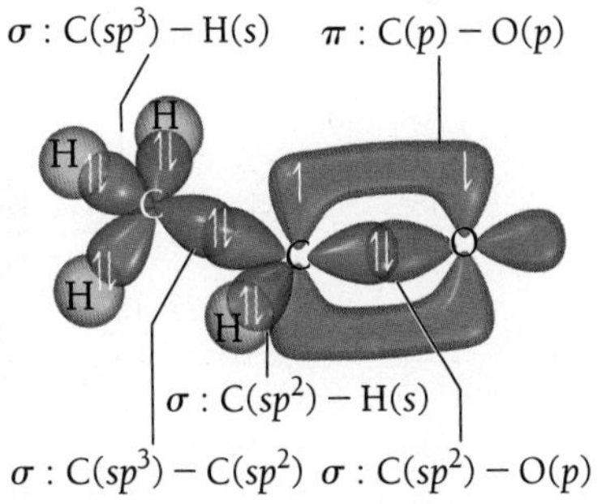

FOR PRACTICE 11.6 Write the hybridization and bonding scheme for XeF_4.

FOR PRACTICE 11.7 Write the hybridization and bonding scheme for HCN.

WATCH **NOW!**

INTERACTIVE WORKED EXAMPLE 11.8

EXAMPLE 11.8 Hybridization and Bonding Scheme

Use valence bond theory to write a hybridization and bonding scheme for ethene, $H_2C{=}CH_2$.

SOLUTION

1. Write the Lewis structure for the molecule.	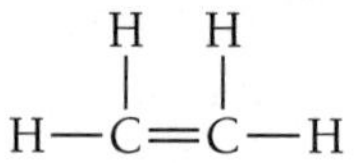
2. Apply VSEPR theory to predict the electron geometry about the central atom (or interior atoms).	The molecule has two interior atoms. Because each atom has three electron groups (one double bond and two single bonds), the electron geometry about each atom is trigonal planar.
3. Select the correct hybridization for the central atom (or interior atoms) based on the electron geometry (see Table 11.3).	A trigonal planar geometry corresponds to sp^2 hybridization.
4. Sketch the molecule, beginning with the central atom and its orbitals. Show overlap with the appropriate orbitals on the terminal atoms.	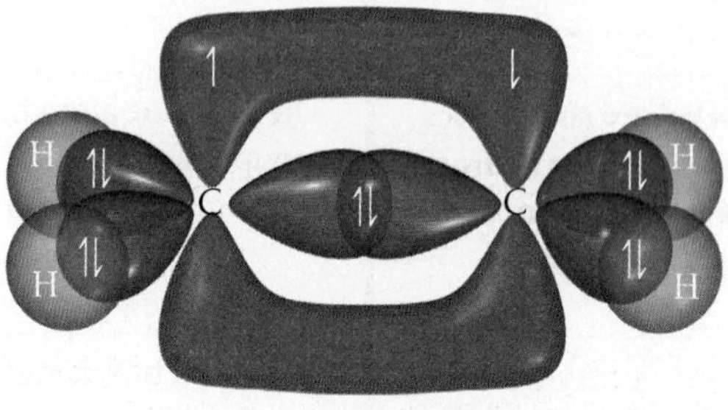
5. Label all bonds using σ or π notation followed by the type of overlapping orbitals.	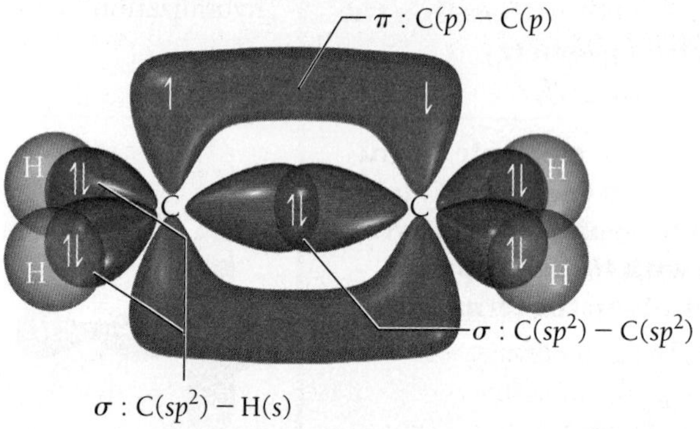

FOR PRACTICE 11.8 Use valence bond theory to write a hybridization and bonding scheme for CO_2.

FOR MORE PRACTICE 11.8 What is the hybridization of the central iodine atom in I_3^-?

11.8 Molecular Orbital Theory: Electron Delocalization

Valence bond theory can explain many aspects of chemical bonding—such as the rigidity of a double bond—but it also has limitations. In valence bond theory, we treat electrons as if they reside in the quantum-mechanical orbitals that we calculated *for atoms*. This is a significant oversimplification that we partially compensate for by hybridization. Nevertheless, we can do better.

In Chapter 8, we stated that the mathematical derivation of energies and orbitals for electrons *in atoms* comes from solving the Schrödinger equation for the atom of interest. For a molecule, we can theoretically do the same thing. The resulting orbitals would be the actual *molecular* orbitals of the molecule as a whole (in contrast to valence bond theory, in which the orbitals are those of individual atoms). As it turns out, however, solving the Schrödinger equation exactly for even the simplest molecules is impossible without making some approximations.

In **molecular orbital (MO) theory**, we do not actually solve the Schrödinger equation for a molecule directly. Instead, we use a trial function, an "educated guess" as to what the solution might be. In other words, rather than mathematically solving the Schrödinger equation, which would give us a mathematical function describing an orbital, we start with a trial mathematical function for the orbital. We then test the trial function to see how well it "works."

Molecular orbital theory is a specific application of a more general quantum-mechanical approximation technique called the variational method. In the variational method, the energy of a trial function within the Schrödinger equation is minimized.

We can understand this process by analogy to solving an algebraic equation. Suppose we want to know x in the equation $4x + 5 = 70$ without actually solving the equation. For an easy equation like this one, we might first estimate that $x = 16$. We can then determine how well our estimate works by substituting $x = 16$ into the equation. If the estimate did not work, we could try again until we found the right value of x. (In this case, we can quickly see that x must be a little more than 16.)

In MO theory, the estimating procedure is analogous. However, we need to add one more important concept to get at the heart of MO theory. In order to determine how well a trial function for an orbital "works" in MO theory, we calculate its energy. No matter how good our trial function, *we can never do better than nature at minimizing the energy of the orbital*. In other words, we can devise any trial function for an orbital in a molecule and calculate its energy. The energy we calculate for the devised orbital will always be greater than or (at best) equal to the energy of the actual orbital.

We calculate the energy of an estimated orbital by substituting it into the Schrödinger equation and solving for the energy.

How does this help us? The best possible orbital is therefore the one with the minimum energy. In modern MO theory, computer programs are designed to try many different variations of a guessed orbital and compare the energies of each one. The variation with the lowest energy is the best approximation for the actual molecular orbital.

Linear Combination of Atomic Orbitals (LCAOs)

The simplest trial functions that work reasonably well in MO theory turn out to be linear combinations of atomic orbitals, or LCAOs. An LCAO molecular orbital is a *weighted linear sum—analogous to a weighted average—of the valence atomic orbitals* of the atoms in the molecule. At first glance, this concept might seem very similar to that of hybridization in valence bond theory. However, in valence bond theory, hybrid orbitals are weighted linear sums of the valence atomic orbitals of a *particular atom*, and the hybrid orbitals remain *localized* on that atom. In MO theory, the molecular orbitals are weighted linear sums of the valence atomic orbitals of *all the atoms* in a molecule, and many of the molecular orbitals are *delocalized* over the entire molecule.

When molecular orbitals are calculated mathematically, it is actually the *wave functions* corresponding to the orbitals that are combined.

Consider the H_2 molecule. One of the molecular orbitals for H_2 is simply an equally weighted sum of the 1*s* orbital from one atom and the 1*s* orbital from the other. We represent this pictorially and energetically as follows:

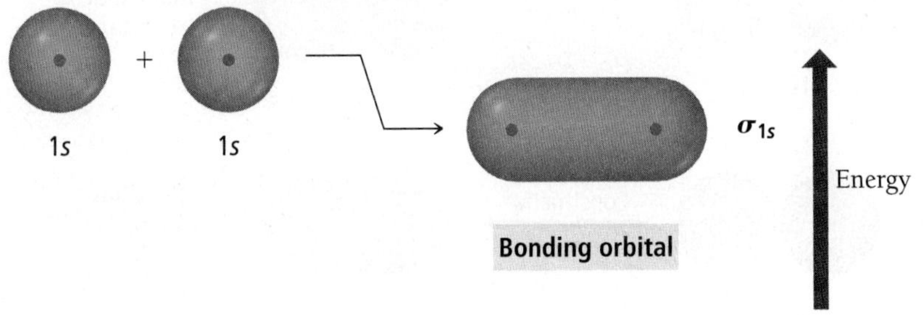

The name of this molecular orbital is σ_{1s}. The σ comes from the shape of the orbital, which looks like a σ bond in valence bond theory, and the 1*s* comes from its formation by a linear sum of 1*s* orbitals. The σ_{1s} orbital is lower in energy than either of the two 1*s* atomic orbitals from which it was formed. For this reason, this orbital is called a **bonding orbital**. When electrons occupy bonding molecular orbitals, the energy of the electrons is lower than it would be if they were occupying atomic orbitals.

We can think of a molecular orbital in a molecule in much the same way that we think about an atomic orbital in an atom. Electrons seek the lowest energy molecular orbital available, but just as an atom has more than one atomic orbital (and some may be empty), a molecule has more than one molecular orbital (and some may be empty). The next molecular orbital of H_2 is approximated by summing the 1*s* orbital on one hydrogen atom with the *negative* (opposite phase) of the 1*s* orbital on the other hydrogen atom:

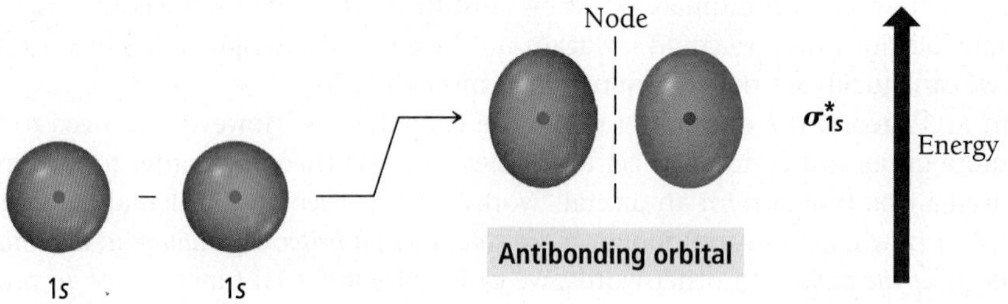

The different phases of the orbitals result in *destructive* interference between them. The resulting molecular orbital therefore has a node between the two atoms. The different colors (red and blue) on either side of the node represent the different phases of the orbital (see Section 8.6). The name of this molecular orbital is σ^*_{1s}. The star indicates that this orbital is an **antibonding orbital**. Electrons in antibonding orbitals have higher energies than they did in their respective atomic orbitals and therefore tend to raise the energy of the system (relative to the unbonded atoms).

In general, when two atomic orbitals are added together to form molecular orbitals, one of the resultant molecular orbitals is lower in energy (the bonding orbital) than the atomic orbitals and the other is higher in energy (the antibonding orbital). Remember that electrons in orbitals behave like waves. The bonding molecular orbital arises out of constructive interference between the overlapping atomic orbitals because both orbitals have the same phase. The antibonding orbital arises out of destructive interference between the overlapping atomic orbitals because *subtracting* one from the other means the two interacting orbitals have opposite phases (Figure 11.13▼).

For this reason, the bonding orbital has an increased electron density in the internuclear region, whereas the antibonding orbital has a node in the internuclear region. Bonding orbitals have greater electron density in the internuclear region, thereby lowering their energy compared to the orbitals in nonbonded atoms. Antibonding orbitals have less electron density in the internuclear region, and their energies are generally higher than in the orbitals of nonbonded atoms.

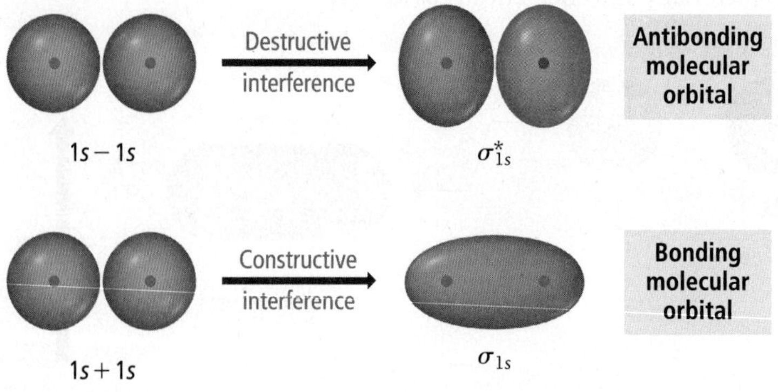

▶ **FIGURE 11.13 Formation of Bonding and Antibonding Orbitals** Constructive interference between two atomic orbitals gives rise to a molecular orbital that is lower in energy than the atomic orbitals. This is the bonding orbital. Destructive interference between two atomic orbitals gives rise to a molecular orbital that is higher in energy than the atomic orbitals. This is the antibonding orbital.

We put all of this together in the molecular orbital energy diagram for H_2:

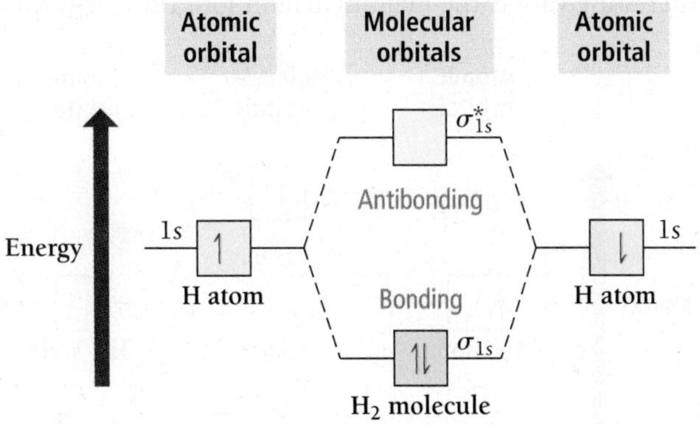

We can represent the molecular orbital energy diagram with a molecular orbital electron configuration (which is analogous to the electron configurations we wrote for elements in Section 9.3):

$$H_2 \qquad (\sigma_{1s})^2$$

In this notation, the σ_{1s} represents the molecular orbital, and the superscript 2 represents the two electrons in the orbital.

The molecular orbital energy diagram shows that two hydrogen atoms can lower their overall energy by forming H_2 because the electrons can move from higher-energy atomic orbitals into the lower-energy σ_{1s} bonding molecular orbital. In MO theory, we define the **bond order** of a diatomic molecule such as H_2 as follows:

$$\text{Bond order} = \frac{(\text{number of electrons in bonding MOs}) - (\text{number of electrons in antibonding MOs})}{2}$$

For H_2, the bond order is 1:

$$H_2 \text{ bond order} = \frac{2-0}{2} = 1$$

A positive bond order means that there are more electrons in bonding molecular orbitals than in antibonding molecular orbitals. The electrons therefore have lower energy than they did in the orbitals of the isolated atoms, and a chemical bond forms. In general, the higher the bond order, the stronger the bond. A negative or zero bond order indicates that a bond does *not* form between the atoms. For example, consider the MO diagram for He_2:

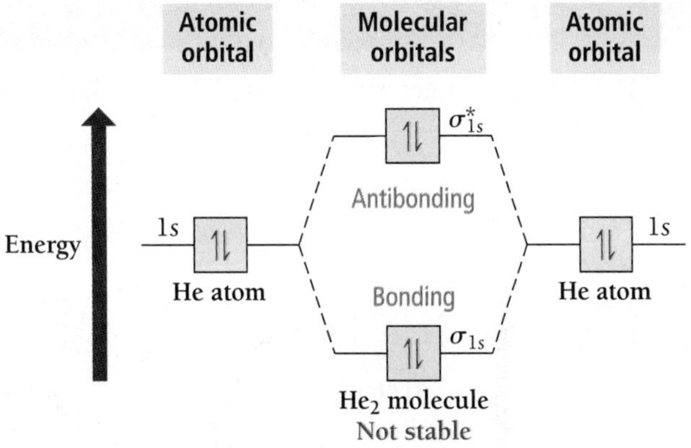

Notice that the two additional electrons must go into the higher-energy antibonding orbital. There is no net stabilization by joining two helium atoms to form a helium molecule, as indicated by the bond order:

$$He_2 \text{ bond order} = \frac{2-2}{2} = 0$$

So according to MO theory, He_2 should not exist as a stable molecule, and in fact it does not. Another interesting case is the helium–helium ion, He_2^+, with the following MO diagram:

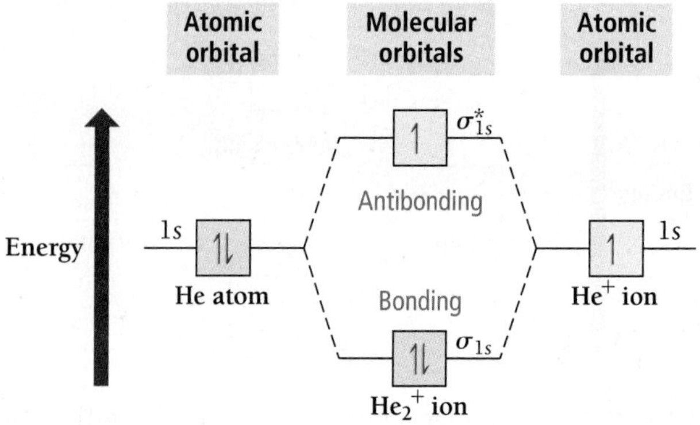

The bond order is $\frac{1}{2}$, indicating that He_2^+ should exist, and indeed it does.

Summarizing LCAO–MO Theory:

- We can approximate MOs as a linear combination of atomic orbitals (AOs). The total number of MOs formed from a particular set of AOs always equals the number of AOs in the set.
- When two AOs combine to form two MOs, one MO is lower in energy (the bonding MO) and the other is higher in energy (the antibonding MO).
- When assigning the electrons of a molecule to MOs, fill the lowest energy MOs first with a maximum of two spin-paired electrons per orbital.
- When assigning electrons to two MOs of the same energy, follow Hund's rule—fill the orbitals singly first, with parallel spins, before pairing.
- The bond order in a diatomic molecule is the number of electrons in bonding MOs minus the number in antibonding MOs divided by two. Stable bonds are associated with a positive bond order (more electrons in bonding MOs than in antibonding MOs).

Notice the power of the molecular orbital approach. Every electron that enters a bonding molecular orbital stabilizes the molecule or polyatomic ion, and every electron that enters an antibonding molecular orbital destabilizes it. The emphasis on electron pairs has been removed. One electron in a bonding molecular orbital stabilizes half as much as two, so a bond order of one-half is nothing mysterious.

EXAMPLE 11.9 Bond Order

Use MO theory to predict the bond order in H_2^-. Is the H_2^- bond a stronger or weaker bond than the H_2 bond?

SOLUTION

The H_2^- ion has three electrons. Assign the three electrons to the molecular orbitals, filling lower-energy orbitals first and proceeding to higher-energy orbitals.	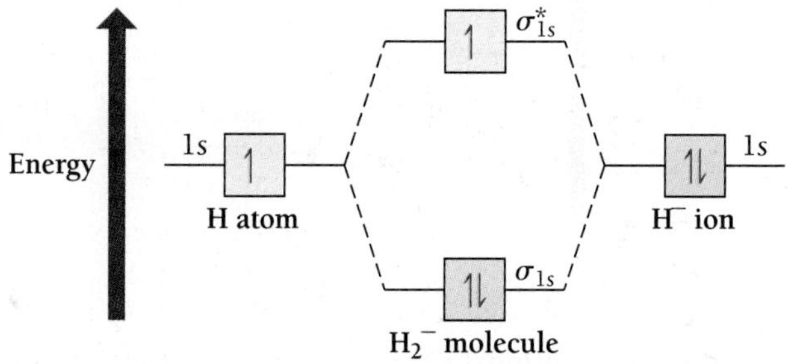
Calculate the bond order by subtracting the number of electrons in antibonding orbitals from the number in bonding orbitals and dividing the result by two.	H_2^- bond order $= \frac{2 - 1}{2} = +\frac{1}{2}$

Since the bond order is positive, H_2^- should be stable. However, the bond order of H_2^- is lower than the bond order of H_2 (which is 1); therefore, the bond in H_2^- is weaker than in H_2.

FOR PRACTICE 11.9 Use MO theory to predict the bond order in H_2^+. Is the H_2^+ bond a stronger or weaker bond than the H_2 bond?

Period Two Homonuclear Diatomic Molecules

Homonuclear diatomic molecules (molecules made up of two atoms of the same kind) formed from second-period elements have between 2 and 16 valence electrons. To explain bonding in these molecules, we must consider the next set of higher-energy molecular orbitals, which can be approximated by linear combinations of the valence atomic orbitals of the period 2 elements.

The core electrons can be ignored (as they are in other models for bonding) because these electrons are held too tightly to individual nuclei to contribute significantly to chemical bonding.

We begin with Li_2. Even though lithium is normally a metal, we can use MO theory to predict whether or not the Li_2 molecule should exist in the gas phase. We approximate the molecular orbitals in Li_2 as linear combinations of the 2*s* atomic orbitals. The resulting molecular orbitals look much like those of the H_2 molecule. The MO diagram for Li_2 therefore looks a lot like the MO diagram for H_2:

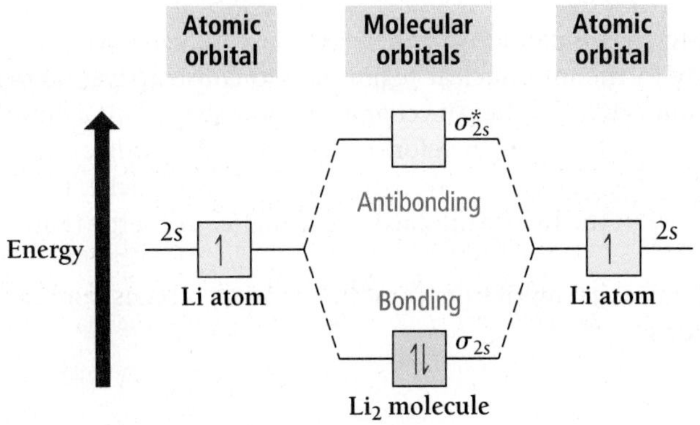

The two valence electrons of Li_2 occupy a bonding molecular orbital. We would predict that the Li_2 molecule is stable with a bond order of 1. Experiments confirm this prediction. In contrast, consider the MO diagram for Be_2:

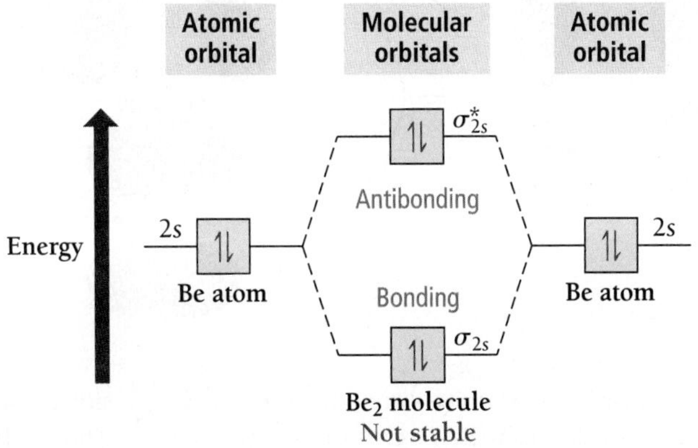

The four valence electrons of Be_2 occupy one bonding MO and one antibonding MO. The bond order is 0; we predict that Be_2 should not be stable, which is again consistent with experimental findings.

The next homonuclear molecule composed of second-row elements is B_2, which has six total valence electrons to accommodate. We can approximate the next higher-energy molecular orbitals for B_2 and the rest of the period 2 diatomic molecules as linear combinations of the 2*p* orbitals taken pairwise. Since the three 2*p* orbitals orient along three orthogonal axes, we must assign similar axes to the molecule. In this book, we assign the internuclear axis to be the *x* direction. Then we represent the LCAO–MOs that result from combining the $2p_x$ orbitals—the ones that lie along the internuclear axis—from each atom as follows:

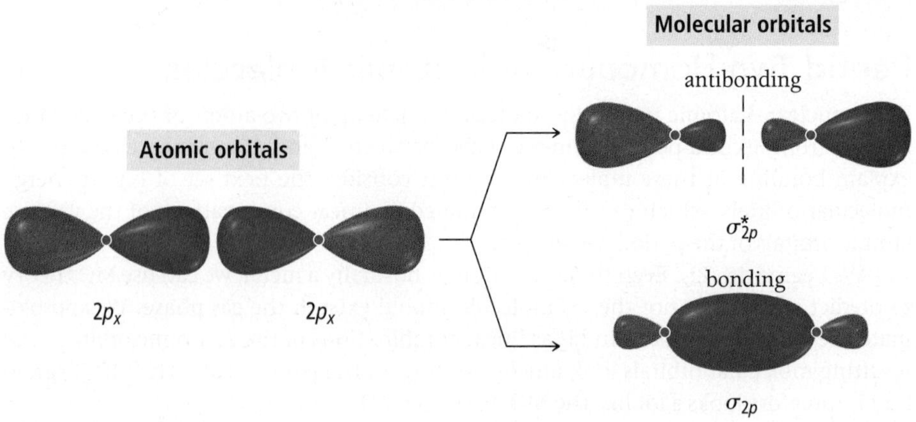

The bonding MO in this pair looks something like candy in a wrapper, with increased electron density in the internuclear region due to constructive interference between the two 2*p* atomic orbitals. It has the characteristic σ shape (it is cylindrically symmetric about the bond axis) and is therefore called the σ_{2p} bonding orbital. The antibonding orbital, called σ^*_{2p}, has a node between the two nuclei (due to destructive interference between the two 2*p* orbitals) and is higher in energy than either of the $2p_x$ orbitals.

The LCAO–MOs that result from combining the $2p_z$ orbitals from each atom are represented as follows:

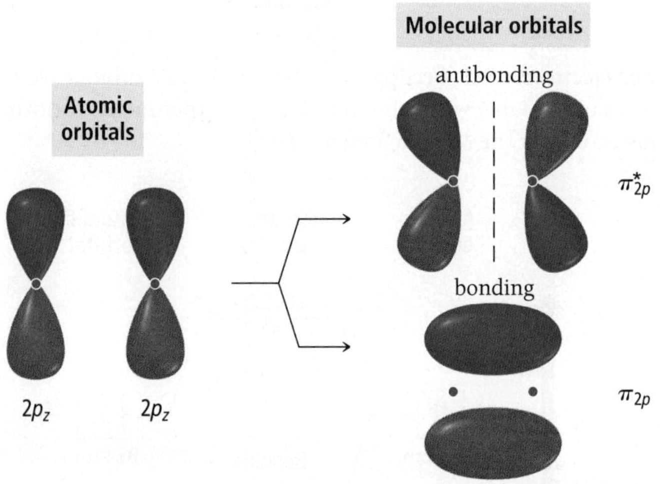

Notice that in this case the *p* orbitals are added together in a side-by-side orientation (in contrast to the $2p_x$ orbitals, which were oriented end to end). The resultant molecular orbitals consequently have a different shape. The electron density in the bonding molecular orbital is above and below the internuclear axis with a nodal plane that includes the internuclear axis. This orbital resembles the electron density distribution of a π bond in valence bond theory. We call this orbital the π_{2p} orbital. The corresponding antibonding orbital has an additional node *between* the nuclei (perpendicular to the internuclear axis) and is called the π^*_{2p} orbital.

The LCAO–MOs that result from combining the $2p_y$ orbitals from each atom are represented as follows:

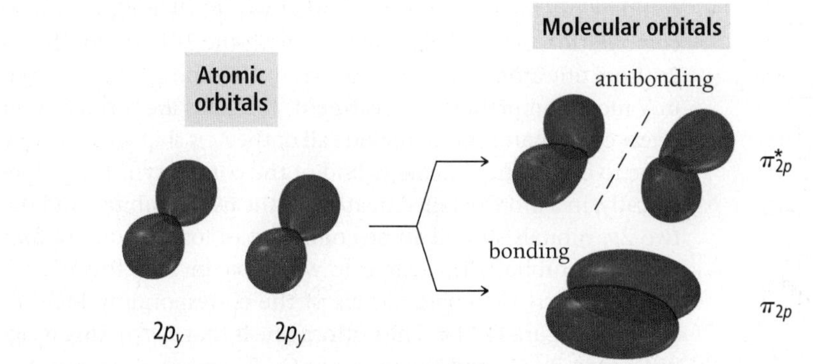

The only difference between the $2p_y$ and the $2p_z$ atomic orbitals is a 90° rotation about the internuclear axis. Consequently, the only difference between the resulting MOs is a 90° rotation about the internuclear axis. The energies and the names of the bonding and antibonding MOs obtained from the combination of the $2p_y$ AOs are identical to those obtained from the combination of the $2p_z$ AOs.

Before we can draw MO diagrams for B_2 and the other second-period diatomic molecules, we must determine the relative energy ordering of the MOs obtained from the $2p$ AO combinations. This is not a simple task. The relative ordering of MOs obtained from LCAO–MO theory is usually determined computationally. There is no single order that works for all molecules. For second-period diatomic molecules, computations reveal that the energy ordering for B_2, C_2, and N_2 is slightly different than that for O_2, F_2, and Ne_2 as follows:

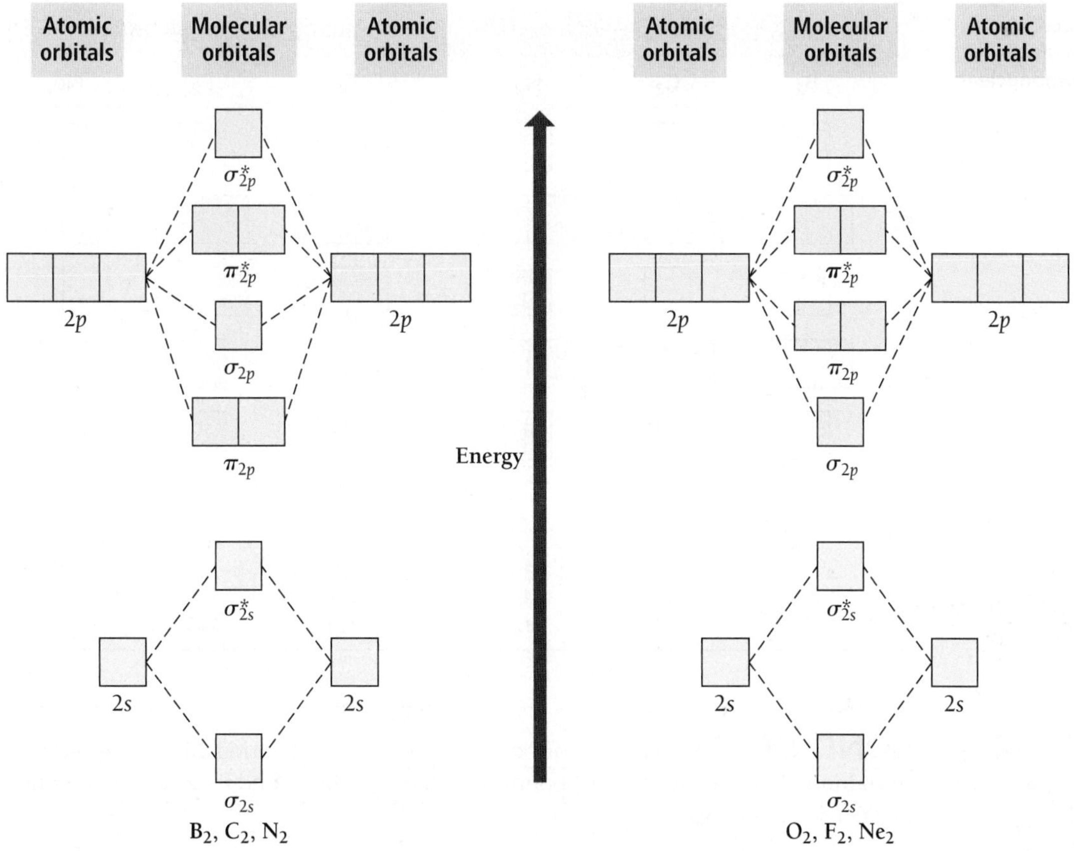

▲ Molecular orbital energy diagrams for second-period diatomic molecules show that the energy ordering of the π_{2p} and σ_{2p} molecular orbitals can vary.

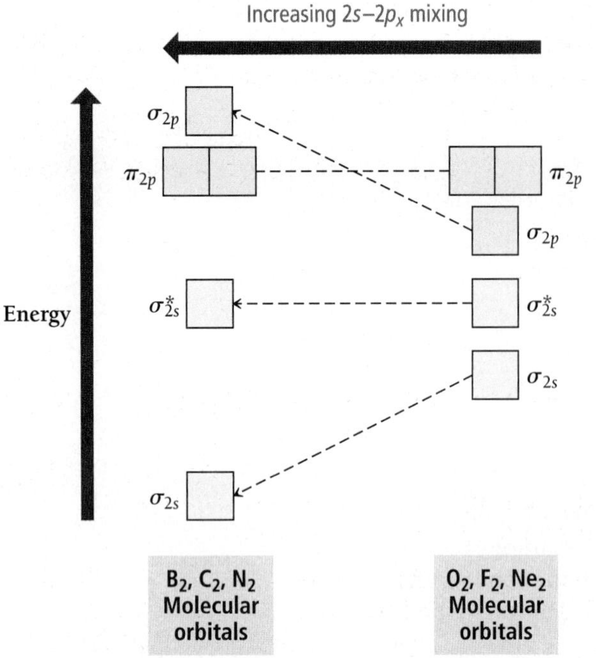

▲ **FIGURE 11.14 The Effects of 2s–2p$_x$ Mixing** The degree of mixing between two orbitals decreases with increasing energy difference between them. Mixing of the 2s and 2p$_x$ orbitals is therefore greater in B_2, C_2, and N_2 than in O_2, F_2, and Ne_2 because in B, C, and N the energy levels of the atomic orbitals are more closely spaced than in O, F, and Ne. This mixing produces a change in energy ordering for the π_{2p} and σ_{2p} molecular orbitals.

The difference in energy ordering can only be explained by revisiting our LCAO–MO model. In our simplified treatment, we assumed that the MOs that result from the second-period AOs could be calculated pairwise. In other words, we took the linear combination of a 2*s* from one atom with the 2*s* from another, a 2p_x from one atom with a 2p_x from the other, and so on. However, in a more comprehensive treatment, the MOs are formed from linear combinations that include all of the AOs that are relatively close to each other in energy and of the correct symmetry. Specifically, in a more detailed treatment, the two 2*s* orbitals and the two 2p_x orbitals should all be combined to form a total of four molecular orbitals. The extent to which we include this type of mixing affects the energy levels of the corresponding MOs, as shown in Figure 11.14◀. The bottom line is that *s–p* mixing is significant in B_2, C_2, and N_2 but not in O_2, F_2, and Ne_2. The result of the mixing is a different energy ordering for some of these diatomic molecules.

Figure 11.15▼ shows the MO energy diagrams for the rest of the second-period homonuclear diatomic molecules, as well as their bond orders, bond energies, and bond lengths. Notice that as bond order increases, the bond gets stronger (greater bond energy) and shorter (smaller bond length). For B_2, with six electrons, the bond order is 1. For C_2, the bond order is 2, and for N_2, the bond order reaches a maximum with a value of 3. Recall that the Lewis structure for N_2 has a triple bond, so both the Lewis model and MO theory predict a strong bond for N_2, which is experimentally observed.

▶ **FIGURE 11.15 Molecular Orbital Energy Diagrams for Second-Row *p*-block Homonuclear Diatomic Molecules**

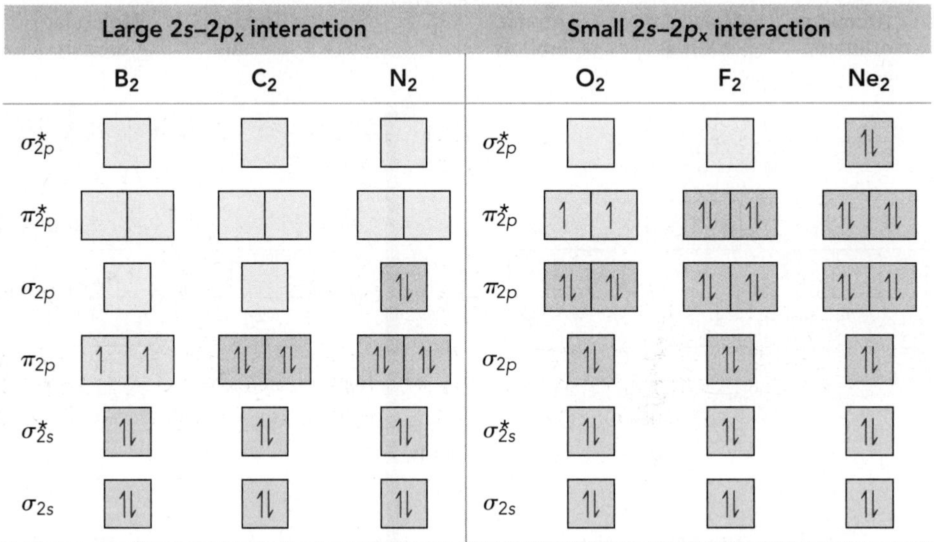

	B_2	C_2	N_2	O_2	F_2	Ne_2
Bond order	1	2	3	2	1	0
Bond energy (kJ/mol)	290	620	946	498	159	—
Bond length (pm)	159	131	110	121	143	—

ANSWER **NOW!** 11.12 Cc Conceptual Connection

BOND ORDER What is the bond order for a second-period diatomic molecule containing three electrons in antibonding molecular orbitals and six electrons in bonding molecular orbitals?

(a) 1 **(b)** 1.5 **(c)** 2 **(d)** 2.5

In O_2, the two additional electrons occupy antibonding orbitals and the bond order is 2. These two electrons are unpaired—they occupy the π^*_{2p} orbitals *singly with parallel spins*, as indicated by Hund's rule. The presence of unpaired electrons in the molecular orbital diagram of oxygen is significant because oxygen is known from experiment to be *paramagnetic*—it is attracted to a magnetic field (see Section 9.7). The paramagnetism of oxygen can be demonstrated by suspending liquid oxygen between the poles of a magnet. This magnetic property is the direct result of *unpaired electrons,* whose spin and movement around the nucleus (more accurately known as orbital angular momentum) generate tiny magnetic fields. When a paramagnetic substance is placed in an external magnetic field, the magnetic fields of each atom or molecule align with the external field, creating the attraction (much as two magnets attract each other when properly oriented). In contrast, when the electrons in an atom or molecule are all *paired,* the magnetic fields caused by electron spin and orbital angular momentum tend to cancel each other, resulting in diamagnetism. A *diamagnetic* substance is not attracted to a magnetic field (and is, in fact, slightly repelled).

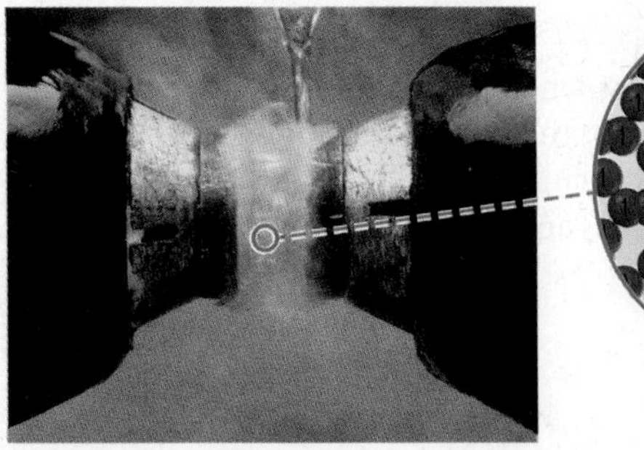

▲ Liquid oxygen can be suspended between the poles of a magnet because it is paramagnetic. It contains unpaired electrons (depicted here in the inset) that generate tiny magnetic fields, which align with and interact with the external field.

In the Lewis structure of O_2, as well as in the valence bond model of O_2, all of the electrons seem to be paired:

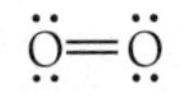

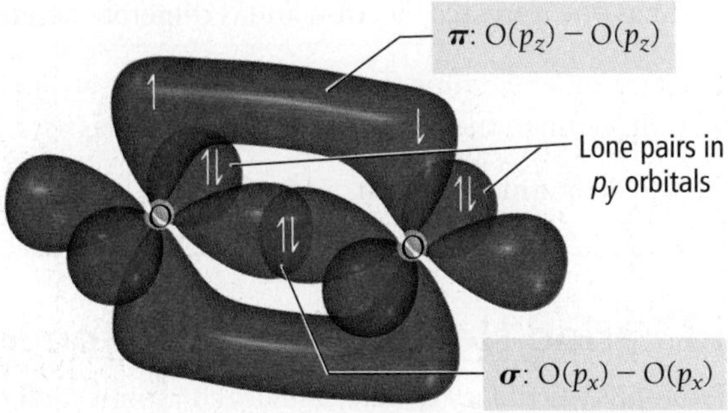

The s orbital on each oxygen atom contains two electrons, but for clarity neither the s orbitals nor the electrons that occupy them are shown.

In the MO diagram for O_2, however, we can see the unpaired electrons. MO theory is the more powerful theory in that it can account for the paramagnetism of O_2—it gives us a picture of bonding that more closely corresponds to what we see in experiments. Continuing along the second-row homonuclear diatomic molecules, we see that F_2 has a bond order of 1 and Ne_2 has a bond order of 0, again consistent with experiment since F_2 exists and Ne_2 does not.

WATCH **NOW!**
INTERACTIVE WORKED EXAMPLE 11.10

EXAMPLE 11.10 Molecular Orbital Theory

Draw an MO energy diagram and determine the bond order for the N_2^- ion. Do you expect the bond in the N_2^- ion to be stronger or weaker than the bond in the N_2 molecule? Is N_2^- diamagnetic or paramagnetic?

SOLUTION

Write an energy-level diagram for the molecular orbitals in N_2^-. Use the energy ordering for N_2.

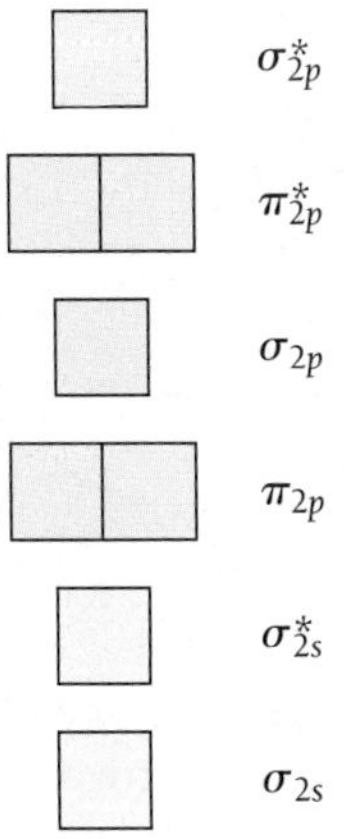

—Continued on the next page

Continued—

The N_2^- ion has 11 valence electrons (five for each nitrogen atom plus one for the negative charge). Assign the electrons to the molecular orbitals beginning with the lowest energy orbitals and following Hund's rule.

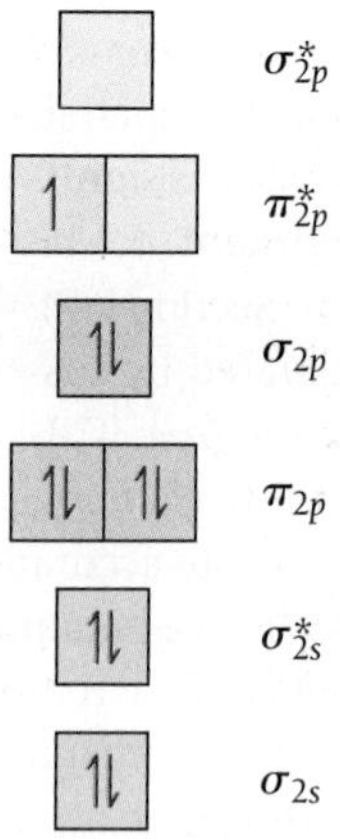

Calculate the bond order by subtracting the number of electrons in antibonding orbitals from the number in bonding orbitals and dividing the result by 2.

$$N_2^- \text{ bond order} = \frac{8 - 3}{2} = +2.5$$

The bond order is 2.5, which is a lower bond order than in the N_2 molecule (bond order = 3); therefore, the bond is weaker. The MO diagram shows that the N_2^- ion has one unpaired electron and is therefore paramagnetic.

FOR PRACTICE 11.10 Draw an MO energy diagram and determine the bond order for the N_2^+ ion. Do you expect the bond in the N_2^+ ion to be stronger or weaker than the bond in the N_2 molecule? Is N_2^+ diamagnetic or paramagnetic?

FOR MORE PRACTICE 11.10 Apply MO theory to determine the bond order of Ne_2.

Second-Period Heteronuclear Diatomic Molecules

We can also apply MO theory to heteronuclear diatomic molecules (two different atoms). For example, we can draw an MO diagram for NO as follows:

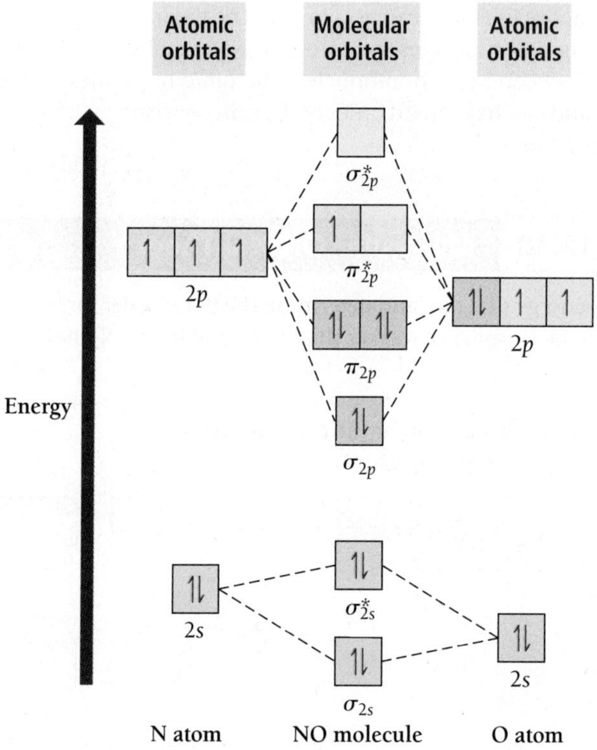

A given orbital will have lower energy in a more electronegative atom. For this reason, electronegative atoms have the ability to attract electrons to themselves.

Oxygen is more electronegative than nitrogen, so its atomic orbitals are lower in energy than nitrogen's atomic orbitals. When two atomic orbitals are identical and of equal energy, the weighting of each orbital in forming a molecular orbital is identical.

However, when two atomic orbitals are different, the weighting of each orbital in forming a molecular orbital may be different. More specifically, when a molecular orbital is approximated as a linear combination of atomic orbitals of different energies, the lower-energy atomic orbital makes a greater contribution to the bonding molecular orbital and the higher-energy atomic orbital makes a greater contribution to the antibonding molecular orbital. For example, notice that the σ_{2s} bonding orbital is closer in energy to the oxygen 2*s* orbital than to the nitrogen 2*s* orbital. We can also see this unequal weighting in the shape of the resultant molecular orbital, in which the electron density is concentrated on the oxygen atom, as shown in Figure 11.16▶.

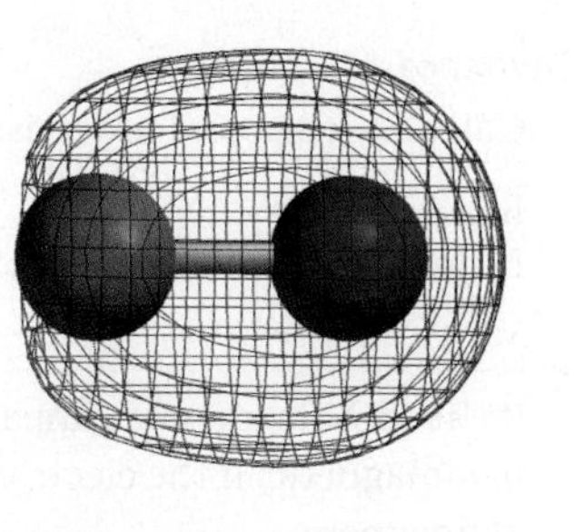

▲ **FIGURE 11.16 Shape of σ_{2s} Bonding Orbital in NO** The molecular orbital shows more electron density at the oxygen end of the molecule because the atomic orbitals of oxygen, the more electronegative element, are lower in energy than those of nitrogen. They therefore contribute more to the bonding molecular orbital.

As another example of a heteronuclear diatomic molecule, consider the MO diagram for HF:

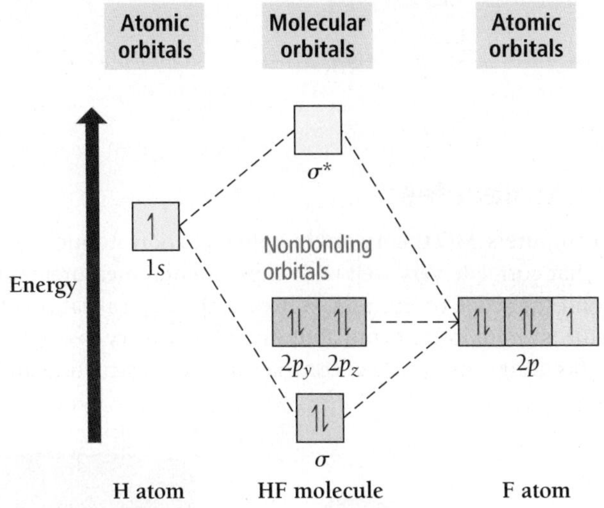

Fluorine is so electronegative that all of its atomic orbitals are lower in energy than hydrogen's atomic orbitals. In fact, fluorine's 2*s* orbital is so low in energy compared to hydrogen's 1*s* orbital that it does not contribute appreciably to the molecular orbitals. The molecular orbitals in HF are approximated by the linear combination of the fluorine $2p_x$ orbital and the hydrogen 1*s* orbital. The other 2*p* orbitals remain localized on the fluorine and appear in the energy diagram as **nonbonding orbitals**. The electrons in the nonbonding orbitals remain localized on the fluorine atom.

EXAMPLE 11.11 Molecular Orbital Theory Applied to Heteronuclear Diatomic Molecules and Ions

Use MO theory to determine the bond order of the CN^- ion. Is the ion paramagnetic or diamagnetic?

SOLUTION

Determine the number of valence electrons in the molecule or ion.	Number of valence electrons = 4 (from C) + 5 (from N) + 1 (from negative charge) = 10
Write an energy-level diagram using Figure 11.15 as a guide. Fill the orbitals beginning with the lowest energy orbital and progressing upward until all electrons have been assigned to an orbital. Remember to allow no more than two electrons (with paired spins) per orbital and to fill degenerate orbitals with single electrons (with parallel spins) before pairing.	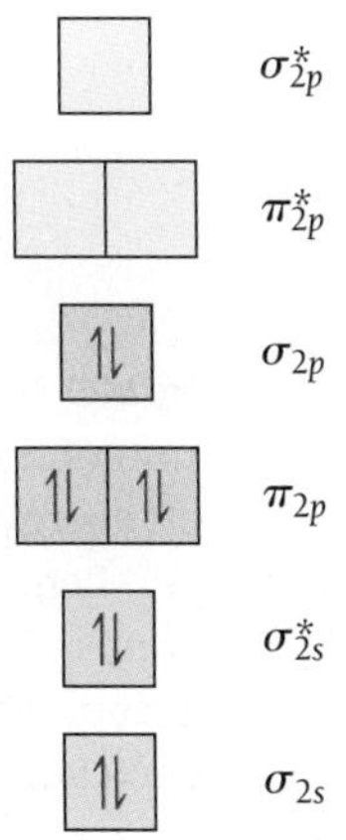

—*Continued on the next page*

Continued—

Calculate the bond order using the appropriate formula: Bond order = $\frac{(\text{number of } e^- \text{ in bonding MOs}) - (\text{number of } e^- \text{ in antibonding MOs})}{2}$	CN^- bond order $= \frac{8-2}{2} = +3$
If the MO diagram has unpaired electrons, the molecule or ion is paramagnetic. If the electrons are all paired, the molecule or ion is diamagnetic.	The MO diagram has no unpaired electrons, so the ion is diamagnetic.

FOR PRACTICE 11.11 Apply MO theory to determine the bond order of NO. (Use the energy ordering of O_2.) Is the molecule paramagnetic or diamagnetic?

Polyatomic Molecules

With the aid of computers, MO theory can be applied to polyatomic molecules and ions, yielding results that correlate very well with experimental measurements. These applications are beyond the scope of this text. However, the delocalization of electrons over an entire molecule is an important contribution of MO theory to our basic understanding of chemical bonding. For example, consider the Lewis structure and valence bond diagram of ozone:

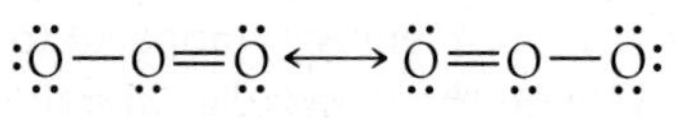

Lewis structure

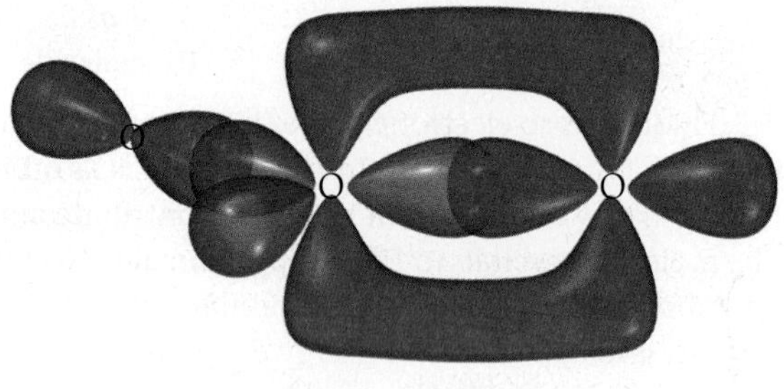

Valence bond model

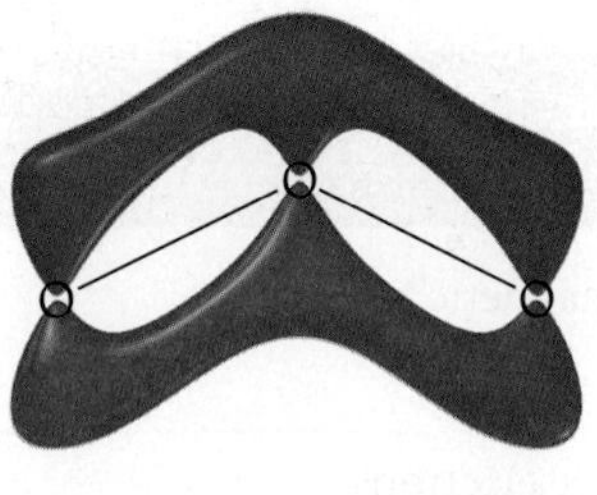

In the Lewis model, we use resonance forms to represent the two equivalent bonds. In valence bond theory, it appears that the two oxygen–oxygen bonds should be different. In MO theory, however, the π molecular orbitals in ozone are formed from a linear combination of the three oxygen $2p$ orbitals and are delocalized over the entire molecule. The lowest energy π bonding molecular orbital is shown in the left margin.

When we examine ozone in nature, we indeed find two equivalent bonds. A similar situation occurs with benzene (C_6H_6). In the Lewis model, we represent the structure with two resonance forms:

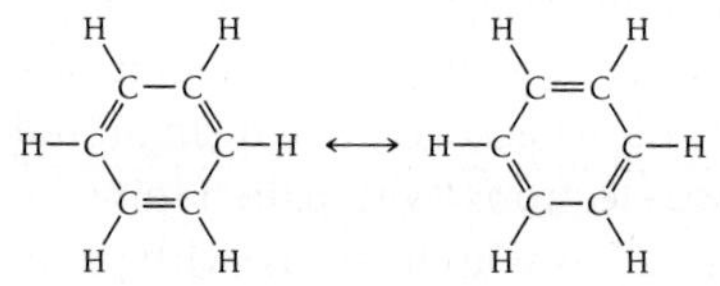

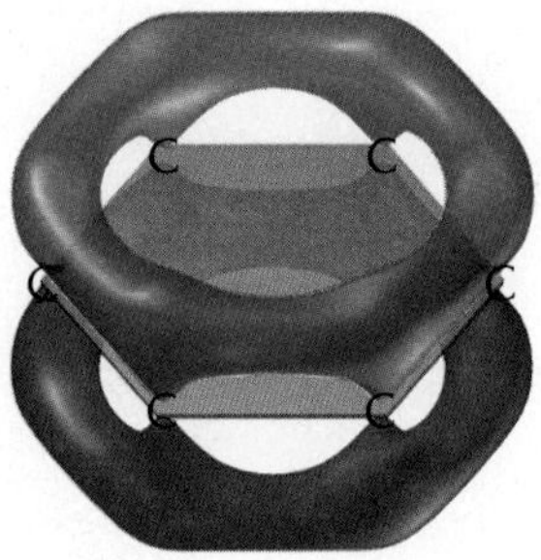

In MO theory, the π molecular orbitals in benzene are formed from a linear combination of the six carbon $2p$ orbitals and are delocalized over the entire molecule. The lowest energy π bonding molecular orbital is shown in the left margin.

Benzene is in fact a highly symmetric molecule with six identical carbon–carbon bonds. The best picture of the π electrons in benzene is one in which the electrons occupy roughly circular-shaped orbitals above and below the plane of the molecule, as depicted in the MO theory approach.

WHAT IS A CHEMICAL BOND? PART II What is a chemical bond according to MO theory?

11.13 Cc Conceptual Connection

ANSWER **NOW!**

(a) According to MO theory, a chemical bond is the overlap between half-filled atomic orbitals.

(b) According to MO theory, a chemical bond is a shared electron pair.

(c) According to MO theory, atoms join together (or bond) when the electrons in the atoms can lower their energy by occupying the molecular orbitals of the resultant molecule.

QUIZ YOURSELF **NOW!**

Self-Assessment Quiz

Q1. Determine the molecular geometry of CBr_4.
MISSED THIS? *Read Section 11.2; Watch KCV 11.2, IWE 11.1*

a) linear
b) trigonal planar
c) tetrahedral
d) trigonal pyramidal

Q2. Determine the molecular geometry of SeF_4. **MISSED THIS?** *Read Sections 11.3, 11.4; Watch KCV 11.3, IWE 11.2*

a) tetrahedral
b) trigonal bipyramidal
c) T-shaped
d) seesaw

Q3. Predict the relative bond angles in BF_3 and SO_2. **MISSED THIS?** *Read Sections 11.3, 11.4; Watch KCV 11.3, IWE 11.2*

a) BF_3 bond angles > SO_2 bond angle
b) SO_2 bond angle > BF_3 bond angles
c) BF_3 bond angles = SO_2 bond angle
d) Relative bond angles cannot be predicted.

Q4. Predict the molecular geometry about nitrogen in the molecule CH_3NHCH_3. **MISSED THIS?** *Read Sections 11.3, 11.4; Watch KCV 11.3, IWE 11.4*

a) linear
b) trigonal planar
c) trigonal pyramidal
d) bent

Q5. Which molecule is polar?
MISSED THIS? *Read Section 11.5; Watch KCV 11.5, IWE 11.5*

a) SF_2 b) BH_3 c) PF_5 d) CS_2

Q6. Determine the hybridization about oxygen in CH_3OH.
MISSED THIS? *Read Sections 11.6, 11.7; Watch KCV 11.6, 11.7, IWE 11.8*

a) *sp* b) sp^2 c) sp^3 d) sp^3d

Q7. Determine the hybridization about carbon in H_2CO. **MISSED THIS?** *Read Sections 11.6, 11.7; Watch KCV 11.6, 11.7, IWE 11.8*

a) *sp* b) sp^2 c) sp^3 d) sp^3d

Q8. According to valence bond theory, which kind of orbitals overlap to form the P—Cl bonds in PCl_5? **MISSED THIS?** *Read Sections 11.6, 11.7; Watch KCV 11.6, 11.7, IWE 11.8*

a) P(sp^3) - Cl(p)
b) P(sp^3d) - Cl(s)
c) P(sp^3) - Cl(s)
d) P(sp^3d) - Cl(p)

Q9. Apply MO theory to determine the bond order in C_2.
MISSED THIS? *Read Section 11.8; Watch IWE 11.10*

a) 0 b) 1 c) 2 d) 3

Q10. Apply MO theory to predict which species has the strongest bond.
MISSED THIS? *Read Section 11.8; Watch IWE 11.10*

a) N_2 b) N_2^- c) N_2^+
d) All bonds are equivalent according to MO theory.

Q11. Apply MO theory to determine which molecule is diamagnetic.
MISSED THIS? *Read Section 11.8; Watch IWE 11.10*

a) CO b) B_2 c) O_2
d) None of the above (all are paramagnetic)

Q12. Which hybridization scheme occurs about nitrogen when nitrogen forms a double bond?
MISSED THIS? *Read Section 11.7; Watch KCV 11.7*

a) *sp* b) sp^2 c) sp^3 d) sp^3d

Q13. Which molecular geometry results when a central atom has five total electron groups, with three of those being bonding groups and two being lone pairs?
MISSED THIS? *Read Sections 11.3, 11.4; Watch KCV 11.3, IWE 11.2*

a) trigonal bipyramidal
b) seesaw
c) T-shaped
d) bent

Q14. Determine the correct molecular geometry (from left to right) about each interior atom in CH_3CH_2OH.
MISSED THIS? *Read Sections 11.3, 11.4; Watch KCV 11.3, IWE 11.4*

a) 1st C tetrahedral; 2nd C trigonal planar; O linear
b) 1st C trigonal planar; 2nd C bent; O linear
c) 1st C trigonal planar; 2nd C trigonal pyramidal; O bent
d) 1st C tetrahedral; 2nd C tetrahedral; O bent

Q15. The central atom in a molecule has a bent molecular geometry. Determine the hybridization of the orbitals in the atom.
MISSED THIS? *Read Section 11.7; Watch KCV 11.7, IWE 11.4*

a) *sp* b) sp^2 c) sp^3
d) Hybridization cannot be determined from the information given.

Answers: **1.** (c) **2.** (d) **3.** (a) **4.** (c) **5.** (a) **6.** (c) **7.** (b) **8.** (d) **9.** (c) **10.** (a) **11.** (a) **12.** (b) **13.** (c) **14.** (d) **15.** (d)

CHAPTER 11 IN REVIEW

TERMS

Section 11.2
valence shell electron pair repulsion (VSEPR) theory (438)
electron groups (438)
linear geometry (439)
trigonal planar geometry (439)
tetrahedral geometry (440)
trigonal bipyramidal geometry (441)
octahedral geometry (441)

Section 11.3
electron geometry (442)
molecular geometry (442)
trigonal pyramidal geometry (442)
bent geometry (443)
seesaw geometry (444)
T-shaped geometry (444)
square pyramidal geometry (445)
square planar geometry (445)

Section 11.6
valence bond theory (455)

Section 11.7
hybridization (457)
hybrid orbitals (457)
pi (π) bond (462)
sigma (σ) bond (462)

Section 11.8
molecular orbital (MO) theory (471)
bonding orbital (472)
antibonding orbital (472)
bond order (473)
nonbonding orbitals (481)

CONCEPTS

Molecular Shape and VSEPR Theory (11.1–11.4)

- The properties of molecules are directly related to their shapes. In VSEPR theory, molecular geometries are determined by the repulsions between electron groups on the central atom. An electron group can be a single bond, double bond, triple bond, lone pair, or even a single electron.
- The five basic molecular shapes are linear (two electron groups), trigonal planar (three electron groups), tetrahedral (four electron groups), trigonal bipyramidal (five electron groups), and octahedral (six electron groups).
- When lone pairs are present on the central atom, the *electron* geometry is still one of the five basic shapes, but one or more positions are occupied by lone pairs. The *molecular* geometry is therefore different from the electron geometry. Lone pairs are positioned so as to minimize repulsions with other lone pairs and with bonding pairs.

Polarity (11.5)

- The polarity of a polyatomic molecule containing polar bonds depends on its geometry. If the dipole moments of the polar bonds are aligned in such a way that they cancel one another, the molecule is not polar. If they are aligned in such a way as to sum together, the molecule is polar.
- Highly symmetric molecules tend to be nonpolar, whereas asymmetric molecules containing polar bonds tend to be polar. The polarity of a molecule dramatically affects its properties.

Valence Bond Theory (11.6–11.7)

- In contrast to the Lewis model, in which a covalent chemical bond is the sharing of electrons represented by dots, in valence bond theory a chemical bond is the overlap of half-filled atomic orbitals (or in some cases the overlap between a completely filled orbital and an empty one).
- The overlapping orbitals may be the standard atomic orbitals, such as 1*s* or 2*p*, or they may be hybridized atomic orbitals, which are mathematical combinations of the standard orbitals on a single atom. The basic hybridized orbitals are sp, sp^2, sp^3, sp^3d, and sp^3d^2.
- The geometry of the molecule is determined by the geometry of the overlapping orbitals.
- In our treatment of valence bond theory, we use the electron geometry determined by VSEPR theory to determine the correct hybridization scheme.
- In valence bond theory, we distinguish between two types of bonds, σ (sigma) and π (pi). In a σ bond, the orbital overlap occurs in the region that lies directly between the two bonding atoms. In a π bond, formed from the side-by-side overlap of *p* orbitals, the overlap occurs above and below the region that lies directly between the two bonding atoms.
- Rotation about a σ bond is relatively free, whereas rotation about a π bond is restricted.

Molecular Orbital Theory (11.8)

- The simplest molecular orbitals are linear combinations of atomic orbitals (LCAOs), weighted averages of the atomic orbitals of the different atoms in the molecule.
- When two atomic orbitals combine to form molecular orbitals, they form one molecular orbital of lower energy (the bonding orbital) and one of higher energy (the antibonding orbital).
- A set of molecular orbitals fills in much the same way as atomic orbitals.
- The stability of the molecule and the strength of the bond depend on the number of electrons in bonding orbitals compared to the number in antibonding orbitals.

EQUATIONS AND RELATIONSHIPS

Bond Order of a Diatomic Molecule (**11.8**)

$$\text{Bond order} = \frac{(\text{number of electrons in bonding MOs}) - (\text{number of electrons in antibonding MOs})}{2}$$

LEARNING OUTCOMES

Chapter Objectives	Assessment
Predict the basic shapes of molecules according to VSEPR theory (**11.2**)	Example 11.1 **For Practice** 11.1 **Exercises** 31–34
Predict how lone pairs and electron groups affect molecular geometry (**11.3, 11.4**)	Examples 11.2, 11.3 **For Practice** 11.2, 11.3 **Exercises** 35–45
Predict the shape of larger molecules (**11.4**)	Example 11.4 **For Practice** 11.4 **Exercises** 46
Predict the polarity of a molecular compound (**11.5**)	Example 11.5 **For Practice** 11.5 **Exercises** 47–52
Determine the hybridization and bonding scheme of a molecule using valence bond theory (**11.6, 11.7**)	Examples 11.6, 11.7, 11.8 **For Practice** 11.6, 11.7, 11.8 **For More Practice** 11.8 **Exercises** 53–68
Predict properties of diatomic molecules using molecular orbital theory (**11.8**)	Examples 11.9, 11.10, 11.11 **For Practice** 11.9, 11.10, 11.11 **For More Practice** 11.10 **Exercises** 69–82

EXERCISES

Mastering Chemistry provides end-of-chapter exercises, feedback-enriched tutorial problems, animations, and interactive activities to encourage problem-solving practice and deeper understanding of key concepts and topics.

REVIEW QUESTIONS

1. Why is molecular geometry important? Cite some examples.

2. According to VSEPR theory, what determines the geometry of a molecule?

3. Name and sketch the five basic electron geometries, and state the number of electron groups corresponding to each. What constitutes an *electron group*?

4. Explain the difference between electron geometry and molecular geometry. Under what circumstances are they not the same?

5. Give the correct electron and molecular geometries that correspond to each set of electron groups around the central atom of a molecule.

- **a.** four electron groups overall; three bonding groups and one lone pair
- **b.** four electron groups overall; two bonding groups and two lone pairs
- **c.** five electron groups overall; four bonding groups and one lone pair
- **d.** five electron groups overall; three bonding groups and two lone pairs
- **e.** five electron groups overall; two bonding groups and three lone pairs
- **f.** six electron groups overall; five bonding groups and one lone pair
- **g.** six electron groups overall; four bonding groups and two lone pairs

6. How do you apply VSEPR theory to predict the shape of a molecule with more than one interior atom?

7. How do you determine whether a molecule is polar? Why is polarity important?

8. What is a chemical bond according to valence bond theory?

9. In valence bond theory, what determines the geometry of a molecule?

10. In valence bond theory, the interaction energy between the electrons and nucleus of one atom with the electrons and nucleus of another atom is usually negative (stabilizing) when ________.

11. What is hybridization? Why is hybridization necessary in valence bond theory?

12. How does hybridization of the atomic orbitals in the central atom of a molecule help lower the overall energy of the molecule?

13. How is the *number* of hybrid orbitals related to the number of standard atomic orbitals that are hybridized?

14. Sketch each set of hybrid orbitals.

a. sp **b.** sp^2 **c.** sp^3
d. sp^3d **e.** sp^3d^2

15. In the Lewis model, the two bonds in a double bond look identical. However, valence bond theory shows that they are not. Describe a double bond according to valence bond theory. Explain why rotation is restricted about a double bond but not about a single bond.

16. Name the hybridization scheme that corresponds to each electron geometry.

- **a.** linear
- **b.** trigonal planar
- **c.** tetrahedral
- **d.** trigonal bipyramidal
- **e.** octahedral

17. What is a chemical bond according to MO theory?

18. Explain the difference between hybrid atomic orbitals in valence bond theory and LCAO molecular orbitals in MO theory.

19. What is a bonding molecular orbital?

20. What is an antibonding molecular orbital?

21. What is the role of wave interference in determining whether a molecular orbital is bonding or antibonding?

22. In MO theory, what is bond order? Why is it important?

23. How is the number of molecular orbitals approximated by a linear combination of atomic orbitals related to the number of atomic orbitals used in the approximation?

24. Sketch each molecular orbital.

a. σ_{2s} b. σ^*_{2s} c. σ_{2p}
d. σ^*_{2p} e. π_{2p} f. π^*_{2p}

25. Draw an energy diagram for the molecular orbitals of period 2 diatomic molecules. Show the difference in ordering for B_2, C_2, and N_2 compared to O_2, F_2, and Ne_2.

26. Why does the energy ordering of the molecular orbitals of the period 2 diatomic molecules change in going from N_2 to O_2?

27. Explain the difference between a paramagnetic species and a diamagnetic one.

28. When applying MO theory to heteronuclear diatomic molecules, the atomic orbitals used may be of different energies. If two atomic orbitals of different energies make two molecular orbitals, how are the energies of the molecular orbitals related to the energies of the atomic orbitals? How is the shape of the resultant molecular orbitals related to the shape of the atomic orbitals?

29. In MO theory, what is a nonbonding orbital?

30. Write a short paragraph describing chemical bonding according to the Lewis model, valence bond theory, and MO theory. Indicate how the theories differ in their description of a chemical bond and describe the strengths and weaknesses of each theory. Which theory is correct?

PROBLEMS BY TOPIC

VSEPR Theory and Molecular Geometry

31. A molecule with the formula AB_3 has a trigonal pyramidal geometry. How many electron groups are on the central atom (A)?
MISSED THIS? *Read Section 11.2; Watch KCV 11.2, IWE 11.1*

32. A molecule with the formula AB_3 has a trigonal planar geometry. How many electron groups are on the central atom?

33. For each molecular geometry, list the number of total electron groups, the number of bonding groups, and the number of lone pairs on the central atom. **MISSED THIS?** *Read Sections 11.2, 11.3; Watch KCV 11.2, 11.3, IWE 11.1, 11.2*

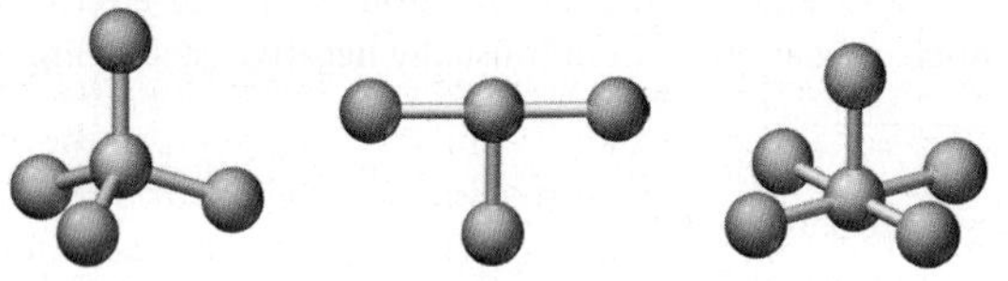

(a) (b) (c)

34. For each molecular geometry, list the number of total electron groups, the number of bonding groups, and the number of lone pairs on the central atom.

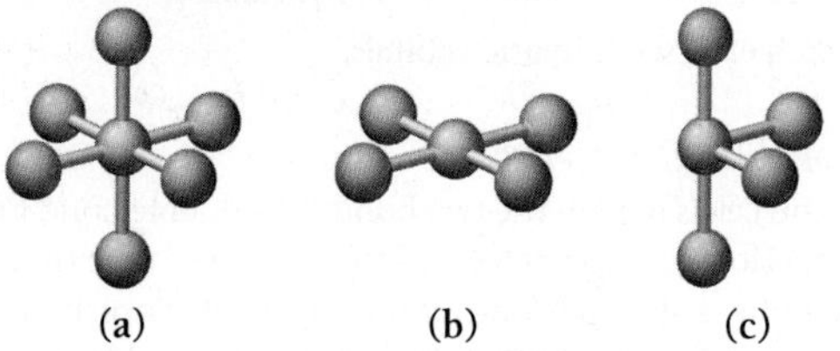

(a) (b) (c)

35. Determine the electron geometry, molecular geometry, and idealized bond angles for each molecule. In which cases do you expect deviations from the idealized bond angle?
MISSED THIS? *Read Sections 11.3, 11.4; Watch KCV 11.3, IWE 11.2*

a. PF_3 b. SBr_2 c. $CHCl_3$ d. CS_2

36. Determine the electron geometry, molecular geometry, and idealized bond angles for each molecule. In which cases do you expect deviations from the idealized bond angle?

a. CF_4 b. NF_3 c. OF_2 d. H_2S

37. Which species has the smaller bond angle, H_3O^+ or H_2O? Explain.
MISSED THIS? *Read Sections 11.3, 11.4; Watch KCV 11.3, IWE 11.2*

38. Which species has the smaller bond angle, ClO_4^- or ClO_3^-? Explain.

39. Determine the molecular geometry and sketch each molecule or ion using the bond conventions shown in "Representing Molecular Geometries on Paper" in Section 11.4.
MISSED THIS? *Read Sections 11.3, 11.4; Watch KCV 11.3, IWE 11.2*

a. SF_4 b. ClF_3 c. IF_2^- d. IBr_4^-

40. Determine the molecular geometry and sketch each molecule or ion, using the bond conventions shown in "Representing Molecular Geometries on Paper" in Section 11.4.

a. BrF_5
b. SCl_6
c. PF_5
d. IF_4^+

41. Determine the molecular geometry about each interior atom and sketch each molecule.
MISSED THIS? *Read Section 11.4; Watch IWE 11.4*

a. C_2H_2 (skeletal structure HCCH)
b. C_2H_4 (skeletal structure H_2CCH_2)
c. C_2H_6 (skeletal structure H_3CCH_3)

42. Determine the molecular geometry about each interior atom and sketch each molecule.

a. N_2
b. N_2H_2 (skeletal structure HNNH)
c. N_2H_4 (skeletal structure H_2NNH_2)

43. Each ball-and-stick model shows the electron and molecular geometry of a generic molecule. Explain what is wrong with each molecular geometry and provide the correct molecular geometry, given the number of lone pairs and bonding groups on the central atom.
MISSED THIS? *Read Sections 11.3, 11.4; Watch KCV 11.3, IWE 11.2*

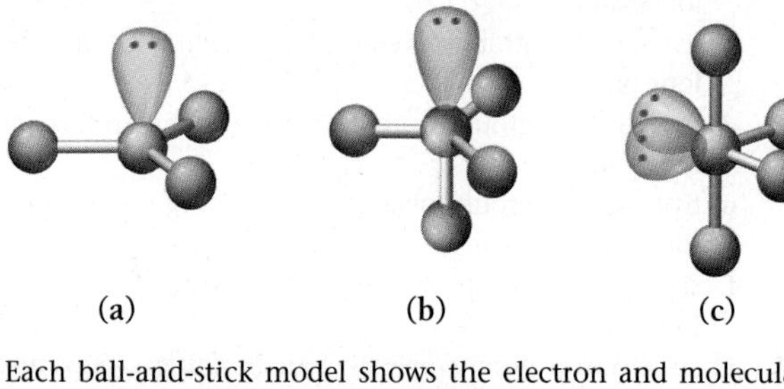

(a) (b) (c)

44. Each ball-and-stick model shows the electron and molecular geometry of a generic molecule. Explain what is wrong with each molecular geometry and provide the correct molecular geometry, given the number of lone pairs and bonding groups on the central atom.

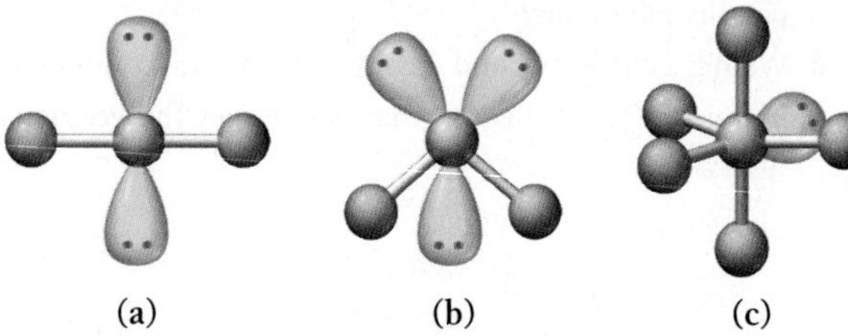

(a) (b) (c)

45. Determine the geometry about each interior atom in each molecule and sketch the molecule. (Skeletal structure is indicated in parentheses.)
MISSED THIS? *Read Section 11.4; Watch IWE 11.4*
a. $CH_3OH(H_3COH)$ b. $CH_3OCH_3(H_3COCH_3)$
c. $H_2O_2(HOOH)$

46. Determine the geometry about each interior atom in each molecule and sketch the molecule. (Skeletal structure is indicated in parentheses.)
a. $CH_3NH_2(H_3CNH_2)$
b. $CH_3CO_2CH_3$ ($H_3CCOOCH_3$ one O atom attached to 2nd C atom; the other O atom is bonded to the 2nd and 3rd C atom)
c. NH_2CO_2H (H_2NCOOH both O atoms attached to C)

Molecular Shape and Polarity

47. Explain why CO_2 and CCl_4 are both nonpolar, even though they contain polar bonds.
MISSED THIS? *Read Section 11.5; Watch KCV 11.5, IWE 11.5*

48. CH_3F is a polar molecule, even though the tetrahedral geometry often leads to nonpolar molecules. Explain.

49. Determine whether each molecule in Exercise 35 is polar or nonpolar.
MISSED THIS? *Read Section 11.5; Watch KCV 11.5, IWE 11.5*

50. Determine whether each molecule in Exercise 36 is polar or nonpolar.

51. Determine whether each molecule is polar or nonpolar.
MISSED THIS? *Read Section 11.5; Watch KCV 11.5, IWE 11.5*
a. SCl_2 b. SCl_4 c. $BrCl_5$

52. Determine whether each molecule is polar or nonpolar.
a. $SiCl_4$ b. CF_2Cl_2
c. SeF_6 d. IF_5

Valence Bond Theory

53. The valence electron configurations of several atoms are shown here. How many bonds can each atom make without hybridization? **MISSED THIS?** *Read Section 11.6; Watch KCV 11.6*
a. Be $2s^2$ b. P $3s^23p^3$ c. F $2s^22p^5$

54. The valence electron configurations of several atoms are shown here. How many bonds can each atom make without hybridization?
a. B $2s^22p^1$ b. N $2s^22p^3$ c. O $2s^22p^4$

55. Write orbital diagrams (boxes with arrows in them) to represent the electron configurations—without hybridization—for all the atoms in PH_3. Circle the electrons involved in bonding. Draw a three-dimensional sketch of the molecule and show orbital overlap. What bond angle do you expect from the unhybridized orbitals? How well does valence bond theory agree with the experimentally measured bond angle of 93.3°?
MISSED THIS? *Read Section 11.6; Watch KCV 11.6*

56. Write orbital diagrams (boxes with arrows in them) to represent the electron configurations—without hybridization—for all the atoms in SF_2. Circle the electrons involved in bonding. Draw a three-dimensional sketch of the molecule and show orbital overlap. What bond angle do you expect from the unhybridized orbitals? How well does valence bond theory agree with the experimentally measured bond angle of 98.2°?

57. Write orbital diagrams (boxes with arrows in them) to represent the electron configuration of carbon before and after sp^3 hybridization.
MISSED THIS? *Read Section 11.7; Watch KCV 11.7*

58. Write orbital diagrams (boxes with arrows in them) to represent the electron configurations of carbon before and after *sp* hybridization.

59. Which hybridization scheme allows the formation of at least one π bond? **MISSED THIS?** *Read Section 11.7; Watch KCV 11.7*

sp^3, sp^2, sp^3d^2

60. Which hybridization scheme allows the central atom to form more than four bonds?

sp^3, sp^3d, sp^2

61. Write a hybridization and bonding scheme for each molecule. Sketch the molecule, including overlapping orbitals, and label all bonds using the notation shown in Examples 11.6 and 11.7.
MISSED THIS? *Read Section 11.7; Watch KCV 11.7, IWE 11.8*
a. CCl_4 b. NH_3 c. OF_2 d. CO_2

62. Write a hybridization and bonding scheme for each molecule. Sketch the molecule, including overlapping orbitals, and label all bonds using the notation shown in Examples 11.6 and 11.7.
a. CH_2Br_2 b. SO_2 c. NF_3 d. BF_3

63. Write a hybridization and bonding scheme for each molecule or ion. Sketch the structure, including overlapping orbitals, and label all bonds using the notation shown in Examples 11.6 and 11.7.
MISSED THIS? *Read Section 11.7; Watch KCV 11.7, IWE 11.8*
a. $COCl_2$ (carbon is the central atom)
b. BrF_5 c. XeF_2 d. I_3^-

64. Write a hybridization and bonding scheme for each molecule or ion. Sketch the structure, including overlapping orbitals, and label all bonds using the notation shown in Examples 11.6 and 11.7.
a. SO_3^{2-} b. PF_6^-
c. BrF_3 d. HCN

65. Write a hybridization and bonding scheme for each molecule that contains more than one interior atom. Indicate the hybridization about each interior atom. Sketch the structure, including overlapping orbitals, and label all bonds using the notation shown in Examples 11.6 and 11.7.
MISSED THIS? *Read Section 11.7; Watch KCV 11.7, IWE 11.8*
a. N_2H_2 (skeletal structure HNNH)
b. N_2H_4 (skeletal structure H_2NNH_2)
c. CH_3NH_2 (skeletal structure H_3CNH_2)

66. Write a hybridization and bonding scheme for each molecule that contains more than one interior atom. Indicate the hybridization about each interior atom. Sketch the structure, including overlapping orbitals, and label all bonds using the notation shown in Examples 11.6 and 11.7.
a. C_2H_2 (skeletal structure HCCH)
b. C_2H_4 (skeletal structure H_2CCH_2)
c. C_2H_6 (skeletal structure H_3CCH_3)

67. Consider the structure of the amino acid alanine. Indicate the hybridization about each interior atom.
MISSED THIS? *Read Section 11.7; Watch KCV 11.7, IWE 11.8*

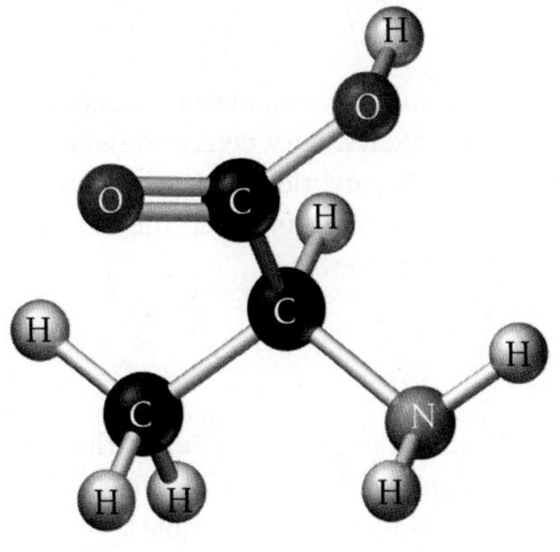

68. Consider the structure of the amino acid aspartic acid. Indicate the hybridization about each interior atom.

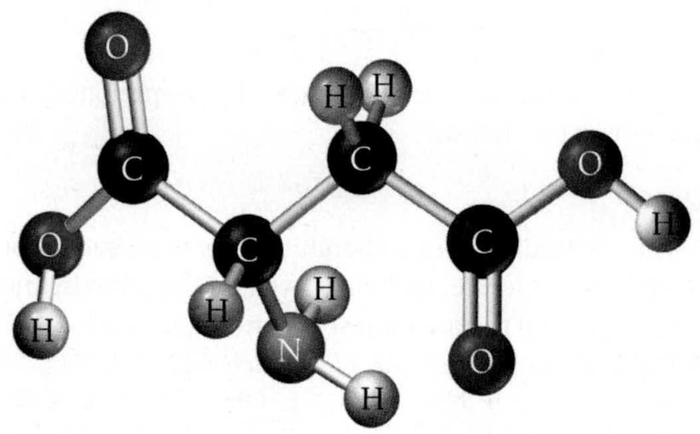

Molecular Orbital Theory

69. Sketch the bonding molecular orbital that results from the linear combination of two 1*s* orbitals. Indicate the region where interference occurs and state the kind of interference (constructive or destructive).
MISSED THIS? *Read Section 11.8*

70. Sketch the antibonding molecular orbital that results from the linear combination of two 1*s* orbitals. Indicate the region where interference occurs and state the kind of interference (constructive or destructive).

71. Draw an MO energy diagram and predict the bond order of Be_2^+ and Be_2^-. Do you expect these molecules to exist in the gas phase?
MISSED THIS? *Read Section 11.8; Watch IWE 11.10*

72. Draw an MO energy diagram and predict the bond order of Li_2^+ and Li_2^-. Do you expect these molecules to exist in the gas phase?

73. Sketch the bonding and antibonding molecular orbitals that result from linear combinations of the $2p_x$ atomic orbitals in a homonuclear diatomic molecule. (The $2p_x$ orbitals are those whose lobes are oriented along the bonding axis.)
MISSED THIS? *Read Section 11.8*

74. Sketch the bonding and antibonding molecular orbitals that result from linear combinations of the $2p_z$ atomic orbitals in a homonuclear diatomic molecule. (The $2p_z$ orbitals are those whose lobes are oriented perpendicular to the bonding axis.) How do these molecular orbitals differ from those obtained from linear combinations of the $2p_y$ atomic orbitals? (The $2p_y$ orbitals are also oriented perpendicular to the bonding axis but are also perpendicular to the $2p_z$ orbitals.)

75. Using the molecular orbital energy ordering for second-row homonuclear diatomic molecules in which the π_{2p} orbitals lie at *lower* energy than the σ_{2p}, draw MO energy diagrams and predict the bond order in a molecule or ion with each number of total valence electrons. Will the molecule or ion be diamagnetic or paramagnetic?
MISSED THIS? *Read Section 11.8; Watch IWE 11.10*
a. 4 b. 6 c. 8 d. 9

76. Using the molecular orbital energy ordering for second-row homonuclear diatomic molecules in which the π_{2p} orbitals lie at *higher* energy than the σ_{2p}, draw MO energy diagrams and predict the bond order in a molecule or ion with each number of total valence electrons. Will the molecule or ion be diamagnetic or paramagnetic?
a. 10 b. 12 c. 13 d. 14

77. Use MO theory to predict if each molecule or ion exists in a relatively stable form.
MISSED THIS? *Read Section 11.8; Watch IWE 11.10*
a. H_2^{2-} b. Ne_2 c. He_2^{2+} d. F_2^{2-}

78. Use MO theory to predict if each molecule or ion exists in a relatively stable form.
a. C_2^{2+} b. Li_2 c. Be_2^{2+} d. Li_2^{2-}

79. According to MO theory, which molecule or ion has the highest bond order? Highest bond energy? Shortest bond length?
MISSED THIS? *Read Section 11.8; Watch IWE 11.10*

$$C_2, C_2^+, C_2^-$$

80. According to MO theory, which molecule or ion has the highest bond order? Highest bond energy? Shortest bond length?

$$O_2, O_2^-, O_2^{2-}$$

81. Draw an MO energy diagram for CO. (Use the energy ordering of O_2.) Predict the bond order and make a sketch of the lowest energy bonding molecular orbital.
MISSED THIS? *Read Section 11.8*

82. Draw an energy diagram for HCl. Predict the bond order and make a sketch of the lowest energy bonding molecular orbital.

CUMULATIVE PROBLEMS

83. For each compound, draw the Lewis structure, determine the geometry using VSEPR theory, determine whether the molecule is polar, identify the hybridization of all interior atoms, and make a sketch of the molecule, according to valence bond theory, showing orbital overlap.
a. COF_2 (carbon is the central atom)
b. S_2Cl_2 (ClSSCl)
c. SF_4

84. For each compound, draw the Lewis structure, determine the geometry using VSEPR theory, determine whether the molecule is polar, identify the hybridization of all interior atoms, and make a sketch of the molecule, according to valence bond theory, showing orbital overlap.
a. IF_5
b. CH_2CHCH_3
c. CH_3SH

85. Amino acids are biological compounds that link together to form proteins, the workhorse molecules in living organisms. The skeletal structures of several simple amino acids are shown here. For each skeletal structure, complete the Lewis structure, determine the geometry and hybridization about each interior atom, and make a sketch of the molecule, using the bond conventions of Section 11.4.

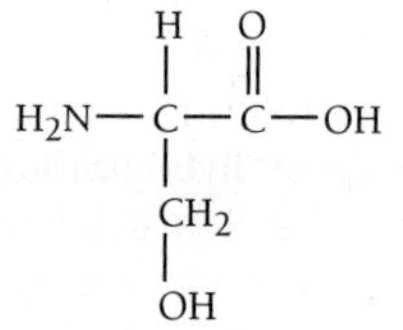
(a) serine

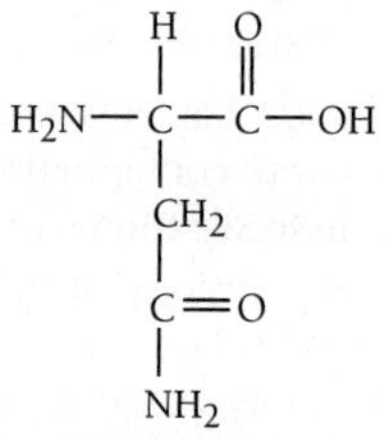
(b) asparagine

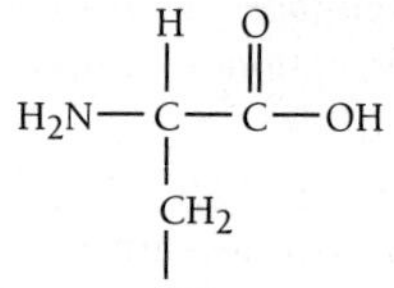
(c) cysteine

86. The genetic code is based on four different bases with the structures shown here. Assign a geometry and hybridization to each interior atom in these four bases.

a. cytosine b. adenine c. thymine d. guanine

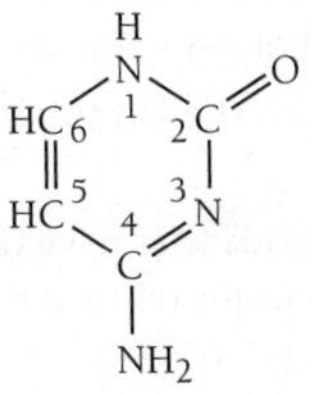
(a)

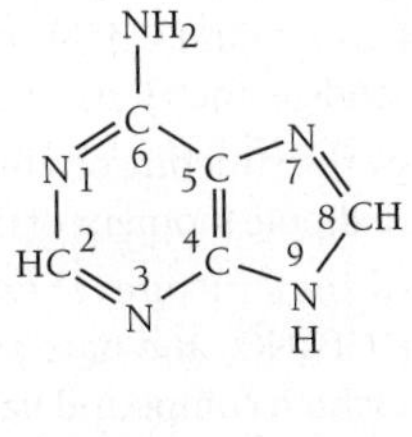
(b)

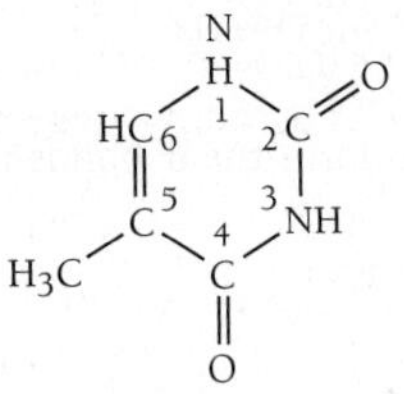
(c)

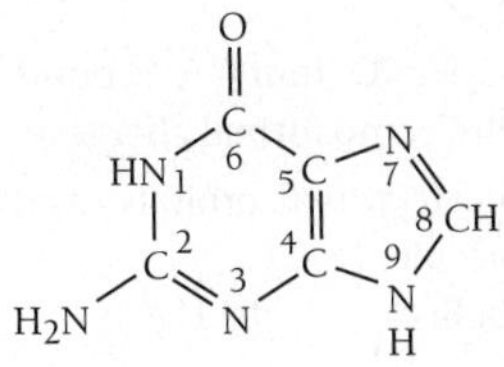
(d)

87. The structure of caffeine, present in coffee and many soft drinks, is shown here. How many pi bonds are present in caffeine? How many sigma bonds? Insert the lone pairs in the molecule. What kinds of orbitals do the lone pairs occupy?

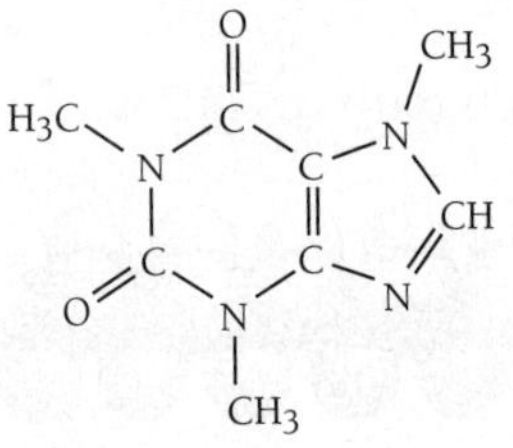

88. The structure of acetylsalicylic acid (aspirin) is shown here. How many pi bonds are present in acetylsalicylic acid? How many sigma bonds? What parts of the molecule are free to rotate? What parts are rigid?

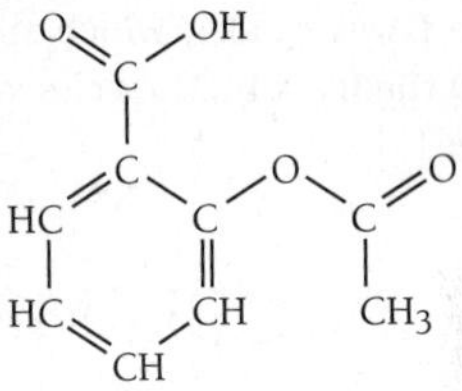

89. Most vitamins can be classified as either fat soluble, which results in their tendency to accumulate in the body (so that taking too much can be harmful), or water soluble, which results in their tendency to be quickly eliminated from the body in urine. Examine the structural formulas and space-filling models of these vitamins and determine whether each one is fat soluble (mostly nonpolar) or water soluble (mostly polar).

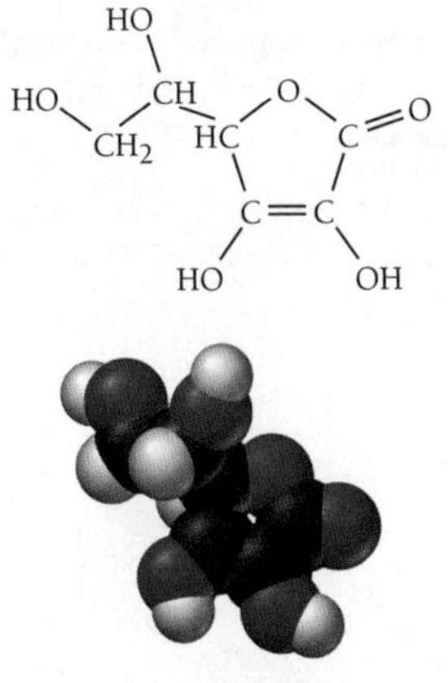
(a) vitamin C

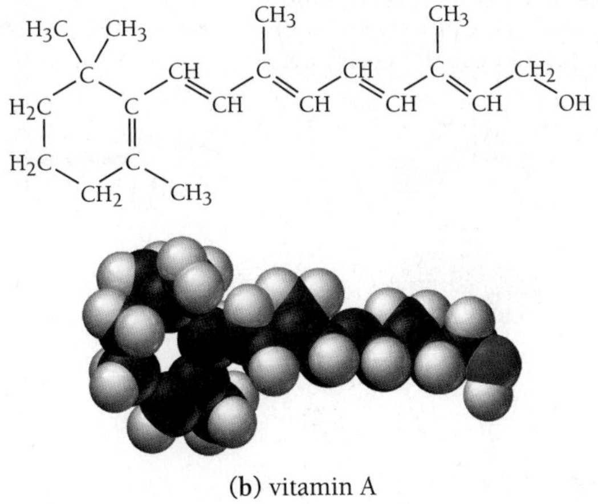
(b) vitamin A

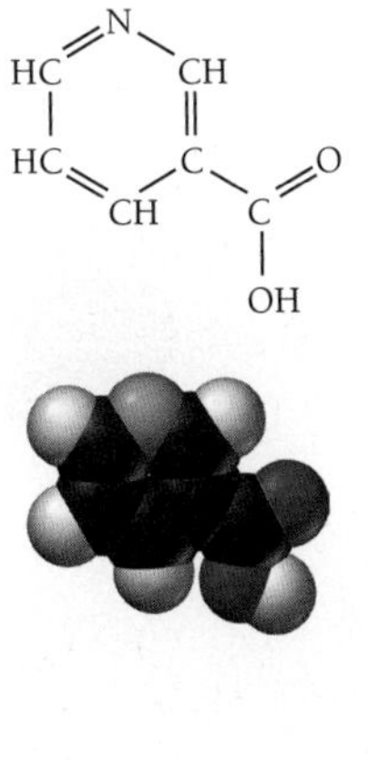
(c) niacin (vitamin B_3)

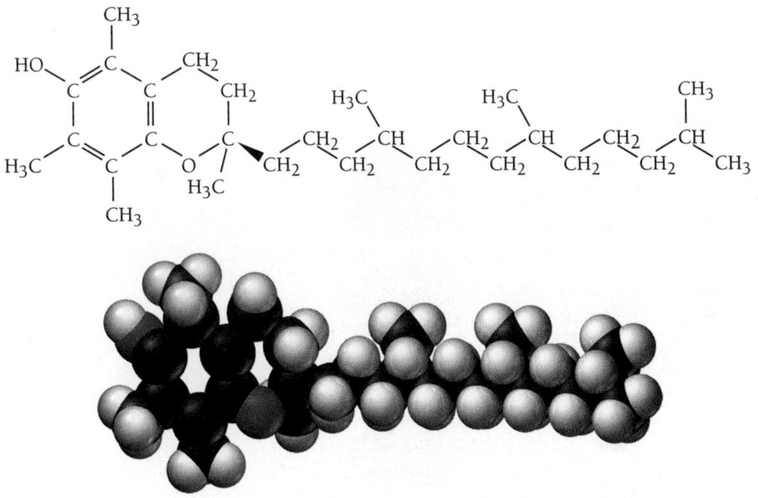
(d) vitamin E

90. Water does not easily remove grease from dishes or hands because grease is nonpolar and water is polar. The addition of soap to water, however, allows the grease to dissolve. Study the structure of sodium stearate (a soap) and describe how it works.

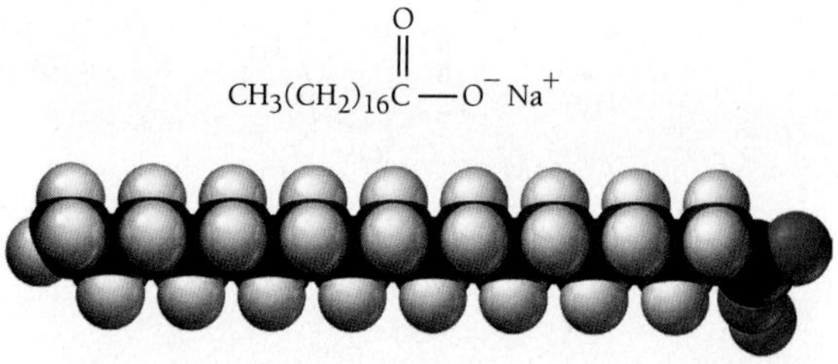

91. Draw a molecular orbital energy diagram for ClF. (Assume that the σ_p orbitals are lower in energy than the π orbitals.) What is the bond order in ClF?

92. Draw Lewis structures and MO diagrams for CN^+, CN, and CN^-. According to the Lewis model, which species is most stable? According to MO theory, which species is most stable? Do the two theories agree?

93. Bromine can form compounds or ions with any number of fluorine atoms from one to five. Write the formulas of all five of these species, assign a hybridization, and describe their electron and molecular geometry.

94. The compound C_3H_4 has two double bonds. Describe its bonding and geometry, using a valence bond approach.

95. Draw the structure of a molecule with the formula $C_4H_6Cl_2$ that has a dipole moment of 0.

96. Draw the structures of two compounds that have the composition CH_3NO_2 and have all three H atoms bonded to the C. Predict which compound has the larger ONO bond angle.

97. How many types of hybrid orbitals do we use to describe each molecule?

a. N_2O_5

b. C_2H_5NO (four C—H bonds and one O—H bond)

c. BrCN (no formal charges)

98. Indicate which orbitals overlap to form the σ bonds in each molecule.

a. $BeBr_2$ b. $HgCl_2$ c. ICN

CHALLENGE PROBLEMS

99. In VSEPR theory, which uses the Lewis model to determine molecular geometry, the trend of decreasing bond angles in CH_4, NH_3, and H_2O is accounted for by the greater repulsion of lone pair electrons compared to bonding pair electrons. How would this trend be accounted for in valence bond theory?

100. The results of a molecular orbital calculation for H_2O are shown here. Examine each of the orbitals and classify them as bonding, antibonding, or nonbonding. Assign the correct number of electrons to the energy diagram. According to this energy diagram, is H_2O stable? Explain.

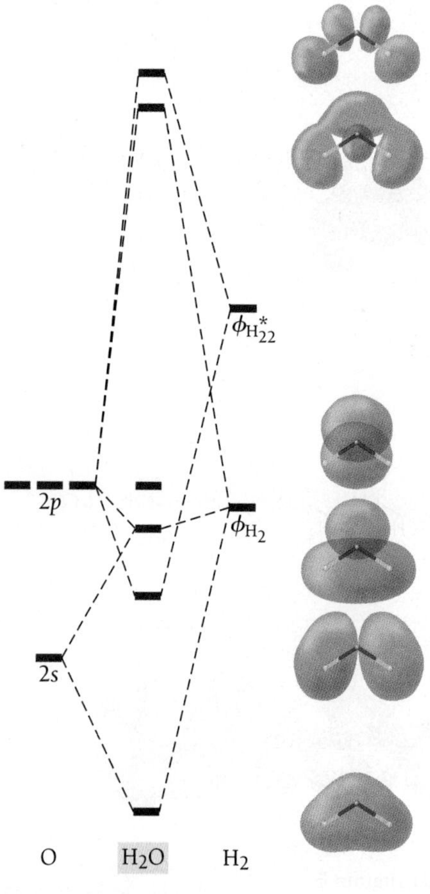

101. The results of a molecular orbital calculation for NH_3 are shown here. Examine each of the orbitals and classify them as bonding, antibonding, or nonbonding. Assign the correct number of electrons to the energy diagram. According to this energy diagram, is NH_3 stable? Explain.

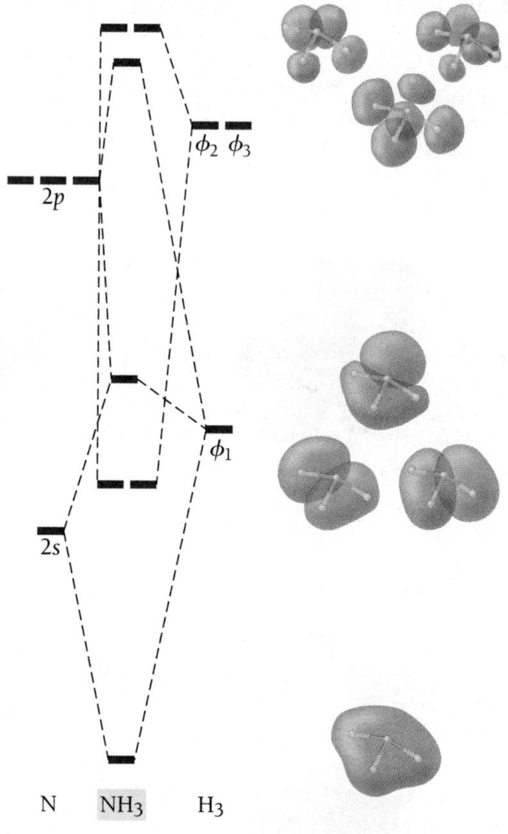

102. *cis*-2-Butene isomerizes to *trans*-2-butene via the reaction shown here.

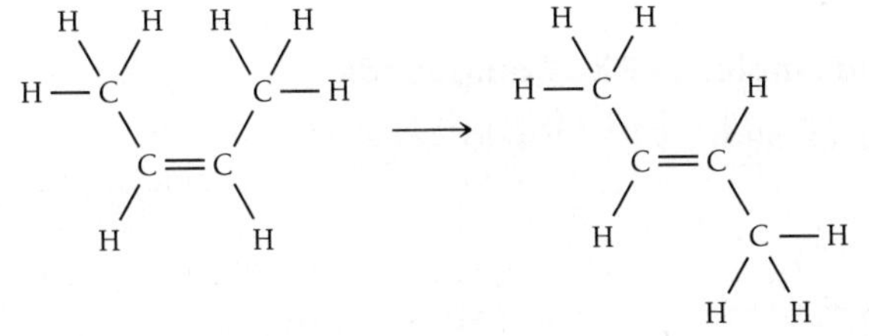

a. If isomerization requires breaking the π bond, what minimum energy is required for isomerization in J/mol? In J/molecule?

b. If the energy for isomerization came from light, what minimum frequency of light would be required? In what portion of the electromagnetic spectrum does this frequency lie?

103. The species NO_2, NO_2^+, and NO_2^- in which N is the central atom have very different bond angles. Predict what these bond angles might be with respect to the ideal angles and justify your prediction.

104. The bond angles increase steadily in the series PF_3, PCl_3, PBr_3, and PI_3. After consulting the data on atomic radii in Chapter 9, provide an explanation for this observation.

105. The ion CH_5^+ can form under very special high-energy conditions in the vapor phase in a mass spectrometer. Propose a hybridization for the carbon atom and predict the geometry.

106. Neither the VSEPR model nor the hybridization model is able to account for the experimental observation that the F—Ba—F bond angle in gaseous BaF_2 is 108° rather than the predicted 180°. Suggest some possible explanations for this observation.

107. Draw the Lewis structure for acetamide (CH_3CONH_2), an organic compound, and determine the geometry about each interior atom. Experiments show that the geometry about the nitrogen atom in acetamide is nearly planar. What resonance structure can account for the planar geometry about the nitrogen atom?

108. Use VSEPR theory to predict the geometry (including bond angles) about each interior atom of methyl azide (CH_3N_3), and make a sketch of the molecule. Would you expect the bond angle between the two interior nitrogen atoms to be the same or different? Would you expect the two nitrogen–nitrogen bond lengths to be the same or different?

CONCEPTUAL PROBLEMS

109. Which statement best captures the fundamental idea behind VSEPR theory? Explain what is wrong with each of the other statements.

a. The angle between two or more bonds is determined primarily by the repulsions between the electrons within those bonds and other (lone pair) electrons on the central atom of a molecule. Each of these electron groups (bonding electrons or lone pair electrons) will lower its potential energy by maximizing its separation from other electron groups, thus determining the geometry of the molecule.

b. The angle between two or more bonds is determined primarily by the repulsions between the electrons within those bonds. Each of these bonding electrons will lower its potential energy by maximizing its separation from other electron groups, thus determining the geometry of the molecule.

c. The geometry of a molecule is determined by the shapes of the overlapping orbitals that form the chemical bonds. Therefore, to determine the geometry of a molecule, you must determine the shapes of the orbitals involved in bonding.

110. Suppose that a molecule has four bonding groups and one lone pair on the central atom. Suppose further that the molecule is confined to two dimensions (this is a purely hypothetical assumption for the sake of understanding the principles behind VSEPR theory). Make a sketch of the molecule and estimate the bond angles.

111. How does each of the three major bonding theories (the Lewis model, valence bond theory, and MO theory) define a single chemical bond? A double bond? A triple bond? How are these definitions similar? How are they different?

112. The most stable forms of the nonmetals in groups 4A, 5A, and 6A of the second period are molecules with multiple bonds. Beginning with the third period, the most stable forms of the nonmetals of these groups are molecules without multiple bonds. Propose an explanation for this observation based on valence bond theory.

QUESTIONS FOR GROUP WORK

Active Classroom Learning

Discuss these questions with the group and record your consensus answer.

113. In complete sentences, describe why someone might expect the bond angles in methane (CH_4) to be 90° even though the bond angles are actually 109.5°.

114. At least two different numbers of electron groups can result in a linear molecule. What are they? What are the numbers of bonding groups and lone pairs in each case? Provide an example of a linear molecule in each case.

115. Have each member of your group select one of the molecules shown below and complete steps a–d. Each member should then present his or her results to the rest of the group, explaining the reasoning used to determine the answers.

CS_2 NCl_3 CF_4 CH_2F_2

a. Draw the Lewis dot structure.

b. Determine the molecular geometry and draw it accurately.

c. Indicate the polarity of any polar bonds within the structure.

d. Classify the molecule as polar or nonpolar.

116. How many atomic orbitals form a set of sp^3 hybrid orbitals? A set of sp^2 hybrid orbitals? A set of sp hybrid orbitals? What is the relationship between these numbers and the number of electron groups around the central atom?

117. Use MO theory to explain in detail why N_2^+ and N_2^- have similar bond strengths and both are very different from neutral N_2.

DATA INTERPRETATION AND ANALYSIS

Using Distances between Atoms to Predict Bond Angles

118. The VSEPR model is useful in predicting bond angles for many compounds. However, as we have seen, other factors (such as type of bond and atomic radii) may also influence bond angles. Consider that data for bond angles in related species in the tables and answer the questions.

Bond Angles in NO_2 and Associated Ions

Species	Bond Angle
NO_2	134°
NO_2^+	180°
NO_2^-	115°

Bond Angles in PX_3 Compounds

Compounds	Bond Angle
PH_3	94°
PF_3	97°
PCl_3	100°
PI_3	102°

a. Draw Lewis structures for all of the species in the Bond Angles in NO_2 and Associated Ions Table.
b. Use the Lewis structures from part a to explain the observed bond angles in NO_2 and its associated ions.
c. Draw Lewis structures for all of the species in the Bond Angles in PX_3 Compounds Table.
d. Make your own table showing the atomic radii of H, F, Cl, and I.
e. Use your answers to parts c and d to explain the observed bond angles in PH_3, PF_3, PCl_3, and PI_3.

Cc ANSWERS TO CONCEPTUAL CONNECTIONS

Electron Groups and Molecular Geometry

11.1 **(b)** Two electron groups with no lone pairs on a central atom in a molecule result in a linear geometry.

Molecular Geometry

11.2 **(a)** Linear. HCN has two electron groups (the single bond and the triple bond) resulting in a linear geometry.

Lone Pairs and Molecular Geometry I

11.3 **(d)** Three bonding groups and one lone pair lead to a trigonal pyramidal geometry.

Lone Pair Repulsions

11.4 **(c)** Positions 1 and 4 would put the greatest distance between the lone pairs and minimize lone pair–lone pair repulsions.

Molecular Geometry and Electron Group Repulsions

11.5 **(d)** All electron groups on the central atom (or interior atoms, if there is more than one) determine the shape of a molecule according to VSEPR theory.

The Shape of Larger Molecules

11.6 **(c)** The nitrogen atom has four electron groups and one lone pair, as the Lewis structure illustrates; therefore, the molecular geometry about the nitrogen atom is trigonal pyramidal.

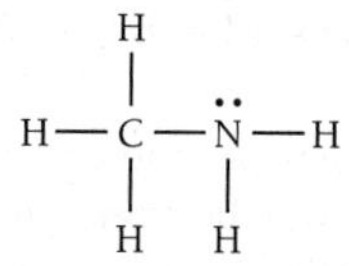

Polarity of Molecules

11.7 **(b)** Even through the molecule has polar bonds, the dipole moments of the three bonds cancel out because of the trigonal planar geometry, and the molecule is not polar.

What Is a Chemical Bond? Part I

11.8 **(b)** In valence bond theory, a covalent chemical bond is the overlap of half-filled atomic orbitals.

Number of Hybrid Orbitals

11.9 **(d)** The number of hybrid orbitals that form must always equal the number of orbitals that are combined. Since one *s* and three *p* orbitals are combined, four hybrid orbitals form. You can also determine the number of hybrid orbitals by summing the superscripts in the hybridization notation. For sp^3, you add the implied 1 superscript on the *s* to the 3 superscript on the *p* and you get $1 + 3 = 4$.

Single and Double Bonds

11.10 **(a)** Applying valence bond theory, we see that a double bond is actually composed of two different kinds of bonds, one σ and one π. The orbital overlap in the π bond is side to side between two *p* orbitals and consequently different from the end-to-end overlap in a σ bond. Since the bonds are different types, the bond energy of the double bond is not just twice the bond energy of the single bond.

Hybridization

11.11 **(a)** Because carbon has two electron groups in carbon dioxide (the two double bonds), the geometry is linear and the hybridization is *sp*.

Bond Order

11.12 **(b)** The bond order is 1.5. Remember that bond order is equal to the number of bonding electrons minus the number of antibonding electrons, all divided by two, so you get that the bond order $= (6 - 3)/2 = 1.5$.

What Is a Chemical Bond? Part II

11.13 **(c)** According to MO theory, atoms join together (or bond) when the electrons in the atoms can lower their energy by occupying the molecular orbitals of the resultant molecule. Unlike the Lewis model or valence bond theory, the chemical "bonds" in MO theory are not localized between atoms but are spread throughout the entire molecule.

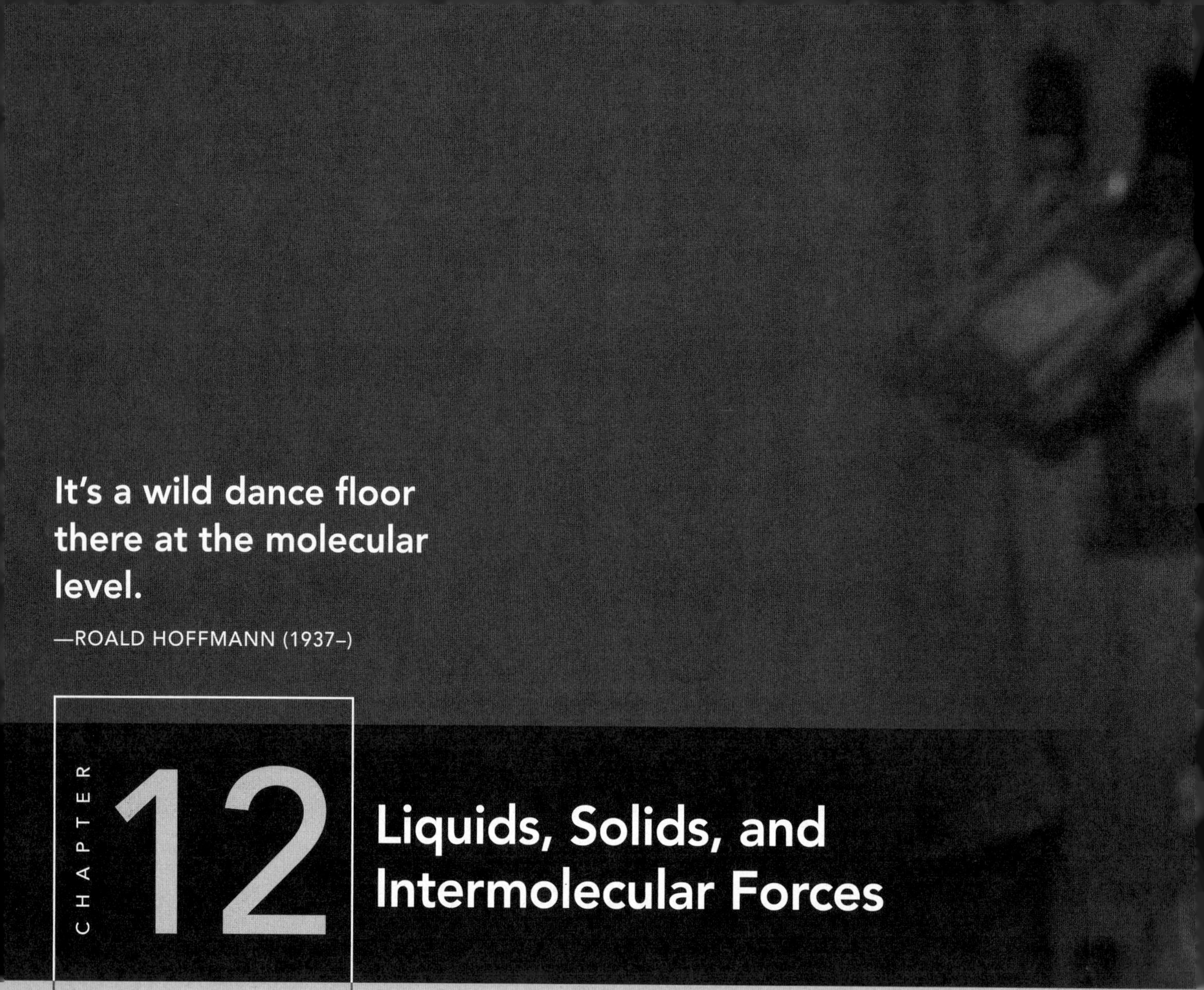

It's a wild dance floor there at the molecular level.

—ROALD HOFFMANN (1937–)

CHAPTER 12 Liquids, Solids, and Intermolecular Forces

Recall from Chapter 1 that matter exists primarily in three states (or phases): solid, liquid, and gas. In Chapter 6, we examined the gas state. In this chapter we turn to the solid and liquid states, known collectively as the *condensed* states. The solid and liquid states are more similar to each other than they are to the gas state. In the gas state, constituent particles—atoms or molecules—are separated by large distances and do not interact with each other very much. In the condensed states, constituent particles are close together and exert moderate to strong attractive forces on one another. Whether a substance is a solid, liquid, or gas at a given temperature depends on the structure of the particles that compose the substance. Remember the theme we have emphasized since Chapter 1 of this book: the properties of matter are determined by the properties of molecules and atoms. In this chapter, we see how the structure of a particular atom or molecule determines the state in which it will exist at a given temperature.

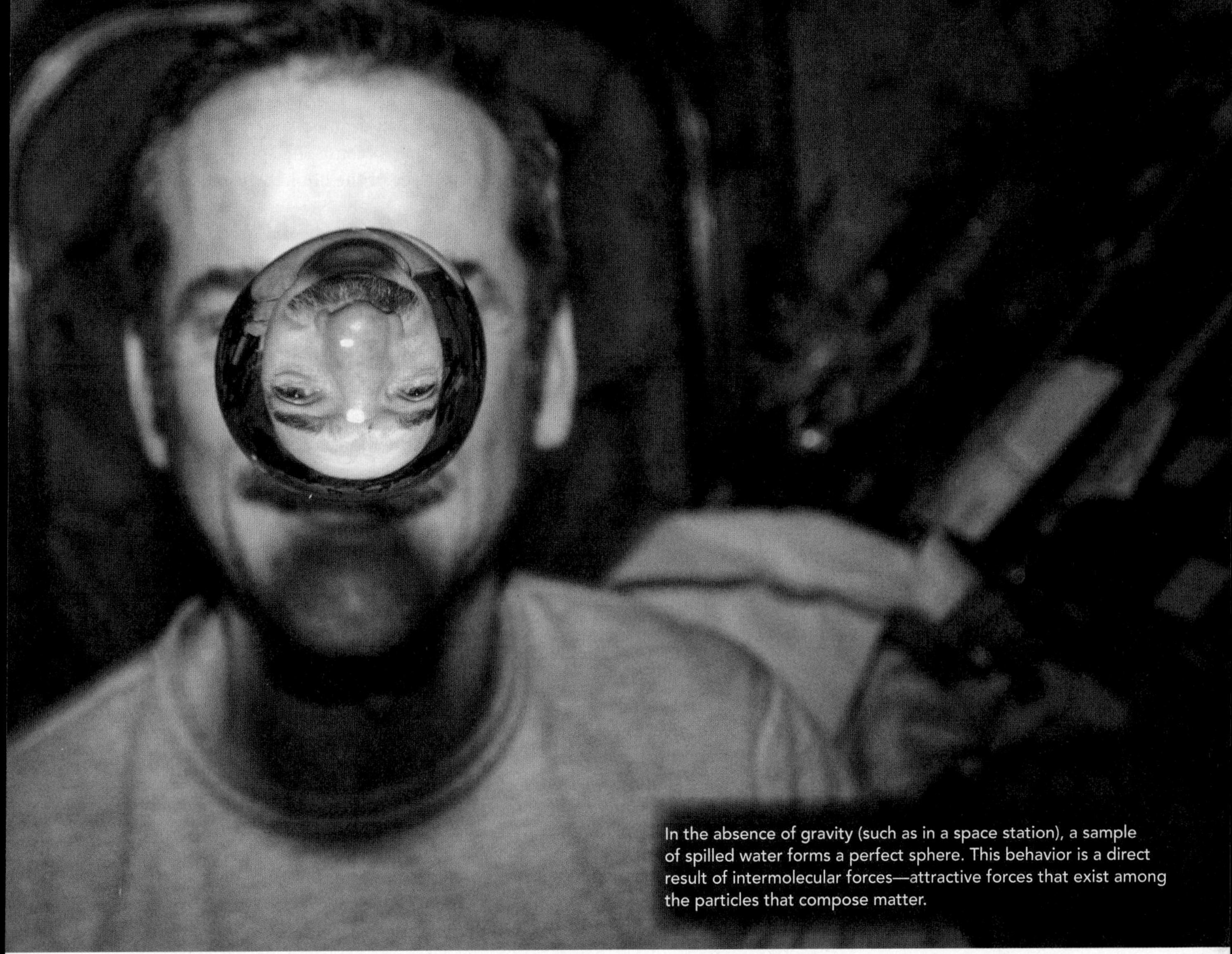
In the absence of gravity (such as in a space station), a sample of spilled water forms a perfect sphere. This behavior is a direct result of intermolecular forces—attractive forces that exist among the particles that compose matter.

12.1 Water, No Gravity 495

12.2 Solids, Liquids, and Gases: A Molecular Comparison 496

12.3 Intermolecular Forces: The Forces That Hold Condensed States Together 499

12.4 Intermolecular Forces in Action: Surface Tension, Viscosity, and Capillary Action 509

12.5 Vaporization and Vapor Pressure 512

12.6 Sublimation and Fusion 522

12.7 Heating Curve for Water 524

12.8 Phase Diagrams 527

12.9 Water: An Extraordinary Substance 529

LEARNING OUTCOMES 533

12.1 Water, No Gravity

In the space station there are no spills. When an astronaut squeezes a full water bottle, the water squirts out like it does on Earth, but instead of falling to the floor and forming a puddle, the water molecules stick together to form a floating, oscillating blob. Over time, the blob stops oscillating and forms a nearly perfect sphere. Why?

The reason is the main topic of this chapter: *intermolecular forces*, the attractive forces that exist among the particles that compose matter. The molecules that compose water are attracted to one another, much like a collection of small magnets are attracted to each other. These attractions hold the water together as a liquid (instead of a gas) at room temperature. These forces also cause samples of water to clump together into a blob, which is clearly seen in the absence of gravity. Over time, irregularities in the shape of the blob smooth out, and the blob becomes a sphere. The sphere is the geometrical shape with the lowest surface area to volume ratio. By forming a sphere, the water molecules maximize their interaction with one another because the sphere results in the minimum number of molecules being at the surface of the liquid, where fewer interactions occur (compared to the interior of the liquid).

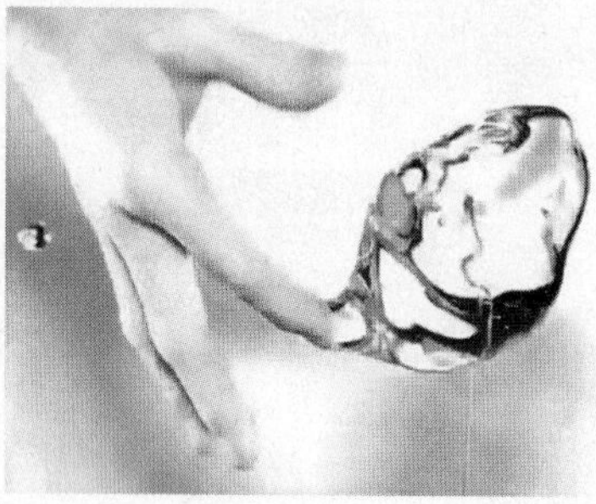

Intermolecular forces exist, not only among water molecules, but among all particles that compose matter. You can see the effect of these attractive forces in the image to the left, which shows an astronaut touching a floating blob of water in the absence of gravity. Notice how the water sticks to the astronaut's finger. The water molecules experience an attractive force to the molecules that compose skin. This attractive force deforms the entire blob of water. *Intermolecular forces exist among all the particles that compose matter.*

The state of a sample of matter—solid, liquid, or gas—depends on the magnitude of intermolecular forces among the constituent particles relative to the amount of thermal energy in the sample. Recall from Chapter 7 that the molecules and atoms composing matter are in constant random motion that increases with increasing temperature. The energy associated with this motion is *thermal energy.* When thermal energy is high relative to intermolecular forces, matter tends to be gaseous. When thermal energy is low relative to intermolecular forces, matter tends to be in a condensed state (liquid or solid). Intermolecular forces are therefore responsible for the very existence of condensed states.

12.2 Solids, Liquids, and Gases: A Molecular Comparison

We are all familiar with solids and liquids. Water, gasoline, rubbing alcohol, and nail polish remover are common liquids. Ice, dry ice, and diamond are familiar solids. What makes these states so different?

Differences between States of Matter

To illustrate the differences between the three common states of matter, Table 12.1 lists the density and molar volume of water in its three different states, along with molecular representations of each state. Notice that the densities of the solid and liquid states are

TABLE 12.1 ■ The Three States of Water

Phase	Temperature (°C)	Density (g/cm^3, at 1 atm)	Molar Volume	Molecular View
Gas (steam)	100	5.90×10^{-4}	30.6 L	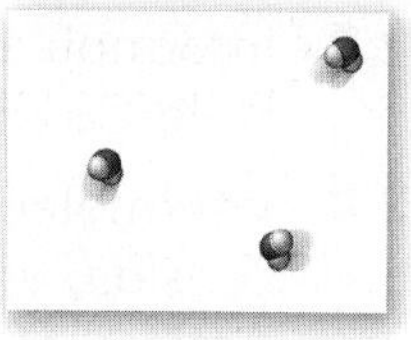
Liquid (water)	20	0.998	18.0 mL	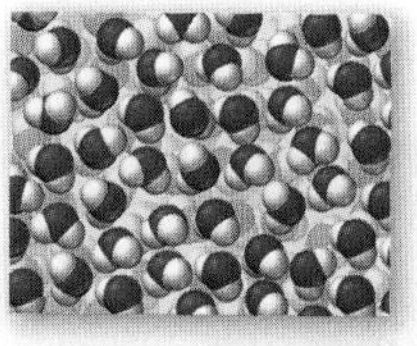
Solid (ice)	0	0.917	19.6 mL	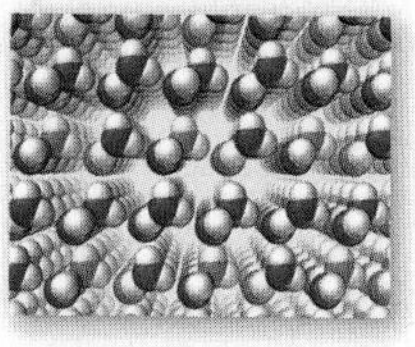

much greater than the density of the gas state. Notice also that the solid and liquid states are more similar in density and molar volume to one another than they are to the gas state. The molecular representations show the reason for these differences. The molecules in liquid water and ice are in close contact with one another—essentially touching—whereas those in gaseous water are separated by large distances. The molecular representation of gaseous water in Table 12.1 is actually out of proportion—the water molecules in the figure should be much farther apart for their size. (Only a fraction of a molecule could be included in the figure if it were drawn to scale.) From the molar volumes, we know that 18.0 mL of liquid water (slightly more than a tablespoon) occupies 30.6 L when converted to gas at 100 °C (at atmospheric pressure). The low density of gaseous water is a direct result of this large separation between molecules.

Notice also that, for water, the solid is slightly less dense than the liquid. This is *atypical* behavior. Most solids are slightly denser than their corresponding liquids because the molecules move closer together upon freezing. As we will discuss in Section 12.9, ice is less dense than liquid water because the unique crystal structure of ice results in water molecules moving slightly farther apart upon freezing.

A major difference between liquids and solids is the freedom of movement of the constituent molecules or atoms. Even though the atoms or molecules in a liquid are in close contact, thermal energy partially overcomes the attractions between them, allowing them to move around one another. This is not the case in solids; the atoms or molecules in a solid are virtually locked in their positions, only vibrating back and forth about a fixed point. Table 12.2 summarizes the properties of liquids and solids, as well as the properties of gases for comparison.

TABLE 12.2 ■ Properties of the States of Matter

State	Density	Shape	Volume	Strength of Intermolecular Forces (Relative to Thermal Energy)
Gas	Low	Indefinite	Indefinite	Weak
Liquid	High	Indefinite	Definite	Moderate
Solid	High	Definite	Definite	Strong

Liquids assume the shape of their containers (to the extent that they fill them) because the atoms or molecules that compose liquids are free to flow (or move around one another). When we pour water into a flask, the water flows and assumes the shape of the flask (Figure 12.1►). Liquids are not easily compressed because the molecules or atoms that compose them are already in close contact—they cannot be pushed much closer together. The molecules in a gas, by contrast, have a great deal of space between them and are easily forced into a smaller volume by an increase in external pressure (Figure 12.2▼).

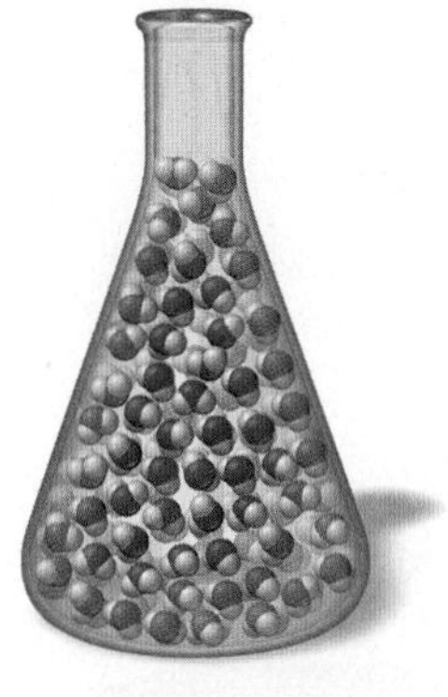

▲ **FIGURE 12.1 Liquids Assume the Shapes of Their Containers** When we pour water into a flask, it assumes the shape of the flask because water molecules are free to flow.

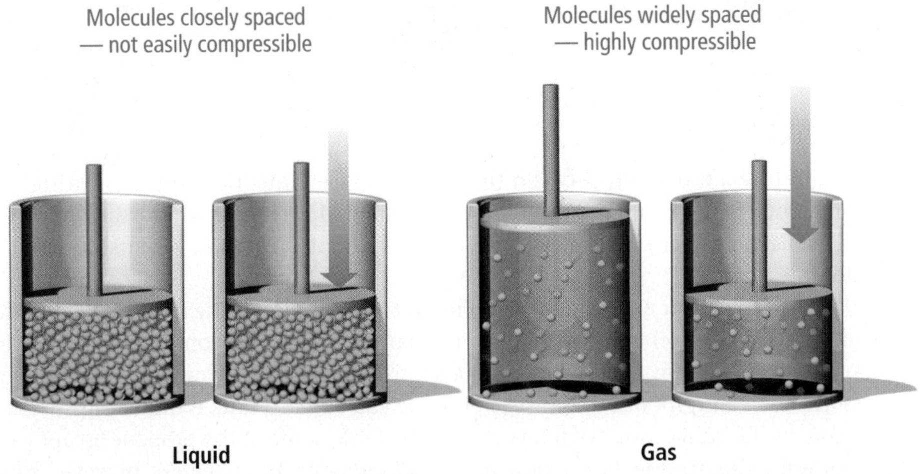

▲ **FIGURE 12.2 Gases Are Compressible** Molecules in a liquid are closely spaced and are not easily compressed. Molecules in a gas have a great deal of space between them, making gases compressible.

According to some definitions, an amorphous solid is considered a unique state, different from the normal solid state because it lacks any long-range order.

Solids have a definite shape because, in contrast to liquids and gases, the molecules or atoms that compose solids are fixed in place—each molecule or atom in a solid merely vibrates about a fixed point. Like liquids, solids have a definite volume and generally cannot be compressed because the molecules or atoms composing them are already in close contact. Solids may be **crystalline**, in which case the atoms or molecules that compose them are arranged in a well-ordered three-dimensional array, or they may be **amorphous**, in which case the atoms or molecules that compose them have no long-range order (Figure 12.3▼).

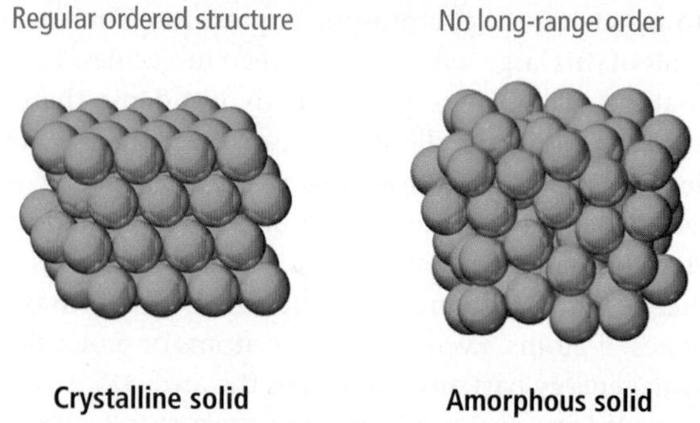

▶ **FIGURE 12.3 Crystalline and Amorphous Solids** In a crystalline solid, the arrangement of the particles displays long-range order. In an amorphous solid, the arrangement of the particles has no long-range order.

ANSWER **NOW!** 12.1 Cc Conceptual Connection

STATES OF MATTER Which state of matter is compressible?

(a) solid
(b) liquid
(c) gas

Changes between States

We can transform one state of matter to another by changing the temperature, pressure, or both. For example, we can convert solid ice to liquid water by heating, and liquid water to solid ice by cooling. The following diagram shows the three states of matter and the changes in conditions that commonly induce transitions between the states:

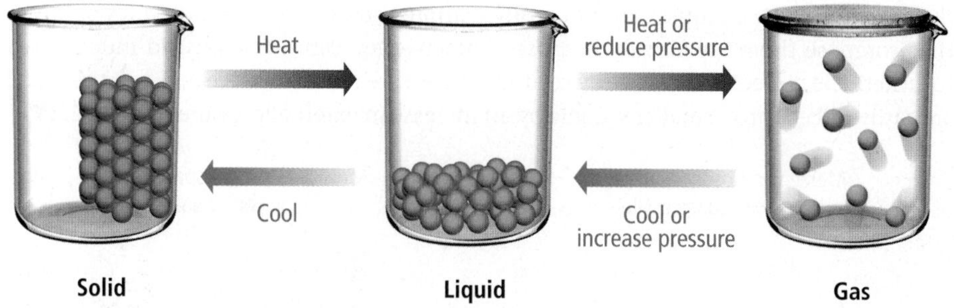

We can induce a transition between the liquid and gas state, not only by heating and cooling, but also by changing the pressure. In general, increases in pressure favor the denser state, so increasing the pressure of a gas sample results in a transition to the liquid state.

The most familiar example of this phenomenon occurs in the LP (liquefied petroleum) gas used as a fuel for outdoor grills and lanterns. LP gas is composed primarily of propane, a gas at room temperature and atmospheric pressure. However, it liquefies at pressures exceeding about 2.7 atm. The propane you buy in a tank is under pressure and therefore in the liquid form. When you open the tank, some of the propane escapes as a gas, lowering the pressure in the tank for a brief moment. Immediately, however, some of the liquid propane evaporates, replacing the gas that escaped. Storing gases like propane as liquids is efficient because, in their liquid form, they occupy much less space.

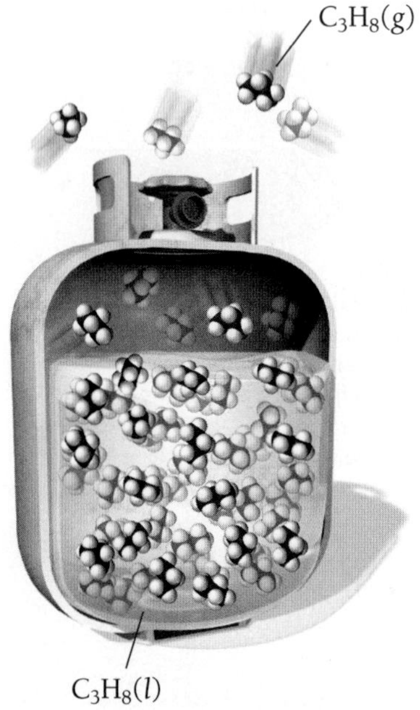

▲ The propane in an LP gas tank is in the liquid state. When you open the tank, some propane vaporizes and escapes as a gas.

12.2 Cc Conceptual Connection

ANSWER NOW!

STATE CHANGES This molecular diagram shows a sample of liquid water:

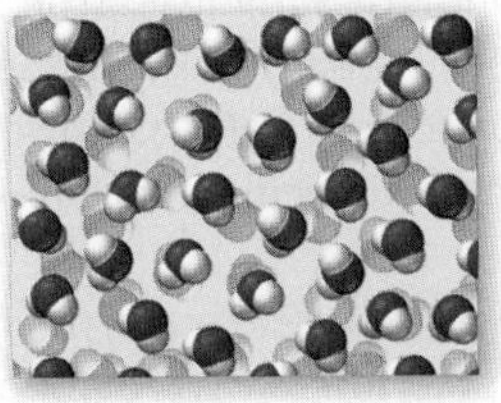

Which of the diagrams below best depicts the vapor emitted from a pot of boiling water?

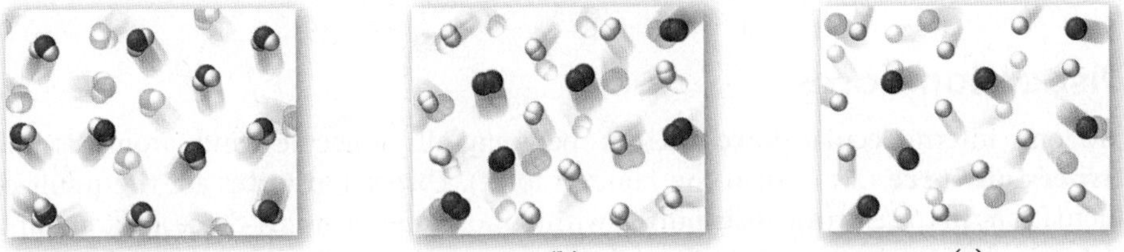

(a) (b) (c)

12.3 Intermolecular Forces: The Forces That Hold Condensed States Together

WATCH **NOW!**

KEY CONCEPT VIDEO 12.3 *Intermolecular Forces*

The structure of the particles that compose a substance determines the strength of the intermolecular forces that hold the substance together, which in turn determines whether the substance is a solid, liquid, or gas at a given temperature. At room temperature, moderate to strong intermolecular forces tend to result in liquids and solids (high melting and boiling points), and weak intermolecular forces tend to result in gases (low melting and boiling points).

Intermolecular forces originate from the interactions among charges, partial charges, and temporary charges on molecules (or atoms and ions), much as bonding forces originate from interactions among charged particles in atoms. Recall from Section 9.3 that according to Coulomb's law, the potential energy (E) of two oppositely charged particles (with charges q_1 and q_2) decreases (becomes more negative) with increasing magnitude of charge and with decreasing separation (r):

$$E = \frac{1}{4\pi\varepsilon_0}\frac{q_1q_2}{r} \quad \text{(When } q_1 \text{ and } q_2 \text{ are opposite in sign, } E \text{ is negative.)}$$

Therefore, as we have seen, protons and electrons are attracted to each other because their potential energy decreases as they get closer together. Similarly, molecules with partial or temporary charges are attracted to each other because *their* potential energy decreases as they get closer together. However, intermolecular forces, even the strongest ones, are generally *much weaker* than bonding forces.

The reason for the relative weakness of intermolecular forces compared to bonding forces is also related to Coulomb's law. Bonding forces are the result of large charges (the charges on protons and electrons) interacting at very close distances. Intermolecular forces are the result of smaller charges (as we shall see in the following discussion) interacting at greater distances. For example, consider the interaction between two water molecules in liquid water:

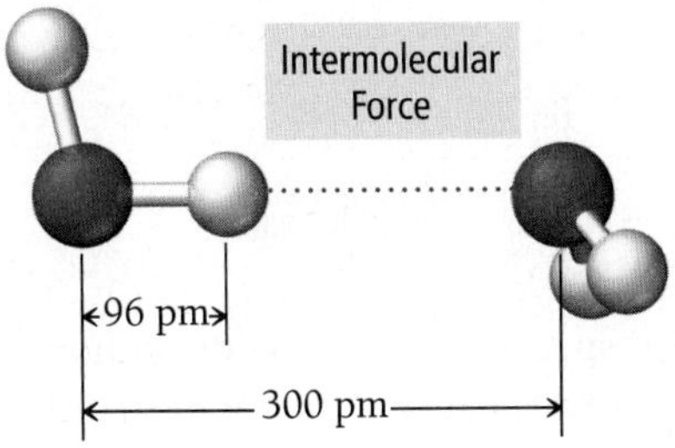

The length of an O—H bond in liquid water is 96 pm; however, the average distance between water molecules in liquid water is about 300 pm. The larger distances between molecules, as well as the smaller charges involved (the partial charges on the hydrogen and oxygen atoms), result in weaker forces. To break the O—H bonds in water, we have to heat the water to thousands of degrees Celsius. However, to completely overcome the intermolecular forces *between* water molecules, we have to heat water only to its boiling point, 100 °C (at sea level).

In this section, we examine several different types of intermolecular forces, including dispersion forces, dipole–dipole forces, hydrogen bonding, and ion–dipole forces. The first three of these can potentially occur in all substances; the last one occurs only in mixtures.

Dispersion Force

The nature of dispersion forces was first recognized by Fritz W. London (1900–1954), a German American physicist.

The one intermolecular force present between all molecules and atoms is the **dispersion force** (also called the London force). Dispersion forces are the result of fluctuations in the electron distribution within molecules or atoms. Since all atoms and molecules have electrons, they all exhibit dispersion forces. The electrons in an atom or molecule may, *at any one instant*, be unevenly distributed. Imagine a frame-by-frame movie of a helium atom in which each "frame" captures the position of the helium atom's two electrons:

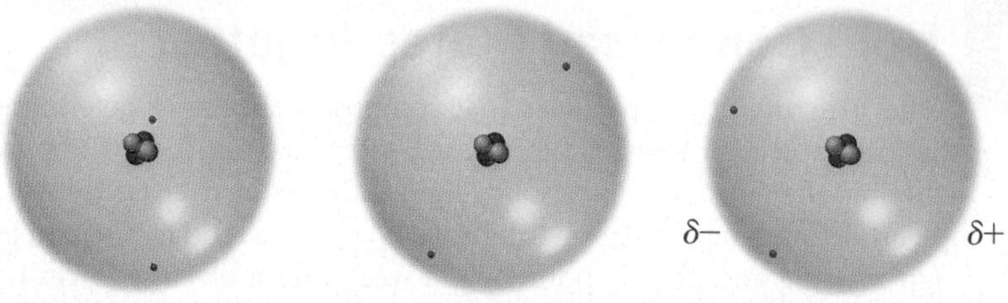

In any one frame, the electrons may not be symmetrically arranged around the nucleus. In frame 3, for example, helium's two electrons are on the left side of the helium atom. At that instant, the left side has a slightly negative charge (δ−). The right side of the atom, which temporarily has no electrons, has a slightly positive charge (δ+) because of the charge of the nucleus. This fleeting charge separation is called an *instantaneous dipole* or a *temporary dipole*. As shown in Figure 12.4▼, an instantaneous dipole on one helium atom induces an instantaneous dipole on its neighboring atoms because the positive end of the instantaneous dipole attracts electrons in the neighboring atoms. The neighboring atoms then attract one another—the positive end of one instantaneous dipole attracting the negative end of another. This attraction is the dispersion force.

▶ **FIGURE 12.4 Dispersion Interactions** The temporary dipole in one helium atom induces a temporary dipole in its neighbor. The resulting attraction between the positive and negative charges creates the dispersion force.

Dispersion Force

An instantaneous dipole on any one helium atom induces instantaneous dipoles on neighboring atoms, which then attract one another.

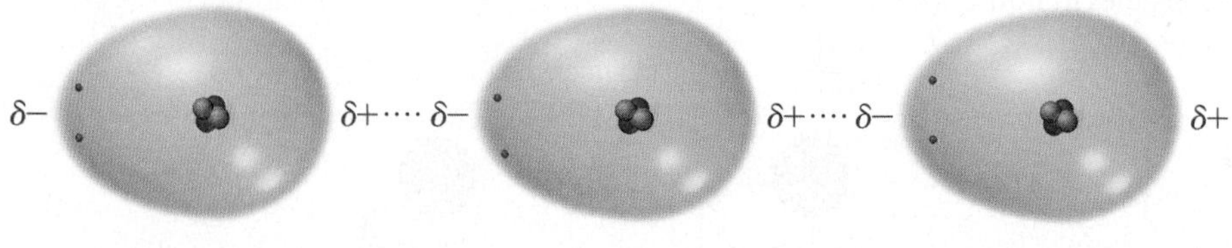

To polarize means to form a dipole moment (see Section 10.6).

The *magnitude* of the dispersion force depends on how easily the electrons in the atom or molecule can move or *polarize* in response to an instantaneous dipole, which in turn depends on the size (or volume) of the electron cloud. A larger electron cloud results in a greater dispersion force because the electrons are held less tightly by the nucleus and therefore polarize more easily. If all other variables are constant, the dispersion force increases with increasing molar mass because molecules or atoms of higher molar mass generally have more electrons dispersed over a greater volume. For example, consider the boiling points of the noble gases displayed in Table 12.3. As the molar masses and electron cloud volumes of the noble gases increase, the greater dispersion forces result in increasing boiling points (because the atoms are more strongly attracted to one another).

Molar mass alone, however, does not always exactly correlate with the magnitude of the dispersion force. Compare the molar masses and boiling points of *n*-pentane and neopentane:

TABLE 12.3 ■ Boiling Points of the Noble Gases

Noble Gas		Molar Mass (g/mol)	Boiling Point (K)
He		4.00	4.2
Ne		20.18	27
Ar		39.95	87
Kr		83.80	120
Xe		131.30	165

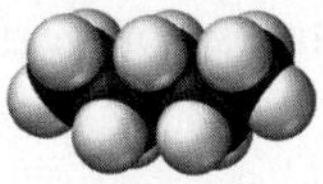

***n*-Pentane**
molar mass = 72.15 g/mol
boiling point = 36.1 °C

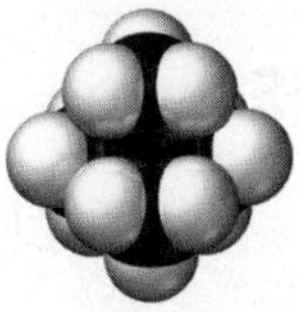

Neopentane
molar mass = 72.15 g/mol
boiling point = 9.5 °C

These molecules have identical molar masses, but *n*-pentane has a higher boiling point than neopentane. Why? Because the two molecules have different shapes. The *n*-pentane molecules are long and can interact with one another along their entire length, as shown in Figure 12.5(a)▼. In contrast, the bulky, round shape of neopentane molecules results in a smaller area of interaction between neighboring molecules, as shown in Figure 12.5(b)▼. The result is a lower boiling point for neopentane.

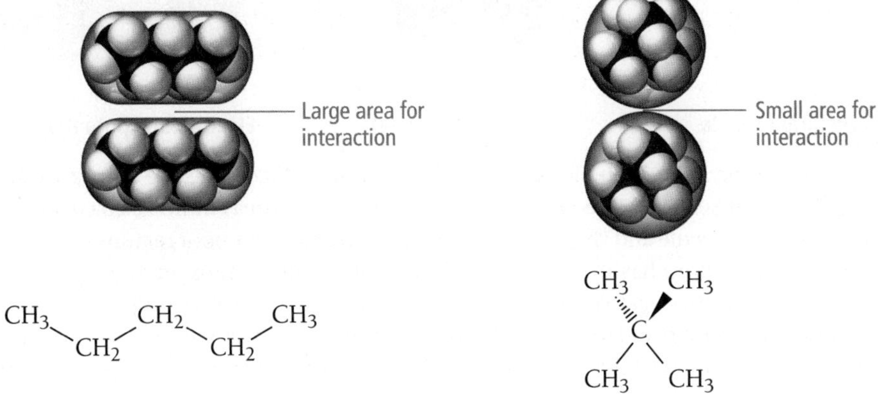

(a) *n*-Pentane **(b) Neopentane**

▲ **FIGURE 12.5 Dispersion Force and Molecular Shape** **(a)** The straight shape of *n*-pentane molecules allows them to interact with one another along the entire length of the molecules. **(b)** The nearly spherical shape of neopentane molecules allows for only a small area of interaction. Thus, dispersion forces are weaker in neopentane than in *n*-pentane, resulting in a lower boiling point.

Although we must always consider molecular shape and other factors in predicting the magnitude of dispersion forces, molar mass can act as a guide when comparing dispersion forces within a family of similar elements or compounds as illustrated in Figure 12.6▶.

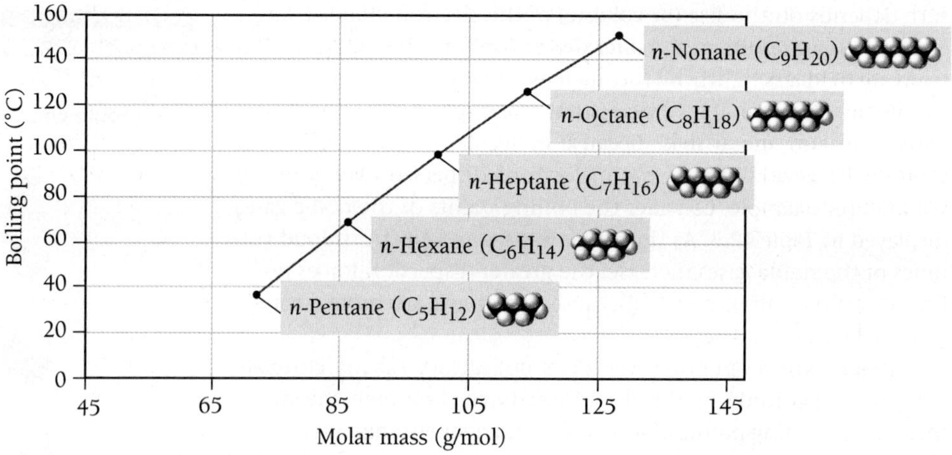

▶ **FIGURE 12.6 Boiling Points of the *n*-Alkanes** The boiling points of the *n*-alkanes rise with increasing molar mass and the consequent stronger dispersion forces.

ANSWER **NOW!**

12.3 Cc Conceptual Connection

DISPERSION FORCES Which halogen has the highest boiling point?

(a) Cl_2 **(b)** Br_2 **(c)** I_2

Dipole–Dipole Force

See Sections 10.6 and 11.5 to review how to determine if a molecule is polar.

The **dipole–dipole force** exists between all molecules that are polar. Polar molecules have electron-rich regions (which have a partial negative charge) and electron-deficient regions (which have a partial positive charge). For example, consider acetone:

Structural formula **Space-filling model** **Electrostatic potential map**

The image on the right is an electrostatic potential map of acetone; we first saw these kinds of maps in Sections 10.6 and 11.5. Recall that the red areas indicate electron-rich regions in the molecule and that the blue areas indicate electron-poor regions.

Notice that acetone has an electron-rich region surrounding the oxygen atom (because oxygen is more electronegative than the rest of the molecule) and electron-poorer regions surrounding the carbon and hydrogen atoms. The result is that acetone has a **permanent dipole** that can interact with other acetone molecules as shown in Figure 12.7▼.

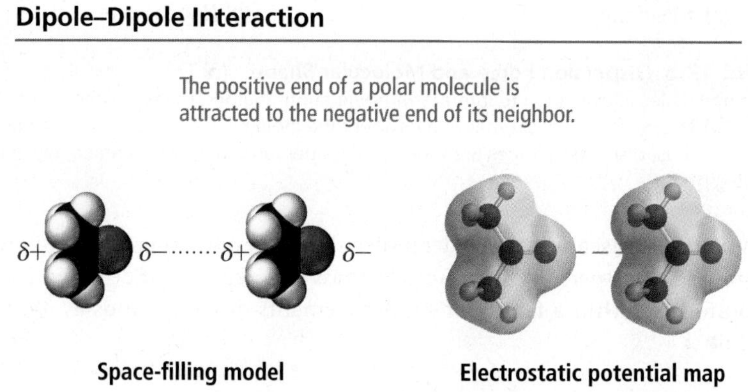

▶ **FIGURE 12.7 Dipole–Dipole Interaction** Molecules with permanent dipoles, such as acetone, are attracted to one another via dipole–dipole interactions.

The positive end of one permanent dipole attracts the negative end of another; this attraction is the dipole–dipole force. Polar molecules, therefore, have higher melting and boiling points than nonpolar molecules of similar molar mass.

Remember that all molecules (including polar ones) have dispersion forces. Polar molecules have, *in addition*, dipole–dipole forces. This additional attractive force raises their melting and boiling points relative to nonpolar molecules of similar molar mass. For example, consider formaldehyde and ethane:

Name	Formula	Molar Mass (g/mol)	Structure	bp (°C)	mp (°C)
Formaldehyde	CH_2O	30.03	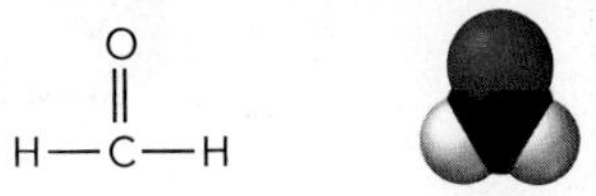	−19.5	−92
Ethane	C_2H_6	30.07	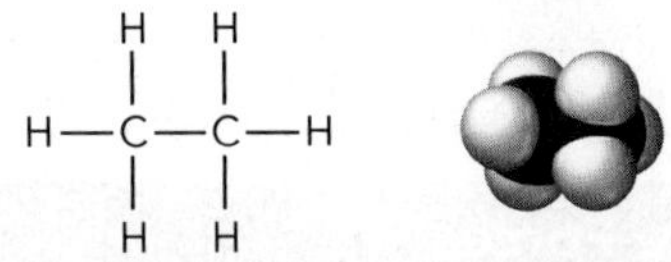	−88	−183

Formaldehyde is polar and has a higher melting point and boiling point than nonpolar ethane, even though the two compounds have the same molar mass. Figure 12.8▼ shows the boiling points of a series of molecules with similar molar mass but progressively greater dipole moments. Notice that the boiling points increase with increasing dipole moment.

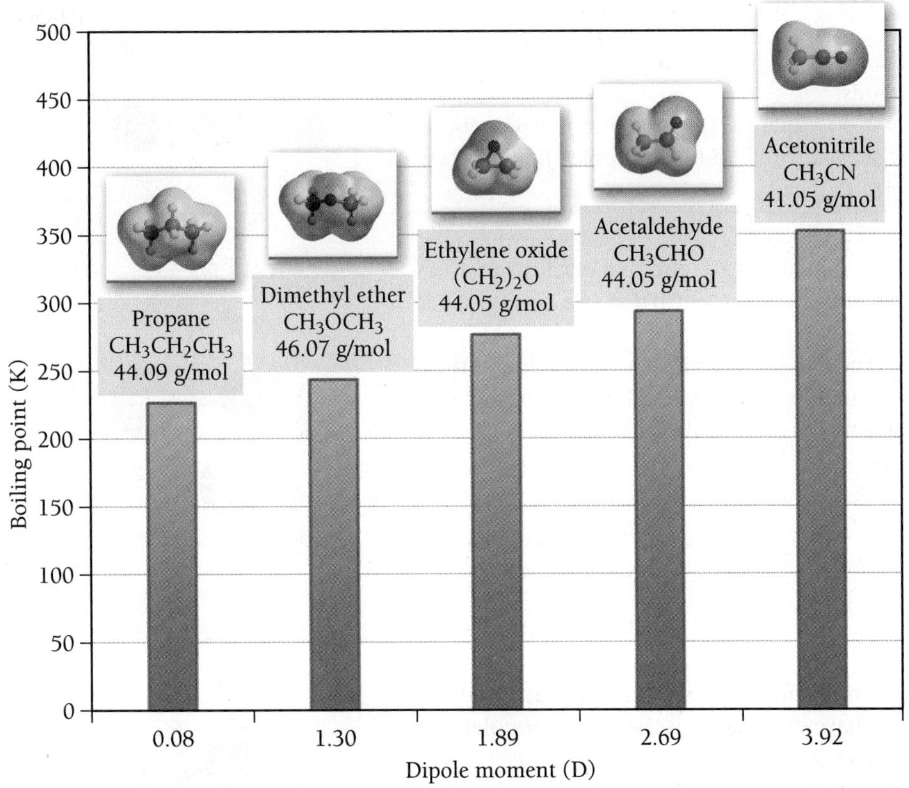

◀ **FIGURE 12.8 Dipole Moment and Boiling Point** The molecules shown here all have similar molar masses but different dipole moments. The boiling points increase with increasing dipole moment.

The polarity of molecules is also important in determining the **miscibility**—the ability to mix without separating into two states—of liquids. This is especially true for water, which is highly polar. In general, polar liquids tend to be miscible with water, while nonpolar liquids are not. For example, pentane (C_5H_{12}) is nonpolar and does not mix with water (Figure 12.9▶). Similarly, water and oil (nonpolar) do not mix. Consequently, oily hands or oily stains on clothes cannot be washed with plain water (see *Chemistry in Your Day: How Soap Works* in Section 11.5).

▶ **FIGURE 12.9 Polar and Nonpolar Substances** Water and pentane do not mix because water molecules are polar and pentane molecules are nonpolar.

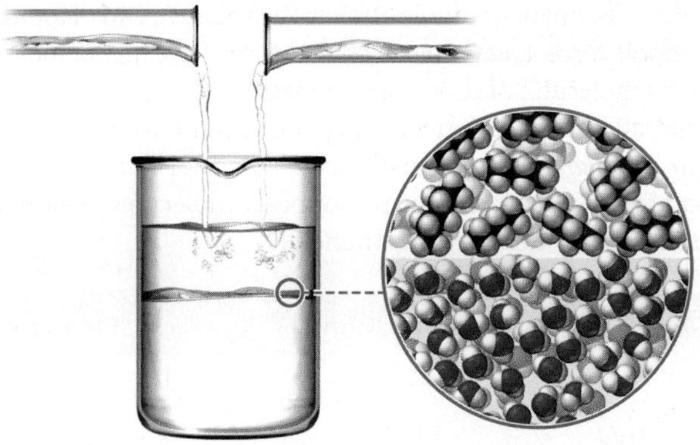

WATCH **NOW!**
INTERACTIVE WORKED EXAMPLE 12.1

EXAMPLE 12.1 Dipole–Dipole Forces

Which molecules have dipole–dipole forces?

(a) CO_2 **(b)** CH_2Cl_2 **(c)** CH_4

SOLUTION

A molecule has dipole–dipole forces if it is polar. To determine if a molecule is polar: (1) *determine if the molecule contains polar bonds* (Section 10.6); and (2) *determine if the polar bonds add together to form a net dipole moment* (Section 11.5).

(a) CO_2

(1) Since the electronegativity of carbon is 2.5 and that of oxygen is 3.5 (see Figure 10.8), CO_2 has polar bonds.

(2) The geometry of CO_2 is linear. Consequently, the dipoles of the polar bonds cancel, so the molecule is *not polar* and does not have dipole–dipole forces.

O=C=O

No dipole forces present

(b) CH_2Cl_2

(1) The electronegativity of C is 2.5, that of H is 2.1, and that of Cl is 3.0. Consequently, CH_2Cl_2 has two polar bonds (C—Cl) and two bonds that are nearly nonpolar (C—H).

(2) The geometry of CH_2Cl_2 is tetrahedral. Because the C—Cl bonds and the C—H bonds are different, their dipoles do not cancel but sum to a net dipole moment. The molecule is polar and has dipole–dipole forces.

CH_2Cl_2

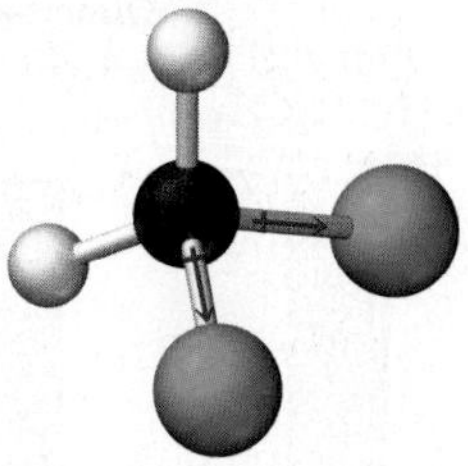

Dipole forces present

(c) CH_4

(1) The electronegativity of C is 2.5 and that of hydrogen is 2.1, so the C—H bonds are nearly nonpolar.

(2) In addition, since the geometry of the molecule is tetrahedral, any slight polarities that the bonds might have cancel. CH_4 is therefore nonpolar and does not have dipole–dipole forces.

CH_4

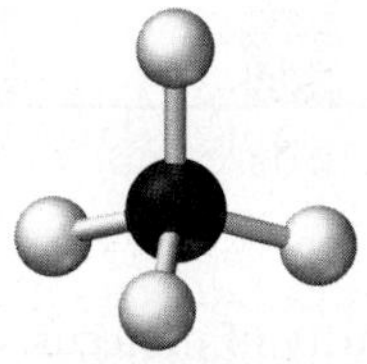

No dipole forces present

FOR PRACTICE 12.1 Which molecules have dipole–dipole forces?

(a) CI_4 **(b)** CH_3Cl **(c)** HCl

12.4 **Cc** Conceptual Connection ANSWER **NOW!**

DIPOLE–DIPOLE INTERACTION An electrostatic potential map for acetonitrile (CH_3CN), which is polar, is shown here: From this map, determine the geometry for how two acetonitrile molecules would interact with each other. Which of the orientations shown here is most likely?

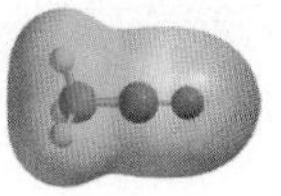

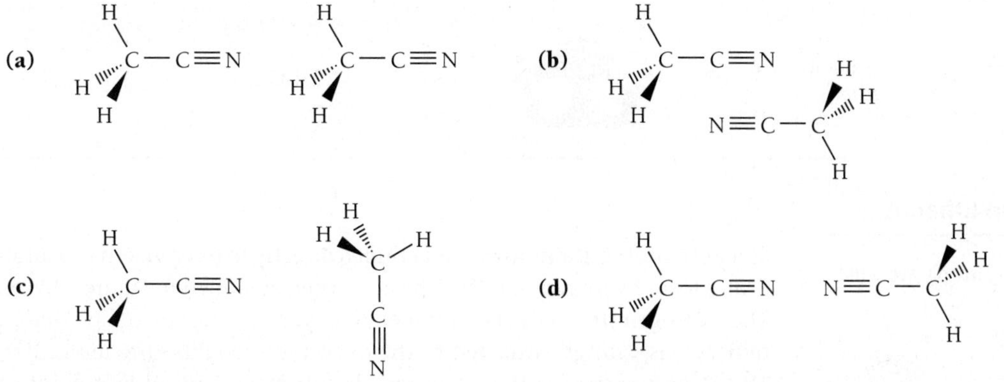

Hydrogen Bonding

Polar molecules containing hydrogen atoms bonded directly to small electronegative atoms—most importantly fluorine, oxygen, or nitrogen—exhibit an intermolecular force called **hydrogen bonding**. HF, NH_3, and H_2O, for example, all exhibit hydrogen bonding. The hydrogen bond is a sort of *super* dipole–dipole force. The large electronegativity difference between hydrogen and any of these electronegative elements causes the hydrogen atom to have a fairly large partial positive charge ($\delta+$) within the bond, while the F, O, or N atom has a fairly large partial negative charge ($\delta-$). In addition, since these atoms are all quite small, the H atom on one molecule can approach the F, O, or N atom on an adjacent molecule very closely. The result is a strong attraction between the H atom on one molecule and the F, O, or N on its neighbor—an attraction called a **hydrogen bond**.

For example, in HF, the hydrogen atom in one molecule is strongly attracted to the fluorine atom on a neighboring molecule (Figure 12.10▼). The electrostatic potential maps in Figure 12.10 illustrate the large differences in electron density that result in unusually large partial charges.

Hydrogen Bonding

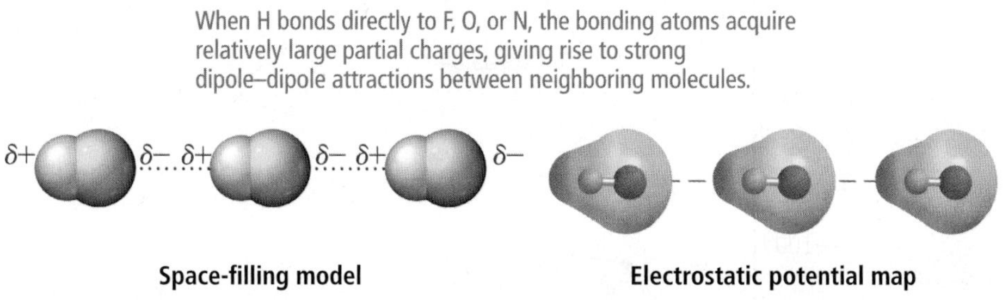

◀ **FIGURE 12.10 Hydrogen Bonding in HF** The hydrogen of one HF molecule, with its partial positive charge, is attracted to the fluorine of its neighbor, with its partial negative charge. This dipole–dipole interaction is an example of a hydrogen bond.

Hydrogen bonds should not be confused with chemical bonds. Chemical bonds occur *between individual atoms within a molecule,* whereas hydrogen bonds—like dispersion forces and dipole–dipole forces—are intermolecular forces that occur *between molecules.* A typical hydrogen bond is only 2–5% as strong as a typical covalent chemical bond. Hydrogen bonds are, however, the strongest of the three *intermolecular* forces we have discussed so far. Substances composed of molecules that form hydrogen bonds have higher melting and boiling points than comparable substances composed of molecules that do not form hydrogen bonds.

For example, consider ethanol and dimethyl ether:

Name	Formula		Molar Mass (g/mol)	Structure	bp (°C)	mp (°C)
Ethanol	C_2H_6O	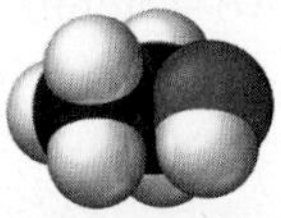	46.07	CH_3CH_2OH	78.3	−114.1
Dimethyl ether	C_2H_6O	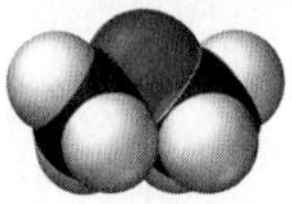	46.07	CH_3OCH_3	−22.0	−138.5

Hydrogen Bonding in Ethanol

The partial positive charge on H is strongly attracted to the partial negative charge on O.

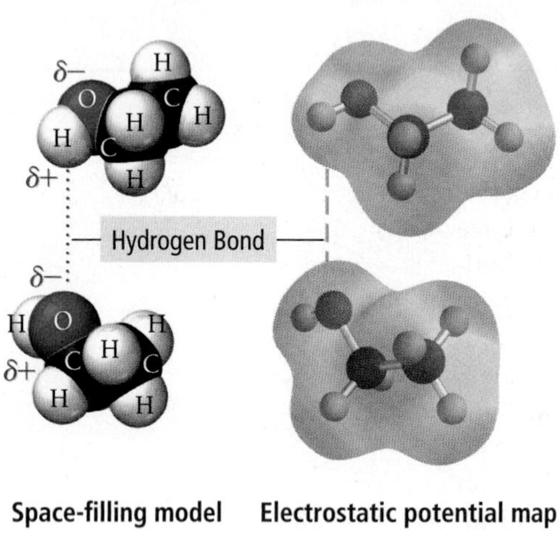

▲ FIGURE 12.11 Hydrogen Bonding in Ethanol The left side shows the space-filling models, and the right side shows the electrostatic potential maps.

Since ethanol contains hydrogen bonded directly to oxygen, ethanol molecules form hydrogen bonds with each other, as shown in Figure 12.11◄. The hydrogen that is directly bonded to oxygen in an individual ethanol molecule is strongly attracted to the oxygen on neighboring molecules. This strong attraction (i.e., hydrogen bond) makes the boiling point of ethanol 78.3 °C. Consequently, ethanol is a liquid at room temperature. In contrast, dimethyl ether has an identical molar mass to ethanol but does not exhibit hydrogen bonding because in the dimethyl ether molecule, the oxygen atom is not bonded directly to hydrogen; this results in lower boiling and melting points, and dimethyl ether is a gas at room temperature.

Water is another good example of a molecule with hydrogen bonding (Figure 12.12▼). Figure 12.13▼ plots the boiling points of the simple hydrogen compounds of the group 4A and group 6A elements. In general, boiling points increase with increasing molar mass, as expected, based on increasing dispersion forces. However, because of hydrogen bonding, the boiling point of water (100 °C) is much higher than expected based on its molar mass (18.0 g/mol). Without hydrogen bonding, all the water on our planet would be gaseous.

Hydrogen Bonding in Water

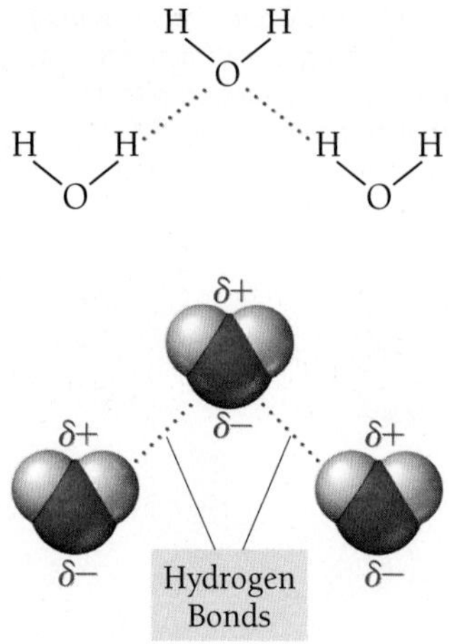

▲ FIGURE 12.12 Hydrogen Bonding in Water

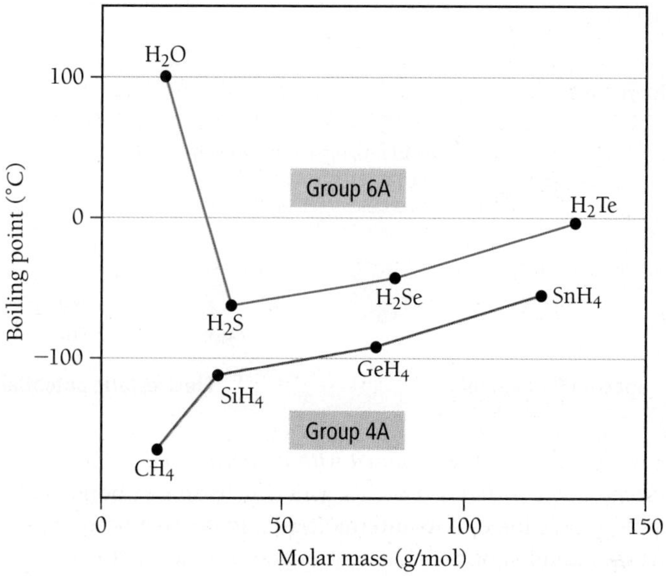

▲ FIGURE 12.13 Boiling Points of Group 4A and 6A Compounds Because of hydrogen bonding, the boiling point of water is anomalous compared to the boiling points of other hydrogen-containing compounds.

WATCH **NOW!**

INTERACTIVE WORKED EXAMPLE 12.2

EXAMPLE 12.2 Hydrogen Bonding

One of these compounds is a liquid at room temperature. Which one and why?

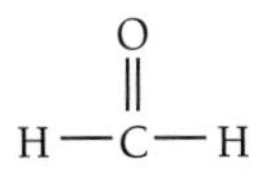

Formaldehyde

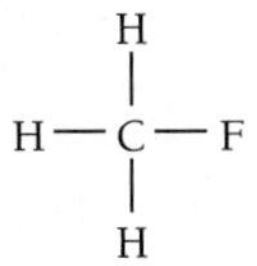

Fluoromethane

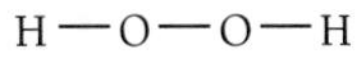

Hydrogen peroxide

SOLUTION

The three compounds have similar molar masses:

Formaldehyde	30.03 g/mol
Fluoromethane	34.03 g/mol
Hydrogen peroxide	34.02 g/mol

As a result, the strengths of their dispersion forces are similar. All three compounds are also polar, so they have dipole–dipole forces. Hydrogen peroxide, however, is the only one of these compounds that also contains H bonded directly to F, O, or N. Therefore, it also has hydrogen bonding and is likely to have the highest boiling point of the three. Since the example stated that only one of the compounds was a liquid, it is safe to assume that hydrogen peroxide is the liquid. Note that, although fluoromethane *contains* both H and F, H is not *directly bonded* to F, so fluoromethane does not have hydrogen bonding as an intermolecular force. Similarly, formaldehyde *contains* both H and O, but H is not *directly bonded* to O, so formaldehyde does not exhibit hydrogen bonding either.

FOR PRACTICE 12.2 Which has the higher boiling point, HF or HCl? Why?

Ion–Dipole Force

The **ion–dipole force** occurs when an ionic compound is mixed with a polar compound; it is especially important in aqueous solutions of ionic compounds. For example, when sodium chloride is mixed with water, the sodium and chloride ions interact with water molecules via ion–dipole forces, as shown in Figure 12.14▶. The positive sodium ions interact with the negative poles of water molecules, while the negative chloride ions interact with the positive poles. Ion–dipole forces are the strongest of the types of intermolecular forces discussed and are responsible for the ability of ionic substances to form solutions with water. We discuss aqueous solutions more thoroughly in Chapter 14.

Ion–Dipole Forces

The positively charged end of a polar molecule such as H_2O is attracted to negative ions, and the negatively charged end of the molecule is attracted to positive ions.

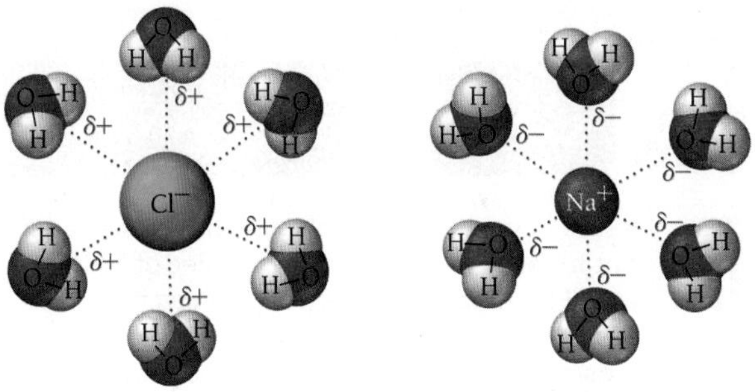

▲ **FIGURE 12.14 Ion–Dipole Forces** Ion–dipole forces exist between Na^+ and the negative ends of H_2O molecules and between Cl^- and the positive ends of H_2O molecules.

***Summarizing Intermolecular Forces* (*as shown in Table 12.4*):**

- Dispersion forces are present in all molecules and atoms and generally increase with increasing molar mass. These forces are always weak in small molecules but can be significant in molecules with high molar masses.
- Dipole–dipole forces are present in polar molecules.
- Hydrogen bonds, the strongest of the intermolecular forces that can occur in pure substances (second only to ion–dipole forces in general), are present in molecules containing hydrogen bonded directly to fluorine, oxygen, or nitrogen.
- Ion–dipole forces are present in mixtures of ionic compounds and polar compounds. These forces are very strong and are especially important in aqueous solutions of ionic compounds.

TABLE 12.4 ■ Types of Intermolecular Forces

Type	Present In	Molecular Perspective	Strength
Dispersion*	All molecules and atoms	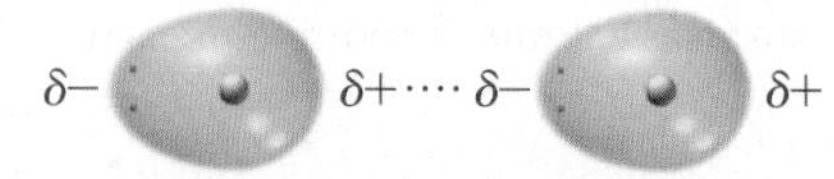	0.05–20+ kJ/mol
Dipole–dipole	Polar molecules	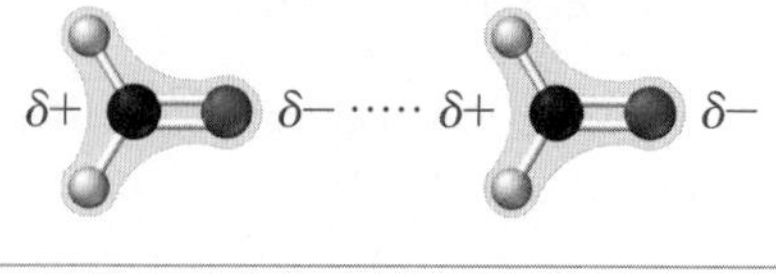	3–20+ kJ/mol
Hydrogen bonding	Molecules containing H bonded to F, O, or N	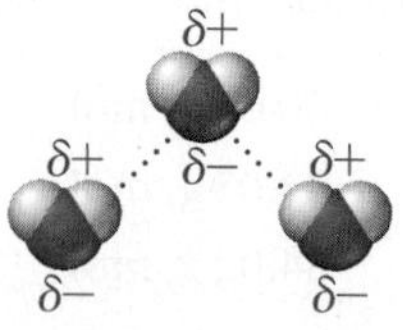	10–40 kJ/mol
Ion–dipole	Mixtures of ionic compounds and polar compounds	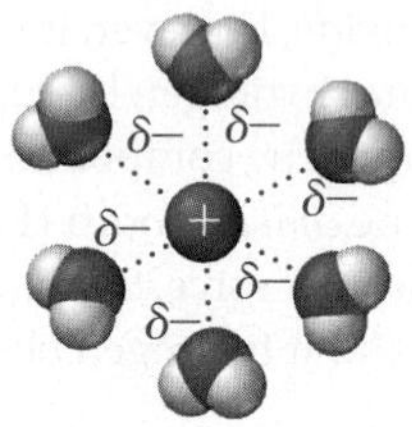	30–100+ kJ/mol

*The dispersion force can become very strong (as strong and even stronger than the others) for molecules of high molar mass.

ANSWER **NOW!**

12.5 Cc Conceptual Connection

INTERMOLECULAR FORCES AND BOILING POINT

Which substance has the highest boiling point?

(a) CH_3OH **(b)** CO **(c)** N_2

CHEMISTRY AND MEDICINE | Hydrogen Bonding in DNA

DNA is a long, chainlike molecule that acts as a blueprint for each living organism. Copies of DNA are passed from parent to offspring, which is how we inherit traits from our parents. A DNA molecule is composed of thousands of repeating units called *nucleotides* (Figure 12.15▼). Each nucleotide contains one of four different *organic bases:* adenine, thymine, cytosine, and guanine (abbreviated A, T, C, and G). The sequence of these bases along DNA encodes the information that determines the nature of the proteins that are made in the body (proteins are the molecules that do most of the work in living organisms). Our proteins in turn determine many of our characteristics, including how we look, what diseases we are at risk of developing, and even our behavior.

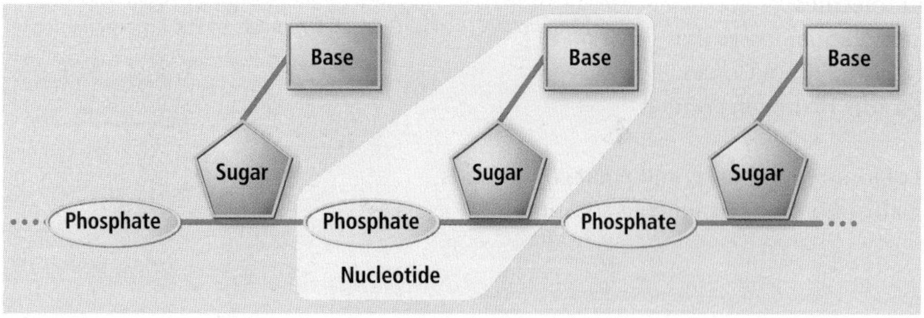

◀ **FIGURE 12.15 Nucleotides**
The individual units in a DNA polymer are nucleotides. Each nucleotide contains one of four bases: adenine, thymine, cytosine, and guanine (abbreviated A, T, C, and G).

The replicating mechanism of DNA is related to its structure, which was discovered in 1953 by James Watson (1928–) and Francis Crick (1916–2004). DNA consists of two *complementary* strands wrapped around each other in the now famous double helix and linked by hydrogen bonds between the bases on each strand. Each base (A, T, C, and G) has a complementary partner with which it forms hydrogen bonds (Figure 12.16▶): adenine (A) with thymine (T) and cytosine (C) with guanine (G). The hydrogen bonding is so specific that each base will pair only with its complementary partner. When a cell is going to divide, enzymes unzip the DNA molecule across the hydrogen bonds that join its two strands (Figure 12.17▼). Then new bases, complementary to the bases in each strand, are added along each of the original strands, forming hydrogen bonds with their complements. The result is two identical copies of the original DNA.

QUESTION *Why would dispersion forces not work as a way to hold the two strands of DNA together? Why would covalent bonds not work?*

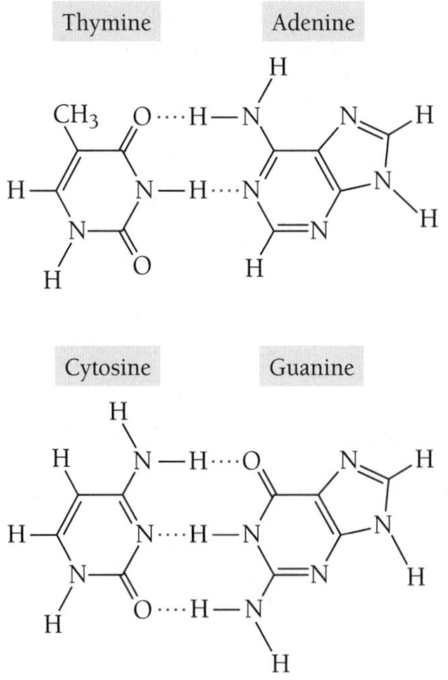

▶ **FIGURE 12.16 Complementary Base Pairing via Hydrogen Bonds** The individual bases in DNA interact with one another via specific hydrogen bonds that form between A and T and between C and G.

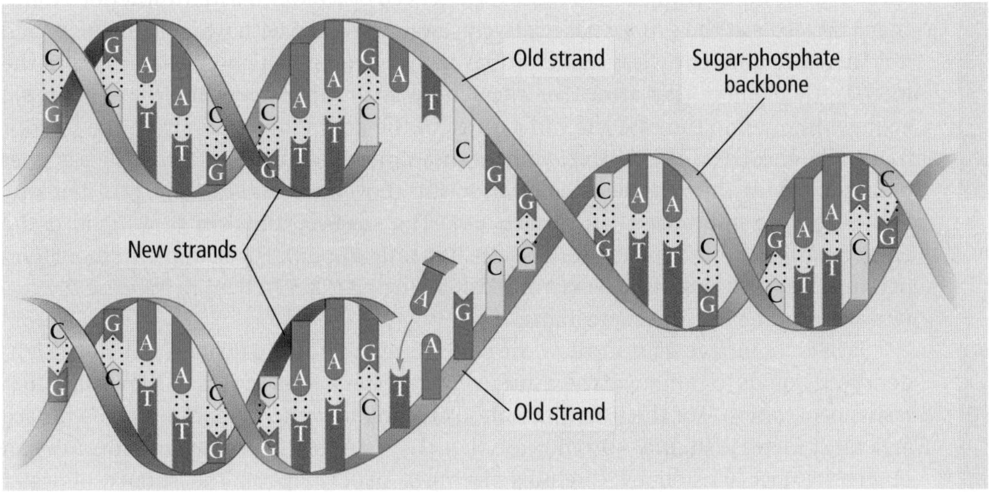

◀ **FIGURE 12.17 Copying DNA** The two strands of the DNA molecule "unzip" by breaking the hydrogen bonds that join the base pairs. New bases complementary to the bases of each strand are assembled and joined together. The result is two molecules, each identical to the original one.

12.4 Intermolecular Forces in Action: Surface Tension, Viscosity, and Capillary Action

The most important manifestation of intermolecular forces is the very existence of liquids and solids. In liquids, we also observe several other manifestations of intermolecular forces, including surface tension, viscosity, and capillary action.

▲ A trout fly can float on water because of surface tension.

Surface Tension

A fly fisherman delicately casts a small fishing fly (a metal hook with a few feathers and strings attached to make it look like an insect) onto the surface of a moving stream. The fly floats on the surface of the water—even though the metal composing the hook is denser than water—and attracts trout. Why? The hook floats because of *surface tension*, the tendency of liquids to minimize their surface area.

Recall from Section 12.3 that the interactions between molecules lower their potential energy in much the same way that the interaction between protons and electrons lowers their potential energy, in accordance with Coulomb's law.

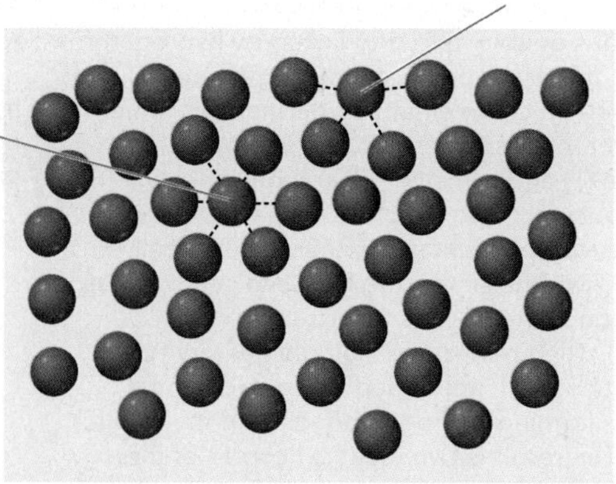

▲ **FIGURE 12.18 The Origin of Surface Tension** Molecules at the liquid surface have a higher potential energy than those in the interior. As a result, a liquid tends to minimize its surface area; its surface behaves like a "skin."

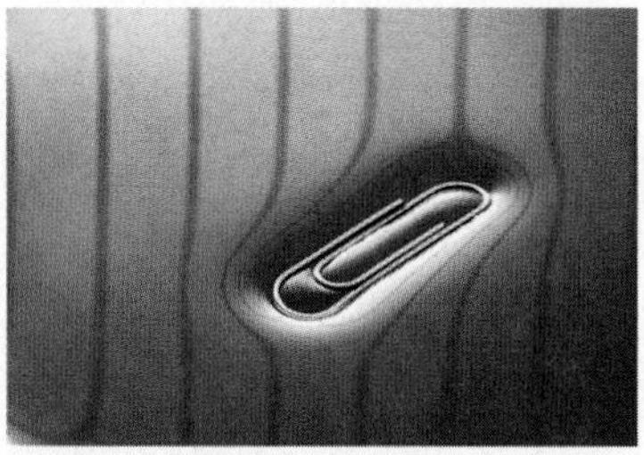

▲ **FIGURE 12.19 Surface Tension in Action** A paper clip floats on water because of surface tension.

▲ **FIGURE 12.20 Spherical Water Droplets** Tiny water droplets are not distorted much by gravity and form nearly perfect spheres held together by intermolecular forces between water molecules.

Figure 12.18▲ depicts the intermolecular forces experienced by a molecule at the surface of the liquid compared to those experienced by a molecule in the interior. Notice that a molecule at the surface has relatively fewer neighbors with which to interact, and it is therefore inherently less stable—it has higher potential energy—than those in the interior. (Remember that attractive interactions with other molecules lower potential energy.) In order to increase the surface area of the liquid, molecules from the interior have to be moved to the surface, and because molecules at the surface have a higher potential energy than those in the interior, this movement requires energy. Therefore, liquids tend to minimize their surface area. The **surface tension** of a liquid is the energy required to increase the surface area by a unit amount. For example, at room temperature, water has a surface tension of $72.8\ \text{mJ/m}^2$; it takes 72.8 mJ to increase the surface area of water by one square meter.

Why does surface tension allow the fly fisherman's hook to float on water? The tendency for liquids to minimize their surface area creates a kind of skin at the surface that resists penetration. For the fisherman's hook to sink into the water, the water's surface area must increase slightly—an increase that is resisted by the surface tension. We can observe surface tension by carefully placing a paper clip on the surface of water (Figure 12.19◀). The paper clip, even though it is denser than water, floats on the surface of the water. A slight tap on the clip provides the energy necessary to overcome the surface tension and causes the clip to sink.

Surface tension decreases as intermolecular forces decrease. You can't float a paper clip on benzene, for example, because the dispersion forces among the molecules composing benzene are significantly weaker than the hydrogen bonds among water molecules. The surface tension of benzene is only $28\ \text{mJ/m}^2$, just 40% that of water.

Surface tension is also the reason for the behavior of water that we discussed in the chapter-opening section on water and gravity. You can see this behavior on Earth by looking at small water droplets (those not large enough to be distorted by gravity) on a leaf or a spider's web (Figure 12.20◀). Just as larger samples of water form spheres in the space station, so smaller samples form spheres on Earth. Why? In the same way that gravity pulls the matter of a planet or star inward to form a sphere, intermolecular forces among collections of water molecules pull the water into a sphere. As we discussed in Section 12.1, the sphere is the geometrical shape with the smallest ratio of surface area to volume; therefore, the formation of a sphere minimizes the number of molecules at the surface, minimizing the potential energy of the system.

Viscosity

Another manifestation of intermolecular forces is **viscosity**, the resistance of a liquid to flow. Motor oil, for example, is more viscous than gasoline, and maple syrup is more viscous than water. Viscosity is measured in a unit called the poise (P), defined as 1 g/cm · s. The viscosity of water at room temperature is approximately one centipoise (cP). Viscosity is greater in substances with stronger intermolecular forces because if molecules are more strongly attracted to each other, they do not flow around each other as freely. Viscosity also depends on molecular shape, increasing in longer molecules that can interact over a greater area and possibly become entangled. Table 12.5 lists the viscosity of several hydrocarbons. Notice the increase in viscosity with increasing molar mass (and therefore increasing magnitude of dispersion forces) and with increasing length (and therefore increasing potential for molecular entanglement).

Viscosity also depends on temperature because thermal energy partially overcomes the intermolecular forces, allowing molecules to flow past each other more easily. Table 12.6 lists the viscosity of water as a function of temperature. Nearly all liquids become less viscous as temperature increases.

TABLE 12.5 ■ Viscosity of Several Hydrocarbons at 20 °C

Hydrocarbon	Molar Mass (g/mol)	Formula	Viscosity (cP)
n-Pentane	72.15	$CH_3CH_2CH_2CH_2CH_3$	0.240
n-Hexane	86.17	$CH_3CH_2CH_2CH_2CH_2CH_3$	0.326
n-Heptane	100.2	$CH_3CH_2CH_2CH_2CH_2CH_2CH_3$	0.409
n-Octane	114.2	$CH_3CH_2CH_2CH_2CH_2CH_2CH_2CH_3$	0.542
n-Nonane	128.3	$CH_3CH_2CH_2CH_2CH_2CH_2CH_2CH_2CH_3$	0.711

TABLE 12.6 ■ Viscosity of Liquid Water at Several Temperatures

Temperature (°C)	Viscosity (cP)
20	1.002
40	0.653
60	0.467
80	0.355
100	0.282

CHEMISTRY IN YOUR DAY | Viscosity and Motor Oil

Viscosity is an important property of the motor oil you put into your car. The oil must be thick enough to adequately coat engine surfaces to lubricate them, but also thin enough to be pumped easily into all the required engine compartments. Motor oil viscosity is usually reported on the SAE scale (named after the Society of Automotive Engineers). The higher the SAE rating, the more viscous the oil. The thinnest motor oils have SAE ratings of 5 or 10, whereas the thickest have SAE ratings of up to 50.

Before the 1950s, most automobile owners changed the oil in their engine to accommodate seasonal changes in weather—a higher SAE rating was required in the summer months and a lower rating in the winter. Today, the advent of multigrade oils allows car owners in many climates to keep the same oil all year long. Multigrade oils, such as the 10W-40 oil shown at right, contain polymers (long molecules made up of repeating structural units) that coil at low temperatures but unwind at high temperatures. At low temperatures, the coiled polymers—because of their compact shape—do not contribute very much to the oil's viscosity. As the temperature increases, however, the molecules unwind, and their long shape results in intermolecular forces and molecular entanglements that prevent the oil's viscosity from decreasing as much as it would normally. The result is an oil whose viscosity is less temperature-dependent than it would be otherwise, allowing the same oil to be used over a wider range of temperatures. The 10W-40 designation indicates that the oil has an SAE rating of 10 at low temperatures and 40 at high temperatures.

Capillary Action

Medical technicians take advantage of **capillary action**—the ability of a liquid to flow against gravity up a narrow tube—when taking a blood sample. The technician pokes the patient's finger with a pin, squeezes some blood out of the puncture, and then collects

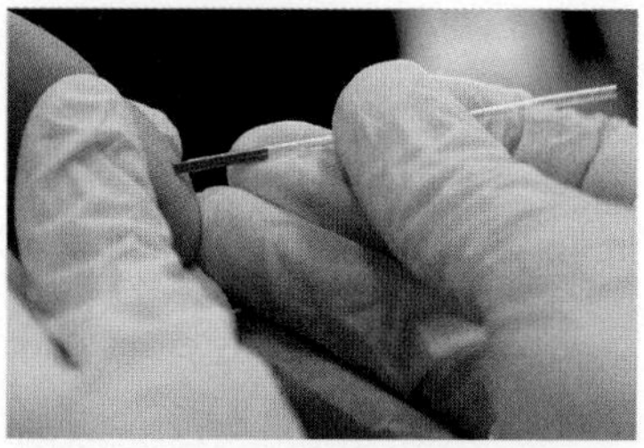

▲ Blood is drawn into a capillary tube by capillary action.

the blood with a thin tube. When the tube's tip comes into contact with the blood, the blood is drawn into the tube by capillary action. The same force helps trees and plants draw water from the soil.

Capillary action results from a combination of two forces: the attraction between molecules in a liquid, called *cohesive forces*, and the attraction between these molecules and the surface of the tube, called *adhesive forces*. The adhesive forces cause the liquid to spread out over the surface of the tube, whereas the cohesive forces cause the liquid to stay together. If the adhesive forces are greater than the cohesive forces (as is the case for water in a glass tube), the attraction to the surface draws the liquid up the tube and the cohesive forces pull along those molecules not in direct contact with the tube walls (Figure 12.21◀). The water rises up the tube until the force of gravity balances the capillary action—the thinner the tube, the higher the rise. If the adhesive forces are less than the cohesive forces (as is the case for liquid mercury), the liquid does not rise up the tube at all (and in fact drops to a level below the level of the surrounding liquid).

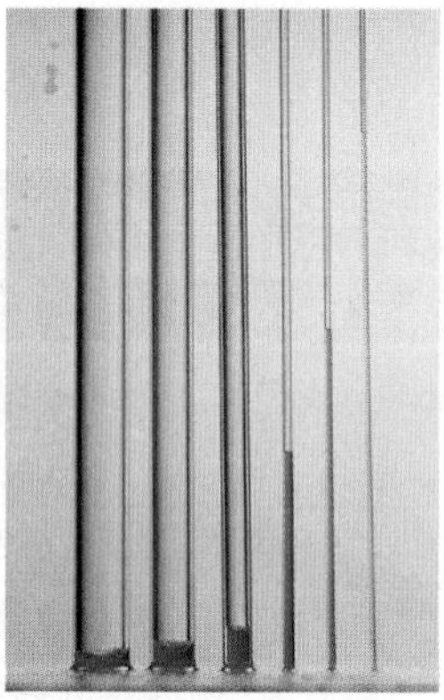

▲ **FIGURE 12.21 Capillary Action** The attraction of water molecules to the glass surface draws the liquid around the edge of the tube up the walls. The water in the rest of the column is pulled along by the attraction of water molecules to one another. As can be seen in this figure, the narrower the tube, the higher the liquid will rise.

We can see the result of the differences in the relative magnitudes of cohesive and adhesive forces by comparing the meniscus of water to the meniscus of mercury (Figure 12.22▶). (The meniscus is the curved shape of a liquid surface within a tube.) The meniscus of water is concave (rounded inward) because the *adhesive forces* are greater than the cohesive forces, causing the edges of the water to creep up the sides of the tube a bit, forming the familiar cupped shape. The meniscus of mercury is convex (rounded outward) because the *cohesive forces*—due to metallic bonding between the atoms—are greater than the adhesive forces. The mercury atoms crowd toward the interior of the liquid to maximize their interactions with each other, resulting in the upward bulge at the center of the surface.

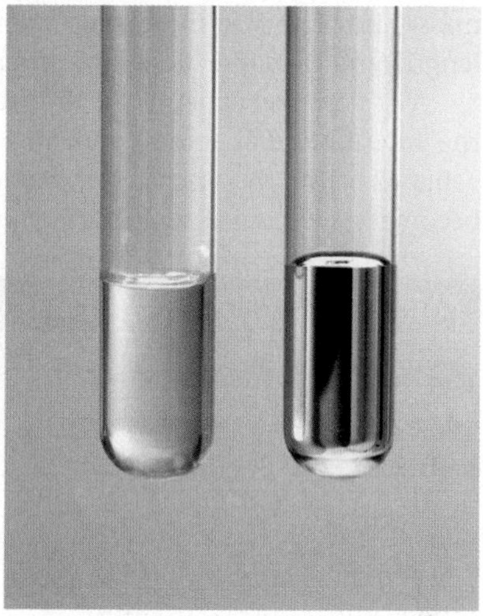

▲ **FIGURE 12.22 Meniscuses of Water and Mercury** The meniscus of water is concave because water molecules are more strongly attracted to the glass wall than to one another. The meniscus of mercury is convex because mercury atoms are more strongly attracted to one another than to the glass walls.

12.5 Vaporization and Vapor Pressure

WATCH **NOW!**

KEY CONCEPT VIDEO 12.5 *Vaporization and Vapor Pressure*

We now turn our attention to *vaporization*, the process by which thermal energy can overcome intermolecular forces and produce a state change from liquid to gas. We first discuss the process of vaporization itself, then the energetics of vaporization, and finally the concepts of *vapor pressure*, *dynamic equilibrium*, and *critical point*. Vaporization is a common occurrence that we experience every day and even depend on to maintain proper body temperature.

The Process of Vaporization

Imagine water molecules in a beaker at room temperature and open to the atmosphere (Figure 12.23◀). The molecules are in constant motion due to thermal energy. If we could actually see the molecules at the surface, we would witness what theoretical chemist Roald Hoffmann describes as a "wild dance floor" (see the chapter-opening quote) because of all the vibrating, jostling, and molecular movement. *The higher the temperature, the greater the average energy of the collection of molecules.* However, at any one time, some molecules have more thermal energy than the average and some have less.

◀ **FIGURE 12.23 Vaporization of Water** Some molecules in an open beaker have enough kinetic energy to vaporize from the surface of the liquid.

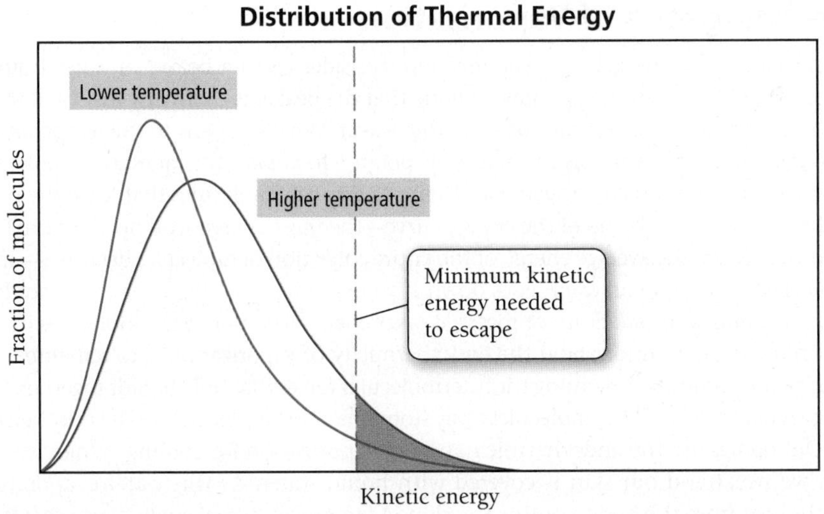

◀ **FIGURE 12.24 Distribution of Thermal Energy** The thermal energies of the molecules in a liquid are distributed over a range. The peak energy increases with increasing temperature.

The distributions of thermal energies for the molecules in a sample of water at two different temperatures are shown in Figure 12.24▲. The molecules at the high end of the distribution curve have enough energy to break free from the surface—where molecules are held less tightly than they are in the interior due to fewer neighbor–neighbor interactions—and into the gas state. This transition, from liquid to gas, is known as **vaporization**. Some of the water molecules in the gas state, at the low end of the energy distribution curve for the gaseous molecules, plunge back into the water and are captured by intermolecular forces. This transition, from gas to liquid, is the opposite of vaporization and is called **condensation**.

Although both vaporization and condensation occur in a beaker open to the atmosphere, under normal conditions (such as relatively dry air at room temperature) evaporation takes place at a greater rate because most of the newly evaporated molecules escape into the surrounding atmosphere and never come back. The result is a noticeable decrease in the water level within an open beaker over time (usually several days).

What happens if we increase the temperature of the water within the beaker? Because of the shift in the energy distribution to higher energies (see Figure 12.24), more molecules now have enough energy to break free and evaporate, so vaporization occurs more quickly. What happens if we spill the water on the table or floor? The same amount of water is now spread over a wider area, resulting in more molecules at the surface of the liquid. Since molecules at the surface have the greatest tendency to evaporate—because they are held less tightly—vaporization also occurs more quickly in this case. You probably know from experience that water in a beaker or glass may take many days to evaporate completely, whereas the same amount of water spilled on a table or floor typically evaporates within a few hours (depending on the exact conditions).

What happens if the liquid in the beaker is not water, but some other substance with weaker intermolecular forces, such as acetone (the main component in nail polish remover)? The weaker intermolecular forces allow more molecules to evaporate at a given temperature, increasing the rate of vaporization. We call liquids that vaporize easily **volatile** and those that do not vaporize easily **nonvolatile**. Acetone is more volatile than water. Motor oil is virtually nonvolatile at room temperature.

***Summarizing the Process of Vaporization*:**

- The rate of vaporization increases with increasing temperature.
- The rate of vaporization increases with increasing surface area.
- The rate of vaporization increases with decreasing strength of intermolecular forces.

VAPORIZATION Which sample of water has the greatest rate of vaporization?

(a) A 100 mL sample of water at 25 °C in 100-mL beaker with a 5 cm diameter.
(b) A 100 mL sample of water at 55 °C in 100-mL beaker with a 5 cm diameter.
(c) A 100 mL sample of water at 25 °C in 250-mL beaker with a 7 cm diameter.
(d) A 100 mL sample of water at 55 °C in 250-mL beaker with a 7 cm diameter.

12.6 Cc Conceptual Connection

ANSWER **NOW!**

The Energetics of Vaporization

To understand the energetics of vaporization, consider again a beaker of water from the molecular point of view, except now imagine that the beaker is thermally insulated so that heat from the surroundings cannot enter the beaker. What happens to the temperature of the water left in the beaker as molecules evaporate? To answer this question, think about the energy distribution curve again (see Figure 12.24). The molecules that leave the beaker are the ones at the high end of the energy curve—the most energetic. If no additional heat enters the beaker, the average energy of the entire collection of molecules decreases—much as the class average on an exam goes down if you eliminate the highest-scoring students. So vaporization is an *endothermic* process; it takes energy to vaporize the molecules in a liquid. Another way to understand the endothermicity of vaporization is to remember that vaporization requires overcoming the intermolecular forces that hold liquids together. Since energy is needed to pull the molecules away from one another, the process is endothermic.

See Chapter 7 to review endothermic and exothermic processes.

▲ When we sweat, water evaporates from the skin. Since evaporation is endothermic, the result is a cooling effect.

Our bodies use the endothermic nature of vaporization for cooling. When we overheat, we sweat and our skin is covered with liquid water. As this water evaporates, it absorbs heat from the body, cooling the skin. A fan makes us feel cooler because it blows newly vaporized water away from our skin, allowing more sweat to vaporize and causing even more cooling. High humidity, in contrast, slows down the net rate of evaporation, preventing cooling. When the air already contains large amounts of water vapor, the sweat evaporates more slowly, making the body's cooling system less efficient.

Condensation, the opposite of vaporization, is exothermic—heat is released when a gas condenses to a liquid. If you have ever accidentally put your hand above a steaming kettle or opened a bag of microwaved popcorn too soon, you may have experienced a *steam burn*. As the steam condenses to a liquid on your skin, it releases a lot of heat, causing the burn. The condensation of water vapor is also the reason that winter overnight temperatures in coastal regions, which tend to have water vapor in the air, do not get as low as in deserts, which tend to have dry air. As the air temperature in a coastal area drops, water condenses out of the air, releasing heat and preventing the temperature from dropping further. In deserts, the air contains almost no moisture to condense, so the temperature drop is more extreme.

The normal boiling point of a substance is its boiling point at a pressure of 1 atm, as discussed later in this section.

The amount of heat required to vaporize one mole of a liquid to gas is its **heat (or enthalpy) of vaporization (ΔH_{vap})**. The heat of vaporization of water at its normal boiling point of 100 °C is +40.7 kJ/mol:

$$H_2O(l) \longrightarrow H_2O(g) \quad \Delta H_{vap} = +40.7 \text{ kJ/mol}$$

The sign conventions of ΔH were introduced in Chapter 7.

The heat of vaporization is always positive because the process is endothermic—energy must be absorbed to vaporize a substance. The heat of vaporization is somewhat temperature dependent. For example, at 25 °C the heat of vaporization of water is +44.0 kJ/mol, slightly more than it is at 100 °C because the water contains less thermal energy at 25 °C. Table 12.7 lists the heats of vaporization of several liquids at their boiling points and at 25 °C.

When a substance condenses from a gas to a liquid, the same amount of heat is involved, but the heat is emitted rather than absorbed:

$$H_2O(g) \longrightarrow H_2O(l) \quad \Delta H = -\Delta H_{vap} = -40.7 \text{ kJ (at 100 °C)}$$

When one mole of water condenses, it releases 40.7 kJ of heat. The sign of ΔH in this case is negative because the process is exothermic.

We can use the heat of vaporization of a liquid to calculate the amount of energy required to vaporize a given mass of the liquid (or the amount of heat given off by the condensation of a given mass of liquid), using concepts similar to those covered in

TABLE 12.7 ■ Heats of Vaporization of Several Liquids at Their Boiling Points and at 25 °C

Liquid	Chemical Formula	Normal Boiling Point (°C)	ΔH_{vap} (kJ/mol) at Boiling Point	ΔH_{vap} (kJ/mol) at 25 °C
Water	H_2O	100	40.7	44.0
Isopropyl alcohol	C_3H_8O	82.3	39.9	45.4
Acetone	C_3H_6O	56.1	29.1	31.0
Diethyl ether	$C_4H_{10}O$	34.6	26.5	27.1

Section 7.6 (stoichiometry of ΔH). The heat of vaporization is like a conversion factor between the number of moles of a liquid and the amount of heat required to vaporize it (or the amount of heat emitted when it condenses), as demonstrated in Example 12.3.

WATCH **NOW!**

INTERACTIVE WORKED EXAMPLE 12.3

EXAMPLE 12.3 Using the Heat of Vaporization in Calculations

Calculate the mass of water (in g) that can be vaporized at its boiling point with 155 kJ of heat.

SORT You are given a certain amount of heat in kilojoules and asked to find the mass of water that can be vaporized.

GIVEN: 155 kJ

FIND: g H_2O

STRATEGIZE The heat of vaporization gives the relationship between heat absorbed and moles of water vaporized. Begin with the given amount of heat (in kJ) and convert to moles of water that can be vaporized. Then use the molar mass as a conversion factor to convert from moles of water to mass of water.

CONCEPTUAL PLAN

kJ → mol H_2O → g H_2O

$$\frac{1 \text{ mol } H_2O}{40.7 \text{ kJ}} \qquad \frac{18.02 \text{ g } H_2O}{1 \text{ mol } H_2O}$$

RELATIONSHIPS USED

$\Delta H_{vap} = 40.7 \text{ kJ/mol (at 100 °C)}$

$18.02 \text{ g } H_2O = 1 \text{ mol } H_2O$

SOLVE Follow the conceptual plan to solve the problem.

SOLUTION

$$155 \text{ kJ} \times \frac{1 \text{ mol } H_2O}{40.7 \text{ kJ}} \times \frac{18.02 \text{ g } H_2O}{1 \text{ mol } H_2O} = 68.6 \text{ g } H_2O$$

FOR PRACTICE 12.3 Calculate the amount of heat (in kJ) required to vaporize 2.58 kg of water at its boiling point.

FOR MORE PRACTICE 12.3 Suppose that 0.48 g of water at 25 °C condenses on the surface of a 55-g block of aluminum that is initially 25 °C. If the heat released during condensation goes only toward heating the metal, what is the final temperature (in °C) of the metal block? (The specific heat capacity of aluminum is 0.903 J/g °C.)

Vapor Pressure and Dynamic Equilibrium

We have already seen that if a container of water is left uncovered at room temperature, the water slowly evaporates away. What happens if the container is sealed? Imagine a sealed evacuated flask—one from which the air has been removed—containing liquid water, as shown in Figure 12.25▼. Initially, the water molecules evaporate, as they did in the open beaker. But because of the seal, the evaporated molecules cannot escape into the atmosphere. As water molecules enter the gas state, some start condensing

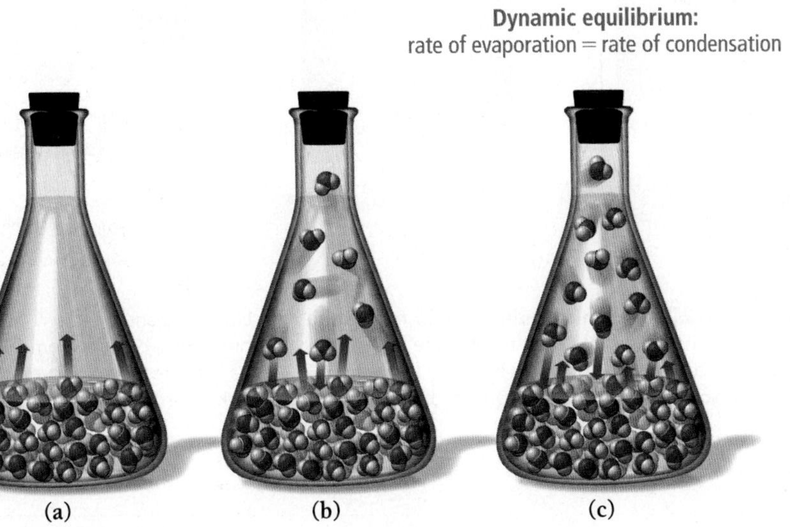

◀ **FIGURE 12.25 Vaporization in a Sealed Flask** **(a)** When water is in a sealed container, water molecules begin to vaporize. **(b)** As water molecules build up in the gas state, they begin to recondense into the liquid. **(c)** When the rate of evaporation equals the rate of condensation, dynamic equilibrium is reached.

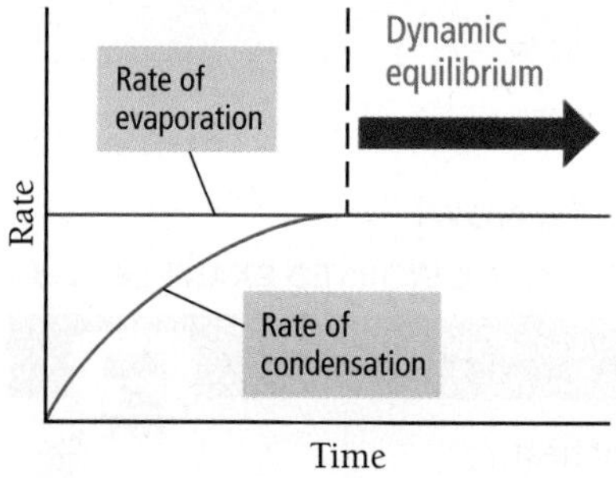

▲ **FIGURE 12.26 Dynamic Equilibrium** Dynamic equilibrium occurs when the rate of condensation is equal to the rate of evaporation.

back into the liquid. As the concentration (or partial pressure) of gaseous water molecules increases, the rate of condensation also increases. However, as long as the water remains at a constant temperature, the rate of evaporation remains constant. Eventually, the rate of condensation and the rate of vaporization become equal—**dynamic equilibrium** has been reached (Figure 12.26◄). Condensation and vaporization continue at equal rates, and the concentration of water vapor above the liquid is constant.

The pressure of a gas in dynamic equilibrium with its liquid is its **vapor pressure.** The vapor pressure of a particular liquid depends on the intermolecular forces present in the liquid and the temperature. Weak intermolecular forces result in volatile (easily vaporizable) substances with high vapor pressures at a given temperature because the intermolecular forces are easily overcome by thermal energy. Strong intermolecular forces result in nonvolatile substances with low vapor pressures at a given temperature.

A liquid in dynamic equilibrium with its vapor is a balanced system that tends to return to equilibrium if disturbed. For example, consider a sample of *n*-pentane (a component of gasoline) at 25 °C in a cylinder equipped with a moveable piston (Figure 12.27(a)▼). The cylinder contains no other gases except *n*-pentane vapor in dynamic equilibrium with the liquid. Since the vapor pressure of *n*-pentane at 25 °C is 510 mmHg, the pressure in the cylinder is 510 mmHg.

Boyle's law is discussed in Section 6.3.

Now, what happens when the piston is moved upward to expand the volume within the cylinder? Initially, the pressure in the cylinder drops below 510 mmHg, in accordance with Boyle's law. Then, however, more liquid vaporizes until equilibrium is reached once again (Figure 12.27(b)▼). If the volume of the cylinder is expanded again, the same thing happens—the pressure initially drops and more *n*-pentane vaporizes to bring the system back into equilibrium. Further expansion causes the same result *as long as some liquid* n*-pentane remains in the cylinder.*

Conversely, what happens if the piston is lowered, decreasing the volume in the cylinder? Initially, the pressure in the cylinder rises above 510 mmHg, but then some of the gas condenses into liquid until equilibrium is reached again (Figure 12.27(c)▼).

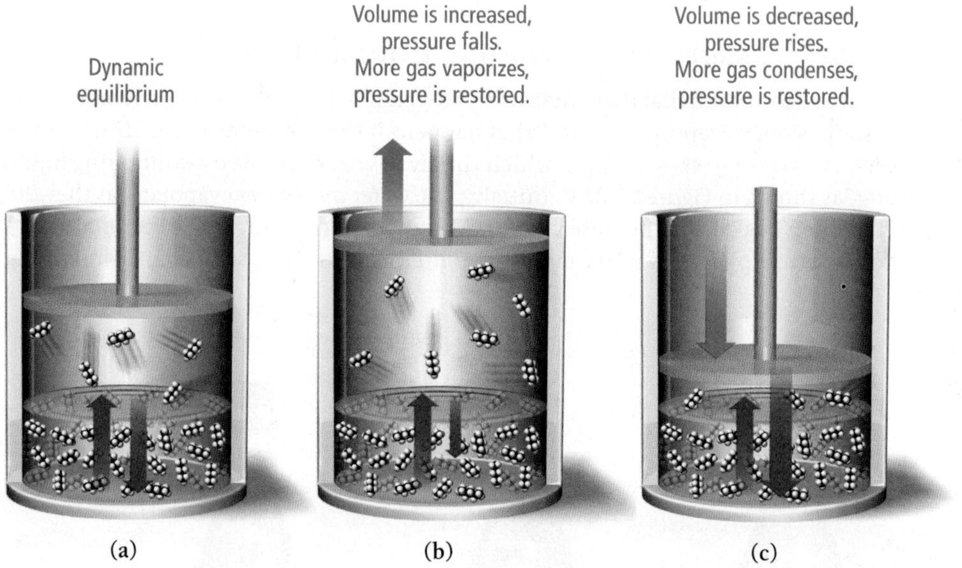

▲ **FIGURE 12.27 Dynamic Equilibrium in *n*-Pentane** **(a)** Liquid *n*-pentane is in dynamic equilibrium with its vapor. **(b)** When the volume is increased, the pressure drops and some liquid converts to gas to bring the pressure back up. **(c)** When the volume is decreased, the pressure increases and some gas converts to liquid to bring the pressure back down.

We describe the tendency of a system in dynamic equilibrium to return to equilibrium with the following general statement:

When a system in dynamic equilibrium is disturbed, the system responds so as to minimize the disturbance and return to a state of equilibrium.

If the pressure above a liquid–vapor system in equilibrium decreases, some of the liquid evaporates, restoring the equilibrium pressure. If the pressure increases, some of the vapor condenses, bringing the pressure back down to the equilibrium pressure. This basic principle—Le Châtelier's principle—is applicable to any chemical system in equilibrium, as we shall see in Chapter 16.

ANSWER **NOW!**

VAPOR PRESSURE What happens to the vapor pressure of a substance when its surface area is increased at constant temperature?

(a) The vapor pressure increases.
(b) The vapor pressure remains the same.
(c) The vapor pressure decreases.

Temperature Dependence of Vapor Pressure and Boiling Point

When the temperature of a liquid increases, its vapor pressure rises because the higher thermal energy increases the number of molecules that have enough energy to vaporize (see Figure 12.24). Because of the shape of the thermal energy distribution curve, a small change in temperature makes a large difference in the number of molecules that have enough energy to vaporize, which results in a large increase in vapor pressure. For example, the vapor pressure of water at 25 °C is 23.3 torr, while at 60 °C the vapor pressure is 149.4 torr. Figure 12.28▼ plots the vapor pressure of water and several other liquids as a function of temperature.

The **boiling point** of a liquid is *the temperature at which the liquid's vapor pressure equals the external pressure.* When a liquid reaches its boiling point, the thermal energy is enough for molecules in the interior of the liquid (not just those at the surface) to break

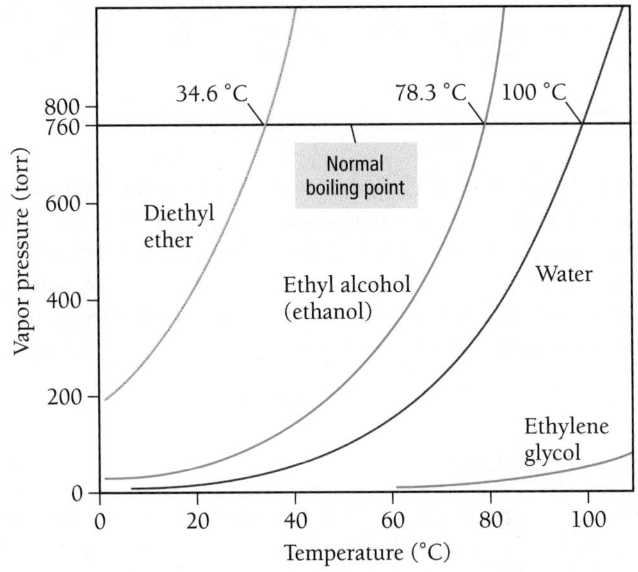

▲ **FIGURE 12.28 Vapor Pressure of Several Liquids at Different Temperatures** At higher temperatures, more molecules have enough thermal energy to escape into the gas state, so vapor pressure increases with increasing temperature.

▶ **FIGURE 12.29 Boiling** A liquid boils when thermal energy is high enough to cause molecules in the interior of the liquid to become gaseous, forming bubbles that rise to the surface.

Sometimes you see bubbles begin to form in hot water below 100 °C. These bubbles are dissolved air—not gaseous water—leaving the liquid. Dissolved air comes out of water as you heat it because the solubility of a gas in a liquid decreases with increasing temperature (as we will see in Chapter 14).

free of their neighbors and enter the gas state (Figure 12.29▲). The bubbles in boiling water are pockets of gaseous water that form within the liquid water. The bubbles float to the surface and leave as gaseous water or steam.

The **normal boiling point** of a liquid is *the temperature at which its vapor pressure equals 1 atm.* The normal boiling point of pure water is 100 °C. However, at a lower pressure, water boils at a lower temperature. In Denver, Colorado, where the altitude is around 1600 meters (5200 feet) above sea level, for example, the average atmospheric pressure is about 83% of what it is at sea level, and water boils at approximately 94 °C. For this reason, it takes slightly longer to cook food in boiling water in Denver than in San Francisco (which is at sea level). Table 12.8 lists the boiling point of water at several locations of varied altitudes.

TABLE 12.8 ■ Boiling Points of Water at Several Locations of Varied Altitudes

Location	Elevation (ft)	Approximate Pressure (atm)*	Approximate Boiling Point of Water (°C)
Mount Everest, Tibet (highest mountain peak on Earth)	29,029 ft.	0.32	78
Denali (formerly Mount McKineley), Alaska (highest mountain peak in North America)	20,310 ft.	0.46	83
Mount Whitney, California (highest mountain peak in 48 contiguous U.S. states)	14,505	0.60	87
Denver, Colorado (mile high city)	5,280	0.83	94
Boston, Massachusetts (sea level)	20	1.0	100

*The atmospheric pressure in each of these locations is subject to weather conditions and can vary significantly from these values.

Once the boiling point of a liquid is reached, additional heating only causes more rapid boiling; it does not raise the temperature of the liquid above its boiling point, as shown in the *heating curve* in Figure 12.30▶. Therefore, at 1 atm, boiling water always has a temperature of 100 °C. *As long as liquid water is present, its temperature cannot rise above its boiling point.* After all the water has been converted to steam, the temperature of the steam can continue to rise beyond 100 °C.

ANSWER NOW!

12.8 Cc Conceptual Connection

BOILING POINT Use Figure 12.28 to estimate the boiling point of water at an external pressure of 200 torr.

(a) 66 °C **(b)** 84 °C **(c)** 100 °C **(d)** 0 °C

The Clausius–Clapeyron Equation

Now, let's return our attention to Figure 12.28. As we can see from the graph, the vapor pressure of a liquid increases with increasing temperature. However, *the relationship is not linear.* In other words, doubling the temperature results in more than doubling the vapor pressure. The relationship between vapor pressure and temperature is exponential, and we can express it as follows:

$$P_{vap} = \beta \exp\left(\frac{-\Delta H_{vap}}{RT}\right) \quad [12.1]$$

In this expression P_{vap} is the vapor pressure, β is a constant that depends on the gas, ΔH_{vap} is the heat of vaporization, R is the gas constant (8.314 J/mol·K), and T is the temperature in kelvins. We can rearrange Equation 12.1 by taking the natural logarithm of both sides:

$$\ln P_{vap} = \ln\left[\beta \exp\left(\frac{-\Delta H_{vap}}{RT}\right)\right] \quad [12.2]$$

Because $\ln AB = \ln A + \ln B$, we can rearrange the right side of Equation 12.2:

$$\ln P_{vap} = \ln \beta + \ln\left[\exp\left(\frac{-\Delta H_{vap}}{RT}\right)\right] \quad [12.3]$$

Because $\ln e^x = x$ (see Appendix IB), we can simplify Equation 12.3:

$$\ln P_{vap} = \ln \beta + \frac{-\Delta H_{vap}}{RT} \quad [12.4]$$

A slight additional rearrangement gives the following important result:

$$\ln P_{vap} = \frac{-\Delta H_{vap}}{R}\left(\frac{1}{T}\right) + \ln \beta \qquad \text{Clausius–Clapeyron equation}$$

$$y = m(x) + b \qquad \text{(equation for a line)}$$

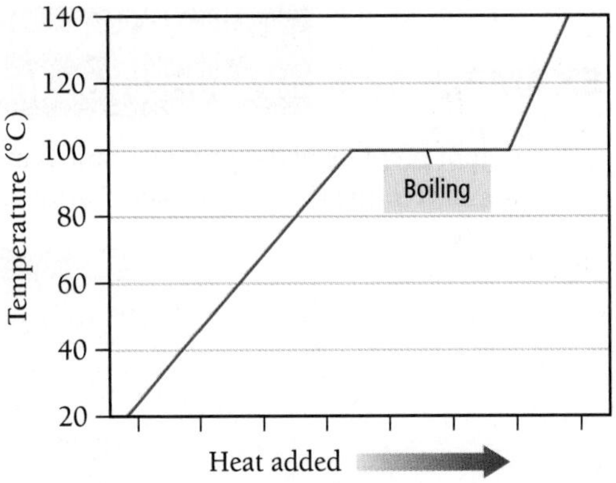

▲ **FIGURE 12.30 The Temperature during Boiling** The temperature of water during boiling remains at 100 °C.

Notice the parallel relationship between the **Clausius-Clapeyron equation** and the equation for a straight line. Just as a plot of y versus x yields a straight line with slope m and intercept b, so a plot of $\ln P_{vap}$ (equivalent to y) versus $1/T$ (equivalent to x) gives a straight line with slope $-\Delta H_{vap}/R$ (equivalent to m) and y-intercept $\ln \beta$ (equivalent to b), as shown in Figure 12.31▼. The Clausius-Clapeyron equation gives a linear relationship—not between the vapor pressure and the temperature (which have an exponential relationship)—but between the *natural* logarithm of the vapor pressure and the *inverse* of temperature. This is a common technique in the analysis of chemical data. If two variables are not linearly related, it is often convenient to find ways to graph *functions of those variables* that are linearly related.

Using the Clausius–Clapeyron equation in this way ignores the relatively small temperature dependence of ΔH_{vap}.

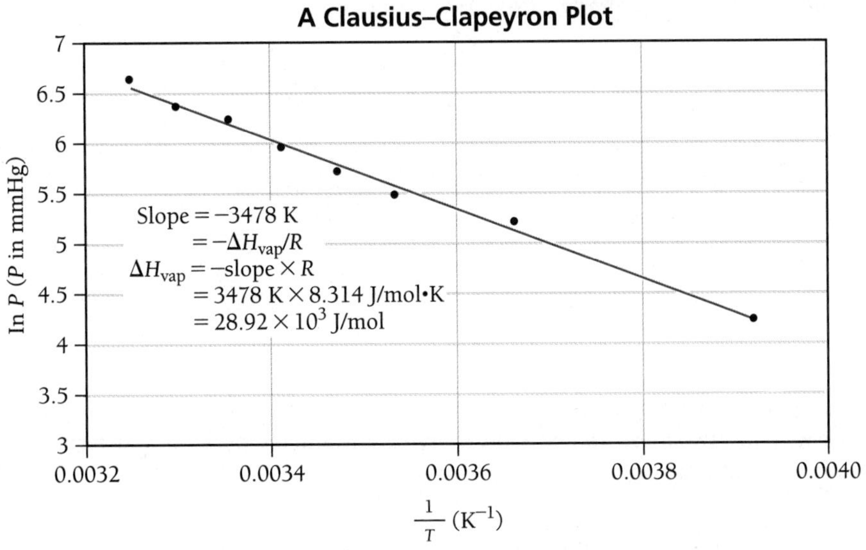

◀ **FIGURE 12.31 A Clausius–Clapeyron Plot for Diethyl Ether ($CH_3CH_2OCH_2CH_3$)** A plot of the natural logarithm of the vapor pressure versus the inverse of the temperature in K yields a straight line with slope $-\Delta H_{vap}/R$.

The Clausius-Clapeyron equation leads to a convenient way to determine the heat of vaporization in the laboratory. We simply measure the vapor pressure of a liquid as a function of temperature and create a plot of the natural logarithm of the vapor pressure versus the inverse of the temperature. We then determine the slope of the line to find the heat of vaporization, as demonstrated in Example 12.4.

EXAMPLE 12.4 Using the Clausius–Clapeyron Equation to Determine Heat of Vaporization from Experimental Measurements of Vapor Pressure

The vapor pressure of dichloromethane is measured as a function of temperature, and the results are tabulated. From the results, determine the heat of vaporization of dichloromethane.

Temperature (K)	Vapor Pressure (torr)
200	0.8
220	4.5
240	21
260	71
280	197
300	391

SOLUTION

To find the heat of vaporization, use an Excel spreadsheet or a graphing calculator to plot the natural logarithm of vapor pressure ($\ln P$) as a function of the inverse of the temperature in kelvins ($1/T$). Then fit the points to a line and determine the slope of the line. The slope of the best-fitting line is −3773 K. Since the slope equals $-\Delta H_{vap}/R$, we find the heat of vaporization as follows:

$$\text{slope} = -\Delta H_{vap}/R$$

$$\Delta H_{vap} = -\text{slope} \times R$$

$$= -(-3773\ \cancel{K})(8.314\ J/mol \cdot \cancel{K})$$

$$= 3.14 \times 10^4\ J/mol$$

$$= 31.4\ kJ/mol$$

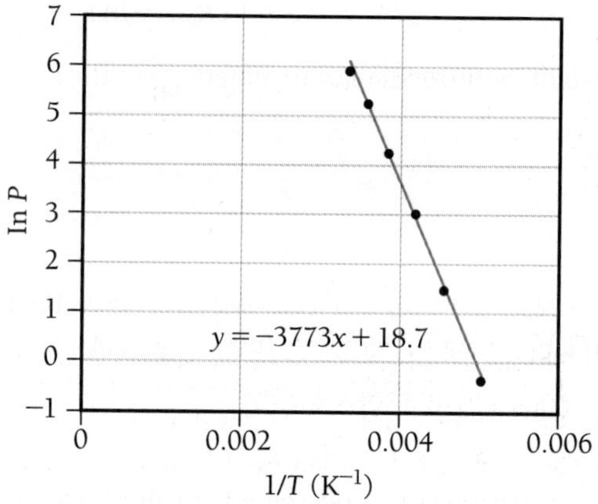

FOR PRACTICE 12.4 The vapor pressure of carbon tetrachloride is measured as a function of the temperature, and the results are tabulated. Determine the heat of vaporization of carbon tetrachloride from the results.

Temperature (K)	Vapor Pressure (torr)
255	11.3
265	21.0
275	36.8
285	61.5
295	99.0
300	123.8

The Clausius–Clapeyron equation can also be expressed in a two-point form that we can use with just two measurements of vapor pressure and temperature to determine the heat of vaporization:

$$\ln\frac{P_2}{P_1} = \frac{-\Delta H_{vap}}{R}\left(\frac{1}{T_2} - \frac{1}{T_1}\right)$$ Clausius–Clapeyron equation (two-point form)

The two-point method is generally inferior to plotting multiple points because fewer data points result in more chance for error.

We can use this form of the equation to predict the vapor pressure of a liquid at any temperature if we know the enthalpy of vaporization and the normal boiling point (or the vapor pressure at some other temperature), as demonstrated in Example 12.5.

WATCH **NOW!**

INTERACTIVE WORKED EXAMPLE 12.5

EXAMPLE 12.5 Using the Two-Point Form of the Clausius–Clapeyron Equation to Predict the Vapor Pressure at a Given Temperature

Methanol has a normal boiling point of 64.6 °C and a heat of vaporization (ΔH_{vap}) of 35.2 kJ/mol. What is the vapor pressure of methanol at 12.0 °C?

SORT You are given the normal boiling point of methanol (the temperature at which the vapor pressure is 760 mmHg) and the heat of vaporization. You are asked to find the vapor pressure at a specified temperature that is also given.

GIVEN: $T_1(°C) = 64.6\ °C$
$P_1 = 760$ torr
$\Delta H_{vap} = 35.2$ kJ/mol
$T_2(°C) = 12.0\ °C$

FIND: P_2

STRATEGIZE The conceptual plan is essentially the Clausius–Clapeyron equation, which relates the given and find quantities.

CONCEPTUAL PLAN

$$\ln\frac{P_2}{P_1} = \frac{-\Delta H_{vap}}{R}\left(\frac{1}{T_2} - \frac{1}{T_1}\right)$$

(Clausius–Clapeyron equation, two-point form)

SOLVE First, convert T_1 and T_2 from °C to K.

SOLUTION

$$\begin{aligned} T_1(\text{K}) &= T_1(°\text{C}) + 273.15 \\ &= 64.6 + 273.15 \\ &= 337.8\ \text{K} \\ T_2(\text{K}) &= T_2(°\text{C}) + 273.15 \\ &= 12.0 + 273.15 \\ &= 285.2\ \text{K} \end{aligned}$$

Then, substitute the required values into the Clausius–Clapeyron equation and solve for P_2.

$$\ln\frac{P_2}{P_1} = \frac{-\Delta H_{vap}}{R}\left(\frac{1}{T_2} - \frac{1}{T_1}\right)$$

$$\ln\frac{P_2}{P_1} = \frac{-35.2 \times 10^3 \frac{\cancel{\text{J}}}{\cancel{\text{mol}}}}{8.314 \frac{\cancel{\text{J}}}{\cancel{\text{mol}} \cdot \cancel{\text{K}}}}\left(\frac{1}{285.2\ \cancel{\text{K}}} - \frac{1}{337.8\ \cancel{\text{K}}}\right)$$

$$= -2.31$$

In order to isolate P_2, you must take the inverse natural logarithm (or inv ln) of $\ln(P_2/P_1)$. Remember that inv ln $(\ln x) = x$.

$$\frac{P_2}{P_1} = e^{-2.31}$$

$$\begin{aligned} P_2 &= P_1(e^{-2.31}) \\ &= 760\ \text{torr}(0.0993) \\ &= 75.4\ \text{torr} \end{aligned}$$

CHECK The units of the answer are correct. The magnitude of the answer makes sense because vapor pressure should be significantly lower at the lower temperature.

FOR PRACTICE 12.5 Propane has a normal boiling point of −42.0 °C and a heat of vaporization (ΔH_{vap}) of 19.04 kJ/mol. What is the vapor pressure of propane at 25.0 °C?

The Critical Point: The Transition to an Unusual State of Matter

We have considered the vaporization of a liquid in a container open to the atmosphere with and without heating, and the vaporization of a liquid in a *sealed* container without heating. We now examine the vaporization of a liquid in a *sealed* container *during heating.*

Consider liquid *n*-pentane in equilibrium with its vapor in a sealed container initially at 25 °C. At this temperature, the vapor pressure of *n*-pentane is 0.67 atm. What happens if we heat the liquid? As the temperature rises, more *n*-pentane vaporizes and the pressure within the container increases. At 100 °C, the pressure is 5.5 atm, and at

190 °C the pressure is 29 atm. As the temperature and pressure increase, more and more gaseous *n*-pentane is forced into the same amount of space, and the density of the *gas* gets higher and higher. At the same time, the increasing temperature causes the density of the *liquid* to become lower and lower. At 197 °C, the meniscus between the liquid and gaseous *n*-pentane disappears, and the gas and liquid states commingle to form a *supercritical fluid* (Figure 12.32▼). For any substance, the *temperature* at which this transition occurs is the **critical temperature (T_c).** The liquid cannot exist (regardless of pressure) above this temperature. The *pressure* at which this transition occurs is the **critical pressure (P_c).**

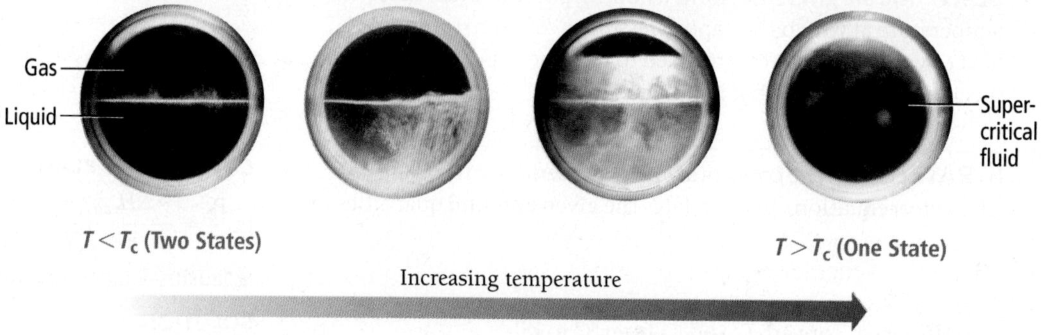

▲ **FIGURE 12.32 Critical Point Transition** As *n*-pentane is heated in a sealed container, it undergoes a transition to a supercritical fluid. At the critical point, the meniscus separating the liquid and gas disappears, and the fluid becomes supercritical—neither a liquid nor a gas.

Researchers are interested in supercritical fluids because of their unique properties. A supercritical fluid has properties of both liquids and gases—it is in some sense intermediate between the two. Supercritical fluids can act as good solvents, selectively dissolving a number of compounds. For example, supercritical carbon dioxide is used as a solvent to extract caffeine from coffee beans. The caffeine dissolves in the supercritical carbon dioxide, but other substances—such as those responsible for the flavor of coffee—do not. Consequently, the caffeine is removed, and the flavor of the coffee is not substantially altered. The supercritical carbon dioxide is easily removed from the mixture by simply lowering the pressure below the critical pressure, at which point the carbon dioxide evaporates, leaving no residue.

12.6 Sublimation and Fusion

In Section 12.5, we examined a beaker of liquid water at room temperature from the molecular viewpoint. Now, let's examine a block of ice at −10 °C from the same molecular perspective, paying close attention to two common processes: sublimation and fusion.

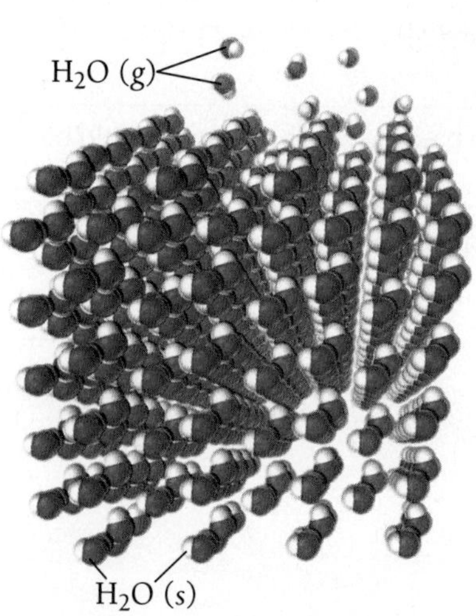

▲ **FIGURE 12.33 The Sublimation of Ice** The water molecules at the surface of an ice cube can sublime directly into the gas state.

Sublimation

Even though a block of ice is solid, the water molecules in the ice have thermal energy, which causes each one to vibrate about a fixed point. The motion is much less vigorous than that in a liquid, but it is significant nonetheless. As in liquids, at any instant some molecules in the block of ice have more thermal energy than the average and some have less. The molecules with high enough thermal energy can break free from the ice surface—where, as in liquids, molecules are held less tightly than in the interior due to fewer neighbor–neighbor interactions—and go directly into the gas state (Figure 12.33◀). This process is **sublimation**, the transition from solid to gas. Some of the water molecules in the gas state (those at the low end of the energy distribution curve for the gaseous molecules) collide with the surface of the ice and are captured by the intermolecular forces with other molecules. This process—the opposite of sublimation—is **deposition**, the transition from gas to solid. As is the case with liquids, the pressure of a gas in dynamic equilibrium with its solid is the vapor pressure of the solid.

Although both sublimation and deposition occur on the surface of an ice block open to the atmosphere at −10 °C, sublimation usually occurs at a greater rate than deposition because most of the newly sublimed molecules escape into the surrounding atmosphere and never come back. The result is a noticeable decrease in the size of the ice block over time (even though the temperature is below the melting point).

If you live in a cold climate, you may have noticed the disappearance of ice and snow from the ground even though the temperature remains below 0 °C. Similarly, ice cubes left in the freezer for a long time slowly shrink, even though the freezer is always below 0 °C. In both cases, the ice is *subliming*, turning directly into water vapor. Ice also sublimes out of frozen foods. You may have noticed, for example, the gradual growth of ice crystals on the *inside* of airtight plastic food-storage bags in a freezer. The ice crystals are composed of water that has sublimed out of the food and redeposited on the surface of the bag or on the surface of the food. For this reason, food that remains frozen for too long becomes dried out. Such dehydration can be avoided to some degree by freezing foods to colder temperatures, a process called deep-freezing. The colder temperature lowers the vapor pressure of ice and preserves the food longer. Freezer burn on meats is another common manifestation of sublimation. When you improperly store meat (for example, in a container that is not airtight) sublimation continues unabated. The result is the dehydration of the surface of the meat, which becomes discolored and loses flavor and texture.

▲ Dry ice (solid CO_2) sublimes but does not melt at atmospheric pressure.

A substance commonly associated with sublimation is solid carbon dioxide or dry ice, which does not melt under atmospheric pressure no matter what the temperature is. However, at −78 °C the CO_2 molecules have enough energy to leave the surface of the dry ice and become gaseous through sublimation.

Fusion

Let's return to our ice block and examine what happens at the molecular level as we increase its temperature. The increasing thermal energy causes the water molecules to vibrate faster and faster. At the **melting point** (0 °C for water), the molecules have enough thermal energy to overcome the intermolecular forces that hold the molecules at their stationary points, and the solid turns into a liquid. This process is **melting** or **fusion**, the transition from solid to liquid. The opposite of melting is **freezing**, the transition from liquid to solid. Once the melting point of a solid is reached, additional heating only causes more rapid melting; it does not raise the temperature of the solid above its melting point (Figure 12.34▶). Only after all of the ice has melted will additional heating raise the temperature of the liquid water past 0 °C. A mixture of water *and* ice always has a temperature of 0 °C (at 1 atm pressure).

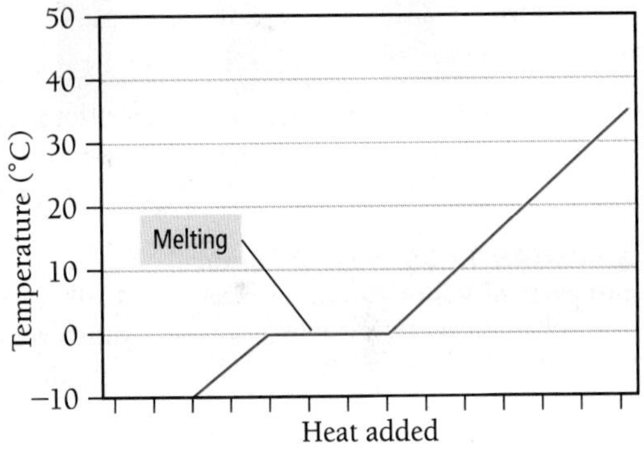

▲ **FIGURE 12.34 Temperature during Melting** The temperature of water during melting remains at 0.0 °C as long as both solid and liquid water remain.

Energetics of Melting and Freezing

The most common way to cool a beverage quickly is to drop several ice cubes into it. As the ice melts, the drink cools because melting is endothermic—the melting ice absorbs heat from the liquid. The amount of heat required to melt 1 mol of a solid is the **heat of fusion (ΔH_{fus})**. The heat of fusion for water is 6.02 kJ/mol:

The term *fusion* is used for melting because if we heat several crystals of a solid, they fuse into a continuous liquid upon melting.

$$H_2O(s) \longrightarrow H_2O(l) \quad \Delta H_{fus} = 6.02 \text{ kJ/mol}$$

The heat of fusion is positive because melting is endothermic.

Freezing, the opposite of melting, is exothermic—heat is released when a liquid freezes into a solid. For example, as water in the freezer turns into ice, it releases heat, which must be removed by the refrigeration system of the freezer. If the refrigeration system did not remove the heat, the water would not completely freeze into ice. The heat released as the water began to freeze would warm the freezer, preventing further freezing. The change in enthalpy for freezing has the same magnitude as the heat of fusion but the opposite sign:

$$H_2O(l) \longrightarrow H_2O(s) \quad \Delta H = -\Delta H_{fus} = -6.02 \text{ kJ/mol}$$

Different substances have different heats of fusion as listed in Table 12.9.

TABLE 12.9 ■ Heats of Fusion of Several Substances

Liquid	Chemical Formula	Melting Point (°C)	ΔH_{fus} (kJ/mol)
Water	H_2O	0.00	6.02
Isopropyl alcohol	C_3H_8O	−89.5	5.37
Acetone	C_3H_6O	−94.8	5.69
Diethyl ether	$C_4H_{10}O$	−116.3	7.27

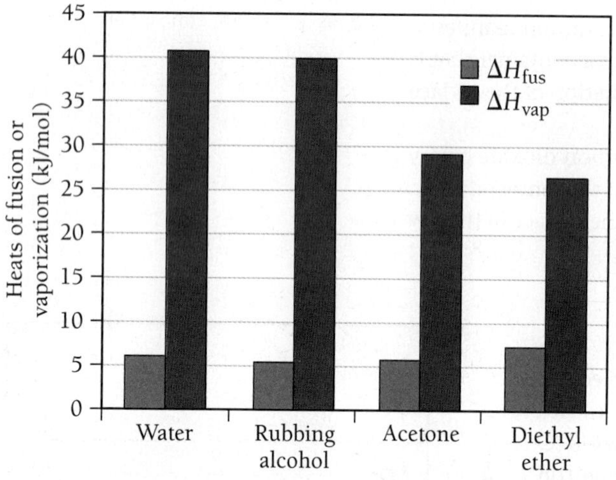

▲ **FIGURE 12.35 Heat of Fusion and Heat of Vaporization** Typical heats of fusion are significantly less than heats of vaporization.

In general, the heat of fusion for a substance is significantly less than its heat of vaporization (Figure 12.35◀). We have already seen that the solid and liquid states are closer to each other in many ways than they are to the gas state. It takes less energy to melt 1 mol of ice into liquid than it does to vaporize 1 mol of liquid water into gas because vaporization requires complete separation of molecules from one another, so the intermolecular forces must be completely overcome. Melting, in contrast, requires that intermolecular forces be only partially overcome, allowing molecules to move around one another while still remaining in contact.

The amount of heat required to sublime one mole of a solid to a gas is its **heat (or enthalpy) of sublimation (ΔH_{sub})**. Since enthalpy is a state function, the change in enthalpy of any two-step process is simply the sum of the changes in enthalpies of each step. Because the sublimation of a substance is equivalent to its fusion followed by its vaporization, the heat of sublimation is the sum of the heat of fusion and the heat of vaporization. For water, we calculate the heat of sublimation at 0 °C as follows:

$$\begin{aligned}\Delta H_{sub} &= \Delta H_{fus} + \Delta H_{vap} \\ &= 6.01 \text{ kJ/mol} + 40.7 \text{ kJ/mol} \\ &= 46.7 \text{ kJ/mol}\end{aligned}$$

WATCH **NOW!**

KEY CONCEPT VIDEO 12.7
Heating Curve for Water

12.7 Heating Curve for Water

We can combine and build on the concepts from Sections 12.5 and 12.6 by examining the *heating curve* for 1.00 mol of water at 1.00 atm pressure shown in Figure 12.36▶. The *y*-axis of the heating curve represents the temperature of the water sample. The *x*-axis represents the amount of heat added (in kilojoules) during heating. In the diagram, we divide the process into five segments: (1) ice warming; (2) ice melting into liquid water; (3) liquid water warming; (4) liquid water vaporizing into steam; and (5) steam warming.

In two of these segments (2 and 4), the temperature is constant as heat is added because the added heat goes into producing the transition between states, not into increasing the temperature. The two states are in equilibrium during the transition, and the temperature remains constant. The amount of heat required to achieve the state change is given by $q = n\Delta H$.

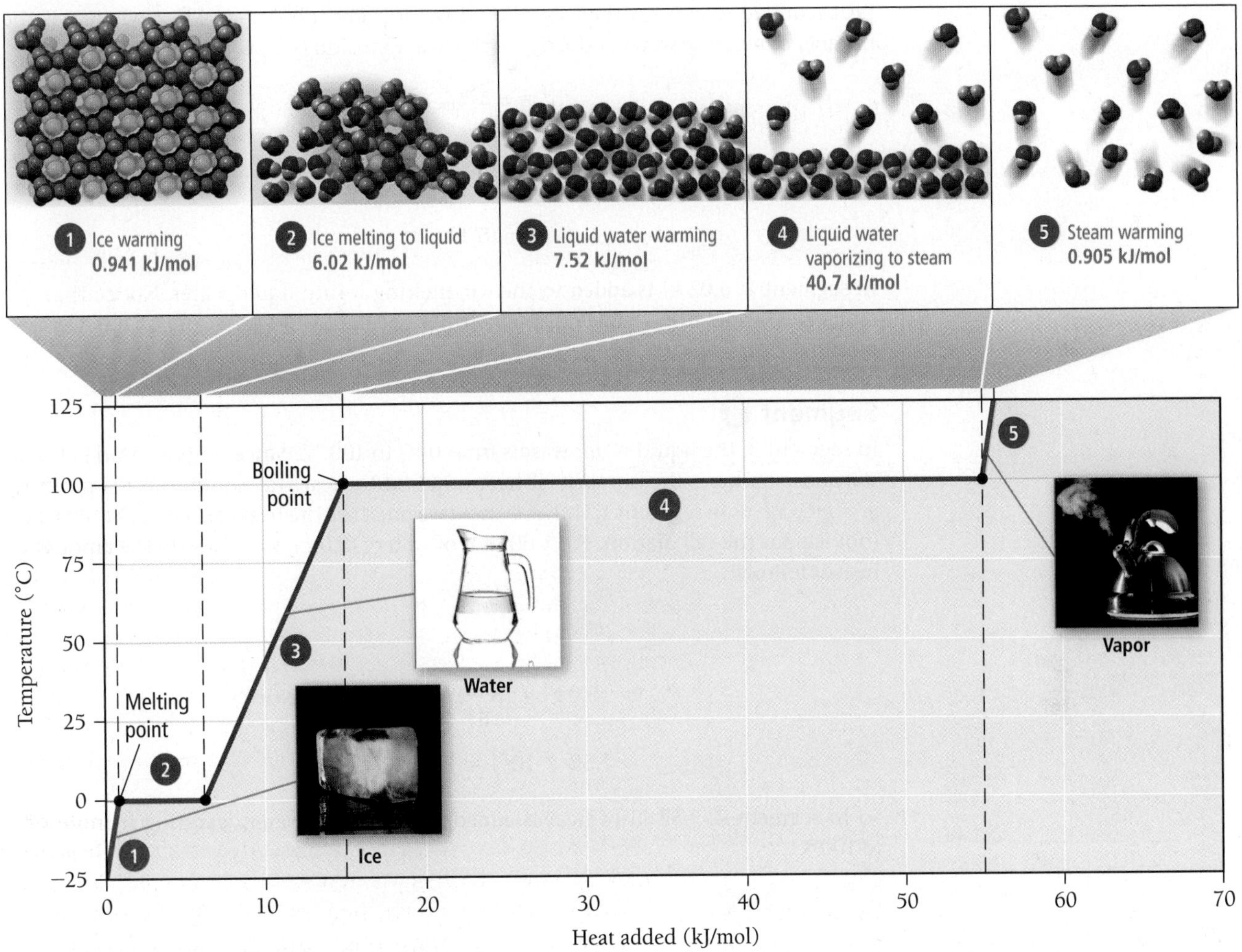

▲ **FIGURE 12.36 Heating Curve for Water**

In the other three segments (1, 3, and 5), temperature increases linearly. These segments represent the heating of a single state in which the deposited heat raises the temperature in accordance with the substance's heat capacity ($q = mC_s\,\Delta T$). We examine each of these segments individually.

Segment 1

In segment 1, solid ice is warmed from −25 °C to 0 °C. Since no transition between states occurs here, the amount of heat required to heat the solid ice is given by $q = mC_s\,\Delta T$ (see Section 7.4), where C_s is the specific heat capacity of ice ($C_{s,\,\text{ice}} = 2.09\,\text{J/g}\cdot{}^\circ\text{C}$). For 1.00 mol of water (18.0 g), we calculate the amount of heat as follows:

$$\begin{aligned} q &= mC_{s,\,\text{ice}}\,\Delta T \\ &= 18.0\,\cancel{\text{g}}\left(2.09\frac{\text{J}}{\cancel{\text{g}}\cdot\cancel{^\circ\text{C}}}\right)[0.0\,\cancel{^\circ\text{C}} - (-25.0\,\cancel{^\circ\text{C}})] \\ &= 941\,\text{J} = 0.941\,\text{kJ} \end{aligned}$$

So in segment 1, 0.941 kJ of heat is added to the ice, warming it from −25° C to 0 °C.

Segment 2

In segment 2, the added heat does not change the temperature of the ice and water mixture because the heat is absorbed by the transition from solid to liquid. The amount of heat required to convert the ice to liquid water is given by $q = n\,\Delta H_{fus}$, where n is the number of moles of water and ΔH_{fus} is the heat of fusion (see Section 12.6):

$$q = n\,\Delta H_{fus}$$

$$= 1.00\,\cancel{mol}\left(\frac{6.02\text{ kJ}}{\cancel{mol}}\right)$$

$$= 6.02\text{ kJ}$$

In segment 2, 6.02 kJ is added to the ice, melting it into liquid water. Notice that the temperature does not change during melting. The liquid and solid coexist at 0 °C as the melting occurs.

Segment 3

In segment 3, the liquid water warms from 0 °C to 100 °C. Since no transition between states occurs here, the amount of heat required to heat the liquid water is given by $q = mC_s\,\Delta T$, as in segment 1. However, now we must use the heat capacity of liquid water (not ice) for the calculation. For 1.00 mol of water (18.0 g), we calculate the amount of heat as follows:

$$q = mC_{s,\,liq}\,\Delta T$$

$$= 18.0\,\cancel{g}\left(4.18\frac{\text{J}}{\cancel{g}\cdot\cancel{°C}}\right)(100.0\,\cancel{°C} - 0.0\,\cancel{°C})$$

$$= 7.52 \times 10^3\text{ J} = 7.52\text{ kJ}$$

So in segment 3, 7.52 kJ of heat is added to the liquid water, warming it from 0 °C to 100 °C.

Segment 4

In segment 4, the water undergoes a second transition between states, this time from liquid to gas. The amount of heat required to convert the liquid to gas is given by $q = n\,\Delta H_{vap}$, where n is the number of moles and ΔH_{vap} is the heat of vaporization (see Section 12.5):

$$q = n\,\Delta H_{vap}$$

$$= 1.00\,\cancel{mol}\left(\frac{40.7\text{ kJ}}{\cancel{mol}}\right)$$

$$= 40.7\text{ kJ}$$

Thus, in segment 4, 40.7 kJ is added to the water, vaporizing it into steam. Notice that the temperature does not change during boiling. The liquid and gas coexist at 100 °C as the boiling occurs.

Segment 5

In segment 5, the steam warms from 100 °C to 125 °C. Since no transition between states occurs here, the amount of heat required to heat the steam is given by $q = mC_s\,\Delta T$ (as in segments 1 and 3) except that we must use the heat capacity of steam (2.01 J/g·°C):

$$q = mC_{s,\,steam}\,\Delta T$$

$$= 18.0\,\cancel{g}\left(2.01\frac{\text{J}}{\cancel{g}\cdot\cancel{°C}}\right)(125.0\,\cancel{°C} - 100.0\,\cancel{°C})$$

$$= 905\text{ J} = 0.905\text{ kJ}$$

So in segment 5, 0.905 kJ of heat is added to the steam, warming it from 100 °C to 125 °C.

COOLING OF WATER WITH ICE You just saw that the heat capacity of ice is $C_{s,\,ice} = 2.09\ J/g \cdot {}^\circ C$ and that the heat of fusion of ice is 6.02 kJ/mol. When a small ice cube at −10 °C is put into a cup of water at room temperature, which of the following plays a greater role in cooling the liquid water: the warming of the ice from −10 °C to 0 °C, or the melting of the ice?

(a) the warming of the ice from −10 °C to 0 °C
(b) the melting of the ice

12.9 Cc Conceptual Connection

ANSWER **NOW!**

12.8 Phase Diagrams

WATCH **NOW!**

KEY CONCEPT VIDEO 12.8
Phase Diagrams

Throughout most of this chapter, we have examined how the state of a substance changes in response to changes in temperature and pressure. We can combine both the temperature dependence and pressure dependence of the state of a particular substance in a graph called a *phase diagram*. A **phase diagram** is a map of the state or *phase* of a substance as a function of pressure (on the *y*-axis) and temperature (on the *x*-axis). In this section, we first examine the major features of a phase diagram, then turn to navigating within a phase diagram, and finally examine and compare the phase diagrams of selected substances.

The Major Features of a Phase Diagram

We can introduce the major features of a phase diagram by examining the phase diagram for water as an example (Figure 12.37▼). The *y*-axis displays the pressure in torr, and the *x*-axis displays the temperature in degrees Celsius. We categorize the main features of the phase diagram as regions, lines, and points.

Phase Diagram for Water

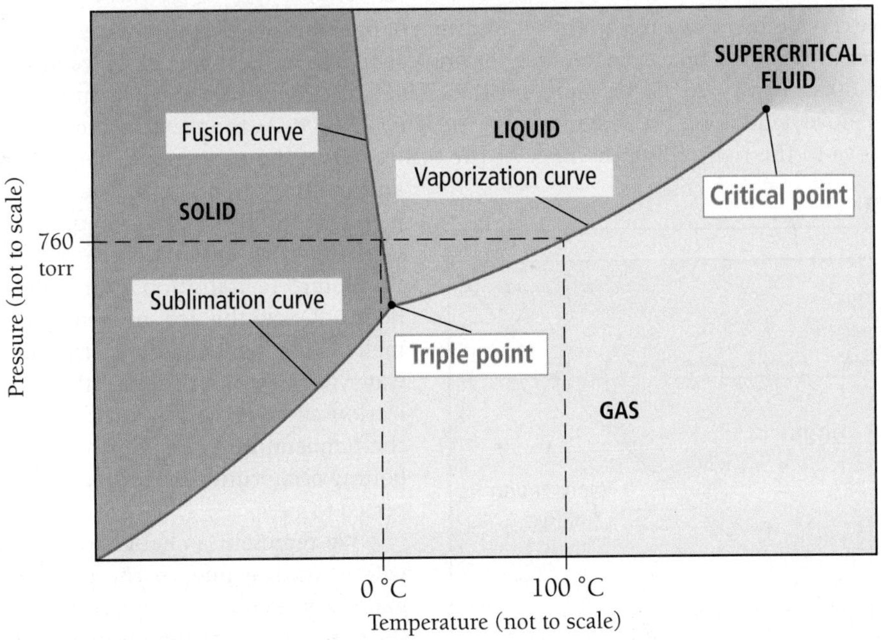

◀ **FIGURE 12.37 Phase Diagram for Water**

Regions

Each of the three main regions—solid, liquid, and gas—in the phase diagram represents conditions under which that particular state is stable. For example, under any of the temperatures and pressures within the liquid region in the phase diagram of water, the liquid is the stable state. Notice that the point 25 °C and 760 torr falls within the liquid region, as we know from everyday experience. In general, low temperature and high pressure favor the solid state, high temperature and low pressure favor the gas state, and intermediate conditions favor the liquid state. A sample of matter that is not in the state indicated by its phase diagram for a given set of conditions converts to that state when those conditions are imposed. For example, steam that is cooled to room temperature at 1 atm condenses to liquid.

Lines

Each of the lines (or curves) in the phase diagram represents a set of temperatures and pressures at which the substance is in equilibrium between the two states on either side of the line. In the phase diagram for water shown in Figure 12.37, consider the curved line beginning just beyond 0 °C separating the liquid from the gas. This line is the vaporization curve (also called the vapor pressure curve) for water that we examined in Section 12.5. At any of the temperatures and pressures that fall along this line, the liquid and gas states of water are equally stable and in equilibrium. For example, at 100 °C and 760 torr pressure, water and its vapor are in equilibrium—they are equally stable and coexist. The other two major lines in a phase diagram are the *sublimation curve* (separating the solid and the gas) and the *fusion curve* (separating the solid and the liquid).

The Triple Point

The triple point of a substance such as water can be reproduced anywhere to calibrate a thermometer or pressure gauge with a known temperature and pressure.

The **triple point** *in a phase diagram represents the unique set of conditions at which the three states are equally stable and in equilibrium.* In the phase diagram for water, the triple point occurs at 0.0098 °C and 4.58 torr. Under these unique conditions (and only under these conditions), the solid, liquid, and gas states of water are equally stable and coexist in equilibrium.

The Critical Point

As we discussed in Section 12.5, at the critical temperature and pressure, the liquid and gas states coalesce into a *supercritical fluid.* The **critical point** *in a phase diagram represents the temperature and pressure above which a supercritical fluid exists.*

Navigation within a Phase Diagram

We can represent changes in the temperature or pressure of a sample of water as movement within the phase diagram. For example, suppose we heat a block of ice initially at 1.0 atm and −25 °C. We represent the change in temperature at constant pressure as movement along the line marked A in Figure 12.38▼. As the temperature rises, we move to the right along the line. At the fusion curve, the temperature stops rising, and melting occurs until the solid ice is completely converted to liquid water. Crossing the fusion curve requires the complete transition from solid to liquid. Once the ice has completely melted, the temperature of the liquid water can begin to rise until the vaporization curve is reached. At this point, the temperature again stops rising and boiling occurs until all the liquid is converted to gas.

We represent a change in pressure with a vertical line on the phase diagram. For example, suppose we lower the pressure above a sample of water initially at 1.0 atm and 25 °C. We represent the change in pressure at constant temperature as movement along the line marked B in Figure 12.38. As the pressure drops, we move down the line and approach the vaporization curve. At the

▼ **FIGURE 12.38 Navigation on the Phase Diagram for Water**

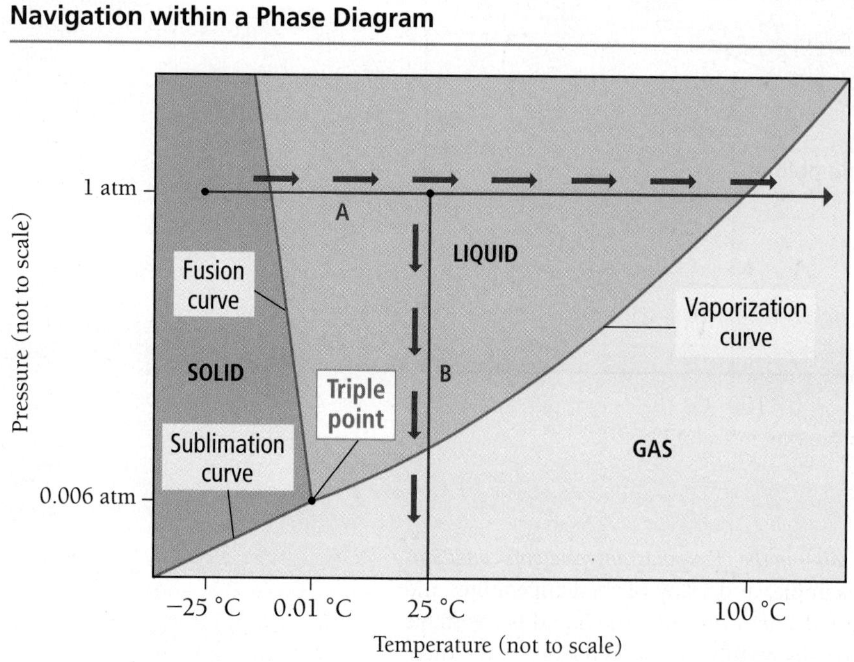

vaporization curve, the pressure stops dropping and vaporization occurs until the liquid completely converts to vapor. Crossing the vaporization curve requires the complete transition from liquid to gas. Only after all the liquid has vaporized can the pressure continue to drop.

The Phase Diagrams of Other Substances

Next, let's examine the phase diagrams of iodine and carbon dioxide in Figure 12.39▶. The phase diagrams are similar to the diagram of water in most of their general features, but some significant differences exist.

Note that the fusion curves for both carbon dioxide and iodine have a positive slope—as the temperature increases, the pressure also increases—in contrast to the fusion curve for water, which has a negative slope. The behavior of water is atypical. The fusion curve within the phase diagrams for most substances has a positive slope because increasing pressure favors the denser state, which for most substances is the solid state.

For example, suppose we increase the pressure on a sample of iodine from 1 atm to 100 atm at 184 °C, as shown by line A in Figure 12.39(a). Notice that this change crosses the fusion curve, converting the liquid into a solid. In contrast, a pressure increase from 1 atm to 100 atm at −0.1 °C in water causes a state transition from solid to liquid. Unlike most substances, the liquid state of water is actually denser than the solid state.

Both water and iodine have stable solid, liquid, and gaseous states at a pressure of 1 atm. However, notice that carbon dioxide has no stable liquid state at a pressure of 1 atm. If we increase the temperature of a block of solid carbon dioxide (dry ice) at 1 atm, as indicated by line B in Figure 12.39(b), we cross the sublimation curve at −78.5 °C. At this temperature, the solid sublimes to a gas, which is one reason that dry ice is useful (it does not melt into a liquid at atmospheric pressure). Carbon dioxide forms a liquid only above pressures of 5.1 atm.

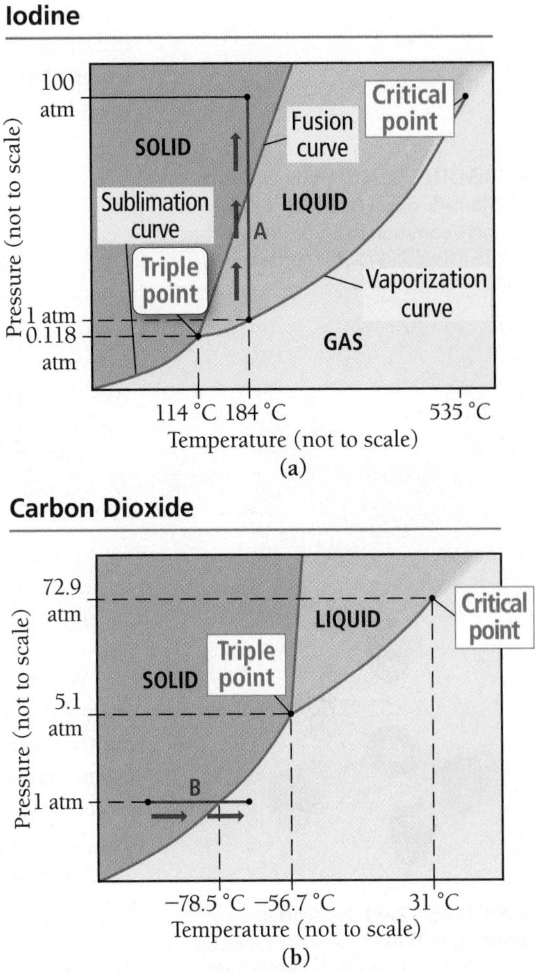

▲ **FIGURE 12.39 Phase Diagrams for Other Substances** **(a)** Iodine, **(b)** Carbon dioxide.

PHASE DIAGRAMS A substance has a triple point at −24.5 °C and 225 mmHg. What is most likely to happen to a solid sample of the substance as it is warmed from −35 °C to 0 °C at a pressure of 220 mmHg?

(a) The solid melts into a liquid.
(b) The solid sublimes into a gas.
(c) Nothing (the solid remains solid).

12.10 Cc Conceptual Connection

ANSWER **NOW!**

12.9 Water: An Extraordinary Substance

Water is the most common and important liquid on Earth. It fills our oceans, lakes, and streams. In its solid form, it caps our mountains, and in its gaseous form, it humidifies our air. We drink water, we sweat water, and we excrete bodily wastes dissolved in water. Indeed, the majority of our body mass *is* water. Life is impossible without water, and in most places on Earth where liquid water exists, life exists. Recent evidence for the existence of water on Mars has fueled hopes of finding life or evidence of past life there. And though it may not be obvious to us (because we take water for granted), this familiar substance has many remarkable properties.

▲ The European Space Agency (ESA) Mars Express Orbiter detected the presence of liquid water under the ice and dust on the planet's south pole.

Among liquids, water is unique. It has a low molar mass (18.02 g/mol), yet it is a liquid at room temperature. Other main-group hydrides have higher molar masses but lower boiling points, as shown in Figure 12.40▼. No other substance of similar molar mass (except HF) comes close to being a liquid at room temperature.

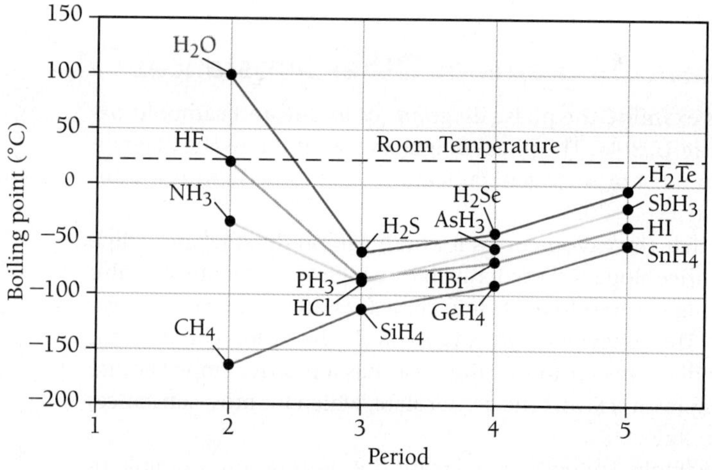

▶ **FIGURE 12.40 Boiling Points of Main-Group Hydrides** Water is the only common main-group hydride that is a liquid at room temperature.

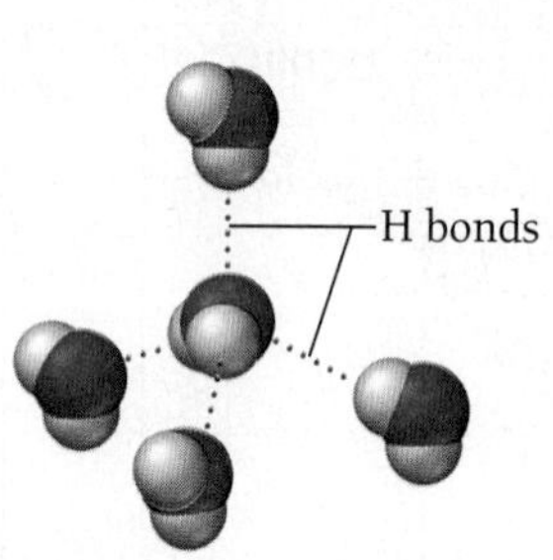

▲ **FIGURE 12.41 Hydrogen Bonding in Water** A water molecule can form four strong hydrogen bonds with four other water molecules.

We can understand water's high boiling point (in spite of its low molar mass) by examining its molecular structure. The bent geometry of the water molecule and the highly polar nature of the O—H bonds result in a molecule with a significant dipole moment. Water's two O—H bonds (hydrogen directly bonded to oxygen) allow a water molecule to form strong hydrogen bonds with four other water molecules (Figure 12.41◀), resulting in a relatively high boiling point.

Water's high polarity allows it to dissolve many other polar and ionic compounds and even a number of nonpolar gases such as oxygen and carbon dioxide (by inducing a dipole moment in their molecules). Consequently, water is the main solvent within living organisms, transporting nutrients and other important compounds throughout the body. Water is the main solvent in our environment as well, allowing aquatic animals, for example, to survive by breathing dissolved oxygen and allowing aquatic plants to survive by using dissolved carbon dioxide for photosynthesis.

Recall from Section 7.4 that water has an exceptionally high specific heat capacity, which has a moderating effect on the climate of coastal cities. In some cities, such as San Francisco, for example, the daily fluctuation in temperature can be less than 10 °C. This same moderating effect occurs over the entire planet, two-thirds of which is covered by water. Without water, the daily temperature fluctuations on our planet might be more like those on Mars, where temperatures fluctuate 63 °C (113 °F) between midday and early morning. Imagine awakening to below-freezing temperatures, only to bake at summer desert temperatures in the afternoon! The presence of water on Earth and water's uniquely high specific heat capacity are largely responsible for our planet's much smaller daily fluctuations.

As we have discussed, the way water freezes is also unique. Unlike other substances, which contract upon freezing, water expands upon freezing. Consequently, ice is less dense than liquid water, which is why ice floats. This seemingly trivial property has significant consequences. The frozen layer of ice at the surface of a winter lake insulates the water in the lake from further freezing. If this ice layer sank, it would kill bottom-dwelling aquatic life and possibly allow the lake to freeze solid, eliminating virtually all life in the lake.

▲ When lettuce freezes, the water within its cells expands, rupturing them.

The expansion of water upon freezing, however, is one reason that most organisms do not survive freezing. When the water within a cell freezes, it expands and often ruptures the cell, just as water freezing within a pipe bursts the pipe. Many foods, especially those with high water content, do not survive freezing very well either. Have you ever tried, for example, to freeze your own vegetables? If you put lettuce or spinach in the freezer, it will be limp and damaged upon thawing. The frozen-food industry gets around this problem by *flash freezing* vegetables and other foods. In this process, foods are frozen nearly instantaneously, which prevents water molecules from settling into their preferred crystalline structure. Consequently, the water does not expand very much, and the food remains largely undamaged.

CHEMISTRY IN THE ENVIRONMENT | Water Pollution

Water quality is critical to human health. Many human diseases—especially in developing nations—are caused by poor water quality. Several kinds of pollutants, including biological and chemical contaminants, can enter water supplies.

◀ Uncontaminated, sanitary water supplies are critical to human health.

Biological contaminants are microorganisms that cause diseases such as hepatitis, cholera, dysentery, and typhoid. They get into drinking water primarily when human or animal waste is dumped into bodies of water. Drinking water in developed nations is usually chemically treated to kill microorganisms. Water containing biological contaminants poses an immediate danger to human health and should not be consumed. Boiling eliminates most biological contaminants from untreated water.

Chemical contaminants enter drinking water supplies as a result of industrial dumping, pesticide and fertilizer use, and household dumping. These contaminants include organic compounds, such as carbon tetrachloride and dioxin, and inorganic elements and compounds, such as mercury, lead, and nitrates. Because many chemical contaminants are neither volatile nor alive (like biological contaminants are), they are usually not eliminated through boiling.

The U.S. Environmental Protection Agency (EPA), under the Safe Drinking Water Act of 1974 and its amendments, sets standards that specify the maximum contamination level (MCL) of nearly 100 biological and chemical contaminants in water. Water providers that serve more than 25 people must periodically test the water they deliver to their consumers for these contaminants. If levels exceed the standards set by the EPA, the water provider must notify consumers and take appropriate measures to remove the contaminant from the water. According to the EPA, water from providers that serve more than 25 people should be safe to consume over a lifetime. If it is not safe to drink for a short period of time, providers must notify consumers.

QUESTION *Why doesn't boiling eliminate nonvolatile contaminants such as lead?*

QUIZ YOURSELF **NOW!**

Self-Assessment Quiz

Q1. Which state of matter is compressible?
MISSED THIS? *Read Section 12.2*

a) gas b) liquid
c) solid d) none of the above

Q2. Liquid nitrogen boils at 77 K. The image shown below depicts a sample of liquid nitrogen.
MISSED THIS? *Read Section 12.2*

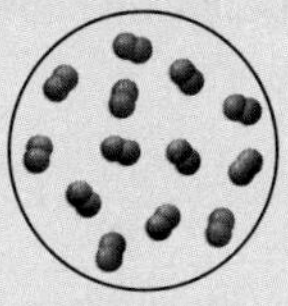

Which image best depicts the nitrogen after it has boiled?

a) 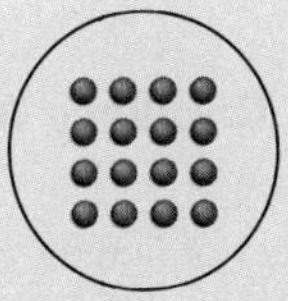

b) 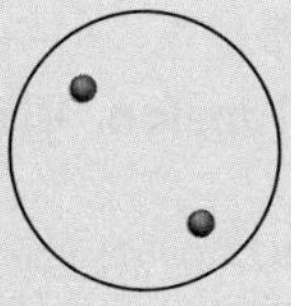

c) 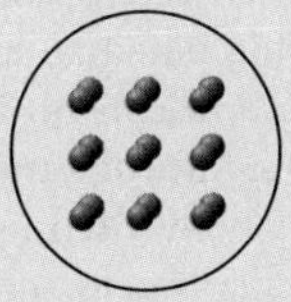

d) 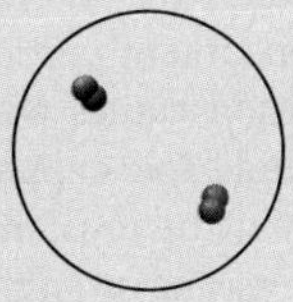

Q3. Based on the expected intermolecular forces, which halogen has the highest boiling point?
MISSED THIS? *Read Section 12.3; Watch KCV 12.3*

a) F_2 b) Cl_2 c) Br_2 d) I_2

Q4. Which substance experiences dipole–dipole forces?
MISSED THIS? *Read Section 12.3; Watch KCV 12.3, IWE 12.1*

a) CCl_4 b) NF_3 c) CS_2 d) SO_3

Q5. One of these substances is a liquid at room temperature. Which one?
MISSED THIS? *Read Section 12.3; Watch KCV 12.3, IWE 12.2*

a) CH_3OH b) CF_4 c) SiH_4 d) CO_2

Q6. Which property of a liquid increases with increasing temperature?
MISSED THIS? *Read Sections 12.4, 12.5; Watch KCV 12.5*

a) surface tension
b) viscosity
c) vapor pressure
d) none of the above

Q7. Determine the amount of heat (in kJ) required to vaporize 1.55 kg of water at its boiling point. For water, $\Delta H_{vap} = 40.7$ kJ/mol (at 100 °C).
MISSED THIS? *Read Section 12.5; Watch KCV 12.5, IWE 12.3*

a) 3.50×10^3 kJ b) 1.14×10^6 kJ
c) 2.11 kJ d) 686 kJ

—Continued on the next page

Continued—

Q8. The vapor pressure of a substance is measured over a range of temperatures. A plot of the natural log of the vapor pressure versus the inverse of the temperature (in kelvin) produces a straight line with a slope of -3.46×10^3 K. Find the enthalpy of vaporization of the substance.
MISSED THIS? *Read Section 12.5*

a) 2.40×10^{-3} kJ/mol
b) 28.8 kJ/mol
c) 0.416 kJ/mol
d) 3.22 kJ/mol

Q9. Acetic acid has a normal boiling point of 118 °C and a ΔH_{vap} of 23.4 kJ/mol. What is the vapor pressure (in mmHg) of acetic acid at 25 °C?
MISSED THIS? *Read Section 12.5; Watch IWE 12.5*

a) 2.92×10^{-39} mmHg
b) 7.16×10^3 mmHg
c) 758 mmHg
d) 80.6 mmHg

Q10. Consider the phase diagram shown here. A sample of the substance in the phase diagram is initially at 175 °C and 925 mmHg. What phase transition occurs when the pressure is decreased to 760 mmHg at constant temperature?
MISSED THIS? *Read Section 12.8; Watch KCV 12.8*

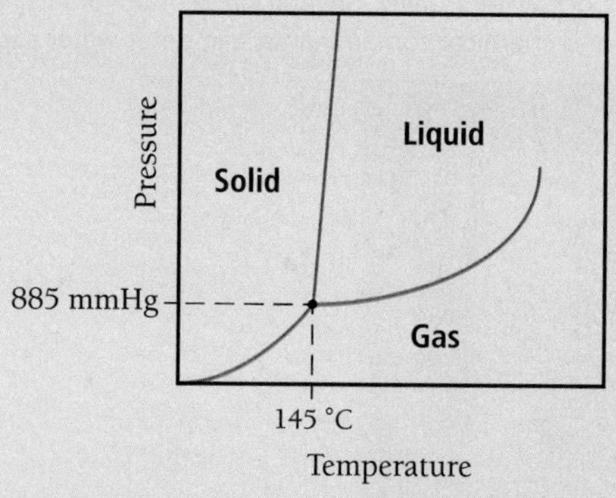

a) solid to liquid
b) liquid to gas
c) solid to gas
d) liquid to solid

Answers: 1. (a) **2.** (d) **3.** (d) **4.** (b) **5.** (a) **6.** (c) **7.** (a) **8.** (b) **9.** (d) **10.** (b)

CHAPTER 12 IN REVIEW

TERMS

Section 12.2
crystalline (498)
amorphous (498)

Section 12.3
dispersion force (500)
dipole–dipole force (502)
permanent dipole (502)
miscibility (503)
hydrogen bonding (505)
hydrogen bond (505)
ion–dipole force (507)

Section 12.4
surface tension (510)
viscosity (511)
capillary action (511)

Section 12.5
vaporization (513)
condensation (513)
volatile (513)
nonvolatile (513)
heat (or enthalpy) of vaporization (ΔH_{vap}) (514)
dynamic equilibrium (516)
vapor pressure (516)
boiling point (517)
normal boiling point (518)
Clausius–Clapeyron equation (519)
critical temperature (T_c) (522)
critical pressure (P_c) (522)

Section 12.6
sublimation (522)
deposition (522)
melting point (523)
melting (fusion) (523)
freezing (523)
heat (or enthalpy) of fusion (ΔH_{fus}) (523)
heat (or enthalpy) of sublimation (ΔH_{sub}) (524)

Section 12.8
phase diagram (527)
triple point (528)
critical point (528)

CONCEPTS

Solids, Liquids, and Intermolecular Forces (12.1, 12.2, 12.3)

- The forces that hold molecules or atoms together in a liquid or solid are intermolecular forces. The strength of the intermolecular forces in a substance determines its state.
- Dispersion forces are present in all elements and compounds; they arise from the fluctuations in electron distribution within atoms and molecules. These are the weakest intermolecular forces, but they are significant in molecules with high molar masses.
- Dipole–dipole forces, generally stronger than dispersion forces, are present in all polar molecules.
- Hydrogen bonding occurs in polar molecules that contain hydrogen atoms bonded directly to fluorine, oxygen, or nitrogen. These are among the strongest intermolecular forces.
- Ion–dipole forces occur when ionic compounds are mixed with polar compounds, and they are especially important in aqueous solutions.

Surface Tension, Viscosity, and Capillary Action (12.4)

- Surface tension results from the tendency of liquids to minimize their surface area in order to maximize the interactions between their constituent particles, thus lowering potential energy. Surface tension causes water droplets to form spheres and allows insects and paper clips to "float" on the surface of water.
- Viscosity is the resistance of a liquid to flow. Viscosity increases with increasing strength of intermolecular forces and decreases with increasing temperature.

- Capillary action is the ability of a liquid to flow against gravity up a narrow tube. It is the result of adhesive forces, the attraction between the molecules and the surface of the tube, and cohesive forces, the attraction between the molecules in the liquid.

Vaporization and Vapor Pressure (12.5, 12.7)

- Vaporization, the transition from liquid to gas, occurs when thermal energy overcomes the intermolecular forces present in a liquid. The opposite process is condensation. Vaporization is endothermic and condensation is exothermic.
- The rate of vaporization increases with increasing temperature, increasing surface area, and decreasing strength of intermolecular forces.
- The heat of vaporization (ΔH_{vap}) is the heat required to vaporize one mole of a liquid.
- In a sealed container, a liquid and its vapor come into dynamic equilibrium, at which point the rate of vaporization equals the rate of condensation. The pressure of a gas that is in dynamic equilibrium with its liquid is its vapor pressure.
- The vapor pressure of a substance increases with increasing temperature and with decreasing strength of its intermolecular forces.
- The boiling point of a liquid is the temperature at which its vapor pressure equals the external pressure.
- The Clausius–Clapeyron equation expresses the relationship between the vapor pressure of a substance and its temperature and can be used to calculate the heat of vaporization from experimental measurements.
- When a liquid is heated in a sealed container, it eventually forms a supercritical fluid, which has properties intermediate between a liquid and a gas. This occurs at critical temperature and critical pressure.

Fusion and Sublimation (12.6, 12.7)

- Sublimation is the transition from solid to gas. The opposite process is deposition.
- Fusion, or melting, is the transition from solid to liquid. The opposite process is freezing.
- The heat of fusion (ΔH_{fus}) is the amount of heat required to melt one mole of a solid. Fusion is endothermic.
- The heat of fusion is generally less than the heat of vaporization because intermolecular forces do not have to be completely overcome for melting to occur.

Phase Diagrams (12.8)

- A phase diagram is a map of the states of a substance as a function of its pressure (y-axis) and temperature (x-axis).
- The regions in a phase diagram represent conditions under which a single stable state (solid, liquid, gas) exists.
- The lines represent conditions under which two states are in equilibrium.
- The triple point represents the conditions under which all three states coexist.
- The critical point is the temperature and pressure above which a supercritical fluid exists.

The Uniqueness of Water (12.9)

- Water is a liquid at room temperature despite its low molar mass. Water forms strong hydrogen bonds, resulting in its high boiling point.
- The polarity of water enables it to dissolve many polar and ionic compounds and even nonpolar gases.
- Water expands upon freezing, so ice is less dense than liquid water. Water is critical both to the existence of life and to human health.

EQUATIONS AND RELATIONSHIPS

Clausius–Clapeyron Equation: Relationship between Vapor Pressure (P_{vap}), the Heat of Vaporization (ΔH_{vap}), and Temperature (T) (**12.5**)

$$\ln P_{vap} = \frac{-\Delta H_{vap}}{RT} + \ln \beta \quad (\beta \text{ is a constant})$$

$$\ln \frac{P_2}{P_1} = \frac{-\Delta H_{vap}}{R}\left(\frac{1}{T_2} - \frac{1}{T_1}\right)$$

LEARNING OUTCOMES

Chapter Objectives	Assessment
Determine the intermolecular forces acting between molecules (**12.2**), (**12.3**)	Example 12.1 **For Practice** 12.1 **Exercises** 35–38
Predict physical properties based on intermolecular forces (**12.4**)	Example 12.2 **For Practice** 12.2 **Exercises** 39–52
Perform calculations using the heat of vaporization (**12.5**)	Example 12.3 **For Practice** 12.3 **For More Practice** 12.3 **Exercises** 53–60
Calculate the heat of vaporization and vapor pressure using the Clausius–Clapeyron equation (**12.5**)	Examples 12.4, 12.5 **For Practice** 12.4, 12.5 **Exercises** 61–66
Perform calculations using the heat of fusion (**12.6**)	**Exercises** 67–70
Calculate heats related to heating and cooling curves (**12.7**)	**Exercises** 71–72
Identify physical properties of a compound from its phase diagram (**12.8**)	**Exercises** 73–78
Describe the physical properties of water (**12.9**)	**Exercises** 79–82

EXERCISES

Mastering Chemistry provides end-of-chapter exercises, feedback-enriched tutorial problems, animations, and interactive activities to encourage problem-solving practice and deeper understanding of key concepts and topics.

REVIEW QUESTIONS

1. Explain why water drops are spherical in the absence of gravity.
2. Why are intermolecular forces important?
3. What are the main properties of liquids (in contrast to gases and solids)?
4. What are the main properties of solids (in contrast to liquids and gases)?
5. What is the fundamental difference between an amorphous solid and a crystalline solid?
6. What factors cause transitions between the solid and liquid state? The liquid and gas state?
7. Describe the relationship between the state of a substance, its temperature, and the strength of its intermolecular forces.
8. From what kinds of interactions do intermolecular forces originate?
9. Why are intermolecular forces generally much weaker than bonding forces?
10. What is the dispersion force? What does the magnitude of the dispersion force depend on? How can you predict the magnitude of the dispersion force for closely related elements or compounds?
11. What is the dipole–dipole force? How can you predict the presence of dipole–dipole forces in a compound?
12. How is the polarity of a liquid generally related to its miscibility with water?
13. What is hydrogen bonding? How can you predict the presence of hydrogen bonding in a compound?
14. What is the ion–dipole force? Why is it important?
15. What is surface tension? How does surface tension result from intermolecular forces? How is it related to the strength of intermolecular forces?
16. What is viscosity? How does viscosity depend on intermolecular forces? What other factors affect viscosity?
17. What is capillary action? How does it depend on the relative strengths of adhesive and cohesive forces?
18. Explain what happens in the processes of vaporization and condensation. Why does the rate of vaporization increase with increasing temperature and surface area?
19. Why is vaporization endothermic? Why is condensation exothermic?
20. How is the volatility of a substance related to the intermolecular forces present within the substance?
21. What is the heat of vaporization for a liquid, and why is it useful?
22. Explain the process of dynamic equilibrium. How is dynamic equilibrium related to vapor pressure?
23. What happens to a system in dynamic equilibrium when it is disturbed in some way?
24. How is vapor pressure related to temperature? What happens to the vapor pressure of a substance when the temperature is increased? Decreased?
25. Define the terms *boiling point* and *normal boiling point*.
26. What is the Clausius–Clapeyron equation, and why is it important?
27. Explain what happens to a substance when it is heated in a closed container to its critical temperature.
28. What is sublimation? Give a common example of sublimation.
29. What is fusion? Is fusion exothermic or endothermic? Why?
30. What is the heat of fusion, and why is it important?
31. Examine the heating curve for water in Section 12.7 (Figure 12.36). Explain why the curve has two segments in which heat is added to the water but the temperature does not rise.
32. Examine the heating curve for water in Section 12.7 (Figure 12.36). Explain the significance of the slopes of each of the three rising segments. Why are the slopes different?
33. What is a phase diagram? Draw a generic phase diagram and label its important features. What is the significance of crossing a line in a phase diagram?
34. How do the properties of water differ from those of most other substances?

PROBLEMS BY TOPIC

Intermolecular Forces

35. Determine the kinds of intermolecular forces that are present in each element or compound.
MISSED THIS? *Read Section 12.3; Watch KCV 12.3*
a. N_2 b. NH_3 c. CO d. CCl_4
36. Determine the kinds of intermolecular forces that are present in each element or compound.
a. Kr b. NCl_3 c. SiH_4 d. HF
37. Determine the kinds of intermolecular forces that are present in each element or compound.
MISSED THIS? *Read Section 12.3; Watch KCV 12.3*
a. HCl b. H_2O c. Br_2 d. He
38. Determine the kinds of intermolecular forces that are present in each element or compound.
a. PH_3 b. HBr c. CH_3OH d. I_2
39. Arrange these compounds in order of increasing boiling point. Explain your reasoning.
MISSED THIS? *Read Section 12.3; Watch KCV 12.3, IWE 12.1, 12.2*
a. CH_4 b. CH_3CH_3 c. CH_3CH_2Cl d. CH_3CH_2OH
40. Arrange these compounds in order of increasing boiling point. Explain your reasoning.
a. H_2S b. H_2Se c. H_2O
41. In each pair of compounds, pick the one with the higher boiling point. Explain your reasoning.
MISSED THIS? *Read Section 12.3; Watch KCV 12.3, IWE 12.2*
a. CH_3OH or CH_3SH b. CH_3OCH_3 or CH_3CH_2OH
c. CH_4 or CH_3CH_3
42. In each pair of compounds, pick the one with the higher boiling point. Explain your reasoning.
a. NH_3 or CH_4 b. CS_2 or CO_2
c. CO_2 or NO_2

43. In each pair of compounds, pick the one with the higher vapor pressure at a given temperature. Explain your reasoning. **MISSED THIS?** *Read Sections 12.3, 12.5; Watch KCV 12.3, 12.5*
a. Br_2 or I_2 b. H_2S or H_2O c. NH_3 or PH_3

44. In each pair of compounds, pick the one with the higher vapor pressure at a given temperature. Explain your reasoning.
a. CH_4 or CH_3Cl
b. $CH_3CH_2CH_2OH$ or CH_3OH
c. CH_3OH or H_2CO

45. Determine whether each pair of compounds forms a homogeneous solution when combined. For those that form homogeneous solutions, indicate the type of forces that are involved. **MISSED THIS?** *Read Section 12.3*
a. CCl_4 and H_2O
b. KCl and H_2O
c. Br_2 and CCl_4
d. CH_3CH_2OH and H_2O

46. Determine whether each pair of compounds forms a homogeneous solution when combined. For those that form homogeneous solutions, indicate the type of forces that are involved.
a. $CH_3CH_2CH_2CH_2CH_3$ and $CH_3CH_2CH_2CH_2CH_2CH_3$
b. CBr_4 and H_2O
c. $LiNO_3$ and H_2O
d. CH_3OH and $CH_3CH_2CH_2CH_2CH_3$

Surface Tension, Viscosity, and Capillary Action

47. Which compound would you expect to have greater surface tension: acetone $[(CH_3)_2CO]$ or water (H_2O)? Explain. **MISSED THIS?** *Read Section 12.4*

48. Water (a) "wets" some surfaces and beads up on others. Mercury (b), in contrast, beads up on almost all surfaces. Explain this difference.

(a) (b)

49. The structures of two isomers of heptane are shown. Which of these two compounds would you expect to have the greater viscosity? **MISSED THIS?** *Read Section 12.4*

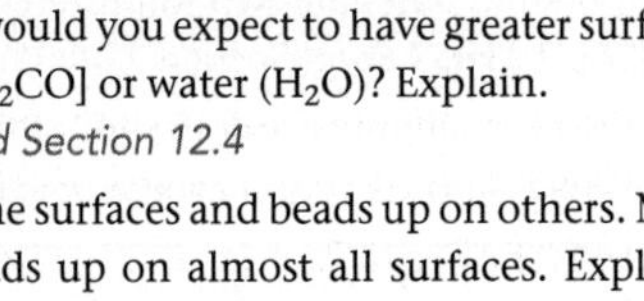

Compound A

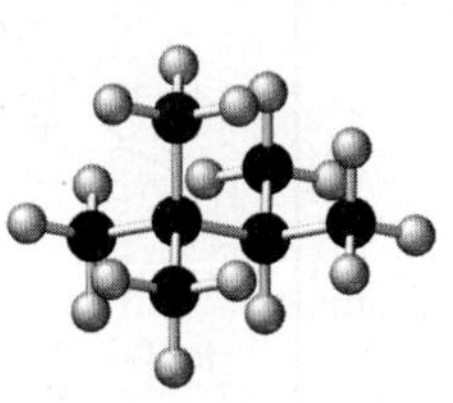

Compound B

50. Explain why the viscosity of multigrade motor oils is less temperature-dependent than that of single-grade motor oils.

51. Water in a glass tube that contains grease or oil residue displays a flat meniscus (left), whereas water in a clean glass tube displays a concave meniscus (right). Explain this observation. **MISSED THIS?** *Read Section 12.4*

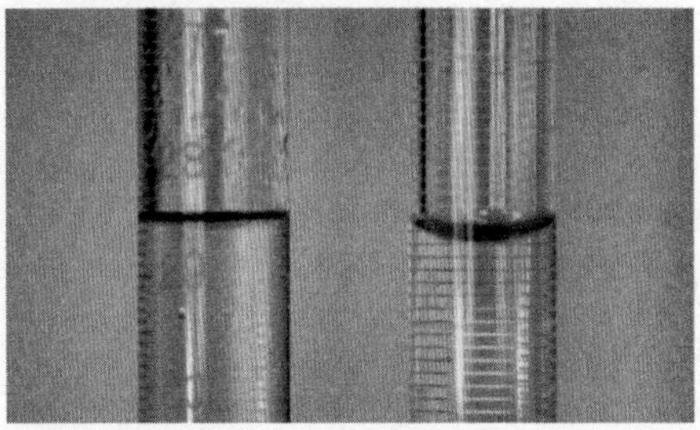

52. When a thin glass tube is put into water, the water rises 1.4 cm. When the same tube is put into hexane, the hexane rises only 0.4 cm. Explain.

Vaporization and Vapor Pressure

53. Which evaporates more quickly: 55 mL of water in a beaker with a diameter of 4.5 cm or 55 mL of water in a dish with a diameter of 12 cm? Is the vapor pressure of the water different in the two containers? Explain. **MISSED THIS?** *Read Section 12.5; Watch KCV 12.5*

54. Which evaporates more quickly: 55 mL of water (H_2O) in a beaker or 55 mL of acetone $[(CH_3)_2CO]$ in an identical beaker under identical conditions? Is the vapor pressure of the two substances different? Explain.

55. Spilling room-temperature water over your skin on a hot day cools you down. Spilling room-temperature vegetable oil over your skin on a hot day does not. Explain the difference. **MISSED THIS?** *Read Section 12.5; Watch KCV 12.5*

56. Why is the heat of vaporization of water greater at room temperature than it is at its boiling point?

57. The human body obtains 915 kJ of energy from a candy bar. If this energy were used to vaporize water at 100.0 °C, how much water (in liters) could be vaporized? (Assume the density of water is 1.00 g/mL.) **MISSED THIS?** *Read Section 12.5; Watch KCV 12.5, IWE 12.3*

58. A 100.0-mL sample of water is heated to its boiling point. How much heat (in kJ) is required to vaporize it? (Assume a density of 1.00 g/mL.)

59. Suppose that 0.95 g of water condenses on a 75.0-g block of iron that is initially at 22 °C. If the heat released during condensation goes only to warming the iron block, what is the final temperature (in °C) of the iron block? (Assume a constant enthalpy of vaporization for water of 44.0 kJ/mol.) **MISSED THIS?** *Read Section 12.5; Watch KCV 12.5, IWE 12.3*

60. Suppose that 1.15 g of rubbing alcohol (C_3H_8O) evaporates from a 65.0-g aluminum block. If the aluminum block is initially at 25 °C, what is the final temperature of the block after the evaporation of the alcohol? Assume that the heat required for the vaporization of the alcohol comes only from the aluminum block and that the alcohol vaporizes at 25 °C.

61. This table displays the vapor pressure of ammonia at several different temperatures. Use the data to determine the heat of vaporization and normal boiling point of ammonia. **MISSED THIS?** *Read Section 12.5*

Temperature (K)	Pressure (torr)
200	65.3
210	134.3
220	255.7
230	456.0
235	597.0

62. This table displays the vapor pressure of nitrogen at several different temperatures. Use the data to determine the heat of vaporization and normal boiling point of nitrogen.

Temperature (K)	Pressure (torr)
65	130.5
70	289.5
75	570.8
80	1028
85	1718

63. Ethanol has a heat of vaporization of 38.56 kJ/mol and a normal boiling point of 78.4 °C. What is the vapor pressure of ethanol at 15 °C?
MISSED THIS? *Read Section 12.5; Watch IWE 12.5*

64. Benzene has a heat of vaporization of 30.72 kJ/mol and a normal boiling point of 80.1 °C. At what temperature does benzene boil when the external pressure is 445 torr?

65. Carbon disulfide has a vapor pressure of 363 torr at 25 °C and a normal boiling point of 46.3 °C. Find ΔH_{vap} for carbon disulfide.
MISSED THIS? *Read Section 12.5; Watch IWE 12.5*

66. Methylamine has a vapor pressure of 344 torr at −25 °C and a boiling point of −6.4 °C. Find ΔH_{vap} for methylamine.

Sublimation and Fusion

67. How much energy is released when 65.8 g of water freezes?
MISSED THIS? *Read Section 12.6*

68. Calculate the amount of heat required to completely sublime 50.0 g of solid dry ice (CO_2) at its sublimation temperature. The heat of sublimation for carbon dioxide is 32.3 kJ/mol.

69. An 8.5-g ice cube is placed into 255 g of water. Calculate the temperature change in the water upon the complete melting of the ice. Assume that all of the energy required to melt the ice comes from the water.
MISSED THIS? *Read Section 12.6*

70. How much ice (in grams) would have to melt to lower the temperature of 352 mL of water from 25 °C to 5 °C? (Assume the density of water is 1.0 g/mL.)

71. How much heat (in kJ) is required to warm 10.0 g of ice, initially at −10.0 °C, to steam at 110.0 °C? The heat capacity of ice is 2.09 J/g·°C, and that of steam is 2.01 J/g·°C.
MISSED THIS? *Read Section 12.7; Watch KCV 12.7*

72. How much heat (in kJ) is evolved in converting 1.00 mol of steam at 145 °C to ice at −50 °C? The heat capacity of steam is 2.01 J/g·°C, and that of ice is 2.09 J/g·°C.

Phase Diagrams

73. Consider the phase diagram shown here. Identify the states present at points *a* through *g*.
MISSED THIS? *Read Section 12.8; Watch KCV 12.8*

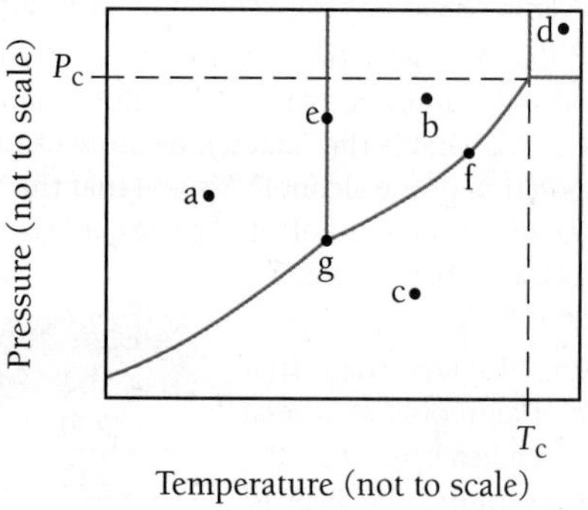

74. Consider the phase diagram for iodine shown here.

a. What is the normal boiling point for iodine?
b. What is the melting point for iodine at 1 atm?
c. What state is present at room temperature and normal atmospheric pressure?
d. What state is present at 186 °C and 1.0 atm?

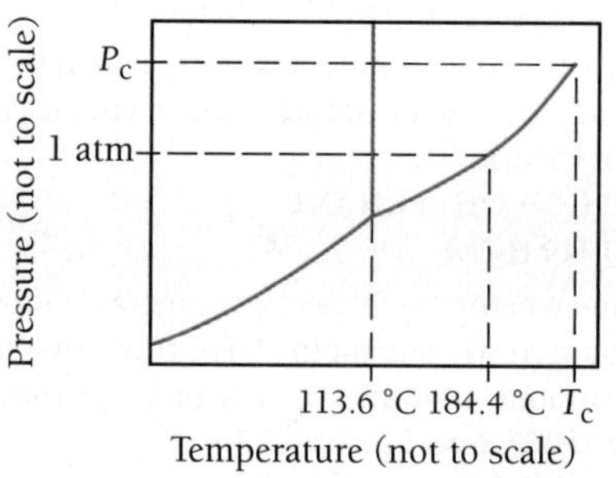

75. Nitrogen has a normal boiling point of 77.3 K and a melting point (at 1 atm) of 63.1 K. Its critical temperature is 126.2 K, and its critical pressure is 2.55×10^4 torr. It has a triple point at 63.1 K and 94.0 torr. Sketch the phase diagram for nitrogen. Does nitrogen have a stable liquid state at 1 atm?
MISSED THIS? *Read Section 12.8; Watch KCV 12.8*

76. Argon has a normal boiling point of 87.2 K and a melting point (at 1 atm) of 84.1 K. Its critical temperature is 150.8 K, and its critical pressure is 48.3 atm. It has a triple point at 83.7 K and 0.68 atm. Sketch the phase diagram for argon. Which has the greater density, solid argon or liquid argon?

77. The phase diagram for sulfur is shown here. The rhombic and monoclinic states are two solid states with different structures.
MISSED THIS? *Read Section 12.8; Watch KCV 12.8*

a. Below what pressure does solid sulfur sublime?
b. Which of the two solid states of sulfur is more dense?

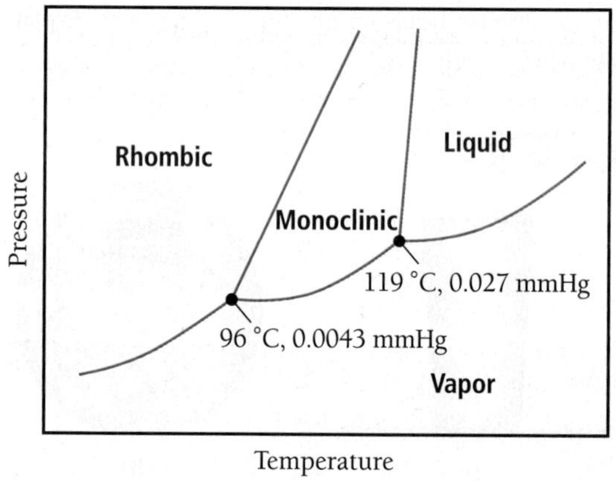

78. The high-pressure phase diagram of ice is shown here. Notice that, under high pressure, ice can exist in several different solid forms. What three forms of ice are present at the triple point marked O? How does the density of ice II compare to ice I (the familiar form of ice)? Would ice III sink or float in liquid water?

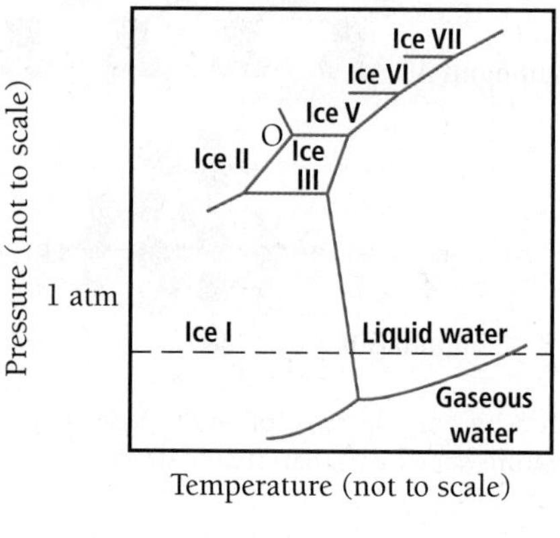

The Uniqueness of Water

79. Water has a high boiling point given its relatively low molar mass. Why?
MISSED THIS? *Read Section 12.9*

80. Water is a good solvent for many substances. What is the molecular basis for this property, and why is it significant?

81. Explain the role of water in moderating Earth's climate.
MISSED THIS? *Read Section 12.9*

82. How is the density of solid water compared to that of liquid water atypical among substances? Why is this significant?

CUMULATIVE PROBLEMS

83. Explain the observed trend in the melting points of the hydrogen halides.

HI	−50.8 °C
HBr	−88.5 °C
HCl	−114.8 °C
HF	−83.1 °C

84. Explain the observed trend in the boiling points of these compounds.

H_2Te	−2 °C
H_2Se	−41.5 °C
H_2S	−60.7 °C
H_2O	100 °C

85. The vapor pressure of water at 25 °C is 23.76 torr. If 1.25 g of water is enclosed in a 1.5-L container, will any liquid be present? If so, what mass of liquid?

86. The vapor pressure of CCl_3F at 300 K is 856 torr. If 11.5 g of CCl_3F is enclosed in a 1.0-L container, will any liquid be present? If so, what mass of liquid?

87. Examine the phase diagram for iodine shown in Figure 12.39(a). What state transitions occur as we uniformly increase the pressure on a gaseous sample of iodine from 0.010 atm at 185 °C to 100 atm at 185 °C? Make a graph, analogous to the heating curve for water shown in Figure 12.36. Plot pressure versus time during the pressure increase.

88. Carbon tetrachloride displays a triple point at 249.0 K and a melting point (at 1 atm) of 250.3 K. Which state of carbon tetrachloride is more dense, the solid or the liquid? Explain.

89. Four ice cubes at exactly 0 °C with a total mass of 53.5 g are combined with 115 g of water at 75 °C in an insulated container. If no heat is lost to the surroundings, what is the final temperature of the mixture?

90. A sample of steam with a mass of 0.552 g and at a temperature of 100 °C condenses into an insulated container holding 4.25 g of water at 5.0 °C. Assuming that no heat is lost to the surroundings, what is the final temperature of the mixture?

91. Draw a heating curve (such as the one in Figure 12.36) for 1 mole of methanol beginning at 170 K and ending at 350 K. Assume that the values given here are constant over the relevant temperature ranges.

Melting point	176 K
Boiling point	338 K
ΔH_{fus}	2.2 kJ/mol
ΔH_{vap}	35.2 kJ/mol
$C_{s,\ solid}$	105 J/K
$C_{s,\ liquid}$	81.3 J/mol · K
$C_{s,\ gas}$	48 J/mol · K

92. Draw a heating curve (such as the one in Figure 12.36) for 1 mol of benzene beginning at 0 °C and ending at 100 °C. Assume that the values given here are constant over the relevant temperature ranges.

Melting point	5.4 °C
Boiling point	80.1 °C
ΔH_{fus}	9.9 kJ/mol
ΔH_{vap}	30.7 kJ/mol
$C_{s,\ solid}$	118 J/mol·K
$C_{s,\ liquid}$	135 J/mol·K
$C_{s,\ gas}$	104 J/mol·K

93. Air conditioners not only cool air but dry it as well. A room in a home measures 6.0 m × 10.0 m × 2.2 m. If the outdoor temperature is 30 °C and the partial pressure of water in the air is 85% of the vapor pressure of water at this temperature, what mass of water must be removed from the air each time the volume of air in the room is cycled through the air conditioner? (Assume that all of the water must be removed from the air.) The vapor pressure for water at 30 °C is 31.8 torr.

94. A sealed flask contains 0.55 g of water at 28 °C. The vapor pressure of water at this temperature is 28.35 mmHg. What is the minimum volume of the flask in order that no liquid water be present in the flask?

95. Based on the phase diagram of CO_2 shown in Figure 12.39(b), describe the state changes that occur when the temperature of CO_2 is increased from 190 K to 350 K at a constant pressure of (a) 1 atm, (b) 5.1 atm, (c) 10 atm, and (d) 100 atm.

96. Consider a planet where the pressure of the atmosphere at sea level is 2500 mmHg. Does water behave in a way that can sustain life on the planet?

CHALLENGE PROBLEMS

97. Liquid nitrogen can be used as a cryogenic substance to obtain low temperatures. Under atmospheric pressure, liquid nitrogen boils at 77 K, allowing low temperatures to be reached. However, if the nitrogen is placed in a sealed, insulated container connected to a vacuum pump, even lower temperatures can be reached. Why? If the vacuum pump has sufficient capacity and is left on for an extended period of time, the liquid nitrogen will start to freeze. Explain.

98. Given that the heat of fusion of water is −6.02 kJ/mol, the heat capacity of $H_2O(l)$ is 75.2 J/mol · K, and the heat capacity of $H_2O(s)$ is 37.7 J/mol · K, calculate the heat of fusion of water at −10 °C.

99. The heat of combustion of CH_4 is 890.4 kJ/mol, and the heat capacity of H_2O is 75.2 J/mol · K. Find the volume of methane measured at 298 K and 1.00 atm required to convert 1.00 L of water at 298 K to water vapor at 373 K.

100. Two liquids, A and B, have vapor pressures at a given temperature of 24 mmHg and 36 mmHg, respectively. We prepare solutions of A and B at a given temperature and measure the total pressures above the solutions. We obtain these data:

Solution	Amt A (mol)	Amt B (mol)	*P* (mmHg)
1	1	1	30
2	2	1	28
3	1	2	32
4	1	3	33

Predict the total pressure above a solution of 5 mol A and 1 mol B.

101. Three 1.0-L flasks, maintained at 308 K, are connected to each other with stopcocks. Initially, the stopcocks are closed. One of the flasks contains 1.0 atm of N_2; the second, 2.0 g of H_2O; and the third, 0.50 g of ethanol, C_2H_6O. The vapor pressure of H_2O at 308 K is 42 mmHg, and that of ethanol is 102 mmHg. The stopcocks are then opened and the contents mix freely. What is the pressure?

102. Butane (C_4H_{10}) has a heat of vaporization of 22.44 kJ/mol and a normal boiling point of −0.4 °C. A 250-mL sealed flask contains 0.55 g of butane at −22 °C. How much butane is present as a liquid? If the butane is warmed to 25 °C, how much is present as a liquid?

CONCEPTUAL PROBLEMS

103. The following image is an electrostatic potential map for ethylene oxide, $(CH_2)_2O$, a polar molecule. Use the electrostatic potential map to predict the geometry for how one ethylene oxide molecule interacts with another. Draw structural formulas, using the 3D bond notation introduced in Section 11.4, to show the geometry of the interaction.

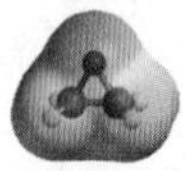

104. One prediction of global warming is the melting of global ice, which may result in coastal flooding. A criticism of this prediction is that the melting of icebergs does not increase ocean levels any more than the melting of ice in a glass of water increases the level of liquid in the glass. Is this a valid criticism? Does the melting of an ice cube in a cup of water raise the level of the liquid in the cup? Why or why not? In response to this criticism, scientists have asserted that they are not worried about melting icebergs, but rather the melting of ice sheets that sit on the continent of Antarctica. Would the melting of this ice increase ocean levels? Why or why not?

105. The rate of vaporization depends on the surface area of the liquid. However, the vapor pressure of a liquid does not depend on the surface area. Explain.

106. Substance A has a smaller heat of vaporization than substance B. Which of the two substances will undergo a larger change in vapor pressure for a given change in temperature?

107. The density of a substance is greater in its solid state than in its liquid state. If the triple point in the phase diagram of the substance is below 1.0 atm, which will necessarily be at a lower temperature, the triple point or the normal melting point?

108. A substance has a heat of vaporization of ΔH_{vap} and a heat of fusion of ΔH_{fus}. Express the heat of sublimation in terms of ΔH_{vap} and ΔH_{fus}.

109. Examine the heating curve for water in Section 12.7 (Figure 12.36). If heat is added to the water at a constant rate, which of the three segments in which temperature is rising will have the least steep slope? Why?

110. A root cellar is an underground chamber used to store fruits, vegetables, and even meats. In extreme cold, farmers put large vats of water into the root cellar to prevent the fruits and vegetables from freezing. Explain why this works.

111. Suggest an explanation for the observation that the heat of fusion of a substance is always smaller than its heat of vaporization.

112. Refer to Figure 12.36 to answer each question.

a. A sample of steam begins on the line segment labeled 5 on the graph. Is heat absorbed or released in moving from the line segment labeled 5 to the line segment labeled 3? What is the sign of *q* for this change?

b. In moving from left to right along the line segment labeled 2 on the graph, heat is absorbed, but the temperature remains constant. Where does the heat go?

c. How would the graph change if it were for another substance (other than water)?

QUESTIONS FOR GROUP WORK

Active Classroom Learning

Discuss these questions with the group and record your consensus answer.

113. The boiling points of three compounds are tabulated here.

	Molar Mass	Boiling Point
2-hexanone	100.16	128 °C
heptane	100.20	98 °C
1-hexanol	102.17	156 °C

Answer the following questions without looking up the structures for these molecules: Which compound experiences hydrogen bonding? Which compound is polar but is unable to experience hydrogen bonding? Which is neither polar nor capable of hydrogen bonding? Explain your answers.

114. The vapor pressure for pure water and pure acetone is measured as a function of temperature. In each case, a graph of the log of the vapor pressure versus $1/T$ is found to be a straight line. The slope of the line for water is −4895 K, and the slope of the line for acetone is −3765 K. Determine ΔH_{vap} for each substance. Account for the difference by discussing the molecular structure of the two molecules.

115. Based on the heating curve for water, does it take more energy to melt a mole of water or to boil a mole of water? Does it take more energy to warm the solid, the liquid, or the gas by 10 °C? Explain your answers clearly.

116. Sketch the phase diagram for carbon dioxide. If you have carbon dioxide at 1.0 atm and 25 °C, could you make it a liquid by cooling it down? How could you make it a liquid at 25 °C? If you increase the pressure of carbon dioxide that is at body temperature (37 °C), will it ever liquefy?

DATA INTERPRETATION AND ANALYSIS

Intermolecular Forces of Group 6A Hydrides

117. We have seen that molar mass and molecular structure influence the boiling point of a substance. We can see these two factors at work in the boiling points of the group 6A hydrides shown in the following graph.

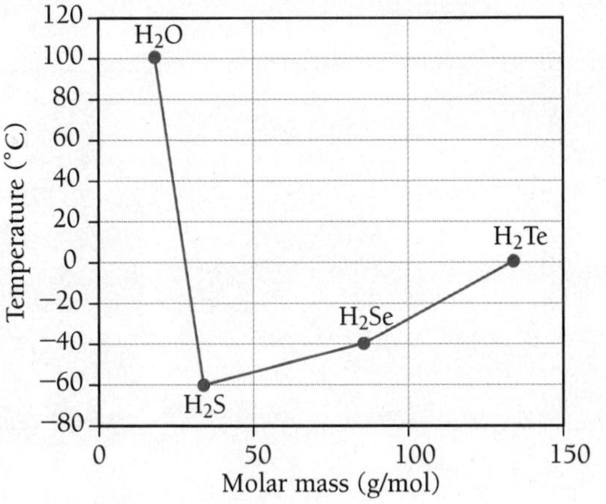

▲ Boiling Point versus Molar Mass of Group 6A Hydrides

In order to disentangle the effects of molar mass and molecular structure on the boiling point, consider the data in the following table.

Compound	Molar Mass (g/mol)	*n*-Boiling Point (°C)	Dipole Moment (D)	Polarizability (10^{-24} cm^3)
H_2O	18.01	100	1.85	1.45
H_2S	34.08	−60	1.10	3.81
H_2Se	80.98	−42.2	0.41	4.71
H_2Te	129.6	−2.2	0.22	5.01

Use the information in the graph and the table to answer the following questions.

a. Does molar mass alone correlate with the trend in the boiling points for the group 6A hydrides?

b. Which boiling points in the graph correlate with polarizability? What type of intermolecular force correlates with polarizability?

c. Use the data in the table to explain the anomalously high boiling point of water.

Cc ANSWERS TO CONCEPTUAL CONNECTIONS

States of Matter

12.1 **(c)** Gases are compressible because the atoms or molecules in a gas are separated by large distances. An increase in pressure forces the atoms or molecules closer together, reducing the gas's volume.

State Changes

12.2 **(a)** When water boils, it simply changes state from liquid to gas. Water molecules do not decompose during boiling.

Dispersion Forces

12.3 **(c)** I_2 has the highest boiling point because it has the highest molar mass. Since the halogens are all similar in other ways, we expect I_2 to have the greatest dispersion forces and therefore the highest boiling point (and in fact it does).

Dipole–Dipole Interaction

12.4 **(a)**

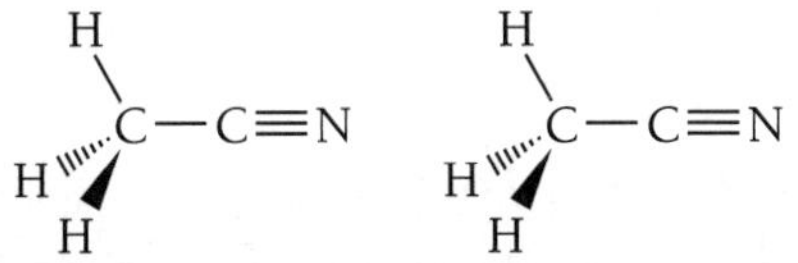

Since acetonitrile is polar, the more negative end (in the electrostatic potential map) is attracted to the positive end (in the electrostatic potential map) of its neighbor.

Intermolecular Forces and Boiling Point

12.5 **(a)** CH_3OH. The compounds all have similar molar masses, so the dispersion forces are similar in all three. CO is polar, but because CH_3OH contains H directly bonded to O, it has hydrogen bonding, resulting in the highest boiling point.

Vaporization

12.6 **(d)** The rate of vaporization increases with increasing temperature and with increasing surface area. This sample has the combined highest temperature and highest surface. (The 250-mL beaker has a greater diameter than the 100-mL beaker, and therefore the water is spread out over a greater area.)

Vapor Pressure

12.7 **(b)** Although the *rate of vaporization* increases with increasing surface area, the *vapor pressure* of a liquid is independent of surface area. An increase in surface area increases both the rate of vaporization and the rate of condensation—the effects exactly cancel, and the vapor pressure does not change.

Boiling Point

12.8 **(a)** According to Figure 12.28, water has a vapor pressure of 200 torr at about 66 °C, so at an external pressure of 200 torr, water boils at 66 °C.

Cooling of Water with Ice

12.9 **(b)** The warming of the ice from −10 °C to 0 °C absorbs only 20.9 J/g of ice. The melting of the ice, however, absorbs about 334 J/g of ice. (You can obtain this value by dividing the heat of fusion of water by its molar mass.) Therefore, the melting of the ice produces a larger temperature decrease in the water than does the warming of the ice.

Phase Diagrams

12.10 **(b)** The solid will sublime into a gas. Since the pressure is below the triple point, the liquid state is not stable.

Should we not suppose that in the formation of a crystal, the particles are not only established in rows and columns set in regular figures, but also by means of some polar property have turned identical sides in identical directions?

—ISAAC NEWTON (1642–1727)

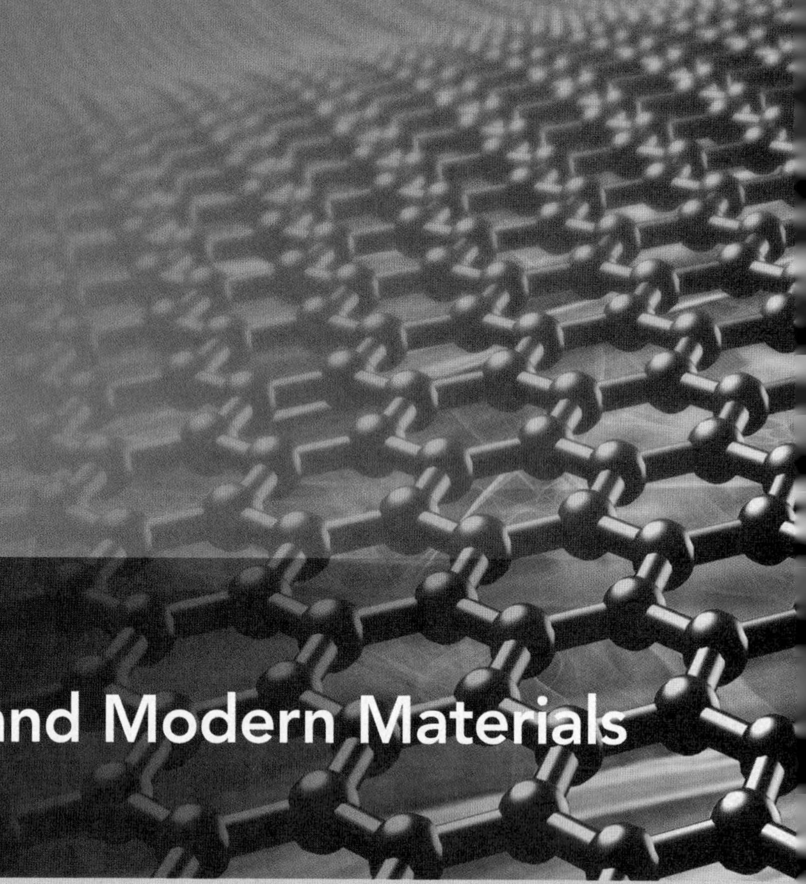

CHAPTER 13 Solids and Modern Materials

In this chapter, we focus on the solid state of matter. We first examine the structures of solids, keeping in mind that these structures determine the properties of solids. For example, the repeating hexagonal pattern of water molecules in crystalline ice determines the hexagonal shape of a snowflake, and the repeating cubic pattern of sodium and chloride ions in sodium chloride determines the cubic shape of salt grains. We then turn our attention to the study and development of solids with unique and useful properties, a field known as *materials science*. The ceramics that compose your coffee cups, the semiconductors in your electronic devices, and the plastics that are most likely all around you even at this moment are materials developed to have specific properties that serve specific purposes. In this chapter, we take a brief look at each of these kinds of materials.

Graphene is the thinnest material known—it is only one atom thick.

13.1 Friday Night Experiments: The Discovery of Graphene 541

13.2 X-Ray Crystallography 542

13.3 Unit Cells and Basic Structures 545

13.4 The Fundamental Types of Crystalline Solids 552

13.5 The Structures of Ionic Solids 556

13.6 Network Covalent Atomic Solids: Carbon and Silicates 558

13.7 Ceramics, Cement, and Glass 561

13.8 Semiconductors and Band Theory 563

13.9 Polymers and Plastics 565

LEARNING OUTCOMES 571

13.1 Friday Night Experiments: The Discovery of Graphene

In 2010, Andre Geim (1958–) and Konstantin Novoselov (1974–) were awarded the Nobel Prize in Physics for the discovery of a new material—**graphene**. Graphene is the thinnest known material (only one atom thick); it is also the strongest. It conducts heat and electricity, it is transparent, and it is completely impermeable to all substances, including helium. Although its many possible applications are yet to be realized, graphene may one day be used to make faster computers, foldable touchscreens, ultrathin light panels, and super-strong plastics to construct satellites, airplanes, ships, and cars. And how did these scientists discover this wonder material? Through *Friday night experiments*.

Most successful modern scientists work in a narrow field of study, chipping away at a problem about which they have become experts. Andre Geim also worked this way—but not all of the time. Geim often ventured into what he calls *lateral ideas*, which were explorations into fields far from his immediate area of expertise. Over a 15-year period, he explored about two dozen such ideas. These explorations became known as *Friday night experiments* (even though they took much longer than just one night). Most of Geim's Friday night experiments were complete failures, but some succeeded. For example, in one Friday night experiment, Geim was able to suspend an entire frog in a magnetic field. In another, he developed a new kind of tape based on mimicking the toes of a gecko. However, his most successful Friday night experiment was the discovery of graphene.

In 2002, Geim assigned his brand-new graduate student a Friday night experiment as a way to give the student time to get acquainted with the laboratory. His assignment was to make films of graphite "as thin as possible." The graduate student tackled the task by attempting to polish a tablet of graphite down to almost nothingness. In spite of his best efforts, the thinnest sheet he could attain by this method was still pretty thick (about 10 μm).

In a breakthrough moment, a colleague brought Geim a piece of scotch tape that had been adhered to a graphite surface and then removed. The tape had remnants of graphite stuck to it. When Geim examined the graphite flakes under a microscope, he realized that these flakes where much thinner than those his graduate student was able to produce through polishing. In fact, some of the flakes were just one layer thick! Over the next several months, Geim and his colleagues were able to isolate these flakes and measure some of their properties. In 2004, Geim and his colleagues published their results—the discovery of atomically thin carbon—in *Nature*. In 2010, Geim and his closest collaborator on the project, Konstantin Novoselov, were awarded the Nobel Prize in Physics for "groundbreaking experiments regarding the two-dimensional material graphene."

Graphene has been right under our noses for some time. Every time you write with a pencil, layers of graphite flake onto the paper, leaving the familiar gray trail. That trail undoubtedly also contains flakes of graphene—too small to see. Geim and Novoselov were able to see what others had missed and as a result discovered a new wonder material. These kinds of discoveries often have huge impacts on society—although it may take decades to realize and refine their applications.

In this chapter, we look into the world of solids and materials and see how they permanently changed societies, just as graphene may someday change our present society. For example, the discovery of cement led to a revolution in building, the discovery of porcelain led to a revolution in dishware, and the discovery of semiconducting materials made possible the computer and Internet revolution which is still unfolding today. The development of new materials continues to be an active and growing area of research. We begin by examining a technique to determine the structure of solids.

▲ The hexagonal shape of a snowflake derives from the hexagonal arrangement of water molecules in crystalline ice.

13.2 X-Ray Crystallography

In Section 12.2, we discussed the differences between solids, liquids, and gases. Recall that solids can be *crystalline* (composed of atoms or molecules arranged in structures with long-range order) or *amorphous* (composed of atoms or molecules with no long-range order). If you have ever visited the mineral section of a natural history museum and seen crystals with smooth faces and well-defined angles, or if you have carefully observed the hexagonal shapes of snowflakes, you have witnessed some of the effects of the underlying long-range order in crystalline solids. The beautiful geometric shapes that are visible on the macroscopic scale are the result of specific structural patterns on the molecular and atomic scales. But how do we study these patterns? How do we look into the atomic and molecular world to determine the arrangement of the atoms and measure the distances between them? In this section, we examine **X-ray diffraction**, a powerful laboratory technique that enables us to do exactly that.

In Section 8.2, we saw that electromagnetic waves (light waves) interact with each other in a characteristic way called *interference*: they can cancel each other out or reinforce each other, depending on the alignment of their crests and troughs. *Constructive interference* occurs when two waves interact with their crests and troughs in alignment. *Destructive interference* occurs when two waves interact with the crests of one aligning with the troughs of the other. Recall also that when light encounters two slits separated by a distance comparable to the wavelength of the light, constructive and destructive interference produces a characteristic *interference pattern*, consisting of alternating bright and dark lines.

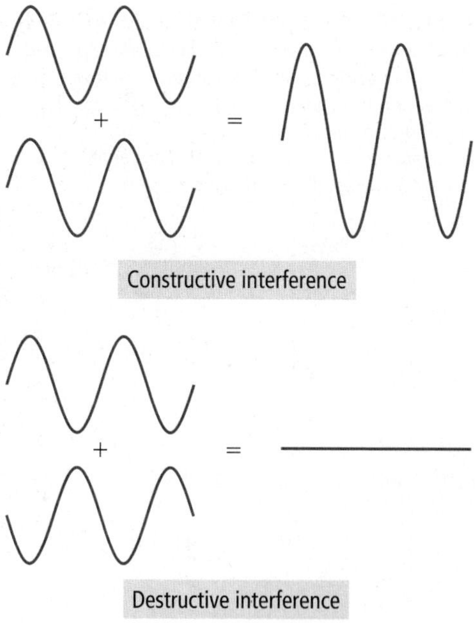

Atomic planes within crystals are separated by about 10^2 pm. As a result, light of similar wavelength (which happens to fall in the X-ray region of the electromagnetic spectrum) forms interference patterns or *diffraction patterns* when it interacts with those atoms. The exact pattern of diffraction reveals the spacing between planes of atoms.

Consider two planes of atoms within a crystalline lattice separated by a distance d, as illustrated in Figure 13.1▼. If two rays of light with wavelength λ that are initially in phase (that is, the crests of one wave are aligned with the crests of the other) diffract from the two planes, the diffracted rays may interfere with each other constructively or destructively, depending on the difference between the path lengths traveled by each ray. If the difference between the two path lengths ($2a$) is an integral number (n) of wavelengths, then the interference is constructive:

$$n\lambda = 2a \quad \text{(criterion for constructive interference)} \qquad [13.1]$$

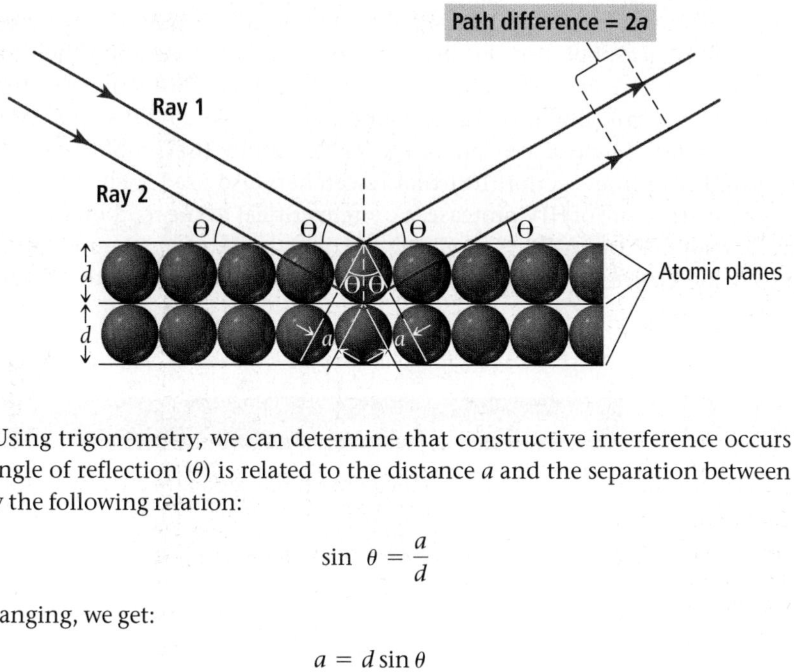

◀ **FIGURE 13.1 Diffraction from a Crystal** When X-rays strike parallel planes of atoms in a crystal, constructive interference occurs if the difference in path length between beams reflected from adjacent planes is an integral number of wavelengths.

Using trigonometry, we can determine that constructive interference occurs when the angle of reflection (θ) is related to the distance a and the separation between layers (d) by the following relation:

$$\sin\theta = \frac{a}{d} \qquad [13.2]$$

Rearranging, we get:

$$a = d\sin\theta \qquad [13.3]$$

By substituting Equation 13.3 into Equation 13.1, we arrive at the following important relationship:

$$n\lambda = 2d\sin\theta \qquad \text{Bragg's law}$$

This equation is *Bragg's law*. For a given wavelength of light incident on atoms arranged in layers, we can measure the angle that produces constructive interference (which appears as a bright spot on the X-ray diffraction pattern) and then calculate d, the distance between the atomic layers:

$$d = \frac{n\lambda}{2\sin\theta} \qquad [13.4]$$

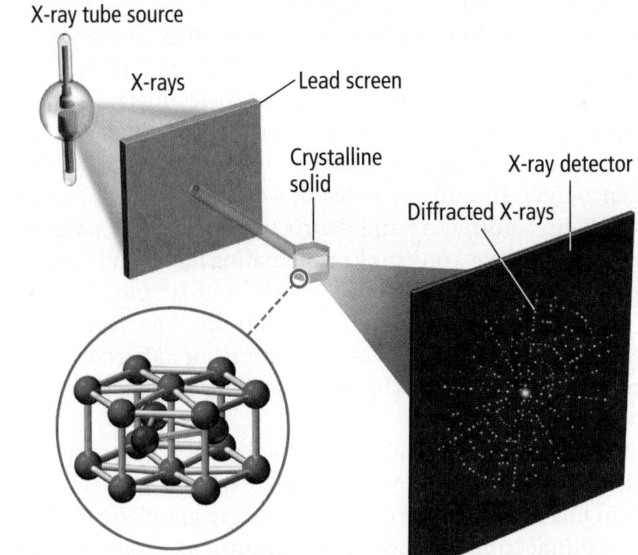

▶ **FIGURE 13.2 X-Ray Diffraction Analysis** In X-ray crystallography, an X-ray beam is passed through a sample, which is rotated to allow diffraction from different crystalline planes. The resulting patterns, representing constructive interference from various planes, are analyzed to determine crystalline structure.

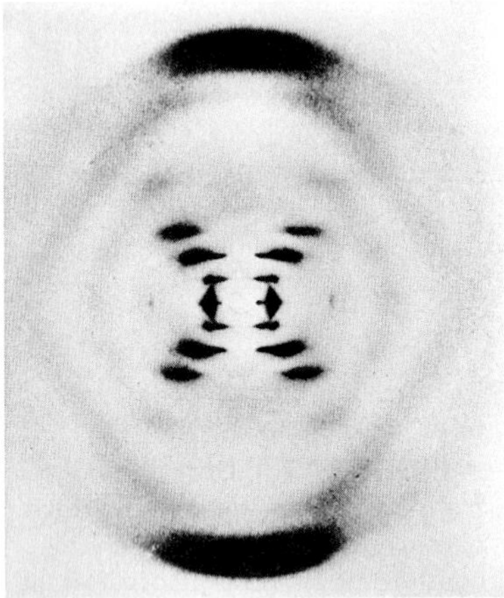

In a modern X-ray diffractometer (Figure 13.2▲), a computer collects and analyzes the diffraction pattern from a crystal. By rotating the crystal and collecting the resulting diffraction patterns at different angles, the distances between various crystalline planes can be measured, eventually yielding the entire crystalline structure. This process is **X-ray crystallography**.

Researchers use X-ray crystallography to determine not only the structures of simple atomic lattices, but also the structures of proteins, DNA, and other biologically important molecules. For example, the famous X-ray diffraction photograph shown in the margin, obtained by Rosalind Franklin (1920–1958) and Maurice Wilkins (1916–2004), helped Watson and Crick determine the double-helical structure of DNA. Recall from Section 10.1 that researchers also used X-ray diffraction to determine the structure of HIV protease, a protein critical to the reproduction of HIV and the development of AIDS. Knowledge of that structure was then employed to design drug molecules to inhibit the action of HIV protease and halt the advance of the disease.

EXAMPLE 13.1 Using Bragg's Law

When an X-ray beam of $\lambda = 154$ pm is incident on the surface of an iron crystal, it produces a maximum diffraction at an angle of $\theta = 32.6°$. Assuming $n = 1$, calculate the separation between layers of iron atoms in the crystal.

SOLUTION

To solve this problem, use Bragg's law in the form given by Equation 13.4. The distance, d, is the separation between layers in the crystal.	$d = \dfrac{n\lambda}{2 \sin \theta}$ $= \dfrac{154 \text{ pm}}{2 \sin(32.6°)}$ $= 143$ pm

FOR PRACTICE 13.1 The spacing between layers of molybdenum atoms is 157 pm. Calculate the angle at which 154-pm X-rays produce a maximum reflection for $n = 1$.

13.3 Unit Cells and Basic Structures

WATCH **NOW!**

KEY CONCEPT VIDEO 13.3
Unit Cells: Simple Cubic, Body-Centered Cubic, and Face-Centered Cubic

X-ray crystallography allows us to determine the regular arrangements of atoms within a crystalline solid. This arrangement is called the **crystalline lattice**. The crystalline lattice of any solid is nature's way of aggregating the particles to minimize their energy. We represent the crystalline lattice with a small collection of atoms, ions, or molecules called the **unit cell**. When the unit cell is repeated over and over—like the tiles of a floor or the pattern in a wallpaper design, but in three dimensions—the entire lattice is reproduced. For example, consider the two-dimensional crystalline lattice shown here:

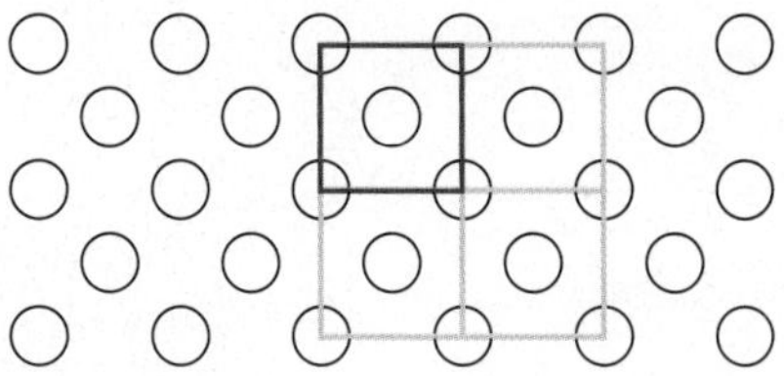

The unit cell for this lattice is the dark-colored square. Each circle represents an atom, ion, or molecule. Repeating the pattern in the square throughout the two-dimensional space generates the entire lattice.

Cubic Unit Cells

Many different unit cells exist, and we often classify unit cells by their symmetry. Figure 13.3▼ shows the different fundamental types of unit cells. In this book, we focus primarily on *cubic unit cells* (although we look at one hexagonal unit cell). Cubic unit cells are characterized by equal edge lengths and 90° angles at their corners. Figure 13.4▶ lists three cubic unit cells—simple cubic, body-centered cubic, and face-centered cubic—along with some of their basic characteristics. The two colors in the images in this table make it easier to visualize the different positions of the atoms; the colors *do not* represent different *kinds* of atoms. For these unit cells, *each atom in any one structure is identical to the other atoms in that structure.*

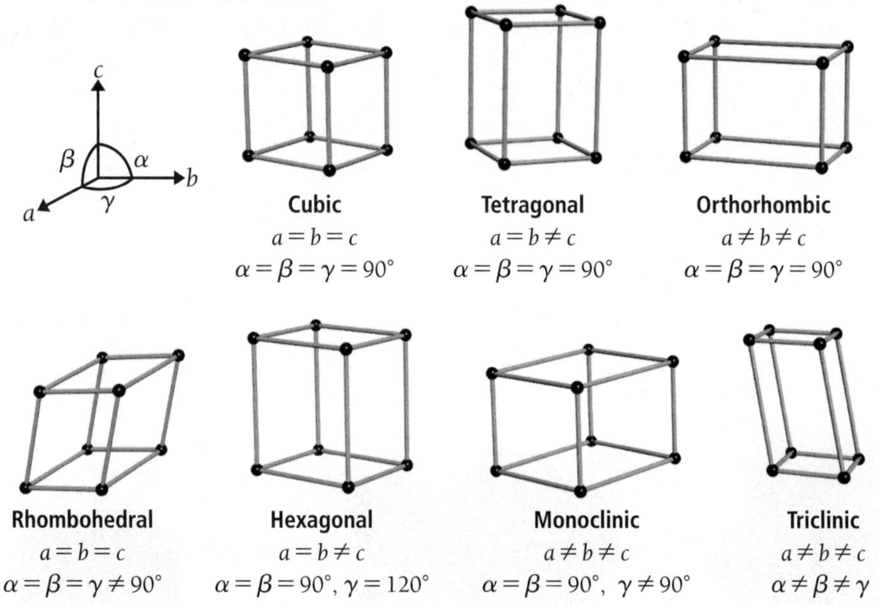

▲ **FIGURE 13.3 The Seven Fundamental Types of Unit Cells** In this book, we focus on cubic unit cells.

Cubic Cell Name	Atoms per Unit Cell	Structure	Coordination Number	Edge Length in terms of r	Packing Efficiency (fraction of volume occupied)
Simple Cubic	1		6	$2r$	52%
Body-Centered Cubic	2		8	$\frac{4r}{\sqrt{3}}$	68%
Face-Centered Cubic	4		12	$2\sqrt{2}r$	74%

▲ **FIGURE 13.4 Cubic Crystalline Lattices** The different colors used for the atoms in this figure are for clarity only. All atoms within each structure are identical. Unit cells, such as the cubic ones shown here, are customarily portrayed with "whole" atoms, even though only a part of the whole atom may actually be in the unit cell.

Simple cubic

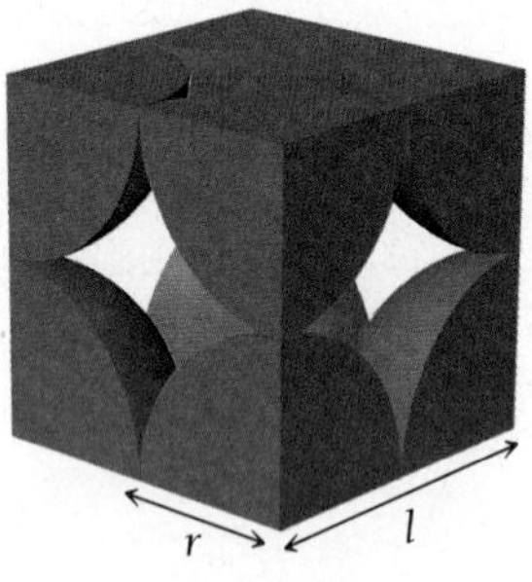

$l = 2r$

▲ In the simple cubic lattice, the atoms touch along each edge so that the edge length is $2r$.

The **simple cubic** unit cell (Figure 13.5▼) consists of a cube with one atom at each corner. As we can see in the figure at the left, the atoms touch along each edge of the cube, so the edge length is twice the radius of the atoms ($l = 2r$).

Even though it may seem like the unit cell contains eight atoms, it actually contains only one as close examination makes evident. Each corner atom is shared by eight other unit cells. In other words, any one unit cell actually contains only one-eighth of each of the eight atoms at its corners, for a total of only one atom per unit cell.

Simple Cubic Unit Cell

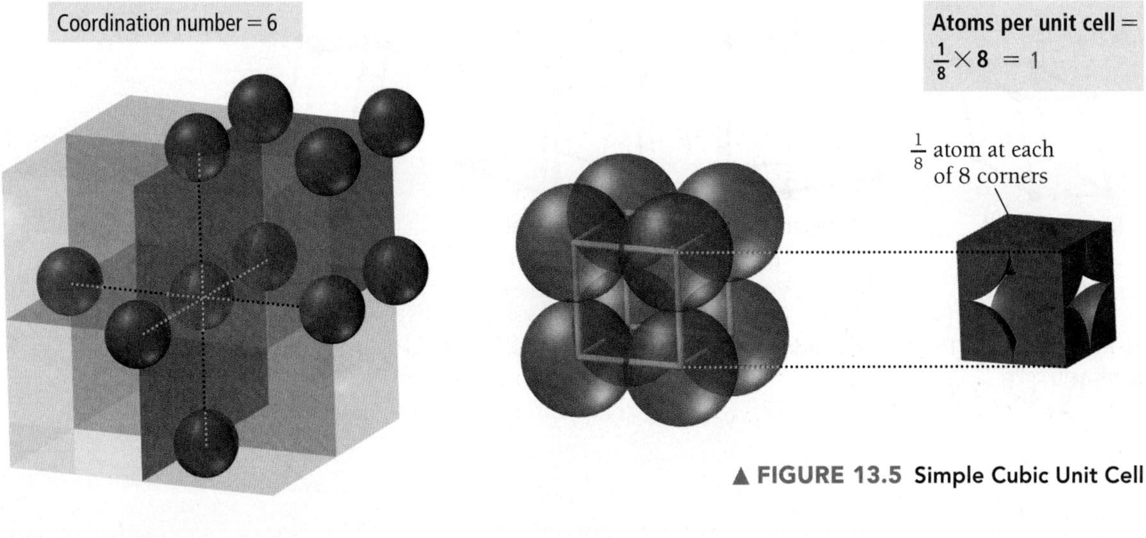

▲ **FIGURE 13.5 Simple Cubic Unit Cell**

A characteristic feature of any unit cell is the **coordination number**, the number of atoms with which each atom is in *direct contact*. The coordination number is the number of atoms with which a particular atom can strongly interact. The simple cubic unit cell has a coordination number of 6; any one atom touches only six others, as you can see in Figure 13.5. A quantity closely related to the coordination number is the **packing efficiency**, the percentage of the volume of the unit cell occupied by the spheres. The higher the coordination number is, the greater the packing efficiency is. The simple cubic unit cell has a packing efficiency of 52%—it contains a lot of empty space.

EXAMPLE 13.2 Calculating the Packing Efficiency of a Unit Cell

Calculate the packing efficiency of the simple cubic unit cell.

SOLUTION

The packing efficiency is defined as the ratio of the volume of the unit cell occupied by atoms to the volume of the unit cell itself, all multiplied by 100%.	$\text{Packing Efficiency} = \dfrac{V_{\text{atom}}}{V_{\text{unit cell}}} \times 100\%$
First, determine the volume occupied by atoms. Each unit cell contains one atom, so the volume of the unit cell occupied by atoms is simply the volume of one atom.	$V_{\text{atom}} = \dfrac{4}{3}\pi r^3$
Next, calculate the volume of the cube in terms of the radius of the atom. The volume of a cube is its edge length cubed, and the edge length of the simple cubic unit cell is $2r$.	$V_{\text{unit cell}} = l^3 = (2r)^3 = 8r^3$
Calculate the packing efficiency by dividing the volume of the atom by the volume of the unit cell and multiplying by 100%.	$\text{Packing Efficiency} = \dfrac{V_{\text{atom}}}{V_{\text{unit cell}}} \times 100\% = \dfrac{\frac{4}{3}\pi r^3}{8r^3} \times 100\% = \dfrac{\frac{4}{3}\pi \cancel{r^3}}{8\cancel{r^3}} \times 100\% = \dfrac{4}{24}\pi \times 100\% = 52.36\%$

FOR PRACTICE 13.2 Calculate the packing efficiency of the two-dimensional lattice shown here:

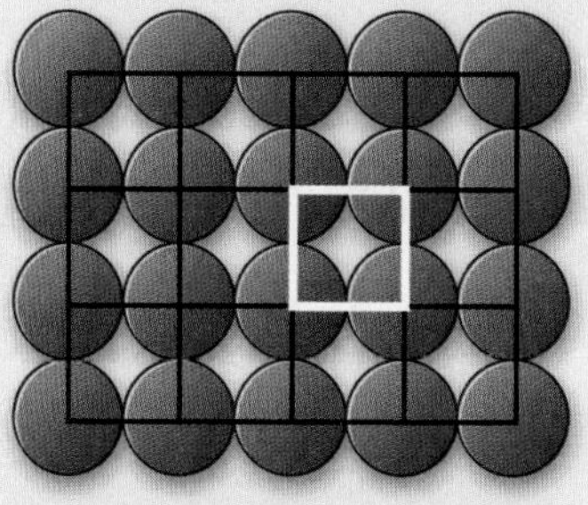

The **body-centered cubic** unit cell (Figure 13.6▶) consists of a cube with one atom at each corner and one atom (of the same kind) in the very center of the cube. Note that in the body-centered unit cell, the atoms *do not* touch along each edge of the cube, but instead touch along the diagonal line that runs from one corner, through the

Body-Centered Cubic Unit Cell

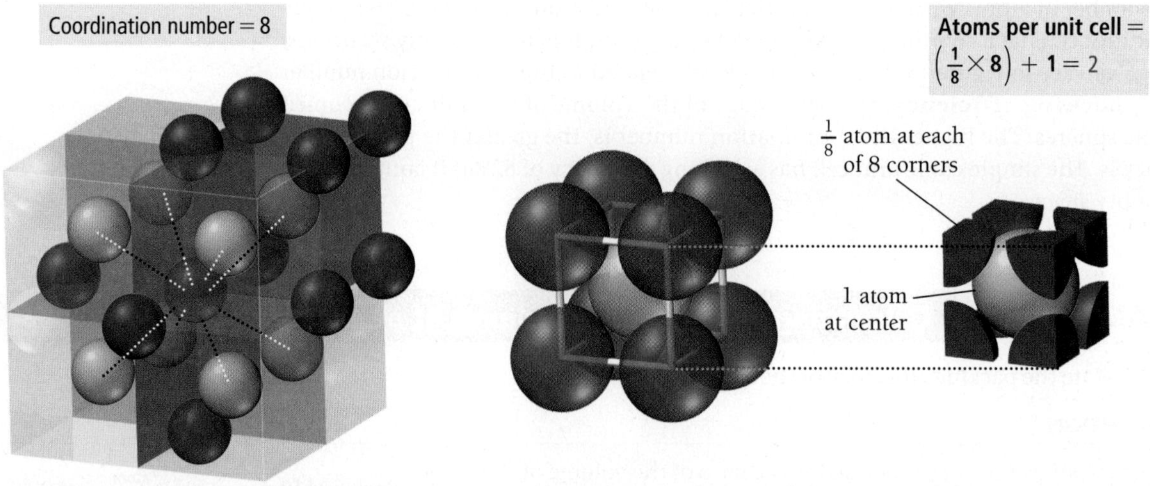

▲ FIGURE 13.6 Body-Centered Cubic Crystal Structure The different colors used for the atoms in this figure are for clarity only. All atoms within the structure are identical.

middle of the cube, to the opposite corner. The edge length in terms of the atomic radius is therefore $l = 4r/\sqrt{3}$ as shown here:

Body-centered cubic

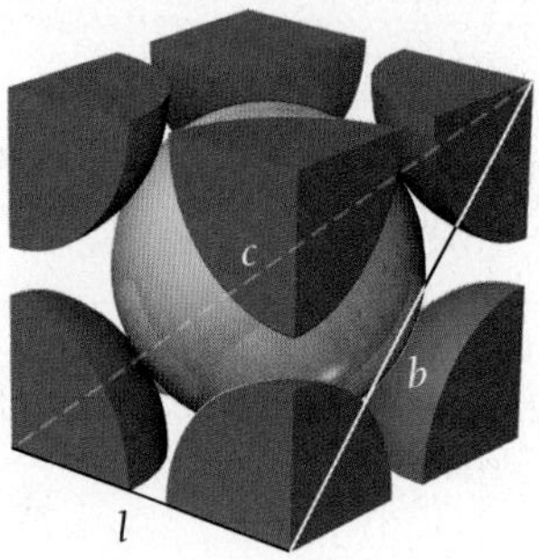

$$c^2 = b^2 + l^2 \qquad b^2 = l^2 + l^2$$
$$c = 4r \qquad b^2 = 2l^2$$
$$(4r)^2 = 2l^2 + l^2$$
$$(4r)^2 = 3l^2$$
$$l^2 = \frac{(4r)^2}{3}$$
$$l = \frac{4r}{\sqrt{3}}$$

► In the body-centered cubic lattice, the atoms touch only along the cube diagonal. The edge length is $4r/\sqrt{3}$.

The body-centered unit cell contains two atoms per unit cell because the center atom is not shared with any other neighboring cells. The coordination number of the body-centered cubic unit cell is 8, which we can see by examining the atom in the very center of the cube, which touches eight atoms at the corners. The packing efficiency for the body-centered unit cell is 68%, significantly higher than for the simple cubic unit cell. Each atom in this structure strongly interacts with more atoms than each atom in the simple cubic unit cell.

ANSWER **NOW!**

13.1 Cc Conceptual Connection

EDGE LENGTH AND ATOMIC RADIUS A body-centered cubic unit cell has an edge length of 588 pm. What is the radius of the atoms composing the unit cell?

(a) 588 pm **(b)** 294 pm **(c)** 255 pm **(d)** 208 pm

WATCH **NOW!**

INTERACTIVE WORKED EXAMPLE 13.3

EXAMPLE 13.3 Relating Unit Cell Volume, Edge Length, and Atomic Radius

A body-centered cubic unit cell has a volume of 4.32×10^{-23} cm^3. Find the radius of the atom in pm.

SORT You are given the volume of a unit cell and asked to find the radius of the atom.

GIVEN: $V = 4.32 \times 10^{-23}$ cm^3

FIND: r (in pm)

STRATEGIZE Use the given volume to find the edge length of the unit cell.

Then use the edge length to determine the radius of the atom.

CONCEPTUAL PLAN

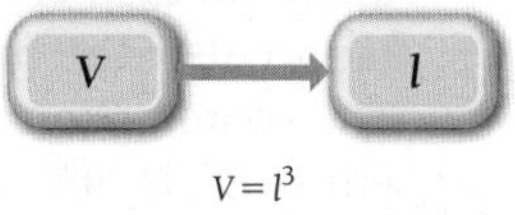

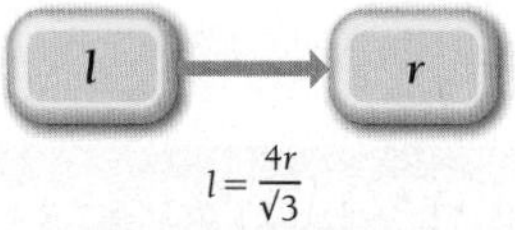

RELATIONSHIPS USED:

$V = l^3$ (Volume of a cube)

$l = \frac{4r}{\sqrt{3}}$ (Edge length of body-centered cubic unit cell)

SOLVE

Solve the equation for the volume of a cube for l and substitute in the given value for V to find l.

Solve the equation for the edge length of a body-centered cubic unit cell for r and substitute in the value of l (from the previous step) to find r.

Convert r from cm to m and then to pm.

SOLUTION

$$V = l^3$$

$$l = \sqrt[3]{V} = \sqrt[3]{4.32 \times 10^{-23}\ \text{cm}^3} = 3.50\underline{8}8 \times 10^{-8}\ \text{cm}$$

$$l = \frac{4r}{\sqrt{3}}$$

$$r = \frac{\sqrt{3}l}{4} = \frac{\sqrt{3}(3.50\underline{8}8 \times 10^{-8}\ \text{cm})}{4} = 1.51\underline{9}3 \times 10^{-8}\ \text{cm}$$

$$1.51\underline{9}3 \times 10^{-8}\ \cancel{\text{cm}} \times \frac{0.01\ \cancel{\text{m}}}{1\ \cancel{\text{cm}}} \times \frac{1\ \text{pm}}{10^{-12}\ \cancel{\text{m}}} = 152\ \text{pm}$$

CHECK The units of the answer (pm) are correct. The magnitude is reasonable because atomic radii range roughly from 50 to 200 pm.

FOR PRACTICE 13.3 An atom has radius of 138 pm and crystallizes in the body-centered cubic unit cell. What is the volume of the unit cell in cm^3?

▶ In the face-centered cubic lattice, the atoms touch along a face diagonal. The edge length is $2\sqrt{2}r$.

The **face-centered cubic** unit cell (Figure 13.7▼) is a cube with one atom at each corner and one atom (of the same kind) in the center of each cube face. Note that in the face-centered unit cell (like the body-centered unit cell), the atoms *do not* touch along each edge of the cube. Instead, the atoms touch *along the face diagonal*. The edge length in terms of the atomic radius is therefore $l = 2\sqrt{2}r$, as shown here.

$$b^2 = l^2 + l^2 = 2l^2$$
$$b = 4r$$
$$(4r)^2 = 2l^2$$
$$l^2 = \frac{(4r)^2}{2}$$
$$l = \frac{4r}{2}$$
$$= 2\ 2r$$

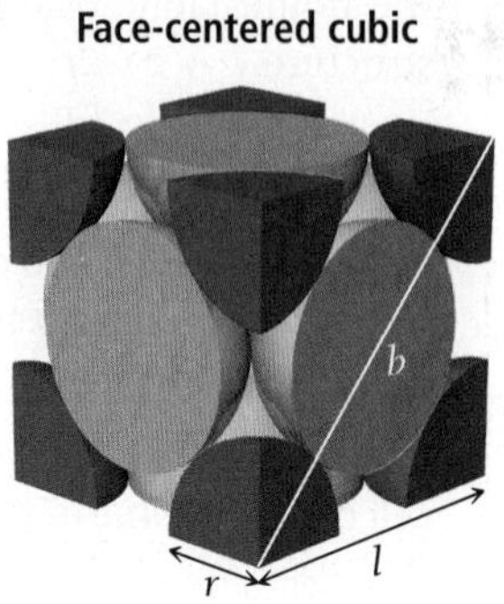

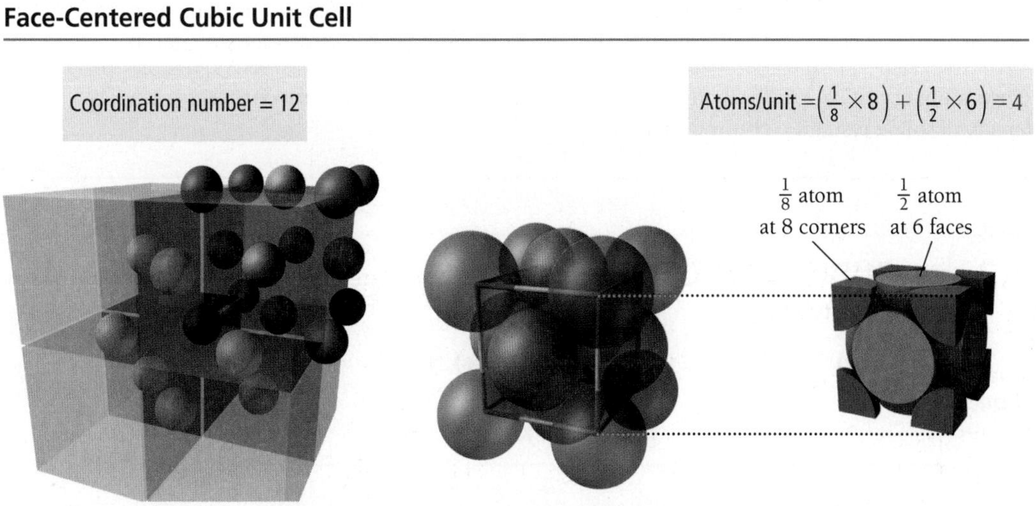

◀ **FIGURE 13.7 Face-Centered Cubic Crystal Structure** The different colors used on the atoms in this figure are for clarity only. All atoms within the structure are identical.

The face-centered unit cell contains four atoms per unit cell because the center atoms on each of the six faces are shared between two unit cells. There are $\frac{1}{2} \times 6 = 3$ face-centered atoms plus $\frac{1}{8} \times 8 = 1$ corner atom, for a total of four atoms per unit cell. The coordination number of the face-centered cubic unit cell is 12, and its packing efficiency is 74%. In this structure, any one atom strongly interacts with more atoms than the atoms in either the simple cubic unit cell or the body-centered cubic unit cell.

WATCH **NOW!**
INTERACTIVE WORKED EXAMPLE 13.4

EXAMPLE 13.4 Relating Density to Crystal Structure

Aluminum crystallizes with a face-centered cubic unit cell. The radius of an aluminum atom is 143 pm. Calculate the density of solid crystalline aluminum in g/cm^3.

SORT You are given the radius of an aluminum atom and its crystal structure. You are asked to find the density of solid aluminum.

GIVEN: $r = 143$ pm, face-centered cubic

FIND: d

STRATEGIZE The conceptual plan is based on the definition of density.
Since the unit cell has the physical properties of the entire crystal, you can find the mass and volume of the unit cell and use these to calculate its density.

CONCEPTUAL PLAN

$$d = m/V$$
$$m = \text{mass of unit cell}$$
$$= \text{number of atoms in unit cell} \times \text{mass of each atom}$$
$$V = \text{volume of unit cell}$$
$$= (\text{edge length})^3$$

SOLVE Begin by finding the mass of the unit cell. Determine the mass of an aluminum atom from its molar mass. Because the face-centered cubic unit cell contains four atoms per unit cell, multiply the mass of aluminum by 4 to get the mass of a unit cell.

SOLUTION

$$m(\text{Al atom}) = 26.98 \frac{\text{g}}{\cancel{\text{mol}}} \times \frac{1\ \cancel{\text{mol}}}{6.022 \times 10^{23}\ \text{atoms}}$$
$$= 4.480 \times 10^{-23}\ \text{g/atom}$$
$$m(\text{unit cell}) = 4\ \cancel{\text{atoms}}(4.480 \times 10^{-23}\ \text{g}/\cancel{\text{atom}})$$
$$= 1.792 \times 10^{-22}\ \text{g}$$

Next, calculate the edge length (l) of the unit cell (in m) from the atomic radius of aluminum. For the face-centered cubic structure, $l = 2\sqrt{2}r$.

$$l = 2\sqrt{2}r$$
$$= 2\sqrt{2}(143\ \text{pm})$$
$$= 2\sqrt{2}(143 \times 10^{-12}\ \text{m})$$
$$= 4.045 \times 10^{-10}\ \text{m}$$

Calculate the volume of the unit cell (in cm) by converting the edge length to cm and cubing the edge length. (Use centimeters because you want to report the density in units of g/cm^3.)

$$V = l^3$$
$$= \left(4.045 \times 10^{-10}\ \cancel{\text{m}} \times \frac{1\ \text{cm}}{10^{-2}\ \cancel{\text{m}}}\right)^3$$
$$= 6.618 \times 10^{-23}\ \text{cm}^3$$

Finally, calculate the density by dividing the mass of the unit cell by the volume of the unit cell.

$$d = \frac{m}{V} = \frac{1.792 \times 10^{-22}\ \text{g}}{6.618 \times 10^{-23}\ \text{cm}^3}$$
$$= 2.71\ \text{g/cm}^3$$

CHECK The units of the answer are correct. The magnitude of the answer is reasonable because the density is greater than 1 g/cm^3 (as you would expect for metals), but still not too high (because aluminum is a low-density metal).

FOR PRACTICE 13.4 Chromium crystallizes with a body-centered cubic unit cell. The radius of a chromium atom is 125 pm. Calculate the density of solid crystalline chromium in g/cm^3.

ANSWER **NOW!**

13.2 Cc Conceptual Connection

CUBIC STRUCTURES How many atoms are in the unit cell in the face-centered cubic structure?

(a) 1 **(b)** 2 **(c)** 4 **(d)** 14

Closest-Packed Structures

Another way to envision crystal structures, especially useful for metals, in which bonds are not usually directional, is to think of the atoms as stacking in layers, much as fruit is stacked at the grocery store. For example, we can envision the simple cubic structure as one layer of atoms arranged in a square pattern, with the next layer stacking directly over the first, so that the atoms in one layer align exactly on top of the atoms in the layer beneath it, as shown here:

As we saw previously, this crystal structure has a great deal of empty space—only 52% of the volume is occupied by the spheres, and the coordination number is 6.

More space-efficient packing can be achieved by aligning neighboring rows of atoms in a pattern, with one row offset from the next by one-half a sphere, as shown here:

In this way, the atoms pack more closely to each other in any one layer. We can further increase the packing efficiency by placing the next layer *not directly on top of the first*, but again offset so that any one atom actually sits in the indentation formed by three atoms in the layer beneath it, as shown here:

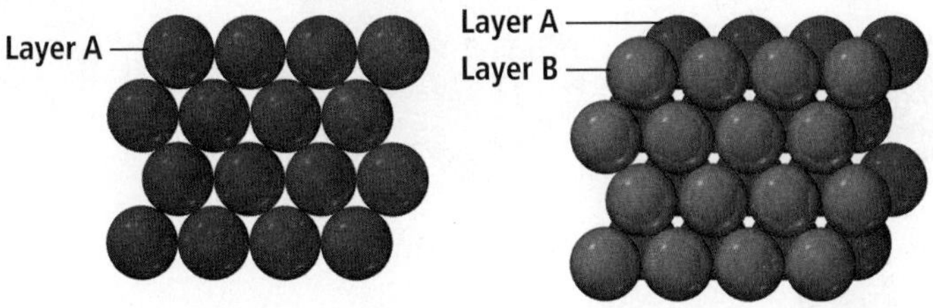

This kind of packing leads to two different crystal structures called *closest-packed structures*, both of which have a packing efficiency of 74% and a coordination number of 12. In the first of these two closest-packed structures—called **hexagonal closest packing**—the third layer of atoms aligns exactly on top of the first, as shown here:

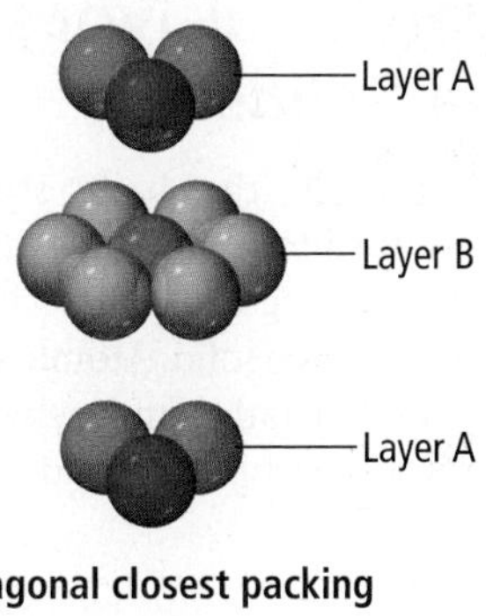

Hexagonal closest packing

Hexagonal Closest Packing

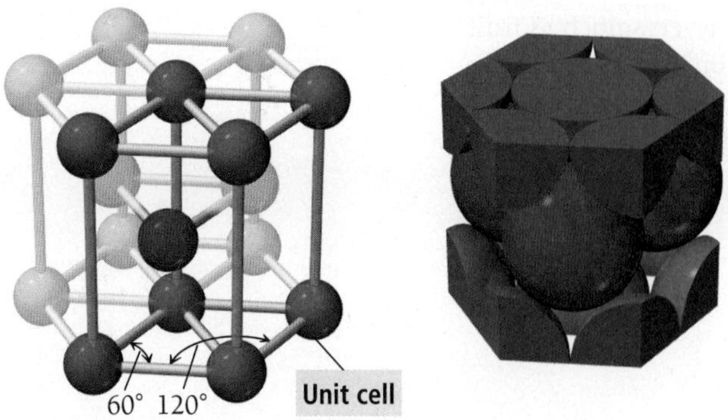

▲ **FIGURE 13.8 Hexagonal Closest-Packing Crystal Structure** The unit cell is shown at left (unfaded part).

The pattern from one layer to the next is ABAB, with the third layer aligning exactly above the first. Notice that the central atom in layer B of this structure is touching six atoms in its own layer, three atoms in the layer above it, and three atoms in the layer below, for a coordination number of 12. The unit cell for this crystal structure is not a cubic unit cell, but a hexagonal one, shown in Figure 13.8◀.

In the second of the two closest-packed structures—called **cubic closest packing**—the third layer of atoms is offset from the first, as shown here:

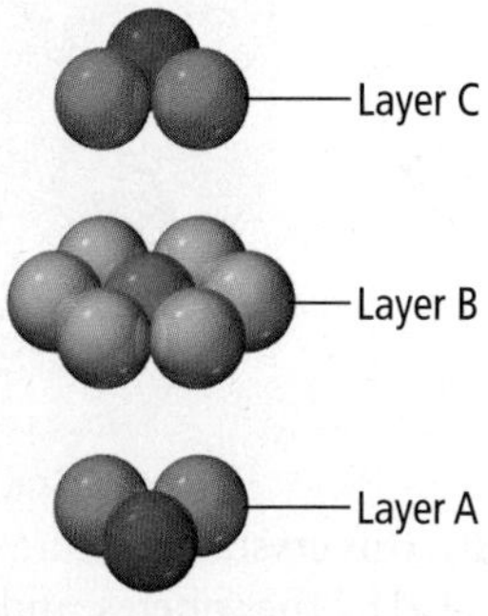

Cubic closest packing

The pattern from one layer to the next is ABCABC, with every fourth layer aligning with the first. Although not simple to visualize, the unit cell for cubic closest packing is the face-centered cubic unit cell, shown in Figure 13.9▼. The cubic closest-packed structure is identical to the face-centered cubic unit cell structure.

Cubic Closest Packed = Face-Centered Cubic

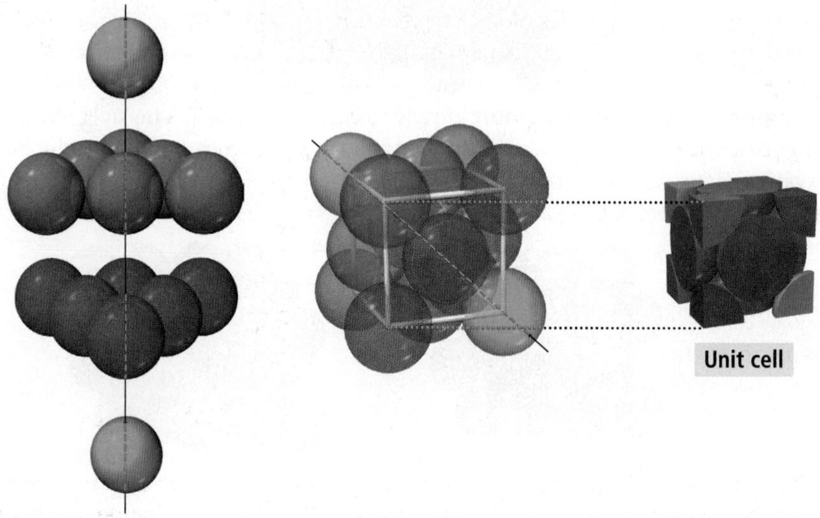

▶ **FIGURE 13.9 Cubic Closest-Packing Crystal Structure** The unit cell of the cubic closest-packed structure is a face-centered cubic.

13.4 The Fundamental Types of Crystalline Solids

We examined some of the basic *structures* of crystalline solids in Section 13.3. In this section, we turn to the different *types* of crystalline solids. We can classify crystalline solids into three categories—molecular, ionic, and atomic—based on the individual particles that compose the solid. Atomic solids can themselves be classified into three categories—nonbonded, metallic, and network covalent—depending on the types of interactions between atoms within the solid. Figure 13.10▶ shows the different categories of crystalline solids.

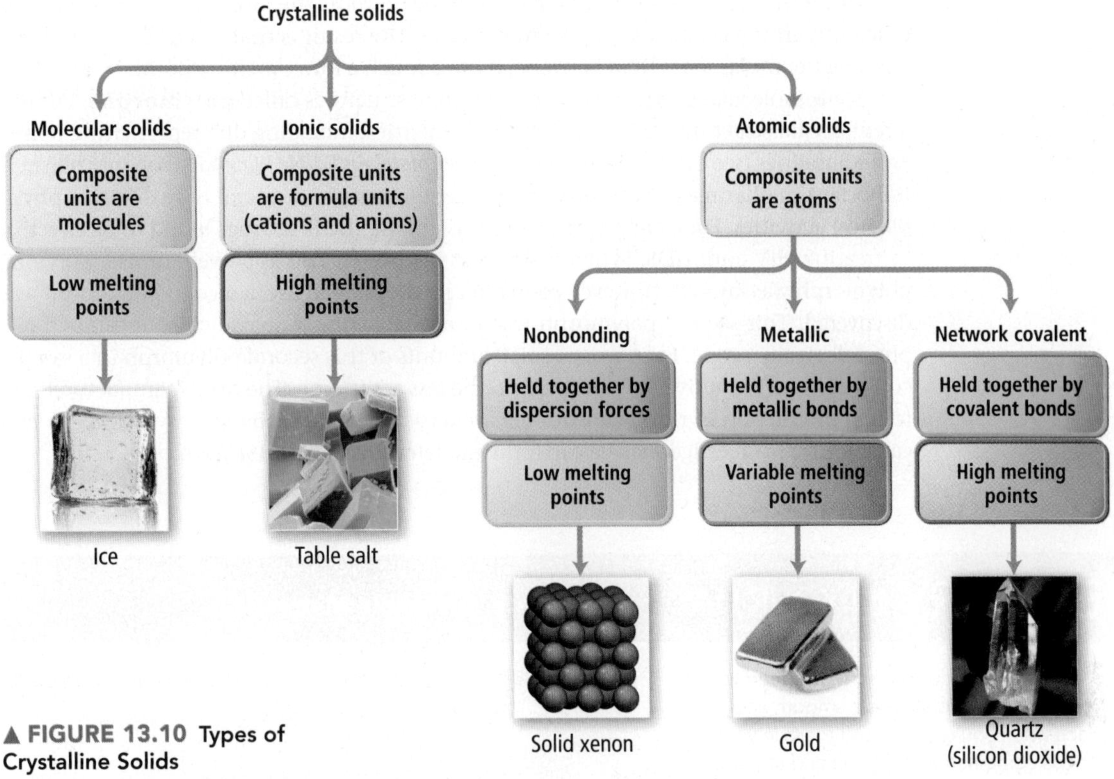

▲ **FIGURE 13.10 Types of Crystalline Solids**

Molecular Solids

Molecular solids are solids in which the composite particles are *molecules*. The unit cells in a crystalline molecular solid are therefore occupied by molecules. Ice (solid H_2O) and dry ice (solid CO_2) are examples of molecular solids. Molecular solids are held together by the kinds of intermolecular forces—dispersion forces, dipole–dipole forces, and hydrogen bonding—discussed in Chapter 12. Although molecular solids as a whole tend to have low to moderately low melting points, their specific properties depend on the types of intermolecular forces between the molecules as well as the structure of the molecule and the crystal structure of the solid. For example, benzene and toluene have similar molar masses and similar intermolecular forces (dispersion forces):

Compound	Structure	Molar Mass	Type of Intermolecular Force	Melting Point of Solid
Benzene (C_6H_6)	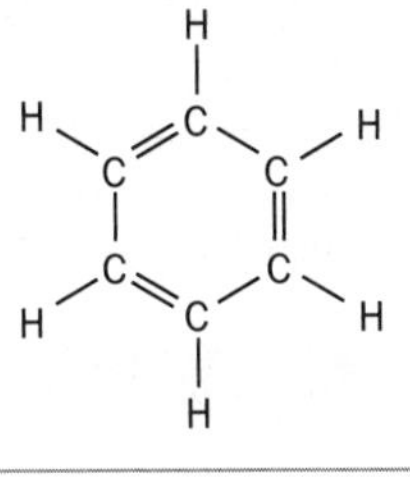	78.11 g/mol	Dispersion	5.5 °C
Toluene (C_7H_8)	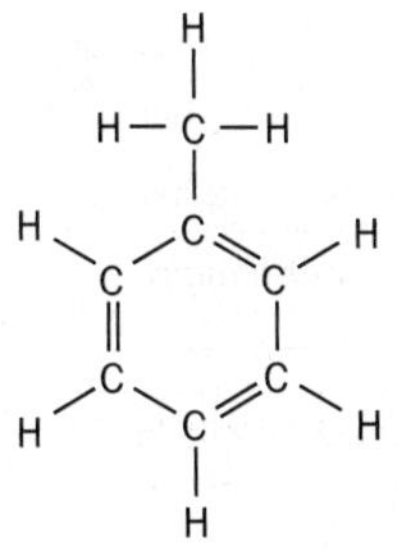	92.14 g/mol	Dispersion	–95.5 °C

However, the extra $—CH_3$ group on toluene prevents the molecules from packing as efficiently in the crystal as they do in benzene. The result is that, even though toluene has a higher molar mass than benzene, it has a much a lower melting point.

Polymorphism can exist in any crystalline material, not just molecular solids.

Some molecular solids crystallize in different structures called **polymorphs**. The different crystal structures can have different properties, including different melting points and solubilities (see *Chemistry in Your Day: Chocolate, An Edible Material*). Polymorphism is important in pharmaceuticals because different forms of a drug can have different physiological activities. For example, ritonavir was among the first drugs found to be effective in treating HIV and AIDS. When it was first discovered and approved for use, only one polymorph was known. However, soon after its widespread use, a second polymorph was discovered. This second polymorph was more stable, less water-soluble, and much less physiologically active. Even worse, small amounts of this second polymorph in a sample could convert the active polymorph into the less active one. The drug manufacturer had to halt production of ritonavir until researchers solved the problem by switching from a capsule form to a refrigerated gelcap form and later to a stable tablet form.

CHEMISTRY IN YOUR DAY | Chocolate, An Edible Material

Chocolate is an edible and delicious material designed to please your senses. Good chocolate has a smooth and shiny surface, snaps when you break it, and melts in your mouth, releasing its delicious combination of flavors and texture. Like all materials, chocolate's properties depend on its structure. The main structural ingredient in chocolate is cocoa butter, a triglyceride. We examine triglycerides more carefully in Chapter 23, but for now, just know that triglycerides are long organic molecules, which means that chocolate is a crystalline molecular solid. Many crystalline molecular solids only have one crystalline structure; however, some (including cocoa butter) have several possible crystalline structures called polymorphs, each with different properties. Cocoa butter has six possible polymorphs, often called Types I–VI, as shown in Table 13.1. For reference, body temperature is 37 °C.

The most desirable crystalline form of cocoa butter in chocolate is Type V. Types I and II are soft and crumbly and show noticeable blooming. *Blooming* is the white residue that forms on the outside of chocolate. If you have ever let a chocolate bar melt and then re-solidify, you have probably noticed this undesirable residue. Types III and IV are firmer, but they don't have a sharp snap when you break or bite into them. Type V is firm, displays a sharp snap, has a smooth and shiny surface, and tends to melt in your mouth rather than your hand. For this reason, chocolatiers aim for this crystal structure. However, this structure is not easy to achieve. If you simply melt chocolate and let it re-solidify, you get a mix of Types I–V with all of their undesirable qualities. Chocolatiers "temper" their chocolate in their quest for primarily Type V characteristics.

▲ The white residue on the surface of the chocolate bon bon on the left is called bloom. The chocolate bon bon on the right has a smooth, shiny surface, characteristic of Type V cocoa butter.

Tempering chocolate requires a specific and carefully controlled heating and cooling sequence (Figure 13.11▶).

TABLE 13.1 ■ Crystalline Forms of Cocoa Butter

Crystalline Structure Type (Polymorph)	Melting Point (°C)	Description	Increasing Density and Stability
I	17.3	Soft, crumbly, noticeable blooming, melts in the hand.	↓
II	23.3	Soft, crumbly, noticeable blooming, melts in the hand.	
III	25.5	Firm, poor snap, some blooming, melts in the hand.	
IV	27.3	Firm, poor snap, some blooming, melts in the hand.	
V	33.8	Firm, good snap, smooth and shiny surface, melts in the mouth, most desirable.	
VI	36.3	Hard, some blooming, cannot be formed from melt, takes several months to form.	

First, chocolatiers heat the chocolate to melt it. Then they allow it to cool slowly. The slow cooling favors the formation of Type V crystals; however, the other types form as well. The final step is to reheat the chocolate to a temperature just below the melting point of the Type V crystals. This step melts all of the Type I–IV crystals, leaving only the Type V crystals to act as "seed crystals."* A seed crystal is a crystal upon which more of the crystal can grow. Seed crystals have the effect of imposing their own structure on the growing crystalline solid. When the properly tempered chocolate cools, the Type V seed crystals cause the majority of the chocolate to crystallize in the Type V structure, resulting in silky smooth, melt-in-your-mouth, chocolate.

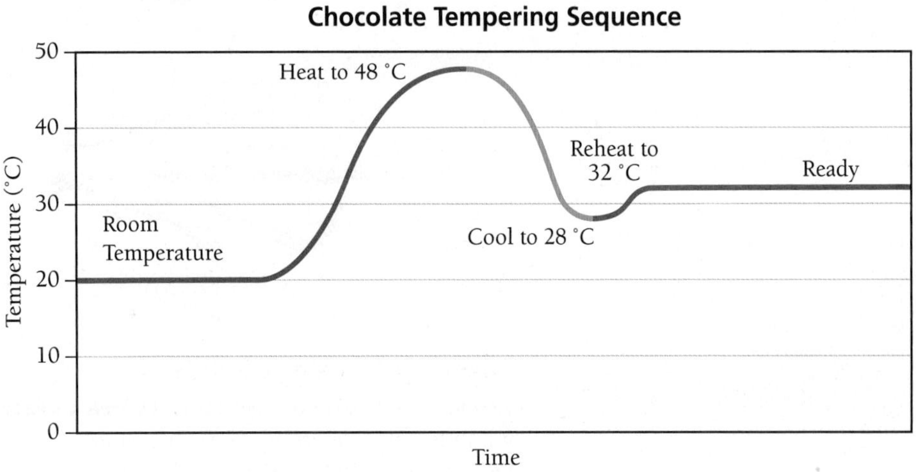

▶ **FIGURE 13.11 Chocolate Tempering** In order to temper chocolate, chocolate makers heat it carefully. After the tempering sequence is completed, the chocolate can be poured into molds or used as coatings. When the tempered chocolate cools, it is primarily Type V and has a shiny smooth surface.

*Sometimes solid bits of tempered chocolate are added at this point to act as additional seed crystals.

Ionic Solids

The composite particles of **ionic solids** are ions. Table salt (NaCl) and calcium fluoride (CaF_2) are examples of ionic solids. The forces holding ionic solids together are strong coulombic forces (or ionic bonds), and because these forces are much stronger than intermolecular forces, ionic solids tend to have much higher melting points than molecular solids. For example, sodium chloride melts at 801 °C, while carbon disulfide (CS_2)—a molecular solid with a higher molar mass—melts at −110 °C. We examine the structure of ionic solids in more detail in Section 13.5.

Atomic Solids

In **atomic solids** the composite particles are individual atoms. Solid xenon (Xe), iron (Fe), and silicon dioxide (SiO_2) are examples of atomic solids. We classify atomic solids into three categories—*nonbonding atomic solids, metallic atomic solids*, and *network covalent atomic solids*—with each type held together by a different kind of force.

Nonbonding Atomic Solids

Nonbonding atomic solids are held together by relatively weak dispersion forces. In order to maximize these interactions, nonbonding atomic solids form closest-packed structures, maximizing their coordination numbers and minimizing the distance between composite units. Nonbonding atomic solids have very low melting points that increase uniformly with molar mass. The only nonbonding atomic solids are noble gases in their solid form. Argon, for example, has a melting point of −189 °C, and xenon has a melting point of −112 °C.

Metallic Atomic Solids

Metallic atomic solids, such as iron or gold, are held together by *metallic bonds*, which in the simplest model are represented by the interaction of metal cations with the sea of electrons that surrounds them, as described in Section 10.11 (Figure 13.12▶).

Because metallic bonds are not directional, many metals tend to form closest-packed crystal structures. For example, nickel crystallizes in the cubic closest-packed structure, and zinc crystallizes in the hexagonal closest-packed structure (Figure 13.13▶). Metallic bonds have varying strengths. Some metals, such as mercury, have melting points below room temperature, whereas other metals, such as iron, have relatively high melting points (iron melts at 1538 °C).

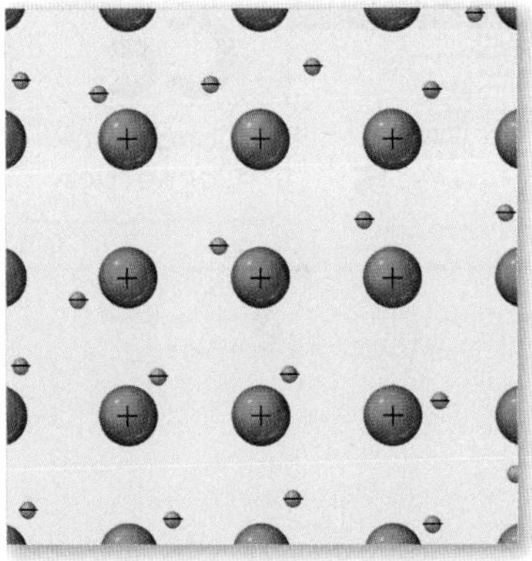

▲ **FIGURE 13.12 The Electron Sea Model** In the electron sea model for metals, the metal cations exist in a "sea" of electrons.

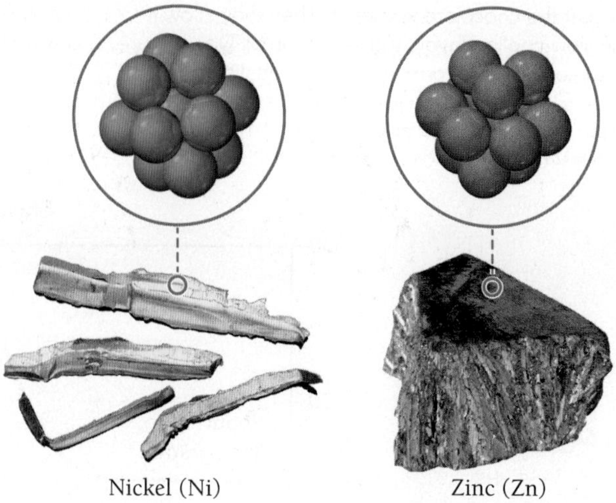

▶ **FIGURE 13.13 Closest-Packed Crystal Structures in Metals** Nickel crystallizes in the cubic closest-packed structure. Zinc crystallizes in the hexagonal closest-packed structure.

Network Covalent Solids

Covalent bonds hold together **network covalent atomic solids**, such as diamond, graphite, and silicon dioxide. The crystal structures of these solids are more restricted by the geometrical constraints of the covalent bonds (which tend to be more directional than intermolecular forces, ionic bonds, or metallic bonds), so they *do not* tend to form closest-packed structures. Network covalent atomic solids have very high melting points because the crystalline solid is held together by covalent bonds. We examine some examples of this class of solids in Section 13.6.

EXAMPLE 13.5 Classifying Crystalline Solids

Classify each crystalline solid as molecular, ionic, or atomic.

(a) Au(*s*) **(b)** $CH_3CH_2OH(s)$ **(c)** $CaF_2(s)$

SOLUTION

(a) Gold (Au) is a metal and is therefore an atomic solid.

(b) Ethanol (CH_3CH_2OH) is a molecular compound. Solid ethanol is therefore a molecular solid.

(c) Calcium fluoride (CaF_2) is an ionic compound, so it is an ionic solid.

FOR PRACTICE 13.5 What type of atomic solid is Au(*s*)?

ANSWER **NOW!**

13.3 Cc Conceptual Connection

CRYSTALLINE SOLID TYPES AND MELTING POINTS

Which solid would you expect to have the highest melting point?

(a) MgO(*s*) **(b)** $I_2(s)$ **(c)** Kr(*s*)

13.5 The Structures of Ionic Solids

Many ionic solids have crystalline structures that are closely related to the unit cells that we examined in Section 13.3. However, because ionic compounds necessarily contain both cations and anions, their structures must accommodate the two different types of ions. In an ionic solid, the cations and anions attract one another. The coordination number of the unit cell represents the number of close cation–anion interactions.

Because these interactions lower potential energy, the crystal structure of a particular ionic compound is the structure that maximizes the coordination number while accommodating both charge neutrality (each unit cell must be charge neutral) and the different sizes of the cations and anions that compose the particular compound. In general, the more similar the radii of the cation and the anion, the higher the coordination number.

Cesium chloride (CsCl) is a good example of an ionic compound with cations and anions of similar size (Cs^+ radius = 167 pm; Cl^- radius = 181 pm). In the cesium chloride structure, the chloride ions occupy the lattice sites of a simple cubic cell, and one cesium ion lies in the very center of the cell, as shown in Figure 13.14▶. (Note that in this and subsequent figures of ionic crystal structures, the different colored spheres represent different ions.) The coordination number for cesium chloride is 8, meaning that each cesium ion is in direct contact with eight chloride ions (and vice versa). The cesium chloride unit cell contains one chloride anion ($8 \times {}^1/_8 = 1$) and one cesium cation for a ratio of Cs to Cl of 1:1, as the formula for the compound indicates. (Note that complete chloride ions are shown in Figure 13.14, even though only ${}^1/_8$ of each ion is in the unit cell.) Calcium sulfide (CaS) has the same structure as cesium chloride.

Cesium chloride (CsCl)

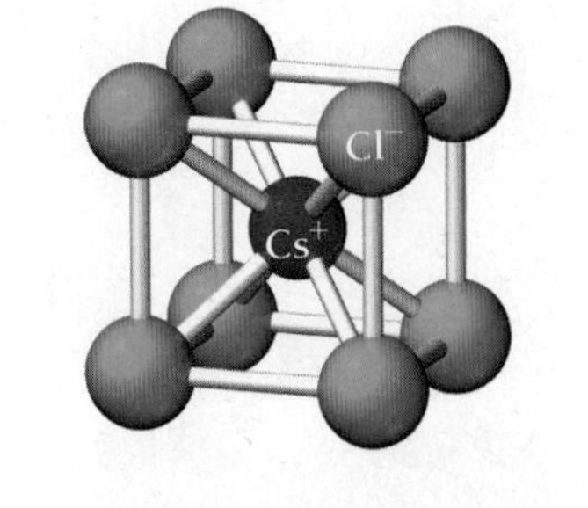

▲ **FIGURE 13.14 Cesium Chloride Unit Cell** The different colored spheres in this figure represent the different ions in the compound.

Sodium chloride is an example of an ionic compound with different ion sizes: Na^+ (radius = 97 pm) and Cl^- (radius = 181 pm). The crystal structure must accommodate the disproportionate sizes. If ion size were the only consideration, the larger chloride anion could theoretically fit many of the smaller sodium cations around it, but charge neutrality requires that each sodium cation be surrounded by an equal number of chloride anions. Therefore, the coordination number is limited by the number of chloride anions that can fit around the relatively small sodium cation. The structure that minimizes the energy is shown in Figure 13.15▶ and has a coordination number of 6 (each chloride anion is surrounded by six sodium cations and vice versa). We can visualize this structure, called the *rock salt* structure, as chloride anions occupying the lattice sites of a face-centered cubic structure with the smaller sodium cations occupying the holes between the anions. (Alternatively, we can visualize this structure as the *sodium cations* occupying the lattice sites of a face-centered cubic structure with the *larger chloride anions* occupying the spaces between the cations.) Each unit cell contains four chloride anions $[(8 \times {}^1/_8) + (6 \times {}^1/_2) = 4]$ and four sodium cations $[(12 \times {}^1/_4) + 1 = 4]$, resulting in a ratio of 1:1, as the formula of the compound specifies. Other compounds exhibiting the sodium chloride structure include LiF, KCl, KBr, AgCl, MgO, and CaO.

Sodium chloride (NaCl)

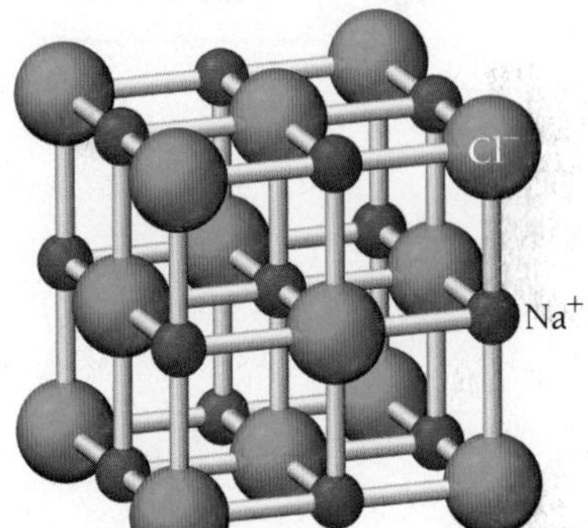

▲ **FIGURE 13.15 Sodium Chloride Unit Cell** The different colored spheres in this figure represent the different ions in the compound.

When there is a greater disproportion between the sizes of the cations and anions in a compound, a coordination number of even 6 is physically impossible. For example, in ZnS (Zn^{2+} radius = 74 pm; S^{2-} radius = 184 pm) the crystal structure, shown in Figure 13.16▶, has a coordination number of only 4. We can visualize this structure, called the *zinc blende* structure, as sulfide anions occupying the lattice sites of a face-centered cubic structure, with the smaller zinc cations occupying four of the eight tetrahedral holes located directly beneath each corner atom. A tetrahedral hole is the empty space that lies in the center of a tetrahedral arrangement of four atoms, as shown in the accompanying figure. Each unit cell contains four sulfide anions $[(8 \times {}^1/_8) + (6 \times {}^1/_2) = 4]$ and four zinc cations (each of the four zinc cations is completely contained within the unit cell), resulting in a ratio of 1:1, just as the formula of the compound indicates. Other compounds that exhibit the zinc blende structure include CuCl, AgI, and CdS.

Zinc blende (ZnS)

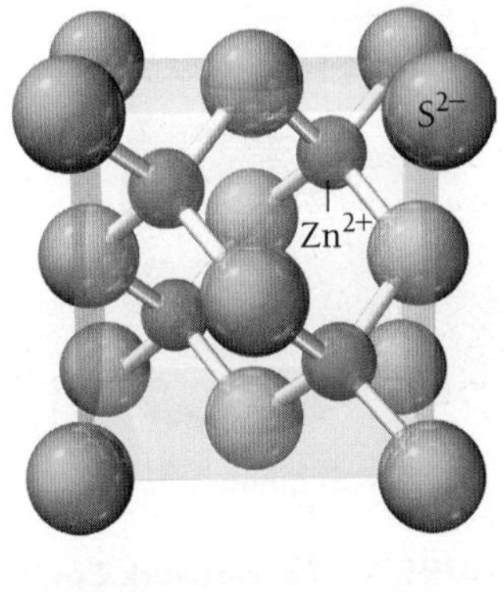

▲ **FIGURE 13.16 Zinc Sulfide (Zinc Blende) Unit Cell** The different colored spheres in this figure represent the different ions in the compound.

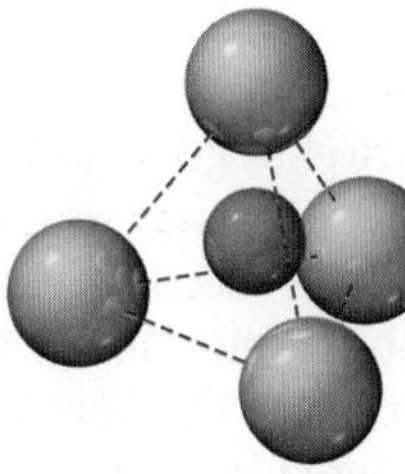

◀ A tetrahedral hole

When the ratio of cations to anions is not 1:1, the crystal structure must accommodate the unequal number of cations and anions. Many compounds that contain a cation-to-anion ratio of 1:2 adopt the *fluorite* (CaF_2) *structure* shown in Figure 13.17▶. We can visualize this structure as calcium cations occupying the lattice sites of a face-centered

Calcium fluoride (CaF_2)

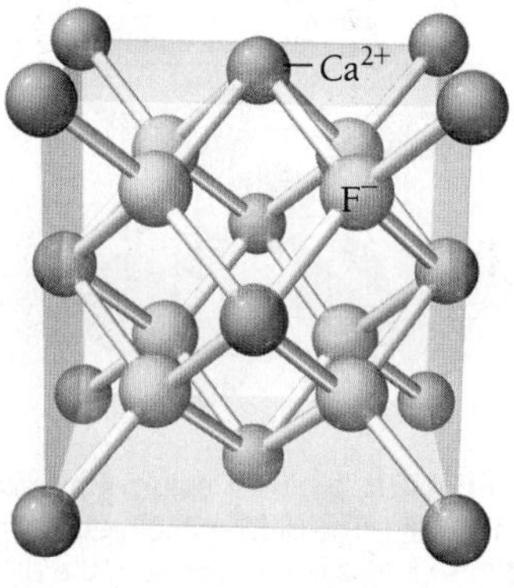

cubic structure with the larger fluoride anions occupying all eight of the tetrahedral holes located directly beneath each corner atom. Each unit cell contains four calcium cations $[(8 \times {}^{1}/_{8}) + (6 \times {}^{1}/_{2}) = 4]$ and eight fluoride anions (each of the eight fluoride anions is completely contained within the unit cell), resulting in a cation-to-anion ratio of 1:2, just as in the formula of the compound. Other compounds exhibiting the fluorite structure include PbF_2, SrF_2, and $BaCl_2$. Compounds with a cation-to-anion ratio of 2:1 often exhibit the *antifluorite structure*, in which the anions occupy the lattice sites of a face-centered cubic structure and the cations occupy the tetrahedral holes beneath each corner atom.

◀ **FIGURE 13.17 Calcium Fluoride (or Fluorite) Unit Cell** The different colored spheres in this figure represent the different ions in the compound.

ANSWER **NOW!**

13.4 Cc Conceptual Connection

IONIC CRYSTALLINE SOLID UNIT CELLS Which compound is most likely to crystallize in the zinc blende structure?

(a) RbCl (Rb^+ radius = 148 pm; Cl^- radius = 181 pm)
(b) $MgCl_2$ (Mg^{2+} radius = 65 pm; Cl^- radius = 181 pm)
(c) CuI (Cu^+ radius = 96 pm; I^- radius = 216 pm)

13.6 Network Covalent Atomic Solids: Carbon and Silicates

As we saw in Section 13.4, network covalent atomic solids are composed of atoms held together by covalent bonds. Because the covalent bonds have to be broken for the solid to melt, network covalent atomic solids have some of the highest melting points of all substances. In this section, we examine two different families of network covalent atomic solids: carbon and silicates.

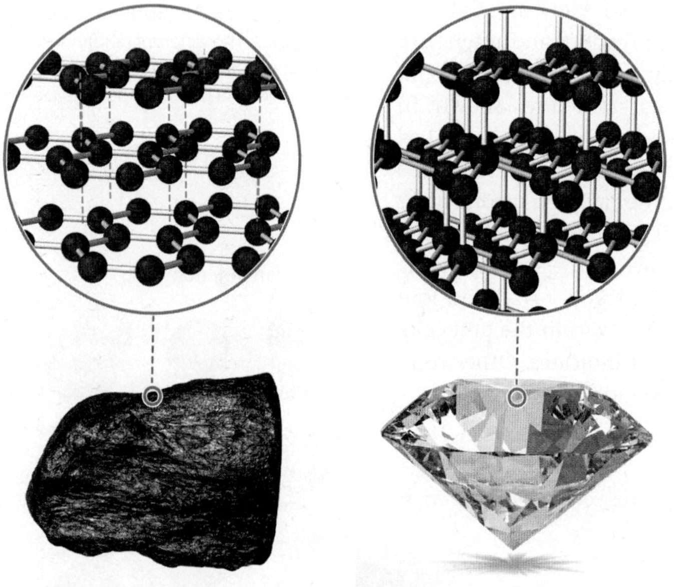

(a) Graphite (b) Diamond

▲ **FIGURE 13.18 Network Covalent Atomic Solids** **(a)** In graphite, carbon atoms are arranged in sheets. Within each sheet, the atoms are covalently bonded to one another by a network of sigma and pi bonds. Neighboring sheets are held together by dispersion forces. **(b)** In diamond, each carbon atom forms four covalent bonds to four other carbon atoms in a tetrahedral geometry.

Carbon

Elemental carbon exists in several different forms (or allotropes) including graphene, which we discussed in Section 13.1. Two well-known naturally occurring crystalline forms of carbon are **graphite** and **diamond**. Graphite's structure, shown in Figure 13.18(a)◀, consists of flat sheets of carbon atoms covalently bonded together as interconnected hexagonal rings. The bond length between carbon atoms *within a sheet* is 142 pm. However, the forces *between* sheets are much different. There are no covalent bonds between sheets, only relatively weak dispersion forces, and the separation between sheets is 341 pm. Consequently, the sheets slide past each other with relative ease, which explains the slippery feel of graphite and its extensive use as a lubricant. The electrons in the extended pi bonding network within a sheet make graphite a good electrical conductor in the direction of the plane of the sheets. Because of its relative stability and electrical properties, graphite is used for electrodes in electrochemical applications and for heating elements in furnaces.

The density of graphite is 2.2 g/cm^3. Under high pressure, the carbon atoms in graphite rearrange to form diamond, which has a higher density of 3.5 g/cm^3.

Diamond forms naturally when carbon is exposed to high pressures deep underground. Through movements in Earth's crust, diamond rises toward the surface. Most diamond is found in Africa, mainly in the Congo region and in South Africa. The first synthetic diamonds were produced in the 1940s, using pressures of 50,000 atm and a temperature of 1600 °C. The unit cell for diamond is shown here:

You can imagine the unit cell for diamond as a face-centered cubic structure with an additional carbon atom in half of the eight tetrahedral holes located directly beneath each corner atom. Notice the similarity between the diamond unit cell and the zinc blende unit cell that we discussed in Section 13.5. Notice also that each carbon atom is covalently bonded to four other carbon atoms at the corners of a tetrahedron. This structure extends throughout the entire crystal, so that a diamond crystal can be thought of as a giant molecule, held together by these covalent bonds.

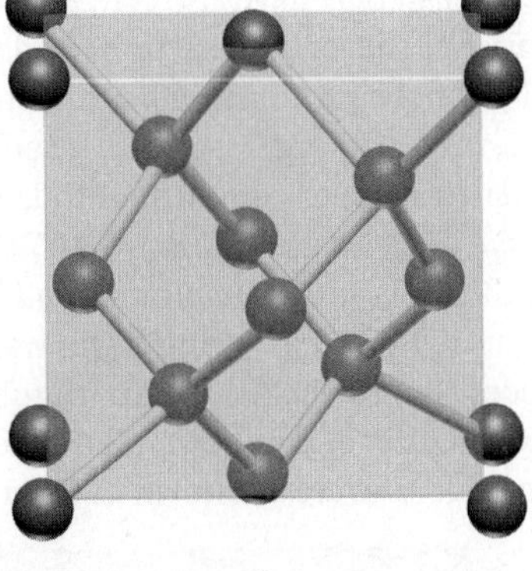

▲ Diamond unit cell

Zinc blende (ZnS)

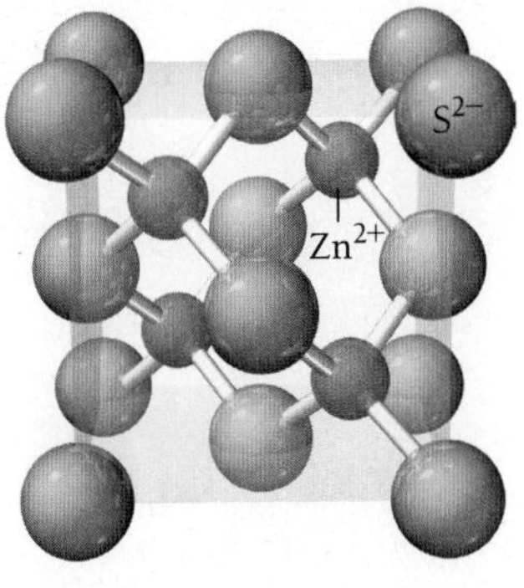

▲ Zinc blende unit cell

Because covalent bonds are very strong, diamond has a very high melting point (it is estimated to melt at about 3800 °C). The electrons in diamond are confined to the covalent bonds and are not free to flow. Therefore, diamond does not conduct electricity. Diamond is very hard and is an excellent conductor of heat. Consequently, the largest use of diamonds is for abrasives and cutting tools. Small diamonds are used at the cutting edge of tools, making the edges much harder and giving them a longer life. Natural diamonds are valued as gems for their brilliance and relative inertness.

13.5 Cc Conceptual Connection — ANSWER **NOW!**

PHASE CHANGES AND PRESSURE High pressure favors the formation of diamond from graphite. What can you conclude about the relative densities of the two substances?

(a) Diamond is denser than graphite.
(b) Graphite is denser than diamond.
(c) Nothing can be determined about the relative densities of the two substances without more information.

In the 1980s, researchers discovered a new form of carbon when they aimed a powerful laser at a graphite surface. This new form of carbon occurs as soccer-ball-shaped clusters of 60 carbon atoms (C_{60}). The atoms form five- and six-membered carbon rings wrapped into a 20-sided icosahedral structure (Figure 13.19▼). The compound was named *buckminsterfullerene*, honoring R. Buckminster Fuller (1895–1983), a twentieth-century engineer and architect who advocated the construction of buildings using a structurally strong geodesic dome shape that he patented.

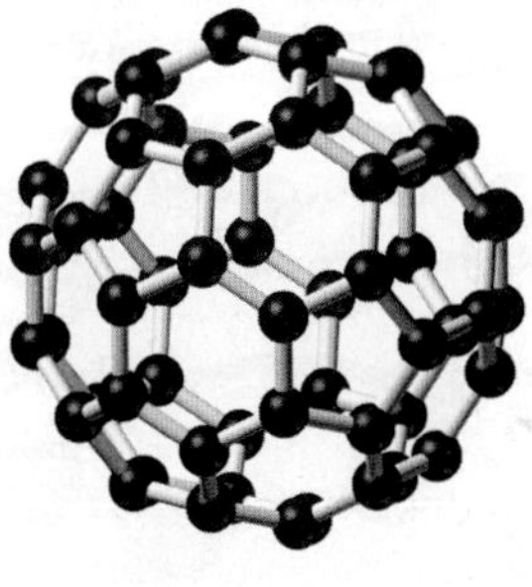

C_{60}

◀ **FIGURE 13.19 C_{60} and a Geodesic Dome** The C_{60} structure resembles Buckminster Fuller's geodesic dome.

Researchers have since identified carbon clusters similar to C_{60} containing from 36 to over 100 carbon atoms. As a class, these carbon clusters are called **fullerenes** and nicknamed *buckyballs*. At room temperature, fullerenes are black solids similar to graphite—the individual clusters are held to one another by dispersion forces. Fullerenes are somewhat soluble in nonpolar solvents, and the different fullerenes form solutions of different colors.

Researchers have also synthesized long carbon structures called **nanotubes**, which consist of sheets of interconnected C_6 rings that assume the shape of a cylinder (like a roll of chicken wire). The first nanotubes discovered consisted of tubes with double walls of C_6 rings with closed ends. The ends of the tubes can be opened when they are heated under the proper conditions. Today, two general types of nanotubes can be produced: (1) *single-walled nanotubes (SWNT)* that have one layer of interconnected C_6 rings forming the walls and (2) *multiwalled nanotubes (MWNT)* that have concentric layers of interconnected C_6 rings forming the walls. In addition, researchers have been able to form *nanoribbons* by slicing open nanotubes. As we discussed in Section 13.1, carbon can also form graphene, long, extended sheets of carbon atoms just one atom thick. These carbon structures are all shown in Figure 13.20▼.

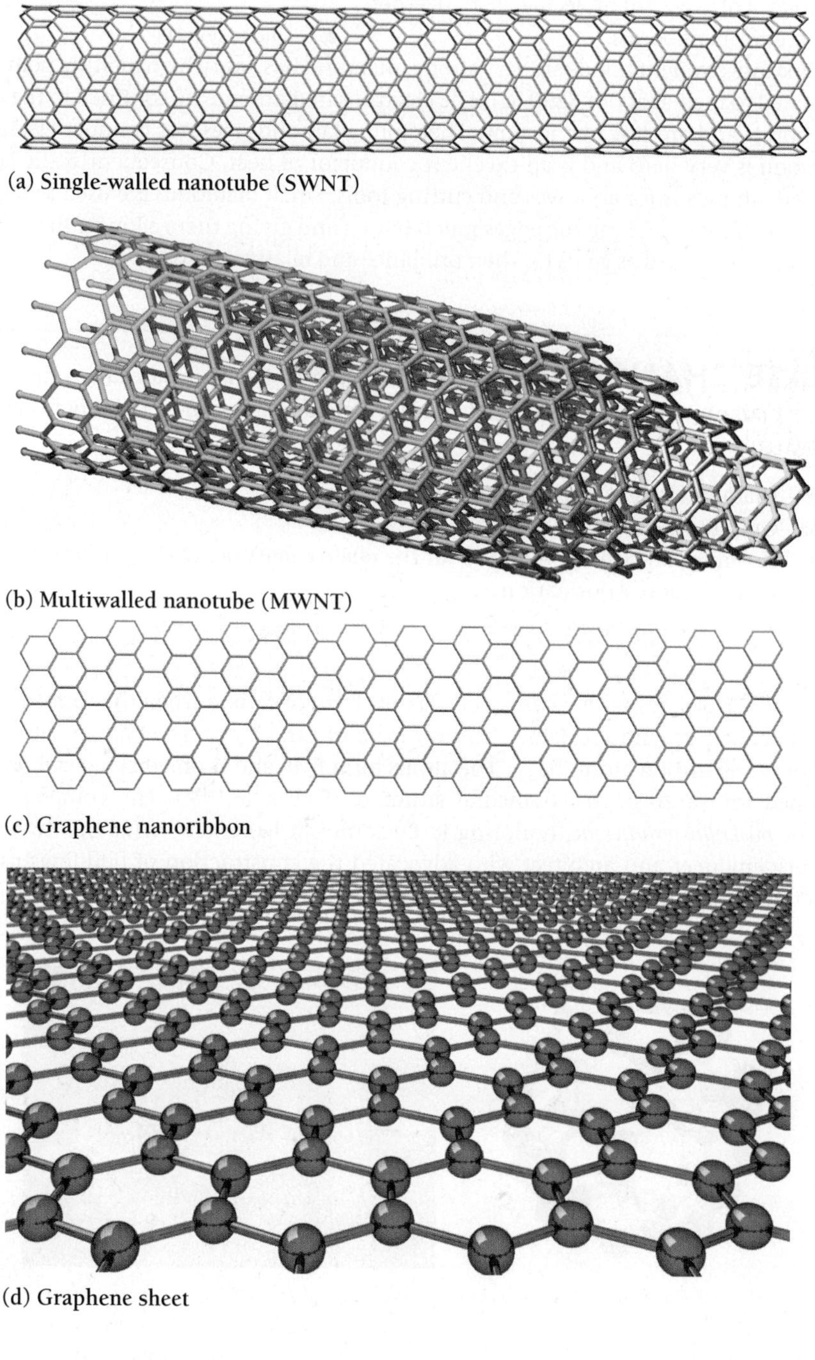

▶ **FIGURE 13.20 Carbon structures include** **(a)** a single-walled nanotube; **(b)** a multiwalled nanotube; **(c)** a graphene nanoribbon; **(d)** a graphene sheet.

Nanotubes are 100 times stronger than steel and only $^1/_{16}$ as dense. Consequently, we use carbon nanotubes commercially for lightweight applications that require strength, such as golf clubs and bicycle frames. When the nanotubes are lined up parallel to one another, a bundle of the tubes forms a "wire" with very low electrical resistance. These tiny wires raise the possibility of making incredibly small electronic devices.

Silicates

The **silicates** (extended arrays of silicon and oxygen) are the most common network covalent atomic solids. Geologists estimate that 90% of Earth's crust is composed of silicates. Silicon and oxygen form a network covalent structure in which a silicon atom bonds to four oxygen atoms, assuming a tetrahedral shape with the silicon atom in the middle and the four oxygen atoms at the corners of the tetrahedron (Figure 13.21▶).

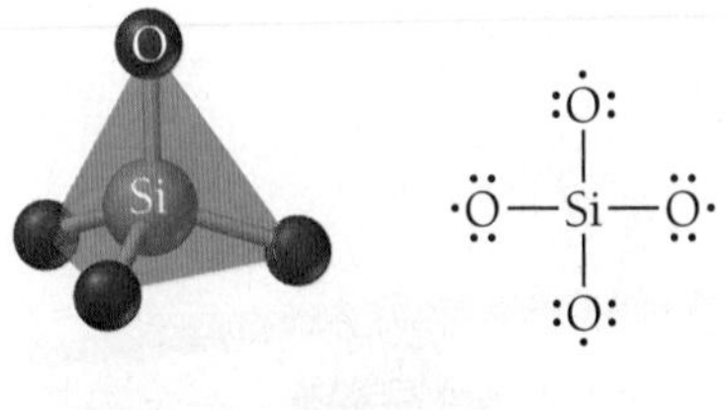

▲ **FIGURE 13.21 SiO_4 Tetrahedron** In an SiO_4 tetrahedron, silicon occupies the center of the tetrahedron, and one oxygen atom occupies each corner.

In this structure, the silicon atom bonds to each oxygen atom with a single covalent sigma bond. In contrast to carbon, which often bonds to oxygen with a double bond (one sigma and one pi bond), silicon typically forms only a single bond with oxygen because the silicon atom is too large to allow substantial overlap between the *p*-orbitals on the two atoms. The silicon atom in this structure, by bonding to four oxygen atoms, obtains a complete octet. However, each oxygen atom is one electron short of an octet. Therefore, each O atom forms a second covalent bond to a different Si atom, resulting in the three-dimensional structure of **quartz**. Quartz has a formula unit of SiO_2 and is generally called **silica**. In silica, each Si atom is in a tetrahedron surrounded by four O atoms, and each O atom acts as a bridge connecting the corners of two tetrahedrons (Figure 13.22▶). See Section 24.3 for a more extended discussion of silicate structures.

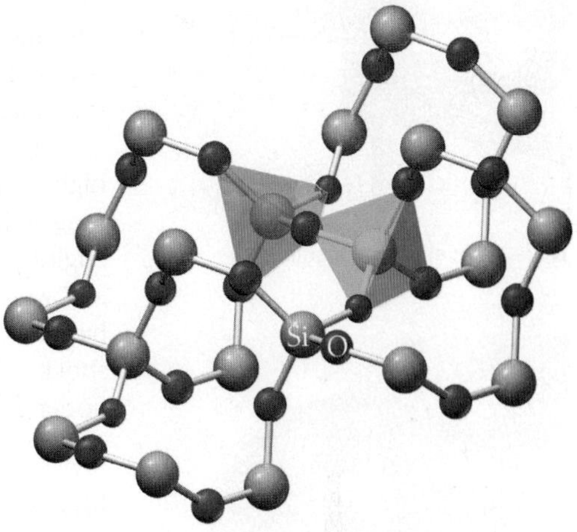

▲ **FIGURE 13.22 Structure of Quartz** In the quartz structure, each Si atom is in a tetrahedron surrounded by four O atoms, and each O atom is a bridge connecting the corners of two tetrahedrons.

13.7 Ceramics, Cement, and Glass

The silicate structures we examined in Section 13.6 are common in ceramics, cement, and glass. These substances are used in buildings, electrical devices, pottery, and kitchenware. If you look around wherever you are sitting at this moment, you are likely to see examples of these materials. In this section of the chapter, we examine each of these amazing classes of materials individually.

Ceramics

Ceramics are traditionally defined as inorganic nonmetallic solids that are prepared from powders usually mixed with water, formed into the desired shape and then heated. Ceramics are extensively used to make bricks, tiles, pottery, dishware, and insulating elements in electrical devices. They display a range of properties but are usually hard, strong, nonconductive, and brittle. The word "ceramics" originates from the Greek *keramikos*. Keramikos is an area of Athens that was the potters' quarter of the city, and the Greeks were among the first accomplished potters. However, pottery itself predates recorded history. The oldest known example is the Venus of Dolni, a figurine that dates to 29,000–25,000 BCE. Ceramics can be categorized into three types: silicate, oxide, and nonoxide.

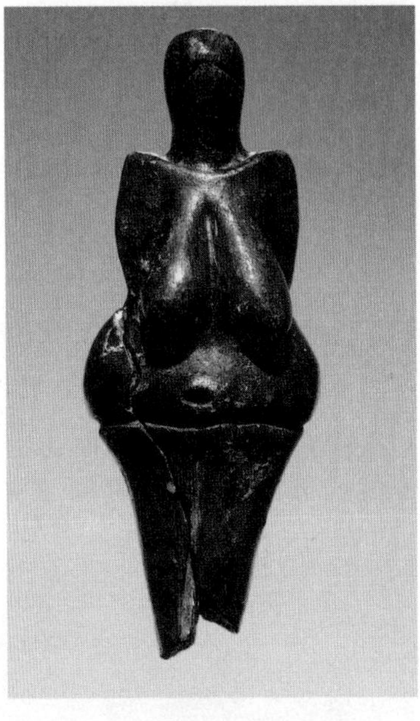

▲ The Venus of Dolni, the oldest known ceramic object, dates to 29,000–25,000 BCE. It was discovered in 1925 in the Czech Republic.

Silicate Ceramics

Many ceramics are composed of aluminosilicates, a class of minerals in which some of the silicon atoms in the silicate structure are replaced by aluminum (see Section 24.3). The weathering of naturally occurring aluminosilicates produces **clays**, which are essentially powdered forms of the minerals mixed with water. When heated, reactions occur that transform the clay into the ceramic substance.

For example, the clay kaolinite, $Al_2Si_2O_5(OH)_4$, undergoes irreversible chemical and structural changes when heated (or fired) above 1500 °C. These changes transform the clay into a white ceramic solid containing an extended network of Si-O and Al-O tetrahedra. Kaolinite is the most important component of porcelain, a ceramic substance that originated in China during the Han dynasty about 2000 years ago. Chinese porcelain was superior to previous ceramics and became highly valued and prized for its beauty and durability, especially when formed into cups for drinking tea. The Chinese profitably exported their porcelain wares to the Middle East and the West and kept their recipe for making it a secret for hundreds of years. The term *china* today still refers to the fine plates, saucers, and cups made from porcelain and related ceramic materials. Silicate ceramics also find extensive use as insulators in electrical applications.

▲ Ceramic electrical insulator

Oxide Ceramics

Among the most common oxide ceramics are Al_2O_3 and MgO. These materials demonstrate the advantages and disadvantages of ceramic materials compared to metals. Al_2O_3 melts at 2072 °C, compared to aluminum metal, which melts at 660 °C. MgO melts at an even higher temperature (2852 °C). Both are physically and chemically stable at high temperatures. The high melting point and chemical stability make Al_2O_3 and MgO outstanding *refractory materials*—materials that can be used in high-temperature applications.

For example, aluminum oxide and magnesium oxide are used in industrial furnaces, high-speed cutting tools, crucibles, heating elements, and fire proofing. Engineers have long desired to take advantage of the high-temperature stability of ceramics to make ceramic engines. A ceramic engine can run at a higher temperature, which makes it more efficient and would require less cooling. However, certain less desirable characteristics of ceramics have made that pursuit difficult. Ceramic materials tend to be brittle and subject to thermal shock (they can crack upon fast changes in temperature). Metals can bend and stretch under stress, but ceramics break. Even though ceramics have found some limited use as components of engines, a completely ceramic mass-produced engine remains elusive.

▲ Aluminum oxide crucible, a container in which substances can be subjected to high temperatures.

Nonoxide Ceramics

The nonoxide ceramics include substances such as Si_3N_4, BN, and SiC. Silicon nitride is a network covalent solid with a structure similar to silica; the silicon atoms sit in the center of nitrogen tetrahedra that are linked. Silicon nitride is used extensively in engine parts and nonmetallic ball bearings. Boron nitride is isoelectronic with C_2 (BN and C_2 have the same number of valence electrons) and forms structures similar to carbon. For example, BN can form layered sheets (similar to graphite), which are covalently bound within the sheets but with only dispersion forces between the sheets. As a result, this form of BN makes a good high-temperature lubricant. Another form of boron nitride has the diamond structure, which results in a hard, strong substance similar to diamond. This form of boron nitride is used as an abrasive and to make cutting tools. Boron nitride can even form nanotubes similar to those formed by carbon. Silicon carbide also has a diamond structure, but in silicon carbide, half of the carbon atoms are replaced by silicon atoms. It too finds applications as an abrasive, and it is also used as a refractory material and an additive to steel.

Cement

Cement was first discovered by the Romans, who used lime, volcanic ash, and clay to make a pourable slurry that hardened into a rocklike substance. The Romans used cement to construct the 43.3-m-diameter dome of the Pantheon, a 2000-year-old edifice. This dome remains the largest unreinforced concrete dome in existence.

▲ The Roman Pantheon, still a popular tourist attraction, sits in the center of the ancient heart of Rome. It boasts a 2000-year-old 43.3 m diameter concrete dome.

The majority of the cement used today is Portland cement. **Portland cement** is a powdered mixture consisting mostly of limestone ($CaCO_3$) and silica (SiO_2), with smaller amounts of alumina (Al_2O_3), iron(III) oxide (Fe_2O_3), and gypsum ($CaSO_4 \cdot 2H_2O$). The powdered mixture reacts with water in a number of complex reactions that produce a final rocklike substance. Unlike clays, which lose water upon setting, Portland cement reacts *with* water as it hardens. The hardening process involves the formation of Si-O-Si bridges that produce fibrous structures. These structures bond strongly to each other (and most other substances). The original Portland cement was patented in 1824 by an English bricklayer named Joseph Aspidin (1788–1855). The hardened cement resembles a prestigious building stone from the Isle of Portland in Southwest England and derives its name from this resemblance.

Portland cement is combined with sand and pebbles to make **concrete**, the most widely used building material in the world. Concrete dramatically revolutionized construction. Before concrete, buildings were made exclusively by arranging the materials piece by piece. With the development of concrete, buildings could literally be poured into place. Concrete is used extensively to make foundations, walls, buildings, bridges, aqueducts, roads, and dams. About half of all the structures humans construct are made of concrete.

Glass

Silica melts when heated above 1500 °C. After melting, if cooled quickly, silica does not crystallize back into the quartz structure. Instead, the Si atoms and O atoms form a randomly ordered amorphous structure called a **glass**. Silicate glass is transparent, impervious to water, and an outstanding material for making windows and drinking vessels. The Egyptians and Greeks likely made glass objects; however, the Romans in the first century BCE were the first to extensively develop glass making. They discovered that adding sodium carbonate to silica dramatically lowers its melting point, allowing glass to form at much lower temperatures. In addition, they developed glassblowing, which involves melting glass and then using a tube to blow the glass into spherical shapes.

▲ Glassblowing involves blowing air into a hot piece of glass to form spherical shapes.

When SiO_2 is made into a glass, the result is called **vitreous silica** or **fused silica**. This type of glass is hard, resists high temperatures, has a low thermal expansion, and is transparent to both visible light and ultraviolet light. Vitreous silica (because of the high temperatures required to produce it) is too expensive for most common applications. The most common modern glass is **soda-lime glass**, which is also referred to as *window glass*. Soda-lime glass is about 70% SiO_2; the balance is mostly Na_2O and CaO. This type of glass is transparent to visible light (not ultraviolet) and has a high thermal expansion, but it is less expensive to make and form into desired shapes than vitreous silica.

One disadvantage of soda-lime glass is its tendency to crack under thermal shock. Adding boric oxide (B_2O_3) to the glass mixture instead of CaO produces **borosilicate glass** (also known as **Pyrex®**), which expands less when heated. As a result, vessels made of Pyrex® can withstand heating and cooling cycles that would shatter soda-lime glass. The beakers, flasks, and other glassware found in most chemistry labs are made of borosilicate glass.

▲ Leaded glass has a higher index of refraction than ordinary glass, making it appear more brilliant.

Leaded glass (often called *crystal*, even though it is not a crystal) results when PbO is mixed with SiO_2 and a couple of other minor components. This type of glass has a higher index of refraction (it bends light more than ordinary glass), which results in glassware with a more brilliant appearance than soda-lime glass. It also makes a ringing sound when tapped, which is a common test to distinguish lead crystal from ordinary glass. Recent concerns about the toxicity of lead in leaded glass have led to the development of lead-free alternatives (often called lead-free crystal) for stemware and drinking glasses, which have properties similar to those of leaded glass, but without the potentially negative health risks.

The amount of lead that leaches into a drink from leaded glass over a short period of time is likely inconsequential. However, storing drinks in leaded glass for long periods of time can lead to elevated lead levels in the liquid.

13.8 Semiconductors and Band Theory

Recall that in Section 13.4 we discussed a model for bonding in metals called the *electron sea model*, which we first introduced and explained in Section 10.11. We now turn to a model for bonding in solids that is both more sophisticated and more broadly applicable—it applies to both metallic solids and covalent solids. The model is **band theory**, and it grows out of molecular orbital theory, first discussed in Section 11.8.

Molecular Orbitals and Energy Bands

Recall that according to molecular orbital theory, the atomic orbitals of the atoms combine within a molecule to form molecular orbitals. These molecular orbitals are not localized on individual atoms but *delocalized over the entire molecule*. Similarly, in band theory, the atomic orbitals of the atoms within a solid crystal combine to form orbitals that are not localized on individual atoms, but delocalized over the entire *crystal*. In some sense, the crystal is like a very large molecule, and its valence electrons occupy the molecular orbitals formed from the atomic orbitals of each atom in the crystal.

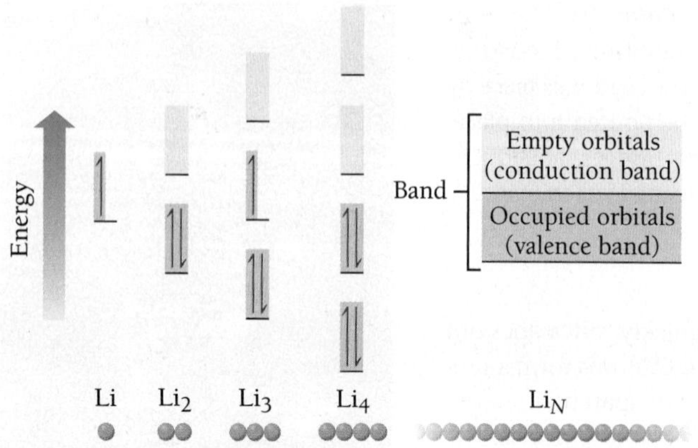

▲ **FIGURE 13.23 Energy Levels of Molecular Orbitals in Lithium Molecules** When many Li atoms are present, the energy levels of the molecular orbitals are so closely spaced that they fuse to form a band. Half of the orbitals are bonding orbitals and contain valence electrons; the other half are antibonding orbitals and are empty.

Consider a series of molecules constructed from individual lithium atoms. The energy levels of the atomic orbitals and resulting molecular orbitals for Li, Li_2, Li_3, Li_4, and Li_N (where N is a large number on the order of 10^{23}) are shown in Figure 13.23◀. The lithium atom has a single electron in a single 2*s* atomic orbital. The Li_2 molecule contains two electrons and two molecular orbitals. The electrons occupy the lower-energy bonding orbital—the higher-energy, or antibonding, molecular orbital is empty. The Li_4 molecule contains four electrons and four molecular orbitals. The electrons occupy the two bonding molecular orbitals—the two antibonding orbitals are completely empty.

The Li_N molecule contains N electrons and N molecular orbitals. However, because there are so many molecular orbitals, the energy spacings between them are infinitesimally small; they are no longer discrete energy levels, but rather they form a *band* of energy levels. One half of the orbitals in the band ($N/2$) are bonding molecular orbitals, and (at 0 K) these orbitals contain the N valence electrons; this band is called the **valence band.** The other $N/2$ molecular orbitals are antibonding and (at 0 K) are completely empty; this band is called the **conduction band**. If the atoms composing a solid have *p* orbitals available, then the same process leads to another set of bands at higher energies.

In lithium metal, the highest occupied molecular orbital lies in the middle of a band of orbitals, and the energy difference between it and the next higher-energy orbital is infinitesimally small. Therefore, above 0 K, electrons can easily make the transition from the valence band to the conduction band. Because electrons in the conduction band are mobile, lithium, like all metals, is a good electrical conductor. Mobile electrons in the conduction band are also responsible for the thermal conductivity of metals. When a metal is heated, electrons are excited to higher-energy molecular orbitals. These electrons quickly transport the thermal energy throughout the crystal lattice.

Recall from Section 2.7 that a semiconductor is a substance of intermediate (and highly temperature-dependent) electrical conductivity.

In metals, the valence band and conduction band are energetically continuous—the energy difference between the top of the valence band and the bottom of the conduction band is infinitesimally small. In semiconductors and insulators, however, an energy gap, called the **band gap,** exists between the valence band and conduction band, as shown in Figure 13.24▼. Band gaps are usually specified in units of electron volts abbreviated as eV ($1\ eV = 1.602 \times 10^{-19}\ J$). In insulators, the band gap is large, and electrons are not promoted into the conduction band at ordinary temperatures, resulting in no electrical conductivity. In semiconductors, the band gap is smaller. As a result, the conductivity of semiconductors increases with increasing temperature because heat allows a greater number of electrons to be thermally promoted into the conduction band.

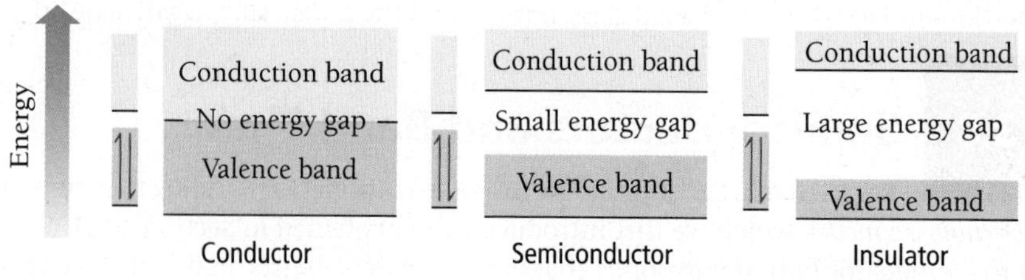

▶ **FIGURE 13.24 Band Gap** In a conductor, there is no energy gap between the valence band and the conduction band. In semiconductors there is a small energy gap, and in insulators there is a large energy gap.

The group 4A elements exhibit a range of band gaps as shown in Table 13.2.

TABLE 13.2 ■ Band Gap of Group 4A Elements

Group 4A Element	Atomic Radius (pm)	Band Gap	Classification
Carbon (diamond)	77	5.5 eV	Insulator
Silicon	118	1.11 eV	Semiconductor
Germanium	122	0.67 eV	Semiconductor
Tin	140	0.08 eV	Metal
Lead	180	none	Metal

Notice that the band gap decreases as you move down the column of elements. Why? We know from our discussion of periodic properties (see Section 9.6) that atomic radius increases as we move down a column in the periodic table. The increasing radius reduces the overlap between orbitals on neighboring atoms, which in turn reduces the energy difference between the antibonding orbitals (the conduction band) and the bonding orbitals (the valence band). This results in a decreasing band gap as you move down the column of elements.

Doping: Controlling the Conductivity of Semiconductors

Doped semiconductors contain minute amounts of impurities that result in additional electrons in the conduction band or electron "holes" in the valence band. For example, silicon is a group 4A semiconductor. Its valence electrons just fill its valence band. The band gap in silicon is large enough that only a few electrons are promoted into the conduction band at room temperature; therefore, silicon is a poor electrical conductor. However, silicon can be doped with phosphorus, a group 5A element with five valence electrons, to increase its conductivity. The phosphorus atoms are incorporated into the silicon crystal structure, and each phosphorous atom brings with it one additional electron. Since the valence band is completely full, the additional electrons must go into the conduction band. These electrons are then mobile and can conduct electrical current. This type of semiconductor is an **n-type semiconductor** because the charge carriers are *negatively* charged electrons in the conduction band.

Silicon can also be doped with a group 3A element, such as gallium, which has only three valence electrons. When gallium is incorporated into the silicon crystal structure, gallium atoms trap some of the electrons in silicon's valence band, resulting in electron "holes," or empty molecular orbitals, in the valence band. The presence of holes also allows for the movement of electrical current because electrons in the valence band can move between holes. In this way, the holes move in the opposite direction as the electrons. This type of semiconductor is a **p-type semiconductor** because each hole acts as a *positive* charge.

At the heart of most modern electronic devices are silicon chips containing millions of **p–n junctions**, tiny spots that are p-type on one side and n-type on the other. These junctions can serve a number of functions, including acting as **diodes** (circuit elements that allow the flow of electrical current in only one direction) or *amplifiers* (elements that amplify a small electrical current into a larger one).

SEMICONDUCTOR TYPE Which element would you dope into germanium to create a p-type semiconductor?

(a) indium **(b)** tin **(c)** arsenic

13.6 Cc Conceptual Connection

ANSWER **NOW!**

13.9 Polymers and Plastics

Polymers are long, chainlike molecules composed of repeating units called **monomers**. In Chapter 23, we discuss natural polymers such as starches, proteins, and DNA, which play important roles in living organisms. In this section, we learn about synthetic polymers, which we encounter daily in plastic products such as PVC tubing, styrofoam coffee cups, nylon rope, and plexiglass windows. Polymeric materials are common in our everyday lives, found in everything from computers to toys to packaging materials. Most polymers are durable, partly because of the length of their molecules. In general, the longer a molecule, the greater the intermolecular forces between molecules and the higher the melting point and boiling point of the substance. Since breaking or tearing a polymeric material involves either overcoming the intermolecular forces between chains or actually breaking the covalent bonds between monomers, polymers tend to be durable materials.

One of the simplest synthetic polymers is polyethylene. The polyethylene monomer is ethene (also called ethylene):

$$H_2C{=}CH_2$$

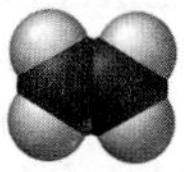

Monomer

Ethene or ethylene

Ethene monomers react with each other, breaking the double bond between carbons and bonding together to form a long polymer chain:

$$\cdots CH_2{-}CH_2{-}CH_2{-}CH_2{-}CH_2{-}CH_2{-}CH_2{-}CH_2{-}CH_2\cdots$$

Polymer

Polyethylene

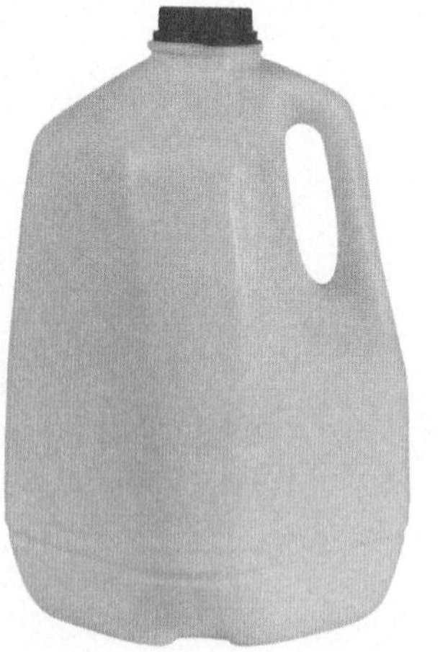

▲ **FIGURE 13.25 Polyethylene** Plastic milk bottles are made from polyethylene.

Polyethylene is an **addition polymer**, a polymer in which the monomers link together without the elimination of any atoms. Polyethylene is the plastic that is used for milk jugs, juice containers, and garbage bags. The properties of polyethylene depend on the exact structure of the ethylene chain and the resulting structure of the material. Although polymers are generally amorphous, they can have regions of crystallinity. For polyethylene, the degree of crystallinity depends in part on the degree of branching in the chain. High-density polyethylene (HDPE), for example, has little branching, so that the chains can align closer to one another, resulting in high crystallinity, high density, and good strength and heat resistance. Common plastic milk jugs are made of HDPE (Figure 13.25◀). Low-density polyethylene (LDPE), in contrast, has more highly branched chains. This branching prevents the chains from interacting as efficiently, resulting in lower crystallinity, density, and strength and heat resistance. Many common plastic bags are made of LDPE.

Substituted polyethylenes make up an entire class of polymers (Table 13.3). For example, polyvinyl chloride (PVC)—the plastic used to make certain kinds of pipes and plumbing fixtures—is composed of monomers in which a chlorine atom has been substituted for one of the hydrogen atoms in ethene (Figure 13.26▼). These monomers, which are shown here, react to form PVC:

$$\cdots CH(Cl){-}CH_2{-}CH(Cl){-}CH_2{-}CH(Cl){-}CH_2{-}CH(Cl){-}CH_2{-}CH(Cl)\cdots$$

$$HC(Cl){=}CH_2$$

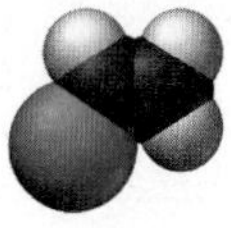

Monomer

Chloroethene

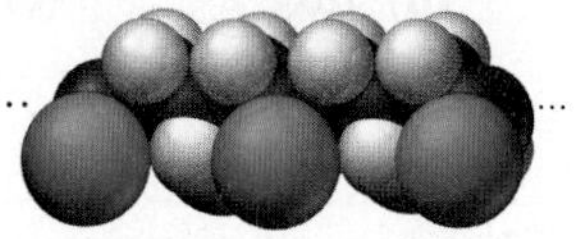

Polymer

Polyvinyl chloride (PVC)

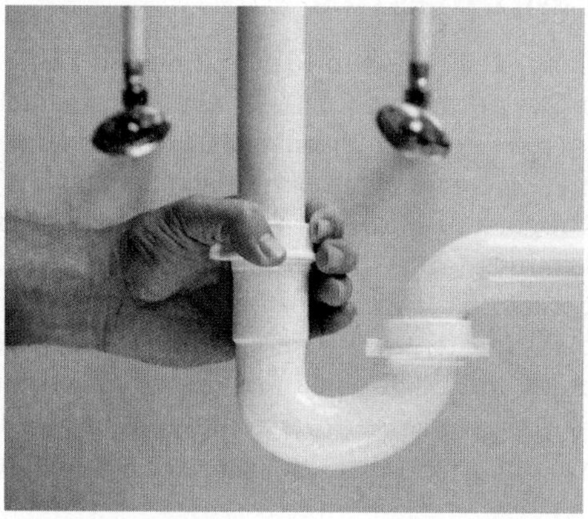

► **FIGURE 13.26 Polyvinyl Chloride** Polyvinyl chloride is used for many plastic plumbing supplies, such as pipes and connectors.

Some polymers—called *copolymers*—consist of two different kinds of monomers. For example, the monomers that compose nylon 6,6 are hexamethylenediamine and adipic acid. These two monomers add together via a condensation reaction as follows:

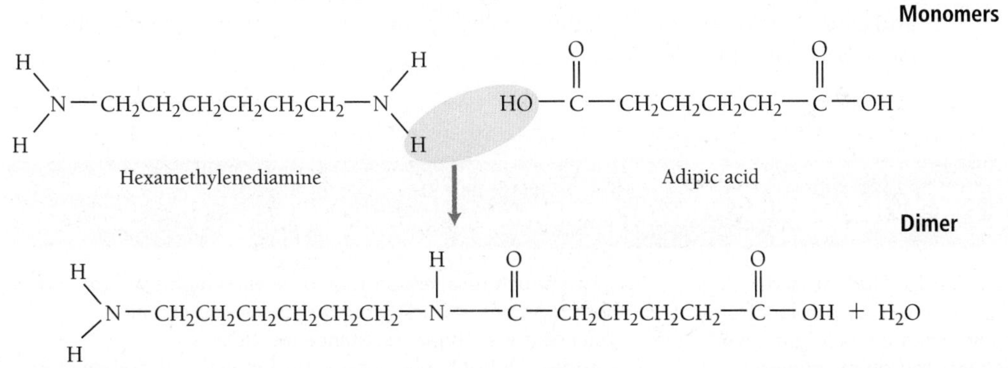

TABLE 13.3 ■ Polymers of Commercial Importance

Polymer	Structure	Uses
Addition Polymers		
Polyethylene	$-(CH_2-CH_2)_n-$	Films, packaging, bottles
Polypropylene	$-[CH_2-CH(CH_3)]_n-$	Kitchenware, fibers, appliances
Polystyrene	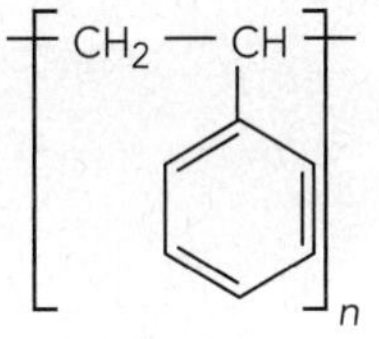	Packaging, disposable food containers, insulation
Polyvinyl chloride	$-[CH_2-CH(Cl)]_n-$	Pipe fittings, clear film for meat packaging
Condensation Polymers		
Polyurethane	$-[C(=O)-NH-R-NH-C(=O)-O-R'-O]_n-$ R, R′ = $-CH_2-CH_2-$ (*for example*)	"Foam" furniture stuffing, spray-on insulation, automotive parts, footwear, water-protective coatings
Polyethylene terephthalate (a polyester)	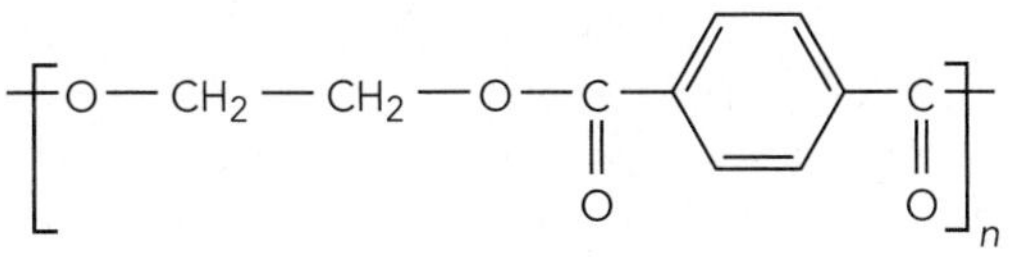	Tire cord, magnetic tape, apparel, soda bottles
Nylon 6,6	$-[NH-(CH_2)_6-NH-C(=O)-(CH_2)_4-C(=O)]_n-$	Home furnishings, apparel, carpet fibers, fish line, polymer blends

The product that forms between the reaction of two monomers is a **dimer**. The polymer (nylon 6,6) forms as the dimer continues to add more monomers. Polymers that eliminate an atom or a small group of atoms during polymerization are **condensation polymers**. Nylon 6,6 and other similar nylons are drawn into fibers and used to make consumer products such as panty hose, carpet fibers, and fishing line (see *Chemistry in Your Day: Kevlar*).

CHEMISTRY IN YOUR DAY | Kevlar

In 1965, Stephanie Kwolek, working for DuPont to develop new polymer fibers, noticed an odd, cloudy product from a polymerization reaction. Some researchers might have rejected the product, but Kwolek insisted on examining its properties more carefully. The results were astonishing—when the polymer was spun into a fiber, it was stronger than any fiber known before. Kwolek had discovered Kevlar, a material that is pound for pound five times stronger than steel.

Kevlar is a condensation polymer featuring aromatic rings and amide linkages:

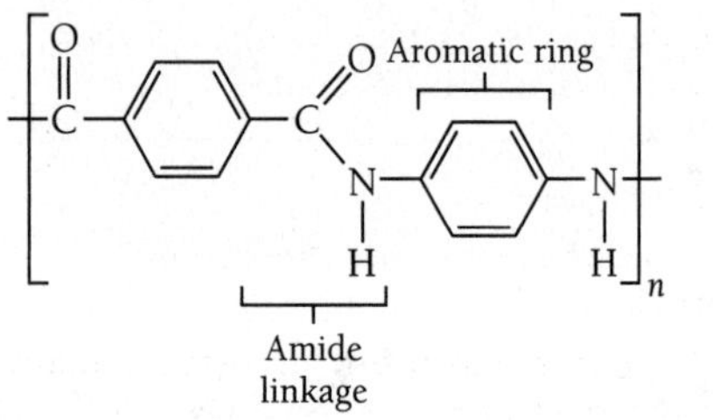

The polymeric chains within Kevlar crystallize in a parallel arrangement (like dry spaghetti noodles in a box), with strong cross-linking between neighboring chains resulting from hydrogen bonding. The hydrogen bonding occurs between the N—H groups on one chain and the C=O groups on neighboring chains:

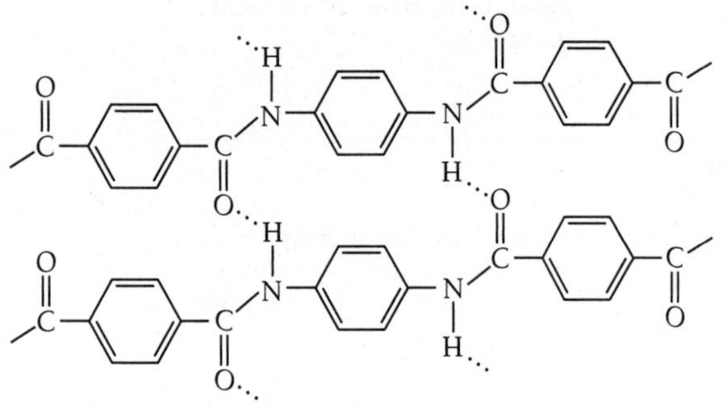

This structure is responsible for Kevlar's high strength and its other properties, including fire resistance and chemical resistance (for example, resistance to acids).

Today, DuPont sells hundreds of millions of dollars worth of Kevlar every year. Kevlar is particularly well known for its use in bulletproof vests. This application of Kwolek's discovery has saved thousands of lives. In addition, Kevlar is used to make helmets, radial tires, brake pads, racing sails, suspension bridge cables, skis, and high-performance hiking and camping gear.

▲ Kevlar is used to make bulletproof vests.

Self-Assessment Quiz

Q1. An X-ray beam of $\lambda = 154$ pm is incident on the surface of an unknown metallic crystal. It produces a maximum diffraction at an angle of $\theta = 29.1°$. Assuming $n = 1$, calculate the separation between layers of metal atoms in the crystal.
MISSED THIS? *Read Section 13.2*

a) 316 pm
b) 105 pm
c) 154 pm
d) 158 pm

Q2. How many atoms are in the body-centered cubic unit cell?
MISSED THIS? *Read Section 13.3; Watch KCV 13.3*

a) 1
b) 2
c) 4
d) 5

Q3. What is the coordination number of an atom in a face-centered unit cell?
MISSED THIS? *Read Section 13.3; Watch KCV 13.3*

a) 4
b) 6
c) 8
d) 12

Q4. What is the packing efficiency of the face-centered cubic unit cell?
MISSED THIS? *Read Section 13.3; Watch KCV 13.3*

a) 52%
b) 68%
c) 74%
d) 88%

Q5. What is the edge length of a body-centered cubic unit cell made up of atoms that each has a radius of 168 pm?
MISSED THIS? *Read Section 13.3; Watch KCV 13.3, IWE 13.3*

a) 388 pm
b) 336 pm
c) 475 pm
d) 84 pm

Q6. Rhodium crystallizes in a face-centered cubic unit cell. The radius of a rhodium atom is 135 pm. Determine the density of rhodium in g/cm^3.
MISSED THIS? *Read Section 13.3; Watch KCV 13.3, IWE 13.4*

a) $3.07\ g/cm^3$
b) $12.3\ g/cm^3$
c) $278\ g/cm^3$
d) $0.337\ g/cm^3$

Q7. Which type of solid is dry ice (solid carbon dioxide)?
MISSED THIS? *Read Section 13.4*

a) ionic
b) molecular
c) atomic
d) none of the above

Q8. Which solid has the highest melting point?
MISSED THIS? *Read Section 13.4*

a) $CS_2(s)$
b) $CaF_2(s)$
c) $C_8H_{18}(s)$
d) $Ar(s)$

Q9. Which material is a common oxide ceramic?
MISSED THIS? *Read Section 13.7*

a) N_2O
b) Al_2O_3
c) Fe_2O_3
d) CuO

Q10. What is the main component of glass?
MISSED THIS? *Read Section 13.7*

a) Al_2O_3
b) SiO_2
c) CaF_2
d) SiC

Q11. Which substance has the greatest band gap?
MISSED THIS? *Read Section 13.8*

a) silicon
b) germanium
c) lead
d) gold

Q12. Which element produces a p-type semiconductor when doped into silicon?
MISSED THIS? *Read Section 13.8*

a) Ge
b) As
c) Ga
d) Sb

Q13. Which monomer produces the addition polymer shown here?
MISSED THIS? *Read Section 13.9*

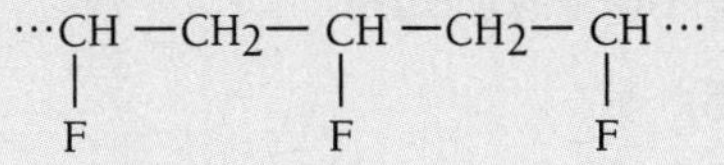

(a) $H_2C{=}CH_2$

(b) 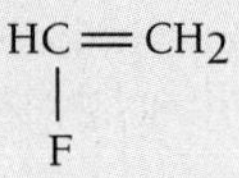

(c) 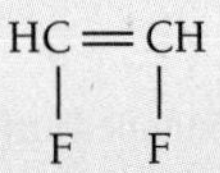

(d) 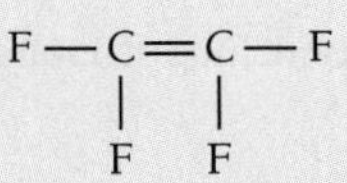

Answers: **1.** (d) **2.** (b) **3.** (d) **4.** (c) **5.** (a) **6.** (b) **7.** (b) **8.** (b) **9.** (b) **10.** (b) **11.** (a) **12.** (c) **13:** (b)

CHAPTER 13 IN REVIEW

TERMS

Section 13.1
graphene (541)

Section 13.2
X-ray diffraction (542)
X-ray crystallography (544)

Section 13.3
crystalline lattice (545)
unit cell (545)
simple cubic (546)
coordination number (547)
packing efficiency (547)
body-centered cubic (547)
face-centered cubic (549)
hexagonal closest packing (551)
cubic closest packing (552)

Section 13.4
molecular solids (553)
polymorphs (554)
ionic solids (555)
atomic solids (555)
nonbonding atomic solids (555)
metallic atomic solids (555)
network covalent atomic solids (556)

Section 13.6
graphite (558)
diamond (558)
fullerenes (560)
nanotubes (560)
silicates (561)
quartz (561)
silica (561)

Section 13.7
ceramics (561)
clay (561)
Portland cement (562)
concrete (563)
glass (563)
vitreous silica (fused silica) (563)
soda-lime glass (563)
borosilicate glass (Pyrex®) (563)
leaded glass (563)

Section 13.8
band theory (563)
valence band (564)
conduction band (564)
band gap (564)
n-type semiconductor (565)
p-type semiconductor (565)
p–n junctions (565)
diodes (565)

Section 13.9
polymer (565)
monomer (565)
addition polymer (566)
dimer (568)
condensation polymer (568)

CONCEPTS

Crystalline Structures (13.2–13.4)

- X-ray crystallography uses the diffraction pattern of X-rays to determine the crystal structure of solids.
- The crystal lattice is represented by a unit cell, a structure that reproduces the entire lattice when repeated in all three dimensions.
- Three basic cubic unit cells are the simple cubic, the body-centered cubic, and the face-centered cubic.
- Some crystal lattices can also be depicted as closest-packed structures, including the hexagonal closest-packing structure (not cubic) and the cubic closest-packing structure (which has a face-centered cubic unit cell).
- The basic types of crystal solids are molecular, ionic, and atomic solids. We divide atomic solids into three different types: nonbonded, metallic, and network covalent.

Ionic Solids (13.5)

- Unit cells in the structures of ionic solids are charge neutral. The unit cells must also accommodate the difference in size between the anion and cation.
- Common unit cells for ionic compounds include the sodium chloride unit cell, the zinc blende unit cell, and the calcium fluoride unit cell.

Network Covalent Atomic Solids (13.6)

- Network covalent solids are composed of extended arrays of atoms held together by covalent bonds.
- Well known network covalent solids include diamond, graphite, graphene, and silica.

Ceramics, Cement, and Glass (13.7)

- Ceramics are inorganic nonmetallic solids that are prepared from powders typically mixed with water, formed into the desired shape, and then heated. Ceramics are usually hard, strong, nonconductive, and brittle.
- Cement is a powdered mixture consisting mostly of limestone ($CaCO_3$) and silica (SiO_2), with smaller amounts of other substances. When cement is mixed with water, it reacts to form a hard, stone-like substance.
- Glass is primarily amorphous SiO_2 or silica. Silicate glass is transparent, impervious to water, and an outstanding material for making windows and drinking vessels.

Semiconductors and Band Theory (13.8)

- Band theory is a model for bonding in solids in which the atomic orbitals of the atoms are combined and delocalized over the entire crystal solid. In band theory, solids form energy bands that are occupied by electrons.
- In metals, the valence band (composed of bonding molecular orbitals) is continuous with the conduction band (composed of antibonding molecular orbitals).
- Semiconductors have a small energy gap—called the band gap—between the valence band and the conduction band.
- Semiconductors can be doped with small amounts of impurities to modify their conductivity.

Polymers and Plastics (13.9)

- Polymers are long, chainlike molecules that consist of repeating units called monomers. They can be natural or synthetic.
- Polyethylene is an addition polymer, a polymer formed without the elimination of any atoms.
- Condensation polymers, such as nylon, are formed by the elimination of small groups of atoms.

EQUATIONS AND RELATIONSHIPS

Bragg's Law: Relationship between Light Wavelength (λ), Angle of Reflection (θ), and Distance (d) between the Atomic Layers (**13.2**) $n\lambda = 2d \sin\theta$ (n = integer)

LEARNING OUTCOMES

Chapter Objectives	Assessment		
Perform X-ray diffraction calculations using Bragg's law (**13.2**)	Example 13.1	**For Practice** 13.1	**Exercises** 27–28
Analyze crystalline solids in terms of unit cell type, coordination number, and packing efficiency (**13.3**)	Example 13.2	**For Practice** 13.2	**Exercises** 29–32
Relate unit cell volume, edge length, and atomic radius (**13.3**)	Example 13.3	**For Practice** 13.3	**Exercises** 33–34
Solve problems involving the density of crystalline solids (**13.3**)	Example 13.4	**For Practice** 13.4	**Exercises** 35–38
Classify crystalline solids by type (molecular, ionic, or atomic) (**13.4**)	Example 13.5	**For Practice** 13.5	**Exercises** 39–40
Predict relative melting points of crystalline solids (**13.4**)	**Exercises** 41–44		
Analyze atomic solids in terms of structure and properties (**13.6**)	**Exercises** 45–52		
Describe the properties of silicates and silicate-based materials (**13.7**)	**Exercises** 53–58		
Analyze semiconductors in terms of band theory and type (n or p) (**13.8**)	**Exercises** 59–68		
Analyze polymers and plastics in terms of structure and properties (**13.9**)	**Exercises** 69–76		

EXERCISES

Mastering Chemistry provides end-of-chapter exercises, feedback-enriched tutorial problems, animations, and interactive activities to encourage problem-solving practice and deeper understanding of key concepts and topics.

REVIEW QUESTIONS

1. What is graphene? Why is graphene unique?

2. Explain the basic principles involved in X-ray crystallography. Include Bragg's law in your explanation.

3. What is a crystalline lattice? How is the lattice represented with the unit cell?

4. Make a drawing of each unit cell: simple cubic, body-centered cubic, and face-centered cubic.

5. For each of the cubic cells in the previous problem, give the coordination number, edge length in terms of r, and number of atoms per unit cell.

6. What is the difference between hexagonal closest packing and cubic closest packing? What are the unit cells for each of these structures?

7. What are the three basic types of solids and the composite units of each? What types of forces hold each type of solid together?

8. What are the three categories of atomic solids?

9. What kinds of forces hold each of the three basic categories of atomic solids together?

10. What is a polymorph?

11. In an ionic compound, how are the relative sizes of the cation and anion related to the coordination number of the crystal structure?

12. Show how the cesium chloride, sodium chloride, and zinc blende unit cells each contain a cation-to-anion ratio of 1:1.

13. Show how the fluorite structure accommodates a cation-to-anion ratio of 1:2.

14. Name and describe the different allotropes of carbon.

15. What are silicates? What is quartz?

16. What is the definition of a *ceramic*? What are the three categories of ceramics?

17. List the major and minor components of Portland cement. What is the difference between the hardening process of Portland cement and the hardening process of clays?

18. How is concrete made from Portland cement? What advantage does concrete have for building compared to the construction methods that predated the development of concrete?

19. Describe what happens on the molecular level when silica is heated and then cooled to make glass.

20. Describe the difference between vitreous silica and soda-lime glass. What are some advantages and disadvantages of each of these types of glass?

21. In band theory of bonding for solids, what is a *band*? What is the difference between the *valence band* and the *conduction band*?

22. In band theory of bonding for solids, what is a band gap? How does the band gap differ in metals, semiconductors, and insulators?

23. Explain how doping can increase the conductivity of a semiconductor. What is the difference between an n-type semiconductor and a p-type semiconductor?

24. What is the trend in the size of the band gap as you move down the column of the group 4A elements?

25. What is a polymer? What is the difference between a polymer and a copolymer?

26. How do an addition polymer and a condensation polymer differ from each other?

PROBLEMS BY TOPIC

Types of Solids and Their Structures

27. An X-ray beam with $\lambda = 154$ pm incident on the surface of a crystal produced a maximum reflection at an angle of $\theta = 28.3°$. Assuming $n = 1$, calculate the separation between layers of atoms in the crystal.
MISSED THIS? *Read Section 13.2*

28. An X-ray beam of unknown wavelength is diffracted from a NaCl surface. If the interplanar distance in the crystal is 286 pm, and the angle of maximum reflection is found to be 7.23°, what is the wavelength of the X-ray beam? (Assume $n = 1$.)

29. Determine the number of atoms per unit cell for each metal.
MISSED THIS? *Read Section 13.3; Watch KCV 13.3*

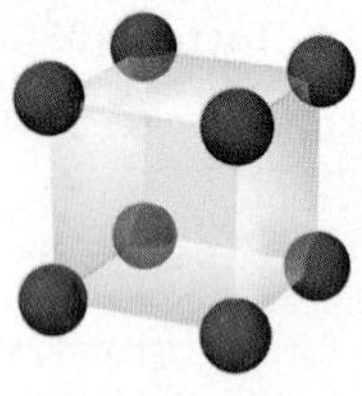

(a) Polonium

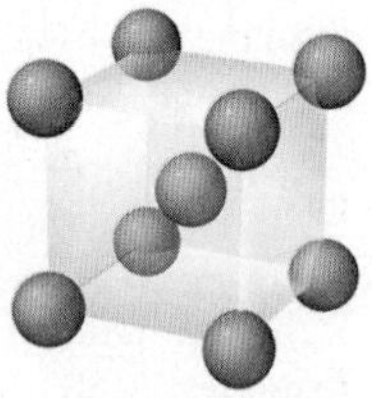

(b) Tungsten

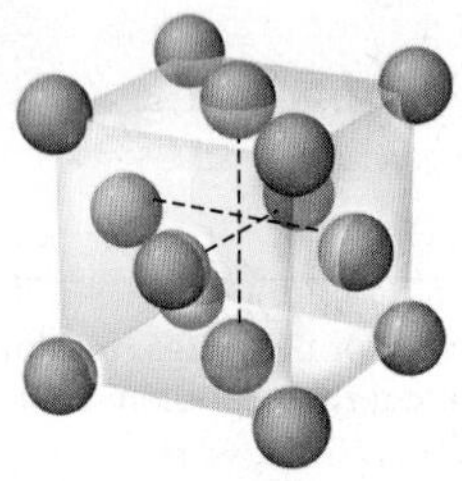

(c) Nickel

30. Determine the coordination number for each structure.

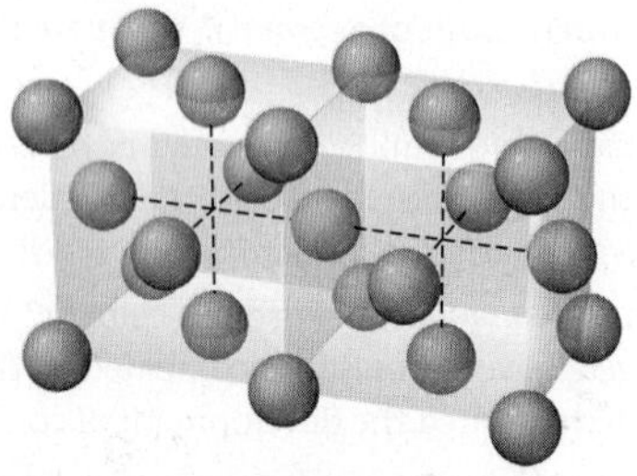

(a) Gold

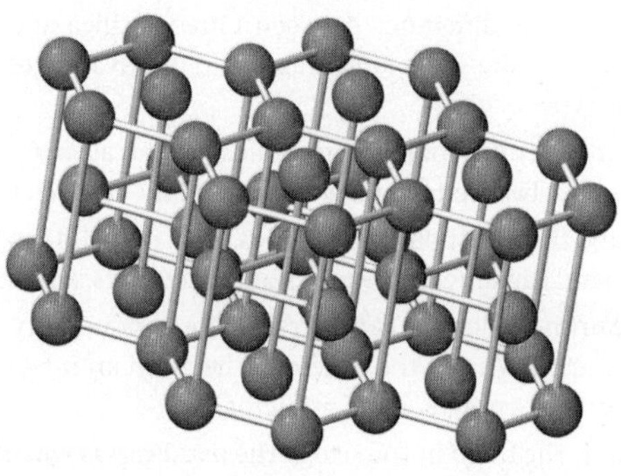

(b) Ruthenium

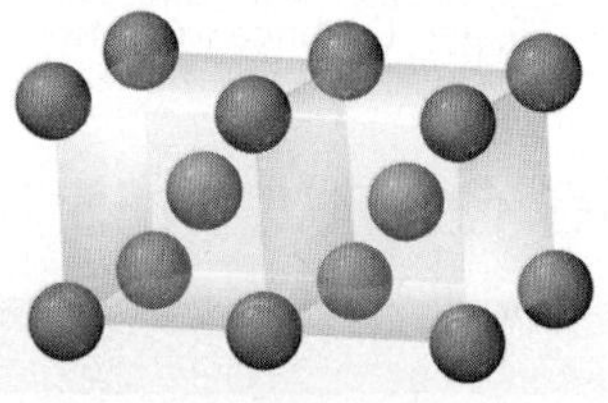

(c) Chromium

31. Calculate the packing efficiency of the body-centered cubic unit cell. Show your work.
MISSED THIS? *Read Section 13.3; Watch KCV 13.3*

32. Calculate the packing efficiency of the face-centered cubic unit cell. Show your work.

33. Platinum crystallizes with the face-centered cubic unit cell. The radius of a platinum atom is 139 pm. Calculate the edge length of the unit cell and the density of platinum in g/cm^3.
MISSED THIS? *Read Section 13.3; Watch KCV 13.3, IWE 13.3, 13.4*

34. Molybdenum crystallizes with the body-centered unit cell. The radius of a molybdenum atom is 136 pm. Calculate the edge length of the unit cell and the density of molybdenum.

35. Rhodium has a density of 12.41 g/cm^3 and crystallizes with the face-centered cubic unit cell. Calculate the radius of a rhodium atom. **MISSED THIS?** *Read Section 13.3; Watch KCV 13.3, IWE 13.3, 13.4*

36. Barium has a density of 3.59 g/cm^3 and crystallizes with the body-centered cubic unit cell. Calculate the radius of a barium atom.

37. Polonium crystallizes with a simple cubic structure. It has a density of 9.3 g/cm^3, a radius of 167 pm, and a molar mass of 209 g/mol. Use these data to calculate Avogadro's number (the number of atoms in one mole).
MISSED THIS? *Read Section 13.3; Watch KCV 13.3, IWE 13.4*

38. Palladium crystallizes with a face-centered cubic structure. It has a density of 12.0 g/cm^3, a radius of 138 pm, and a molar mass of 106.42 g/mol. Use these data to calculate Avogadro's number.

39. Identify each solid as molecular, ionic, or atomic.
MISSED THIS? *Read Section 13.4*

a. $Ar(s)$
b. $H_2O(s)$
c. $K_2O(s)$
d. $Fe(s)$

40. Identify each solid as molecular, ionic, or atomic.

a. $CaCl_2(s)$
b. $CO_2(s)$
c. $Ni(s)$
d. $I_2(s)$

41. Which solid has the highest melting point? Why?

$Ar(s)$, $CCl_4(s)$, $LiCl(s)$, $CH_3OH(s)$

MISSED THIS? *Read Section 13.4*

42. Which solid has the highest melting point? Why?

$C(s$, diamond$)$, $Kr(s)$, $NaCl(s)$, $H_2O(s)$

43. Which solid in each pair has the higher melting point and why?
MISSED THIS? *Read Section 13.4*

a. $TiO_2(s)$ or $HOOH(s)$
b. $CCl_4(s)$ or $SiCl_4(s)$
c. $Kr(s)$ or $Xe(s)$
d. $NaCl(s)$ or $CaO(s)$

44. Which solid in each pair has the higher melting point and why?

a. $Fe(s)$ or $CCl_4(s)$
b. $KCl(s)$ or $HCl(s)$
c. $Ti(s)$ or $Ne(s)$
d. $H_2O(s)$ or $H_2S(s)$

45. An oxide of titanium crystallizes with the unit cell shown here (titanium = gray; oxygen = red). What is the formula of the oxide? **MISSED THIS?** *Read Section 13.5; Watch KCV 13.5*

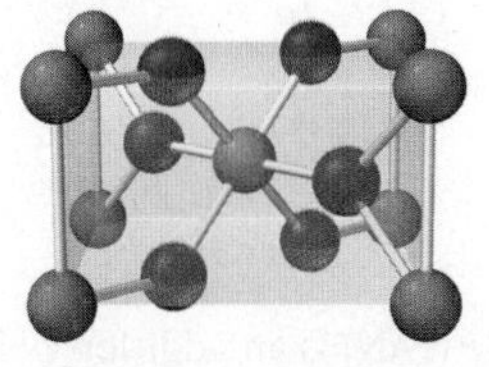

46. An oxide of rhenium crystallizes with the unit cell shown here (rhenium = gray; oxygen = red). What is the formula of the oxide?

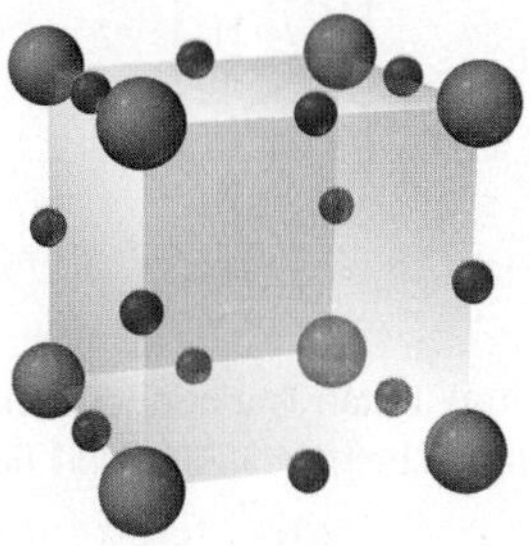

47. The unit cells for cesium chloride and barium chloride are shown here. Show that the ratio of cations to anions in each unit cell corresponds to the ratio of cations to anions in the formula of each compound.
MISSED THIS? *Read Section 13.5; Watch KCV 13.3*

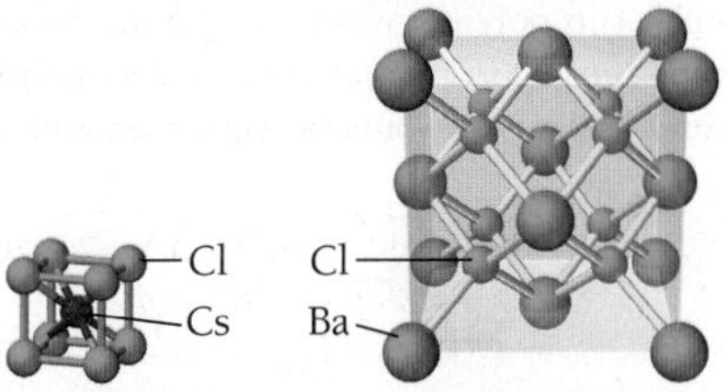

Cesium chloride Barium chloride

48. The unit cells for lithium oxide and silver iodide are shown here. Show that the ratio of cations to anions in each unit cell corresponds to the ratio of cations to anions in the formula of each compound.

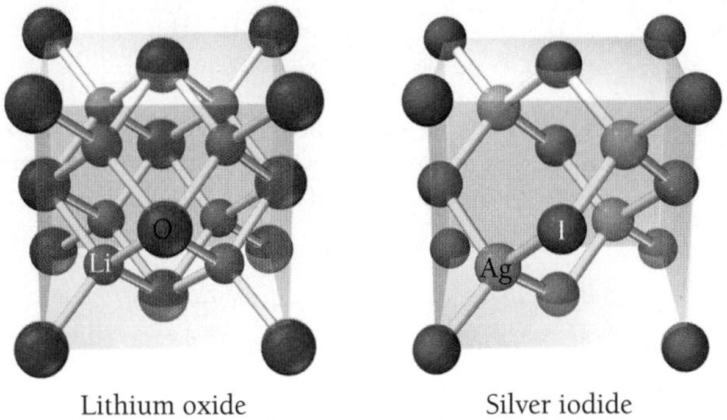

Lithium oxide Silver iodide

49. Identify the structure of each of the two unit cells shown in Problem 47 as the rock salt structure, zinc blende structure, fluorite structure, antifluorite structure, or none of these.
MISSED THIS? *Read Section 13.5*

50. Identify the structure of each of the two unit cells shown in Problem 48 as the rock salt structure, zinc blende structure, fluorite structure, antifluorite structure, or none of these.

51. Consider the rock salt structure in Figure 13.15. What type of structure would result if all the anions were somehow removed, leaving only cations?
MISSED THIS? *Read Section 13.5; Watch KCV 13.3*

52. Consider the zinc blende structure in Figure 13.16. What type of structure would result if the remaining tetrahedral sites in the unit cell were also filled with cations?

Ceramics, Cement, and Glass

53. Classify each of the following as a component of a silicate ceramic, an oxide ceramic, or a nonoxide ceramic.
MISSED THIS? *Read Section 13.7*

a. B_4C
b. Mg_2SiO_4
c. $MoSi_2$

54. Classify each of the following as a component of a silicate ceramic, an oxide ceramic, or a nonoxide ceramic.

a. TiB_2
b. ZrO_2
c. $NaAlSi_3O_8$

55. What are the name and formula of the compound commonly used in the manufacture of glass to reduce its tendency to crack or shatter under thermal shock?
MISSED THIS? *Read Section 13.7*

56. What are the name and formula of the compound commonly used in the manufacture of glass to increase the index of refraction?

57. One of the key components in the manufacture of Portland cement is Ca_3SiO_5, a compound that is obtained by firing the reactants in a kiln at 1400–1500 °C. Assign an oxidation state to each element in this compound.
MISSED THIS? *Read Section 5.9, 13.7; Watch KCV 5.13*

58. Replacement of aluminum ions in kaolinite with magnesium ions yields a compound with the formula $Mg_3Si_2O_5(OH)_4$. Assign an oxidation state to each element in this compound.

Semiconductors and Band Theory

59. Which solid would you expect to have little or no band gap?
MISSED THIS? *Read Section 13.8*

a. Zn(*s*)
b. Si(*s*)
c. As(*s*)

60. Which solid would you expect to have the largest band gap?

a. As(*s*)
b. Sb(*s*)
c. Bi(*s*)

61. How many molecular orbitals are present in the conduction band of a lithium crystal with a mass of 11.2 g?
MISSED THIS? *Read Section 13.8*

62. How many molecular orbitals are present in the valence band of a sodium crystal with a mass of 5.45 g?

63. A substance has a band gap of 6.9 eV at 273 K. Is this substance best classified as an insulator, a semiconductor, or a metal?
MISSED THIS? *Read Section 13.8*

64. A substance has a band gap of 0.85 eV at 273 K. Is this substance best classified as an insulator, a semiconductor, or a metal?

65. Indicate if each solid forms an n-type or a p-type semiconductor. **MISSED THIS?** *Read Section 13.8*

a. germanium doped with gallium
b. silicon doped with arsenic

66. Indicate if each solid forms an n-type or a p-type semiconductor.

a. silicon doped with gallium
b. germanium doped with antimony

67. Does a photon of red light with a frequency of 4.29×10^{14} Hz have sufficient energy to promote an electron from the valence band to the conduction band in a sample of silicon (the band gap in silicon is 1.11 eV)? **MISSED THIS?** *Read Section 13.8*

68. Which wavelength of light (in nm) is emitted if an electron moves from the conduction band to the valence band in a sample of diamond (diamond has a band gap of 5.5 eV)?

Polymers

69. Teflon is an addition polymer formed from the monomer shown here. Draw the structure of the polymer. **MISSED THIS?** *Read Section 13.9*

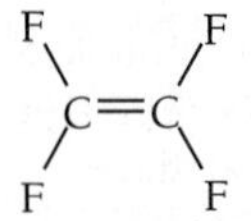

70. Saran, the polymer used to make Saran Wrap, is an addition polymer formed from two monomers—vinylidene chloride and vinyl chloride. Draw the structure of the polymer. (*Hint:* The monomers alternate.)

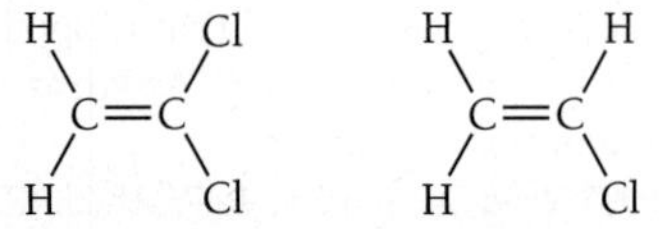

Vinylidene chloride   Vinyl chloride

71. One kind of polyester is a condensation copolymer formed from terephthalic acid and ethylene glycol. Draw the structure of the dimer. [*Hint:* Water (circled) is eliminated when the bond between the monomers forms.] **MISSED THIS?** *Read Section 13.9*

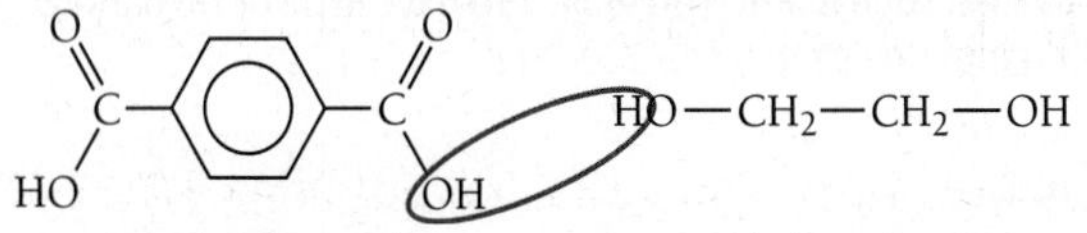

Terephthalic acid   Ethylene glycol

72. Nomex, a condensation copolymer used by firefighters because of its flame-resistant properties, forms from isophthalic acid and *m*-aminoaniline. Draw the structure of the dimer. (*Hint:* Water is eliminated when the bond between the monomers forms.)

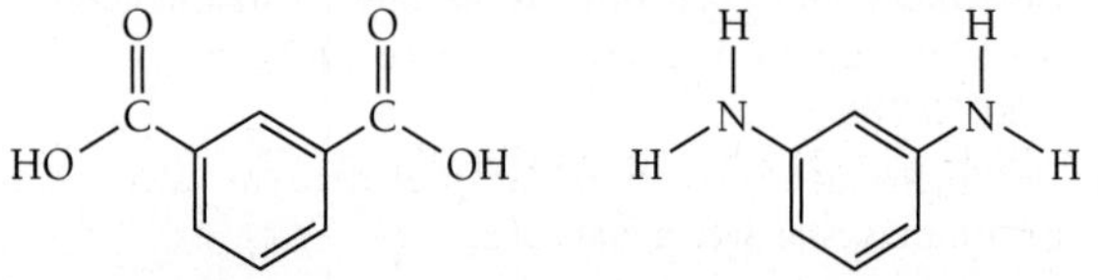

Isophthalic acid   *m*-Aminoaniline

73. Polyacetylene is an addition polymer with the structure shown here. Draw the structure of the monomer. **MISSED THIS?** *Read Section 13.9*

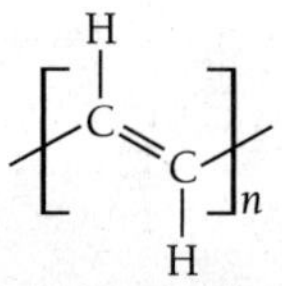

74. Polyacrylonitrile (PAN) is an addition polymer with the structure shown here. Draw the structure of the monomer.

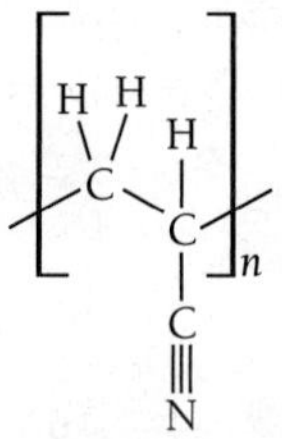

75. The polycarbonate Lexan is a condensation polymer and has the structure shown here: **MISSED THIS?** *Read Section 13.9*

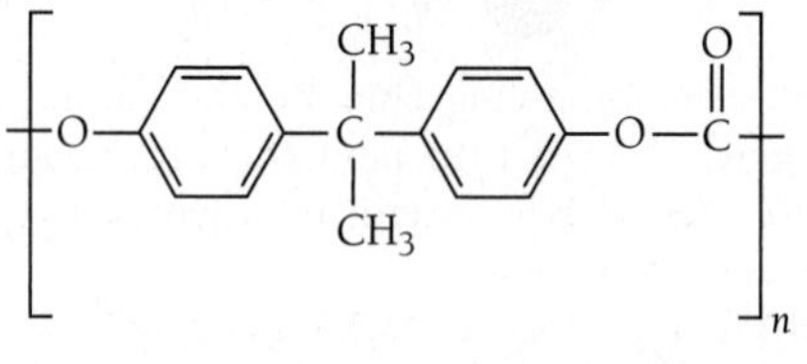

Assuming this polymer was formed from the monomer shown here plus another monomer, provide a possible structure for the other monomer that would be required to form Lexan.

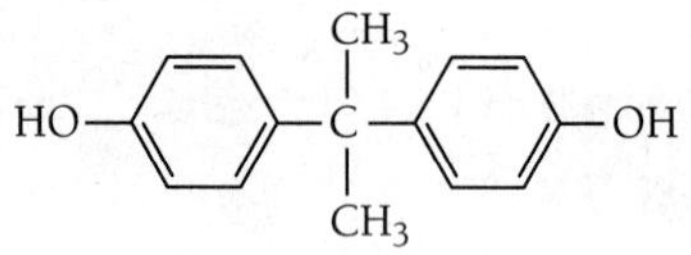

76. Consider the condensation polymer with the structure shown here:

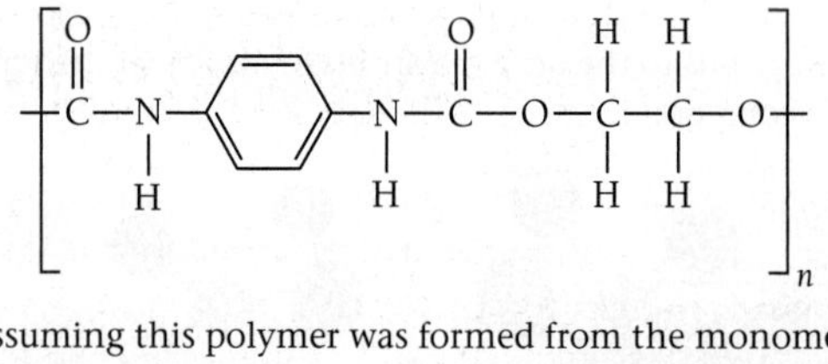

Assuming this polymer was formed from the monomer shown here plus another monomer, provide the structure of the other monomer that would be required to form this polymer.

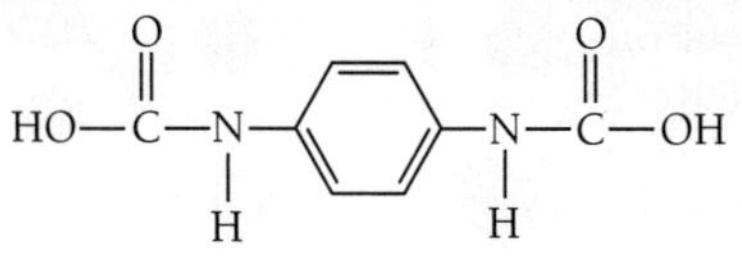

CUMULATIVE PROBLEMS

77. Silver iodide crystallizes in the zinc blende structure. The separation between nearest-neighbor cations and anions is approximately 325 pm, and the melting point is 558 °C. Cesium chloride, by contrast, crystallizes in the structure shown in Figure 13.14. Even though the separation between nearest-neighbor cations and anions is greater (348 pm), the melting point of cesium chloride is higher (645 °C). Explain.

78. Copper iodide crystallizes in the zinc blende structure. The separation between nearest-neighbor cations and anions is approximately 311 pm, and the melting point is 606 °C. Potassium chloride, by contrast, crystallizes in the rock salt structure. Even though the separation between nearest-neighbor cations and anions is greater (319 pm), the melting point of potassium chloride is higher (776 °C). Explain.

79. Consider the face-centered cubic structure shown here:

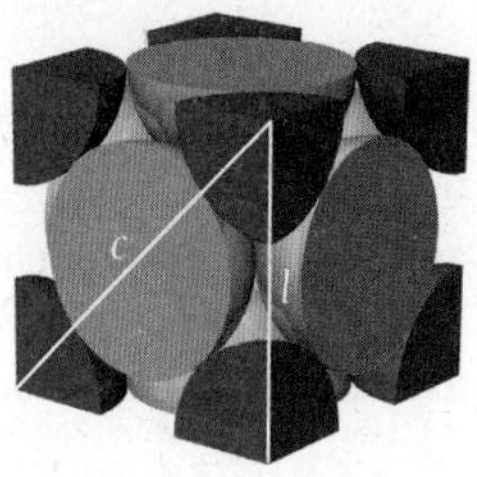

a. What is the length of the line (labeled *c*) that runs diagonally across one of the faces of the cube in terms of *r* (the atomic radius)?

b. Use the answer to part a and the Pythagorean theorem to derive the expression for the edge length (*l*) in terms of *r*.

80. Consider the body-centered cubic structure shown here:

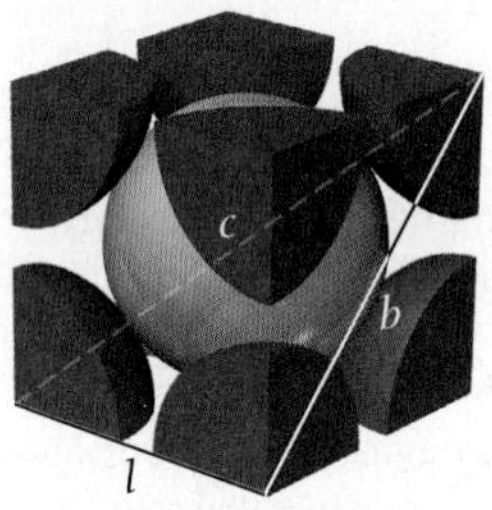

a. What is the length of the line (labeled *c*) that runs from one corner of the cube diagonally through the center of the cube to the other corner in terms of *r* (the atomic radius)?

b. Use the Pythagorean theorem to derive an expression for the length of the line (labeled *b*) that runs diagonally across one of the faces of the cube in terms of the edge length (*l*).

c. Use the answer to parts a and b along with the Pythagorean theorem to derive the expression for the edge length (*l*) in terms of *r*.

81. The volume of a unit cell of diamond is 0.0454 nm^3, and the density of diamond is 3.52 g/cm^3. Find the number of carbon atoms in a unit cell of diamond.

82. The density of an unknown metal is 12.3 g/cm^3, and its atomic radius is 0.134 nm. It has a face-centered cubic lattice. Find the atomic mass of this metal.

83. An unknown metal is found to have a density of 7.8748 g/cm^3 and to crystallize in a body-centered cubic lattice. The edge of the unit cell is 0.28664 nm. Calculate the atomic mass of the metal.

84. When spheres of radius *r* are packed in a body-centered cubic arrangement, they occupy 68.0% of the available volume. Use the fraction of occupied volume to calculate the value of *a*, the length of the edge of the cube, in terms of *r*.

85. Potassium chloride crystallizes in the rock salt structure. Estimate the density of potassium chloride using the ionic radii provided in Chapter 9.

86. Calculate the fraction of empty space in cubic closest packing to five significant figures.

87. A tetrahedral site in a closest-packed lattice is formed by four spheres at the corners of a regular tetrahedron. This is equivalent to placing the spheres at alternate corners of a cube. In such a closest-packed arrangement the spheres are in contact, and if the spheres have a radius *r*, the diagonal of the face of the cube is 2*r*. The tetrahedral hole is inside the middle of the cube. Find the length of the body diagonal of this cube and then find the radius of the tetrahedral hole.

88. X-ray diffractometers often use metals that have had their core electrons excited as a source of X-rays. Consider the $2p \longrightarrow 1s$ transition for copper, which is called the $K\alpha$ transition. Calculate the wavelength of X-rays (in Å) given off by the $K\alpha$ transition if the energy given off by a mole of copper atoms is 7.77×10^5 kJ. ($1\ \text{Å} = 10^{-10}$ m)

89. Why is it necessary to use the $K\alpha$ transition ($2p \longrightarrow 1s$) in copper (see Problem 88) to generate X-rays? Why not use, for example, the $4s \longrightarrow 3p$ transition?

90. In certain cases where X-ray diffraction is unsuitable for determining the structure of a crystal, *neutron diffraction* can be used. Instead of X-rays, a beam of neutrons is used to analyze the sample. Calculate the velocity of a beam of neutrons with a wavelength of 2.00 Å.

CHALLENGE PROBLEMS

91. The structure of the addition polymer polypropylene is shown in Table 13.3.

a. Draw the structure of the monomer.

b. Show how an alternate version of the polypropylene polymer (with a different arrangement) could be formed from the monomer you found in part a.

92. Perovskite is a compound with a cubic unit cell and has a strontium atom at the center of the cell, titanium atoms at the corners of the unit cell, and oxygen atoms at the centers of each face of the unit cell.

a. What is the formula of perovskite?

b. What is the coordination number of strontium in the perovskite structure?

c. If the edge length of the unit cell is 3.905 Å, calculate the density of perovskite in g/cm^3.

93. A compound with the formula Rb_3C_{60} has been shown to demonstrate superconductivity below 30.0 K. Given that the C_{60} molecules have a face-centered cubic arrangement, which of the tetrahedral and octahedral sites are occupied by Rb atoms?

94. Despite Dalton's laws, it is now known that many ionic compounds do not always contain atoms in small integer ratios. For example, a sample of iron(II) oxide may, in fact, contain a significant amount of Fe^{3+} in addition to Fe^{2+}. This is an example of a *nonstoichiometric* compound. A sample of iron(II) oxide is found to be 75.65% iron by mass. Determine the percentage of Fe^{3+} ions in the sample.

CONCEPTUAL PROBLEMS

95. During the glass manufacturing process, the liquid must be cooled relatively quickly to form the glass. Why?

96. Why are X-rays used for crystallography? Why not use some other, more accessible type of electromagnetic radiation such as ultraviolet light?

97. Compare the crystal structure of diamond (C) and zinc blende (ZnS). What are the key similarities and differences between the two structures?

98. In X-ray crystallography, a small amount of oil is often used to mount the crystal sample on a glass fiber. Explain why neither the oil nor the glass fiber interferes with the diffraction pattern of the crystal.

99. Which is not likely to lead to an increase in electrical conductivity?

a. Increasing the temperature of a semiconductor

b. Choosing a semiconductor with a smaller band gap

c. Doping the semiconductor

d. All of the above would likely lead to an increase in electrical conductivity.

QUESTIONS FOR GROUP WORK

Active Classroom Learning

Discuss these questions with the group and record your consensus answer.

100. Have each group member select one of the cubic crystalline lattices. Learn everything you can about your lattice and present it to the group.

101. Using group members to play the role of atoms or molecules, demonstrate the main structural features of the following categories of crystalline solids: molecular solid, ionic solid, nonbonded solid, metallic solid, network covalent solid. Clearly identify what you represent and how you are representing various interactions between particles (e.g., covalent bond, ionic bond).

102. Make a list of questions you would need to ask in order to classify a solid into one of the categories of crystalline solids (molecular solid, ionic solid, nonbonded solid, metallic solid, and network covalent solid). Determine a good order to ask them. (You may need a branching decision tree.) Once you have agreed on a good set of questions, have each group member choose a substance from the chapter and then have the other group members ask the questions in turn until the correct classification is reached. You may agree to edit your questions if you discover ways to improve them when you are using your decision tree.

103. Have each group member select and study a material from the section on ceramics, cement, and glass. Take turns describing your material to the group, and see if they can identify the type of material based on your description (without consulting the text).

104. Describe how a common object or toy (e.g., a train, building blocks, or beads on a string) could represent the structure of a polymer. Describe how the following terms would be represented using your model: monomer, dimer, addition polymer, condensation polymer, branching.

DATA INTERPRETATION AND ANALYSIS

Alloy Composition and Phase

105. An *alloy* is a metallic mixture composed of two or more elements. As is the case in all mixtures, the relative amounts of the elements in an alloy can vary. In some cases, the components of an alloy can have different crystal structures. For example, a nickel–chromium alloy consists of nickel, which has face-centered cubic structure, and chromium, which has a body-centered cubic structure. Which structure does the alloy adopt? It depends on the relative compositions. The phase diagrams for alloys such as these reveal the structure as a function of the alloy composition and temperature. For example, the nickel and chromium phase diagram from 700 °C to 1900 °C is shown here:

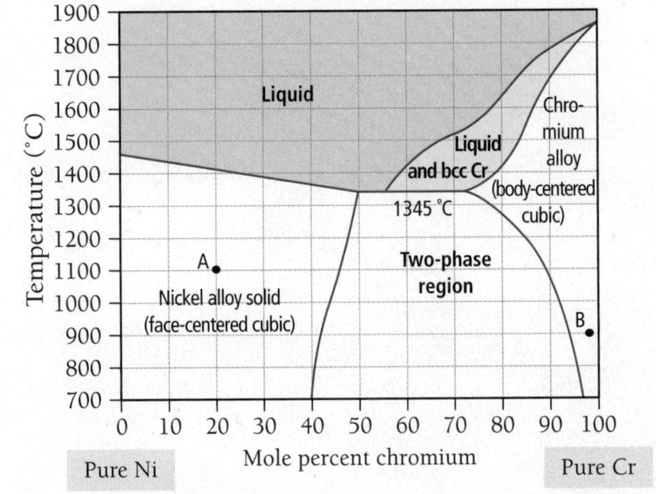

▲ Cr-Ni Phase Diagram

Notice that the diagram has two different solid phases: face-centered cubic and body-centered cubic. From pure nickel (0 mol % chromium) to about 40–50 mol % chromium, the structure is face-centered cubic. In this structure, Cr atoms substitute for Ni atoms in the face-centered cubic structure of nickel. However, when an amount of chromium beyond a certain percentage (which depends on temperature) is added, that structure is no longer stable. At the other end of the diagram, from pure chromium to about 75% chromium (depending on temperature), the structure is body-centered cubic, with nickel substituting into the body-centered cubic structure of the chromium. The region in between the two phases is called the *two-phase region*. At these compositions, the two phases (nickel-rich face-centered cubic and chromium-rich body-centered cubic) exist together (the solution is not homogeneous in this region). Use the phase diagram to answer the following questions.

a. What is the relative composition of the mixture at point A? At what temperature does a solid mixture having this composition melt?

b. Is it possible to have a homogeneous solid mixture that is 50% Ni and 50% Cr? If so, what crystalline structure would it have?

c. What is the relative composition at point B? What is the crystalline structure at point B?

d. At what temperature does the solid present at point B begin to melt?

Cc ANSWERS TO CONCEPTUAL CONNECTIONS

Edge Length and Atomic Radius

13.1 **(c)** 255 pm The relationship between the edge length and the radius for the body-centered cubic unit cell is $l = 4r\sqrt{3}$. Therefore, $r = l\sqrt{3}/4$.

Cubic Structures

13.2 **(c)** The face-centered cubic structure has four atoms per unit cell.

Crystalline Solid Types and Melting Points

13.3 **(a)** MgO, an ionic compound, has the highest melting point because the solid is held together by ionic bonds. I_2 is a molecular compound with only dispersion forces, and Kr is a nonbonding atomic solid with only dispersion forces. As a result, these two substances have much lower melting points.

Ionic Crystalline Solid Unit Cells

13.4 **(c)** The zinc blende structure occurs in ionic compounds with a one-to-one cation-to-anion ratio in which the cation is much smaller than the anion.

Phase Changes and Pressure

13.5 **(a)** An increase in pressure favors the denser phase, in this case diamond.

Semiconductor Type

13.6 **(a)** Since indium has three valence electrons and germanium has four, the presence of indium would introduce holes into the valence band, resulting in a p-type semiconductor.

One molecule of nonsaline substance (held in the solvent) dissolved in 100 molecules of any volatile liquid decreases the vapor pressure of this liquid by a nearly constant fraction, nearly 0.0105.

—FRANÇOIS-MARIE RAOULT (1830–1901)

CHAPTER 14 Solutions

We learned in Chapter 1 that most of the matter we encounter is in the form of mixtures. In this chapter, we focus on homogeneous mixtures, known as solutions. Solutions are mixtures in which atoms and molecules intermingle on the molecular and atomic scale. Common examples of solutions include ocean water, gasoline, and air. Why do solutions form? How are their properties different from the properties of the pure substances that compose them? As you read this chapter, keep in mind the large number of solutions that surround you at every moment, including those that exist within your own body.

Drinking seawater causes dehydration because seawater draws water out of body tissues.

14.1 Thirsty Solutions: Why You Shouldn't Drink Seawater 579

14.2 Types of Solutions and Solubility 581

14.3 Energetics of Solution Formation 586

14.4 Solution Equilibrium and Factors Affecting Solubility 589

14.5 Expressing Solution Concentration 594

14.6 Colligative Properties: Vapor Pressure Lowering, Freezing Point Depression, Boiling Point Elevation, and Osmotic Pressure 601

14.7 Colligative Properties of Strong Electrolyte Solutions 613

14.8 Colloids 616

LEARNING OUTCOMES 621

14.1 Thirsty Solutions: Why You Shouldn't Drink Seawater

In the popular novel *Life of Pi* by Yann Martel, the main character (whose name is Pi) is stranded on a lifeboat with a Bengal tiger in the middle of the Pacific Ocean for 227 days. Pi survives in part by rigging a solar still to distill seawater for drinking. However, in the first three days of his predicament (before he rigs the still), he becomes severely dehydrated from lack of water. He is surrounded by seawater, but drinking *that* water would only have made his condition worse. Why? Seawater actually draws water

In some cases, the concepts of solute and solvent are not useful. For example, a homogeneous mixture of water and ethanol can contain equal amounts of both components, and neither component can then be identified as the solvent.

out of the body as it passes through the stomach and intestines, resulting in diarrhea and further dehydration. We can think of seawater as a *thirsty solution*—one that draws more water to itself. Consequently, seawater should never be consumed as drinking water.

Seawater is a **solution**, a homogeneous mixture of two or more substances or components, as shown in Figure 14.1▼. The majority component in a solution is typically called the **solvent**, and the minority component is called the **solute**. In seawater, water is the solvent, and sodium chloride is the primary solute. Solutions form in part because of the intermolecular forces we discussed in Chapter 12. In most solutions, the particles of the solute interact with the particles of the solvent through intermolecular forces.

▶ **FIGURE 14.1 A Typical Solution** In seawater, sodium chloride is the primary solute. Water is the solvent.

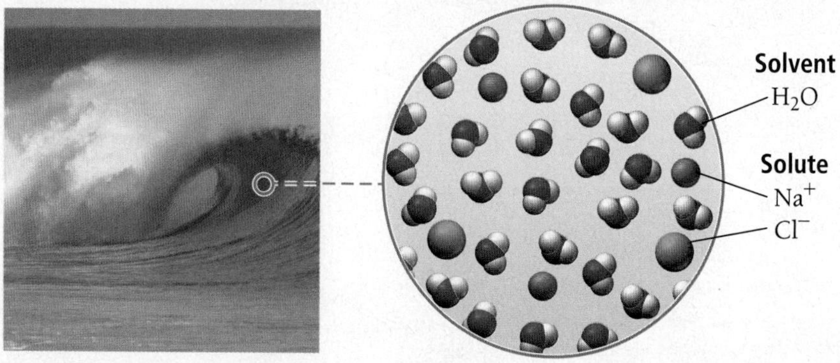

The reason that seawater draws water to itself is related to nature's tendency toward spontaneous mixing, which we discuss in more detail later in this chapter and in Chapter 19. For now, we simply observe that unless the mixing process is highly unfavorable energetically, substances tend to combine into uniform mixtures and do not separate into pure substances. For example, suppose pure water and a sodium chloride solution are in separate compartments with a removable barrier between them, as shown in Figure 14.2(a)▼. If we remove the barrier, the two liquids spontaneously mix, eventually forming a more dilute sodium chloride solution of uniform concentration, as shown in Figure 14.2(b)▼. The tendency toward mixing results in a uniform concentration of the final solution.

Seawater is a *thirsty* solution because of this tendency toward mixing. As seawater moves through the intestine, it flows past cells that line the digestive tract. These cells consist of largely fluid interiors surrounded by membranes. Cellular fluids themselves contain dissolved ions, including sodium and chloride, but the fluids in the cells are more dilute than seawater. Nature's tendency toward mixing (which tends to produce

Spontaneous Mixing

When the barrier that separates pure water and a sodium chloride solution is removed, spontaneous mixing occurs, producing a solution of uniform concentration.

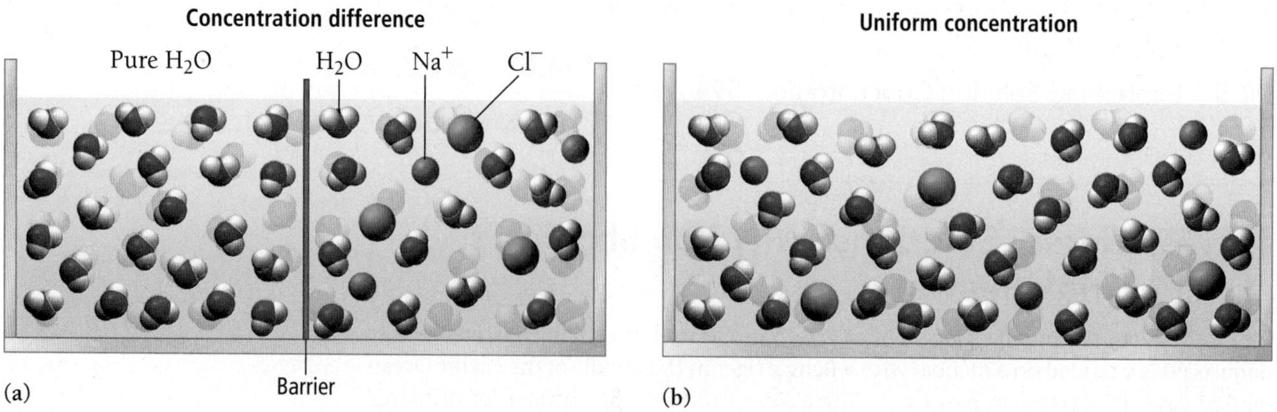

▲ **FIGURE 14.2 The Tendency to Mix** **(a)** A barrier separates pure water and a sodium chloride solution. **(b)** When the barrier is removed, the two liquids spontaneously mix, producing a single solution of uniform concentration.

solutions of uniform concentration), together with the selective permeability of the cell membranes (which allows water to flow in and out, but restricts the flow of dissolved solids), cause a *flow of solvent out of the body's cells into the seawater*. In this way, the two solutions become more similar in concentration (as though they had mixed). The solution in the intestine becomes somewhat more dilute than it was, and the solution in the cells becomes somewhat more concentrated. The accumulation of extra fluid in the intestines causes diarrhea, and the decreased fluid in the cells causes dehydration. If Pi had drunk the seawater instead of constructing the solar still, neither he nor his companion, the large Bengal tiger, would have survived their ordeal.

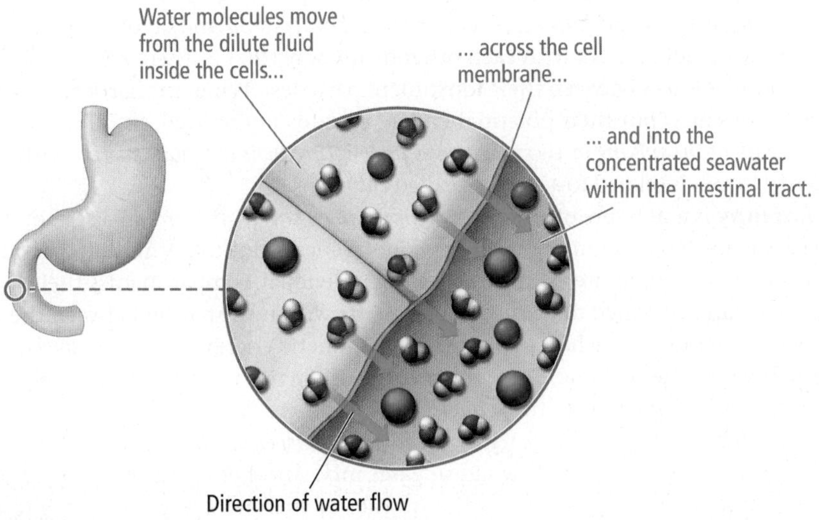

◀ Seawater is a more concentrated solution than the fluids in body cells. As a result, when seawater flows through the digestive tract, it draws water out of the surrounding tissues.

14.2 Types of Solutions and Solubility

A solution may be composed of a solid and a liquid (such as the salt and water that are the primary components of seawater), but it may also be composed of a gas and a liquid, two different liquids, or other combinations (see Table 14.1). In **aqueous solutions**, water is the solvent, and a solid, liquid, or gas is the solute. For example, sugar water and salt water are both aqueous solutions. Similarly, ethyl alcohol—the alcohol in alcoholic beverages—readily mixes with water to form a solution, and carbon dioxide dissolves in water to form the aqueous solution that we know as club soda.

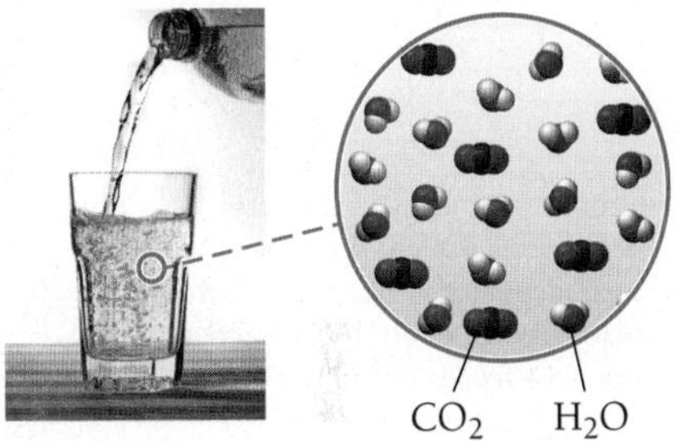

▲ Club soda is a solution of carbon dioxide and water.

TABLE 14.1 ■ Common Types of Solutions

Solution Phase	Solute Phase	Solvent Phase	Example
Gaseous solution	Gas	Gas	Air (mainly oxygen and nitrogen)
Liquid solution	Gas	Liquid	Club soda (CO_2 and water)
	Liquid	Liquid	Vodka (ethanol and water)
	Solid	Liquid	Seawater (salt and water)
Solid solution	Solid	Solid	Brass (copper and zinc) and other alloys

You probably know from experience that a particular solvent, such as water, does not dissolve all possible solutes. For example, you cannot clean your greasy hands with water alone because the water does not dissolve the grease. However, another solvent, such as paint thinner, can easily dissolve the grease. The grease is *insoluble* in water but *soluble* in the paint thinner. The **solubility** of a substance is the amount of the substance that dissolves in a given amount of solvent. The solubility of sodium chloride in water at 25 °C is 36 g NaCl per 100 g water, whereas the solubility of grease in water is nearly zero. The solubility of one substance in another depends both on the tendency toward mixing that we discussed in Section 14.1 and on the types of intermolecular forces that we discussed in Chapter 12.

The general solubilities of a number of ionic compounds are described by the solubility rules in Section 5.4.

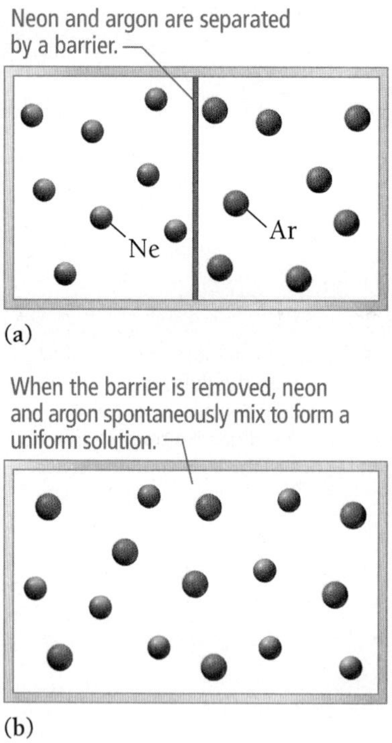

▲ **FIGURE 14.3 Spontaneous Mixing of Two Ideal Gases** **(a)** A barrier separates neon and argon. **(b)** When the barrier is removed, the two gases spontaneously mix to form a uniform solution.

Nature's Tendency toward Mixing: Entropy

So far in this book, we have seen that many physical systems tend toward lower *potential energy*. For example, two particles with opposite charges (such as a proton and an electron or a cation and an anion) move toward each other because their potential energy decreases as their separation decreases according to Coulomb's law. The formation of a solution, however, *does not necessarily* lower the potential energy of its constituent particles. The clearest example of this phenomenon is the formation of a homogeneous mixture (a *solution*) of two ideal gases. Suppose that we enclose neon and argon in a container with a removable barrier between them, as shown in Figure 14.3(a)◀. As soon as we remove the barrier, the neon and argon mix together to form a solution, as shown in Figure 14.3(b)◀. *Why?*

At low pressures and moderate temperatures, both neon and argon behave as ideal gases—they do not interact with each other in any way (that is, there are no significant intermolecular forces between their constituent particles). When the barrier is removed, the two gases mix, but their potential energy remains unchanged. In other words, *we cannot think of the mixing of two ideal gases as lowering their potential energy*. Rather, the tendency to mix is related to a concept called *entropy*.

Entropy is a measure of *energy randomization* or *energy dispersal* in a system. Recall that a gas at any temperature above 0 K has kinetic energy due to the motion of its atoms. When neon and argon are confined to their individual compartments, their kinetic energies are also confined to those compartments. When the barrier between the compartments is removed, each gas—along with its kinetic energy—becomes *spread out* or *dispersed* over a larger volume. Thus, the mixture of the two gases has greater energy dispersal, or greater *entropy*, than the separated components.

The pervasive tendency for energy to spread out, or disperse, whenever it is not restrained from doing so is the reason that two ideal gases mix. Another common example of the tendency toward energy dispersal is the transfer of thermal energy from hot to cold. When we heat one end of an iron rod, the thermal energy added to the end of the rod spontaneously spreads along the rod's entire length. In contrast to the mixing of two ideal gases—where the kinetic energy of the particles becomes dispersed over a larger volume because the particles themselves become dispersed—the thermal energy in the rod, initially concentrated in relatively fewer particles, becomes dispersed by being distributed over a larger number of particles. The tendency for energy to disperse is why thermal energy flows from the hot end of the rod to the cold one, and not the other way around. Imagine a metal rod that became spontaneously hotter on one end and ice cold on the other—this does not happen because energy does not spontaneously concentrate itself. In Chapter 19, we will see that the dispersal of energy is actually the fundamental criterion that ultimately determines the spontaneity of any process.

The potential energy of the gas particles does not change upon mixing because the gas is ideal; the particles do not exert any attractive or repulsive forces on each other, so mixing does not change their potential energy.

ANSWER **NOW!**

14.1 Cc Conceptual Connection

MIXING OF IDEAL GASES Which statement is true?

(a) Ideal gases mix because mixing decreases their potential energy.
(b) Ideal gases mix because mixing increases their potential energy.
(c) Ideal gases mix because mixing decreases their entropy.
(d) Ideal gases mix because mixing increases their entropy.

The Effect of Intermolecular Forces

We have just seen that, in the absence of intermolecular forces, two substances spontaneously mix to form a homogeneous solution. We know from Chapter 12, however, that solids and liquids exhibit a number of different types of intermolecular forces, including dispersion forces, dipole–dipole forces, hydrogen bonding, and ion–dipole forces (Figure 14.4▶). These forces may promote the formation of a solution or prevent it, depending on the nature of the forces in the particular combination of solute and solvent.

Intermolecular forces exist between (a) the solvent and solute particles, (b) the solvent particles themselves, and (c) the solute particles themselves, as shown in Figure 14.5▶.

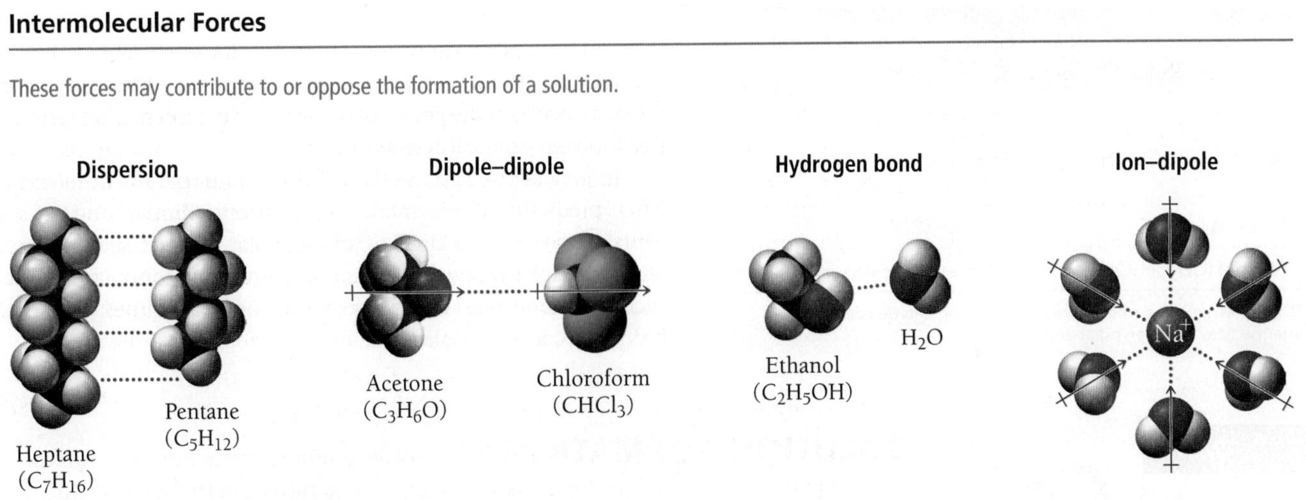

▲ **FIGURE 14.4 Intermolecular Forces Involved in Solutions**

Solvent–solute interactions:	The interactions between a solvent particle and a solute particle.
Solvent–solvent interactions:	The interactions between a solvent particle and another solvent particle.
Solute–solute interactions:	The interactions between a solute particle and another solute particle.

As Table 14.2 indicates, a solution always forms if the solvent–solute interactions are comparable to, or stronger than, the solvent–solvent interactions and the solute–solute interactions. For example, consider mixing the hydrocarbons pentane (C_5H_{12}) and heptane (C_7H_{16}). The intermolecular forces present *within* pentane (that is, the pentane–pentane attractions) and within heptane (the heptane–heptane attractions) are dispersion forces. Similarly, the intermolecular forces present *between* heptane and pentane (the pentane–heptane attractions) are also dispersion forces. All three interactions are of similar magnitude, so the two substances are soluble in each other in all proportions—they are said to be **miscible**. The formation of the solution is driven by the tendency toward mixing, or toward greater entropy, that we just discussed.

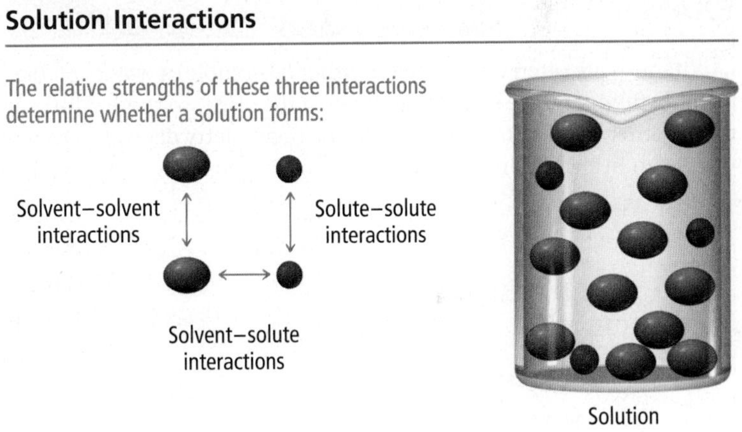

▲ **FIGURE 14.5 Forces in a Solution**

TABLE 14.2 ■ Relative Interactions and Solution Formation

Solvent–solute interactions	>	Solvent–solvent and solute–solute interactions	Solution forms
Solvent–solute interactions	=	Solvent–solvent and solute–solute interactions	Solution forms
Solvent–solute interactions	<	Solvent–solvent and solute–solute interactions	Solution may or may not form, depending on relative disparity

A solution sometimes forms even when solvent–solute interactions are weak. For example, if solvent molecules and solute molecules each interact more strongly with molecules of their own kind than with molecules of the other kind, then a solution may still form, depending on the relative disparities between the interactions. If the disparity is small, the tendency to mix results in the formation of a solution even though the process is energetically uphill. If the disparity is large, however, a solution does not form. For example, consider mixing hexane and water. The water molecules have strong hydrogen-bonding attractions to each other but cannot form hydrogen bonds with hexane. The energy required to pull water molecules away from one another is too great, and too little energy is returned when

TABLE 14.3 ■ Common Laboratory Solvents

Common Polar Solvents	Common Nonpolar Solvents
Water (H_2O)	Hexane (C_6H_{14})
Acetone (CH_3COCH_3)	Diethyl ether ($CH_3CH_2OCH_2CH_3$)*
Methanol (CH_3OH)	Toluene (C_7H_8)
Ethanol (CH_3CH_2OH)	Carbon tetrachloride (CCl_4)

*Diethyl ether has a small dipole moment and can be considered intermediate between polar and nonpolar.

the water molecules interact with hexane molecules. As a result, a solution does not form when we mix hexane and water. Although the tendency to mix is strong, it cannot overcome the large energy disparity between the powerful solvent–solvent interactions and the weak solvent–solute interactions.

In general, we can use the rule of thumb that *like dissolves like* when predicting the formation of solutions. Similar kinds of solvents dissolve similar kinds of solutes. Polar solvents, such as water, tend to dissolve many polar or ionic solutes, and nonpolar solvents, such as hexane, tend to dissolve many nonpolar solutes. Table 14.3 lists some common polar and nonpolar laboratory solvents.

ANSWER **NOW!**

14.2 Cc Conceptual Connection

SOLUTION FORMATION If the solvent–solute interactions in a mixture are comparable in strength to the solvent–solvent interactions and the solute–solute interactions, what can you conclude about solution formation in this mixture?

(a) A homogeneous solution forms.
(b) A homogeneous solution does not form.
(c) The formation of a homogeneous solution is uncertain.

EXAMPLE 14.1 Solubility

Vitamins are often categorized as either fat-soluble or water-soluble. Water-soluble vitamins, on one hand, dissolve in body fluids and are easily eliminated in the urine, so there is little danger of overconsumption. Fat-soluble vitamins, on the other hand, can accumulate in the body's fatty deposits. Overconsumption of a fat-soluble vitamin can be dangerous to your health. Examine the structure of the vitamins shown here and classify each as either fat-soluble or water-soluble.

(a) Vitamin C

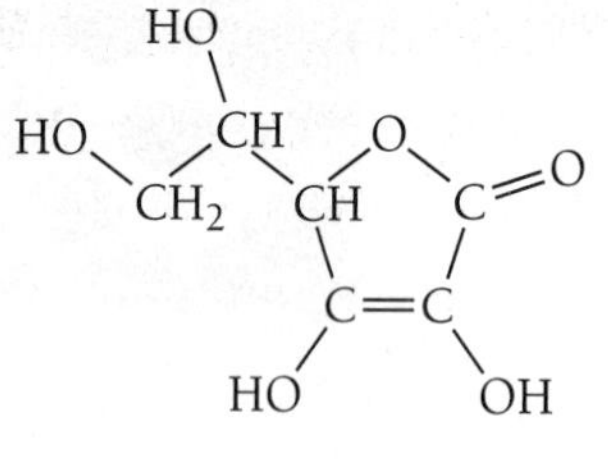

(b) Vitamin K_3

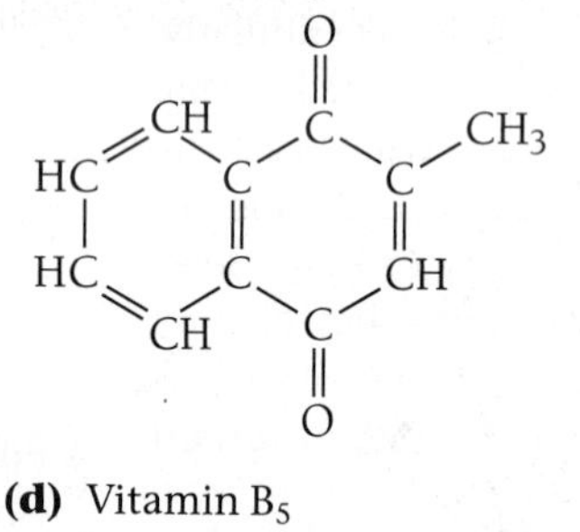

(c) Vitamin A

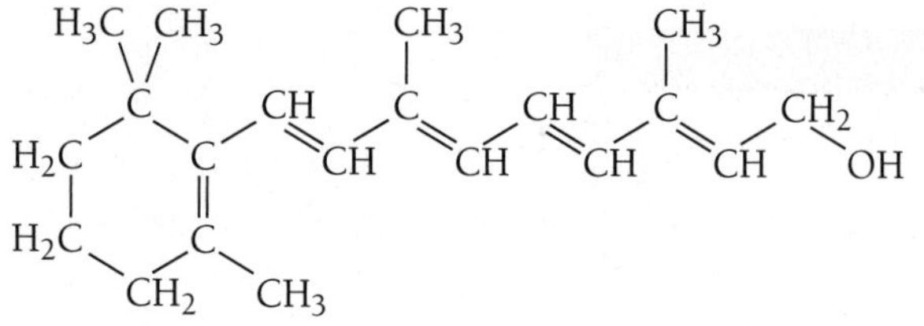

(d) Vitamin B_5

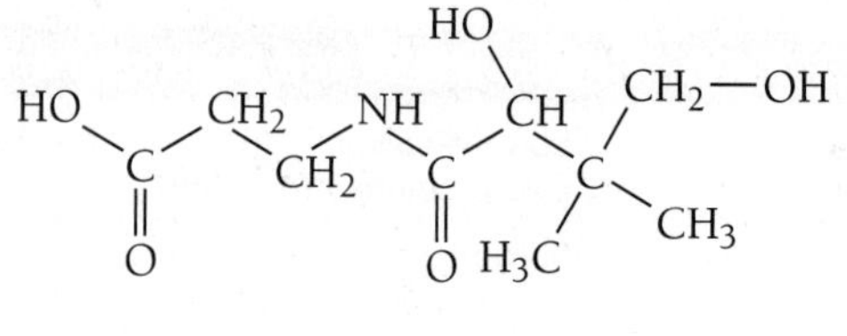

SOLUTION

(a) The four —OH bonds in vitamin C make it highly polar and allow it to hydrogen-bond with water. Vitamin C is water-soluble.

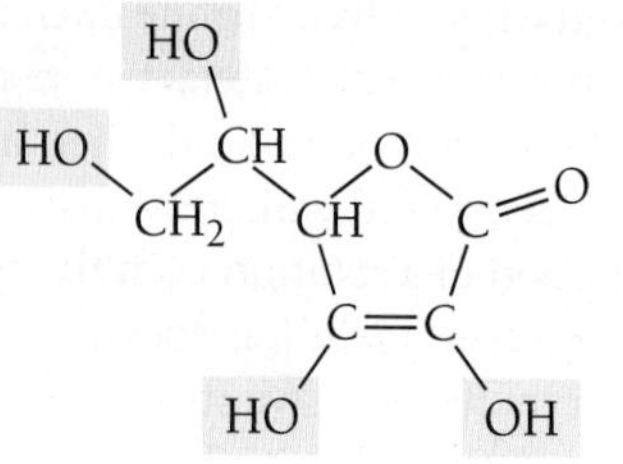

(b) The C—C bonds in vitamin K_3 are nonpolar and the C—H bonds are nearly so. The C=O bonds are polar, but the bond dipoles oppose and largely cancel each other, so the molecule is dominated by the nonpolar bonds. Vitamin K_3 is fat-soluble.

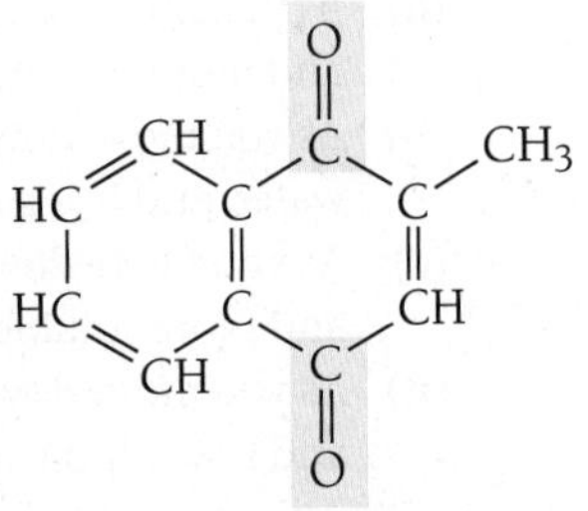

(c) The C—C bonds in vitamin A are nonpolar, and the C—H bonds are nearly so. The one polar —OH bond may increase its water solubility slightly, but overall vitamin A is nonpolar and therefore fat-soluble.

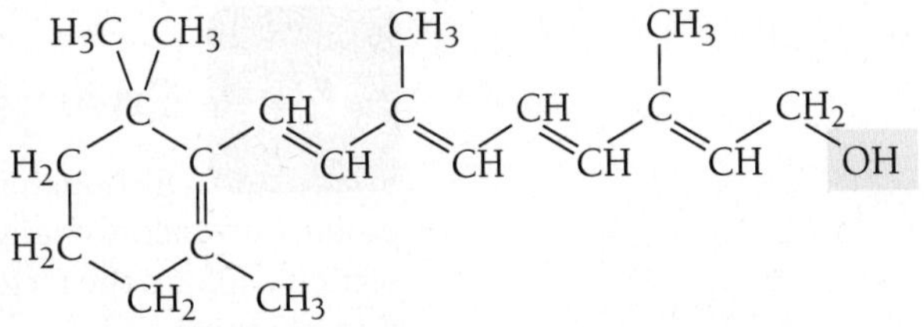

(d) The three —OH bonds and one —NH bond in vitamin B_5 make it highly polar and allow it to hydrogen-bond with water. Vitamin B_5 is water-soluble.

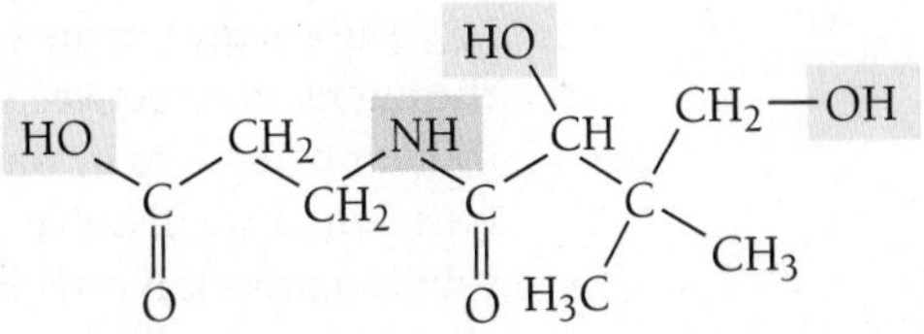

FOR PRACTICE 14.1 Determine whether each compound is soluble in hexane.

(a) water (H_2O) **(b)** propane ($CH_3CH_2CH_3$) **(c)** ammonia (NH_3) **(d)** hydrogen chloride (HCl)

14.3 Cc Conceptual Connection — ANSWER NOW!

SOLUBILITY Consider the table listing the solubilities of several alcohols in water and in hexane. Which statement best describes the observed trend in terms of intermolecular forces?

Alcohol	Space-Filling Model	Solubility in H_2O (mol alcohol/100 g H_2O)	Solubility in Hexane (C_6H_{14}) (mol alcohol/100 g C_6H_{14})
Methanol (CH_3OH)		Miscible	0.12
Ethanol (CH_3CH_2OH)		Miscible	Miscible
Propanol ($CH_3CH_2CH_2OH$)		Miscible	Miscible
Butanol ($CH_3CH_2CH_2CH_2OH$)		0.11	Miscible
Pentanol ($CH_3CH_2CH_2CH_2CH_2OH$)		0.030	Miscible

—*Continued on the next page*

Continued—

(a) As you move down the list, molecules become more polar, less soluble in water, and more soluble in hexane.
(b) As you move down the list, molecules become more polar, more soluble in water, and less soluble in hexane.
(c) As you move down the list, molecules become less polar, less soluble in water, and more soluble in hexane.
(d) As you move down the list, molecules become less polar, more soluble in water, and less soluble in hexane.

14.3 Energetics of Solution Formation

Although forming a solution does not involve a chemical reaction, it can produce an energy change—just like the chemical reactions discussed in Chapter 7. This section explores the factors that determine if energy is absorbed or released when a solution is formed.

The energy changes that occur when a solution forms depend on the magnitude of the interactions between the solute and solvent particles. For example, when we dissolve sodium hydroxide in water, heat is evolved—the solution process is *exothermic*. In contrast, when we dissolve ammonium nitrate (NH_4NO_3) in water, heat is absorbed—this solution process is *endothermic*. Other solutions, such as sodium chloride in water, barely absorb or evolve heat upon formation. What causes these different behaviors?

Energy Changes in Solution Formation

We can understand the energy changes associated with solution formation by envisioning the process as occurring in three steps, each with an associated change in enthalpy:

1. Separating the solute into its constituent particles.

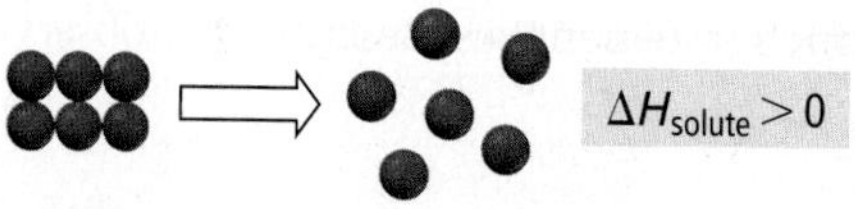

This step is always endothermic (positive ΔH) because energy is required to overcome the forces that hold the solute particles together.

2. Separating the solvent particles from each other to make room for the solute particles.

This step is also endothermic because energy is required to overcome the intermolecular forces among the solvent particles.

3. Mixing the solute particles with the solvent particles.

This step is exothermic because energy is released as the solute particles interact (through intermolecular forces) with the solvent particles.

According to Hess's law, the overall enthalpy change upon solution formation, called the **enthalpy of solution (ΔH_{soln})**, is the sum of the changes in enthalpy for each step:

$$\underset{}{\Delta H_{soln}} = \underset{\text{endothermic (+)}}{\Delta H_{solute}} + \underset{\text{endothermic (+)}}{\Delta H_{solvent}} + \underset{\text{exothermic (−)}}{\Delta H_{mix}}$$

Since the first two terms are endothermic (positive ΔH) and the third term is exothermic (negative ΔH), the overall sign of ΔH_{soln} depends on the magnitudes of the individual terms, as shown in Figure 14.6▼.

- $\Delta H_{soln} \approx 0$ *If the sum of the endothermic terms is approximately equal in magnitude to the exothermic term, then ΔH_{soln} is about zero.* The increasing entropy upon mixing drives the formation of a solution while the overall energy of the system remains nearly constant.
- $\Delta H_{soln} < 0$ *If the sum of the endothermic terms is smaller in magnitude than the exothermic term, then ΔH_{soln} is negative and the solution process is exothermic.* In this case, both the tendency toward lower energy and the tendency toward greater entropy drive the formation of a solution.
- $\Delta H_{soln} > 0$ *If the sum of the endothermic terms is greater in magnitude than the exothermic term, then ΔH_{soln} is positive and the solution process is endothermic.* As long as ΔH_{soln} is not too large, the tendency toward greater entropy still drives the formation of a solution. However, if ΔH_{soln} is too large, a solution does not form.

▼ **FIGURE 14.6 Energetics of the Solution Process** **(a)** When ΔH_{mix} is greater in magnitude than the sum of ΔH_{solute} and $\Delta H_{solvent}$, the heat of solution is negative (exothermic). **(b)** When ΔH_{mix} is smaller in magnitude than the sum of ΔH_{solute} and $\Delta H_{solvent}$, the heat of solution is positive (endothermic).

Energetics of Solution Formation

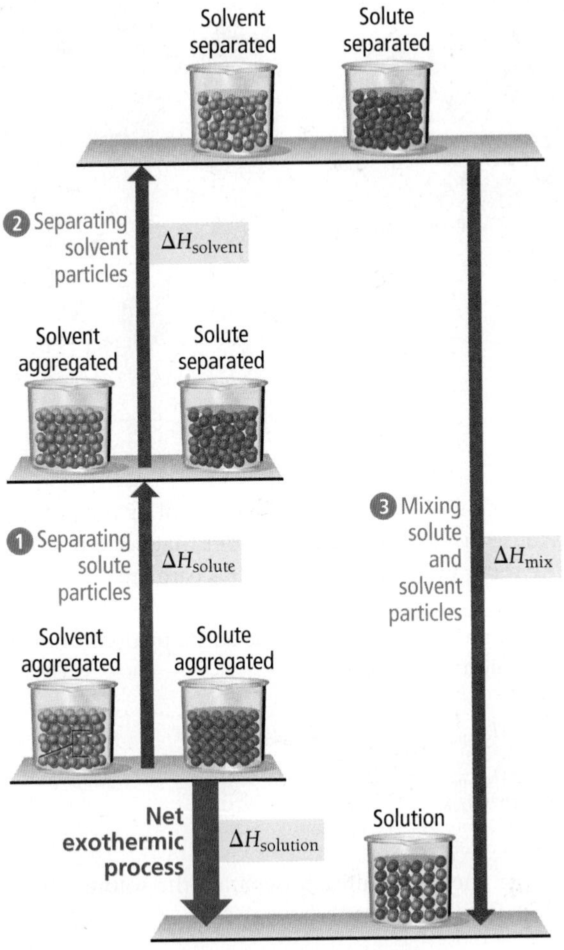

(a) Exothermic

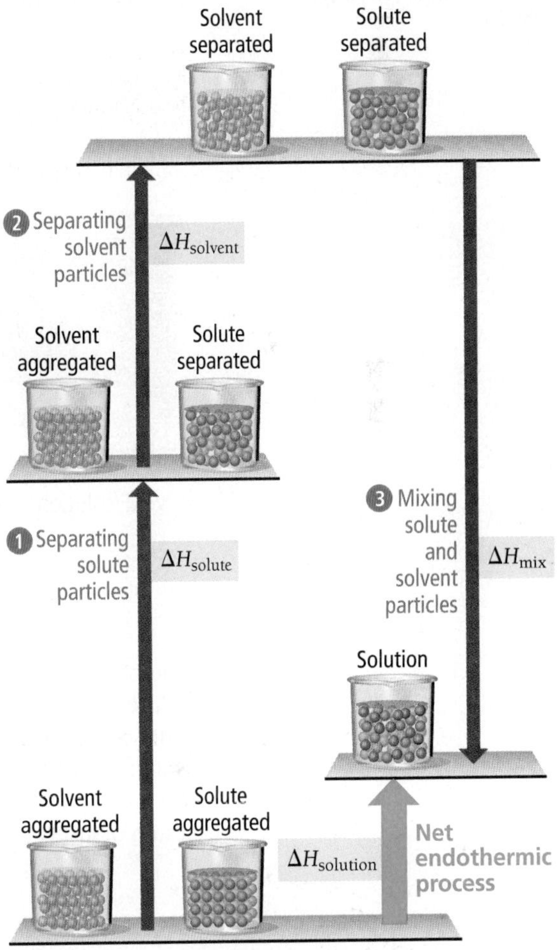

(b) Endothermic

Aqueous Solutions and Heats of Hydration

Many common solutions, such as the seawater mentioned in Section 14.1, contain an ionic compound dissolved in water. In these aqueous solutions, $\Delta H_{solvent}$ and ΔH_{mix} can be combined into a single term called the **heat of hydration ($\Delta H_{hydration}$)** (Figure 14.7▼).

▶ **FIGURE 14.7 Heat of Hydration and Heat of Solution** The heat of hydration is the heat emitted when 1 mol of gaseous solute ions is dissolved in water. The sum of the negative of the lattice energy (which is ΔH_{solute}) and the heat of hydration is the heat of solution.

Heat of Hydration

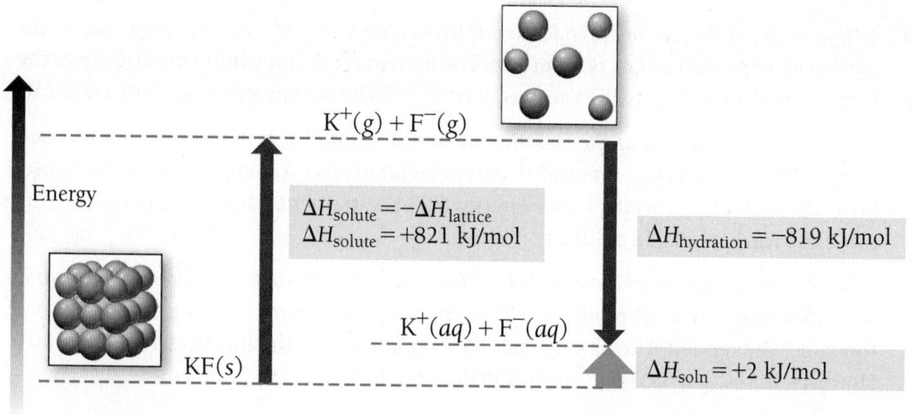

▶ **FIGURE 14.8 Ion–Dipole Interactions**

Ion–Dipole Interactions

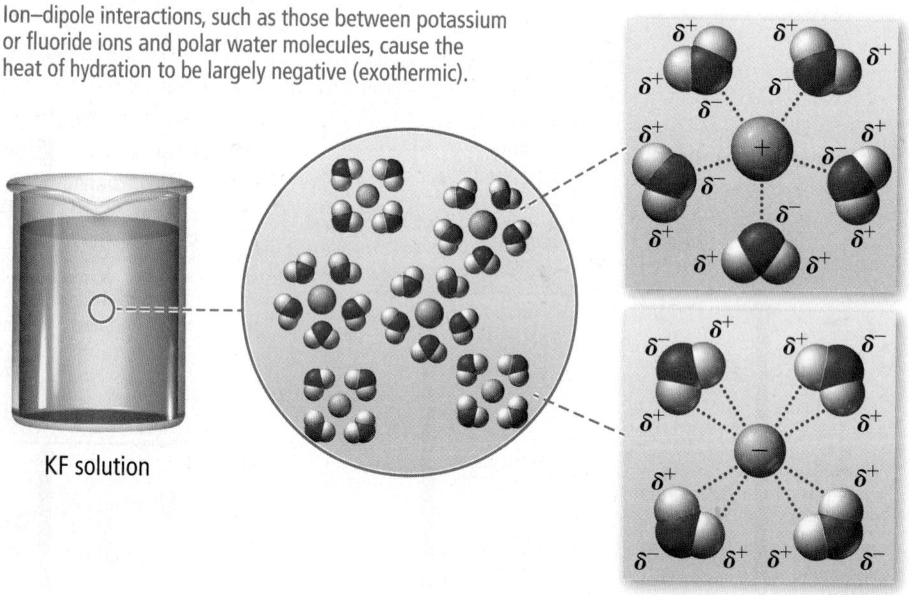

The heat of hydration is the enthalpy change that occurs when 1 mol of the gaseous solute ions is dissolved in water. Because the ion–dipole interactions that occur between a dissolved ion and the surrounding water molecules (Figure 14.8▲) are much stronger than the hydrogen bonds in water, $\Delta H_{hydration}$ is always largely negative (exothermic) for ionic compounds. Using the heat of hydration, we can write the enthalpy of solution as a sum of just two terms, one endothermic and one exothermic:

$$\Delta H_{soln} = \Delta H_{solute} + \underbrace{\Delta H_{solvent} + \Delta H_{mix}}$$

$$\Delta H_{soln} = \underset{\substack{\text{endothermic} \\ \text{(positive)}}}{\Delta H_{solute}} + \underset{\substack{\text{exothermic} \\ \text{(negative)}}}{\Delta H_{hydration}}$$

For ionic compounds, ΔH_{solute}, the energy required to separate the solute into its constituent particles, is the negative of the solute's lattice energy ($\Delta H_{solute} = -\Delta H_{lattice}$), discussed in Section 10.4. For ionic aqueous solutions, then, the overall enthalpy of solution depends on the relative magnitudes of ΔH_{solute} and $\Delta H_{hydration}$, with three possible scenarios (in each case we refer to the *magnitude (absolute value)* of ΔH):

1. $|\Delta H_{solute}| < |\Delta H_{hydration}|$. **EXOTHERMIC SOLUTION PROCESS** The amount of energy required to separate the solute into its constituent ions is less than the energy given off when the ions are hydrated. ΔH_{soln} is therefore negative, and the solution process is exothermic. Solutes with negative enthalpies of solution include lithium bromide and potassium hydroxide. When these solutes dissolve in water, the resulting solutions feel warm to the touch:

$$LiBr(s) \xrightarrow[H_2O]{} Li^+(aq) + Br^-(aq) \qquad \Delta H_{soln} = -48.78 \text{ kJ/mol}$$
$$KOH(s) \xrightarrow[H_2O]{} K^+(aq) + OH^-(aq) \qquad \Delta H_{soln} = -57.56 \text{ kJ/mol}$$

2. $|\Delta H_{solute}| > |\Delta H_{hydration}|$. **ENDOTHERMIC SOLUTION PROCESS** The amount of energy required to separate the solute into its constituent ions is greater than the energy given off when the ions are hydrated. ΔH_{soln} is therefore positive, and the solution process is endothermic (if a solution forms at all). Solutes that form aqueous solutions with positive enthalpies of solution include ammonium nitrate and silver nitrate. When these solutes dissolve in water, the resulting solutions feel cool to the touch:

$$NH_4NO_3(s) \xrightarrow[H_2O]{} NH_4^+(aq) + NO_3^-(aq) \qquad \Delta H_{soln} = +25.67 \text{ kJ/mol}$$
$$AgNO_3(s) \xrightarrow[H_2O]{} Ag^+(aq) + NO_3^-(aq) \qquad \Delta H_{soln} = +36.91 \text{ kJ/mol}$$

3. $|\Delta H_{solute}| \approx |\Delta H_{hydration}|$. The amount of energy required to separate the solute into its constituent ions is roughly equal to the energy given off when the ions are hydrated. ΔH_{soln} is therefore approximately zero, and the solution process is neither appreciably exothermic nor appreciably endothermic. Solutes with enthalpies of solution near zero include sodium chloride and sodium fluoride. When these solutes dissolve in water, the resulting solutions do not undergo a noticeable change in temperature:

$$NaCl(s) \xrightarrow[H_2O]{} Na^+(aq) + Cl^-(aq) \qquad \Delta H_{soln} = +3.88 \text{ kJ/mol}$$
$$NaF(s) \xrightarrow[H_2O]{} Na^+(aq) + F^-(aq) \qquad \Delta H_{soln} = +0.91 \text{ kJ/mol}$$

ENERGETICS OF AQUEOUS SOLUTION FORMATION

14.4 Cc Conceptual Connection

ANSWER **NOW!**

The enthalpy of solution for cesium fluoride is −36.8 kJ/mol. What can you conclude about the relative magnitudes of ΔH_{solute} and $\Delta H_{hydration}$?

(a) $|\Delta H_{solute}| > |\Delta H_{hydration}|$
(b) $|\Delta H_{solute}| < |\Delta H_{hydration}|$
(c) $|\Delta H_{solute}| = |\Delta H_{hydration}|$

14.4 Solution Equilibrium and Factors Affecting Solubility

WATCH **NOW!**

KEY CONCEPT VIDEO 14.4
Solution Equilibrium and the Factors Affecting Solubility

The dissolution of a solute in a solvent is an equilibrium process similar to the equilibrium process associated with a phase change (discussed in Chapter 12). Imagine, from a molecular viewpoint, the dissolution of a solid solute such as sodium chloride in a liquid solvent such as water (Figure 14.9▼). Initially, water molecules rapidly solvate sodium cations and chloride anions, resulting in a noticeable decrease in the amount of

Solution Equilibrium

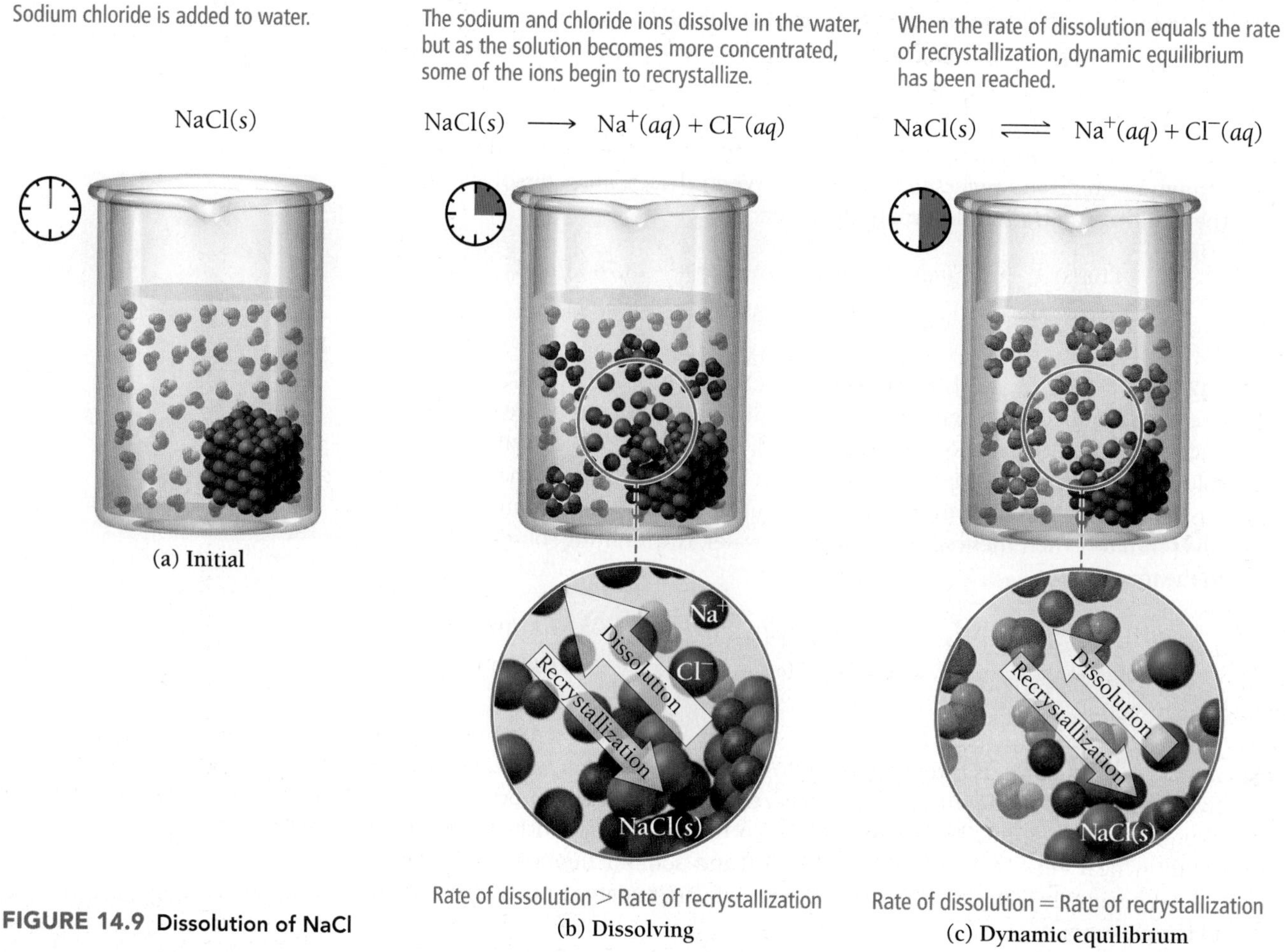

▲ **FIGURE 14.9 Dissolution of NaCl**

solid sodium chloride in the water. Over time, however, the concentration of dissolved sodium chloride in the solution increases. This dissolved sodium chloride then begins to recrystallize as solid sodium chloride. Initially, the rate of dissolution far exceeds the rate of recrystallization, but as the concentration of dissolved sodium chloride increases, the rate of recrystallization also increases. Eventually, the rates of dissolution and recrystallization become equal—**dynamic equilibrium** has been reached.

$$\mathrm{NaCl}(s) \rightleftharpoons \mathrm{Na}^+(aq) + \mathrm{Cl}^-(aq)$$

A solution in which the dissolved solute is in dynamic equilibrium with the solid (undissolved) solute is a **saturated solution**. *If you add additional solute to a saturated solution, it will not dissolve.* A solution containing less than the equilibrium amount of solute is an **unsaturated solution**. *If you add additional solute to an unsaturated solution, it will dissolve.*

Under certain circumstances, a **supersaturated solution**—one containing more than the equilibrium amount of solute—may form. Supersaturated solutions are unstable, and the excess solute normally precipitates out of the solution. However, in some cases, if left undisturbed, a supersaturated solution can exist for an extended period of time. For example, in a common classroom demonstration, a tiny piece of solid sodium acetate is added to a supersaturated solution of sodium acetate. This triggers the precipitation of the solute, which crystallizes out of solution in a dramatic and often beautiful way (Figure 14.10◀).

▲ **FIGURE 14.10 Precipitation from a Supersaturated Solution** When a small piece of solid sodium acetate is added to a supersaturated sodium acetate solution, the excess solid precipitates out of the solution.

The Temperature Dependence of the Solubility of Solids

The solubility of solids in water can be highly dependent on temperature. Have you ever noticed how much more sugar you can dissolve in hot tea than in cold tea? Although exceptions exist, *the solubility of most solids in water increases with increasing temperature*, as shown in Figure 14.11▶. For example, the solubility of potassium nitrate (KNO_3) at room temperature is about 37 g KNO_3 per 100 g of water. At 50 °C, the solubility rises to 88 g KNO_3 per 100 g of water.

In the case of sugar dissolving in water, the higher temperature increases both *how fast* the sugar dissolves and *how much* sugar dissolves.

A common way to purify a solid is through a technique called **recrystallization**. In this technique, enough solid is added to water (or some other solvent) to create a saturated solution at an elevated temperature. As the solution cools, it becomes supersaturated and the excess solid precipitates out of solution. If the solution cools slowly, the solid forms crystals as it comes out of solution. The crystalline structure tends to reject impurities, resulting in a purer solid.

You can use the temperature dependence of the solubility of solids to make rock candy. Prepare a saturated sucrose (table sugar) solution at an elevated temperature, and allow a string or stick to dangle into the solution for several days. As the solution cools and the solvent evaporates, the solution becomes supersaturated and sugar crystals grow on the string or stick. After several days, beautiful edible crystals or "rocks" of sugar cover the string.

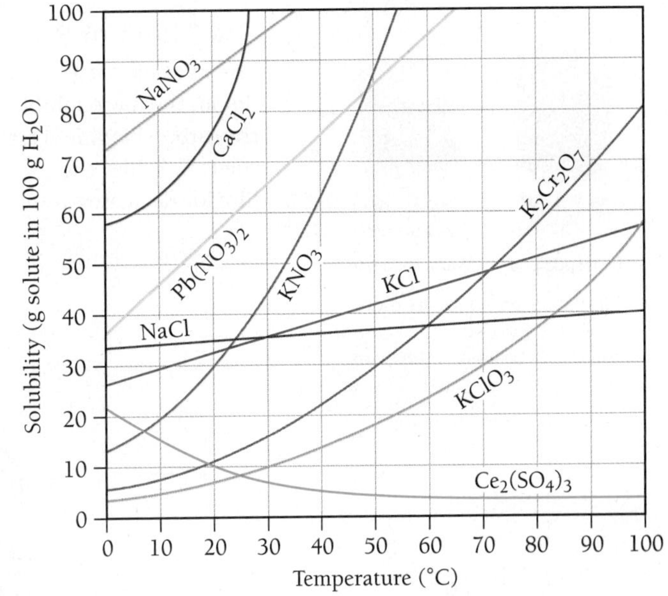

▲ **FIGURE 14.11 Solubility and Temperature** The solubility of most solids increases with increasing temperature.

Factors Affecting the Solubility of Gases in Water

Solutions of gases dissolved in water are common. Club soda, for example, is a solution of carbon dioxide and water, and most liquids exposed to air contain dissolved gases from air. Fish and other aquatic animals depend on the oxygen dissolved in lake or ocean water for life, and our blood contains dissolved nitrogen, oxygen, and carbon dioxide. Even tap water contains dissolved gases. The solubility of a gas in a liquid is affected by both temperature and pressure.

The Effect of Temperature

You can observe the effect of temperature on the solubility of a gas in water by heating ordinary tap water on a stove. Before the water reaches its boiling point, small bubbles develop in the water. These bubbles are the dissolved air (mostly nitrogen and oxygen) coming out of solution. (Once the water boils, the bubbling becomes more vigorous—these larger bubbles are composed of water vapor.) The dissolved air comes out of the heated solution because—unlike solids, whose solubility generally increases with increasing temperature—*the solubility of gases in water decreases with increasing temperature.*

▲ Rock candy is formed by the recrystallization of sugar.

The inverse relationship between gas solubility and temperature is the reason that warm soda pop bubbles more than cold soda pop when you open it and warm beer goes flat faster than cold beer. More carbon dioxide comes out of these solutions at room

SOLUBILITY AND TEMPERATURE A solution is saturated in both nitrogen gas and potassium bromide at 75 °C. When the solution is cooled to room temperature, what is most likely to happen?

(a) Some nitrogen gas bubbles out of solution.
(b) Some potassium bromide precipitates out of solution.
(c) Some nitrogen gas bubbles out of solution, *and* some potassium bromide precipitates out of solution.
(d) Nothing happens.

14.5 Cc Conceptual Connection

ANSWER **NOW!**

▲ Warm soda pop bubbles more than cold soda pop because carbon dioxide is less soluble in the warm solution.

temperature than at a lower temperature because the gas is less soluble at room temperature. The decreasing solubility of gases with increasing temperature is also the reason that fish don't bite much in a warm lake. The warm temperature results in a lower oxygen concentration. With lower oxygen levels, the fish become lethargic and do not strike as aggressively at the lure or bait you cast their way.

The Effect of Pressure

The solubility of gases also depends on pressure. The higher the pressure of a gas above a liquid, the more soluble the gas is in the liquid. In a sealed can of soda pop, for example, the carbon dioxide is maintained in solution by a high pressure of carbon dioxide within the can. When the can is opened, this pressure is released and the solubility of carbon dioxide decreases, resulting in bubbling as shown in Figure 14.12▼.

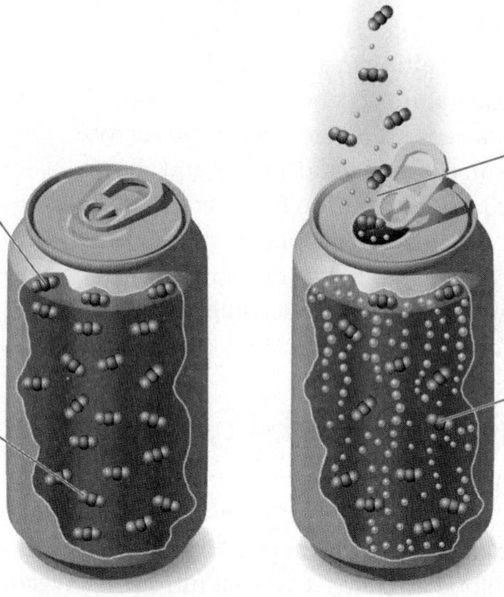

▶ **FIGURE 14.12 Soda Fizz** The bubbling that occurs when a can of soda is opened results from the reduced pressure of carbon dioxide over the liquid. At lower pressure, the carbon dioxide is less soluble and bubbles out of solution.

The increased solubility of a gas in a liquid can be understood by considering cylinders containing water and carbon dioxide gas:

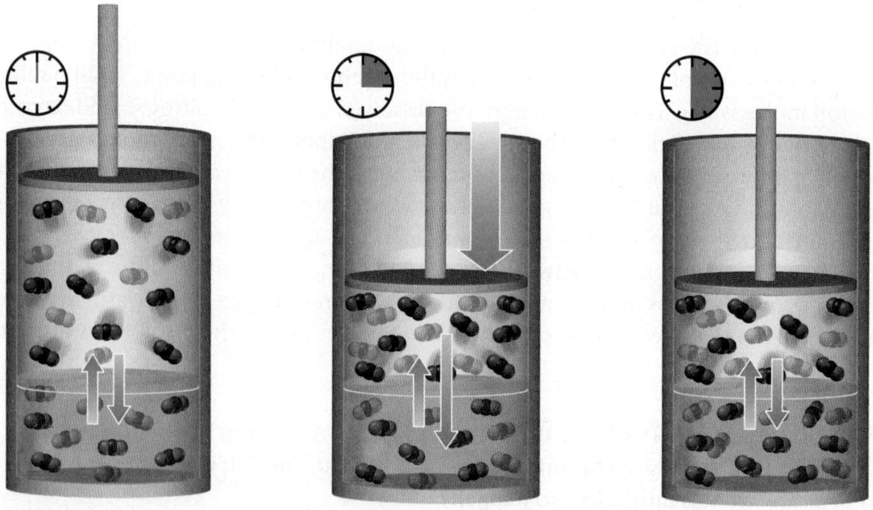

The first cylinder represents an equilibrium between gaseous and dissolved carbon dioxide—the rate of carbon dioxide molecules entering solution exactly equals the rate of molecules leaving the solution. Now imagine decreasing the volume, as we have done in the second cylinder. The pressure of carbon dioxide increases, causing the rate of molecules entering the solution to rise. The number of molecules in solution increases until equilibrium is established again, as shown in the third cylinder. However, the amount of carbon dioxide in solution in the third cylinder is greater.

We quantify the solubility of gases with increasing pressure with **Henry's law**:

$$S_{gas} = k_H P_{gas}$$

where S_{gas} is the solubility of the gas (usually in M), k_H is a constant of proportionality (called the *Henry's law constant*) that depends on the specific solute and solvent and also on temperature, and P_{gas} is the partial pressure of the gas (usually in atm). The equation shows that the solubility of a gas in a liquid is directly proportional to the pressure of the gas above the liquid. Table 14.4 lists the Henry's law constants for several common gases.

TABLE 14.4 ■ Henry's Law Constants for Several Gases in Water at 25 °C

Gas	k_H (M/atm)
O_2	1.3×10^{-3}
N_2	6.1×10^{-4}
CO_2	3.4×10^{-2}
NH_3	5.8×10^{1}
He	3.7×10^{-4}

14.6 Cc Conceptual Connection ANSWER **NOW!**

HENRY'S LAW Examine the Henry's law constants in Table 14.4. Why is the constant for ammonia larger than the others?

(a) Because ammonia is polar and the other substances in the table are nonpolar.
(b) Because ammonia has the highest molar mass of the substances listed in the table.
(c) Because ammonia is nonpolar and the other substances in the table are polar.

WATCH **NOW!**
INTERACTIVE WORKED EXAMPLE 14.2

EXAMPLE 14.2 Henry's Law

What pressure of carbon dioxide is required to keep the carbon dioxide concentration in a bottle of club soda at 0.12 M at 25 °C?

SORT You are given the desired solubility of carbon dioxide and asked to find the pressure required to achieve this solubility.

GIVEN: $S_{CO_2} = 0.12\ \text{M}$

FIND: P_{CO_2}

STRATEGIZE Use Henry's law to find the required pressure from the solubility. You will need the Henry's law constant for carbon dioxide, which is listed in Table 14.4.

CONCEPTUAL PLAN

$S_{CO_2} \rightarrow P_{CO_2}$

$S_{CO_2} = k_{H,CO_2} P_{CO_2}$

RELATIONSHIPS USED

$S_{gas} = k_H P_{gas}$ (Henry's law)

$k_{H,CO_2} = 3.4 \times 10^{-2}\ \text{M/atm}$ (from Table 14.4)

SOLVE Solve the Henry's law equation for P_{CO_2} and substitute the other quantities to calculate it.

SOLUTION

$$S_{CO_2} = k_{H,CO_2} P_{CO_2}$$

$$P_{CO_2} = \frac{S_{CO_2}}{k_{H,CO_2}} = \frac{0.12\ \cancel{\text{M}}}{3.4 \times 10^{-2} \frac{\cancel{\text{M}}}{\text{atm}}} = 3.5\ \text{atm}$$

CHECK The answer is in the correct units and seems reasonable. A small answer (for example, less than 1 atm) would be suspect because you know that the soda is under a pressure greater than atmospheric pressure when you open it. A very large answer (for example, over 100 atm) would be suspect because an ordinary can or bottle probably could not sustain such high pressures without bursting.

FOR PRACTICE 14.2 Determine the solubility of oxygen in water at 25 °C exposed to air at 1.0 atm. Assume a partial pressure for oxygen of 0.21 atm.

WATCH **NOW!**

KEY CONCEPT VIDEO 14.5

Solution Concentration: Molarity, Molality, Parts by Mass and Volume, Mole Fraction

14.5 Expressing Solution Concentration

As we have seen, the amount of solute in a solution is an important property of the solution. For example, the amount of sodium chloride in a solution determines whether or not the solution will cause dehydration if consumed. A **dilute solution** contains small quantities of solute relative to the amount of solvent. Drinking

CHEMISTRY IN THE ENVIRONMENT | Lake Nyos

Most people living near Lake Nyos in the West African country of Cameroon began August 22, 1986, like any other day. Unfortunately, their day ended in tragedy. On that evening, a large cloud of carbon dioxide gas burped

▲ Lake Nyos, in Cameroon, has a deceptively peaceful appearance; in the summer of 1986, more than 1700 people died around its shores.

up from the depths of Lake Nyos, killing over 1700 people and about 3000 cattle. Two years before, a similar tragedy had occurred in Lake Monoun, just 60 miles away, killing 37 people. Today, scientists have taken steps to prevent these lakes from accumulating the carbon dioxide that caused the disasters.

Lake Nyos is a water-filled volcanic crater. Some 50 miles beneath the surface of the lake, molten volcanic rock (magma) produces carbon dioxide gas that seeps into the lake. The carbon dioxide forms a solution with the lake water. The high pressure at the bottom of the deep lake allows the solution to become highly concentrated in carbon dioxide. The 1986 disaster occurred because over time—either because of the high concentration itself or because of some other natural trigger such as a landslide or small earthquake—some gaseous carbon dioxide escaped. The rising bubbles disrupted the stratified layers of lake water, causing water at the bottom of the lake to rise to a region of lower pressure. The drop in pressure decreased the solubility of the carbon dioxide, so more carbon dioxide bubbles formed. This in turn caused more churning and still more carbon dioxide release. The result was a massive cloud of carbon dioxide gas that escaped from the lake. Since carbon dioxide is heavier than air, the carbon dioxide traveled down the sides of the volcano and into the nearby valley, displacing air and asphyxiating many of the local residents.

In an effort to keep these events from recurring, scientists have constructed a piping system that slowly vents carbon dioxide from the lake bottom, preventing the buildup that led to the tragedy.

◄ A plumbing system slowly vents carbon dioxide from Lake Nyos.

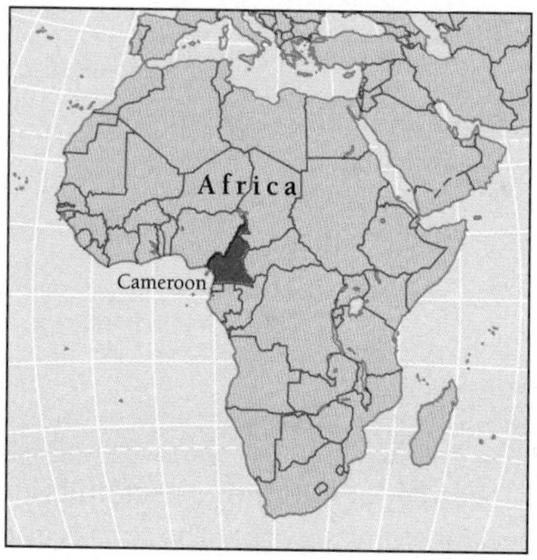

QUESTION *Suppose that the water pressure at the bottom of Lake Nyos is 25 atm. What is the solubility of carbon dioxide at that depth?*

a dilute sodium chloride solution does not cause dehydration. A **concentrated solution** contains large quantities of solute relative to the amount of solvent. Drinking a concentrated sodium chloride solution does cause dehydration. Common ways of reporting solution concentration include molarity, molality, parts by mass, parts by volume, mole fraction, and mole percent, as summarized in Table 14.5. We have seen two of these units before: molarity in Section 5.2, and mole fraction in Section 6.6. In the following section, we review the terms we have already covered and introduce the new ones.

TABLE 14.5 ■ Solution Concentration Terms

Unit	Definition	Units
Molarity (M)	$\frac{\text{amount solute (in mol)}}{\text{volume solution (in L)}}$	$\frac{\text{mol}}{\text{L}}$
Molality (m)	$\frac{\text{amount solute (in mol)}}{\text{mass solvent (in kg)}}$	$\frac{\text{mol}}{\text{kg}}$
Mole fraction (χ)	$\frac{\text{amount solute (in mol)}}{\text{total amount of solute and solvent (in mol)}}$	None
Mole percent (mol %)	$\frac{\text{amount solute (in mol)}}{\text{total amount of solute and solvent (in mol)}} \times 100\%$	%
Parts by mass	$\frac{\text{mass solute}}{\text{mass solution}} \times \text{multiplication factor}$	
Percent by mass (%)	Multiplication factor = 100	%
Parts per million by mass (ppm)	Multiplication factor = 10^6	ppm
Parts per billion by mass (ppb)	Multiplication factor = 10^9	ppb
Parts by volume (%, ppm, ppb)	$\frac{\text{volume solute}}{\text{volume solution}} \times \text{multiplication factor*}$	

*Multiplication factors for parts by volume are identical to those for parts by mass.

Molarity

The **molarity (M)** of a solution is the amount of solute (in moles) divided by the volume of solution (in liters):

$$\text{Molarity (M)} = \frac{\text{amount solute (in mol)}}{\text{volume solution (in L)}}$$

Note that molarity is moles of solute per liter of *solution*, not per liter of solvent. To make a solution of a specified molarity, we usually put the solute into a flask and then add water (or another solvent) to the desired volume of solution, as shown in Figure 14.13►. Molarity is a convenient unit to use when making, diluting, and transferring solutions because it specifies the amount of solute per unit of solution.

Molarity depends on volume, and because volume varies with temperature, molarity also varies with temperature. For example, a 1 M aqueous solution at room temperature is slightly less than 1 M at an elevated temperature because the volume of the solution is slightly greater at the elevated temperature.

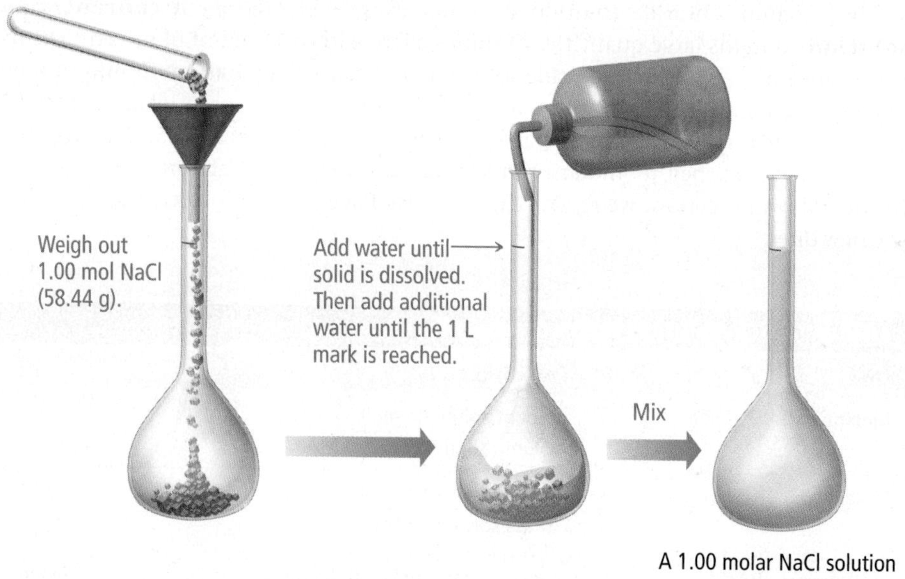

▶ **FIGURE 14.13 Preparing a Solution of Known Concentration** To make a 1 M NaCl solution, we add 1 mol of the solid to a flask and dilute with water to make 1 L of solution.

Molality

A concentration unit that is independent of temperature is **molality (*m*)**, the amount of solute (in moles) divided by the mass of solvent (in kilograms):

Molality is abbreviated with a lowercase italic *m*, and molarity is abbreviated with a capital M.

$$\text{Molality } (m) = \frac{\text{amount solute (in mol)}}{\text{mass solvent (in kg)}}$$

Notice that molality is defined with respect to kilograms *solvent*, not kilograms solution. Molality is particularly useful when we need to compare concentrations over a range of different temperatures.

ANSWER **NOW!**

14.7 Cc Conceptual Connection

MOLALITY If you combine 25.0 g of a solute that has a mass of 25.0 g/mol with 100.0 g of a solvent, what is the molality of the resulting solution?

(a) 0.25 *m* **(b)** 10.0 *m* **(c)** 1.0 *m* **(d)** 8.0 *m*

Parts by Mass and Parts by Volume

It is often convenient to report a concentration as a ratio of masses. A **parts by mass** concentration is the ratio of the mass of the solute to the mass of the solution, all multiplied by a multiplication factor:

$$\frac{\text{Mass solute}}{\text{Mass solution}} \times \text{multiplication factor}$$

The concentration of the solution determines the best parts by mass unit (and therefore the multiplication factor) to use. For example, for **percent by mass** the multiplication factor is 100:

$$\text{Percent by mass} = \frac{\text{mass solute}}{\text{mass solution}} \times 100\%$$

Percent means *per hundred*; a solution with a concentration of 14% by mass contains 14 g of solute per 100 g of solution.

For more dilute solutions, we might use **parts per million (ppm)**, which has a multiplication factor of 10^6, or **parts per billion (ppb)**, which has a multiplication factor of 10^9.

$$\text{ppm} = \frac{\text{mass solute}}{\text{mass solution}} \times 10^6$$

$$\text{ppb} = \frac{\text{mass solute}}{\text{mass solution}} \times 10^9$$

A solution with a concentration of 15 ppm by mass, for example, contains 15 g of solute per 10^6 g of solution.

Sometimes, we report concentrations as a ratio of volumes, especially for solutions in which both the solute and solvent are liquids. A **parts by volume** concentration is usually the ratio of the volume of the solute to the volume of the solution, all multiplied by a multiplication factor:

$$\frac{\text{Volume solute}}{\text{Volume solution}} \times \text{multiplication factor}$$

The multiplication factors are identical to those just described for parts by mass concentrations. For example, a 22% ethanol solution by volume contains 22 mL of ethanol for every 100 mL of solution.

For dilute aqueous solutions near room temperature, the units of ppm are equivalent to milligrams solute per liter of solution. This is because the density of a dilute aqueous solution near room temperature is 1.0 g/mL, so that 1 L has a mass of 1000 g.

Using Parts by Mass (or Parts by Volume) in Calculations

We can use the parts by mass (or parts by volume) concentration of a solution as a conversion factor between mass (or volume) of the solute and mass (or volume) of the solution. For example, for a solution containing 3.5% sodium chloride by mass, we write the following conversion factor:

$$\frac{3.5 \text{ g NaCl}}{100 \text{ g solution}}$$ converts g solution → g NaCl

This conversion factor converts from grams solution to grams NaCl. To convert the other way, we invert the conversion factor:

$$\frac{100 \text{ g solution}}{3.5 \text{ g NaCl}}$$ converts g NaCl → g solution

WATCH **NOW!**
INTERACTIVE WORKED EXAMPLE 14.3

EXAMPLE 14.3 Using Parts by Mass in Calculations

What volume (in mL) of a soft drink that is 10.5% sucrose ($C_{12}H_{22}O_{11}$) by mass contains 78.5 g of sucrose? (The density of the solution is 1.04 g/mL.)

SORT You are given a mass of sucrose and the concentration and density of a sucrose solution, and you are asked to find the volume of solution containing the given mass.	**GIVEN:** 78.5 g $C_{12}H_{22}O_{11}$ 10.5% $C_{12}H_{22}O_{11}$ by mass density = 1.04 g/mL **FIND:** mL

—Continued on the next page

Continued—

STRATEGIZE Begin with the mass of sucrose in grams. Use the mass percent concentration of the solution (written as a ratio, as shown under Relationships Used) to find the number of grams of solution containing this quantity of sucrose. Then use the density of the solution to convert grams to milliliters of solution.

CONCEPTUAL PLAN

$$\text{g } C_{12}H_{22}O_{11} \xrightarrow{\frac{100 \text{ g soln}}{10.5 \text{ g } C_{12}H_{22}O_{11}}} \text{g soln} \xrightarrow{\frac{1 \text{ mL}}{1.04 \text{ g}}} \text{mL soln}$$

RELATIONSHIPS USED

$\dfrac{10.5 \text{ g } C_{12}H_{22}O_{11}}{100 \text{ g soln}}$ (percent by mass written as ratio)

$\dfrac{1.04 \text{ g}}{1 \text{ mL}}$ (given density of the solution)

SOLVE Begin with 78.5 g $C_{12}H_{22}O_{11}$ and multiply by the conversion factors to arrive at the volume of solution.

SOLUTION

$$78.5 \text{ g } C_{12}H_{22}O_{11} \times \frac{100 \text{ g soln}}{10.5 \text{ g } C_{12}H_{22}O_{11}} \times \frac{1 \text{ mL}}{1.04 \text{ g}} = 719 \text{ mL soln}$$

CHECK The units of the answer are correct. The magnitude seems correct because the solution is approximately 10% sucrose by mass. Since the density of the solution is approximately 1 g/mL, the volume containing 78.5 g sucrose should be roughly 10 times larger, as calculated ($719 \approx 10 \times 78.5$).

FOR PRACTICE 14.3 What mass of sucrose ($C_{12}H_{22}O_{11}$), in g, is contained in 355 mL (12 ounces) of a soft drink that is 11.5% sucrose by mass? (Assume a density of 1.04 g/mL.)

FOR MORE PRACTICE 14.3 A water sample is found to contain the pollutant chlorobenzene with a concentration of 15 ppb (by mass). What volume of this water contains 5.00×10^2 mg of chlorobenzene? (Assume a density of 1.00 g/mL.)

Mole Fraction and Mole Percent

The mole fraction can also be defined for the solvent:

$$\chi_{\text{solvent}} = \frac{n_{\text{solvent}}}{n_{\text{solute}} + n_{\text{solvent}}}$$

For some applications, especially those in which the ratio of solute to solvent can vary widely, the most useful way to express concentration is the amount of solute (in moles) divided by the total amount of solute and solvent (in moles). This ratio is the **mole fraction (χ_{solute})**:

$$\chi_{\text{solute}} = \frac{\text{amount solute (in mol)}}{\text{total amount of solute and solvent (in mol)}} = \frac{n_{\text{solute}}}{n_{\text{solute}} + n_{\text{solvent}}}$$

Also in common use is the **mole percent (mol %)**, which is simply the mole fraction × 100 percent:

$$\text{mol \%} = \chi_{\text{solute}} \times 100\%$$

CHEMISTRY IN THE ENVIRONMENT | The Dirty Dozen

A number of potentially harmful chemicals—such as DDT, dioxin, and polychlorinated biphenyls (PCBs)—can make their way into water sources from industrial dumping, atmospheric emissions, agricultural use, and household dumping. Since crops, livestock, and fish consume water, they too can accumulate these chemicals. Human consumption of food or water contaminated with harmful chemicals can lead to a number of diseases and adverse health effects such as increased cancer risk, liver damage, and central nervous system damage. Governments around the world have joined forces to ban the production of a number of these kinds of chemicals—called persistent organic pollutants or POPs. The original treaty named the Stockholm Convention on Persistent Organic Pollutants was signed in 2001. It targeted 12 such substances referred to as the "dirty dozen" (Table 14.6).

One problem common to all of these chemicals is their persistence in the environment. These compounds are fairly stable and do not break down under normal environmental conditions. Once they get into the environment, they stay there for a long time. A second problem with these chemicals is their contribution to a process called *bioamplification*. Because they are nonpolar, these chemicals are stored and concentrated in the

TABLE 14.6 ■ The Dirty Dozen

1. Aldrin—insecticide	7. Furan—industrial by-product
2. Chlordane—insecticide	8. Heptachlor—insecticide
3. DDT—insecticide	9. Hexachlorobenzene—fungicide, industrial by-product
4. Dieldrin—insecticide	10. Mirex—insecticide, fire retardant
5. Dioxin—industrial by-product	11. Polychlorinated biphenyls (PCBs)—electrical insulators
6. Eldrin—insecticide	12. Toxaphene—insecticide

▲ Potentially harmful chemicals make their way into water sources in many ways.

fatty tissues of the organisms that consume them. As larger organisms eat smaller ones, they consume more of the stored chemicals. The result is an increase in the concentrations of these chemicals as they move up the food chain.

For example, the use of DDT nearly drove the bald eagle (whose egg shells were greatly weakened by eating fish contaminated with DDT) to extinction. In 1963, the population dwindled to less than 500 nesting pairs. Fortunately, nearly all intentional production of DDT (and the other chemicals on this list) has been banned. The bald eagle population has recovered to an estimated 10,000 nesting pairs. The recovery has been so strong that the bald eagle has been removed from both the endangered and threatened species lists.

◀ The bald eagle was nearly driven to extinction by human use of DDT. Bald eagles eat fish, which became contaminated due to bioamplification. The DDT consumed with the fish caused the eagle's egg shells to become fragile. The DDT ban has allowed the bald eagle population to recover.

In the United States, the presence of these contaminants in water supplies is monitored by the Environmental Protection Agency (EPA). The EPA has set limits, called maximum contaminant levels (MCLs), for each of these contaminants in food and drinking water. Table 14.7 lists some MCLs for selected compounds in water supplies. Notice the units that the EPA uses to express the concentration of the contaminants, mg/L. This unit is a conversion factor between liters of water consumed and the mass (in mg) of the pollutant. According to the EPA, as long as the contaminant concentrations are below these levels, the water is safe to drink.

TABLE 14.7 ■ EPA Maximum Contaminant Level (MCL) for Several "Dirty Dozen" Chemicals

Chlordane	0.002 mg/L
Dioxin	0.00000003 mg/L
Heptachlor	0.0004 mg/L
Hexachlorobenzene	0.001 mg/L

QUESTION *Calculate how much of each chemical in Table 14.7 at the MCL is present in 715 L of water, the approximate amount of water consumed by an adult in one year.*

WATCH **NOW!**

INTERACTIVE WORKED EXAMPLE 14.4

EXAMPLE 14.4 Calculating Concentrations

A solution is prepared by dissolving 17.2 g of ethylene glycol ($C_2H_6O_2$) in 0.500 kg of water. The final volume of the solution is 515 mL. Calculate the concentration of the solution in each unit.

(a) molarity **(b)** molality **(c)** percent by mass **(d)** mole fraction **(e)** mole percent

SOLUTION

(a) To calculate molarity, first find the amount of ethylene glycol in moles from the mass and molar mass. Then divide the amount in moles by the volume of the solution in liters.

$$\text{mol } C_2H_6O_2 = 17.2\ \cancel{\text{g } C_2H_6O_2} \times \frac{1 \text{ mol g } C_2H_6O_2}{62.07\ \cancel{\text{g } C_2H_6O_2}} = 0.27\underline{7}1 \text{ mol } C_2H_6O_2$$

$$\text{Molarity (M)} = \frac{\text{amount solute (in mol)}}{\text{volume solution (in L)}}$$

$$= \frac{0.27\underline{7}1 \text{ mol } C_2H_6O_2}{0.515 \text{ L solution}}$$

$$= 0.538 \text{ M}$$

—Continued on the next page

Continued—

(b) To calculate molality, use the amount of ethylene glycol in moles from part a, and divide by the mass of the water in kilograms.

$$\text{Molality } (m) = \frac{\text{amount solute (in mol)}}{\text{mass solvent (in kg)}}$$

$$= \frac{0.2771 \text{ mol } C_2H_6O_2}{0.500 \text{ kg } H_2O}$$

$$= 0.554\, m$$

(c) To calculate percent by mass, divide the mass of the solute by the sum of the masses of the solute and solvent and multiply the ratio by 100%.

$$\text{Percent by mass} = \frac{\text{mass solute}}{\text{mass solution}} \times 100\%$$

$$= \frac{17.2 \text{ g}}{17.2 \text{ g} + 5.00 \times 10^2 \text{ g}} \times 100\%$$

$$= 3.33\%$$

(d) To calculate mole fraction, first determine the amount of water in moles from the mass of water and its molar mass. Then divide the amount of ethylene glycol in moles (from part a) by the total number of moles.

$$\text{mol } H_2O = 5.00 \times 10^2 \text{ g } H_2O \times \frac{1 \text{ mol } H_2O}{18.02 \text{ g } H_2O}$$

$$= 27.75 \text{ mol } H_2O$$

$$\chi_{\text{solute}} = \frac{n_{\text{solute}}}{n_{\text{solute}} + n_{\text{solvent}}}$$

$$= \frac{0.2771 \text{ mol}}{0.2771 \text{ mol} + 27.75 \text{ mol}}$$

$$= 9.89 \times 10^{-3}$$

(e) To calculate mole percent, multiply the mole fraction by 100%.

$$\text{mol } \% = \chi_{\text{solute}} \times 100\%$$

$$= 0.989\%$$

FOR PRACTICE 14.4 A solution is prepared by dissolving 50.4 g sucrose ($C_{12}H_{22}O_{11}$) in 0.332 kg of water. The final volume of the solution is 355 mL. Calculate the concentration of the solution in each unit.

(a) molarity **(b)** molality **(c)** percent by mass **(d)** mole fraction **(e)** mole percent

WATCH **NOW!**

INTERACTIVE WORKED EXAMPLE 14.5

EXAMPLE 14.5 Converting between Concentration Units

What is the molarity of a 6.56% by mass glucose ($C_6H_{12}O_6$) solution? (The density of the solution is 1.03 g/mL.)

SORT You are given the concentration of a glucose solution in percent by mass and the density of the solution. Find the concentration of the solution in molarity.

GIVEN: 6.56% $C_6H_{12}O_6$

density = 1.03 g/mL

FIND: M

STRATEGIZE Begin with the mass percent concentration of the solution written as a ratio, and separate the numerator from the denominator. Convert the numerator from g $C_6H_{12}O_6$ to mol $C_6H_{12}O_6$. Convert the denominator from g solution to mL of solution and then to L solution. Divide the numerator (now in mol) by the denominator (now in L) to obtain molarity.

CONCEPTUAL PLAN

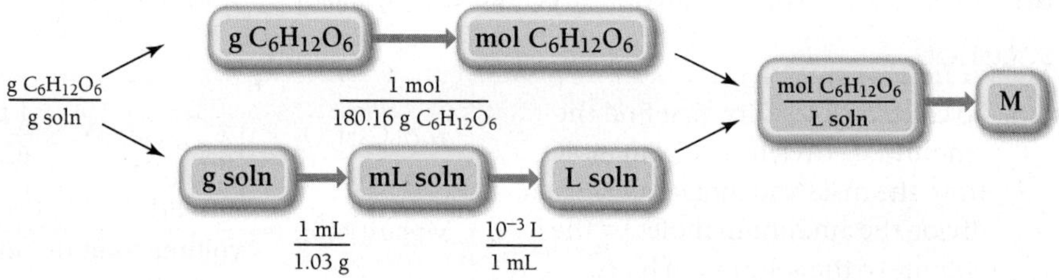

RELATIONSHIPS USED

$\frac{6.56\ \text{g}\ C_6H_{12}O_6}{100\ \text{g soln}}$ (percent by mass written as ratio)

$\frac{1\ \text{mol}}{180.16\ \text{g}\ C_6H_{12}O_6}$ (from molar mass of glucose)

$\frac{1\ \text{mL}}{1.03\ \text{g}}$ (from given density of the solution)

SOLVE Begin with the numerator (6.56 g $C_6H_{12}O_6$) and use the molar mass to convert to mol $C_6H_{12}O_6$.

SOLUTION

$$6.56\ \cancel{\text{g}\ C_6H_{12}O_6} \times \frac{1\ \text{mol}\ C_6H_{12}O_6}{180.16\ \cancel{\text{g}\ C_6H_{12}O_6}} = 0.036\underline{4}12\ \text{mol}\ C_6H_{12}O_6$$

Convert the denominator (100 g solution) into mL of solution (using the density) and then to L of solution.

$$100\ \text{g soln} \times \frac{1\ \cancel{\text{mL}}}{1.03\ \text{g}} \times \frac{10^{-3}\ \text{L}}{\cancel{\text{mL}}} = 0.097\underline{0}87\ \text{L soln}$$

Finally, divide mol $C_6H_{12}O_6$ by L solution to arrive at molarity.

$$\frac{0.036\underline{4}12\ \text{mol}\ C_6H_{12}O_6}{0.097\underline{0}87\ \text{L soln}} = 0.375\ \text{M}\ C_6H_{12}O_6$$

CHECK The units of the answer are correct. The magnitude seems correct. Very high molarities (especially above 25 M) should immediately appear suspect. One liter of water contains about 55 moles of water molecules, so molarities higher than 55 M are physically impossible.

FOR PRACTICE 14.5 What is the molarity of a 10.5% by mass glucose ($C_6H_{12}O_6$) solution? (The density of the solution is 1.03 g/mL.)

FOR MORE PRACTICE 14.5 What is the molality of a 10.5% by mass glucose ($C_6H_{12}O_6$) solution? (The density of the solution is 1.03 g/mL.)

14.6 Colligative Properties: Vapor Pressure Lowering, Freezing Point Depression, Boiling Point Elevation, and Osmotic Pressure

WATCH **NOW!**

KEY CONCEPT VIDEO 14.6
Colligative Properties

Have you ever wondered why you add salt to the ice in an ice-cream maker? Or why salt is scattered on icy roads in cold climates? Salt lowers the temperature at which a saltwater solution freezes. A salt and water solution remains liquid even below 0 °C. When salt is added to ice in the ice-cream maker, an ice/water/salt mixture forms that can reach a temperature of about −10 °C, at which point the cream freezes. On the winter road, the salt allows the ice to melt when the ambient temperature is below freezing.

The depression of the freezing point of water by salt is an example of a **colligative property**, a property that depends on the number of particles dissolved in solution, not on the type of particle. In this section, we examine four colligative properties: vapor pressure lowering, freezing point depression, boiling point elevation, and osmotic pressure.

▲ In winter, salt is often applied to roads so that the ice will melt at lower temperatures.

Since these properties depend on the *number* of dissolved particles, nonelectrolytes are treated slightly differently than electrolytes when determining colligative properties. When 1 mol of a nonelectrolyte dissolves in water, it forms 1 mol of dissolved

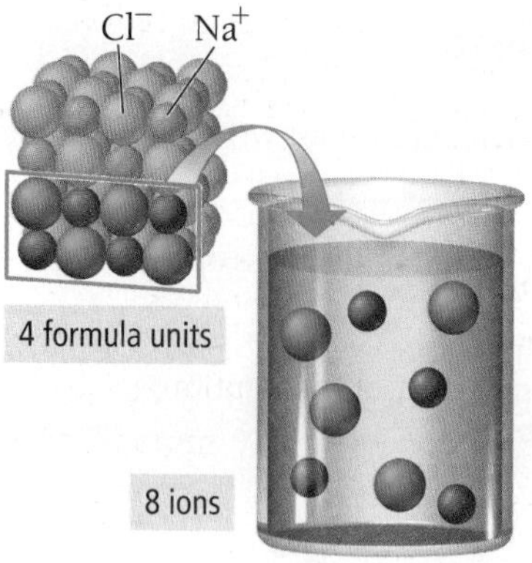

▶ **FIGURE 14.14 NaCl in Water** When sodium chloride is dissolved in water, each mole of NaCl produces 2 mol of particles: 1 mol of Na^+ cations and 1 mol of Cl^- anions.

particles. When 1 mol of an electrolyte dissolves in water, however, it normally forms more than 1 mol of dissolved particles (as shown in Figure 14.14◀). For example, when 1 mol of NaCl dissolves in water, it forms 1 mol of dissolved Na^+ ions and 1 mol of dissolved Cl^- ions. Therefore, the resulting solution has 2 mol of dissolved particles. The colligative properties of electrolyte solutions reflect this higher concentration of dissolved particles. In this section, we examine colligative properties of nonelectrolyte solutions; we expand the concept to include electrolyte solutions in Section 14.7.

Vapor Pressure Lowering

Recall from Section 12.5 that the vapor pressure of a liquid is the pressure of the gas above the liquid when the two are in dynamic equilibrium (that is, when the rate of vaporization equals the rate of condensation). How does a nonvolatile nonelectrolyte solute affect the vapor pressure of the liquid into which it dissolves? The basic answer to this question is that *the vapor pressure of the solution is lower than the vapor pressure of the pure solvent.* We can understand why this happens in two different ways.

The simplest explanation for why the vapor pressure of a solution is lower than that of the pure solvent is related to the concept of dynamic equilibrium itself. Consider the following representation of a liquid in dynamic equilibrium with its vapor. Here the rate of vaporization is equal to the rate of condensation:

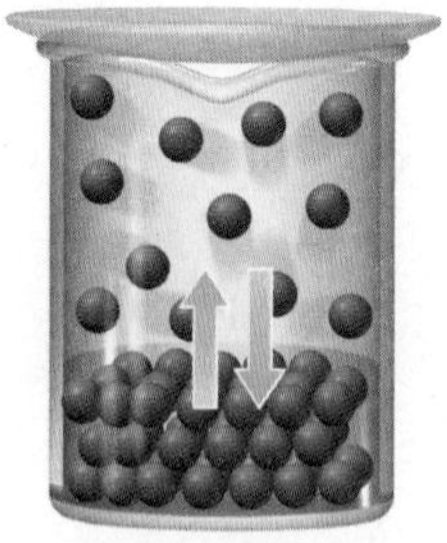

Dynamic equilibrium

When a nonvolatile solute is added, however, the solute particles (shown in red) interfere with the ability of the solvent particles (blue) to vaporize. The rate of vaporization is thus diminished compared to that of the pure solvent:

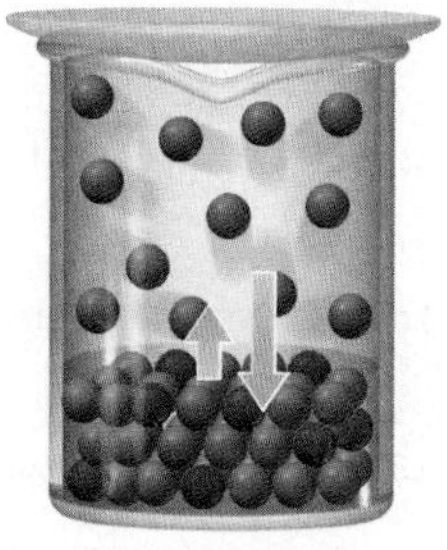

Rate of vaporization reduced by solute

The change in the rate of vaporization creates an imbalance in the rates; the rate of condensation is now *greater* than the rate of vaporization. The net effect is that some of the molecules that were in the gas state condense into the liquid state. As they condense, the reduced number of molecules in the gas state causes the rate of condensation to decrease. Eventually, the two rates become equal again, but only after the concentration of solvent molecules in the gas state has decreased:

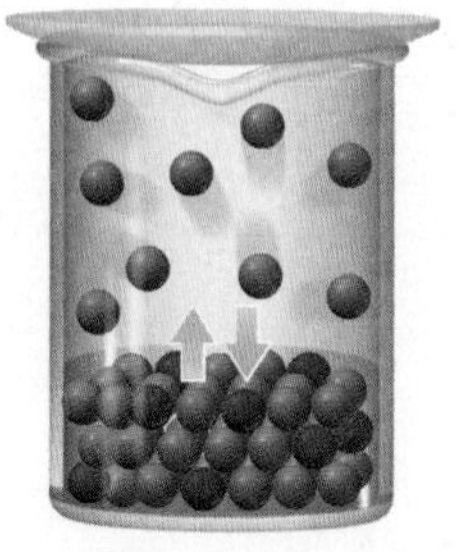

Equilibrium reestablished but with fewer molecules in gas phase

The result is a lower vapor pressure for the solution compared to the pure solvent.

A more fundamental explanation of why the vapor pressure of a solution is lower than that of the pure solvent is related to the tendency toward mixing (toward greater entropy) that we discussed in Sections 14.1 and 14.2. Recall that a concentrated solution is a *thirsty* solution—it has the ability to draw solvent to itself. We can see a dramatic demonstration of this tendency by placing a concentrated solution of a nonvolatile solute and a beaker of the pure solvent in a sealed container. Over time, the level of the pure solvent will drop, and the level of the solution will rise as molecules vaporize out of the pure solvent and condense into the solution.

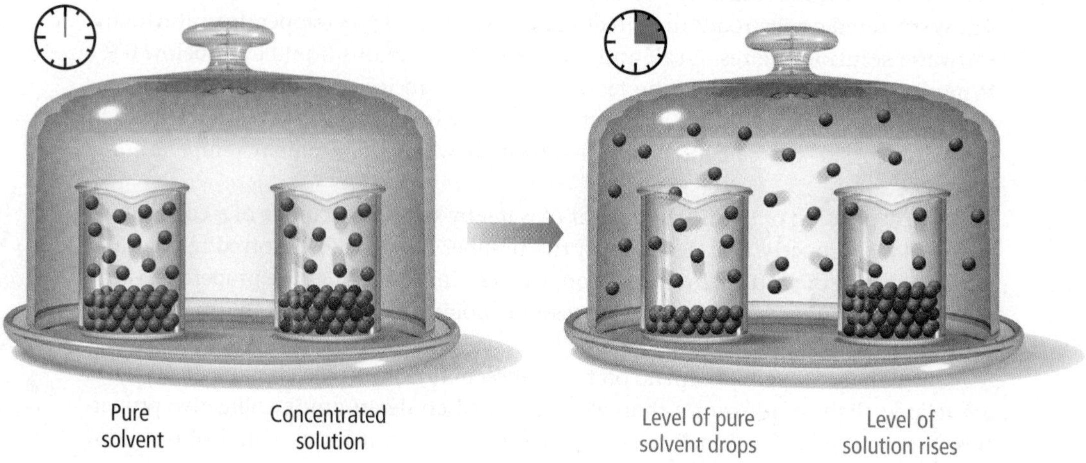

Notice the similarity between this process and the dehydration caused by drinking seawater. In both cases, a concentrated solution has the ability to draw solvent to itself. The reason is nature's tendency to mix. If a pure solvent and concentrated solution are combined in a beaker, they naturally form a mixture in which the concentrated solution becomes less concentrated than it was initially. Similarly, if a pure solvent and concentrated solution are combined in a sealed container—even though they are in separate beakers—the two mix so that the concentrated solution becomes less concentrated.

The net transfer of solvent from the beaker containing pure solvent to the one containing the solution shows that the vapor pressure of the solution is lower than that of the pure solvent. As solvent molecules vaporize, the vapor pressure in the sealed container rises. Before dynamic equilibrium can be attained, however, the pressure exceeds the vapor pressure of the solution, causing molecules to condense into the solution (the beaker on the right). Therefore, molecules constantly vaporize from the pure solvent, but the solvent's vapor pressure is never reached because molecules are constantly condensing into the solution. The result is a continuous transfer of solvent molecules from the pure solvent to the solution.

We can quantify the vapor pressure of a solution with **Raoult's law**:

$$P_{\text{solution}} = \chi_{\text{solvent}} P^{\circ}_{\text{solvent}}$$

In this equation, P_{solution} is the vapor pressure of the solution, χ_{solvent} is the mole fraction of the solvent, and $P^{\circ}_{\text{solvent}}$ is the vapor pressure of the pure solvent at the same temperature. For example, suppose a water sample at 25 °C contains 0.900 mol of water and 0.100 mol of a nonvolatile solute such as sucrose. The pure water has a vapor pressure of 23.8 torr. We calculate the vapor pressure of the solution by substituting into Raoult's law:

$$\begin{aligned} P_{\text{solution}} &= \chi_{H_2O} P^{\circ}_{H_2O} \\ &= 0.900(23.8 \text{ torr}) \\ &= 21.4 \text{ torr} \end{aligned}$$

Notice that the vapor pressure of the solution is directly proportional to the amount of the solvent in the solution. Since the solvent particles compose 90% of all of the particles in the solution, the vapor pressure of the solution is 90% of the vapor pressure of the pure solvent.

SOLUTION VAPOR PRESSURE What is the vapor pressure of a solution in which the mole fraction of the solute is 0.200 and the vapor pressure of the pure solvent is 100.0 torr? (Assume a single nonvolatile, nonelectrolyte solute).

(a) 20.0 torr **(b)** 80.0 torr **(c)** 100.0 torr **(d)** 120.0 torr

14.8 Cc Conceptual Connection

ANSWER **NOW!**

To arrive at an equation that shows how much the vapor pressure is lowered by a solute, we define the **vapor pressure lowering (ΔP)** as the difference in vapor pressure between the pure solvent and the solution:

$$\Delta P = P^{\circ}_{\text{solvent}} - P_{\text{solution}}$$

Then, for a two-component solution, we can substitute $\chi_{\text{solvent}} = 1 - \chi_{\text{solute}}$ into Raoult's law:

$$\begin{aligned} P_{\text{solution}} &= \chi_{\text{solvent}} P^{\circ}_{\text{solvent}} \\ P_{\text{solution}} &= (1 - \chi_{\text{solute}}) P^{\circ}_{\text{solvent}} \\ P^{\circ}_{\text{solvent}} - P_{\text{solution}} &= \chi_{\text{solute}} P^{\circ}_{\text{solvent}} \\ \Delta P &= \chi_{\text{solute}} P^{\circ}_{\text{solvent}} \end{aligned}$$

This last equation indicates that the lowering of the vapor pressure is directly proportional to the mole fraction of the solute.

WATCH **NOW!**

INTERACTIVE WORKED EXAMPLE 14.6

EXAMPLE 14.6 Calculating the Vapor Pressure of a Solution Containing a Nonelectrolyte and Nonvolatile Solute

Calculate the vapor pressure at 25 °C of a solution containing 99.5 g sucrose ($C_{12}H_{22}O_{11}$) and 300.0 mL water. The vapor pressure of pure water at 25 °C is 23.8 torr. Assume the density of water is 1.00 g/mL.

SORT You are given the mass of sucrose and volume of water in a solution. You are also given the vapor pressure and density of pure water and asked to find the vapor pressure of the solution.

GIVEN: 99.5 g $C_{12}H_{22}O_{11}$
300.0 mL H_2O
$P^{\circ}_{H_2O} = 23.8$ torr at 25 °C
$d_{H_2O} = 1.00$ g/mL

FIND: $P_{solution}$

STRATEGIZE Raoult's law relates the vapor pressure of a solution to the mole fraction of the solvent and the vapor pressure of the pure solvent. Begin by calculating the amount in moles of sucrose and water.

CONCEPTUAL PLAN

g $C_{12}H_{22}O_{11}$ → mol $C_{12}H_{22}O_{11}$

$$\frac{1\text{ mol } C_{12}H_{22}O_{11}}{342.30\text{ g } C_{12}H_{22}O_{11}}$$

mL H_2O → g H_2O → mol H_2O

$$\frac{1.00\text{ g}}{1\text{ mL}} \qquad \frac{1\text{ mol } H_2O}{18.02\text{ g } H_2O}$$

Calculate the mole fraction of the solvent from the calculated amounts of solute and solvent.

mol $C_{12}H_{22}O_{11}$, mol H_2O → χ_{H_2O}

$$\chi_{H_2O} = \frac{n_{H_2O}}{n_{H_2O} + n_{C_{12}H_{22}O_{11}}}$$

Then use Raoult's law to calculate the vapor pressure of the solution.

χ_{H_2O}, $P^{\circ}_{H_2O}$ → $P_{solution}$

$$P_{solution} = \chi_{H_2O}P^{\circ}_{H_2O}$$

SOLVE Calculate the number of moles of each solution component.

SOLUTION

$$99.5\ \cancel{\text{g } C_{12}H_{22}O_{11}} \times \frac{1\text{ mol } C_{12}H_{22}O_{11}}{342.30\ \cancel{\text{g } C_{12}H_{22}O_{11}}} = 0.29\underline{0}7\text{ mol } C_{12}H_{22}O_{11}$$

$$300.0\ \cancel{\text{mL } H_2O} \times \frac{1.00\text{ g}}{1\ \cancel{\text{mL}}} \times \frac{1\text{ mol } H_2O}{18.02\ \cancel{\text{g } H_2O}} = 16.\underline{6}5\text{ mol } H_2O$$

Use the number of moles of each component to calculate the mole fraction of the solvent (H_2O).

$$\chi_{H_2O} = \frac{n_{H_2O}}{n_{C_{12}H_{22}O_{11}} + n_{H_2O}} = \frac{16.\underline{6}5\ \cancel{\text{mol}}}{0.29\underline{0}7\ \cancel{\text{mol}} + 16.\underline{6}5\ \cancel{\text{mol}}} = 0.98\underline{2}8$$

Use the mole fraction of water and the vapor pressure of pure water to calculate the vapor pressure of the solution.

$$P_{solution} = \chi_{H_2O}P^{\circ}_{H_2O} = 0.98\underline{2}8\ (23.8\text{ torr}) = 23.4\text{ torr}$$

CHECK The units of the answer are correct. The magnitude of the answer seems right because the calculated vapor pressure of the solution is just below that of the pure liquid, as you would expect for a solution with a large mole fraction of solvent.

FOR PRACTICE 14.6 Calculate the vapor pressure at 25 °C of a solution containing 55.3 g ethylene glycol ($HOCH_2CH_2OH$) and 285.2 g water. The vapor pressure of pure water at 25 °C is 23.8 torr.

FOR MORE PRACTICE 14.6 A solution containing ethylene glycol and water has a vapor pressure of 7.88 torr at 10 °C. Pure water has a vapor pressure of 9.21 torr at 10 °C. What is the mole fraction of ethylene glycol in the solution?

Vapor Pressures of Solutions Containing a Volatile (Nonelectrolyte) Solute

Some solutions contain not only a volatile solvent, but also a volatile *solute*. In this case, *both* the solvent and the solute contribute to the overall vapor pressure of the solution. A solution like this may be an **ideal solution** (in which case its behavior follows Raoult's law at all concentrations for both the solvent and the solute), or it may be nonideal (in which case it does not follow Raoult's law).

An ideal solution is similar in concept to an ideal gas. Just as an ideal gas follows the ideal gas law exactly, so an ideal solution follows Raoult's law exactly. In an ideal solution, the solute–solvent interactions are similar in magnitude to the solute–solute and solvent–solvent interactions. In this type of solution, the solute simply dilutes the solvent and ideal behavior is observed. The vapor pressure of each solution component is described by Raoult's law throughout the entire composition range of the solution. For a two-component solution containing liquids A and B, we write:

Over a complete range of composition of a solution, it no longer makes sense to designate a solvent and solute, so we simply label the two components A and B.

$$P_A = \chi_A P_A^\circ$$
$$P_B = \chi_B P_B^\circ$$

The total pressure above such a solution is the sum of the partial pressures of the components:

$$P_{tot} = P_A + P_B$$

Figure 14.15(a)▼ is a plot of vapor pressure versus solution composition for an ideal two-component solution.

In a nonideal solution, the solute–solvent interactions are either stronger or weaker than the solvent–solvent interactions.

For example, if the solute–solvent interactions are stronger, then the solute tends to prevent the solvent from vaporizing as readily as it would otherwise. If the solution is sufficiently dilute, then the effect will be small and Raoult's law works as an approximation. However, if the solution is not dilute, the effect will be significant and the vapor pressure of the solution will be *less than* that predicted by Raoult's law, as shown in Figure 14.15(b)▼.

If, however, the solute–solvent interactions are weaker than solvent–solvent interactions, then the solute tends to allow more vaporization than would occur with just the solvent. If the solution is not dilute, the effect will be significant and the vapor pressure of the solution will be *greater than* predicted by Raoult's law, as shown in Figure 14.15(c)▼.

Deviations from Raoult's Law

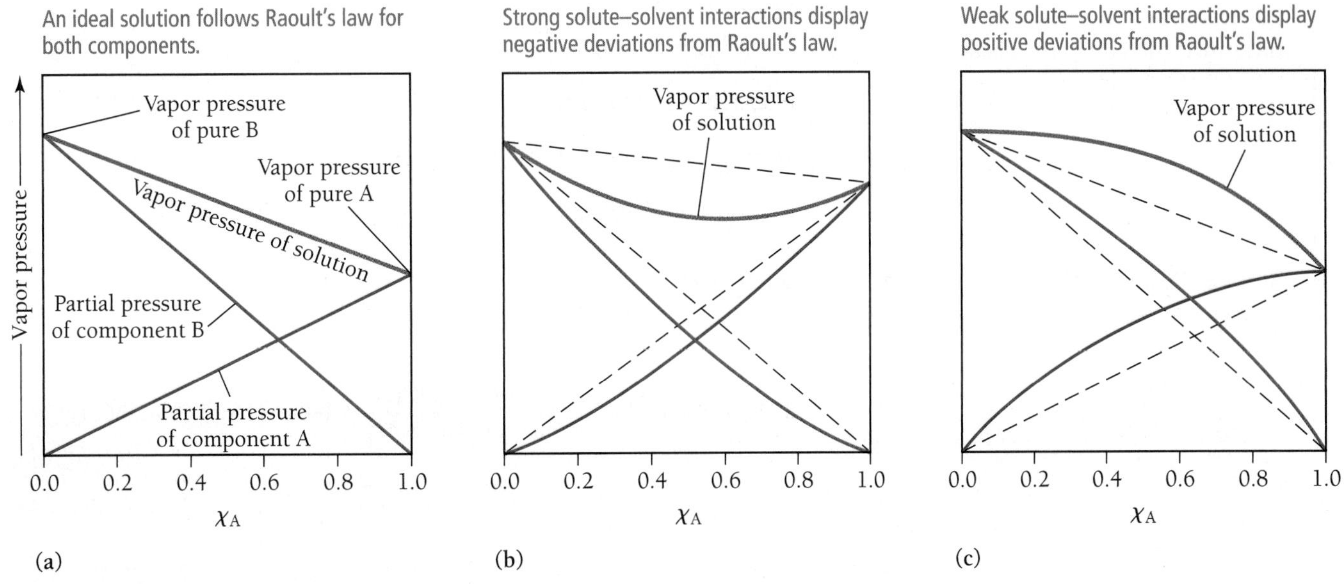

▲ **FIGURE 14.15 Behavior of Ideal and Nonideal Solutions** **(a)** Ideal behavior **(b)** Strong solute-solvent interactions **(c)** Weak solute-solvent interactions (The dashed lines in parts b and c represent ideal behavior.)

EXAMPLE 14.7 Calculating the Vapor Pressure of a Two-Component Solution

A solution contains 3.95 g of carbon disulfide (CS_2) and 2.43 g of acetone (CH_3COCH_3). At 35 °C the vapor pressures of pure carbon disulfide and pure acetone are 515 torr and 332 torr, respectively. Assuming ideal behavior, calculate the vapor pressures of each component and the total vapor pressure above the solution. The experimentally measured total vapor pressure of the solution at 35 °C is 645 torr. Is the solution ideal? If not, what can you say about the relative strength of carbon disulfide–acetone interactions compared to the acetone–acetone and carbon disulfide–carbon disulfide interactions?

SORT You are given the masses and vapor pressures of carbon disulfide and acetone and are asked to find the vapor pressures of each component in the mixture and the total pressure assuming ideal behavior.

GIVEN: 3.95 g CS_2

2.43 g CH_3COCH_3

$P^\circ_{CS_2} = 515$ torr (at 35 °C)

$P^\circ_{CH_3COCH_3} = 332$ torr (at 35 °C)

$P_{tot}(\text{exp}) = 645$ torr (at 35 °C)

FIND: $P_{CS_2}, P_{CH_3COCH_3}, P_{tot}(\text{ideal})$

STRATEGIZE This problem requires that you use Raoult's law to calculate the partial pressures of each component. In order to use Raoult's law, first calculate the mole fractions of the two components. Convert the masses of each component to moles and then use the definition of mole fraction to calculate the mole fraction of carbon disulfide. You can then find the mole fraction of acetone because the mole fractions of the two components add up to 1.

CONCEPTUAL PLAN

3.95 g CS_2 → mol CS_2

$$\frac{1 \text{ mol } CS_2}{76.15 \text{ g } CS_2}$$

2.43 g CH_3COCH_3 → mol CH_3COCH_3

$$\frac{1 \text{ mol } CH_3COCH_3}{58.08 \text{ g } CH_3COCH_3}$$

mol CS_2, mol CH_3COCH_3 → χ_{CS_2}, $\chi_{CH_3COCH_3}$

$$\chi_{CS_2} = \frac{n_{CS_2}}{n_{CS_2} + n_{CH_3COCH_3}}$$

Use the mole fraction of each component along with Raoult's law to calculate the partial pressure of each component. The total pressure is the sum of the partial pressures.

$$P_{CS_2} = \chi_{CS_2} P^\circ_{CS_2}$$

$$P_{CH_3COCH_3} = \chi_{CH_3COCH_3} P^\circ_{CH_3COCH_3}$$

$$P_{tot} = P_{CS_2} + P_{CH_3COCH_3}$$

RELATIONSHIPS USED

$$\chi_A = \frac{n_A}{n_A + n_B} \text{ (mole fraction definition)}$$

$$P_A = \chi_A P^\circ_A \text{ (Raoult's law)}$$

SOLVE Begin by converting the mass of each component to the amounts in moles.

SOLUTION

$$3.95 \text{ g } CS_2 \times \frac{1 \text{ mol } CS_2}{76.15 \text{ g } CS_2} = 0.05187 \text{ mol } CS_2$$

$$2.43 \text{ g } CH_3COCH_3 \times \frac{1 \text{ mol } CH_3COCH_3}{58.08 \text{ g } CH_3COCH_3} = 0.04184 \text{ mol } CH_3COCH_3$$

Then calculate the mole fraction of carbon disulfide.	$\chi_{CS_2} = \dfrac{n_{CS_2}}{n_{CS_2} + n_{CH_3COCH_3}}$ $= \dfrac{0.05187 \text{ mol}}{0.05187 \text{ mol} + 0.04184 \text{ mol}}$ $= 0.5535$
Calculate the mole fraction of acetone by subtracting the mole fraction of carbon disulfide from 1.	$\chi_{CH_3COCH_3} = 1 - 0.5535$ $= 0.4465$
Calculate the partial pressures of carbon disulfide and acetone by using Raoult's law and the given values of the vapor pressures of the pure substances.	$P_{CS_2} = \chi_{CS_2} P^{\circ}_{CS_2}$ $= 0.5535\ (515 \text{ torr})$ $= 285 \text{ torr}$ $P_{CH_3COCH_3} = \chi_{CH_3COCH_3} P^{\circ}_{CH_3COCH_3}$ $= 0.4465\ (332 \text{ torr})$ $= 148 \text{ torr}$
Calculate the total pressure by summing the partial pressures.	$P_{tot}(\text{ideal}) = 285 \text{ torr} + 148 \text{ torr}$ $= 433 \text{ torr}$
Lastly, compare the calculated total pressure for the ideal case to the experimentally measured total pressure. Since the experimentally measured pressure is greater than the calculated pressure, we can conclude that the interactions between the two components are weaker than the interactions between the components themselves.	$P_{tot}(\text{exp}) = 645 \text{ torr}$ $P_{tot}(\text{exp}) > P_{tot}(\text{ideal})$ The solution is not ideal and shows positive deviations from Raoult's law. Therefore, carbon disulfide–acetone interactions must be weaker than acetone–acetone and carbon disulfide–carbon disulfide interactions.

CHECK The units of the answer (torr) are correct. The magnitude seems reasonable given the partial pressures of the pure substances.

FOR PRACTICE 14.7 A solution of benzene (C_6H_6) and toluene (C_7H_8) is 25.0% benzene by mass. At 25 °C the vapor pressures of pure benzene and pure toluene are 94.2 torr and 28.4 torr, respectively. Assuming ideal behavior, calculate the following:

(a) The vapor pressure of each of the solution components in the mixture.
(b) The total pressure above the solution.
(c) The composition of the vapor in mass percent.

Why is the composition of the vapor different from the composition of the solution?

RAOULT'S LAW A solution contains equal amounts (in moles) of liquid components A and B. The vapor pressure of pure A is 100 mmHg and that of pure B is 200 mmHg. The experimentally measured vapor pressure of the solution is 120 mmHg. What are the relative strengths of the solute–solute, solute–solvent, and solvent–solvent interactions in this solution?

14.9 Cc Conceptual Connection

ANSWER **NOW!**

(a) Solute–solvent interactions > solute–solute and solvent–solvent interactions
(b) Solute–solvent interactions = solute–solute and solvent–solvent interactions
(c) Solute–solute and solvent–solvent interactions > solute–solvent interactions

Freezing Point Depression and Boiling Point Elevation

Vapor pressure lowering occurs at all temperatures. We can see the effect of vapor pressure lowering over a range of temperatures by comparing the phase diagrams for a pure solvent and for a solution containing a nonvolatile solute:

▶ A nonvolatile solute lowers the vapor pressure of a solution, resulting in a lower freezing point and an elevated boiling point.

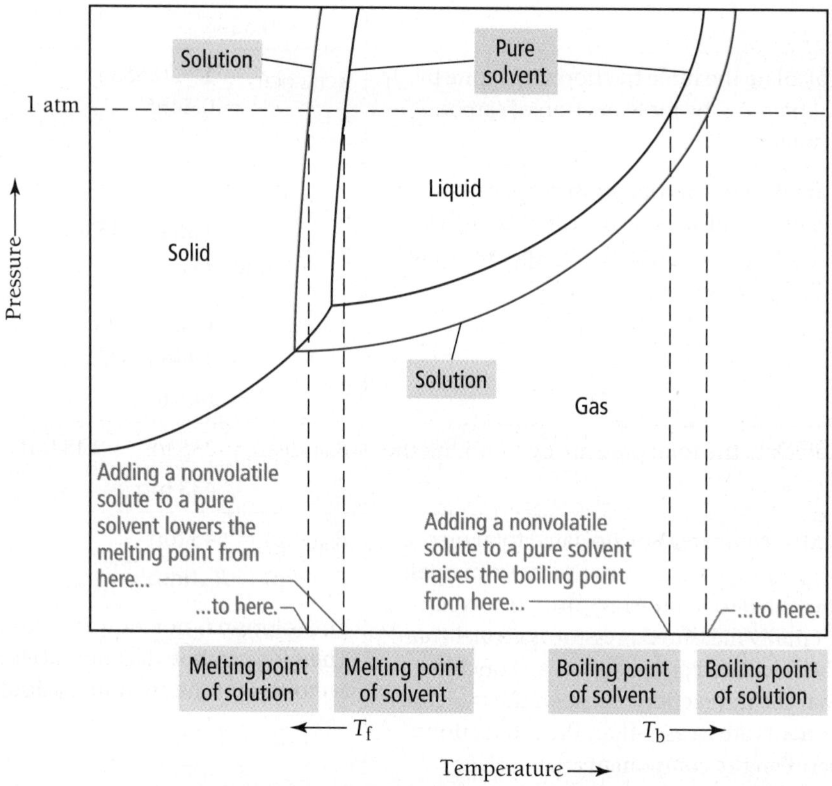

Notice that the vapor pressure for the solution is shifted downward and to the left compared to that of the pure solvent. Consequently, the vapor pressure curve intersects the solid–gas curve at a lower temperature. The net effect is that the solution has a *lower melting point* and a *higher boiling point* than the pure solvent. These effects are called **freezing point depression** and **boiling point elevation**, respectively, both of which are colligative properties (like vapor pressure lowering).

The freezing point of a solution containing a nonvolatile solute is lower than the freezing point of the pure solvent. For example, antifreeze, used to prevent the freezing of engine blocks in cold climates, is an aqueous solution of ethylene glycol ($C_2H_6O_2$). The more concentrated the solution, the lower the freezing point becomes.

▲ Antifreeze is an aqueous solution of ethylene glycol. The solution has a lower freezing point and higher boiling point than pure water.

The amount that the freezing point decreases is given by the following equation:

$$\Delta T_f = m \times K_f$$

where

- ΔT_f is the change in temperature of the freezing point in degrees Celsius (relative to the freezing point of the pure solvent), usually reported as a positive number;
- m is the molality of the solution in moles solute per kilogram solvent; and
- K_f is the freezing point depression constant for the solvent.

For water,

$$K_f = 1.86\ °C/m$$

When an aqueous solution containing a dissolved solid solute freezes slowly, the ice that forms does not normally contain much of the solute. For example, when ice forms in ocean water, the ice is not salt water, but freshwater. As the ice forms, the crystal structure of the ice tends to exclude the solute particles. You can verify this yourself by partially freezing a saltwater solution in the freezer. Take out the newly formed ice, rinse it several times, and taste it. Compare its taste to the taste of the original solution. The ice is much less salty.

TABLE 14.8 ■ Freezing Point Depression and Boiling Point Elevation Constants for Several Liquid Solvents

Solvent	Normal Freezing Point (°C)	K_f (°C/m)	Normal Boiling Point (°C)	K_b (°C/m)
Benzene (C_6H_6)	5.5	5.12	80.1	2.53
Carbon tetrachloride (CCl_4)	−22.9	29.9	76.7	5.03
Chloroform ($CHCl_3$)	−63.5	4.70	61.2	3.63
Ethanol (C_2H_5OH)	−114.1	1.99	78.3	1.22
Diethyl ether ($C_4H_{10}O$)	−116.3	1.79	34.6	2.02
Water (H_2O)	0.00	1.86	100.0	0.512

Table 14.8 provides freezing point depression and boiling point elevation constants for several liquids. Calculating the freezing point of a solution involves substituting into the freezing point depression equation as Example 14.8 demonstrates.

EXAMPLE 14.8 Freezing Point Depression

Calculate the freezing point of a 1.7 m aqueous ethylene glycol solution.

SORT You are given the molality of a solution and asked to find its freezing point.

GIVEN: 1.7 m solution
FIND: freezing point (from ΔT_f)

STRATEGIZE To solve this problem, use the freezing point depression equation.

CONCEPTUAL PLAN

$m \rightarrow \Delta T_f$

$\Delta T_f = m \times K_f$

SOLVE Substitute into the equation to calculate ΔT_f. The actual freezing point is the freezing point of pure water (0.00 °C) − ΔT_f.

SOLUTION

$$\Delta T_f = m \times K_f$$
$$= 1.7\, \cancel{m} \times 1.86\ °\text{C}/\cancel{m}$$
$$= 3.2\ °\text{C}$$

$$\text{Freezing point} = 0.00\ °\text{C} - 3.2\ °\text{C}$$
$$= -3.2\ °\text{C}$$

CHECK The units of the answer are correct. The magnitude seems about right. The expected range for freezing points of an aqueous solution is anywhere from −10 °C to just below 0 °C. Any answers out of this range would be suspect.

FOR PRACTICE 14.8 Calculate the freezing point of a 2.6 m aqueous sucrose solution.

The boiling point of a solution containing a nonvolatile solute is higher than the boiling point of the pure solvent. In automobiles, antifreeze not only prevents the freezing of water within engine blocks in cold climates, it also prevents the boiling of water within engine blocks in hot climates. The amount that boiling points rise in solutions is given by the equation:

$$\Delta T_b = m \times K_b$$

where

- ΔT_b is the change in temperature of the boiling point in degrees Celsius (relative to the boiling point of the pure solvent);
- m is the molality of the solution in moles solute per kilogram solvent; and
- K_b is the boiling point elevation constant for the solvent.

For water,

$$K_b = 0.512\ ^\circ\text{C}/m$$

Calculating the boiling point of a solution involves substituting into the boiling point elevation equation, as Example 14.9 demonstrates.

ANSWER **NOW!**

14.10 Cc Conceptual Connection

BOILING POINT ELEVATION Solution A is a 1.0 m solution with a nonionic solute and water as the solvent. Solution B is a 1.0 m solution with the same nonionic solute and ethanol as the solvent. Which solution has the greater increase in its boiling point (relative to the pure solvent)?

(a) Solution A **(b)** Solution B

WATCH **NOW!**

INTERACTIVE WORKED EXAMPLE 14.9

EXAMPLE 14.9 Boiling Point Elevation

What mass of ethylene glycol ($C_2H_6O_2$), in grams, must be added to 1.0 kg of water to produce a solution that boils at 105.0 °C?

SORT You are given the desired boiling point of an ethylene glycol solution containing 1.0 kg of water and asked to find the mass of ethylene glycol you need to add to raise the boiling point.

GIVEN: $\Delta T_b = 5.0\ ^\circ\text{C}$, 1.0 kg H_2O

FIND: g $C_2H_6O_2$

STRATEGIZE To solve this problem, use the boiling point elevation equation to calculate the desired molality of the solution from ΔT_b.

CONCEPTUAL PLAN

$\Delta T_b \rightarrow m$

$\Delta T_b = m \times K_b$

Then use that molality to determine how many moles of ethylene glycol are needed per kilogram of water. Finally, calculate the molar mass of ethylene glycol and use it to convert from moles of ethylene glycol to mass of ethylene glycol.

kg H_2O $\rightarrow$ mol $C_2H_6O_2$ $\rightarrow$ g $C_2H_6O_2$

$\dfrac{\text{mol } C_2H_6O_2}{\text{kg } H_2O}$ $\qquad \dfrac{62.07 \text{ g } C_2H_6O_2}{1 \text{ mol } C_2H_6O_2}$

from first step

RELATIONSHIPS USED $C_2H_6O_2$ molar mass = 62.07 g/mol

$\Delta T_b = m \times K_b$ (boiling point elevation)

SOLVE Begin by solving the boiling point elevation equation for molality and substituting the required quantities to calculate m.

SOLUTION

$$\Delta T_b = m \times K_b$$

$$m = \frac{\Delta T_b}{K_b} = \frac{5.0\ \cancel{^\circ\text{C}}}{0.512 \dfrac{\cancel{^\circ\text{C}}}{m}}$$

$$= 9.7\underline{7}\ m$$

$$1.0\ \cancel{\text{kg } H_2O} \times \frac{9.7\underline{7}\ \cancel{\text{mol } C_2H_6O_2}}{\cancel{\text{kg } H_2O}} \times \frac{62.07 \text{ g } C_2H_6O_2}{1\ \cancel{\text{mol } C_2H_6O_2}} = 6.1 \times 10^2 \text{ g } C_2H_6O_2$$

CHECK The units of the answer are correct. The magnitude might seem a little high initially, but the boiling point elevation constant is so small that a lot of solute is required to raise the boiling point by a small amount.

FOR PRACTICE 14.9 Calculate the boiling point of a 3.60 m aqueous sucrose solution.

CHEMISTRY IN YOUR DAY | Antifreeze in Frogs

Wood frogs (*Rana sylvatica*) look like most other frogs. They are a few inches long and have characteristic greenish-brown skin. However, wood frogs survive cold winters in a remarkable way—they partially freeze. In its partially frozen state, a wood frog has no heartbeat, no blood circulation, no breathing, and no brain activity. Within 1–2 hours of thawing, however, these vital functions return, and the frog hops off to find food. How does the wood frog do this?

Most cold-blooded animals cannot survive freezing temperatures because the water within their cells freezes. As we learned in Section 12.9, when water freezes, it expands, irreversibly damaging cells. When the wood frog hibernates for the winter, however, it produces large amounts of glucose that is secreted into its bloodstream and fills the interior of its cells. When the temperature drops below freezing, extracellular body fluids, such as those in the frog's abdominal cavity, freeze solid. Fluids within cells, however, remain liquid because the high glucose concentration lowers their freezing point. In other words, the concentrated glucose solution within the frog's cells acts as antifreeze, preventing the water within the cells from freezing and allowing the frog to survive.

▲ The wood frog survives winter by partially freezing. It protects its cells by flooding them with glucose, which acts as an antifreeze.

QUESTION *The wood frog can survive at body temperatures as low as −8.0 °C. Calculate the molality of a glucose solution ($C_6H_{12}O_6$) required to lower the freezing point of water to −8.0 °C.*

Osmotic Pressure

The process by which seawater causes dehydration (discussed in Section 14.1) is *osmosis*. **Osmosis** is the flow of solvent from a solution of lower solute concentration to one of higher solute concentration. Concentrated solutions draw solvent from more dilute solutions because of nature's tendency to mix.

Figure 14.16▼ illustrates an osmosis cell. The left side of the cell contains a concentrated saltwater solution, and the right side of the cell contains pure water. A **semipermeable membrane**—a membrane that selectively allows some substances to pass through but not others—separates the two halves of the cell. Water flows by osmosis from the pure-water side of the cell through the semipermeable membrane and into the

Osmosis and Osmotic Pressure

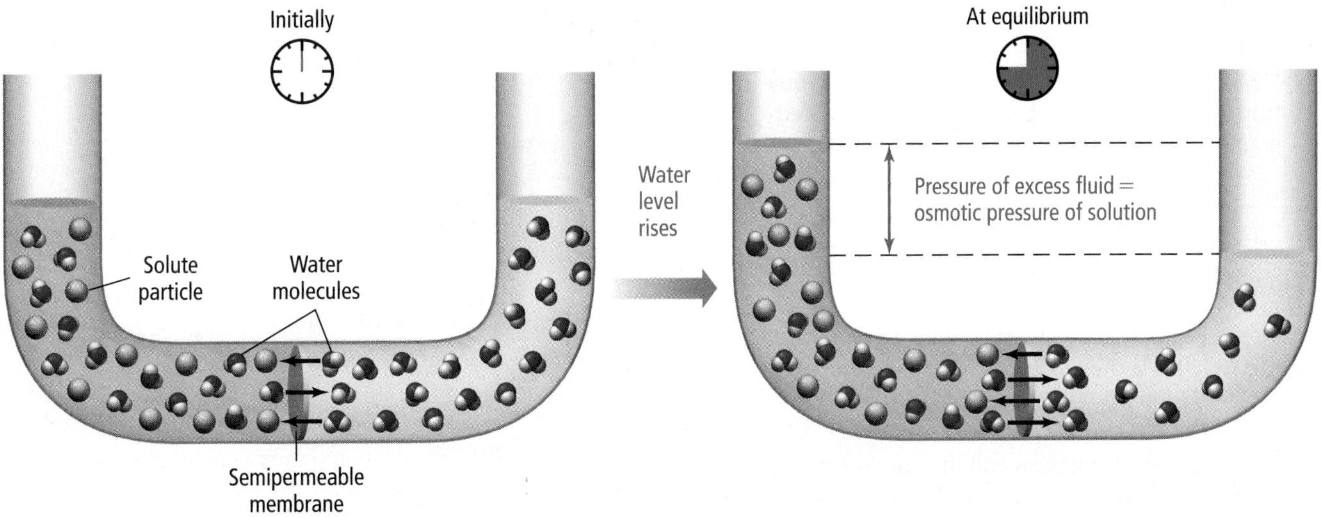

▲ **FIGURE 14.16 An Osmosis Cell** In an osmosis cell, water flows from the pure-water side of the cell through the semipermeable membrane to the saltwater side.

saltwater side. Over time, the water level on the left side of the cell rises, while the water level on the right side of the cell falls. If external pressure is applied to the water in the left side, this process can be opposed and even reversed. The pressure required to stop the osmotic flow, called the **osmotic pressure**, is given by the following equation:

$$\Pi = MRT$$

where M is the molarity of the solution, R is the ideal gas constant (0.08206 L · atm/mol · K), and T is the temperature (in Kelvin).

EXAMPLE 14.10 Osmotic Pressure

The osmotic pressure of a solution containing 5.87 mg of an unknown protein per 10.0 mL of solution is 2.45 torr at 25 °C. Find the molar mass of the unknown protein.

SORT You are told that a solution of an unknown protein contains 5.87 mg of the protein per 10.0 mL of solution. You are also given the osmotic pressure of the solution at a particular temperature and asked to find the molar mass of the unknown protein.

GIVEN: 5.87 mg protein
10.0 mL solution
$\Pi = 2.45$ torr
$T = 25$ °C

FIND: molar mass of protein (g/mol)

STRATEGIZE

Step 1: Use the given osmotic pressure and temperature to find the molarity of the protein solution.

CONCEPTUAL PLAN

$\Pi, T \rightarrow$ M

$\Pi = MRT$

Step 2: Use the molarity calculated in step 1 to find the number of moles of protein in 10 mL of solution.

mL solution $\rightarrow$ L solution $\rightarrow$ mol protein

$\frac{1\ \text{L}}{1000\ \text{mL}}$ $\quad$ $\frac{\text{mol protein}}{\text{L solution}}$ (from first step)

Step 3: Finally, use the number of moles of the protein calculated in step 2 and the given mass of the protein in 10.0 mL of solution to find the molar mass.

$$\text{Molar mass} = \frac{\text{mass protein}}{\text{moles protein}}$$

RELATIONSHIPS USED $\Pi = MRT$ (osmotic pressure equation)

SOLVE

SOLUTION

Step 1: Begin by solving the osmotic pressure equation for molarity and substituting in the required quantities in the correct units to calculate M.

$$\Pi = MRT$$

$$M = \frac{\Pi}{RT} = \frac{2.45\ \text{torr} \times \frac{1\ \text{atm}}{760\ \text{torr}}}{0.08206\ \frac{\text{L} \cdot \text{atm}}{\text{mol} \cdot \text{K}}(298\ \text{K})}$$

$$= 1.318 \times 10^{-4}\ \text{M}$$

Step 2: Begin with the given volume, convert to liters, then use the molarity to find the number of moles of protein.

$$10.0\ \text{mL} \times \frac{1\ \text{L}}{1000\ \text{mL}} \times \frac{1.318 \times 10^{-4}\ \text{mol}}{\text{L}} = 1.318 \times 10^{-6}\ \text{mol}$$

Step 3: Use the given mass and the number of moles from step 2 to calculate the molar mass of the protein.

$$\text{Molar mass} = \frac{\text{mass protein}}{\text{moles protein}}$$

$$= \frac{5.87 \times 10^{-3}\ \text{g}}{1.318 \times 10^{-6}\ \text{mol}} = 4.45 \times 10^{3}\ \text{g/mol}$$

CHECK The units of the answer are correct. The magnitude might seem a little high initially, but proteins are large molecules and therefore have high molar masses.

FOR PRACTICE 14.10 Calculate the osmotic pressure (in atm) of a solution containing 1.50 g ethylene glycol ($C_2H_6O_2$) in 50.0 mL of solution at 25 °C.

14.7 Colligative Properties of Strong Electrolyte Solutions

At the beginning of Section 14.6, we saw that colligative properties depend on the number of dissolved particles and that we must therefore treat electrolytes slightly differently than nonelectrolytes when determining colligative properties. For example, the freezing point depression of a 0.10 m sucrose solution is $\Delta T_f = 0.186$ °C. However, the freezing point depression of a 0.10 m sodium chloride solution is nearly twice this large. Why? Because 1 mol of sodium chloride dissociates into nearly 2 mol of ions in solution. The ratio of moles of particles in solution to moles of formula units dissolved is called the **van't Hoff factor (i)**:

$$i = \frac{\text{moles of particles in solution}}{\text{moles of formula units dissolved}}$$

TABLE 14.9 ■ Van't Hoff Factors at 0.05 m Concentration in Aqueous Solution

Solute	i Expected	i Measured
Nonelectrolyte	1	1
NaCl	2	1.9
$MgSO_4$	2	1.3
$MgCl_2$	3	2.7
K_2SO_4	3	2.6
$FeCl_3$	4	3.4

Since 1 mol of NaCl produces 2 mol of particles in solution, we expect the van't Hoff factor for NaCl to be exactly 2. In reality, this expected factor only occurs in very dilute solutions. For example, the van't Hoff factor for a 0.10 m NaCl solution is 1.87, and for a 0.010 m NaCl solution the van't Hoff factor is 1.94. The van't Hoff factor approaches the expected value at infinite dilution (as the concentration approaches zero). Table 14.9 lists the actual and expected van't Hoff factors for a number of solutes.

The reason that van't Hoff factors do not exactly equal expected values is that some ions effectively pair in solution. We expect the dissociation of an ionic compound to be complete in solution. In reality, however, the dissociation is not complete—at any moment, some cations pair with anions (Figure 14.17▶), slightly reducing the number of particles in solution.

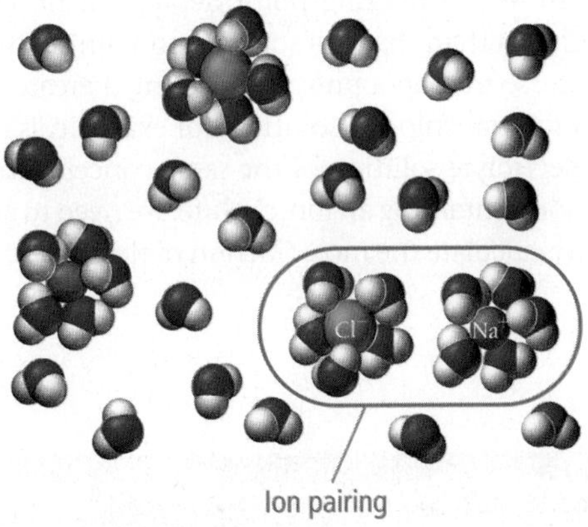

◀ **FIGURE 14.17 Ion Pairing** Hydrated anions and cations may get close enough together to effectively pair, lowering the concentration of particles below what would be expected.

To calculate freezing point depression, boiling point elevation, and osmotic pressure of ionic solutions, we use the van't Hoff factor in each equation as follows:

$$\Delta T_f = im \times K_f \text{ (freezing point depression)}$$
$$\Delta T_b = im \times K_b \text{ (boiling point elevation)}$$
$$\Pi = iMRT \text{ (osmotic pressure)}$$

COLLIGATIVE PROPERTIES Which aqueous solution has the highest boiling point?

(a) 0.50 M $C_{12}H_{22}O_{11}$
(b) 0.50 M NaCl
(c) 0.50 M $MgCl_2$

14.11 Cc Conceptual Connection

ANSWER **NOW!**

EXAMPLE 14.11 Van't Hoff Factor and Freezing Point Depression

The freezing point of an aqueous 0.050 *m* $CaCl_2$ solution is –0.27 °C. What is the van't Hoff factor (*i*) for $CaCl_2$ at this concentration? How does it compare to the expected value of *i*?

SORT You are given the molality of a solution and its freezing point. You are asked to find the value of *i*, the van't Hoff factor, and compare it to the expected value.

GIVEN: 0.050 *m* $CaCl_2$ solution, $\Delta T_f = 0.27\ °C$

FIND: i

STRATEGIZE To solve this problem, use the freezing point depression equation including the van't Hoff factor.

CONCEPTUAL PLAN

$\Delta T_f = im \times K_f$

SOLVE Solve the freezing point depression equation for *i*, substituting in the given quantities to calculate its value.

SOLUTION

$$\Delta T_f = im \times K_f$$

$$i = \frac{\Delta T_f}{m \times K_f} = \frac{0.27\ \cancel{°C}}{0.050\ \cancel{m} \times \frac{1.86\ \cancel{°C}}{\cancel{m}}} = 2.9$$

The expected value of *i* for $CaCl_2$ is 3 because calcium chloride forms 3 mol of ions for each mole of calcium chloride that dissolves. Because of ion pairing, the experimental value is slightly less than 3.

CHECK The answer has no units, which is as expected since *i* is a ratio. The magnitude is about right since it is close to the value you would expect upon complete dissociation of $CaCl_2$.

FOR PRACTICE 14.11 Calculate the freezing point of an aqueous 0.10 *m* $FeCl_3$ solution using a van't Hoff factor of 3.2.

Strong Electrolytes and Vapor Pressure

Just as the freezing point depression of a solution containing an electrolyte solute is greater than that of a solution containing the same concentration of a nonelectrolyte solute, so the vapor pressure lowering is greater (for the same reasons). The vapor pressure for a sodium chloride solution, for example, is lowered about twice as much as it is for a nonelectrolyte solution of the same concentration. To calculate the vapor pressure of a solution containing an ionic solute, we need to account for the dissociation of the solute when we calculate the mole fraction of the solvent, as we demonstrate in Example 14.12.

WATCH **NOW!**

INTERACTIVE WORKED EXAMPLE 14.12

EXAMPLE 14.12 Calculating the Vapor Pressure of a Solution Containing an Ionic Solute

A solution contains 0.102 mol $Ca(NO_3)_2$ and 0.927 mol H_2O. Calculate the vapor pressure of the solution at 55 °C. The vapor pressure of pure water at 55 °C is 118.1 torr. (Assume that the solute completely dissociates.)

SORT You are given the number of moles of each component of a solution and asked to find the vapor pressure of the solution. You are also given the vapor pressure of pure water at the appropriate temperature.

GIVEN: 0.102 mol $Ca(NO_3)_2$

0.927 mol H_2O

$P^\circ_{H_2O} = 118.1$ torr (at 55 °C)

FIND: $P_{solution}$

STRATEGIZE To solve this problem, use Raoult's law as you did in Example 14.6. Calculate $\chi_{solvent}$ from the given amounts of solute and solvent.

CONCEPTUAL PLAN

$\chi_{H_2O}, P^\circ_{H_2O}$ → $P_{solution}$

$P_{solution} = \chi_{H_2O} P^\circ_{H_2O}$

SOLVE The key to this problem is to understand the dissociation of calcium nitrate. Write the equation showing the dissociation.	**SOLUTION** $Ca(NO_3)_2(s) \longrightarrow Ca^{2+}(aq) + 2\,NO_3^{-}(aq)$
Since 1 mol of calcium nitrate dissociates into 3 mol of dissolved particles, multiply the number of moles of calcium nitrate by 3 when calculating the mole fraction.	$\chi_{H_2O} = \dfrac{n_{H_2O}}{3 \times n_{Ca(NO_3)_2} + n_{H_2O}}$ $= \dfrac{0.927\,\cancel{mol}}{3\,(0.102)\,\cancel{mol} + 0.927\,\cancel{mol}}$ $= 0.75\underline{1}8$
Use the mole fraction of water and the vapor pressure of pure water to calculate the vapor pressure of the solution.	$P_{solution} = \chi_{H_2O} P^{\circ}_{H_2O}$ $= 0.75\underline{1}8\,(118.1\ torr)$ $= 88.8\ torr$

CHECK The units of the answer are correct. The magnitude also seems right because the calculated vapor pressure of the solution is significantly less than that of the pure solvent, as you would expect for a solution with a significant amount of solute.

FOR PRACTICE 14.12 A solution contains 0.115 mol H_2O and an unknown number of moles of sodium chloride. The vapor pressure of the solution at 30 °C is 25.7 torr. The vapor pressure of pure water at 30 °C is 31.8 torr. Calculate the number of moles of sodium chloride in the solution. (Assume that the solute completely dissociates.)

Colligative Properties and Medical Solutions

Doctors and other health care workers often administer solutions to patients. The osmotic pressure of these solutions is controlled for the desired effect on the patient. Solutions having osmotic pressures greater than those of body fluids are called *hyperosmotic*. These solutions take water out of cells and tissues. When a human cell is placed in a hyperosmotic solution, it tends to shrivel as it loses water to the surrounding solution (Figure 14.18(b)▼). Solutions having osmotic pressures less than those of body fluids are called *hyposmotic*. These solutions pump water into cells. When a human cell is placed in a hyposmotic solution—such as pure water, for example—water enters the cell, sometimes causing it to burst (Figure 14.18(c)▼).

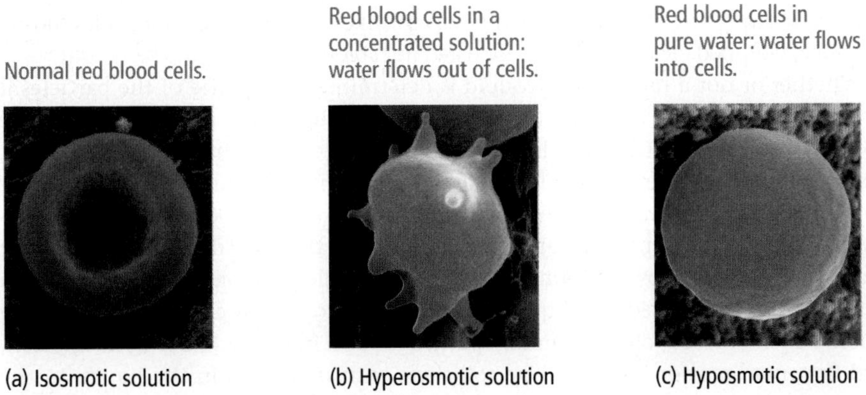

▲ **FIGURE 14.18 Red Blood Cells and Osmosis** **(a)** In an isosmotic solution, red blood cells have the normal shape shown here. In a hyperosmotic solution **(b)**, they lose water and shrivel. In a hyposmotic solution **(c)**, they swell up and may burst as water flows into the cell.

Intravenous solutions—those that are administered directly into a patient's veins—must have osmotic pressures equal to those of body fluids. These solutions are called *isosmotic* (or *isotonic*). When a patient is given an IV in a hospital, the majority of the fluid is usually an isosmotic saline solution—a solution containing 0.9 g NaCl per 100 mL of solution. In medicine and in other health-related fields, solution concentrations are often reported in units that indicate the mass of the solute per given volume of solution. Also common is *percent mass to volume*—which is the mass of the solute in grams divided by the volume of the solution in milliliters times 100%. In these units, the concentration of an isotonic saline solution is 0.9% mass/volume.

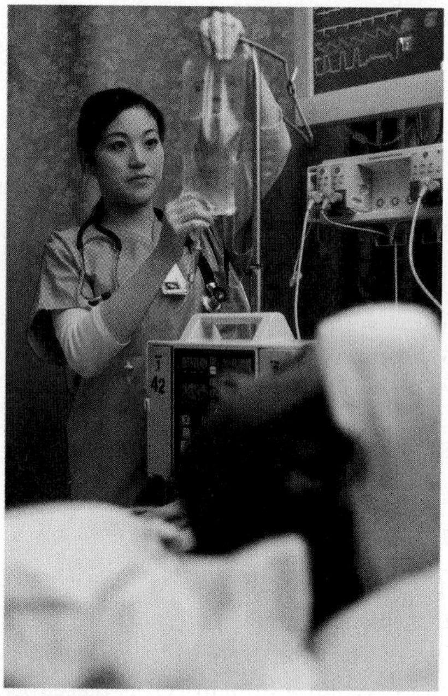

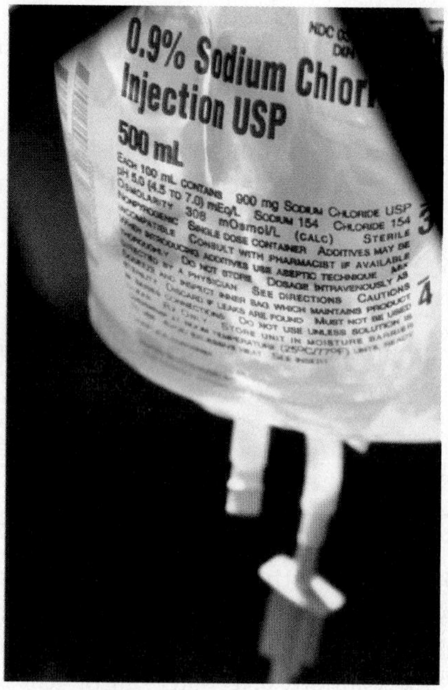

▶ Fluids used for intravenous transfusion must be isosmotic with bodily fluids—that is, they must have the same osmotic pressure as body fluids.

14.8 Colloids

When you mix water and soap together, the resulting mixture has a distinctive haze (Figure 14.19◀). Soapy water is hazy because soap and water form a *colloidal dispersion* rather than a true solution. A **colloidal dispersion**, or more simply a **colloid**, is a mixture in which a dispersed substance (which is solute-like) is finely divided in a dispersing medium (which is solvent-like). Examples of colloids including fog, smoke, whipped cream, and milk are listed in Table 14.10.

▲ **FIGURE 14.19 A Colloid** Soapy water is an example of a colloidal dispersion. The haze is due to the scattering of light by the colloidal particles.

Whether or not a mixture is a colloid is determined by the size of the particles it contains. If the particles are small (for example, individual small molecules), then the mixture is a solution. If the particles have a diameter greater than 1 μm (for example, grains of sand), then the mixture is a heterogeneous mixture. Sand stirred into water slowly settles out of the water. *If the particles are between 1 nm and 1000 nm in size, the mixture is a colloid.* Colloidal particles are small enough that they stay dispersed throughout the dispersing medium by collisions with other molecules or atoms. When you view a colloidal particle dispersed in a liquid under a microscope, you can witness its jittery motion, which proceeds along a random path, as shown in Figure 14.20▶. This motion, called Brownian motion, is caused by collisions with molecules in the liquid. In the beginning of the twentieth century, Brownian motion was a decisive factor in confirming the molecular and atomic nature of matter.

Soap forms a colloid because of its unique structure, shown in Figure 14.21▶. One end of the molecule is ionic and therefore interacts strongly with water molecules via ion–dipole interactions. The other end of the soap molecule is a long, nonpolar, hydrocarbon tail.

TABLE 14.10 ■ Types of Colloidal Dispersions

Classification	Dispersing Substance (Solute-like)	Dispersing Medium (Solvent-like)	Example	
Aerosol	Liquid	Gas		Fog (water droplets in air)
Solid aerosol	Solid	Gas		Smoke (ash in air)
Foam	Gas	Liquid		Whipped cream (air bubbles in butterfat)
Emulsion	Liquid	Liquid		Milk (milk fat globules in water)
Solid emulsion	Liquid	Solid	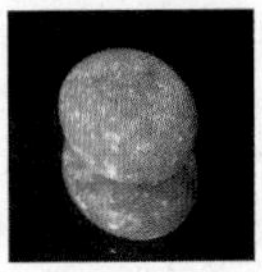	Opal (water in silica glass)

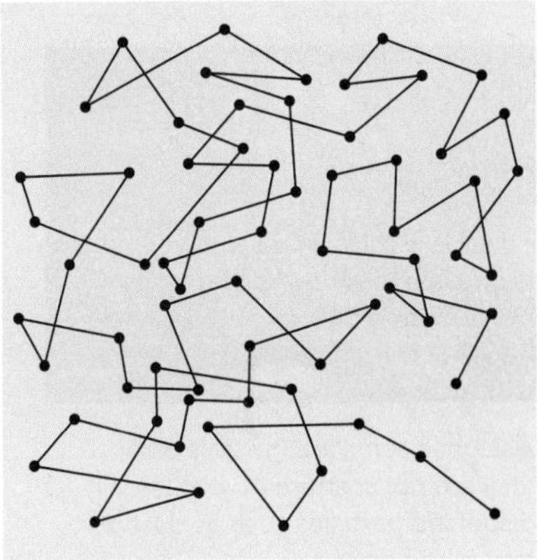

▲ **FIGURE 14.20 Brownian Motion** A colloidal particle exhibits Brownian motion (Section 2.1), moving in a jerky, haphazard path as it undergoes collisions with molecules in the liquid.

When enough soap is added to water, the soap molecules aggregate in structures called *micelles* (Figure 14.22▼). In a micelle, the nonpolar hydrocarbon tails crowd into the center of a sphere to maximize their interactions with one another. The ionic heads orient toward the surface of the sphere where they can interact with water molecules. The micelle structures are responsible for the haze seen in soapy water—they are too small to be seen by the naked eye, but they still scatter light (as particles in other types of colloids do).

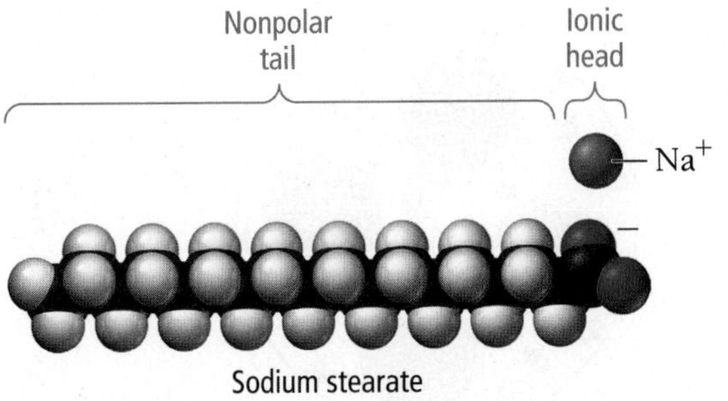

▲ **FIGURE 14.21 Soap Molecule Structure** A soap molecule has a charged ionic head and a long nonpolar hydrocarbon tail.

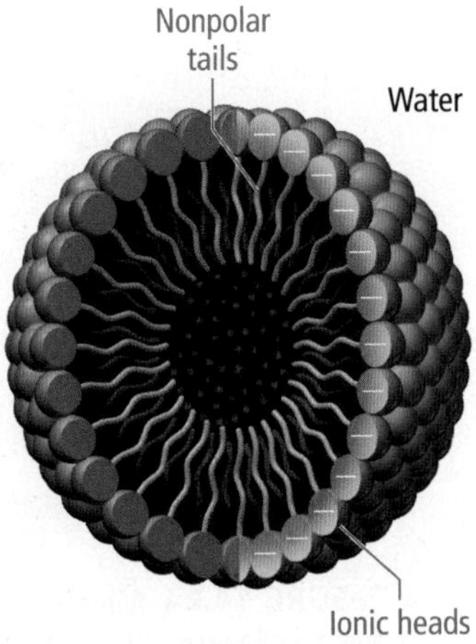

◀ **FIGURE 14.22 Micelle Structure** In a micelle, the nonpolar tails of soap molecules (or of other molecules that have properties that are similar to soap) are oriented inward (where they can interact with one another), and the ionic heads are oriented outward (where they can interact with the polar water molecules).

▲ **FIGURE 14.23 The Tyndall Effect** When a light beam passes through a colloidal suspension (left), it is visible because the colloid particles scatter some of the light. The beam is not visible in a noncolloidal solution (right), nor would it be visible in pure water.

▲ Light beams are invisible when they are not scattered by colloidally dispersed particles such as dust or mist in the air.

This scattering of light by a colloidal dispersion is known as the **Tyndall effect** (Figure 14.23▲). You can observe the Tyndall effect in other colloids such as fog (water droplets dispersed in air) or dusty air. In fact, you can use the Tyndall effect as a test to determine whether a mixture is a solution or a colloid, since solutions contain completely dissolved solute molecules that are too small to scatter light.

Colloidal suspensions of micelles are kept stable by electrostatic repulsions that occur at their surfaces. For example, in soap, the ionic heads of the soap molecules compose the surface of the spherical particle (Figure 14.24▼). These ionic heads interact strongly with water molecules but repel other colloid particles. Heating a colloid composed of micelles can destroy the micelles because collisions occur with enough force to overcome the electrostatic repulsions and allow the molecules within the micelles to coalesce with those in other micelles. Similarly, adding an electrolyte to a colloidal suspension of micelles can also disrupt the electrostatic repulsions that occur between the particles and thus destroy the colloid. For this reason, soap does not work well in a saltwater solution.

The particles in a colloid need not be clusters of molecules. Some colloids, such as many protein solutions, contain dispersed macromolecules. For example, a solution containing hemoglobin is a colloid. The hemoglobin molecules are so large that they scatter light.

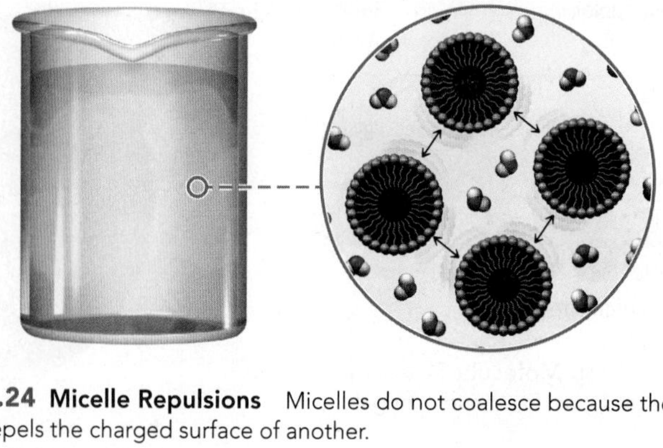

▲ **FIGURE 14.24 Micelle Repulsions** Micelles do not coalesce because the charged surface of one micelle repels the charged surface of another.

Self-Assessment Quiz

Q1. Which compound do you expect to be most soluble in octane (C_8H_{18})? **MISSED THIS?** *Read Section 14.2*

a) CH_3OH b) CBr_4 c) H_2O d) NH_3

Q2. An aqueous solution is saturated in both potassium chlorate and carbon dioxide gas at room temperature. What happens when the solution is warmed to 85 °C?

MISSED THIS? *Read Section 14.4; Watch KCV 14.4*

a) Potassium chlorate precipitates out of solution.
b) Carbon dioxide bubbles out of solution.
c) Potassium chlorate precipitates out of solution and carbon dioxide bubbles out of solution.
d) Nothing happens; all of the potassium chloride and the carbon dioxide remain dissolved in solution.

Q3. A 500.0-mL sample of pure water is allowed to come to equilibrium with pure oxygen gas at a pressure of 755 mmHg. What mass of oxygen gas dissolves in the water? (The Henry's law constant for oxygen gas is 1.3×10^{-3} M/atm.)

MISSED THIS? *Read Section 14.4; Watch IWE 14.2*

a) 15.7 g b) 6.5×10^{-3} g
c) 0.041 g d) 0.021 g

Q4. A potassium bromide solution is 7.55% potassium bromide by mass, and its density is 1.03 g/mL. What mass of potassium bromide is contained in 35.8 mL of the solution?

MISSED THIS? *Read Section 14.5; Watch IWE 14.3*

a) 2.78 g b) 2.70 g
c) 4.88 g d) 2.62 g

Q5. A solution contains 22.4 g glucose ($C_6H_{12}O_6$) dissolved in 0.500 L of water. What is the molality of the solution? (Assume a density of 1.00 g/mL for water.) **MISSED THIS?** *Read Section 14.5; Watch KCV 14.5; Watch IWE 14.4*

a) 0.238 *m* b) 44.8 *m*
c) 0.249 *m* d) 4.03 *m*

Q6. A sodium nitrate solution is 12.5% $NaNO_3$ by mass and has a density of 1.02 g/mL. Calculate the molarity of the solution. **MISSED THIS?** *Read Section 14.5; Watch KCV 14.5; Watch IWE 14.5*

a) 1.44 M b) 12.8 M
c) 6.67 M d) 1.50 M

Q7. Determine the vapor pressure at 25 °C of an aqueous ethylene glycol ($C_2H_6O_2$) solution that is 14.8% $C_2H_6O_2$ by mass. The vapor pressure of pure water at 25 °C is 23.8 torr. **MISSED THIS?** *Read Section 14.6; Watch KCV 14.6; Watch IWE 14.6*

a) 3.52 torr b) 22.7 torr
c) 1.14 torr d) 20.3 torr

Q8. A solution contains a mixture of substance A and substance B, both of which are volatile. The mole fraction of substance A is 0.35. At 32 °C the vapor pressure of pure A is 87 mmHg, and the vapor pressure of pure B is 122 mmHg. What is the total vapor pressure of the solution at this temperature?

MISSED THIS? *Read Section 14.6*

a) 110 mmHg b) 209 mmHg
c) 99.3 mmHg d) 73.2 mmHg

Q9. What mass of glucose ($C_6H_{12}O_6$) should be dissolved in 10.0 kg of water to obtain a solution with a freezing point of −4.2 °C? **MISSED THIS?** *Read Section 14.6; Watch KCV 14.6; Watch IWE 14.9*

a) 0.023 kg b) 4.1 kg
c) 0.41 kg d) 14.1 kg

Q10. Which of these aqueous solutions has the highest boiling point? **MISSED THIS?** *Read Section 14.6; Watch KCV 14.6*

a) 1.25 M $C_6H_{12}O_6$
b) 1.25 M KNO_3
c) 1.25 M $Ca(NO_3)_2$
d) None of the above (they all have the same boiling point)

Q11. The osmotic pressure of a solution containing 22.7 mg of an unknown protein in 50.0 mL of solution is 2.88 mmHg at 25 °C. Determine the molar mass of the protein.

MISSED THIS? *Read Section 14.6*

a) 246 g/mol b) 3.85 g/mol
c) 2.93×10^3 g/mol d) 147 g/mol

Q12. The enthalpy of solution for NaOH is −44.46 kJ/mol. What can you conclude about the relative magnitudes of the absolute values of ΔH_{solute} and $\Delta H_{hydration}$, where ΔH_{solute} is the heat associated with separating the solute particles and $\Delta H_{hydration}$ is the heat associated with dissolving the solute particles in water? **MISSED THIS?** *Read Section 14.3*

a) $|\Delta H_{solute}| > |\Delta H_{hydration}|$
b) $|\Delta H_{solute}| < |\Delta H_{hydration}|$
c) $|\Delta H_{solute}| = |\Delta H_{hydration}|$
d) None of the above (nothing can be concluded about the relative magnitudes)

Q13. A 2.4 *m* aqueous solution of an ionic compound with the formula MX_2 has a boiling point of 103.4 °C. Calculate the van't Hoff factor (*i*) for MX_2 at this concentration.

MISSED THIS? *Read Section 14.7*

a) 2.8 b) 83
c) 0.73 d) 1.0

Q14. A solution is an equimolar mixture of two volatile components A and B. Pure A has a vapor pressure of 50 torr, and pure B has a vapor pressure of 100 torr. The vapor pressure of the mixture is 85 torr. What can you conclude about the relative strengths of the intermolecular forces between particles of A and B (relative to those between particles of A and those between particles of B)?

MISSED THIS? *Read Section 14.6*

a) The intermolecular forces between particles A and B are *weaker* than those between particles of A and those between particles of B.
b) The intermolecular forces between particles A and B are *stronger* than those between particles of A and those between particles of B.
c) The intermolecular forces between particles A and B are *the same as* those between particles of A and those between particles of B.
d) Nothing can be concluded about the relative strengths of intermolecular forces from this observation.

—Continued on the next page

Continued—

Q15. An aqueous solution at 25 °C is in equilibrium with a gaseous mixture containing an equal number of moles of oxygen, nitrogen, and helium. Rank the relative concentrations of each gas in the aqueous solution from highest to lowest.

MISSED THIS? *Read Section 14.4*

a) $[O_2] > [N_2] > [He]$
b) $[He] > [N_2] > [O_2]$
c) $[N_2] > [He] > [O_2]$
d) $[N_2] > [O_2] > [He]$

Answers: **1.** (b) **2.** (b) **3.** (d) **4.** (a) **5.** (c) **6.** (d) **7.** (b) **8.** (a) **9.** (b) **10.** (c) **11.** (c) **12.** (b) **13.** (a) **14.** (a) **15.** (a)

CHAPTER 14 IN REVIEW

TERMS

Section 14.1
solution (580)
solvent (580)
solute (580)

Section 14.2
aqueous solution (581)
solubility (581)
entropy (582)
miscible (583)

Section 14.3
enthalpy of solution (ΔH_{soln}) (587)
heat of hydration ($\Delta H_{hydration}$) (588)

Section 14.4
dynamic equilibrium (590)
saturated solution (590)
unsaturated solution (590)
supersaturated solution (590)
recrystallization (591)
Henry's law (593)

Section 14.5
dilute solution (594)
concentrated solution (595)
molarity (M) (595)
molality (*m*) (596)
parts by mass (596)
percent by mass (596)
parts per million (ppm) (597)
parts per billion (ppb) (597)
parts by volume (597)
mole fraction (χ_{solute}) (598)
mole percent (mol %) (598)

Section 14.6
colligative property (601)
Raoult's law (603)
vapor pressure lowering (ΔP) (603)
ideal solution (605)
freezing point depression (608)
boiling point elevation (608)
osmosis (611)
semipermeable membrane (611)
osmotic pressure (612)

Section 14.7
van't Hoff factor (*i*) (613)

Section 14.8
colloidal dispersion (colloid) (616)
Tyndall effect (618)

CONCEPTS

Solutions (14.1, 14.2)

- A solution is a homogeneous mixture of two or more substances. In a solution, the majority component is the solvent, and the minority component is the solute.
- The tendency toward greater entropy (or greater energy dispersal) is the driving force for solution formation.
- In aqueous solutions, water is a solvent, and a solid, liquid, or gas is the solute.

Solubility and Energetics of Solution Formation (14.2, 14.3)

- The solubility of a substance is the amount of the substance that dissolves in a given amount of solvent. The solubility of one substance in another depends on the types of intermolecular forces that exist *between* the substances as well as *within* each substance.
- We can determine the overall enthalpy change upon solution formation by adding the enthalpy changes for the three steps of solution formation: (1) separation of the solute particles, (2) separation of the solvent particles, and (3) mixing of the solute and solvent particles. The first two steps are both endothermic, whereas the last is exothermic.
- In aqueous solutions of an ionic compound, the combined change in enthalpy for steps 2 and 3 is the heat of hydration ($\Delta H_{hydration}$), which is always negative.

Solution Equilibrium (14.4)

- Dynamic equilibrium in a solution occurs when the rates of dissolution and recrystallization in a solution are equal. A solution in this state is saturated. Solutions containing less than or more than the equilibrium amount of solute are unsaturated or supersaturated, respectively.
- The solubility of most solids in water increases with increasing temperature.
- The solubility of gases in water generally decreases with increasing temperature, but it increases with increasing pressure.

Concentration Units (14.5)

- Common units to express solution concentration include molarity (M), molality (*m*), mole fraction (χ), mole percent (mol %), percent (%) by mass or volume, parts per million (ppm) by mass or volume, and parts per billion (ppb) by mass or volume. Table 14.5 summarizes these units.

Vapor Pressure Lowering, Freezing Point Depression, Boiling Point Elevation, and Osmosis (14.6, 14.7)

- The presence of a nonvolatile solute in a liquid results in a lower vapor pressure of the solution relative to the vapor pressure of the pure liquid. Raoult's law for an ideal solution predicts this lower vapor pressure.
- If the solute–solvent interactions are particularly strong, the actual vapor pressure is lower than that predicted by Raoult's law.
- If the solute–solvent interactions are particularly weak, the actual vapor pressure is higher than that predicted by Raoult's law.
- The addition of a nonvolatile solute to a liquid results in a solution with a lower freezing point and a higher boiling point than those of the pure solvent.
- The flow of solvent from a solution of lower concentration to a solution of higher concentration is osmosis.
- All of these phenomena (vapor pressure lowering, freezing point depression, boiling point elevation, and osmosis) are colligative properties and depend only on the number of solute particles added, not the type of solute particles.
- Electrolyte solutes have a greater effect on these properties than the corresponding amount of a nonelectrolyte solute as specified by the van't Hoff factor.

Colloids (14.8)

- A colloid is a mixture in which a substance is finely divided in a dispersing medium.
- Colloidal mixtures occur when the dispersed substance ranges in size from 1 nm to 1000 nm.
- One way to identify colloidal mixtures is by their tendency to scatter light, known as the Tyndall effect.

EQUATIONS AND RELATIONSHIPS

Henry's Law: Solubility of Gases with Increasing Pressure (**14.4**)

$$S_{gas} = k_H P_{gas} \text{ } (k_H \text{ is Henry's law constant})$$

Molarity (M) of a Solution (**14.5**)

$$\text{M} = \frac{\text{amount solute (in mol)}}{\text{volume solution (in L)}}$$

Molality (m) of a Solution (**14.5**)

$$m = \frac{\text{amount solute (in mol)}}{\text{mass solvent (in kg)}}$$

Concentration of a Solution in Parts by Mass and Parts by Volume (**14.5**)

$$\text{Percent by mass} = \frac{\text{mass solute} \times 100\%}{\text{mass solution}}$$

$$\text{Parts per million (ppm)} = \frac{\text{mass solute} \times 10^6}{\text{mass solution}}$$

$$\text{Parts per billion (ppb)} = \frac{\text{mass solute} \times 10^9}{\text{mass solution}}$$

$$\text{Parts by volume} = \frac{\text{volume solute} \times \text{multiplication factor}}{\text{volume solution}}$$

Concentration of a Solution in Mole Fraction (χ) and Mole Percent (**14.5**)

$$\chi_{solute} = \frac{n_{solute}}{n_{solute} + n_{solvent}}$$

$$\text{Mol \%} = \chi \times 100\%$$

Raoult's Law: Relationship between the Vapor Pressure of a Solution ($P_{solution}$), the Mole Fraction of the Solvent ($\chi_{solvent}$), and the Vapor Pressure of the Pure Solvent ($P^{\circ}_{solvent}$) (**14.6**)

$$P_{solution} = \chi_{solvent} P^{\circ}_{solvent}$$

The Vapor Pressure of a Solution Containing Two Volatile Components (**14.6**)

$$P_A = \chi_A P^{\circ}_A$$
$$P_B = \chi_B P^{\circ}_B$$
$$P_{tot} = P_A + P_B$$

Relationship between Freezing Point Depression (ΔT_f), Molality (m), and Freezing Point Depression Constant (K_f) (**14.6**)

$$\Delta T_f = m \times K_f$$

Relationship between Boiling Point Elevation (ΔT_b), Molality (m), and Boiling Point Elevation Constant (K_b) (**14.6**)

$$\Delta T_b = m \times K_b$$

Relationship between Osmotic Pressure (Π), Molarity (M), the Ideal Gas Constant (R), and Temperature (T, in K) (**14.6**)

$$\Pi = MRT \text{ } (R = 0.08206 \text{ L} \cdot \text{atm/mol} \cdot \text{K})$$

van't Hoff Factor (i): Ratio of Moles of Particles in Solution to Moles of Formula Units Dissolved (**14.7**)

$$i = \frac{\text{moles of particles in solution}}{\text{moles of formula units dissolved}}$$

LEARNING OUTCOMES

Chapter Objectives	Assessment
Determine the solubility of a solute (**14.2**)	Example 14.1 **For Practice** 14.1 **Exercises** 31–34
Analyze energy transfer for the formation of a solution (**14.3**)	Exercises 35–40
Evaluate the solubility of solids and gases with changing temperature and pressure (**14.4**)	Example 14.2 **For Practice** 14.2 **Exercises** 41–50

Perform calculations using varying concentration units (**14.5**)	Examples 14.3, 14.4, 14.5 **For Practice** 14.3, 14.4, 14.5 **For More Practice** 14.3, 14.5 **Exercises** 51–68
Determine colligative properties of solutions containing a nonelectrolyte (**14.6**)	Examples 14.6, 14.7, 14.8, 14.9, 14.10 **For Practice** 14.6, 14.7, 14.8, 14.9, 14.10 **For More Practice** 14.6 **Exercises** 69–86
Calculate colligative properties of solutions containing an ionic solute (**14.7**)	Example 14.11 **For Practice** 14.11, 14.12 **Exercises** 87–98

EXERCISES

Mastering Chemistry provides end-of-chapter exercises, feedback-enriched tutorial problems, animations, and interactive activities to encourage problem-solving practice and deeper understanding of key concepts and topics.

REVIEW QUESTIONS

1. Explain why drinking seawater results in dehydration.
2. What is a solution? What are the solute and solvent?
3. What does it mean to say that a substance is soluble in another substance? Which units are used in reporting solubility?
4. Why do two ideal gases thoroughly mix when combined? What drives the mixing?
5. What is entropy? Why is entropy important in discussing the formation of solutions?
6. What kinds of intermolecular forces are involved in solution formation?
7. Explain how the relative strengths of solute–solute interactions, solvent–solvent interactions, and solvent–solute interactions affect solution formation.
8. What does the statement *like dissolves like* mean with respect to solution formation?
9. What are the three steps involved in evaluating the enthalpy changes associated with solution formation?
10. What is the heat of hydration ($\Delta H_{hydration}$)? How does the enthalpy of solution depend on the relative magnitudes of ΔH_{solute} and $\Delta H_{hydration}$?
11. Explain dynamic equilibrium with respect to solution formation. What is a saturated solution? An unsaturated solution? A supersaturated solution?
12. How does the solubility of a solid in a liquid depend on temperature? How is this temperature dependence exploited to purify solids through recrystallization?
13. How does the solubility of a gas in a liquid depend on temperature? How does this temperature dependence affect the amount of oxygen available for fish and other aquatic animals?
14. How does the solubility of a gas in a liquid depend on pressure? How does this pressure dependence account for the bubbling that occurs upon opening a can of soda?
15. What is Henry's law? For what kinds of calculations is Henry's law useful?
16. What are the common units for expressing solution concentration?
17. How are parts by mass and parts by volume used in calculations?
18. What is the effect of a nonvolatile solute on the vapor pressure of a liquid? Why is the vapor pressure of a solution different from the vapor pressure of the pure liquid solvent?
19. What is Raoult's law? For what kind of calculations is Raoult's law useful?
20. Explain the difference between an ideal and a nonideal solution.
21. What is the effect on vapor pressure of a solution with particularly *strong* solute–solvent interactions? With particularly *weak* solute–solvent interactions?
22. Explain why the lower vapor pressure for a solution containing a nonvolatile solute results in a higher boiling point and lower melting point compared to the pure solvent.
23. What are colligative properties?
24. What is osmosis? What is osmotic pressure?
25. Explain the meaning of the van't Hoff factor and its role in determining the colligative properties of solutions containing ionic solutes.
26. Describe a colloidal dispersion. What is the difference between a colloidal dispersion and a true solution?
27. What is the Tyndall effect, and how can it be used to help identify colloidal dispersions?
28. What keeps the particles in a colloidal dispersion from coalescing?

PROBLEMS BY TOPIC

Solubility

29. Pick an appropriate solvent from Table 14.3 to dissolve each substance. State the kind of intermolecular forces that would occur between the solute and solvent in each case.
MISSED THIS? *Read Section 14.2*

a. motor oil (nonpolar)
b. ethanol (polar, contains an OH group)
c. lard (nonpolar)
d. potassium chloride (ionic)

30. Pick an appropriate solvent from Table 14.3 to dissolve each substance. State the kind of intermolecular forces that would occur between the solute and solvent in each case.

a. isopropyl alcohol (polar, contains an OH group)
b. sodium chloride (ionic)
c. vegetable oil (nonpolar)
d. sodium nitrate (ionic)

31. Which molecule would you expect to be more soluble in water: $CH_3CH_2CH_2OH$ or $HOCH_2CH_2CH_2OH$?
MISSED THIS? *Read Section 14.2*

32. Which molecule would you expect to be more soluble in water: CCl_4 or CH_2Cl_2?

33. For each compound, would you expect greater solubility in water or in hexane? Indicate the kinds of intermolecular forces that occur between the solute and the solvent in which the molecule is most soluble. **MISSED THIS?** *Read Section 14.2*

a. glucose

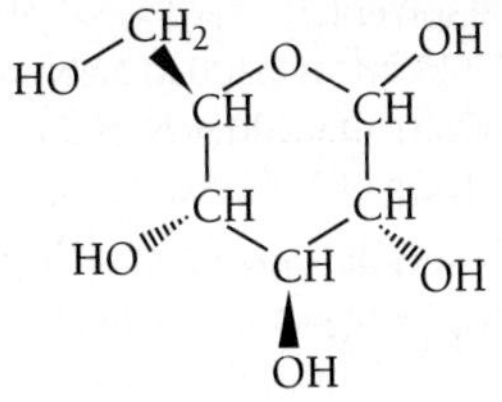

b. naphthalene

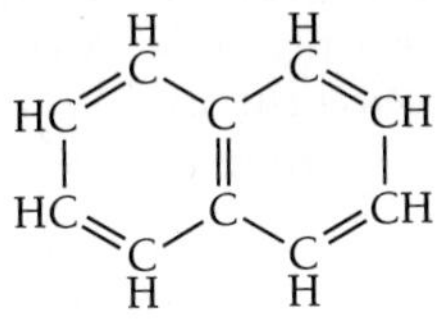

c. dimethyl ether

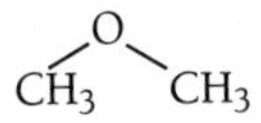

34. For each compound, would you expect greater solubility in water or in hexane? Indicate the kinds of intermolecular forces that would occur between the solute and the solvent in which the molecule is most soluble.

a. toluene

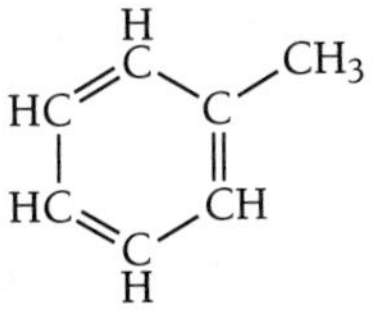

b. sucrose (table sugar)

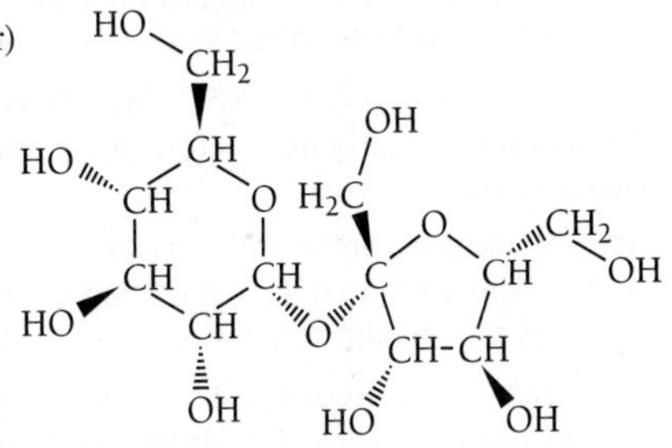

c. isobutene

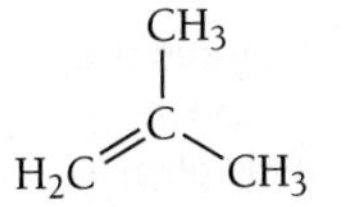

d. ethylene glycol

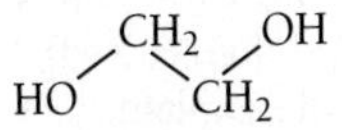

Energetics of Solution Formation

35. When ammonium chloride (NH_4Cl) is dissolved in water, the solution becomes colder. **MISSED THIS?** *Read Section 14.3*

a. Is the dissolution of ammonium chloride endothermic or exothermic?
b. What can you conclude about the relative magnitudes of the lattice energy of ammonium chloride and its heat of hydration?
c. Sketch a qualitative energy diagram similar to Figure 14.7 for the dissolution of NH_4Cl.
d. Why does the solution form? What drives the process?

36. When lithium iodide (LiI) is dissolved in water, the solution becomes hotter.

a. Is the dissolution of lithium iodide endothermic or exothermic?
b. What can you conclude about the relative magnitudes of the lattice energy of lithium iodide and its heat of hydration?
c. Sketch a qualitative energy diagram similar to Figure 14.7 for the dissolution of LiI.
d. Why does the solution form? What drives the process?

37. Silver nitrate has a lattice energy of −820 kJ/mol and a heat of solution of 22.6 kJ/mol. Calculate the heat of hydration for silver nitrate. **MISSED THIS?** *Read Section 14.3*

38. Use the data to calculate the heats of hydration of lithium chloride and sodium chloride. Which of the two cations, lithium or sodium, has stronger ion–dipole interactions with water? Why?

Compound	Lattice Energy (kJ/mol)	ΔH_{soln} (kJ/mol)
LiCl	−834	−37.0
NaCl	−769	+3.88

39. Lithium iodide has a lattice energy of -7.3×10^2 kJ/mol and a heat of hydration of −793 kJ/mol. Find the heat of solution for lithium iodide and determine how much heat is evolved or absorbed when 15.0 g of lithium iodide completely dissolves in water. **MISSED THIS?** *Read Section 14.3*

40. Potassium nitrate has a lattice energy of −163.8 kcal/mol and a heat of hydration of −155.5 kcal/mol. How much potassium nitrate has to dissolve in water to absorb 1.00×10^2 kJ of heat?

Solution Equilibrium and Factors Affecting Solubility

41. A solution contains 25 g of NaCl per 100.0 g of water at 25 °C. Is the solution unsaturated, saturated, or supersaturated? (Use Figure 14.11.) **MISSED THIS?** *Read Section 14.4; Watch KCV 14.4*

42. A solution contains 32 g of KNO_3 per 100.0 g of water at 25 °C. Is the solution unsaturated, saturated, or supersaturated? (Use Figure 14.11.)

43. A KNO_3 solution containing 45 g of KNO_3 per 100.0 g of water is cooled from 40 °C to 0 °C. What happens during cooling? (Use Figure 14.11.) **MISSED THIS?** *Read Section 14.4; Watch KCV 14.4*

44. A KCl solution containing 42 g of KCl per 100.0 g of water is cooled from 60 °C to 0 °C. What happens during cooling? (Use Figure 14.11.)

45. Some laboratory procedures involving oxygen-sensitive reactants or products call for using water that has been boiled (and then cooled). Explain.
MISSED THIS? *Read Section 14.4; Watch KCV 14.4*

46. A person preparing a fish tank fills the tank with water that has been boiled (and then cooled). When the person puts fish into the tank, they die. Explain.

47. Scuba divers breathing air at increased pressure can suffer from nitrogen narcosis—a condition resembling drunkenness—when the partial pressure of nitrogen exceeds about 4 atm. What property of gas/water solutions causes this to happen? How can a diver reverse this effect?
MISSED THIS? *Read Section 14.4; Watch KCV 14.4*

48. Scuba divers breathing air at increased pressure can suffer from oxygen toxicity—too much oxygen in their bloodstream—when the partial pressure of oxygen exceeds about 1.4 atm. What happens to the amount of oxygen in a diver's bloodstream when he or she breathes oxygen at elevated pressures? How can this be reversed?

49. Calculate the mass of nitrogen dissolved at room temperature in an 80.0-L home aquarium. Assume a total pressure of 1.0 atm and a mole fraction for nitrogen of 0.78.
MISSED THIS? *Read Section 14.4; Watch KCV 14.4, IWE 14.2*

50. Use Henry's law to determine the molar solubility of helium at a pressure of 1.0 atm and 25 °C.

Concentrations of Solutions

51. An aqueous NaCl solution is made using 112 g of NaCl diluted to a total solution volume of 1.00 L. Calculate the molarity, molality, and mass percent of the solution. (Assume a density of 1.08 g/mL for the solution.)
MISSED THIS? *Read Section 14.5; Watch KCV 14.5, IWE 14.4*

52. An aqueous KNO_3 solution is made using 72.5 g of KNO_3 diluted to a total solution volume of 2.00 L. Calculate the molarity, molality, and mass percent of the solution. (Assume a density of 1.05 g/mL for the solution.)

53. To what volume should you dilute 50.0 mL of a 5.00 M KI solution so that 25.0 mL of the diluted solution contains 3.05 g of KI?
MISSED THIS? *Read Section 14.5; Watch KCV 14.5*

54. To what volume should you dilute 125 mL of an 8.00 M $CuCl_2$ solution so that 50.0 mL of the diluted solution contains 4.67 g $CuCl_2$?

55. Silver nitrate solutions are often used to plate silver onto other metals. What is the maximum amount of silver (in grams) that can be plated out of 4.8 L of an $AgNO_3$ solution containing 3.4% Ag by mass? Assume that the density of the solution is 1.01 g/mL.
MISSED THIS? *Read Section 14.5; Watch KCV 14.5, IWE 14.3*

56. A dioxin-contaminated water source contains 0.085% dioxin by mass. How much dioxin is present in 2.5 L of this water? Assume a density of 1.00 g/mL.

57. A hard water sample contains 0.0085% Ca by mass (in the form of Ca^{2+} ions). How much water (in grams) contains 1.2 g of Ca? (1.2 g of Ca is the recommended daily allowance of calcium for adults between 19 and 24 years old.)
MISSED THIS? *Read Section 14.5; Watch KCV 14.5, IWE 14.3*

58. Lead is a toxic metal that affects the central nervous system. A Pb-contaminated water sample contains 0.0011% Pb by mass. How much of the water (in mL) contains 150 mg of Pb? (Assume a density of 1.0 g/mL.)

59. You can purchase nitric acid in a concentrated form that is 70.3% HNO_3 by mass and has a density of 1.41 g/mL. Describe exactly how you would prepare 1.15 L of 0.100 M HNO_3 from the concentrated solution.
MISSED THIS? *Read Section 14.5; Watch KCV 14.5, IWE 14.3*

60. You can purchase hydrochloric acid in a concentrated form that is 37.0% HCl by mass and that has a density of 1.20 g/mL. Describe exactly how to prepare 2.85 L of 0.500 M HCl from the concentrated solution.

61. Describe how to prepare each solution from the dry solute and the solvent. **MISSED THIS?** *Read Section 14.5; Watch KCV 14.5*
a. 1.00×10^2 mL of 0.500 M KCl
b. 1.00×10^2 g of 0.500 *m* KCl
c. 1.00×10^2 g of 5.0% KCl solution by mass

62. Describe how to prepare each solution from the dry solute and the solvent.
a. 125 mL of 0.100 M $NaNO_3$
b. 125 g of 0.100 *m* $NaNO_3$
c. 125 g of 1.0% $NaNO_3$ solution by mass

63. A solution is prepared by dissolving 28.4 g of glucose ($C_6H_{12}O_6$) in 355 g of water. The final volume of the solution is 378 mL. For this solution, calculate the concentration in each unit.
MISSED THIS? *Read Section 14.5; Watch KCV 14.5, IWE 14.4*
a. molarity
b. molality
c. percent by mass
d. mole fraction
e. mole percent

64. A solution is prepared by dissolving 20.2 mL of methanol (CH_3OH) in 100.0 mL of water at 25 °C. The final volume of the solution is 118 mL. The densities of methanol and water at this temperature are 0.782 g/mL and 1.00 g/mL, respectively. For this solution, calculate the concentration in each unit.
a. molarity
b. molality
c. percent by mass
d. mole fraction
e. mole percent

65. Household hydrogen peroxide is an aqueous solution containing 3.0% hydrogen peroxide by mass. What is the molarity of this solution? (Assume a density of 1.01 g/mL.)
MISSED THIS? *Read Section 14.5; Watch KCV 14.5, IWE 14.5*

66. One brand of laundry bleach is an aqueous solution containing 4.55% sodium hypochlorite (NaOCl) by mass. What is the molarity of this solution? (Assume a density of 1.02 g/mL.)

67. An aqueous solution contains 36% HCl by mass. Calculate the molality and mole fraction of the solution.
MISSED THIS? *Read Section 14.5; Watch KCV 14.5, IWE 14.5*

68. An aqueous solution contains 5.0% NaCl by mass. Calculate the molality and mole fraction of the solution.

Vapor Pressure of Solutions

69. A beaker contains 100.0 mL of pure water. A second beaker contains 100.0 mL of seawater. The two beakers are left side by side on a lab bench for 1 week. At the end of the week, the liquid level in both beakers has decreased. However, the level has decreased more in one of the beakers than in the other. Which one and why? **MISSED THIS?** *Read Section 14.6; Watch KCV 14.6*

70. Which solution has the highest vapor pressure?
    a. 20.0 g of glucose ($C_6H_{12}O_6$) in 100.0 mL of water
    b. 20.0 g of sucrose ($C_{12}H_{22}O_{11}$) in 100.0 mL of water
    c. 10.0 g of potassium acetate $KC_2H_3O_2$ in 100.0 mL of water

71. Calculate the vapor pressure of a solution containing 24.5 g of glycerin ($C_3H_8O_3$) in 135 mL of water at 30.0 °C. The vapor pressure of pure water at this temperature is 31.8 torr. Assume that glycerin is not volatile and dissolves molecularly (i.e., it is not ionic), and use a density of 1.00 g/mL for the water.
MISSED THIS? *Read Section 14.6; Watch KCV 14.6, IWE 14.6*

72. A solution contains naphthalene ($C_{10}H_8$) dissolved in hexane (C_6H_{14}) at a concentration of 12.35% naphthalene by mass. Calculate the vapor pressure at 25 °C of hexane above the solution. The vapor pressure of pure hexane at 25 °C is 151 torr.

73. A solution contains 50.0 g of heptane (C_7H_{16}) and 50.0 g of octane (C_8H_{18}) at 25 °C. The vapor pressures of pure heptane and pure octane at 25 °C are 45.8 torr and 10.9 torr, respectively. Assuming ideal behavior, answer the following:
MISSED THIS? *Read Section 14.6; Watch KCV 14.6*
    a. What is the vapor pressure of each of the solution components in the mixture?
    b. What is the total pressure above the solution?
    c. What is the composition of the vapor in mass percent?
    d. Why is the composition of the vapor different from the composition of the solution?

74. A solution contains a mixture of pentane and hexane at room temperature. The solution has a vapor pressure of 258 torr. Pure pentane and hexane have vapor pressures of 425 torr and 151 torr, respectively, at room temperature. What is the mole fraction composition of the mixture? (Assume ideal behavior.)

75. A solution contains 4.08 g of chloroform ($CHCl_3$) and 9.29 g of acetone (CH_3COCH_3). The vapor pressures at 35 °C of pure chloroform and pure acetone are 295 torr and 332 torr, respectively. Assuming ideal behavior, calculate the vapor pressures of each of the components and the total vapor pressure above the solution. The experimentally measured total vapor pressure of the solution at 35 °C is 312 torr. Is the solution ideal? If not, what can you say about the relative strength of chloroform–acetone interactions compared to the acetone–acetone and chloroform–chloroform interactions?
MISSED THIS? *Read Section 14.6; Watch KCV 14.6, IWE 14.6*

76. A solution of methanol and water has a mole fraction of water of 0.312 and a total vapor pressure of 211 torr at 39.9 °C. The vapor pressures of pure methanol and pure water at this temperature are 256 torr and 55.3 torr, respectively. Is the solution ideal? If not, what can you say about the relative strengths of the solute–solvent interactions compared to the solute–solute and solvent–solvent interactions?

Freezing Point Depression, Boiling Point Elevation, and Osmosis

77. A glucose solution contains 55.8 g of glucose ($C_6H_{12}O_6$) in 455 g of water. Determine the freezing point and boiling point of the solution.
MISSED THIS? *Read Section 14.6; Watch KCV 14.6, IWE 14.9*

78. An ethylene glycol solution contains 21.2 g of ethylene glycol ($C_2H_6O_2$) in 85.4 mL of water. Determine the freezing point and boiling point of the solution. (Assume a density of 1.00 g/mL for water.)

79. Calculate the freezing point and boiling point of a solution containing 10.0 g of naphthalene ($C_{10}H_8$) in 100.0 mL of benzene. Benzene has a density of 0.877 g/cm^3.
MISSED THIS? *Read Section 14.6; Watch KCV 14.6, IWE 14.9*

80. Calculate the freezing point and boiling point of a solution containing 7.55 g of ethylene glycol ($C_2H_6O_2$) in 85.7 mL of ethanol. Ethanol has a density of 0.789 g/cm^3.

81. An aqueous solution containing 17.5 g of an unknown molecular (nonelectrolyte) compound in 100.0 g of water has a freezing point of −1.8 °C. Calculate the molar mass of the unknown compound. **MISSED THIS?** *Read Section 14.6; Watch KCV 14.6*

82. An aqueous solution containing 35.9 g of an unknown molecular (nonelectrolyte) compound in 150.0 g of water has a freezing point of −1.3 °C. Calculate the molar mass of the unknown compound.

83. Calculate the osmotic pressure of a solution containing 24.6 g of glycerin ($C_3H_8O_3$) in 250.0 mL of solution at 298 K.
MISSED THIS? *Read Section 14.6; Watch KCV 14.6*

84. What mass of sucrose ($C_{12}H_{22}O_{11}$) would you combine with 5.00×10^2 g of water to make a solution with an osmotic pressure of 8.55 atm at 298 K? (Assume a density of 1.0 g/mL for the solution.)

85. A solution containing 27.55 mg of an unknown protein per 25.0 mL solution was found to have an osmotic pressure of 3.22 torr at 25 °C. What is the molar mass of the protein?
MISSED THIS? *Read Section 14.6; Watch KCV 14.6*

86. Calculate the osmotic pressure of a solution containing 18.75 mg of hemoglobin in 15.0 mL of solution at 25 °C. The molar mass of hemoglobin is 6.5×10^4 g/mol.

87. Calculate the freezing point and boiling point of each aqueous solution, assuming complete dissociation of the solute.
MISSED THIS? *Read Section 14.7*
    a. 0.100 m K_2S
    b. 21.5 g of $CuCl_2$ in 4.50×10^2 g water
    c. 5.5% $NaNO_3$ by mass (in water)

88. Calculate the freezing point and boiling point in each solution, assuming complete dissociation of the solute.
    a. 10.5 g $FeCl_3$ in 1.50×10^2 g water
    b. 3.5% KCl by mass (in water)
    c. 0.150 m MgF_2

89. What mass of salt (NaCl) should you add to 1.00 L of water in an ice-cream maker to make a solution that freezes at −10.0 °C? Assume complete dissociation of the NaCl and density of 1.00 g/mL for water. **MISSED THIS?** *Read Section 14.7*

90. Determine the required concentration (in percent by mass) for an aqueous ethylene glycol ($C_2H_6O_2$) solution to have a boiling point of 104.0 °C.

91. Use the van't Hoff factors in Table 14.9 to calculate each colligative property: **MISSED THIS?** *Read Section 14.7*
    a. the melting point of a 0.100 m iron(III) chloride solution
    b. the osmotic pressure of a 0.085 M potassium sulfate solution at 298 K
    c. the boiling point of a 1.22% by mass magnesium chloride solution

92. Using the van't Hoff factors in Table 14.9, calculate the mass of solute required to make each aqueous solution:

a. a sodium chloride solution containing 1.50×10^2 g of water that has a melting point of −1.0 °C

b. 2.50×10^2 mL of a magnesium sulfate solution that has an osmotic pressure of 3.82 atm at 298 K

c. an iron(III) chloride solution containing 2.50×10^2 g of water that has a boiling point of 102 °C

93. A 1.2 *m* aqueous solution of an ionic compound with the formula MX_2 has a boiling point of 101.4 °C. Calculate the van't Hoff factor (*i*) for MX_2 at this concentration.
MISSED THIS? *Read Section 14.7*

94. A 0.95 *m* aqueous solution of an ionic compound with the formula MX has a freezing point of −3.0 °C. Calculate the van't Hoff factor (*i*) for MX at this concentration.

95. A 0.100 M ionic solution has an osmotic pressure of 8.3 atm at 25 °C. Calculate the van't Hoff factor (*i*) for this solution.
MISSED THIS? *Read Section 14.7*

96. A solution contains 8.92 g of KBr in 500.0 mL of solution and has an osmotic pressure of 6.97 atm at 25 °C. Calculate the van't Hoff factor (*i*) for KBr at this concentration.

97. Calculate the vapor pressure at 25 °C of an aqueous solution that is 5.50% NaCl by mass. (Assume complete dissociation of the solute.)
MISSED THIS? *Read Section 14.7; Watch IWE 14.12*

98. An aqueous $CaCl_2$ solution has a vapor pressure of 81.6 mmHg at 50 °C. The vapor pressure of pure water at this temperature is 92.6 mmHg. What is the concentration of $CaCl_2$ in mass percent? (Assume complete dissociation of the solute.)

CUMULATIVE PROBLEMS

99. The solubility of carbon tetrachloride (CCl_4) in water at 25 °C is 1.2 g/L. The solubility of chloroform ($CHCl_3$) at the same temperature is 10.1 g/L. Why is chloroform almost ten times more soluble in water than carbon tetrachloride?

100. The solubility of phenol in water at 25 °C is 87 g/L. The solubility of naphthol at the same temperature is only 0.74 g/L. Examine the structures of phenol and naphthol shown here and explain why phenol is so much more soluble than naphthol.

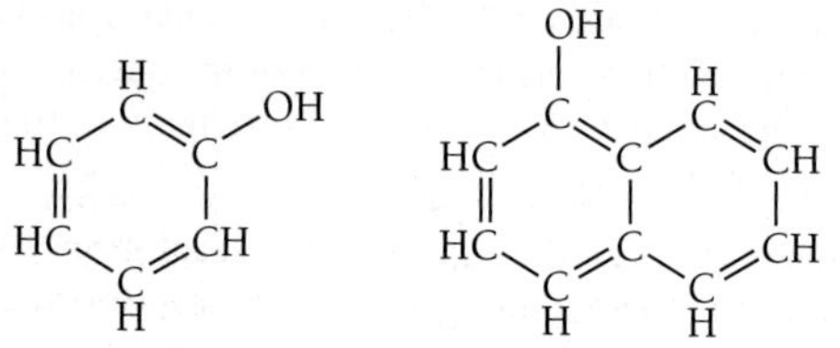

Phenol Naphthol

101. Potassium perchlorate ($KClO_4$) has a lattice energy of −599 kJ/mol and a heat of hydration of −548 kJ/mol. Find the heat of solution for potassium perchlorate and determine the temperature change that occurs when 10.0 g of potassium perchlorate is dissolved with enough water to make 100.0 mL of solution. (Assume a heat capacity of 4.05 J/g · °C for the solution and a density of 1.05 g/mL.)

102. Sodium hydroxide (NaOH) has a lattice energy of −887 kJ/mol and a heat of hydration of −932 kJ/mol. How much solution could be heated to boiling by the heat evolved by the dissolution of 25.0 g of NaOH? (For the solution, assume a heat capacity of 4.0 J/g · °C, an initial temperature of 25.0 °C, a boiling point of 100.0 °C, and a density of 1.05 g/mL.)

103. A saturated solution forms when 0.0537 L of argon, at a pressure of 1.0 atm and a temperature of 25 °C, is dissolved in 1.0 L of water. Calculate the Henry's law constant for argon.

104. A gas has a Henry's law constant of 0.112 M/atm. What total volume of solution is needed to completely dissolve 1.65 L of the gas at a pressure of 725 torr and a temperature of 25 °C?

105. The Safe Drinking Water Act (SDWA) sets a limit for mercury—a toxin to the central nervous system—at 0.0020 ppm by mass. Water suppliers must periodically test their water to ensure that mercury levels do not exceed this limit. Suppose water becomes contaminated with mercury at twice the legal limit (0.0040 ppm). How much of this water would a person have to consume to ingest 50.0 mg of mercury?

106. Water softeners often replace calcium ions in hard water with sodium ions. Since sodium compounds are soluble, the presence of sodium ions in water does not cause the white, scaly residues caused by calcium ions. However, calcium is more beneficial to human health than sodium because calcium is a necessary part of the human diet, while high levels of sodium intake are linked to increases in blood pressure. The U.S. Food and Drug Administration (FDA) recommends that adults ingest less than 2.4 g of sodium per day. How many liters of softened water, containing a sodium concentration of 0.050% sodium by mass, would a person have to consume to exceed the FDA recommendation? (Assume a water density of 1.0 g/mL.)

107. An aqueous solution contains 12.5% NaCl by mass. What mass of water (in grams) is contained in 2.5 L of the vapor above this solution at 55 °C? The vapor pressure of pure water at 55 °C is 118 torr. (Assume complete dissociation of NaCl.)

108. The vapor above an aqueous solution contains 19.5 mg water per liter at 25 °C. Assuming ideal behavior, what is the concentration of the solute within the solution in mole percent?

109. What is the freezing point of an aqueous solution that boils at 106.5 °C?

110. What is the boiling point of an aqueous solution that has a vapor pressure of 20.5 torr at 25 °C? (Assume a nonvolatile solute.)

111. An isotonic solution contains 0.90% NaCl mass to volume. Calculate the percent mass to volume for isotonic solutions containing each solute at 25 °C. Assume a van't Hoff factor of 1.9 for all *ionic* solutes.

a. KCl b. NaBr c. glucose ($C_6H_{12}O_6$)

112. Magnesium citrate, $Mg_3(C_6H_5O_7)_2$, belongs to a class of laxatives called *hyperosmotics*, which cause rapid emptying of the bowel. When a concentrated solution of magnesium citrate is consumed, it passes through the intestines, drawing water and promoting diarrhea, usually within 6 hours. Calculate the osmotic pressure of a magnesium citrate laxative solution containing 28.5 g of magnesium citrate in 235 mL of solution at 37 °C (approximate body temperature). Assume complete dissociation of the ionic compound.

113. A solution is prepared from 4.5701 g of magnesium chloride and 43.238 g of water. The vapor pressure of water above this solution is 0.3624 atm at 348.0 K. The vapor pressure of pure water at this temperature is 0.3804 atm. Find the value of the van't Hoff factor (*i*) for magnesium chloride in this solution.

114. When HNO_2 is dissolved in water, it partially dissociates according to the equation $HNO_2 \rightleftharpoons H^+ + NO_2^-$. A solution is prepared that contains 7.050 g of HNO_2 in 1.000 kg of water. Its freezing point is –0.2929 °C. Calculate the fraction of HNO_2 that has dissociated.

115. A solution of a nonvolatile solute in water has a boiling point of 375.3 K. Calculate the vapor pressure of water above this solution at 338 K. The vapor pressure of pure water at this temperature is 0.2467 atm.

116. The density of a 0.438 M solution of potassium chromate (K_2CrO_4) at 298 K is 1.063 g/mL. Calculate the vapor pressure of water above the solution. The vapor pressure of pure water at this temperature is 0.0313 atm. (Assume complete dissociation of the solute.)

117. The vapor pressure of carbon tetrachloride, CCl_4, is 0.354 atm, and the vapor pressure of chloroform, $CHCl_3$, is 0.526 atm at 316 K. A solution is prepared from equal masses of these two compounds at this temperature. Calculate the mole fraction of the chloroform in the vapor above the solution. If the vapor above the original solution is condensed and isolated into a separate flask, what will the vapor pressure of chloroform be above this new solution?

118. Distillation is a method of purification based on successive separations and recondensations of vapor above a solution. Use the result of the previous problem to calculate the mole fraction of chloroform in the vapor above a solution obtained by three successive separations and condensations of the vapors above the original solution of carbon tetrachloride and chloroform. Show how this result explains the use of distillation as a separation method.

119. A solution of 49.0% H_2SO_4 by mass has a density of 1.39 g/cm^3 at 293 K. A 25.0-cm^3 sample of this solution is mixed with enough water to increase the volume of the solution to 99.8 cm^3. Find the molarity of sulfuric acid in this solution.

120. Find the mass of urea (CH_4N_2O) needed to prepare 50.0 g of a solution in water in which the mole fraction of urea is 0.0770.

121. A solution contains 10.05 g of unknown compound dissolved in 50.0 mL of water. (Assume a density of 1.00 g/mL for water.) The freezing point of the solution is –3.16 °C. The mass percent composition of the compound is 60.97% C, 11.94% H, and the rest is O. What is the molecular formula of the compound?

122. The osmotic pressure of a solution containing 2.10 g of an unknown compound dissolved in 175.0 mL of solution at 25 °C is 1.93 atm. The combustion of 24.02 g of the unknown compound produced 28.16 g CO_2 and 8.64 g H_2O. What is the molecular formula of the compound (which contains only carbon, hydrogen, and oxygen)?

123. A 100.0-mL aqueous sodium chloride solution is 13.5% NaCl by mass and has a density of 1.12 g/mL. What would you add (solute or solvent), and what mass of it, to make the boiling point of the solution 104.4 °C? (Use i = 1.8 for NaCl.)

124. A 50.0-mL solution is initially 1.55% $MgCl_2$ by mass and has a density of 1.05 g/mL. What is the freezing point of the solution after you add an additional 1.35 g $MgCl_2$? (Use i = 2.5 for $MgCl_2$.)

CHALLENGE PROBLEMS

125. The small bubbles that form on the bottom of a water pot that is being heated (before boiling) are due to dissolved air coming out of solution. Use Henry's law and the solubilities given to calculate the total volume of nitrogen and oxygen gas that should bubble out of 1.5 L of water upon warming from 25 °C to 50 °C. Assume that the water is initially saturated with nitrogen and oxygen gas at 25 °C and a total pressure of 1.0 atm. Assume that the gas bubbles out at a temperature of 50 °C. The solubility of oxygen gas at 50 °C is 27.8 mg/L at an oxygen pressure of 1.00 atm. The solubility of nitrogen gas at 50 °C is 14.6 mg/L at a nitrogen pressure of 1.00 atm. Assume that the air above the water contains an oxygen partial pressure of 0.21 atm and a nitrogen partial pressure of 0.78 atm.

126. The vapor above a mixture of pentane and hexane at room temperature contains 35.5% pentane by mass. What is the mass percent composition of the solution? Pure pentane and hexane have vapor pressures of 425 torr and 151 torr, respectively, at room temperature.

127. A 1.10-g sample contains only glucose ($C_6H_{12}O_6$) and sucrose ($C_{12}H_{22}O_{11}$). When the sample is dissolved in water to a total solution volume of 25.0 mL, the osmotic pressure of the solution is 3.78 atm at 298 K. What is the mass percent composition of glucose and sucrose in the sample?

128. A solution is prepared by mixing 631 mL of methanol with 501 mL of water. The molarity of methanol in the resulting solution is 14.29 M. The density of methanol at this temperature is 0.792 g/mL. Calculate the difference in volume between this solution and the total volume of water and methanol that were mixed to prepare the solution.

129. Two alcohols, isopropyl alcohol and propyl alcohol, have the same molecular formula, C_3H_8O. A solution of the two that is two-thirds by mass isopropyl alcohol has a vapor pressure of 0.110 atm at 313 K. A solution that is one-third by mass isopropyl alcohol has a vapor pressure of 0.089 atm at 313 K. Calculate the vapor pressure of each pure alcohol at this temperature. Explain the difference given that the formula of propyl alcohol is $CH_3CH_2CH_2OH$ and that of isopropyl alcohol is $(CH_3)_2CHOH$.

130. A metal, M, of atomic mass 96 amu reacts with fluorine to form a salt that can be represented as MF_x. In order to determine x and therefore the formula of the salt, a boiling point elevation experiment is performed. A 9.18-g sample of the salt is dissolved in 100.0 g of water, and the boiling point of the solution is found to be 374.38 K. Find the formula of the salt. (Assume complete dissociation of the salt in solution.)

131. Sulfuric acid in water dissociates completely into H^+ and HSO_4^- ions. The HSO_4^- ion dissociates to a limited extent into H^+ and SO_4^{2-}. The freezing point of a 0.1000 m solution of sulfuric acid in water is 272.76 K. Calculate the molality of SO_4^{2-} in the solution, assuming ideal solution behavior.

132. A solution of 75.0 g of benzene (C_6H_6) and 75.0 g of toluene (C_7H_8) has a total vapor pressure of 80.9 mmHg at 303 K. Another solution of 100.0 g benzene and 50.0 g toluene has a total vapor pressure of 93.9 mmHg at this temperature. Find the vapor pressure of pure benzene and pure toluene at 303 K.

133. A solution is prepared by dissolving 11.60 g of a mixture of sodium carbonate and sodium bicarbonate in 1.00 L of water. A 300.0 cm^3 sample of the solution is treated with excess HNO_3 and boiled to remove all the dissolved gas. A total of 0.940 L of dry CO_2 is collected at 298 K and 0.972 atm. Find the molarity of the carbonate and bicarbonate in the solution.

CONCEPTUAL PROBLEMS

134. Substance A is a nonpolar liquid and has only dispersion forces among its constituent particles. Substance B is also a nonpolar liquid and has about the same magnitude of dispersion forces among its constituent particles as substance A. When substance A and substance B are combined, they spontaneously mix.

a. Why do the two substances mix?

b. Predict the sign and magnitude of ΔH_{soln}.

c. Determine the signs and relative magnitudes of ΔH_{solute}, $\Delta H_{solvent}$, and ΔH_{mix}.

135. A power plant built on a river uses river water as a coolant. The water is warmed as it is used in heat exchangers within the plant. Should the warm water be immediately cycled back into the river? Why or why not?

137. If each substance listed here costs the same amount per kilogram, which would be most cost-effective as a way to lower the freezing point of water? (Assume complete dissociation for all ionic compounds.) Explain.

a. $HOCH_2CH_2OH$ b. NaCl c. KCl

d. $MgCl_2$ e. $SrCl_2$

138. A helium balloon inflated on one day will fall to the ground by the next day. The volume of the balloon decreases somewhat overnight but not by enough to explain why it no longer floats. (If you inflate a new balloon with helium to the same size as the balloon that fell to the ground, the newly inflated balloon floats.) Explain.

136. The vapor pressure of a 1 M ionic solution is different from the vapor pressure of a 1 M nonelectrolyte solution. In both cases, the solute is nonvolatile. Which set of diagrams best represents the differences between the two solutions and their vapors?

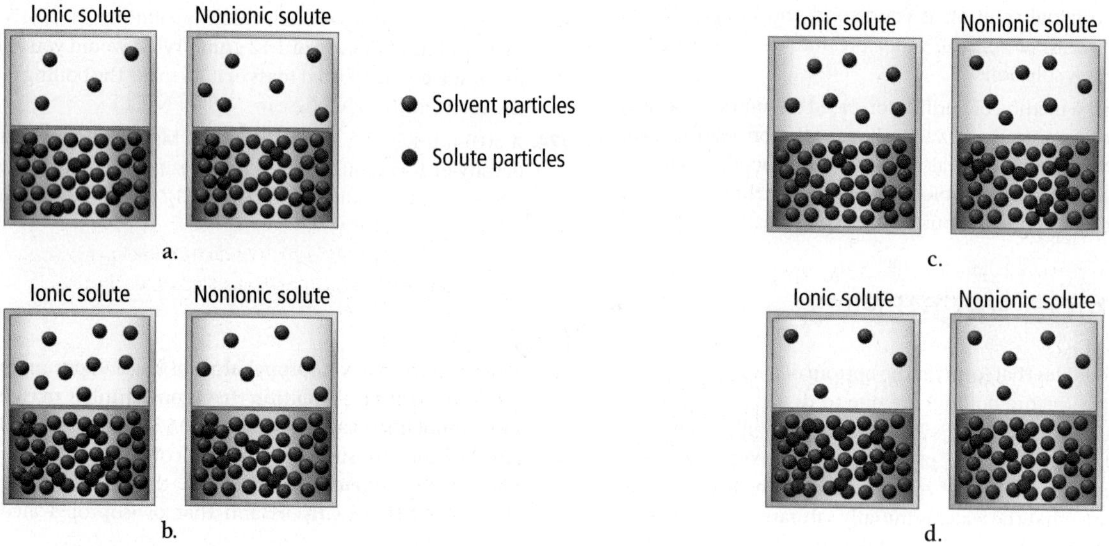

QUESTIONS FOR GROUP WORK

Active Classroom Learning

Discuss these questions with the group and record your consensus answer.

139. Explain why 1-propanol ($CH_3CH_2CH_2OH$) is miscible in both water (H_2O) and hexane (C_6H_6) when hexane and water are barely soluble in each other.

140. Have each group member make a flashcard with one of the following on the front: ΔH_{soln}, $\Delta H_{lattice}$, $\Delta H_{solvent}$, ΔH_{mix}, and $\Delta H_{hydration}$. On the back of the card, each group member should describe (in words) the ΔH process his or her card lists and how that ΔH relates to other ΔH values mathematically. Each member presents his or her ΔH to the group. After everyone has presented, members should trade cards and quiz each other.

141. Complete the following table by adding *increases, decreases,* or *no effect*:

	Increasing Temperature	Increasing Pressure
solubility of gas in water		
solubility of a solid in water		

142. When 13.62 g (about one tablespoon) of table sugar (sucrose, $C_{12}H_{22}O_{11}$) is dissolved in 241.5 mL of water (density 0.997 g/mL), the final volume is 250.0 mL (about one cup). Have each group member calculate one of the following for the solution and present his or her answer to the group:

a. mass percent

b. molarity

c. molality

143. Calculate the expected boiling and freezing point for the solution in the previous problem. If you had to bring this syrup to the boiling point for a recipe, would you expect it to take much more time than it takes to boil the same amount of pure water? Why or why not? Would the syrup freeze in a typical freezer (−18 °C)? Why or why not?

DATA INTERPRETATION AND ANALYSIS

Freezing Point of Salt Water

144. The salinity of seawater can vary in the world's oceans as shown in the map, which indicates salinity in units of percent by mass NaCl. Examine the image and answer the questions that follow.

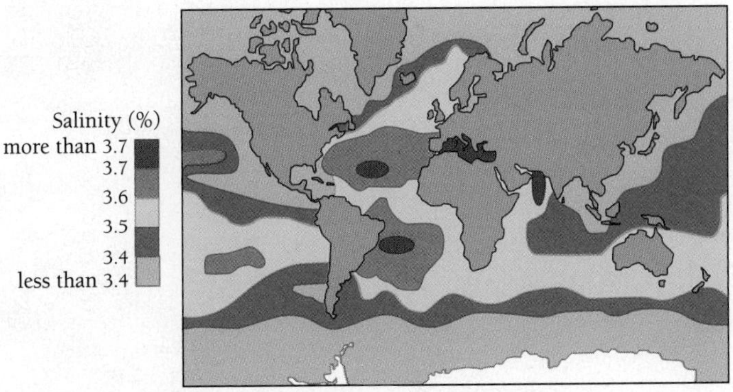

Salinity of Seawater

a. Which regions of the globe generally have higher salinity? Lower salinity? State your answer as a general trend in the salinity of seawater.

b. Speculate on possible reasons for the trend you observed in part a.

c. Calculate the freezing point of a sample of seawater taken from the middle of the Atlantic Ocean. Use a van't Hoff factor of 1.9 for your calculation.

d. Make a graph of the freezing point of the seawater versus salinity for the range of salinities in the world's oceans.

Cc ANSWERS TO CONCEPTUAL CONNECTIONS

Mixing of Ideal Gases

14.1 **(d)** When gases mix, the kinetic energy of each gas is spread out over more space, so entropy increases.

Solution Formation

14.2 **(a)** When solvent–solute interactions in a mixture are comparable in strength to the solvent–solvent interactions and the solute–solute interactions, entropy drives the formation of a homogeneous mixture.

Solubility

14.3 **(c)** The first alcohol on the list is methanol, which is highly polar and forms hydrogen bonds with water. It is miscible in water and has only limited solubility in hexane, which is nonpolar. However, as the carbon chain gets longer in the series of alcohols, the OH group becomes less important relative to the growing nonpolar carbon chain. Therefore, the alcohols become progressively less soluble in water and more soluble in hexane. This table demonstrates the rule of thumb *like dissolves like*. Methanol is like water and therefore dissolves in water. It is unlike hexane and therefore has limited solubility in hexane. As you move down the list, the alcohols become increasingly like hexane and increasingly unlike water and therefore become increasingly soluble in hexane and increasingly insoluble in water.

Energetics of Aqueous Solution Formation

14.4 **(b)** You can conclude that $|\Delta H_{solute}| < |\Delta H_{hydration}|$. Since ΔH_{soln} is negative, the absolute value of the negative term ($\Delta H_{hydration}$) must be greater than the absolute value of the positive term (ΔH_{solute}).

Solubility and Temperature

14.5 **(b)** Some potassium bromide precipitates out of solution. The solubility of most solids decreases with decreasing temperature. However, the solubility of gases increases with decreasing temperature. Therefore, the nitrogen becomes more soluble and will not bubble out of solution.

Henry's Law

14.6 **(a)** Ammonia is the only compound on the list that is polar, so we would expect its solubility in water to be greater than the solubilities of the other gases (which are all nonpolar).

Molality

14.7 **(b)** The solution has a molality of 10.0 *m*. You combined 1.00 mol of solute with 0.100 kg of solvent, so the molality is 1.00 mol/0.100 kg $=$ 10.0 *m*.

Solution Vapor Pressure

14.8 **(b)** The vapor pressure of a solution is the mole fraction of the solvent times the vapor pressure of the pure solvent. Since the mole fraction of the solvent is 0.800, the vapor pressure of the solution is 0.800×100.0 torr, which equals 80.0 torr.

Raoult's Law

14.9 **(a)** The solute–solvent interactions must be stronger than the solute–solute and solvent–solvent interactions. The stronger interactions lower the vapor pressure from the expected ideal value of 150 mmHg.

Boiling Point Elevation

14.10 **(b)** Solution B because K_b for ethanol is greater than K_b for water.

Colligative Properties

14.11 **(c)** The 0.50 M $MgCl_2$ solution has the highest boiling point because it has the highest concentration of particles. We expect 1 mol of $MgCl_2$ to form 3 mol of particles in solution (although it effectively forms slightly fewer).

Nobody, I suppose, could devote many years to the study of chemical kinetics without being deeply conscious of the fascination of time and change: this is something that goes outside science into poetry. . . .

—SIR CYRIL N. HINSHELWOOD (1897–1967)

CHAPTER

15 Chemical Kinetics

In this chapter-opening quotation, Oxford chemistry professor Sir Cyril Hinshelwood calls attention to an aspect of chemistry often overlooked by the casual observer—the mystery of change with time. Since the opening chapter of this book, you have learned that the goal of chemistry is to understand the macroscopic world by examining the molecular one. In this chapter, we focus on understanding how this molecular world changes with time, an area of study called chemical kinetics. The molecular world is anything but static. Thermal energy produces constant molecular motion, causing molecules to repeatedly collide with one another. In a tiny fraction of these collisions, something extraordinary happens—the electrons on one molecule or atom are attracted to the nuclei of another. Some bonds weaken and new bonds form—a chemical reaction occurs. Chemical kinetics is the study of how these kinds of changes occur in time.

Pouring ice water on a lizard slows it down, making it easier to catch.

15.1 Catching Lizards 631

15.2 The Rate of a Chemical Reaction 632

15.3 The Rate Law: The Effect of Concentration on Reaction Rate 637

15.4 The Integrated Rate Law: The Dependence of Concentration on Time 642

15.5 The Effect of Temperature on Reaction Rate 650

15.6 Reaction Mechanisms 656

15.7 Catalysis 661

LEARNING OUTCOMES 670

15.1 Catching Lizards

The children who live in my neighborhood (including my own kids) have a unique way of catching lizards. Armed with cups of ice water, they chase one of these cold-blooded reptiles into a corner, and take aim and pour the cold water directly onto the lizard's body. The lizard's body temperature drops, and it becomes virtually immobilized—easy prey for little hands. The kids scoop up the lizard and place it in a tub filled with sand and leaves. They then watch as the lizard warms back up and becomes active again. They usually release the lizard back into the yard within hours. I guess you could call them catch-and-release lizard hunters.

Unlike mammals, which actively regulate their body temperature through metabolic activity, lizards are *ectotherms*—their body temperature depends on their surroundings. When splashed with cold water, a lizard's body simply gets colder. The drop in body temperature immobilizes the lizard because its movement depends on chemical reactions that occur within its muscles, and the *rates* of those reactions—how fast they occur—are highly sensitive to temperature. In other words, when the temperature drops, the reactions that produce movement in the lizard occur more slowly; therefore, the movement itself slows down. When reptiles get cold, they become lethargic, unable to move very quickly. For this reason, reptiles try to maintain their body temperature within a narrow range by moving between sun and shade.

The rates of chemical reactions, and especially the ability to *control* those rates, are important not just in reptile movement but in many other phenomena as well. For example, a successful rocket launch depends on the rate at which fuel burns—too quickly and the rocket can explode, too slowly and it will not leave the ground. Chemists must always consider reaction rates when synthesizing compounds. No matter how stable a compound might be, its synthesis is impossible if the rate at which it forms is too slow. As we have seen with reptiles, reaction rates are important to life. In fact, the human body's ability to switch a specific reaction on or off at a specific time is achieved partly by controlling the rate of that reaction through the use of enzymes (biological molecules that we explore more fully in Section 15.7).

The first person to measure the rate of a chemical reaction carefully was Ludwig Wilhelmy (1812–1864). In 1850, he measured how fast sucrose, upon treatment with acid, hydrolyzed (broke up with the addition of water) into glucose and fructose. This reaction occurred over several hours, and Wilhelmy was able to show how the rate depended on the initial amount of sugar present—the greater the initial amount, the faster the initial rate. Today we can measure the rates of reactions that occur in times as short as several femtoseconds (femto $= 10^{-15}$). The knowledge of reaction rates is not only practically important—giving us the ability to control how fast a reaction occurs—but also theoretically important. As we will discuss in Section 15.6, the rate of a reaction can tell us much about how the reaction occurs on the molecular scale.

WATCH **NOW!**

KEY CONCEPT VIDEO 15.2

The Rate of a Chemical Reaction

15.2 The Rate of a Chemical Reaction

The rate of a chemical reaction is a measure of how fast the reaction occurs, as shown in Figure 15.1▶. If a chemical reaction has a fast rate, a large fraction of molecules react to form products in a given period of time. If a chemical reaction has a slow rate, only a relatively small fraction of molecules reacts to form products in a given period of time.

Definition of Reaction Rate

When we measure how fast something occurs, or more specifically the *rate* at which it occurs, we usually express the measurement as a change in some quantity per unit of time. For example, we measure the speed of a car—the rate at which it travels—in *miles per hour*, and we measure how quickly (or slowly) people lose weight in *pounds per week*. We report these rates in units that represent the change in what we are measuring (distance or weight) divided by the change in time:

$$\text{Speed} = \frac{\text{change in distance}}{\text{change in time}} = \frac{\Delta x}{\Delta t} \qquad \text{Weight loss} = \frac{\text{change in weight}}{\text{change in time}} = \frac{\Delta\ \text{weight}}{\Delta t}$$

Similarly, the rate of a chemical reaction is measured as a change in the amounts of reactants or products (usually in concentration units) divided by the change in time. For example, consider the gas-phase reaction between $H_2(g)$ and $I_2(g)$:

$$H_2(g) + I_2(g) \longrightarrow 2\,HI(g)$$

We can define the rate of this reaction in the time interval t_1 to t_2 as follows:

Recall that [A] means the concentration of A in M (mol/L).

$$\text{Rate} = -\frac{\Delta[H_2]}{\Delta t} = -\frac{[H_2]_{t_2} - [H_2]_{t_1}}{t_2 - t_1} \qquad [15.1]$$

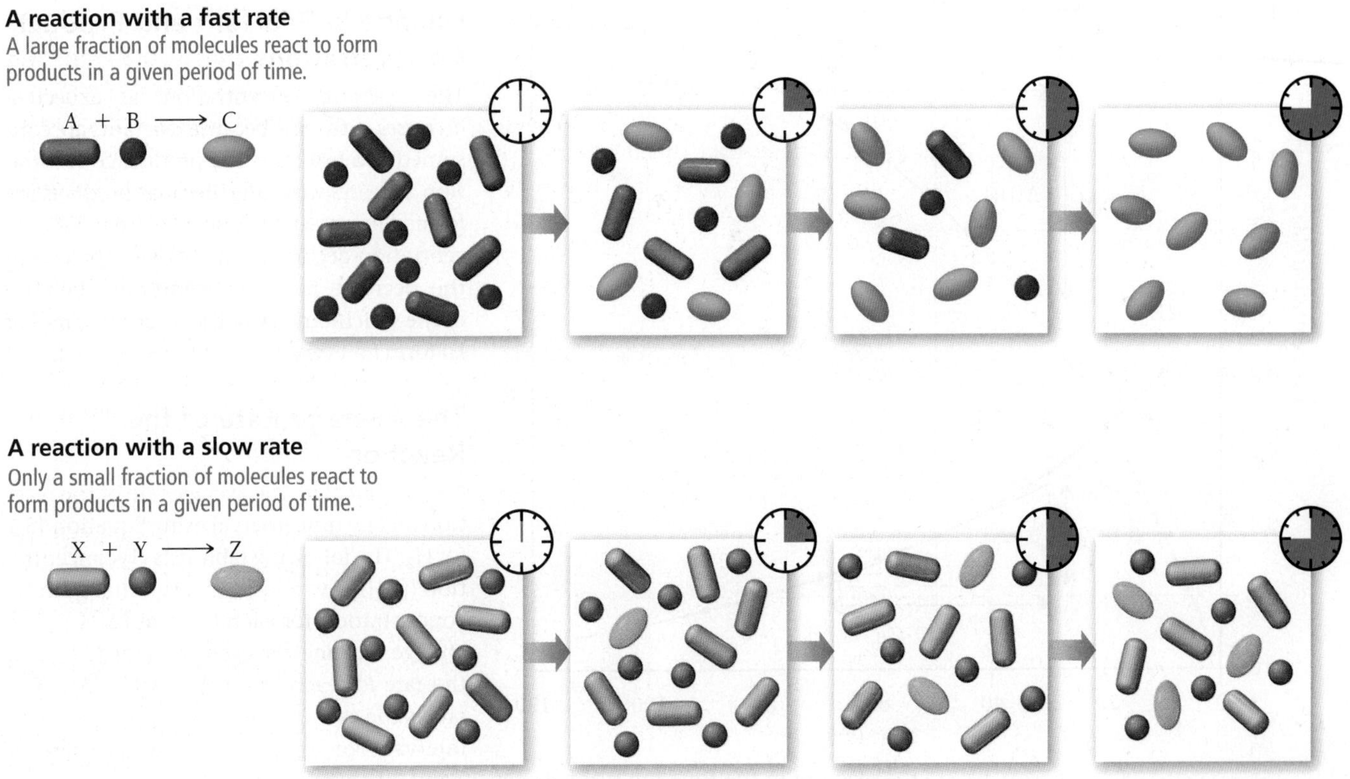

▲ **FIGURE 15.1 The Rate of a Chemical Reaction**

In this expression, $[H_2]_{t_2}$ is the hydrogen concentration at time t_2 and $[H_2]_{t_1}$ is the hydrogen concentration at time t_1. The reaction rate is defined as *the negative* of the change in concentration of a reactant divided by the change in time. The negative sign is part of the definition when we define the reaction rate with respect to a reactant because reactant concentrations decrease as a reaction proceeds; therefore, *the change in the concentration of a reactant is negative*. The negative sign thus makes the overall *rate* positive. (By convention, we report reaction rates as positive quantities.)

Similarly, we can define the reaction rate with respect to the other reactant:

$$\text{Rate} = -\frac{\Delta[I_2]}{\Delta t} \qquad [15.2]$$

Since 1 mol of H_2 reacts with 1 mol of I_2, we define the rate in the same way. We can also define the rate with respect to the *product* of the reaction:

$$\text{Rate} = +\frac{1}{2}\frac{\Delta[HI]}{\Delta t} \qquad [15.3]$$

Because product concentrations *increase* as the reaction proceeds, the change in concentration of a product is positive. Therefore, when we define the rate with respect to a product, we do not include a negative sign in the definition—the rate is naturally positive. The factor of $\frac{1}{2}$ in this definition is related to the stoichiometry of the reaction. In order to have a single rate for the entire reaction, the definition of the rate with respect to each reactant and product must reflect the stoichiometric coefficients of the reaction. For this particular reaction, 2 mol of HI is produced from 1 mol of H_2 and 1 mol of I_2:

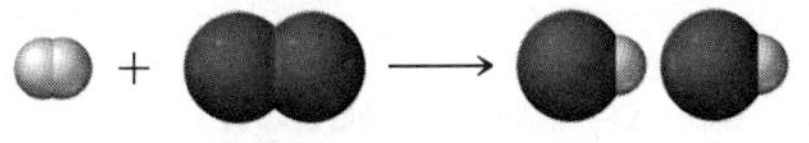

The concentration of HI increases at twice the rate that the concentration of H_2 or I_2 decreases. In other words, if 100 I_2 molecules react per second, then 200 HI molecules form per second. In order for the overall rate to have the same value when defined with respect to any of the reactants or products, we must multiply the change in HI concentration by a factor of one-half.

Consider the graph in Figure 15.2▶, which represents the changes in concentration for H_2 (one of the reactants) and HI (the product) versus time. Let's examine several features of this graph individually.

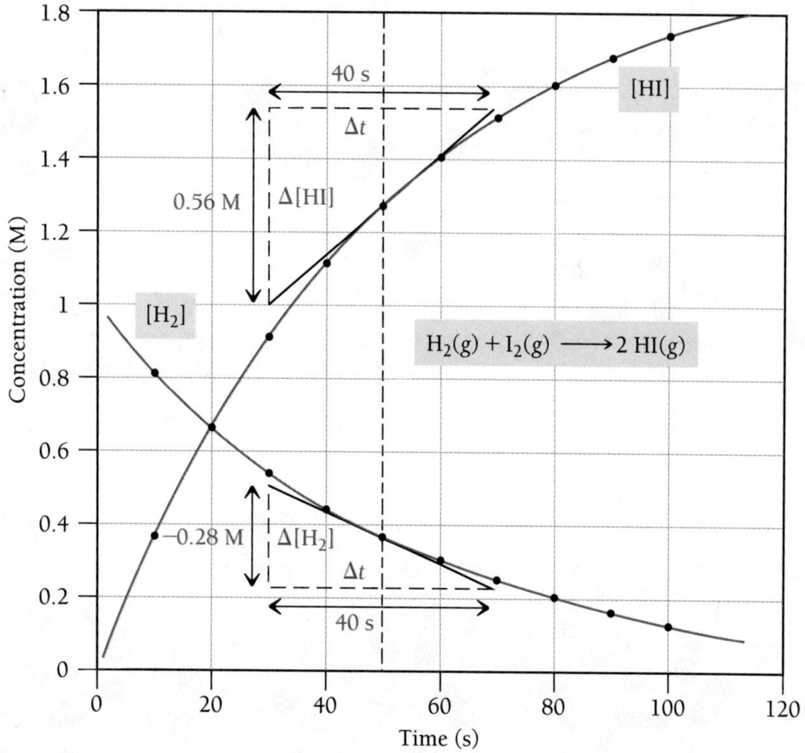

▲ **FIGURE 15.2 Reactant and Product Concentrations as a Function of Time** The graph shows the concentration of one of the reactants (H_2) and the product (HI) as a function of time. The other reactant (I_2) is omitted for clarity.

Change in Reactant and Product Concentrations

The reactant concentration, as expected, *decreases* with time because reactants are consumed in a reaction. The product concentration *increases* with time because products are formed in a reaction. The increase in HI concentration occurs at exactly twice the rate of the decrease in H_2 concentration because of the stoichiometry of the reaction: 2 mol of HI form for every 1 mol of H_2 consumed.

The Average Rate of the Reaction

We can calculate the average rate of the reaction for any time interval using Equation 15.1 for H_2. The following table lists H_2 concentration ($[H_2]$) at various times, the change in H_2 concentration for each interval ($\Delta[H_2]$), the change in time for each interval (Δt), and the rate for each interval ($-\Delta[H_2]/\Delta t$). The rate is the average rate within the given time interval. For example, the average rate of the reaction in the time interval between 10 and 20 seconds is 0.0149 M/s, whereas the average rate in the time interval between 20 and 30 seconds is 0.0121 M/s.

Time (s)	$[H_2]$ (M)	$\Delta[H_2]$ (M)	Δt (s)	Rate $= -\Delta[H_2]/\Delta t$ (M/s)
0.000	1.000			
		−0.181	10.000	0.0181
10.000	0.819			
		−0.149	10.000	0.0149
20.000	0.670			
		−0.121	10.000	0.0121
30.000	0.549			
		−0.100	10.000	0.0100
40.000	0.449			
		−0.081	10.000	0.0081
50.000	0.368			
		−0.067	10.000	0.0067
60.000	0.301			
		−0.054	10.000	0.0054
70.000	0.247			
		−0.045	10.000	0.0045
80.000	0.202			
		−0.037	10.000	0.0037
90.000	0.165			
		−0.030	10.000	0.0030
100.000	0.135			

Notice that the average rate *decreases* as the reaction progresses. In other words, the reaction slows down as it proceeds. We discuss this further in the next section, where we will see that, for most reactions, the rate depends on the concentrations of the reactants. As the reactants transform to products, their concentrations decrease, and the reaction slows down.

The Instantaneous Rate of the Reaction

The instantaneous rate of the reaction is the rate at any one point in time and is represented by the instantaneous slope of the curve at that point. We can determine the instantaneous rate by calculating the slope of the tangent to the curve at the point of interest. In Figure 15.2, we have drawn the tangent lines for both $[H_2]$ and [HI] at 50 seconds. We calculate the instantaneous rate at 50 seconds as follows:

Using $[H_2]$

$$\text{Instantaneous rate (at 50 s)} = -\frac{\Delta[H_2]}{\Delta t} = -\frac{-0.28\text{ M}}{40\text{ s}} = 0.0070\text{ M/s}$$

Using [HI]

$$\text{Instantaneous rate (at 50 s)} = +\frac{1}{2}\frac{\Delta[\text{HI}]}{\Delta t} = +\frac{1}{2}\frac{0.56\ \text{M}}{40\ \text{s}} = 0.0070\ \text{M/s}$$

As we would expect, the rate is the same whether we use one of the reactants or the product for the calculation. Notice that the instantaneous rate at 50 seconds (0.0070 M/s) is between the average rates calculated for the 10-second intervals just before and just after 50 seconds.

We can generalize our definition of reaction rate for the generic reaction:

$$a\text{A} + b\text{B} \longrightarrow c\text{C} + d\text{D} \qquad [15.4]$$

where A and B are reactants, C and D are products, and a, b, c, and d are the stoichiometric coefficients. We define the rate of the reaction as follows:

$$\text{Rate} = -\frac{1}{a}\frac{\Delta[\text{A}]}{\Delta t} = -\frac{1}{b}\frac{\Delta[\text{B}]}{\Delta t} = +\frac{1}{c}\frac{\Delta[\text{C}]}{\Delta t} = +\frac{1}{d}\frac{\Delta[\text{D}]}{\Delta t} \qquad [15.5]$$

From the definition, we can see that knowing the rate of change in the concentration of any one reactant or product at a point in time allows us to determine the rate of change in the concentration of any other reactant or product at that point in time (from the balanced equation). *However, predicting the rate at some future time is not possible from just the balanced equation.*

WATCH **NOW!**

INTERACTIVE WORKED EXAMPLE 15.1

EXAMPLE 15.1 Expressing Reaction Rates

Consider this balanced chemical equation:

$$H_2O_2(aq) + 3\,I^-(aq) + 2\,H^+(aq) \longrightarrow I_3^-(aq) + 2\,H_2O(l)$$

In the first 10.0 seconds of the reaction, the concentration of I^- drops from 1.000 M to 0.868 M.

(a) Calculate the average rate of this reaction in this time interval.

(b) Determine the rate of change in the concentration of H^+ (that is, $\Delta[H^+]/\Delta t$) during this time interval.

SOLUTION

(a) Use Equation 15.5 to calculate the average rate of the reaction.

$$\text{Rate} = -\frac{1}{3}\frac{\Delta[I^-]}{\Delta t} = -\frac{1}{3}\frac{(0.868\ \text{M} - 1.000\ \text{M})}{10.0\ \text{s}} = 4.40 \times 10^{-3}\ \text{M/s}$$

(b) Use Equation 15.5 again for the relationship between the rate of the reaction and $\Delta[H^+]/\Delta t$. After solving for $\Delta[H^+]/\Delta t$, substitute the calculated rate from part (a) and calculate $\Delta[H^+]/\Delta t$.

$$\text{Rate} = -\frac{1}{2}\frac{\Delta[H^+]}{\Delta t}$$

$$\frac{\Delta[H^+]}{\Delta t} = -2(\text{rate}) = -2(4.40 \times 10^{-3}\ \text{M/s}) = -8.80 \times 10^{-3}\ \text{M/s}$$

FOR PRACTICE 15.1 For the reaction shown in Example 15.1, predict the rate of change in concentration of H_2O_2 ($\Delta[H_2O_2]/\Delta t$) and I_3^- ($\Delta[I_3^-]/\Delta t$) during this time interval.

REACTION RATES For the reaction $\text{A} + 2\text{B} \longrightarrow \text{C}$ under a given set of conditions, the initial rate is 0.100 M/s. What is $\Delta[\text{B}]/\Delta t$ under the same conditions?

(a) −0.0500 M/s **(b)** −0.100 M/s **(c)** −0.200 M/s **(d)** +0.200 M/s

15.1 Cc Conceptual Connection

ANSWER **NOW!**

Measuring Reaction Rates

In order to study the kinetics of a reaction, we must have an experimental way to measure the concentration of at least one of the reactants or products as a function of time. For example, Ludwig Wilhelmy, whose experiment on the rate of the conversion of sucrose to glucose and fructose we discussed briefly in Section 15.1, took advantage of sucrose's ability to rotate polarized light. (Polarized light is light with an electric field oriented along one plane.) When a beam of polarized light is passed through a sucrose solution, the polarization of the light is rotated clockwise. In contrast, the products of the reaction (glucose and fructose) rotate polarized light counterclockwise. By measuring the degree of polarization of light passing through a reacting solution—a technique known as polarimetry—Wilhelmy was able to determine the relative concentrations of the reactants and products as a function of time.

Perhaps the most common way to study the kinetics of a reaction is through spectroscopy (see Section 8.3). For example, the reaction of H_2 and I_2 to form HI can be followed spectroscopically because I_2 is violet and H_2 and HI are colorless. As I_2 reacts with H_2 to form HI, the violet color of the reaction mixture fades. We can monitor the fading color with a spectrometer, a device that passes light through a sample and measures how strongly the light is absorbed (Figure 15.3▼). If the sample contains the reacting mixture, the intensity of the light absorption will decrease as the reaction proceeds, providing a direct measure of the concentration of I_2 as a function of time. Because light travels so fast and because experimental techniques can produce very short pulses of light, spectroscopy can be used to measure reactions that happen on time scales as short as several femtoseconds.

▼ FIGURE 15.3 The Spectrometer In a spectrometer, light of a specific wavelength is passed through the sample, and the intensity of the transmitted light—which depends on how much light is absorbed by the sample—is measured and recorded.

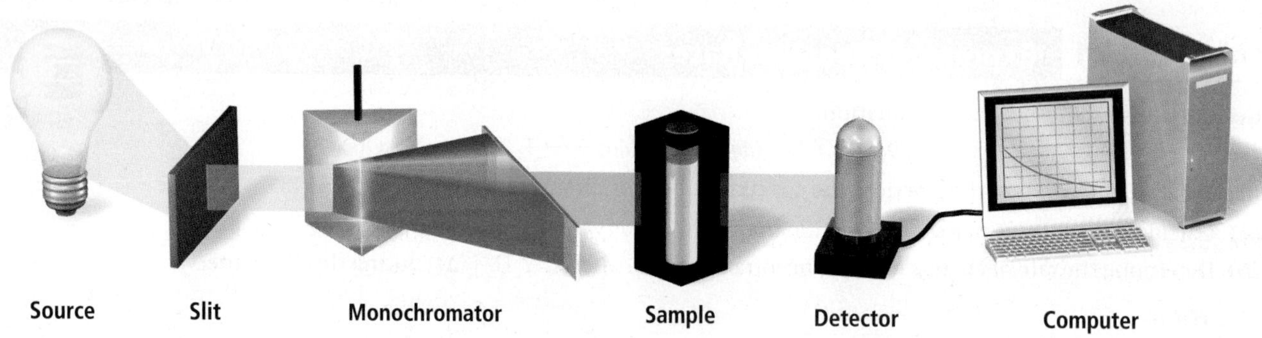

By measuring changes in pressure, we can also monitor reactions in which the number of moles of gaseous reactants and products changes as the reaction proceeds. Consider the reaction in which dinitrogen monoxide reacts to form nitrogen and oxygen gas:

$$2\,N_2O(g) \longrightarrow 2\,N_2(g) + O_2(g)$$

For every 2 mol of N_2O that reacts, the reaction vessel contains one additional mole of gas. As the reaction proceeds and the amount of gas increases, the pressure steadily rises. We can use the rise in pressure to determine the relative concentrations of reactants and products as a function of time.

We can use all of the three techniques mentioned here—polarimetry, spectroscopy, and pressure measurement—to monitor a reaction as it occurs in a reaction vessel. Some reactions occur slowly enough that samples, or *aliquots*, can be periodically withdrawn from the reaction vessel and analyzed to determine the progress of the reaction. We can use instrumental techniques such as gas chromatography (Figure 15.4◀) or mass spectrometry, as well as wet chemical techniques such as titration, to measure the relative amounts of reactants or products in the aliquot. By taking aliquots at regular time intervals, we can determine the relative amounts of reactants and products as a function of time.

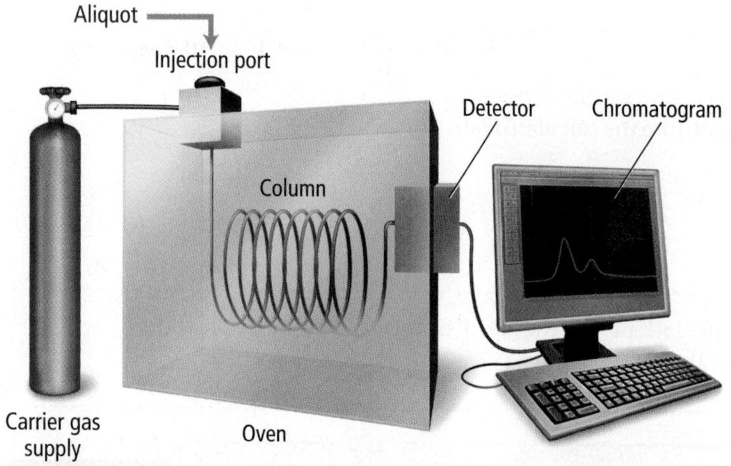

▲ FIGURE 15.4 The Gas Chromatograph In a gas chromatograph (GC), a sample of the reaction mixture, or aliquot, is injected into a specially constructed column. Because of their characteristic physical and chemical properties, different components of the mixture pass through the column at different rates and thus exit at different times. As each component leaves the column, it is detected electronically and a chromatogram is recorded. The area under each peak in the chromatogram is proportional to the amount of one particular component in the sample mixture.

15.3 The Rate Law: The Effect of Concentration on Reaction Rate

WATCH **NOW!**

KEY CONCEPT VIDEO 15.3
The Rate Law for a Chemical Reaction

The rate of a reaction often depends on the concentration of one or more of the reactants. As we have already seen, Ludwig Wilhelmy noticed this effect for the hydrolysis of sucrose. For simplicity, let's consider a reaction in which a single reactant, A, decomposes into products:

$$A \longrightarrow \text{products}$$

As long as the rate of the reverse reaction (in which the products return to reactants) is negligibly slow, we can express the relationship between the rate of the reaction and the concentration of the reactant—called the **rate law**—as follows:

$$\text{Rate} = k[A]^n \qquad [15.6]$$

where k is a constant of proportionality called the **rate constant** and n is the **reaction order**. The value of n (usually an integer) determines how the rate depends on the concentration of the reactant:

- If $n = 0$, the reaction is *zero order* and the rate is independent of the concentration of A.
- If $n = 1$, the reaction is *first order* and the rate is directly proportional to the concentration of A.
- If $n = 2$, the reaction is *second order* and the rate is proportional to the square of the concentration of A.

By definition, $[A]^0 = 1$, so the rate is equal to k regardless of [A].

Although other orders are possible, including noninteger (or fractional) orders, these three are the most common.

The Three Common Reaction Orders ($n = 0$, 1, and 2)

Figure 15.5▼ shows three plots illustrating how the *concentration of A changes with time* for the three common reaction orders with identical numerical values for the rate constant (k) and identical initial concentrations. Figure 15.6▼ has three plots showing the *rate of the reaction* (the slope of the lines in Figure 15.5) *as a function of the reactant concentration* for each reaction order.

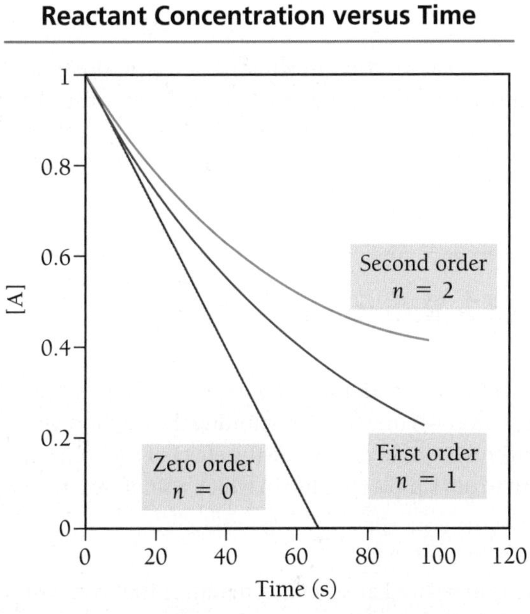

▲ **FIGURE 15.5 Reactant Concentration as a Function of Time for Different Reaction Orders**

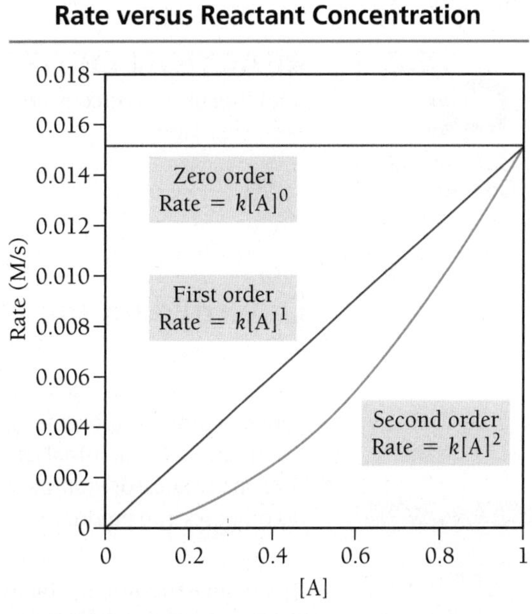

▲ **FIGURE 15.6 Reaction Rate as a Function of Reactant Concentration for Different Reaction Orders**

Sublimation Is Zero Order

When one layer of particles sublimes, the next layer is exposed. The number of particles available to sublime remains constant.

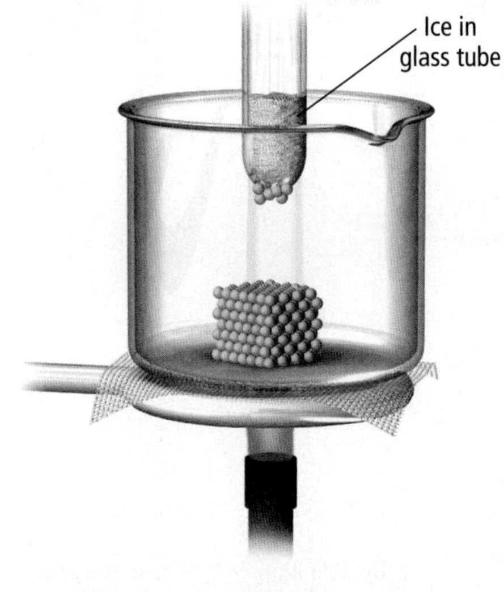

▲ **FIGURE 15.7 Sublimation** When a layer of particles sublimes, another identical layer is just below it. Consequently, the number of particles available to sublime at any one time does not change with the total number of particles in the sample, and the process is zero order.

Zero-Order Reaction

In a zero-order reaction, the rate of the reaction is independent of the concentration of the reactant:

$$\text{Rate} = k[\text{A}]^0 = k \qquad [15.7]$$

Consequently, for a zero-order reaction, the concentration of the reactant decreases linearly with time, as shown in Figure 15.5. The slope of the line is constant, indicating a constant rate. The rate is constant because the reaction does not slow down as the concentration of A decreases. The graph in Figure 15.6 shows that the rate of a zero-order reaction is the same at any concentration of A.

Zero-order reactions occur under conditions where the amount of reactant actually *available for reaction* is unaffected by changes in the *overall quantity of reactant.* For example, sublimation is normally zero order because only molecules at the surface of a substance can sublime, and the concentration of the surface molecules does not change as the amount of subliming substance decreases (Figure 15.7◀).

First-Order Reaction

In a first-order reaction, the rate of the reaction is directly proportional to the concentration of the reactant:

$$\text{Rate} = k[\text{A}]^1 \qquad [15.8]$$

For a first-order reaction, the rate slows down as the reaction proceeds because the concentration of the reactant decreases. We can see this in Figure 15.5—the slope of the curve (the rate) becomes less steep (slower) with time. Figure 15.6 shows the rate as a function of the concentration of A. Notice the linear relationship—the rate is directly proportional to the concentration.

Second-Order Reaction

In a second-order reaction, the rate of the reaction is proportional to the square of the concentration of the reactant:

$$\text{Rate} = k[\text{A}]^2 \qquad [15.9]$$

Consequently, for a second-order reaction, the rate is even more sensitive to the reactant concentration. We can see this in Figure 15.5—the slope of the curve (the rate) flattens out more quickly than it does for a first-order reaction. Figure 15.6 shows the rate as a function of the concentration of A. Notice the quadratic relationship—the rate is proportional to the square of the concentration.

ANSWER **NOW!**

15.2 Cc Conceptual Connection

REACTION ORDER For a particular reaction in which A ⟶ products, a doubling of the concentration of A causes the reaction rate to double. What is the order of the reaction?

(a) 0 **(b)** 1 **(c)** 2

Determining the Order of a Reaction

The order of a reaction can be determined only by experiment. A common way to determine reaction order is the *method of initial rates*. In this method, the initial rate—the rate for a short period of time at the beginning of the reaction—is measured by running the reaction several times with different initial reactant concentrations to determine the effect of the concentration on the rate. For example, let's return to our simple reaction in which a single reactant, A, decomposes into products:

$$\text{A} \longrightarrow \text{products}$$

In an experiment, the initial rate is measured at several different initial concentrations with the results shown in the table in the margin.

[A] (M)	Initial Rate (M/s)
0.10	0.015
0.20	0.030
0.40	0.060

In this data set, when the concentration of A doubles, the rate doubles—the initial rate is directly proportional to the initial concentration. The reaction is therefore first order in A, and the rate law takes the first-order form:

$$\text{Rate} = k[\text{A}]^1$$

We can determine the value of the rate constant, k, by solving the rate law for k and substituting the concentration and the initial rate from any one of the three measurements. Here we use the first measurement:

$$\text{Rate} = k[\text{A}]^1$$

$$k = \frac{\text{rate}}{[\text{A}]} = \frac{0.015\ \cancel{\text{M}}/\text{s}}{0.10\ \cancel{\text{M}}} = 0.15\ \text{s}^{-1}$$

Notice that the rate constant for a first-order reaction has units of s^{-1}.

The following two data sets show how measured initial rates are different for zero-order and for second-order reactions having the same initial rate at [A] = 0.10 M:

Zero Order ($n = 0$)

[A] (M)	Initial Rate (M/s)
0.10	0.015
0.20	0.015
0.40	0.015

Second Order ($n = 2$)

[A] (M)	Initial Rate (M/s)
0.10	0.015
0.20	0.060
0.40	0.240

For a zero-order reaction, the initial rate is independent of the reactant concentration—the rate is the same at all measured initial concentrations. For a second-order reaction, the initial rate quadruples for a doubling of the reactant concentration—the relationship between concentration and rate is quadratic. If we are unsure about how the initial rate is changing with the initial reactant concentration, or if the numbers are not as obvious as they are in these examples, we can substitute any two initial concentrations and the corresponding initial rates into a ratio of the rate laws to determine the order (n):

$$\frac{\text{rate 2}}{\text{rate 1}} = \frac{k[\text{A}]_2^n}{k[\text{A}]_1^n}$$

For example, we can substitute the last two measurements in the data set just given for the second-order reaction as follows:

$$\frac{0.240\ \cancel{\text{M/s}}}{0.060\ \cancel{\text{M/s}}} = \frac{\cancel{k}(0.40\ \cancel{\text{M}})^n}{\cancel{k}(0.20\ \cancel{\text{M}})^n}$$

$$4.0 = \left(\frac{0.40}{0.20}\right)^n = 2^n$$

$$\log 4.0 = \log(2^n)$$

$$= n \log 2$$

$$n = \frac{\log 4}{\log 2}$$

$$= 2$$

Remember that $\frac{x^n}{y^n} = \left(\frac{x}{y}\right)^n$.

Remember that $\log x^n = n \log x$.

The rate constants for zero- and second-order reactions have different units than for first-order reactions. The rate constant for a zero-order reaction has units of $\text{M} \cdot \text{s}^{-1}$, and the rate constant for a second-order reaction has units of $\text{M}^{-1} \cdot \text{s}^{-1}$.

The general expression for the units of the rate constant for an nth-order reaction is $\text{M}^{(1-n)}\ \text{s}^{-1}$.

RATE AND CONCENTRATION I The reaction A ⟶ B has been experimentally determined to be second order. The initial rate is 0.0100 M/s at an initial concentration of A of 0.100 M. What is the initial rate at [A] = 0.500 M?

(a) 0.00200 M/s **(b)** 0.0100 M/s **(c)** 0.0500 M/s **(d)** 0.250 M/s

15.3 Cc Conceptual Connection

ANSWER **NOW!**

Reaction Order for Multiple Reactants

So far, we have considered a simple reaction with only one reactant. How do we define the rate law for reactions with more than one reactant? Consider the generic reaction:

$$aA + bB \longrightarrow cC + dD$$

As long as the reverse reaction is negligibly slow, the rate law is proportional to the concentration of [A] raised to the m power multiplied by the concentration of [B] raised to the n power:

$$\text{Rate} = k[A]^m[B]^n \qquad [15.10]$$

where m is the reaction order with respect to A and n is the reaction order with respect to B. The **overall order** is the sum of the exponents $(m + n)$. For example, the reaction between hydrogen and iodine has been experimentally determined to be first order with respect to hydrogen, first order with respect to iodine, and thus second order overall:

$$H_2(g) + I_2(g) \longrightarrow 2\,HI(g) \quad \text{Rate} = k[H_2]^1[I_2]^1$$

Similarly, the reaction between hydrogen and nitrogen monoxide has been experimentally determined to be first order with respect to hydrogen, second order with respect to nitrogen monoxide, and thus third order overall:

$$2\,H_2(g) + 2\,NO(g) \longrightarrow N_2(g) + 2\,H_2O(g) \quad \text{Rate} = k[H_2]^1[NO]^2$$

The rate law for any reaction must always be determined by experiment, often by the method of initial rates described previously. We can't simply look at a chemical equation and determine the rate law for the reaction. When the reaction has two or more reactants, the concentration of each reactant is usually varied independently of the others to determine the dependence of the rate on the concentration of that reactant. Example 15.2 demonstrates how to use the method of initial rates to determine the order of a reaction with multiple reactants.

WATCH **NOW!**

INTERACTIVE WORKED EXAMPLE 15.2

EXAMPLE 15.2 Determining the Order and Rate Constant of a Reaction

Consider the reaction between nitrogen dioxide and carbon monoxide:

$$NO_2(g) + CO(g) \longrightarrow NO(g) + CO_2(g)$$

The initial rate of the reaction is measured at several different concentrations of the reactants, and the tabulated results are shown here.

From the data, determine:

(a) the rate law for the reaction

(b) the rate constant (k) for the reaction

$[NO_2]$ (M)	[CO] (M)	Initial Rate (M/s)
0.10	0.10	0.0021
0.20	0.10	0.0082
0.20	0.20	0.0083
0.40	0.10	0.033

SOLUTION

(a) Begin by examining how the rate changes for each change in concentration. Between the first two experiments, the concentration of NO_2 doubles, the concentration of CO stays constant, and the rate quadruples, suggesting that the reaction is second order in NO_2.

Between the second and third experiments, the concentration of NO_2 stays constant, the concentration of CO doubles, and the rate remains constant (the small change in the least significant figure is simply experimental error), suggesting that the reaction is zero order in CO.

Between the third and fourth experiments, the concentration of NO_2 again doubles and the concentration of CO halves, yet the rate quadruples again, confirming that the reaction is second order in NO_2 and zero order in CO.

$[NO_2]$ (M)	[CO] (M)	Initial Rate (M/s)
0.10	0.10	0.0021
↓ $\times 2$	↓ constant	↓ $\times 4$
0.20	0.10	0.0082
↓ constant	↓ $\times 2$	↓ $\times 1$
0.20	0.20	0.0083
↓ $\times 2$	↓ $\times \frac{1}{2}$	↓ $\times 4$
0.40	0.10	0.033

Write the overall rate expression.

$$\text{Rate} = k[NO_2]^2[CO]^0 = k[NO_2]^2$$

(a) ALTERNATIVE APPROACH

If the relationship between the changes in concentrations and the changes in initial rates is not immediately obvious, you can determine the reaction order for any reactant by substituting any two initial rates and the corresponding initial concentrations into a ratio of the rate laws to determine the order (n).

$$\frac{\text{rate 2}}{\text{rate 1}} = \frac{k[A]_2^n}{k[A]_1^n}$$

For NO_2 use the first and second concentrations and rates (because $[NO_2]$ changes here, but [CO] is constant). Substitute the rates and concentrations into the expression for the ratio of the rate constants.

For NO_2
$$\frac{\text{rate 2}}{\text{rate 1}} = \frac{k[NO_2]_2^n}{k[NO_2]_1^n}$$
$$\frac{0.0082\ \cancel{M/s}}{0.0021\ \cancel{M/s}} = \frac{\cancel{k}(0.20\ \cancel{M})^n}{\cancel{k}(0.10\ \cancel{M})^n}$$
$$3.9 = \left(\frac{0.20}{0.10}\right)^n = 2^n$$

Take the log of both sides of the equation and solve for n.

$$\log 3.9 = \log 2^n$$
$$= n \log 2$$
$$n = \frac{\log 3.9}{\log 2}$$
$$= 1.96 = 2$$

For CO, use the second and third concentrations and rates (because [CO] changes here, but $[NO_2]$ is constant).

Substitute the rates and concentrations into the expression for the ratio of the rate laws.

For CO
$$\frac{\text{rate 3}}{\text{rate 2}} = \frac{k[CO]_3^n}{k[CO_2]_2^n}$$
$$\frac{0.0083\ \cancel{M/s}}{0.0082\ \cancel{M/s}} = \frac{\cancel{k}(0.20\ \cancel{M})^n}{\cancel{k}(0.10\ \cancel{M})^n}$$
$$1.01 = \left(\frac{0.20}{0.10}\right)^n = 2^n$$

Take the log of both sides of the equation and solve for n.

$$\log 1.01 = \log 2^n$$
$$= n \log 2$$
$$n = \frac{\log 1.01}{\log 2}$$
$$= 0.01 = 0$$

Write the overall rate expression from the order of each reactant.

$$\text{Rate} = k[NO_2]^2[CO]^0 = k[NO_2]^2$$

(b) To determine the rate constant for the reaction, solve the rate law for k and substitute the concentration and the initial rate from any one of the four measurements. In this case, we use the first measurement.

$$\text{Rate} = k[NO_2]^2$$
$$k = \frac{\text{rate}}{[NO_2]^2} = \frac{0.0021\ \text{M/s}}{(0.10\ \text{M})^2} = 0.21\ \text{M}^{-1}\cdot\text{s}^{-1}$$

FOR PRACTICE 15.2 Consider the equation:

$$CHCl_3(g) + Cl_2(g) \longrightarrow CCl_4(g) + HCl(g)$$

The initial rate of reaction is measured at several different concentrations of the reactants with the tabulated results shown here.

$[CHCl_3]$ (M)	$[Cl_2]$ (M)	Initial Rate (M/s)
0.010	0.010	0.0035
0.020	0.010	0.0069
0.020	0.020	0.0098
0.040	0.040	0.027

From the data, determine:

(a) the rate law for the reaction **(b)** the rate constant (k) for the reaction

ANSWER **NOW!**

15.4 Cc Conceptual Connection

RATE AND CONCENTRATION II This reaction was experimentally determined to be first order with respect to O_2 and second order with respect to NO:

$$O_2(g) + 2\,NO(g) \longrightarrow 2\,NO_2(g)$$

The diagrams shown here represent reaction mixtures in which the number of each type of molecule represents its relative initial concentration. Which mixture has the fastest initial rate?

(a) (b) (c)

WATCH **NOW!**

KEY CONCEPT VIDEO 15.4
The Integrated Rate Law

15.4 The Integrated Rate Law: The Dependence of Concentration on Time

The rate laws we have examined so far show the relationship between *the rate of a reaction and the concentration of a reactant.* But we often want to know the relationship between *the concentration of a reactant and time.* For example, the presence of chlorofluorocarbons (CFCs) in the atmosphere threatens the ozone layer. One of the reasons that CFCs pose such a significant threat is that the reactions that consume them are so slow (Table 15.1). Legislation has significantly reduced CFC emissions, but even if humans were to completely stop adding CFCs to the atmosphere, their concentration would decrease only very slowly. Nonetheless, we would like to know how their concentration changes with time. How much will be left in 20 years? In 50 years?

TABLE 15.1 ■ Atmospheric Lifetimes of Several CFCs

CFC Name	Structure	Atmospheric Lifetime*
CFC-11 (CCl_3F) Trichlorofluoromethane		45 years
CFC-12 (CCl_2F_2) Dichlorodifluoromethane		100 years
CFC-113 ($C_2F_3Cl_3$) 1,1,2-Trichloro-1,2,2-trifluoroethane		85 years
CFC-114 ($C_2F_4Cl_2$) 1,2-Dichlorotetrafluoroethane		300 years
CFC-115 (C_2F_5Cl) Monochloropentafluoroethane		1700 years

*Data taken from EPA site (under section 602 of Clean Air Act).

The Integrated Rate Law

The **integrated rate law** for a chemical reaction is a relationship between the concentrations of the reactants and time. For simplicity, we return to a single reactant decomposing into products:

$$A \longrightarrow \text{products}$$

The integrated rate law for this reaction depends on the order of the reaction; let's examine each of the common reaction orders individually.

First-Order Integrated Rate Law

If our simple reaction is first order, the rate is directly proportional to the concentration of A:

$$\text{Rate} = k[A]$$

Since Rate $= -\Delta[A]/\Delta t$, we can write:

$$-\frac{\Delta[A]}{\Delta t} = k[A] \qquad [15.11]$$

In this form, the rate law is also known as the *differential rate law*.

We can use calculus (see margin) to integrate the differential rate law and obtain the first-order *integrated rate law*:

$$\ln[A]_t = -kt + \ln[A]_0 \qquad [15.12]$$

$$-\frac{d[A]}{dt} = k[A]$$
$$\frac{d[A]}{[A]} = -kdt$$
$$\int_{[A]_0}^{[A]} \frac{d[A]}{[A]} = -\int_0^t kdt$$
$$[\ln[A]]_{[A]_0}^{[A]} = -k[t]_0^t$$
$$\ln[A] - \ln[A]_0 = -kt$$
$$\ln[A] = -kt + \ln[A]_0$$

We can also rearrange the integrated rate law by subtracting $\ln[A]_0$ from both sides of Equation 15.12:

$$\ln[A]_t = -kt + \ln[A]_0$$
$$\ln[A]_t - \ln[A]_0 = -kt$$

Since $\ln A - \ln B = \ln(A/B)$, we can rearrange this equation to get:

$$\ln\frac{[A]_t}{[A]_0} = -kt \qquad [15.13]$$

where $[A]_t$ is the concentration of A at any time t, k is the rate constant, and $[A]_0$ is the initial concentration of A.

Notice that the integrated rate law shown in Equation 15.12 has the form of an equation for a straight line:

$$\ln[A]_t = -kt + \ln[A]_0$$
$$y = mx + b$$

For a first-order reaction, a plot of the natural logarithm of the reactant concentration as a function of time yields a straight line with a slope of $-k$ and a y-intercept of $\ln[A]_0$, as shown in Figure 15.8▶. (Note that the slope is negative but that the rate constant is always positive.)

First-Order Integrated Rate Law

A plot of the natural log of the reactant concentration as a function of time yields a straight line.

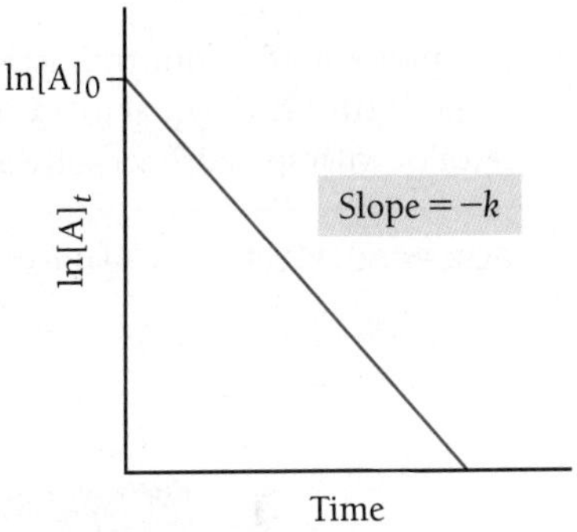

▲ **FIGURE 15.8 First-Order Integrated Rate Law** The slope of the line is equal to $-k$ and the y-intercept is $\ln[A]_0$.

EXAMPLE 15.3 The First-Order Integrated Rate Law: Using Graphical Analysis of Reaction Data

Consider the equation for the decomposition of SO_2Cl_2:

$$SO_2Cl_2(g) \longrightarrow SO_2(g) + Cl_2(g)$$

The concentration of SO_2Cl_2 is monitored at a fixed temperature as a function of time during the decomposition reaction, and the following data are tabulated:

Time (s)	$[SO_2Cl_2]$ (M)	Time (s)	$[SO_2Cl_2]$ (M)
0	0.100	800	0.0793
100	0.0971	900	0.0770
200	0.0944	1000	0.0748
300	0.0917	1100	0.0727
400	0.0890	1200	0.0706
500	0.0865	1300	0.0686
600	0.0840	1400	0.0666
700	0.0816	1500	0.0647

Show that the reaction is first order, and determine the rate constant for the reaction.

—*Continued on the next page*

Continued—

SOLUTION

In order to show that the reaction is first order, prepare a graph of the natural logarithm of $[SO_2Cl_2]$ versus time as shown:

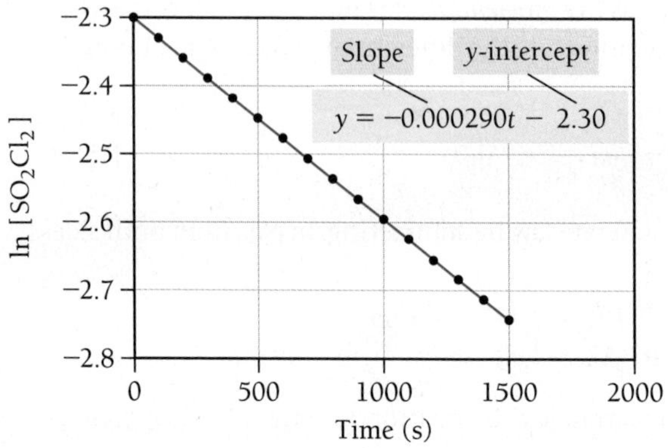

The plot is linear, confirming that the reaction is indeed first order. To obtain the rate constant, fit the data to a line. The slope of the line is equal to $-k$. Since the slope of the best-fitting line (which is most easily determined on a graphing calculator or with spreadsheet software such as Microsoft Excel) is $-2.90 \times 10^{-4}\,s^{-1}$, the rate constant is $+2.90 \times 10^{-4}\,s^{-1}$.

FOR PRACTICE 15.3 Use the graph and the best-fitting line in Example 15.3 to predict the concentration of SO_2Cl_2 at 1900 s.

WATCH **NOW!**

INTERACTIVE WORKED EXAMPLE 15.4

EXAMPLE 15.4 The First-Order Integrated Rate Law: Determining the Concentration of a Reactant at a Given Time

In Example 15.3, you determined that the decomposition of SO_2Cl_2 (under the given reaction conditions) is first order and has a rate constant of $+2.90 \times 10^{-4}\,s^{-1}$. If the reaction is carried out at the same temperature and the initial concentration of SO_2Cl_2 is 0.0225 M, what is the SO_2Cl_2 concentration after 865 s?

SORT You are given the rate constant of a first-order reaction and the initial concentration of the reactant and asked to find the concentration at 865 seconds.	**GIVEN:** $k = +2.90 \times 10^{-4}\,s^{-1}$ $[SO_2Cl_2]_0 = 0.0225\ M$ **FIND:** $[SO_2Cl_2]$ at $t = 865\ s$
STRATEGIZE Refer to the first-order integrated rate law to determine the SO_2Cl_2 concentration at $t = 865$ s.	**EQUATION** $\ln [A]_t = -kt + \ln [A]_0$
SOLVE Substitute the rate constant, the initial concentration, and the time into the integrated rate law. Solve the integrated rate law for the concentration of $[SO_2Cl_2]_t$.	**SOLUTION** $\ln[SO_2Cl_2]_t = -kt + \ln[SO_2Cl_2]_0$ $\ln[SO_2Cl_2]_t = -(2.90 \times 10^{-4}\,\cancel{s^{-1}})865\,\cancel{s} + \ln(0.0225)$ $\ln[SO_2Cl_2]_t = -0.251 - 3.79$ $[SO_2Cl_2]_t = e^{-4.04}$ $= 0.0176\ M$

CHECK The concentration is smaller than the original concentration as expected. If the concentration were larger than the initial concentration, this would indicate a mistake in the signs of one of the quantities on the right-hand side of the equation.

FOR PRACTICE 15.4 Cyclopropane rearranges to form propene in the gas phase.

The reaction is first order in cyclopropane and has a measured rate constant of $3.36 \times 10^{-5}\,s^{-1}$ at 720 K. If the initial cyclopropane concentration is 0.0445 M, what is the cyclopropane concentration after 235.0 minutes?

Second-Order Integrated Rate Law

If our simple reaction (A ⟶ products) is second order, the rate is proportional to the square of the concentration of A:

$$\text{Rate} = k[A]^2$$

Since Rate $= -\Delta[A]/\Delta t$, we can write the differential rate law:

$$-\frac{\Delta[A]}{\Delta t} = k[A]^2 \quad [15.14]$$

Again, we can use calculus to integrate the second-order differential rate law. We leave this derivation to an exercise (see Exercise 115 at the end of this chapter). The derivation results in the *second-order integrated rate law*:

$$\frac{1}{[A]_t} = kt + \frac{1}{[A]_0} \quad [15.15]$$

The second-order integrated rate law is also in the form of an equation for a straight line:

$$\frac{1}{[A]_t} = kt + \frac{1}{[A]_0}$$
$$y = mx + b$$

However, you must plot the inverse of the concentration of the reactant as a function of time. The plot yields a straight line with a slope of k and an intercept of $1/[A]_0$, as shown in Figure 15.9▶.

Second-Order Integrated Rate Law

A plot of the inverse of the reactant concentration as a function of time yields a straight line.

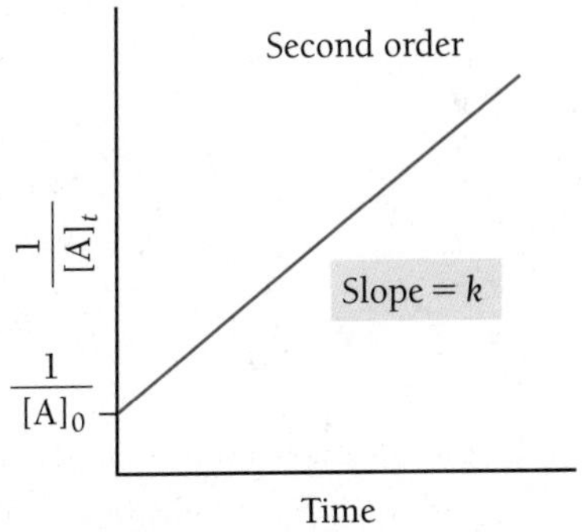

▲ **FIGURE 15.9 Second-Order Integrated Rate Law** The slope of the line is equal to k, and the y-intercept is $1/[A]_0$.

EXAMPLE 15.5 The Second-Order Integrated Rate Law: Using Graphical Analysis of Reaction Data

Consider the equation for the decomposition of NO_2:

$$NO_2(g) \longrightarrow NO(g) + O(g)$$

The concentration of NO_2 is monitored at a fixed temperature as a function of time during the decomposition reaction and the data tabulated in the margin at right. Show by graphical analysis that the reaction is not first order and that it is second order. Determine the rate constant for the reaction.

Time (s)	$[NO_2]$ (M)
0	0.01000
50	0.00887
100	0.00797
150	0.00723
200	0.00662
250	0.00611
300	0.00567
350	0.00528
400	0.00495
450	0.00466
500	0.00440
550	0.00416
600	0.00395
650	0.00376
700	0.00359
750	0.00343
800	0.00329
850	0.00316
900	0.00303
950	0.00292
1000	0.00282

SOLUTION

In order to show that the reaction is *not* first order, prepare a graph of $\ln[NO_2]$ versus time as shown:

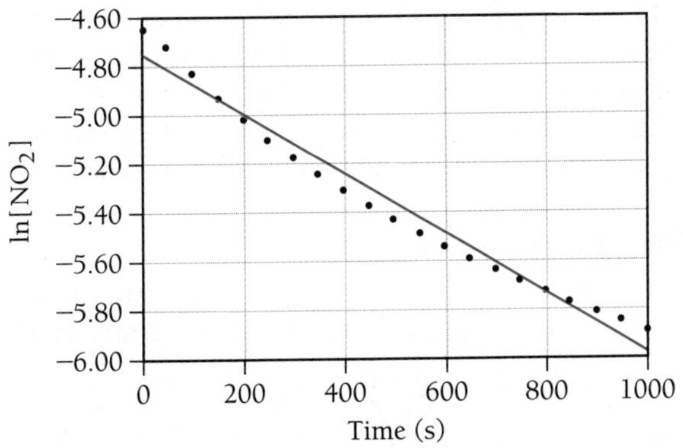

The plot is *not* linear (the straight line does not fit the data points), confirming that the reaction is not first order. In order to show that the reaction is second order, prepare a graph of $1/[NO_2]$ versus time as shown:

—*Continued on the next page*

Continued—

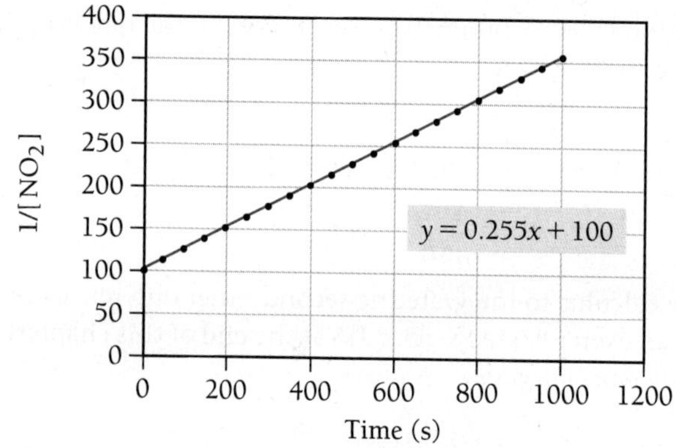

This graph is linear (the data points fit well to a straight line), confirming that the reaction is indeed second order. To obtain the rate constant, determine the slope of the best-fitting line. The slope is $0.255\ M^{-1} \cdot s^{-1}$; therefore, the rate constant is $0.255\ M^{-1} \cdot s^{-1}$.

FOR PRACTICE 15.5 Use the graph and the best-fitting line in Example 15.5 to predict the concentration of NO_2 at 2000 s.

$$-\frac{d[A]}{dt} = k[A]^0$$
$$-\frac{d[A]}{dt} = k$$
$$\int_{[A]_0}^{[A]} d[A] = -k\int_0^t dt$$
$$[[A]]_{[A]_0}^{[A]} = -k[t]_0^t$$
$$[A] - [A]_0 = -kt$$
$$[A] = -kt + [A]_0$$

Zero-Order Integrated Rate Law

If our simple reaction is zero order, the rate is proportional to a constant:

$$\text{Rate} = k[A]^0 = k$$

Since Rate $= -\Delta[A]/\Delta t$, we can write:

$$-\frac{\Delta[A]}{\Delta t} = k \qquad [15.16]$$

We can integrate the zero-order differential rate law (see margin) to obtain the *zero-order integrated rate law*:

$$[A]_t = -kt + [A]_0 \qquad [15.17]$$

The zero-order integrated rate law in Equation 15.17 is also in the form of an equation for a straight line. A plot of the concentration of the reactant as a function of time yields a straight line with a slope of $-k$ and an intercept of $[A]_0$, shown in Figure 15.10◀.

Zero-Order Integrated Rate Law

A plot of the reactant concentration as a function of time yields a straight line.

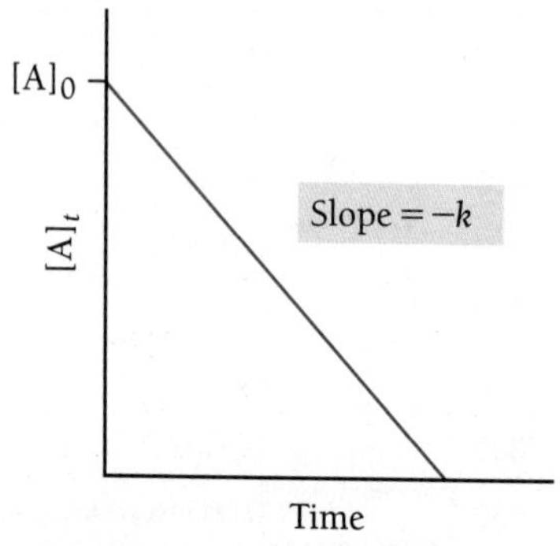

▲ **FIGURE 15.10 Zero-Order Integrated Rate Law** The slope of the line is equal to $-k$ and the y-intercept is $[A]_0$.

The Half-Life of a Reaction

The **half-life ($t_{1/2}$)** of a reaction is the time required for the concentration of a reactant to fall to one-half of its initial value. For example, if a reaction has a half-life of 100 seconds, and if the initial concentration of the reactant is 1.0 M, the concentration will fall to 0.50 M in 100 s. The half-life expression—which defines the dependence of half-life on the rate constant and the initial concentration—is different for different reaction orders.

First-Order Reaction Half-Life

From the definition of half-life and from the integrated rate law, we can derive an expression for the half-life. For a first-order reaction, the integrated rate law is:

$$\ln\frac{[A]_t}{[A]_0} = -kt$$

At a time equal to the half-life ($t = t_{1/2}$), the concentration is exactly half of the initial concentration: ($[A]_{t_{1/2}} = \frac{1}{2}[A]_0$). Therefore, when $t = t_{1/2}$ we can write the following expression:

$$\ln\frac{\frac{1}{2}\cancel{[A]_0}}{\cancel{[A]_0}} = \ln\frac{1}{2} = -kt_{1/2} \qquad [15.18]$$

Solving for $t_{1/2}$, and substituting -0.693 for $\ln \frac{1}{2}$, we arrive at the expression for the half-life of a first-order reaction:

$$t_{1/2} = \frac{0.693}{k} \qquad [15.19]$$

Notice that, for a first-order reaction, $t_{1/2}$ *is independent of the initial concentration*. For example, if $t_{1/2}$ is 100 s, and if the initial concentration is 1.0 M, the concentration falls to 0.50 M in 100 s, to 0.25 M in another 100 s, to 0.125 M in another 100 s, and so on (Figure 15.11▶). Even though the concentration is changing as the reaction proceeds, the half-life (how long it takes for the concentration to halve) is constant. A constant half-life is unique to first-order reactions, making the concept of half-life particularly useful for first-order reactions.

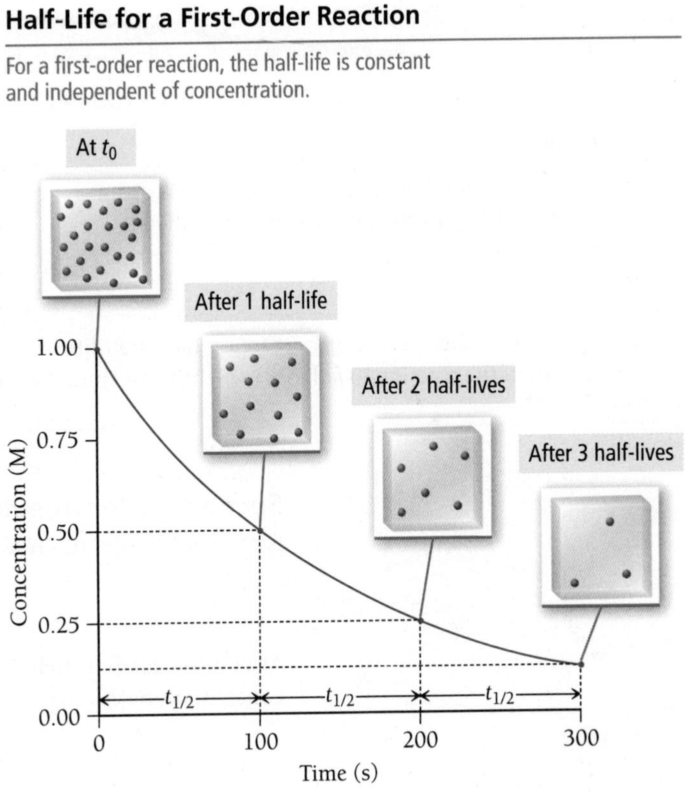

▶ **FIGURE 15.11 Half-Life: Concentration versus Time for a First-Order Reaction** For this reaction, the concentration decreases by one-half every 100 seconds ($t_{1/2}$ = 100 s). The blue spheres represent reactant molecules (the products are omitted for clarity).

15.5 Cc Conceptual Connection — ANSWER NOW!

HALF-LIFE I The images shown here depict the first-order reaction A ⟶ B at various times during the reaction process. The black circles represent reactant A, and the red circles represent product B. What is the half-life of the reaction?

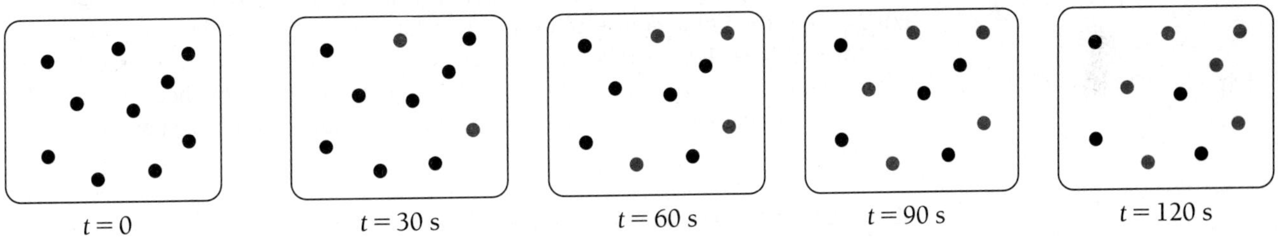

(a) 30 s **(b)** 60 s **(c)** 90 s **(d)** 120 s

15.6 Cc Conceptual Connection — ANSWER NOW!

HALF-LIFE II A first-order reaction (A ⟶ B) has a half-life of 25 minutes. If the initial concentration of A is 0.300 M, what is the concentration of B after 50 minutes? (Do not use a calculator to solve this problem.)

(a) 0.300 M **(b)** 0.225 M **(c)** 0.150 M **(d)** 0.100 M

EXAMPLE 15.6 Half-Life

Molecular iodine dissociates at 625 K with a first-order rate constant of 0.271 s^{-1}. What is the half-life of this reaction?

SOLUTION

Because the reaction is first order, the half-life is given by Equation 15.19. Substitute the value of k into the expression and calculate $t_{1/2}$.

$$t_{1/2} = \frac{0.693}{k}$$

$$= \frac{0.693}{0.271\ s^{-1}} = 2.56\ s$$

FOR PRACTICE 15.6 A first-order reaction has a half-life of 26.4 seconds. How long does it take for the concentration of the reactant in the reaction to fall to one-eighth of its initial value?

Second-Order Reaction Half-Life

For a second-order reaction, the integrated rate law is:

$$\frac{1}{[A]_t} = kt + \frac{1}{[A]_0}$$

At a time equal to the half-life ($t = t_{1/2}$), the concentration is exactly one-half of the initial concentration ($[A]_t = \frac{1}{2}[A]_0$). We can therefore write the following expression at $t = t_{1/2}$:

$$\frac{1}{\frac{1}{2}[A]_0} = kt_{1/2} + \frac{1}{[A]_0} \quad [15.20]$$

And then solve for $t_{1/2}$:

$$kt_{1/2} = \frac{1}{\frac{1}{2}[A]_0} - \frac{1}{[A]_0}$$

$$kt_{1/2} = \frac{2}{[A]_0} - \frac{1}{[A]_0}$$

$$t_{1/2} = \frac{1}{k[A]_0} \quad [15.21]$$

Notice that, for a second-order reaction, the half-life depends on the initial concentration. So if the initial concentration of a reactant in a second-order reaction is 1.0 M and the half-life is 100 s, the concentration falls to 0.50 M in 100 s. However, the time it takes for the concentration to fall to 0.25 M is now *longer than 100 s* because the initial concentration has decreased. Thus, the half-life continues to get longer as the concentration decreases.

Zero-Order Reaction Half-Life

For a zero-order reaction, the integrated rate law is:

$$[A]_t = -kt + [A]_0$$

Making the substitutions ($t = t_{1/2}$; $[A]_t = \frac{1}{2}[A]_0$), we can write the expression at $t = t_{1/2}$:

$$\tfrac{1}{2}[A]_0 = -kt_{1/2} + [A]_0 \quad [15.22]$$

We then solve for $t_{1/2}$:

$$t_{1/2} = \frac{[A]_0}{2k} \quad [15.23]$$

Notice that, for a zero-order reaction, the half-life also depends on the initial concentration; however, unlike in the second-order case, the two are directly proportional—the half-life gets shorter as the concentration decreases.

Summarizing Basic Kinetic Relationships (see Table 15.2):

- The reaction order and rate law must be determined experimentally.
- The rate law relates the *rate* of the reaction to the *concentration* of the reactant(s).
- The integrated rate law (which is mathematically derived from the rate law) relates the *concentration* of the reactant(s) to *time*.
- The half-life is the time it takes for the concentration of a reactant to fall to one-half of its initial value.
- The half-life of a first-order reaction is independent of the initial concentration.
- The half-lives of zero-order and second-order reactions depend on the initial concentrations.

15.7 Cc Conceptual Connection

ANSWER **NOW!**

RATE LAW AND INTEGRATED RATE LAW A decomposition reaction, with a rate that is observed to slow down as the reaction proceeds, has a half-life that depends on the initial concentration of the reactant. Which statement is most likely true for this reaction?

(a) A plot of the natural log of the concentration of the reactant as a function of time is linear.

(b) The half-life of the reaction increases as the initial concentration increases.

(c) A doubling of the initial concentration of the reactant results in a quadrupling of the rate.

TABLE 15.2 ■ Rate Law Summary Table

Order	Rate Law	Units of k	Integrated Rate Law	Straight-Line Plot	Half-Life Expression
0	Rate $= k[A]^0$	$M \cdot s^{-1}$	$[A]_t = -kt + [A]_0$	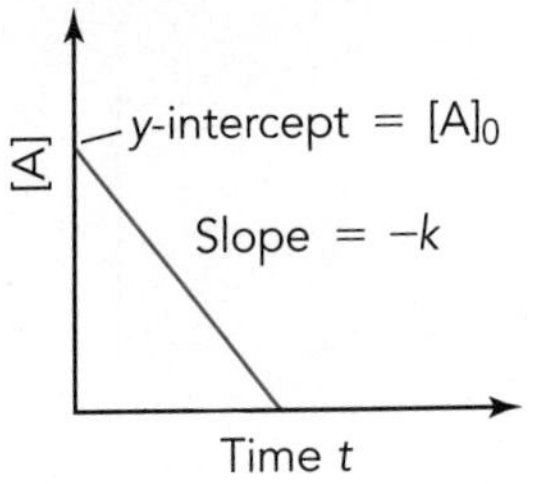	$t_{1/2} = \frac{[A]_0}{2k} = \frac{1}{k}\frac{[A]_0}{2}$
1	Rate $= k[A]^1$	s^{-1}	$\ln[A]_t = -kt + \ln[A]_0$ $\ln\frac{[A]_t}{[A]_0} = -kt$	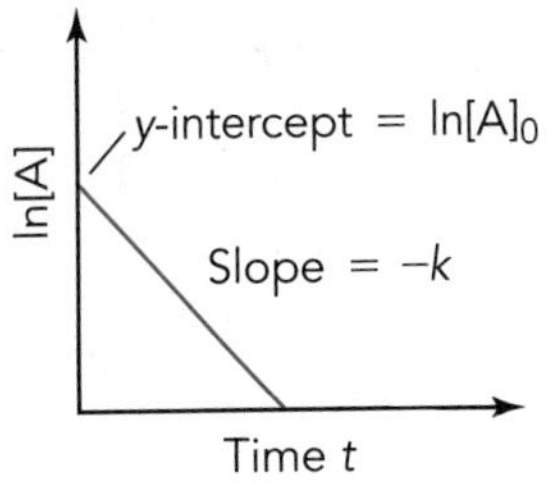	$t_{1/2} = \frac{0.693}{k} = \frac{1}{k}(0.693)$
2	Rate $= k[A]^2$	$M^{-1} \cdot s^{-1}$	$\frac{1}{[A]_t} = kt + \frac{1}{[A]_0}$	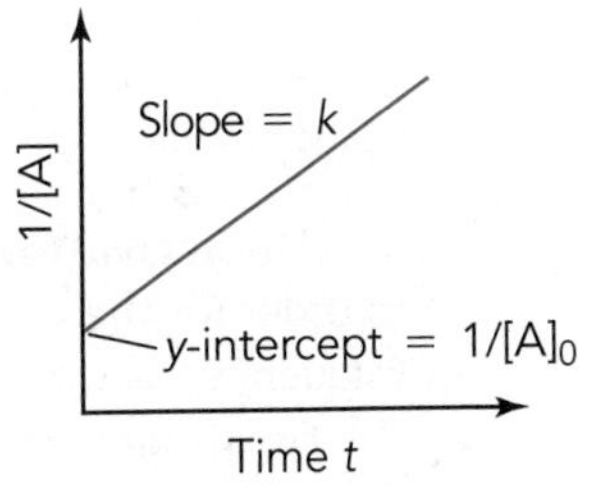	$t_{1/2} = \frac{1}{k[A]_0} = \frac{1}{k}\frac{1}{[A]_0}$

WATCH **NOW!**

KEY CONCEPT VIDEO 15.5
The Effect of Temperature on Reaction Rate

15.5 The Effect of Temperature on Reaction Rate

In the opening section of this chapter, we discussed how lizards become lethargic when their body temperature drops and the chemical reactions that control their muscle movement slow. The rates of chemical reactions are, in general, highly sensitive to temperature. For example, at around room temperature, a 10 °C increase in temperature increases the rate of a typical biological reaction by two or three times. How do we explain this highly sensitive temperature dependence?

The Arrhenius Equation

Recall that the rate law for a reaction is Rate $= k[A]^n$. *The temperature dependence of the reaction rate is contained in the rate constant, k* (which is actually a constant only when the temperature remains constant). An increase in temperature generally results in an increase in k, which results in a faster rate. In 1889, Swedish chemist Svante Arrhenius (1859–1927) wrote a paper quantifying the temperature dependence of the rate constant.

The modern form of the **Arrhenius equation** shows the relationship between the rate constant (k) and the temperature in kelvin (T):

$$k = Ae^{\frac{-E_a}{RT}} \qquad [15.24]$$

Activation energy ($-E_a$); Frequency factor (A); Exponential factor ($e^{\frac{-E_a}{RT}}$)

In this equation, R is the gas constant (8.314 J/mol · K), A is a constant called the *frequency factor* (or the *pre-exponential factor*), and E_a is the *activation energy* (or *activation barrier*).

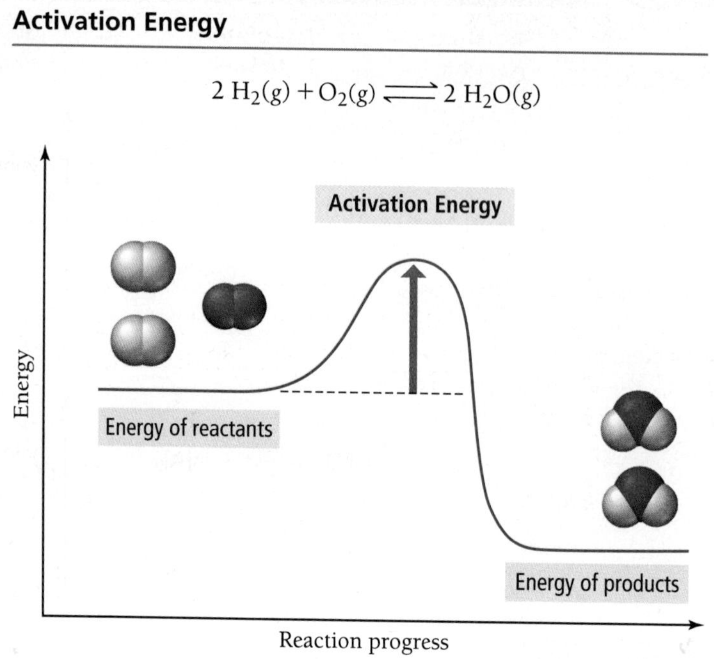

▲ **FIGURE 15.12 The Activation Energy Barrier** Even though the reaction is energetically favorable (the energy of the products is lower than that of the reactants), an input of energy is needed for the reaction to take place.

The **activation energy (E_a)** is an energy barrier or hump that must be surmounted in order for the reactants to transform into products (Figure 15.12▲). We examine the frequency factor more closely in the next section; for now, we can think of the **frequency factor (*A*)** as the number of times that the reactants approach the activation barrier per unit time.

The Activation Energy, Frequency Factor, and Exponential Factor

To understand each of these quantities better, consider the simple reaction in which CH_3NC (methyl isonitrile) rearranges to form CH_3CN (acetonitrile):

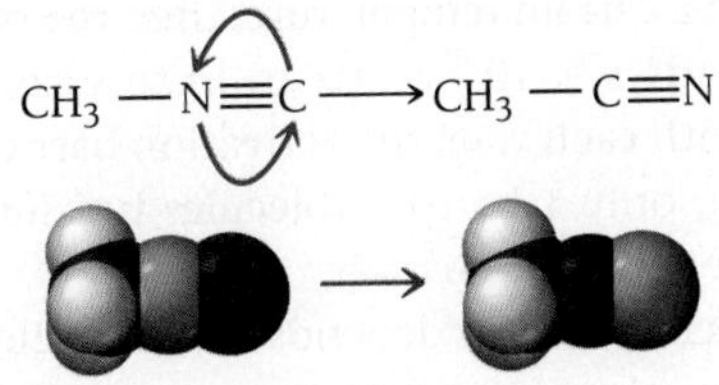

Let's examine the physical meaning of the activation energy, frequency factor, and exponential factor for this reaction.

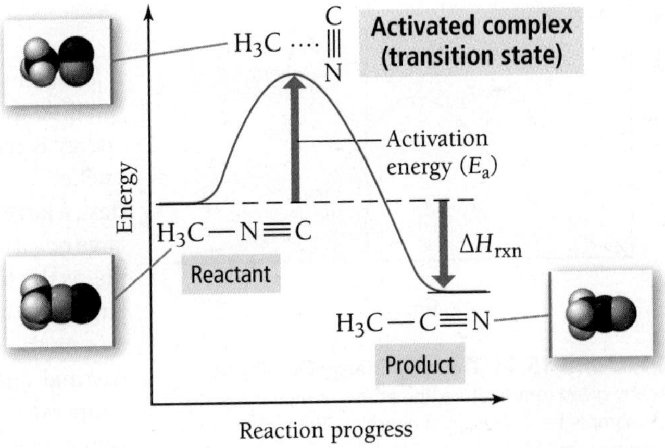

▲ **FIGURE 15.13 The Activated Complex** The reaction pathway includes a transitional state—the activated complex—that has a higher energy than either the reactant or the product.

The Activation Energy

Figure 15.13▶ shows the energy of a molecule as the reaction proceeds. The *x*-axis represents the progress of the reaction from left (reactant) to right (product). To get from the reactant to the product, the molecule must go through a high-energy state called the **activated complex** or **transition state**. Even though the overall reaction is energetically downhill (exothermic), it must first go uphill to reach the activated complex because energy is required to initially weaken the H_3C—N bond and allow the NC group to begin to rotate:

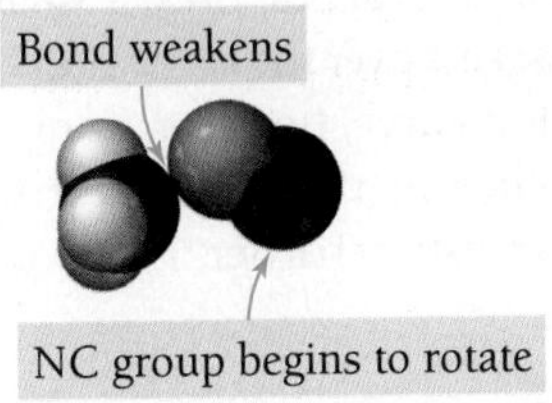

The energy required to reach the activated complex is the *activation energy. The higher the activation energy, the slower the reaction rate (at a given temperature).*

The Frequency Factor

Recall that the frequency factor represents the number of approaches to the activation barrier per unit time. Any time that the NC group begins to rotate, it approaches the activation barrier. For this reaction, the frequency factor represents the rate at which the NC part of the molecule wags (vibrates side to side). With each wag, the reactant approaches the activation barrier:

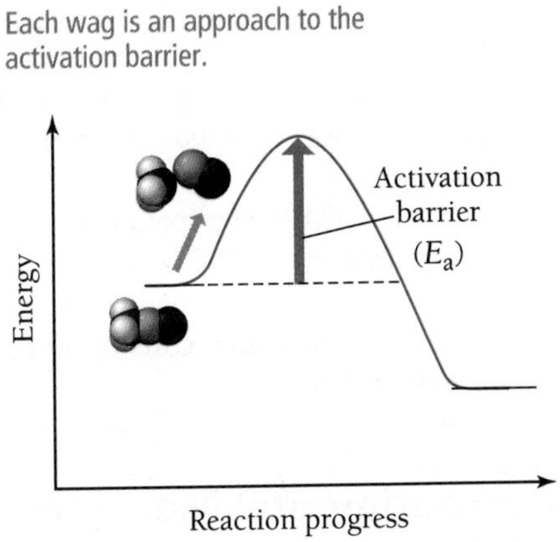

However, approaching the activation barrier is not equivalent to surmounting it. Most of the approaches do not have enough total energy to make it over the activation barrier.

The Exponential Factor

The **exponential factor** is a number between 0 and 1 that represents the fraction of molecules that have enough energy to make it over the activation barrier on a given approach. The exponential factor is the fraction of approaches that are actually successful and result in the product. For example, if the frequency factor is 10^9/s and the exponential factor is 10^{-7} at a certain temperature, then the overall rate constant at that temperature is $10^9/\text{s} \times 10^{-7} = 10^2/\text{s}$. In this case, the CN group wags at a rate of 10^9/s. With each wag, the activation barrier is approached. However, for a given wag, only 1 in 10^7 molecules has sufficient energy to actually make it over the activation barrier.

The exponential factor depends on both the temperature (T) and the activation energy (E_a) of the reaction:

$$\text{Exponential factor} = e^{-E_a/RT}$$

A low activation energy and a high temperature make the negative exponent small, so the exponential factor approaches one. For example, if the activation energy is zero, then the exponent is zero, and the exponential factor is exactly one ($e^{-0} = 1$)—every approach to the activation barrier is successful. By contrast, a large activation energy and a low temperature make the exponent a very large negative number, so the exponential factor becomes very small. For example, as the temperature approaches 0 K, the exponent approaches an infinitely large negative number, and the exponential factor approaches zero ($e^{-\infty} = 0$).

As the temperature increases, the number of molecules having enough thermal energy to surmount the activation barrier increases. At any given temperature, a sample of molecules has a distribution of energies, as shown in Figure 15.14◀. Under common circumstances, only a small fraction of the molecules has enough energy to make it over the activation barrier. Because of the shape of the energy distribution curve, however, a small change in temperature results in a large difference in the number of molecules having enough energy to surmount the activation barrier. This explains the sensitivity of reaction rates to temperature.

Thermal Energy Distribution

As temperature increases, the fraction of molecules with enough energy to surmount the activation energy barrier also increases.

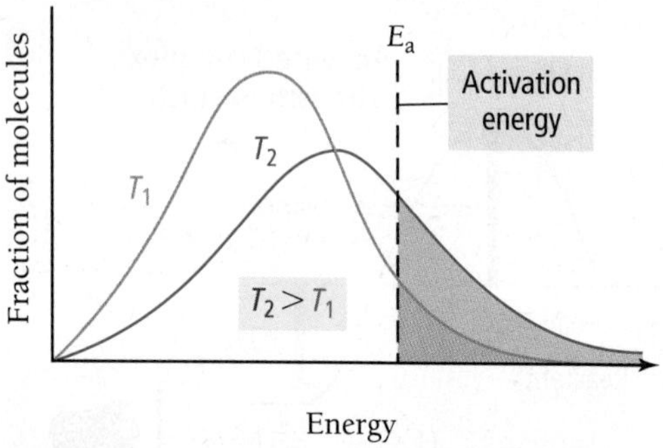

▲ **FIGURE 15.14 Thermal Energy Distribution** At any given temperature, the atoms or molecules in a gas sample have a range of energies. The higher the temperature, the wider the energy distribution and the greater the average energy. The fraction of molecules with enough energy to surmount the activation energy barrier and react (shaded regions) increases sharply as the temperature rises.

Summarizing Temperature and Reaction Rate:

- The frequency factor is the number of times that the reactants approach the activation barrier per unit time.
- The exponential factor is the fraction of the approaches that are successful in surmounting the activation barrier and forming products.
- The exponential factor increases with increasing temperature but decreases with increasing activation energy.

ANSWER **NOW!**

15.8 Cc Conceptual Connection

REACTION RATE AND TEMPERATURE Which statement best explains why reaction rates generally increase with increasing temperature?

(a) Reaction rates increase with increasing temperature because, as temperature increases, a greater fraction of molecules have enough thermal energy to surmount the activation barrier.

(b) Reaction rates increase with increasing temperature because, as temperature increases, the pre-exponential factor of the rate constant increases.

(c) Reaction rates increase with increasing temperature because, as temperature increases, molecules decompose into their constituent atoms, which can then form new bonds to form the products.

Arrhenius Plots: Experimental Measurements of the Frequency Factor and the Activation Energy

The frequency factor and activation energy are important quantities in understanding the kinetics of any reaction. To see how we measure these factors in the laboratory, consider again Equation 15.24: $k = Ae^{-E_a/RT}$. Taking the natural logarithm of both sides of this equation, we get the following result:

$$\ln k = \ln(Ae^{-E_a/RT})$$

$$\ln k = \ln A + \ln e^{-E_a/RT}$$

$$\ln k = \ln A - \frac{E_a}{RT} \quad [15.25]$$

$$\ln k = -\frac{E_a}{R}\left(\frac{1}{T}\right) + \ln A \quad [15.26]$$

$$y = \quad mx \quad + \; b$$

Remember that $\ln(AB) = \ln A + \ln B$.

Remember that $\ln e^x = x$.

In an Arrhenius analysis, the pre-exponential factor (*A*) is assumed to be independent of temperature. Although the pre-exponential factor does depend on temperature to some degree, its temperature dependence is much less than that of the exponential factor and is often ignored.

Equation 15.26 is in the form of a straight line. *A plot of the natural logarithm of the rate constant (ln k) versus the inverse of the temperature in kelvins (1/T) yields a straight line with a slope of $-E_a/R$ and a y-intercept of ln A.* Such a plot is called an **Arrhenius plot** and is commonly used in the analysis of kinetic data, as shown in Example 15.7.

EXAMPLE 15.7 Using an Arrhenius Plot to Determine Kinetic Parameters

The decomposition of ozone shown here is important to many atmospheric reactions:

$$O_3(g) \longrightarrow O_2(g) + O(g)$$

A study of the kinetics of the reaction results in the following data:

Temperature (K)	Rate Constant ($M^{-1} \cdot s^{-1}$)	Temperature (K)	Rate Constant ($M^{-1} \cdot s^{-1}$)
600	3.37×10^3	1300	7.83×10^7
700	4.85×10^4	1400	1.45×10^8
800	3.58×10^5	1500	2.46×10^8
900	1.70×10^6	1600	3.93×10^8
1000	5.90×10^6	1700	5.93×10^8
1100	1.63×10^7	1800	8.55×10^8
1200	3.81×10^7	1900	1.19×10^9

Determine the value of the frequency factor and activation energy for the reaction.

SOLUTION

To determine the frequency factor and activation energy, prepare a graph of the natural log of the rate constant (ln *k*) versus the inverse of the temperature (1/*T*).

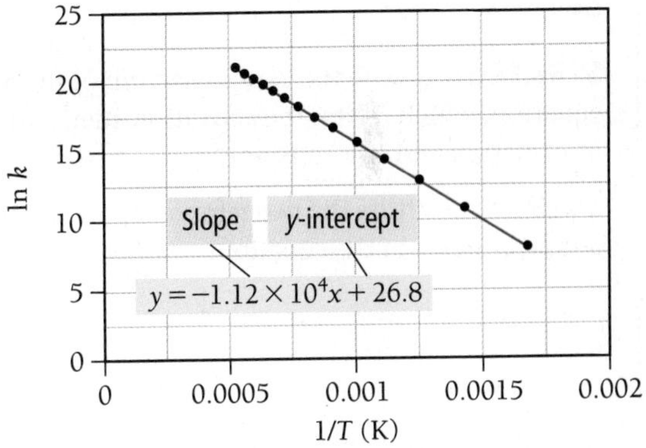

The plot is linear, as expected for Arrhenius behavior. The line that fits best has a slope of -1.12×10^4 K and a *y*-intercept of 26.8. Calculate the activation energy from the slope by setting the slope equal to $-E_a/R$ and solving for E_a:

$$-1.12 \times 10^4\ \text{K} = \frac{-E_a}{R}$$

$$E_a = 1.12 \times 10^4\ \cancel{\text{K}}\left(8.314 \frac{\text{J}}{\text{mol} \cdot \cancel{\text{K}}}\right)$$

$$= 9.31 \times 10^4\ \text{J/mol}$$

$$= 93.1\ \text{kJ/mol}$$

Calculate the frequency factor (*A*) by setting the intercept equal to ln *A*.

$$26.8 = \ln A$$

$$A = e^{26.8}$$

$$= 4.36 \times 10^{11}$$

Since the rate constants are measured in units of $M^{-1} \cdot s^{-1}$, the frequency factor is in the same units. Consequently, you can conclude that the reaction has an activation energy of 93.1 kJ/mol and a frequency factor of $4.36 \times 10^{11}\ M^{-1} \cdot s^{-1}$.

FOR PRACTICE 15.7 For the decomposition of ozone reaction in Example 15.7, use the results of the Arrhenius analysis to predict the rate constant at 298 K.

In some cases, when either data are limited or plotting capabilities are absent, we can calculate the activation energy if we know the rate constant at just two different temperatures. We can apply the Arrhenius expression in Equation 15.26 to the two different temperatures as follows:

$$\ln k_2 = -\frac{E_a}{R}\left(\frac{1}{T_2}\right) + \ln A$$

$$\ln k_1 = -\frac{E_a}{R}\left(\frac{1}{T_1}\right) + \ln A$$

We can then subtract $\ln k_1$ from $\ln k_2$:

$$\ln k_2 - \ln k_1 = \left[-\frac{E_a}{R}\left(\frac{1}{T_2}\right) + \ln A\right] - \left[-\frac{E_a}{R}\left(\frac{1}{T_1}\right) + \ln A\right]$$

Rearranging, we get the two-point form of the Arrhenius equation:

$$\ln\frac{k_2}{k_1} = \frac{E_a}{R}\left(\frac{1}{T_1} - \frac{1}{T_2}\right) \qquad [15.27]$$

Example 15.8 demonstrates how to use this equation to calculate the activation energy from experimental measurements of the rate constant at two different temperatures.

WATCH **NOW!**
INTERACTIVE WORKED EXAMPLE 15.8

EXAMPLE 15.8 Using the Two-Point Form of the Arrhenius Equation

Consider the reaction between nitrogen dioxide and carbon monoxide:

$$NO_2(g) + CO(g) \longrightarrow NO(g) + CO_2(g)$$

The rate constant at 701 K is measured as 2.57 $M^{-1} \cdot s^{-1}$ and that at 895 K is measured as 567 $M^{-1} \cdot s^{-1}$. Find the activation energy for the reaction in kJ/mol.

SORT You are given the rate constant of a reaction at two different temperatures and asked to find the activation energy.

GIVEN: $T_1 = 701\text{ K}, k_1 = 2.57\text{ M}^{-1}\cdot\text{s}^{-1}$
$T_2 = 895\text{ K}, k_2 = 567\text{ M}^{-1}\cdot\text{s}^{-1}$

FIND: E_a

STRATEGIZE Use the two-point form of the Arrhenius equation, which relates the activation energy to the given information and R (a constant).

EQUATION $\ln\frac{k_2}{k_1} = \frac{E_a}{R}\left(\frac{1}{T_1} - \frac{1}{T_2}\right)$

SOLVE Substitute the two rate constants and the two temperatures into the equation.

SOLUTION

$$\ln\frac{567\text{ M}^{-1}\cdot\text{s}^{-1}}{2.57\text{ M}^{-1}\cdot\text{s}^{-1}} = \frac{E_a}{R}\left(\frac{1}{701\text{ K}} - \frac{1}{895\text{ K}}\right)$$

$$5.40 = \frac{E_a}{R}\left(\frac{3.09 \times 10^{-4}}{\text{K}}\right)$$

Solve the equation for E_a, the activation energy, and convert to kJ/mol.

$$E_a = 5.40\left(\frac{\text{K}}{3.09 \times 10^{-4}}\right)R$$

$$= 5.40\left(\frac{\text{K}}{3.09 \times 10^{-4}}\right)8.314\frac{\text{J}}{\text{mol}\cdot\text{K}}$$

$$= 1.45 \times 10^5\text{ J/mol}$$

$$= 1.5 \times 10^2\text{ kJ/mol}$$

CHECK The magnitude of the answer is reasonable. Activation energies for most reactions range from tens to hundreds of kilojoules per mole.

FOR PRACTICE 15.8 Use the results from Example 15.8 and the given rate constant of the reaction at either of the two temperatures to predict the rate constant for this reaction at 525 K.

REACTION RATE AND ACTIVATION ENERGY Reaction A and reaction B have identical frequency factors. However, reaction B has a higher activation energy than reaction A. Which reaction has a greater rate constant at room temperature?

(a) Reaction A
(b) Reaction B

15.9 Cc Conceptual Connection

ANSWER **NOW!**

The Collision Model: A Closer Look at the Frequency Factor

Recall that the frequency factor in the Arrhenius equation represents the number of approaches to the activation barrier per unit time. Let's refine that idea for a reaction involving two gas-phase reactants:

$$A(g) + B(g) \longrightarrow \text{products}$$

In the **collision model**, a chemical reaction occurs after a sufficiently energetic collision between two reactant molecules (Figure 15.15▶). In collision theory, therefore, each approach to the activation barrier is a collision between the reactant molecules. Consequently, the value of the frequency factor should simply be the number of collisions that occur per second. However, the frequency factors of most (though not all) gas-phase chemical reactions tend to be smaller than the number of collisions that occur per second. Why?

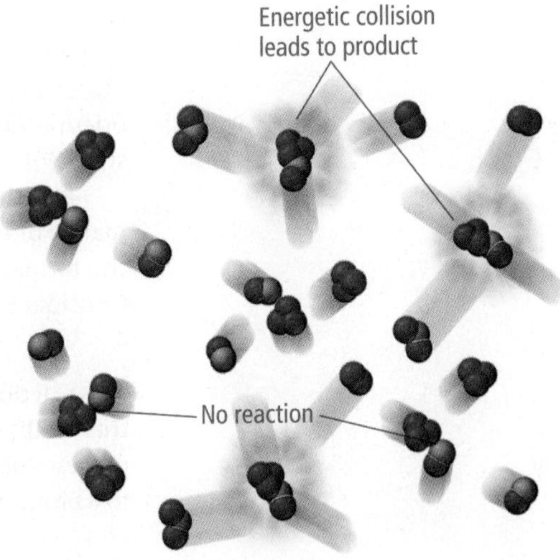

▲ **FIGURE 15.15 The Collision Model** In the collision model, two molecules react after a sufficiently energetic collision with the correct orientation brings the reacting groups together.

In the collision model, we can separate the frequency factor into two distinct parts, as shown in the following equations:

$$k = Ae^{\frac{-E_a}{RT}}$$

$$= pze^{\frac{-E_a}{RT}}$$

Orientation factor (p) Collision frequency (z)

where p is the **orientation factor** and z is the **collision frequency**. The collision frequency is the number of collisions that occur per unit time, which we calculate for a gas-phase reaction from the pressure of the gases and the temperature of the reaction mixture. Under typical conditions, a single molecule undergoes on the order of 10^9 collisions every second. The orientation factor is a number, usually between 0 and 1, which represents the fraction of collisions with an orientation that allows the reaction to occur.

To better understand the orientation factor, consider the reaction represented by the following equation:

$$NOCl(g) + NOCl(g) \longrightarrow 2\,NO(g) + Cl_2(g)$$

In order for the reaction to occur, two NOCl molecules must collide with sufficient energy. However, not all collisions with sufficient energy lead to products because the reactant molecules must also be properly oriented.

Consider the three possible collision orientations of the reactant molecules shown here:

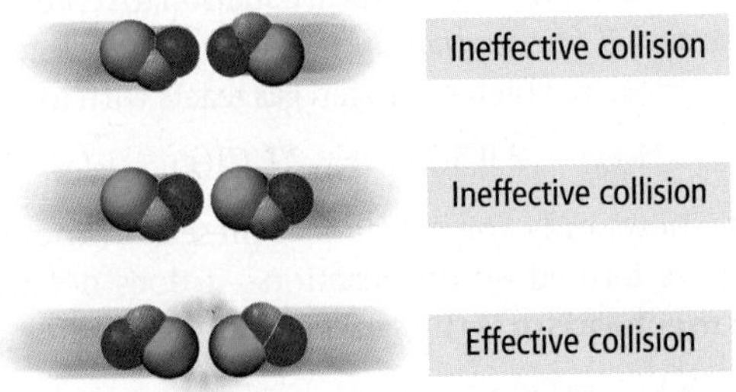

The first two collisions, even if they occur with sufficient energy, do not result in a reaction because the reactant molecules are not oriented in a way that allows the chlorine atoms to bond. In other words, if two molecules are to react with each other, they must collide in such a way that allows the necessary bonds to break and form. For the reaction of $NOCl(g)$, the orientation factor is $p = 0.16$. This means that only 16 out of 100 sufficiently energetic collisions are successful in forming the products.

Some reactions have orientation factors that are much smaller than one. Consider the reaction between hydrogen and ethene:

$$H_2(g) + CH_2{=}CH_2(g) \longrightarrow CH_3{-}CH_3(g)$$

The orientation factor for this reaction is 1.7×10^{-6}, which means that fewer than two out of each million sufficiently energetic collisions actually form products. The small orientation factor indicates that the orientational requirements for this reaction are very stringent—the molecules must be aligned in a *very specific way* for the reaction to occur.

Reactions between *individual atoms* usually have orientation factors of approximately one because atoms are spherically symmetrical; thus any orientation can lead to the formation of products. A few reactions have orientation factors greater than one. Consider the reaction between potassium and bromine:

$$K(g) + Br_2(g) \longrightarrow KBr(g) + Br(g)$$

This reaction has an orientation factor of $p = 4.8$. In other words, there are more reactions than collisions—the reactants do not even have to collide to react! Apparently, through a process dubbed *the harpoon mechanism*, a potassium atom can actually transfer an electron to a bromine molecule without a collision. The resulting positive charge on the potassium and the negative charge on the bromine cause the two species to attract each other and form a bond. The potassium atom essentially *harpoons* a passing bromine molecule with an electron and *reels it in* through the coulombic attraction between opposite charges.

We can picture a sample of reactive gases as a frenzy of collisions between the reacting atoms or molecules. At normal temperatures, the vast majority of these collisions do not have sufficient energy to overcome the activation barrier, and the atoms or molecules simply bounce off one another. Of the collisions having sufficient energy to overcome the activation barrier, most do not have the proper orientation for the reaction to occur (for the majority of common reactions). When two molecules with sufficient energy *and* the correct orientation collide, something extraordinary happens. The electrons on one of the atoms or molecules are attracted to the nuclei of the other; some bonds begin to weaken while other bonds begin to form, and, if all goes well, the reactants go through the transition state and are transformed into the products. This is how a chemical reaction occurs.

ANSWER **NOW!**

15.10 Cc Conceptual Connection

COLLISION THEORY Which reaction do you expect to have the smallest orientation factor?

(a) $H(g) + I(g) \longrightarrow HI(g)$
(b) $H_2(g) + I_2(g) \longrightarrow 2\,HI(g)$
(c) $HCl(g) + HCl(g) \longrightarrow H_2(g) + Cl_2(g)$

WATCH **NOW!**

KEY CONCEPT VIDEO 15.6
Reaction Mechanisms

15.6 Reaction Mechanisms

Most chemical reactions do not occur in a single step but rather over the course of several steps. When we write a chemical equation to represent a chemical reaction, *we usually represent the overall reaction, not the series of individual steps by which the reaction occurs*. Consider the reaction in which hydrogen gas reacts with iodine monochloride:

$$H_2(g) + 2\,ICl(g) \longrightarrow 2\,HCl(g) + I_2(g)$$

The overall equation shows only the substances present at the beginning of the reaction and the substances formed by the reaction—it does not show the intermediate steps. The **reaction mechanism** is the series of individual chemical steps by which an overall chemical reaction occurs. For example, the proposed mechanism for the reaction between hydrogen and iodine monochloride contains two steps:

$$\textbf{Step 1} \quad H_2(g) + ICl(g) \longrightarrow HI(g) + HCl(g)$$

$$\textbf{Step 2} \quad HI(g) + ICl(g) \longrightarrow HCl(g) + I_2(g)$$

In the first step, an H_2 molecule collides with an ICl molecule and forms an HI molecule and an HCl molecule. In the second step, the HI molecule formed in the first step collides with a second ICl molecule to form another HCl molecule and an I_2 molecule. Each step in a reaction mechanism is an **elementary step**. Elementary steps cannot be broken down into simpler steps—they occur as written (they represent the exact species that are colliding in the reaction).

An elementary step represents an actual interaction between the reactant molecules in the step. An overall reaction equation shows only the starting substances and the ending substances, not the path between them.

One of the requirements for a valid reaction mechanism is that the individual steps in the mechanism add to the overall reaction. For example, the mechanism just shown sums to the overall reaction as shown here:

$$H_2(g) + ICl(g) \longrightarrow \cancel{HI}(g) + HCl(g)$$

$$\cancel{HI}(g) + ICl(g) \longrightarrow HCl(g) + I_2(g)$$

$$\overline{H_2(g) + 2\,ICl(g) \longrightarrow 2\,HCl(g) + I_2(g)}$$

Notice that the HI molecule appears in the reaction mechanism but not in the overall reaction equation. We call species such as HI *reaction intermediates*. A **reaction intermediate** forms in one elementary step and is consumed in another. The reaction mechanism is a complete, detailed description of the reaction at the molecular level—it specifies the individual collisions and reactions that result in the overall reaction. As such, reaction mechanisms are highly sought-after pieces of chemical knowledge.

How do we determine reaction mechanisms? Recall from the opening section of this chapter that chemical kinetics are not only practically important (because they allow us to control the rate of a particular reaction), but they are also theoretically important because they can help us determine the mechanism of the reaction. We can piece together possible reaction mechanisms by measuring the kinetics of the overall reaction and working backward to write a mechanism consistent with the measured kinetics.

Rate Laws for Elementary Steps

We characterize elementary steps by their **molecularity,** the number of reactant particles involved in the step. The most common molecularities are **unimolecular** and **bimolecular**:

$A \longrightarrow$ products	**Unimolecular**
$A + A \longrightarrow$ products	**Bimolecular**
$A + B \longrightarrow$ products	**Bimolecular**

Elementary steps in which three reactant particles collide, called **termolecular** steps, are very rare because the probability of three particles simultaneously colliding is small.

Although we cannot deduce the rate law for an *overall chemical reaction* from the balanced chemical equation, we can deduce the rate law for an *elementary step* from its equation. Since we know that an elementary step occurs through the collision of the reactant particles, the rate is proportional to the product of the concentrations of those particles. For example, the rate for the bimolecular elementary step in which A reacts with B is proportional to the concentration of A multiplied by the concentration of B:

$$A + B \longrightarrow \text{products} \qquad \text{Rate} = k[A][B]$$

Similarly, the rate law for the bimolecular step in which A reacts with A is proportional to the square of the concentration of A:

$$A + A \longrightarrow \text{products} \qquad \text{Rate} = k[A]^2$$

Table 15.3 summarizes the rate laws for the common elementary steps, as well as those for the rare termolecular step. Notice that the molecularity of the elementary step is equal to the overall order of the step.

TABLE 15.3 ■ Rate Laws for Elementary Steps

Elementary Step	Molecularity	Rate Law
A ⟶ products	1	Rate = k[A]
A + A ⟶ products	2	Rate = k[A]^2
A + B ⟶ products	2	Rate = k[A][B]
A + A + A ⟶ products	3 (rare)	Rate = k[A]^3
A + A + B ⟶ products	3 (rare)	Rate = k[A]^2[B]
A + B + C ⟶ products	3 (rare)	Rate = k[A][B][C]

ANSWER **NOW!**

15.11 Cc Conceptual Connection

ELEMENTARY STEPS What is the rate law for the elementary step Cl + CO ⟶ ClCO?

(a) Rate = k[Cl]

(b) Rate = k[CO]

(c) Rate = k[ClCO]

(d) Rate = k[Cl][CO]

Rate-Determining Steps and Overall Reaction Rate Laws

In most chemical reactions, one of the elementary steps—called the **rate-determining step**—is much slower than the others. The rate-determining step in a chemical reaction is analogous to the narrowest section on a freeway. If a section of a freeway narrows from four lanes to two lanes, for even a short distance, the rate at which cars travel along the freeway is limited by the rate at which they can travel through the narrow section (even though the rate might be much faster along the four-lane section). Similarly, the rate-determining step in a reaction mechanism limits the overall rate of the reaction (even though the other steps occur much faster) and therefore determines *the rate law for the overall reaction*.

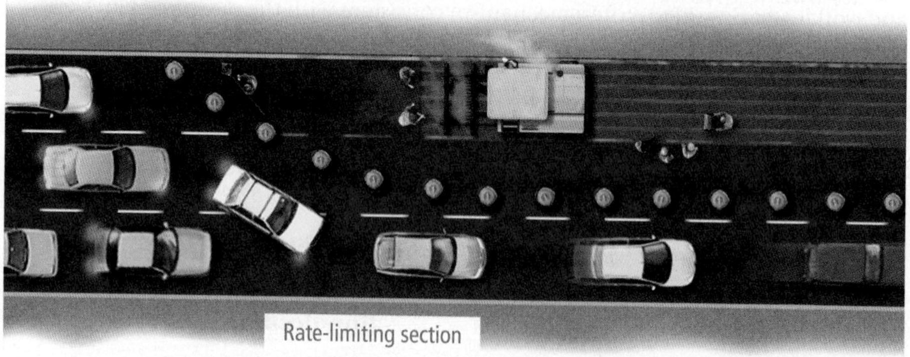

▶ The rate-limiting step in a reaction mechanism limits the overall rate of the reaction just as the narrowest section of a highway limits the rate at which traffic can pass.

As an example, consider the reaction between nitrogen dioxide gas and carbon monoxide gas:

$$NO_2(g) + CO(g) \longrightarrow NO(g) + CO_2(g)$$

The experimentally determined rate law for this reaction is Rate = $k[NO_2]^2$. We can see from this rate law that the reaction must not be a single-step reaction—otherwise the rate law would be Rate = $k[NO_2][CO]$. A possible mechanism for this reaction involves two steps:

$$NO_2(g) + NO_2(g) \longrightarrow NO_3(g) + NO(g) \quad \text{Slow}$$
$$NO_3(g) + CO(g) \longrightarrow NO_2(g) + CO_2(g) \quad \text{Fast}$$

Figure 15.16▶ shows the energy diagram for this mechanism. The first step has a much larger activation energy than the second step. This greater activation energy results in a much smaller rate constant for the first step compared to the second step. The first step determines the overall rate of the reaction, and the predicted *overall* rate law is therefore Rate = $k[NO_2]^2$, which is consistent with the observed experimental rate law.

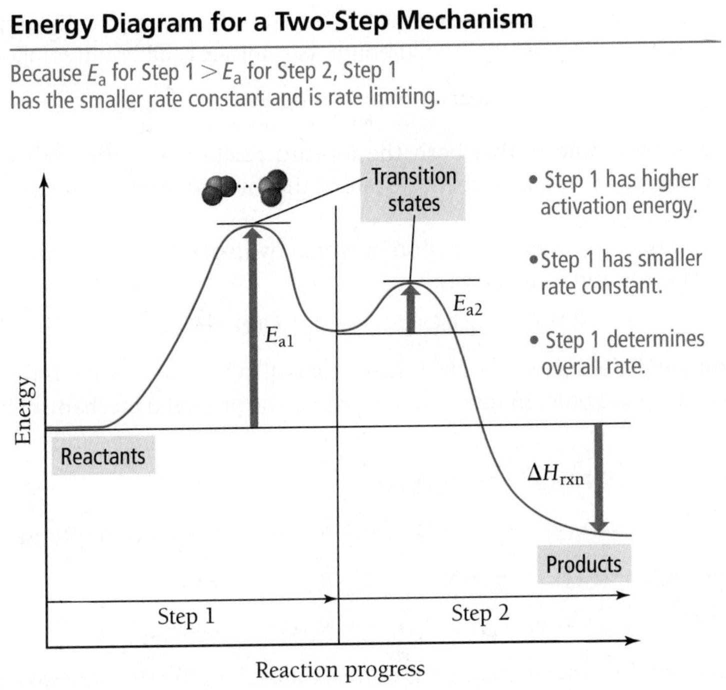

◀ **FIGURE 15.16 Energy Diagram for a Two-Step Mechanism**

For a proposed reaction mechanism, such as the one shown here for NO_2 and CO, to be *valid* (mechanisms can only be validated, not proven), two conditions must be met:

1. **The elementary steps in the mechanism must sum to the overall reaction.**
2. **The rate law predicted by the mechanism must be consistent with the experimentally observed rate law.**

We have already seen that the rate law predicted by the earlier mechanism is consistent with the experimentally observed rate law. We can check whether the elementary steps sum to the overall reaction by adding them together:

$$NO_2(g) + \cancel{NO_2}(g) \longrightarrow \cancel{NO_3}(g) + NO(g) \qquad \text{Slow}$$
$$\cancel{NO_3}(g) + CO(g) \longrightarrow \cancel{NO_2}(g) + CO_2(g) \qquad \text{Fast}$$
$$NO_2(g) + CO(g) \longrightarrow NO(g) + CO_2(g) \qquad \text{Overall}$$

The mechanism fulfills both of the given requirements and is therefore valid. A valid mechanism is not a *proven* mechanism (because other mechanisms may also fulfill both of the given requirements). We can only say that a given mechanism is consistent with kinetic observations of the reaction and is therefore possible. Other types of data—such as the experimental evidence for a proposed intermediate—are necessary to further strengthen the validity of a proposed mechanism.

Mechanisms with a Fast Initial Step

When the proposed mechanism for a reaction has a slow initial step—such as the one shown previously for the reaction between NO_2 and CO—the rate law predicted by the mechanism normally contains only reactants involved in the overall reaction. However, when a mechanism begins with a fast initial step, some other subsequent step in the mechanism is the rate-limiting step. In these cases, the rate law predicted by the rate-limiting step may contain reaction intermediates. Because reaction intermediates do not appear in the overall reaction equation, a rate law containing intermediates cannot generally correspond to the experimental rate law. Fortunately, however, we can often express the concentration of intermediates in terms of the concentrations of the reactants of the overall reaction.

In a multistep mechanism where the first step is fast, the products of the first step may build up because the rate at which they are consumed is limited by some slower step further down the line. As those products build up, they can begin to react with one another to re-form the reactants. As long as the first step is fast enough compared to the rate-limiting step, the first-step reaction will reach equilibrium. We indicate equilibrium as follows:

$$\text{reactants} \underset{k_{-1}}{\overset{k_1}{\rightleftharpoons}} \text{products}$$

The double arrows indicate that both the forward reaction and the reverse reaction occur. If equilibrium is reached, then the rate of the forward reaction equals the rate of the reverse reaction.

As an example, consider the reaction by which hydrogen reacts with nitrogen monoxide to form water and nitrogen gas:

$$2\,H_2(g) + 2\,NO(g) \longrightarrow 2\,H_2O(g) + N_2(g)$$

The experimentally observed rate law is Rate $= k[H_2][NO]^2$. The reaction is first order in hydrogen and second order in nitrogen monoxide. The proposed mechanism has a slow second step:

$2\,NO(g) \underset{k_{-1}}{\overset{k_1}{\rightleftharpoons}} \cancel{N_2O_2(g)}$		Fast
$H_2(g) + \cancel{N_2O_2(g)} \xrightarrow[k_2]{} H_2O(g) + \cancel{N_2O(g)}$		Slow (rate limiting)
$\cancel{N_2O(g)} + H_2(g) \xrightarrow[k_3]{} N_2(g) + H_2O(g)$		Fast
$2\,H_2(g) + 2\,NO(g) \longrightarrow 2\,H_2O(g) + N_2(g)$		Overall

To determine whether the mechanism is valid, we must find whether the two conditions described previously are met. As we can see, the steps do indeed sum to the overall reaction, so the first condition is met.

The second condition is that the rate law predicted by the mechanism must be consistent with the experimentally observed rate law. Because the second step is rate limiting, we write the following expression for the rate law:

$$\text{Rate} = k_2[H_2][N_2O_2] \qquad [15.28]$$

This rate law contains an intermediate (N_2O_2) and therefore cannot be consistent with the experimentally observed rate law (which does not contain intermediates). Because of the equilibrium in the first step, however, *we can express the concentration of the intermediate in terms of the reactants of the overall equation.* Since the first step reaches equilibrium, the rate of the forward reaction in the first step equals the rate of the reverse reaction:

$$\text{Rate (forward)} = \text{Rate (reverse)}$$

The rate of the forward reaction is given by the rate law:

$$\text{Rate} = k_1[NO]^2$$

The rate of the reverse reaction is given by the rate law:

$$\text{Rate} = k_{-1}[N_2O_2]$$

Since these two rates are equal at equilibrium, we write the expression:

$$k_1[NO]^2 = k_{-1}[N_2O_2]$$

Rearranging, we get:

$$[N_2O_2] = \frac{k_1}{k_{-1}}[NO]^2$$

We can now substitute this expression into Equation 15.28, the rate law obtained from the slow step:

$$\begin{aligned}\text{Rate} &= k_2[H_2][N_2O_2]\\ &= k_2[H_2]\frac{k_1}{k_{-1}}[NO]^2\\ &= \frac{k_2k_1}{k_{-1}}[H_2][NO]^2\end{aligned}$$

If we combine the individual rate constants into one overall rate constant, we get the predicted rate law:

$$\text{Rate} = k[H_2][NO]^2$$

Since this rate law is consistent with the experimentally observed rate law, condition 2 is met and the proposed mechanism is valid.

WATCH **NOW!**

INTERACTIVE WORKED EXAMPLE 15.9

EXAMPLE 15.9 Reaction Mechanisms

Ozone naturally decomposes to oxygen by this reaction:

$$2\,O_3(g) \longrightarrow 3\,O_2(g)$$

The experimentally observed rate law for this reaction is:

$$\text{Rate} = k[O_3]^2[O_2]^{-1}$$

Show that this proposed mechanism is consistent with the experimentally observed rate law.

$$O_3(g) \underset{k_{-1}}{\overset{k_1}{\rightleftharpoons}} O_2(g) + O(g) \quad \text{Fast} \qquad O_3(g) + O(g) \xrightarrow[k_2]{} 2\,O_2(g) \quad \text{Slow}$$

SOLUTION

To determine whether the mechanism is valid, you must first determine whether the steps sum to the overall reaction. The steps do indeed sum to the overall reaction, so the first condition is met.	$O_3(g) \underset{k_{-1}}{\overset{k_1}{\rightleftharpoons}} O_2(g) + \cancel{O}(g)$ $O_3(g) + \cancel{O}(g) \xrightarrow[k_2]{} 2\,O_2(g)$ $2\,O_3(g) \longrightarrow 3\,O_2(g)$
The second condition is that the rate law predicted by the mechanism is consistent with the experimentally observed rate law. Because the second step is rate limiting, write the rate law based on the second step.	$\text{Rate} = k_2[O_3][O]$
Because the rate law contains an intermediate (O), you must express the concentration of the intermediate in terms of the concentrations of the reactants of the overall reaction. To do this, set the rates of the forward reaction and the reverse reaction of the first step equal to each other. Solve the expression from the previous step for [O], the concentration of the intermediate.	Rate (forward) = Rate (backward) $k_1[O_3] = k_{-1}[O_2][O]$ $[O] = \dfrac{k_1[O_3]}{k_{-1}[O_2]}$
Finally, substitute [O] into the rate law predicted by the slow step.	$\text{Rate} = k_2[O_3][O]$ $= k_2[O_3]\dfrac{k_1[O_3]}{k_{-1}[O_2]}$ $= k_2\dfrac{k_1}{k_{-1}}\dfrac{[O_3]^2}{[O_2]} = k[O_3]^2[O_2]^{-1}$

CHECK Because the two steps in the proposed mechanism sum to the overall reaction, and because the rate law obtained from the proposed mechanism is consistent with the experimentally observed rate law, the proposed mechanism is valid. The −1 reaction order with respect to $[O_2]$ indicates that the rate slows down as the concentration of oxygen increases—oxygen inhibits, or slows down, the reaction.

FOR PRACTICE 15.9 Predict the overall reaction and rate law that results from the following two-step mechanism:

$$2\,A \longrightarrow A_2 \quad \text{Slow}$$

$$A_2 + B \longrightarrow A_2B \quad \text{Fast}$$

15.7 Catalysis

Throughout this chapter, we have learned about ways to control the rates of chemical reactions. We can speed up the rate of a reaction by increasing the concentration of the reactants or by increasing the temperature. However, these approaches are not always feasible. There are limits to how concentrated we can make a reaction mixture, and increases in temperature may allow unwanted reactions—such as the decomposition of a reactant—to occur.

Alternatively, we can increase reaction rates by using a **catalyst**, a substance that increases the rate of a chemical reaction but is not consumed by the reaction. A catalyst works by providing an alternative mechanism for the reaction—one in which the rate-determining step has a lower activation energy.

For example, consider the noncatalytic destruction of ozone in the upper atmosphere, discussed in Section 7.10, which happens according to this reaction:

$$O_3(g) + O(g) \longrightarrow 2\,O_2(g)$$

In this reaction, an ozone molecule collides with an oxygen atom to form two oxygen molecules in a single elementary step.

Photodissociation means *light-induced* dissociation. The energy from a photon of light can break chemical bonds and therefore dissociate, or break apart, a molecule.

Earth has a protective ozone layer in the upper atmosphere because the activation energy for this reaction is fairly high; the reaction, therefore, proceeds at a fairly slow rate, and the ozone layer does not rapidly decompose into O_2. However, the addition of Cl atoms (which come from the photodissociation of human-made chlorofluorocarbons) to the upper atmosphere makes available another pathway by which O_3 can be destroyed. The first step in this pathway—called the catalytic destruction of ozone—is the reaction of Cl with O_3 to form ClO and O_2:

$$Cl + O_3 \longrightarrow ClO + O_2$$

This is followed by a second step in which ClO reacts with O, regenerating Cl:

$$ClO + O \longrightarrow Cl + O_2$$

If we add the two reactions, the overall reaction is identical to the noncatalytic reaction:

$$\cancel{Cl} + O_3 \longrightarrow \cancel{ClO} + O_2$$
$$\cancel{ClO} + O \longrightarrow \cancel{Cl} + O_2$$
$$O_3 + O \longrightarrow 2\,O_2$$

However, the activation energy for the rate-limiting step in this pathway is much smaller than that for the first, uncatalyzed pathway (as shown in Figure 15.17◀), and therefore the reaction occurs at a much faster rate. Note that the Cl is not consumed in the overall reaction—this is characteristic of a catalyst.

In the case of the catalytic destruction of ozone, the catalyst speeds up a reaction that we *do not* want to happen. Most of the time, however, catalysts are used to speed up reactions that we *do* want to happen. For example, your car most likely has a catalytic converter in its exhaust system. The catalytic converter contains solid catalysts, such as platinum, rhodium, or palladium, dispersed on an underlying high-surface-area ceramic structure. These catalysts convert exhaust pollutants such as nitrogen monoxide and carbon monoxide into less harmful substances:

$$2\,NO(g) + 2\,CO(g) \xrightarrow[\text{catalyst}]{} N_2(g) + 2\,CO_2(g)$$

The catalytic converter also promotes the complete combustion of any fuel fragments present in the exhaust:

$$CH_3CH_2CH_3(g) + 5\,O_2(g) \xrightarrow[\text{catalyst}]{} 3\,CO_2(g) + 4\,H_2O(g)$$

Fuel fragment

Energy Diagram for Catalyzed and Uncatalyzed Pathways

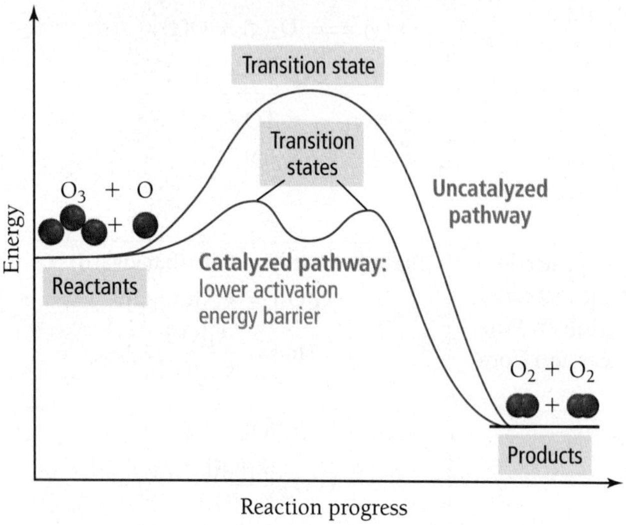

▲ **FIGURE 15.17 Catalyzed and Uncatalyzed Decomposition of Ozone** In the catalytic destruction of ozone (red), the activation barrier for the rate-limiting step is much lower than that in the uncatalyzed process (blue).

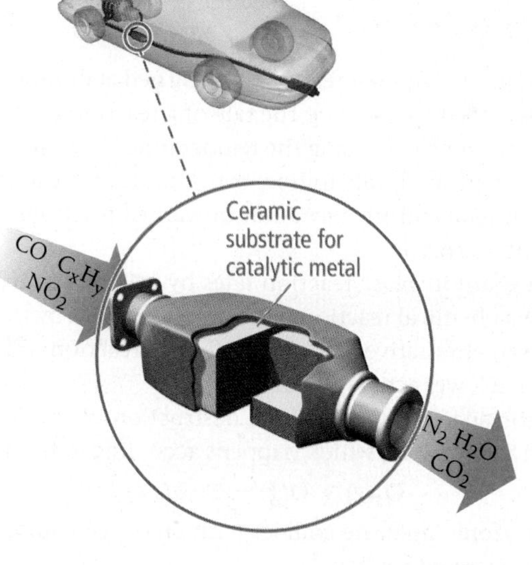

▶ The catalytic converter in the exhaust system of a car helps eliminate pollutants in the exhaust.

Fuel fragments in exhaust are harmful because they lead to the formation of ozone. Recall from Section 7.10 that although ozone is a natural part of our *upper* atmosphere that protects us from excess exposure to ultraviolet light, it is a pollutant in the *lower* atmosphere, interfering with cardiovascular function and acting as an eye and lung irritant. The use of catalytic converters in motor vehicles has resulted in lower levels of these pollutants over most U.S. cities in the last 30 years, even though the number of cars on the roadways has dramatically increased (see Table 15.4).

TABLE 15.4 ■ Change in Pollutant Levels

Pollutant	Change 1980–2013
NO_2	−60%
O_3	−33%
CO	−84%

Source: *EPA's National Air Trends.*

▲ Polar stratospheric clouds contain ice particles that catalyze reactions by which chlorine is released from its atmospheric chemical reservoirs.

Homogeneous and Heterogeneous Catalysis

We categorize catalysts into two types: homogeneous and heterogeneous (Figure 15.18▼). In **homogeneous catalysis**, the catalyst exists in the same phase (or state) as the reactants. The catalytic destruction of ozone by Cl is an example of homogeneous catalysis—the chlorine atoms exist in the gas phase with the gas-phase reactants. In **heterogeneous catalysis**, the catalyst exists in a different phase than the reactants. The solid catalysts used in catalytic converters are examples of heterogeneous catalysts—they are solids while the reactants are gases. The use of solid catalysts with gas-phase or solution-phase reactants is the most common type of heterogeneous catalysis.

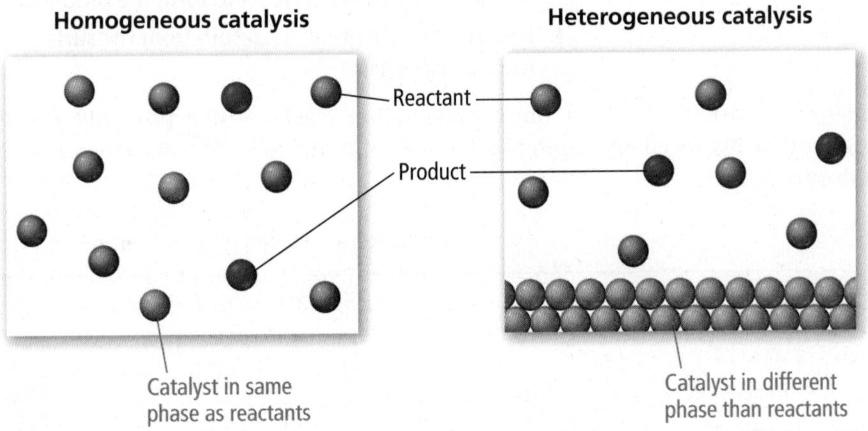

▲ **FIGURE 15.18 Homogeneous and Heterogeneous Catalysis** A homogeneous catalyst exists in the same phase as the reactants. A heterogeneous catalyst exists in a different phase than the reactants. Often, a heterogeneous catalyst provides a solid surface on which the reaction can take place.

Research has shown that heterogeneous catalysis is most likely responsible for the annual formation of an ozone hole over Antarctica. After the discovery of the Antarctic ozone hole in 1985, scientists wondered why there was such a dramatic drop in ozone over Antarctica but not over the rest of the planet. After all, the chlorine from chlorofluorocarbons that catalyzes ozone destruction is evenly distributed throughout the entire atmosphere.

As it turns out, most of the chlorine that enters the atmosphere from chlorofluorocarbons gets bound up in chlorine *reservoirs*, which are substances such as $ClONO_2$ that hold chlorine and prevent it from catalyzing ozone destruction. The unique conditions over Antarctica—especially the cold, isolated air mass that exists during the long dark winter—result in clouds that contain solid ice particles. These unique clouds are called polar stratospheric clouds (or PSCs), and the surfaces of the ice particles within these clouds appear to catalyze the release of chlorine from their reservoirs:

$$ClONO_2 + HCl \xrightarrow[\text{PSCs}]{} Cl_2 + HNO_3$$

When the sun rises in the Antarctic spring, the sunlight dissociates the chlorine molecules into chlorine atoms:

$$Cl_2 \xrightarrow[\text{light}]{} 2\,Cl$$

The chlorine atoms then catalyze the destruction of ozone by the mechanism discussed previously. This continues until the sun melts the stratospheric clouds, allowing chlorine

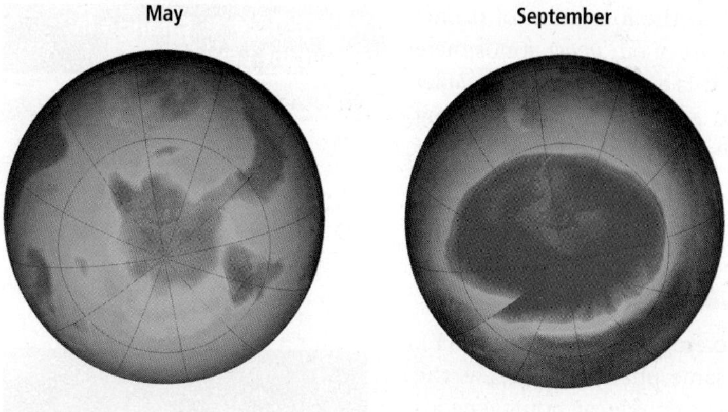

▲ **FIGURE 15.19 Ozone Depletion in the Antarctic Spring** The concentration of ozone over Antarctica drops sharply during the months of September and October due to the catalyzed destruction of ozone by chlorine. The image on the left shows the average ozone levels in May 2017, and the image on the right shows the average levels from September 2017. (The lowest ozone levels are represented in blue.) Source: NASA Ozone Watch, OMI instrument (KNMI/NASA) onboard the Aura satellite.

atoms to be reincorporated into their reservoirs. The result is an ozone hole that forms every spring and lasts about six to eight weeks (Figure 15.19◀).

A second example of heterogeneous catalysis involves the **hydrogenation** of double bonds within alkenes. Consider the reaction between ethene and hydrogen, which is relatively slow at normal temperatures:

$$H_2C{=}CH_2(g) + H_2(g) \longrightarrow H_3C{-}CH_3(g)$$

Slow at room temperature

However, in the presence of finely divided platinum, palladium, or nickel, the reaction happens rapidly. The catalysis occurs by the four-step process depicted in Figure 15.20▼:

1. Adsorption: the reactants are adsorbed onto the metal surface.
2. Diffusion: the reactants diffuse on the surface until they approach each other.
3. Reaction: the reactants react to form the products.
4. Desorption: the products desorb from the surface into the gas phase.

The large activation energy of the hydrogenation reaction—due primarily to the strength of the hydrogen–hydrogen bond in H_2—is greatly lowered when the reactants adsorb onto the surface.

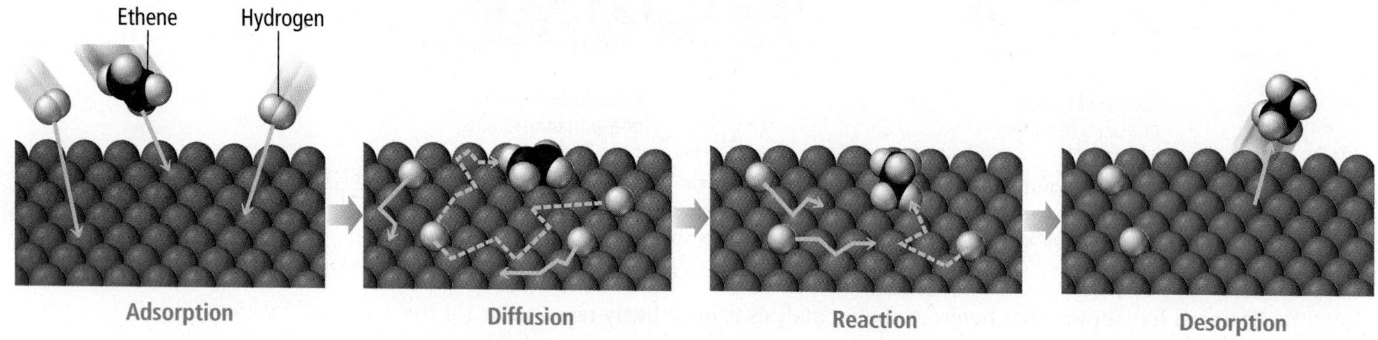

▲ **FIGURE 15.20 Catalytic Hydrogenation of Ethene**

Enzymes: Biological Catalysts

The strategies used to speed up chemical reactions in the laboratory—high temperatures, high pressures, strongly acidic or alkaline conditions—are not available to living organisms, since they would be fatal to cells.

We find perhaps the best example of chemical catalysis in living organisms. Most of the thousands of reactions that must occur for an organism to survive are too slow at normal temperatures. So living organisms rely on **enzymes**, biological catalysts that increase the rates of biochemical reactions. Enzymes are usually large protein molecules with complex three-dimensional structures. Within each enzyme's structure is a specific area called the **active site**. The properties and shape of the active site are just right to bind the reactant molecule, usually called the **substrate**. The substrate fits into the active site in a manner that is analogous to a key fitting into a lock (Figure 15.21▶). When the substrate binds to the active site of the enzyme—through intermolecular forces such as hydrogen bonding and dispersion forces, or even covalent bonds—the activation energy of the reaction is greatly lowered, allowing the reaction to occur at a much faster rate. The general mechanism by which an enzyme (E) binds a substrate (S) and then reacts to form the products (P) is:

$$E + S \rightleftharpoons ES \qquad \text{Fast}$$

$$ES \longrightarrow E + P \qquad \text{Slow, rate limiting}$$

Enzyme–Substrate Binding

A substrate (or reactant) fits into the active site of an enzyme much as a key fits into a lock.

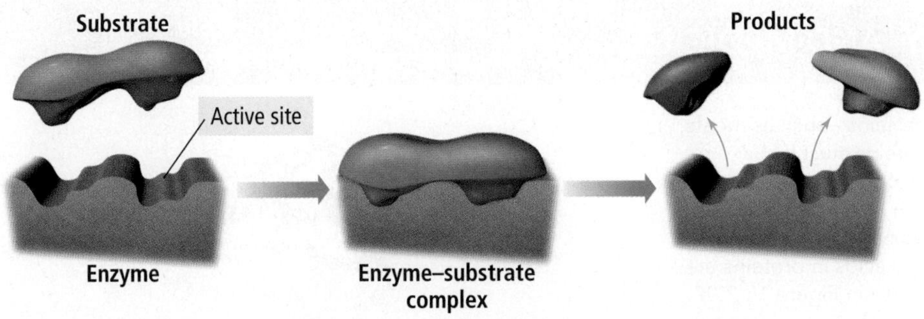

▲ **FIGURE 15.21 Enzyme–Substrate Binding** Intermolecular forces hold the substrate in place and form an enzyme–substrate complex. (Sometimes temporary covalent bonding may also be involved.) After the reaction occurs, the products are released from the active site.

Sucrase, for example, is an enzyme that catalyzes the breaking up of sucrose (table sugar) into glucose and fructose within the body. At body temperature, sucrose does not break into glucose and fructose because the activation energy is high, resulting in a slow reaction rate. However, when a sucrose molecule binds to the active site within sucrase, the bond between the glucose and fructose units weakens because glucose is forced into a geometry that stresses the bond (Figure 15.22▶). Weakening of this bond lowers the activation energy for the reaction, increasing the reaction rate. The reaction can then proceed toward equilibrium—which favors the products—at a much lower temperature.

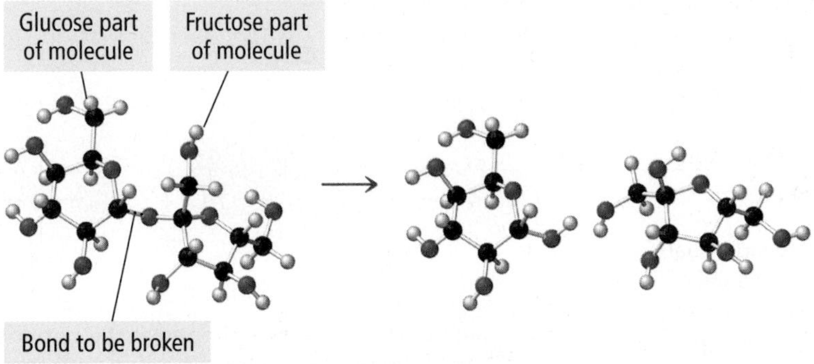

$$\underset{\text{Sucrose}}{C_{12}H_{22}O_{11}} + H_2O \longrightarrow \underset{\text{Glucose}}{C_6H_{12}O_6} + \underset{\text{Fructose}}{C_6H_{12}O_6}$$

▲ Sucrose breaks up into glucose and fructose during digestion.

By allowing otherwise slow reactions to occur at reasonable rates, enzymes give living organisms tremendous control over which reactions occur and when they occur. Enzymes are extremely specific (each enzyme catalyzes only a single reaction) and efficient, speeding up reaction rates by factors of as much as a billion. (and sometimes even more).

To turn a particular reaction on, a living organism produces or activates the correct enzyme to catalyze that reaction. Because organisms are so dependent on the reactions enzymes catalyze, many substances that inhibit the action of enzymes are highly toxic. Locking up a single enzyme molecule can stop the reaction

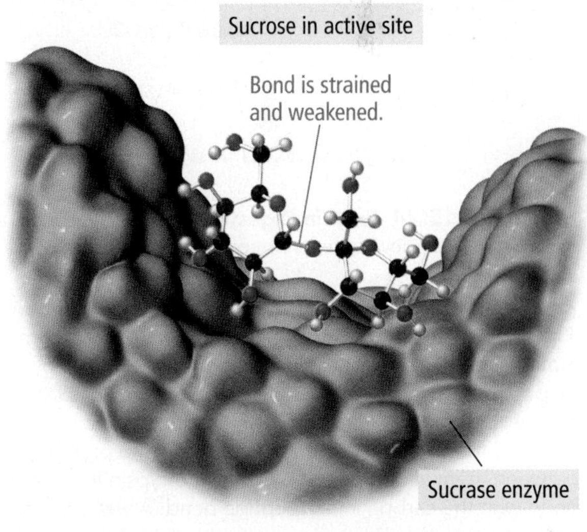

▲ **FIGURE 15.22 An Enzyme-Catalyzed Reaction** Sucrase catalyzes the conversion of sucrose into glucose and fructose by weakening the bond that joins the two rings.

of billions of substrates, much as one motorist stalled at a tollbooth can paralyze an entire highway full of cars. (For another example of enzyme action, see the *Chemistry and Medicine* box on the role of chymotrypsin in digestion.)

CHEMISTRY AND MEDICINE | Enzyme Catalysis and the Role of Chymotrypsin in Digestion

When we eat foods containing proteins—such as meats, eggs, beans, and nuts—the proteins must be digested. Proteins are large biological molecules composed of individual units called amino acids. (We discuss the structure of proteins and other biologically important molecules more fully in Chapter 23.) The amino acids in proteins are linked together via peptide bonds, as shown in Figure 15.23▼.

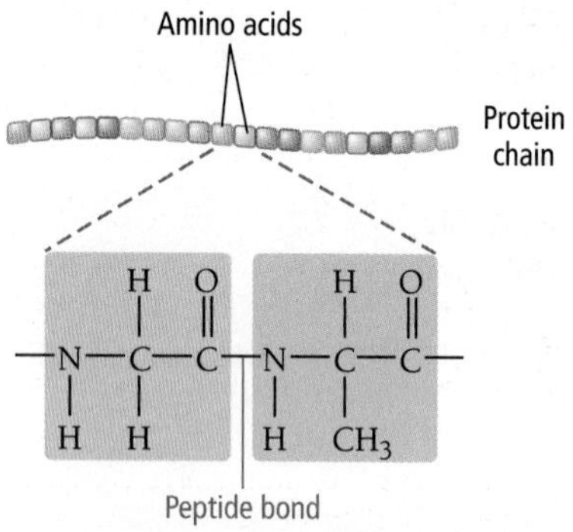

▲ **FIGURE 15.23 The Structure of a Protein** Proteins are chains of amino acids linked together by peptide bonds.

During digestion, the protein must be broken up into individual amino acids (Figure 15.24▼), which can pass through the walls of the small intestine and into the bloodstream. However, the peptide bonds that link amino acids together are relatively stable, and under ordinary conditions the reaction is slow.

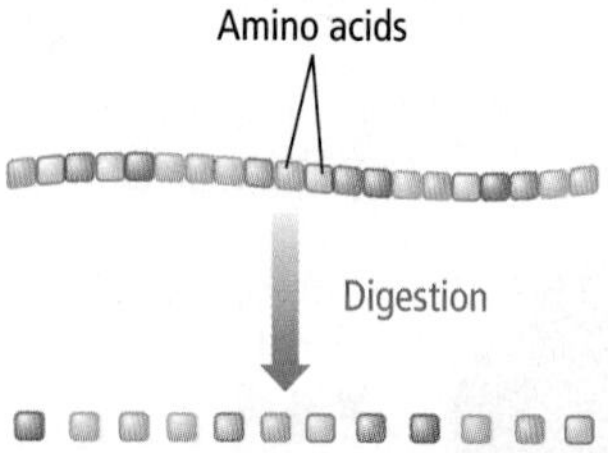

▲ **FIGURE 15.24 Protein Digestion** During digestion, a protein is broken down into its component amino acids.

The pancreas secretes an enzyme called chymotrypsin (Figure 15.25►) into the small intestine. Like many enzymes, chymotrypsin is highly selective in its action—it operates only on peptide bonds between certain kinds of amino acids. When a protein molecule containing such a pair of amino acids is attached to the active site of chymotrypsin, the peptide bond between them is weakened as the chymotrypsin forms a covalent bond with the carbon in the peptide bond. A water molecule can then come in and cleave the bond, with an —OH from the water binding to the carbon atom and the remaining —H bonding to the nitrogen (Figure 15.26►).

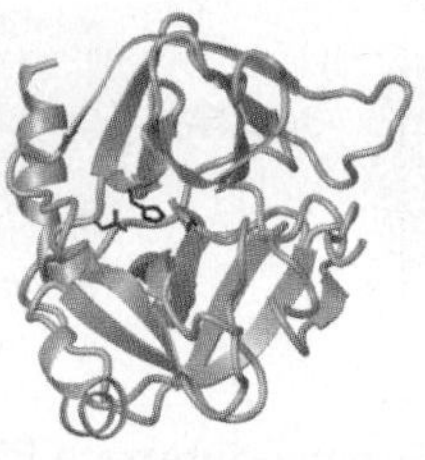

▲ **FIGURE 15.25 Chymotrypsin, a Digestive Enzyme** This model of chymotrypsin shows a section of a protein substrate (red) in the active site.

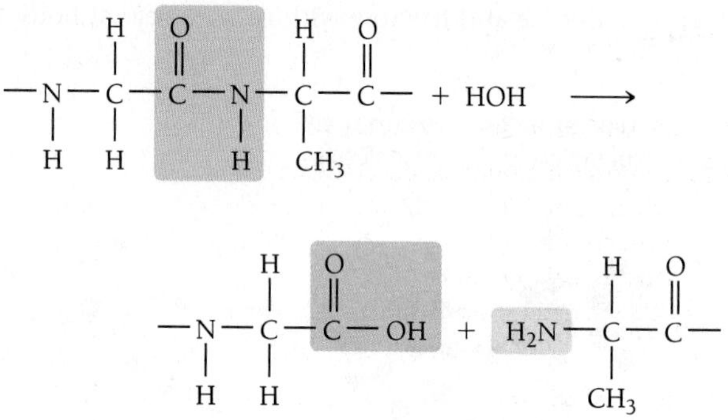

The amino acid chain is thus clipped at the peptide bond. The products of the reaction leave the active site, another protein binds to the chymotrypsin, and the process is repeated. Other digestive enzymes cleave protein chains between other pairs of amino acids. Together, these enzymes eventually reduce the entire protein to its constituent amino acids.

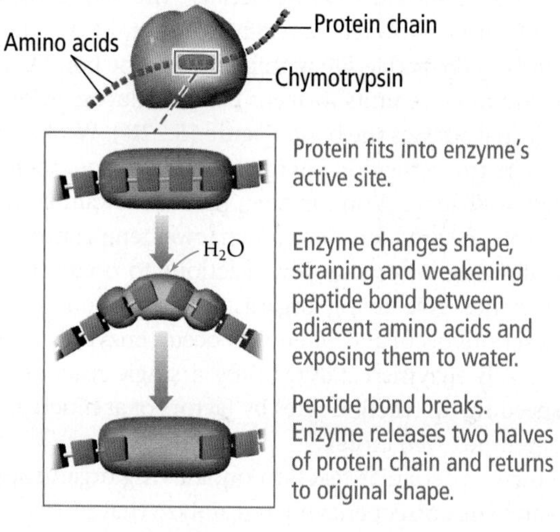

▲ **FIGURE 15.26 The Action of Chymotrypsin**

Self-Assessment Quiz

Q1. This graph shows the concentration of the reactant A in the reaction A $\longrightarrow$ B. Determine the average rate of the reaction between 0 and 10 seconds.
MISSED THIS? *Read Section 15.2; Watch KCV 15.2, IWE 15.1*

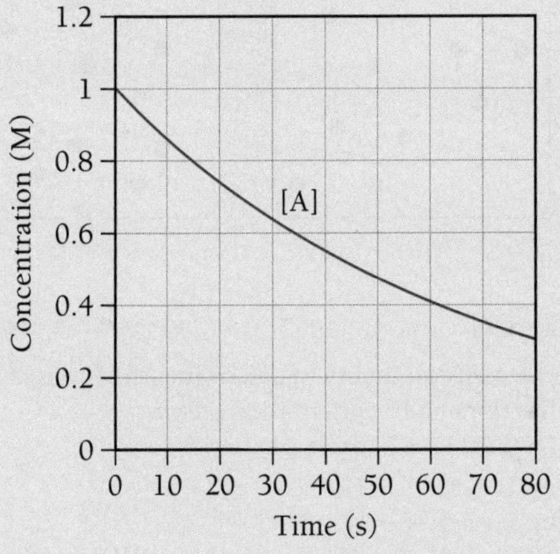

a) 0.07 M/s b) 0.007 M/s c) 0.86 M/s d) 0.014 M/s

Q2. Dinitrogen monoxide decomposes into nitrogen and oxygen when heated. The initial rate of the reaction is 0.022 M/s. What is the initial rate of change of the concentration of N_2O (that is, $\Delta[N_2O]/\Delta t$)?
MISSED THIS? *Read Section 15.2; Watch KCV 15.2, IWE 15.1*

$$2\,N_2O(g) \longrightarrow 2\,N_2(g) + O_2(g)$$

a) −0.022 M/s
b) −0.011 M/s
c) −0.044 M/s
d) +0.022 M/s

Q3. This plot shows the rate of the decomposition of SO_2Cl_2 into SO_2 and Cl_2 as a function of the concentration of SO_2Cl_2. What is the order of the reaction?
MISSED THIS? *Read Section 15.3; Watch KCV 15.3*

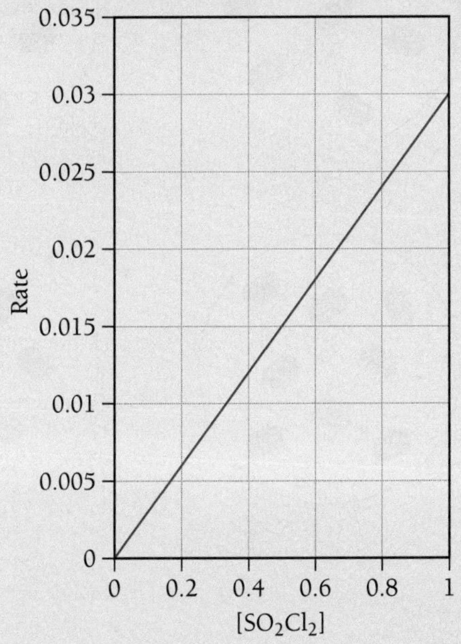

a) first order
b) second order
c) zero order
d) Order cannot be determined without more information.

Q4. For the reaction 2 A + B $\longrightarrow$ C, the initial rate is measured at several different reactant concentrations. From the resulting tabulated data, determine the rate law for the reaction.
MISSED THIS? *Read Section 15.3; Watch KCV 15.3, IWE 15.2*

[A] (M)	[B] (M)	Initial Rate (M/s)
0.05	0.05	0.035
0.10	0.05	0.070
0.20	0.10	0.56

a) Rate = $k[A][B]$
b) Rate = $k[A]^2[B]$
c) Rate = $k[A][B]^2$
d) Rate = $k[A]^2[B]^2$

Q5. What is the rate constant for the reaction in Question 4?
MISSED THIS? *Read Section 15.3; Watch KCV 15.3, IWE 15.2*

a) $2.8 \times 10^2\ M^{-2} \cdot s^{-1}$
b) $14\ M^{-2} \cdot s^{-1}$
c) $1.4 \times 10^2\ M^{-2} \cdot s^{-1}$
d) $1.4 \times 10^3\ M^{-2} \cdot s^{-1}$

Q6. The decomposition of Br_2 is followed as a function of time; two different plots of the data are shown. Determine the order and rate constant for the reaction.
MISSED THIS? *Read Section 15.4; Watch KCV 15.4*

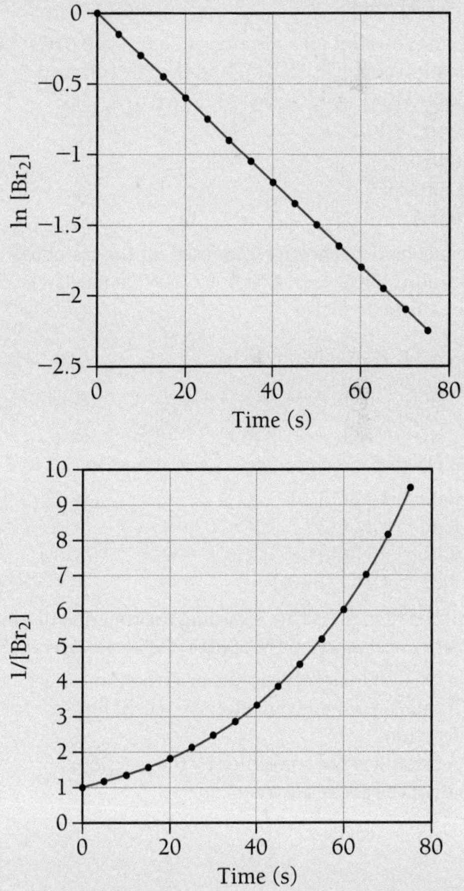

a) first order; $0.030\ s^{-1}$
b) first order; $33.3\ s^{-1}$
c) second order; $0.045\ M^{-1} \cdot s^{-1}$
d) second order; $22.2\ M^{-1} \cdot s^{-1}$

—Continued on the next page

Continued—

Q7. The reaction X $\longrightarrow$ products is second order in X and has a rate constant of 0.035 $M^{-1}s^{-1}$. If a reaction mixture is initially 0.45 M in X, what is the concentration of X after 155 seconds?
MISSED THIS? *Read Section 15.4; Watch KCV 15.4, IWE 15.4*

a) 7.6 M
b) 2.0×10^{-3} M
c) 0.13 M
d) 0.00 M

Q8. A decomposition reaction has a half-life that does not depend on the initial concentration of the reactant. What is the order of the reaction? **MISSED THIS?** *Read Section 15.4*

a) zero order
b) first order
c) second order
d) Order cannot be determined without more information.

Q9. The rate constant of a reaction is measured at different temperatures. A plot of the natural log of the rate constant as a function of the inverse of the temperature (in kelvins) yields a straight line with a slope of -8.55×10^3 K^{-1}. What is the activation energy (E_a) for the reaction?
MISSED THIS? *Read Section 15.5*

a) −71 kJ/mol
b) 71 kJ/mol
c) 1.0 kJ/mol
d) −1.0 kJ/mol

Q10. The rate constant for a reaction at 25.0 °C is 0.010 s^{-1}, and its activation energy is 35.8 kJ. Find the rate constant at 50.0 °C.
MISSED THIS? *Read Section 15.5; Watch IWE 15.8*

a) 0.021 s^{-1}
b) 0.010 s^{-1}
c) 0.0033 s^{-1}
d) 0.031 s^{-1}

Q11. The mechanism shown is proposed for the gas-phase reaction, $2\,N_2O_5 \longrightarrow 4\,NO_2 + O_2$. What rate law does the mechanism predict?

$N_2O_5 \underset{k_{-1}}{\overset{k_1}{\rightleftharpoons}} NO_2 + NO_3$ Fast

$NO_2 + NO_3 \longrightarrow NO_2 + O_2 + NO$ Slow

$NO + N_2O_5 \longrightarrow 3\,NO_2$ Fast

MISSED THIS? *Read Section 15.6; Watch KCV 15.6, IWE 15.9*

a) Rate = $k[N_2O_5]$
b) Rate = $k[N_2O_5]^2$
c) Rate = $k[N_2O_5]^0$
d) Rate = $k[NO_2][NO_3]$

Q12. Which statement is true regarding the function of a catalyst in a chemical reaction? **MISSED THIS?** *Read Section 15.7*

a) A catalyst increases the rate of a reaction.
b) A catalyst provides an alternate mechanism for the reaction.
c) A catalyst is not consumed by the reaction.
d) All of the above are true.

Q13. These images represent the first-order reaction A $\longrightarrow$ B initially and at some later time. The rate law for the reaction is Rate = 0.010 s^{-1} [A]. How much time has passed between the two images?
MISSED THIS? *Read Section 15.4; Watch KCV 15.4, IWE 15.4*

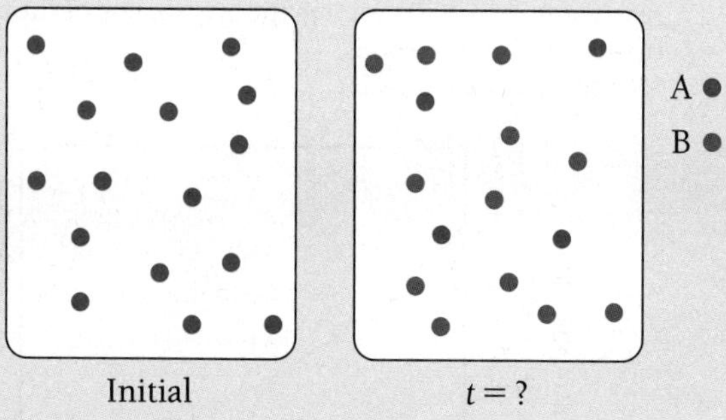

a) 69 s b) 139 s c) 60 s d) 12.5 s

Q14. Use collision theory to determine which single-step reaction has the smallest orientation factor.
MISSED THIS? *Read Section 15.5*

a) $H + H \longrightarrow H_2$
b) $I + HI \longrightarrow I_2 + H$
c) $H_2 + H_2C{=}CH_2 \longrightarrow H_3C{-}CH_3$
d) All of these reactions have the same orientation factor.

Q15. Carbon monoxide and chlorine gas react to form phosgene ($COCl_2$) according to the equation:

$$CO(g) + Cl_2(g) \longrightarrow COCl_2(g)$$

The rate law for the reaction is Rate = $k[Cl_2]^{3/2}[CO]$. Which representation of a mixture of chlorine gas and carbon monoxide gas has the fastest initial rate?
MISSED THIS? *Read Section 15.3; Watch KCV 15.3*

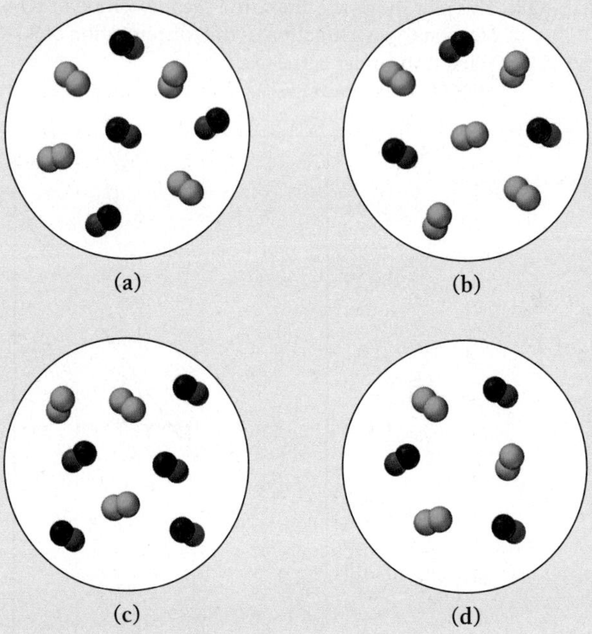

Answers: 1. (d) 2. (c) 3. (a) 4. (c) 5. (a) 6. (a) 7. (c) 8. (b) 9. (b) 10. (d) 11. (a) 12. (d) 13. (b) 14. (c) 15. (b)

CHAPTER 15 IN REVIEW

TERMS

Section 15.3
rate law (637)
rate constant (k) (637)
reaction order (n) (637)
overall order (640)

Section 15.4
integrated rate law (642)
half-life ($t_{1/2}$) (646)

Section 15.5
Arrhenius equation (650)
activation energy (E_a) (650)
frequency factor (A) (650)
activated complex (transition state) (651)
exponential factor (652)
Arrhenius plot (653)
collision model (655)
orientation factor (655)
collision frequency (655)

Section 15.6
reaction mechanism (656)
elementary step (657)
reaction intermediate (657)
molecularity (657)
unimolecular (657)
bimolecular (657)
termolecular (657)
rate-determining step (658)

Section 15.7
catalyst (661)
homogeneous catalysis (663)
heterogeneous catalysis (663)
hydrogenation (664)
enzyme (664)
active site (664)
substrate (664)

CONCEPTS

Reaction Rates, Orders, and Rate Laws (15.1–15.3)

- The rate of a chemical reaction is a measure of how fast a reaction occurs. The rate reflects the change in the concentration of a reactant or product per unit time and is usually reported in units of M/s.
- Reaction rates generally depend on the concentration of the reactants. The rate of a first-order reaction is directly proportional to the concentration of the reactant, the rate of a second-order reaction is proportional to the square of the concentration of the reactant, and the rate of a zero-order reaction is independent of the concentration of the reactant.
- For a reaction with more than one reactant, the order with respect to each reactant is, in general, independent of the order with respect to other reactants. The rate law shows the relationship between the rate and the concentrations of each reactant and must be determined experimentally.

Integrated Rate Laws and Half-Life (15.4)

- The rate law for a reaction describes the relationship between the rate of the reaction and the concentrations of the reactants.
- The integrated rate law for a reaction describes the relationship between the concentration of a reactant and time.
- The integrated rate law for a zero-order reaction shows that the concentration of the reactant varies linearly with time. For a first-order reaction, the *natural log* of the concentration of the reactant varies linearly with time, and for a second-order reaction, the *inverse* of the concentration of the reactant varies linearly with time.
- The half-life of a reaction can be derived from the integrated rate law and represents the time required for the concentration of a reactant to fall to one-half of its initial value. The half-life of a first-order reaction is *independent* of initial concentration of the reactant. The half-life of a zero-order or second-order reaction *depends* on the initial concentration of reactant.

The Effect of Temperature on Reaction Rate (15.5)

- The rate constant of a reaction generally depends on temperature and can be expressed by the Arrhenius equation, which consists of a frequency factor and an exponential factor.
- The frequency factor represents the number of times that the reactants approach the activation barrier per unit time. The exponential factor is the fraction of approaches that are successful in surmounting the activation barrier and forming products.
- The exponential factor depends on both the temperature and the activation energy, a barrier that the reactants must overcome to become products. The exponential factor increases with increasing temperature but decreases with increasing activation energy.
- We can determine the frequency factor and activation energy for a reaction by measuring the rate constant at different temperatures and constructing an Arrhenius plot.
- For reactions in the gas phase, Arrhenius behavior can be modeled with the collision model. In this model, reactions occur as a result of sufficiently energetic collisions. The colliding molecules must be oriented in such a way that the reaction can occur. The frequency factor contains two terms: p, which represents the fraction of collisions that have the proper orientation, and z, which represents the number of collisions per unit time.

Reaction Mechanisms (15.6)

- Most chemical reactions occur not in a single step, but in several steps. The series of individual steps by which a reaction occurs is the reaction mechanism.
- In order for a proposed reaction mechanism to be valid, it must fulfill two conditions: (a) the steps must sum to the overall reaction, and (b) the mechanism must predict the experimentally observed rate law.
- For mechanisms with a slow initial step, we derive the rate law from the slow step.
- For mechanisms with a fast initial step, we first write the rate law based on the slow step but then assume that the fast steps reach equilibrium, so we can write concentrations of intermediates in terms of the reactants.

Catalysis (15.7)

- A catalyst is a substance that increases the rate of a chemical reaction by providing an alternative mechanism that has a lower activation energy for the rate-determining step.
- Catalysts can be homogeneous or heterogeneous. A homogeneous catalyst exists in the same phase as the reactants and forms a homogeneous mixture with them. A heterogeneous catalyst exists in a different phase than the reactants.
- Enzymes are biological catalysts capable of increasing the rate of specific biochemical reactions by many orders of magnitude.

EQUATIONS AND RELATIONSHIPS

The Rate of Reaction (**15.2**)

For a reaction, $aA + bB \longrightarrow cC + dD$, the rate is defined as:

$$\text{Rate} = -\frac{1}{a}\frac{\Delta[A]}{\Delta t} = -\frac{1}{b}\frac{\Delta[B]}{\Delta t} = +\frac{1}{c}\frac{\Delta[C]}{\Delta t} = +\frac{1}{d}\frac{\Delta[D]}{\Delta t}$$

The Rate Law (**15.3**)

$\text{Rate} = k[A]^n$ (single reactant)

$\text{Rate} = k[A]^m[B]^n$ (multiple reactants)

Integrated Rate Laws and Half-Life (**15.4**)

Reaction Order	Integrated Rate Law	Units of k	Half-Life Expression
0	$[A]_t = -kt + [A]_0$	$M \cdot s^{-1}$	$t_{1/2} = \frac{[A]_0}{2k}$
1	$\ln [A]_t = -kt + \ln [A]_0$	s^{-1}	$t_{1/2} = \frac{0.693}{k}$
2	$\frac{1}{[A]_t} = kt + \frac{1}{[A]_0}$	$M^{-1} \cdot s^{-1}$	$t_{1/2} = \frac{1}{k[A]_0}$

Arrhenius Equation (**15.5**)

$k = Ae^{-E_a/RT}$

$\ln k = -\frac{E_a}{R}\left(\frac{1}{T}\right) + \ln A$ (linearized form)

$\ln\frac{k_2}{k_1} = \frac{E_a}{R}\left(\frac{1}{T_1} - \frac{1}{T_2}\right)$ (two-point form)

$k = pze^{-E_a/RT}$ (collision theory)

Rate Laws for Elementary Steps (**15.6**)

Elementary Step	Molecularity	Rate Law
$A \longrightarrow$ products	1	$\text{Rate} = k[A]$
$A + A \longrightarrow$ products	2	$\text{Rate} = k[A]^2$
$A + B \longrightarrow$ products	2	$\text{Rate} = k[A][B]$
$A + A + A \longrightarrow$ products	3 (rare)	$\text{Rate} = k[A]^3$
$A + A + B \longrightarrow$ products	3 (rare)	$\text{Rate} = k[A]^2[B]$
$A + B + C \longrightarrow$ products	3 (rare)	$\text{Rate} = k[A][B][C]$

LEARNING OUTCOMES

Chapter Objectives	Assessment
Express reaction rates (15.2)	Example 15.1 **For Practice** 15.1 **Exercises** 25–34
Analyze reactions in terms of the rate law (rate constant and reaction order) (15.3)	Example 15.2 **For Practice** 15.2 **Exercises** 35–46
Analyze graphical reaction data using the integrated rate law to determine the reaction order and the rate constant (15.4)	Examples 15.3–15.5 **For Practice** 15.3–15.5 **Exercises** 47–52
Perform half-life calculations (15.4)	Example 15.6 **For Practice** 15.6 **Exercises** 53–58
Perform rate calculations involving the Arrhenius equation (15.5)	Examples 15.7, 15.8 **For Practice** 15.7, 15.8 **Exercises** 59–74
Determine whether a reaction mechanism is valid (15.6)	**Exercises** 75–78
Describe the affects of catalysts on rates of reaction (15.7)	**Exercises** 79–82

EXERCISES

Mastering Chemistry provides end-of-chapter exercises, feedback-enriched tutorial problems, animations, and interactive activities to encourage problem-solving practice and deeper understanding of key concepts and topics.

REVIEW QUESTIONS

1. Explain why lizards become sluggish in cold weather. How is this phenomenon related to chemistry?

2. Why are reaction rates important (both practically and theoretically)?

3. What units are typically used to express the rate of a reaction?

4. Why is the reaction rate for reactants defined as the *negative* of the change in reactant concentration with respect to time, whereas for products it is defined as the change in reactant concentration with respect to time (with a positive sign)?

5. Explain the difference between the average rate of reaction and the instantaneous rate of reaction.

6. Consider a simple reaction in which reactant A forms products:

$$A \longrightarrow \text{products}$$

What is the rate law if the reaction is zero order with respect to A? First order? Second order? For each case, explain how a doubling of the concentration of A would affect the rate of reaction.

7. How is the order of a reaction generally determined?

8. For a reaction with multiple reactants, how is the overall order of the reaction defined?

9. Explain the difference between the rate law for a reaction and the integrated rate law for a reaction. What relationship does each kind of rate law express?

10. Write integrated rate laws for zero-order, first-order, and second-order reactions of the form A $\longrightarrow$ products.

11. What does the term *half-life* mean? Write the expressions for the half-lives of zero-order, first-order, and second-order reactions.

12. How do reaction rates typically depend on temperature? What part of the rate law is temperature dependent?

13. Explain the meaning of each term within the Arrhenius equation: activation energy, frequency factor, and exponential factor. Use these terms and the Arrhenius equation to explain why small changes in temperature can result in large changes in reaction rates.

14. What is an Arrhenius plot? Explain the significance of the slope and intercept of an Arrhenius plot.

15. Explain how a chemical reaction occurs according to the collision model. Explain the meaning of the orientation factor in this model.

16. Explain the difference between a normal chemical equation for a chemical reaction and the mechanism of that reaction.

17. In a reaction mechanism, what is an elementary step? Write down the three most common elementary steps and the corresponding rate law for each one.

18. What are the two requirements for a proposed mechanism to be valid for a given reaction?

19. What is an intermediate within a reaction mechanism?

20. What is a catalyst? How does a catalyst increase the rate of a chemical reaction?

21. Explain the difference between homogeneous catalysis and heterogeneous catalysis.

22. What are the four basic steps involved in heterogeneous catalysis?

23. What are enzymes? What is the active site of an enzyme? What is a substrate?

24. What is the general two-step mechanism by which most enzymes work?

PROBLEMS BY TOPIC

Reaction Rates

25. Consider the reaction:
MISSED THIS? *Read Section 15.2; Watch KCV 15.2, IWE 15.1*

$$2\,HBr(g) \longrightarrow H_2(g) + Br_2(g)$$

a. Express the rate of the reaction in terms of the change in concentration of each of the reactants and products.
b. In the first 25.0 s of this reaction, the concentration of HBr dropped from 0.600 M to 0.512 M. Calculate the average rate of the reaction during this time interval.
c. If the volume of the reaction vessel in part b was 1.50 L, what amount of Br_2 (in moles) was formed during the first 15.0 s of the reaction?

26. Consider the reaction:

$$2\,N_2O(g) \longrightarrow 2\,N_2(g) + O_2(g)$$

a. Express the rate of the reaction in terms of the change in concentration of each of the reactants and products.
b. In the first 15.0 s of the reaction, 0.015 mol of O_2 is produced in a reaction vessel with a volume of 0.500 L. What is the average rate of the reaction during this time interval?
c. Predict the rate of change in the concentration of N_2O during this time interval. In other words, what is $\Delta[N_2O]/\Delta t$?

27. For the reaction $2\,A(g) + B(g) \longrightarrow 3\,C(g)$,
MISSED THIS? *Read Section 15.2; Watch KCV 15.2, IWE 15.1*

a. determine the expression for the rate of the reaction in terms of the change in concentration of each of the reactants and products.
b. when A is decreasing at a rate of 0.100 M/s, how fast is B decreasing? How fast is C increasing?

28. For the reaction $A(g) + \frac{1}{2}\,B(g) \longrightarrow 2\,C(g)$,

a. determine the expression for the rate of the reaction in terms of the change in concentration of each of the reactants and products.
b. when C is increasing at a rate of 0.025 M/s, how fast is B decreasing? How fast is A decreasing?

29. Consider the reaction:
MISSED THIS? *Read Section 15.2; Watch KCV 15.2, IWE 15.1*

$$Cl_2(g) + 3\,F_2(g) \longrightarrow 2\,ClF_3(g)$$

Complete the table.

$\Delta[Cl_2]/\Delta t$	$\Delta[F_2]/\Delta t$	$\Delta[ClF_3]/\Delta t$	Rate
−0.012 M/s			

30. Consider the reaction:

$$8\,H_2S(g) + 4\,O_2(g) \longrightarrow 8\,H_2O(g) + S_8(g)$$

Complete the table.

$\Delta[H_2S]/\Delta t$	$\Delta[O_2]/\Delta t$	$\Delta[H_2O]/\Delta t$	$\Delta[S_8]/\Delta t$	Rate
−0.080 M/s				

31. Consider the reaction:
MISSED THIS? *Read Section 15.2; Watch KCV 15.2, IWE 15.1*

$$C_4H_8(g) \longrightarrow 2\,C_2H_4(g)$$

The tabulated data were collected for the concentration of C_4H_8 as a function of time:

Time (s)	$[C_4H_8]$ (M)
0	1.000
10	0.913
20	0.835
30	0.763
40	0.697
50	0.637

a. What is the average rate of the reaction between 0 and 10 s? Between 40 and 50 s?
b. What is the rate of formation of C_2H_4 between 20 and 30 s?

32. Consider the reaction:

$$NO_2(g) \longrightarrow NO(g) + \frac{1}{2}O_2(g)$$

The tabulated data were collected for the concentration of NO_2 as a function of time:

Time (s)	$[NO_2]$ (M)
0	1.000
10	0.951
20	0.904
30	0.860
40	0.818
50	0.778
60	0.740
70	0.704
80	0.670
90	0.637
100	0.606

a. What is the average rate of the reaction between 10 and 20 s? Between 50 and 60 s?

b. What is the rate of formation of O_2 between 50 and 60 s?

33. Consider the reaction:
MISSED THIS? *Read Section 15.2; Watch KCV 15.2, IWE 15.1*

$$H_2(g) + Br_2(g) \longrightarrow 2\,HBr(g)$$

The graph shows the concentration of Br_2 as a function of time.

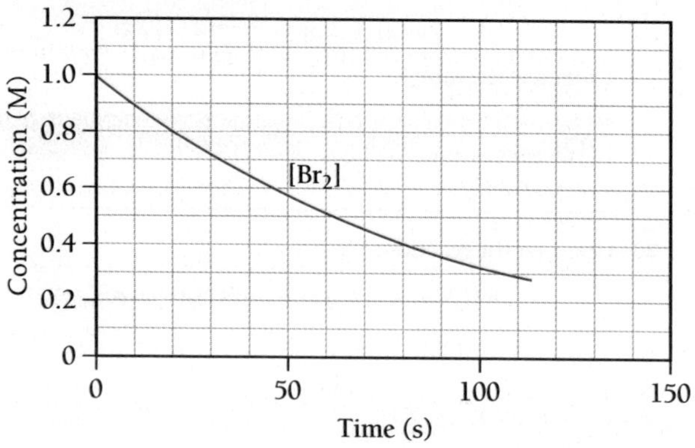

a. Use the graph to calculate each quantity:
   i. the average rate of the reaction between 0 and 25 s
   ii. the instantaneous rate of the reaction at 25 s
   iii. the instantaneous rate of formation of HBr at 50 s

b. Make a rough sketch of a curve representing the concentration of HBr as a function of time. Assume that the initial concentration of HBr is zero.

34. Consider the reaction:

$$2\,H_2O_2(aq) \longrightarrow 2\,H_2O(l) + O_2(g)$$

The graph shows the concentration of H_2O_2 as a function of time.

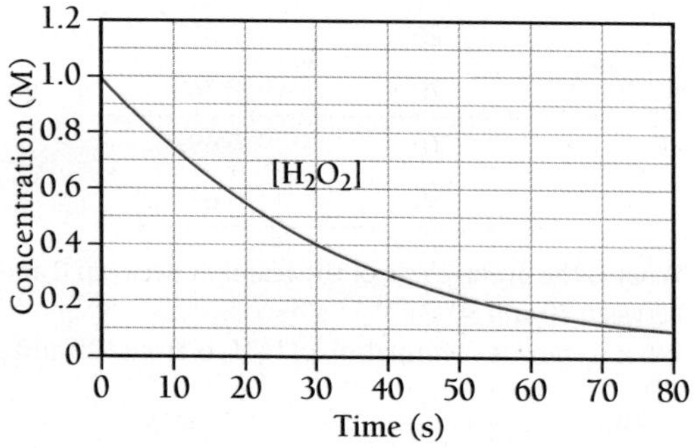

Use the graph to calculate each quantity:

a. the average rate of the reaction between 10 and 20 s
b. the instantaneous rate of the reaction at 30 s
c. the instantaneous rate of formation of O_2 at 50 s
d. If the initial volume of the H_2O_2 is 1.5 L, what total amount of O_2 (in moles) is formed in the first 50 s of reaction?

The Rate Law and Reaction Orders

35. This graph shows a plot of the rate of a reaction versus the concentration of the reactant A for the reaction A $\longrightarrow$ products.
MISSED THIS? *Read Section 15.3; Watch KCV 15.3*

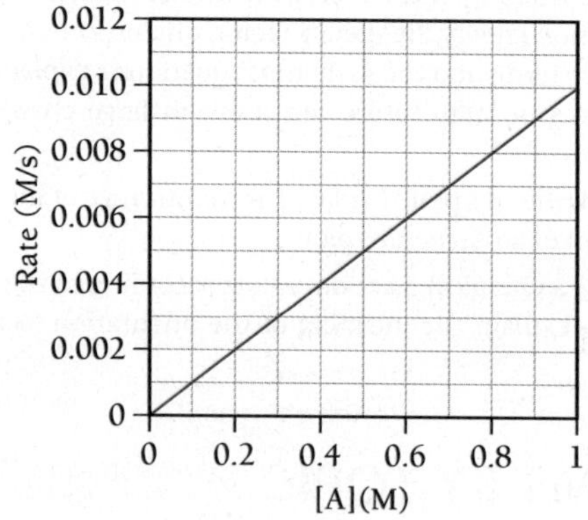

a. What is the order of the reaction with respect to A?
b. Make a rough sketch of a plot of [A] versus *time*.
c. Write a rate law for the reaction including an estimate for the value of *k*.

36. This graph shows a plot of the rate of a reaction versus the concentration of the reactant.

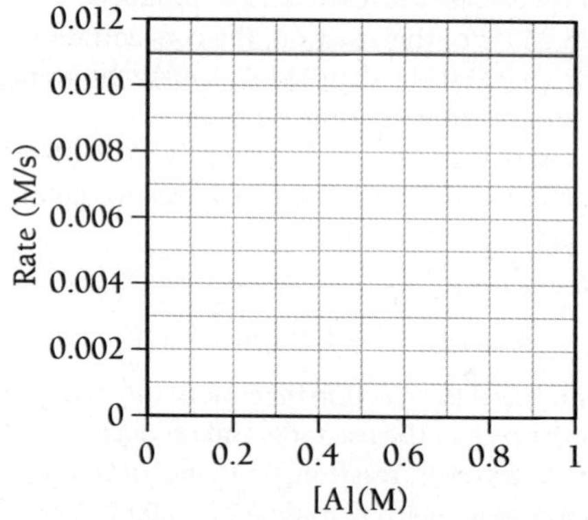

a. What is the order of the reaction with respect to A?
b. Make a rough sketch of a plot of [A] versus *time*.
c. Write a rate law for the reaction including the value of *k*.

37. What are the units of *k* for each type of reaction?
MISSED THIS? *Read Section 15.3*

a. first-order reaction
b. second-order reaction
c. zero-order reaction

38. This reaction is first order in N_2O_5:

$$N_2O_5(g) \longrightarrow NO_3(g) + NO_2(g)$$

The rate constant for the reaction at a certain temperature is 0.053/s.

a. Calculate the rate of the reaction when $[N_2O_5] = 0.055$ M.
b. What would the rate of the reaction be at the concentration indicated in part a if the reaction were second order? Zero order? (Assume the same *numerical* value for the rate constant with the appropriate units.)

39. A reaction in which A, B, and C react to form products is first order in A, second order in B, and zero order in C.
MISSED THIS? *Read Section 15.3; Watch KCV 15.3*

a. Write a rate law for the reaction.
b. What is the overall order of the reaction?
c. By what factor does the reaction rate change if [A] is doubled (and the other reactant concentrations are held constant)?
d. By what factor does the reaction rate change if [B] is doubled (and the other reactant concentrations are held constant)?
e. By what factor does the reaction rate change if [C] is doubled (and the other reactant concentrations are held constant)?
f. By what factor does the reaction rate change if the concentrations of all three reactants are doubled?

40. A reaction in which A, B, and C react to form products is zero order in A, one-half order in B, and second order in C.

a. Write a rate law for the reaction.
b. What is the overall order of the reaction?
c. By what factor does the reaction rate change if [A] is doubled (and the other reactant concentrations are held constant)?
d. By what factor does the reaction rate change if [B] is doubled (and the other reactant concentrations are held constant)?
e. By what factor does the reaction rate change if [C] is doubled (and the other reactant concentrations are held constant)?
f. By what factor does the reaction rate change if the concentrations of all three reactants are doubled?

41. Consider the data showing the initial rate of a reaction (A ⟶ products) at several different concentrations of A. What is the order of the reaction? Write a rate law for the reaction, including the value of the rate constant, *k*.
MISSED THIS? *Read Section 15.3; Watch KCV 15.3, IWE 15.2*

[A] (M)	Initial Rate (M/s)
0.100	0.053
0.200	0.210
0.300	0.473

42. Consider the data showing the initial rate of a reaction (A ⟶ products) at several different concentrations of A. What is the order of the reaction? Write a rate law for the reaction, including the value of the rate constant, *k*.

[A] (M)	Initial Rate (M/s)
0.15	0.008
0.30	0.016
0.60	0.032

43. Consider the tabulated data showing the initial rate of a reaction (A ⟶ products) at several different concentrations of A. What is the order of the reaction? Write a rate law for the reaction, including the value of the rate constant, *k*.
MISSED THIS? *Read Section 15.3; Watch KCV 15.3, IWE 15.2*

[A] (M)	Initial Rate (M/s)
0.12	0.0078
0.16	0.0104
0.20	0.0130

44. Consider the tabulated data showing the initial rate of a reaction (A ⟶ products) at several different concentrations of A. What is the order of the reaction? Write a rate law for the reaction, including the value of the rate constant, *k*.

[A] (M)	Initial Rate (M/s)
0.12	3.89×10^{-4}
0.18	8.75×10^{-4}
0.28	2.12×10^{-3}

45. The tabulated data were collected for this reaction:
MISSED THIS? *Read Section 15.3; Watch KCV 15.3, IWE 15.2*

$$2\,NO_2(g) + F_2(g) \longrightarrow 2\,NO_2F(g)$$

$[NO_2]$	$[F_2]$ (M)	Initial Rate (M/s)
0.100	0.100	0.026
0.200	0.100	0.051
0.200	0.200	0.103
0.400	0.400	0.411

Write an expression for the reaction rate law and calculate the value of the rate constant, *k*. What is the overall order of the reaction?

46. The tabulated data were collected for this reaction:

$$CH_3Cl(g) + 3\,Cl_2(g) \longrightarrow CCl_4(g) + 3\,HCl(g)$$

$[CH_3Cl]$ (M)	$[Cl_2]$ (M)	Initial Rate (M/s)
0.050	0.050	0.014
0.100	0.050	0.029
0.100	0.100	0.041
0.200	0.200	0.115

Write an expression for the reaction rate law and calculate the value of the rate constant, *k*. What is the overall order of the reaction?

The Integrated Rate Law and Half-Life

47. Indicate the order of reaction consistent with each observation.
MISSED THIS? *Read Section 15.4; Watch KCV 15.4*

a. A plot of the concentration of the reactant versus time yields a straight line.
b. The reaction has a half-life that is independent of initial concentration.
c. A plot of the inverse of the concentration versus time yields a straight line.

48. Indicate the order of reaction consistent with each observation.

a. The half-life of the reaction gets shorter as the initial concentration is increased.
b. A plot of the natural log of the concentration of the reactant versus time yields a straight line.
c. The half-life of the reaction gets longer as the initial concentration is increased.

49. The tabulated data show the concentration of AB versus time for this reaction:
MISSED THIS? *Read Section 15.4; Watch KCV 15.4*

$$AB(g) \longrightarrow A(g) + B(g)$$

Time (s)	[AB] (M)
0	0.950
50	0.459
100	0.302
150	0.225
200	0.180
250	0.149
300	0.128
350	0.112
400	0.0994
450	0.0894
500	0.0812

Determine the order of the reaction and the value of the rate constant. Predict the concentration of AB at 25 s.

50. The tabulated data show the concentration of N_2O_5 versus time for this reaction:

$$N_2O_5(g) \longrightarrow NO_3(g) + NO_2(g)$$

Time (s)	$[N_2O_5]$ (M)
0	1.000
25	0.822
50	0.677
75	0.557
100	0.458
125	0.377
150	0.310
175	0.255
200	0.210

Determine the order of the reaction and the value of the rate constant. Predict the concentration of N_2O_5 at 250 s.

51. The tabulated data show the concentration of cyclobutane (C_4H_8) versus time for this reaction:
MISSED THIS? *Read Section 15.4; Watch KCV 15.4*

$$C_4H_8 \longrightarrow 2\,C_2H_4$$

Time (s)	$[C_4H_8]$ (M)
0	1.000
10	0.894
20	0.799
30	0.714
40	0.638
50	0.571
60	0.510
70	0.456
80	0.408
90	0.364
100	0.326

Determine the order of the reaction and the value of the rate constant. What is the rate of reaction when $[C_4H_8] = 0.25$ M?

52. The reaction A $\longrightarrow$ products was monitored as a function of time. The results are shown here.

Time (s)	[A] (M)
0	1.000
25	0.914
50	0.829
75	0.744
100	0.659
125	0.573
150	0.488
175	0.403
200	0.318

Determine the order of the reaction and the value of the rate constant. What is the rate of reaction when $[A] = 0.10$ M?

53. This reaction was monitored as a function of time:
MISSED THIS? *Read Section 15.4; Watch KCV 15.4, IWE 15.4*

$$A \longrightarrow B + C$$

A plot of ln[A] versus time yields a straight line with slope $-0.0045/s$.

a. What is the value of the rate constant (k) for this reaction at this temperature?
b. Write the rate law for the reaction.
c. What is the half-life?
d. If the initial concentration of A is 0.250 M, what is the concentration after 225 s?

54. This reaction was monitored as a function of time:

$$AB \longrightarrow A + B$$

A plot of 1/[AB] versus time yields a straight line with a slope of $+0.55/M \cdot s$.

a. What is the value of the rate constant (k) for this reaction at this temperature?
b. Write the rate law for the reaction.
c. What is the half-life when the initial concentration is 0.55 M?
d. If the initial concentration of AB is 0.250 M and the reaction mixture initially contains no products, what are the concentrations of A and B after 75 s?

55. The decomposition of SO_2Cl_2 is first order in SO_2Cl_2 and has a rate constant of $1.42 \times 10^{-4} s^{-1}$ at a certain temperature.
MISSED THIS? *Read Section 15.4; Watch KCV 15.4, IWE 15.4*

a. What is the half-life for this reaction?
b. How long will it take for the concentration of SO_2Cl_2 to decrease to 25% of its initial concentration?
c. If the initial concentration of SO_2Cl_2 is 1.00 M, how long will it take for the concentration to decrease to 0.78 M?
d. If the initial concentration of SO_2Cl_2 is 0.150 M, what is the concentration of SO_2Cl_2 after 2.00×10^2 s? After 5.00×10^2 s?

56. The decomposition of XY is second order in XY and has a rate constant of $7.02 \times 10^{-3} M^{-1} \cdot s^{-1}$ at a certain temperature.

a. What is the half-life for this reaction at an initial concentration of 0.100 M?
b. How long will it take for the concentration of XY to decrease to 12.5% of its initial concentration when the initial concentration is 0.100 M? When the initial concentration is 0.200 M?
c. If the initial concentration of XY is 0.150 M, how long will it take for the concentration to decrease to 0.062 M?
d. If the initial concentration of XY is 0.050 M, what is the concentration of XY after 5.0×10^1 s? After 5.50×10^2 s?

57. The half-life for the radioactive decay of U-238 is 4.5 billion years and is independent of initial concentration. How long will it take for 10% of the U-238 atoms in a sample of U-238 to decay? If a sample of U-238 initially contained 1.5×10^{18} atoms when the universe was formed 13.8 billion years ago, how many U-238 atoms does it contain today?
MISSED THIS? *Read Section 15.4; Watch KCV 15.4, IWE 15.4*

58. The half-life for the radioactive decay of C-14 is 5730 years and is independent of the initial concentration. How long does it take for 25% of the C-14 atoms in a sample of C-14 to decay? If a sample of C-14 initially contains 1.5 mmol of C-14, how many millimoles are left after 2255 years?

The Effect of Temperature and the Collision Model

59. The diagram shows the energy of a reaction as the reaction progresses. Label each blank box in the diagram.
MISSED THIS? *Read Section 15.5; Watch KCV 15.5*

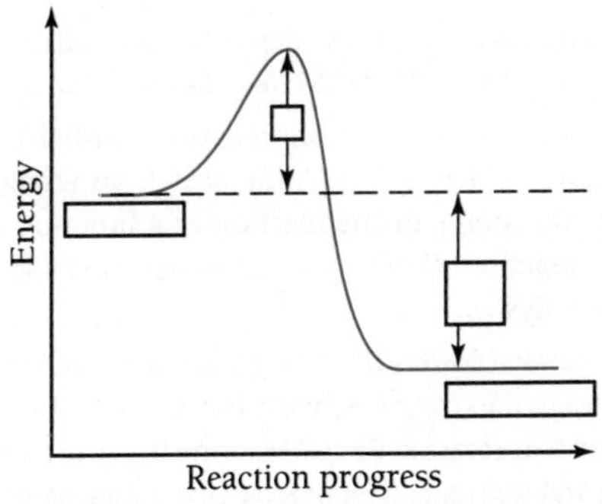

a. reactants b. products
c. activation energy (E_a)
d. enthalpy of reaction (ΔH_{rxn})

60. A chemical reaction is endothermic and has an activation energy that is twice the value of the enthalpy change of the reaction. Draw a diagram depicting the energy of the reaction as it progresses. Label the position of the reactants and products and indicate the activation energy and enthalpy of reaction.

61. The activation energy of a reaction is 56.8 kJ/mol, and the frequency factor is 1.5×10^{11}/s. Calculate the rate constant of the reaction at 25 °C.
MISSED THIS? *Read Section 15.5; Watch KCV 15.5*

62. The rate constant of a reaction at 32 °C is 0.055/s. If the frequency factor is 1.2×10^{13}/s, what is the activation barrier?

63. The rate constant (k) for a reaction was measured as a function of temperature. A plot of ln k versus $1/T$ (in K) is linear and has a slope of −7445 K. Calculate the activation energy for the reaction.
MISSED THIS? *Read Section 15.5*

64. The rate constant (k) for a reaction was measured as a function of temperature. A plot of ln k versus $1/T$ (in K) is linear and has a slope of -1.01×10^4 K. Calculate the activation energy for the reaction.

65. The data shown here were collected for the first-order reaction:
MISSED THIS? *Read Section 15.5*

$$N_2O(g) \longrightarrow N_2(g) + O(g)$$

Use an Arrhenius plot to determine the activation barrier and frequency factor for the reaction.

Temperature (K)	Rate Constant (1/s)
800	3.24×10^{-5}
900	0.00214
1000	0.0614
1100	0.955

66. The tabulated data show the rate constant of a reaction measured at several different temperatures. Use an Arrhenius plot to determine the activation barrier and frequency factor for the reaction.

Temperature (K)	Rate Constant (1/s)
300	0.0134
310	0.0407
320	0.114
330	0.303
340	0.757

67. The tabulated data were collected for the second-order reaction:
MISSED THIS? *Read Section 15.5*

$$Cl(g) + H_2(g) \longrightarrow HCl(g) + H(g)$$

Use an Arrhenius plot to determine the activation barrier and frequency factor for the reaction.

Temperature (K)	Rate Constant (L/mol · s)
90	0.00357
100	0.0773
110	0.956
120	7.781

68. The tabulated data show the rate constant of a reaction measured at several different temperatures. Use an Arrhenius plot to determine the activation barrier and frequency factor for the reaction.

Temperature (K)	Rate Constant (1/s)
310	0.00434
320	0.0140
330	0.0421
340	0.118
350	0.316

69. A reaction has a rate constant of 0.0117/s at 400.0 K and 0.689/s at 450.0 K.
MISSED THIS? *Read Section 15.5; Watch IWE 15.8*

a. Determine the activation barrier for the reaction.
b. What is the value of the rate constant at 425 K?

70. A reaction has a rate constant of 0.000122/s at 27 °C and 0.228/s at 77 °C.

a. Determine the activation barrier for the reaction.
b. What is the value of the rate constant at 17 °C?

71. If a temperature increase from 10.0 °C to 20.0 °C doubles the rate constant for a reaction, what is the value of the activation barrier for the reaction?
MISSED THIS? *Read Section 15.5; Watch IWE 15.8*

72. If a temperature increase from 20.0 °C to 35.0 °C triples the rate constant for a reaction, what is the value of the activation barrier for the reaction?

73. Consider these two gas-phase reactions:
MISSED THIS? *Read Section 15.5*

a. $AA(g) + BB(g) \longrightarrow 2\,AB(g)$
b. $AB(g) + CD(g) \longrightarrow AC(g) + BD(g)$

If the reactions have identical activation barriers and are carried out under the same conditions, which one would you expect to have the faster rate?

74. Which of these two reactions would you expect to have the smaller orientation factor? Explain.

a. $O(g) + N_2(g) \longrightarrow NO(g) + N(g)$
b. $NO(g) + Cl_2(g) \longrightarrow NOCl(g) + Cl(g)$

Reaction Mechanisms

75. Consider this overall reaction, which is experimentally observed to be second order in AB and zero order in C:
MISSED THIS? *Read Section 15.6; Watch KCV 15.6, IWE 15.9*

$$AB + C \longrightarrow A + BC$$

Is the following mechanism valid for this reaction?

$$AB + AB \xrightarrow[k_1]{} AB_2 + A \quad \text{Slow}$$

$$AB_2 + C \xrightarrow[k_2]{} AB + BC \quad \text{Fast}$$

76. Consider this overall reaction, which is experimentally observed to be second order in X and first order in Y:

$$X + Y \longrightarrow XY$$

a. Does the reaction occur in a single step in which X and Y collide?

b. Is this two-step mechanism valid?

$$2\,X \underset{k_2}{\overset{k_1}{\rightleftharpoons}} X_2 \qquad \text{Fast}$$

$$X_2 + Y \xrightarrow[k_3]{} XY + X \qquad \text{Slow}$$

77. Consider this three-step mechanism for a reaction:
MISSED THIS? *Read Section 15.6; Watch KCV 15.6, IWE 15.9*

$$Cl_2(g) \underset{k_2}{\overset{k_1}{\rightleftharpoons}} 2\,Cl(g) \qquad \text{Fast}$$

$$Cl(g) + CHCl_3(g) \xrightarrow[k_3]{} HCl(g) + CCl_3(g) \qquad \text{Slow}$$

$$Cl(g) + CCl_3(g) \xrightarrow[k_4]{} CCl_4(g) \qquad \text{Fast}$$

a. What is the overall reaction?

b. Identify the intermediates in the mechanism.

c. What is the predicted rate law?

78. Consider this two-step mechanism for a reaction:

$$NO_2(g) + Cl_2(g) \xrightarrow[k_1]{} ClNO_2(g) + Cl(g) \qquad \text{Slow}$$

$$NO_2(g) + Cl(g) \xrightarrow[k_2]{} ClNO_2(g) \qquad \text{Fast}$$

a. What is the overall reaction?

b. Identify the intermediates in the mechanism.

c. What is the predicted rate law?

Catalysis

79. Many heterogeneous catalysts are deposited on high-surface-area supports. Why? **MISSED THIS?** *Read Section 15.7*

80. Suppose that the reaction A $\longrightarrow$ products is exothermic and has an activation barrier of 75 kJ/mol. Sketch an energy diagram showing the energy of the reaction as a function of the progress of the reaction. Draw a second energy curve showing the effect of a catalyst.

81. Suppose that a catalyst lowers the activation barrier of a reaction from 125 kJ/mol to 55 kJ/mol. By what factor would you expect the reaction rate to increase at 25 °C? (Assume that the frequency factors for the catalyzed and uncatalyzed reactions are identical.)
MISSED THIS? *Read Sections 15.5, 15.7*

82. The activation barrier for the hydrolysis of sucrose into glucose and fructose is 108 kJ/mol. If an enzyme increases the rate of the hydrolysis reaction by a factor of 1 million, how much lower must the activation barrier be when sucrose is in the active site of the enzyme? (Assume that the frequency factors for the catalyzed and uncatalyzed reactions are identical and a temperature of 25 °C.)

CUMULATIVE PROBLEMS

83. The tabulated data were collected for this reaction at 500 °C:

$$CH_3CN(g) \longrightarrow CH_3NC(g)$$

Time (h)	[CH_3CN] (M)
0.0	1.000
5.0	0.794
10.0	0.631
15.0	0.501
20.0	0.398
25.0	0.316

a. Determine the order of the reaction and the value of the rate constant at this temperature.

b. What is the half-life for this reaction (at the initial concentration)?

c. How long will it take for 90% of the CH_3CN to convert to CH_3NC?

84. The tabulated data were collected for this reaction at a certain temperature:

$$X_2Y \longrightarrow 2\,X + Y$$

Time (h)	[X_2Y] (M)
0.0	0.100
1.0	0.0856
2.0	0.0748
3.0	0.0664
4.0	0.0598
5.0	0.0543

a. Determine the order of the reaction and the value of the rate constant at this temperature.

b. What is the half-life for this reaction (at the initial concentration)?

c. What is the concentration of X after 10.0 hours?

85. Consider the reaction:

$$A + B + C \longrightarrow D$$

The rate law for this reaction is:

$$\text{Rate} = k\frac{[A][C]^2}{[B]^{1/2}}$$

Suppose the rate of the reaction at certain initial concentrations of A, B, and C is 0.0115 M/s. What is the rate of the reaction if the concentrations of A and C are doubled and the concentration of B is tripled?

86. Consider the reaction:

$$2\,O_3(g) \longrightarrow 3\,O_2(g)$$

The rate law for this reaction is:

$$\text{Rate} = k\frac{[O_3]^2}{[O_2]}$$

Suppose that a 1.0-L reaction vessel initially contains 1.0 mol of O_3 and 1.0 mol of O_2. What fraction of the O_3 will have reacted when the rate falls to one-half of its initial value?

87. At 700 K, acetaldehyde decomposes in the gas phase to methane and carbon monoxide. The reaction is:

$$CH_3CHO(g) \longrightarrow CH_4(g) + CO(g)$$

A sample of CH_3CHO is heated to 700 K, and the pressure is measured as 0.22 atm before any reaction takes place. The kinetics of the reaction are followed by measurements of total pressure, and these data are obtained:

t (s)	0	1000	3000	7000
P_{Total} (atm)	0.22	0.24	0.27	0.31

Find the rate law, the rate constant, and the total pressure after 2.00×10^4 s.

88. At 400 K, oxalic acid decomposes according to the reaction:

$$H_2C_2O_4(g) \longrightarrow CO_2(g) + HCOOH(g)$$

In three separate experiments, the initial pressure of oxalic acid and final total pressure after 20,000 s are measured.

Experiment	1	2	3
$P_{H_2C_2O_4}$ at $t = 0$	65.8	92.1	111
P_{Total} at $t = 20{,}000$ s	94.6	132	160

Find the rate law of the reaction and its rate constant.

89. Dinitrogen pentoxide decomposes in the gas phase to form nitrogen dioxide and oxygen gas. The reaction is first order in dinitrogen pentoxide and has a half-life of 2.81 h at 25 °C. If a 1.5-L reaction vessel initially contains 745 torr of N_2O_5 at 25 °C, what partial pressure of O_2 is present in the vessel after 215 minutes?

90. Cyclopropane (C_3H_6) reacts to form propene (C_3H_6) in the gas phase. The reaction is first order in cyclopropane and has a rate constant of 5.87×10^{-4}/s at 485 °C. If a 2.5-L reaction vessel initially contains 722 torr of cyclopropane at 485 °C, how long will it take for the partial pressure of cyclopropane to drop to below 1.00×10^2 torr?

91. Iodine atoms combine to form I_2 in liquid hexane solvent with a rate constant of 1.5×10^{10} L/mol · s. The reaction is second order in I. Since the reaction occurs so quickly, the only way to study the reaction is to create iodine atoms almost instantaneously, usually by photochemical decomposition of I_2. Suppose a flash of light creates an initial [I] concentration of 0.0100 M. How long will it take for 95% of the newly created iodine atoms to recombine to form I_2?

92. The hydrolysis of sucrose ($C_{12}H_{22}O_{11}$) into glucose and fructose in acidic water has a rate constant of $1.8 \times 10^{-4}\ s^{-1}$ at 25 °C. Assuming the reaction is first order in sucrose, determine the mass of sucrose that is hydrolyzed when 2.55 L of a 0.150 M sucrose solution is allowed to react for 195 minutes.

93. The reaction $AB(aq) \longrightarrow A(g) + B(g)$ is second order in AB and has a rate constant of $0.0118\ M^{-1} \cdot s^{-1}$ at 25.0 °C. A reaction vessel initially contains 250.0 mL of 0.100 M AB that is allowed to react to form the gaseous product. The product is collected over water at 25.0 °C. How much time is required to produce 200.0 mL of the products at a barometric pressure of 755.1 mmHg? (The vapor pressure of water at this temperature is 23.8 mmHg.)

94. The reaction $2\,H_2O_2(aq) \longrightarrow 2\,H_2O(l) + O_2(g)$ is first order in H_2O_2 and under certain conditions has a rate constant of $0.00752\ s^{-1}$ at 20.0 °C. A reaction vessel initially contains 150.0 mL of 30.0% H_2O_2 by mass solution (the density of the solution is 1.11 g/mL). The gaseous oxygen is collected over water at 20.0 °C as it forms. What volume of O_2 forms in 85.0 seconds at a barometric pressure of 742.5 mmHg? (The vapor pressure of water at this temperature is 17.5 mmHg.)

95. Consider this energy diagram:

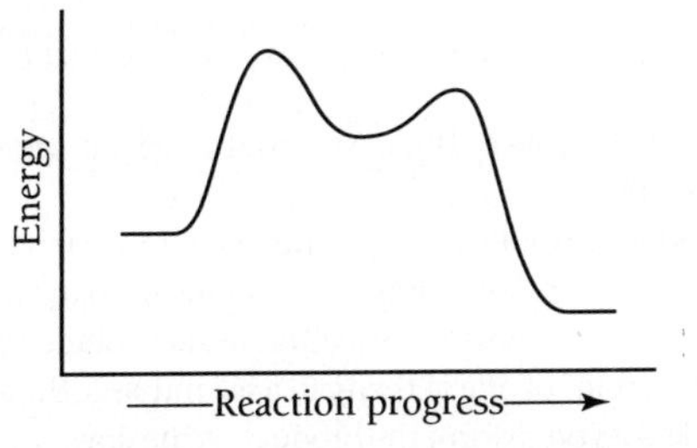

a. How many elementary steps are involved in this reaction?

b. Label the reactants, products, and intermediates.

c. Which step is rate limiting?

d. Is the overall reaction endothermic or exothermic?

96. Consider the reaction in which HCl adds across the double bond of ethene:

$$HCl + H_2C{=}CH_2 \longrightarrow H_3C{-}CH_2Cl$$

The following mechanism, with the accompanying energy diagram, has been suggested for this reaction:

Step 1 $HCl + H_2C{=}CH_2 \longrightarrow H_3C{=}CH_2^{+} + Cl^{-}$

Step 2 $H_3C{=}CH_2^{+} + Cl^{-} \longrightarrow H_3C{-}CH_2Cl$

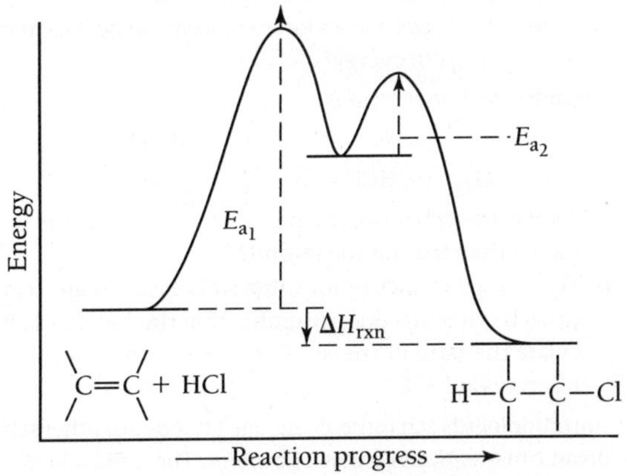

a. Based on the energy diagram, determine which step is rate limiting.

b. What is the expected order of the reaction based on the proposed mechanism?

c. Is the overall reaction exothermic or endothermic?

97. The desorption (leaving of the surface) of a single molecular layer of *n*-butane from a single crystal of aluminum oxide is found to be first order with a rate constant of 0.128/s at 150 K.

a. What is the half-life of the desorption reaction?

b. If the surface is initially completely covered with *n*-butane at 150 K, how long will it take for 25% of the molecules to desorb (leave the surface)? For 50% to desorb?

c. If the surface is initially completely covered, what fraction will remain covered after 10 s? After 20 s?

98. The evaporation of a 120-nm film of *n*-pentane from a single crystal of aluminum oxide is zero order with a rate constant of 1.92×10^{13} molecules/cm^2 · s at 120 K.

a. If the initial surface coverage is 8.9×10^{16} molecules/cm^2, how long will it take for one-half of the film to evaporate?

b. What fraction of the film is left after 10 s? Assume the same initial coverage as in part a.

99. The kinetics of this reaction were studied as a function of temperature. (The reaction is first order in each reactant and second order overall.)

$$C_2H_5Br(aq) + OH^-(aq) \longrightarrow C_2H_5OH(l) + Br^-(aq)$$

Temperature (°C)	*k* (L/mol · s)
25	8.81×10^{-5}
35	0.000285
45	0.000854
55	0.00239
65	0.00633

a. Determine the activation energy and frequency factor for the reaction.

b. Determine the rate constant at 15 °C.

c. If a reaction mixture is 0.155 M in C_2H_5Br and 0.250 M in OH^-, what is the initial rate of the reaction at 75 °C?

100. The reaction $2\,N_2O_5 \longrightarrow 2\,N_2O_4 + O_2$ takes place at around room temperature in solvents such as CCl_4. The rate constant at 293 K is found to be $2.35 \times 10^{-4}\,s^{-1}$, and at 303 K the rate constant is found to be $9.15 \times 10^{-4}\,s^{-1}$. Calculate the frequency factor for the reaction.

101. This reaction has an activation energy of zero in the gas phase:

$$CH_3 + CH_3 \longrightarrow C_2H_6$$

a. Would you expect the rate of this reaction to change very much with temperature?
b. Why might the activation energy be zero?
c. What other types of reactions would you expect to have little or no activation energy?

102. Consider the two reactions:

$$O + N_2 \longrightarrow NO + N \qquad E_a = 315\ \text{kJ/mol}$$
$$Cl + H_2 \longrightarrow HCl + H \qquad E_a = 23\ \text{kJ/mol}$$

a. Why is the activation barrier for the first reaction so much higher than that for the second?
b. The frequency factors for these two reactions are very close to each other in value. Assuming that they are the same, calculate the ratio of the reaction rate constants for these two reactions at 25 °C.

103. Anthropologists can estimate the age of a bone or other sample of organic matter by its carbon-14 content. The carbon-14 in a living organism is constant until the organism dies, after which carbon-14 decays with first-order kinetics and a half-life of 5730 years. Suppose a bone from an ancient human contains 19.5% of the C-14 found in living organisms. How old is the bone?

104. Geologists can estimate the age of rocks by their uranium-238 content. The uranium is incorporated in the rock as it hardens and then decays with first-order kinetics and a half-life of 4.5 billion years. A rock contains 83.2% of the amount of uranium-238 that it contained when it was formed. (The amount that the rock contained when it was formed can be deduced from the presence of the decay products of U-238.) How old is the rock?

105. Consider the gas-phase reaction:

$$H_2(g) + I_2(g) \longrightarrow 2\,HI(g)$$

The reaction was experimentally determined to be first order in H_2 and first order in I_2. Consider the proposed mechanisms.

Proposed mechanism I:

$$H_2(g) + I_2(g) \longrightarrow 2\,HI(g) \qquad \text{Single step}$$

Proposed mechanism II:

$$I_2(g) \underset{k_{-1}}{\overset{k_1}{\rightleftharpoons}} 2\,I(g) \qquad \text{Fast}$$
$$H_2(g) + 2\,I(g) \xrightarrow[k_2]{} 2\,HI(g) \qquad \text{Slow}$$

a. Show that both of the proposed mechanisms are valid.
b. What kind of experimental evidence might lead you to favor mechanism II over mechanism I?

106. Phosgene (Cl_2CO), a poison gas used in World War I, is formed by the reaction of Cl_2 and CO. The proposed mechanism for the reaction is:

$$Cl_2 \rightleftharpoons 2\,Cl \qquad \text{(fast, equilibrium)}$$
$$Cl + CO \rightleftharpoons ClCO \qquad \text{(fast, equilibrium)}$$
$$ClCO + Cl_2 \longrightarrow Cl_2CO + Cl \qquad \text{(slow)}$$

What rate law is consistent with this mechanism?

107. The proposed mechanism for the formation of hydrogen bromide can be written in a simplified form as:

$$Br_2(g) \underset{k_{-1}}{\overset{k_1}{\rightleftharpoons}} 2Br(g) \qquad \text{Fast}$$
$$Br(g) + H_2(g) \xrightarrow{k_2} HBr(g) + H(g) \qquad \text{Slow}$$
$$H(g) + Br_2(g) \xrightarrow{k_3} HBr(g) + Br(g) \qquad \text{Fast}$$

What rate law corresponds to this mechanism?

108. A proposed mechanism for the formation of hydrogen iodide can be written in simplified form as

$$I_2 \underset{k_{-1}}{\overset{k_1}{\rightleftharpoons}} 2\,I \qquad \text{Fast}$$
$$I + H_2 \underset{k_{-2}}{\overset{k_2}{\rightleftharpoons}} H_2I \qquad \text{Fast}$$
$$H_2I + I \xrightarrow[k_3]{} 2\,HI \qquad \text{Slow}$$

What rate law corresponds to this mechanism?

109. A certain substance X decomposes. Fifty percent of X remains after 100 minutes. How much X remains after 200 minutes if the reaction order with respect to X is (a) zero order, (b) first order, (c) second order?

110. The half-life for radioactive decay (a first-order process) of plutonium-239 is 24,000 years. How many years does it take for one mole of this radioactive material to decay until just one atom remains?

111. The energy of activation for the decomposition of 2 mol of HI to H_2 and I_2 in the gas phase is 185 kJ. The heat of formation of HI(*g*) from $H_2(g)$ and $I_2(g)$ is −5.65 kJ/mol. Find the energy of activation for the reaction of 1 mol of H_2 and 1 mol of I_2 to form 2 mol of HI in the gas phase.

112. Ethyl chloride vapor decomposes by the first-order reaction:

$$C_2H_5Cl \longrightarrow C_2H_4 + HCl$$

The activation energy is 249 kJ/mol, and the frequency factor is $1.6 \times 10^{14}\,s^{-1}$. Find the value of the rate constant at 710 K. What fraction of the ethyl chloride decomposes in 15 minutes at this temperature? Find the temperature at which the rate of the reaction would be twice as fast.

CHALLENGE PROBLEMS

113. In this chapter, we have seen a number of reactions in which a single reactant forms products. For example, consider the following first-order reaction:

$$CH_3NC(g) \longrightarrow CH_3CN(g)$$

However, we also learned that gas-phase reactions occur through collisions.

a. One possible explanation for how this reaction occurs is that two molecules of CH_3NC collide with each other and form two molecules of the product in a single elementary step. If that were the case, what reaction order would you expect?
b. Another possibility is that the reaction occurs through more than one step. For example, a possible mechanism involves one step in which the two CH_3NC molecules collide, resulting in the "activation" of one of them. In a second step, the activated molecule goes on to form the product. Write down this mechanism and determine which step must be rate determining in order for the kinetics of the reaction to be first order. Show explicitly how the mechanism predicts first-order kinetics.

114. The first-order *integrated* rate law for the reaction A $\longrightarrow$ products is derived from the rate law using calculus:

$$\text{Rate} = k[\text{A}] \text{ (first-order rate law)}$$

$$\text{Rate} = -\frac{d[\text{A}]}{dt}$$

$$\frac{d[\text{A}]}{dt} = -k[\text{A}]$$

The equation just given is a first-order, separable differential equation that can be solved by separating the variables and integrating:

$$\frac{d[\text{A}]}{[\text{A}]} = -kdt$$

$$\int_{[\text{A}]_0}^{[\text{A}]} \frac{d[\text{A}]}{[\text{A}]} = -\int_0^t kdt$$

In the integral just given, $[\text{A}]_0$ is the initial concentration of A. We then evaluate the integral:

$$[\ln[\text{A}]]_{[\text{A}]_0}^{[\text{A}]} = -k[t]_0^t$$

$$\ln[\text{A}] - \ln[\text{A}]_0 = -kt$$

$$\ln[\text{A}] = -kt + \ln[\text{A}]_0 \text{ (integrated rate law)}$$

a. Use a procedure similar to the one just shown to derive an integrated rate law for a reaction A $\longrightarrow$ products, which is one-half order in the concentration of A (that is, Rate $= k[\text{A}]^{1/2}$).

b. Use the result from part a to derive an expression for the half-life of a one-half-order reaction.

115. The previous exercise shows how the first-order integrated rate law is derived from the first-order differential rate law. Begin with the second-order differential rate law and derive the second-order integrated rate law.

116. The rate constant for the first-order decomposition of $N_2O_5(g)$ to $NO_2(g)$ and $O_2(g)$ is $7.48 \times 10^{-3}\ \text{s}^{-1}$ at a given temperature.

a. Find the length of time required for the total pressure in a system containing N_2O_5 at an initial pressure of 0.100 atm to rise to 0.145 atm.

b. To 0.200 atm.

c. Find the total pressure after 100 s of reaction.

117. The rate of decomposition of $N_2O_3(g)$ to $NO_2(g)$ and $NO(g)$ is followed by measuring $[NO_2]$ at different times. The following data are obtained.

$[NO_2]$(mol/L)	0	0.193	0.316	0.427	0.784
t (s)	0	884	1610	2460	50,000

The reaction follows a first-order rate law. Calculate the rate constant. Assume that after 50,000 s all $N_2O_3(g)$ had decomposed.

118. At 473 K, for the elementary reaction $2\,NOCl(g) \underset{k_{-1}}{\overset{k_1}{\rightleftharpoons}} 2\,NO(g) + Cl_2(g)$

$$k_1 = 7.8 \times 10^{-2}\ \text{L/mol s} \quad \text{and}$$

$$k_{-1} = 4.7 \times 10^{2}\ \text{L}^2/\text{mol}^2\ \text{s}$$

A sample of NOCl is placed in a container and heated to 473 K. When the system comes to equilibrium, [NOCl] is found to be 0.12 mol/L. What are the concentrations of NO and Cl_2?

CONCEPTUAL PROBLEMS

119. Consider the reaction:

$$CHCl_3(g) + Cl_2(g) \longrightarrow CCl_4(g) + HCl(g)$$

The reaction is first order in $CHCl_3$ and one-half order in Cl_2. Which reaction mixture would you expect to have the fastest initial rate?

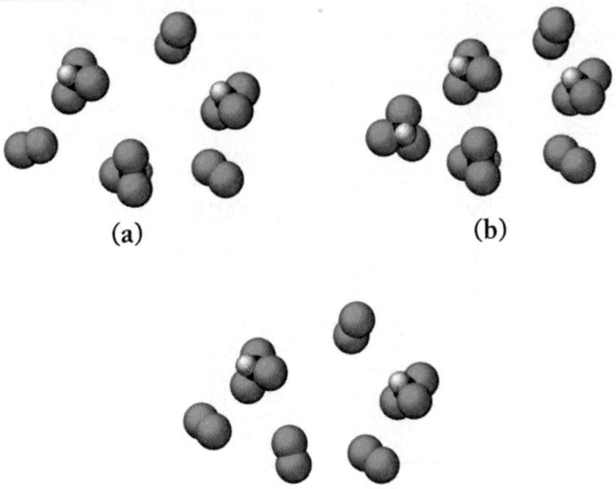

(a) (b) (c)

120. Three different reactions involve a single reactant converting to products. Reaction A has a half-life that is independent of the initial concentration of the reactant, reaction B has a half-life that doubles when the initial concentration of the reactant doubles, and reaction C has a half-life that doubles when the initial concentration of the reactant is halved. Which statement is most consistent with these observations?

a. Reaction A is first order; reaction B is second order; and reaction C is zero order.

b. Reaction A is first order; reaction B is zero order; and reaction C is zero order.

c. Reaction A is zero order; reaction B is first order; and reaction C is second order.

d. Reaction A is second order; reaction B is first order; and reaction C is zero order.

121. The accompanying graph shows the concentration of a reactant as a function of time for two different reactions. One of the reactions is first order, and the other is second order. Which of the two reactions is first order? Second order? How would you change each plot to make it linear?

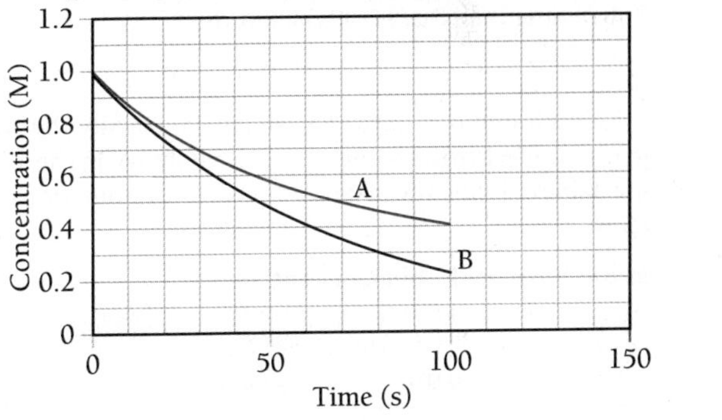

122. A particular reaction, A $\longrightarrow$ products, has a rate that slows down as the reaction proceeds. The half-life of the reaction is found to depend on the initial concentration of A. Determine whether each statement is likely to be true or false for this reaction.

a. A doubling of the concentration of A doubles the rate of the reaction.

b. A plot of 1/[A] versus time is linear.

c. The half-life of the reaction gets longer as the initial concentration of A increases.

d. A plot of the concentration of A versus time has a constant slope.

QUESTIONS FOR GROUP WORK

Active Classroom Learning

Discuss these questions with the group and record your consensus answer.

123. A student says, "The initial concentration of a reactant was doubled, and the rate doubled. Therefore the reaction is second order in that reactant." Why might the student say that? What is wrong with the statement? What is the actual order with respect to the reactant? Explain your reasoning clearly.

124. A certain compound, A, reacts to form products according to the reaction A $\longrightarrow$ P. The amount of A is measured as a function of time under a variety of different conditions, and the tabulated results are shown here:

Time (s)	25.0 °C [A] (M)	35.0 °C [A] (M)	45.0 °C [A] (M)
0	1.000	1.000	1.000
10	0.779	0.662	0.561
20	0.591	0.461	0.312
30	0.453	0.306	0.177
40	0.338	0.208	0.100
50	0.259	0.136	0.057
60	0.200	0.093	0.032

Have one group member make a graph of [A] versus *t*, one group member make a graph of ln[A] versus *t*, and one group member make a graph of 1/[A] versus *t* using the data for 25 °C. Additional group members can make similar graphs for the other temperatures. What is the order of the reaction with respect to A? Explain your answer.

a. Use the data to determine the rate constant at each temperature.

b. What is the activation energy for this reaction?

c. The same reaction is conducted in the presence of a catalyst, and the following data are obtained:

Time (s)	25.0 °C [A] (M)	35.0 °C [A] (M)	45.0 °C [A] (M)
0	1.000	1.000	1.000
0.1	0.724	0.668	0.598
0.2	0.511	0.433	0.341
0.3	0.375	0.291	0.202
0.4	0.275	0.190	0.119
0.5	0.198	0.122	0.071
0.6	0.141	0.080	0.043

What effect does a catalyst have on the rate of the reaction? What is the activation energy for this reaction in the presence of the catalyst? How does it compare with the activation energy for the reaction when the catalyst isn't present?

DATA INTERPRETATION AND ANALYSIS

Atmospheric Methane Degredation

125. Methane (CH_4) is a greenhouse gas emitted by industry, agriculture, and waste systems. Methane is the second most prevalent greenhouse gas (after carbon dioxide). Methane plays an important role in climate change because it absorbs infrared radiation more efficiently than carbon dioxide. Methane is broken down in the atmosphere by ozone (O_3), making its atmospheric lifetime shorter than that of carbon dioxide.

$$CH_4(g) + O_3(g) \longrightarrow \text{products}$$

A research group studied the rate of the reaction by which methane reacts with ozone; the data are shown in the following tables. Study the data and answer the questions that follow.

Initial Rate vs. Initial Concentrations

$[CH_4]$	$[O_3]$	Initial Rate (M/s)
0.010	0.010	3.94×10^{-7}
0.020	0.010	7.88×10^{-7}
0.020	0.020	1.58×10^{-6}

Rate Constant vs. Temperature

Temperature (K)	$k(M^{-1} \cdot s^{-1})$
260	2.26×10^{-5}
265	3.95×10^{-5}
270	6.76×10^{-5}
275	0.000114
280	0.000187
285	0.000303
290	0.000483
295	0.000758
300	0.001171
305	0.001783

a. Use the data in the first table to determine the order of the reaction with respect to each reactant.

b. Use the data in the second table to determine the activation barrier and pre-exponential factor for the reaction.

c. Atmospheric concentrations of methane and ozone can vary depending on the location and altitude. Calculate the rate of the reaction at 273 K for a methane concentration of 1.8 ppm (by volume) and an ozone concentration of 5.0 ppm (by volume). Note that 1 ppm of CH_4 by volume means 1 L $CH_4/10^6$ L air. Assume STP (standard temperature and pressure) so that 1 mol gas occupies 22.4 L.

d. What is the half-life of methane in the atmosphere in years at 323 K? (Assume that $[CH_4] = [O_3] = [A]_0 = 5.0 \times 10^{-7}$ M.)

Cc ANSWERS TO CONCEPTUAL CONNECTIONS

Reaction Rates

15.1 **(c)** The rate at which B changes is twice the rate of the reaction because its coefficient is 2, and it is negative because B is a reactant.

Reaction Order

15.2 **(b)** For a first-order reaction, a doubling of the reactant concentration doubles the reaction rate.

Rate and Concentration I

15.3 **(d)** Since the reaction is second order, increasing the concentration of A by a factor of 5 causes the rate to increase by 5^2 or 25.

Rate and Concentration II

15.4 **(c)** All three mixtures have the same total number of molecules, but mixture **(c)** has the greatest number of NO molecules. Since the reaction is second order in NO and only first order in O_2, mixture **(c)** has the fastest initial rate.

Half-Life I

15.5 **(c)** The half-life is 90 s because it takes 90 s for the reactant to fall to one-half of its intitial concentration.

Half-Life II

15.6 **(b)** The concentration of B after 50 seconds (two half-lives) is 0.225 M as you can see from this table.

Time (min)	[A] (M)	[B] (M)
0	0.300	0.0
25	0.150	0.150
50	0.075	0.225

Rate Law and Integrated Rate Law

15.7 **(c)** The reaction is most likely second order because its rate depends on the concentration (therefore it cannot be zero order), and its half-life depends on the initial concentration (therefore it cannot be first order). For a second-order reaction, a doubling of the initial concentration results in the quadrupling of the rate.

Reaction Rate and Temperature

15.8 **(a)** As temperature increases, a greater fraction of molecules have enough thermal energy to surmount the activation barrier.

Reaction Rate and Activation Energy

15.9 **(a)** Reaction A has a faster rate because it has a lower activation energy; therefore, the exponential factor is larger at a given temperature, making the rate constant larger. (With a larger rate constant and the same initial concentration, the rate is faster.)

Collision Theory

15.10 **(c)** Since the reactants in part **(a)** are atoms, the orientation factor should be about one. The reactants in parts **(b)** and **(c)** are both molecules, so we expect orientation factors of less than one. Since the reactants in **(b)** are symmetrical, we would not expect the collision to have as specific an orientation requirement as in **(c)**, where the reactants are asymmetrical and must therefore collide in such way that a hydrogen atom is in close proximity to another hydrogen atom. Therefore, we expect **(c)** to have the smallest orientation factor.

Elementary Steps

15.11 **(d)** Since the elementary step is of the form $A + B \longrightarrow$ products, the rate law is rate $= k[A][B]$.

Every system in chemical equilibrium, under the influence of a change of any one of the factors of equilibrium, undergoes a transformation . . . [that produces a change] . . . in the opposite direction of the factor in question.

—HENRI LE CHÂTELIER (1850–1936)

CHAPTER 16

Chemical Equilibrium

In Chapter 15, we examined *how fast* a chemical reaction occurs. In this chapter, we examine *how far* a chemical reaction goes. The *speed* of a chemical reaction is determined by kinetics. The *extent* of a chemical reaction is determined by thermodynamics. Our focus is on describing how far a chemical reaction goes based on an experimentally measurable quantity called *the equilibrium constant*. A reaction with a large equilibrium constant proceeds nearly to completion—almost all the reactants react to form products. A reaction with a small equilibrium constant barely proceeds at all—almost all the reactants remain as reactants, hardly forming any products. For now, we simply accept the equilibrium constant as an experimentally measurable quantity and learn how to use it to predict and quantify the extent of a reaction. In Chapter 19, we will explore the reasons underlying the magnitude of equilibrium constants.

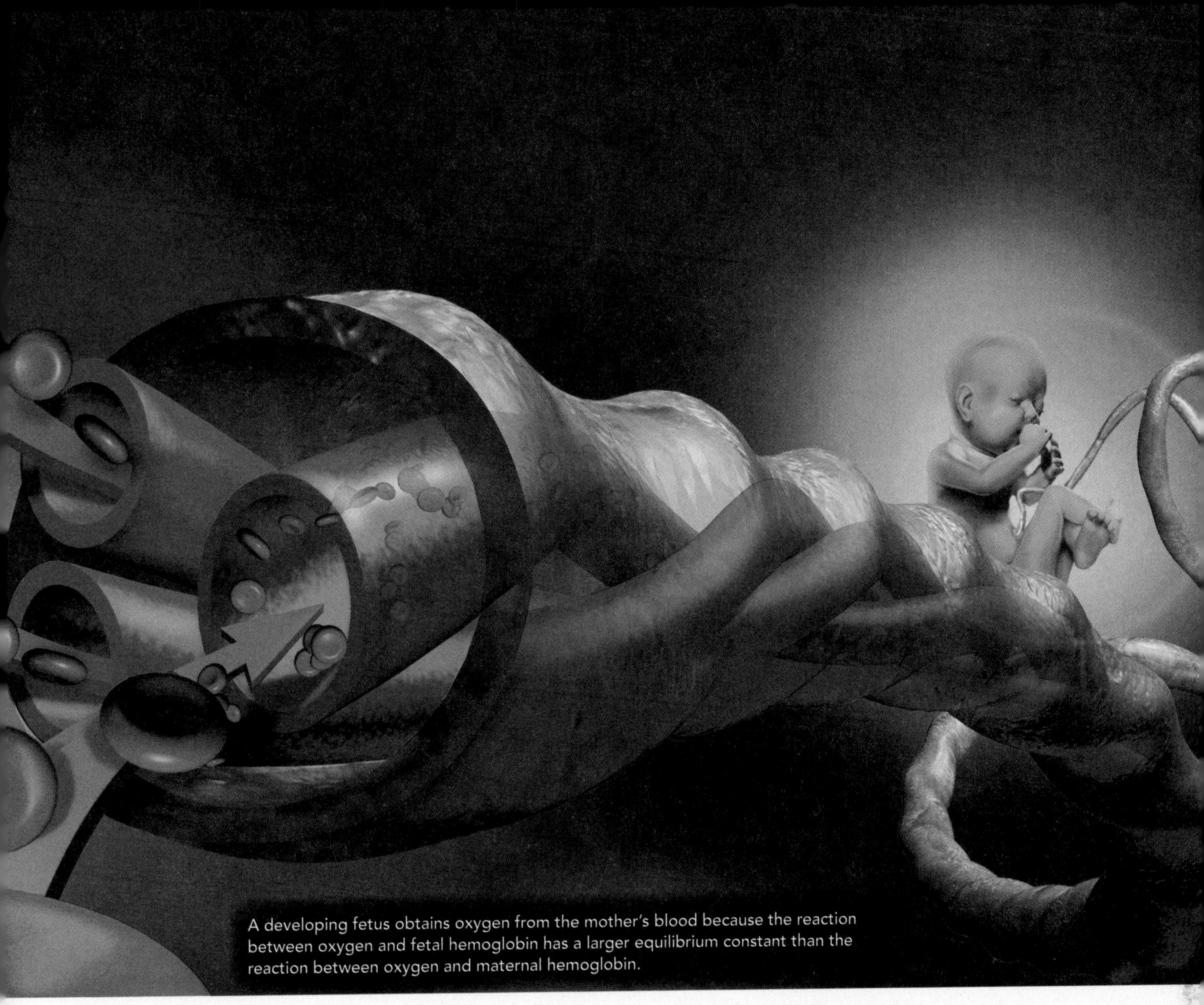

A developing fetus obtains oxygen from the mother's blood because the reaction between oxygen and fetal hemoglobin has a larger equilibrium constant than the reaction between oxygen and maternal hemoglobin.

16.1 Fetal Hemoglobin and Equilibrium 683
16.2 The Concept of Dynamic Equilibrium 685
16.3 The Equilibrium Constant (K) 688
16.4 Expressing the Equilibrium Constant in Terms of Pressure 692
16.5 Heterogeneous Equilibria: Reactions Involving Solids and Liquids 695
16.6 Calculating the Equilibrium Constant from Measured Equilibrium Concentrations 696
16.7 The Reaction Quotient: Predicting the Direction of Change 699
16.8 Finding Equilibrium Concentrations 701
16.9 Le Châtelier's Principle: How a System at Equilibrium Responds to Disturbances 711
LEARNING OUTCOMES 720

16.1 Fetal Hemoglobin and Equilibrium

Have you ever wondered how a baby in the womb gets oxygen? Unlike you and me, a fetus does not breathe air. Yet, like you and me, a fetus needs oxygen. Where does that oxygen come from? After we are born, we inhale air into our lungs and that air diffuses into capillaries, where it comes into contact with our blood. Within our red blood cells, a protein called hemoglobin (Hb) reacts with oxygen according to the chemical equation:

$$Hb + O_2 \rightleftharpoons HbO_2$$

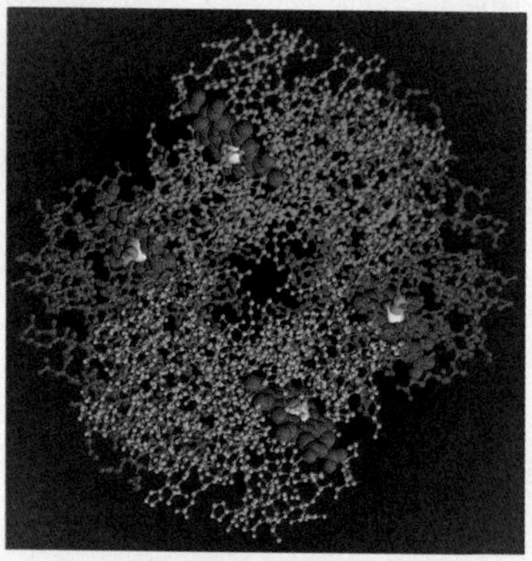

▲ Hemoglobin is the oxygen-carrying protein in red blood cells. Oxygen binds to iron atoms, which are depicted here in white.

The double arrows in this equation indicate that the reaction can occur in both the forward and reverse directions and can reach chemical *equilibrium*. We encountered this term in Chapters 12 and 14, and we define it more carefully in the next section. For now, understand that the relative concentrations of the reactants and products in a reaction at equilibrium are described by the *equilibrium constant, K*. A large value of *K* means that the reaction lies far to the right at equilibrium—a high concentration of products and a low concentration of reactants. A small value of *K* means that the reaction lies far to the left at equilibrium—a high concentration of reactants and a low concentration of products. In short, the value of *K* is a measure of how far a reaction proceeds—the larger the value of *K*, the more the reaction proceeds toward the products.

The equilibrium constant for the reaction between hemoglobin and oxygen is such that hemoglobin efficiently binds oxygen at typical lung oxygen concentrations, but it can also release oxygen under the appropriate conditions. Any system at equilibrium, including the hemoglobin–oxygen system, responds to changes in ways that maintain equilibrium. If any of the concentrations of the reactants or products change, the reaction shifts to counteract that change. For the hemoglobin system, as blood flows through the lungs where oxygen concentrations are high, the equilibrium shifts to the right—hemoglobin binds oxygen:

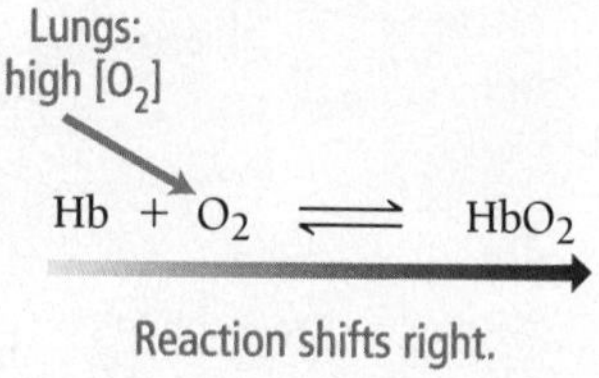

In our bodies, as blood flows out of the lungs and into muscles and organs where oxygen concentrations have been depleted (because muscles and organs use oxygen), the equilibrium shifts to the left—hemoglobin releases oxygen:

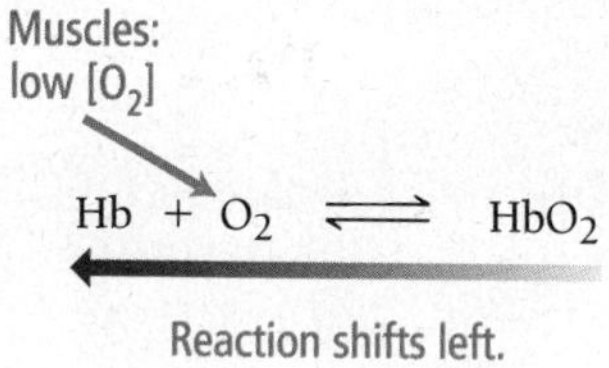

In other words, to maintain equilibrium, *hemoglobin binds oxygen when the surrounding oxygen concentration is high, but it releases oxygen when the surrounding oxygen concentration is low*. In this way, hemoglobin transports oxygen from the lungs to all parts of the body that use oxygen.

A fetus has its own circulatory system. The mother's blood never flows into the fetus's body, and the fetus cannot get any air in the womb. How, then, does the fetus get oxygen? The answer lies in the properties of fetal hemoglobin (HbF), which is slightly different from adult hemoglobin. Like adult hemoglobin, fetal hemoglobin is in equilibrium with oxygen:

$$\text{HbF} + \text{O}_2 \rightleftharpoons \text{HbFO}_2$$

However, the equilibrium constant for fetal hemoglobin is larger than the equilibrium constant for adult hemoglobin, meaning that the reaction tends to go farther in the direction of the product. Consequently, fetal hemoglobin loads oxygen at a lower oxygen concentration than does adult hemoglobin. In the placenta, fetal blood flows in close proximity to maternal blood. Although the two never mix, because of the different equilibrium constants, the maternal hemoglobin releases oxygen that the fetal hemoglobin then binds and carries into its own circulatory system (Figure 16.1▶). Nature has evolved a chemical system through which the mother's hemoglobin can in effect *hand off* oxygen to the hemoglobin of the fetus.

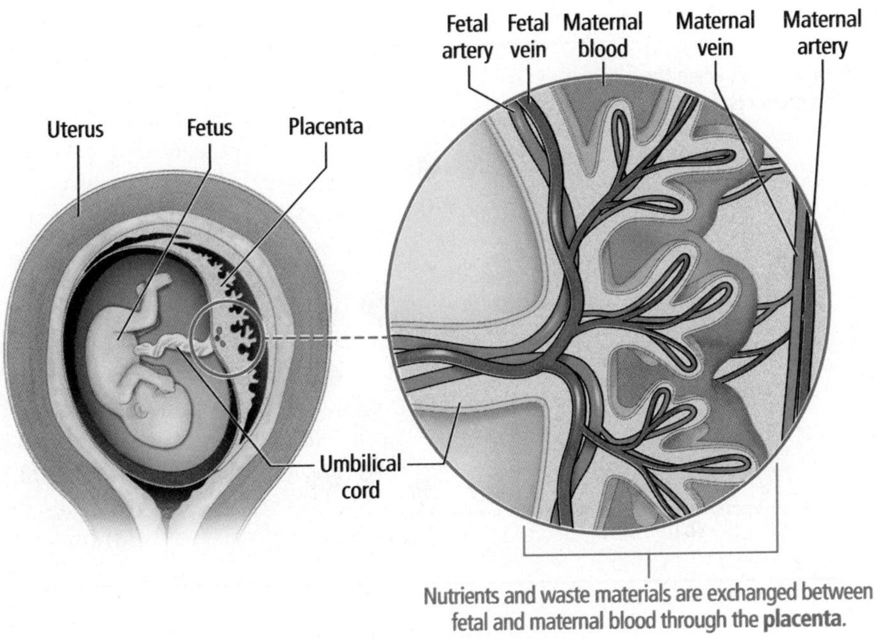

◀ **FIGURE 16.1 Oxygen Exchange between the Maternal and Fetal Circulation** In the placenta, the blood of the fetus comes into close proximity with the blood of the mother, although the two do not mix directly. Because the reaction of fetal hemoglobin with oxygen has a larger equilibrium constant than the reaction of maternal hemoglobin with oxygen, the fetus receives oxygen from the mother's blood.

16.2 The Concept of Dynamic Equilibrium

Recall from the previous chapter that reaction rates generally increase with increasing concentration of the reactants and decrease with decreasing concentration of the reactants (unless the reaction order is zero). With this in mind, consider the reaction between hydrogen and iodine:

$$H_2(g) + I_2(g) \rightleftharpoons 2\,HI(g)$$

In this reaction, H_2 and I_2 react to form 2 HI molecules, but the 2 HI molecules can also react to re-form H_2 and I_2. A reaction such as this one—that can proceed in both the forward and reverse directions—is **reversible**. Suppose we begin with only H_2 and I_2 in a container (Figure 16.2a▶). What happens? Initially H_2 and I_2 begin to react to form HI (Figure 16.2b). However, as H_2 and I_2 react, their concentrations decrease, which in turn *decreases the rate of the forward reaction*. At the same time, HI begins to form. As the concentration of HI increases, the reverse reaction begins to occur at a faster and faster rate. Eventually the rate of the reverse reaction (which has been increasing) equals the rate of the forward reaction (which has been decreasing). At that point, **dynamic equilibrium** is reached (Figure 16.2c, d▶):

Nearly all chemical reactions are at least theoretically reversible. In many cases, however, the reversibility is so small that it can be ignored.

Dynamic equilibrium for a chemical reaction is the condition in which the rate of the forward reaction equals the rate of the reverse reaction.

Dynamic equilibrium is "dynamic" because the forward and reverse reactions are still occurring; however, they are occurring at the same rate. When dynamic equilibrium is reached, the concentrations of H_2, I_2, and HI no longer change. They remain constant because the reactants and products form at the same rate that they are depleted. Note that just because the concentrations of reactants and products no longer change at equilibrium *does not mean that the concentrations of reactants and products are equal to one another* at equilibrium. Some reactions reach equilibrium only after most of the reactants have formed products. Others reach equilibrium when only a small fraction of the reactants have formed products. It depends on the reaction.

Dynamic Equilibrium

Equilibrium is reached in a chemical reaction when the concentrations of the reactants and products no longer change.

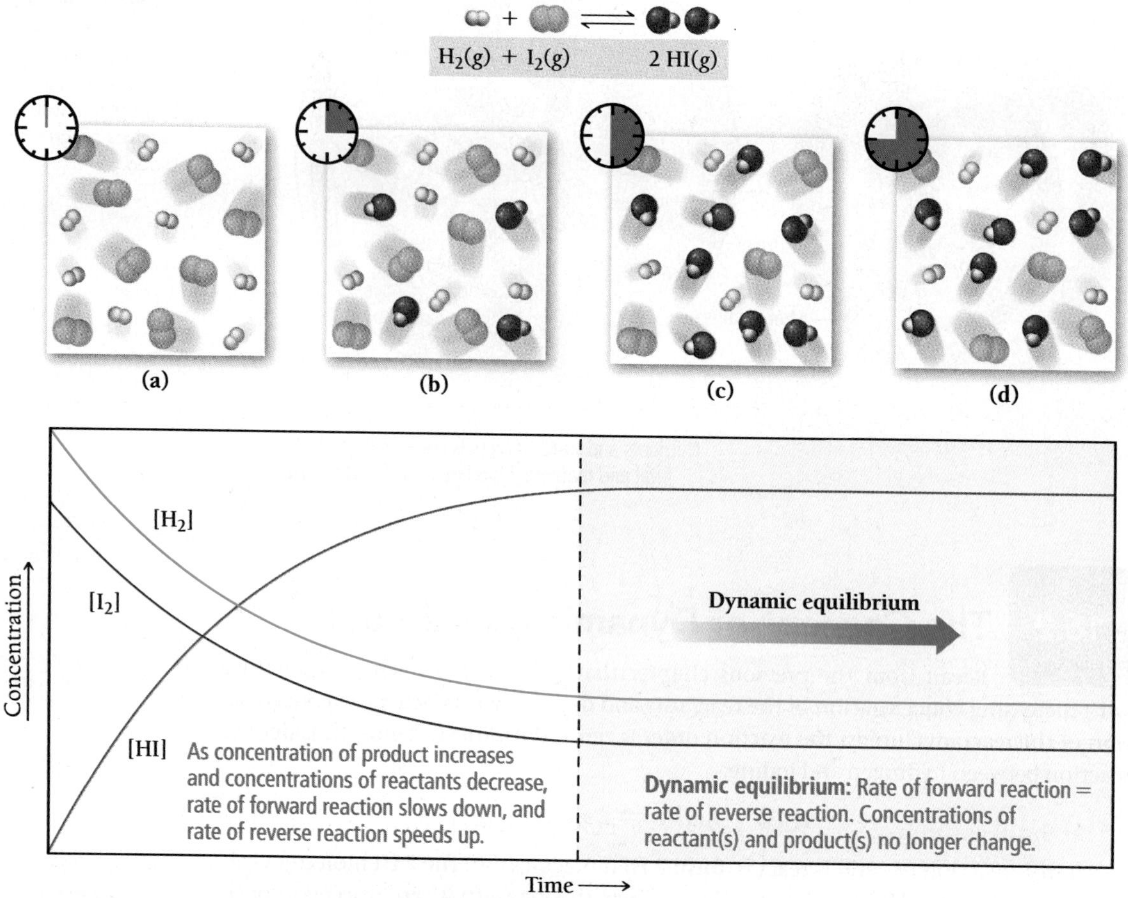

▲ **FIGURE 16.2 Dynamic Equilibrium** Equilibrium is reached in a chemical reaction when the concentrations of the reactants and products no longer change. The molecular images depict the progress of the reaction $H_2(g) + I_2(g) \rightleftharpoons 2\,HI(g)$. The graph shows the concentrations of H_2, I_2, and HI as a function of time. When the reaction reaches equilibrium, both the forward and reverse reactions continue, but at equal rates, so the concentrations of the reactants and products remain constant.

We can better understand dynamic equilibrium with a simple analogy. Imagine two neighboring countries (A and B) with a closed border between them (Figure 16.3▶). Country A is overpopulated and Country B is underpopulated. One day, the border between the two countries opens, and people immediately begin to leave Country A for Country B:

$$\text{Country A} \longrightarrow \text{Country B}$$

The population of Country A goes down as the population of Country B goes up. As people leave Country A, however, the *rate* at which they leave slows down because as Country A becomes less populated, the pool of potential emigrants gets smaller. (In other words, the rate of emigration is directly proportional to the population—as the population decreases, the emigration rate goes down.) In contrast, as people move into Country B, it gets more crowded and some people begin to move from Country B to Country A:

$$\text{Country A} \longleftarrow \text{Country B}$$

Dynamic Equilibrium: An Analogy

Initial: Net movement from A to B

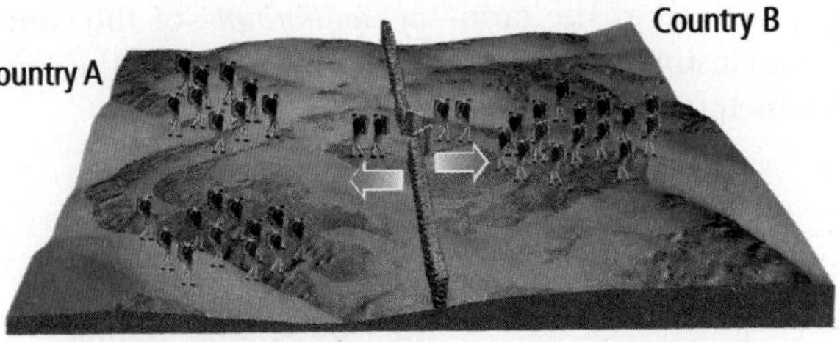

Equilibrium: Equal movement in both directions

▲ **FIGURE 16.3 A Population Analogy for Chemical Equilibrium** Because Country A is initially overpopulated, people migrate from Country A to Country B. As the population of Country A falls and that of Country B rises, the rate of migration from Country A to Country B decreases and the rate of migration from Country B to Country A increases. Eventually, the two rates become equal. Equilibrium has been reached.

As the population of Country B continues to grow, the rate of people moving out of Country B accelerates. Eventually, the *rate* of people moving out of Country A (which has been slowing down as people leave) equals the *rate* of people moving out of Country B (which has been increasing as Country B gets more crowded). Dynamic equilibrium has been reached:

$$\text{Country A} \rightleftharpoons \text{Country B}$$

Notice that when the two countries reach dynamic equilibrium, their populations no longer change because the number of people moving out of either country equals the number of people moving in. However, one country—because of its charm or the availability of good jobs or lower taxes, or for whatever other reason—may have a higher population than the other country, even when dynamic equilibrium is reached.

Similarly, when a chemical reaction reaches dynamic equilibrium, the rate of the forward reaction equals the rate of the reverse reaction, and the concentrations of reactants and products become *constant*. But the concentrations of reactants and products will not necessarily be *equal* at equilibrium, just as the populations of the two countries are not necessarily equal at equilibrium.

DYNAMIC EQUILIBRIUM Which statement does NOT generally apply to a chemical reaction in dynamic equilibrium?

(a) The rates of the forward and reverse reactions are equal.
(b) The concentrations of the reactants and products are constant.
(c) The concentrations of the reactants and products are equal.

16.1 Cc Conceptual Connection

ANSWER **NOW!**

WATCH **NOW!**

KEY CONCEPT VIDEO 16.3
The Equilibrium Constant

16.3 The Equilibrium Constant (*K*)

We have just seen that the *concentrations of reactants and products* are not equal at equilibrium—rather, the *rates of the forward and reverse reactions* are equal. So what about the concentrations? What can we know about them? The concentrations, as we can see by reexamining Figure 16.2, become constant; they don't change once equilibrium is reached (as long as the temperature is constant). We quantify the relative concentrations of reactants and products at equilibrium with a quantity called the *equilibrium constant* (*K*). Consider an equation for a generic chemical reaction:

$$aA + bB \rightleftharpoons cC + dD$$

We distinguish between the equilibrium constant (*K*) and the Kelvin unit of temperature (K) by italicizing the equilibrium constant.

where A and B are reactants, C and D are products, and *a*, *b*, *c*, and *d* are the respective stoichiometric coefficients in the chemical equation. The **equilibrium constant (*K*)** for the reaction is defined as the ratio—*at equilibrium*—of the concentrations of the products raised to their stoichiometric coefficients divided by the concentrations of the reactants raised to their stoichiometric coefficients:

$$K = \frac{\overbrace{[C]^c[D]^d}^{\text{Products}}}{\underbrace{[A]^a[B]^b}_{\text{Reactants}}} \qquad \textbf{The Law of Mass Action}$$

In this notation, [A] represents the molar concentration of A.

Why is *this* particular ratio of concentrations at equilibrium—and not some other ratio—defined as the equilibrium constant? *Because this particular ratio is always a constant when the reactants and products are at equilibrium* (at constant temperature). As we can see from the expression, the equilibrium constant *quantifies* the relative concentrations of reactants and products *at equilibrium*. The relationship between the balanced chemical equation and the expression of the equilibrium constant is the **law of mass action**.

ANSWER **NOW!**

16.2 Cc Conceptual Connection

THE LAW OF MASS ACTION According to the law of mass action, what is the correct expression for the equilibrium constant for the reaction $2\,A + B \rightleftharpoons 3\,C$?

(a) $K = \frac{[C]}{[A][B]}$ **(b)** $K = \frac{3[C]}{2[A][B]}$ **(c)** $K = \frac{[A]^2[B]}{[C]^3}$ **(d)** $K = \frac{[C]^3}{[A]^2[B]}$

Expressing Equilibrium Constants for Chemical Reactions

To express an equilibrium constant for a chemical reaction, we examine the balanced chemical equation and apply the law of mass action. For example, suppose we want to express the equilibrium constant for the reaction:

$$2\,N_2O_5(g) \rightleftharpoons 4\,NO_2(g) + O_2(g)$$

The equilibrium constant is $[NO_2]$ raised to the fourth power multiplied by $[O_2]$ raised to the first power divided by $[N_2O_5]$ raised to the second power:

$$K = \frac{[NO_2]^4[O_2]}{[N_2O_5]^2}$$

Notice that the *coefficients* in the chemical equation become the *exponents* in the expression of the equilibrium constant.

WATCH **NOW!**

INTERACTIVE WORKED EXAMPLE 16.1

EXAMPLE 16.1 Expressing Equilibrium Constants for Chemical Equations

Express the equilibrium constant for the chemical equation:

$$CH_3OH(g) \rightleftharpoons CO(g) + 2\,H_2(g)$$

SOLUTION

The equilibrium constant is the equilibrium concentrations of the products raised to their stoichiometric coefficients divided by the equilibrium concentrations of the reactants raised to their stoichiometric coefficients.

$$K = \frac{[CO][H_2]^2}{[CH_3OH]}$$

FOR PRACTICE 16.1 Express the equilibrium constant for the combustion of propane:

$$C_3H_8(g) + 5\,O_2(g) \rightleftharpoons 3\,CO_2(g) + 4\,H_2O(g)$$

The Significance of the Equilibrium Constant

You now know how to express the equilibrium constant, but what does it mean? What, for example, does a large equilibrium constant ($K \gg 1$) imply about a reaction? A large equilibrium constant indicates that the numerator (which specifies the amounts of products at equilibrium) is larger than the denominator (which specifies the amounts of reactants at equilibrium). Therefore, when the equilibrium constant is large, the forward reaction is favored. For example, consider the reaction:

$$H_2(g) + Br_2(g) \rightleftharpoons 2\,HBr(g) \qquad K = 1.9 \times 10^{19} \text{ (at 25 °C)}$$

The equilibrium constant is large, indicating that the equilibrium point for the reaction lies far to the right—high concentrations of products, low concentrations of reactants (Figure 16.4▶). Remember that the equilibrium constant says nothing about *how fast* a reaction reaches equilibrium, only *how far* the reaction has proceeded once equilibrium is reached. A reaction with a large equilibrium constant may be kinetically very slow and take a long time to reach equilibrium.

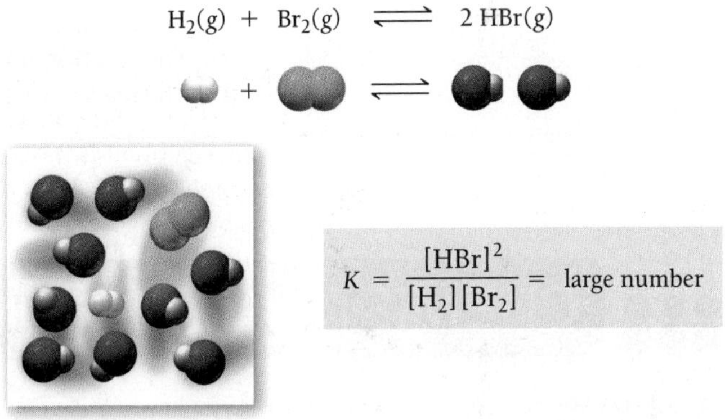

▲ **FIGURE 16.4 The Meaning of a Large Equilibrium Constant** If the equilibrium constant for a reaction is large, the equilibrium point of the reaction lies far to the right—the concentration of products is large and the concentration of reactants is small.

Conversely, what does a *small* equilibrium constant ($K \ll 1$) mean? It indicates that the reverse reaction is favored and that there will be more reactants than products when equilibrium is reached. For example, consider the reaction:

$$N_2(g) + O_2(g) \rightleftharpoons 2\,NO(g) \qquad K = 4.1 \times 10^{-31} \text{ (at 25 °C)}$$

The equilibrium constant is very small, indicating that the equilibrium point for the reaction lies far to the left—high concentrations of reactants, low concentrations of products (Figure 16.5▶). This is fortunate because N_2 and O_2 are the main components of air. If this equilibrium constant were large, much of the N_2 and O_2 in air would react to form NO, a toxic gas.

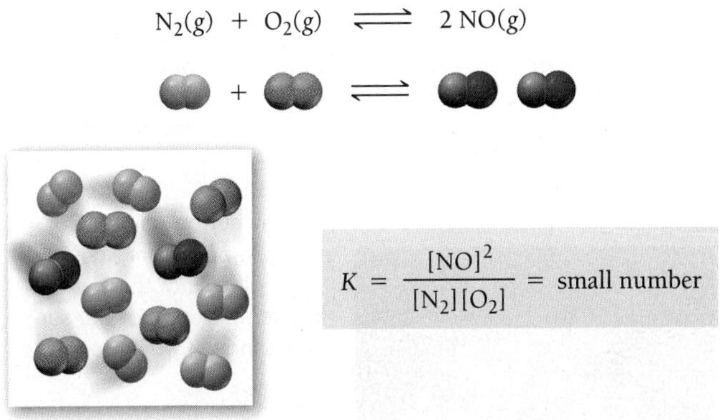

▲ **FIGURE 16.5 The Meaning of a Small Equilibrium Constant** If the equilibrium constant for a reaction is small, the equilibrium point of the reaction lies far to the left—the concentration of products is small and the concentration of reactants is large.

Summarizing the Significance of the Equilibrium Constant:

- $K \ll 1$ Reverse reaction is favored; forward reaction does not proceed very far.
- $K \approx 1$ Neither direction is favored; forward reaction proceeds about halfway.
- $K \gg 1$ Forward reaction is favored; forward reaction proceeds essentially to completion.

ANSWER **NOW!**

16.3 Cc Conceptual Connection

THE MAGNITUDE OF THE EQUILIBRIUM CONSTANT

Consider the reaction $A(g) \rightleftharpoons B(g)$. The images shown here illustrate equilibrium mixtures of A (red) and B (black) at three different temperatures. At which temperature is the equilibrium constant the largest?

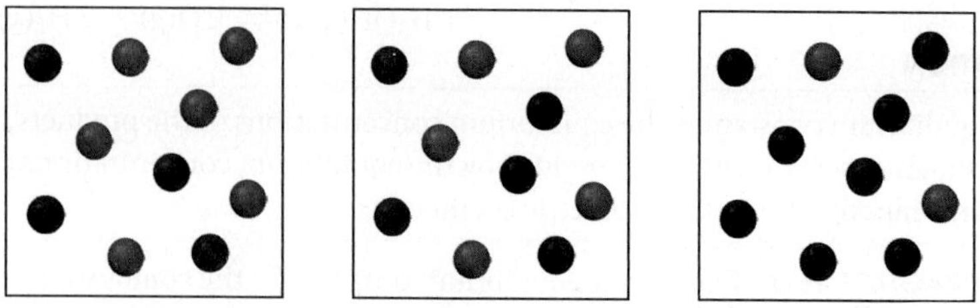

(a) T_1 **(b)** T_2 **(c)** T_3

ANSWER **NOW!**

16.4 Cc Conceptual Connection

EQUILIBRIUM CONSTANTS AND EQUILIBRIUM CONCENTRATIONS

The equilibrium constant for the reaction $A(g) \rightleftharpoons B(g)$ is 10. A reaction mixture initially contains [A] = 1.1 M and [B] = 0.0 M. Which statement is true at equilibrium?

(a) The reaction mixture contains [A] = 1.0 M and [B] = 0.1 M.
(b) The reaction mixture contains [A] = 0.1 M and [B] = 1.0 M.
(c) The reaction mixture contains equal concentrations of A and B.

CHEMISTRY AND MEDICINE | Life and Equilibrium

Have you ever tried to define life? If you have, you probably know that a definition is elusive. How are living things different from nonliving things? You may try to define living things as those things that can move. But of course many living things do not move (most plants, for example), and some nonliving things, such as glaciers and Earth itself, do move. So motion is neither unique to nor definitive of life. You may try to define living things as those things that can reproduce. But again, many living things, such as mules or sterile humans, cannot reproduce; yet they are alive. In addition, some nonliving things, such as crystals, for example, reproduce (in some sense). So what is unique about living things?

One definition of life involves the concept of equilibrium—living things *are not* in equilibrium with their surroundings. Our body temperature, for example, is not the same as the temperature of our surroundings. If we jump into a swimming pool, the acidity of our blood does not become the same as the acidity of the surrounding water. Living things, even the simplest ones, maintain some measure of *disequilibrium* with their environment.

◀ What makes these cells alive?

We must add one more concept, however, to complete our definition of life with respect to equilibrium. A cup of hot water is in disequilibrium with its environment with respect to temperature, yet it is not alive. The cup of hot water has no control over its disequilibrium, however, and will slowly come to equilibrium with its environment. In contrast, living things—as long as they are alive—maintain and *control* their disequilibrium. Your body temperature, for example, is not *only* in disequilibrium with your surroundings—it is in *controlled disequilibrium*. Your body maintains your temperature within a specific range that is not in equilibrium with the surrounding temperature.

So, one criterion for life is that living things are in *controlled disequilibrium* with their environment. Maintaining disequilibrium is a main activity of living organisms, requiring energy obtained from their environment. Plants derive that energy from sunlight; animals eat plants (or other animals that have eaten plants), and thus they too ultimately derive their energy from the sun. A living thing comes into equilibrium with its surroundings only after it dies.

Relationships between the Equilibrium Constant and the Chemical Equation

If a chemical equation is modified in some way, then the equilibrium constant for the equation changes because of the modification. The following three modifications are common:

1. **If you reverse the equation, invert the equilibrium constant.** For example, consider this equilibrium equation:

$$\mathrm{A} + 2\,\mathrm{B} \rightleftharpoons 3\,\mathrm{C}$$

The expression for the equilibrium constant of this reaction is:

$$K_{\text{forward}} = \frac{[\mathrm{C}]^3}{[\mathrm{A}][\mathrm{B}]^2}$$

If you reverse the equation:

$$3\,\mathrm{C} \rightleftharpoons \mathrm{A} + 2\,\mathrm{B}$$

then, according to the law of mass action, the expression for the equilibrium constant becomes:

$$K_{\text{reverse}} = \frac{[\mathrm{A}][\mathrm{B}]^2}{[\mathrm{C}]^3} = \frac{1}{K_{\text{forward}}}$$

2. **If you multiply the coefficients in the equation by a factor, raise the equilibrium constant to the same factor.** Consider again this chemical equation and corresponding expression for the equilibrium constant:

$$\mathrm{A} + 2\,\mathrm{B} \rightleftharpoons 3\,\mathrm{C} \qquad K = \frac{[\mathrm{C}]^3}{[\mathrm{A}][\mathrm{B}]^2}$$

If you multiply the equation by n, you get:

$$n\,\mathrm{A} + 2n\,\mathrm{B} \rightleftharpoons 3n\,\mathrm{C}$$

Applying the law of mass action, the expression for the equilibrium constant becomes:

$$K' = \frac{[\mathrm{C}]^{3n}}{[\mathrm{A}]^n[\mathrm{B}]^{2n}} = \left(\frac{[\mathrm{C}]^3}{[\mathrm{A}][\mathrm{B}]^2}\right)^n = K^n$$

If n is a fractional quantity, raise K to the same fractional quantity.

Remember that $(x^a)^b = x^{ab}$.

3. **If you add two or more individual chemical equations to obtain an overall equation, multiply the corresponding equilibrium constants by each other to obtain the overall equilibrium constant.** Consider these two chemical equations and their corresponding equilibrium constant expressions:

$$\mathrm{A} \rightleftharpoons 2\,\mathrm{B} \qquad K_1 = \frac{[\mathrm{B}]^2}{[\mathrm{A}]}$$

$$2\,\mathrm{B} \rightleftharpoons 3\,\mathrm{C} \qquad K_2 = \frac{[\mathrm{C}]^3}{[\mathrm{B}]^2}$$

The two equations sum as follows:

$$\begin{array}{l} \mathrm{A} \rightleftharpoons \cancel{2\,\mathrm{B}} \\ \underline{\cancel{2\,\mathrm{B}} \rightleftharpoons 3\,\mathrm{C}} \\ \mathrm{A} \rightleftharpoons 3\,\mathrm{C} \end{array}$$

According to the law of mass action, the equilibrium constant for this overall equation is then:

$$K_{\text{overall}} = \frac{[\mathrm{C}]^3}{[\mathrm{A}]}$$

Notice that K_{overall} is the product of K_1 and K_2:

$$\begin{aligned} K_{\text{overall}} &= K_1 \times K_2 \\ &= \frac{\cancel{[\mathrm{B}]^2}}{[\mathrm{A}]} \times \frac{[\mathrm{C}]^3}{\cancel{[\mathrm{B}]^2}} \\ &= \frac{[\mathrm{C}]^3}{[\mathrm{A}]} \end{aligned}$$

ANSWER **NOW!**

16.5
Cc
Conceptual Connection

THE EQUILIBRIUM CONSTANT AND THE CHEMICAL EQUATION The reaction $A(g) \rightleftharpoons 2\,B(g)$ has an equilibrium constant of $K = 0.010$. What is the equilibrium constant for the reaction $B(g) \rightleftharpoons \frac{1}{2}A(g)$?

(a) 1 **(b)** 10 **(c)** 100 **(d)** 0.0010

EXAMPLE 16.2 Manipulating the Equilibrium Constant to Reflect Changes in the Chemical Equation

Consider the chemical equation and equilibrium constant for the synthesis of ammonia at 25 °C:

$$N_2(g) + 3\,H_2(g) \rightleftharpoons 2\,NH_3(g) \qquad K = 5.6 \times 10^5$$

Calculate the equilibrium constant for the following reaction at 25 °C:

$$NH_3(g) \rightleftharpoons \tfrac{1}{2}N_2(g) + \tfrac{3}{2}H_2(g) \qquad K' = ?$$

SOLUTION

You want to manipulate the given reaction and value of K to obtain the desired reaction and value of K. You can see that the given reaction is the reverse of the desired reaction, and its coefficients are twice those of the desired reaction.

Begin by reversing the given reaction and taking the inverse of the value of K.	$N_2(g) + 3\,H_2(g) \rightleftharpoons 2\,NH_3(g) \qquad K = 5.6 \times 10^5$ $2\,NH_3(g) \rightleftharpoons N_2(g) + 3\,H_2(g) \qquad K_{reverse} = \dfrac{1}{5.6 \times 10^5}$
Next, multiply the reaction by $\frac{1}{2}$ and raise the equilibrium constant to the $\frac{1}{2}$ power.	$NH_3(g) \rightleftharpoons \frac{1}{2}N_2(g) + \frac{3}{2}H_2(g)$ $K' = K_{reverse}^{1/2} = \left(\dfrac{1}{5.6 \times 10^5}\right)^{1/2}$
Calculate the value of K'.	$K' = 1.3 \times 10^{-3}$

FOR PRACTICE 16.2 Consider the following chemical equation and equilibrium constant at 25 °C:

$$2\,COF_2(g) \rightleftharpoons CO_2(g) + CF_4(g) \qquad K = 2.2 \times 10^6$$

Calculate the equilibrium constant for the following reaction at 25 °C:

$$2\,CO_2(g) + 2\,CF_4(g) \rightleftharpoons 4\,COF_2(g) \qquad K' = ?$$

FOR MORE PRACTICE 16.2 Predict the equilibrium constant for the first reaction shown here given the equilibrium constants for the second and third reactions:

$$CO_2(g) + 3\,H_2(g) \rightleftharpoons CH_3OH(g) + H_2O(g) \qquad K_1 = ?$$

$$CO(g) + H_2O(g) \rightleftharpoons CO_2(g) + H_2(g) \qquad K_2 = 1.0 \times 10^5$$

$$CO(g) + 2\,H_2(g) \rightleftharpoons CH_3OH(g) \qquad K_3 = 1.4 \times 10^7$$

16.4 Expressing the Equilibrium Constant in Terms of Pressure

So far, we have expressed the equilibrium constant only in terms of the *concentrations* of the reactants and products. For gaseous reactions, the partial pressure of a particular gas is proportional to its concentration. Therefore, we can also express the equilibrium constant in terms of the *partial pressures* of the reactants and products. Consider the gaseous reaction:

$$2\,SO_3(g) \rightleftharpoons 2\,SO_2(g) + O_2(g)$$

From this point on, we designate K_c as the equilibrium constant with respect to concentration in molarity. For the reaction just given, we can express K_c using the law of mass action:

$$K_c = \frac{[SO_2]^2[O_2]}{[SO_3]^2}$$

We now designate K_p as the equilibrium constant with respect to partial pressures in atmospheres. *The expression for K_p takes the form of the expression for K_c, except that we use the partial pressure of each gas in place of its concentration.* For the SO_3 reaction, we write K_p as:

$$K_p = \frac{(P_{SO_2})^2 P_{O_2}}{(P_{SO_3})^2}$$

where P_A is simply the partial pressure of gas A in units of atmospheres.

Relationship Between K_p and K_c

Since the partial pressure of a gas in atmospheres is not the same as its concentration in molarity, the value of K_p for a reaction is not necessarily equal to the value of K_c. However, as long as the gases are behaving ideally, we can derive a relationship between the two constants. The concentration of an ideal gas A is the number of moles of A (n_A) divided by its volume (V) in liters:

$$[A] = \frac{n_A}{V}$$

From the ideal gas law, we can relate the quantity n_A/V to the partial pressure of A as follows:

$$P_A V = n_A RT$$

$$P_A = \frac{n_A}{V} RT$$

Since $[A] = n_A/V$, we can write:

$$P_A = [A]RT \quad \text{or} \quad [A] = \frac{P_A}{RT} \qquad [16.1]$$

Now consider the following general equilibrium chemical equation:

$$aA + bB \rightleftharpoons cC + dD$$

According to the law of mass action, we write K_c as follows:

$$K_c = \frac{[C]^c[D]^d}{[A]^a[B]^b}$$

Substituting $[X] = P_X/RT$ for each concentration term, we get:

$$K_c = \frac{\left(\frac{P_C}{RT}\right)^c\left(\frac{P_D}{RT}\right)^d}{\left(\frac{P_A}{RT}\right)^a\left(\frac{P_B}{RT}\right)^b} = \frac{P_C^c P_D^d\left(\frac{1}{RT}\right)^{c+d}}{P_A^a P_B^b\left(\frac{1}{RT}\right)^{a+b}} = \frac{P_C^c P_D^d}{P_A^a P_B^b}\left(\frac{1}{RT}\right)^{c+d-(a+b)}$$

$$= K_p\left(\frac{1}{RT}\right)^{c+d-(a+b)}$$

Rearranging,

$$K_p = K_c(RT)^{c+d-(a+b)}$$

Finally, if we let $\Delta n = c + d - (a + b)$, which is the sum of the stoichiometric coefficients of the gaseous products minus the sum of the stoichiometric coefficients of the gaseous reactants, we get the following general result:

$$K_p = K_c(RT)^{\Delta n} \qquad [16.2]$$

In the equation $K_p = K_c(RT)^{\Delta n}$, the quantity Δn represents the difference between the number of moles of gaseous products and gaseous reactants.

Notice that if the total number of moles of gas is the same after the reaction as before, then $\Delta n = 0$, and K_p is equal to K_c.

WATCH **NOW!**

INTERACTIVE WORKED EXAMPLE 16.3

EXAMPLE 16.3 Relating K_p and K_c

Nitrogen monoxide, a pollutant in automobile exhaust, is oxidized to nitrogen dioxide in the atmosphere according to the equation:

$$2\,NO(g) + O_2(g) \rightleftharpoons 2\,NO_2(g) \qquad K_p = 2.2 \times 10^{12} \text{ at } 25\,°C$$

Find K_c for this reaction.

SORT You are given K_p for the reaction and asked to find K_c.

GIVEN: $K_p = 2.2 \times 10^{12}$

FIND: K_c

STRATEGIZE Use Equation 16.2 to relate K_p and K_c.

EQUATION $K_p = K_c(RT)^{\Delta n}$

SOLVE Solve the equation for K_c.

SOLUTION

$$K_c = \frac{K_p}{(RT)^{\Delta n}}$$

Calculate Δn.

$$\Delta n = 2 - 3 = -1$$

Substitute the required quantities to calculate K_c. The temperature must be in kelvins. The units are dropped when reporting K_c, as described later in this section.

$$K_c = \frac{2.2 \times 10^{12}}{\left(0.08206 \dfrac{L \cdot atm}{mol \cdot K} \times 298\,K\right)^{-1}}$$

$$= 5.4 \times 10^{13}$$

CHECK The easiest way to check this answer is to substitute it back into Equation 16.2 and confirm that you get the original value for K_p.

$$K_p = K_c(RT)^{\Delta n}$$

$$= 5.4 \times 10^{13}\left(0.08206 \frac{L \cdot atm}{mol \cdot K} \times 298\,K\right)^{-1}$$

$$= 2.2 \times 10^{12}$$

FOR PRACTICE 16.3 Consider the following reaction and corresponding value of K_c:

$$H_2(g) + I_2(g) \rightleftharpoons 2\,HI(g) \qquad K_c = 6.2 \times 10^2 \text{ at } 25\,°C$$

What is the value of K_p at this temperature?

Units of K

Throughout this book, we express concentrations and partial pressures within the equilibrium constant expression in units of molarity and atmospheres, respectively. When expressing the value of the equilibrium constant, however, we have not included the units. Formally, the values of concentration or partial pressure that we substitute into the equilibrium constant expression are ratios of the concentration or pressure to a reference concentration (exactly 1 M) or a reference pressure (exactly 1 atm).

For example, within the equilibrium constant expression, a pressure of 1.5 atm becomes:

$$\frac{1.5\,\cancel{atm}}{1\,\cancel{atm}} = 1.5$$

Similarly, a concentration of 1.5 M becomes:

$$\frac{1.5\,\cancel{M}}{1\,\cancel{M}} = 1.5$$

As long as concentration units are expressed in molarity for K_c and pressure units are expressed in atmospheres for K_p, we can skip this formality and enter the quantities directly into the equilibrium expression, dropping their corresponding units.

THE RELATIONSHIP BETWEEN K_p AND K_c Under which circumstances are K_p and K_c equal for the reaction shown here?

16.6 Cc Conceptual Connection — ANSWER NOW!

$$aA(g) + bB(g) \rightleftharpoons cC(g) + dD(g)$$

(a) If $a + b = c + d$.
(b) If the reaction is reversible.
(c) If the equilibrium constant is small.

16.5 Heterogeneous Equilibria: Reactions Involving Solids and Liquids

Many chemical reactions involve pure solids or pure liquids as reactants or products. Consider, for example, the reaction:

$$2\,CO(g) \rightleftharpoons CO_2(g) + C(s)$$

We might expect the expression for the equilibrium constant to be:

$$K_c = \frac{[CO_2][C]}{[CO]^2} \quad \text{(incorrect)}$$

However, since carbon is a solid, its concentration is constant (if you double the amount of carbon its *concentration* remains the same). The concentration of a solid does not change because a solid does not expand to fill its container. Its concentration, therefore, depends only on its density, which is constant as long as *some* solid is present (Figure 16.6▼). Consequently, pure solids—those reactants or products labeled in the chemical equation with an (*s*)—are not included in the equilibrium expression (because their constant value is incorporated into the value of *K*). The correct equilibrium expression for this reaction is therefore:

$$K_c = \frac{[CO_2]}{[CO]^2}$$

Similarly, the concentration of a pure liquid does not change. So, pure liquids—reactants or products labeled in the chemical equation with an (ℓ)—are also excluded from the equilibrium expression. For example, consider the equilibrium expression for the reaction between carbon dioxide and water:

$$CO_2(g) + H_2O(\ell) \rightleftharpoons H^+(aq) + HCO_3^-(aq)$$

Since $H_2O(\ell)$ is pure liquid, it is omitted from the equilibrium expression:

$$K_c = \frac{[H^+][HCO_3^-]}{[CO_2]}$$

A Heterogeneous Equilibrium

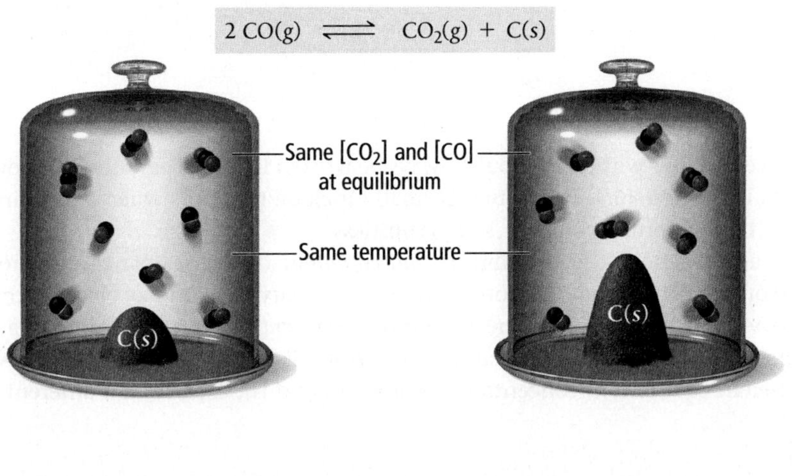

◀ **FIGURE 16.6 Heterogeneous Equilibrium** The concentration of solid carbon (the number of atoms per unit volume) is constant as long as some solid carbon is present. The same is true for pure liquids. For this reason, the concentrations of solids and pure liquids are not included in equilibrium constant expressions.

EXAMPLE 16.4 Writing Equilibrium Expressions for Reactions Involving a Solid or a Liquid

Write an expression for the equilibrium constant (K_c) for this chemical equation:

$$CaCO_3(s) \rightleftharpoons CaO(s) + CO_2(g)$$

SOLUTION

Since $CaCO_3(s)$ and $CaO(s)$ are both solids, omit them from the equilibrium expression.	$K_c = [CO_2]$

FOR PRACTICE 16.4 Write an equilibrium expression (K_c) for the equation:

$$4\,HCl(g) + O_2(g) \rightleftharpoons 2\,H_2O(\ell) + 2\,Cl_2(g)$$

ANSWER **NOW!**

16.7 Cc Conceptual Connection

HETEROGENEOUS EQUILIBRIA, K_p AND K_c For which reaction does $K_p = K_c$?

(a) $2\,Na_2O_2(s) + 2\,CO_2(g) \rightleftharpoons 2\,Na_2CO_3(s) + O(g)$
(b) $Fe_2O_3(s) + 3\,CO(g) \rightleftharpoons 2\,Fe(s) + 3\,CO_2(g)$
(c) $NH_4NO_3(s) \rightleftharpoons N_2O(g) + 2\,H_2O(g)$

16.6 Calculating the Equilibrium Constant from Measured Equilibrium Concentrations

The most direct way to obtain an experimental value for the equilibrium constant of a reaction is to measure the concentrations of the reactants and products in a reaction mixture at equilibrium. Consider the following reaction:

$$H_2(g) + I_2(g) \rightleftharpoons 2\,HI(g)$$

Since equilibrium constants depend on temperature, many equilibrium problems state the temperature even though it has no formal part in the calculation.

Suppose a mixture of H_2 and I_2 is allowed to come to equilibrium at 445 °C. The measured equilibrium concentrations are $[H_2] = 0.11$ M, $[I_2] = 0.11$ M, and $[HI] = 0.78$ M. What is the value of the equilibrium constant at this temperature?

We can write the expression for K_c from the balanced equation:

$$K_c = \frac{[HI]^2}{[H_2][I_2]}$$

To calculate the value of K_c, we substitute the correct equilibrium concentrations into the expression for K_c:

$$\begin{aligned} K_c &= \frac{[HI]^2}{[H_2][I_2]} \\ &= \frac{(0.78)^2}{(0.11)(0.11)} \\ &= 5.0 \times 10^1 \end{aligned}$$

The concentrations within K_c should always be written in moles per liter (M); however, as noted in Section 16.4, we do not normally include the units when expressing the value of the equilibrium constant, so K_c is unitless.

For any reaction, the equilibrium *concentrations* of the reactants and products depend on the initial concentrations (and in general vary from one set of initial concentrations to another). However, the equilibrium *constant* is always the same at a given temperature, regardless of the initial concentrations. For example, Table 16.1 shows several different equilibrium concentrations of H_2, I_2, and HI, each from a different set of

TABLE 16.1 ■ Initial and Equilibrium Concentrations for the Reaction $H_2(g) + I_2(g) \rightleftharpoons 2\,HI(g)$ at 445 °C

Initial Concentrations			Equilibrium Concentrations			Equilibrium Constant
$[H_2]$	$[I_2]$	$[HI]$	$[H_2]$	$[I_2]$	$[HI]$	$K_c = \frac{[HI]^2}{[H_2][I_2]}$
0.50	0.50	0.0	0.11	0.11	0.78	$\frac{(0.78)^2}{(0.11)(0.11)} = 50$
0.0	0.0	0.50	0.055	0.055	0.39	$\frac{(0.39)^2}{(0.055)(0.055)} = 50$
0.50	0.50	0.50	0.165	0.165	1.17	$\frac{(1.17)^2}{(0.165)(0.165)} = 50$
1.0	0.50	0.0	0.53	0.033	0.934	$\frac{(0.934)^2}{(0.53)(0.033)} = 50$
0.50	1.0	0.0	0.033	0.53	0.934	$\frac{(0.934)^2}{(0.033)(0.53)} = 50$

initial concentrations. Notice that the equilibrium constant is always the same, regardless of the initial concentrations. Whether we start with only reactants or only products, the reaction reaches equilibrium concentrations at which the equilibrium constant is the same. No matter what the initial concentrations are, the reaction always goes in a direction that ensures that the equilibrium concentrations—when substituted into the equilibrium expression—give the same constant, *K*.

So far, we have calculated equilibrium constants from values of the equilibrium concentrations of all the reactants and products. In most cases, however, we need only know the initial concentrations of the reactant(s) and the equilibrium concentration of any *one* reactant or product. We can deduce the other equilibrium concentrations from the stoichiometry of the reaction.

For example, consider the simple reaction:

$$A(g) \rightleftharpoons 2\,B(g)$$

Suppose that we have a reaction mixture in which the initial concentration of A is 1.00 M and the initial concentration of B is 0.00 M. When equilibrium is reached, the concentration of A is 0.75 M. Since [A] has changed by −0.25 M, we can deduce (based on the stoichiometry) that [B] must have changed by 2 × (+0.25 M) or +0.50 M. We summarize the initial conditions, the changes, and the equilibrium conditions in the following table:

	[A]	[B]
Initial	1.00	0.00
Change	−0.25	+2(0.25)
Equilibrium	0.75	0.50

We refer to this type of table as an ICE table (I = initial, C = change, E = equilibrium). To calculate the equilibrium constant, we use the balanced equation to write an expression for the equilibrium constant and then substitute the equilibrium concentrations from the ICE table:

$$K = \frac{[B]^2}{[A]} = \frac{(0.50)^2}{(0.75)} = 0.33$$

In Examples 16.5 and 16.6, we show the general procedure for solving these kinds of equilibrium problems in the left column and work two examples exemplifying the procedure in the center and right columns.

WATCH **NOW!**

INTERACTIVE WORKED EXAMPLE VIDEO 16.5

HOW TO: *Find Equilibrium Constants from Experimental Concentration Measurements*

To solve these types of problems, follow the given procedure.

EXAMPLE 16.5

Finding Equilibrium Constants from Experimental Concentration Measurements

Consider the following reaction:

$$CO(g) + 2\,H_2(g) \rightleftharpoons CH_3OH(g)$$

A reaction mixture at 780 °C initially contains [CO] = 0.500 M and $[H_2]$ = 1.00 M. At equilibrium, the CO concentration is found to be 0.15 M. What is the value of the equilibrium constant?

EXAMPLE 16.6

Finding Equilibrium Constants from Experimental Concentration Measurements

Consider the following reaction:

$$2\,CH_4(g) \rightleftharpoons C_2H_2(g) + 3\,H_2(g)$$

A reaction mixture at 1700 °C initially contains $[CH_4]$ = 0.115 M. At equilibrium, the mixture contains $[C_2H_2]$ = 0.035 M. What is the value of the equilibrium constant?

1. Using the balanced equation as a guide, prepare an ICE table showing the known initial concentrations and equilibrium concentrations of the reactants and products. Leave space in the middle of the table for determining the changes in concentration that occur during the reaction.

Example 16.5:

$$CO(g) + 2\,H_2(g) \rightleftharpoons CH_3OH(g)$$

	[CO]	$[H_2]$	$[CH_3OH]$
Initial	0.500	1.00	0.00
Change			
Equil	0.15		

Example 16.6:

$$2\,CH_4(g) \rightleftharpoons C_2H_2(g) + 3\,H_2(g)$$

	$[CH_4]$	$[C_2H_2]$	$[H_2]$
Initial	0.115	0.00	0.00
Change			
Equil		0.035	

2. For the reactant or product whose concentration is known both initially and at equilibrium, calculate the change in concentration that occurs.

Example 16.5:

$$CO(g) + 2\,H_2(g) \rightleftharpoons CH_3OH(g)$$

	[CO]	$[H_2]$	$[CH_3OH]$
Initial	0.500	1.00	0.00
Change	−0.35		
Equil	0.15		

Example 16.6:

$$2\,CH_4(g) \rightleftharpoons C_2H_2(g) + 3\,H_2(g)$$

	$[CH_4]$	$[C_2H_2]$	$[H_2]$
Initial	0.115	0.00	0.00
Change		+0.035	
Equil		0.035	

3. Use the change you calculated in step 2 and the stoichiometric relationships from the balanced chemical equation to determine the changes in concentration of all other reactants and products. Since reactants are consumed during the reaction, the changes in their concentrations are negative. Since products are formed, the changes in their concentrations are positive.

Example 16.5:

$$CO(g) + 2\,H_2(g) \rightleftharpoons CH_3OH(g)$$

	[CO]	$[H_2]$	$[CH_3OH]$
Initial	0.500	1.00	0.00
Change	−0.35	−2(0.35)	+0.35
Equil	0.15		

Example 16.6:

$$2\,CH_4(g) \rightleftharpoons C_2H_2(g) + 3\,H_2(g)$$

	$[CH_4]$	$[C_2H_2]$	$[H_2]$
Initial	0.115	0.00	0.00
Change	−2(0.035)	+0.035	+3(0.035)
Equil		0.035	

4. Sum each column for each reactant and product to determine the equilibrium concentrations.

Example 16.5:

	[CO]	$[H_2]$	$[CH_3OH]$
Initial	0.500	1.00	0.00
Change	−0.35	−0.70	+0.35
Equil	0.15	0.30	0.35

Example 16.6:

	$[CH_4]$	$[C_2H_2]$	$[H_2]$
Initial	0.115	0.00	0.00
Change	−0.070	+0.035	+0.105
Equil	0.045	0.035	0.105

5. Use the balanced equation to write an expression for the equilibrium constant and substitute the equilibrium concentrations to calculate *K*.	$K_c = \frac{[CH_3OH]}{[CO][H_2]^2}$ $= \frac{0.35}{(0.15)(0.30)^2}$ $= 26$	$K_c = \frac{[C_2H_2][H_2]^3}{[CH_4]^2}$ $= \frac{(0.035)(0.105)^3}{(0.045)^2}$ $= 0.020$
	FOR PRACTICE 16.5 The reaction in Example 16.5 between CO and H_2 is carried out at a different temperature with initial concentrations of [CO] = 0.27 M and $[H_2]$ = 0.49 M. At equilibrium, the concentration of CH_3OH is 0.11 M. Find the equilibrium constant at this temperature.	**FOR PRACTICE 16.6** The reaction of CH_4 in Example 16.6 is carried out at a different temperature with an initial concentration of $[CH_4]$ = 0.087 M. At equilibrium, the concentration of H_2 is 0.012 M. Find the equilibrium constant at this temperature.

WATCH **NOW!**

KEY CONCEPT VIDEO 16.7
The Reaction Quotient

16.7 The Reaction Quotient: Predicting the Direction of Change

When the reactants of a chemical reaction mix, they generally react to form products—we say that the reaction proceeds to the right (toward the products). The amount of products formed when a reaction reaches equilibrium depends on the magnitude of the equilibrium constant, as we have seen. However, what if a reaction mixture that is not at equilibrium contains both reactants *and products*? Can we predict the direction of change for such a mixture?

To gauge the progress of a reaction relative to equilibrium, we use a quantity called the *reaction quotient*. The definition of the reaction quotient takes the same form as the definition of the equilibrium constant, except that the reaction need not be at equilibrium. So, for the general reaction:

$$aA + bB \rightleftharpoons cC + dD$$

we define the **reaction quotient (Q_c)** as the ratio—at any point in the reaction—of the concentrations of the products raised to their stoichiometric coefficients divided by the concentrations of the reactants raised to their stoichiometric coefficients. For gases with amounts measured in atmospheres, the reaction quotient uses the partial pressures in place of concentrations and is called Q_p:

$$Q_c = \frac{[C]^c[D]^d}{[A]^a[B]^b} \qquad Q_p = \frac{P_C^c P_D^d}{P_A^a P_B^b}$$

The difference between the reaction quotient and the equilibrium constant is that, at a given temperature, the equilibrium constant has only one value and it specifies the relative amounts of reactants and products *at equilibrium*. The reaction quotient, by contrast, depends on the current state of the reaction and has many different values as the reaction proceeds. For example, in a reaction mixture containing only reactants, the reaction quotient is zero ($Q_c = 0$):

$$Q_c = \frac{[0]^c[0]^d}{[A]^a[B]^b} = 0$$

In a reaction mixture containing only products, the reaction quotient is infinite ($Q_c = \infty$):

$$Q_c = \frac{[C]^c[D]^d}{[0]^a[0]^b} = \infty$$

In a reaction mixture containing both reactants and products, each at a concentration of 1 M, the reaction quotient is one ($Q_c = 1$):

$$Q_c = \frac{(1)^c(1)^d}{(1)^a(1)^b} = 1$$

The reaction quotient is useful because *the value of Q relative to K is a measure of the progress of the reaction toward equilibrium. At equilibrium, the reaction quotient is equal to the*

Q, K, and the Direction of a Reaction

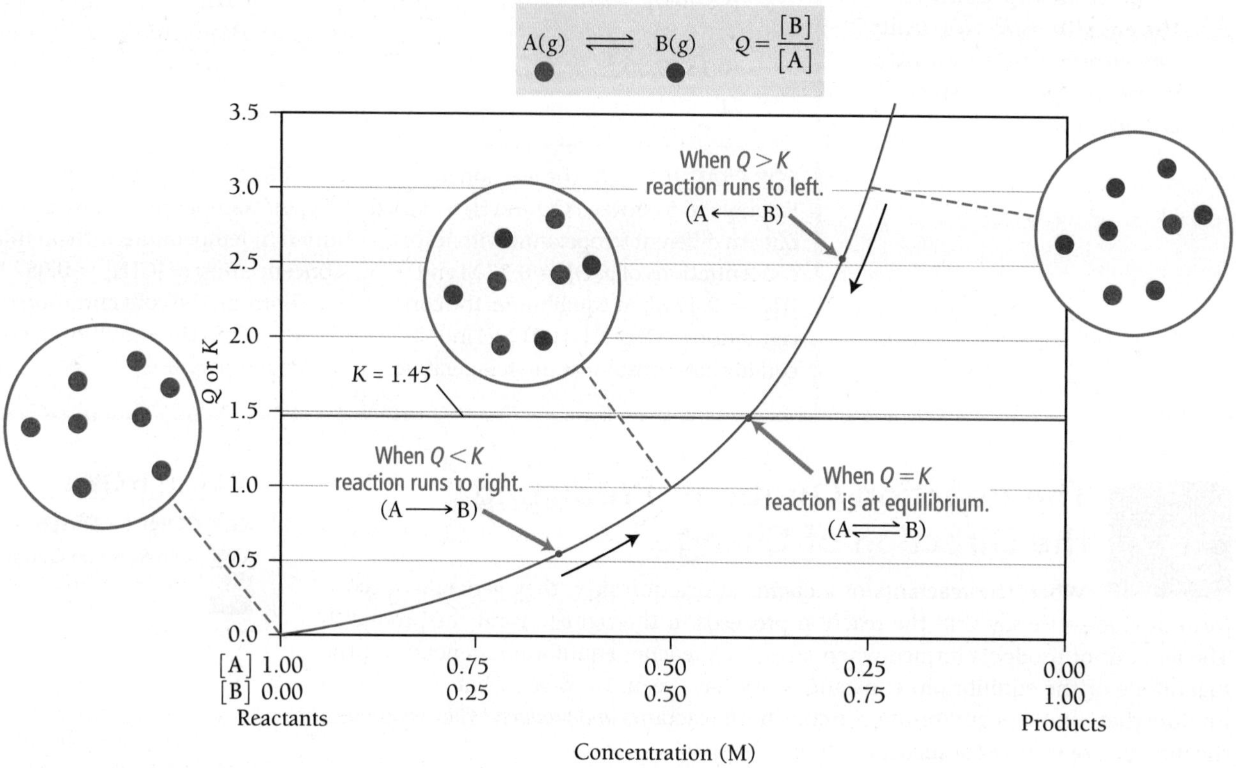

▲ FIGURE 16.7 Q, K, and the Direction of a Reaction The graph shows a plot of Q as a function of the concentrations of the reactants and products in a simple reaction A ⇌ B, in which $K = 1.45$ and the sum of the reactant and product concentrations is 1 M. The far left of the graph represents pure reactant, and the far right represents pure product. The midpoint of the graph represents an equal mixture of A and B. When Q is less than K, the reaction moves in the forward direction (A ⟶ B). When Q is greater than K, the reaction moves in the reverse direction (A ⟵ B). When Q is equal to K, the reaction is at equilibrium.

equilibrium constant. Figure 16.7▲ shows a plot of Q as a function of the concentrations of A and B for the simple reaction $A(g) \rightleftharpoons B(g)$, which has an equilibrium constant of $K = 1.45$. The following points are representative of three possible conditions:

Q	K	Predicted Direction of Reaction
0.55	1.45	To the right (toward products)
2.55	1.45	To the left (toward reactants)
1.45	1.45	No change (at equilibrium)

For the first set of values in the table, Q is less than K and must therefore get larger as the reaction proceeds toward equilibrium. Q becomes larger as the reactant concentration decreases and the product concentration increases—the reaction proceeds to the right. For the second set of values, Q is greater than K and must therefore get smaller as the reaction proceeds toward equilibrium. Q gets smaller as the reactant concentration increases and the product concentration decreases—the reaction proceeds to the left. In the third set of values, $Q = K$, implying that the reaction is at equilibrium—the reaction will not proceed in either direction.

Summarizing Direction of Change Predictions:

The reaction quotient (Q) relative to the equilibrium constant (K) is a measure of the progress of a reaction toward equilibrium.

- $Q < K$ Reaction goes to the right (toward products).
- $Q > K$ Reaction goes to the left (toward reactants).
- $Q = K$ Reaction is at equilibrium.

WATCH NOW!
INTERACTIVE WORKED EXAMPLE 16.7

EXAMPLE 16.7 Predicting the Direction of a Reaction by Comparing Q and K

Consider the reaction and its equilibrium constant at 25.0 °C:

$$I_2(g) + Cl_2(g) \rightleftharpoons 2\,ICl(g) \qquad K_p = 81.9$$

A reaction mixture contains $P_{I_2} = 0.114$ atm, $P_{Cl_2} = 0.102$ atm, and $P_{ICl} = 0.355$ atm. Is the reaction mixture at equilibrium? If not, in which direction will the reaction proceed?

SOLUTION

To determine the progress of the reaction relative to the equilibrium state, first calculate Q.	$Q_p = \left(\dfrac{P_{ICl}^2}{P_{I_2}P_{Cl_2}}\right) = \dfrac{(0.355)^2}{(0.114)(0.102)} = 10.8$
Compare Q to K.	$Q_p = 10.8;\ K_p = 81.9$ Since $Q_p < K_p$, the reaction is not at equilibrium and will proceed to the right.

FOR PRACTICE 16.7 Consider the reaction and its equilibrium constant:

$$N_2O_4(g) \rightleftharpoons 2\,NO_2(g) \qquad K_c = 5.85 \times 10^{-3} \text{ (at some temperature)}$$

A reaction mixture contains $[NO_2] = 0.0255$ M and $[N_2O_4] = 0.0331$ M. Calculate Q_c and determine the direction in which the reaction will proceed.

Q AND K For the reaction $N_2O_4(g) \rightleftharpoons 2\,NO_2(g)$, a reaction mixture at a certain temperature initially contains both N_2O_4 and NO_2 in their standard states, which means that $P_{N_2O_4} = 1$ atm and $P_{NO_2} = 1$ atm (see the definition of standard state in Section 7.9). If $K_p = 0.15$, which statement is true of the reaction mixture before any reaction occurs?

16.8 Cc Conceptual Connection — ANSWER NOW!

(a) $Q = K$; the reaction is at equilibrium.
(b) $Q < K$; the reaction will proceed to the right.
(c) $Q > K$; the reaction will proceed to the left.

16.8 Finding Equilibrium Concentrations

WATCH NOW!
KEY CONCEPT VIDEO 16.8
Finding Equilibrium Concentrations from Initial Concentrations

In Section 16.6, we discussed how to calculate an equilibrium constant from the equilibrium concentrations of the reactants and products. Just as commonly, we will want to calculate equilibrium concentrations of reactants or products from the equilibrium constant. These kinds of calculations are important because they allow us to calculate the amount of a reactant or product at equilibrium. For example, in a synthesis reaction, we might want to know how much of the product forms when the reaction reaches equilibrium. Or for the hemoglobin–oxygen equilibrium discussed in Section 16.1, we might want to know the concentration of oxygenated hemoglobin present under certain oxygen concentrations within the lungs or muscles.

We divide these types of problems into two categories: (1) finding equilibrium concentrations when we know the equilibrium constant and all but one of the equilibrium concentrations of the reactants and products, and (2) finding equilibrium concentrations when we know the equilibrium constant and only initial concentrations. The second category of problem is more difficult than the first. Let's examine each separately.

Finding Equilibrium Concentrations from the Equilibrium Constant and All but One of the Equilibrium Concentrations of the Reactants and Products

We can use the equilibrium constant to calculate the equilibrium concentration of one of the reactants or products, given the equilibrium concentrations of the others. To solve this type of problem, we follow our general problem-solving procedure.

WATCH **NOW!**

INTERACTIVE WORKED EXAMPLE 16.8

EXAMPLE 16.8 Finding Equilibrium Concentrations When You Know the Equilibrium Constant and All but One of the Equilibrium Concentrations of the Reactants and Products

Consider the following reaction:

$$2\,COF_2(g) \rightleftharpoons CO_2(g) + CF_4(g) \qquad K_c = 2.00 \text{ at } 1000\,°C$$

In an equilibrium mixture, the concentration of COF_2 is 0.255 M and the concentration of CF_4 is 0.118 M. What is the equilibrium concentration of CO_2?

SORT You are given the equilibrium constant of a chemical reaction, together with the equilibrium concentrations of the reactant and one product. You are asked to find the equilibrium concentration of the other product.

GIVEN: $[COF_2] = 0.255$ M
$[CF_4] = 0.118$ M
$K_c = 2.00$

FIND: $[CO_2]$

STRATEGIZE Calculate the concentration of the product using the given quantities and the expression for K_c.

CONCEPTUAL PLAN

$[COF_2], [CF_4], K_c$ → $[CO_2]$

$$K_c = \frac{[CO_2][CF_4]}{[COF_2]^2}$$

SOLVE Solve the equilibrium expression for $[CO_2]$ and then substitute in the appropriate values to calculate it.

SOLUTION

$$[CO_2] = K_c \frac{[COF_2]^2}{[CF_4]}$$

$$[CO_2] = 2.00\left(\frac{(0.255)^2}{0.118}\right) = 1.10\,\text{M}$$

CHECK Check your answer by mentally substituting the given values of $[COF_2]$ and $[CF_4]$, as well as your calculated value for CO_2, back into the equilibrium expression:

$$K_c = \frac{[CO_2][CF_4]}{[COF_2]^2}$$

$[CO_2]$ is roughly equal to 1. $[COF_2]^2 \approx 0.06$ and $[CF_4] \approx 0.12$. Therefore, K_c is approximately 2, as given in the problem.

FOR PRACTICE 16.8 Diatomic iodine $[I_2]$ decomposes at high temperature to form I atoms according to the reaction:

$$I_2(g) \rightleftharpoons 2\,I(g) \qquad K_c = 0.011 \text{ at } 1200\,°C$$

In an equilibrium mixture, the concentration of I_2 is 0.10 M. What is the equilibrium concentration of I?

FINDING EQUILIBRIUM CONCENTRATIONS For the reaction, $A(g) \rightleftharpoons 2\,B(g)$, $K_c = 4.0$. A reaction mixture at equilibrium contains $[A] = 1.0$ M. What is the concentration of B in the reaction mixture?

(a) 0.50 M **(b)** 1.0 M **(c)** 2.0 M **(d)** 4.0 M

16.9
Cc
Conceptual Connection

ANSWER **NOW!**

Finding Equilibrium Concentrations from the Equilibrium Constant and Initial Concentrations or Pressures

More commonly, we know the equilibrium constant and only initial concentrations of reactants and need to find the *equilibrium concentrations* of the reactants or products. These kinds of problems are generally more involved than those we just examined and require a specific procedure to solve them. The procedure has some similarities to the one used in Examples 16.5 and 16.6 in that we set up an ICE table showing the initial concentrations, the changes, and the equilibrium concentrations. However, unlike in Examples 16.5 and 16.6, here the changes in concentration are not known and are represented with the variable x.

For example, consider again the simple reaction:

$$A(g) \rightleftharpoons 2\,B(g)$$

Suppose that, as before (see Section 16.6), we have a reaction mixture in which the initial concentration of A is 1.0 M and the initial concentration of B is 0.00 M. However, now we know the equilibrium constant, $K = 0.33$, and want to find the equilibrium concentrations. We know that because $Q = 0$, the reaction proceeds to the right (toward the products). We set up the ICE table with the given initial concentrations and then *represent the unknown change in [A] with the variable x* as follows:

	[A]	[B]
Initial	1.0	0.00
Change	$-x$	$+2x$
Equil	$1.0 - x$	$2x$

Represent changes from initial conditions with the variable *x*.

Notice that, due to the stoichiometry of the reaction, the change in [B] must be $+2x$. As before, each *equilibrium* concentration is the sum of the two entries above it in the ICE table. In order to find the equilibrium concentrations of A and B, we must find the value of the variable x. Since we know the value of the equilibrium constant, we can use the equilibrium constant expression to set up an equation in which x is the only variable:

$$K = \frac{[B]^2}{[A]} = \frac{(2x)^2}{1.0 - x} = 0.33$$

or more simply:

$$\frac{4x^2}{1.0 - x} = 0.33$$

This equation is a *quadratic* equation—it contains the variable x raised to the second power. In general, we can solve quadratic equations with the quadratic formula (see Appendix IC), which we introduce in Example 16.10. If the quadratic equation is a perfect square, however, we can solve it by simpler means, as shown in Example 16.9. For both of these examples, we give the general procedure in the left column and apply the procedure to the two examples to the right. Later in this section, we see that quadratic equations can often be simplified by making some approximations based on our chemical knowledge.

WATCH **NOW!**

INTERACTIVE WORKED EXAMPLE VIDEO 16.9

HOW TO: *Find Equilibrium Concentrations from Initial Concentrations and the Equilibrium Constant*

To solve these types of problems, follow the given procedure.

EXAMPLE 16.9

Finding Equilibrium Concentrations from Initial Concentrations and the Equilibrium Constant

Consider the reaction:

$$N_2(g) + O_2(g) \rightleftharpoons 2\,NO(g) \qquad K_c = 0.10 \text{ (at 2000 °C)}$$

A reaction mixture at 2000 °C initially contains $[N_2] = 0.200$ M and $[O_2] = 0.200$ M. Find the equilibrium concentrations of the reactants and product at this temperature.

EXAMPLE 16.10

Finding Equilibrium Concentrations from Initial Concentrations and the Equilibrium Constant

Consider the reaction:

$$N_2O_4(g) \rightleftharpoons 2\,NO_2(g) \qquad K_c = 0.36 \text{ (at 100 °C)}$$

A reaction mixture at 100 °C initially contains $[NO_2] = 0.100$ M. Find the equilibrium concentrations of NO_2 and N_2O_4 at this temperature.

---

1. Using the balanced equation as a guide, prepare a table showing the known initial concentrations of the reactants and products. Leave room in the table for the changes in concentrations and for the equilibrium concentrations.

Example 16.9:

$$N_2(g) + O_2(g) \rightleftharpoons 2\,NO(g)$$

	$[N_2]$	$[O_2]$	$[NO]$
Initial	0.200	0.200	0.00
Change			
Equil			

Example 16.10:

$$N_2O_4(g) \rightleftharpoons 2\,NO_2(g)$$

	$[N_2O_4]$	$[NO_2]$
Initial	0.00	0.100
Change		
Equil		

2. Use the initial concentrations to calculate the reaction quotient (*Q*) for the initial concentrations. Compare *Q* to *K* to predict the direction in which the reaction proceeds.

Example 16.9:

$$Q_c = \frac{[NO]^2}{[N_2][O_2]} = \frac{(0.00)^2}{(0.200)(0.200)} = 0$$

$Q < K$; therefore, the reaction will proceed to the right.

Example 16.10:

$$Q_c = \frac{[NO_2]^2}{[N_2O_4]} = \frac{(0.100)^2}{0.00} = \infty$$

$Q > K$; therefore, the reaction will proceed to the left.

3. Represent the change in the concentration of one of the reactants or products with the variable *x*. Define the changes in the concentrations of the other reactants or products in terms of *x*. It is usually most convenient to let *x* represent the change in concentration of the reactant or product with the smallest stoichiometric coefficient.

Example 16.9:

$$N_2(g) + O_2(g) \rightleftharpoons 2\,NO(g)$$

	$[N_2]$	$[O_2]$	$[NO]$
Initial	0.200	0.200	0.00
Change	$-x$	$-x$	$+2x$
Equil			

Example 16.10:

$$N_2O_4(g) \rightleftharpoons 2\,NO_2(g)$$

	$[N_2O_4]$	$[NO_2]$
Initial	0.00	0.100
Change	$+x$	$-2x$
Equil		

4. Sum each column for each reactant and each product to determine the equilibrium concentrations in terms of the initial concentrations and the variable *x*.

Example 16.9:

$$N_2(g) + O_2(g) \rightleftharpoons 2\,NO(g)$$

	$[N_2]$	$[O_2]$	$[NO]$
Initial	0.200	0.200	0.00
Change	$-x$	$-x$	$+2x$
Equil	$0.200 - x$	$0.200 - x$	$2x$

Example 16.10:

$$N_2O_4(g) \rightleftharpoons 2\,NO_2(g)$$

	$[N_2O_4]$	$[NO_2]$
Initial	0.00	0.100
Change	$+x$	$-2x$
Equil	x	$0.100 - 2x$

5. Substitute the expressions for the equilibrium concentrations (from step 4) into the expression for the equilibrium constant. Using the given value of the equilibrium constant, solve the expression for the variable *x*. In some cases, such as Example 16.9, you can take the square root of both sides of the expression to solve for *x*. In other cases, such as Example 16.10, you must solve a quadratic equation to find *x*. Remember the quadratic formula: $ax^2 + bx + c = 0$ $x = \frac{-b \pm \sqrt{b^2 - 4ac}}{2a}$	$K_c = \frac{[NO]^2}{[N_2][O_2]}$ $= \frac{(2x)^2}{(0.200 - x)(0.200 - x)}$ $0.10 = \frac{(2x)^2}{(0.200 - x)^2}$ $\sqrt{0.10} = \frac{2x}{0.200 - x}$ $\sqrt{0.10}\,(0.200 - x) = 2x$ $\sqrt{0.10}\,(0.200) - \sqrt{0.10}\,x = 2x$ $0.063 = 2x + \sqrt{0.10}\,x$ $0.063 = 2.3x$ $x = 0.027$	$K_c = \frac{[NO_2]^2}{[N_2O_4]}$ $= \frac{(0.100 - 2x)^2}{x}$ $0.36 = \frac{0.0100 - 0.400x + 4x^2}{x}$ $0.36x = 0.0100 - 0.400x + 4x^2$ $4x^2 - 0.76x + 0.0100 = 0$ (*quadratic*) $x = \frac{-b \pm \sqrt{b^2 - 4ac}}{2a}$ $= \frac{-(-0.76) \pm \sqrt{(-0.76)^2 - 4(4)(0.0100)}}{2(4)}$ $= \frac{0.76 \pm 0.65}{8}$ $x = 0.176$ or $x = 0.014$
6. Substitute *x* into the expressions for the equilibrium concentrations of the reactants and products (from step 4) and calculate the concentrations. In cases where you solved a quadratic and have two values for *x*, choose the value for *x* that gives a physically realistic answer. For example, reject the value of *x* that results in any negative concentrations.	$[N_2] = 0.200 - 0.027$ $= 0.173\ M$ $[O_2] = 0.200 - 0.027$ $= 0.173\ M$ $[NO] = 2(0.027)$ $= 0.054\ M$	We reject the root $x = 0.176$ because it gives a negative concentration for NO_2. Using $x = 0.014$, we get the following concentrations: $[NO_2] = 0.100 - 2x$ $= 0.100 - 2(0.014) = 0.072\ M$ $[N_2O_4] = x$ $= 0.014\ M$
7. Check your answer by substituting the calculated equilibrium values into the equilibrium expression. The calculated value of *K* should match the given value of *K*. Note that rounding errors could cause a difference in the least significant digit when comparing values of the equilibrium constant.	$K_c = \frac{[NO]^2}{[N_2][O_2]}$ $= \frac{(0.054)^2}{(0.173)(0.173)} = 0.097$ Since the calculated value of K_c matches the given value (to within one digit in the least significant figure), the answer is valid.	$K_c = \frac{[NO_2]^2}{[N_2O_4]} = \frac{(0.072)^2}{0.014}$ $= 0.37$ Since the calculated value of K_c matches the given value (to within one digit in the least significant figure), the answer is valid.
	FOR PRACTICE 16.9 The reaction in Example 16.9 is carried out at a different temperature at which $K_c = 0.055$. This time, however, the reaction mixture starts with only the product, $[NO] = 0.0100\ M$, and no reactants. Find the equilibrium concentrations of N_2, O_2, and NO at equilibrium.	**FOR PRACTICE 16.10** The reaction in Example 16.10 is carried out at the same temperature, but this time the reaction mixture initially contains only the reactant, $[N_2O_4] = 0.0250\ M$, and no NO_2. Find the equilibrium concentrations of N_2O_4 and NO_2.

When the initial conditions are given in terms of partial pressures (instead of concentrations) and the equilibrium constant is given as K_p instead of K_c, use the same procedure, but substitute partial pressures for concentrations, as shown in Example 16.11.

EXAMPLE 16.11 Finding Equilibrium Partial Pressures When You Are Given the Equilibrium Constant and Initial Partial Pressures

Consider the reaction:

$$I_2(g) + Cl_2(g) \rightleftharpoons 2\,ICl(g) \qquad K_p = 81.9 \text{ (at 25 °C)}$$

A reaction mixture at 25 °C initially contains $P_{I_2} = 0.100$ atm, $P_{Cl_2} = 0.100$ atm, and $P_{ICl} = 0.100$ atm. Find the equilibrium partial pressures of I_2, Cl_2, and ICl at this temperature.

SOLUTION

Follow the procedure used in Examples 16.5 and 16.6 (using partial pressures in place of concentrations) to solve the problem.

1. Using the balanced equation as a guide, prepare an ICE table showing the known initial partial pressures of the reactants and products.

$$I_2(g) + Cl_2(g) \rightleftharpoons 2\,ICl(g)$$

	P_{I_2} (atm)	P_{Cl_2} (atm)	P_{ICl} (atm)
Initial	0.100	0.100	0.100
Change			
Equil			

2. Use the initial partial pressures to calculate the reaction quotient (Q). Compare Q to K to predict the direction in which the reaction will proceed.

$$Q_p = \frac{(P_{ICl})^2}{P_{I_2}P_{Cl_2}} = \frac{(0.100)^2}{(0.100)(0.100)} = 1$$

$K_p = 81.9$ (given)

$Q < K$; therefore, the reaction will proceed to the right.

3. Represent the change in the partial pressure of one of the reactants or products with the variable x. Define the changes in the partial pressures of the other reactants or products in terms of x.

$$I_2(g) + Cl_2(g) \rightleftharpoons 2\,ICl(g)$$

	P_{I_2} (atm)	P_{Cl_2} (atm)	P_{ICl} (atm)
Initial	0.100	0.100	0.100
Change	−x	−x	+2x
Equil			

4. Sum each column for each reactant and product to determine the equilibrium partial pressures in terms of the initial partial pressures and the variable x.

$$I_2(g) + Cl_2(g) \rightleftharpoons 2\,ICl(g)$$

	P_{I_2} (atm)	P_{Cl_2} (atm)	P_{ICl} (atm)
Initial	0.100	0.100	0.100
Change	−x	−x	+2x
Equil	0.100 − x	0.100 − x	0.100 + 2x

5. Substitute the expressions for the equilibrium partial pressures (from step 4) into the expression for the equilibrium constant. Use the given value of the equilibrium constant to solve the expression for the variable x.

$$K_p = \frac{(P_{ICl})^2}{P_{I_2}P_{Cl_2}} = \frac{(0.100 + 2x)^2}{(0.100 - x)(0.100 - x)}$$

$$81.9 = \frac{(0.100 + 2x)^2}{(0.100 - x)^2} \quad \text{(perfect square)}$$

$$\sqrt{81.9} = \frac{(0.100 + 2x)}{(0.100 - x)}$$

$$\sqrt{81.9}\,(0.100 - x) = 0.100 + 2x$$

$$\sqrt{81.9}\,(0.100) - \sqrt{81.9}\,x = 0.100 + 2x$$

$$\sqrt{81.9}\,(0.100) - 0.100 = 2x + \sqrt{81.9}\,x$$

$$0.805 = 11.05x$$

$$x = 0.0729$$

6. Substitute x into the expressions for the equilibrium partial pressures of the reactants and products (from step 4) and calculate the partial pressures.

$P_{I_2} = 0.100 - 0.0729 = 0.027$ atm

$P_{Cl_2} = 0.100 - 0.0729 = 0.027$ atm

$P_{ICl} = 0.100 + 2(0.0729) = 0.246$ atm

7. Check your answer by substituting the calculated equilibrium partial pressures into the equilibrium expression. The calculated value of *K* should match the given value of *K*.	$K_p = \dfrac{(P_{ICl})^2}{P_{I_2}P_{Cl_2}} = \dfrac{(0.246)^2}{(0.027)(0.027)} = 83$ Since the calculated value of K_p matches the given value (within the uncertainty indicated by the significant figures), the answer is valid.

FOR PRACTICE 16.11 The reaction between I_2 and Cl_2 in Example 16.11 is carried out at the same temperature, but with these initial partial pressures: $P_{I_2} = 0.150$ atm, $P_{Cl_2} = 0.150$ atm, $P_{ICl} = 0.00$ atm. Find the equilibrium partial pressures of all three substances.

Simplifying Approximations in Working Equilibrium Problems

For some equilibrium problems of the type shown in Examples 16.9, 16.10, and 16.11, we can make an approximation that simplifies the calculations without any significant loss of accuracy. For example, if the equilibrium constant is relatively small, the reaction will not proceed very far to the right. Therefore, if the initial reactant concentration is relatively large, we can make the assumption that *x* is small relative to the initial concentration of reactant.

To see how this approximation works, consider again the simple reaction $A \rightleftharpoons 2\,B$. Suppose that, as before, we have a reaction mixture in which the initial concentration of A is 1.0 M and the initial concentration of B is 0.0 M and that we want to find the equilibrium concentrations. However, suppose that in this case the equilibrium constant is much smaller, say $K = 3.3 \times 10^{-5}$. The ICE table is identical to the one we set up previously:

	[A]	[B]
Initial	1.0	0.0
Change	−x	+2x
Equil	1.0 − x	2x

Except for the value of *K*, we end up with the exact quadratic equation that we had before:

$$K = \frac{[B]^2}{[A]} = \frac{(2x)^2}{1.0 - x} = 3.3 \times 10^{-5}$$

or more simply:

$$\frac{4x^2}{1.0 - x} = 3.3 \times 10^{-5}$$

We can rearrange this quadratic equation into standard form and solve it using the quadratic formula. But since *K* is small, the reaction will not proceed very far toward products and, therefore, *x* will also be small. If *x* is much smaller than 1.0, then $(1.0 - x)$ (the quantity in the denominator) can be approximated by (1.0):

$$\frac{4x^2}{(1.0 - \cancel{x})} = 3.3 \times 10^{-5}$$

This approximation greatly simplifies the equation, which we can then solve for *x* as follows:

$$\frac{4x^2}{1.0} = 3.3 \times 10^{-5}$$

$$4x^2 = 3.3 \times 10^{-5}$$

$$x = \sqrt{\frac{3.3 \times 10^{-5}}{4}} = 0.0029$$

We can check the validity of this approximation by comparing the calculated value of *x* to the number it was subtracted from. The ratio of *x* to the number it is subtracted from should be less than 0.05 (or 5%) for the approximation to be valid. In this case, we subtracted *x* from 1.0, and we calculate the ratio of the value of *x* to 1.0 as follows:

$$\frac{0.0029}{1.0} \times 100\% = 0.29\%$$

The approximation is therefore valid.

In Examples 16.12 and 16.13, we treat two nearly identical problems—the only difference is the initial concentration of the reactant. In Example 16.12, the initial concentration of the reactant is relatively large, the equilibrium constant is small, and the *x is small* approximation works well. In Example 16.13, however, the initial concentration of the reactant is much smaller, and even though the equilibrium constant is the same, the *x is small* approximation does not work (because the initial concentration is also small). In cases such as this, we have a couple of options to solve the problem. We can either solve the equation exactly (using the quadratic formula, for example), or we can use the *method of successive approximations*, which is introduced in Example 16.13. In this method, we essentially solve for x as if it were small, and then substitute the value obtained back into the equation (where x was initially neglected) to solve for x again. We repeat this process until the calculated value of x stops changing with each iteration, an indication that we have arrived at an acceptable value for x.

Note that the *x is small* approximation does not imply that *x is zero*. If that were the case, the reactant and product concentrations would not change from their initial values. The *x is small* approximation just means that when x is added or subtracted to another number, it does not change that number by very much. For example, we can calculate the value of the difference $1.0 - x$ when $x = 3.0 \times 10^{-4}$:

$$1.0 - x = 1.0 - 3.0 \times 10^{-4} = 0.9\underline{9}97 = 1.0$$

Since the value of 1.0 is known only to two significant figures, subtracting the small x does not change the value at all. This situation is similar to weighing yourself on a bathroom scale with and without a penny in your pocket. Unless your scale is unusually precise, removing the penny from your pocket will not change the reading on the scale. This does not imply that the penny is weightless, only that its weight is small when compared to your body weight. You can neglect the weight of the penny in reading your weight with no detectable loss in accuracy.

WATCH **NOW!**

INTERACTIVE WORKED EXAMPLE VIDEO 16.12

HOW TO: *Determine Equilibrium Concentrations from Initial Concentrations and the Equilibrium Constant*

To solve these types of problems, follow the given procedure.

EXAMPLE 16.12

Finding Equilibrium Concentrations from Initial Concentrations in Cases with a Small Equilibrium Constant

Consider the reaction for the decomposition of hydrogen disulfide:

$$2\,H_2S(g) \rightleftharpoons 2\,H_2(g) + S_2(g)$$

$$K_c = 1.67 \times 10^{-7} \text{ at } 800\,°C$$

A 0.500-L reaction vessel initially contains 0.0125 mol of H_2S at 800 °C. Find the equilibrium concentrations of H_2 and S_2.

EXAMPLE 16.13

Finding Equilibrium Concentrations from Initial Concentrations in Cases with a Small Equilibrium Constant

Consider the reaction for the decomposition of hydrogen disulfide:

$$2\,H_2S(g) \rightleftharpoons 2\,H_2(g) + S_2(g)$$

$$K_c = 1.67 \times 10^{-7} \text{ at } 800\,°C$$

A 0.500-L reaction vessel initially contains 1.25×10^{-4} mol of H_2S at 800 °C. Find the equilibrium concentrations of H_2 and S_2.

1. Using the balanced equation as a guide, prepare a table showing the known initial concentrations of the reactants and products. (In these examples, you first calculate the concentration of H_2S from the given number of moles and volume.)

Example 16.12:

$$[H_2S] = \frac{0.0125\text{ mol}}{0.500\text{ L}} = 0.0250\text{ M}$$

$$2\,H_2S(g) \rightleftharpoons 2\,H_2(g) + S_2(g)$$

	$[H_2S]$	$[H_2]$	$[S_2]$
Initial	0.0250	0.00	0.00
Change			
Equil			

Example 16.13:

$$[H_2S] = \frac{1.25 \times 10^{-4}\text{ mol}}{0.500\text{ L}}$$

$$= 2.50 \times 10^{-4}\text{ M}$$

$$2\,H_2S(g) \rightleftharpoons 2\,H_2(g) + S_2(g)$$

	$[H_2S]$	$[H_2]$	$[S_2]$
Initial	2.50×10^{-4}	0.00	0.00
Change			
Equil			

2. Use the initial concentrations to calculate the reaction quotient (Q). Compare Q to K to predict the direction in which the reaction proceeds.

By inspection, $Q = 0$; the reaction proceeds to the right.

By inspection, $Q = 0$; the reaction proceeds to the right.

3. Represent the change in the concentration of one of the reactants or products with the variable x. Define the changes in the concentrations of the other reactants or products with respect to x.

$$2\,H_2S(g) \rightleftharpoons 2\,H_2(g) + S_2(g)$$

	$[H_2S]$	$[H_2]$	$[S_2]$
Initial	0.0250	0.00	0.00
Change	$-2x$	$+2x$	$+x$
Equil			

$$2\,H_2S(g) \rightleftharpoons 2\,H_2(g) + S_2(g)$$

	$[H_2S]$	$[H_2]$	$[S_2]$
Initial	2.50×10^{-4}	0.00	0.00
Change	$-2x$	$+2x$	$+x$
Equil			

4. Sum each column for each reactant and product to determine the equilibrium concentrations in terms of the initial concentrations and the variable x.

$$2H_2S(g) \rightleftharpoons 2H_2(g) + S_2(g)$$

	$[H_2S]$	$[H_2]$	$[S_2]$
Initial	0.0250	0.00	0.00
Change	$-2x$	$+2x$	$+x$
Equil	$0.0250 - 2x$	$2x$	x

$$2H_2S(g) \rightleftharpoons 2H_2(g) + S_2(g)$$

	$[H_2S]$	$[H_2]$	$[S_2]$
Initial	2.50×10^{-4}	0.00	0.00
Change	$-2x$	$+2x$	$+x$
Equil	$2.50 \times 10^{-4} - 2x$	$2x$	x

5. Substitute the expressions for the equilibrium concentrations (from step 4) into the expression for the equilibrium constant. Use the given value of the equilibrium constant to solve the resulting equation for the variable x. In this case, the resulting equation is cubic in x. Although cubic equations can be solved, the solutions are not usually simple. However, since the equilibrium constant is small, we know that the reaction does not proceed very far to the right. Therefore, x is a small number and can be dropped from any quantities in which it is added to or subtracted from another number (as long as the number itself is not too small).

$$K_c = \frac{[H_2]^2[S_2]}{[H_2S]^2} = \frac{(2x)^2x}{(0.0250 - 2x)^2}$$

$$1.67 \times 10^{-7} = \frac{4x^3}{(0.0250 - 2x)^2}$$

x is small.

$$1.67 \times 10^{-7} = \frac{4x^3}{(0.0250 - \cancel{2x})^2}$$

$$1.67 \times 10^{-7} = \frac{4x^3}{6.25 \times 10^{-4}}$$

$$6.25 \times 10^{-4}(1.67 \times 10^{-7}) = 4x^3$$

$$x^3 = \frac{6.25 \times 10^{-4}(1.67 \times 10^{-7})}{4}$$

$$x = 2.97 \times 10^{-4}$$

$$K_c = \frac{[H_2]^2[S_2]}{[H_2S]^2} = \frac{(2x)^2x}{(2.50 \times 10^{-4} - 2x)^2}$$

$$1.67 \times 10^{-7} = \frac{4x^3}{(2.50 \times 10^{-4} - 2x)^2}$$

x is small.

$$1.67 \times 10^{-7} = \frac{4x^3}{(2.50 \times 10^{-4} - \cancel{2x})^2}$$

$$1.67 \times 10^{-7} = \frac{4x^3}{6.25 \times 10^{-8}}$$

$$6.25 \times 10^{-8}(1.67 \times 10^{-7}) = 4x^3$$

$$x^3 = \frac{6.25 \times 10^{-8}(1.67 \times 10^{-7})}{4}$$

$$x = 1.38 \times 10^{-5}$$

Check whether your approximation is valid by comparing the calculated value of x to the number it was added to or subtracted from. The ratio of the two numbers should be less than 0.05 (or 5%) for the approximation to be valid. If the approximation is not valid, proceed to step 5a.

Checking the *x is small* approximation:

$$\frac{2.97 \times 10^{-4}}{0.0250} \times 100\% = 1.19\%$$

The *x is small* approximation is valid; proceed to step 6.

Checking the *x is small* approximation:

$$\frac{1.38 \times 10^{-5}}{2.50 \times 10^{-4}} \times 100\% = 5.52\%$$

The approximation does not satisfy the <5% rule (although it is close).

—Continued on the next page

Continued—

5a. If the approximation is not valid, you can either solve the equation exactly (by hand or with your calculator) or use the method of successive approximations. In this example, the method of successive approximations is used. Substitute the value obtained for x in step 5 back into the original cubic equation, but only at the exact spot where you assumed x was negligible, and then solve the equation for x again. Continue this procedure until the value of x you obtain from solving the equation is the same as the one that you substituted into the equation.		$1.67 \times 10^{-7} = \dfrac{4x^3}{(2.50 \times 10^{-4} - 2x)^2}$ $x = 1.38 \times 10^{-5}$ $1.67 \times 10^{-7} = \dfrac{4x^3}{(2.50 \times 10^{-4} - 2.76 \times 10^{-5})^2}$ $x = 1.27 \times 10^{-5}$ If we substitute this value of x back into the cubic equation and solve it, we get $x = 1.28 \times 10^{-5}$, which is nearly identical to 1.27×10^{-5}. Therefore, we have arrived at the best approximation for x.
6. Substitute x into the expressions for the equilibrium concentrations of the reactants and products (from step 4) and calculate the concentrations.	$[H_2S] = 0.0250 - 2(2.97 \times 10^{-4})$ $= 0.0244\ M$ $[H_2] = 2(2.97 \times 10^{-4})$ $= 5.94 \times 10^{-4}\ M$ $[S_2] = 2.97 \times 10^{-4}\ M$	$[H_2S] = 2.50 \times 10^{-4} - 2(1.28 \times 10^{-5})$ $= 2.24 \times 10^{-4}\ M$ $[H_2] = 2(1.28 \times 10^{-5})$ $= 2.56 \times 10^{-5}\ M$ $[S_2] = 1.28 \times 10^{-5}\ M$
7. Check your answer by substituting the calculated equilibrium values into the equilibrium expression. The calculated value of K should match the given value of K. Note that the approximation method and rounding errors could cause a difference of up to about 5% when comparing values of the equilibrium constant.	$K_c = \dfrac{(5.94 \times 10^{-4})^2(2.97 \times 10^{-4})}{(0.0244)^2}$ $= 1.76 \times 10^{-7}$ The calculated value of K is close enough to the given value when you consider the uncertainty introduced by the approximation. Therefore, the answer is valid.	$K_c = \dfrac{(2.56 \times 10^{-5})^2(1.28 \times 10^{-5})}{(2.24 \times 10^{-4})^2}$ $= 1.67 \times 10^{-7}$ The calculated value of K is equal to the given value. Therefore, the answer is valid.
	FOR PRACTICE 16.12 The reaction in Example 16.12 is carried out at the same temperature with the following initial concentrations: $[H_2S] = 0.100\ M$, $[H_2] = 0.100\ M$, and $[S_2] = 0.00\ M$. Find the equilibrium concentration of $[S_2]$.	**FOR PRACTICE 16.13** The reaction in Example 16.13 is carried out at the same temperature with the following initial concentrations: $[H_2S] = 1.00 \times 10^{-4}\ M$, $[H_2] = 0.00\ M$, and $[S_2] = 0.00\ M$. Find the equilibrium concentration of $[S_2]$.

ANSWER **NOW!**

16.10 Cc Conceptual Connection

THE *X IS SMALL* APPROXIMATION For the generic reaction, $A(g) \rightleftharpoons B(g)$, consider each value of K and initial concentration of A. For which set of values does the *x is small* approximation most likely apply?

(a) $K = 1.0 \times 10^{-5}$; $[A] = 0.250\ M$
(b) $K = 1.0 \times 10^{-2}$; $[A] = 0.250\ M$
(c) $K = 1.0 \times 10^{-5}$; $[A] = 0.00250\ M$
(d) $K = 1.0 \times 10^{-2}$; $[A] = 0.00250\ M$

16.9 Le Châtelier's Principle: How a System at Equilibrium Responds to Disturbances

WATCH **NOW!**

KEY CONCEPT VIDEO 16.9
Le Châtelier's Principle

We have seen that a chemical system not in equilibrium tends to progress toward equilibrium and that the relative concentrations of the reactants and products at equilibrium are characterized by the equilibrium constant, *K*. What happens, however, when a chemical system already at equilibrium is disturbed? **Le Châtelier's principle** states that the chemical system responds to minimize the disturbance.

Pronounced "Le-sha-te-lyay"

Le Châtelier's principle: When a chemical system at equilibrium is disturbed, the system shifts in a direction that minimizes the disturbance.

In other words, a system at equilibrium tends to maintain that equilibrium—it bounces back when disturbed.

We can understand Le Châtelier's principle by returning to our two neighboring countries analogy. Suppose the populations of Country A and Country B are at equilibrium. This means that the rate of people moving out of Country A and into Country B is equal to the rate of people moving into Country A and out of Country B, and the populations of the two countries are stable:

$$\text{Country A} \rightleftharpoons \text{Country B}$$

Now imagine disturbing the balance (Figure 16.8▼). Suppose there is a notable increase in the birthrate in Country B. What happens? After Country B becomes more crowded, the rate of people leaving Country B increases. The net flow of people is out of Country B and into Country A. Equilibrium is disturbed by the addition of more people to Country B, and people leave Country B in response. In effect, the system responded by shifting in the direction that minimized the disturbance.

On the other hand, what happens if there is a baby boom in Country A? As Country A gets more crowded, the rate of people leaving Country A increases. The net flow of people is out of Country A and into Country B. The number of people in Country A initially increases, and the system responds; people move out of Country A.

The two-country analogy should help you see the effects of disturbing a system in equilibrium—it should not be taken as an exact parallel.

Le Châtelier's Principle: An Analogy

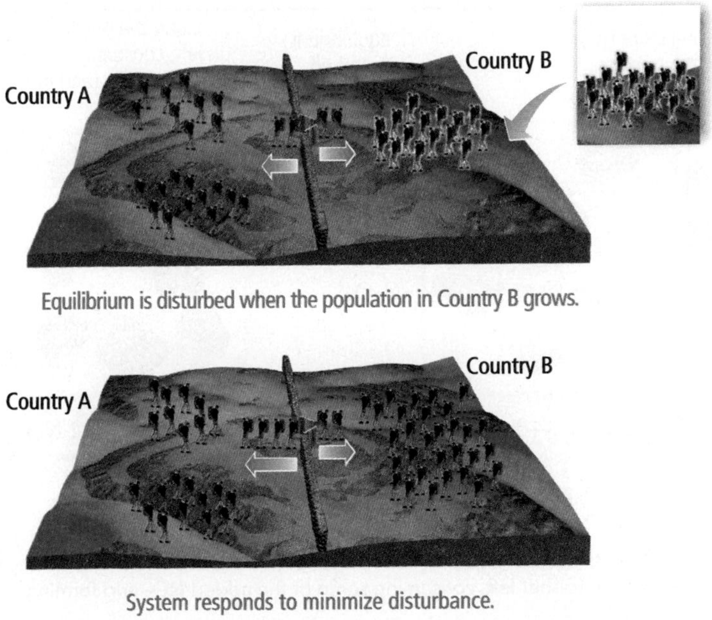

◄ **FIGURE 16.8 A Population Analogy for Le Châtelier's Principle** A baby boom in Country B shifts the equilibrium to the left. People leave Country B (because it has become too crowded) and migrate to Country A until equilibrium is reestablished.

Chemical systems behave similarly: when their equilibrium is disturbed, they react to counter the disturbance. We can disturb a system in chemical equilibrium in several different ways, including changing the concentration of a reactant or product, changing the volume or pressure, and changing the temperature. We consider each of these separately.

The Effect of a Concentration Change on Equilibrium

Consider the following reaction in chemical equilibrium:

$$N_2O_4(g) \rightleftharpoons 2\,NO_2(g)$$

Suppose we disturb the equilibrium by adding NO_2 to the equilibrium mixture (Figure 16.9▼). In other words, we increase the concentration of NO_2, the product. What happens? According to Le Châtelier's principle, the system shifts in a direction to minimize the disturbance. The reaction goes to the left (it proceeds in the reverse direction), consuming some of the added NO_2 and thus bringing its concentration back down, as shown graphically in Figure 16.10a▶:

Add NO_2.

$$N_2O_4(g) \rightleftharpoons 2\,NO_2(g)$$

Reaction shifts left.

The reaction shifts to the left because the value of Q changes as follows:

- Before addition of $NO_2: Q = K$.
- Immediately after addition of $NO_2: Q > K$.
- Reaction shifts to the left to reestablish equilibrium.

But what happens if we add extra N_2O_4 (the reactant), increasing its concentration? In this case, the reaction shifts to the right, consuming some of the added N_2O_4 and bringing *its* concentration back down, as shown graphically in Figure 16.10b▶:

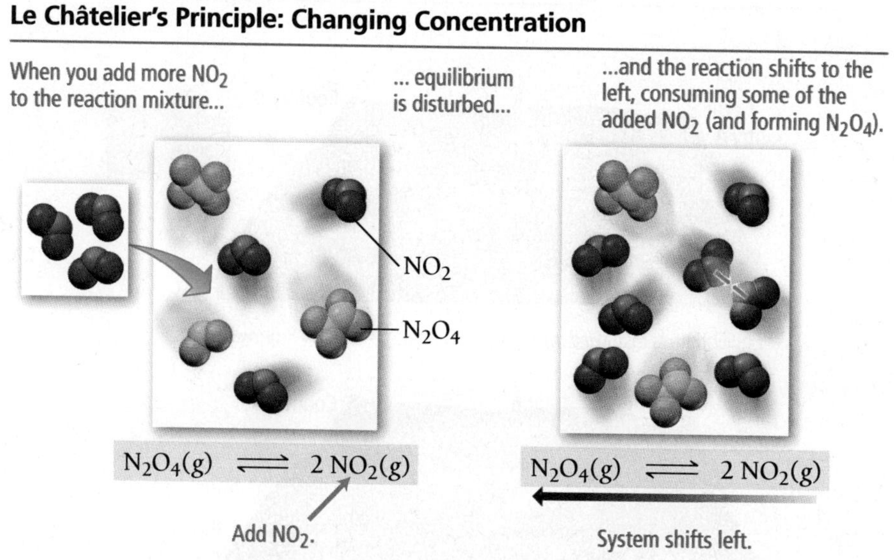

▲ **FIGURE 16.9 Le Châtelier's Principle: The Effect of a Concentration Change** Adding NO_2 causes the reaction to shift left, consuming some of the added NO_2 and forming more N_2O_4.

Le Châtelier's Principle: Graphical Representation

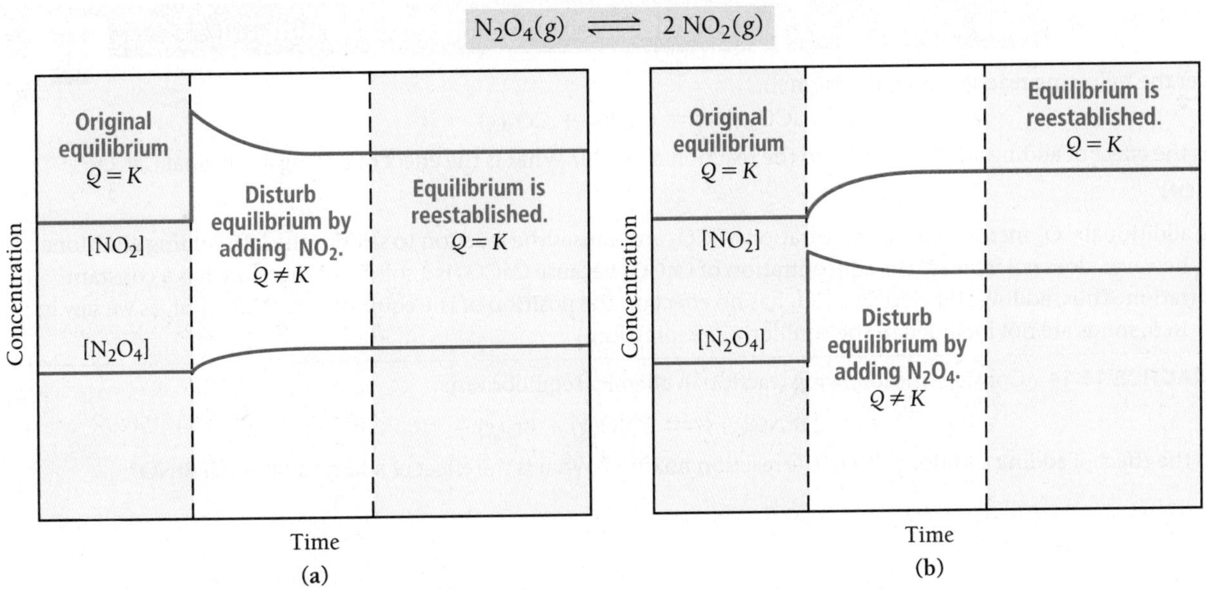

▲ **FIGURE 16.10 Le Châtelier's Principle: Changing Concentration** The graph shows the concentrations of NO_2 and N_2O_4 for the reaction $N_2O_4(g) \longrightarrow 2\ NO_2(g)$ as a function of time in three distinct stages of the reaction: initially at equilibrium (left), upon disturbance of the equilibrium by addition of more NO_2 **(a)** or N_2O_4 **(b)** to the reaction mixture (center), and upon reestablishment of equilibrium (right).

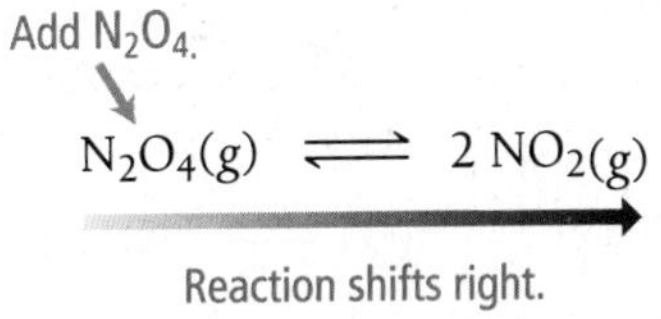

The reaction shifts to the right because the value of Q changes as follows:

- Before addition of $N_2O_4 : Q = K$.
- Immediately after addition of $N_2O_4 : Q < K$.
- Reaction shifts to the right to reestablish equilibrium.

In both of these cases (either adding NO_2 or adding N_2O_4), the system shifts in a direction that minimizes the disturbance. Lowering the concentration of a reactant (which makes $Q > K$) causes the system to shift in the direction of the reactants to minimize the disturbance. Lowering the concentration of a product (which makes $Q < K$) causes the system to shift in the direction of products.

Summarizing the Effect of a Concentration Change on Equilibrium:

If a chemical system is at equilibrium:

- *Increasing* the concentration of one or more of the *reactants* (which makes $Q < K$) causes the reaction to *shift to the right* (in the direction of the products).
- *Increasing* the concentration of one or more of the *products* (which makes $Q > K$) causes the reaction to *shift to the left* (in the direction of the reactants).
- *Decreasing* the concentration of one or more of the *reactants* (which makes $Q > K$) causes the reaction to *shift to the left* (in the direction of the reactants).
- *Decreasing* the concentration of one or more of the *products* (which makes $Q < K$) causes the reaction to *shift to the right* (in the direction of the products).

WATCH **NOW!**

INTERACTIVE WORKED EXAMPLE 16.14

EXAMPLE 16.14 The Effect of a Concentration Change on Equilibrium

Consider the following reaction at equilibrium:

$$CaCO_3(s) \rightleftharpoons CaO(s) + CO_2(g)$$

What is the effect of adding additional CO_2 to the reaction mixture? What is the effect of adding additional $CaCO_3$?

SOLUTION

Adding additional CO_2 increases the concentration of CO_2 and causes the reaction to shift to the left. Adding additional $CaCO_3$, however, does *not* increase the concentration of $CaCO_3$ because $CaCO_3$ is a solid and therefore has a constant concentration. Thus, adding additional $CaCO_3$ has no effect on the position of the equilibrium. (Note that, as we saw in Section 16.5, solids are not included in the equilibrium expression.)

FOR PRACTICE 16.14 Consider the following reaction in chemical equilibrium:

$$2\,BrNO(g) \rightleftharpoons 2\,NO(g) + Br_2(g)$$

What is the effect of adding additional Br_2 to the reaction mixture? What is the effect of adding additional BrNO?

The Effect of a Volume (or Pressure) Change on Equilibrium

In considering the effect of a change in volume, we are assuming that the change in volume is carried out at constant temperature.

How does a system in chemical equilibrium respond to a volume change? Recall from Chapter 6 that changing the volume of a gas (or a gas mixture) results in a change in pressure. Remember also that pressure and volume are inversely related: a *decrease* in volume causes an *increase* in pressure, and an *increase* in volume causes a *decrease* in pressure. So, if the volume of a reaction mixture at chemical equilibrium is changed, the pressure changes and the system shifts in a direction to minimize that change.

For example, consider the following reaction at equilibrium in a cylinder equipped with a moveable piston:

$$N_2(g) + 3\,H_2(g) \rightleftharpoons 2\,NH_3(g)$$

What happens if we push down on the piston, lowering the volume and raising the pressure (Figure 16.11▶)? How can the chemical system respond to bring the pressure back down? Look carefully at the reaction coefficients. If the reaction shifts to the right, 4 mol of gas particles are converted to 2 mol of gas particles. From the ideal gas law ($PV = nRT$), we know that decreasing the number of moles of a gas (n) results in a lower pressure (P). Therefore, the system shifts to the right, decreasing the number of gas molecules and bringing the pressure back down, minimizing the disturbance.

Consider the same reaction mixture at equilibrium again. What happens if, this time, we pull *up* on the piston, *increasing* the volume (Figure 16.11b▶)? The higher volume results in a lower pressure and the system responds to bring the pressure back up. It does this by shifting to the left, converting 2 mol of gas particles into 4 mol of gas particles, increasing the pressure and minimizing the disturbance.

Consider again the same reaction mixture at equilibrium. What happens if, this time, we keep the volume the same but increase the pressure *by adding an inert gas* to the mixture? Although the overall pressure of the mixture increases, the partial pressures of the reactants and products do not change. Consequently, there is no effect, and the reaction does not shift in either direction.

Summarizing the Effect of Volume Change on Equilibrium:

If a chemical system is at equilibrium:

- *Decreasing* the volume causes the reaction to shift in the direction that has *the fewer moles of gas particles*.
- *Increasing* the volume causes the reaction to shift in the direction that has *the greater number of moles of gas particles*.

- If a reaction has an equal number of moles of gas on both sides of the chemical equation, then a change in volume produces no effect on the equilibrium.
- Adding an inert gas to the mixture at a fixed volume has no effect on the equilibrium.

Le Châtelier's Principle: Changing Pressure

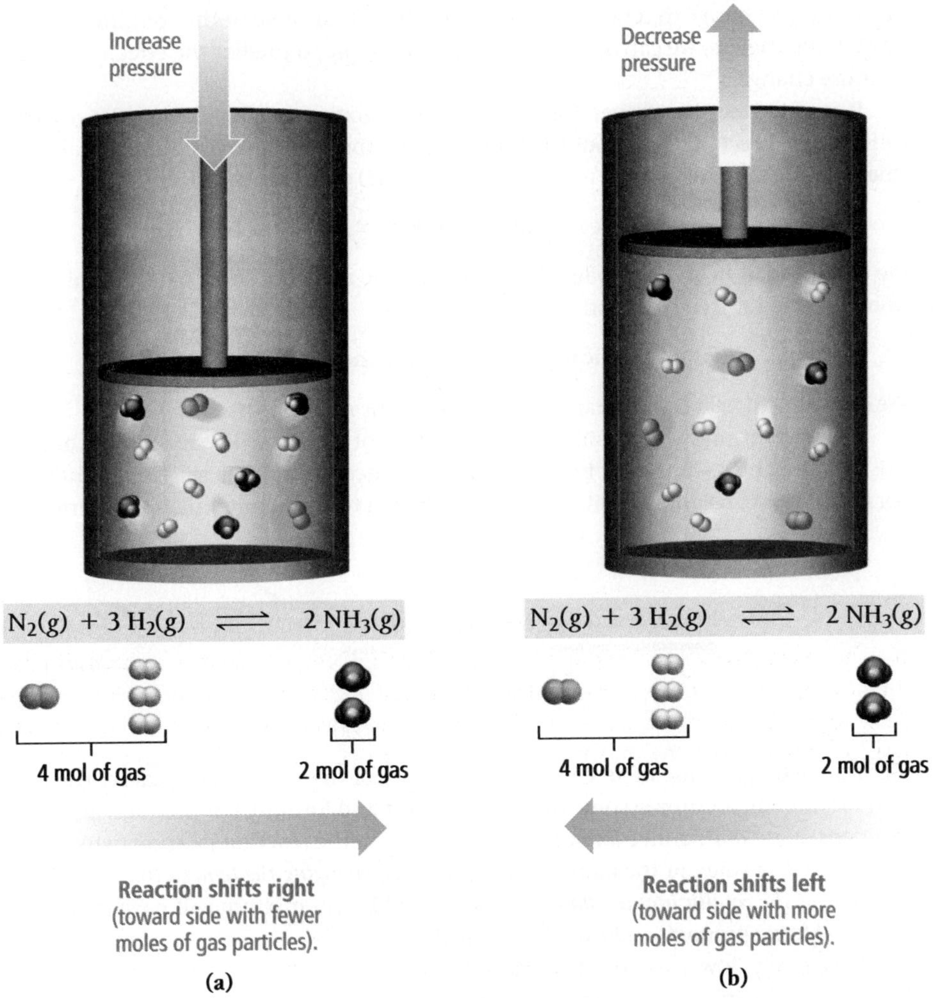

◀ **FIGURE 16.11 Le Châtelier's Principle: The Effect of a Pressure Change** **(a)** Decreasing the volume increases the pressure, causing the reaction to shift to the right (fewer moles of gas, lower pressure). **(b)** Increasing the volume reduces the pressure, causing the reaction to shift to the left (more moles of gas, higher pressure).

EXAMPLE 16.15 The Effect of a Volume Change on Equilibrium

Consider the following reaction at chemical equilibrium:

$$2\,KClO_3(s) \rightleftharpoons 2\,KCl(s) + 3\,O_2(g)$$

What is the effect of decreasing the volume of the reaction mixture? Increasing the volume of the reaction mixture? Adding an inert gas at constant volume?

SOLUTION

The chemical equation has 3 mol of gas on the right and zero moles of gas on the left. Decreasing the volume of the reaction mixture increases the pressure and causes the reaction to shift to the left (toward the side with fewer moles of gas particles). Increasing the volume of the reaction mixture decreases the pressure and causes the reaction to shift to the right (toward the side with more moles of gas particles.) Adding an inert gas has no effect.

FOR PRACTICE 16.15 Consider the following reaction at chemical equilibrium:

$$2\,SO_2(g) + O_2(g) \rightleftharpoons 2\,SO_3(g)$$

What is the effect of decreasing the volume of the reaction mixture? Increasing the volume of the reaction mixture?

In considering the effect of a change in temperature, we are assuming that the heat is added (or removed) at constant pressure.

The Effect of a Temperature Change on Equilibrium

When a system at equilibrium is disturbed by a change in concentration or a change in volume, the equilibrium shifts to counter the change, but *the equilibrium constant does not change*. In other words, changes in volume or concentration generally change Q, not K, and the system responds by shifting so that Q becomes equal to K. In contrast, a change in temperature changes the actual value of the equilibrium constant. Nonetheless, we can use Le Châtelier's principle to predict the effects of a temperature change.

If we increase the temperature of a reaction mixture at equilibrium, the reaction shifts in the direction that tends to decrease the temperature and vice versa. Recall from Chapter 7 that an exothermic reaction (negative ΔH) emits heat:

$$\text{Exothermic reaction:}\quad A + B \rightleftharpoons C + D + \text{heat}$$

We can think of heat as a product in an exothermic reaction. In an endothermic reaction (positive ΔH), the reaction absorbs heat:

$$\text{Endothermic reaction:}\quad A + B + \text{heat} \rightleftharpoons C + D$$

We can think of heat as a reactant in an endothermic reaction.

At constant pressure, raising the temperature of an *exothermic* reaction—think of this as adding heat—is similar to adding more product, causing the reaction to shift left. For example, the reaction of nitrogen with hydrogen to form ammonia is exothermic:

Add heat

$$N_2(g) + 3\,H_2(g) \rightleftharpoons 2\,NH_3(g) + \text{heat}$$

Reaction shifts left.
Smaller K

Raising the temperature of an equilibrium mixture of these three gases causes the reaction to shift left, absorbing some of the added heat and forming less products and more reactants. Note that, unlike adding additional NH_3 to the reaction mixture (which does *not* change the value of the equilibrium constant), *changing the temperature does change the value of the equilibrium constant.* The new equilibrium mixture will have more reactants and fewer products and therefore a smaller value of K.

Conversely, lowering the temperature causes the reaction to shift right, releasing heat and producing more products because the value of K has increased:

Remove heat

$$N_2(g) + 3\,H_2(g) \rightleftharpoons 2\,NH_3(g) + \text{heat}$$

Reaction shifts right.
Larger K

In contrast, for an *endothermic* reaction, raising the temperature (adding heat) causes the reaction to shift right to absorb the added heat. For example, the following reaction is endothermic:

Add heat

$$\underset{\text{colorless}}{N_2O_4(g)} + \text{heat} \rightleftharpoons \underset{\text{brown}}{2\,NO_2(g)}$$

Reaction shifts right.
Larger K

Le Châtelier's Principle: Changing Temperature

$$\underset{\text{colorless}}{N_2O_4(g) + \text{heat}} \rightleftharpoons \underset{\text{brown}}{2\,NO_2(g)}$$

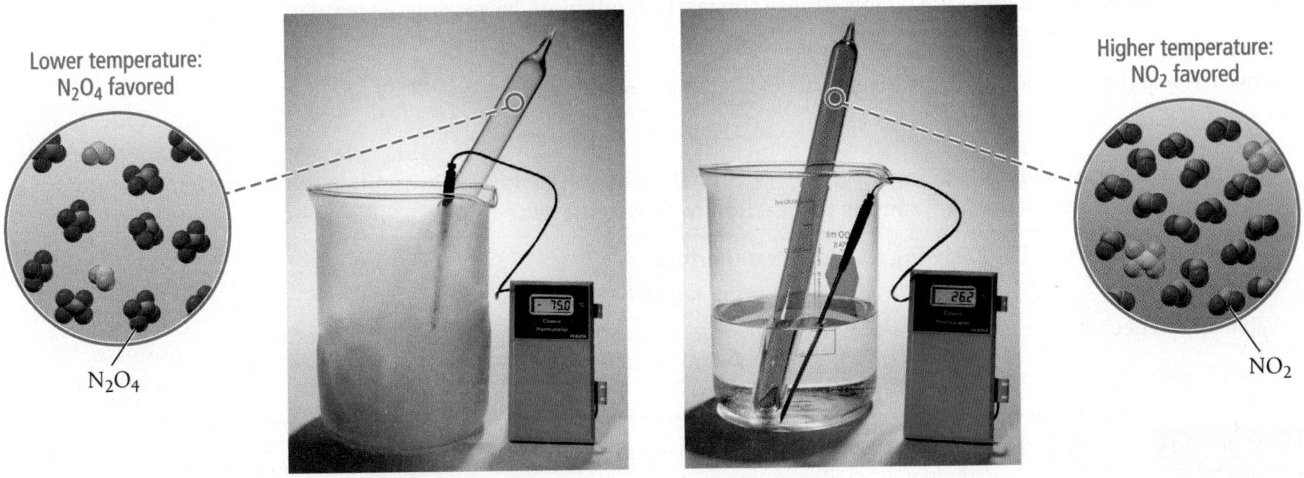

▲ **FIGURE 16.12 Le Châtelier's Principle: The Effect of a Temperature Change**
Because the reaction is endothermic, raising the temperature causes a shift to the right, toward the formation of brown NO_2.

On the one hand, raising the temperature of an equilibrium mixture of these two gases causes the reaction to shift right, absorbing some of the added heat and producing more products because the value of K has increased. Because N_2O_4 is colorless and NO_2 is brown, the effects of changing the temperature of this reaction are easily seen (Figure 16.12▲).

On the other hand, lowering the temperature (removing heat) of a reaction mixture of these two gases causes the reaction to shift left, releasing heat, forming less products, and lowering the value of K:

Remove heat

$$\underset{\text{colorless}}{N_2O_4(g) + \text{heat}} \rightleftharpoons \underset{\text{brown}}{2\,NO_2(g)}$$

Reaction shifts left.
Smaller K

Summarizing the Effect of a Temperature Change on Equilibrium:
In an *exothermic* chemical reaction, heat is a product.

- *Increasing* the temperature causes an exothermic reaction to *shift left* (in the direction of the reactants); the value of the equilibrium constant decreases.
- *Decreasing* the temperature causes an exothermic reaction to *shift right* (in the direction of the products); the value of the equilibrium constant increases.

In an *endothermic* chemical reaction, heat is a reactant.

- *Increasing* the temperature causes an endothermic reaction to *shift right* (in the direction of the products); the equilibrium constant increases.
- *Decreasing* the temperature causes an endothermic reaction to *shift left* (in the direction of the reactants); the equilibrium constant decreases.

Adding heat favors the endothermic direction. Removing heat favors the exothermic direction.

EXAMPLE 16.16 The Effect of a Temperature Change on Equilibrium

The following reaction is endothermic:

$$CaCO_3(s) \rightleftharpoons CaO(s) + CO_2(g)$$

What is the effect of increasing the temperature of the reaction mixture? Decreasing the temperature?

SOLUTION

Since the reaction is endothermic, we can think of heat as a reactant:

$$\text{Heat} + CaCO_3(s) \rightleftharpoons CaO(s) + CO_2(g)$$

Raising the temperature is like adding a reactant, causing the reaction to shift to the right. Lowering the temperature is equivalent to removing a reactant, causing the reaction to shift to the left.

FOR PRACTICE 16.16 The following reaction is exothermic:

$$2\,SO_2(g) + O_2(g) \rightleftharpoons 2\,SO_3(g)$$

What is the effect of increasing the temperature of the reaction mixture? Decreasing the temperature?

ANSWER **NOW!**

16.11 Cc Conceptual Connection

LE CHÂTELIER'S PRINCIPLE Consider the exothermic reaction $2\,NO(g) + Cl_2(g) \rightleftharpoons 2\,NOCl(g)$. Which change causes a reaction mixture at equilibrium to shift right?

(a) Adding NOCl to the reaction mixture.
(b) Increasing the volume of the reaction vessel at constant temperature.
(c) Increasing the temperature of the reaction vessel.
(d) None of the above.

QUIZ YOURSELF **NOW!**

Self-Assessment Quiz

Q1. What is the correct expression for the equilibrium constant (K_c) for the reaction between carbon and hydrogen gas to form methane shown here?

$$C(s) + 2\,H_2(g) \rightleftharpoons CH_4(g)$$

MISSED THIS? *Read Section 16.3; Watch KCV 16.3*

a) $K_c = \frac{[CH_4]}{[H_2]}$ b) $K_c = \frac{[CH_4]}{[C][H_2]}$

c) $K_c = \frac{[CH_4]}{[C][H_2]^2}$ d) $K_c = \frac{[CH_4]}{[H_2]^2}$

Q2. The equilibrium constant for the reaction shown here is $K_c = 1.0 \times 10^3$. A reaction mixture at equilibrium contains $[A] = 1.0 \times 10^{-3}$ M. What is the concentration of B in the mixture?

$$A(g) \rightleftharpoons B(g)$$

MISSED THIS? *Read Section 16.3; Watch KCV 16.3*

a) 1.0×10^{-3} M b) 1.0 M
c) 2.0 M d) 1.0×10^3 M

Q3. Use the data shown here to find the equilibrium constant (K_c) for the reaction $A(g) \rightleftharpoons 2\,B(g) + C(g)$.

$$A(g) \rightleftharpoons 2\,X(g) + C(g) \quad K_c = 1.55$$
$$B(g) \rightleftharpoons X(g) \quad K_c = 25.2$$

MISSED THIS? *Read Section 16.3*

a) 984 b) 26.8
c) 6.10×10^{-4} d) 2.44×10^{-3}

Q4. The reaction shown here has a $K_p = 4.5 \times 10^2$ at 825 K. Find K_c for the reaction at this temperature.

$$CH_4(g) + CO_2(g) \rightleftharpoons 2\,CO(g) + 2\,H_2(g)$$

MISSED THIS? *Read Section 16.4; Watch IWE 16.3*

a) 0.098 b) 2.1×10^6 c) 6.6 d) 4.5×10^{-2}

Q5. Consider the reaction between NO and Cl_2 to form NOCl:

$$2\,NO(g) + Cl_2(g) \rightleftharpoons 2\,NOCl(g)$$

A reaction mixture at a certain temperature initially contains only $[NO] = 0.50$ M and $[Cl_2] = 0.50$ M. After the reaction comes to equilibrium, the concentration of NOCl is 0.30 M. Find the value of the equilibrium constant (K_c) at this temperature.

MISSED THIS? *Read Section 16.6; Watch IWE 16.5*

a) 11 b) 4.3 c) 6.4 d) 0.22

Q6. For the reaction $2\,A(g) \rightleftharpoons B(g)$, the equilibrium constant is $K_p = 0.76$. A reaction mixture initially contains 2.0 atm of each gas ($P_A = 2.0$ atm and $P_B = 2.0$ atm). Which statement is true of the reaction mixture?

MISSED THIS? *Read Section 16.7; Watch KCV 16.7, IWE 16.7*

a) The reaction mixture is at equilibrium.
b) The reaction mixture will proceed toward products.
c) The reaction mixture will proceed toward reactants.
d) It is not possible to determine from the information given the future direction of the reaction mixture.

Q7. Consider the reaction between iodine gas and chlorine gas to form iodine monochloride:

$I_2(g) + Cl_2(g) \rightleftharpoons 2\,ICl(g)$ $\quad K_p = 81.9$ (at 296 K)

A reaction mixture at 298 K initially contains $P_{I_2} = 0.25$ atm and $P_{Cl_2} = 0.25$ atm. What is the partial pressure of iodine monochloride when the reaction reaches equilibrium?

MISSED THIS? *Read Section 16.8; Watch KCV 16.8, IWE 16.9*

a) 0.18 atm b) 0.64 atm c) 0.41 atm d) 2.3 atm

Q8. Consider the reaction of A to form B:

$2\,A(g) \rightleftharpoons B(g)$ $\quad K_c = 1.8 \times 10^{-5}$ (at 298 K)

A reaction mixture at 298 K initially contains [A] = 0.50 M. What is the concentration of B when the reaction reaches equilibrium?

MISSED THIS? *Read Section 16.8; Watch KCV 16.8, IWE 16.12*

a) 9.0×10^{-6} M b) 0.060 M
c) 0.030 M d) 4.5×10^{-6} M

Q9. The decomposition of NH_4HS is endothermic:

$$NH_4HS(s) \rightleftharpoons NH_3(g) + H_2S(g)$$

Which change to an equilibrium mixture of this reaction results in the formation of more H_2S?

MISSED THIS? *Read Section 16.9; Watch KCV 16.9, IWE 16.14*

a) a decrease in the volume of the reaction vessel (at constant temperature)
b) an increase in the amount of NH_4HS in the reaction vessel
c) an increase in temperature
d) all of the above

Q10. The solid XY decomposes into gaseous X and Y:

$XY(s) \rightleftharpoons X(g) + Y(g)$ $\quad K_p = 4.1$ (at 0 °C)

If the reaction is carried out in a 22.4-L container, which initial amounts of X and Y result in the formation of solid XY?

MISSED THIS? *Read Section 16.7; Watch KCV 16.7, IWE 16.7*

a) 5 mol X; 0.5 mol Y b) 2.0 mol X; 2.0 mol Y
c) 1 mol X; 1 mol Y d) none of the above

Q11. What is the effect of adding helium gas (at constant volume) to an equilibrium mixture of the reaction:

$$CO(g) + Cl_2(g) \rightleftharpoons COCl_2(g)$$

MISSED THIS? *Read Section 16.9*

a) The reaction shifts toward the products.
b) The reaction shifts toward the reactants.
c) The reaction does not shift in either direction.
d) The reaction slows down.

Q12. The reaction $X_2(g) \rightleftharpoons 2\,X(g)$ occurs in a closed reaction vessel at constant volume and temperature. Initially, the vessel contains only X_2 at a pressure of 1.55 atm. After the reaction reaches equilibrium, the total pressure is 2.85 atm. What is the value of the equilibrium constant, K_p, for the reaction?

MISSED THIS? *Read Section 16.6; Watch IWE 16.5*

a) 27 b) 10 c) 5.2 d) 32

Answers: 1. (d) **2.** (b) **3.** (d) **4.** (a) **5.** (c) **6.** (b) **7.** (c)
8. (d) **9.** (c) **10.** (d) **11.** (c) **12.** (a)

CHAPTER 16 IN REVIEW

TERMS

Section 16.2
reversible (685)
dynamic equilibrium (685)

Section 16.3
equilibrium constant (*K*) (688)
law of mass action (688)

Section 16.7
reaction quotient (Q_c) (699)

Section 16.9
Le Châtelier's principle (711)

CONCEPTS

The Equilibrium Constant (16.1)

- The relative concentrations of the reactants and the products at equilibrium are expressed by the equilibrium constant, *K*.
- The equilibrium constant measures how far a reaction proceeds toward products: a large *K* (greater than 1) indicates a high concentration of products at equilibrium, and a small *K* (less than 1) indicates a low concentration of products at equilibrium.

Dynamic Equilibrium (16.2)

- Most chemical reactions are reversible; they can proceed in either the forward or the reverse direction.
- When a chemical reaction is in dynamic equilibrium, the rate of the forward reaction equals the rate of the reverse reaction, so the net concentrations of reactants and products do not change. However, this does *not* imply that the concentrations of the reactants and the products are equal at equilibrium.

The Equilibrium Constant Expression (16.3)

- The equilibrium constant expression is given by the law of mass action and is equal to the concentrations of the products, raised to their stoichiometric coefficients, divided by the concentrations of the reactants, raised to their stoichiometric coefficients.
- When the equation for a chemical reaction is reversed, multiplied, or added to another equation, *K* must be modified accordingly.

The Equilibrium Constant, *K* (16.4)

- The equilibrium constant can be expressed in terms of concentrations (K_c) or in terms of partial pressures (K_p). These two constants are related by Equation 16.2. Concentration must always be expressed in units of molarity for K_c. Partial pressures must always be expressed in units of atmospheres for K_p.

States of Matter and the Equilibrium Constant (16.5)

- The equilibrium constant expression contains only partial pressures or concentrations of reactants and products that exist as gases or solutes dissolved in solution. Pure liquids and solids are not included in the expression for the equilibrium constant.

Calculating *K* (16.6)

- We can calculate the equilibrium constant from equilibrium concentrations or partial pressures by substituting measured values into the expression for the equilibrium constant (as obtained from the law of mass action).
- In most cases, we can calculate the equilibrium concentrations of the reactants and products—and therefore the value of the equilibrium constant—from the initial concentrations of the reactants and products and the equilibrium concentration of *just one* reactant or product.

The Reaction Quotient, Q (16.7)

- The reaction quotient, *Q*, is the ratio of the concentrations (or partial pressures) of products raised to their stoichiometric coefficients to the concentrations of reactants raised to their stoichiometric coefficients *at any point in the reaction.*
- Like *K*, *Q* can be expressed in terms of concentrations (Q_c) or partial pressures (Q_p).
- At equilibrium, *Q* is equal to *K*; therefore, we can determine the direction in which a reaction proceeds by comparing *Q* to *K*. If $Q < K$, the reaction moves in the direction of the products; if $Q > K$, the reaction moves in the reverse direction.

Finding Equilibrium Concentrations (16.8)

- There are two general types of problems in which *K* is given and we can determine one (or more) equilibrium concentrations:
  (1) We are given *K* and all but one equilibrium concentration.
  (2) We are given *K* and *only* initial concentrations.
- We solve the first type by rearranging the law of mass action and substituting the given values.
- We solve the second type by creating an ICE table and using a variable *x* to represent the change in concentration.

Le Châtelier's Principle (16.9)

- When a system at equilibrium is disturbed—by a change in the amount of a reactant or product, a change in volume, or a change in temperature—the system shifts in the direction that minimizes the disturbance.

EQUATIONS AND RELATIONSHIPS

Expression for the Equilibrium Constant, K_c (**16.3**)

$$aA + bB \rightleftharpoons cC + dD$$

$$K = \frac{[C]^c[D]^d}{[A]^a[B]^b} \quad \text{(equilibrium concentrations only)}$$

Relationship between the Equilibrium Constant and the Chemical Equation (**16.3**)

1. If you reverse the equation, invert the equilibrium constant.
2. If you multiply the coefficients in the equation by a factor, raise the equilibrium constant to the same factor.
3. If you add two or more individual chemical equations to obtain an overall equation, multiply the corresponding equilibrium constants by each other to obtain the overall equilibrium constant.

Expression for the Equilibrium Constant, K_p (**16.4**)

$$aA + bB \rightleftharpoons cC + dD$$

$$K_p = \frac{P_C^c P_D^d}{P_A^a P_B^b} \quad \text{(equilibrium partial pressures only)}$$

Relationship between the Equilibrium Constants, K_c and K_p (**16.4**)

$$K_p = K_c(RT)^{\Delta n}$$

The Reaction Quotient, Q_c (**16.7**)

$$aA + bB \rightleftharpoons cC + dD$$

$$Q_c = \frac{[C]^c[D]^d}{[A]^a[B]^b} \quad \text{(concentrations at any point in the reaction)}$$

The Reaction Quotient, Q_p (**16.7**)

$$aA + bB \rightleftharpoons cC + dD$$

$$Q_p = \frac{P_C^c P_D^d}{P_A^a P_B^b} \quad \text{(partial pressures at any point in the reaction)}$$

Relationship of Q to the Direction of the Reaction (**16.7**)

$Q < K$ Reaction goes to the right.

$Q > K$ Reaction goes to the left.

$Q = K$ Reaction is at equilibrium.

LEARNING OUTCOMES

Chapter Objectives	Assessment
Write equilibrium constant expressions for chemical equations (**16.2, 16.3**)	Example 16.1 **For Practice 16.1** **Exercises 21–26**
Predict how changes in the chemical equation affect the equilibrium constant (**16.3**)	Example 16.2 **For Practice 16.2** **For More Practice 16.2** **Exercises 27–30**
Write equilibrium constants in terms of partial pressures (K_p) or concentrations (K_c) (**16.4**)	Example 16.3 **For Practice 16.3** **Exercises 31–32**

Write equilibrium constants for chemical equations that contain solids and pure liquids (**16.5**)	Example 16.4 **For Practice** 16.4 **Exercises** 33–34
Calculate equilibrium constants from experimental concentration measurements (**16.6**)	Examples 16.5, 16.6 **For Practices** 16.5, 16.6 **Exercises** 35–46
Predict the direction of a reaction by comparing the reaction quotient (Q_c) to the equilibrium constant (K_c) (**16.7**)	Example 16.7 **For Practice** 16.7 **Exercises** 47–50
Calculate unknown equilibrium concentrations from known equilibrium constants and all but one of the reactant and product equilibrium concentrations (**16.8**)	Example 16.8 **For Practice** 16.8
Calculate unknown equilibrium concentrations from known equilibrium constants and initial concentrations or pressures (**16.8**)	Examples 16.9–16.11 **For Practices** 16.9–16.11 **Exercises** 51–60
Calculate unknown equilibrium concentrations from known equilibrium constants and initial concentration or pressures in cases with a relatively small equilibrium constant (**16.8**)	Examples 16.12, 16.13 **For Practice** 16.12, 16.13 **Exercises** 61–62
Predict the effect of a concentration change on equilibrium (**16.9**)	Example 16.14 **For Practices** 16.14 **Exercises** 63–66
Predict the effect of a volume or pressure change on equilibrium (**16.9**)	Example 16.15 **For Practice** 16.15 **Exercises** 67–68
Predict the effect of a temperature change on equilibrium (**16.9**)	Example 16.16 **For Practice** 16.16 **Exercises** 69–72

EXERCISES

Mastering Chemistry provides end-of-chapter exercises, feedback-enriched tutorial problems, animations, and interactive activities to encourage problem-solving practice and deeper understanding of key concepts and topics.

REVIEW QUESTIONS

1. How does a developing fetus get oxygen in the womb?

2. What is dynamic equilibrium? Why is it called *dynamic*?

3. Give the general expression for the equilibrium constant of the following generic reaction:

$$aA + bB \rightleftharpoons cC + dD$$

4. What is the significance of the equilibrium constant? What does a large equilibrium constant tell us about a reaction? A small one?

5. What happens to the value of the equilibrium constant for a reaction if the reaction equation is reversed? Multiplied by a constant?

6. If two reactions sum to an overall reaction, and the equilibrium constants for the two reactions are K_1 and K_2, what is the equilibrium constant for the overall reaction?

7. Explain the difference between K_c and K_p. For a given reaction, how are the two constants related?

8. What units should be used when expressing concentrations or partial pressures in the equilibrium constant? What are the units of K_p and K_c? Explain.

9. Why are the concentrations of solids and liquids omitted from equilibrium expressions?

10. Does the value of the equilibrium constant depend on the initial concentrations of the reactants and products? Do the equilibrium concentrations of the reactants and products depend on their initial concentrations? Explain.

11. Explain how you might deduce the equilibrium constant for a reaction in which you know the initial concentrations of the reactants and products and the equilibrium concentration of only one reactant or product.

12. What is the definition of the reaction quotient (*Q*) for a reaction? What does *Q* measure?

13. What is the value of *Q* when each reactant and product is in its standard state? (See Section 7.9 for the definition of standard states.)

14. In what direction will a reaction proceed for each condition:

a. $Q < K$; b. $Q > K$; and c. $Q = K$?

15. Many equilibrium calculations involve finding the equilibrium concentrations of reactants and products given their initial concentrations and the equilibrium constant. Outline the general procedure used in solving these kinds of problems.

16. In equilibrium problems involving equilibrium constants that are small relative to the initial concentrations of reactants, we can often assume that the quantity *x* (which represents how far the reaction proceeds toward products) is small. When this assumption is made, we can ignore the quantity *x* when it is subtracted from a large number but not when it is multiplied by a large number. In other words, $2.5 - x \approx 2.5$, but $2.5x \neq 2.5$. Explain why we can ignore a small *x* in the first case but not in the second.

17. What happens to a chemical system at equilibrium when that equilibrium is disturbed?

18. What is the effect of a change in concentration of a reactant or product on a chemical reaction initially at equilibrium?

19. What is the effect of a change in volume on a chemical reaction (that includes gaseous reactants or products) initially at equilibrium?

20. What is the effect of a temperature change on a chemical reaction initially at equilibrium? How does the effect differ for an exothermic reaction compared to an endothermic one?

PROBLEMS BY TOPIC

Equilibrium and the Equilibrium Constant Expression

21. Write an expression for the equilibrium constant of each chemical equation.
MISSED THIS? *Read Section 16.3; Watch KCV 16.3*

a. $SbCl_5(g) \rightleftharpoons SbCl_3(g) + Cl_2(g)$
b. $2\,BrNO(g) \rightleftharpoons 2\,NO(g) + Br_2(g)$
c. $CH_4(g) + 2\,H_2S(g) \rightleftharpoons CS_2(g) + 4\,H_2(g)$
d. $2\,CO(g) + O_2(g) \rightleftharpoons 2\,CO_2(g)$

22. Find and fix each mistake in the equilibrium constant expressions.

a. $2\,H_2S(g) \rightleftharpoons 2\,H_2(g) + S_2(g) \quad K = \dfrac{[H_2][S_2]}{[H_2S]}$

b. $CO(g) + Cl_2(g) \rightleftharpoons COCl_2(g) \quad K = \dfrac{[CO][Cl_2]}{[COCl_2]}$

23. When this reaction comes to equilibrium, will the concentrations of the reactants or products be greater? Does the answer to this question depend on the initial concentrations of the reactants and products?
MISSED THIS? *Read Section 16.3; Watch KCV 16.3*

$$A(g) + B(g) \rightleftharpoons 2\,C(g) \quad K_c = 1.4 \times 10^{-5}$$

24. Ethene (C_2H_4) can be halogenated by this reaction:

$$C_2H_4(g) + X_2(g) \rightleftharpoons C_2H_4X_2(g)$$

where X_2 can be Cl_2 (green), Br_2 (brown), or I_2 (purple). Examine the three figures representing equilibrium concentrations in this reaction at the same temperature for the three different halogens. Rank the equilibrium constants for the three reactions from largest to smallest.

a. b. c.

25. H_2 and I_2 are combined in a flask and allowed to react according to the reaction:
MISSED THIS? *Read Section 16.3; Watch KCV 16.3*

$$H_2(g) + I_2(g) \rightleftharpoons 2\,HI(g)$$

Examine the figures (sequential in time) and answer the questions:

a. Which figure represents the point at which equilibrium is reached?
b. How would the series of figures change in the presence of a catalyst?
c. Would there be different amounts of reactants and products in the final figure (vi) in the presence of a catalyst?

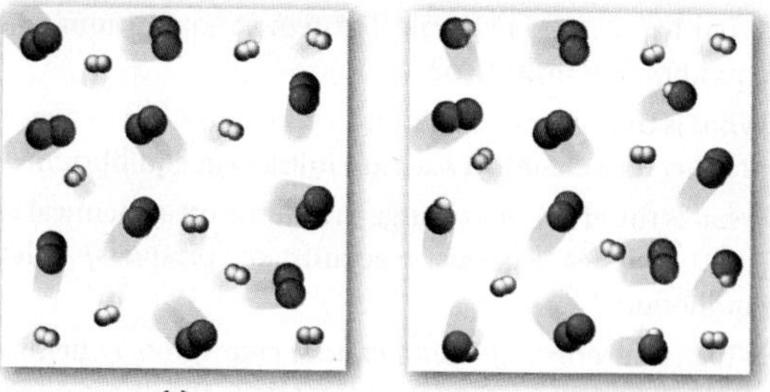

(i) (ii)

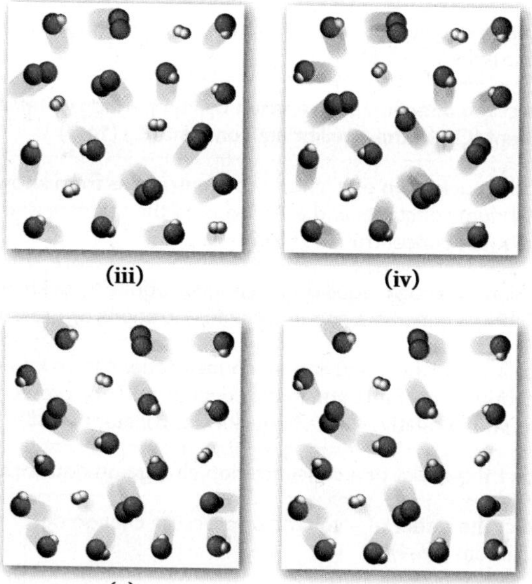

(iii) (iv) (v) (vi)

26. A chemist trying to synthesize a particular compound attempts two different synthesis reactions. The equilibrium constants for the two reactions are 23.3 and 2.2×10^4 at room temperature. However, upon carrying out both reactions for 15 minutes, the chemist finds that the reaction with the smaller equilibrium constant produces more of the desired product. Explain how this might be possible.

27. This reaction has an equilibrium constant of $K_p = 2.26 \times 10^4$ at 298 K.
MISSED THIS? *Read Section 16.3*

$$CO(g) + 2\,H_2(g) \rightleftharpoons CH_3OH(g)$$

Calculate K_p for each reaction and predict whether reactants or products will be favored at equilibrium.

a. $CH_3OH(g) \rightleftharpoons CO(g) + 2\,H_2(g)$
b. $\frac{1}{2}CO(g) + H_2(g) \rightleftharpoons \frac{1}{2}CH_3OH(g)$
c. $2\,CH_3OH(g) \rightleftharpoons 2\,CO(g) + 4\,H_2(g)$

28. This reaction has an equilibrium constant of $K_p = 2.2 \times 10^6$ at 298 K.

$$2\,COF_2(g) \rightleftharpoons CO_2(g) + CF_4(g)$$

Calculate K_p for each reaction and predict whether reactants or products will be favored at equilibrium.

a. $COF_2(g) \rightleftharpoons \frac{1}{2}CO_2(g) + \frac{1}{2}CF_4(g)$
b. $6\,COF_2(g) \rightleftharpoons 3\,CO_2(g) + 3\,CF_4(g)$
c. $2\,CO_2(g) + 2\,CF_4(g) \rightleftharpoons 4\,COF_2(g)$

29. Consider the reactions and their respective equilibrium constants:
MISSED THIS? *Read Section 16.3*

$NO(g) + \frac{1}{2}Br_2(g) \rightleftharpoons NOBr(g) \qquad K_p = 5.3$
$2\,NO(g) \rightleftharpoons N_2(g) + O_2(g) \qquad K_p = 2.1 \times 10^{30}$

Use these reactions and their equilibrium constants to predict the equilibrium constant for the following reaction:

$$N_2(g) + O_2(g) + Br_2(g) \rightleftharpoons 2\,NOBr(g)$$

30. Use the reactions and their equilibrium constants to predict the equilibrium constant for the reaction $2\,A(s) \rightleftharpoons 3\,D(g)$.

$A(s) \rightleftharpoons \frac{1}{2}B(g) + C(g) \qquad K_1 = 0.0334$
$3\,D(g) \rightleftharpoons B(g) + 2\,C(g) \qquad K_2 = 2.35$

K_p, K_c, and Heterogeneous Equilibria

31. Calculate K_c for each reaction.
MISSED THIS? *Read Section 16.4; Watch IWE 16.3*

a. $I_2(g) \rightleftharpoons 2\,I(g)$ $K_p = 6.26 \times 10^{-22}$ (at 298 K)
b. $CH_4(g) + H_2O(g) \rightleftharpoons CO(g) + 3\,H_2(g)$
$K_p = 7.7 \times 10^{24}$ (at 298 K)
c. $I_2(g) + Cl_2(g) \rightleftharpoons 2\,ICl(g)$ $K_p = 81.9$ (at 298 K)

32. Calculate K_p for each reaction.

a. $N_2O_4(g) \rightleftharpoons 2\,NO_2(g)$ $K_c = 5.9 \times 10^{-3}$ (at 298 K)
b. $N_2(g) + 3\,H_2(g) \rightleftharpoons 2\,NH_3(g)$ $K_c = 3.7 \times 10^{8}$ (at 298 K)
c. $N_2(g) + O_2(g) \rightleftharpoons 2\,NO(g)$ $K_c = 4.10 \times 10^{-31}$ (at 298 K)

33. Write an equilibrium expression for each chemical equation involving one or more solid or liquid reactants or products.
MISSED THIS? *Read Section 16.4*

a. $CO_3^{2-}(aq) + H_2O(l) \rightleftharpoons HCO_3^-(aq) + OH^-(aq)$
b. $2\,KClO_3(s) \rightleftharpoons 2\,KCl(s) + 3\,O_2(g)$
c. $HF(aq) + H_2O(l) \rightleftharpoons H_3O^+(aq) + F^-(aq)$
d. $NH_3(aq) + H_2O(l) \rightleftharpoons NH_4^+(aq) + OH^-(aq)$

34. Find and fix the mistake in the equilibrium expression.

$$PCl_5(g) \rightleftharpoons PCl_3(l) + Cl_2(g) \qquad K_c = \frac{[PCl_3][Cl_2]}{[PCl_5]}$$

Relating the Equilibrium Constant to Equilibrium Concentrations and Equilibrium Partial Pressures

35. Consider the reaction:
MISSED THIS? *Read Section 16.6*

$$CO(g) + 2\,H_2(g) \rightleftharpoons CH_3OH(g)$$

An equilibrium mixture of this reaction at a certain temperature has [CO] = 0.105 M, $[H_2]$ = 0.114 M, and $[CH_3OH]$ = 0.185 M. What is the value of the equilibrium constant (K_c) at this temperature?

36. Consider the reaction:

$$NH_4HS(s) \rightleftharpoons NH_3(g) + H_2S(g)$$

An equilibrium mixture of this reaction at a certain temperature has $[NH_3]$ = 0.278 M and $[H_2S]$ = 0.355 M. What is the value of the equilibrium constant (K_c) at this temperature?

37. Consider the reaction:
MISSED THIS? *Read Section 16.6; Watch IWE 16.5*

$$N_2(g) + 3\,H_2(g) \rightleftharpoons 2\,NH_3(g)$$

Complete the table. Assume that all concentrations are equilibrium concentrations in M.

T (K)	$[N_2]$	$[H_2]$	$[NH_3]$	K_c
500	0.115	0.105	0.439	______
575	0.110	______	0.128	9.6
775	0.120	0.140	______	0.0584

38. Consider the following reaction:

$$H_2(g) + I_2(g) \rightleftharpoons 2\,HI(g)$$

Complete the table. Assume that all concentrations are equilibrium concentrations in M.

T (°C)	$[H_2]$	$[I_2]$	[HI]	K_c
25	0.0355	0.0388	0.922	______
340	______	0.0455	0.387	9.6
445	0.0485	0.0468	______	50.2

39. Consider the reaction:
MISSED THIS? *Read Section 16.8; Watch IWE 16.8*

$$2\,NO(g) + Br_2(g) \rightleftharpoons 2\,NOBr(g) \qquad K_p = 28.4 \text{ at } 298\text{ K}$$

In a reaction mixture at equilibrium, the partial pressure of NO is 108 torr and that of Br_2 is 126 torr. What is the partial pressure of NOBr in this mixture?

40. Consider the reaction:

$$SO_2Cl_2(g) \rightleftharpoons SO_2(g) + Cl_2(g) \quad K_p = 2.91 \times 10^3 \text{ at } 298\text{ K}$$

In a reaction at equilibrium, the partial pressure of SO_2 is 137 torr and that of Cl_2 is 285 torr. What is the partial pressure of SO_2Cl_2 in this mixture?

41. For the reaction $A(g) \rightleftharpoons 2\,B(g)$, a reaction vessel initially contains only A at a pressure of P_A = 1.32 atm. At equilibrium, P_A = 0.25 atm. Calculate the value of K_p. (Assume no changes in volume or temperature.)
MISSED THIS? *Read Section 16.6; Watch IWE 16.5*

42. For the reaction $2\,A(g) \rightleftharpoons B(g) + 2\,C(g)$, a reaction vessel initially contains only A at a pressure of P_A = 255 mmHg. At equilibrium, P_A = 55 mmHg. Calculate the value of K_p. (Assume no changes in volume or temperature.)

43. Consider the reaction:
MISSED THIS? *Read Section 16.6; Watch IWE 16.5*

$$Fe^{3+}(aq) + SCN^-(aq) \rightleftharpoons FeSCN^{2+}(aq)$$

A solution is made containing an initial $[Fe^{3+}]$ of 1.0×10^{-3} M and an initial $[SCN^-]$ of 8.0×10^{-4} M. At equilibrium, $[FeSCN^{2+}] = 1.7 \times 10^{-4}$ M. Calculate the value of the equilibrium constant (K_c).

44. Consider the reaction:

$$SO_2Cl_2(g) \rightleftharpoons SO_2(g) + Cl_2(g)$$

A reaction mixture is made containing an initial $[SO_2Cl_2]$ of 0.020 M. At equilibrium, $[Cl_2] = 1.2 \times 10^{-2}$ M. Calculate the value of the equilibrium constant (K_c).

45. Consider the reaction:
MISSED THIS? *Read Section 16.6; Watch IWE 16.5*

$$H_2(g) + I_2(g) \rightleftharpoons 2\,HI(g)$$

A reaction mixture in a 3.67-L flask at a certain temperature initially contains 0.763 g H_2 and 96.9 g I_2. At equilibrium, the flask contains 90.4 g HI. Calculate the equilibrium constant (K_c) for the reaction at this temperature.

46. Consider the reaction:

$$CO(g) + 2\,H_2(g) \rightleftharpoons CH_3OH(g)$$

A reaction mixture in a 5.19-L flask at a certain temperature contains 26.9 g CO and 2.34 g H_2. At equilibrium, the flask contains 8.65 g CH_3OH. Calculate the equilibrium constant (K_c) for the reaction at this temperature.

The Reaction Quotient and Reaction Direction

47. Consider the reaction:
MISSED THIS? *Read Section 16.7; Watch KCV 16.7, IWE 16.7*

$$NH_4HS(s) \rightleftharpoons NH_3(g) + H_2S(g)$$

At a certain temperature, $K_c = 8.5 \times 10^{-3}$. A reaction mixture at this temperature containing solid NH_4HS has $[NH_3]$ = 0.166 M and $[H_2S]$ = 0.166 M. Will more of the solid form or will some of the existing solid decompose as equilibrium is reached?

48. Consider the reaction:

$$2\,H_2S(g) \rightleftharpoons 2\,H_2(g) + S_2(g) \qquad K_p = 2.4 \times 10^{-4} \text{ at } 1073\text{ K}$$

A reaction mixture contains 0.112 atm of H_2, 0.055 atm of S_2, and 0.445 atm of H_2S. Is the reaction mixture at equilibrium? If not, in what direction will the reaction proceed?

49. Silver sulfate dissolves in water according to the reaction:
MISSED THIS? *Read Section 16.7; Watch KCV 16.7, IWE 16.7*

$$Ag_2SO_4(s) \rightleftharpoons 2\,Ag^+(aq) + SO_4^{2-}(aq)$$
$$K_c = 1.1 \times 10^{-5} \text{ at } 298\text{ K}$$

A 1.5-L solution contains 6.55 g of dissolved silver sulfate. If additional solid silver sulfate is added to the solution, will it dissolve?

50. Nitrogen dioxide dimerizes according to the reaction:

$$2\,NO_2(g) \rightleftharpoons N_2O_4(g) \qquad K_p = 6.7 \text{ at } 298\text{ K}$$

A 2.25-L container contains 0.055 mol of NO_2 and 0.082 mol of N_2O_4 at 298 K. Is the reaction at equilibrium? If not, in what direction will the reaction proceed?

Finding Equilibrium Concentrations from Initial Concentrations and the Equilibrium Constant

51. Consider the reaction and the associated equilibrium constant:
MISSED THIS? *Read Section 16.8; Watch KCV 16.8, IWE 16.9*

$$aA(g) \rightleftharpoons bB(g) \qquad K_c = 4.0$$

Find the equilibrium concentrations of A and B for each value of a and b. Assume that the initial concentration of A in each case is 1.0 M and that no B is present at the beginning of the reaction.

a. $a = 1; b = 1$ b. $a = 2; b = 2$ c. $a = 1; b = 2$

52. Consider the reaction and the associated equilibrium constant:

$$aA(g) + bB(g) \rightleftharpoons cC(g) \qquad K_c = 5.0$$

Find the equilibrium concentrations of A, B, and C for each value of a, b, and c. Assume that the initial concentrations of A and B are each 1.0 M and that no product is present at the beginning of the reaction.

a. $a = 1; b = 1; c = 2$
b. $a = 1; b = 1; c = 1$
c. $a = 2; b = 1; c = 1$ (set up equation for x; don't solve)

53. For the reaction shown here, $K_c = 0.513$ at 500 K.
MISSED THIS? *Read Section 16.8; Watch KCV 16.8, IWE 16.9*

$$N_2O_4(g) \rightleftharpoons 2\,NO_2(g)$$

If a reaction vessel initially contains an N_2O_4 concentration of 0.0500 M at 500 K, what are the equilibrium concentrations of N_2O_4 and NO_2 at 500 K?

54. For the reaction shown here, $K_c = 255$ at 1000 K.

$$CO(g) + Cl_2(g) \rightleftharpoons COCl_2(g)$$

If a reaction mixture initially contains a CO concentration of 0.1500 M and a Cl_2 concentration of 0.175 M at 1000 K, what are the equilibrium concentrations of CO, Cl_2, and $COCl_2$ at 1000 K?

55. Consider the reaction:
MISSED THIS? *Read Section 16.8; Watch KCV 16.8, IWE 16.9*

$$NiO(s) + CO(g) \rightleftharpoons Ni(s) + CO_2(g)$$
$$K_c = 4.0 \times 10^3 \text{ at } 1500\text{ K}$$

If a mixture of solid nickel(II) oxide and 0.20 M carbon monoxide comes to equilibrium at 1500 K, what is the equilibrium concentration of CO_2?

56. Consider the reaction:

$$CO(g) + H_2O(g) \rightleftharpoons CO_2(g) + H_2(g) \quad K_c = 102 \text{ at } 500\text{ K}$$

If a reaction mixture initially contains 0.110 M CO and 0.110 M H_2O, what will the equilibrium concentration of each of the reactants and products be?

57. Consider the reaction:
MISSED THIS? *Read Section 16.8; Watch KCV 16.8, IWE 16.12*

$$HC_2H_3O_2(aq) + H_2O(l) \rightleftharpoons H_3O^+(aq) + C_2H_3O_2^-(aq)$$
$$K_c = 1.8 \times 10^{-5} \text{ at } 25\text{ °C}$$

If a solution initially contains 0.210 M $HC_2H_3O_2$, what is the equilibrium concentration of H_3O^+ at 25 °C?

58. Consider the reaction:

$$SO_2Cl_2(g) \rightleftharpoons SO_2(g) + Cl_2(g)$$
$$K_c = 2.99 \times 10^{-7} \text{ at } 227\text{ °C}$$

If a reaction mixture initially contains 0.175 M SO_2Cl_2, what is the equilibrium concentration of Cl_2 at 227 °C?

59. Consider the reaction:
MISSED THIS? *Read Section 16.8; Watch KCV 16.8, IWE 16.12*

$$Br_2(g) + Cl_2(g) \rightleftharpoons 2\,BrCl(g) \quad K_p = 1.11 \times 10^{-4} \text{ at } 150\text{ K}$$

A reaction mixture initially contains a Br_2 partial pressure of 755 torr and a Cl_2 partial pressure of 735 torr at 150 K. Calculate the equilibrium partial pressure of BrCl.

60. Consider the reaction:

$$CO(g) + H_2O(g) \rightleftharpoons CO_2(g) + H_2(g)$$
$$K_p = 0.0611 \text{ at } 2000\text{ K}$$

A reaction mixture initially contains a CO partial pressure of 1344 torr and a H_2O partial pressure of 1766 torr at 2000 K. Calculate the equilibrium partial pressures of each of the products.

61. Consider the reaction:
MISSED THIS? *Read Section 16.8; Watch KCV 16.8, IWE 16.9, 16.12*

$$A(g) \rightleftharpoons B(g) + C(g)$$

Find the equilibrium concentrations of A, B, and C for each value of K_c. Assume that the initial concentration of A in each case is 1.0 M and that the reaction mixture initially contains no products. Make any appropriate simplifying assumptions.

a. $K_c = 1.0$
b. $K_c = 0.010$
c. $K_c = 1.0 \times 10^{-5}$

62. Consider the reaction:

$$A(g) \rightleftharpoons 2\,B(g)$$

Find the equilibrium partial pressures of A and B for each value of K_p. Assume that the initial partial pressure of B in each case is 1.0 atm and that the initial partial pressure of A is 0.0 atm. Make any appropriate simplifying assumptions.

a. $K_p = 1.0$
b. $K_p = 1.0 \times 10^{-4}$
c. $K_p = 1.0 \times 10^5$

Le Châtelier's Principle

63. Consider this reaction at equilibrium:
MISSED THIS? *Read Section 16.9; Watch KCV 16.9, IWE 16.14*

$$CO(g) + Cl_2(g) \rightleftharpoons COCl_2(g)$$

Predict whether the reaction will shift left, shift right, or remain unchanged after each disturbance.

a. $COCl_2$ is added to the reaction mixture.
b. Cl_2 is added to the reaction mixture.
c. $COCl_2$ is removed from the reaction mixture.

64. Consider this reaction at equilibrium:

$$2\,BrNO(g) \rightleftharpoons 2\,NO(g) + Br_2(g)$$

Predict whether the reaction will shift left, shift right, or remain unchanged after each disturbance.

a. NO is added to the reaction mixture.
b. BrNO is added to the reaction mixture.
c. Br_2 is removed from the reaction mixture.

65. Consider this reaction at equilibrium:
MISSED THIS? *Read Section 16.9; Watch KCV 16.9, IWE 16.14*

$$2\,KClO_3(s) \rightleftharpoons 2\,KCl(s) + 3\,O_2(g)$$

Predict whether the reaction will shift left, shift right, or remain unchanged after each disturbance.

a. O_2 is removed from the reaction mixture.
b. KCl is added to the reaction mixture.
c. $KClO_3$ is added to the reaction mixture.
d. O_2 is added to the reaction mixture.

66. Consider this reaction at equilibrium:

$$C(s) + H_2O(g) \rightleftharpoons CO(g) + H_2(g)$$

Predict whether the reaction will shift left, shift right, or remain unchanged after each disturbance.

a. C is added to the reaction mixture.
b. H_2O is condensed and removed from the reaction mixture.
c. CO is added to the reaction mixture.
d. H_2 is removed from the reaction mixture.

67. Each reaction is allowed to come to equilibrium, and then the volume is changed as indicated. Predict the effect (shift right, shift left, or no effect) of the indicated volume change.
MISSED THIS? *Read Section 16.9; Watch KCV 16.9*

a. $I_2(g) \rightleftharpoons 2\,I(g)$ (volume is increased)
b. $2\,H_2S(g) \rightleftharpoons 2\,H_2(g) + S_2(g)$ (volume is decreased)
c. $I_2(g) + Cl_2(g) \rightleftharpoons 2\,ICl(g)$ (volume is decreased)

68. Each reaction is allowed to come to equilibrium, and then the volume is changed as indicated. Predict the effect (shift right, shift left, or no effect) of the indicated volume change.

a. $CO(g) + H_2O(g) \rightleftharpoons CO_2(g) + H_2(g)$ (volume is decreased)
b. $PCl_3(g) + Cl_2(g) \rightleftharpoons PCl_5(g)$ (volume is increased)
c. $CaCO_3(s) \rightleftharpoons CaO(s) + CO_2(g)$ (volume is increased)

69. This reaction is endothermic.
MISSED THIS? *Read Section 16.9; Watch KCV 16.9*

$$C(s) + CO_2(g) \rightleftharpoons 2\,CO(g)$$

Predict the effect (shift right, shift left, or no effect) of increasing and decreasing the reaction temperature. How does the value of the equilibrium constant depend on temperature?

70. This reaction is exothermic.

$$C_6H_{12}O_6(s) + 6\,O_2(g) \rightleftharpoons 6\,CO_2(g) + 6\,H_2O(g)$$

Predict the effect (shift right, shift left, or no effect) of increasing and decreasing the reaction temperature. How does the value of the equilibrium constant depend on temperature?

71. Coal, which is primarily carbon, can be converted to natural gas, primarily CH_4, by the exothermic reaction:
MISSED THIS? *Read Section 16.9; Watch KCV 16.9, IWE 16.14*

$$C(s) + 2\,H_2(g) \rightleftharpoons CH_4(g)$$

Which disturbance will favor CH_4 at equilibrium?

a. adding more C to the reaction mixture
b. adding more H_2 to the reaction mixture
c. raising the temperature of the reaction mixture
d. lowering the volume of the reaction mixture
e. adding a catalyst to the reaction mixture
f. adding neon gas to the reaction mixture

72. Coal can be used to generate hydrogen gas (a potential fuel) by the endothermic reaction:

$$C(s) + H_2O(g) \rightleftharpoons CO(g) + H_2(g)$$

If this reaction mixture is at equilibrium, predict whether each disturbance will result in the formation of additional or less hydrogen gas, or have no effect on the quantity of hydrogen gas.

a. adding more C to the reaction mixture
b. adding more H_2O to the reaction mixture
c. raising the temperature of the reaction mixture
d. increasing the volume of the reaction mixture
e. adding a catalyst to the reaction mixture
f. adding an inert gas to the reaction mixture

CUMULATIVE PROBLEMS

73. Carbon monoxide replaces oxygen in oxygenated hemoglobin according to the reaction:

$$HbO_2(aq) + CO(aq) \rightleftharpoons HbCO(aq) + O_2(aq)$$

a. Use the reactions and associated equilibrium constants at body temperature given here to find the equilibrium constant for the reaction just shown.

$$Hb(aq) + O_2(aq) \rightleftharpoons HbO_2(aq) \qquad K_c = 1.8$$

$$Hb(aq) + CO(aq) \rightleftharpoons HbCO(aq) \qquad K_c = 306$$

b. Suppose that an air mixture becomes polluted with carbon monoxide at a level of 0.10% (by volume). Assuming that the air contains 20.0% oxygen and that the oxygen and carbon monoxide ratios that dissolve in the blood are identical to the ratios in the air, what is the ratio of HbCO to HbO_2 in the bloodstream? Comment on the toxicity of carbon monoxide.

74. Nitrogen monoxide is a pollutant in the lower atmosphere that irritates the eyes and lungs and leads to the formation of acid rain. Nitrogen monoxide forms naturally in atmosphere according to the endothermic reaction:

$$N_2(g) + O_2(g) \rightleftharpoons 2\,NO(g) \quad K_p = 4.1 \times 10^{-31} \text{ at } 298\text{ K}$$

Use the ideal gas law to calculate the concentrations of nitrogen and oxygen present in air at a pressure of 1.0 atm and a temperature of 298 K. Assume that nitrogen composes 78% of air by volume and that oxygen composes 21% of air. Find the "natural" equilibrium concentration of NO in air in units of molecules/cm^3. How would you expect this concentration to change in an automobile engine in which combustion is occurring?

75. The reaction $CO_2(g) + C(s) \rightleftharpoons 2\,CO(g)$ has $K_p = 5.78$ at 1200 K.

a. Calculate the total pressure at equilibrium when 4.45 g of CO_2 is introduced into a 10.0-L container and heated to 1200 K in the presence of 2.00 g of graphite.

b. Repeat the calculation of part a in the presence of 0.50 g of graphite.

76. A mixture of water and graphite is heated to 600 K. When the system comes to equilibrium, it contains 0.13 mol of H_2, 0.13 mol of CO, 0.43 mol of H_2O, and some graphite. Some O_2 is added to the system, and a spark is applied so that the H_2 reacts completely with the O_2. Find the amount of CO in the flask when the system returns to equilibrium.

77. At 650 K, the reaction $MgCO_3(s) \rightleftharpoons MgO(s) + CO_2(g)$ has $K_p = 0.026$. A 10.0-L container at 650 K has 1.0 g of $MgO(s)$ and CO_2 at $P = 0.0260$ atm. The container is then compressed to a volume of 0.100 L. Find the mass of $MgCO_3$ that is formed.

78. A system at equilibrium contains $I_2(g)$ at a pressure of 0.21 atm and $I(g)$ at a pressure of 0.23 atm. The system is then compressed to half its volume. Find the pressure of each gas when the system returns to equilibrium.

79. Consider the exothermic reaction:

$$C_2H_4(g) + Cl_2(g) \rightleftharpoons C_2H_4Cl_2(g)$$

If you were trying to maximize the amount of $C_2H_4Cl_2$ produced, which tactic might you try? Assume that the reaction mixture reaches equilibrium.

a. increasing the reaction volume

b. removing $C_2H_4Cl_2$ from the reaction mixture as it forms

c. lowering the reaction temperature

d. adding Cl_2

80. Consider the endothermic reaction:

$$C_2H_4(g) + I_2(g) \rightleftharpoons C_2H_4I_2(g)$$

If you were trying to maximize the amount of $C_2H_4I_2$ produced, which tactic might you try? Assume that the reaction mixture reaches equilibrium.

a. decreasing the reaction volume

b. removing I_2 from the reaction mixture

c. raising the reaction temperature

d. adding C_2H_4 to the reaction mixture

81. Consider the reaction:

$$H_2(g) + I_2(g) \rightleftharpoons 2\,HI(g)$$

A reaction mixture at equilibrium at 175 K contains $P_{H_2} = 0.958$ atm, $P_{I_2} = 0.877$ atm, and $P_{HI} = 0.020$ atm. A second reaction mixture, also at 175 K, contains $P_{H_2} = P_{I_2} = 0.621$ atm and $P_{HI} = 0.101$ atm. Is the second reaction at equilibrium? If not, what will be the partial pressure of HI when the reaction reaches equilibrium at 175 K?

82. Consider the reaction:

$$2\,H_2S(g) + SO_2(g) \rightleftharpoons 3\,S(s) + 2\,H_2O(g)$$

A reaction mixture initially containing 0.500 M H_2S and 0.500 M SO_2 contains 0.0011 M H_2O at equilibrium at a certain temperature. A second reaction mixture at the same temperature initially contains $[H_2S] = 0.250$ M and $[SO_2] = 0.325$ M. Calculate the equilibrium concentration of H_2O in the second mixture at this temperature.

83. Ammonia can be synthesized according to the reaction:

$$N_2(g) + 3\,H_2(g) \rightleftharpoons 2\,NH_3(g) \quad K_p = 5.3 \times 10^{-5} \text{ at } 725\text{ K}$$

A 200.0-L reaction container initially contains 1.27 kg of N_2 and 0.310 kg of H_2 at 725 K. Assuming ideal gas behavior, calculate the mass of NH_3 (in g) present in the reaction mixture at equilibrium. What is the percent yield of the reaction under these conditions?

84. Hydrogen can be extracted from natural gas according to the reaction:

$$CH_4(g) + CO_2(g) \rightleftharpoons 2\,CO(g) + 2\,H_2(g) \quad K_p = 4.5 \times 10^{2} \text{ at } 825\text{ K}$$

An 85.0-L reaction container initially contains 22.3 kg of CH_4 and 55.4 kg of CO_2 at 825 K. Assuming ideal gas behavior, calculate the mass of H_2 (in g) present in the reaction mixture at equilibrium. What is the percent yield of the reaction under these conditions?

85. The system described by the reaction $CO(g) + Cl_2(g) \rightleftharpoons COCl_2(g)$ is at equilibrium at a given temperature when $P_{CO} = 0.30$ atm, $P_{Cl_2} = 0.10$ atm, and $P_{COCl_2} = 0.60$ atm. An additional pressure of $Cl_2(g) = 0.40$ atm is added. Find the pressure of CO when the system returns to equilibrium.

86. A reaction vessel at 27 °C contains a mixture of SO_2 ($P = 3.00$ atm) and O_2 ($P = 1.00$ atm). When a catalyst is added, this reaction takes place: $2\,SO_2(g) + O_2(g) \rightleftharpoons 2\,SO_3(g)$. At equilibrium, the total pressure is 3.75 atm. Find the value of K_c.

87. At 70 K, CCl_4 decomposes to carbon and chlorine. The K_p for the decomposition is 0.76. Find the starting pressure of CCl_4 at this temperature that will produce a total pressure of 1.0 atm at equilibrium.

88. The equilibrium constant for the reaction $SO_2(g) + NO_2(g) \rightleftharpoons SO_3(g) + NO(g)$ is $K_c = 3.0$. Find the amount of NO_2 that must be added to 2.4 mol of SO_2 in order to form 1.2 mol of SO_3 at equilibrium.

89. A sample of $CaCO_3(s)$ is introduced into a sealed container of volume 0.654 L and heated to 1000 K until equilibrium is reached. The K_p for the reaction $CaCO_3(s) \rightleftharpoons CaO(s) + CO_2(g)$ is 3.9×10^{-2} at this temperature. Calculate the mass of $CaO(s)$ that is present at equilibrium.

90. An equilibrium mixture contains N_2O_4 ($P = 0.28$ atm) and NO_2 ($P = 1.1$ atm) at 350 K. The volume of the container is doubled at constant temperature. Write a balanced chemical equation for the reaction and calculate the equilibrium pressures of the two gases when the system reaches a new equilibrium.

91. Carbon monoxide and chlorine gas react to form phosgene:

$$CO(g) + Cl_2(g) \rightleftharpoons COCl_2(g) \quad K_p = 3.10 \text{ at } 700\text{ K}$$

If a reaction mixture initially contains 215 torr of CO and 245 torr of Cl_2, what is the mole fraction of $COCl_2$ when equilibrium is reached?

92. Solid carbon can react with gaseous water to form carbon monoxide gas and hydrogen gas. The equilibrium constant for the reaction at 700.0 K is $K_p = 1.60 \times 10^{-3}$. If a 1.55-L reaction vessel initially contains 145 torr of water at 700.0 K in contact with excess solid carbon, find the percent by mass of hydrogen gas of the gaseous reaction mixture at equilibrium.

CHALLENGE PROBLEMS

93. Consider the reaction:

$$2\,NO(g) + O_2(g) \rightleftharpoons 2\,NO_2(g)$$

a. A reaction mixture at 175 K initially contains 522 torr of NO and 421 torr of O_2. At equilibrium, the total pressure in the reaction mixture is 748 torr. Calculate K_p at this temperature.

b. A second reaction mixture at 175 K initially contains 255 torr of NO and 185 torr of O_2. What is the equilibrium partial pressure of NO_2 in this mixture?

94. Consider the reaction:

$$2\,SO_2(g) + O_2(g) \rightleftharpoons 2\,SO_3(g) \qquad K_p = 0.355 \text{ at } 950\text{ K}$$

A 2.75-L reaction vessel at 950 K initially contains 0.100 mol of SO_2 and 0.100 mol of O_2. Calculate the total pressure (in atmospheres) in the reaction vessel when equilibrium is reached.

95. Nitric oxide reacts with chlorine gas according to the reaction:

$$2\,NO(g) + Cl_2(g) \rightleftharpoons 2\,NOCl(g)$$

$$K_p = 0.27 \text{ at } 700\text{ K}$$

A reaction mixture initially contains equal partial pressures of NO and Cl_2. At equilibrium, the partial pressure of NOCl is 115 torr. What were the initial partial pressures of NO and Cl_2?

96. At a given temperature, a system containing $O_2(g)$ and some oxides of nitrogen can be described by these reactions:

$$2\,NO(g) + O_2(g) \rightleftharpoons 2\,NO_2(g) \qquad K_p = 10^4$$

$$2\,NO_2(g) \rightleftharpoons N_2O_4(g) \qquad K_p = 0.10$$

A pressure of 1 atm of $N_2O_4(g)$ is placed in a container at this temperature. Predict which, if any, component (other than N_2O_4) will be present at a pressure greater than 0.2 atm at equilibrium.

97. A sample of pure NO_2 is heated to 337 °C, at which temperature it partially dissociates according to the equation:

$$2\,NO_2(g) \rightleftharpoons 2\,NO(g) + O_2(g)$$

At equilibrium the density of the gas mixture is 0.520 g/L at 0.750 atm. Calculate K_c for the reaction.

98. When $N_2O_5(g)$ is heated, it dissociates into $N_2O_3(g)$ and $O_2(g)$ according to the reaction:

$$N_2O_5(g) \rightleftharpoons N_2O_3(g) + O_2(g)$$

$$K_c = 7.75 \text{ at a given temperature}$$

The $N_2O_3(g)$ dissociates to give $N_2O(g)$ and $O_2(g)$ according the reaction:

$$N_2O_3(g) \rightleftharpoons N_2O(g) + O_2(g)$$

$$K_c = 4.00 \text{ at the same temperature}$$

When 4.00 mol of $N_2O_5(g)$ is heated in a 1.00-L reaction vessel to this temperature, the concentration of $O_2(g)$ at equilibrium is 4.50 mol/L. Find the concentrations of all the other species in the equilibrium system.

99. A sample of SO_3 is introduced into an evacuated sealed container and heated to 600 K. The following equilibrium is established:

$$2\,SO_3(g) \rightleftharpoons 2\,SO_2(g) + O_2(g)$$

The total pressure in the system is 3.0 atm, and the mole fraction of O_2 is 0.12. Find K_p.

CONCEPTUAL PROBLEMS

100. A reaction $A(g) \rightleftharpoons B(g)$ has an equilibrium constant of 1.0×10^{-4}. For which of the initial reaction mixtures is the *x is small* approximation most likely to apply?

a. [A] = 0.0010 M; [B] = 0.00 M
b. [A] = 0.00 M; [B] = 0.10 M
c. [A] = 0.10 M; [B] = 0.10 M
d. [A] = 0.10 M; [B] = 0.00 M

101. The reaction $A(g) \rightleftharpoons 2\,B(g)$ has an equilibrium constant of $K_c = 1.0$ at a given temperature. If a reaction vessel contains equal initial amounts (in moles) of A and B, does the direction in which the reaction proceeds depend on the volume of the reaction vessel? Explain.

102. A particular reaction has an equilibrium constant of $K_p = 0.50$. A reaction mixture is prepared in which all the reactants and products are in their standard states. In which direction does the reaction proceed?

103. Consider the reaction:

$$aA(g) \rightleftharpoons bB(g)$$

Each of the entries in the following table represents equilibrium partial pressures of A and B under different initial conditions. What are the values of *a* and *b* in the reaction?

P_A (atm)	P_B (atm)
4.0	2.0
2.0	1.4
1.0	1.0
0.50	0.71
0.25	0.50

104. Consider the simple one-step reaction:

$$A(g) \rightleftharpoons B(g)$$

Since the reaction occurs in a single step, the forward reaction has a rate of $k_{for}[A]$ and the reverse reaction has a rate of $k_{rev}[B]$. What happens to the rate of the forward reaction when we increase the concentration of A? How does this explain the reason behind Le Châtelier's principle?

105. Consider the reaction: $A(g) \rightleftharpoons 2\,B(g)$. The graph plots the concentrations of A and B as a function of time at a constant temperature. What is the equilibrium constant for this reaction at this temperature?

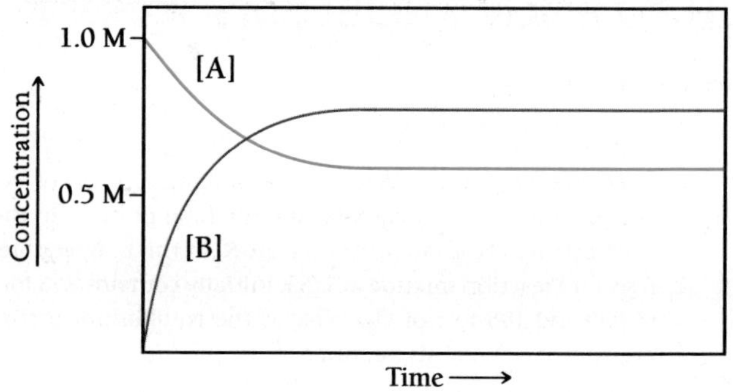

QUESTIONS FOR GROUP WORK

Active Classroom Learning

Discuss these questions with the group and record your consensus answer.

106. The reactions shown here can be combined to make the overall reaction $C(s) + H_2O(g) \longrightarrow CO(g) + H_2(g)$ by reversing some and/or dividing all the coefficients by a number. As a group, determine how the reactions need to be modified to sum to the overall process. Then have each group member determine the value of *K* for one of the reactions to be combined. Finally, combine all the values of *K* to determine the value of *K* for the overall reaction.

a. $C(s) + O_2(g) \longrightarrow CO_2(g)$ $K = 1.363 \times 10^{69}$
b. $2\,H_2(g) + O_2(g) \longrightarrow 2\,H_2O(g)$ $K = 1.389 \times 10^{80}$
c. $2\,CO(g) + O_2(g) \longrightarrow 2\,CO_2(g)$ $K = 1.477 \times 10^{90}$

107. Consider the reaction: $N_2(g) + 3\,H_2(g) \longrightarrow 2\,NH_3(g)$.

a. Write the equilibrium constant expression for this reaction.
If some hydrogen is added, before the reaction shifts,
b. How will the numerator and denominator of the expression in part a compare to the value at equilibrium?
c. Will *Q* be larger or smaller than *K*? Why?
d. Will the reaction have to shift forward or backward to retain equilibrium? Explain.
e. Are your answers above consistent with Le Châtelier's principle? Explain.

108. For the reaction $A \longrightarrow B$, the ratio of products to reactants at equilibrium is always the same number, no matter how much A or B is initially present. Interestingly, in contrast, the ratio of products to reactants for the reaction $C \longrightarrow 2\,D$ does depend on how much of C and D you have initially. Explain this observation. Which ratio is independent of the starting amounts of C and D? Answer in complete sentences.

109. Solve each of the expressions for *x* using the quadratic formula and the *x is small* approximation. In which of the following expressions is the *x is small* approximation valid?

a. $x^2/(0.2 - x) = 1.3 \times 10^4$
b. $x^2/(0.2 - x) = 1.3$
c. $x^2/(0.2 - x) = 1.3 \times 10^{-4}$
d. $x^2/(0.01 - x) = 1.3 \times 10^{-4}$

In a complete sentence, describe the factor(s) that tend to make the *x is small* approximation valid in an expression.

110. Have each group member explain to the group what happens if a system at equilibrium is subject to one of the following changes and why:

a. the concentration of a reactant is increased
b. a solid product is added
c. the volume is decreased
d. the temperature is raised

DATA INTERPRETATION AND ANALYSIS

Chemical Equilibrium on Venus

111. The atmosphere of the planet Venus is almost entirely composed of carbon dioxide (about 96.5% carbon dioxide). The carbon dioxide on Venus might be in equilibrium with carbonate ions in minerals on the planet's crust. Two possible equilibrium systems involve $CaSiO_3$ and $MgSiO_3$:

$CaSiO_3(s) + CO_2(g) \rightleftharpoons CaCO_3(s) + SiO_2(s)$ System 1

$MgSiO_3(s) + CaCO_3(s) + SiO_2(s) \rightleftharpoons CaMgSi_2O_6(s) + CO_2(g)$ System 2

The first graph shows the expected pressures of carbon dioxide (in atm) at different temperatures for each of these equilibrium systems. (Note that both axes on this graph are logarithmic.) The second graph is a phase diagram for carbon dioxide. Examine the graphs and answer the questions.

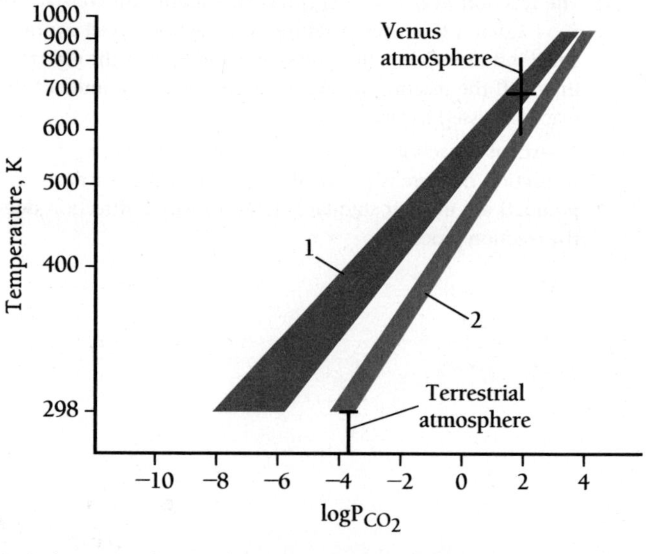

▲ Carbon Dioxide Partial Pressures for Systems 1 and 2

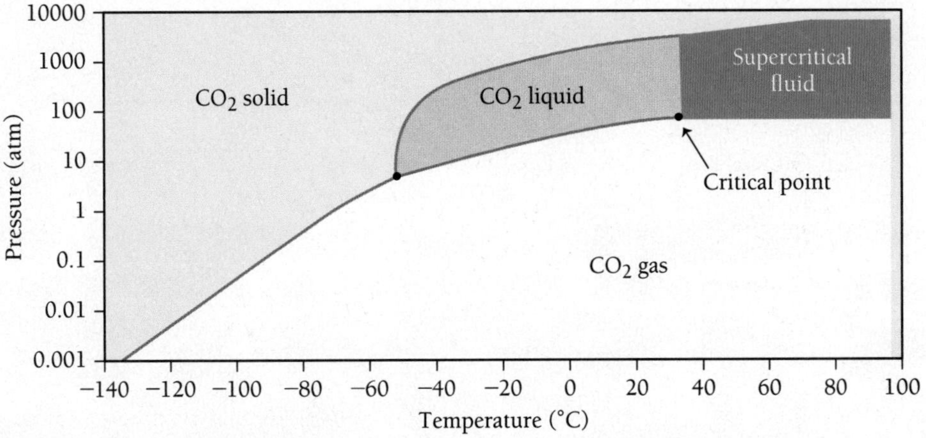

▲ Carbon Dioxide Phase Diagram

a. The partial pressure of carbon dioxide on the surface of Venus is 91 atm. What is the value of the equilibrium constant (K_p) if the Venusian carbon dioxide is in equilibrium according to system 1? According to system 2?

b. The approximate temperature on the surface of Venus is about 740 K. What is the approximate carbon dioxide concentration for system 1 at this temperature? For system 2? (Use a point at approximately the middle of each colored band, which represents the range of possible values, to estimate the carbon dioxide concentration.)

c. Use the partial pressure of carbon dioxide on the surface of Venus given in part a to determine which of the two equilibrium systems is more likely to be responsible for the carbon dioxide on the surface of Venus.

d. From the carbon dioxide phase diagram, determine the minimum pressure required for supercritical carbon dioxide to form. If the partial pressure of carbon dioxide on the surface of Venus was higher in the distant past, could supercritical carbon dioxide have existed on the surface of Venus?

Cc ANSWERS TO CONCEPTUAL CONNECTIONS

Dynamic Equilibrium

16.1 **(c)** For a chemical reaction in dynamic equilibrium, the concentrations of the reactants and products are generally *not* equal.

The Law of Mass Action

16.2 **(d)** The equilibrium constant is defined as the ratio—*at equilibrium*—of the concentrations of the products raised to their stoichiometric coefficients divided by the concentrations of the reactants raised to their stoichiometric coefficients.

The Magnitude of the Equilibrium Contstant

16.3 **(c)** The equilibrium constant is largest for temperature T_3 (because the reaction mixture has the most products relative to reactants at that temperature).

Equilibrium Constants and Equilibrium Concentrations

16.4 **(b)** The reaction mixture will contain [A] = 0.1 M and [B] = 1.0 M so that [B]/[A] = 10.

The Equilibrium Constant and the Chemical Equation

16.5 **(b)** The reaction is reversed and divided through by two. Therefore, you invert the equilibrium constant and take the square root of the result. $K = (1/0.010)^{1/2} = 10$.

The Relationship between K_p and K_c

16.6 **(a)** When $a + b = c + d$, the quantity Δn is zero so that $K_p = K_c(RT)^0$. Since $(RT)^0$ is equal to 1, $K_p = K_c$.

Heterogeneous Equilibria, K_p, and K_c

16.7 **(b)** Since Δn for gaseous reactants and products is zero, $K_p = K_c$.

Q and K

16.8 **(c)** Because N_2O_4 and NO_2 are both in their standard states, they each have a partial pressure of 1.0 atm. Consequently, $Q_p = 1$. Since $K_p = 0.15$, $Q_p > K_p$, and the reaction proceeds to the left.

Finding Equilibrium Concentrations

16.9 **(c)** $K_c = \dfrac{[B]^2}{[A]}$

$$[B] = \sqrt{[A]K_c} = \sqrt{1.0 \times 4.0} = 2.0$$

The *x is small* Approximation

16.10 **(a)** The *x is small* approximation is most likely to apply to a reaction with a small equilibrium constant and an initial concentration of reactant that is not too small. The bigger the equilibrium constant and the smaller the initial concentration of reactant, the less likely that the *x is small* approximation will apply.

Le Châtelier's Principle

16.11 **(d)** None of the changes listed here causes the reaction to shift right. They all cause the reaction to shift left.

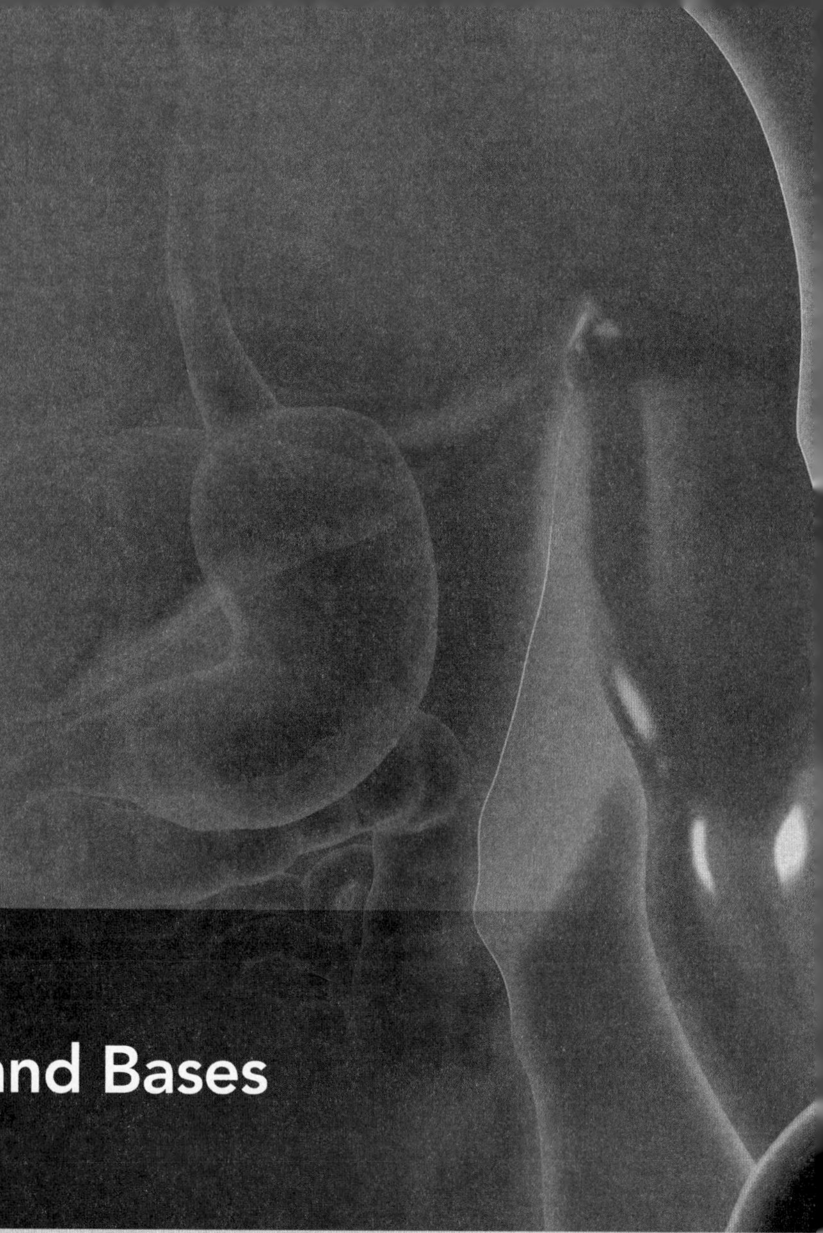

The differences between the various acid–base concepts are not concerned with which is right, but which is most convenient to use in a particular situation.

—JAMES E. HUHEEY (1935–)

CHAPTER 17 Acids and Bases

In this chapter, we apply the equilibrium concepts learned in the previous chapter to acid–base phenomena. Acids are common in many foods, such as limes, lemons, and vinegar, and in a number of consumer products, such as toilet cleaners and batteries. Bases are less common in foods but are key ingredients in consumer products such as drain openers and antacids. We will examine three different models for acid–base behavior, all of which define that behavior differently. In spite of their differences, the three models coexist, each being useful at explaining a particular range of acid–base phenomena. We also examine how to calculate the acidity or basicity of solutions and define a useful scale, called the pH scale, to quantify acidity and basicity. These types of calculations often involve solving the kind of equilibrium problems that we explored in Chapter 16.

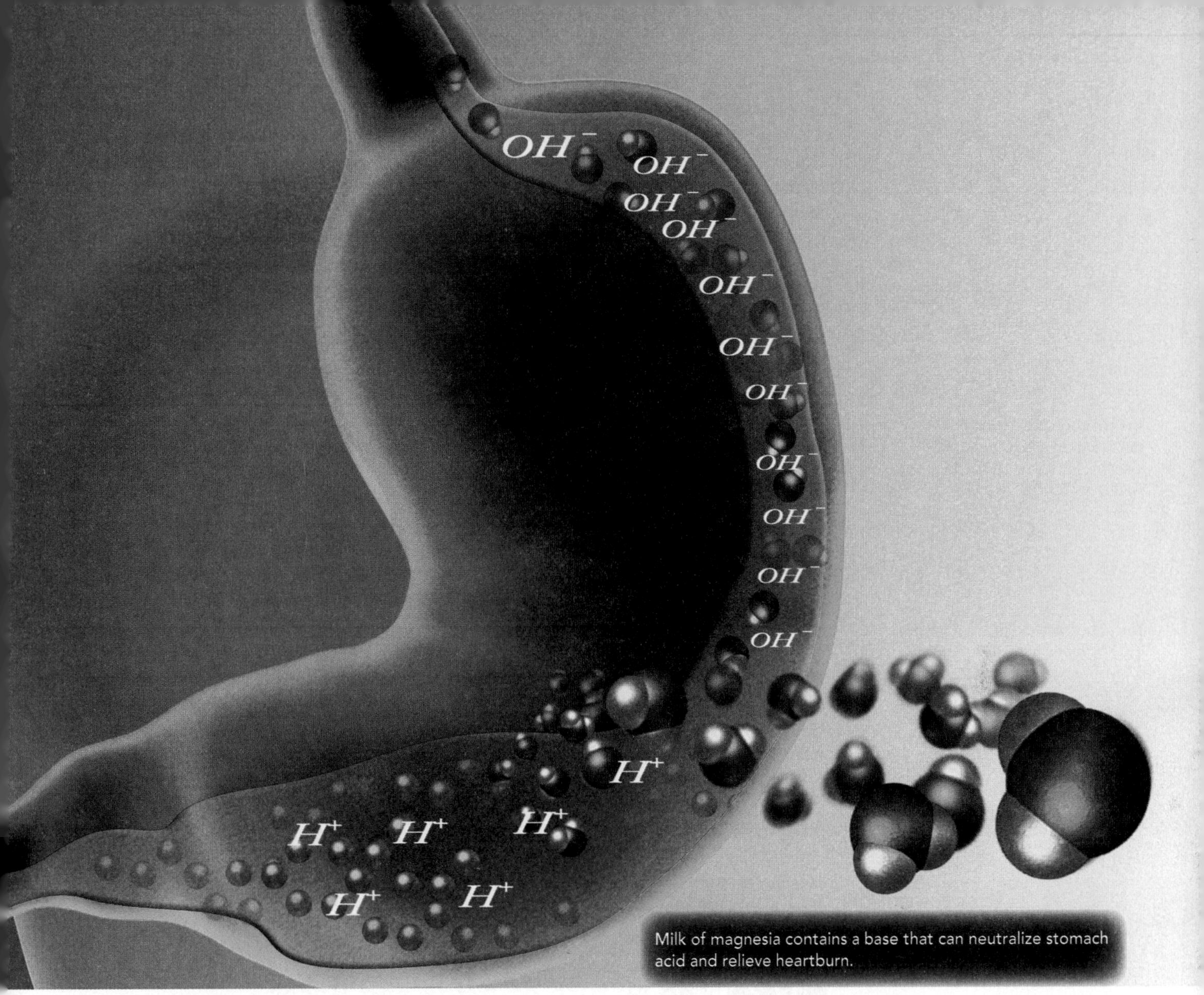

Milk of magnesia contains a base that can neutralize stomach acid and relieve heartburn.

17.1 Heartburn 731

17.2 The Nature of Acids and Bases 732

17.3 Definitions of Acids and Bases 734

17.4 Acid Strength and the Acid Ionization Constant (K_a) 737

17.5 Autoionization of Water and pH 740

17.6 Finding the $[H_3O^+]$ and pH of Strong and Weak Acid Solutions 745

17.7 Base Solutions 754

17.8 The Acid–Base Properties of Ions and Salts 758

17.9 Polyprotic Acids 765

17.10 Acid Strength and Molecular Structure 770

17.11 Lewis Acids and Bases 772

17.12 Acid Rain 773

LEARNING OUTCOMES 778

17.1 Heartburn

Heartburn is a painful burning sensation in the esophagus (the tube that joins the throat to the stomach) just below the chest. The pain is caused by hydrochloric acid (HCl), which the stomach excretes to kill microorganisms and to activate enzymes that break down food. Hydrochloric acid sometimes backs up out of the stomach and into the esophagus, a phenomenon called *acid reflux*. Recall from Section 5.7 that acids are substances that—by one definition that we elaborate on shortly—produce H^+ ions in solution. When hydrochloric acid from the stomach comes in contact with the lining of the esophagus, the H^+ ions irritate the tissues, resulting in the burning sensation. Some of the acid can work its way into the lower throat and even the mouth, producing pain in the throat and a sour taste (characteristic of acids) in the mouth. Almost everyone experiences heartburn at some time, most commonly after a large meal when the stomach is full. Strenuous activity or lying in a horizontal position after a large meal increases the likelihood of stomach acid reflux and the resulting heartburn.

Bases were first defined in Section 5.7.

The simplest way to relieve mild heartburn is to swallow repeatedly. Saliva contains the bicarbonate ion (HCO_3^-), which acts as a base and, when swallowed, neutralizes some of the acid in the esophagus. Later in this chapter, we will see how bicarbonate acts as a base. You can also treat heartburn with antacids such as Tums, milk of magnesia, or Mylanta. These over-the-counter medications contain more base than saliva does and therefore are effective at neutralizing esophageal acid. We look at the bases in these medicines more carefully later (see *Chemistry and Medicine: What's in My Antacid?* in Section 17.7).

The bicarbonate ion neutralizes stomach acid according to the reaction: $H^+(aq) + HCO_3^-(aq) \longrightarrow H_2O(l) + CO_2(g)$.

For some people, heartburn becomes a chronic problem. Gastroesophageal reflux disease (GERD) is the medical condition associated with chronic heartburn. In patients with GERD, the band of muscles (called the esophageal sphincter) at the bottom of the esophagus just above the stomach does not close tightly enough, allowing stomach contents to leak back into the esophagus on a regular basis. Medical researchers have developed a wireless sensor to help diagnose and evaluate treatment of GERD. Using a tube that goes down through the throat, a physician attaches the sensor to tissues in the patient's esophagus. The sensor reads pH—a measure of acidity that we discuss in Section 17.5—and transmits the readings to a recorder worn on the patient's body. The patient goes about his or her normal activities for the next few days while the recorder monitors esophageal pH. The physician then reads the record of esophageal pH to make a diagnosis or evaluate treatment.

The concentration of stomach acid, $[H_3O^+]$, varies from about 0.01 to 0.1 M.

In this chapter, we examine acid and base behavior. Acids and bases are not only important to our health (as we have just seen), but are also found in many household products, foods, medicines, and of course in nearly every chemistry laboratory. Acid–base chemistry is central to much of biochemistry and molecular biology. The building blocks of proteins, for example, are acids (called amino acids), and the molecules that carry the genetic code in DNA are bases.

17.2 The Nature of Acids and Bases

Acids have the following general properties: a sour taste, the ability to dissolve many metals, the ability to turn blue litmus paper red, and the ability to neutralize bases. Table 17.1 lists some common acids.

For a review of acid naming, see Section 3.6.

Litmus paper contains dyes that change color in the presence of acids and bases.

TABLE 17.1 ■ Some Common Acids

Name	Occurrence/Uses
Hydrochloric acid (HCl)	Metal cleaning; food preparation; ore refining; primary component of stomach acid
Sulfuric acid (H_2SO_4)	Fertilizer and explosives manufacturing; dye and glue production; in automobile batteries; electroplating of copper
Nitric acid (HNO_3)	Fertilizer and explosives manufacturing; dye and glue production
Acetic acid ($HC_2H_3O_2$)	Plastic and rubber manufacturing; food preservation; active component of vinegar
Citric acid ($H_3C_6H_5O_7$)	In citrus fruits such as lemons and limes; used to adjust pH in foods and beverages
Carbonic acid (H_2CO_3)	In carbonated beverages due to the reaction of carbon dioxide with water
Hydrofluoric acid (HF)	Metal cleaning; glass frosting and etching
Phosphoric acid (H_3PO_4)	Fertilizer manufacturing; biological buffering; beverage preservation

The formula for acetic acid can also be written as CH_3COOH.

You can find hydrochloric acid in most chemistry laboratories. In industry, it is used to clean metals, to prepare and process some foods, and to refine metal ores. As we discussed in Section 17.1, hydrochloric acid is also the main component of stomach acid.

HCl 

Hydrochloric acid

Sulfuric acid and nitric acid are also common in the laboratory. They play major roles in the manufacture of fertilizers, explosives, dyes, and glues. Sulfuric acid, produced in larger quantities than any other industrial chemical, is used in most automobile batteries.

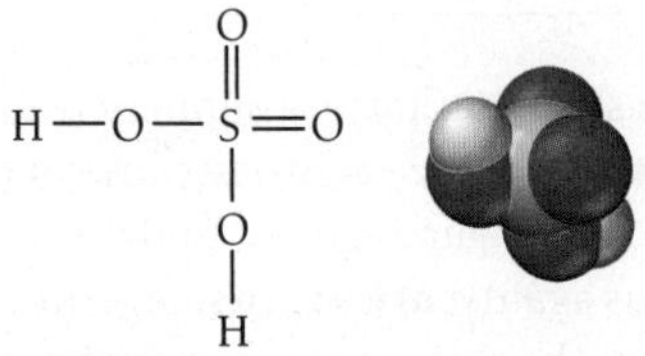

H_2SO_4

Sulfuric acid

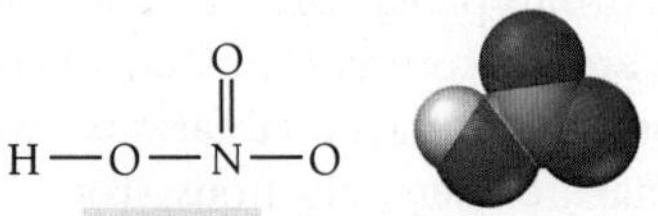

HNO_3

Nitric acid

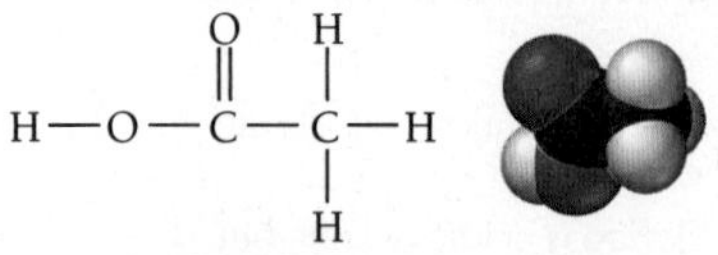

$HC_2H_3O_2$

Acetic acid

You can probably find acetic acid in your home—it is the active component of vinegar. It is also produced in improperly stored wines. The word *vinegar* originates from the French words *vin aigre*, which means "sour wine." Wine experts consider the presence of vinegar in wines a serious fault, since it makes the wine taste like salad dressing.

Acetic acid is a **carboxylic acid**, an acid that contains the following grouping of atoms:

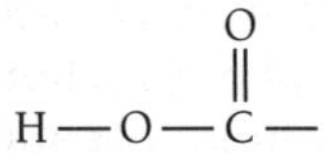

Carboxylic acid group

Carboxylic acids are often found in substances derived from living organisms. Other examples of carboxylic acids are citric acid, found in lemons and limes, and malic acid, found in apples, grapes, and wine.

▲ Acetic acid makes vinegar taste sour.

$H_3C_6H_5O_7$

Citric acid

$H_2C_4H_4O_5$

Malic acid

▲ Citrus fruits, apples, and grapes all contain acids.

▲ Many common household products and remedies contain bases.

TABLE 17.2 ■ Common Bases

Name	Occurrence/Uses
Sodium hydroxide (NaOH)	Petroleum processing; soap and plastic manufacturing
Potassium hydroxide (KOH)	Cotton processing; electroplating; soap production; batteries
Sodium bicarbonate ($NaHCO_3$)	Sold as baking soda; antacid; source of CO_2
Sodium carbonate (Na_2CO_3)	Glass and soap manufacturing; general cleanser; water softener
Ammonia (NH_3)	Detergent; fertilizer and explosives manufacturing; synthetic fiber production

Bases have the following general properties: a bitter taste, a slippery feel, the ability to turn red litmus paper blue, and the ability to neutralize acids. Because of their bitterness, bases are less common in foods than are acids. Our aversion to the taste of bases is probably an evolutionary adaptation to warn us against **alkaloids**, organic bases found in plants that are often poisonous. (For example, the active component of hemlock—the poisonous plant that killed the Greek philosopher Socrates—is the alkaloid coniine.) Nonetheless, some foods, such as coffee and chocolate (especially dark chocolate), contain bitter flavors. Many people enjoy the bitterness, but only after acquiring the taste over time.

Coffee is acidic overall, but bases present in coffee—such as caffeine—and other compounds impart a bitter flavor.

Bases feel slippery because they react with oils on the skin to form soap-like substances. Some household cleaning solutions, such as ammonia, are basic and have the characteristic slippery feel of a base. Bases turn red litmus paper blue; in the laboratory, litmus paper is routinely used to test the basicity of solutions.

Some common bases are listed in Table 17.2. You can find sodium hydroxide and potassium hydroxide in most chemistry laboratories. They are used in petroleum and cotton processing and in soap and plastic manufacturing. Sodium hydroxide is the active ingredient in products such as Drāno that unclog drains. In many homes, you can find sodium bicarbonate in the medicine cabinet (it is an active ingredient in some antacids) as well as in the kitchen (labeled as baking soda).

ANSWER **NOW!**

17.1 Cc Conceptual Connection

ACID PROPERTIES Which property is not associated with an acid?

(a) dissolves metals
(b) turns blue litmus red
(c) has a bitter taste

WATCH **NOW!**

KEY CONCEPT VIDEO 17.3
Definitions of Acids and Bases

17.3 Definitions of Acids and Bases

What are the key characteristics of the molecules and ions that exhibit acid and base behavior? In this chapter, we examine three different definitions: the Arrhenius definition, the Brønsted–Lowry definition, and the Lewis definition. Why three definitions, and which one is correct? As inorganic chemist and author James Huheey notes in the quotation that opens this chapter, no single definition is "correct." Rather, each definition is useful in a given instance. We discuss the Lewis definition of acids and bases in Section 17.11; here we discuss the other two.

The Arrhenius Definition

In the 1880s, Swedish chemist Svante Arrhenius (1859–1927) proposed the following molecular definitions of acids and bases:

Acid: A substance that produces H^+ ions in aqueous solution.

Base: A substance that produces OH^- ions in aqueous solution.

According to the **Arrhenius definition**, HCl is an acid because it produces H^+ ions in solution (Figure 17.1▶):

$$HCl(aq) \longrightarrow H^+(aq) + Cl^-(aq)$$

Hydrogen chloride (HCl) is a covalent compound and does not contain ions. However, in water it *ionizes* completely to form $H^+(aq)$ ions and $Cl^-(aq)$ ions. The H^+ ions are highly reactive. In aqueous solution, the H^+ ions bond to water to form H_3O^+:

$$H^+ + \ddot{\underset{\cdot\cdot}{O}}{:}H \text{ (with H above O)} \longrightarrow \left[H{:}\ddot{\underset{\cdot\cdot}{O}}{:}H \text{ (with H above O)}\right]^+$$

The H_3O^+ ion is the **hydronium ion**. In water, H^+ ions *always* associate with H_2O molecules to form hydronium ions and other associated species with the general formula $H(H_2O)_n{}^+$. For example, an H^+ ion can associate with two water molecules to form $H(H_2O)_2{}^+$, with three to form $H(H_2O)_3{}^+$, and so on. Chemists often use $H^+(aq)$ and $H_3O^+(aq)$ interchangeably to mean the same thing—an H^+ ion that has been solvated (or dissolved) in water.

According to the Arrhenius definition, NaOH is a base because it produces OH^- ions in solution (Figure 17.2▶):

$$NaOH(aq) \longrightarrow Na^+(aq) + OH^-(aq)$$

NaOH is an ionic compound and therefore contains Na^+ and OH^- ions. When NaOH is added to water, it *dissociates* (breaks apart) into its component ions.

Under the Arrhenius definition, acids and bases combine to form water, neutralizing each other in the process:

$$H^+(aq) + OH^-(aq) \longrightarrow H_2O(l)$$

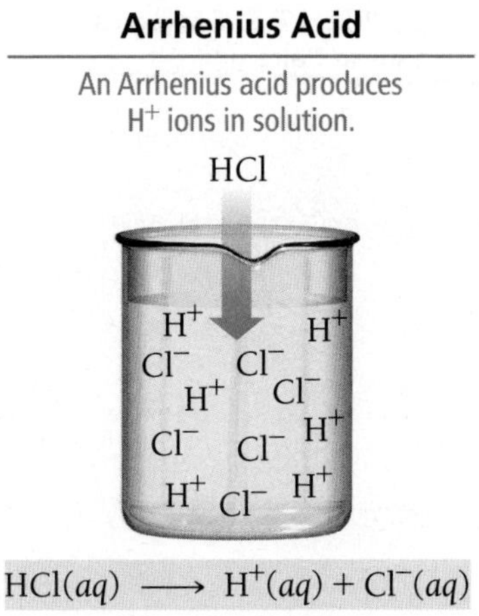

▲ **FIGURE 17.1 Arrhenius Acid**

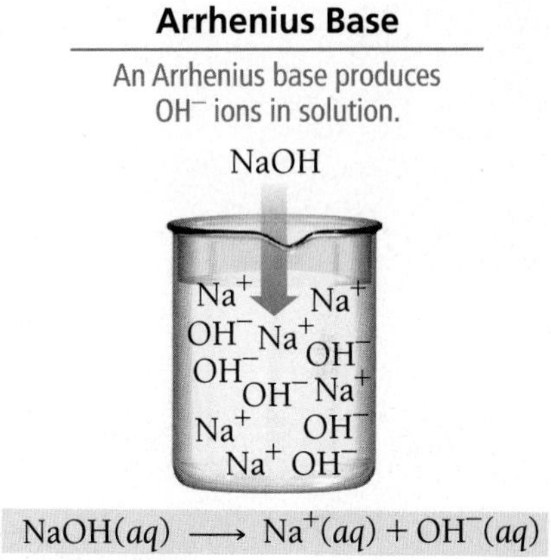

▲ **FIGURE 17.2 Arrhenius Base**

The Brønsted–Lowry Definition

A second, more widely applicable definition of acids and bases, the **Brønsted–Lowry definition**, was introduced in 1923. This definition focuses on the *transfer of H^+ ions* in an acid–base reaction. Since an H^+ ion is a proton—a hydrogen atom without its electron—this definition focuses on the idea of a proton donor and a proton acceptor:

Acid: proton (H^+ ion) *donor*

Base: proton (H^+ ion) *acceptor*

According to this definition, HCl is an acid because, in solution, it donates a proton to water:

$$HCl(aq) + H_2O(l) \longrightarrow H_3O^+(aq) + Cl^-(aq)$$

This definition clearly describes what happens to the H^+ ion from an acid—it associates with a water molecule to form H_3O^+ (a hydronium ion). The Brønsted–Lowry definition also applies nicely to bases (such as NH_3) that do not inherently contain OH^- ions but still produce OH^- ions in solution. According to the Brønsted–Lowry definition, NH_3 is a base because it accepts a proton from water:

$$NH_3(aq) + H_2O(l) \rightleftharpoons NH_4{}^+(aq) + OH^-(aq)$$

All Arrhenius acids and bases are acids and bases under the Brønsted–Lowry definition. However, some Brønsted–Lowry acids and bases cannot be classified as Arrhenius acids and bases.

According to the Brønsted–Lowry definition, acids (proton donors) and bases (proton acceptors) always occur together in an acid–base reaction. In the reaction between HCl and H_2O, HCl is the proton donor (acid) and H_2O is the proton acceptor (base):

$$\underset{\substack{\text{acid}\\\text{(proton donor)}}}{HCl(aq)} + \underset{\substack{\text{base}\\\text{(proton acceptor)}}}{H_2O(l)} \longrightarrow H_3O^+(aq) + Cl^-(aq)$$

In the reaction between NH_3 and H_2O, H_2O is the proton donor (acid) and NH_3 is the proton acceptor (base):

$$\underset{\substack{\text{base}\\\text{(proton acceptor)}}}{NH_3(aq)} + \underset{\substack{\text{acid}\\\text{(proton donor)}}}{H_2O(l)} \rightleftharpoons NH_4{}^+(aq) + OH^-(aq)$$

According to the Brønsted–Lowry definition, some substances—such as water in the previous two equations—can act as acids *or* bases. Substances that can act as acids or bases are **amphoteric**. Notice what happens when we reverse an equation representing a Brønsted–Lowry acid–base reaction:

$$\underset{\substack{\text{acid}\\\text{(proton donor)}}}{NH_4{}^+(aq)} + \underset{\substack{\text{base}\\\text{(proton acceptor)}}}{OH^-(aq)} \rightleftharpoons NH_3(aq) + H_2O(l)$$

▶ **FIGURE 17.3 Conjugate Acid–Base Pairs**

Conjugate Acid–Base Pairs

A conjugate acid–base pair consists of two substances related to each other by the transfer of a proton.

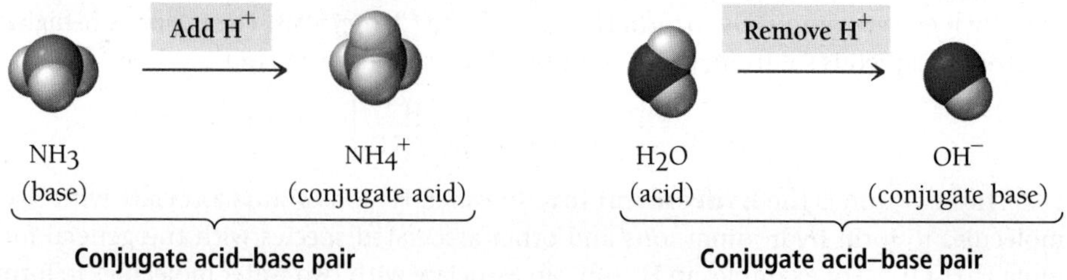

In this reaction, NH_4^+ is the proton donor (acid) and OH^- is the proton acceptor (base). The substance that was the base (NH_3) has become the acid (NH_4^+) and vice versa. NH_4^+ and NH_3 are often referred to as a **conjugate acid–base pair**, two substances related to each other by the transfer of a proton (Figure 17.3▲). A **conjugate acid** is any base to which a proton has been added, and a **conjugate base** is any acid from which a proton has been removed. Going back to the original forward reaction, we can identify the conjugate acid–base pairs:

$$NH_3(aq) + H_2O(l) \rightleftharpoons NH_4^+(aq) + OH^-(aq)$$

$NH_3(aq)$	$H_2O(l)$	$NH_4^+(aq)$	$OH^-(aq)$
Base	Acid	Conjugate acid	Conjugate base

Summarizing the Brønsted–Lowry Definition of Acids and Bases:

- A base accepts a proton and becomes a conjugate acid.
- An acid donates a proton and becomes a conjugate base.

WATCH **NOW!**

INTERACTIVE WORKED EXAMPLE 17.1

EXAMPLE 17.1 Identifying Brønsted–Lowry Acids and Bases and Their Conjugates

In each reaction, identify the Brønsted–Lowry acid, the Brønsted–Lowry base, the conjugate acid, and the conjugate base.

(a) $H_2SO_4(aq) + H_2O(l) \longrightarrow HSO_4^-(aq) + H_3O^+(aq)$

(b) $HCO_3^-(aq) + H_2O(l) \rightleftharpoons H_2CO_3(aq) + OH^-(aq)$

SOLUTION

(a) Because H_2SO_4 donates a proton to H_2O in this reaction, it is the acid (proton donor). After H_2SO_4 donates the proton, it becomes HSO_4^-, the conjugate base. Because H_2O accepts a proton, it is the base (proton acceptor). After H_2O accepts the proton, it becomes H_3O^+, the conjugate acid.	$H_2SO_4(aq) + H_2O(l) \longrightarrow HSO_4^-(aq) + H_3O^+(aq)$ $H_2SO_4(aq)$ (Acid) + $H_2O(l)$ (Base) $\longrightarrow$ $HSO_4^-(aq)$ (Conjugate base) + $H_3O^+(aq)$ (Conjugate acid)
(b) Because H_2O donates a proton to HCO_3^- in this reaction, it is the acid (proton donor). After H_2O donates the proton, it becomes OH^-, the conjugate base. Because HCO_3^- accepts a proton, it is the base (proton acceptor). After HCO_3^- accepts the proton, it becomes H_2CO_3, the conjugate acid.	$HCO_3^-(aq) + H_2O(l) \rightleftharpoons H_2CO_3(aq) + OH^-(aq)$ $HCO_3^-(aq)$ (Base) + $H_2O(l)$ (Acid) $\rightleftharpoons$ $H_2CO_3(aq)$ (Conjugate acid) + $OH^-(aq)$ (Conjugate base)

FOR PRACTICE 17.1 In each reaction, identify the Brønsted–Lowry acid, the Brønsted–Lowry base, the conjugate acid, and the conjugate base.

(a) $C_5H_5N(aq) + H_2O(l) \rightleftharpoons C_5H_5NH^+(aq) + OH^-(aq)$

(b) $HNO_3(aq) + H_2O(l) \rightleftharpoons H_3O^+(aq) + NO_3^-(aq)$

CONJUGATE ACID–BASE PAIRS Which pair is *not* a conjugate acid–base pair?

17.2 Cc Conceptual Connection — ANSWER NOW!

(a) $(CH_3)_3N$; $(CH_3)_3NH^+$

(b) H_2SO_4; H_2SO_3

(c) HNO_2; NO_2^-

17.4 Acid Strength and the Acid Ionization Constant (K_a)

WATCH **NOW!**

KEY CONCEPT VIDEO 17.4
Acid Strength and the Acid Ionization Constant

The strength of an electrolyte, first discussed in Section 5.4, depends on the extent of its dissociation into its component ions in solution. A *strong electrolyte* completely dissociates into ions in solution, whereas a *weak electrolyte* only partially dissociates. We define strong and weak acids accordingly. A **strong acid** completely ionizes in solution, whereas a **weak acid** only partially ionizes. In other words, the strength of an acid depends on the equilibrium:

$$HA(aq) + H_2O(l) \rightleftharpoons H_3O^+(aq) + A^-(aq)$$

In the preceding equation, HA is a generic formula for an acid. If the equilibrium lies far to the right, the acid is strong—it completely ionizes. If the equilibrium lies to the left, the acid is weak—only a small percentage of the acid molecules ionize. Of course, the range of acid strength is continuous, but for most purposes, the categories of strong and weak are useful.

Strong Acids

Hydrochloric acid (HCl) is an example of a strong acid:

Single arrow indicates complete ionization.

$$HCl(aq) + H_2O(l) \longrightarrow H_3O^+(aq) + Cl^-(aq)$$

An HCl solution contains virtually no intact HCl; the HCl has essentially all ionized to form $H_3O^+(aq)$ and $Cl^-(aq)$ (Figure 17.4▼). A 1.0 M HCl solution has an H_3O^+ concentration of 1.0 M. Abbreviating the concentration of H_3O^+ as $[H_3O^+]$, we say that a 1.0 M HCl solution has $[H_3O^+] = 1.0$ M.

Table 17.3 lists the six important strong acids. The first five acids in the table are **monoprotic acids**, acids containing only one ionizable proton. Sulfuric acid is an example of a **diprotic acid**, an acid containing two ionizable protons.

An ionizable proton is one that ionizes in solution. We discuss polyprotic acids in more detail in Section 17.9.

TABLE 17.3 ■ Strong Acids

Hydrochloric acid (HCl)	Nitric acid (HNO_3)
Hydrobromic acid (HBr)	Perchloric acid ($HClO_4$)
Hydroiodic acid (HI)	Sulfuric acid (H_2SO_4) (*diprotic*)

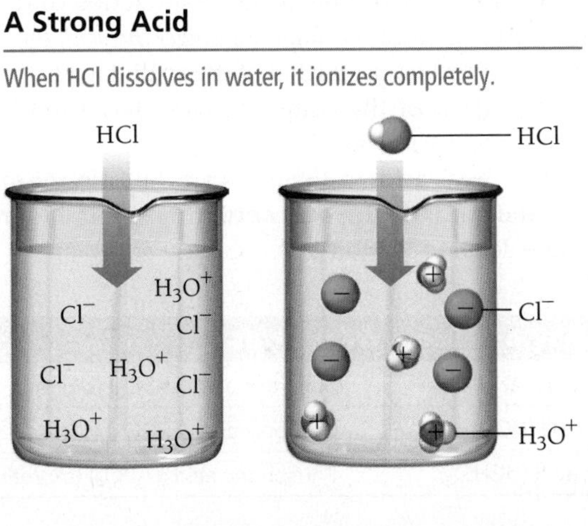

◀ **FIGURE 17.4 Ionization of a Strong Acid** HCl completely ionizes in water to form H_3O^+ and Cl^-. The solution contains virtually no intact HCl.

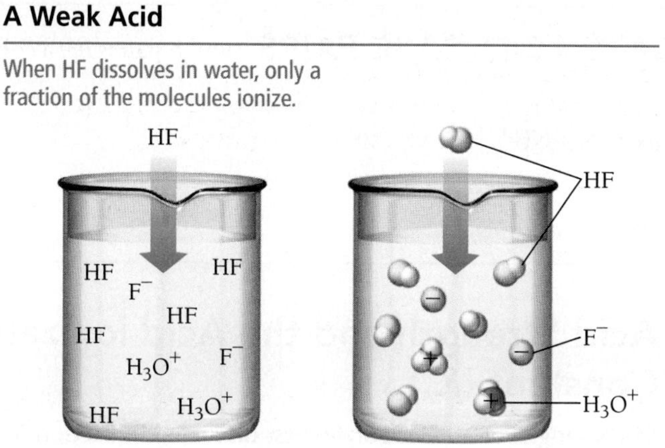

▲ **FIGURE 17.5 Ionization of a Weak Acid** HF partially ionizes in water to form H_3O^+ and F^-. The solution contains many intact HF molecules.

Weak Acids

In contrast to HCl, HF is a weak acid, one that does not completely ionize in solution:

Equilibrium arrow indicates partial ionization.

$$HF(aq) + H_2O(l) \rightleftharpoons H_3O^+(aq) + F^-(aq)$$

The terms *strong* and *weak* acids are often confused with the terms *concentrated* and *dilute* acids. Can you articulate the difference between these terms?

An HF solution contains a large number of intact (or un-ionized) HF molecules; it also contains some $H_3O^+(aq)$ and $F^-(aq)$ (Figure 17.5▲). In other words, a 1.0 M HF solution has an $[H_3O^+]$ that is much less than 1.0 M because only some of the HF molecules ionize to form H_3O^+.

The degree to which an acid is strong or weak depends on the attraction between the anion of the acid (the conjugate base) and the hydrogen ion, relative to the attractions of these ions to water. Recall that HA is a generic formula for an acid. The degree to which the following reaction proceeds in the forward direction depends on the strength of the attraction between H^+ and A^-:

$$\underset{\text{acid}}{HA(aq)} + H_2O(l) \rightleftharpoons H_3O^+(aq) + \underset{\text{conjugate base}}{A^-(aq)}$$

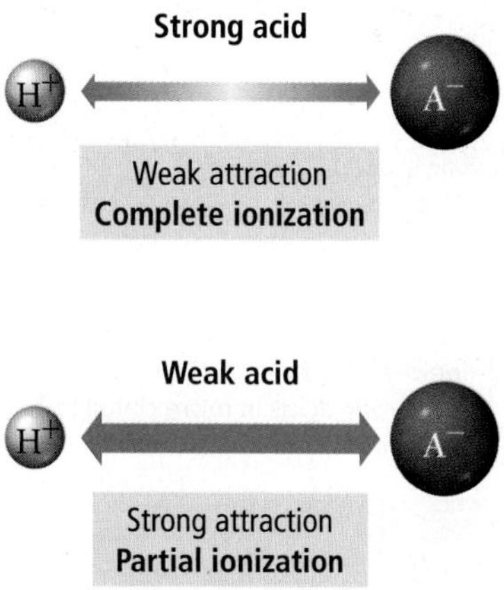

▲ **FIGURE 17.6 Ionic Attraction and Acid Strength** In a strong acid, the attraction between H^+ and A^- is weak, resulting in complete ionization. In a weak acid, the attraction between H^+ and A^- is strong, resulting in only partial ionization.

If the attraction between H^+ and A^- is *weak*, then the reaction favors the forward direction and the acid is *strong*. If the attraction between H^+ and A^- is *strong*, then the reaction favors the reverse direction and the acid is *weak*, as shown in Figure 17.6◀.

For example, in HCl, on one hand, the conjugate base (Cl^-) has a relatively weak attraction to H^+—the reverse reaction does not occur to any significant extent. In HF, on the other hand, the conjugate base (F^-) has a greater attraction to H^+—the reverse reaction occurs to a significant degree. *In general, the stronger the acid, the weaker the conjugate base and vice versa.* If the forward reaction (that of the acid) has a high tendency to occur, then the reverse reaction (that of the conjugate base) has a low tendency to occur. Table 17.4 lists some common weak acids.

Notice that two of the weak acids in Table 17.4 are diprotic, meaning that they have two ionizable protons, and one is a **triprotic acid** (three ionizable protons). We discuss polyprotic acids in more detail in Section 17.9.

Alternatively, we can write the formulas for acetic acid and formic acid as CH_3COOH and $HCOOH$, respectively, to indicate that in these compounds the only H that ionizes is the one attached to an oxygen atom.

TABLE 17.4 ■ Some Weak Acids

Hydrofluoric acid (HF)	Sulfurous acid (H_2SO_3) (*diprotic*)
Acetic acid ($HC_2H_3O_2$)	Carbonic acid (H_2CO_3) (*diprotic*)
Formic acid ($HCHO_2$)	Phosphoric acid (H_3PO_4) (*triprotic*)

The Acid Ionization Constant (K_a)

We quantify the relative strength of a weak acid with the **acid ionization constant (K_a)**, which is the equilibrium constant for the ionization reaction of the weak acid. As we saw in Section 16.3, for the two equivalent reactions:

$$HA(aq) + H_2O(l) \rightleftharpoons H_3O^+(aq) + A^-(aq)$$
$$HA(aq) \rightleftharpoons H^+(aq) + A^-(aq)$$

Sometimes K_a is referred to as the acid dissociation constant.

the equilibrium constant is:

$$K_a = \frac{[H_3O^+][A^-]}{[HA]} = \frac{[H^+][A^-]}{[HA]}$$

Recall from Chapter 16 that the concentrations of pure solids or pure liquids are not included in the expression for K_c; therefore, $H_2O(l)$ is not included in the expression for K_a.

Since $[H_3O^+]$ is equivalent to $[H^+]$, both forms of the expression are equal. Although the ionization constants for all weak acids are relatively small (otherwise the acid would not be a weak acid), they do vary in magnitude. The smaller the constant, the less the acid ionizes, and the weaker the acid. Table 17.5 lists the acid ionization constants for a number of common weak acids in order of decreasing acid strength. Appendix IIC contains a more complete list.

TABLE 17.5 ■ Acid Ionization Constants (K_a) for Some Monoprotic Weak Acids at 25 °C

Acid	Formula	Structural Formula	Ionization Reaction	K_a	pK_a
Chlorous acid	$HClO_2$	H—O—Cl=O	$HClO_2(aq) + H_2O(l) \rightleftharpoons H_3O^+(aq) + ClO_2^-(aq)$	1.1×10^{-2}	1.96
Nitrous acid	HNO_2	H—O—N=O	$HNO_2(aq) + H_2O(l) \rightleftharpoons H_3O^+(aq) + NO_2^-(aq)$	4.6×10^{-4}	3.34
Hydrofluoric acid	HF	H—F	$HF(aq) + H_2O(l) \rightleftharpoons H_3O^+(aq) + F^-(aq)$	6.8×10^{-4}	3.17
Formic acid	$HCHO_2$	H—O—C(=O)—H	$HCHO_2(aq) + H_2O(l) \rightleftharpoons H_3O^+(aq) + CHO_2^-(aq)$	1.8×10^{-4}	3.74
Benzoic acid	$HC_7H_5O_2$	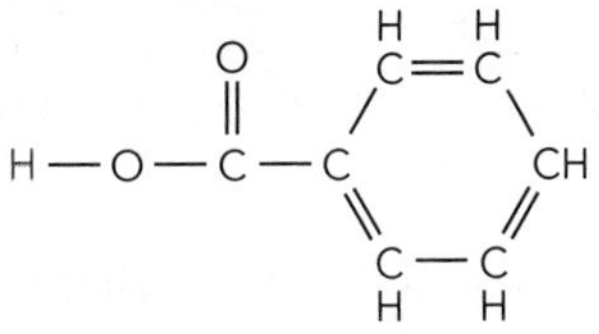	$HC_7H_5O_2(aq) + H_2O(l) \rightleftharpoons H_3O^+(aq) + C_7H_5O_2^-(aq)$	6.5×10^{-5}	4.19
Acetic acid	$HC_2H_3O_2$	H—O—C(=O)—CH_3	$HC_2H_3O_2(aq) + H_2O(l) \rightleftharpoons H_3O^+(aq) + C_2H_3O_2^-(aq)$	1.8×10^{-5}	4.74
Hypochlorous acid	HClO	H—O—Cl	$HClO(aq) + H_2O(l) \rightleftharpoons H_3O^+(aq) + ClO^-(aq)$	2.9×10^{-8}	7.54
Hydrocyanic acid	HCN	H—C≡N	$HCN(aq) + H_2O(l) \rightleftharpoons H_3O^+(aq) + CN^-(aq)$	4.9×10^{-10}	9.31
Phenol	HC_6H_5O	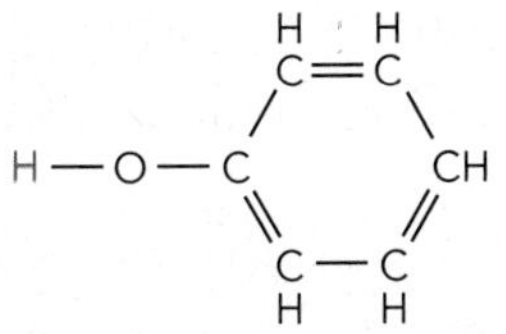	$HC_6H_5O(aq) + H_2O(l) \rightleftharpoons H_3O^+(aq) + C_6H_5O^-(aq)$	1.3×10^{-10}	9.89

ANSWER **NOW!**

17.3 Cc Conceptual Connection

THE MAGNITUDE OF THE ACID IONIZATION CONSTANT

Consider the three generic weak acids HA, HB, and HC. The images shown here represent the ionization of each acid at room temperature. Which acid has the largest K_a?

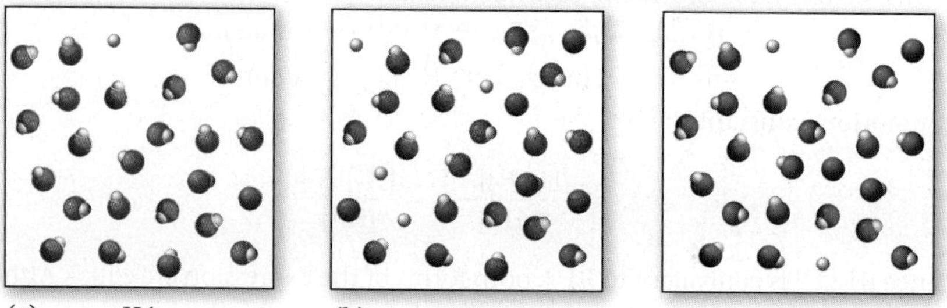

(a) HA (b) HB (c) HC

ANSWER **NOW!**

17.4 Cc Conceptual Connection

RELATIVE STRENGTHS OF WEAK ACIDS

Consider these two acids and their K_a values:

(a) HF $K_a = 6.8 \times 10^{-4}$

(b) HClO $K_a = 2.9 \times 10^{-8}$

Which acid is stronger?

17.5 Autoionization of Water and pH

We saw previously that water acts as a base when it reacts with HCl and as an acid when it reacts with NH_3:

Water acting as a base

$$HCl(aq) + H_2O(l) \longrightarrow H_3O^+(aq) + Cl^-(aq)$$

Acid (proton donor) — Base (proton acceptor)

Water acting as an acid

$$NH_3(aq) + H_2O(l) \rightleftharpoons NH_4^+(aq) + OH^-(aq)$$

Base (proton acceptor) — Acid (proton donor)

Water is *amphoteric*; it can act as either an acid or a base. Even when pure, water acts as an acid and a base with itself, a process called **autoionization:**

Water acting as both an acid and a base

$$H_2O(l) + H_2O(l) \rightleftharpoons H_3O^+(aq) + OH^-(aq)$$

Acid (proton donor) — Base (proton acceptor)

We can write the autoionization reaction as:

$$H_2O(l) \rightleftharpoons H^+(aq) + OH^-(aq)$$

The equilibrium constant expression for this reaction is the product of the concentration of the two ions:

$$K_w = [H_3O^+][OH^-] = [H^+][OH^-]$$

This equilibrium constant is called the **ion product constant for water (K_w)** (sometimes called the *dissociation constant for water*). At 25 °C, $K_w = 1.0 \times 10^{-14}$. In pure water, since H_2O is the only source of these ions, the concentrations of H_3O^+ and OH^- are equal, and the solution is **neutral**. Since the concentrations of the two ions are equal, we can easily calculate them from K_w.

$$[H_3O^+] = [OH^-] = \sqrt{K_w} = 1.0 \times 10^{-7} \qquad \text{(in pure water at 25 °C)}$$

As you can see, in pure water, the concentrations of H_3O^+ and OH^- are *very small* (1.0×10^{-7} M) at room temperature.

An **acidic solution** contains an acid that creates additional H_3O^+ ions, causing $[H_3O^+]$ to increase. However, the *ion product constant still applies*:

$$[H_3O^+][OH^-] = K_w = 1.0 \times 10^{-14}$$

The concentration of H_3O^+ times the concentration of OH^- is always 1.0×10^{-14} *at 25 °C.* If $[H_3O^+]$ increases, then $[OH^-]$ must decrease for the ion product constant to remain 1.0×10^{-14}. For example, if $[H_3O^+] = 1.0 \times 10^{-3}$, then we can find $[OH^-]$ by solving the ion product constant expression for $[OH^-]$:

$$(1.0 \times 10^{-3})\,[OH^-] = 1.0 \times 10^{-14}$$

$$[OH^-] = \frac{1.0 \times 10^{-14}}{1.0 \times 10^{-3}} = 1.0 \times 10^{-11}\,\text{M}$$

In an acidic solution $[H_3O^+] > [OH^-]$.

A **basic solution** contains a base that creates additional OH^- ions, causing $[OH^-]$ to increase and $[H_3O^+]$ to decrease, but again the *ion product constant still applies*. Suppose $[OH^-] = 1.0 \times 10^{-2}$; we can find $[H_3O^+]$ by solving the ion product constant expression for $[H_3O^+]$:

$$[H_3O^+](1.0 \times 10^{-2}) = 1.0 \times 10^{-14}$$

$$[H_3O^+] = \frac{1.0 \times 10^{-14}}{1.0 \times 10^{-2}} = 1.0 \times 10^{-12}\,\text{M}$$

In a basic solution $[OH^-] > [H_3O^+]$.

Notice that changing $[H_3O^+]$ in an aqueous solution produces an inverse change in $[OH^-]$ and vice versa.

Summarizing K_w:

- A *neutral solution* contains $[H_3O^+] = [OH^-] = 1.0 \times 10^{-7}$ M (at 25 °C).
- An *acidic solution* contains $[H_3O^+] > [OH^-]$.
- A *basic solution* contains $[OH^-] > [H_3O^+]$.
- In *all aqueous solutions* both H_3O^+ and OH^- are present, with $[H_3O^+][OH^-] = K_w = 1.0 \times 10^{-14}$ (at 25 °C).

The ion product constant K_w depends on temperature. For all calculations in this book, assume 25 °C unless otherwise noted.

ACIDITY OF SOLUTIONS The H_3O^+ concentrations of three solutions at room temperature are as follows. Which solution is acidic?

(a) $[H_3O^+] = 1 \times 10^{-3}$ M **(b)** $[H_3O^+] = 1 \times 10^{-7}$ M
(c) $[H_3O^+] = 1 \times 10^{-9}$ M

17.5 Cc Conceptual Connection

ANSWER **NOW!**

EXAMPLE 17.2 Using K_W in Calculations

Calculate $[OH^-]$ at 25 °C for each solution and determine if the solution is acidic, basic, or neutral.

(a) $[H_3O^+] = 7.5 \times 10^{-5}$ M **(b)** $[H_3O^+] = 1.5 \times 10^{-9}$ M **(c)** $[H_3O^+] = 1.0 \times 10^{-7}$ M

SOLUTION

(a) To find $[OH^-]$, use the ion product constant. Substitute the given value for $[H_3O^+]$ and solve the equation for $[OH^-]$.

$$[H_3O^+][OH^-] = K_w = 1.0 \times 10^{-14}$$

$$(7.5 \times 10^{-5})[OH^-] = 1.0 \times 10^{-14}$$

Since $[H_3O^+] > [OH^-]$, the solution is acidic.

$$[OH^-] = \frac{1.0 \times 10^{-14}}{7.5 \times 10^{-5}} = 1.3 \times 10^{-10}\,\text{M}$$

Acidic solution

—Continued on the next page

Continued—

(b) Substitute the given value for $[H_3O^+]$ and solve the acid ionization equation for $[OH^-]$. Since $[H_3O^+] < [OH^-]$, the solution is basic.	$(1.5 \times 10^{-9})[OH^-] = 1.0 \times 10^{-14}$ $[OH^-] = \frac{1.0 \times 10^{-14}}{1.5 \times 10^{-9}} = 6.7 \times 10^{-6}\,M$ Basic solution
(c) Substitute the given value for $[H_3O^+]$ and solve the acid ionization equation for $[OH^-]$. Since $[H_3O^+] = 1.0 \times 10^{-7}$ and $[OH^-] = 1.0 \times 10^{-7}$, the solution is neutral.	$(1.0 \times 10^{-7})[OH^-] = 1.0 \times 10^{-14}$ $[OH^-] = \frac{1.0 \times 10^{-14}}{1.0 \times 10^{-7}} = 1.0 \times 10^{-7}\,M$ Neutral solution

FOR PRACTICE 17.2 Calculate $[H_3O^+]$ at 25 °C for each solution and determine if the solution is acidic, basic, or neutral.
(a) $[OH^-] = 1.5 \times 10^{-2}\,M$ **(b)** $[OH^-] = 1.0 \times 10^{-7}\,M$ **(c)** $[OH^-] = 8.2 \times 10^{-10}\,M$

WATCH **NOW!**

KEY CONCEPT VIDEO 17.5
The pH Scale

The pH Scale: A Way to Quantify Acidity and Basicity

The pH scale is a compact way to specify the acidity of a solution. We define **pH** as the negative of the logarithm of the hydronium ion concentration:

$$pH = -\log[H_3O^+]$$

A solution with $[H_3O^+] = 1.0 \times 10^{-3}\,M$ (acidic) has a pH of:

$$\begin{aligned} pH &= -\log[H_3O^+] \\ &= -\log(1.0 \times 10^{-3}) \\ &= -(-3.00) \\ &= 3.00 \end{aligned}$$

Notice that we report the pH to two *decimal places* in this example. This is because only the numbers to the right of the decimal point are significant in a logarithm. Because our original value for the concentration had two significant figures, the log of that number has two decimal places:

2 significant digits → 2 decimal places

$$\log 1.0 \times 10^{-3} = 3.00$$

If the original number has three significant digits, we report the log to three decimal places:

3 significant digits → 3 decimal places

$$\log 1.00 \times 10^{-3} = 3.000$$

A solution with $[H_3O^+] = 1.0 \times 10^{-7}\,M$ (neutral at 25 °C) has a pH of:

$$\begin{aligned} pH &= -\log[H_3O^+] \\ &= -\log(1.0 \times 10^{-7}) \\ &= -(-7.00) \\ &= 7.00 \end{aligned}$$

In general, at 25 °C:

- $pH < 7$ The solution is *acidic.*
- $pH > 7$ The solution is *basic.*
- $pH = 7$ The solution is *neutral.*

Table 17.6 lists the pH of some common substances. As we discussed in Section 17.2, many foods, especially fruits, are acidic and have low pH values. Relatively few foods are basic. The foods with the lowest pH values are limes and lemons, and they are among the sourest. Because the pH scale is a *logarithmic scale,* a change of 1 pH unit corresponds to a 10-fold change in H_3O^+ concentration (Figure 17.7▶). For example, a lime with a pH of 2.0 is 10 times more acidic than a plum with a pH of 3.0 and 100 times more acidic than a cherry with a pH of 4.0.

The log of a number is the exponent to which 10 must be raised to obtain that number. Thus, $\log 10^1 = 1$; $\log 10^2 = 2$; $\log 10^{-1} = -1$; $\log 10^{-2} = -2$, and so (see Appendix I).

When we take the log of a quantity, the result has the same number of decimal places as the number of significant figures in the original quantity.

Concentrated acid solutions can have negative pH. For example, if $[H_3O^+] = 2.0\,M$, the pH is -0.30.

TABLE 17.6 ■ The pH of Some Common Substances

Substance	pH
Gastric juice (human stomach)	1.0–3.0
Limes	1.8–2.0
Lemons	2.2–2.4
Soft drinks	2.0–4.0
Plums	2.8–3.0
Wines	2.8–3.8
Apples	2.9–3.3
Peaches	3.4–3.6
Cherries	3.2–4.0
Beers	4.0–5.0
Rainwater (unpolluted)	5.6
Human blood	7.3–7.4
Egg whites	7.6–8.0
Milk of magnesia	10.5
Household ammonia	10.5–11.5
4% NaOH solution	14

The pH Scale

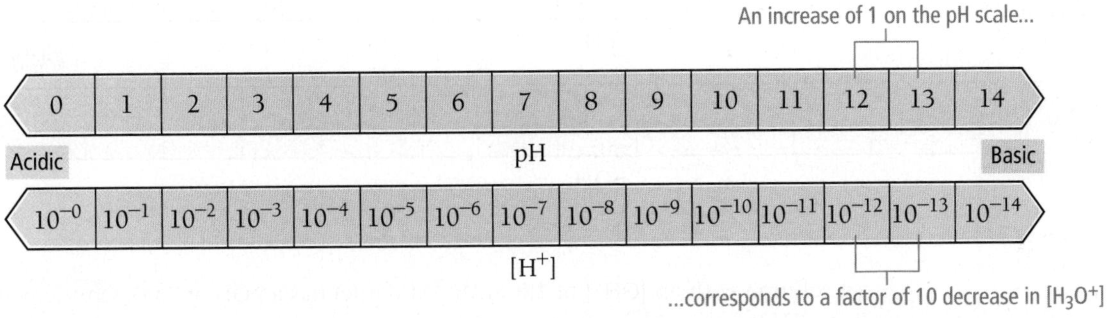

▲ **FIGURE 17.7 The pH Scale** An increase of 1 on the pH scale corresponds to a factor of 10 decrease in $[H_3O^+]$.

WATCH **NOW!**
INTERACTIVE WORKED EXAMPLE 17.3

EXAMPLE 17.3 Calculating pH from $[H_3O^+]$ or $[OH^-]$

Calculate the pH of each solution at 25 °C and indicate whether the solution is acidic or basic.

(a) $[H_3O^+] = 1.8 \times 10^{-4}$ M **(b)** $[OH^-] = 1.3 \times 10^{-2}$ M

SOLUTION

(a) To calculate pH, substitute the given $[H_3O^+]$ into the pH equation. Since pH < 7, this solution is acidic.	$\text{pH} = -\log[H_3O^+]$ $= -\log(1.8 \times 10^{-4})$ $= -(-3.74)$ $= 3.74$ (acidic)
(b) First use K_w to find $[H_3O^+]$ from $[OH^-]$.	$[H_3O^+][OH^-] = K_w = 1.0 \times 10^{-14}$ $[H_3O^+](1.3 \times 10^{-2}) = 1.0 \times 10^{-14}$ $[H_3O^+] = \dfrac{1.0 \times 10^{-14}}{1.3 \times 10^{-2}} = 7.7 \times 10^{-13}$ M
Then substitute $[H_3O^+]$ into the pH expression to find pH.	$\text{pH} = -\log[H_3O^+]$ $= -\log(7.7 \times 10^{-13})$ $= -(-12.11)$
Since pH > 7, this solution is basic.	$= 12.11$ (basic)

FOR PRACTICE 17.3 Calculate the pH of each solution and indicate whether the solution is acidic or basic.

(a) $[H_3O^+] = 9.5 \times 10^{-9}$ M **(b)** $[OH^-] = 7.1 \times 10^{-3}$ M

EXAMPLE 17.4 Calculating $[H_3O^+]$ from pH

Calculate $[H_3O^+]$ for a solution with a pH of 4.80.

SOLUTION

(a) To find $[H_3O^+]$ from pH, start with the equation that defines pH. Substitute the given value of pH and then solve for $[H_3O^+]$. Since the given pH value was reported to two decimal places, report the $[H_3O^+]$ to two significant figures. (Remember that $10^{\log x} = x$ (see Appendix I). Some calculators use an inv log key to represent this function.)	$\text{pH} = -\log[H_3O^+]$ $4.80 = -\log[H_3O^+]$ $-4.80 = \log[H_3O^+]$ $10^{-4.80} = 10^{\log[H_3O^+]}$ $10^{-4.80} = [H_3O^+]$ $[H_3O^+] = 1.6 \times 10^{-5}$ M

FOR PRACTICE 17.4 Calculate $[H_3O^+]$ for a solution with a pH of 8.37.

pOH and Other p Scales

The pOH scale is analogous to the pH scale but is defined with respect to $[OH^-]$ instead of $[H_3O^+]$:

$$\text{pOH} = -\log[OH^-]$$

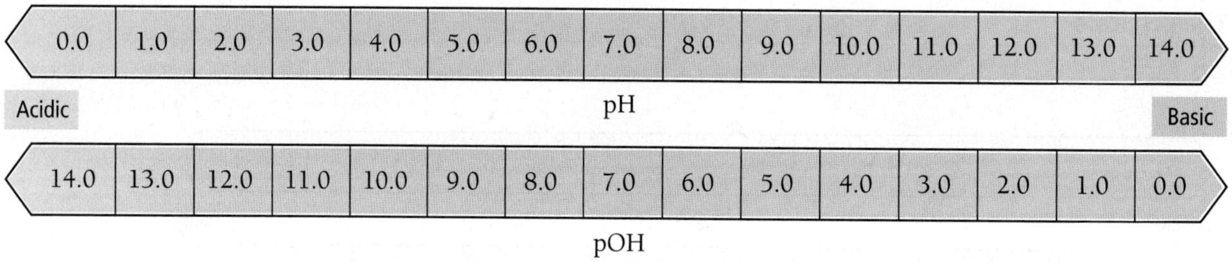

▲ **FIGURE 17.8 pH and pOH**

Notice that p is the mathematical operator $-\log$; thus, $pX = -\log X$.

A solution with an $[OH^-]$ of 1.0×10^{-3} M (basic) has a pOH of 3.00. On the pOH scale, a pOH less than 7 is basic and a pOH greater than 7 is acidic. A pOH of 7 is neutral (Figure 17.8▲). We can derive a relationship between pH and pOH at 25 °C from the expression for K_w:

$$[H_3O^+][OH^-] = 1.0 \times 10^{-14}$$

Taking the log of both sides, we get:

$$\log([H_3O^+][OH^-]) = \log(1.0 \times 10^{-14})$$
$$\log[H_3O^+] + \log[OH^-] = -14.00$$
$$-\log[H_3O^+] - \log[OH^-] = 14.00$$
$$\text{pH} + \text{pOH} = 14.00$$

The sum of pH and pOH is always equal to 14.00 at 25 °C. Therefore, a solution with a pH of 3 has a pOH of 11.

Another common p scale is the pK_a scale defined as:

$$pK_a = -\log K_a$$

The pK_a of a weak acid is another way to quantify its strength. The smaller the pK_a, the stronger the acid. For example, chlorous acid, with a K_a of 1.1×10^{-2}, has a pK_a of 1.96; and formic acid, with a K_a of 1.8×10^{-4}, has a pK_a of 3.74 (see Table 17.5).

ANSWER **NOW!**

17.6 Cc Conceptual Connection

pH AND ACIDITY As the pH of a solution increases (gets higher), what happens to the acidity of the solution?

(a) The acidity increases.
(b) The acidity decreases.
(c) The acidity remains constant.

CHEMISTRY AND MEDICINE | Ulcers

An ulcer is a lesion on the wall of the stomach or small intestine. Under normal circumstances, a thick layer of mucus lines the stomach wall and protects it from the hydrochloric acid and other gastric juices in the stomach. If that mucous layer is damaged, however, stomach juices come in direct contact with the stomach wall and begin to digest it, creating an ulcer. The main symptom of an ulcer is a burning or gnawing pain in the stomach.

Acidic drugs, such as aspirin, and acidic foods, such as citrus fruits and pickling fluids, irritate ulcers. When consumed, these substances increase the acidity of the stomach juices, exacerbating the irritation to the stomach wall. On the other hand, antacids—which contain bases—relieve ulcers. Common antacids include Tums and milk of magnesia.

The causes of ulcers are manifold. For many years, a stressful lifestyle and a rich diet were blamed. More recent research, however, has shown that a bacterial infection of the stomach lining is responsible for many ulcers. (The 2005 Nobel Prize in Physiology or Medicine was awarded to Australians Barry J. Marshall and J. Robin Warren, for their discovery of the bacterial cause of ulcers.) Long-term use of some over-the-counter pain relievers, such as aspirin, is also believed to produce ulcers.

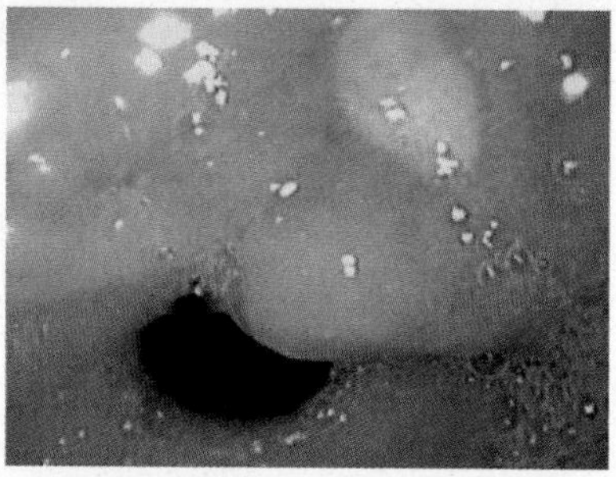

▲ An ulcer is a lesion in the stomach wall.

QUESTION *Which dessert is less likely to irritate an ulcer, key lime pie or meringue (made of egg whites)?*

17.6 Finding the [H_3O^+] and pH of Strong and Weak Acid Solutions

WATCH **NOW!**

KEY CONCEPT VIDEO 17.6
Finding the [H_3O^+] and pH of Strong and Weak Acid Solutions

A solution containing a strong or weak acid has two potential sources of H_3O^+: the ionization of the acid itself and the autoionization of water. If we let HA be a strong or weak acid, the ionization equations are:

$$HA(aq) + H_2O(l) \rightleftharpoons H_3O^+(aq) + A^-(aq) \quad \text{Strong or Weak Acid}$$

$$H_2O(l) + H_2O(l) \rightleftharpoons H_3O^+(aq) + OH^-(aq) \quad K_w = 1.0 \times 10^{-14}$$

Except in extremely dilute acid solutions, the autoionization of water contributes a negligibly small amount of H_3O^+ compared to the ionization of the strong or weak acid. Recall from Section 17.5 that autoionization in pure water at 25 °C produces an H_3O^+ concentration of 1.0×10^{-7} M. In a strong or weak acid solution, the additional H_3O^+ from the acid causes the autoionization of water equilibrium to shift left (as described by Le Châtelier's principle). Consequently, in most strong or weak acid solutions, the autoionization of water produces even less H_3O^+ than in pure water and can be ignored. Therefore we can focus exclusively on the amount of H_3O^+ produced by the acid.

The only exceptions would be extremely dilute ($< 10^{-5}$ M) strong acid solutions.

Strong Acids

Because strong acids, by definition, completely ionize in solution and because we can (in nearly all cases) ignore the contribution of the autoionization of water, *the concentration of H_3O^+ in a strong acid solution is equal to the concentration of the strong acid.* For example, a 0.10 M HCl solution has an H_3O^+ concentration of 0.10 M and a pH of 1.00:

$$0.10 \text{ M HCl} \Rightarrow [H_3O^+] = 0.10 \text{ M} \Rightarrow pH = -\log(0.10) = 1.00$$

Weak Acids

Finding the pH of a weak acid solution is more complicated because the concentration of H_3O^+ is *not equal* to the concentration of the weak acid. For example, if we make a solution of 0.10 M HCl (a strong acid) and a solution of 0.10 M acetic acid (a weak acid) in the laboratory and measure the pH of each, we get the following results:

$$0.10 \text{ M HCl} \qquad pH = 1.00$$

$$0.10 \text{ M } HC_2H_3O_2 \qquad pH = 2.87$$

The pH of the acetic acid solution is higher (it is less acidic) because acetic acid only partially ionizes. Calculating the [H_3O^+] formed by the ionization of a weak acid requires solving an equilibrium problem similar to those in Chapter 16. Consider, for example, a 0.10 M solution of the generic weak acid HA with an acid ionization constant K_a. Since we can ignore the contribution of the autoionization of water, we only have to determine the concentration of H_3O^+ formed by the following equilibrium:

$$HA(aq) + H_2O(l) \rightleftharpoons H_3O^+(aq) + A^-(aq) \qquad K_a$$

We can summarize the initial conditions, the changes, and the equilibrium conditions in the following ICE table:

ICE tables were first introduced in Section 16.6. The reactant $H_2O(l)$ is a pure liquid and is therefore not included either in the equilibrium constant or in the ICE table (see Section 16.5).

	[HA]	[H_3O^+]	[A^-]
Initial	0.10	≈0.00	0.00
Change	$-x$	$+x$	$+x$
Equilibrium	$0.10 - x$	x	x

The initial H_3O^+ concentration is listed as *approximately* zero because of the negligibly small contribution of H_3O^+ due to the autoionization of water (discussed previously). The variable x represents the amount of HA that ionizes. As discussed in Chapter 16, each *equilibrium* concentration is the sum of the two entries above it in the ICE table. In order to find the equilibrium concentration of H_3O^+, we must find the value of the variable x. We can use the equilibrium expression to set up an equation in which x is the only variable:

$$K_a = \frac{[H_3O^+][A^-]}{[HA]} = \frac{x^2}{0.10 - x}$$

As is often the case with equilibrium problems, we arrive at a quadratic equation in x, which we can solve using the quadratic formula (see Appendix IC). However, in many cases we can apply the *x is small* approximation (first discussed in Section 16.8). In Examples 17.5 and 17.6, we examine the general procedure for solving weak acid equilibrium problems. In both of these examples, the *x is small* approximation works well. In Example 17.7, we solve a problem in which the *x is small* approximation does not work. In such cases, we can solve the quadratic equation explicitly, or apply the method of successive approximations (also discussed in Section 16.8). Finally, in Example 17.8, we work a problem in which we find the equilibrium constant of a weak acid from its pH.

WATCH **NOW!**

INTERACTIVE WORKED EXAMPLE VIDEO 17.5

HOW TO: *Find the pH (or $[H_3O^+]$) of a Weak Acid Solution*

To solve these types of problems, follow the outlined procedure.

EXAMPLE 17.5

Finding the $[H_3O^+]$ of a Weak Acid Solution

Find the $[H_3O^+]$ of a 0.100 M HCN solution.

EXAMPLE 17.6

Finding the pH of a Weak Acid Solution

Find the pH of a 0.200 M HNO_2 solution.

1. Write the balanced equation for the ionization of the acid and use it as a guide to prepare an ICE table showing the given concentration of the weak acid as its initial concentration. Leave room in the table for the changes in concentrations and for the equilibrium concentrations. (Note that $[H_3O^+]$ is listed as approximately zero because the autoionization of water produces a negligibly small amount of H_3O^+.)

Example 17.5:

$$HCN(aq) + H_2O(l) \rightleftharpoons H_3O^+(aq) + CN^-(aq)$$

	[HCN]	$[H_3O^+]$	$[CN^-]$
Initial	0.100	≈0.00	0.00
Change			
Equil			

Example 17.6:

$$HNO_2(aq) + H_2O(l) \rightleftharpoons H_3O^+(aq) + NO_2^-(aq)$$

	$[HNO_2]$	$[H_3O^+]$	$[NO_2^-]$
Initial	0.200	≈0.00	0.00
Change			
Equil			

2. Represent the change in the concentration of H_3O^+ with the variable x. Define the changes in the concentrations of the other reactants and products in terms of x. Always keep in mind the stoichiometry of the reaction.

Example 17.5:

$$HCN(aq) + H_2O(l) \rightleftharpoons H_3O^+(aq) + CN^-(aq)$$

	[HCN]	$[H_3O^+]$	$[CN^-]$
Initial	0.100	≈0.00	0.00
Change	−x	+x	+x
Equil			

Example 17.6:

$$HNO_2(aq) + H_2O(l) \rightleftharpoons H_3O^+(aq) + NO_2^-(aq)$$

	$[HNO_2]$	$[H_3O^+]$	$[NO_2^-]$
Initial	0.200	≈0.00	00.00
Change	−x	+x	+x
Equil			

3. Sum each column to determine the equilibrium concentrations in terms of the initial concentrations and the variable x.

Example 17.5:

$$HCN(aq) + H_2O(l) \rightleftharpoons H_3O^+(aq) + CN^-(aq)$$

	[HCN]	$[H_3O^+]$	$[CN^-]$
Initial	0.100	≈0.00	0.00
Change	−x	+x	+x
Equil	0.100 − x	x	x

Example 17.6:

$$HNO_2(aq) + H_2O(l) \rightleftharpoons H_3O^+(aq) + NO_2^-(aq)$$

	$[HNO_2]$	$[H_3O^+]$	$[NO_2^-]$
Initial	0.200	≈0.00	0.00
Change	−x	+x	+x
Equil	0.200 − x	x	x

4. Substitute the expressions for the equilibrium concentrations (from step 3) into the expression for the acid ionization constant (K_a). In many cases, you can make the approximation that *x is small* (as discussed in Section 16.8). **Substitute the value of the acid ionization constant (from Table 17.5) into the K_a expression and solve for *x*.** Confirm that the *x is small* approximation is valid by calculating the ratio of *x* to the number it was subtracted from in the approximation. The ratio should be less than 0.05 (or 5%).	$K_a = \frac{[H_3O^+][CN^-]}{[HCN]}$ $= \frac{x^2}{0.100 - \cancel{x}}$ (*x is small*) $4.9 \times 10^{-10} = \frac{x^2}{0.100}$ $\sqrt{4.9 \times 10^{-10}} = \sqrt{\frac{x^2}{0.100}}$ $x = \sqrt{(0.100)(4.9 \times 10^{-10})}$ $= 7.0 \times 10^{-6}$ $\frac{7.0 \times 10^{-6}}{0.100} \times 100\% = 7.0 \times 10^{-3}\%$ Therefore, the approximation is valid.	$K_a = \frac{[H_3O^+][NO_2^-]}{[HNO_2]}$ $= \frac{x^2}{0.200 - \cancel{x}}$ (*x is small*) $4.6 \times 10^{-4} = \frac{x^2}{0.200}$ $\sqrt{4.6 \times 10^{-4}} = \sqrt{\frac{x^2}{0.200}}$ $x = \sqrt{(0.200)(4.6 \times 10^{-4})}$ $= 9.6 \times 10^{-3}$ $\frac{9.6 \times 10^{-3}}{0.200} \times 100\% = 4.8\%$ Therefore, the approximation is valid (but barely so).
5. Determine $[H_3O^+]$ from the calculated value of *x* and calculate the pH if necessary.	$[H_3O^+] = 7.0 \times 10^{-6}$ M (pH was not asked for in this problem.)	$[H_3O^+] = 9.6 \times 10^{-3}$ M $pH = -\log[H_3O^+]$ $= -\log(9.6 \times 10^{-3})$ $= 2.02$
6. Check your answer by substituting the calculated equilibrium values into the acid ionization expression. The calculated value of K_a should match the given value of K_a. Note that rounding errors and the *x is small* approximation may result in a difference in the least significant digit when comparing values of K_a.	$K_a = \frac{[H_3O^+][CN^-]}{[HCN]} = \frac{(7.0 \times 10^{-6})^2}{0.100}$ $= 4.9 \times 10^{-10}$ Since the calculated value of K_a matches the given value, the answer is valid. **FOR PRACTICE 17.5** Find the H_3O^+ concentration of a 0.250 M hydrofluoric acid solution.	$K_a = \frac{[H_3O^+][NO_2^-]}{[HNO_2]} = \frac{(9.6 \times 10^{-3})^2}{0.200}$ $= 4.6 \times 10^{-4}$ Since the calculated value of K_a matches the given value, the answer is valid. **FOR PRACTICE 17.6** Find the pH of a 0.0150 M acetic acid solution.

WATCH **NOW!**

INTERACTIVE WORKED EXAMPLE 17.7

EXAMPLE 17.7 Finding the pH of a Weak Acid Solution in Cases Where the *x is small* Approximation Does Not Work

Find the pH of a 0.100 M $HClO_2$ solution.

SOLUTION

1. Write the balanced equation for the ionization of the acid and use it as a guide to prepare an ICE table showing the given concentration of the weak acid as its initial concentration.
(Note that the H_3O^+ concentration is listed as approximately zero. Although a little H_3O^+ is present from the autoionization of water, this amount is negligibly small compared to the amount of $HClO_2$ or H_3O^+ formed by the acid.)

$$HClO_2(aq) + H_2O(l) \rightleftharpoons H_3O^+(aq) + ClO_2^-(aq)$$

	$[HClO_2]$	$[H_3O^+]$	$[ClO_2^-]$
Initial	0.100	≈0.00	0.00
Change			
Equil			

2. Represent the change in $[H_3O^+]$ with the variable *x*. Define the changes in the concentrations of the other reactants and products in terms of *x*.

$$HClO_2(aq) + H_2O(l) \rightleftharpoons H_3O^+(aq) + ClO_2^-(aq)$$

	$[HClO_2]$	$[H_3O^+]$	$[ClO_2^-]$
Initial	0.100	≈0.00	0.00
Change	−x	+x	+x
Equil			

—*Continued on the next page*

Continued—

Step	Solution
3. Sum each column to determine the equilibrium concentrations in terms of the initial concentrations and the variable *x*.	$HClO_2(aq) + H_2O(l) \rightleftharpoons H_3O^+(aq) + ClO_2^-(aq)$

	$[HClO_2]$	$[H_3O^+]$	$[ClO_2^-]$
Initial	0.100	≈0.00	0.00
Change	−x	+x	+x
Equil	0.100 − x	x	x

4. Substitute the expressions for the equilibrium concentrations (from step 3) into the expression for the acid ionization constant (K_a). Make the *x is small* approximation and substitute the value of the acid ionization constant (from Table 17.5) into the K_a expression. Solve for *x*.

$$K_a = \frac{[H_3O^+][ClO_2^-]}{[HClO_2]}$$

$$= \frac{x^2}{0.100 - \cancel{x}} \quad (x \text{ is small})$$

$$0.011 = \frac{x^2}{0.100}$$

$$\sqrt{0.011} = \sqrt{\frac{x^2}{0.100}}$$

$$x = \sqrt{(0.100)(0.011)}$$

$$= 0.033$$

Check to see if the *x is small* approximation is valid by calculating the ratio of *x* to the number it was subtracted from in the approximation. The ratio should be less than 0.05 (or 5%).

$$\frac{0.033}{0.100} \times 100\% = 33\%$$

Therefore, the *x is small* approximation is *not valid.*

4a. If the *x is small* approximation is not valid, solve the quadratic equation explicitly or use the method of successive approximations to find *x*. In this case, you solve the quadratic equation.

$$0.011 = \frac{x^2}{0.100 - x}$$

$$0.011(0.100 - x) = x^2$$

$$0.0011 - 0.011x = x^2$$

$$x^2 + 0.011x - 0.0011 = 0$$

$$x = \frac{-b \pm \sqrt{b^2 - 4ac}}{2a}$$

$$= \frac{-(0.011) \pm \sqrt{(0.011)^2 - 4(1)(-0.0011)}}{2(1)}$$

$$= \frac{-0.011 \pm 0.06\underline{7}2}{2}$$

$$x = -0.039 \quad or \quad x = 0.028$$

Since *x* represents the concentration of H_3O^+, and since concentrations cannot be negative, you reject the negative root.

$x = 0.028$

5. Determine the H_3O^+ concentration from the calculated value of *x* and calculate the pH (if necessary).

$$[H_3O^+] = 0.028\ M$$

$$pH = -\log[H_3O^+]$$

$$= -\log 0.028$$

$$= 1.55$$

6. Check your answer by substituting the calculated equilibrium values into the acid ionization expression. The calculated value of K_a should match the given value of K_a. Note that rounding errors could result in a difference in the least significant digit when comparing values of K_a.

$$K_a = \frac{[H_3O^+][ClO_2^-]}{[HClO_2]} = \frac{0.028^2}{0.100 - 0.028}$$

$$= 0.011$$

Since the calculated value of K_a matches the given value, the answer is valid.

FOR PRACTICE 17.7 Find the pH of a 0.010 M HNO_2 solution.

WATCH **NOW!**

INTERACTIVE WORKED EXAMPLE 17.8

EXAMPLE 17.8 Finding the Equilibrium Constant from pH

A 0.100 M weak acid (HA) solution has a pH of 4.25. Find K_a for the acid.

SOLUTION

Use the given pH to find the equilibrium concentration of H_3O^+. Then write the balanced equation for the ionization of the acid and use it as a guide to prepare an ICE table showing all known concentrations.

$$pH = -\log[H_3O^+]$$
$$4.25 = -\log[H_3O^+]$$
$$[H_3O^+] = 5.6 \times 10^{-5}\,M$$
$$HA(aq) + H_2O(l) \rightleftharpoons H_3O^+(aq) + A^-(aq)$$

	[HA]	$[H_3O^+]$	$[A^-]$
Initial	0.100	≈0.00	0.00
Change			
Equil		5.6×10^{-5}	

Use the equilibrium concentration of H_3O^+ and the stoichiometry of the reaction to predict the changes and equilibrium concentration for all species. For most weak acids, the initial and equilibrium concentrations of the weak acid (HA) are effectively equal because the amount that ionizes is usually very small compared to the initial concentration.

$$HA(aq) + H_2O(l) \rightleftharpoons H_3O^+(aq) + A^-(aq)$$

	[HA]	$[H_3O^+]$	$[A^-]$
Initial	0.100	≈0.00	0.00
Change	-5.6×10^{-5}	$+5.6 \times 10^{-5}$	$+5.6 \times 10^{-5}$
Equil	$(0.100 - 5.6 \times 10^{-5})$ ≈0.100	5.6×10^{-5}	5.6×10^{-5}

Substitute the equilibrium concentrations into the expression for K_a and calculate its value.

$$K_a = \frac{[H_3O^+][A^-]}{[HA]}$$
$$= \frac{(5.6 \times 10^{-5})(5.6 \times 10^{-5})}{0.100}$$
$$= 3.1 \times 10^{-8}$$

FOR PRACTICE 17.8 A 0.175 M weak acid solution has a pH of 3.25. Find K_a for the acid.

THE *X IS SMALL* APPROXIMATION The initial concentration and K_a of several weak acid (HA) solutions are listed. For which solution is the *x is small* approximation *least* likely to work in finding the pH?

(a) initial [HA] = 0.100 M; $K_a = 1.0 \times 10^{-5}$
(b) initial [HA] = 1.00 M; $K_a = 1.0 \times 10^{-6}$
(c) initial [HA] = 0.0100 M; $K_a = 1.0 \times 10^{-3}$
(d) initial [HA] = 1.0 M; $K_a = 1.5 \times 10^{-3}$

17.7 Cc Conceptual Connection — ANSWER **NOW!**

STRONG AND WEAK ACIDS Which solution is most acidic (that is, which one has the lowest pH)?

(a) 0.10 M HCl
(b) 0.10 M HF
(c) 0.20 M HF

17.8 Cc Conceptual Connection — ANSWER **NOW!**

Percent Ionization of a Weak Acid

We can quantify the ionization of a weak acid according to the percentage of acid molecules that actually ionizes. We define the **percent ionization** of a weak acid as the ratio of the ionized acid concentration to the initial acid concentration, multiplied by 100%:

$$\text{Percent ionization} = \frac{\text{concentration of ionized acid}}{\text{initial concentration of acid}} \times 100\% = \frac{[H_3O^+]_{equil}}{[HA]_{init}} \times 100\%$$

Since the concentration of ionized acid is equal to the H_3O^+ concentration at equilibrium (for a monoprotic acid), we can use $[H_3O^+]_{equil}$ and $[HA]_{init}$ in the formula to calculate the percent ionization. For example, in Example 17.6, we found that a 0.200 M HNO_2 solution contains 9.6×10^{-3} M H_3O^+. The 0.200 M HNO_2 solution therefore has the following percent ionization:

$$\begin{aligned}\%\ \text{ionization} &= \frac{[H_3O^+]_{equil}}{[HA]_{init}} \times 100\% \\ &= \frac{9.6 \times 10^{-3}\ \cancel{M}}{0.200\ \cancel{M}} \times 100\% \\ &= 4.8\%\end{aligned}$$

As you can see, the percent ionization is relatively small. In this case, even though HNO_2 has the second largest K_a in Table 17.5, fewer than 5 molecules out of 100 ionize. For most other weak acids (with smaller K_a values) the percent ionization is even less.

In Example 17.9, we calculate the percent ionization of a more concentrated HNO_2 solution. In the example, notice that the calculated H_3O^+ concentration is much greater (as we would expect for a more concentrated solution), but the *percent ionization* is actually smaller.

WATCH **NOW!**

INTERACTIVE WORKED EXAMPLE 17.9

EXAMPLE 17.9 Finding the Percent Ionization of a Weak Acid

Find the percent ionization of a 2.5 M HNO_2 solution.

SOLUTION

To find the percent ionization, you must find the equilibrium concentration of H_3O^+. Follow the procedure in Example 17.5, shown in condensed form here.

$$HNO_2(aq) + H_2O(l) \rightleftharpoons H_3O^+(aq) + NO_2^-(aq)$$

	$[HNO_2]$	$[H_3O^+]$	$[NO_2^-]$
Initial	2.5	≈0.00	0.00
Change	−x	+x	+x
Equil	2.5 − x	x	x

$$K_a = \frac{[H_3O^+][NO_2^-]}{[HNO_2]} = \frac{x^2}{2.5 - \cancel{x}} \quad (x \text{ is small})$$

$$4.6 \times 10^{-4} = \frac{x^2}{2.5}$$

$$x = 0.034$$

Therefore, $[H_3O^+] = 0.034$ M.

Use the definition of percent ionization to calculate it. (Since the percent ionization is less than 5%, the *x is small* approximation is valid.)

$$\begin{aligned}\%\ \text{ionization} &= \frac{[H_3O^+]_{equil}}{[HA]_{init}} \times 100\% \\ &= \frac{0.034\ \cancel{M}}{2.5\ \cancel{M}} \times 100\% \\ &= 1.4\%\end{aligned}$$

FOR PRACTICE 17.9 Find the percent ionization of a 0.250 M $HC_2H_3O_2$ solution at 25 °C.

We can now compare the results of Examples 17.6 and 17.9. From the table shown here, we can see that the more concentrated HNO_2 solution has a lower percent ionization. This trend applies to all weak acid solutions.

$[HNO_2]$	$[H_3O^+]$	Percent Ionization
0.200	0.0096	4.8%
2.5	0.034	1.4%

Summarizing $[H_3O^+]$ and Percent Ionization:

- The *equilibrium H_3O^+ concentration* of a weak acid *increases* with increasing initial concentration of the acid.
- The *percent ionization* of a weak acid *decreases* with increasing concentration of the acid.

In other words, as the concentration of a weak acid solution increases, the concentration of the hydronium ion also increases, but the increase is not linear. The H_3O^+ concentration increases less than the concentration of the acid because as the acid concentration increases, a smaller fraction of weak acid molecules ionize.

We can understand this behavior by analogy with Le Châtelier's principle. Consider the following weak acid ionization equilibrium:

$$\underset{\text{1 mol dissolved particles}}{HA(aq)} \rightleftharpoons \underset{\text{2 mol dissolved particles}}{H^+(aq) + A^-(aq)}$$

If we dilute a weak acid solution initially at equilibrium, the system (according to Le Châtelier's principle) responds to minimize the disturbance. The equilibrium shifts to the right because the right side of the equation contains more particles in solution (2 mol versus 1 mol) than the left side. If the system shifts to the right, the percent ionization is greater in the more dilute solution, which is what we observe.

PERCENT IONIZATION Which weak acid solution has the greatest percent ionization?

(a) 0.100 M $HC_2H_3O_2$
(b) 0.500 M $HC_2H_3O_2$
(c) 0.0100 M $HC_2H_3O_2$

17.9 Cc Conceptual Connection

ANSWER **NOW!**

Mixtures of Acids

Finding the pH of a mixture of acids may seem difficult at first. However, in many cases, the relative strengths of the acids in the mixture allow us to neglect the weaker acid and focus only on the stronger one. Here, we consider two possible acid mixtures: a strong acid with a weak acid and a weak acid with another weak acid.

A Strong Acid and a Weak Acid

Consider a mixture that is 0.10 M in HCl and 0.10 M in $HCHO_2$. There are three sources of H_3O^+ ions: the strong acid (HCl), the weak acid ($HCHO_2$), and the autoionization of water:

$$HCl(aq) + H_2O(l) \longrightarrow H_3O^+(aq) + Cl^-(aq) \qquad \text{Strong}$$
$$HCHO_2(aq) + H_2O(l) \rightleftharpoons H_3O^+(aq) + CHO_2^-(aq) \qquad K_a = 1.8 \times 10^{-4}$$
$$H_2O(l) + H_2O(l) \rightleftharpoons H_3O^+(aq) + OH^-(aq) \qquad K_w = 1.0 \times 10^{-14}$$

Since HCl is strong, we know that it completely ionizes to produce a significant concentration of H_3O^+(0.10 M). The H_3O^+ formed by HCl then *suppresses* the formation of additional H_3O^+ formed by the ionization of $HCHO_2$ or the autoionization of water. In other words, according to Le Châtelier's principle, the formation of H_3O^+ by the strong acid causes the weak acid to ionize even less than it would in the absence of the strong acid. To see this clearly, we calculate $[H_3O^+]$ and $[CHO_2^-]$ in this solution.

In an initial estimate of $[H_3O^+]$, we can neglect the contribution of $HCHO_2$ and H_2O. The concentration of H_3O^+ is then equal to the initial concentration of HCl:

$$[H_3O^+] = [HCl] = 0.10\ M$$

To find $[CHO_2^-]$ we must solve an equilibrium problem. However, the initial concentration of H_3O^+ in this case is not negligible (as it has been in all the other weak acid equilibrium problems that we have worked so far) because HCl has formed a significant amount of H_3O^+. The concentration of H_3O^+ formed by HCl becomes the *initial* concentration of H_3O^+ in the ICE table for $HCHO_2$ as shown here:

$$HCHO_2(aq) + H_2O(l) \rightleftharpoons H_3O^+(aq) + CHO_2^-(aq)$$

	$[HCHO_2]$	$[H_3O^+]$	$[CHO_2^-]$
Initial	0.10	0.10	0.00
Change	−x	+x	+x
Equil	0.10 − x	0.10 + x	x

We then use the equilibrium expression to set up an equation in which x is the only variable:

$$K_a = \frac{[H_3O^+][CHO_2^-]}{[HCHO_2]} = \frac{(0.10 + x)x}{0.10 - x}$$

Since the equilibrium constant is small relative to the initial concentration of the acid, we can make the *x is small* approximation:

$$K_a = \frac{(0.10 + \cancel{x})x}{0.10 - \cancel{x}}$$

$$1.8 \times 10^{-4} = \frac{(0.10)x}{0.10}$$

$$x = 1.8 \times 10^{-4}$$

Checking the *x is small* approximation:

$$\frac{1.8 \times 10^{-4}}{0.10} \times 100\% = 0.18\%$$

We find that the approximation is valid. Therefore, $[CHO_2^-] = 1.8 \times 10^{-4}$ M. We can now see that we can completely ignore the ionization of the weak acid ($HCHO_2$) in calculating $[H_3O^+]$ for the mixture. The contribution to the concentration of H_3O^+ by the weak acid must necessarily be equal to the concentration of CHO_2^- that we just calculated (because of the stoichiometry of the ionization reaction). Therefore, we have the following contributions to $[H_3O^+]$:

HCl contributes 0.10 M

$HCHO_2$ contributes 1.8×10^{-4} M or 0.00018 M

Total $[H_3O^+] = 0.10\ M + 0.00018\ M = 0.10\ M$

As we can see, since the significant figure rules for addition limit the answer to two decimal places, the amount of H_3O^+ contributed by $HCHO_2$ is completely negligible. The amount of H_3O^+ contributed by the autoionization of water is even smaller and therefore similarly negligible.

A Mixture of Two Weak Acids

When two weak acids are mixed, we again have three potential sources of H_3O^+ to consider: each of the two weak acids and the autoionization of water. However, if the values of K_a for the two weak acids are sufficiently different in magnitude (if they differ by more than a factor of several hundred), then as long as the concentrations of the two acids are similar in magnitude (or the concentration of the stronger one is greater than that of the weaker), we can assume that the weaker acid will not make a significant contribution to the concentration of H_3O^+. We make this assumption for the same reason that we made a similar assumption for a mixture of a strong acid and a weak one: the H_3O^+ formed by the stronger acid suppresses the ionization of the weaker one, in accordance with Le Châtelier's principle. Example 17.10 shows how to calculate the concentration of H_3O^+ in a mixture of two weak acids.

EXAMPLE 17.10 Mixtures of Weak Acids

Find the pH of a mixture that is 0.300 M in HF and 0.100 M in HClO.

SOLUTION

The three possible sources of H_3O^+ ions are HF, HClO, and H_2O. Write the ionization equations for the three sources and their corresponding equilibrium constants. Since the equilibrium constant for the ionization of HF is about 24,000 times larger than that for the ionization of HClO, the contribution of HF to $[H_3O^+]$ is by far the greatest. You can therefore just calculate the $[H_3O^+]$ formed by HF and neglect the other two potential sources of H_3O^+.

$$HF(aq) + H_2O(l) \rightleftharpoons H_3O^+(aq) + F^-(aq) \qquad K_a = 6.8 \times 10^{-4}$$

$$HClO(aq) + H_2O(l) \rightleftharpoons H_3O^+(aq) + ClO^-(aq) \qquad K_a = 2.9 \times 10^{-8}$$

$$H_2O(l) + H_2O(l) \rightleftharpoons H_3O^+(aq) + OH^-(aq) \qquad K_w = 1.0 \times 10^{-14}$$

Write the balanced equation for the ionization of HF and use it as a guide to prepare an ICE table.

$$HF(aq) + H_2O(l) \rightleftharpoons H_3O^+(aq) + F^-(aq)$$

	[HF]	$[H_3O^+]$	$[F^-]$
Initial	0.300	≈0.00	0.00
Change	−x	+x	+x
Equil	0.300 − x	x	x

Substitute the expressions for the equilibrium concentrations into the expression for the acid ionization constant (K_a). Since the equilibrium constant is small relative to the initial concentration of HF, you can make the *x is small* approximation. Substitute the value of the acid ionization constant (from Table 17.5) into the K_a expression and solve for x.

$$K_a = \frac{[H_3O^+][F^-]}{[HF]} = \frac{x^2}{0.300 - x} \quad (x \text{ is small})$$

$$6.8 \times 10^{-4} = \frac{x^2}{0.300}$$

$$\sqrt{(0.300)(6.8 \times 10^{-4})} = \sqrt{x^2}$$

$$x = 1.4\underline{2}8 \times 10^{-2}$$

Confirm that the *x is small* approximation is valid by calculating the ratio of x to the number it was subtracted from in the approximation. The ratio should be less than 0.05 (or 5%).

$$\frac{1.4\underline{2}8 \times 10^{-2}}{0.300} \times 100\% = 4.8\%$$

Therefore, the approximation is valid (though barely so).

Determine the H_3O^+ concentration from the calculated value of x and find the pH.

$$[H_3O^+] = 1.4 \times 10^{-2}\,M$$

$$pH = -\log(1.4 \times 10^{-2}) = 1.85$$

FOR PRACTICE 17.10 Find the ClO^- concentration of the mixture of HF and HClO discussed in Example 17.10.

JUDGING RELATIVE pH Which solution is most acidic (that is, has the lowest pH)?

(a) 1.0 M HCl
(b) 2.0 M HF
(c) A solution that is 1.0 M in HF and 1.0 M in HClO

17.10 Cc Conceptual Connection

ANSWER **NOW!**

17.7 Base Solutions

We have seen that bases are solutions that produce OH^- in solution (Arrhenius definition) or accept protons (Brønsted–Lowry definition). In analogy to acids, which can be strong or weak, bases can also be strong or weak.

Strong Bases

Just as we define a strong acid as one that completely ionizes in solution, analogously we define a **strong base** as a base that completely dissociates in solution. NaOH, for example, is a strong base:

$$NaOH(aq) \longrightarrow Na^+(aq) + OH^-(aq)$$

An NaOH solution contains no intact NaOH—it has all dissociated to form $Na^+(aq)$ and $OH^-(aq)$ (Figure 17.9▼). In other words, a 1.0 M NaOH solution has $[OH^-] = 1.0$ M and $[Na^+] = 1.0$ M. Table 17.7 lists the common strong bases.

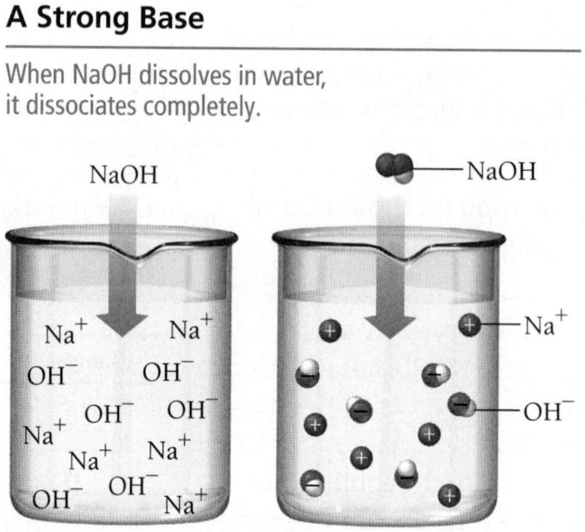

▶ **FIGURE 17.9 Ionization of a Strong Base** NaOH dissociates completely in water to form Na^+ and OH^-. The solution contains virtually no intact NaOH.

TABLE 17.7 ■ Strong Bases

Lithium hydroxide (LiOH)
Sodium hydroxide (NaOH)
Potassium hydroxide (KOH)
Strontium hydroxide [$Sr(OH)_2$]
Calcium hydroxide [$Ca(OH)_2$]
Barium hydroxide [$Ba(OH)_2$]

As we can see in the table, most strong bases are group 1A or group 2A metal hydroxides. The group 1A metal hydroxides are highly soluble in water and can form concentrated base solutions. The group 2A metal hydroxides, however, are only slightly soluble, a useful property for some applications (see *Chemistry and Medicine: What's in My Antacid?* in this section). Notice that the general formula for the group 2A metal hydroxides is $M(OH)_2$. When they dissolve in water, they produce 2 mol of OH^- per mole of the base. For example, $Sr(OH)_2$ dissociates as follows:

$$Sr(OH)_2(aq) \longrightarrow Sr^{2+}(aq) + 2\,OH^-(aq)$$

Unlike diprotic acids, which ionize in two steps, bases containing two OH^- ions dissociate in one step.

Weak Bases

The behavior of a **weak base** is analogous to that of a weak acid. Unlike strong bases that contain OH^- and *dissociate* in water, the most common weak bases produce OH^- by accepting a proton from water, ionizing water to form OH^- according to the general equation:

$$B(aq) + H_2O(l) \rightleftharpoons BH^+(aq) + OH^-(aq)$$

In this equation, B is a generic symbol for a weak base. Ammonia, for example, ionizes water as follows:

$$NH_3(aq) + H_2O(l) \rightleftharpoons NH_4^+(aq) + OH^-(aq)$$

The double arrow indicates that the ionization is not complete. An NH_3 solution contains mostly NH_3 with only some NH_4^+ and OH^- (Figure 17.10▶). A 1.0 M NH_3 solution will have $[OH^-] < 1.0$ M.

A Weak Base

When NH_3 dissolves in water, it partially ionizes.

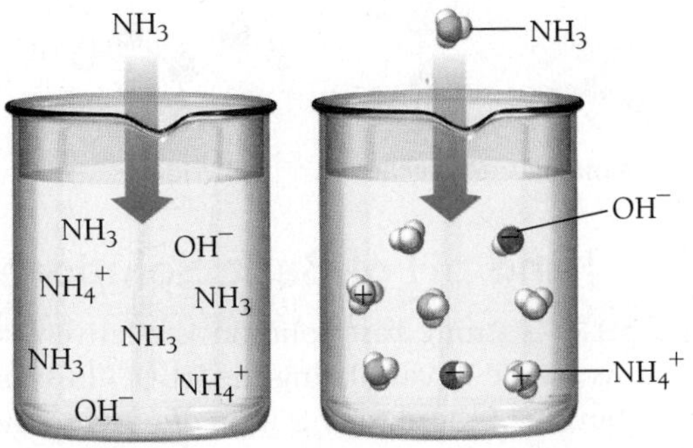

◀ **FIGURE 17.10 Ionization of a Weak Base** NH_3 partially ionizes in water to form NH_4^+ and OH^-. Most of the NH_3 molecules in solution remain as NH_3.

The extent of ionization of a weak base is quantified with the **base ionization constant (K_b)**. For the general reaction in which a weak base ionizes water, we define K_b as follows:

$$B(aq) + H_2O(l) \rightleftharpoons BH^+(aq) + OH^-(aq) \qquad K_b = \frac{[BH^+][OH^-]}{[B]}$$

By analogy with K_a, the smaller the value of K_b, the weaker the base. Table 17.8 lists some common weak bases, their ionization reactions, and values for K_b. Appendix IIC contains a more complete table. We can also apply the "p" scale to K_b, so that $pK_b = -\log K_b$.

All but two of the weak bases listed in Table 17.8 are either ammonia or an amine, which we can think of as ammonia with one or more hydrocarbon groups substituted for one or more hydrogen atoms. All of these bases have a nitrogen atom with a lone pair (Figure 17.11▶). This lone pair acts as the proton acceptor that makes the substance a base, as shown in the reactions for ammonia and methylamine:

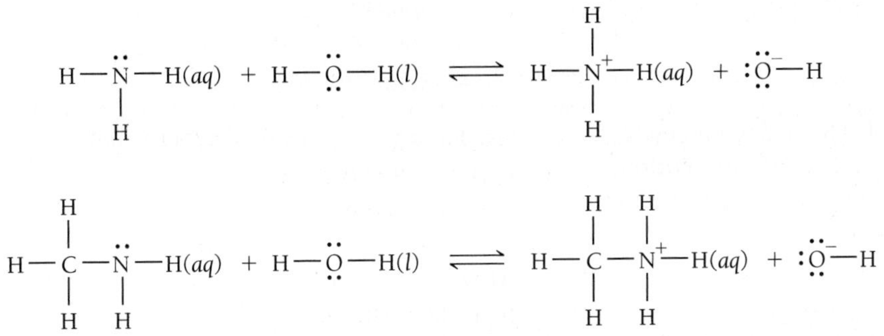

TABLE 17.8 ■ Some Common Weak Bases

Weak Base	Ionization Reaction	K_b (at 25 °C)
Carbonate ion (CO_3^{2-})*	$CO_3^{2-}(aq) + H_2O(l) \rightleftharpoons HCO_3^-(aq) + OH^-(aq)$	1.8×10^{-4}
Methylamine (CH_3NH_2)	$CH_3NH_2(aq) + H_2O(l) \rightleftharpoons CH_3NH_3^+(aq) + OH^-(aq)$	4.4×10^{-4}
Ethylamine ($C_2H_5NH_2$)	$C_2H_5NH_2(aq) + H_2O(l) \rightleftharpoons C_2H_5NH_3^+(aq) + OH^-(aq)$	5.6×10^{-4}
Ammonia (NH_3)	$NH_3(aq) + H_2O(l) \rightleftharpoons NH_4^+(aq) + OH^-(aq)$	1.76×10^{-5}
Bicarbonate ion (HCO_3^-)* (or hydrogen carbonate)	$HCO_3^-(aq) + H_2O(l) \rightleftharpoons H_2CO_3(aq) + OH^-(aq)$	2.3×10^{-8}
Pyridine (C_5H_5N)	$C_5H_5N(aq) + H_2O(l) \rightleftharpoons C_5H_5NH^+(aq) + OH^-(aq)$	1.7×10^{-9}
Aniline ($C_6H_5NH_2$)	$C_6H_5NH_2(aq) + H_2O(l) \rightleftharpoons C_6H_5NH_3^+(aq) + OH^-(aq)$	3.9×10^{-10}

*The carbonate and bicarbonate ions must occur with a positively charged ion such as Na^+ that serves to balance the charge but does not have any part in the ionization reaction. For example, it is the bicarbonate ion that makes sodium bicarbonate ($NaHCO_3$) basic. We look more closely at ionic bases in Section 17.8.

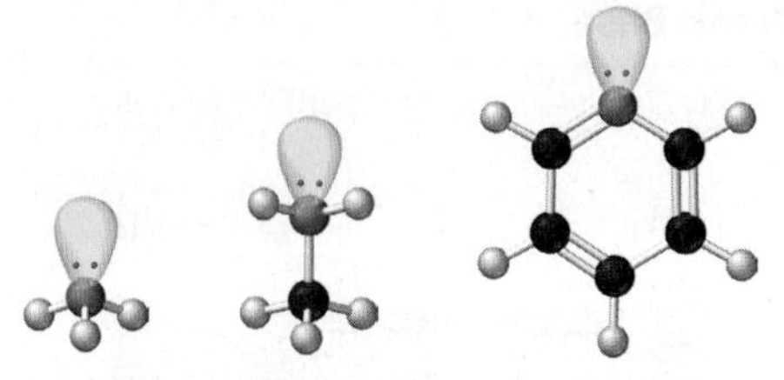

▶ **FIGURE 17.11 Lone Pairs in Weak Bases** Many weak bases have a nitrogen atom with a lone pair that acts as the proton acceptor.

Finding the $[OH^-]$ and pH of Basic Solutions

Finding the $[OH^-]$ and pH of a strong base solution is relatively straightforward, as shown in Example 17.11. As we did in calculating the $[H_3O^+]$ in strong acid solutions, we can neglect the contribution of the autoionization of water to the $[OH^-]$ and focus solely on the strong base itself.

EXAMPLE 17.11 Finding the $[OH^-]$ and pH of a Strong Base Solution

Determine the OH^- concentration and pH in each solution.

(a) 0.225 M KOH

(b) 0.0015 M $Sr(OH)_2$

SOLUTION

(a) Since KOH is a strong base, it completely dissociates into K^+ and OH^- in solution. The concentration of OH^- is therefore the same as the given concentration of KOH. Use this concentration and K_w to find $[H_3O^+]$.	$KOH(aq) \longrightarrow K^+(aq) + OH^-(aq)$ $[OH^-] = 0.225\ M$ $[H_3O^+][OH^-] = K_w = 1.0 \times 10^{-14}$ $[H_3O^+](0.225) = 1.0 \times 10^{-14}$ $[H_3O^+] = 4.\underline{4}4 \times 10^{-14}\ M$
Then substitute $[H_3O^+]$ into the pH expression to find the pH.	$pH = -\log[H_3O^+]$ $= -\log(4.44 \times 10^{-14})$ $= 13.35$
(b) Since $Sr(OH)_2$ is a strong base, 1 mol of $Sr(OH)_2$ completely dissociates into 1 mol of Sr^{2+} and 2 mol of OH^- in solution. The concentration of OH^- is therefore twice the given concentration of $Sr(OH)_2$.	$Sr(OH)_2(aq) \longrightarrow Sr^{2+}(aq) + 2\ OH^-(aq)$ $[OH^-] = 2(0.0015)\ M$ $= 0.0030\ M$
Use this concentration and K_w to find $[H_3O^+]$.	$[H_3O^+][OH^-] = K_w = 1.0 \times 10^{-14}$ $[H_3O^+](0.0030) = 1.0 \times 10^{-14}$ $[H_3O^+] = 3.3 \times 10^{-12}\ M$
Substitute $[H_3O^+]$ into the pH expression to find the pH.	$pH = -\log[H_3O^+]$ $= -\log(3.3 \times 10^{-12})$ $= 11.48$

FOR PRACTICE 17.11 Find the $[OH^-]$ and pH of a 0.010 M $Ba(OH)_2$ solution.

Finding the $[OH^-]$ and pH of a *weak base* solution is analogous to finding the $[H_3O^+]$ and pH of a weak acid. Similarly, we neglect the contribution of the autoionization of water to the $[OH^-]$ and focus solely on the weak base itself. We find the contribution of the weak base by preparing an ICE table showing the relevant concentrations of all species and then use the base ionization constant expression to find the $[OH^-]$. Example 17.12 demonstrates how to find the $[OH^-]$ and pH of a weak base solution.

WATCH **NOW!**

INTERACTIVE WORKED EXAMPLE 17.12

EXAMPLE 17.12 Finding the $[OH^-]$ and pH of a Weak Base Solution

Find the $[OH^-]$ and pH of a 0.100 M NH_3 solution.

SOLUTION

1. Write the balanced equation for the ionization of water by the base and use it as a guide to prepare an ICE table showing the given concentration of the weak base as its initial concentration. Leave room in the table for the changes in concentrations and for the equilibrium concentrations. (Note that you should list the OH^- concentration as approximately zero. Although a little OH^- is present from the autoionization of water, this amount is negligibly small compared to the amount of OH^- formed by the base.)

$$NH_3(aq) + H_2O(l) \rightleftharpoons NH_4^+(aq) + OH^-(aq)$$

	$[NH_3]$	$[NH_4^+]$	$[OH^-]$
Initial	0.100	0.00	≈0.00
Change			
Equil			

2. Represent the change in the concentration of OH^- with the variable x. Define the changes in the concentrations of the other reactants and products in terms of x.

$$NH_3(aq) + H_2O(l) \rightleftharpoons NH_4^+(aq) + OH^-(aq)$$

	$[NH_3]$	$[NH_4^+]$	$[OH^-]$
Initial	0.100	0.00	≈0.00
Change	$-x$	$+x$	$+x$
Equil			

3. Sum each column to determine the equilibrium concentrations in terms of the initial concentrations and the variable x.

$$NH_3(aq) + H_2O(l) \rightleftharpoons NH_4^+(aq) + OH^-(aq)$$

	$[NH_3]$	$[NH_4^+]$	$[OH^-]$
Initial	0.100	0.00	≈0.00
Change	$-x$	$+x$	$+x$
Equil	$0.100 - x$	x	x

4. Substitute the expressions for the equilibrium concentrations (from step 3) into the expression for the base ionization constant. In many cases, you can make the approximation that *x is small* (as discussed in Chapter 16).

$$K_b = \frac{[NH_4^+][OH^-]}{[NH_3]}$$

$$= \frac{x^2}{0.100 - \cancel{x}} \quad (x \text{ is small})$$

Substitute the value of the base ionization constant (from Table 17.8) into the K_b expression and solve for x.

$$1.76 \times 10^{-5} = \frac{x^2}{0.100}$$

$$\sqrt{1.76 \times 10^{-5}} = \sqrt{\frac{x^2}{0.100}}$$

$$x = \sqrt{(0.100)(1.76 \times 10^{-5})}$$

$$= 1.33 \times 10^{-3}$$

Confirm that the *x is small* approximation is valid by calculating the ratio of x to the number it was subtracted from in the approximation. The ratio should be less than 0.05 (or 5%).

$$\frac{1.33 \times 10^{-3}}{0.100} \times 100\% = 1.33\%$$

Therefore, the approximation is valid.

5. Determine the OH^- concentration from the calculated value of x. Use the expression for K_w to find $[H_3O^+]$.

$$[OH^-] = 1.33 \times 10^{-3}\ M$$

$$[H_3O^+][OH^-] = K_w = 1.00 \times 10^{-14}$$

$$[H_3O^+](1.33 \times 10^{-3}) = 1.00 \times 10^{-14}$$

$$[H_3O^+] = 7.52 \times 10^{-12}\ M$$

Substitute $[H_3O^+]$ into the pH equation to find pH.

$$pH = -\log[H_3O^+]$$

$$= -\log(7.52 \times 10^{-12})$$

$$= 11.124$$

FOR PRACTICE 17.12 Find the $[OH^-]$ and pH of a 0.33 M methylamine solution.

CHEMISTRY AND MEDICINE | What's in My Antacid?

In the opening section of this chapter, we discussed heartburn and its treatment with antacids. Some common antacids and their active ingredients include the following:

Amphogel	$Al(OH)_3$
Milk of magnesia	$Mg(OH)_2$
Maalox	$Mg(OH)_2$ and $Al(OH)_3$
Mylanta	$Mg(OH)_2$ and $Al(OH)_3$
Tums	$CaCO_3$

We categorize antacids into three main groups: calcium-based, magnesium-based, and aluminum-based. Calcium-based antacids may cause acid rebound—which means that, although they initially relieve heartburn, they can also cause the stomach to produce more acid, resulting in a quick return of the symptoms. Aluminum- and magnesium-based antacids do not cause acid rebound but have downsides of their own. Aluminum-based antacids tend to cause constipation, and magnesium-based ones tend to cause diarrhea. (In fact, milk of magnesia is sometimes used as a laxative.) A person who takes repeated doses of these antacids should alternate between the two or choose a product that contains both.

Notice the absence of group 1A metal hydroxides, such as KOH or NaOH, in the list of antacids. Why are those substances—which are completely soluble and act as strong bases—not used in antacids? Because a solution that contains sufficient KOH or NaOH to neutralize stomach acid would also burn the mouth and throat. In contrast, $Mg(OH)_2$ and $Al(OH)_3$ are only slightly soluble. Therefore liquid antacids containing these are actually *suspensions* of $Mg(OH)_2$ and $Al(OH)_3$—they are heterogeneous mixtures in which the solid is finely divided into the liquid. As a result, the concentration of OH^- in these suspensions is relatively small compared to what it would be with a group 1A metal hydroxide.

▶ Antacids contain a variety of bases that effectively neutralize excess stomach acid.

Initially, it might seem as though the relatively lower OH^- concentration would make the antacid much less effective. However, the solid $Mg(OH)_2$ or $Al(OH)_3$ continues to dissolve as the OH^- neutralizes stomach acid. For example, a suspension of magnesium hydroxide contains solid $Mg(OH)_2$ in equilibrium with dissolved Mg^{2+} and OH^- ions:

$$Mg(OH)_2(s) \rightleftharpoons Mg^{2+}(aq) + 2\ OH^-(aq)$$

As stomach acid is neutralized, OH^- is used up, and the equilibrium shifts to the right providing additional OH^- ions. In this way, a suspension of $Mg(OH)_2$ provides a steady concentration of dissolved OH^- ions to neutralize stomach acid.

QUESTION *Write chemical equations showing the reactions of each of the bases in the antacids discussed here with stomach acid (HCl).*

WATCH **NOW!**

KEY CONCEPT VIDEO 17.8
The Acid–Base Properties of Ions and Salts

17.8 The Acid–Base Properties of Ions and Salts

We have already seen that some ions act as bases. For example, the bicarbonate ion acts as a base according to the following equation:

$$HCO_3^-(aq) + H_2O(l) \rightleftharpoons H_2CO_3(aq) + OH^-(aq)$$

The bicarbonate ion, like any ion, does not exist by itself—in order to be charge-neutral, it must pair with a counterion (in this case a cation) to form an ionic compound, called a *salt.* For example, the sodium salt of bicarbonate is sodium bicarbonate. Like all soluble salts, sodium bicarbonate dissociates in solution to form a sodium cation and bicarbonate anion:

$$NaHCO_3(s) \rightleftharpoons Na^+(aq) + HCO_3^-(aq)$$

The sodium ion has neither acidic nor basic properties (it does not ionize water), as we will see shortly. The bicarbonate ion, by contrast, acts as a weak base, ionizing water as just shown to form a basic solution. Consequently, the pH of a sodium bicarbonate solution is above 7 (the solution is basic). In this section, we consider some of the acid–base properties of salts and the ions they contain. Some salts are pH-neutral when put into water, others are acidic, and still others are basic, depending on their constituent anions and cations. In general, anions tend to form either *basic* or neutral solutions, while cations tend to form either *acidic* or neutral solutions.

Anions as Weak Bases

We can think of any anion as the conjugate base of an acid. Consider the following anions and their corresponding acids:

This anion	is the conjugate base of	this acid
Cl^-		HCl
F^-		HF
NO_3^-		HNO_3
$C_2H_3O_2^-$		$HC_2H_3O_2$

In general, the anion A^- is the conjugate base of the acid HA. Since every anion can be regarded as the conjugate base of an acid, every anion itself can potentially act as a base. However, *not every anion does act as a base*—it depends on the strength of the corresponding acid. In general:

- An anion that is the conjugate base of a *weak acid* is itself a *weak base.*
- An anion that is the conjugate base of a *strong acid* is pH-*neutral* (forms solutions that are neither acidic nor basic).

For example, the Cl^- anion is the conjugate base of HCl, a strong acid. Therefore, the Cl^- anion is pH-neutral (neither acidic nor basic). The F^- anion, however, is the conjugate base of HF, a weak acid. Therefore, the F^- ion is itself a weak base and ionizes water according to the reaction:

$$F^-(aq) + H_2O(l) \rightleftharpoons OH^-(aq) + HF(aq)$$

We can understand why the conjugate base of a weak acid is basic by asking ourselves why an acid is weak to begin with. Hydrofluoric acid is a weak acid because the following reaction lies to the left:

$$HF(aq) + H_2O(l) \rightleftharpoons H_3O^+(aq) + F^-(aq)$$

The equilibrium lies to the left because the F^- ion has a significant affinity for H^+ ions. Consequently, when F^- is put into water, its affinity for H^+ ions allows it to remove H^+ ions from water molecules, thus acting as a weak base. In general, as shown in Figure 17.12▼,

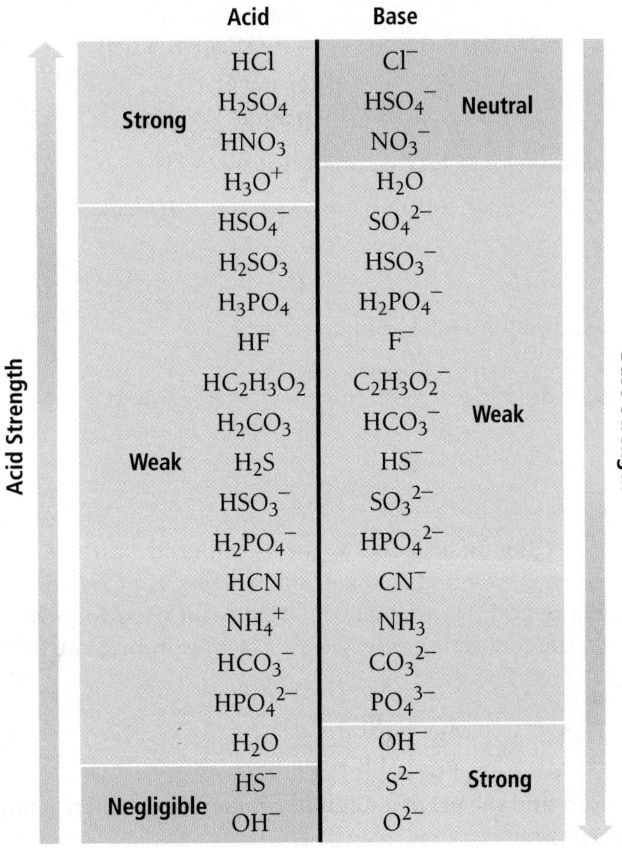

◀ **FIGURE 17.12 Strength of Conjugate Acid–Base Pairs** The stronger an acid, the weaker its conjugate base.

the weaker the acid, the stronger the conjugate base (as we saw in Section 17.4). In contrast, the conjugate base of a strong acid, such as Cl^-, does not act as a base because this reaction lies far to the right:

$$HCl(aq) + H_2O(l) \longrightarrow H_3O^+(aq) + Cl^-(aq)$$

The reaction lies far to the right because the Cl^- ion has a low affinity for H^+ ions. Consequently, when Cl^- is put into water, it does not remove H^+ ions from water molecules.

EXAMPLE 17.13 Determining Whether an Anion Is Basic or pH-Neutral

Classify each anion as a weak base or pH-neutral.

(a) NO_3^- **(b)** NO_2^- **(c)** $C_2H_3O_2^-$

SOLUTION

(a) From Table 17.3, you can see that NO_3^- is the conjugate base of a *strong* acid (HNO_3) and is therefore pH-neutral.

(b) From Table 17.5 (or from its absence in Table 17.3), you know that NO_2^- is the conjugate base of a weak acid (HNO_2) and is therefore a weak base.

(c) From Table 17.5 (or from its absence in Table 17.3), you know that $C_2H_3O_2^-$ is the conjugate base of a weak acid ($HC_2H_3O_2$) and is therefore a weak base.

FOR PRACTICE 17.13 Classify each anion as a weak base or pH-neutral.
(a) CHO_2^- **(b)** ClO_4^-

We can determine the pH of a solution containing an anion that acts as a weak base in a manner similar to how we determine the pH of any weak base solution. However, we need to know K_b for the anion acting as a base, which we can readily determine from K_a of the corresponding acid. Recall from Section 17.4 the expression for K_a for a generic acid HA:

$$HA(aq) + H_2O(l) \rightleftharpoons H_3O^+(aq) + A^-(aq)$$

$$K_a = \frac{[H_3O^+][A^-]}{[HA]}$$

Similarly, the expression for K_b for the conjugate base (A^-) is:

$$A^-(aq) + H_2O(l) \rightleftharpoons OH^-(aq) + HA(aq)$$

$$K_b = \frac{[OH^-][HA]}{[A^-]}$$

If we multiply the expressions for K_a and K_b, we get K_w:

$$K_a \times K_b = \frac{[H_3O^+]\cancel{[A^-]}[OH^-]\cancel{[HA]}}{\cancel{[HA]} \quad \cancel{[A^-]}} = [H_3O^+][OH^-] = K_w$$

Or simply,

$$K_a \times K_b = K_w$$

The product of K_a for an acid and K_b for its conjugate base is K_w (1.0×10^{-14} at 25 °C). Consequently, we can find K_b for an anion acting as a base from the value of K_a for the corresponding acid. For example, for acetic acid ($HC_2H_3O_2$), $K_a = 1.8 \times 10^{-5}$. We calculate K_b for the conjugate base ($C_2H_3O_2^-$) by substituting into the equation:

$$K_a \times K_b = K_w$$

$$K_b = \frac{K_w}{K_a} = \frac{1.0 \times 10^{-14}}{1.8 \times 10^{-5}} = 5.6 \times 10^{-10}$$

Knowing K_b, we can find the pH of a solution containing an anion acting as a base, as Example 17.14 demonstrates.

WATCH **NOW!**

INTERACTIVE WORKED EXAMPLE 17.14

EXAMPLE 17.14 Determining the pH of a Solution Containing an Anion Acting as a Base

Find the pH of a 0.100 M $NaCHO_2$ solution. The salt completely dissociates into $Na^+(aq)$ and $CHO_2^-(aq)$, and the Na^+ ion has no acid or base properties.

SOLUTION

1. Since the Na^+ ion does not have any acidic or basic properties, you can ignore it. Write the balanced equation for the ionization of water by the basic anion and use it as a guide to prepare an ICE table showing the given concentration of the weak base as its initial concentration.

$$CHO_2^-(aq) + H_2O(l) \rightleftharpoons HCHO_2(aq) + OH^-(aq)$$

	$[CHO_2^-]$	$[HCHO_2]$	$[OH^-]$
Initial	0.100	0.00	≈0.00
Change			
Equil			

2. Represent the change in the concentration of OH^- with the variable x. Define the changes in the concentrations of the other reactants and products in terms of x.

$$CHO_2^-(aq) + H_2O(l) \rightleftharpoons HCHO_2(aq) + OH^-(aq)$$

	$[CHO_2^-]$	$[HCHO_2]$	$[OH^-]$
Initial	0.100	0.00	≈0.00
Change	$-x$	$+x$	$+x$
Equil			

3. Sum each column to determine the equilibrium concentrations in terms of the initial concentrations and the variable x.

$$CHO_2^-(aq) + H_2O(l) \rightleftharpoons HCHO_2(aq) + OH^-(aq)$$

	$[CHO_2^-]$	$[HCHO_2]$	$[OH^-]$
Initial	0.100	0.00	≈0.00
Change	$-x$	$+x$	$+x$
Equil	$0.100 - x$	x	x

4. Find K_b from K_a (for the conjugate acid).

$$K_a \times K_b = K_w$$

$$K_b = \frac{K_w}{K_a} = \frac{1.0 \times 10^{-14}}{1.8 \times 10^{-4}} = 5.6 \times 10^{-11}$$

Substitute the expressions for the equilibrium concentrations (from step 3) into the expression for K_b. In many cases, you can make the approximation that *x is small*.

$$K_b = \frac{[HCHO_2][OH^-]}{[CHO_2^-]} = \frac{x^2}{0.100 - \cancel{x}}$$

Substitute the value of K_b into the K_b expression and solve for x.

$$5.6 \times 10^{-11} = \frac{x^2}{0.100}$$

$$x = 2.4 \times 10^{-6}$$

Confirm that the *x is small* approximation is valid by calculating the ratio of x to the number it was subtracted from in the approximation. The ratio should be less than 0.05 (or 5%).

$$\frac{2.4 \times 10^{-6}}{0.100} \times 100\% = 0.0024\%$$

Therefore, the approximation is valid.

5. Determine the OH^- concentration from the calculated value of x.

$$[OH^-] = 2.4 \times 10^{-6}\,M$$

Use the expression for K_w to find $[H_3O^+]$.

$$[H_3O^+][OH^-] = K_w = 1.0 \times 10^{-14}$$
$$[H_3O^+](2.4 \times 10^{-6}) = 1.0 \times 10^{-14}$$
$$[H_3O^+] = 4.2 \times 10^{-9}\,M$$

Substitute $[H_3O^+]$ into the pH equation to find pH.

$$pH = -\log[H_3O^+] = -\log(4.2 \times 10^{-9}) = 8.38$$

FOR PRACTICE 17.14 Find the pH of a 0.250 M $NaC_2H_3O_2$ solution.

We can also express the relationship between K_a and K_b in terms of pK_a and pK_b. By taking the log of both sides of $K_a \times K_b = K_w$, we get:

$$\log(K_a \times K_b) = \log K_w$$
$$\log K_a + \log K_b = \log K_w$$

Since $K_w = 10^{-14}$, we can rearrange the equation to get:

$$\log K_a + \log K_b = \log 10^{-14} = -14$$

Rearranging further:

$$-\log K_a - \log K_b = 14$$

Since $-\log K = pK$, we get:

$$pK_a + pK_b = 14$$

ANSWER **NOW!**

17.11 Cc Conceptual Connection

ANIONS AS WEAK BASES Which anion acts as a weak base?

(a) Cl^-
(b) Br^-
(c) F^-

Cations as Weak Acids

In contrast to anions, which in some cases act as weak bases, cations can in some cases act as *weak acids*. Although some exceptions exist, we can generally divide cations into three categories: cations that are the counterions of strong bases; cations that are the conjugate acids of *weak* bases; and cations that are small, highly charged metals. We examine each individually.

Cations That Are the Counterions of Strong Bases

Strong bases such as NaOH or $Ca(OH)_2$ generally contain hydroxide ions and a counterion. In solution, a strong base completely dissociates to form $OH^-(aq)$ and the solvated (in solution) counterion. Although these counterions interact with water molecules via ion–dipole forces, they do not ionize water and they do not contribute to the acidity or basicity of the solution. In general, *cations that are the counterions of strong bases are themselves pH-neutral* (they form solutions that are neither acidic nor basic). For example, Na^+, K^+, and Ca^{2+} are the counterions of the strong bases NaOH, KOH, and $Ca(OH)_2$ and are therefore themselves pH-neutral.

Cations That Are the Conjugate Acids of Weak Bases

A cation can be formed from any nonionic weak base by adding a proton (H^+) to its formula. The cation is the conjugate acid of the base. Consider the following cations and their corresponding weak bases:

This cation	**is the conjugate acid of**	**this weak base**
NH_4^+		NH_3
$C_2H_5NH_3^+$		$C_2H_5NH_2$
$CH_3NH_3^+$		CH_3NH_2

Any of these cations, with the general formula BH^+, will act as a weak acid according to the equation:

$$BH^+(aq) + H_2O(aq) \rightleftharpoons H_3O^+(aq) + B(aq)$$

In general, *a cation that is the conjugate acid of a weak base is a weak acid.*

We can calculate the pH of a solution containing the conjugate acid of a weak base just like that of any other weak acidic solution. However, we must derive the value of K_a for the acid from K_b using the previously derived relationship: $K_a \times K_b = K_w$.

Cations That Are Small, Highly Charged Metals

Small, highly charged metal cations such as Al^{3+} and Fe^{3+} form weakly acidic solutions. For example, when Al^{3+} is dissolved in water, it becomes hydrated according to the equation:

$$Al^{3+}(aq) + 6\,H_2O(l) \longrightarrow Al(H_2O)_6^{3+}(aq)$$

The hydrated form of the ion then acts as a Brønsted–Lowry acid:

$$Al(H_2O)_6^{3+}(aq) + H_2O(aq) \rightleftharpoons Al(H_2O)_5(OH)^{2+}(aq) + H_3O^+(aq)$$

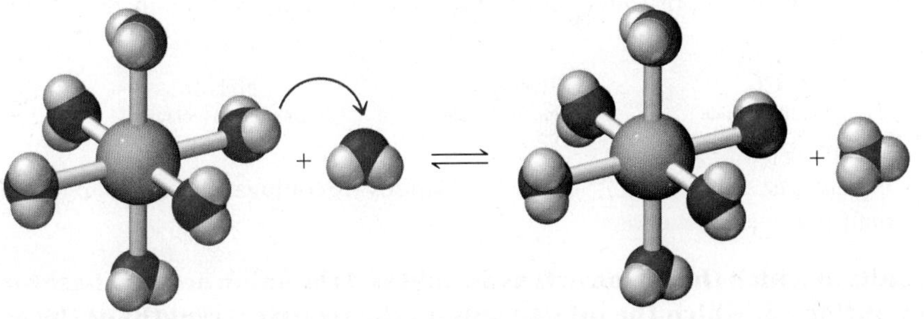

In effect, the binding of a water molecule to the cation makes the water more acidic. See Section 17.10.

Neither the alkali metal cations nor the alkaline earth metal cations ionize water in this way, but the cations of many other metals do. The smaller and more highly charged the cation, the more acidic its behavior.

EXAMPLE 17.15 Determining Whether a Cation Is Acidic or pH-Neutral

Classify each cation as a weak acid or pH-neutral.

(a) $C_5H_5NH^+$ **(b)** Ca^{2+} **(c)** Cr^{3+}

SOLUTION

(a) The $C_5H_5NH^+$ cation is the conjugate acid of a weak base and is therefore a weak acid.

(b) The Ca^{2+} cation is the counterion of a strong base and is therefore pH-neutral (neither acidic nor basic).

(c) The Cr^{3+} cation is a small, highly charged metal cation and is therefore a weak acid.

FOR PRACTICE 17.15 Classify each cation as a weak acid or pH-neutral.

(a) Li^+ **(b)** $CH_3NH_3^+$ **(c)** Fe^{3+}

Classifying Salt Solutions as Acidic, Basic, or Neutral

Since salts contain both a cation and an anion, they can form acidic, basic, or neutral solutions when dissolved in water. The pH of the solution depends on the specific cation and anion involved. We examine the four possibilities individually.

1. **Salts in which neither the cation nor the anion acts as an acid or a base form pH-neutral solutions.** A salt in which the cation is the counterion of a strong base and in which the anion is the conjugate base of strong acid forms a *neutral* solution. Some salts in this category include:

$NaCl$	$Ca(NO_3)_2$	KBr
sodium chloride	calcium nitrate	potassium bromide

Cations are pH–neutral. Anions are conjugate bases of strong acids.

2. **Salts in which the cation does not act as an acid and the anion acts as a base form basic solutions.** A salt in which the cation is the counterion of a strong base and in which the anion is the conjugate base of *weak* acid forms a *basic* solution. Salts in this category include:

NaF	$Ca(C_2H_3O_2)_2$	KNO_2
sodium fluoride	calcium acetate	potassium nitrite

Cations are pH–neutral. Anions are conjugate bases of weak acids.

3. **Salts in which the cation acts as an acid and the anion does not act as a base form acidic solutions.** A salt in which the cation is either the conjugate acid of a weak base or a small, highly charged metal ion and in which the anion is the conjugate base of *strong* acid forms an *acidic* solution. Salts in this category include:

$FeCl_3$	$Al(NO_3)_3$	NH_4Br
iron(III) chloride	aluminum nitrate	ammonium bromide

Cations are conjugate acids of *weak* bases or small, highly charged metal ions.

Anions are conjugate bases of *strong* acids.

4. **Salts in which the cation acts as an acid and the anion acts as a base form solutions in which the pH depends on the relative strengths of the acid and the base.** A salt in which the cation is either the conjugate acid of a weak base or a small, highly charged metal ion and in which the anion is the conjugate base of a *weak* acid forms a solution in which the pH depends on the relative strengths of the acid and base. Salts in this category include:

FeF_3	$Al(C_2H_3O_2)_3$	NH_4NO_2
iron(III) fluoride	aluminum acetate	ammonium nitrite

Cations are conjugate acids of *weak* bases or small, highly charged metal ions.

Anions are conjugate bases of *weak* acids.

We can determine the overall acidity or basicity of a solution containing one of these salts by comparing the K_a of the acid to the K_b of the base—the ion with the higher value of K dominates and determines whether the solution will be acidic or basic, as shown in part (e) of Example 17.16. Table 17.9 summarizes all of these possibilities.

TABLE 17.9 ■ pH of Salt Solutions

		ANION	
		Conjugate base of strong acid	Conjugate base of weak acid
CATION	Conjugate acid of weak base	*Acidic*	*Depends on relative strengths*
	Small, highly charged metal ion	*Acidic*	*Depends on relative strengths*
	Counterion of strong base	*Neutral*	*Basic*

WATCH **NOW!**
INTERACTIVE WORKED EXAMPLE 17.16

EXAMPLE 17.16 Determining the Overall Acidity or Basicity of Salt Solutions

Determine if the solution formed by each salt is acidic, basic, or neutral.

(a) $SrCl_2$ **(b)** $AlBr_3$ **(c)** $CH_3NH_3NO_3$
(d) $NaCHO_2$ **(e)** NH_4F

SOLUTION

(a) The Sr^{2+} cation is the counterion of a strong base ($Sr(OH)_2$) and is pH-neutral. The Cl^- anion is the conjugate base of a strong acid (HCl) and is pH-neutral as well. The $SrCl_2$ solution is therefore pH-neutral (neither acidic nor basic).

$SrCl_2$
pH-neutral cation | pH-neutral anion
Neutral solution

(b) The Al^{3+} cation is a small, highly charged metal ion (that is not an alkali metal or an alkaline earth metal) and is a weak acid. The Br^- anion is the conjugate base of a strong acid (HBr) and is pH-neutral. The $AlBr_3$ solution is therefore acidic.

$AlBr_3$
acidic cation | pH-neutral anion
Acidic solution

(c) The $CH_3NH_3^+$ ion is the conjugate acid of a weak base (CH_3NH_2) and is acidic. The NO_3^- anion is the conjugate base of a strong acid (HNO_3) and is pH-neutral. The $CH_3NH_3NO_3$ solution is therefore acidic.	$CH_3NH_3NO_3$ acidic cation — pH-neutral anion **Acidic solution**
(d) The Na^+ cation is the counterion of a strong base and is pH-neutral. The CHO_2^- anion is the conjugate base of a weak acid and is basic. The $NaCHO_2$ solution is therefore basic.	$NaCHO_2$ pH-neutral cation — basic anion **Basic solution**
(e) The NH_4^+ ion is the conjugate acid of a weak base (NH_3) and is acidic. The F^- ion is the conjugate base of a weak acid and is basic. To determine the overall acidity or basicity of the solution, compare the values of K_a for the acidic cation and K_b for the basic anion. Obtain each value of K from the conjugate by using $K_a \times K_b = K_w$.	NH_4F acidic cation — basic anion $K_a(NH_4^+) = \dfrac{K_w}{K_b(NH_3)} = \dfrac{1.0 \times 10^{-14}}{1.76 \times 10^{-5}} = 5.68 \times 10^{-10}$ $K_b(F^-) = \dfrac{K_w}{K_a(HF)} = \dfrac{1.0 \times 10^{-14}}{6.8 \times 10^{-4}} = 1.5 \times 10^{-11}$
Since K_a is greater than K_b, the solution is acidic.	$K_a > K_b$ **Acidic solution**

FOR PRACTICE 17.16 Determine if the solution formed by each salt is acidic, basic, or neutral.

(a) $NaHCO_3$ **(b)** $CH_3CH_2NH_3Cl$ **(c)** KNO_3 **(d)** $Fe(NO_3)_3$

ACIDITY OR BASICITY OF IONIC COMPOUNDS Which ionic compound forms an acidic solution when dissolved in water?

(a) NH_4Br **(b)** KCl **(c)** $NaHCO_3$

17.12 Cc Conceptual Connection

ANSWER **NOW!**

17.9 Polyprotic Acids

In Section 17.4, we discussed that some acids, called polyprotic acids, contain two or more ionizable protons. Recall that sulfurous acid (H_2SO_3) is a diprotic acid containing two ionizable protons and that phosphoric acid (H_3PO_4) is a triprotic acid containing three ionizable protons.

Typically, a **polyprotic acid** ionizes in successive steps, each with its own K_a. For example, sulfurous acid ionizes in two steps:

$$H_2SO_3(aq) \rightleftharpoons H^+(aq) + HSO_3^-(aq) \qquad K_{a_1} = 1.6 \times 10^{-2}$$
$$HSO_3^-(aq) \rightleftharpoons H^+(aq) + SO_3^{2-}(aq) \qquad K_{a_2} = 6.4 \times 10^{-8}$$

K_{a_1} is the acid ionization constant for the first step, and K_{a_2} is the acid ionization constant for the second step. Notice that K_{a_2} is much smaller than K_{a_1}. This is true for all polyprotic acids and makes sense because the first proton separates from a neutral molecule, while the second must separate from an anion. The negatively charged anion holds the positively charged proton more tightly, making the proton more difficult to remove and resulting in a smaller value of K_a.

Table 17.10 lists some common polyprotic acids and their acid ionization constants. Notice that in all cases, the value of K_a for each step becomes successively smaller. The value of K_{a_1} for sulfuric acid is identified as strong because sulfuric acid is strong in the first step and weak in the second.

TABLE 17.10 ■ Common Polyprotic Acids and Ionization Constants at 25 °C

Name (Formula)	Structure	Space-Filling Model	K_{a_1}	K_{a_2}	K_{a_3}
Sulfuric Acid (H_2SO_4)	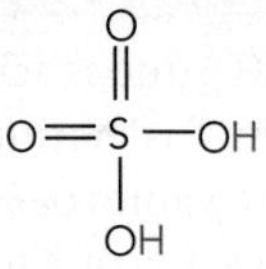		Strong	1.2×10^{-2}	
Oxalic Acid ($H_2C_2O_4$)	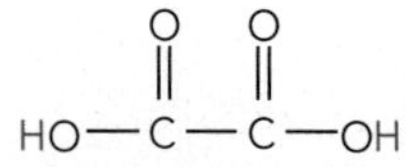		6.0×10^{-2}	6.1×10^{-5}	
Sulfurous Acid (H_2SO_3)	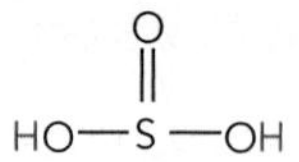		1.6×10^{-2}	6.4×10^{-8}	
Phosphoric Acid (H_3PO_4)	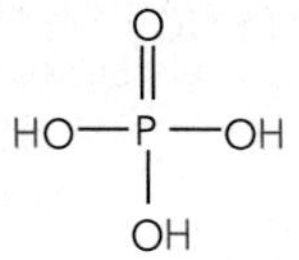		7.5×10^{-3}	6.2×10^{-8}	4.2×10^{-13}
Citric Acid ($H_3C_6H_5O_7$)	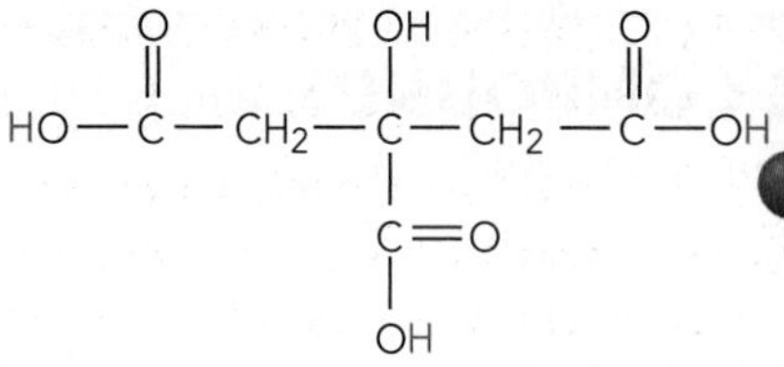		7.4×10^{-4}	1.7×10^{-5}	4.0×10^{-7}
Ascorbic Acid ($H_2C_6H_6O_6$)	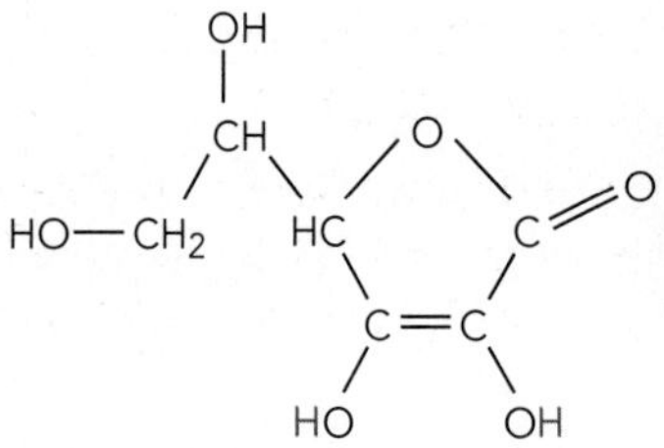	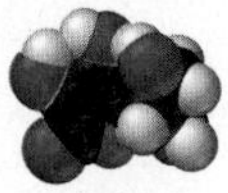	8.0×10^{-5}	1.6×10^{-12}	
Carbonic Acid (H_2CO_3)	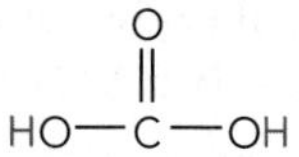	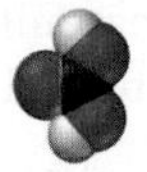	4.3×10^{-7}	5.6×10^{-11}	

Finding the pH of Polyprotic Acid Solutions

Finding the pH of a polyprotic acid solution is less difficult than we might first imagine because, for most polyprotic acids, K_{a_1} is much larger than K_{a_2} (or K_{a_3} for triprotic acids). Therefore, the amount of H_3O^+ formed by the first ionization step is much larger than that formed by the second or third ionization step. In addition, the formation of H_3O^+ in the first step inhibits the formation of additional H_3O^+ in the second step (because of Le Châtelier's principle). Consequently, we treat most polyprotic acid solutions as if the first step were the only one that contributes to the H_3O^+ concentration, as illustrated in Example 17.17. A major exception is a dilute solution of sulfuric acid, which we examine in Example 17.18.

EXAMPLE 17.17 Finding the pH of a Polyprotic Acid Solution

Find the pH of a 0.100 M ascorbic acid ($H_2C_6H_6O_6$) solution.

SOLUTION

To find the pH, you must find the equilibrium concentration of H_3O^+. Treat the problem as a weak acid pH problem with a single ionizable proton. The second proton contributes a negligible amount to the concentration of H_3O^+ and can be ignored. Follow the procedure from Example 17.6, shown in condensed form here. Use K_{a_1} for ascorbic acid from Table 17.10.

$$H_2C_6H_6O_6(aq) + H_2O(l) \rightleftharpoons H_3O^+(aq) + HC_6H_6O_6^-(aq)$$

	$[H_2C_6H_6O_6]$	$[H_3O^+]$	$[HC_6H_6O_6^-]$
Initial	0.100	≈ 0.00	0.00
Change	−x	+x	+x
Equil	0.100 − x	x	x

$$K_{a_1} = \frac{[H_3O^+][HC_6H_6O_6^-]}{[H_2C_6H_6O_6]}$$

$$= \frac{x^2}{0.100 - \cancel{x}} \qquad (x \text{ is small})$$

$$8.0 \times 10^{-5} = \frac{x^2}{0.100}$$

$$x = 2.8 \times 10^{-3}$$

Confirm that the *x is small* approximation is valid by calculating the ratio of *x* to the number it was subtracted from in the approximation. The ratio should be less than 0.05 (or 5%).

$$\frac{2.8 \times 10^{-3}}{0.100} \times 100\% = 2.8\%$$

The approximation is valid. Therefore,

Calculate the pH from H_3O^+ concentration.

$$[H_3O^+] = 2.8 \times 10^{-3}\text{ M}$$

$$\text{pH} = -\log(2.8 \times 10^{-3}) = 2.55$$

FOR PRACTICE 17.17 Find the pH of a 0.050 M H_2CO_3 solution.

EXAMPLE 17.18 Dilute H_2SO_4 Solutions

Find the pH of a 0.0100 M sulfuric acid (H_2SO_4) solution.

SOLUTION

Sulfuric acid is strong in its first ionization step and weak in its second. Begin by writing the equations for the two steps. As the concentration of an H_2SO_4 solution becomes smaller, the second ionization step becomes more significant because the percent ionization increases (as discussed in Section 17.6). Therefore, for a concentration of 0.0100 M, you can't neglect the H_3O^+ contribution from the second step, as you can for other polyprotic acids. You must calculate the H_3O^+ contributions from both steps.

$$H_2SO_4(aq) + H_2O(l) \longrightarrow H_3O^+(aq) + HSO_4^-(aq) \quad \text{Strong}$$

$$HSO_4^-(aq) + H_2O(l) \rightleftharpoons H_3O^+(aq) + SO_4^{2-}(aq) \quad K_{a_2} = 0.012$$

—*Continued on the next page*

Continued—

The $[H_3O^+]$ that results from the first ionization step is 0.0100 M (because the first step is strong). To determine the $[H_3O^+]$ formed by the second step, prepare an ICE table for the second step in which the initial concentration of H_3O^+ is 0.0100 M. The initial concentration of HSO_4^- must also be 0.0100 M (due to the stoichiometry of the ionization reaction).	(ICE table below)
Substitute the expressions for the equilibrium concentrations (from the table just shown) into the expression for K_{a_2}. In this case, you cannot make the *x is small* approximation because the equilibrium constant (0.012) *is not small* relative to the initial concentration (0.0100).	$K_{a_2} = \frac{[H_3O^+][SO_4^{2-}]}{[HSO_4^-]}$ $= \frac{(0.0100 + x)x}{0.0100 - x}$
Substitute the value of K_{a_2} and multiply out the expression to arrive at the standard quadratic form.	$0.012 = \frac{0.0100x + x^2}{0.0100 - x}$ $0.012(0.0100 - x) = 0.0100x + x^2$ $0.00012 - 0.012x = 0.0100x + x^2$ $x^2 + 0.022x - 0.00012 = 0$
Solve the quadratic equation using the quadratic formula.	$x = \frac{-b \pm \sqrt{b^2 - 4ac}}{2a}$ $= \frac{-(0.022) \pm \sqrt{(0.022)^2 - 4(1)(-0.00012)}}{2(1)}$ $= \frac{-0.022 \pm 0.031}{2}$ $x = -0.027$ or $x = 0.0045$ Since x represents a concentration and since concentrations cannot be negative, we reject the negative root. $x = 0.0045$
Determine the H_3O^+ concentration from the calculated value of x and calculate the pH. Notice that the second step produces almost half as much H_3O^+ as the first step—an amount that must not be ignored. This is always the case with dilute H_2SO_4 solutions.	$[H_3O^+] = 0.0100 + x$ $= 0.0100 + 0.0045$ $= 0.0145$ M $pH = -\log[H_3O^+]$ $= -\log(0.0145)$ $= 1.84$

	$[HSO_4^-]$	$[H_3O^+]$	$[SO_4^{2-}]$
Initial	0.0100	≈ 0.0100	0.000
Change	−x	+x	+x
Equil	0.0100 − x	0.0100 + x	x

FOR PRACTICE 17.18 Find the pH and $[SO_4^{2-}]$ of a 0.0075 M sulfuric acid solution.

Finding the Concentration of the Anions for a Weak Diprotic Acid Solution

In some cases, we may want to know the concentrations of the anions formed by a polyprotic acid. Consider the following generic polyprotic acid H_2X and its ionization steps:

$$H_2X(aq) + H_2O(l) \rightleftharpoons H_3O^+(aq) + HX^-(aq) \qquad K_{a_1}$$

$$HX^-(aq) + H_2O(l) \rightleftharpoons H_3O^+(aq) + X^{2-}(aq) \qquad K_{a_2}$$

In Examples 17.17 and 17.18, we illustrated how to find the concentration of H_3O^+ for such a solution, which is equal to the concentration of HX^-. What if instead we needed to find the concentration of X^{2-}? To find the concentration of X^{2-}, we use the concentration of HX^- and H_3O^+ (from the first ionization step) as the initial concentrations for the second ionization step. We then solve a second equilibrium problem using the second ionization equation and K_{a_2}, as demonstrated in Example 17.19.

EXAMPLE 17.19 Finding the Concentration of the Anions for a Weak Diprotic Acid Solution

Find the $[C_6H_6O_6^{2-}]$ of the 0.100 M ascorbic acid ($H_2C_6H_6O_6$) solution in Example 17.17.

SOLUTION

To find the $[C_6H_6O_6^{2-}]$, use the concentrations of $[HC_6H_6O_6^-]$ and H_3O^+ produced by the first ionization step (as calculated in Example 17.17) as the initial concentrations for the second step. Because of the 1:1 stoichiometry, $[HC_6H_6O_6^-] = [H_3O^+]$. Then solve an equilibrium problem for the second step similar to that of Example 17.5, shown in condensed form here. You can find the value of K_{a_2} for ascorbic acid in Table 17.10.

$$HC_6H_6O_6^-(aq) + H_2O(l) \rightleftharpoons H_3O^+(aq) + C_6H_6O_6^{2-}(aq)$$

	$[HC_6H_6O_6^-]$	$[H_3O^+]$	$[C_6H_6O_6^{2-}]$
Initial	2.8×10^{-3}	2.8×10^{-3}	0.000
Change	$-x$	$+x$	$+x$
Equil	$2.8 \times 10^{-3} - x$	$2.8 \times 10^{-3} + x$	x

$$K_{a_2} = \frac{[H_3O^+][C_6H_6O_6^{2-}]}{[HC_6H_6O_6^-]}$$

$$= \frac{(2.8 \times 10^{-3} + \cancel{x})x}{2.8 \times 10^{-3} - \cancel{x}} \quad (x \text{ is small})$$

$$= \frac{\cancel{(2.8 \times 10^{-3})}x}{\cancel{2.8 \times 10^{-3}}}$$

$$x = K_{a_2} = 1.6 \times 10^{-12}\ \text{M}$$

Since x is much smaller than 2.8×10^{-3}, the *x is small* approximation is valid. Therefore,

$[C_6H_6O_6^{2-}] = 1.6 \times 10^{-12}$ M

FOR PRACTICE 17.19 Find the $[CO_3^{2-}]$ of the 0.050 M carbonic acid (H_2CO_3) solution in For Practice 17.17.

Notice from the results of Example 17.19 that the concentration of X^{2-} for a weak diprotic acid H_2X is equal to K_{a_2}. This general result applies to all diprotic acids in which the *x is small* approximation is valid. Notice also that the concentration of H_3O^+ produced by the second ionization step of a diprotic acid is very small compared to the concentration produced by the first step, as shown in Figure 17.13▼.

Dissociation of a Polyprotic Acid

$$H_2C_6H_6O_6(aq) + H_2O(l) \rightleftharpoons H_3O^+(aq) + HC_6H_6O_6^-(aq)$$

$$[H_3O^+] = 2.8 \times 10^{-3}\ \text{M}$$

$$HC_6H_6O_6^-(aq) + H_2O(l) \rightleftharpoons H_3O^+(aq) + C_6H_6O_6^{2-}(aq)$$

$$[H_3O^+] = 1.6 \times 10^{-12}\ \text{M}$$

$$\text{Total } [H_3O^+] = 2.8 \times 10^{-3}\ \text{M} + 1.6 \times 10^{-12}\ \text{M}$$

$$= 2.8 \times 10^{-3}\ \text{M}$$

0.100 M $H_2C_6H_6O_6$

▲ **FIGURE 17.13 Dissociation of a Polyprotic Acid** A 0.100 M $H_2C_6H_6O_6$ solution contains an H_3O^+ concentration of 2.8×10^{-3} M from the first step. The amount of H_3O^+ contributed by the second step is only 1.6×10^{-12} M, which is insignificant compared to the amount produced by the first step.

17.10 Acid Strength and Molecular Structure

We have learned that a Brønsted–Lowry acid is a proton (H^+) donor. However, we have not explored why some hydrogen-containing molecules act as acids while others do not, or why some acids are strong and others weak. For example, why is H_2S acidic while CH_4 is not? Or why is HF a weak acid while HCl is a strong acid? We divide our discussion about these issues into two categories: binary acids (those containing hydrogen and only one other element) and oxyacids (those containing hydrogen bonded to an oxygen atom that is bonded to another element).

Binary Acids

Consider the bond between a hydrogen atom and some other generic element (which we call Y):

$$\mathrm{H{-}Y}$$

The factors affecting the ease with which this hydrogen is donated (and therefore will be acidic) are the *polarity* of the bond and the *strength* of the bond.

Bond Polarity

Using the notation introduced in Chapter 10, the H—Y bond must be polarized with the hydrogen atom as the positive pole in order for HY to be acidic:

$$^{\delta+}\mathrm{H{-}Y}^{\delta-}$$

This requirement makes physical sense because the hydrogen atom must be lost as a positively charged ion (H^+). A partial positive charge on the hydrogen atom facilitates its loss. Consider the following three bonds and their corresponding dipole moments:

H—Li	H—C	H—F
Not acidic	Not acidic	Acidic

LiH is ionic with *the negative charge on the hydrogen atom*; therefore, LiH is not acidic. The C—H bond is virtually nonpolar because the electronegativities of carbon and hydrogen are similar; therefore C—H is not acidic. In contrast, the H—F bond is polar with the positive charge on the hydrogen atom. As we have discussed in this chapter, HF is an acid. This is because the partial positive charge on the hydrogen atom makes it easier for the hydrogen to be lost as an H^+ ion.

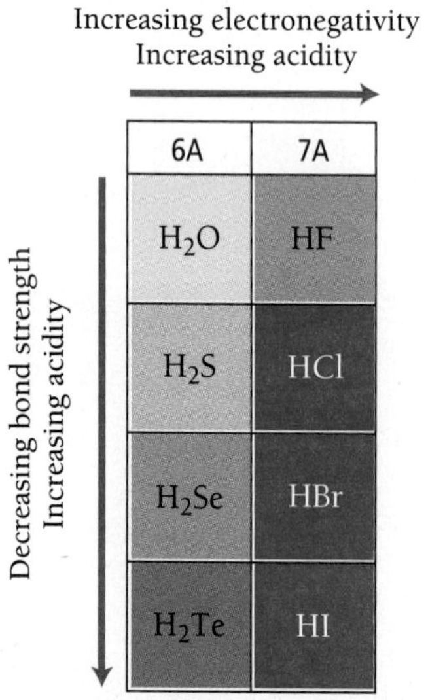

▲ FIGURE 17.14 Acidity of the Group 6A and 7A Hydrides From left to right, the hydrides become more acidic because the H—Y bond becomes more polar. From top to bottom, these hydrides become more acidic because the H—Y bond becomes weaker.

Bond Strength

The strength of the H—Y bond also affects the strength of the corresponding acid. As we might expect, the stronger the bond, the weaker the acid—the more tightly the hydrogen atom is held, the less likely it is to come off. We can see the effect of bond strength by comparing the bond strengths and acidities of the hydrogen halides:

Acid	Bond Energy (kJ/mol)	Type of Acid
H—F	565	Weak
H—Cl	431	Strong
H—Br	364	Strong

HCl and HBr have weaker bonds and are both strong acids. HF, however, has a stronger bond and is therefore a weak acid, despite the greater bond polarity of HF.

The Combined Effect of Bond Polarity and Bond Strength

We can see the combined effect of bond polarity and bond strength by examining the trends in acidity of the group 6A and 7A hydrides as shown in Figure 17.14◄. The hydrides become more acidic from left to right as the H—Y bond becomes more polar. The hydrides also become more acidic from top to bottom as the H—Y bond becomes weaker.

Oxyacids

Oxyacids contain a hydrogen atom bonded to an oxygen atom. The oxygen atom is in turn bonded to another atom (which we call Y):

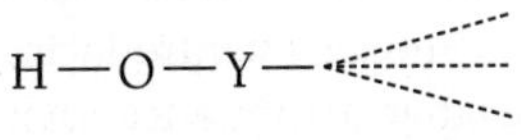

Y may or may not be bonded to yet other atoms. The factors affecting the ease with which the hydrogen in an oxyacid is donated (and therefore is acidic) are the *electronegativity of the element Y* and the *number of oxygen atoms attached to the element Y.*

Oxyacids are sometimes called oxoacids.

The Electronegativity of Y

The more electronegative the element Y, the more it weakens and polarizes the H—O bond and the more acidic the oxyacid is. We can see this effect by comparing the electronegativity of Y and the acid ionization constants of the following oxyacids:

Acid	Electronegativity of Y	K_a
H—O—I	2.5	2.3×10^{-11}
H—O—Br	2.8	2.0×10^{-9}
H—O—Cl	3.0	2.9×10^{-8}

Chlorine is the most electronegative of the three elements, and the corresponding acid has the greatest K_a.

The Number of Oxygen Atoms Bonded to Y

Oxyacids may contain additional oxygen atoms bonded to the element Y. Because these additional oxygen atoms are electronegative, they draw electron density away from Y, which in turn draws electron density away from the H—O bond, further weakening and polarizing it, and leading to increasing acidity. We can see this effect by comparing the following series of acid ionization constants:

Acid	Structure	K_a
$HClO_4$	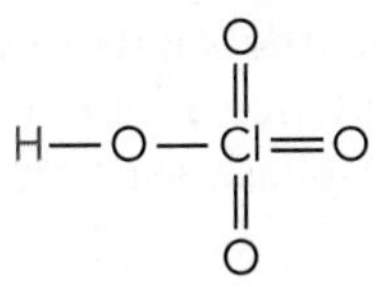	Strong
$HClO_3$	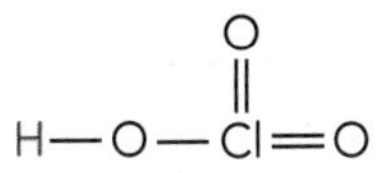	1
$HClO_2$	H—O—Cl=O	1.1×10^{-2}
HClO	H—O—Cl	2.9×10^{-8}

The greater the number of oxygen atoms bonded to Y, the stronger the acid. On this basis we would predict that H_2SO_4 is a stronger acid than H_2SO_3 and that HNO_3 is stronger than HNO_2. As we have seen in this chapter, both H_2SO_4 and HNO_3 are strong acids, while H_2SO_3 and HNO_2 are weak acids, as predicted.

ACID STRENGTH AND MOLECULAR STRUCTURE Which of the protons shown in red is more acidic?

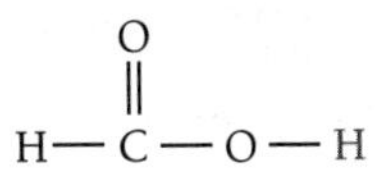

(a)

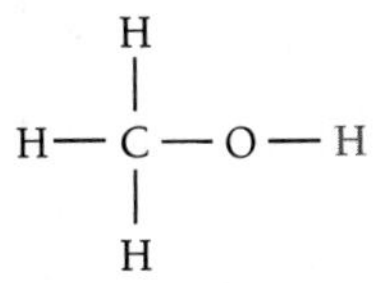

(b)

17.13 Cc Conceptual Connection

ANSWER **NOW!**

17.11 Lewis Acids and Bases

We began our definitions of acids and bases with the Arrhenius model. We then saw how the Brønsted–Lowry model, by introducing the concept of a proton donor and proton acceptor, expands the range of substances that we consider acids and bases. We now introduce a third model, which further broadens the range of substances that we can consider acids. This third model is the *Lewis model*, named after G. N. Lewis, the American chemist who devised the electron-dot representation of chemical bonding (Section 10.1).

While the Brønsted–Lowry model focuses on the transfer of a proton, the Lewis model focuses on the transfer of an electron pair. Consider the simple acid–base reaction between the H^+ ion and NH_3, shown here with Lewis structures:

$$H^+ + :NH_3 \longrightarrow [H:NH_3]^+$$

Brønsted–Lowry model focuses on the proton

Lewis model focuses on the electron pair

According to the Brønsted–Lowry model, the ammonia accepts a proton, thus acting as a base. According to the Lewis model, the ammonia acts as a base by *donating an electron pair*. The general definitions of acids and bases according to the Lewis model focus on the electron pair:

Lewis acid: electron pair acceptor

Lewis base: electron pair donor

According to the Lewis definition, H^+ in the reaction just shown is acting as an acid because it is accepting an electron pair from NH_3. NH_3 is acting as a Lewis base because it is donating an electron pair to H^+.

Although the Lewis model does not significantly expand the substances that can be considered bases—because all proton acceptors must have an electron pair to bind the proton—it does significantly expand the substances that can be considered acids. According to the Lewis model, a substance need not even contain hydrogen to be an acid. For example, consider the gas-phase reaction between boron trifluoride and ammonia shown here:

$$\underset{\text{Lewis acid}}{BF_3} + \underset{\text{Lewis base}}{:NH_3} \longrightarrow \underset{\text{adduct}}{F_3B:NH_3}$$

Boron trifluoride has an empty orbital that can accept the electron pair from ammonia and form the product (the product of a Lewis acid–base reaction is sometimes called an *adduct*). The reaction just shown demonstrates an important property of Lewis acids:

A Lewis acid has an empty orbital (or can rearrange electrons to create an empty orbital) that can accept an electron pair.

Consequently, the Lewis definition subsumes a whole new class of acids. Next we examine a few examples.

Molecules That Act as Lewis Acids

Since molecules with incomplete octets have empty orbitals, they can serve as Lewis acids. For example, both $AlCl_3$ and BCl_3 have incomplete octets:

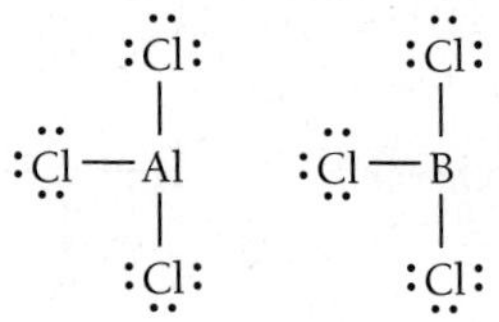

These both act as Lewis acids, as shown in the following reactions:

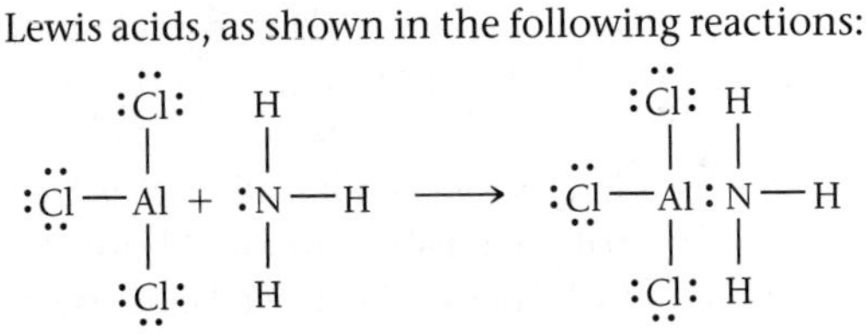

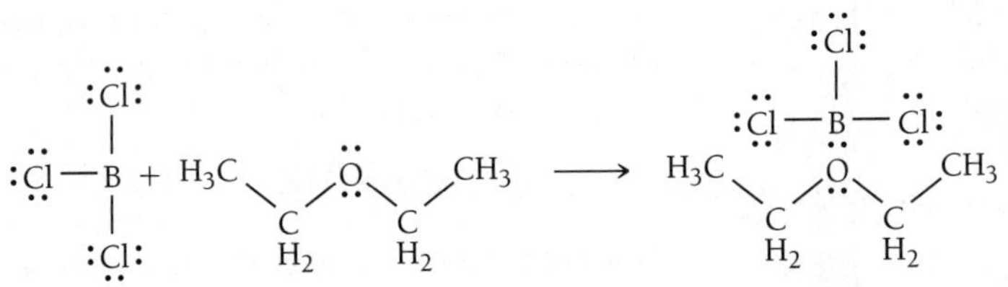

Some molecules that may not initially contain empty orbitals can rearrange their electrons to act as Lewis acids. Consider the reaction between carbon dioxide and water:

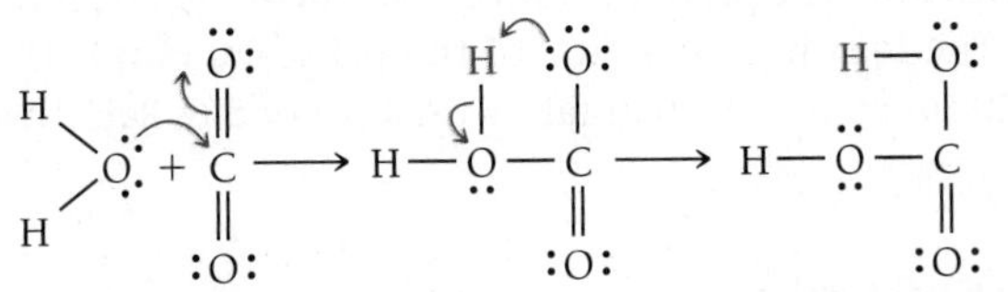

Water
Lewis base

Carbon dioxide
Lewis acid

Carbonic acid

The electrons in the double bond on carbon move to the terminal oxygen atom, allowing carbon dioxide to act as a Lewis acid by accepting an electron pair from water. The molecule then undergoes a rearrangement in which the hydrogen atom shown in red bonds with the terminal oxygen atom instead of the internal one.

Cations That Act as Lewis Acids

Some cations, because they are positively charged and have lost some electrons, have empty orbitals that allow them to also act as Lewis acids. Consider the hydration process of the Al^{3+} ion discussed in Section 17.8 and shown here:

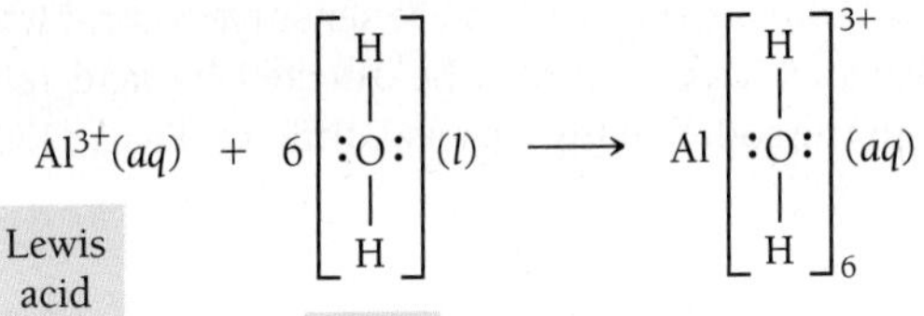

Lewis
acid

Lewis
base

The aluminum ion acts as a Lewis acid, accepting lone pairs from six water molecules to form the hydrated ion. Many other small, highly charged metal ions also act as Lewis acids in this way.

17.12 Acid Rain

About 82% of U.S. energy comes from the combustion of fossil fuels, including petroleum, natural gas, and coal (Figure 17.15▶). Some fossil fuels, especially coal, contain small amounts of sulfur impurities. During combustion, these impurities react with oxygen to form SO_2. In addition, during combustion of any fossil fuel, nitrogen from the air reacts with oxygen to form NO_2. Sulfur dioxide and nitrogen dioxide react with water and diatomic oxygen (O_2) in the atmosphere to form sulfuric acid and nitric acid:

$$2\,SO_2 + O_2 + 2\,H_2O \longrightarrow 2\,H_2SO_4$$
$$4\,NO_2 + O_2 + 2\,H_2O \longrightarrow 4\,HNO_3$$

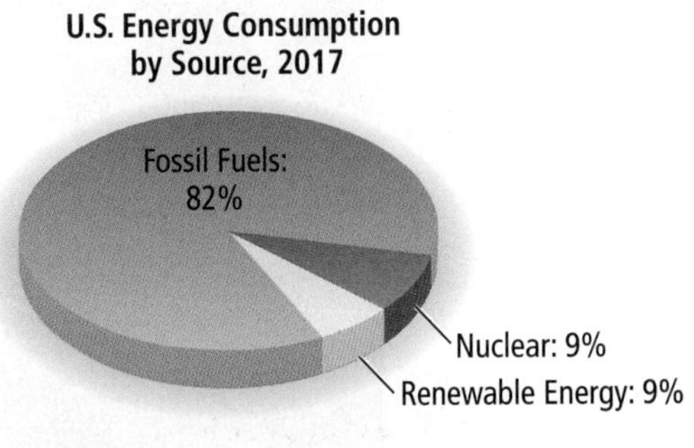

▲ **FIGURE 17.15 Sources of U.S. Energy** About 82% of U.S. energy comes from fossil fuel combustion.
Source: U.S. EIA Annual Energy Review 2017

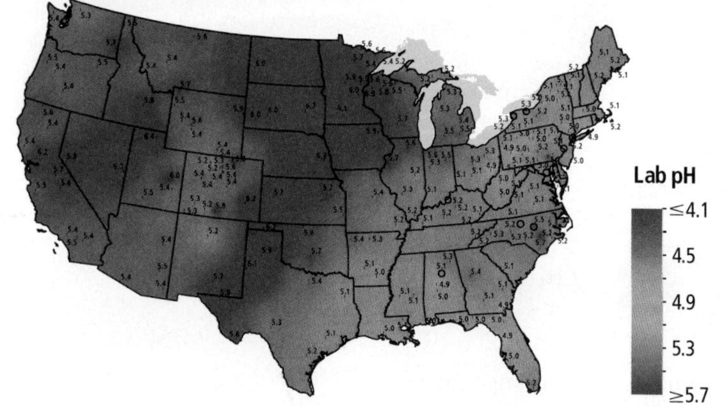

▲ FIGURE 17.16 Acid Rain Acid rain is a significant problem in the northeastern United States. The map shows the pH of rain that falls across the United States.
Source: National Atmospheric Deposition Program, National Trends Network

These acids combine with rain to form *acid rain*. The problem is greatest in the northeastern portion of the United States, where the rain is significantly acidic because the sulfur and nitrogen oxides produced by coal combustion in the Midwest are carried toward the Northeast by natural air currents.

Even in relatively unpolluted areas, rain is naturally somewhat acidic because of atmospheric carbon dioxide. Carbon dioxide combines with rainwater to form carbonic acid:

$$CO_2 + H_2O \longrightarrow H_2CO_3$$

However, carbonic acid is a relatively weak acid. Rain that is saturated with CO_2 has a pH of about 5.6, which is only mildly acidic. When nitric acid and sulfuric acid mix with rain, the pH of the rain can fall below 4.3 (Figure 17.16◀). Remember that because of the logarithmic nature of the pH scale, rain with a pH of 4.3 has an $[H_3O^+]$ that is 20 times greater than rain with a pH of 5.6. Rain that is this acidic has a harmful impact.

Effects of Acid Rain

Acids dissolve metals and acid rain degrades metal structures. Bridges, railroads, and even automobiles can be damaged by acid rain. Since acids react with carbonates, acid rain also harms building materials that contain carbonates (CO_3^{2-}), including marble, cement, and limestone. Statues, buildings, and pathways in the Northeast show significant signs of acid rain damage (Figure 17.17a▼).

Acid rain also accumulates in lakes and rivers and affects aquatic life. Many lakes, especially those that are surrounded by land that contains significant amounts of limestone ($CaCO_3$), have the ability to neutralize acidic rain. In the Midwest, for example, limestone-rich soils prevent most lakes from becoming acidified. In the northeastern United States, however, the lack of limestone makes lakes more susceptible, and over 2000 lakes and streams have increased acidity levels due to acid rain. Aquatic plants, frogs, salamanders, and some species of fish are sensitive to acid levels and cannot survive in the acidified water. Trees can also be affected by acid rain because the acid removes nutrients from the soil, making survival difficult (Figure 17.17b▼).

▼ FIGURE 17.17 The Effects of Acid Rain **(a)** Buildings, gravestones, and statues damaged by acid rain are a common sight in the northeastern United States and in many other industrialized nations. **(b)** Some species of trees are highly susceptible to the effects of acid rain.

(a) (b)

Acid Rain Legislation

In 1990, the U.S. Congress passed amendments to the Clean Air Act specifically targeted at reducing acid rain. These amendments force electrical utilities—which are the most significant source of SO_2—to lower their SO_2 emissions gradually over time. The result has been a 76% decrease in SO_2 pollutant levels in the United States since 1990 (Figure 17.18▼). The acidity of rain over the northeastern United States has begun to decrease, and lakes are beginning to recover. In the early 1990s, scientists categorized 30% of the lakes in the Northeast as being of *acute concern*, which means that a complete loss of fish population is expected. Today, the fraction of lakes in this category has been reduced to less than 18%. The acid rain program has been a dramatic success, and today's environmental legislation—such as legislation aimed at global warming—is using the acid rain legislation as a model for what can work.

SO_2 AIR QUALITY, 1990–2016

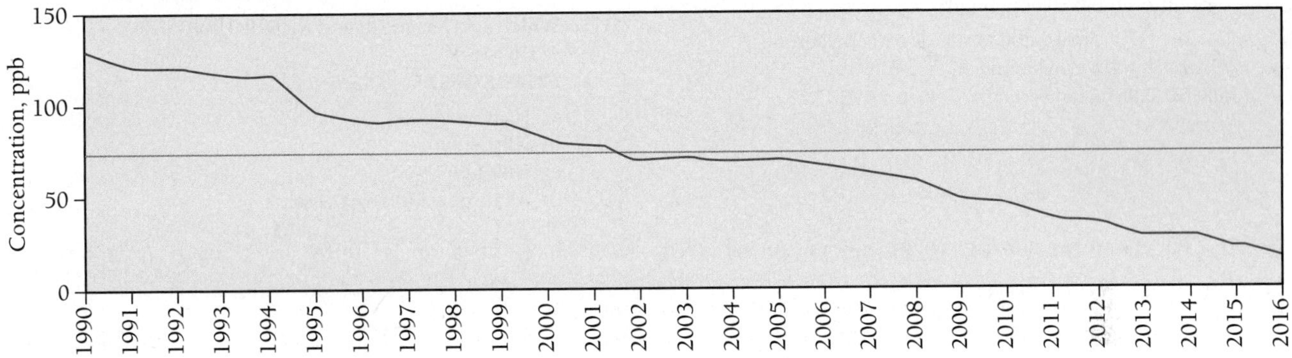

▲ **FIGURE 17.18 U.S. Sulfur Dioxide Pollutant Levels** As a result of amendments to the Clean Air Act passed in 1990, SO_2 levels continue to decrease.
Source: U.S. EPA Air Trends

QUIZ YOURSELF **NOW!**

Self-Assessment Quiz

Q1. Identify the conjugate base in the reaction shown here:

$$HClO_2(aq) + H_2O(aq) \rightleftharpoons H_3O^+(aq) + ClO_2^-(aq)$$

MISSED THIS? *Read Section 17.3; Watch KCV 17.3, IWE 17.1*

a) $HClO_2$ b) H_2O c) H_3O^+ d) ClO_2^-

Q2. Which pair is a Brønsted–Lowry conjugate acid–base pair?

MISSED THIS? *Read Section 17.3; Watch KCV 17.3, IWE 17.1*

a) NH_3; NH_4^+ b) H_3O^+; OH^-
c) HCl; HBr d) ClO_4^-; ClO_3^-

Q3. Consider the given acid ionization constants. Identify the strongest conjugate base.

MISSED THIS? *Read Sections 17.4, 17.8*

Acid	K_a
$HNO_2(aq)$	4.6×10^{-4}
$HCHO_2(aq)$	1.8×10^{-4}
$HClO(aq)$	2.9×10^{-8}
$HCN(aq)$	4.9×10^{-10}

a) $NO_2^-(aq)$ b) $CHO_2^-(aq)$
c) $ClO^-(aq)$ d) $CN^-(aq)$

Q4. What is the OH^- concentration in an aqueous solution at 25 °C in which $[H_3O^+] = 1.9 \times 10^{-9}$ M?

MISSED THIS? *Read Section 17.5*

a) 1.9×10^{-9} M b) 5.3×10^{-6} M
c) 5.3×10^{6} M d) 1.9×10^{-23} M

Q5. An $HNO_3(aq)$ solution has a pH of 1.75. What is the molar concentration of the $HNO_3(aq)$ solution?

MISSED THIS? *Read Section 17.6; Watch KCV 17.6*

a) 1.75 M b) 5.6×10^{-13} M
c) 56 M d) 0.018 M

Q6. Find the pH of a 0.350 M aqueous benzoic acid solution. For benzoic acid, $K_a = 6.5 \times 10^{-5}$.

MISSED THIS? *Read Section 17.6; Watch KCV 17.6, IWE 17.5*

a) 4.64 b) 4.19
c) 2.32 d) 11.68

Q7. Find the pH of a 0.155 M $HClO_2(aq)$ solution. For $HClO_2$, $K_a = 0.011$.

MISSED THIS? *Read Section 17.6; Watch KCV 17.6, IWE 17.7*

a) 0.92 b) 1.44
c) 1.39 d) 0.69

—Continued on the next page

Continued—

Q8. Calculate the percent ionization of 1.45 M aqueous acetic acid solution. For acetic acid, $K_a = 1.8 \times 10^{-5}$.
MISSED THIS? *Read Section 17.6; Watch KCV 17.6, IWE 17.9*

a) 0.35% b) 0.0018%
c) 0.29% d) 0.0051%

Q9. Consider two aqueous solutions of nitrous acid (HNO_2). Solution A has a concentration of $[HNO_2] = 0.55$ M and solution B has a concentration of $[HNO_2] = 1.25$ M. Which statement about the two solutions is true?
MISSED THIS? *Read Section 17.6*

a) Solution A has the higher percent ionization and the higher pH.
b) Solution B has the higher percent ionization and the higher pH.
c) Solution A has the higher percent ionization and solution B has the higher pH.
d) Solution B has the higher percent ionization and solution A has the higher pH.

Q10. Find the $[OH^-]$ in a 0.200 M solution of ethylamine ($C_2H_5NH_2$). For ethylamine, $K_b = 5.6 \times 10^{-4}$.
MISSED THIS? *Read Section 17.7; Watch IWE 17.12*

a) 11.52 M b) 2.48 M
c) 0.033 M d) 0.011 M

Q11. Which ion forms a basic solution when dissolved in water?
MISSED THIS? *Read Section 17.8; Watch KCV 17.8*

a) Br^- b) NO_3^- c) HSO_4^- d) SO_3^{2-}

Q12. Which compound forms an acidic solution when dissolved in water?
MISSED THIS? *Read Section 17.8; Watch KCV 17.8, IWE 17.16*

a) NH_4Cl b) NaCl c) KNO_2 d) $Ca(NO_3)_2$

Q13. Find the pH of 0.175 M NaCN solution. For HCN, $K_a = 4.9 \times 10^{-10}$.
MISSED THIS? *Read Section 17.8; Watch KCV 17.8, IWE 17.14*

a) 5.03 b) 11.28 c) 2.31 d) 8.97

Q14. What is the concentration of X^{2-} in a 0.150 M solution of the diprotic acid H_2X? For H_2X, $K_{a_1} = 4.5 \times 10^{-6}$ and $K_{a_2} = 1.2 \times 10^{-11}$.
MISSED THIS? *Read Section 17.9*

a) 9.9×10^{-8} M b) 2.0×10^{-9} M
c) 8.2×10^{-4} M d) 1.2×10^{-11} M

Q15. Which acid has the largest K_a: $HClO_2(aq)$, $HBrO_2(aq)$, or $HIO_2(aq)$?
MISSED THIS? *Read Section 17.10*

a) $HClO_2(aq)$
b) $HBrO_2(aq)$
c) $HIO_2(aq)$
d) All three acids have the same K_a.

Answers: **1.** (d) **2.** (a) **3.** (d) **4.** (b) **5.** (d) **6.** (c) **7.** (b) **8.** (a) **9.** (a) **10.** (d) **11.** (d) **12.** (a) **13.** (b) **14.** (d) **15.** (a)

CHAPTER 17 IN REVIEW

TERMS

Section 17.2
carboxylic acid (733)
alkaloid (734)
conjugate acid–base pair (736)
conjugate acid (736)
conjugate base (736)

Section 17.3
Arrhenius definitions (of acids and bases) (735)
hydronium ion (735)
Brønsted–Lowry definitions (of acids and bases) (735)
amphoteric (735)

Section 17.4
strong acid (737)
weak acid (737)
monoprotic acid (737)
diprotic acid (737)
triprotic acid (738)
acid ionization constant (K_a) (739)

Section 17.5
autoionization (740)
ion product constant for water (K_w) (741)
neutral (741)
acidic solution (741)
basic solution (741)
pH (742)

Section 17.6
percent ionization (750)

Section 17.7
strong base (754)
weak base (754)
base ionization constant (K_b) (755)

Section 17.9
polyprotic acid (765)

Section 17.11
Lewis acid (772)
Lewis base (772)

CONCEPTS

Heartburn (17.1)
- Hydrochloric acid from the stomach sometimes comes in contact with the esophageal lining, resulting in irritation, called heartburn. Heartburn is treated with antacids, bases that neutralize stomach acid.

The Nature of Acids and Bases (17.2)
- Acids generally taste sour, dissolve metals, turn blue litmus paper red, and neutralize bases. Common acids are hydrochloric, sulfuric, nitric, and carboxylic acids.

- Bases generally taste bitter, feel slippery, turn red litmus paper blue, and neutralize acids. Common bases are sodium hydroxide, sodium bicarbonate, and potassium hydroxide.

Definitions of Acids and Bases (17.3)

- The Arrhenius definition of acids and bases states that in an aqueous solution, an acid produces hydrogen ions and a base produces hydroxide ions.
- The Brønsted–Lowry definition states that an acid is a proton (hydrogen ion) donor and a base is a proton acceptor. According to the Brønsted–Lowry definition, two substances related by the transfer of a proton are a conjugate acid–base pair.

Acid Strength and the Acid Dissociation Constant, K_a (17.4)

- In a solution, a strong acid completely ionizes but a weak acid only partially ionizes.
- Generally, the stronger the acid, the weaker the conjugate base, and vice versa.
- The extent of dissociation of a weak acid is quantified by the acid dissociation constant, K_a, which is the equilibrium constant for the ionization of the weak acid.

Autoionization of Water and pH (17.5)

- In an acidic solution, the concentration of hydrogen ions is always greater than the concentration of hydroxide ions. $[H_3O^+]$ multiplied by $[OH^-]$ is always constant at a constant temperature.
- There are two types of logarithmic acid–base scales: pH and pOH. At 25 °C, the sum of a solution's pH and pOH is always 14.

Finding the $[H_3O^+]$ and pH of Strong and Weak Acid Solutions (17.6)

- In a strong acid solution, the hydrogen ion concentration equals the initial concentration of the acid.
- In a weak acid solution, the hydrogen ion concentration—which can be determined by solving an equilibrium problem—is lower than the initial acid concentration.
- The percent ionization of weak acids decreases as the acid (and hydrogen ion) concentration increases.
- In mixtures of two acids with large K_a differences, the concentration of hydrogen ions can usually be determined by considering only the stronger of the two acids.

Base Solutions (17.7)

- A strong base dissociates completely; a weak base does not.
- Most weak bases produce hydroxide ions through the ionization of water. The base ionization constant, K_b, indicates the extent of ionization.

Ions as Acids and Bases (17.8)

- A cation is a weak acid if it is the conjugate acid of a weak base; it is neutral if it is the counterion of a strong base.
- An anion is a weak base if it is the conjugate base of a weak acid; it is neutral if it is the conjugate base of a strong acid.
- To calculate the pH of a solution of an acidic cation or basic anion, we determine K_a or K_b from the equation $K_a \times K_b = K_w$.

Polyprotic Acids (17.9)

- Polyprotic acids contain two or more ionizable protons.
- Generally, polyprotic acids ionize in successive steps, and the value of K_a becomes smaller for each step.
- In many cases, we can determine the $[H_3O^+]$ of a polyprotic acid solution by considering only the first ionization step; then, the concentration of the anion formed in the second ionization step is equivalent to the value of K_{a_2}.

Acid Strength and Molecular Structure (17.10)

- For binary acids, acid strength decreases with increasing bond energy and increases with increasing bond polarity.
- For oxyacids, acid strength increases with the electronegativity of the atoms bonded to the oxygen atom and also increases with the number of oxygen atoms in the molecule.

Lewis Acids and Bases (17.11)

- A third model of acids and bases, the Lewis model, defines a base as an electron pair donor and an acid as an electron pair acceptor. According to this definition, an acid does not have to contain hydrogen. A Lewis acid can be a compound with an empty orbital—or one that will rearrange to make an empty orbital—or a cation.

Acid Rain (17.12)

- The combustion of fossil fuels produces oxides of sulfur and nitrogen, which react with oxygen and water to form sulfuric and nitric acids. These acids combine with rain to form acid rain.
- Acid rain corrodes human-made structures and damages aquatic environments and forests. Environmental legislation has helped stabilize the amount of acid rain being produced.

EQUATIONS AND RELATIONSHIPS

Note: In all of these equations $[H^+]$ is interchangeable with $[H_3O^+]$.

Expression for the Acid Ionization Constant, K_a (**17.4**)

$$K_a = \frac{[H_3O^+][A^-]}{[HA]}$$

The Ion Product Constant for Water, K_w (**17.5**)

$$K_w = [H_3O^+][OH^-] = 1.0 \times 10^{-14} \text{ (at 25 °C)}$$

Expression for the pH Scale (**17.5**)

$$\text{pH} = -\log[H_3O^+]$$

Expression for the pOH Scale (**17.5**)

$$\text{pOH} = -\log[OH^-]$$

Relationship between pH and pOH (**17.5**)

$$\text{pH} + \text{pOH} = 14.00$$

Expression for the pK_a Scale (**17.5**)

$$pK_a = -\log K_a$$

Expression for Percent Ionization (**17.6**)

$$\text{Percent ionization} = \frac{\text{concentration of ionized acid}}{\text{initial concentration of acid}} \times 100\%$$

$$= \frac{[H_3O^+]_{equil}}{[HA]_{init}} \times 100\%$$

Relationship between K_a, K_b, and K_w (**17.8**)

$$K_a \times K_b = K_w$$

LEARNING OUTCOMES

Chapter Objectives	Assessment
Analyze acids and bases by definition (Arrhenius or Brønsted–Lowry) and their corresponding properties (**17.2**, **17.3**)	Example 17.1 **For Practice** 17.1 **Exercises** 33–40
Perform calculations involving K_a (**17.4**)	**Exercises** 41–46
Perform calculations involving K_w (**17.5**)	Example 17.2 **For Practice** 17.2 **Exercises** 47–48
Quantify the acidity of a solution using the pH scale (**17.5**)	Examples 17.3, 17.4 **For Practice** 17.3, 17.4 **Exercises** 49–56
Perform pH calculations of strong acids and weak acids (**17.6**)	Examples 17.5–17.8 **For Practice** 17.5–17.8 **Exercises** 57–70
Perform percent ionization calculations for acids (**17.6**)	Example 17.9 **For Practice** 17.9 **Exercises** 71–78
Perform pH calculations for mixtures of acids (**17.6**)	Example 17.10 **For Practice** 17.10 **Exercises** 79–80
Perform pH calculations for a strong base (**17.7**)	Example 17.11 **For Practice** 17.11 **Exercises** 81–86
Perform pH calculations for a weak base (**17.7**)	Example 17.12 **For Practice** 17.12 **Exercises** 87–94
Classify an anion in solution as basic or neutral (**17.8**)	Example 17.13 **For Practice** 17.13 **Exercises** 95–96
Perform pH calculations for solutions containing anions that act as a base (**17.8**)	Example 17.14 **For Practice** 17.14 **Exercises** 97–98
Classify a cation in solution as acidic or neutral (**17.8**)	Example 17.15 **For Practice** 17.15 **Exercises** 99–100
Classify salts solutions as acidic, basic, or neutral (**17.8**)	Example 17.16 **For Practice** 17.16 **Exercises** 101–108
Perform pH calculations of polyprotic acid solutions (**17.9**)	Examples 17.17, 17.18 **For Practice** 17.17, 17.18 **Exercises** 109–112
Calculate the concentration of anions for weak diprotic acid solutions (**17.9**)	Example 17.19 **For Practice** 17.19 **Exercises** 113–116
Predict acidity based on molecular structure (**17.10**)	**Exercises** 117–122
Analyze acids and bases in terms of the Lewis model definition (**17.11**)	**Exercises** 123–126

EXERCISES

Mastering Chemistry provides end-of-chapter exercises, feedback-enriched tutorial problems, animations, and interactive activities to encourage problem-solving practice and deeper understanding of key concepts and topics.

REVIEW QUESTIONS

1. What causes heartburn? What are some possible ways to alleviate heartburn?

2. What are the general physical and chemical properties of acids? Of bases?

3. What is a carboxylic acid? Give an example.

4. What is the Arrhenius definition of an acid? Of a base?

5. What is a hydronium ion? Does H^+ exist in solution by itself?

6. What is the Brønsted–Lowry definition of an acid? Of a base?

7. Why is there more than one definition of acid–base behavior? Which definition is the right one?

8. Describe amphoteric behavior and give an example.

9. What is a conjugate acid–base pair? Provide an example.

10. Explain the difference between a strong acid and a weak acid and list one example of each.

11. What are diprotic and triprotic acids? List an example of each.

12. Define the acid ionization constant and explain its significance.

13. Write an equation for the autoionization of water and an expression for the ion product constant for water (K_w). What is the value of K_w at 25 °C?

14. What happens to the $[OH^-]$ of a solution when the $[H_3O^+]$ is increased? Decreased?

15. Define pH. What pH range is considered acidic? Basic? Neutral? (Assume 25 °C.)

16. Define pOH. What pOH range is considered acidic? Basic? Neutral? (Assume 25 °C.)

17. In most solutions containing a strong or weak acid, the autoionization of water can be neglected when calculating $[H_3O^+]$. Explain why this statement is valid.

18. When calculating $[H_3O^+]$ for weak acid solutions, we can often use the *x is small* approximation. Explain the nature of this approximation and why it is valid.

19. What is the percent ionization of an acid? Explain what happens to the percent ionization of a weak acid as a function of the concentration of the weak acid solution.

20. In calculating $[H_3O^+]$ for a mixture of a strong acid and weak acid, the weak acid can often be neglected. Explain why this statement is valid.

21. Write a generic equation showing how a weak base ionizes water.

22. How can you determine if an anion will act as a weak base? Write a generic equation showing the reaction by which an anion, A^-, acts as a weak base.

23. What is the relationship between the acid ionization constant for a weak acid (K_a) and the base ionization constant for its conjugate base (K_b)?

24. What kinds of cations act as weak acids? List some examples.

25. When calculating the $[H_3O^+]$ for a polyprotic acid, the second ionization step can often be neglected. Explain why this statement is valid.

26. For a weak diprotic acid H_2X, what is the relationship between $[X^{2-}]$ and K_{a_2}? Under what conditions does this relationship exist?

27. For a binary acid, H—Y, which factors affect the relative ease with which the acid ionizes?

28. Which factors affect the relative acidity of an oxyacid?

29. What is the Lewis definition of an acid? Of a base?

30. What is a general characteristic of a Lewis acid? Of a Lewis base?

31. What is acid rain? What causes it, and where is the problem the greatest?

32. What are the main detrimental effects of acid rain? What is being done to address the problem of acid rain?

PROBLEMS BY TOPIC

The Nature and Definitions of Acids and Base

33. Identify each substance as an acid or a base and write a chemical equation showing how it is an acid or a base according to the Arrhenius definition.
MISSED THIS? Read Section 17.3; Watch KCV 17.3
a. $HNO_3(aq)$ b. $NH_4^+(aq)$
c. $KOH(aq)$ d. $HC_2H_3O_2(aq)$

34. Identify each substance as an acid or a base and write a chemical equation showing how it is an acid or a base in aqueous solution according to the Arrhenius definition.
a. $NaOH(aq)$ b. $H_2SO_4(aq)$
c. $HBr(aq)$ d. $Sr(OH)_2(aq)$

35. In each reaction, identify the Brønsted–Lowry acid, the Brønsted–Lowry base, the conjugate acid, and the conjugate base.
MISSED THIS? Read Section 17.3; Watch KCV 17.3, IWE 17.1
a. $H_2CO_3(aq) + H_2O(l) \rightleftharpoons H_3O^+(aq) + HCO_3^-(aq)$
b. $NH_3(aq) + H_2O(l) \rightleftharpoons NH_4^+(aq) + OH^-(aq)$
c. $HNO_3(aq) + H_2O(l) \longrightarrow H_3O^+(aq) + NO_3^-(aq)$
d. $C_5H_5N(aq) + H_2O(l) \rightleftharpoons C_5H_5NH^+(aq) + OH^-(aq)$

36. In each reaction, identify the Brønsted–Lowry acid, the Brønsted–Lowry base, the conjugate acid, and the conjugate base.
a. $HI(aq) + H_2O(l) \longrightarrow H_3O^+(aq) + I^-(aq)$
b. $CH_3NH_2(aq) + H_2O(l) \rightleftharpoons CH_3NH_3^+(aq) + OH^-(aq)$
c. $CO_3^{2-}(aq) + H_2O(l) \rightleftharpoons HCO_3^-(aq) + OH^-(aq)$
d. $HBr(aq) + H_2O(l) \longrightarrow H_3O^+(aq) + Br^-(aq)$

37. Write the formula for the conjugate base of each acid.
MISSED THIS? Read Section 17.3; Watch KCV 17.3, IWE 17.1
a. HCl b. H_2SO_3 c. $HCHO_2$ d. HF

38. Write the formula for the conjugate acid of each base.
a. NH_3 b. ClO_4^- c. HSO_4^- d. CO_3^{2-}

39. Both H_2O and $H_2PO_4^-$ are amphoteric. Write an equation to show how each substance can act as an acid and another equation to show how each can act as a base.
MISSED THIS? Read Sections 17.3, 17.5; Watch KCV 17.3, IWE 17.1

40. Both HCO_3^- and HS^- are amphoteric. Write an equation to show how each substance can act as an acid and another equation to show how each can act as a base.

Acid Strength and K_a

41. Classify each acid as strong or weak. If the acid is weak, write an expression for the acid ionization constant (K_a).
MISSED THIS? Read Section 17.4; Watch KCV 17.4
a. HNO_3 b. HCl c. HBr d. H_2SO_3

42. Classify each acid as strong or weak. If the acid is weak, write an expression for the acid ionization constant (K_a).
a. HF b. $HCHO_2$ c. H_2SO_4 d. H_2CO_3

43. The three diagrams represent three different solutions of the binary acid HA. Water molecules have been omitted for clarity, and hydronium ions (H_3O^+) are represented by hydrogen ions (H^+). Rank the acids in order of decreasing acid strength.
MISSED THIS? Read Section 17.4; Watch KCV 17.4

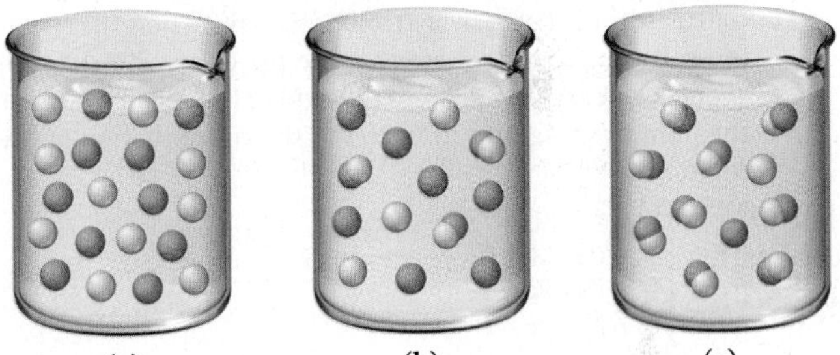

(a) (b) (c)

44. Rank the solutions in order of decreasing $[H_3O^+]$: 0.10 M HCl; 0.10 M HF; 0.10 M HClO; 0.10 M HC_6H_5O.

45. Pick the stronger base from each pair.
MISSED THIS? Read Sections 17.4, 17.8
a. F^- or Cl^- b. NO_2^- or NO_3^- c. F^- or ClO^-

46. Pick the stronger base from each pair.
a. ClO_4^- or ClO_2^- b. Cl^- or H_2O c. CN^- or ClO^-

Autoionization of Water and pH

47. Calculate $[OH^-]$ in each aqueous solution at 25 °C, and classify the solution as acidic or basic.
MISSED THIS? Read Section 17.5
a. $[H_3O^+] = 1.2 \times 10^{-8}$ M b. $[H_3O^+] = 8.5 \times 10^{-5}$ M
c. $[H_3O^+] = 3.5 \times 10^{-2}$ M

48. Calculate $[H_3O^+]$ in each aqueous solution at 25 °C, and classify each solution as acidic or basic.
a. $[OH^-] = 1.1 \times 10^{-9}$ M b. $[OH^-] = 2.9 \times 10^{-2}$ M
c. $[OH^-] = 6.9 \times 10^{-12}$ M

49. Calculate the pH and pOH of each solution at 25 °C.
MISSED THIS? Read Section 17.5; Watch IWE 17.3
a. $[H_3O^+] = 1.7 \times 10^{-8}$ M b. $[H_3O^+] = 1.0 \times 10^{-7}$ M
c. $[H_3O^+] = 2.2 \times 10^{-6}$ M

50. Calculate $[H_3O^+]$ and $[OH^-]$ for each solution at 25 °C.
a. pH = 8.55 b. pH = 11.23 c. pH = 2.87

51. Complete the table. (All solutions are at 25 °C.)
MISSED THIS? *Read Section 17.5; Watch IWE 17.3*

$[H_3O^+]$	$[OH^-]$	pH	Acidic or Basic
______	______	3.15	______
3.7×10^{-9}	______	______	______
______	______	11.1	______
______	1.6×10^{-11}	______	______

52. Complete the table. (All solutions are at 25 °C.)

$[H_3O^+]$	$[OH^-]$	pH	Acidic or Basic
3.5×10^{-3}	______	______	______
______	3.8×10^{-7}	______	______
1.8×10^{-9}	______	______	______
______	______	7.15	______

53. Like all equilibrium constants, the value of K_w depends on temperature. At body temperature (37 °C), $K_w = 2.4 \times 10^{-14}$. What are the $[H_3O^+]$ and pH of pure water at body temperature?
MISSED THIS? *Read Sections 17.5, 17.6; Watch KCV 17.6, IWE 17.5*

54. The value of K_w increases with increasing temperature. Is the autoionization of water endothermic or exothermic?

55. Calculate the pH of each acid solution. Explain how the resulting pH values demonstrate that the pH of an acid solution should carry as many digits to the right of the decimal place as the number of significant figures in the concentration of the solution.
MISSED THIS? *Read Section 17.5*

$[H_3O^+] = 0.044$ M
$[H_3O^+] = 0.045$ M
$[H_3O^+] = 0.046$ M

56. Determine the concentration of H_3O^+ to the correct number of significant figures in a solution with each pH. Describe how these calculations show the relationship between the number of digits to the right of the decimal place in pH and the number of significant figures in concentration.

pH = 2.50
pH = 2.51
pH = 2.52

Acid Solutions

57. For each strong acid solution, determine $[H_3O^+]$, $[OH^-]$, and pH.
MISSED THIS? *Read Section 17.6*
a. 0.25 M HCl
b. 0.015 M HNO_3
c. a solution that is 0.052 M in HBr and 0.020 M in HNO_3
d. a solution that is 0.655% HNO_3 by mass (assume a density of 1.01 g/mL for the solution)

58. Determine the pH of each solution.
a. 0.048 M HI
b. 0.0895 M $HClO_4$
c. a solution that is 0.045 M in $HClO_4$ and 0.048 M in HCl
d. a solution that is 1.09% HCl by mass (assume a density of 1.01 g/mL for the solution)

59. What mass of HI must be present in 0.250 L of solution to obtain a solution with each pH value?
MISSED THIS? *Read Section 17.6*
a. pH = 1.25 b. pH = 1.75 c. pH = 2.85

60. What mass of $HClO_4$ must be present in 0.500 L of solution to obtain a solution with each pH value?
a. pH = 2.50 b. pH = 1.50 c. pH = 0.50

61. What is the pH of a solution in which 224 mL of HCl(*g*), measured at 27.2 °C and 1.02 atm, is dissolved in 1.5 L of aqueous solution?
MISSED THIS? *Read Section 17.6*

62. What volume of a concentrated HCl solution, which is 36.0% HCl by mass and has a density of 1.179 g/mL, should be used to make 5.00 L of an HCl solution with a pH of 1.8?

63. Determine the $[H_3O^+]$ and pH of a 0.100 M solution of benzoic acid. **MISSED THIS?** *Read Section 17.6; Watch KCV 17.6, IWE 17.5*

64. Determine the $[H_3O^+]$ and pH of a 0.200 M solution of formic acid.

65. Determine the pH of an HNO_2 solution of each concentration. In which cases can you *not* make the simplifying assumption that *x is small*?
MISSED THIS? *Read Section 17.6; Watch KCV 17.6, IWE 17.5, 17.7*
a. 0.500 M b. 0.100 M c. 0.0100 M

66. Determine the pH of an HF solution of each concentration. In which cases can you *not* make the simplifying assumption that *x is small*? (K_a for HF is 6.8×10^{-4}.)
a. 0.250 M b. 0.0500 M c. 0.0250 M

67. If 15.0 mL of glacial acetic acid (pure $HC_2H_3O_2$) is diluted to 1.50 L with water, what is the pH of the resulting solution? The density of glacial acetic acid is 1.05 g/mL.
MISSED THIS? *Read Section 17.6; Watch KCV 17.6, IWE 17.5*

68. Calculate the pH of a formic acid solution that contains 1.35% formic acid by mass. (Assume a density of 1.01 g/mL for the solution.)

69. A 0.185 M solution of a weak acid (HA) has a pH of 2.95. Calculate the acid ionization constant (K_a) for the acid.
MISSED THIS? *Read Section 17.6; Watch KCV 17.6, IWE 17.8*

70. A 0.115 M solution of a weak acid (HA) has a pH of 3.29. Calculate the acid ionization constant (K_a) for the acid.

71. Determine the percent ionization of a 0.125 M HCN solution.
MISSED THIS? *Read Section 17.6; Watch KCV 17.6, IWE 17.9*

72. Determine the percent ionization of a 0.225 M solution of benzoic acid.

73. Calculate the percent ionization of an acetic acid solution having the given concentration.
MISSED THIS? *Read Section 17.6; Watch KCV 17.6, IWE 17.9*
a. 1.00 M b. 0.500 M c. 0.100 M d. 0.0500 M

74. Calculate the percent ionization of a formic acid solution having the given concentration.
a. 1.00 M b. 0.500 M c. 0.100 M d. 0.0500 M

75. A 0.148 M solution of a monoprotic acid has a percent ionization of 1.55%. Determine the acid ionization constant (K_a) for the acid.
MISSED THIS? *Read Section 17.6; Watch KCV 17.6, IWE 17.9*

76. A 0.085 M solution of a monoprotic acid has a percent ionization of 0.59%. Determine the acid ionization constant (K_a) for the acid.

77. Find the pH and percent ionization of each HF solution. (K_a for HF is 6.8×10^{-4}.) **MISSED THIS?** *Read Section 17.6; Watch KCV 17.6, IWE 17.5, 17.7, 17.9*
a. 0.250 M HF b. 0.100 M HF c. 0.050 M HF

78. Find the pH and percent ionization of a 0.100 M solution of a weak monoprotic acid having the given K_a values.
a. $K_a = 1.0 \times 10^{-5}$
b. $K_a = 1.0 \times 10^{-3}$
c. $K_a = 1.0 \times 10^{-1}$

79. Find the pH of each mixture of acids.
MISSED THIS? *Read Section 17.6*
a. 0.115 M in HBr and 0.125 M in $HCHO_2$
b. 0.150 M in HNO_2 and 0.085 M in HNO_3
c. 0.185 M in $HCHO_2$ and 0.225 M in $HC_2H_3O_2$
d. 0.050 M in acetic acid and 0.050 M in hydrocyanic acid

80. Find the pH of each mixture of acids.
a. 0.075 M in HNO_3 and 0.175 M in $HC_7H_5O_2$
b. 0.020 M in HBr and 0.015 M in $HClO_4$
c. 0.095 M in HF and 0.225 M in HC_6H_5O
d. 0.100 M in formic acid and 0.050 M in hypochlorous acid

Base Solutions

81. For each strong base solution, determine $[OH^-]$, $[H_3O^+]$, pH, and pOH. **MISSED THIS?** *Read Section 17.7*
a. 0.15 M NaOH
b. 1.5×10^{-3} M $Ca(OH)_2$
c. 4.8×10^{-4} M $Sr(OH)_2$
d. 8.7×10^{-5} M KOH

82. For each strong base solution, determine $[OH^-]$, $[H_3O^+]$, pH, and pOH.
a. 8.77×10^{-3} M LiOH
b. 0.0112 M $Ba(OH)_2$
c. 1.9×10^{-4} M KOH
d. 5.0×10^{-4} M $Ca(OH)_2$

83. Determine the pH of a solution that is 3.85% KOH by mass. Assume that the solution has density of 1.01 g/mL.
MISSED THIS? *Read Section 17.7*

84. Determine the pH of a solution that is 1.55% NaOH by mass. Assume that the solution has density of 1.01 g/mL.

85. What volume of 0.855 M KOH solution is required to make 3.55 L of a solution with pH of 12.4?
MISSED THIS? *Read Section 17.7*

86. What volume of a 15.0% by mass NaOH solution, which has a density of 1.116 g/mL, should be used to make 5.00 L of an NaOH solution with a pH of 10.8?

87. Write equations showing how each weak base ionizes water to form OH^-. Also write the corresponding expression for K_b.
MISSED THIS? *Read Section 17.7*
a. NH_3
b. HCO_3^-
c. CH_3NH_2

88. Write equations showing how each weak base ionizes water to form OH^-. Also write the corresponding expression for K_b.
a. CO_3^{2-}
b. $C_6H_5NH_2$
c. $C_2H_5NH_2$

89. Determine the $[OH^-]$, pH, and pOH of a 0.15 M ammonia solution. **MISSED THIS?** *Read Section 17.7; Watch IWE 17.12*

90. Determine the $[OH^-]$, pH, and pOH of a solution that is 0.125 M in CO_3^{2-}.

91. Caffeine ($C_8H_{10}N_4O_2$) is a weak base with a pK_b of 10.4. Calculate the pH of a solution containing a caffeine concentration of 455 mg/L.
MISSED THIS? *Read Section 17.7; Watch IWE 17.12*

92. Amphetamine ($C_9H_{13}N$) is a weak base with a pK_b of 4.2. Calculate the pH of a solution containing an amphetamine concentration of 225 mg/L.

93. Morphine is a weak base. A 0.150 M solution of morphine has a pH of 10.7. What is K_b for morphine?
MISSED THIS? *Read Section 17.7; Watch IWE 17.8, 17.12*

94. A 0.135 M solution of a weak base has a pH of 11.23. Determine K_b for the base.

Acid–Base Properties of Ions and Salts

95. Determine if each anion acts as a weak base in solution. For those anions that are basic, write an equation that shows how the anion acts as a base.
MISSED THIS? *Read Section 17.8; Watch KCV 17.8*
a. Br^-
b. ClO^-
c. CN^-
d. Cl^-

96. Determine whether each anion is basic or neutral. For those anions that are basic, write an equation that shows how the anion acts as a base.
a. $C_7H_5O_2^-$
b. I^-
c. NO_3^-
d. F^-

97. Determine the $[OH^-]$ and pH of a solution that is 0.140 M in F^-.
MISSED THIS? *Read Section 17.8; Watch KCV 17.8, IWE 17.14*

98. Determine the $[OH^-]$ and pH of a solution that is 0.250 M in HCO_3^-.

99. Determine whether each cation is acidic or pH-neutral. For those cations that are acidic, write an equation that shows how the cation acts as an acid.
MISSED THIS? *Read Section 17.8; Watch KCV 17.8*
a. NH_4^+
b. Na^+
c. Co^{3+}
d. $CH_2NH_3^+$

100. Determine whether each cation is acidic or pH-neutral. For each cation that is acidic, write an equation that shows how the cation acts as an acid.
a. Sr^{2+}
b. Mn^{3+}
c. $C_5H_5NH^+$
d. Li^+

101. Determine if each salt will form a solution that is acidic, basic, or pH-neutral.
MISSED THIS? *Read Section 17.8; Watch KCV 17.8, IWE 17.16*
a. $FeCl_3$
b. NaF
c. $CaBr_2$
d. NH_4Br
e. $C_6H_5NH_3NO_2$

102. Determine if each salt will form a solution that is acidic, basic, or pH-neutral.
a. $Al(NO_3)_3$
b. $C_2H_5NH_3NO_3$
c. K_2CO_3
d. RbI
e. NH_4ClO

103. Arrange the solutions in order of increasing acidity.
MISSED THIS? *Read Section 17.8; Watch KCV 17.8*

NaCl, NH_4Cl, $NaHCO_3$, NH_4ClO_2, NaOH

104. Arrange the solutions in order of increasing basicity.

CH_3NH_3Br, KOH, KBr, KCN, $C_5H_5NHNO_2$

105. Determine the pH of each solution.
MISSED THIS? *Read Section 17.8; Watch KCV 17.8, 17.14, 17.16*
a. 0.10 M NH_4Cl
b. 0.10 M $NaC_2H_3O_2$
c. 0.10 M NaCl

106. Determine the pH of each solution.
a. 0.20 M $KCHO_2$
b. 0.20 M CH_3NH_3I
c. 0.20 M KI

107. Calculate the concentration of all species in a 0.15 M KF solution.
MISSED THIS? *Read Section 17.8; Watch KCV 17.8, 17.14, 17.16*

108. Calculate the concentration of all species in a 0.225 M $C_6H_5NH_3Cl$ solution.

Polyprotic Acids

109. Write chemical equations and corresponding equilibrium expressions for each of the three ionization steps of phosphoric acid.
MISSED THIS? *Read Section 17.9*

110. Write chemical equations and corresponding equilibrium expressions for each of the two ionization steps of carbonic acid.

111. Calculate the $[H_3O^+]$ and pH of each polyprotic acid solution.
MISSED THIS? *Read Section 17.9*
a. 0.350 M H_3PO_4
b. 0.350 M $H_2C_2O_4$

112. Calculate the $[H_3O^+]$ and pH of each polyprotic acid solution.
a. 0.125 M H_2CO_3
b. 0.125 M $H_3C_6H_5O_7$

113. Calculate the concentration of all species in a 0.500 M solution of H_2SO_3.
MISSED THIS? *Read Section 17.9*

114. Calculate the concentration of all species in a 0.155 M solution of H_2CO_3.

115. Calculate the $[H_3O^+]$ and pH of each H_2SO_4 solution. At approximately what concentration does the *x is small* approximation break down?
MISSED THIS? *Read Section 17.9*
a. 0.50 M
b. 0.10 M
c. 0.050 M

116. Consider a 0.10 M solution of a weak polyprotic acid (H_2A) with the possible values of K_{a_1} and K_{a_2} given here.
a. $K_{a_1} = 1.0 \times 10^{-4}$; $K_{a_2} = 5.0 \times 10^{-5}$
b. $K_{a_1} = 1.0 \times 10^{-4}$; $K_{a_2} = 1.0 \times 10^{-5}$
c. $K_{a_1} = 1.0 \times 10^{-4}$; $K_{a_2} = 1.0 \times 10^{-6}$
Calculate the contributions to $[H_3O^+]$ from each ionization step. At what point can the contribution of the second step be neglected?

Molecular Structure and Acid Strength

117. Based on their molecular structure, pick the stronger acid from each pair of binary acids. Explain your choice.
MISSED THIS? *Read Section 17.10*
a. HF and HCl
b. H_2O or HF
c. H_2Se or H_2S

118. Based on molecular structure, arrange the binary compounds in order of increasing acid strength. Explain your choice.

H_2Te, HI, H_2S, NaH

119. Based on their molecular structure, pick the stronger acid from each pair of oxyacids. Explain your choice.
MISSED THIS? *Read Section 17.10*
a. H_2SO_4 or H_2SO_3
b. $HClO_2$ or HClO
c. HClO or HBrO
d. CCl_3COOH or CH_3COOH

120. Based on molecular structure, arrange the oxyacids in order of increasing acid strength. Explain your choice.

$HClO_3$, HIO_3, $HBrO_3$

121. Which is a stronger base, S^{2-} or Se^{2-}? Explain.
MISSED THIS? *Read Section 17.10*

122. Which is a stronger base, PO_4^{3-} or AsO_4^{3-}? Explain.

Lewis Acids and Bases

123. Classify each species as either a Lewis acid or a Lewis base.
MISSED THIS? *Read Section 17.11*
a. Fe^{3+}
b. BH_3
c. NH_3
d. F^-

124. Classify each species as either a Lewis acid or a Lewis base.
a. $BeCl_2$
b. OH^-
c. $B(OH)_3$
d. CN^-

125. Identify the Lewis acid and Lewis base from among the reactants in each equation.
MISSED THIS? *Read Section 17.11*
a. $Fe^{3+}(aq) + 6\,H_2O(l) \rightleftharpoons Fe(H_2O)_6^{3+}(aq)$
b. $Zn^{2+}(aq) + 4\,NH_3(aq) \rightleftharpoons Zn(NH_3)_4^{2+}(aq)$
c. $(CH_3)_3N(g) + BF_3(g) \rightleftharpoons (CH_3)_3NBF_3(s)$

126. Identify the Lewis acid and Lewis base from among the reactants in each equation.
a. $Ag^+(aq) + 2\,NH_3(aq) \rightleftharpoons Ag(NH_3)_2^+(aq)$
b. $AlBr_3 + NH_3 \rightleftharpoons H_3NAlBr_3$
c. $F^-(aq) + BF_3(aq) \rightleftharpoons BF_4^-(aq)$

CUMULATIVE PROBLEMS

127. Based on these molecular views, determine whether each pictured acid is weak or strong.

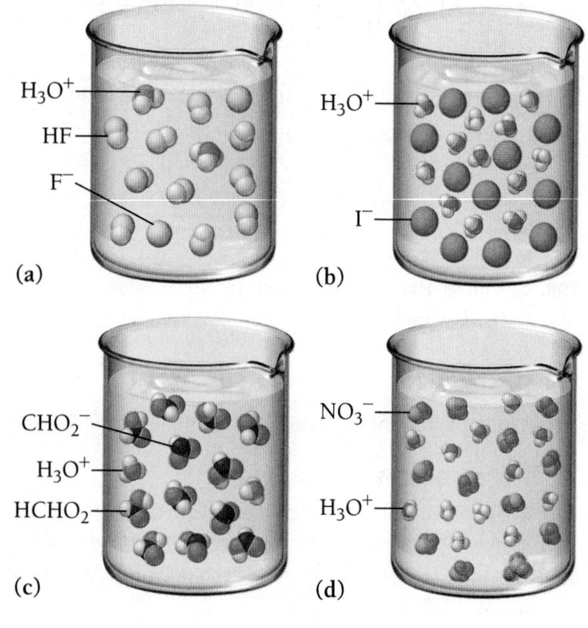

128. Based on these molecular views, determine whether each pictured base is weak or strong.

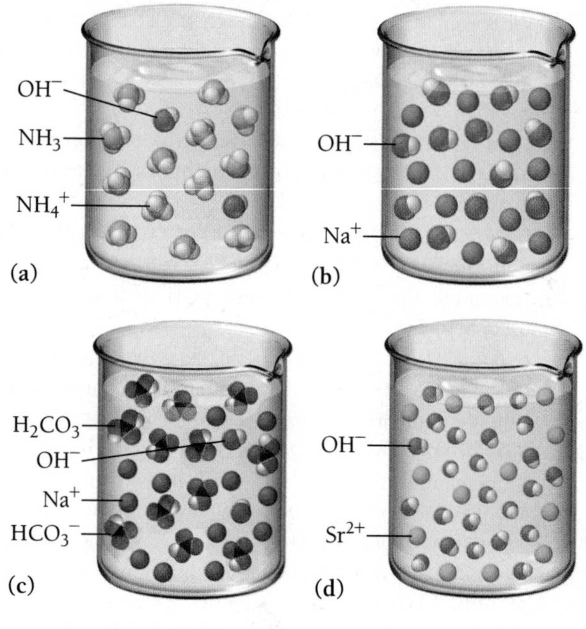

129. The binding of oxygen by hemoglobin in the blood involves the equilibrium reaction:

$$HbH^+(aq) + O_2(aq) \rightleftharpoons HbO_2(aq) + H^+(aq)$$

In this equation, Hb is hemoglobin. The pH of normal human blood is highly controlled within a range of 7.35 to 7.45. Given the above equilibrium, why is this important? What would happen to the oxygen-carrying capacity of hemoglobin if blood became too acidic (a dangerous condition known as acidosis)?

130. Carbon dioxide dissolves in water according to the equations:

$$CO_2(g) + H_2O(l) \rightleftharpoons H_2CO_3(aq)$$

$$H_2CO_3(aq) + H_2O(l) \rightleftharpoons HCO_3^-(aq) + H_3O^+(aq)$$

Carbon dioxide levels in the atmosphere have increased about 20% over the last century. Given that Earth's oceans are exposed to atmospheric carbon dioxide, what effect might the increased CO_2 be having on the pH of the world's oceans? What effect might this change be having on the limestone structures (primarily $CaCO_3$) of coral reefs and marine shells?

131. People often take milk of magnesia to reduce the discomfort associated with acid stomach or heartburn. The recommended dose is 1 teaspoon, which contains 4.00×10^2 mg of $Mg(OH)_2$. What volume of an HCl solution with a pH of 1.3 can be neutralized by one dose of milk of magnesia? If the stomach contains 2.00×10^2 mL of pH 1.3 solution, is all the acid neutralized? If not, what fraction is neutralized?

132. Lakes that have been acidified by acid rain can be neutralized by liming, the addition of limestone ($CaCO_3$). How much limestone (in kg) is required to completely neutralize a 4.3 billion liter lake with a pH of 5.5?

▲ Liming a lake.

133. Acid rain over the Great Lakes has a pH of about 4.5. Calculate the $[H_3O^+]$ of this rain and compare that value to the $[H_3O^+]$ of rain over the West Coast that has a pH of 5.4. How many times more concentrated is the acid in rain over the Great Lakes?

134. White wines tend to be more acidic than red wines. Find the $[H_3O^+]$ in a Sauvignon Blanc with a pH of 3.23 and a Cabernet Sauvignon with a pH of 3.64. How many times more acidic is the Sauvignon Blanc?

135. Common aspirin is acetylsalicylic acid, which has the structure shown here and a pK_a of 3.5.

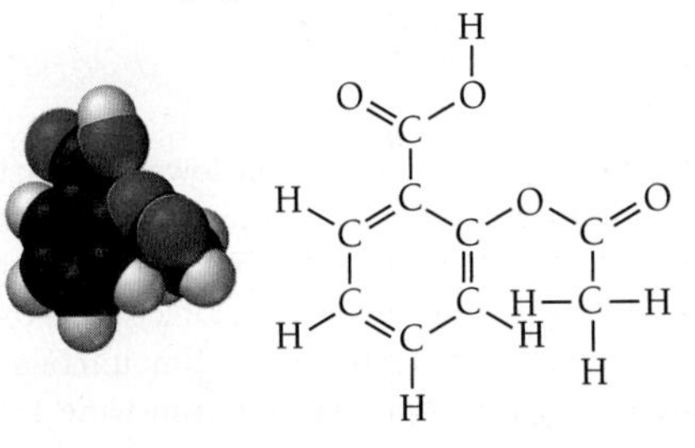

Calculate the pH of a solution in which one normal adult dose of aspirin (6.5×10^2 mg) is dissolved in 8.0 ounces of water.

136. The AIDS drug zalcitabine (also known as ddC) is a weak base with a pK_b of 9.8.

What percentage of the base is protonated in an aqueous zalcitabine solution containing 565 mg/L?

137. Determine the pH of each solution.
a. 0.0100 M $HClO_4$
b. 0.115 M $HClO_2$
c. 0.045 M $Sr(OH)_2$
d. 0.0852 M KCN
e. 0.155 M NH_4Cl

138. Determine the pH of each solution.
a. 0.0650 M HNO_3
b. 0.150 M HNO_2
c. 0.0195 M KOH
d. 0.245 M CH_3NH_3I
e. 0.318 M KC_6H_5O

139. Determine the pH of each two-component solution.
a. 0.0550 M in HI and 0.00850 M in HF
b. 0.112 M in NaCl and 0.0953 M in KF
c. 0.132 M in NH_4Cl and 0.150 M HNO_3
d. 0.0887 M in sodium benzoate and 0.225 M in potassium bromide
e. 0.0450 M in HCl and 0.0225 M in HNO_3

140. Determine the pH of each two-component solution.
a. 0.050 M KOH and 0.015 M $Ba(OH)_2$
b. 0.265 M NH_4NO_3 and 0.102 M HCN
c. 0.075 M RbOH and 0.100 M $NaHCO_3$
d. 0.088 M $HClO_4$ and 0.022 M KOH
e. 0.115 M NaClO and 0.0500 M KI

141. Write net ionic equations for the reactions that take place when aqueous solutions of the following substances are mixed:
a. sodium cyanide and nitric acid
b. ammonium chloride and sodium hydroxide
c. sodium cyanide and ammonium bromide
d. potassium hydrogen sulfate and lithium acetate
e. sodium hypochlorite and ammonia

142. Morphine has the formula $C_{17}H_{19}NO_3$. It is a base and accepts one proton per molecule. It is isolated from opium. A 0.682-g sample of opium is found to require 8.92 mL of a 0.0116 M solution of sulfuric acid for neutralization. Assuming that morphine is the only acid or base present in opium, calculate the percent morphine in the sample of opium.

143. The pH of a 1.00 M solution of urea, a weak organic base, is 7.050. Calculate the K_a of protonated urea.

144. A solution is prepared by dissolving 0.10 mol of acetic acid and 0.10 mol of ammonium chloride in enough water to make 1.0 L of solution. Find the concentration of ammonia in the solution.

145. Lactic acid is a weak acid found in milk. Its calcium salt is a source of calcium for growing animals. A saturated solution of this salt, which we can represent as $Ca(Lact)_2$, has a $[Ca^{2+}] = 0.26$ M and a pH = 8.78. Assuming the salt is completely dissociated, calculate the K_a of lactic acid.

146. A solution of 0.23 mol of the chloride salt of protonated quinine (QH^+), a weak organic base, in 1.0 L of solution has pH = 4.58. Find the K_b of quinine (Q).

CHALLENGE PROBLEMS

147. A student mistakenly calculates the pH of a 1.0×10^{-7} M HI solution to be 7.0. Explain why the student is incorrect and calculate the correct pH.

148. When 2.55 g of an unknown weak acid (HA) with a molar mass of 85.0 g/mol is dissolved in 250.0 g of water, the freezing point of the resulting solution is −0.257 °C. Calculate K_a for the unknown weak acid.

149. Calculate the pH of a solution that is 0.00115 M in HCl and 0.0100 M in $HClO_2$.

150. To what volume should you dilute 1 L of a solution of a weak acid HA to reduce the $[H^+]$ to one-half of that in the original solution?

151. HA, a weak acid, with $K_a = 1.0 \times 10^{-8}$, also forms the ion HA_2^-. The reaction is $HA(aq) + A^-(aq) \rightleftharpoons HA_2^-(aq)$ and its $K = 4.0$. Calculate the $[H^+]$, $[A^-]$, and $[HA_2^-]$ in a 1.0 M solution of HA.

152. Basicity in the gas phase can be defined as the proton affinity of the base, for example, $CH_3NH_2(g) + H^+(g) \rightleftharpoons CH_3NH_3^+(g)$. In the gas phase, $(CH_3)_3N$ is more basic than CH_3NH_2, while in solution the reverse is true. Explain this observation.

153. Calculate the pH of a solution prepared from 0.200 mol of NH_4CN and enough water to make 1.00 L of solution.

154. To 1.0 L of a 0.30 M solution of $HClO_2$ is added 0.20 mol of NaF. Calculate the $[HClO_2]$ at equilibrium.

155. A mixture of Na_2CO_3 and $NaHCO_3$ has a mass of 82.2 g. It is dissolved in 1.00 L of water, and the pH is found to be 9.95. Find the mass of $NaHCO_3$ in the mixture.

156. A mixture of NaCN and $NaHSO_4$ consists of a total of 0.60 mol. When the mixture is dissolved in 1.0 L of water and comes to equilibrium, the pH is found to be 9.9. Find the amount of NaCN in the mixture.

CONCEPTUAL PROBLEMS

157. Without doing any calculations, determine which solution in each pair is more acidic.

a. 0.0100 M in HCl and 0.0100 M in KOH
b. 0.0100 M in HF and 0.0100 M in KBr
c. 0.0100 M in NH_4Cl and 0.0100 M in CH_3NH_3Br
d. 0.100 M in NaCN and 0.100 M in $CaCl_2$

158. Without doing any calculations, determine which solution in each pair is more basic.

a. 0.100 M in NaClO and 0.100 M in NaF
b. 0.0100 M in KCl and 0.0100 M in $KClO_2$
c. 0.0100 M in HNO_3 and 0.0100 M in NaOH
d. 0.0100 M in NH_4Cl and 0.0100 M in HCN

159. Rank the acids in order of increasing acid strength.

CH_3COOH $CH_2ClCOOH$ $CHCl_2COOH$ CCl_3COOH

160. Without using a calculator, determine the pH and pOH of each solution. Rank the solutions from most acidic to most basic.

a. 1.0×10^{-2} M HCl
b. 1.0×10^{-4} M HCl
c. 1.0×10^{-2} M NaOH
d. 1.0×10^{-4} M NaOH

QUESTIONS FOR GROUP WORK

Active Classroom Learning

Discuss these questions with the group and record your consensus answer.

161. Without referring to the text, have each member of your group mention a different property of either an acid or a base, such as "Acids turn blue litmus paper red." Record as many properties as your group can recall without the text.

162. Have each group member make two flashcards with an acid or base on one side and its conjugate on the other side. Check each other's cards and quiz each other until each group member is proficient at identifying conjugate pairs.

163. Answer the following questions in a complete sentence or two:

a. How do you know if an acid is strong or weak?
b. How do you calculate the pH of a strong acid solution?
c. How do you calculate the pH of a weak acid solution?
d. If you know the K_a of an acid, how do you determine the K_b of its conjugate base?
e. If you know $[OH^-]$ for a solution, how do you determine $[H_3O^+]$?

164. Solve the following problem, taking turns in your group to explain how to do the next step: What is the pH when 5.3 g of sodium acetate, $NaC_2H_3O_2$, is dissolved in 100.0 mL of water? (The K_a of acetic acid, $HC_2H_3O_2$, is 1.8×10^{-5}.)

165. Define each of the following with complete sentences, and provide an example chemical equation: an Arrhenius acid, a Brønsted–Lowry base, and a Lewis acid.

DATA INTERPRETATION AND ANALYSIS

Sulfur Dioxide in Wine

166. Sulfur dioxide is a common preservative in wine; it prevents oxidation and bacterial growth. When SO_2 is added to wine, it reacts with water to form an equilibrium system with the bisulfite ion:

$$SO_2(aq) + H_2O(l) \rightleftharpoons H^+(aq) + HSO_3^-(aq)$$

In this equilibrium system, SO_2 is called "molecular SO_2"; in its HSO_3^- form, it is called "free SO_2." Only molecular SO_2 acts as a preservative. The amount of molecular SO_2 in the equilibrium system is highly pH dependent—the lower the pH, the more the equilibrium shifts to the left and the greater the amount of free SO_2. The recommended amount of free SO_2 is 0.8 ppm for white wine and 0.5 ppm for red wine. The table shows the amount of free SO_2 required to obtain the correct amount of molecular SO_2 as a function of pH for both red and white wine. For dilute solutions such as these, 1 ppm = 1 mg/L.

Study the table and and answer the questions.

pH	White Wine 0.8 ppm molecular SO_2	Red Wine 0.5 ppm molecular SO_2
3	13	8
3.05	15	9
3.1	16	10
3.15	19	12
3.2	21	13
3.25	23	15
3.3	26	16
3.35	29	18
3.4	32	20
3.45	37	23
3.5	40	25
3.55	46	29
3.6	50	31
3.65	57	36
3.7	63	39
3.75	72	45
3.8	79	49
3.85	91	57
3.9	99	62

Amount of Free SO_2 Required to Maintain Correct Amount of Molecular SO_2 in White and Red Wine.

a. A 225-L barrel of white wine has an initial free SO_2 concentration of 22 ppm and a pH of 3.70. How much SO_2 (in grams) should be added to the barrel to result in the required SO_2 level?

b. A 225-L barrel of red wine has an initial free SO_2 concentration of 11 ppm and a pH of 3.80. How much SO_2 (in grams) should be added to this barrel to result in the required SO_2 level?

c. Gaseous SO_2 is highly toxic and can be difficult to handle, so winemakers often use potassium metabisulfite ($K_2S_2O_5$), also known as KMBS, as a source of SO_2 in wine. When KMBS is added to wine, the metabisulfite ion ($S_2O_5^{2-}$) reacts with water to form the bisulfite ion (HSO_3^-). Write the balanced equation for the reaction that occurs when the metabisulfite ion reacts with water.

d. Determine the percent by mass of SO_2 in KMBS.

e. How much KMBS must a winemaker add to the barrels of wine in problems (a) and (b) to achieve the required amount of molecular SO_2?

Cc ANSWERS TO CONCEPTUAL CONNECTIONS

Acid Properties

17.1 **(c)** Acids typically have a sour taste. The bitter taste is associated with bases.

Conjugate Acid–Base Pairs

17.2 **(b)** H_2SO_4 and H_2SO_3 are both acids; this is not a conjugate acid–base pair.

The Magnitude of the Acid Ionization Constant

17.3 **(b)** HB has the largest K_a.

Relative Strengths of Weak Acids

17.4 **(a)** HF is stronger because it has a larger acid ionization constant.

Acidity of Solutions

17.5 **(a)** Since the H_3O^+ concentration is greater than 10^{-7} M at room temperature, this solution is acidic.

pH and Acidity

17.6 **(b)** As pH increases, acidity decreases.

The *x is small* Approximation

17.7 **(c)** The validity of the *x is small* approximation depends on both the value of the equilibrium constant and the initial concentration—the closer that these are to one another, the less likely the approximation is valid.

Strong and Weak Acids

17.8 **(a)** A weak acid solution is usually less than 5% dissociated. Since HCl is a strong acid, the 0.10 M solution is much more acidic than either a weak acid with the same concentration or even a weak acid that is twice as concentrated.

Percent Ionization

17.9 Solution **(c)** has the greatest percent ionization because percent ionization increases with decreasing weak acid concentration.

Judging Relative pH

17.10 **(a)** A weak acid solution is usually less than 5% dissociated. Therefore, since HCl is the only strong acid, the 1.0 M solution is much more acidic than either a weak acid that is twice as concentrated or a combination of two weak acids with the same concentrations.

Anions as Weak Bases

17.11 **(c)** The F^- ion is the conjugate base of a *weak* acid (HF) and is therefore a weak base.

Acidity or Basicity of Ionic Compounds

17.12 **(a)** The NH_4^+ cation is the conjugate acid of a weak base and is therefore a weak acid. The Br^- ion is the conjugate base of a *strong* acid (HBr) and is therefore pH-neutral. Therefore, the compound forms an acidic solution when dissolved in water.

Acid Strength and Molecular Structure

17.13 **(a)** Since the carbon atom in **(a)** is bonded to another oxygen atom, which draws electron density away from the O—H bond (weakening and polarizing it), and the carbon atom in **(b)** is bonded only to other hydrogen atoms, the proton in structure **(a)** is more acidic.

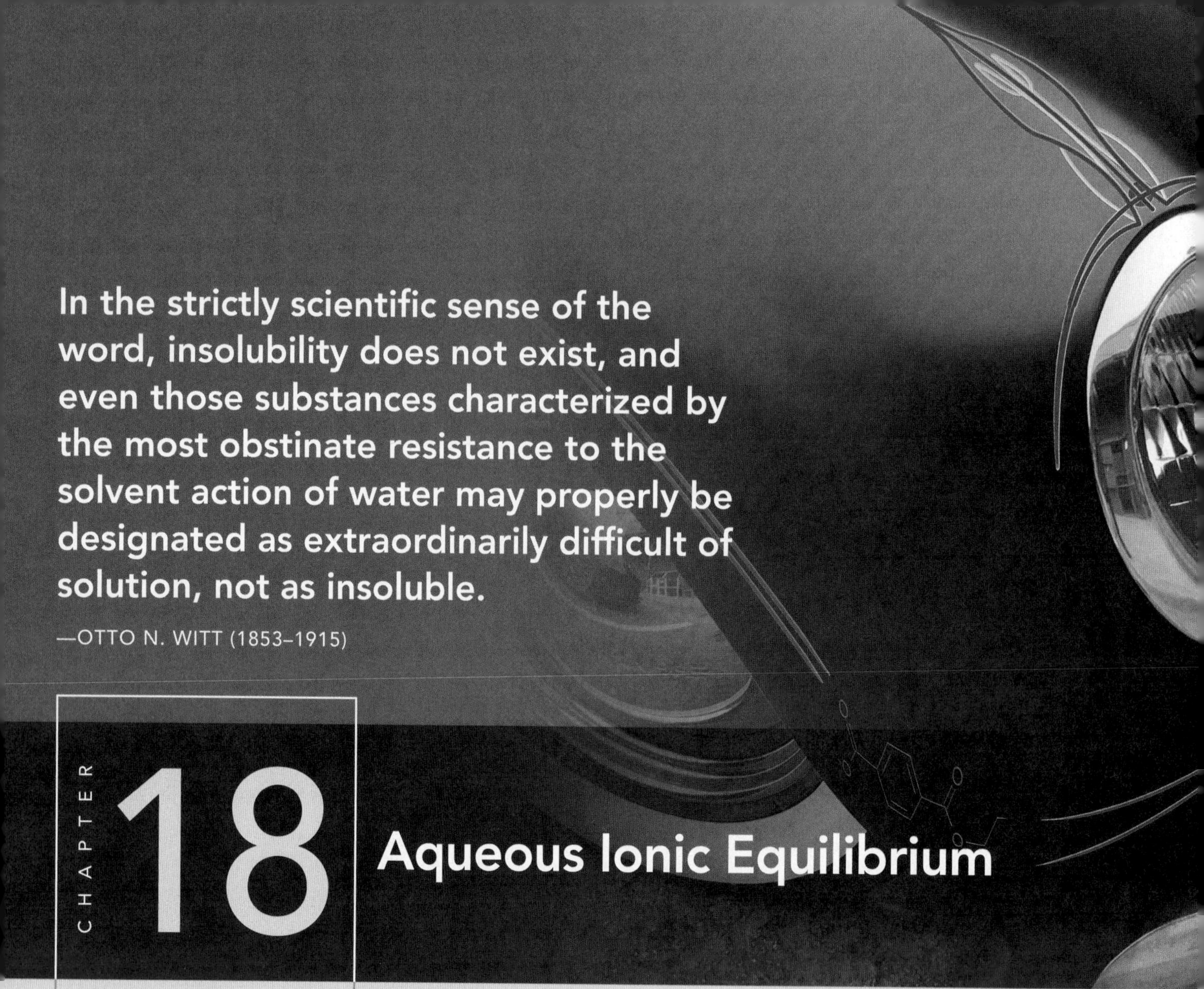

In the strictly scientific sense of the word, insolubility does not exist, and even those substances characterized by the most obstinate resistance to the solvent action of water may properly be designated as extraordinarily difficult of solution, not as insoluble.

—OTTO N. WITT (1853–1915)

CHAPTER 18 Aqueous Ionic Equilibrium

We have already seen the importance of aqueous solutions, first in Chapters 5, 14, and 16, and most recently in Chapter 17 on acids and bases. We now turn our attention to two additional topics involving aqueous solutions: buffers (solutions that resist pH change) and solubility equilibria (the extent to which slightly soluble ionic compounds dissolve in water). Buffers are tremendously important in biology because nearly all physiological processes must occur within a narrow pH range. Solubility equilibria are related to the solubility rules that we discussed in Chapter 5. In this chapter, we find a more complicated picture: solids that we considered insoluble under the simple "solubility rules" are actually better described as being only very slightly soluble, as the chapter-opening quotation from Otto Witt suggests. Solubility equilibria are important in predicting not only solubility, but also precipitation reactions that might occur when aqueous solutions are mixed.

Antifreeze is a dangerous poison that affects the blood's ability to carry oxygen.

18.1 The Danger of Antifreeze 787

18.2 Buffers: Solutions That Resist pH Change 788

18.3 Buffer Effectiveness: Buffer Range and Buffer Capacity 799

18.4 Titrations and pH Curves 803

18.5 Solubility Equilibria and the Solubility Product Constant 817

18.6 Precipitation 823

18.7 Qualitative Chemical Analysis 826

18.8 Complex Ion Equilibria 829

LEARNING OUTCOMES 835

18.1 The Danger of Antifreeze

Every year, thousands of dogs and cats die from consuming a common household product: improperly stored or leaked antifreeze. Most types of auto antifreeze are aqueous solutions of ethylene glycol:

Some brands of antifreeze use propylene glycol, which is less toxic than ethylene glycol.

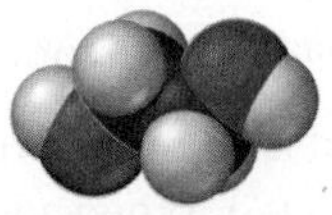

$HOCH_2CH_2OH$

Ethylene glycol has a somewhat sweet taste that can attract curious dogs and cats—and sometimes even young children, who are also vulnerable to this toxic compound. The first stage of ethylene glycol poisoning is a state resembling drunkenness. Because the compound is an alcohol, it affects the brain much as an alcoholic beverage would. Once ethylene glycol starts to be metabolized, however, a second and more deadly stage commences.

In the liver, ethylene glycol is oxidized to glycolic acid ($HOCH_2COOH$), which enters the bloodstream. The acidity of blood is critically important and tightly regulated because many proteins only function in a narrow pH range. In human blood, for example, pH is held between 7.36 and 7.42. This nearly constant blood pH is maintained by *buffers*. We discuss buffers more carefully later in this chapter, but for now know that a buffer is a chemical system that resists pH changes by neutralizing added acid or base. An important buffer in blood is a mixture of carbonic acid (H_2CO_3) and the bicarbonate ion (HCO_3^-). The carbonic acid neutralizes added base:

$$H_2CO_3(aq) + \underset{\text{added base}}{OH^-(aq)} \longrightarrow H_2O(l) + HCO_3^-(aq)$$

The bicarbonate ion neutralizes added acid:

$$HCO_3^-(aq) + \underset{\text{added acid}}{H^+(aq)} \longrightarrow H_2CO_3(aq)$$

In this way, the carbonic acid and bicarbonate ion buffering system keeps blood pH nearly constant.

When the glycolic acid generated by antifreeze consumption first enters the bloodstream, the acid's tendency to lower blood pH is countered by the buffering action of the bicarbonate ion. However, if the quantities of consumed antifreeze are large enough, the glycolic acid overwhelms the capacity of the buffer (we discuss buffer capacity in Section 18.3), causing blood pH to drop to dangerously low levels.

Low blood pH results in *acidosis*, a condition in which the acid affects the equilibrium between hemoglobin (Hb) and oxygen:

Excess H^+

$$HbH^+(aq) + O_2(g) \rightleftharpoons HbO_2(aq) + H^+(aq)$$

Shift left

The excess acid causes the equilibrium to shift to the left, reducing the blood's ability to carry oxygen. At this point, the cat or dog may begin hyperventilating in an effort to overcome the acidic blood's lowered oxygen-carrying capacity. If no treatment is administered, the animal will eventually go into a coma and die.

One treatment for ethylene glycol poisoning is the administration of ethyl alcohol (the alcohol found in alcoholic beverages). The two molecules are similar enough that the liver enzyme that catalyzes the metabolism of ethylene glycol also acts on ethyl alcohol, but the enzyme has a higher affinity for ethyl alcohol than for ethylene glycol. Consequently, the enzyme preferentially metabolizes ethyl alcohol, allowing the unmetabolized ethylene glycol to escape through the urine. If administered early, this treatment can save the life of a dog or cat that has consumed ethylene glycol.

WATCH NOW!

KEY CONCEPT VIDEO 18.2A
Buffers

18.2 Buffers: Solutions That Resist pH Change

Most solutions significantly change pH when an acid or base is added to them. As we have just learned, however, a **buffer** resists pH change by neutralizing added acid or added base. A buffer contains either:

1. significant amounts of a weak acid and its conjugate base or
2. significant amounts of a weak base and its conjugate acid.

For example, the buffer in blood is composed of carbonic acid (H_2CO_3) and its conjugate base, the bicarbonate ion (HCO_3^-). When additional base is added to a buffer, the weak acid reacts with the base, neutralizing it. When additional acid is added to a buffer, the conjugate base reacts with the acid, neutralizing it. In this way, a buffer can maintain a nearly constant pH.

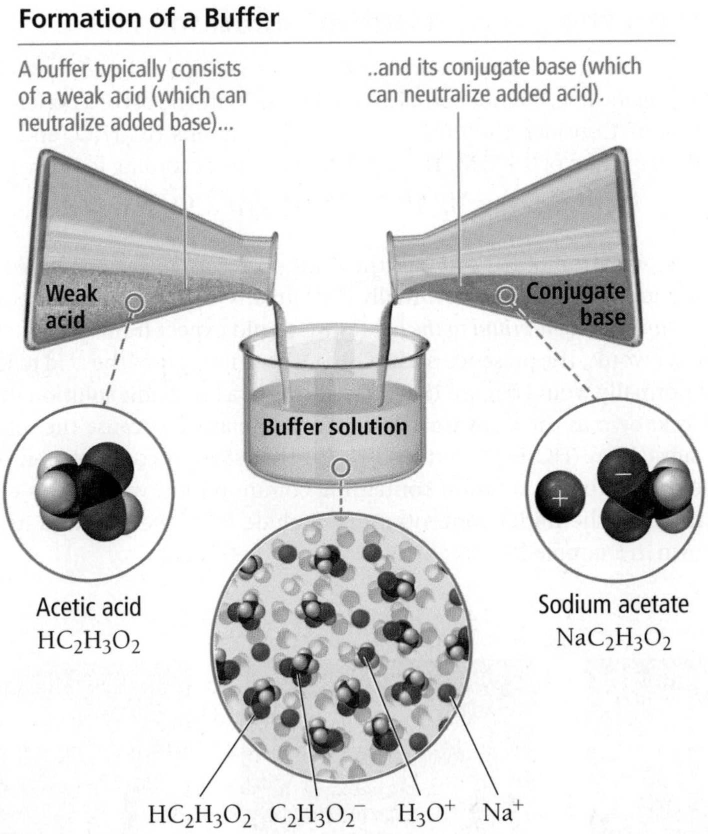

◀ **FIGURE 18.1 A Buffer Solution**

A weak acid by itself, even though it partially ionizes to form some of its conjugate base, does not contain sufficient base to be a buffer. Similarly, a weak base by itself, even though it partially ionizes water to form some of its conjugate acid, does not contain sufficient acid to be a buffer. *A buffer must contain significant amounts of both a weak acid and its conjugate base (or vice versa)*. Consider the simple buffer made by dissolving acetic acid ($HC_2H_3O_2$) and sodium acetate ($NaC_2H_3O_2$) in water (Figure 18.1▲).

Suppose, on one hand, that we add a strong base, such as NaOH, to this solution. The acetic acid neutralizes the base:

$$NaOH(aq) + HC_2H_3O_2(aq) \longrightarrow H_2O(l) + NaC_2H_3O_2(aq)$$

$C_2H_3O_2^-$ is the conjugate base of $HC_2H_3O_2$.

As long as the amount of added NaOH is less than the amount of $HC_2H_3O_2$ in solution, the buffer neutralizes the added NaOH and the resulting pH change is small.

Suppose, on the other hand, that we add a strong acid, such as HCl, to the solution. In this case, the conjugate base, $NaC_2H_3O_2$, neutralizes the added HCl:

$$HCl(aq) + NaC_2H_3O_2(aq) \longrightarrow HC_2H_3O_2(aq) + NaCl(aq)$$

As long as the amount of added HCl is less than the amount of $NaC_2H_3O_2$ in solution, the buffer neutralizes the added HCl and the resulting pH change is small.

Summarizing Buffer Characteristics:

- Buffers resist pH change.
- A buffer contains significant amounts of either (1) a weak acid and its conjugate base, or (2) a weak base and its conjugate acid.
- The acid neutralizes added base.
- The base neutralizes added acid.

BUFFERS Which solution is a buffer?

(a) a solution that is 0.100 M in HNO_2 and 0.100 M in HCl
(b) a solution that is 0.100 M in HNO_3 and 0.100 M in $NaNO_3$
(c) a solution that is 0.100 M in HNO_2 and 0.100 M in NaCl
(d) a solution that is 0.100 M in HNO_2 and 0.100 M in $NaNO_2$

18.1 Cc Conceptual Connection

ANSWER **NOW!**

WATCH **NOW!**

KEY CONCEPT VIDEO 18.2B
Finding pH and pH Changes in Buffer Solutions

Calculating the pH of a Buffer Solution

In Chapter 17, we discussed how to calculate the pH of a solution containing either a weak acid or its conjugate base, but not both. How do we calculate the pH of a buffer—a solution containing both? Consider a solution that initially contains $HC_2H_3O_2$ and $NaC_2H_3O_2$, each at a concentration of 0.100 M. The acetic acid ionizes according to the reaction:

$$HC_2H_3O_2(aq) + H_2O(l) \rightleftharpoons H_3O^+(aq) + C_2H_3O_2^-(aq)$$

Initial concentration: 0.100 M (for $HC_2H_3O_2$); 0.100 M (for $C_2H_3O_2^-$)

Le Châtelier's principle is discussed in Section 16.9.

However, the ionization of $HC_2H_3O_2$ in the solution is suppressed compared to its ionization in a solution that does not initially contain any $C_2H_3O_2^-$, because the presence of $C_2H_3O_2^-$ *shifts the equilibrium to the left* (as we would expect from Le Châtelier's principle). In other words, the presence of the $C_2H_3O_2^-(aq)$ ion causes the acid to ionize even less than it normally would (Figure 18.2▼), resulting in a less acidic solution (higher pH). This effect is known as the **common ion effect**, so named because the solution contains two substances ($HC_2H_3O_2$ and $NaC_2H_3O_2$) that share a common ion ($C_2H_3O_2^-$). To find the pH of a buffer solution containing common ions, we work an equilibrium problem in which the initial concentrations include both the acid and its conjugate base, as shown in Example 18.1.

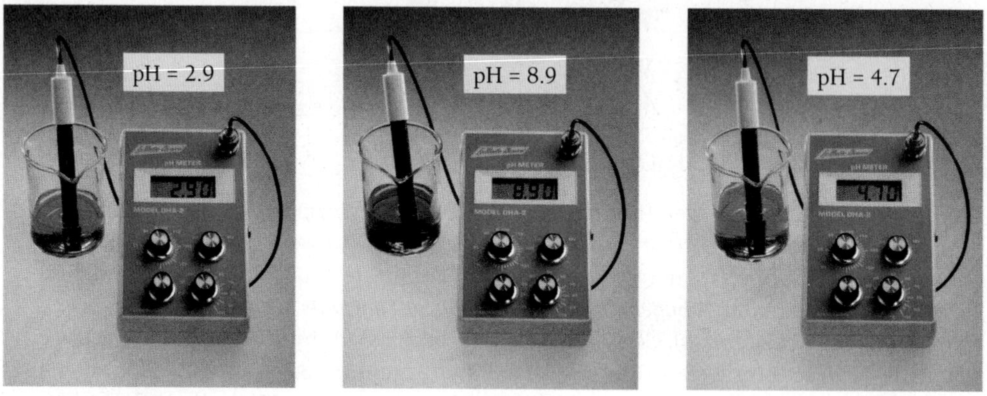

0.100 M $HC_2H_3O_2$ | 0.100 M $NaC_2H_3O_2$ | 0.100 M $HC_2H_3O_2$, 0.100 M $NaC_2H_3O_2$

▶ **FIGURE 18.2 The Common Ion Effect** The pH of a 0.100 M acetic acid solution is 2.9. The pH of a 0.100 M sodium acetate solution is 8.9. The pH of a solution that is 0.100 M in acetic acid and 0.100 M in sodium acetate is 4.7.

EXAMPLE 18.1 Calculating the pH of a Buffer Solution

Calculate the pH of a buffer solution that is 0.100 M in $HC_2H_3O_2$ and 0.100 M in $NaC_2H_3O_2$.

SOLUTION

1. Write the balanced equation for the ionization of the acid and use it as a guide to prepare an ICE table showing the given concentrations of the acid and its conjugate base as the initial concentrations. Leave room in the table for the changes in concentrations and for the equilibrium concentrations.

$$HC_2H_3O_2(aq) + H_2O(l) \rightleftharpoons H_3O^+(aq) + C_2H_3O_2^-(aq)$$

	$[HC_2H_3O_2]$	$[H_3O^+]$	$[C_2H_3O_2^-]$
Initial	0.100	≈ 0.00	0.100
Change			
Equil			

2. Represent the change in the concentration of H_3O^+ with the variable x. Express the changes in the concentrations of the other reactants and products in terms of x.

$$HC_2H_3O_2(aq) + H_2O(l) \rightleftharpoons H_3O^+(aq) + C_2H_3O_2^-(aq)$$

	$[HC_2H_3O_2]$	$[H_3O^+]$	$[C_2H_3O_2^-]$
Initial	0.100	≈ 0.00	0.100
Change	$-x$	$+x$	$+x$
Equil			

3. Sum each column to determine the equilibrium concentrations in terms of the initial concentrations and the variable x.

$$HC_2H_3O_2(aq) + H_2O(l) \rightleftharpoons H_3O^+(aq) + C_2H_3O_2^-(aq)$$

	$[HC_2H_3O_2]$	$[H_3O^+]$	$[C_2H_3O_2^-]$
Initial	0.100	≈ 0.00	0.100
Change	−x	+x	+x
Equil	0.100 − x	x	0.100 + x

4. Substitute the expressions for the equilibrium concentrations (from step 3) into the expression for the acid ionization constant.

In most cases, you can make the approximation that *x is small*. (See Sections 16.8 and 17.6 to review the *x is small* approximation.)

$$K_a = \frac{[H_3O^+][C_2H_3O^-]}{[HC_2H_3O_2]}$$

$$= \frac{x(0.100 + \cancel{x})}{0.100 - \cancel{x}} \qquad (x \text{ is small})$$

Substitute the value of the acid ionization constant (from Table 17.5) into the K_a expression and solve for x.

$$1.8 \times 10^{-5} = \frac{x(\cancel{0.100})}{\cancel{0.100}}$$

Confirm that *x is small* by calculating the ratio of x and the number it was subtracted from in the approximation. The ratio should be less than 0.05 (5%).

$$x = 1.8 \times 10^{-5}$$

$$\frac{1.8 \times 10^{-5}}{0.100} \times 100\% = 0.018\%$$

Therefore the approximation is valid.

5. Determine the H_3O^+ concentration from the calculated value of x and substitute into the pH equation to find pH.

$$[H_3O^+] = x = 1.8 \times 10^{-5}\,M$$

$$pH = -\log[H_3O^+]$$

$$= -\log(1.8 \times 10^{-5})$$

$$= 4.74$$

FOR PRACTICE 18.1 Calculate the pH of a buffer solution that is 0.200 M in $HC_2H_3O_2$ and 0.100 M in $NaC_2H_3O_2$.

FOR MORE PRACTICE 18.1 Calculate the pH of the buffer that results from mixing 60.0 mL of 0.250 M $HCHO_2$ and 15.0 mL of 0.500 M $NaCHO_2$.

The Henderson–Hasselbalch Equation

We can derive an equation that relates the pH of a buffer solution to the initial concentration of the buffer components, thus simplifying the calculation of the pH of a buffer solution. Consider a buffer containing the generic weak acid HA and its conjugate base A^-. The acid ionizes as follows:

$$HA(aq) + H_2O(l) \rightleftharpoons H_3O^+(aq) + A^-(aq)$$

We derive an expression for the concentration of H_3O^+ from the acid ionization equilibrium expression by solving the expression for $[H_3O^+]$:

$$K_a = \frac{[H_3O^+][A^-]}{[HA]}$$

$$[H_3O^+] = K_a \frac{[HA]}{[A^-]} \qquad [18.1]$$

If we make the same *x is small* approximation that we make for weak acid or weak base equilibrium problems, *we can consider the equilibrium concentrations of HA and A^- to be essentially identical to the initial concentrations of HA and A^-* (see step 4 of Example 18.1). Therefore, to determine $[H_3O^+]$ for any buffer solution, we multiply K_a by the ratio of the

Recall that the variable x in a weak acid equilibrium problem represents the change in the initial acid concentration. The *x is small* approximation is valid because so little of the weak acid ionizes compared to its initial concentration.

concentrations of the acid and the conjugate base. To find the $[H_3O^+]$ of the buffer in Example 18.1 (a solution that is 0.100 M in $HC_2H_3O_2$ and 0.100 M in $NaC_2H_3O_2$), we substitute the concentrations of $HC_2H_3O_2$ and $C_2H_3O_2^-$ into Equation 18.1:

$$[H_3O^+] = K_a \frac{[HC_2H_3O_2]}{[C_2H_3O_2^-]}$$
$$= K_a \frac{0.100}{0.100}$$
$$= K_a$$

In this buffer solution, as in any in which the acid and conjugate base concentrations are equal, $[H_3O^+]$ is equal to K_a.

We can derive an equation for the pH of a buffer by taking the negative logarithm of both sides of Equation 18.1:

Recall that log AB = log A + log B, so −log AB = −log A − log B.

$$[H_3O^+] = K_a \frac{[HA]}{[A^-]}$$
$$-\log[H_3O^+] = -\log\left(K_a \frac{[HA]}{[A^-]}\right)$$
$$-\log[H_3O^+] = -\log K_a - \log\frac{[HA]}{[A^-]} \quad [18.2]$$

We can rearrange Equation 18.2 to get:

Recall that log (A/B) = −log (B/A), so −log (A/B) = log (B/A).

$$-\log[H_3O^+] = -\log K_a + \log\frac{[A^-]}{[HA]}$$

Since pH $= -\log [H_3O^+]$ and since $pK_a = -\log K_a$, we obtain the result:

$$pH = pK_a + \log\frac{[A^-]}{[HA]}$$

Since A^- is a weak base and HA is a weak acid, we can generalize the equation:

Note that, as expected, the pH of a buffer increases with an increase in the amount of base relative to the amount of acid.

$$pH = pK_a + \log\frac{[\text{base}]}{[\text{acid}]} \quad [18.3]$$

where the base is the conjugate base of the acid or the acid is the conjugate acid of the base. This equation, known as the **Henderson–Hasselbalch equation**, allows us to quickly calculate the pH of a buffer solution from the initial concentrations of the buffer components *as long as the x is small approximation is valid*. In Example 18.2, we show how to find the pH of a buffer in two ways: in the left column we solve a common ion effect equilibrium problem using a method similar to the one we used in Example 18.1; in the right column we use the Henderson–Hasselbalch equation.

WATCH **NOW!**

INTERACTIVE WORKED EXAMPLE 18.2

EXAMPLE 18.2 Calculating the pH of a Buffer Solution as an Equilibrium Problem and with the Henderson–Hasselbalch Equation

Calculate the pH of a buffer solution that is 0.050 M in benzoic acid ($HC_7H_5O_2$) and 0.150 M in sodium benzoate ($NaC_7H_5O_2$). For benzoic acid, $K_a = 6.5 \times 10^{-5}$.

SOLUTION

Equilibrium Approach	Henderson–Hasselbalch Approach
Write the balanced equation for the ionization of the acid and use it as a guide to prepare an ICE table.	To find the pH of this solution, determine which component is the acid and which is the base and substitute their concentrations into the Henderson–Hasselbalch equation to calculate pH.

$$HC_7H_5O_2(aq) + H_2O(l) \rightleftharpoons H_3O^+(aq) + C_7H_5O_2^-(aq)$$

	$[HC_7H_5O_2]$	$[H_3O^+]$	$[C_7H_5O_2^-]$
Initial	0.050	≈ 0.00	0.150
Change	−x	+x	+x
Equil	0.050 − x	x	0.150 + x

Substitute the expressions for the equilibrium concentrations into the expression for the acid ionization constant. Make the *x is small* approximation and solve for *x*.

$$K_a = \frac{[H_3O^+][C_7H_5O_2^-]}{[HC_7H_5O_2]}$$

$$= \frac{x(0.150 + \cancel{x})}{0.050 - \cancel{x}} \quad (x \text{ is small})$$

$$6.5 \times 10^{-5} = \frac{x(0.150)}{0.050}$$

$$x = 2.2 \times 10^{-5}$$

Since $[H_3O^+] = x$, we calculate pH as follows:

$$pH = -\log[H_3O^+]$$

$$= -\log(2.2 \times 10^{-5})$$

$$= 4.66$$

$HC_7H_5O_2$ is the acid and $NaC_7H_5O_2$ is the base. Therefore, we calculate the pH as follows:

$$pH = pK_a + \log\frac{[\text{base}]}{[\text{acid}]}$$

$$= -\log(6.5 \times 10^{-5}) + \log\frac{0.150}{0.050}$$

$$= 4.1\underline{8}7 + 0.4\underline{7}7$$

$$= 4.66$$

Confirm that the *x is small* approximation is valid by calculating the ratio of *x* to the number it was subtracted from in the approximation. The ratio should be less than 0.05 (5%). (See Sections 16.8 and 17.6 to review the *x is small* approximation.)

$$\frac{2.2 \times 10^{-5}}{0.050} \times 100\% = 0.044\%$$

The approximation is valid.

Confirm that the *x is small* approximation is valid by calculating the $[H_3O^+]$ from the pH. Since $[H_3O^+]$ is formed by ionization of the acid, the calculated $[H_3O^+]$ has to be less than 0.05 (or 5%) of the initial concentration of the acid in order for the *x is small* approximation to be valid.

$$pH = 4.66 = -\log[H_3O^+]$$

$$[H_3O^+] = 10^{-4.66} = 2.2 \times 10^{-5}\,M$$

$$\frac{2.2 \times 10^{-5}}{0.050} \times 100\% = 0.044\%$$

The approximation is valid.

FOR PRACTICE 18.2 Calculate the pH of a buffer solution that is 0.250 M in HCN and 0.170 M in KCN. For HCN, $K_a = 4.9 \times 10^{-10}$ ($pK_a = 9.31$). Use both the equilibrium approach and the Henderson–Hasselbalch approach.

You may be wondering how to decide whether to use the equilibrium approach or the Henderson–Hasselbalch equation when calculating the pH of buffer solutions. The answer depends on the specific problem. In cases where you can make the *x is small* approximation, the Henderson–Hasselbalch equation is adequate. However, as you can see from Example 18.2, checking the *x is small* approximation is not as convenient with the Henderson–Hasselbalch equation (because the approximation is implicit). Thus, the equilibrium approach, though lengthier, gives you a better sense of the important quantities in the problem and the nature of the approximation.

When first working buffer problems, use the equilibrium approach until you get a good sense for when the *x is small* approximation is adequate. Then you can switch to the more streamlined approach in cases where the approximation applies (and only in those cases). In general, remember that the *x is small* approximation applies to problems in which both of the following are true: (a) the initial concentrations of acids (and/or bases) are not too dilute; and (b) the equilibrium constant is fairly small. Although the exact values depend on the details of the problem, for many buffer problems this means that the initial concentrations of acids and conjugate bases should be at least 10^2–10^3 times greater than the equilibrium constant (depending on the required accuracy).

ANSWER NOW!

18.2 Cc Conceptual Connection

pH OF BUFFER SOLUTIONS A buffer contains the weak acid HA and its conjugate base A^-. The weak acid has a pK_a of 4.82 and the buffer has a pH of 4.25. Which statement is true of the relative concentrations of the weak acid and conjugate base in the buffer?

(a) $[HA] > [A^-]$ **(b)** $[HA] < [A^-]$ **(c)** $[HA] = [A^-]$

Calculating pH Changes in a Buffer Solution

When we add acid or base to a buffer, the buffer resists a pH change. Nonetheless, the pH does change by a small amount. Calculating the pH change requires breaking up the problem into two parts:

1. **The stoichiometry calculation** in which we calculate how the addition changes the relative amounts of acid and conjugate base.
2. **The equilibrium calculation** in which we calculate the pH based on the new amounts of acid and conjugate base.

We demonstrate this calculation with a 1.0-L buffer solution that is 0.100 M in the generic acid HA and 0.100 M in its conjugate base A^-. Since the concentrations of the weak acid and the conjugate base are equal, the pH of the buffer is equal to pK_a. Let's calculate the pH of the solution after we add 0.025 mol of strong acid (H^+) (assuming that the change in volume from adding the acid is negligible).

The Stoichiometry Calculation

As the added acid is neutralized, it converts a stoichiometric amount of the base into its conjugate acid through the neutralization reaction (Figure 18.3a▶, on p. 796):

$$\underset{\text{added acid}}{H^+(aq)} + \underset{\text{weak base in buffer}}{A^-(aq)} \longrightarrow HA(aq)$$

Neutralizing 0.025 mol of the strong acid (H^+) requires 0.025 mol of the weak base (A^-). Consequently, the amount of A^- *decreases* by 0.025 mol, and the amount of HA *increases* by 0.025 mol (because of the 1:1:1 stoichiometry of the neutralization reaction). We can track these changes in tabular form as follows:

It is best to work with amounts in moles instead of concentrations when tracking these changes, as explained later in this chapter.

	$H^+(aq)$	+	$A^-(aq)$	$\longrightarrow$	$HA(aq)$
Before addition	≈0.00 mol		0.100 mol		0.100 mol
Addition	+0.025 mol		—		—
After addition	≈0.00 mol		0.075 mol		0.125 mol

Notice that this table is not an ICE table. This table simply tracks the stoichiometric changes that occur during the neutralization of the added acid. We write ≈0.00 mol for the amount of H^+ because the amount is so small compared to the amounts of A^- and HA. (Remember that weak acids ionize only to a small extent and that the presence of the common ion further suppresses the ionization.) The amount of H^+, of course, is not *exactly* zero, as we can see by completing the equilibrium part of the calculation.

The Equilibrium Calculation

We have just seen that adding a small amount of acid to a buffer is equivalent to changing the initial concentrations of the acid and conjugate base present in the buffer (in this case, since the volume is 1.0 L, [HA] increased from 0.100 M to 0.125 M and $[A^-]$ decreased from 0.100 M to 0.075 M). Knowing these new initial concentrations, we can calculate the new pH in the same way that we calculate the pH of any buffer: either by working a full equilibrium problem or by using the Henderson–Hasselbalch equation (see Examples 18.1 and 18.2).

In this case, we work the full equilibrium problem. We begin by writing the balanced equation for the ionization of the acid and using it as a guide to prepare an ICE table. The initial concentrations for the ICE table are those that we calculated in the stoichiometry part of the calculation:

$$HA(aq) + H_2O(l) \rightleftharpoons H_3O^+(aq) + A^-(aq)$$

	$[HA]$	$[H_3O^+]$	$[A^-]$
Initial	0.125	≈0.00	0.075
Change	$-x$	$+x$	$+x$
Equil	$0.125 - x$	x	$0.075 + x$

From stoichiometry calculation

We then substitute the expressions for the equilibrium concentrations into the expression for the acid ionization constant. As long as K_a is sufficiently small relative to the initial concentrations, we can make the *x is small* approximation and solve for x, which is equal to $[H_3O^+]$:

$$K_a = \frac{[H_3O^+][A^-]}{[HA]}$$

$$= \frac{x(0.075 + \cancel{x})}{0.125 - \cancel{x}} \quad (x \text{ is small})$$

$$K_a = \frac{x(0.075)}{0.125}$$

$$x = [H_3O^+] = K_a \frac{0.125}{0.075}$$

Once we calculate $[H_3O^+]$, we can calculate the pH with the equation $pH = -\log[H_3O^+]$.

Notice that, since the expression for x contains a *ratio* of concentrations $[HA]/[A^-]$, the *amounts of acid and base in moles* may be substituted in place of concentration because, in a single buffer solution, the volume is the same for both the acid and the base. Therefore, the volumes cancel:

$$[HA]/[A^-] = \frac{\frac{n_{HA}}{\cancel{V}}}{\frac{n_{A^-}}{\cancel{V}}} = n_{HA}/n_{A^-}$$

The effect of adding a small amount of strong base to the buffer is exactly the opposite of adding acid. The added base converts a stoichiometric amount of the acid into its conjugate base through the neutralization reaction (Figure 18.3b▶):

$$\underset{\text{added base}}{OH^-(aq)} + \underset{\text{weak acid in buffer}}{HA(aq)} \longrightarrow H_2O(l) + A^-(aq)$$

If we add 0.025 mol of OH^-, the amount of A^- goes *up* by 0.025 mol and the amount of HA goes *down* by 0.025 mol, as shown in the following table:

	$OH^-(aq)$	+	$HA(aq)$	⟶	$H_2O(l)$	+	$A^-(aq)$
Before addition	≈0.00 mol		0.100 mol				0.100 mol
Addition	+0.025 mol		—				—
After addition	≈0.00 mol		0.075 mol				0.125 mol

When you calculate the pH of a buffer after adding small amounts of acid or base, remember the following:

- Adding a small amount of strong acid to a buffer converts a stoichiometric amount of the base to the conjugate acid and decreases the pH of the buffer (adding acid decreases pH just as we would expect).
- Adding a small amount of strong base to a buffer converts a stoichiometric amount of the acid to the conjugate base and increases the pH of the buffer (adding base increases the pH just as we would expect).

The easiest way to remember these changes is relatively simple: adding acid creates more acid; adding base creates more base.

▶ **FIGURE 18.3 Buffering Action** **(a)** When a strong acid is added to a buffer, a stoichiometric amount of the weak base is converted to the conjugate acid. **(b)** When a strong base is added to a buffer, a stoichiometric amount of the weak acid is converted to the conjugate base.

Action of a Buffer

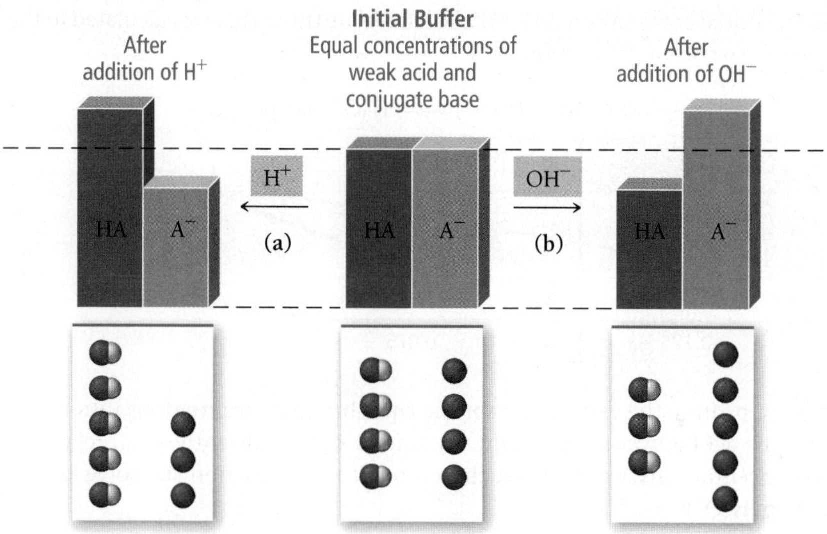

HOW TO: *Calculate pH Changes in a Buffer Solution after Adding Small Amounts of Strong Acid or Strong Base*

1. **Stoichiometry Calculation** Use the stoichiometry of the neutralization equation to calculate the changes in the amounts (in moles) of the buffer components upon addition of the acid or base.
2. **Equilibrium Calculation** Use the new amounts of buffer components to work an equilibrium problem to find pH. (For most buffers, this can also be done with the Henderson–Hasselbalch equation.)

Example 18.3 and the For Practice Problems that follow apply this procedure.

ANSWER **NOW!**

18.3 Cc Conceptual Connection

BUFFERING ACTION Closely examine Figure 18.3▲. Which image best represents the amount of OH^- added to the buffer in part (b) of the figure?

a. 
b. 
c. 

WATCH **NOW!**
INTERACTIVE WORKED EXAMPLE 18.3

EXAMPLE 18.3 Calculating the pH Change in a Buffer Solution after the Addition of a Small Amount of Strong Acid or Base

A 1.0-L buffer solution contains 0.100 mol $HC_2H_3O_2$ and 0.100 mol $NaC_2H_3O_2$. The value of K_a for $HC_2H_3O_2$ is 1.8×10^{-5}. Because the initial amounts of acid and conjugate base are equal, the pH of the buffer is equal to $pK_a = -\log(1.8 \times 10^{-5}) = 4.74$. Calculate the new pH after adding 0.010 mol of solid NaOH to the buffer. For comparison, calculate the pH after adding 0.010 mol of solid NaOH to 1.0 L of pure water. (Ignore any small changes in volume that might occur upon addition of the base.)

SOLUTION

1. **Stoichiometry Calculation** The addition of the base converts a stoichiometric amount of acid to the conjugate base (adding base creates more base). Write an equation showing the neutralization reaction and then set up a table to track the changes.

	$OH^-(aq)$ +	$HC_2H_3O_2(aq)$ ⟶	$H_2O(l)$ +	$C_2H_3O_2^-(aq)$
Before addition	≈0.00 mol	0.100 mol		0.100 mol
Addition	0.010 mol	—		—
After addition	≈0.00 mol	0.090 mol		0.110 mol

2. Equilibrium Calculation Write the balanced equation for the ionization of the acid and use it as a guide to prepare an ICE table. Use the amounts of acid and conjugate base from part I as the initial amounts of acid and conjugate base in the ICE table.

$$HC_2H_3O_2(aq) + H_2O(l) \rightleftharpoons H_3O^+(aq) + C_2H_3O_2^-(aq)$$

	$[HC_2H_3O_2]$	$[H_3O^+]$	$[C_2H_3O_2^-]$
Initial	0.090	≈0.00	0.110
Change	−x	+x	+x
Equil	0.090 − x	x	0.110 + x

Substitute the expressions for the equilibrium concentrations of acid and conjugate base into the expression for the acid ionization constant. Make the *x is small* approximation and solve for *x*. Calculate the pH from the value of *x*, which is equal to $[H_3O^+]$.

$$K_a = \frac{[H_3O^+][C_2H_3O_2^-]}{[HC_2H_3O_2]}$$

$$= \frac{x(0.110 + \cancel{x})}{0.090 - \cancel{x}} \quad (x \text{ is small})$$

$$1.8 \times 10^{-5} = \frac{x(0.110)}{0.090}$$

$$x = [H_3O^+] = 1.4\underline{7} \times 10^{-5} \text{ M}$$

$$pH = -\log[H_3O^+]$$

$$= -\log(1.4\underline{7} \times 10^{-5})$$

$$= 4.83$$

Confirm that the *x is small* approximation is valid by calculating the ratio of *x* to the smallest number it was subtracted from in the approximation. The ratio should be less than 0.05 (5%).

$$\frac{1.4\underline{7} \times 10^{-5}}{0.090} \times 100\% = 0.016\%$$

The approximation is valid.

2. Equilibrium Alternative (using the Henderson–Hasselbalch equation). As long as the *x is small* approximation is valid, you can substitute the quantities of acid and conjugate base after the addition (from part I) into the Henderson–Hasselbalch equation and calculate the new pH.

$$pH = pK_a + \log\frac{[\text{base}]}{[\text{acid}]}$$

$$= -\log(1.8 \times 10^{-5}) + \log\frac{0.110}{0.090}$$

$$= 4.74 + 0.087$$

$$= 4.83$$

The pH of 1.0 L of water after adding 0.010 mol of NaOH is calculated from the $[OH^-]$. For a strong base, $[OH^-]$ is simply the number of moles of OH^- divided by the number of liters of solution.

$$[OH^-] = \frac{0.010 \text{ mol}}{1.0 \text{ L}} = 0.010 \text{ M}$$

$$pOH = -\log[OH^-] = -\log(0.010)$$

$$= 2.00$$

$$pOH + pH = 14.00$$

$$pH = 14.00 - pOH$$

$$= 14.00 - 2.00$$

$$= 12.00$$

CHECK Notice that the buffer solution changed from pH = 4.74 to pH = 4.83 upon addition of the base (a small fraction of a single pH unit). In contrast, the pure water changed from pH = 7.00 to pH = 12.00, five whole pH units (a factor of 10^5). Notice also that even the buffer solution got slightly more basic upon addition of a base, as we would expect. To check your answer, always make sure the pH goes in the direction you expect: adding base should make the solution more basic (higher pH); adding acid should make the solution more acidic (lower pH).

FOR PRACTICE 18.3 Calculate the pH of the solution in Example 18.3 upon addition of 0.015 mol of NaOH to the original buffer.

FOR MORE PRACTICE 18.3 Calculate the pH of the solution in Example 18.3 upon addition of 10.0 mL of 1.00 M HCl to the original buffer.

ANSWER NOW!

18.4 Cc Conceptual Connection

ADDING ACID OR BASE TO A BUFFER A buffer contains equal amounts of a weak acid and its conjugate base and has a pH of 5.25. Which would be a reasonable value of buffer pH after the addition of a small amount of acid?

(a) 4.15
(b) 5.15
(c) 5.35
(d) 6.35

Buffers Containing a Base and Its Conjugate Acid

So far, we have seen examples of buffers composed of an acid and its conjugate base (where the conjugate base is an ion). A buffer can also be composed of a base and its conjugate acid (where the conjugate acid is an ion). For example, a solution containing significant amounts of both NH_3 and NH_4Cl acts as a buffer (Figure 18.4▼). The NH_3 is a weak base that neutralizes small amounts of added acid, and the NH_4^+ ion is the conjugate acid that neutralizes small amounts of added base.

We calculate the pH of a solution like this in the same way that we calculated the pH of a buffer containing a weak acid and its conjugate base. When using the Henderson–Hasselbalch equation, however, we must first calculate pK_a for the conjugate acid of the weak base. Recall from Section 17.8 that for a conjugate acid–base pair, $K_a \times K_b = K_w$ and $pK_a + pK_b = 14$. Consequently, we can find pK_a of the conjugate acid by subtracting pK_b of the weak base from 14. Example 18.4 illustrates the procedure for calculating the pH of a buffer composed of a weak base and its conjugate acid.

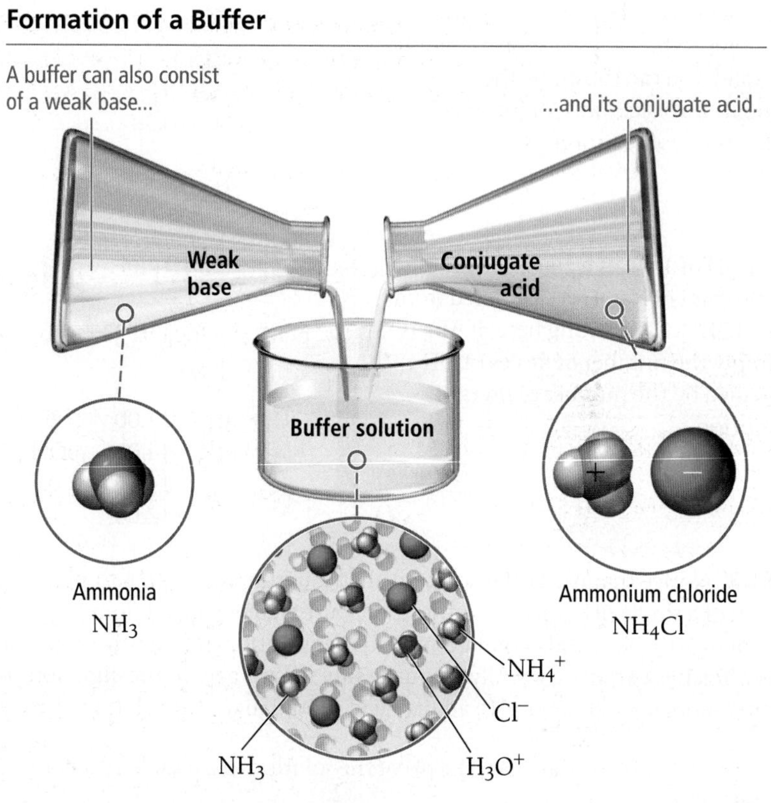

▲ **FIGURE 18.4 Buffer Containing a Base**

WATCH **NOW!**

INTERACTIVE WORKED EXAMPLE 18.4

EXAMPLE 18.4 Using the Henderson–Hasselbalch Equation to Calculate the pH of a Buffer Solution Composed of a Weak Base and Its Conjugate Acid

Use the Henderson–Hasselbalch equation to calculate the pH of a buffer solution that is 0.50 M in NH_3 and 0.20 M in NH_4Cl. For ammonia, $pK_b = 4.75$.

SOLUTION

Since K_b for NH_3 (1.76×10^{-5}) is much smaller than the initial concentrations in this problem, you can use the Henderson–Hasselbalch equation to calculate the pH of the buffer. First calculate pK_a from pK_b.

$$pK_a + pK_b = 14$$
$$pK_a = 14 - pK_b = 14 - 4.75 = 9.25$$

Then substitute the given quantities into the Henderson–Hasselbalch equation and calculate pH.

$$pH = pK_a + \log\frac{[\text{base}]}{[\text{acid}]}$$
$$= 9.25 + \log\frac{0.50}{0.20}$$
$$= 9.25 + 0.40$$
$$= 9.65$$

FOR PRACTICE 18.4 Calculate the pH of 1.0 L of the solution in Example 18.4 upon addition of 0.010 mol of solid NaOH to the original buffer solution.

FOR MORE PRACTICE 18.4 Calculate the pH of 1.0 L of the solution in Example 18.4 upon addition of 30.0 mL of 1.0 M HCl to the original buffer solution.

18.3 Buffer Effectiveness: Buffer Range and Buffer Capacity

An effective buffer neutralizes small to moderate amounts of added acid or base. Recall from Section 18.1, however, that a buffer can be destroyed by the addition of too much acid or too much base. What factors influence the effectiveness of a buffer? In this section, we examine two such factors: *the relative amounts of the acid and conjugate base* and *the absolute concentrations of the acid and conjugate base*. We then define the *capacity of a buffer* (how much added acid or base it can effectively neutralize) and the *range of a buffer* (the pH range over which a particular acid and its conjugate base can be effective).

Relative Amounts of Acid and Base

A buffer is most effective (most resistant to pH changes) when the concentrations of acid and conjugate base are equal. Let's explore this idea by considering the behavior of a generic buffer composed of HA and A^- for which $pK_a = 5.00$ and calculating the percent change in pH upon addition of 0.010 mol of NaOH for two different 1.0-liter solutions of this buffer system. Both solutions have 0.20 mol of *total* acid and conjugate base. However, solution I has equal amounts of acid and conjugate base (0.10 mol of each), while solution II has much more acid than conjugate base (0.18 mol HA and 0.020 mol A^-). We can calculate the initial pH values of each solution using the Henderson–Hasselbalch equation. Solution I has an initial pH of 5.00 and solution II has an initial pH of 4.05:

Solution I: 0.10 mol HA and 0.10 mol A^-; initial pH = 5.00

	$OH^-(aq)$	+ $HA(aq)$	$\longrightarrow$ $H_2O(l)$ + $A^-(aq)$
Before addition	≈0.00 mol	0.100 mol	0.100 mol
Addition	0.010 mol	—	—
After addition	≈0.00 mol	0.090 mol	0.110 mol

$$\begin{aligned} pH &= pK_a + \log\frac{[\text{base}]}{[\text{acid}]} \\ &= 5.00 + \log\frac{0.110}{0.090} \\ &= 5.09 \end{aligned}$$

$$\begin{aligned} \%\ \text{change} &= \frac{5.09 - 5.00}{5.00} \times 100\% \\ &= 1.8\% \end{aligned}$$

Solution II: 0.18 mol HA and 0.020 mol A^-; initial pH = 4.05

	$OH^-(aq)$	+ $HA(aq)$	$\longrightarrow$ $H_2O(l)$ + $A^-(aq)$
Before addition	≈0.00 mol	0.18 mol	0.020 mol
Addition	0.010 mol	—	—
After addition	≈0.00 mol	0.17 mol	0.030 mol

$$\begin{aligned} pH &= pK_a + \log\frac{[\text{base}]}{[\text{acid}]} \\ &= 5.00 + \log\frac{0.030}{0.17} \\ &= 4.25 \end{aligned}$$

$$\begin{aligned} \%\ \text{change} &= \frac{4.25 - 4.05}{4.05} \times 100\% \\ &= 4.9\% \end{aligned}$$

As you can see, the buffer with equal amounts of acid and conjugate base is more resistant to pH change and is therefore the more effective buffer. A buffer becomes less effective as the difference in the relative amounts of acid and conjugate base increases. As a guideline, we can say that an effective buffer must have a [base]/[acid] ratio in the range of 0.10 to 10. *In order for a buffer to be reasonably effective, the relative concentrations of acid and conjugate base should not differ by more than a factor of 10.*

Absolute Concentrations of the Acid and Conjugate Base

A buffer is most effective (most resistant to pH changes) when the concentrations of acid and conjugate base are high. Let's explore this idea by again considering a generic buffer composed of HA and A^- and a pK_a of 5.00 and calculating the percent change in pH upon addition of 0.010 mol of NaOH for two 1.0-liter solutions of this buffer system. In this case, both the acid and the base in solution I are ten times more concentrated than the acid and base in solution II. Both solutions have equal relative amounts of acid and conjugate base and therefore have the same initial pH of 5.00:

Solution I: 0.50 mol HA and 0.50 mol A^-; initial pH = 5.00

	$OH^-(aq)$	+ $HA(aq)$	$\longrightarrow$ $H_2O(l)$ + $A^-(aq)$
Before addition	≈0.00 mol	0.50 mol	0.50 mol
Addition	0.010 mol	—	—
After addition	≈0.00 mol	0.49 mol	0.51 mol

$$\begin{aligned} pH &= pK_a + \log\frac{[\text{base}]}{[\text{acid}]} \\ &= 5.00 + \log\frac{0.51}{0.49} \\ &= 5.02 \end{aligned}$$

$$\begin{aligned} \%\ \text{change} &= \frac{5.02 - 5.00}{5.00} \times 100\% \\ &= 0.4\% \end{aligned}$$

Solution II: 0.050 mol HA and 0.050 mol A^-; initial pH = 5.00

	$OH^-(aq)$	+ $HA(aq)$	$\longrightarrow$ $H_2O(l)$ + $A^-(aq)$
Before addition	≈0.00 mol	0.050 mol	0.050 mol
Addition	0.010 mol	—	—
After addition	≈0.00 mol	0.040 mol	0.060 mol

$$\begin{aligned} pH &= pK_a + \log\frac{[\text{base}]}{[\text{acid}]} \\ &= 5.00 + \log\frac{0.060}{0.040} \\ &= 5.18 \end{aligned}$$

$$\begin{aligned} \%\ \text{change} &= \frac{5.18 - 5.00}{5.00} \times 100\% \\ &= 3.6\% \end{aligned}$$

As you can see, the buffer with greater amounts of acid and conjugate base is more resistant to pH changes and therefore is the more effective buffer. The more dilute the buffer components, the less effective the buffer.

Buffer Range

In light of the guideline that the relative concentrations of acid and conjugate base should not differ by more than a factor of 10 in order for a buffer to be reasonably effective, we can calculate the pH range over which a particular acid and its conjugate base make an effective buffer. Because the pH of a buffer is given by the Henderson–Hasselbalch equation, we can calculate the outermost points of the effective range as follows:

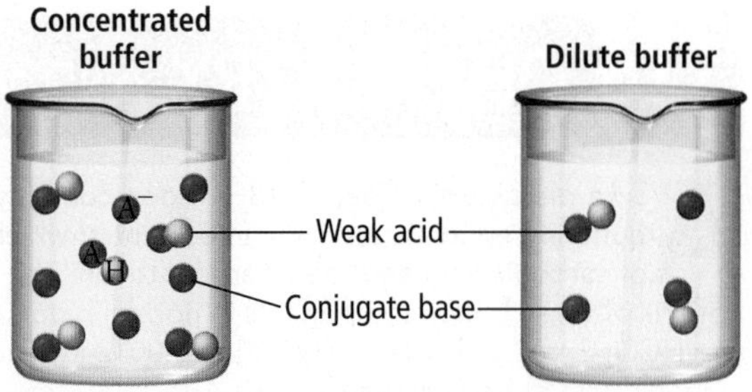

▲ A concentrated buffer contains more of the weak acid and its conjugate base than a weak buffer does. It can therefore neutralize more added acid or added base.

Lowest pH for effective buffer occurs when the base is one-tenth as concentrated as the acid.

$$\begin{aligned} pH &= pK_a + \log\frac{[\text{base}]}{[\text{acid}]} \\ &= pK_a + \log 0.10 \\ &= pK_a - 1 \end{aligned}$$

Highest pH for effective buffer occurs when the base is ten times as concentrated as the acid.

$$\begin{aligned} pH &= pK_a + \log\frac{[\text{base}]}{[\text{acid}]} \\ &= pK_a + \log 10 \\ &= pK_a + 1 \end{aligned}$$

The effective range for a buffering system is one pH unit on either side of pK_a. For example, we can use a weak acid with a pK_a of 5.0 (and its conjugate base) to prepare a buffer in the range of 4.0–6.0. We can adjust the relative amounts of acid and conjugate base to achieve any pH within this range. As we noted earlier, however, the buffer would be most effective at pH 5.0 because the buffer components would be exactly equal at that pH. Example 18.5 demonstrates how to pick an acid/conjugate base system for a buffer and how to calculate the relative amounts of acid and conjugate base required for a desired pH.

EXAMPLE 18.5 Preparing a Buffer

Which acid would you choose to combine with its sodium salt to make a solution buffered at pH 4.25? For the best choice, calculate the ratio of the conjugate base to the acid required to attain the desired pH.

chlorous acid ($HClO_2$)	$pK_a = 1.95$	formic acid ($HCHO_2$)	$pK_a = 3.74$
nitrous acid (HNO_2)	$pK_a = 3.34$	hypochlorous acid ($HClO$)	$pK_a = 7.54$

SOLUTION

The best choice is formic acid because its pK_a lies closest to the desired pH. You can calculate the ratio of conjugate base (CHO_2^-) to acid ($HCHO_2$) required by using the Henderson–Hasselbalch equation as follows:

$$pH = pK_a + \log\frac{[\text{base}]}{[\text{acid}]}$$

$$4.25 = 3.74 + \log\frac{[\text{base}]}{[\text{acid}]}$$

$$\begin{aligned} \log\frac{[\text{base}]}{[\text{acid}]} &= 4.25 - 3.74 \\ &= 0.51 \end{aligned}$$

$$\begin{aligned} \frac{[\text{base}]}{[\text{acid}]} &= 10^{0.51} \\ &= 3.24 \end{aligned}$$

FOR PRACTICE 18.5 Which acid in Example 18.5 would you choose to create a buffer with pH = 7.35? If you have 500.0 mL of a 0.10 M solution of the acid, what mass of the corresponding sodium salt of the conjugate base do you need to make the buffer?

CHEMISTRY AND MEDICINE | Buffer Effectiveness in Human Blood

As we discussed in Section 18.1, blood contains several buffering systems, the most important of which consists of carbonic acid and the bicarbonate ion. The concentrations of these buffer components in normal blood plasma are $[HCO_3^-] = 0.024$ M and $[H_2CO_3] = 0.0012$ M. The pK_a for carbonic acid at body temperature is 6.1.

If we substitute these quantities into the Henderson–Hasselbalch equation, we can calculate the normal pH of blood:

$$\begin{aligned} pH &= pK_a + \log\frac{[\text{base}]}{[\text{acid}]} \\ &= 6.1 + \log\frac{[HCO_3^-]}{[H_2CO_3]} \\ &= 6.1 + \log\frac{0.024 \text{ M}}{0.0012 \text{ M}} \\ &= 7.4 \end{aligned}$$

Normal blood has a pH of 7.4. Notice that the concentration of the bicarbonate ion is 20 times higher than the concentration of carbonic acid and the pH of the buffer is more than one pH unit away from pK_a. Why?

The higher bicarbonate ion concentration in blood makes the buffer capacity of blood greater for acid than for base, which is necessary because the products of metabolism that enter blood are mostly acidic. For example, when we exercise, our bodies produce lactic acid ($HC_3H_5O_3$). The lactic acid enters the bloodstream and must be neutralized. The bicarbonate ion neutralizes the lactic acid according to the equation:

$$HCO_3^-(aq) + HC_3H_5O_3(aq) \longrightarrow H_2CO_3(aq) + C_3H_5O_3^-(aq)$$

An enzyme called carbonic anhydrase then catalyzes the conversion of carbonic acid into carbon dioxide and water:

$$H_2CO_3(aq) \rightleftharpoons CO_2(g) + H_2O(l)$$

We eliminate the carbon dioxide from our blood when we breathe. When large amounts of lactic acid are produced, we must breathe faster to keep up with the need to eliminate carbon dioxide. This is why we pant when we exert ourselves.

QUESTION *A 70-kg person has a total blood volume of about 5.0 L. Given the carbonic acid and bicarbonate concentrations stated, what volume (in mL) of 6.0 M HCl can be neutralized by blood without the blood pH dropping below 7.0 (which would result in death)?*

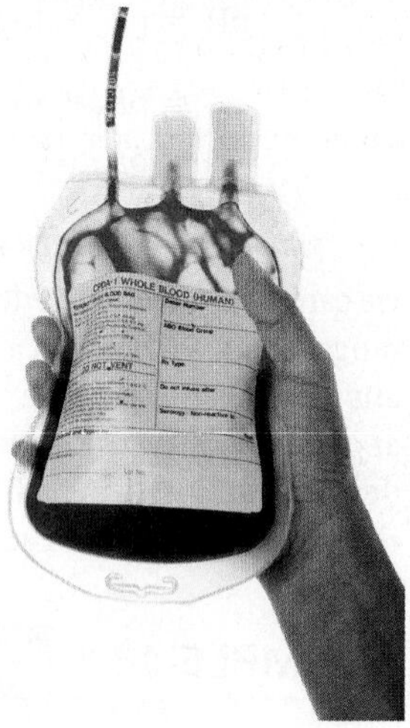

▶ Normal blood has a pH of 7.4.

Buffer Capacity

Buffer capacity is the amount of acid or base that we can add to a buffer without causing a large change in pH. Given what we just learned about the absolute concentrations of acid and conjugate base in an effective buffer, we can conclude that the *buffer capacity increases with increasing absolute concentrations of the buffer components*. The more concentrated the weak acid and conjugate base that compose the buffer, the higher the buffer capacity. In addition, *overall buffer capacity increases as the relative concentrations of the buffer components become more similar to each other*. As the ratio of the buffer components gets closer to 1, the *overall* capacity of the buffer (the ability to neutralize added acid *and* added base) becomes greater. In some cases, however, a buffer that must neutralize primarily added acid (or primarily added base) may be overweighted in one of the buffer components, as shown in the *Chemistry and Medicine* box in this section.

ANSWER **NOW!**

18.5 Cc Conceptual Connection

BUFFER CAPACITY A 1.0-L buffer solution is 0.10 M in HF and 0.050 M in NaF. Which action destroys the buffer?

(a) adding 0.050 mol of HCl
(b) adding 0.050 mol of NaOH
(c) adding 0.050 mol of NaF
(d) none of the above

18.4 Titrations and pH Curves

We first examined acid–base titrations in Section 5.7. In an **acid–base titration**, a basic (or acidic) solution of unknown concentration reacts with an acidic (or basic) solution of known concentration. The known solution is slowly added to the unknown one while the pH is monitored with either a pH meter or an **indicator** (a substance whose color depends on the pH). As the acid and base combine, they neutralize each other. At the **equivalence point**—the point in the titration when the number of moles of base is stoichiometrically equal to the number of moles of acid—the titration is complete. When the equivalence point is reached, neither reactant is in excess and the number of moles of the reactants are related by the reaction stoichiometry (Figure 18.5▼).

The equivalence point is so named because the number of moles of acid and base are stoichiometrically equivalent at this point.

In this section, we examine acid–base titrations more closely, concentrating on the pH changes that occur during the titration. A plot of the pH of the solution during a titration is known as a *titration curve* or *pH curve*. Figure 18.6▼ is a pH curve for the titration of HCl with NaOH. Before any base is added to the solution, the pH is low (as we would expect for a solution of HCl). As the NaOH is added, the solution becomes less

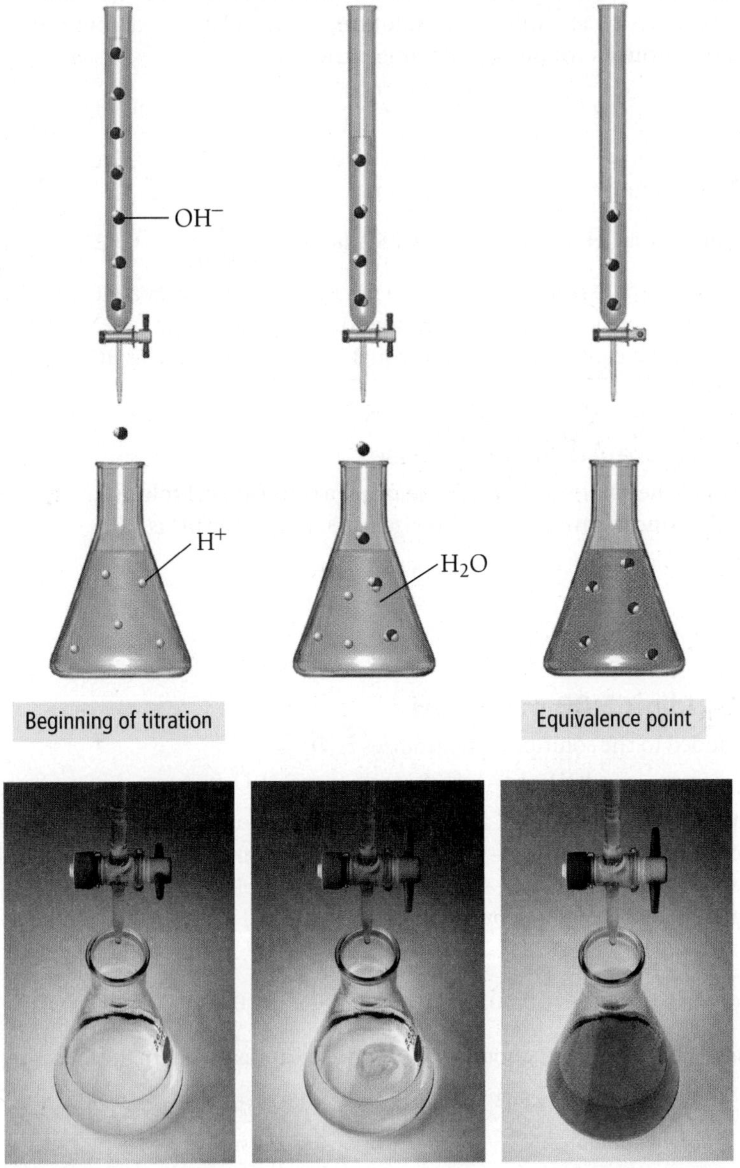

▲ **FIGURE 18.5 Acid–Base Titration** As OH^- is added in a titration, it neutralizes the H^+, forming water. At the equivalence point, the titration is complete.

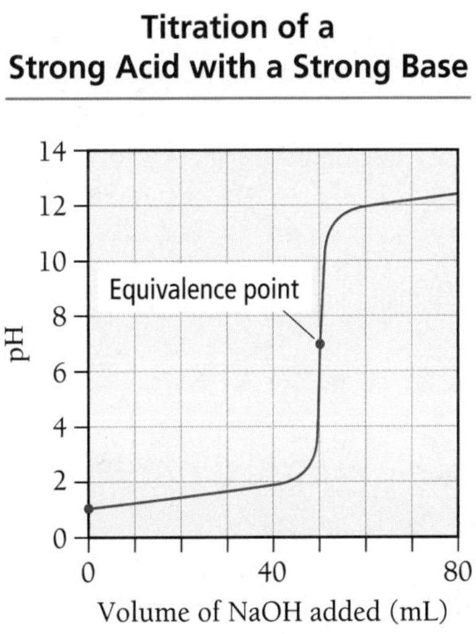

▲ **FIGURE 18.6 Titration Curve: Strong Acid + Strong Base** This curve represents the titration of 50.0 mL of 0.100 M HCl with 0.100 M NaOH.

acidic because the NaOH begins to neutralize the HCl. The point of inflection in the middle of the curve is the equivalence point. Notice that the pH changes very quickly near the equivalence point (small amounts of added base cause large changes in pH). Beyond the equivalence point, the solution is basic because the HCl has been completely neutralized and excess base is being added to the solution. The exact shape of the pH curve depends on several factors, including the strength of the acid or base being titrated. Let's consider several combinations individually.

WATCH **NOW!**

KEY CONCEPT VIDEO 18.4A

The Titration of a Strong Acid with a Strong Base

The Titration of a Strong Acid with a Strong Base

Consider the titration of 25.0 mL of 0.100 M HCl with 0.100 M NaOH. We begin by calculating the volume of base required to reach the equivalence point and then the pH at several points during the titration.

Volume of NaOH Required to Reach the Equivalence Point

During the titration, the added sodium hydroxide neutralizes the hydrochloric acid:

$$HCl(aq) + NaOH(aq) \longrightarrow H_2O(l) + NaCl(aq)$$

The equivalence point is reached when the number of moles of base added equals the number of moles of acid initially in solution. We calculate the amount of acid initially in solution from its volume and its concentration:

$$\text{Initial mol HCl} = 0.0250\,\cancel{L} \times \frac{0.100\text{ mol}}{1\,\cancel{L}} = 0.00250\text{ mol HCl}$$

The amount of NaOH that must be added is 0.00250 mol NaOH. We calculate the volume of NaOH required from its concentration:

$$\text{Volume NaOH solution} = 0.00250\,\cancel{\text{mol}} \times \frac{1\text{ L}}{0.100\,\cancel{\text{mol}}} = 0.0250\text{ L}$$

The equivalence point is reached when 25.0 mL of NaOH has been added. In this case, the concentrations of both solutions are identical, so the volume of NaOH solution required to reach the equivalence point is equal to the volume of the HCl solution that is being titrated.

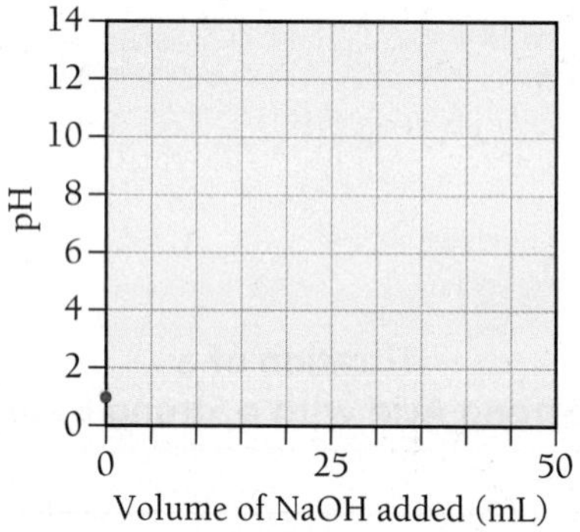

Initial pH (before Adding Any Base)

The initial pH of the solution is simply the pH of a 0.100 M HCl solution. Since HCl is a strong acid, the concentration of H_3O^+ is also 0.100 M and the pH is 1.00:

$$\begin{aligned} pH &= -\log[H_3O^+] \\ &= -\log(0.100) \\ &= 1.00 \end{aligned}$$

pH after Adding 5.00 mL NaOH

As NaOH is added to the solution, it neutralizes H_3O^+:

$$OH^-(aq) + H_3O^+(aq) \longrightarrow 2\,H_2O(l)$$

We calculate the amount of H_3O^+ at any given point (before the equivalence point) by using the reaction stoichiometry—1 mol of NaOH neutralizes 1 mol of H_3O^+. The initial number of moles of H_3O^+ (as just calculated) is 0.00250 mol. We calculate the number of moles of NaOH added at 5.00 mL by multiplying the added volume (in L) by the concentration of the NaOH solution:

$$\text{mol NaOH added} = 0.00500\,\cancel{L} \times \frac{0.100\text{ mol}}{1\,\cancel{L}} = 0.000500\text{ mol NaOH}$$

The addition of OH^- causes the amount of H_3O^+ to decrease as shown in the following table:

	$OH^-(aq)$	+	$H_3O^+(aq) \longrightarrow 2\,H_2O(l)$
Before addition	≈0.00 mol		0.00250 mol
Addition	0.000500 mol		—
After addition	≈0.00 mol		0.00200 mol

We calculate the H_3O^+ concentration by dividing the number of moles of H_3O^+ remaining by the *total volume* (initial volume plus added volume):

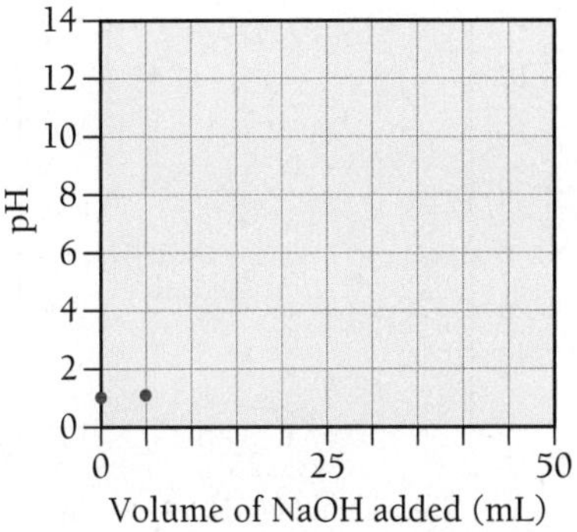

$$[H_3O^+] = \frac{0.00200 \text{ mol } H_3O^+}{0.0250 \text{ L} + 0.00500 \text{ L}} = 0.0667 \text{ M}$$

Initial volume (0.0250 L) — Added volume (0.00500 L)

The pH is therefore 1.18:

$$\begin{aligned} pH &= -\log 0.0667 \\ &= 1.18 \end{aligned}$$

pH after Adding 10.0, 15.0, and 20.0 mL NaOH

As more NaOH is added, it further neutralizes the H_3O^+ in the solution. We calculate the pH at each of these points in the same way that we calculated the pH at the 5.00 mL point. The results are tabulated as follows:

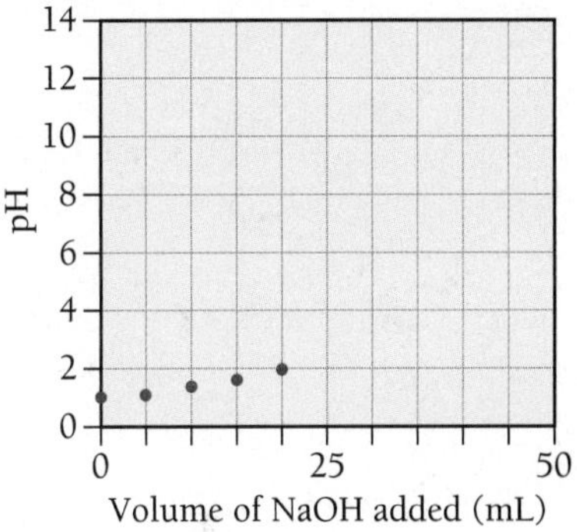

Volume (mL)	pH
10.0	1.37
15.0	1.60
20.0	1.95

pH after Adding 25.0 mL NaOH (Equivalence Point)

The pH at the equivalence point of a strong acid–strong base titration will always be 7.00 (at 25 °C). At the equivalence point, the strong base has completely neutralized the strong acid. The only source of hydronium ions then is the ionization of water. The $[H_3O^+]$ at 25 °C from the ionization of water is 1.00×10^{-7} M and the pH is 7.00.

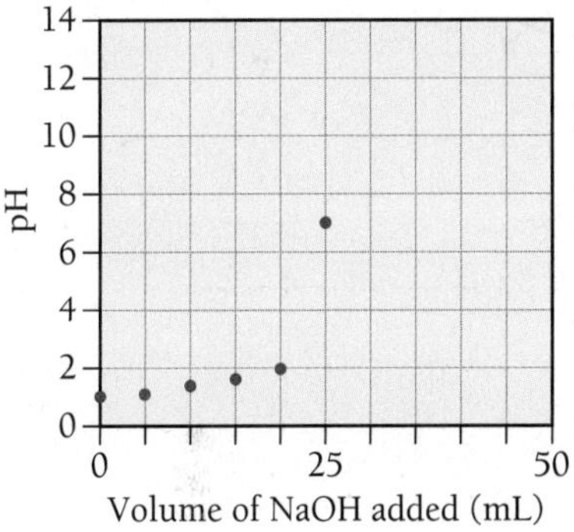

pH after Adding 30.00 mL NaOH

As NaOH is added beyond the equivalence point, it becomes the excess reagent. We calculate the amount of OH^- at any given point (past the equivalence point) by subtracting the initial amount of H_3O^+ from the amount of added OH^-. The number of moles of OH^- added at 30.00 mL is:

$$\text{mol } OH^- \text{ added} = 0.0300 \,\cancel{\text{L}} \times \frac{0.100 \text{ mol}}{1 \,\cancel{\text{L}}} = 0.00300 \text{ mol } OH^-$$

The number of moles of OH^- remaining after neutralization is shown in the following table:

	$OH^-(aq)$ +	$H_3O^+(aq) \longrightarrow 2\,H_2O(l)$
Before addition	≈0.00 mol	0.00250 mol
Addition	0.00300 mol	—
After addition	0.00050 mol	≈0.00 mol

We calculate the OH^- concentration by dividing the number of moles of OH^- remaining by the *total volume* (initial volume plus added volume):

$$[OH^-] = \frac{0.000500 \text{ mol } OH^-}{0.0250 \text{ L} + 0.0300 \text{ L}} = 0.00909 \text{ M}$$

We can then calculate the $[H_3O^+]$ and pH:

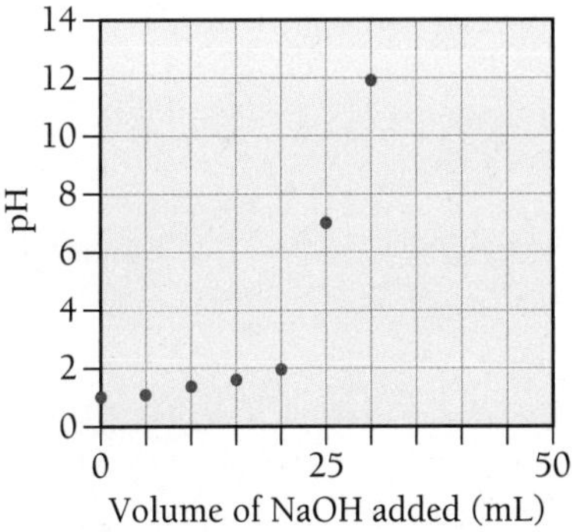

$$\begin{aligned} [H_3O^+][OH^-] &= 10^{-14} \\ [H_3O^+] &= \frac{10^{-14}}{[OH^-]} = \frac{10^{-14}}{0.00909} \\ &= 1.10 \times 10^{-12} \text{ M} \\ pH &= -\log(1.10 \times 10^{-12}) \\ &= 11.96 \end{aligned}$$

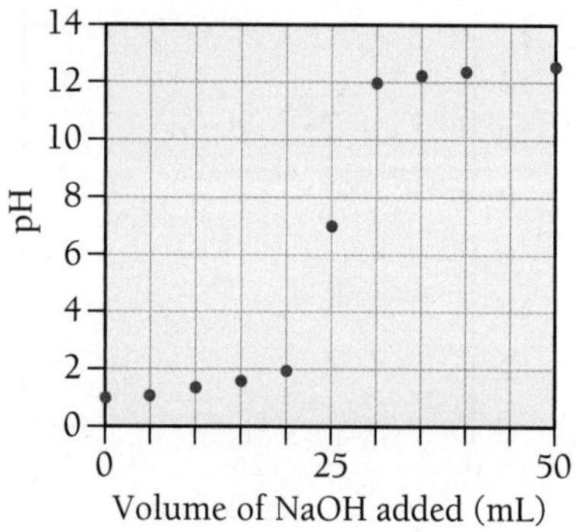

pH after Adding 35.0, 40.0, and 50.0 mL NaOH

As more NaOH is added, it further increases the basicity of the solution. We calculate the pH at each of these points in the same way that we calculated the pH at the 30.00 mL point. The results are tabulated as follows:

Volume (mL)	pH
35.0	12.22
40.0	12.36
50.0	12.52

The Overall pH Curve

The overall pH curve for the titration of a strong acid with a strong base has the characteristic S-shape we just plotted. The overall curve is as follows:

Titration of a Strong Acid with a Strong Base

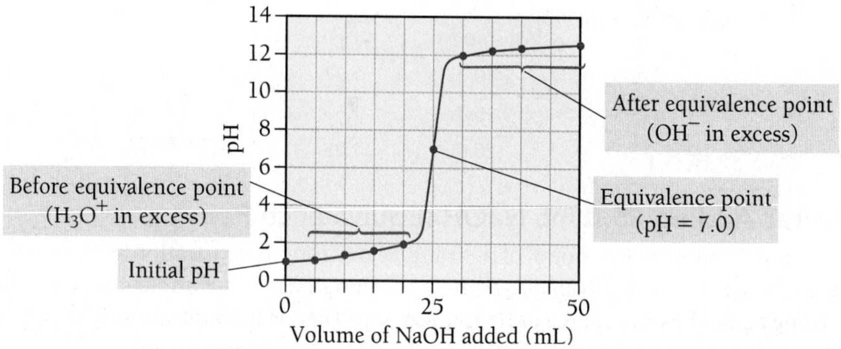

Summarizing the Titration of a Strong Acid with a Strong Base:

- The initial pH is simply the pH of the strong acid solution to be titrated.
- Before the equivalence point, H_3O^+ is in excess. Calculate the $[H_3O^+]$ by subtracting the number of moles of added OH^- from the initial number of moles of H_3O^+ and dividing by the *total* volume.
- At the equivalence point, neither reactant is in excess and the pH = 7.00.
- Beyond the equivalence point, OH^- is in excess. Calculate the $[OH^-]$ by subtracting the initial number of moles of H_3O^+ from the number of moles of added OH^- and dividing by the *total* volume.

The pH curve for the titration of a strong base with a strong acid is shown in Figure 18.7▼. Calculating the points along this curve is very similar to calculating the points along the pH curve for the titration of a strong acid with a strong base. The main difference is that the curve starts basic and then becomes acidic after the equivalence point (instead of vice versa).

Titration of a Strong Base with a Strong Acid

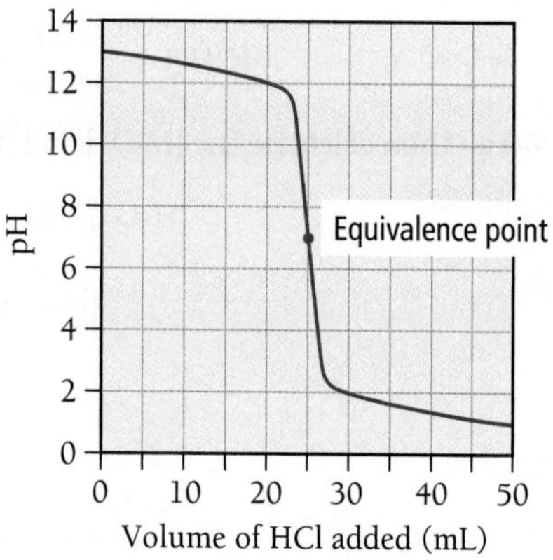

▶ **FIGURE 18.7 Titration Curve: Strong Base + Strong Acid** This curve represents the titration of 25.0 mL of 0.100 M NaOH with 0.100 M HCl.

WATCH **NOW!**

INTERACTIVE WORKED EXAMPLE 18.6

EXAMPLE 18.6 Strong Acid–Strong Base Titration pH Curve

A 50.0-mL sample of 0.200 M sodium hydroxide is titrated with 0.200 M nitric acid. Calculate pH:

(a) after adding 30.00 mL of HNO_3

(b) at the equivalence point

SOLUTION

(a) Begin by calculating the initial amount of NaOH (in moles) from the volume and molarity of the NaOH solution. Because NaOH is a strong base, it dissociates completely, so the amount of OH^- is equal to the amount of NaOH.

$$\text{moles NaOH} = 0.0500\,\cancel{\text{L}} \times \frac{0.200\text{ mol}}{1\,\cancel{\text{L}}} = 0.0100\text{ mol}$$

$$\text{moles OH}^- = 0.0100\text{ mol}$$

Calculate the amount of HNO_3 (in moles) added at 30.0 mL from the molarity of the HNO_3 solution.

$$\text{mol HNO}_3\text{ added} = 0.0300\text{ L} \times \frac{0.200\text{ mol}}{1\text{ L}} = 0.00600\text{ mol HNO}_3$$

As HNO_3 is added to the solution, it neutralizes some of the OH^-. Calculate the number of moles of OH^- remaining by setting up a table based on the neutralization reaction that shows the amount of OH^- before the addition, the amount of H_3O^+ added, and the amounts left after the addition.

	$OH^-(aq)$ +	$H_3O^+(aq) \longrightarrow 2H_2O(l)$
Before addition	0.0100 mol	≈0.00 mol
Addition	—	0.00600 mol
After addition	0.0040 mol	0.00 mol

Calculate the OH^- concentration by dividing the amount of OH^- remaining by the *total volume* (initial volume plus added volume).

$$[OH^-] = \frac{0.0040\text{ mol}}{0.0500\text{ L} + 0.0300\text{ L}} = 0.0500\text{M}$$

Calculate the pOH from $[OH^-]$.

$$\text{pOH} = -\log(0.0500) = 1.30$$

Calculate the pH from the pOH using the equation pH + pOH = 14.

$$\text{pH} = 14 - \text{pOH} = 14 - 1.30 = 12.70$$

(b) At the equivalence point, the strong base has completely neutralized the strong acid. The $[H_3O^+]$ at 25 °C from the ionization of water is 1.00×10^{-7} M and the pH is therefore 7.00.

$$\text{pH} = 7.00$$

FOR PRACTICE 18.6 Calculate the pH in the titration in Example 18.6 after the addition of 60.0 mL of 0.200 M HNO_3.

18.6 Cc Conceptual Connection ANSWER **NOW!**

TITRATION EQUIVALENCE POINT The amount of strong acid in the flask shown here is to be titrated by a strong base. Which mark on the burette next to the flask indicates the amount of base required to reach the equivalence point?

(a) A
(b) B
(c) C
(d) D

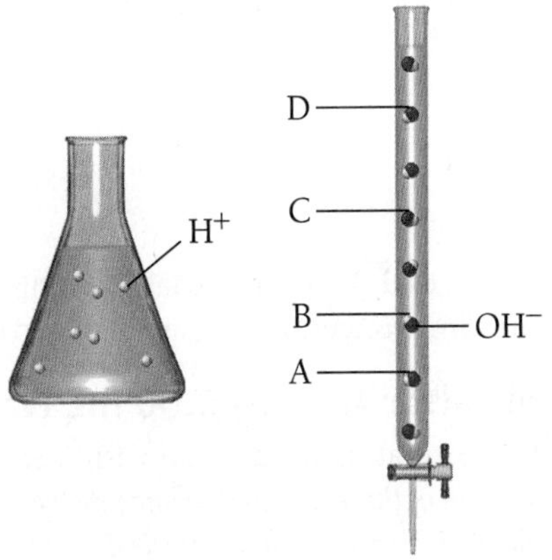

WATCH **NOW!**

KEY CONCEPT VIDEO 18.4B
The Titration of a Weak Acid and a Strong Base

The Titration of a Weak Acid with a Strong Base

Consider the titration of 25.0 mL of 0.100 M $HCHO_2$ with 0.100 M NaOH:

$$NaOH(aq) + HCHO_2(aq) \longrightarrow H_2O(l) + NaCHO_2(aq)$$

The concentrations and the volumes here are identical to those in our previous titration, in which we calculated the pH curve for the titration of a *strong* acid with a strong base. The only difference is that $HCHO_2$ is a *weak* acid rather than a strong one. We begin by calculating the volume required to reach the equivalence point of the titration.

Volume of NaOH Required to Reach the Equivalence Point

From the stoichiometry of the equation, we can see that the equivalence point occurs when the amount (in moles) of added base equals the amount (in moles) of acid initially in solution:

$$\text{Initial mol } HCHO_2 = 0.0250\,\cancel{L} \times \frac{0.100\text{ mol}}{1\,\cancel{L}} = 0.00250\text{ mol } HCHO_2$$

The amount of NaOH that must be added is 0.00250 mol NaOH. The volume of NaOH required is therefore:

$$\text{Volume NaOH solution} = 0.00250\,\cancel{\text{mol}} \times \frac{1\text{ L}}{0.100\,\cancel{\text{mol}}} = 0.0250\text{ L NaOH solution}$$

The equivalence point occurs when 25.0 mL of base has been added. Notice that the volume of NaOH required to reach the equivalence point for this weak acid is identical to that required for a strong acid. *The volume at the equivalence point in an acid–base titration does not depend on whether the acid being titrated is a strong acid or a weak acid; it depends only on the amount (in moles) of acid present in solution before the titration begins and on the concentration of the added base.*

Initial pH (before Adding Any Base)

The initial pH of the solution is the pH of a 0.100 M $HCHO_2$ solution. Since $HCHO_2$ is a weak acid, we calculate the concentration of H_3O^+ and the pH by doing an equilibrium problem for the ionization of $HCHO_2$. The procedure for solving weak acid ionization problems is given in Examples 17.5 and 17.6. We show a highly condensed calculation here (K_a for $HCHO_2$ is 1.8×10^{-4}):

$$HCHO_2(aq) + H_2O(l) \rightleftharpoons H_3O^+(aq) + CHO_2^-(aq)$$

	$[HCHO_2]$	$[H_3O^+]$	$[CHO_2^-]$
Initial	0.100	≈0.00	0.00
Change	$-x$	$+x$	$+x$
Equil	$0.100 - x$	x	x

$$K_a = \frac{[H_3O^+][CHO_2^-]}{[HCHO_2]}$$

$$= \frac{x^2}{0.100 - \cancel{x}} \quad (x \text{ is small})$$

$$1.8 \times 10^{-4} = \frac{x^2}{0.100}$$

$$x = 4.\underline{2}4 \times 10^{-3}$$

Therefore, $[H_3O^+] = 4.\underline{2}4 \times 10^{-3}$ M.

$$pH = -\log(4.\underline{2}4 \times 10^{-3})$$
$$= 2.37$$

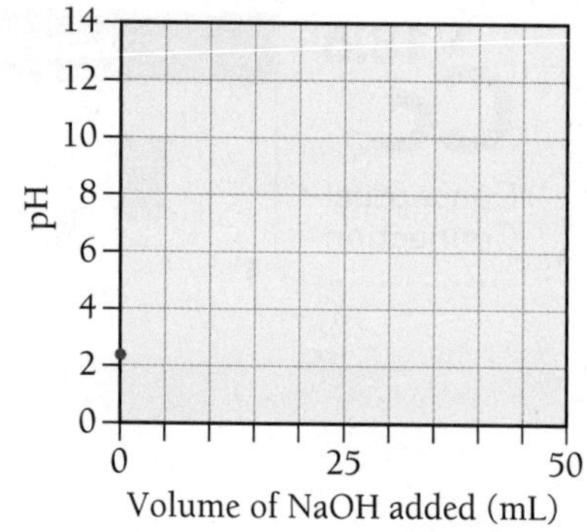

Notice that the pH is initially at a higher value (less acidic) than it is for a strong acid of the same concentration, as we would expect because the acid is weak.

pH after Adding 5.00 mL NaOH

When titrating a *weak acid* with a strong base, the added NaOH *converts a stoichiometric amount of the acid into its conjugate base*. As we calculated previously, 5.00 mL of the 0.100 M NaOH solution contains 0.000500 mol OH^-. When the 0.000500 mol OH^- is added to the weak acid solution, the OH^- reacts stoichiometrically with $HCHO_2$ causing the amount of $HCHO_2$ to *decrease* by 0.000500 mol and the amount of CHO_2^- to *increase* by 0.000500 mol.

This is very similar to what happens when we add strong base to a buffer, and it is summarized in the following table:

	$OH^-(aq)$ +	$HCHO_2(aq)$ ⟶	$H_2O(l)$ +	$CHO_2^-(aq)$
Before addition	≈0.00 mol	0.00250 mol	—	0.00 mol
Addition	0.000500 mol	—	—	—
After addition	≈0.00 mol	0.00200 mol	—	0.000500 mol

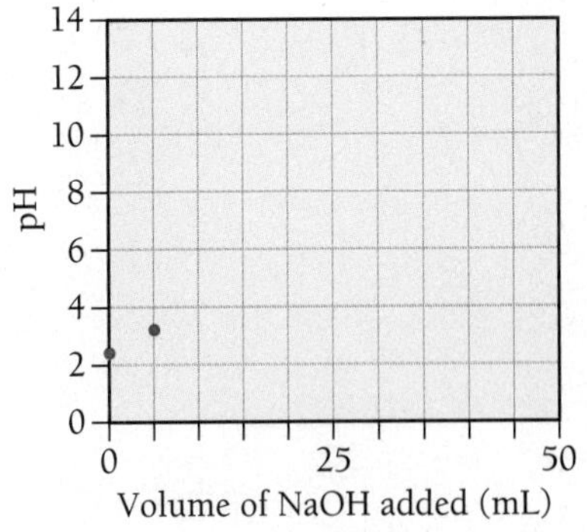

Notice that, after the addition, the solution contains significant amounts of both an acid ($HCHO_2$) and its conjugate base (CHO_2^-)—*the solution is now a buffer*. To calculate the pH of a buffer (when the *x is small* approximation applies as it does here), we can use the Henderson–Hasselbalch equation and pK_a for $HCHO_2$ (which is 3.74):

$$\begin{aligned} pH &= pK_a + \log\frac{[\text{base}]}{[\text{acid}]} \\ &= 3.74 + \log\frac{0.000500}{0.00200} \\ &= 3.74 - 0.60 \\ &= 3.14 \end{aligned}$$

pH after Adding 10.0, 12.5, 15.0, and 20.0 mL NaOH

As more NaOH is added, it converts more $HCHO_2$ into CHO_2^-. We calculate the relative amounts of $HCHO_2$ and CHO_2^- at each of these volumes using the reaction stoichiometry and then calculate the pH of the resulting buffer using the Henderson–Hasselbalch equation (as we did for the pH at 5.00 mL). The amounts of $HCHO_2$ and CHO_2^- (after addition of the OH^-) at each volume and the corresponding values of pH are tabulated as follows:

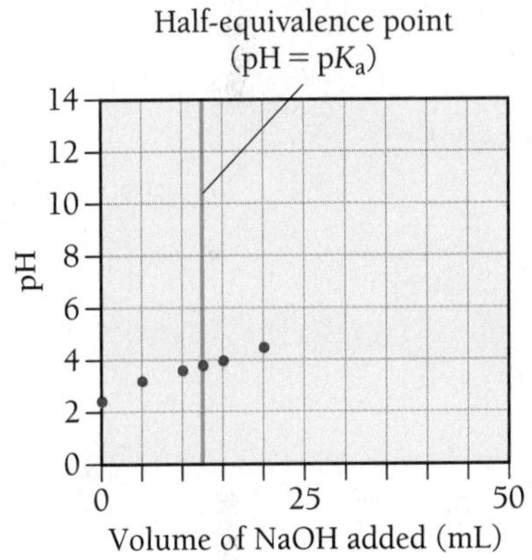

Volume (mL)	mol $HCHO_2$	mol CHO_2^-	pH
10.0	0.00150	0.00100	3.56
12.5	0.00125	0.00125	3.74
15.0	0.00100	0.00150	3.92
20.0	0.00050	0.00200	4.34

As the titration proceeds, more of the $HCHO_2$ is converted to the conjugate base (CHO_2^-). Notice that an added NaOH volume of 12.5 mL corresponds to one-half of the equivalence point. At this volume, one-half of the initial amount of $HCHO_2$ has been converted to CHO_2^-, resulting in *equal amounts of weak acid and conjugate base*. For any buffer in which the amounts of weak acid and conjugate base are equal, the pH = pK_a:

$$pH = pK_a + \log\frac{[\text{base}]}{[\text{acid}]}$$

If [base] = [acid], then [base]/[acid] = 1.

$$\begin{aligned} pH &= pK_a + \log 1 \\ &= pK_a + 0 \\ &= pK_a \end{aligned}$$

Since pH = pK_a halfway to the equivalence point, titrations can be used to measure the pK_a of an acid.

pH after Adding 25.0 mL NaOH (Equivalence Point)

At the equivalence point, 0.00250 mol of OH^- has been added and therefore all of the $HCHO_2$ has been converted into its conjugate base (CHO_2^-) as summarized in the following table:

	$OH^-(aq)$ +	$HCHO_2(aq)$ ⟶	$H_2O(l)$ +	$CHO_2^-(aq)$
Before addition	≈0.00 mol	0.00250 mol	—	0.00 mol
Addition	0.00250 mol	—	—	—
After addition	≈0.00 mol	0.00 mol	—	0.00250 mol

The solution is no longer a buffer (it no longer contains significant amounts of both a weak acid and its conjugate base). Instead, the solution contains an ion (CHO_2^-) acting as a weak base. We discussed how to calculate the pH of solutions such as this in Section 17.8 (see Example 17.14) by solving an equilibrium problem involving the ionization of water by the weak base (CHO_2^-):

$$CHO_2^-(aq) + H_2O(l) \rightleftharpoons HCHO_2(aq) + OH^-(aq)$$

We calculate the initial concentration of CHO_2^- for the equilibrium problem by dividing the number of moles of CHO_2^- (0.00250 mol) by the *total* volume at the equivalence point (initial volume plus added volume):

Moles CHO_2^- at equivalence point

$$[CHO_2^-] = \frac{0.00250 \text{ mol}}{0.0250 \text{ L} + 0.0250 \text{ L}} = 0.0500 \text{ M}$$

Initial volume — Added volume at equivalence point

We then proceed to solve the equilibrium problem as shown in condensed form as follows:

$$CHO_2^-(aq) + H_2O(l) \rightleftharpoons HCHO_2(aq) + OH^-(aq)$$

	$[CHO_2^-]$	$[HCHO_2]$	$[OH^-]$
Initial	0.0500	0.00	≈0.00
Change	$-x$	$+x$	$+x$
Equil	$0.0500 - x$	x	x

Before substituting into the expression for K_b, we find the value of K_b from K_a for formic acid ($K_a = 1.8 \times 10^{-4}$) and K_w:

$$K_a \times K_b = K_w$$

$$K_b = \frac{K_w}{K_a} = \frac{1.0 \times 10^{-14}}{1.8 \times 10^{-4}} = 5.6 \times 10^{-11}$$

Then we substitute the equilibrium concentrations from the previous table into the expression for K_b:

$$K_b = \frac{[HCHO_2][OH^-]}{[CHO_2^-]}$$

$$= \frac{x^2}{0.0500 - \cancel{x}} \quad (x \textit{ is small})$$

$$5.6 \times 10^{-11} = \frac{x^2}{0.0500}$$

$$x = 1.7 \times 10^{-6}$$

Remember that x represents the concentration of the hydroxide ion. We calculate $[H_3O^+]$ and pH:

$$[OH^-] = 1.7 \times 10^{-6} \text{ M}$$

$$[H_3O^+][OH^-] = K_w = 1.0 \times 10^{-14}$$

$$[H_3O^+](1.7 \times 10^{-6}) = 1.0 \times 10^{-14}$$

$$[H_3O^+] = 5.9 \times 10^{-9} \text{ M}$$

$$\text{pH} = -\log[H_3O^+]$$

$$= -\log(5.9 \times 10^{-9})$$

$$= 8.23$$

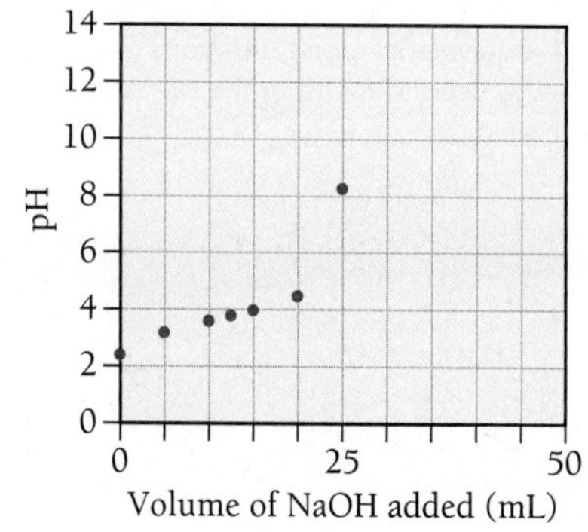

Notice that the pH at the equivalence point is *not* neutral but basic. *The titration of a weak acid by a strong base always has a basic equivalence point* because, at the equivalence point, all of the acid has been converted into its conjugate base, resulting in a weakly basic solution.

pH after Adding 30.00 mL NaOH

At this point in the titration, 0.00300 mol of OH^- has been added. NaOH has thus become the excess reagent as shown in the following table:

	$OH^-(aq)$ +	$HCHO_2(aq)$ ⟶	$H_2O(l)$ +	$CHO_2^-(aq)$
Before addition	≈0.00 mol	0.00250 mol	—	0.00 mol
Addition	0.00300 mol	—	—	—
After addition	0.00050 mol	≈0.00 mol	—	0.00250 mol

The solution is now a mixture of a strong base (NaOH) and a weak base (CHO_2^-). The strong base completely overwhelms the weak base, and we can calculate the pH by considering the strong base alone (as we did for the titration of a strong acid and a strong base). We calculate the OH^- concentration by dividing the amount of OH^- remaining by the *total volume* (initial volume plus added volume):

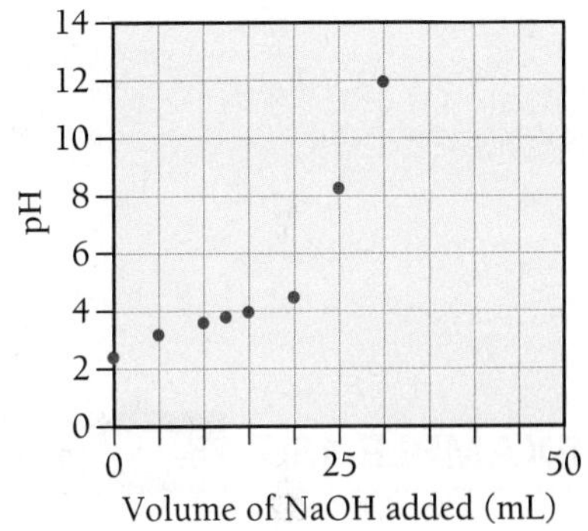

$$[OH^-] = \frac{0.00050 \text{ mol } OH^-}{0.0250 \text{ L} + 0.0300 \text{ L}} = 0.0091 \text{ M}$$

We can then calculate the $[H_3O^+]$ and pH:

$$[H_3O^+][OH^-] = 10^{-14}$$

$$[H_3O^+] = \frac{10^{-14}}{[OH^-]} = \frac{10^{-14}}{0.0091} = 1.1 \times 10^{-12} \text{ M}$$

$$\text{pH} = -\log(1.10 \times 10^{-12})$$

$$= 11.96$$

pH after Adding 35.0, 40.0, and 50.0 mL NaOH

As more NaOH is added, the basicity of the solution increases further. We calculate the pH at each of these volumes in the same way we calculated the pH at 30.00 mL of added NaOH. The results are tabulated as follows:

Volume (mL)	pH
35.0	12.22
40.0	12.36
50.0	12.52

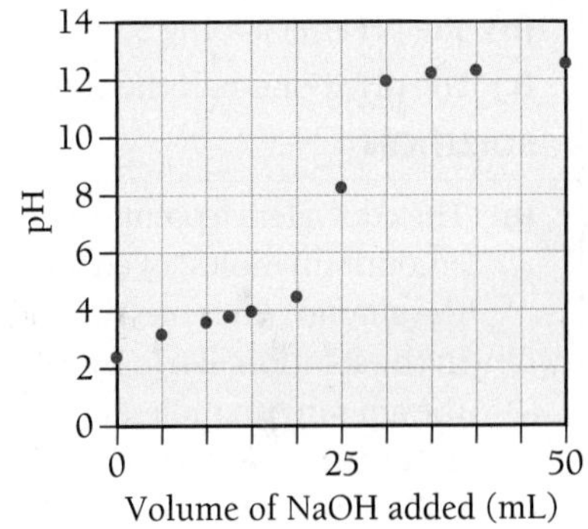

The Overall pH Curve

The overall pH curve for the titration of a weak acid with a strong base has a characteristic S-shape similar to that for the titration of a strong acid with a strong base. The main difference is that the equivalence point pH is basic (not neutral). Notice that calculating the pH in different regions throughout the titration involves working different kinds of acid–base problems, all of which we have encountered before.

Titration of a Weak Acid with a Strong Base

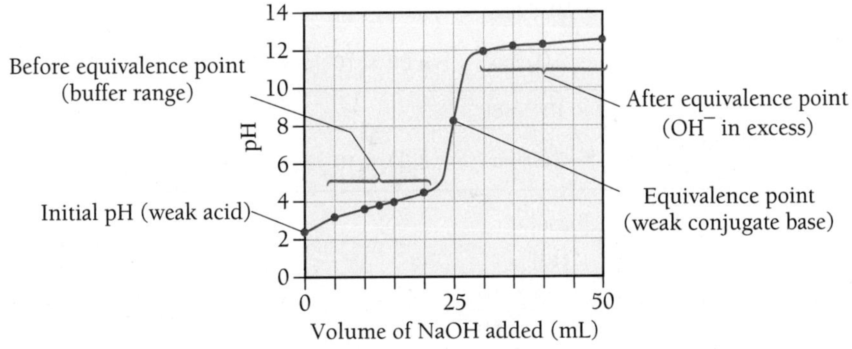

Summarizing Titration of a Weak Acid with a Strong Base:

- The initial pH is that of the weak acid solution to be titrated. Calculate the pH by working an equilibrium problem (similar to Examples 17.5 and 17.6) using the concentration of the weak acid as the initial concentration.
- Between the initial pH and the equivalence point, the solution becomes a buffer. Use the reaction stoichiometry to calculate the amounts of each buffer component and then use the Henderson–Hasselbalch equation to calculate the pH (as in Example 18.3).
- Halfway to the equivalence point, the buffer components are exactly equal and $pH = pK_a$.
- At the equivalence point, the acid has all been converted into its conjugate base. Calculate the pH by working an equilibrium problem for the ionization of water by the ion acting as a weak base (similar to Example 17.14). (Calculate the concentration of the ion acting as a weak base by dividing the number of moles of the ion by the total volume at the equivalence point.)
- Beyond the equivalence point, OH^- is in excess. Ignore the weak base and calculate the $[OH^-]$ by subtracting the initial number of moles of the weak acid from the number of moles of added OH^- and dividing by the *total* volume.

WATCH **NOW!**

INTERACTIVE WORKED EXAMPLE 18.7

EXAMPLE 18.7 Weak Acid–Strong Base Titration pH Curve

A 40.0-mL sample of 0.100 M HNO_2 is titrated with 0.200 M KOH. Calculate:

(a) the volume required to reach the equivalence point

(b) the pH after adding 5.00 mL of KOH

(c) the pH at one-half the equivalence point

SOLUTION

(a) The equivalence point occurs when the amount (in moles) of added base equals the amount (in moles) of acid initially in the solution. Begin by calculating the amount (in moles) of acid initially in the solution. The amount (in moles) of KOH that must be added is equal to the amount of the weak acid.

$$\text{mol } HNO_2 = 0.0400\ \cancel{L} \times \frac{0.100\text{ mol}}{\cancel{L}} = 4.00 \times 10^{-3}\text{ mol}$$

$$\text{mol KOH required} = 4.00 \times 10^{-3}\text{ mol}$$

Calculate the volume of KOH required from the number of moles of KOH and the molarity.

$$\text{volume KOH solution} = 4.00 \times 10^{-3}\ \cancel{\text{mol}} \times \frac{1\text{ L}}{0.200\ \cancel{\text{mol}}} = 0.0200\text{ L KOH solution} = 20.0\text{ mL KOH solution}$$

(b) Use the concentration of the KOH solution to calculate the amount (in moles) of OH^- in 5.00 mL of the solution.

$$\text{mol } OH^- = 5.00 \times 10^{-3}\ \cancel{L} \times \frac{0.200\text{ mol}}{1\ \cancel{L}} = 1.00 \times 10^{-3}\text{ mol } OH^-$$

Prepare a table showing the amounts of HNO_2 and NO_2^- before and after the addition of 5.00 mL KOH. The addition of the KOH stoichiometrically reduces the concentration of HNO_2 and increases the concentration of NO_2^-.

	$OH^-(aq)$ +	$HNO_2(aq)$ ⟶	$H_2O(l)$ +	$NO_2^-(aq)$
Before addition	≈0.00 mol	4.00×10^{-3} mol	—	0.00 mol
Addition	1.00×10^{-3} mol	—	—	—
After addition	≈0.00 mol	3.00×10^{-3} mol	—	1.00×10^{-3} mol

Since the solution now contains significant amounts of a weak acid and its conjugate base, use the Henderson–Hasselbalch equation and pK_a for HNO_2 (which is 3.34) to calculate the pH of the solution.

$$pH = pK_a + \log\frac{[\text{base}]}{[\text{acid}]} = 3.34 + \log\frac{1.00 \times 10^{-3}}{3.00 \times 10^{-3}} = 3.34 - 0.48 = 2.86$$

(c) At one-half the equivalence point, the amount of added base is exactly one-half the initial amount of acid. The base converts exactly half of the HNO_2 into NO_2^-, resulting in equal amounts of the weak acid and its conjugate base. The pH is therefore equal to pK_a.

	$OH^-(aq)$	+ $HNO_2(aq)$	$\longrightarrow$ $H_2O(l)$	+ $NO_2^-(aq)$
Before addition	≈0.00 mol	4.00×10^{-3} mol	—	0.00 mol
Addition	2.00×10^{-3} mol	—	—	—
After addition	≈0.00 mol	2.00×10^{-3} mol	—	2.00×10^{-3} mol

$$pH = pK_a + \log \frac{[\text{base}]}{[\text{acid}]}$$

$$= 3.34 + \log \frac{2.00 \times 10^{-3}}{2.00 \times 10^{-3}} = 3.34 + 0 = 3.34$$

FOR PRACTICE 18.7 Determine the pH at the equivalence point for the titration of HNO_2 and KOH in Example 18.7.

18.7 Cc Conceptual Connection ANSWER **NOW!**

WEAK ACID–STRONG BASE TITRATION Two 25.0-mL samples of unknown monoprotic weak acids, A and B, are titrated with 0.100 M NaOH solutions. The titration curve for each acid is shown below. Which of the two weak acid solutions is more concentrated? Which of the two weak acids has the larger K_a?

Acid A

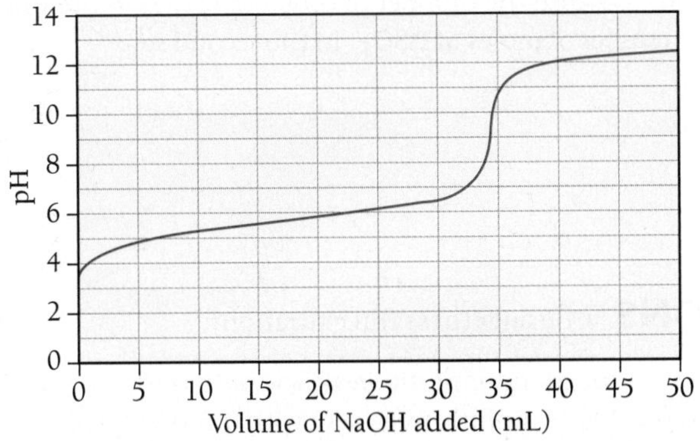

Acid B

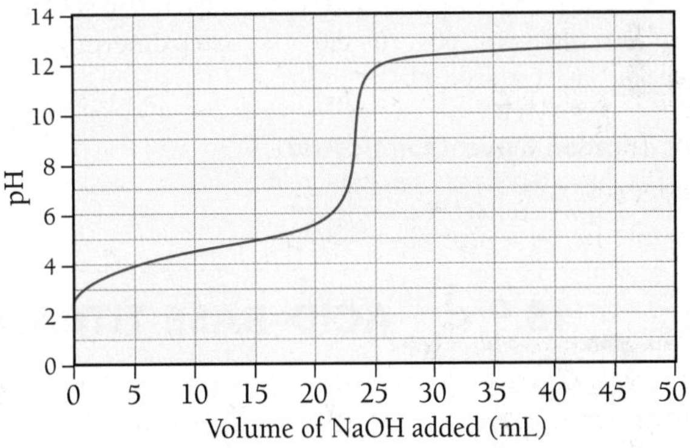

(a) Acid B is more concentrated and has the larger K_a.
(b) Acid A is more concentrated and has the larger K_a.
(c) Acid A is more concentrated and Acid B has the larger K_a.
(d) Acid B is more concentrated and Acid A has the larger K_a.

The Titration of a Weak Base with a Strong Acid

The pH curve for the titration of a weak base with a strong acid is shown in Figure 18.8▶. Calculating the points along this curve is very similar to calculating the points along the pH curve for the titration of a weak acid with a strong base (which we just did). The main differences are that the curve starts basic and has an acidic equivalence point. We calculate the pH in the buffer region using $pH = pK_a + \log \frac{[\text{base}]}{[\text{acid}]}$ where the pK_a corresponds to the conjugate acid of the base being titrated.

Titration of a Weak Base with a Strong Acid

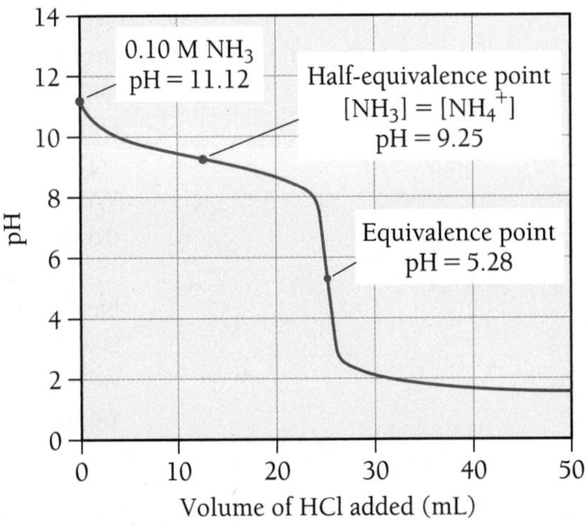

▶ **FIGURE 18.8 Titration Curve: Weak Base + Strong Acid** This curve represents the titration of 0.100 M NH_3 with 0.100 M HCl.

ANSWER NOW!

18.8
Cc
Conceptual Connection

THE HALF-EQUIVALENCE POINT What is the pH at the half-equivalence point in the titration of a weak base with a strong acid? The pK_b of the weak base is 8.75.

(a) 8.75 **(b)** 7.0 **(c)** 5.25 **(d)** 4.37

Titration of a Polyprotic Acid

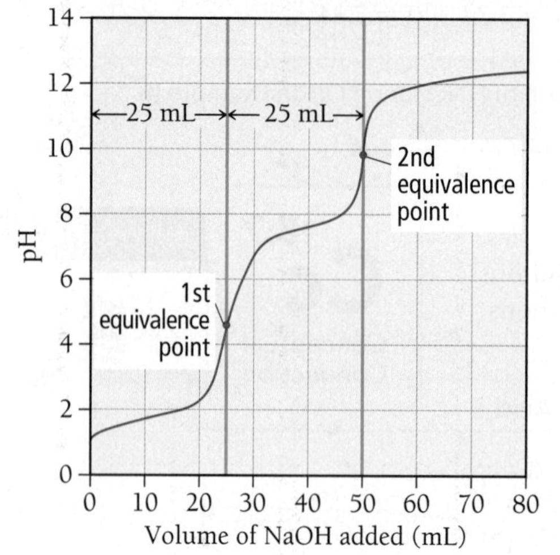

▲ **FIGURE 18.9 Titration Curve: Diprotic Acid + Strong Base** This curve represents the titration of 25.0 mL of 0.100 M H_2SO_3 with 0.100 M NaOH.

The Titration of a Polyprotic Acid

When a diprotic acid is titrated with a strong base, if K_{a_1} and K_{a_2} are sufficiently different, the pH curve will have two equivalence points. For example, Figure 18.9◀ shows the pH curve for the titration of sulfurous acid (H_2SO_3) with sodium hydroxide. Recall from Section 17.9 that sulfurous acid ionizes in two steps as follows:

$$H_2SO_3(aq) \rightleftharpoons H^+(aq) + HSO_3^-(aq) \qquad K_{a_1} = 1.6 \times 10^{-2}$$

$$HSO_3^-(aq) \rightleftharpoons H^+(aq) + SO_3^{2-}(aq) \qquad K_{a_2} = 6.4 \times 10^{-8}$$

The first equivalence point in the titration curve represents the titration of the first proton, whereas the second equivalence point represents the titration of the second proton. Notice that the volume required to reach the first equivalence point is identical to the volume required to reach the second point because the number of moles of H_2SO_3 in the first step determines the number of moles of HSO_3^- in the second step.

ANSWER NOW!

18.9
Cc
Conceptual Connection

ACID–BASE TITRATIONS Consider these three titrations:

(i) the titration of 25.0 mL of a 0.100 M monoprotic weak acid with 0.100 M NaOH
(ii) the titration of 25.0 mL of a 0.100 M diprotic weak acid with 0.100 M NaOH
(iii) the titration of 25.0 mL of a 0.100 M strong acid with 0.100 M NaOH

Which statement is most likely to be true?

(a) All three titrations have the same initial pH.
(b) All three titrations have the same pH at their first equivalence points.
(c) All three titrations require the same volume of NaOH to reach their first equivalence points.

Indicators: pH-Dependent Colors

We can monitor the pH of a titration with either a pH meter or an indicator. The direct monitoring of pH with a meter yields data like the pH curves we have examined previously, allowing determination of the equivalence point from the pH curve itself, as shown in Figure 18.10▶. With an indicator, we rely on the point where the indicator changes color—called the **endpoint**—to determine the equivalence point, as shown in Figure 18.11▶. With the correct indicator, the endpoint of the titration (indicated by the color change) occurs at the equivalence point (when the amount of acid equals the amount of base).

An indicator is itself a weak organic acid that is a different color than its conjugate base. For example, phenolphthalein (whose structure is shown in Figure 18.12▶) is a common indicator whose acid form is colorless and conjugate base form is pink. If we let HIn represent the acid form of a generic indicator and In^- the conjugate base form, we have the following equilibrium:

$$\underset{\text{color 1}}{HIn(aq)} + H_2O(l) \rightleftharpoons H_3O^+(aq) + \underset{\text{color 2}}{In^-(aq)}$$

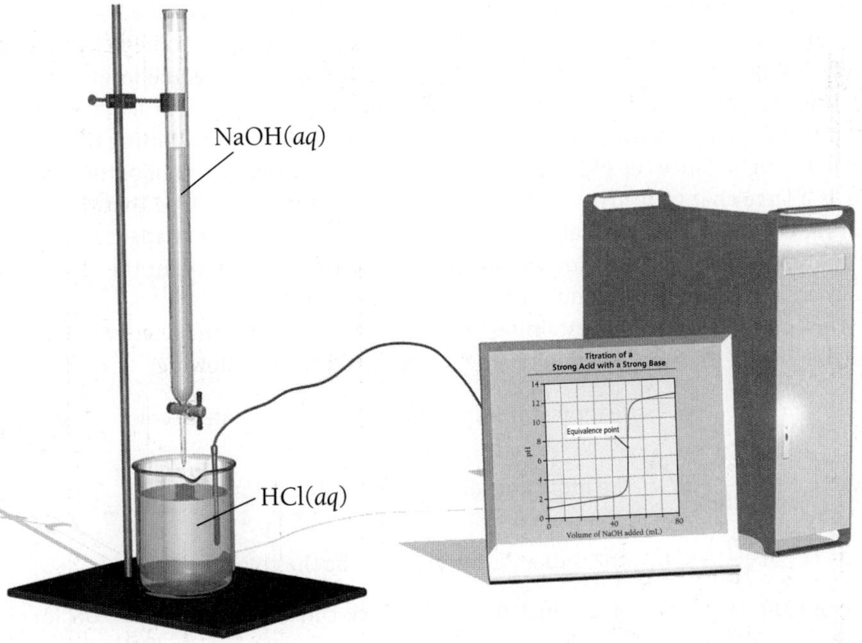

◀ **FIGURE 18.10 Monitoring the pH during a Titration** A pH meter monitors pH during titration. The inflection point in the resulting pH curve signifies the equivalence point.

Using an Indicator

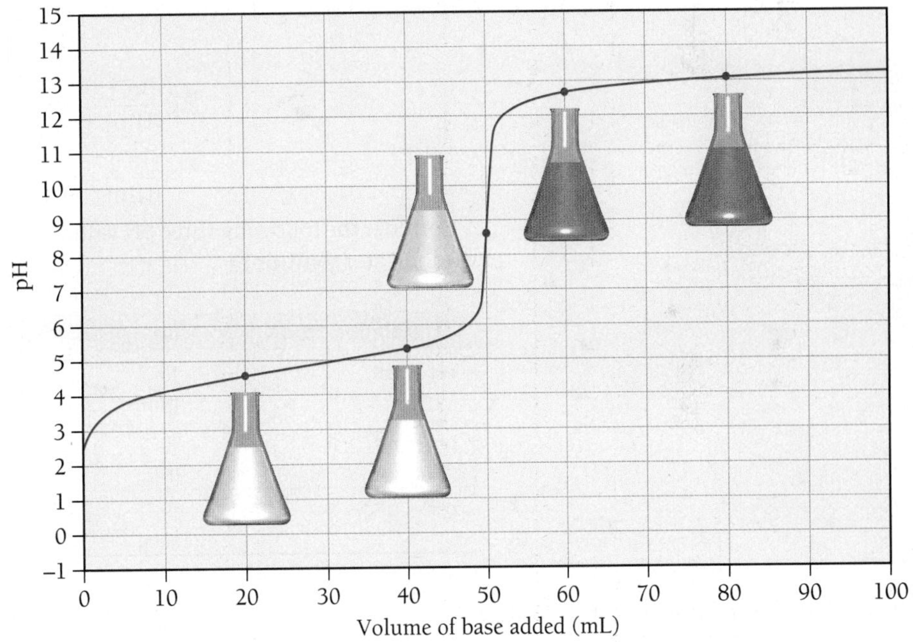

▶ **FIGURE 18.11 Monitoring the Color Change during a Titration** Titration of 0.100 M $HC_2H_3O_2$ with 0.100 M NaOH. The endpoint of a titration is signaled by a color change in an appropriate indicator (in this case, phenolphthalein).

▼ **FIGURE 18.12 Phenolphthalein** Phenolphthalein, a weakly acidic compound, is colorless. Its conjugate base is pink.

Phenolphthalein, a Common Indicator

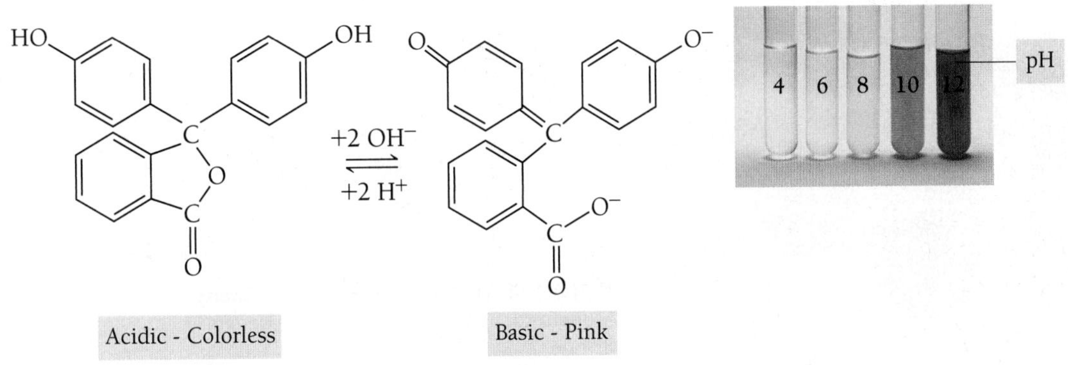

Because its color is intense, only a small amount of indicator is required—an amount that will not affect the pH of the solution or the equivalence point of the neutralization reaction. When the $[H_3O^+]$ changes during the titration, the equilibrium shifts in response. At low pH, the $[H_3O^+]$ is high and the equilibrium lies far to the left, resulting in a solution of color 1. As the titration proceeds, the $[H_3O^+]$ decreases, shifting the equilibrium to the right. Since the pH change is large near the equivalence point of the titration, there is a large change in $[H_3O^+]$ near the equivalence point. Provided that the correct indicator is chosen, there will also be a correspondingly significant change in color. For the titration of a strong acid with a strong base, one drop of the base near the endpoint is usually enough to change the indicator from color 1 to color 2.

The color of a solution containing an indicator depends on the relative concentrations of HIn and In^-. As a useful guideline, we can assume the following:

If $\frac{[In^-]}{HIn} = 1$, the indicator solution will be intermediate in color.

If $\frac{[In^-]}{HIn} > 10$, the indicator solution will be the color of In^-.

If $\frac{[In^-]}{HIn} < 0.1$, the indicator solution will be the color of HIn.

From the Henderson–Hasselbalch equation, we can derive an expression for the ratio of $[In^-]/[HIn]$:

$$pH = pK_a + \log\frac{[base]}{[acid]}$$

$$= pK_a + \log\frac{[In^-]}{[HIn]}$$

$$\log\frac{[In^-]}{[HIn]} = pH - pK_a$$

$$\frac{[In^-]}{[HIn]} = 10^{(pH - pK_a)}$$

Consider the following three pH values relative to pK_a and the corresponding colors of the indicator solution:

pH (relative to pK_a)	$[In^-]/[HIn]$ Ratio	Color of Indicator Solution
$pH = pK_a$	$\frac{[In^-]}{[HIn]} = 10^0 = 1$	Intermediate color
$pH = pK_a + 1$	$\frac{[In^-]}{[HIn]} = 10^1 = 10$	Color of In^-
$pH = pK_a - 1$	$\frac{[In^-]}{[HIn]} = 10^{-1} = 0.10$	Color of HIn

When the pH of the solution equals the pK_a of the indicator, the solution has an intermediate color. When the pH is 1 unit (or more) above pK_a, the indicator is the color of In^-, and when the pH is 1 unit (or more) below pK_a, the indicator is the color of HIn. As you can see, the indicator changes color within a range of two pH units centered at pK_a (Figure 18.13◀). Table 18.1 shows various indicators and their colors as a function of pH.

Indicator Color Change: Methyl Red

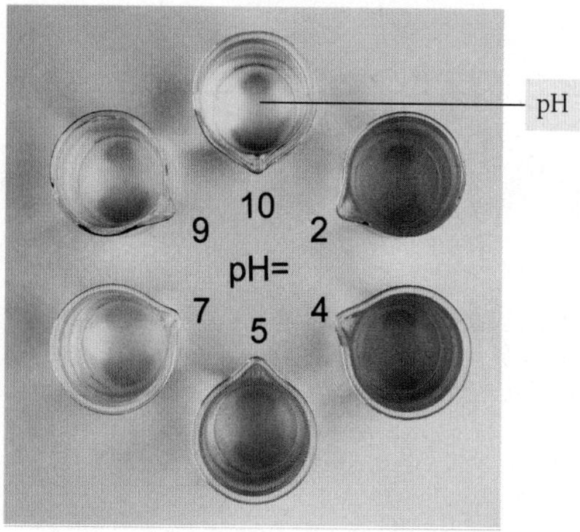

◀ **FIGURE 18.13 Indicator Color Change** An indicator (in this case, methyl red) generally changes color within a range of two pH units.

TABLE 18.1 ■ Ranges of Color Changes for Several Acid–Base Indicators

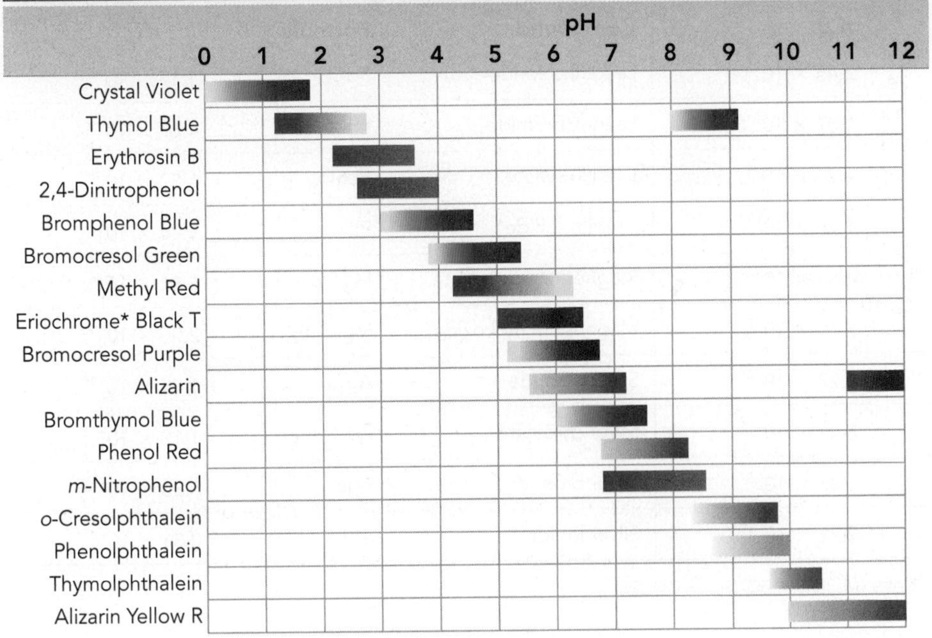

*Trademark of CIBA GEIGY CORP.

18.5 Solubility Equilibria and the Solubility Product Constant

Recall from Chapter 5 that a compound is considered *soluble* if it dissolves in water and *insoluble* if it does not. Recall also that, with the solubility rules in Table 5.1, we were able to classify ionic compounds simply as soluble or insoluble. Now we have the tools to examine *degrees* of solubility.

We can better understand the solubility of an ionic compound by applying the concept of equilibrium to the process of dissolution. For example, we can represent the dissolution of calcium fluoride in water as an equilibrium:

$$CaF_2(s) \rightleftharpoons Ca^{2+}(aq) + 2\ F^-(aq)$$

The equilibrium constant for a chemical equation representing the dissolution of an ionic compound is the **solubility product constant (K_{sp})**. For CaF_2, the expression of the solubility product constant is:

$$K_{sp} = [Ca^{2+}][F^-]^2$$

Notice that, as we discussed in Section 16.5, solids are omitted from the equilibrium expression because the concentration of a solid is constant (it is determined by its density and does not change when more solid is added).

The value of K_{sp} is a measure of the solubility of a compound. Table 18.2 lists the values of K_{sp} for a number of ionic compounds. A more complete list can be found in Appendix IIC.

K_{sp} and Molar Solubility

Recall from Section 14.2 that the *solubility* of a compound is the quantity of the compound that dissolves in a certain amount of liquid. The **molar solubility** is the solubility in units of moles per liter (mol/L). We can calculate the molar solubility of a compound directly from K_{sp}.

Consider silver chloride:

$$AgCl(s) \rightleftharpoons Ag^+(aq) + Cl^-(aq) \qquad K_{sp} = 1.77 \times 10^{-10}$$

TABLE 18.2 ■ Selected Solubility Product Constants (K_{sp}) at 25 °C

Compound	Formula	K_{sp}	Compound	Formula	K_{sp}
Barium fluoride	BaF_2	2.45×10^{-5}	Lead(II) chloride	$PbCl_2$	1.17×10^{-5}
Barium sulfate	$BaSO_4$	1.07×10^{-10}	Lead(II) bromide	$PbBr_2$	4.67×10^{-6}
Calcium carbonate	$CaCO_3$	4.96×10^{-9}	Lead(II) sulfate	$PbSO_4$	1.82×10^{-8}
Calcium fluoride	CaF_2	1.46×10^{-10}	Lead(II) sulfide*	PbS	9.04×10^{-29}
Calcium hydroxide	$Ca(OH)_2$	4.68×10^{-6}	Magnesium carbonate	$MgCO_3$	6.82×10^{-6}
Calcium sulfate	$CaSO_4$	7.10×10^{-5}	Magnesium hydroxide	$Mg(OH)_2$	2.06×10^{-13}
Copper(II) sulfide*	CuS	1.27×10^{-36}	Silver chloride	AgCl	1.77×10^{-10}
Iron(II) carbonate	$FeCO_3$	3.07×10^{-11}	Silver chromate	Ag_2CrO_4	1.12×10^{-12}
Iron(II) hydroxide	$Fe(OH)_2$	4.87×10^{-17}	Silver bromide	AgBr	5.35×10^{-13}
Iron(II) sulfide*	FeS	3.72×10^{-19}	Silver iodide	AgI	8.51×10^{-17}

*Sulfide equilibrium is of the type: $MS(s) + H_2O(l) \rightleftharpoons M^{2+}(aq) + HS^-(aq) + OH^-(aq)$

Notice that K_{sp} is *not* the molar solubility, but the solubility product constant. The solubility product constant has only one value at a given temperature. The solubility, however, can have different values in different kinds of solutions. For example, due to the common ion effect, the solubility of AgCl in pure water is different from its solubility in an NaCl solution, even though the solubility product constant is the same for both solutions. Notice also that the solubility of AgCl is directly related (by the reaction stoichiometry) to the amount of Ag^+ or Cl^- present in solution when equilibrium is reached. Consequently, finding molar solubility from K_{sp} involves solving an equilibrium problem.

For AgCl, we set up an ICE table for the dissolution of AgCl into its ions in pure water:

$$AgCl(s) \rightleftharpoons Ag^+(aq) + Cl^-(aq)$$

	$[Ag^+]$	$[Cl^-]$
Initial	0.00	0.00
Change	$+S$	$+S$
Equil	S	S

Alternatively, the variable x can be used in place of S, as it was for other equilibrium calculations.

We let S represent the concentration of AgCl that dissolves (which is the molar solubility) and then represent the concentrations of the ions formed in terms of S. In this case, for every 1 mol of AgCl that dissolves, 1 mol of Ag^+ and 1 mol of Cl^- are produced. Therefore, the concentrations of Ag^+ or Cl^- present in solution are equal to S. Substituting the equilibrium concentrations of Ag^+ and Cl^- into the expression for the solubility product constant, we get:

$$\begin{aligned} K_{sp} &= [Ag^+][Cl^-] \\ &= S \times S \\ &= S^2 \end{aligned}$$

Therefore,

$$\begin{aligned} S &= \sqrt{K_{sp}} \\ &= \sqrt{1.77 \times 10^{-10}} \\ &= 1.33 \times 10^{-5}\ M \end{aligned}$$

The molar solubility of AgCl is 1.33×10^{-5} mol per liter.

WATCH **NOW!**

INTERACTIVE WORKED EXAMPLE 18.8

EXAMPLE 18.8 Calculating Molar Solubility from K_{sp}

Calculate the molar solubility of $PbCl_2$ in pure water.

SOLUTION

Begin by writing the reaction by which solid $PbCl_2$ dissolves into its constituent aqueous ions and write the corresponding expression for K_{sp}.

$$PbCl_2(s) \rightleftharpoons Pb^{2+}(aq) + 2\,Cl^-(aq)$$
$$K_{sp} = [Pb^{2+}][Cl^-]^2$$

Refer to the stoichiometry of the reaction and prepare an ICE table, showing the equilibrium concentrations of Pb^{2+} and Cl^- relative to S, the amount of $PbCl_2$ that dissolves.

$$PbCl_2(s) \rightleftharpoons Pb^{2+}(aq) + 2\,Cl^-(aq)$$

	$[Pb^{2+}]$	$[Cl^-]$
Initial	0.00	0.00
Change	$+S$	$+2S$
Equil	S	$2S$

Substitute the equilibrium expressions for $[Pb^{2+}]$ and $[Cl^-]$ from the previous step into the expression for K_{sp}.

$$K_{sp} = [Pb^{2+}][Cl^-]^2$$
$$= S(2S)^2 = 4S^3$$

Solve for S and substitute the numerical value of K_{sp} (from Table 18.2) to calculate S.

$$S = \sqrt[3]{\frac{K_{sp}}{4}}$$

$$S = \sqrt[3]{\frac{1.17 \times 10^{-5}}{4}} = 1.43 \times 10^{-2}\,\text{M}$$

FOR PRACTICE 18.8 Calculate the molar solubility of $Fe(OH)_2$ in pure water.

CHEMISTRY IN YOUR DAY | Hard Water

In many parts of the United States, significant concentrations of $CaCO_3$ and $MgCO_3$ dissolve into rainwater runoff as it flows through soils rich in these compounds. Water containing dissolved calcium and magnesium ions is known as *hard water*. Hard water is not a health hazard because both calcium and magnesium are part of a healthy diet. However, their presence in water can be a nuisance. Because of their relatively low solubility, hard water becomes saturated with $CaCO_3$ and $MgCO_3$ as it evaporates. If evaporation continues, some dissolved ions precipitate out as salts. These precipitates show up as scaly deposits on faucets, sinks, or cookware. Washing cars or dishes with hard water leaves spots of $CaCO_3$ and $MgCO_3$.

Water can be softened with water softeners. These devices replace the Ca^{2+} and Mg^{2+} ions present in hard water with ions such as K^+ or Na^+. Since potassium and sodium salts are soluble, they do not form scaly deposits in the way that Ca^{2+} and Mg^{2+} ions do. However, when sodium is used to soften drinking water, the resulting water is high in sodium content, a disadvantage to those who must control their sodium intake due to high blood pressure.

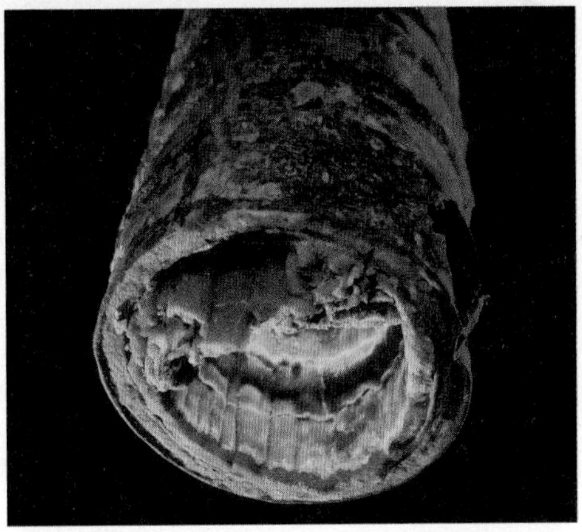

▲ The water in reservoirs where the soil is rich in limestone (calcium carbonate) contains Ca^{2+} ions. This so-called hard water contains dissolved $CaCO_3$ and $MgCO_3$. When hard water evaporates, it can leave deposits of these salts on the shores of lakes and reservoirs (at left) and on plumbing fixtures (such as the pipe shown here).

QUESTION *Use the K_{sp} values from Table 18.2 to calculate the molar solubility of $CaCO_3$ and $MgCO_3$. What mass of $CaCO_3$ (in grams) is in 5 L of water that is saturated with $CaCO_3$?*

EXAMPLE 18.9 Calculating K_{sp} from Molar Solubility

The molar solubility of Ag_2SO_4 in pure water is 1.4×10^{-2} M. Calculate K_{sp}.

SOLUTION

Begin by writing the reaction by which solid Ag_2SO_4 dissolves into its constituent aqueous ions; then write the corresponding expression for K_{sp}.

$$Ag_2SO_4(s) \rightleftharpoons 2\,Ag^+(aq) + SO_4^{2-}(aq)$$
$$K_{sp} = [Ag^+]^2[SO_4^{2-}]$$

Use an ICE table to define $[Ag^+]$ and $[SO_4^{2-}]$ in terms of S, the amount of Ag_2SO_4 that dissolves.

$$Ag_2SO_4(s) \rightleftharpoons 2\,Ag^+(aq) + SO_4^{2-}(aq)$$

	$[Ag^+]$	$[SO_4^{2-}]$
Initial	0.00	0.00
Change	$+2S$	$+S$
Equil	$2S$	S

Substitute the expressions for $[Ag^+]$ and $[SO_4^{2-}]$ from the previous step into the expression for K_{sp}. Substitute the given value *of the molar solubility for S and calculate* K_{sp}.

$$\begin{aligned} K_{sp} &= [Ag^+]^2[SO_4^{2-}] \\ &= (2S)^2S \\ &= 4S^3 \\ &= 4(1.4 \times 10^{-2})^3 \\ &= 1.1 \times 10^{-5} \end{aligned}$$

FOR PRACTICE 18.9 The molar solubility of AgBr in pure water is 7.3×10^{-7} M. Calculate K_{sp}.

K_{sp} and Relative Solubility

As we have just seen, molar solubility and K_{sp} are related, and each can be calculated from the other; however, we cannot generally use the K_{sp} values of two different compounds to directly compare their relative solubilities.

For example, consider the following compounds, their K_{sp} values, and their molar solubilities:

Compound	K_{sp}	Solubility
$Mg(OH)_2$	2.06×10^{-13}	3.72×10^{-5} M
$FeCO_3$	3.07×10^{-11}	5.54×10^{-6} M

Magnesium hydroxide has a smaller K_{sp} than iron(II) carbonate, but a higher molar solubility. Why? The relationship between K_{sp} and molar solubility depends on the stoichiometry of the dissociation reaction. Consequently, any direct comparison of K_{sp} values for different compounds can only be made if the compounds have the same dissociation stoichiometry.

Consider the following compounds with the same dissociation stoichiometry, their K_{sp} values, and their molar solubilities:

Compound	K_{sp}	Solubility
$Mg(OH)_2$	2.06×10^{-13}	3.72×10^{-5} M
CaF_2	1.46×10^{-10}	3.32×10^{-4} M

In this case, magnesium hydroxide and calcium fluoride have the same dissociation stoichiometry (1 mol of each compound produces 3 mol of dissolved ions); therefore, the K_{sp} values can be directly compared as a measure of relative solubility.

The Effect of a Common Ion on Solubility

How is the solubility of an ionic compound affected when the compound is dissolved in a solution that already contains one of its ions? For example, what is the solubility of CaF_2 in a solution that is 0.100 M in NaF? We can determine the change in solubility by considering the common ion effect, which we first encountered in Section 18.2. We represent the dissociation of CaF_2 in a 0.100 M NaF solution as shown in the margin.

In accordance with Le Châtelier's principle, the presence of the F^- ion in solution causes the equilibrium to shift to the left (compared to its position in pure water), which means that less CaF_2 dissolves—that is, its solubility is decreased.

Common ion
0.100 M $F^-(aq)$

$$CaF_2(s) \rightleftharpoons Ca^{2+}(aq) + 2\,F^-(aq)$$

Equilibrium shifts left

In general, the solubility of an ionic compound is lower in a solution containing a common ion than in pure water.

We can calculate the exact value of the solubility by working an equilibrium problem in which the concentration of the common ion is accounted for in the initial conditions, as shown in Example 18.10.

EXAMPLE 18.10 Calculating Molar Solubility in the Presence of a Common Ion

What is the molar solubility of CaF_2 in a solution containing 0.100 M NaF?

SOLUTION

Begin by writing the reaction by which solid CaF_2 dissolves into its constituent aqueous ions. Write the corresponding expression for K_{sp}.

$$CaF_2(s) \rightleftharpoons Ca^{2+}(aq) + 2\,F^-(aq)$$

$$K_{sp} = [Ca^{2+}][F^-]^2$$

Use the stoichiometry of the reaction to prepare an ICE table showing the initial concentration of the common ion. Fill in the equilibrium concentrations of Ca^{2+} and F^- relative to S, the amount of CaF_2 that dissolves.

$$CaF_2(s) \rightleftharpoons Ca^{2+}(aq) + 2\,F^-(aq)$$

	$[Ca^{2+}]$	$[F^-]$
Initial	0.00	0.100
Change	$+S$	$+2S$
Equil	S	$0.100 + 2S$

Substitute the equilibrium expressions for $[Ca^{2+}]$ and $[F^-]$ from the previous step into the expression for K_{sp}. Because K_{sp} is small, you can make the approximation that $2S$ is much less than 0.100 and will therefore be insignificant when added to 0.100 (this is similar to the *x is small* approximation in equilibrium problems).

$$K_{sp} = [Ca^{2+}][F^-]^2$$
$$= S(0.100 + \cancel{2S})^2 \quad (S \text{ is small})$$
$$= S(0.100)^2$$

Solve for S and substitute the numerical value of K_{sp} (from Table 18.2) to calculate S. Note that the calculated value of S is indeed small compared to 0.100; our approximation is valid.

$$K_{sp} = S(0.100)^2$$

$$S = \frac{K_{sp}}{0.0100} = \frac{1.46 \times 10^{-10}}{0.0100} = 1.46 \times 10^{-8}\,\text{M}$$

For comparison, the molar solubility of CaF_2 in pure water is 3.32×10^{-4} M, which means CaF_2 is over 20,000 times more soluble in water than in the NaF solution. (Confirm this for yourself by calculating its solubility in pure water from the value of K_{sp}.)

FOR PRACTICE 18.10 Calculate the molar solubility of CaF_2 in a solution containing 0.250 M $Ca(NO_3)_2$.

COMMON ION EFFECT In which solution is $BaSO_4$ most soluble?

(a) a solution that is 0.10 M in $BaNO_3$
(b) a solution that is 0.10 M in Na_2SO_4
(c) a solution that is 0.10 M in $NaNO_3$

18.10 Cc Conceptual Connection

ANSWER **NOW!**

The Effect of pH on Solubility

The pH of a solution can affect the solubility of a compound in that solution. For example, consider the dissociation of $Mg(OH)_2$, the active ingredient in milk of magnesia:

$$Mg(OH)_2(s) \rightleftharpoons Mg^{2+}(aq) + 2OH^-(aq)$$

The solubility of this compound is highly dependent on the pH of the solution into which it dissolves. If the pH is high, then the concentration of OH^- in the solution is high. In accordance with the common ion effect, this shifts the equilibrium to the left, lowering the solubility:

High $[OH^-]$

$$Mg(OH)_2(s) \rightleftharpoons Mg^{2+}(aq) + 2\,OH^-(aq)$$

Equilibrium shifts left

If the pH is low, then the concentration of $H_3O^+(aq)$ in the solution is high. As the $Mg(OH)_2$ dissolves, these H_3O^+ ions neutralize the newly dissolved OH^- ions, driving the reaction to the right:

H_3O^+ reacts with OH^-

$$Mg(OH)_2(s) \rightleftharpoons Mg^{2+}(aq) + 2\,OH^-(aq)$$

Equilibrium shifts right

▲ Stalactites (which hang from the ceiling) and stalagmites (which grow up from the ground) form as calcium carbonate precipitates out of the water evaporating in underground caves.

Consequently, the solubility of $Mg(OH)_2$ in an acidic solution is higher than that in a pH-neutral or basic solution.

In general, the solubility of an ionic compound with a strongly basic or weakly basic anion increases with increasing acidity (decreasing pH).

Common basic anions include OH^-, S^{2-}, and $CO_3{}^{2-}$. Therefore, hydroxides, sulfides, and carbonates are more soluble in acidic water than in pure water. Since rainwater is naturally acidic due to dissolved carbon dioxide, it can dissolve rocks high in limestone ($CaCO_3$) as it flows through the ground. This process sometimes results in huge underground caverns such as those at Carlsbad Caverns National Park in New Mexico. Dripping water saturated in $CaCO_3$ within the cave creates the dramatic mineral formations known as stalagmites and stalactites.

EXAMPLE 18.11 The Effect of pH on Solubility

Determine whether each compound is more soluble in an acidic solution than it is in a neutral solution.

(a) BaF_2 **(b)** AgI **(c)** $Ca(OH)_2$

SOLUTION

(a) The solubility of BaF_2 is greater in an acidic solution than it is in a neutral solution because the F^- ion is a weak base. (F^- is the conjugate base of the weak acid HF and is therefore a weak base.)

(b) The solubility of AgI is not greater in an acidic solution than it is in a neutral solution because the I^- is *not* a base. (I^- is the conjugate base of the *strong* acid HI and is therefore pH-neutral.)

(c) The solubility of $Ca(OH)_2$ is greater in an acidic solution than it is in a neutral solution because the OH^- ion is a strong base.

FOR PRACTICE 18.11 Which compound, $FeCO_3$ or $PbBr_2$, is more soluble in acid than in base? Why?

18.6 Precipitation

In Chapter 5, we learned that a precipitation reaction can occur when we mix two solutions containing ionic compounds when one of the possible cross products—the combination of a cation from one solution and the anion from the other—is insoluble. In this chapter, however, we have seen that the terms *soluble* and *insoluble* are extremes in a continuous range of solubility—many compounds are slightly soluble, and even those that we categorize as insoluble in Chapter 5 actually have some limited degree of solubility (they have very small solubility product constants).

We can better understand precipitation reactions by revisiting a concept from Chapter 16—the reaction quotient (Q). The reaction quotient for the reaction by which an ionic compound dissolves is the product of the concentrations of the ionic components raised to their stoichiometric coefficients. For example, consider the reaction by which CaF_2 dissolves:

$$CaF_2(s) \rightleftharpoons Ca^{2+}(aq) + 2\,F^-(aq)$$

The reaction quotient for this reaction is:

$$Q = [Ca^{2+}][F^-]^2$$

▲ Precipitation reaction

The difference between Q and K_{sp} is that K_{sp} is the value of this product *at equilibrium only*, whereas Q is the value of the product under any conditions. We can therefore use the value of Q to compare a solution containing any concentrations of the component ions to a solution that is at equilibrium.

Consider a solution of calcium fluoride in which Q is less than K_{sp}. Recall from Chapter 16 that if Q is less than K_{sp}, the reaction will proceed to the right (toward products). Consequently, as long as solid CaF_2 is present, the CaF_2 will continue to dissolve. If all of the solid has already dissolved, the solution will simply remain as it is, containing less than the equilibrium amount of the dissolved ions. Such a solution is an *unsaturated solution*. If more solid is added to an unsaturated solution, it will dissolve, as long as Q remains less than K_{sp}.

Now consider a solution in which Q is exactly equal to K_{sp}. In this case, the reaction is at equilibrium and does not make progress in either direction. Such a solution most likely contains at least a small amount of the solid in equilibrium with its component ions. However, the amount of solid may be too small to be visible. Such a solution is a *saturated solution*.

Finally, consider a solution in which Q is greater than K_{sp}. In this case, the reaction proceeds to the left (toward the reactants) and solid calcium fluoride forms from the dissolved calcium and fluoride ions. In other words, the solid normally precipitates out of a solution in which Q is greater than K_{sp}. Under certain circumstances, however, Q can remain greater than K_{sp} for an unlimited period of time. Such a solution, called a *supersaturated solution*, is unstable and forms a precipitate when sufficiently disturbed. Figure 18.14▶ shows a supersaturated solution of sodium acetate. When a small seed crystal of solid sodium acetate is dropped into the solution, it triggers the precipitation reaction.

***Summarizing the Relationship of Q and K_{sp} in Solutions Containing an Ionic Compound*:**

- If $Q < K_{sp}$, the solution is unsaturated and more of the solid ionic compound can dissolve in the solution.
- If $Q = K_{sp}$, the solution is saturated. The solution is holding the equilibrium amount of the dissolved ions, and additional solid does not dissolve in the solution.
- If $Q > K_{sp}$, the solution is supersaturated. Under most circumstances, the excess solid precipitates out of a supersaturated solution.

▼ FIGURE 18.14 Precipitation from a Supersaturated Solution The excess solute in a supersaturated solution of sodium acetate precipitates out if a small sodium acetate crystal is added.

We can use Q to predict whether a precipitation reaction will occur upon the mixing of two solutions containing dissolved ionic compounds. For example, consider mixing a silver nitrate solution with a potassium iodide solution to form a mixture that is 0.010 M in $AgNO_3$ and 0.015 M in KI. Will a precipitate form in the newly mixed solution? From Chapter 5 we know that one of the cross products, KNO_3, is soluble and will therefore not precipitate. The other cross product, AgI, *may* precipitate if the concentrations of Ag^+ and I^- are high enough in the newly mixed solution: we can compare Q to K_{sp} to determine if a precipitate will form. For AgI, $K_{sp} = 8.51 \times 10^{-17}$. For the newly mixed solution, $[Ag^+] = 0.010$ M and $[I^-] = 0.015$ M. We calculate Q as follows:

$$Q = [Ag^+][I^-] = (0.010)(0.015) = 1.5 \times 10^{-4}$$

The value of Q is much greater than K_{sp}; therefore, AgI should precipitate out of the newly mixed solution.

WATCH **NOW!**

INTERACTIVE WORKED EXAMPLE 18.12

EXAMPLE 18.12 Predicting Precipitation Reactions by Comparing Q and K_{sp}

A solution containing lead(II) nitrate is mixed with one containing sodium bromide to form a solution that is 0.0150 M in $Pb(NO_3)_2$ and 0.00350 M in NaBr. Does a precipitate form in the newly mixed solution?

SOLUTION

First, determine the possible cross products and their K_{sp} values (Table 18.2). Any cross products that are soluble do *not* precipitate (see Table 4.1).	Possible cross products: $NaNO_3$ soluble $PbBr_2$ $K_{sp} = 4.67 \times 10^{-6}$
Calculate Q and compare it to K_{sp}. A precipitate will only form if $Q > K_{sp}$.	$Q = [Pb^{2+}][Br^-]^2$ $= (0.0150)(0.00350)^2$ $= 1.84 \times 10^{-7}$ $Q < K_{sp}$; therefore no precipitate forms.

FOR PRACTICE 18.12 If the original solutions in Example 18.12 are concentrated through evaporation and mixed again to form a solution that is 0.0600 M in $Pb(NO_3)_2$ and 0.0158 M in NaBr, will a precipitate form in this newly mixed solution?

Selective Precipitation

The difference in K_{sp} values required for selective precipitation is a factor of at least 10^3.

A solution may contain several different dissolved metal cations that can often be separated by **selective precipitation**, a process involving the addition of a reagent that forms a precipitate with one of the dissolved cations but not the others. For example, seawater contains dissolved magnesium and calcium cations with the concentrations $[Mg^{2+}] = 0.059$ M and $[Ca^{2+}] = 0.011$ M. We can separate these ions by adding a reagent that will precipitate one of the ions but not the other. From Table 18.2, we find that $Mg(OH)_2$ has a K_{sp} of 2.06×10^{-13} and that $Ca(OH)_2$ has a K_{sp} of 4.68×10^{-6}, indicating that the hydroxide ion forms a precipitate with magnesium at a much lower concentration than it does with calcium. Consequently, a soluble hydroxide—such as KOH or NaOH—is a good choice for the precipitating reagent. When we add an appropriate amount of KOH or NaOH to seawater, the hydroxide ion causes the precipitation of $Mg(OH)_2$ (the compound with the lowest K_{sp}) but not $Ca(OH)_2$. Calculations for this selective precipitation are shown in Examples 18.13 and 18.14. In these calculations, you compare Q to K_{sp} to determine the concentration that triggers precipitation.

SELECTIVE PRECIPITATION A solution contains equal concentrations of Ba^{2+}, Pb^{2+}, and Ca^{2+} ions. When postassium sulfate is added to this solution, which cation precipitates first? (*Hint:* See Table 18.2.)

(a) Ba^{2+} **(b)** Pb^{2+} **(c)** Ca^{2+}

18.11 Cc Conceptual Connection

ANSWER **NOW!**

EXAMPLE 18.13 Finding the Minimum Required Reagent Concentration for Selective Precipitation

The magnesium and calcium ions present in seawater ($[Mg^{2+}] = 0.059$ M and $[Ca^{2+}] = 0.011$ M) can be separated by selective precipitation with KOH. What minimum $[OH^-]$ triggers the precipitation of the Mg^{2+} ion?

SOLUTION

The precipitation commences when the value of Q for the precipitating compound just equals the value of K_{sp}. Set the expression for Q for magnesium hydroxide equal to the value of K_{sp}, and solve for $[OH^-]$. This is the concentration above which $Mg(OH)_2$ precipitates.	$Q = [Mg^{2+}][OH^-]^2$ $= (0.059)[OH^-]^2$ When $Q = K_{sp}$, $(0.059)[OH^-]^2 = K_{sp} = 2.06 \times 10^{-13}$ $[OH^-]^2 = \dfrac{2.06 \times 10^{-13}}{0.059}$ $[OH^-] = 1.9 \times 10^{-6}$ M

FOR PRACTICE 18.13 If the concentration of Mg^{2+} in the previous solution was 0.025 M, what minimum $[OH^-]$ triggers precipitation of the Mg^{2+} ion?

EXAMPLE 18.14 Finding the Concentrations of Ions Left in Solution after Selective Precipitation

You add potassium hydroxide to the solution in Example 18.13. When the $[OH^-]$ reaches 1.9×10^{-6} M (as you just calculated), magnesium hydroxide begins to precipitate out of solution. As you continue to add KOH, the magnesium hydroxide continues to precipitate. However, at some point, the $[OH^-]$ becomes high enough to begin to precipitate the calcium ions as well. What is the concentration of Mg^{2+} when Ca^{2+} begins to precipitate?

SOLUTION

First, find the OH^- concentration at which Ca^{2+} begins to precipitate by writing the expression for Q for calcium hydroxide and substituting the concentration of Ca^{2+} from Example 18.13.	$Q = [Ca^{2+}][OH^-]^2$ $= (0.011)[OH^-]^2$
Set the expression for Q equal to the value of K_{sp} for calcium hydroxide and solve for $[OH^-]$. This is the concentration above which $Ca(OH)_2$ precipitates.	When $Q = K_{sp}$, $(0.011)[OH^-]^2 = K_{sp} = 4.68 \times 10^{-6}$ $[OH^-]^2 = \dfrac{4.68 \times 10^{-6}}{0.011}$ $[OH^-] = 2.\underline{0}6 \times 10^{-2}$ M
Find the concentration of Mg^{2+} when OH^- reaches the concentration you just calculated by writing the expression *for Q for magnesium hydroxide* and substituting the concentration of OH^- that you just calculated. Then set the expression for Q equal to the value of K_{sp} for magnesium hydroxide and solve for $[Mg^{2+}]$. This is the concentration of Mg^{2+} that remains when $Ca(OH)_2$ begins to precipitate.	$Q = [Mg^{2+}][OH^-]^2$ $= [Mg^{2+}](2.\underline{0}6 \times 10^{-2})^2$ When $Q = K_{sp}$, $[Mg^{2+}](2.\underline{0}6 \times 10^{-2})^2 = K_{sp} = 2.06 \times 10^{-13}$ $[Mg^{2+}] = \dfrac{2.06 \times 10^{-13}}{(2.\underline{0}6 \times 10^{-2})^2}$ $[Mg^{2+}] = 4.9 \times 10^{-10}$ M

—*Continued on the next page*

Continued—

As you can see from the results, the selective precipitation worked very well. The concentration of Mg^{2+} dropped from 0.059 M to 4.9×10^{-10} M before any calcium began to precipitate, which means that the process separated 99.99% of the magnesium out of the solution.

FOR PRACTICE 18.14 A solution is 0.085 M in Pb^{2+} and 0.025 M in Ag^{+}. (a) If selective precipitation is to be achieved using NaCl, what minimum concentration of NaCl do you need to begin to precipitate the ion that precipitates first? (b) What is the concentration of each ion left in solution at the point where the second ion begins to precipitate?

18.7 Qualitative Chemical Analysis

Selective precipitation as discussed in Section 18.6 can be used in a systematic way to determine which metal ions are present in an unknown solution. This method is known as **qualitative analysis**. The word *qualitative* means *involving quality or kind.* Qualitative analysis involves finding the *kind* of ions present in the solution. This stands in contrast to **quantitative analysis**, which is concerned with quantity, or the amounts of substances in a solution or mixture.

In the past, qualitative analysis by selective precipitation was used extensively to determine the metals present in a sample. This process—dubbed *wet chemistry* because it involves the mixing of many aqueous solutions in the lab—has been replaced by more precise and less time-intensive instrumental techniques. Nonetheless, both for the sake of history and also because of the importance of the principles involved, we now examine a traditional qualitative analysis scheme. You may use such a scheme in your general chemistry laboratory as an exercise in qualitative analysis.

The basic idea behind qualitative analysis is straightforward. A sample containing a mixture of metal cations is subjected to the addition of several precipitating agents. At each step, some of the metal cations—those that form insoluble compounds with the precipitating agent—precipitate from the mixture and are separated out as solids. The remaining aqueous mixture is then subjected to the next precipitating agent, and so on (Figure 18.15▼).

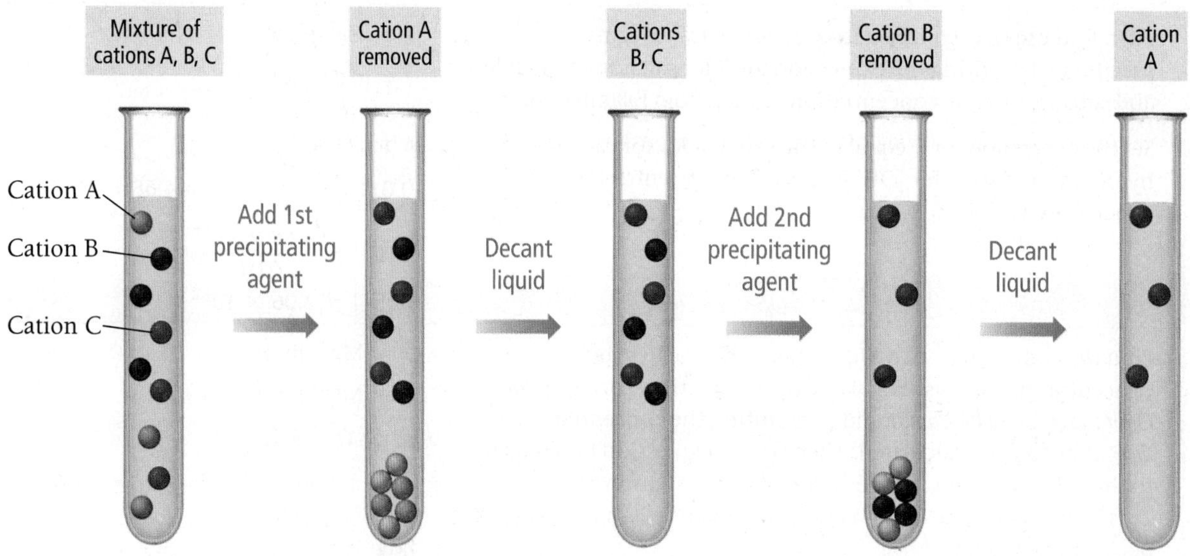

▲ **FIGURE 18.15 Qualitative Analysis** In qualitative analysis, specific ions are precipitated successively by the addition of appropriate reagents.

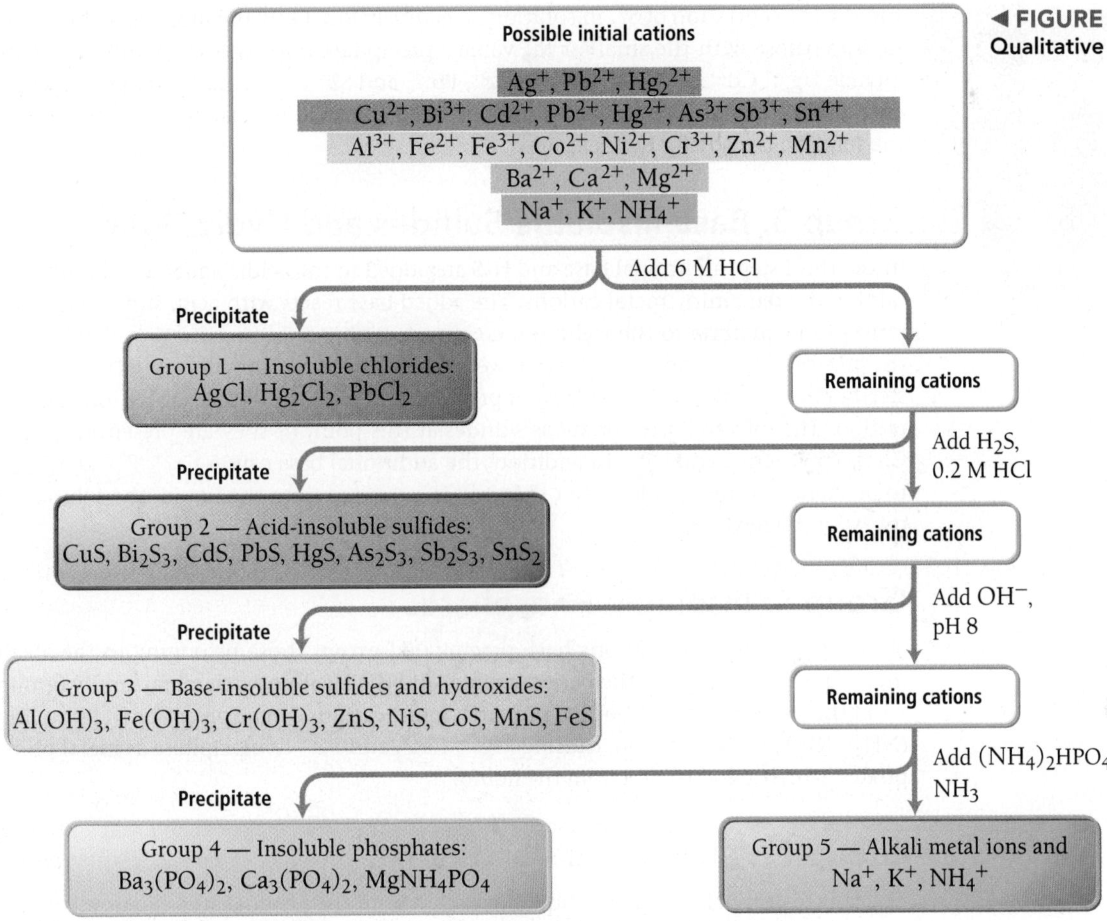

◀ **FIGURE 18.16 A General Qualitative Analysis Scheme**

Figure 18.16▲ is a diagram of a general qualitative analysis scheme. The scheme involves separating a mixture of the common ions into five groups by sequentially adding five different precipitating agents. After each precipitating agent is added, the mixture is put into a centrifuge to separate the solid from the liquid. The liquid is decanted for the next step, and the solid is set aside for subsequent analysis. We examine each group separately.

Group 1: Insoluble Chlorides

In the first step, the aqueous mixture containing the metal cations is treated with 6 M HCl. Since most chlorides are soluble, the chloride ions *do not form* a precipitate with the majority of the cations in the mixture. However, Ag^+, Pb^{2+}, and Hg_2^{2+} *do form* insoluble chlorides. So, if any of those metal cations are present, they precipitate out. The absence of a precipitate constitutes a negative test for Ag^+, Pb^{2+}, and Hg_2^{2+}. If a precipitate forms, one or more of these ions is present. After the solid is separated from the liquid, the solution is ready for the next step.

Group 2: Acid-Insoluble Sulfides

In the second step, the acidic aqueous mixture containing the remaining metal cations is treated with H_2S, a weak diprotic acid that dissociates in two steps:

$$H_2S \rightleftharpoons H^+ + HS^-$$

$$HS^- \rightleftharpoons H^+ + S^{2-}$$

The concentration of S^{2-} ions in an H_2S solution is pH-dependent. At low pH (high H^+ concentration) the equilibria shift left, minimizing the amount of available S^{2-}. At high pH (low H^+ concentration) the equilbria shift right, maximizing the amount of available S^{2-}. At this stage, the solution is acidic (from the addition of HCl in the previous step),

$(NH_4)_2S$ CdS Sb_2S_3 PbS

and the concentration of S^{2-} in solution is relatively low. Only the most insoluble metal sulfides (those with the smallest K_{sp} values) precipitate under these conditions. These include Hg^{2+}, Cd^{2+}, Bi^{3+}, Cu^{2+}, Sn^{4+}, As^{3+}, Pb^{2+}, and Sb^{3+}. If any of these metal cations are present, they precipitate out as sulfides. After the solid is separated from the liquid, the solution is ready for the next step.

Group 3: Base-Insoluble Sulfides and Hydroxides

In the third step, additional base and H_2S are added to the acidic aqueous mixture containing the remaining metal cations. The added base reacts with acid, shifting the H_2S ionization equilibria to the right and creating a higher S^{2-} concentration. This causes the precipitation of those sulfides that were too soluble to precipitate out in the previous step but not soluble enough to prevent precipitation with the higher sulfide ion concentration. The ions that precipitate as sulfides at this point (if they are present) are Fe^{2+}, Co^{2+}, Zn^{2+}, Mn^{2+}, and Ni^{2+}. In addition, the additional base causes Cr^{3+}, Fe^{3+}, and Al^{3+} to precipitate as hydroxides. After the solid is separated from the liquid, the solution is ready for the next step.

Group 4: Insoluble Phosphates

At this stage, all of the cations have precipitated except those belonging to the alkali metal family (group 1A in the periodic table) and the alkaline earth metal family (group 2A in the periodic table). The alkaline earth metal cations can be precipitated by adding $(NH_4)_2HPO_4$ to the solution, causing Mg^{2+}, Ca^{2+}, and Ba^{2+} to precipitate as metal phosphates, which are separated from the liquid.

Group 5: Alkali Metals and NH_4^+

The only dissolved ions that the liquid decanted from the previous step can now contain are Na^+, K^+, and NH_4^+. These cations do not form insoluble compounds with any anions and cannot be precipitated from the solution. Their presence can be determined, however, by other means. Sodium and potassium ions, for example, are usually identified through flame tests. The sodium ion produces a yellow-orange flame, and the potassium ion produces a violet flame, as shown in Figure 18.17▼.

By applying this procedure, nearly two dozen metal cations can be separated from a solution initially containing all of them. Each of the groups can be further analyzed to determine which specific ions are present. The procedures for these steps are found in many general chemistry laboratory manuals.

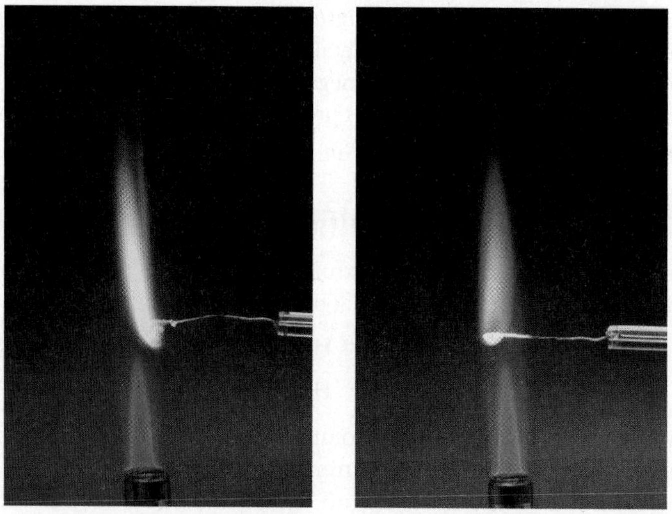
Sodium Potassium

▶ **FIGURE 18.17 Flame Tests** The sodium ion produces a yellow-orange flame. The potassium ion produces a violet flame.

18.8 Complex Ion Equilibria

We have discussed several different types of equilibria so far, including acid–base equilibria and solubility equilibria. We now turn to equilibria of another type, which primarily involve transition metal ions in solution. Transition metal ions tend to be good electron acceptors (good Lewis acids). In aqueous solutions, water molecules can act as electron donors (Lewis bases) to hydrate transition metal ions. For example, silver ions are hydrated by water in solution to form $Ag(H_2O)_2^+(aq)$. Chemists often write $Ag^+(aq)$ as a shorthand notation for the hydrated silver ion, but the bare ion does not really exist by itself in solution.

Species such as $Ag(H_2O)_2^+$ are known as *complex ions*. A **complex ion** contains a central metal ion bound to one or more *ligands*. A **ligand** is a neutral molecule or ion that acts as a Lewis base with the central metal ion. In $Ag(H_2O)_2^+$, water is the ligand. If a stronger Lewis base is put into a solution containing $Ag(H_2O)_2^+$, the stronger Lewis base displaces the water in the complex ion. For example, ammonia reacts with $Ag(H_2O)_2^+$ according to the following reaction:

$$Ag(H_2O)_2^+(aq) + 2\,NH_3(aq) \rightleftharpoons Ag(NH_3)_2^+(aq) + 2\,H_2O(l)$$

For simplicity, we often leave water out of the equation:

$$Ag^+(aq) + 2\,NH_3(aq) \rightleftharpoons Ag(NH_3)_2^+(aq) \qquad K_f = 1.7 \times 10^7$$

We cover complex ions in more detail in Chapter 26. Here, we focus on the equilibria associated with their formation.

The equilibrium constant associated with the reaction for the formation of a complex ion, such as the one just shown, is called the **formation constant (K_f)**. The expression for K_f is determined by the law of mass action, like any equilibrium constant. For $Ag(NH_3)_2^+$, the expression for K_f is:

$$K_f = \frac{[Ag(NH_3)_2^+]}{[Ag^+][NH_3]^2}$$

Notice that the value of K_f for $Ag(NH_3)_2^+$ is large, indicating that the formation of the complex ion is highly favored. Table 18.3 lists the formation constants for a number of common complex ions. You can see that, in general, values of K_f are very large, indicating that the formation of complex ions is highly favored in each case. Example 18.15 illustrates how to use K_f in calculations.

TABLE 18.3 ■ Formation Constants of Selected Complex Ions in Water at 25 °C

Complex Ion	K_f	Complex Ion	K_f
$Ag(CN)_2^-$	1×10^{21}	$Cu(NH_3)_4^{2+}$	1.7×10^{13}
$Ag(NH_3)_2^+$	1.7×10^{7}	$Fe(CN)_6^{4-}$	1.5×10^{35}
$Ag(S_2O_3)_2^{3-}$	2.8×10^{13}	$Fe(CN)_6^{3-}$	2×10^{43}
AlF_6^{3-}	7×10^{19}	$Hg(CN)_4^{2-}$	1.8×10^{41}
$Al(OH)_4^-$	3×10^{33}	$HgCl_4^{2-}$	1.1×10^{16}
$CdBr_4^{2-}$	5.5×10^{3}	HgI_4^{2-}	2×10^{30}
CdI_4^{2-}	2×10^{6}	$Ni(NH_3)_6^{2+}$	2.0×10^{8}
$Cd(CN)_4^{2-}$	3×10^{18}	$Pb(OH)_3^-$	8×10^{13}
$Co(NH_3)_6^{3+}$	2.3×10^{33}	$Sn(OH)_3^-$	3×10^{25}
$Co(OH)_4^{2-}$	5×10^{9}	$Zn(CN)_4^{2-}$	2.1×10^{19}
$Co(SCN)_4^{2-}$	1×10^{3}	$Zn(NH_3)_4^{2+}$	2.8×10^{9}
$Cr(OH)_4^-$	8.0×10^{29}	$Zn(OH)_4^{2-}$	2×10^{15}
$Cu(CN)_4^{2-}$	1.0×10^{25}		

EXAMPLE 18.15 Complex Ion Equilibria

You mix a 200.0-mL sample of a solution that is 1.5×10^{-3} M in $Cu(NO_3)_2$ with a 250.0-mL sample of a solution that is 0.20 M in NH_3. After the solution reaches equilibrium, what concentration of $Cu^{2+}(aq)$ remains?

SOLUTION

Write the balanced equation for the complex ion equilibrium that occurs and look up the value of K_f in Table 18.3. Since this is an equilibrium problem, you have to create an ICE table, which requires the initial concentrations of Cu^{2+} and NH_3. Calculate those concentrations from the given values.

$$Cu^{2+}(aq) + 4\,NH_3(aq) \rightleftharpoons Cu(NH_3)_4^{2+}(aq)$$

$$K_f = 1.7 \times 10^{13}$$

$$[Cu^{2+}]_{initial} = \frac{0.200\,\cancel{L} \times \dfrac{1.5 \times 10^{-3}\,mol}{\cancel{L}}}{0.200\,L + 0.250\,L} = 6.7 \times 10^{-4}\,M$$

$$[NH_3]_{initial} = \frac{0.250\,\cancel{L} \times \dfrac{0.20\,mol}{1\,\cancel{L}}}{0.200\,L + 0.250\,L} = 0.11\,M$$

Construct an ICE table for the reaction and write down the initial concentrations of each species.

$$Cu^{2+}(aq) + 4\,NH_3(aq) \rightleftharpoons Cu(NH_3)_4^{2+}(aq)$$

	$[Cu^{2+}]$	$[NH_3]$	$[Cu(NH_3)_4^{2+}]$
Initial	6.7×10^{-4}	0.11	0.0
Change			
Equil			

Since the equilibrium constant is large and the concentration of ammonia is much larger than the concentration of Cu^{2+}, you can assume that the reaction will be driven to the right so that most of the Cu^{2+} is consumed. Unlike previous ICE tables, where you used x to represent the change in concentration in going to equilibrium, here you let x represent the small amount of Cu^{2+} that remains when equilibrium is reached.

$$Cu^{2+}(aq) + 4\,NH_3(aq) \rightleftharpoons Cu(NH_3)_4^{2+}(aq)$$

	$[Cu^{2+}]$	$[NH_3]$	$[Cu(NH_3)_4^{2+}]$
Initial	6.7×10^{-4}	0.11	0.0
Change	$\approx(-6.7 \times 10^{-4})$	$\approx 4(-6.7 \times 10^{-4})$	$\approx(+6.7 \times 10^{-4})$
Equil	x	0.11	6.7×10^{-4}

Substitute the expressions for the equilibrium concentrations into the expression for K_f and solve for x.

$$K_f = \frac{[Cu(NH_3)_4^{2+}]}{[Cu^{2+}][NH_3]^4}$$

$$= \frac{6.7 \times 10^{-4}}{x(0.11)^4}$$

$$x = \frac{6.7 \times 10^{-4}}{K_f(0.11)^4}$$

$$= \frac{6.7 \times 10^{-4}}{1.7 \times 10^{13}(0.11)^4}$$

$$= 2.7 \times 10^{-13}$$

Confirm that x is indeed small compared to the initial concentration of the metal cation.

The remaining Cu^{2+} is very small because the formation constant is very large.

Since $x = 2.7 \times 10^{-13} \ll 6.7 \times 10^{-4}$, the approximation is valid. The remaining $[Cu^{2+}] = 2.7 \times 10^{-13}$ M.

FOR PRACTICE 18.15 You mix a 125.0-mL sample of a solution that is 0.0117 M in $NiCl_2$ with a 175.0-mL sample of a solution that is 0.250 M in NH_3. After the solution reaches equilibrium, what concentration of $Ni^{2+}(aq)$ remains?

The Effect of Complex Ion Equilibria on Solubility

Recall from Section 18.5 that the solubility of an ionic compound with a basic anion increases with increasing acidity because the acid reacts with the anion and drives the reaction to the right. Similarly, *the solubility of an ionic compound containing a metal cation that forms complex ions increases in the presence of Lewis bases that complex with the cation.* The most common Lewis bases that increase the solubility of metal cations are NH_3, CN^-, and OH^-.

For example, silver chloride is only slightly soluble in pure water:

$$AgCl(s) \rightleftharpoons Ag^+(aq) + Cl^-(aq) \qquad K_{sp} = 1.77 \times 10^{-10}$$

However, adding ammonia increases its solubility dramatically because, as we saw previously in this section, the ammonia forms a complex ion with the silver cations:

$$Ag^+(aq) + 2\,NH_3(aq) \rightleftharpoons Ag(NH_3)_2^{\,+}(aq) \qquad K_f = 1.7 \times 10^7$$

The large value of K_f significantly lowers the concentration of $Ag^+(aq)$ in solution and therefore drives the dissolution of $AgCl(s)$. The two previous reactions can be added together:

$$\begin{array}{rll} AgCl(s) \rightleftharpoons & \cancel{Ag^+(aq)} + Cl^-(aq) & K_{sp} = 1.77 \times 10^{-10} \\ \cancel{Ag^+(aq)} + 2\,NH_3(aq) \rightleftharpoons & Ag(NH_3)_2^{\,+}(aq) & K_f = 1.7 \times 10^7 \\ \hline AgCl(s) + 2\,NH_3(aq) \rightleftharpoons & Ag(NH_3)_2^{\,+}(aq) + Cl^-(aq) & K = K_{sp} \times 3.0 \times 10^{-3} \end{array}$$

As we learned in Section 16.3, the equilibrium constant for a reaction that is the sum of two other reactions is the product of the equilibrium constants for the two other reactions. Adding ammonia changes the equilibrium constant for the dissolution of $AgCl(s)$ by a factor of $3.0 \times 10^{-3}/1.77 \times 10^{-10} = 1.7 \times 10^7$ (17 million), which makes the otherwise relatively insoluble AgCl(s) quite soluble, as shown in Figure 18.18▼.

Complex Ion Formation

$$2\,NH_3(aq) + AgCl(s) \rightleftharpoons Ag(NH_3)_2^{\,+}(aq) + Cl^-(aq)$$

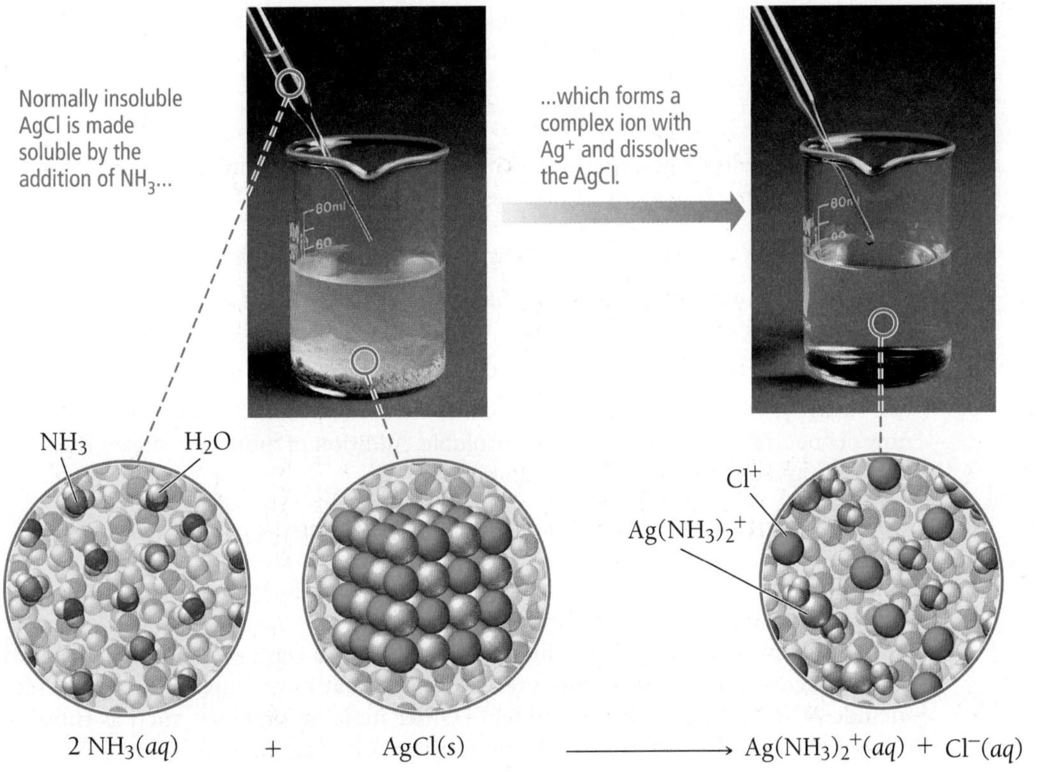

◀ **FIGURE 18.18**
Complex Ion Formation

ANSWER NOW!

18.12 **Cc** Conceptual Connection

SOLUBILITY AND COMPLEX ION EQUILIBRIA Which compound, when added to water, is most likely to increase the solubility of CuS?

(a) NaCl **(b)** KNO_3 **(c)** NaCN **(d)** $MgBr_2$

The Solubility of Amphoteric Metal Hydroxides

Many metal hydroxides are insoluble or only very slightly soluble in pH-neutral water. For example, $Al(OH)_3$ has $K_{sp} = 1.3 \times 10^{-33}$, which means that if we put $Al(OH)_3$ in water, the vast majority of it will settle to the bottom as an undissolved solid. All metal hydroxides, however, have a basic anion (OH^-) and therefore become more soluble in acidic solutions (see the previous subsection and Section 18.5). The metal hydroxides become more soluble because they can act as bases and react with $H_3O^+(aq)$. For example, $Al(OH)_3$ dissolves in acid according to the reaction:

$$Al(OH)_3(s) + 3\,H_3O^+(aq) \longrightarrow Al^{3+}(aq) + 6\,H_2O(l)$$

$Al(OH)_3$ acts as a base in this reaction.

Recall from Section 17.3 that a substance that can act as either an acid or a base is said to be amphoteric.

Interestingly, some metal hydroxides can also act as acids—they are *amphoteric*. The ability of an amphoteric metal hydroxide to act as an acid increases its solubility in basic solution. For example, $Al(OH)_3(s)$ dissolves in basic solution according to the reaction:

$$Al(OH)_3(s) + OH^-(aq) \longrightarrow Al(OH)_4^-(aq)$$

$Al(OH)_3$ acts as an acid in this reaction.

$Al(OH)_3$ is soluble at high pH and soluble at low pH but *insoluble* in a pH-neutral solution.

We can observe the whole range of the pH-dependent solubility behavior of Al^{3+} by considering a hydrated aluminum ion in solution, beginning at an acidic pH. We know from Section 17.8 that Al^{3+} in solution is inherently acidic because it complexes with water to form $Al(H_2O)_6^{3+}(aq)$. The complex ion then acts as an acid by losing a proton from one of the complexed water molecules according to the reaction:

$$Al(H_2O)_6^{3+}(aq) + H_2O(l) \rightleftharpoons Al(H_2O)_5(OH)^{2+}(aq) + H_3O^+(aq)$$

Addition of base to the solution drives the reaction to the right and continues to remove protons from complexed water molecules:

$$Al(H_2O)_5(OH)^{2+}(aq) + OH^-(aq) \rightleftharpoons Al(H_2O)_4(OH)_2^+(aq) + H_2O(l)$$

$$Al(H_2O)_4(OH)_2^+(aq) + OH^-(aq) \rightleftharpoons \underbrace{Al(H_2O)_3(OH)_3(s)}_{\text{equivalent to } Al(OH)_3(s)} + H_2O(l)$$

The result of removing three protons from $Al(H_2O)_6^{3+}(aq)$ is the solid white precipitate $Al(H_2O)_3(OH)_3(s)$, which is more commonly written as $Al(OH)_3(s)$. The solution is now pH-neutral and the hydroxide is insoluble. Addition of more OH^- makes the solution basic and dissolves the solid precipitate:

$$Al(H_2O)_3(OH)_3(s) + OH^-(aq) \rightleftharpoons Al(H_2O)_2(OH)_4^-(aq) + H_2O(l)$$

As the solution goes from acidic to neutral to basic, the solubility of Al^{3+} changes accordingly, as illustrated in Figure 18.19▶.

The extent to which a metal hydroxide dissolves in both acid and base depends on the degree to which it is amphoteric. Cations that form amphoteric hydroxides include Al^{3+}, Cr^{3+}, Zn^{2+}, Pb^{2+}, and Sn^{2+}. Other metal hydroxides, such as those of Ca^{2+}, Fe^{2+}, and Fe^{3+}, are not amphoteric—they become soluble in acidic solutions, but not in basic ones.

pH-Dependent Solubility of an Amphoteric Hydroxide

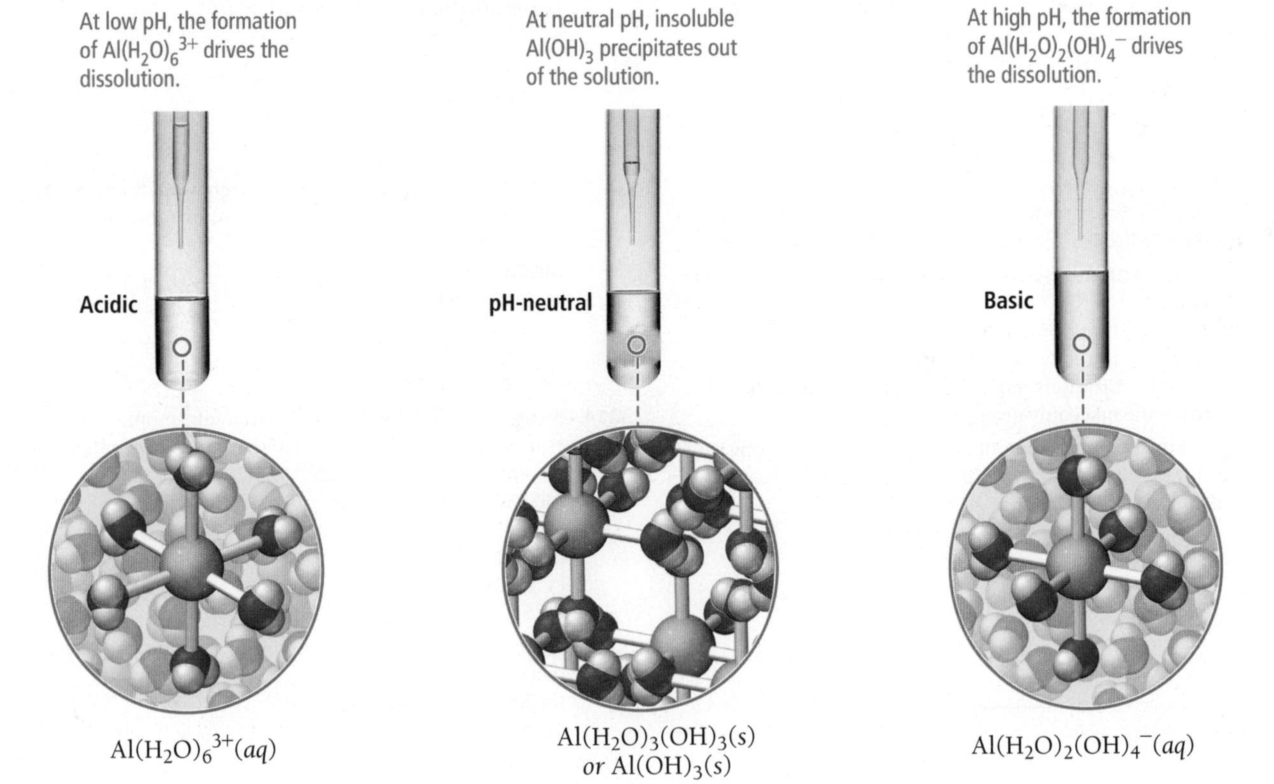

▲ **FIGURE 18.19 Solubility of an Amphoteric Hydroxide** Because aluminum hydroxide is amphoteric, its solubility is pH-dependent.

QUIZ YOURSELF **NOW!**

Self-Assessment Quiz

Q1. A buffer is 0.100 M in NH_4Cl and 0.100 M in NH_3. When a small amount of hydrobromic acid is added to this buffer, which buffer component neutralizes the added acid?
MISSED THIS? *Read Section 18.2; Watch KCV 18.2A*

a) NH_4^+ b) Cl^- c) NH_3
d) None of the above (hydrobromic acid will not be neutralized by this buffer).

Q2. What is the pH of a buffer that is 0.120 M in formic acid ($HCHO_2$) and 0.080 M in potassium formate ($KCHO_2$)? For formic acid, $K_a = 1.8 \times 10^{-4}$.
MISSED THIS? *Read Section 18.2; Watch KCV 18.2B, IWE 18.2*

a) 2.33 b) 3.57 c) 3.74 d) 3.91

Q3. A buffer with a pH of 9.85 contains CH_3NH_2 and CH_3NH_3Cl in water. What can you conclude about the relative concentrations of CH_3NH_2 and CH_3NH_3Cl in this buffer? For CH_3NH_2, $pK_b = 3.36$.
MISSED THIS? *Read Section 18.2; Watch KCV 18.2B, IWE 18.2*

a) $CH_3NH_2 > CH_3NH_3Cl$ b) $CH_3NH_2 < CH_3NH_3Cl$
c) $CH_3NH_2 = CH_3NH_3Cl$
d) Nothing can be concluded about the relative concentrations of CH_3NH_2 and CH_3NH_3Cl.

Q4. A 500.0-mL buffer solution is 0.10 M in benzoic acid and 0.10 M in sodium benzoate and has an initial pH of 4.19. What is the pH of the buffer upon addition of 0.010 mol of NaOH?
MISSED THIS? *Read Section 18.2; Watch KCV 18.2B, IWE 18.3*

a) 1.70 b) 4.01 c) 4.29 d) 4.37

Q5. Consider a buffer composed of the weak acid HA and its conjugate base A^-. Which pair of concentrations results in the most effective buffer?
MISSED THIS? *Read Section 18.3*

a) 0.10 M HA; 0.10 M A^- b) 0.50 M HA; 0.50 M A^-
c) 0.90 M HA; 0.10 M A^- d) 0.10 M HA; 0.90 M A^-

Q6. Which combination is the best choice to prepare a buffer with a pH of 9.0?
MISSED THIS? *Read Section 18.3*

a) NH_3; NH_4Cl (pK_b for NH_3 is 4.75)
b) C_5H_5N; C_5H_5NHCl (pK_b for C_5H_5N is 8.76)
c) HNO_2; $NaNO_2$ (pK_a for HNO_2 is 3.33)
d) $HCHO_2$; $NaCHO_2$ (pK_a for $HCHO_2$ is 3.74)

Q7. A 25.0-mL sample of an unknown HBr solution is titrated with 0.100 M NaOH. The equivalence point is reached upon the addition of 18.88 mL of the base. What is the concentration of the HBr solution?
MISSED THIS? *Read Section 18.4; Watch KCV 18.4A, IWE 18.6*

a) 0.0755 M b) 0.0376 M
c) 0.100 M d) 0.00188 M

Q8. A 10.0-mL sample of 0.200 M hydrocyanic acid (HCN) is titrated with 0.0998 M NaOH. What is the pH at the equivalence point? For hydrocyanic acid, $pK_a = 9.31$.
MISSED THIS? *Read Section 18.4; Watch KCV 18.4B, IWE 18.7*

a) 7.00 b) 8.76 c) 9.31 d) 11.07

—Continued on the next page

Continued—

Q9. A 20.0-mL sample of 0.150 M ethylamine is titrated with 0.0981 M HCl. What is the pH after the addition of 5.0 mL of HCl? For ethylamine, $pK_b = 3.25$.
MISSED THIS? *Read Section 18.4; Watch KCV 18.4B, IWE 18.7*

a) 10.75 b) 11.04 c) 2.96 d) 11.46

Q10. Three 15.0-mL acid samples—0.10 M HA, 0.10 M HB, and 0.10 M H_2C—are all titrated with 0.100 M NaOH. If HA is a weak acid, HB is a strong acid, and H_2C is a diprotic acid, which statement is true of all three titrations?
MISSED THIS? *Read Section 18.4; Watch KCV 18.4A, KCV 18.4B*

a) All three titrations have the same pH at the first equivalence point.
b) All three titrations have the same initial pH.
c) All three titrations have the same final pH.
d) All three titrations require the same volume of NaOH to reach the first equivalence point.

Q11. A weak unknown monoprotic acid is titrated with a strong base. The titration curve is shown. Find K_a for the unknown acid.
MISSED THIS? *Read Section 18.4; Watch KCV 18.4B, IWE 18.7*

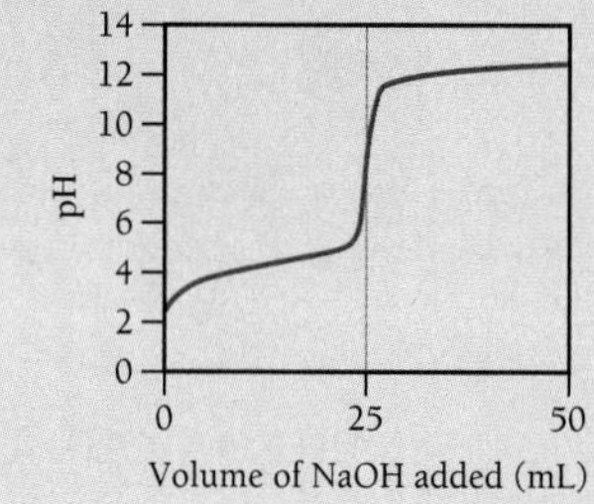

a) 2.5×10^{-3} b) 3.2×10^{-5}
c) 3.2×10^{-7} d) 2.5×10^{-9}

Q12. Calculate the molar solubility of lead(II) bromide ($PbBr_2$). For lead(II) bromide, $K_{sp} = 4.67 \times 10^{-6}$.
MISSED THIS? *Read Section 18.5; Watch IWE 18.8*

a) 0.00153 M
b) 0.0105 M
c) 0.0167 M
d) 0.0211 M

Q13. Calculate the molar solubility of magnesium fluoride (MgF_2) in a solution that is 0.250 M in NaF. For magnesium fluoride, $K_{sp} = 5.16 \times 10^{-11}$.
MISSED THIS? *Read Section 18.5*

a) 2.35×10^{-4} M
b) 2.06×10^{-10} M
c) 2.87×10^{-5} M
d) 8.26×10^{-10} M

Q14. A solution is 0.0250 M in Pb^{2+}. What minimum concentration of Cl^- is required to begin to precipitate $PbCl_2$? For $PbCl_2$, $K_{sp} = 1.17 \times 10^{-5}$.
MISSED THIS? *Read Section 18.6; Watch IWE 18.12*

a) 1.17×10^{-5} M
b) 0.0108 M
c) 0.0216 M
d) 5.41×10^{-4} M

Q15. Which compound is more soluble in an acidic solution than in a neutral solution?
MISSED THIS? *Read Section 18.5*

a) $PbBr_2$
b) CuCl
c) AgI
d) BaF_2

Answers: 1. (c) **2.** (b) **3.** (b) **4.** (d) **5.** (b) **6.** (a) **7.** (a) **8.** (d) **9.** (d) **10.** (d) **11.** (b) **12.** (b) **13.** (d) **14.** (c) **15.** (d)

CHAPTER 18 IN REVIEW

TERMS

Section 18.2
buffer (788)
common ion effect (790)
Henderson–Hasselbalch equation (792)

Section 18.3
buffer capacity (802)

Section 18.4
acid–base titration (803)
indicator (803)
equivalence point (803)
endpoint (814)

Section 18.5
solubility product constant (K_{sp}) (817)
molar solubility (817)

Section 18.6
selective precipitation (824)

Section 18.7
qualitative analysis (826)
quantitative analysis (826)

Section 18.8
complex ion (829)
ligand (829)
formation constant (K_f) (829)

CONCEPTS

The Danger of Antifreeze (18.1)

- Although buffers closely regulate the pH of mammalian blood, the capacity of these buffers to neutralize can be overwhelmed.
- Ethylene glycol, the main component of antifreeze, is metabolized by the liver into glycolic acid. The resulting acidity can exceed the buffering capacity of blood and cause acidosis, a serious condition that results in oxygen deprivation.

Buffers: Solutions That Resist pH Change (18.2)

- Buffers contain significant amounts of both a weak acid and its conjugate base (or a weak base and its conjugate acid), enabling the buffer to neutralize added acid or added base.
- Adding a small amount of acid to a buffer converts a stoichiometric amount of base to the conjugate acid. Adding a small amount of base to a buffer converts a stoichiometric amount of the acid to the conjugate base.

- We can determine the pH of a buffer solution by solving an equilibrium problem, focusing on the common ion effect, or by using the Henderson–Hasselbalch equation.

Buffer Range and Buffer Capacity (18.3)

- A buffer works best when the amounts of acid and conjugate base it contains are large and approximately equal.
- If the relative amounts of acid and base in a buffer differ by more than a factor of 10, the ability of the buffer to neutralize added acid and added base diminishes. The maximum pH range at which a buffer is effective is one pH unit on either side of the acid's pK_a.

Titrations and pH Curves (18.4)

- A titration curve is a graph of the change in pH versus added volume of acid or base during a titration.
- This chapter examines three types of titration curves, representing three types of acid–base reactions: a strong acid with a strong base, a weak acid with a strong base (or vice versa), and a polyprotic acid with a strong base.
- The equivalence point of a titration can be made visible by an indicator, a compound that changes color over a specific pH range.

Solubility Equilibria and the Solubility Product Constant (18.5)

- The solubility product constant (K_{sp}) is an equilibrium constant for the dissolution of an ionic compound in water.
- We can determine the molar solubility of an ionic compound from K_{sp} and vice versa. Although the value of K_{sp} is constant at a given temperature, the solubility of an ionic substance can depend on other factors such as the presence of common ions and the pH of the solution.

Precipitation (18.6)

- We can compare the magnitude of K_{sp} to the reaction quotient, Q, in order to determine the relative saturation of a solution.
- Substances with cations that have sufficiently different values of K_{sp} can be separated by selective precipitation, in which an added reagent forms a precipitate with one of the dissolved cations but not others.

Qualitative Chemical Analysis (18.7)

- Qualitative analysis operates on the principle that a mixture of cations can be separated and analyzed based on the differences in the solubilities of their salts.
- In a classic qualitative analysis scheme, an unknown mixture of cations is sequentially treated with different reagents, each of which precipitates a known subgroup of cations.

Complex Ion Equilibria (18.8)

- A complex ion contains a central metal ion coordinated to two or more ligands.
- The equilibrium constant for the formation of a complex ion is called a formation constant and is usually quite large.
- The solubility of an ionic compound containing a metal cation that forms complex ions increases in the presence of Lewis bases that complex with the cation because the formation of the complex ion drives the dissolution reaction to the right.
- All metal hydroxides become more soluble in the presence of acids, but amphoteric metal hydroxides also become more soluble in the presence of bases.

EQUATIONS AND RELATIONSHIPS

The Henderson–Hasselbalch Equation (**18.2**)

$$\text{pH} = \text{p}K_a + \log\frac{[\text{base}]}{[\text{acid}]}$$

Effective Buffer Range (**18.3**)

$$\text{pH range} = \text{p}K_a \pm 1$$

The Relation between Q and K_{sp} (**18.6**)

If $Q < K_{sp}$, the solution is unsaturated. More of the solid ionic compound can dissolve in the solution.

If $Q = K_{sp}$, the solution is saturated. The solution is holding the equilibrium amount of the dissolved ions, and additional solid will not dissolve in the solution.

If $Q > K_{sp}$, the solution is supersaturated. Under most circumstances, the solid will precipitate out of a supersaturated solution.

LEARNING OUTCOMES

Chapter Objectives	Assessment
Perform pH calculations for buffer solutions containing a common ion (**18.2**)	Example 18.1 **For Practice** 18.1 **For More Practice** 18.1 Exercises 27–34
Perform pH calculations for buffer solutions using the Henderson–Hasselbalch equation (**18.2**)	Example 18.2 **For Practice** 18.2 **Exercises** 35–46
Perform pH calculations for buffer solutions after the addition of a small amount of strong acid or strong base (**18.2**)	Example 18.3 **For Practice** 18.3 **For More Practice** 18.3 Exercises 47–50
Perform pH calculations for buffer solutions containing a weak base and its conjugate acid before and after the addition of an acid or base (**18.2**)	Example 18.4 **For Practice** 18.4 **For More Practice** 18.4 Exercises 51–52
Describe the preparation of an effective buffer solution (**18.3**)	Example 18.5 **For Practice** 18.5 **Exercises** 53–60
Perform pH calculations for the titration of a strong acid with a strong base (**18.4**)	Example 18.6 **For Practice** 18.6 **Exercise** 61

Perform calculations for the titration of a weak acid with a strong base (**18.4**)	Example 18.7 **For Practice** 18.7 **Exercises** 62–77
Identify specific points along the titration curve for a diprotic acid with a strong base (**18.4**)	**Exercises** 78–80
Predict properties of indicators in solutions (**18.4**)	**Exercises** 81–84
Perform K_{sp} calculations for ionic compounds in pure water (**18.5**)	Examples 18.8, 18.9 **For Practice** 18.8, 18.9 **Exercises** 85–94
Perform K_{sp} calculations involving the common ion effect (**18.5**)	Example 18.10 **For Practice** 18.10 **Exercises** 95–96
Determine the effect of pH on solubility (**18.5**)	Example 18.11 **For Practice** 18.11 **Exercises** 97–100
Predict precipitation reactions by comparing Q to K_{sp} (**18.6**)	Example 18.12 **For Practice** 18.12 **Exercises** 101–106
Perform calculations involving selective precipitation (**18.6**)	Examples 18.13, 18.14 **For Practice** 18.13, 18.14 **Exercises** 107–108
Perform calculations involving complex ion equilibria (**18.8**)	Example 18.15 **For Practice** 18.15 **Exercises** 109–111

EXERCISES

Mastering Chemistry provides end-of-chapter exercises, feedback-enriched tutorial problems, animations, and interactive activities to encourage problem-solving practice and deeper understanding of key concepts and topics.

REVIEW QUESTIONS

1. What is the pH range of human blood? How is human blood maintained in this pH range?

2. What is a buffer? How does a buffer work? How does it neutralize added acid? Added base?

3. What is the common ion effect?

4. What is the Henderson–Hasselbalch equation, and why is it useful?

5. What is the pH of a buffer solution when the concentrations of both buffer components (the weak acid and its conjugate base) are equal? What happens to the pH when the buffer contains more of the weak acid than the conjugate base? More of the conjugate base than the weak acid?

6. Suppose that a buffer contains equal amounts of a weak acid and its conjugate base. What happens to the relative amounts of the weak acid and conjugate base when a small amount of strong acid is added to the buffer? What happens when a small amount of strong base is added?

7. How do you use the Henderson–Hasselbalch equation to calculate the pH of a buffer containing a base and its conjugate acid? Specifically, how do you determine the correct value for pK_a?

8. What factors influence the effectiveness of a buffer? What are the characteristics of an effective buffer?

9. What is the effective pH range of a buffer (relative to the pK_a of the weak acid component)?

10. Describe acid–base titration. What is the equivalence point?

11. The pH at the equivalence point of the titration of a strong acid with a strong base is 7.0. However, the pH at the equivalence point of the titration of a *weak* acid with a strong base is above 7.0. Explain.

12. The volume required to reach the equivalence point of an acid–base titration depends on the volume and concentration of the acid or base to be titrated and on the concentration of the acid or base used to do the titration. It does not, however, depend on whether or not the acid or base being titrated is strong or weak. Explain.

13. In the titration of a strong acid with a strong base, how do you calculate these quantities?

a. initial pH
b. pH before the equivalence point
c. pH at the equivalence point
d. pH beyond the equivalence point

14. In the titration of a weak acid with a strong base, how do you calculate these quantities?

a. initial pH
b. pH before the equivalence point
c. pH at one-half the equivalence point
d. pH at the equivalence point
e. pH beyond the equivalence point

15. The titration of a polyprotic acid with sufficiently different pK_as displays two equivalence points. Why?

16. In the titration of a polyprotic acid, the volume required to reach the first equivalence point is identical to the volume required to reach the second one. Why?

17. What is the difference between the endpoint and the equivalence point in a titration?

18. What is an indicator? How can an indicator signal the equivalence point of a titration?

19. What is the solubility product constant? Write a general expression for the solubility constant of a compound with the general formula A_mX_n.

20. What is molar solubility? How can you obtain the molar solubility of a compound from K_{sp}?

21. How does a common ion affect the solubility of a compound? More specifically, how is the solubility of a compound with the general formula AX different in a solution containing one of the common ions (A^+ or X^-) than it is in pure water? Explain.

22. How is the solubility of an ionic compound with a basic anion affected by pH? Explain.

23. For a given solution containing an ionic compound, what is the relationship between Q, K_{sp}, and the relative saturation of the solution?

24. What is selective precipitation? Under which conditions does selective precipitation occur?

25. What is qualitative analysis? How does *qualitative* analysis differ from *quantitative* analysis?

26. What are the main groups in the general qualitative analysis scheme described in this chapter? Describe the steps and reagents necessary to identify each group.

PROBLEMS BY TOPIC

The Common Ion Effect and Buffers

27. In which of these solutions will HNO_2 ionize less than it does in pure water? **MISSED THIS?** *Read Section 18.2*
    a. 0.10 M NaCl
    b. 0.10 M KNO_3
    c. 0.10 M NaOH
    d. 0.10 M $NaNO_2$

28. A formic acid solution has a pH of 3.25. Which of these substances will raise the pH of the solution upon addition? Explain your answer.
    a. HCl
    b. NaBr
    c. $NaCHO_2$
    d. KCl

29. Solve an equilibrium problem (using an ICE table) to calculate the pH of each solution.
    MISSED THIS? *Read Section 18.2; Watch KCV 18.2A, 18.2B, IWE 18.2*
    a. a solution that is 0.20 M in $HCHO_2$ and 0.15 M in $NaCHO_2$
    b. a solution that is 0.16 M in NH_3 and 0.22 M in NH_4Cl

30. Solve an equilibrium problem (using an ICE table) to calculate the pH of each solution.
    a. a solution that is 0.195 M in $HC_2H_3O_2$ and 0.125 M in $KC_2H_3O_2$
    b. a solution that is 0.255 M in CH_3NH_2 and 0.135 M in CH_3NH_3Br

31. Calculate the percent ionization of a 0.15 M benzoic acid solution in pure water and in a solution containing 0.10 M sodium benzoate. Why does the percent ionization differ significantly in the two solutions?
    MISSED THIS? *Read Section 18.2; Watch KCV 18.2A*

32. Calculate the percent ionization of a 0.13 M formic acid solution in pure water and also in a solution containing 0.11 M potassium formate. Explain the difference in percent ionization in the two solutions.

33. Solve an equilibrium problem (using an ICE table) to calculate the pH of each solution.
    MISSED THIS? *Read Section 18.2; Watch KCV 18.2B, IWE 18.2*
    a. 0.15 M HF
    b. 0.15 M NaF
    c. a mixture that is 0.15 M in HF and 0.15 M in NaF

34. Solve an equilibrium problem (using an ICE table) to calculate the pH of each solution.
    a. 0.18 M CH_3NH_2
    b. 0.18 M CH_3NH_3Cl
    c. a mixture that is 0.18 M in CH_3NH_2 and 0.18 M in CH_3NH_3Cl

35. A buffer contains significant amounts of acetic acid and sodium acetate. Write equations showing how this buffer neutralizes added acid and added base.
    MISSED THIS? *Read Section 18.2; Watch KCV 18.2A*

36. A buffer contains significant amounts of ammonia and ammonium chloride. Write equations showing how this buffer neutralizes added acid and added base.

37. Use the Henderson–Hasselbalch equation to calculate the pH of each solution in Problem 29.
    MISSED THIS? *Read Section 18.2; Watch KCV 18.2B, IWE 18.2*

38. Use the Henderson–Hasselbalch equation to calculate the pH of each solution in Problem 30.

39. Use the Henderson–Hasselbalch equation to calculate the pH of each solution.
    MISSED THIS? *Read Section 18.2; Watch KCV 18.2B, IWE 18.2*
    a. a solution that is 0.135 M in HClO and 0.155 M in KClO
    b. a solution that contains 1.05% $C_2H_5NH_2$ by mass and 1.10% $C_2H_5NH_3Br$ by mass
    c. a solution that contains 10.0 g of $HC_2H_3O_2$ and 10.0 g of $NaC_2H_3O_2$ in 150.0 mL of solution

40. Use the Henderson–Hasselbalch equation to calculate the pH of each solution.
    a. a solution that is 0.145 M in propanoic acid and 0.115 M in potassium propanoate
    b. a solution that contains 0.785% C_5H_5N by mass and 0.985% C_5H_5NHCl by mass
    c. a solution that contains 15.0 g of HF and 25.0 g of NaF in 125 mL of solution

41. Calculate the pH of the solution that results from each mixture.
    MISSED THIS? *Read Section 18.2; Watch KCV 18.2B, IWE 18.2*
    a. 50.0 mL of 0.15 M $HCHO_2$ with 75.0 mL of 0.13 M $NaCHO_2$
    b. 125.0 mL of 0.10 M NH_3 with 250.0 mL of 0.10 M NH_4Cl

42. Calculate the pH of the solution that results from each mixture.
    a. 150.0 mL of 0.25 M HF with 225.0 mL of 0.30 M NaF
    b. 175.0 mL of 0.10 M $C_2H_5NH_2$ with 275.0 mL of 0.20 M $C_2H_5NH_3Cl$

43. Calculate the ratio of NaF to HF required to create a buffer with pH = 4.00.
    MISSED THIS? *Read Section 18.2; Watch KCV 18.2B, IWE 18.2*

44. Calculate the ratio of CH_3NH_2 to CH_3NH_3Cl concentration required to create a buffer with pH = 10.24.

45. What mass of sodium benzoate should you add to 150.0 mL of a 0.15 M benzoic acid solution to obtain a buffer with a pH of 4.25? (Assume no volume change.)
    MISSED THIS? *Read Section 18.2; Watch KCV 18.2B, IWE 18.2*

46. What mass of ammonium chloride should you add to 2.55 L of a 0.155 M NH_3 to obtain a buffer with a pH of 9.55? (Assume no volume change.)

47. A 250.0-mL buffer solution is 0.250 M in acetic acid and 0.250 M in sodium acetate.
    MISSED THIS? *Read Section 18.2; Watch KCV 18.2B, IWE 18.2, 18.3*
    a. What is the initial pH of this solution?
    b. What is the pH after addition of 0.0050 mol of HCl?
    c. What is the pH after addition of 0.0050 mol of NaOH?

48. A 100.0-mL buffer solution is 0.175 M in HClO and 0.150 M in NaClO.

a. What is the initial pH of this solution?
b. What is the pH after addition of 150.0 mg of HBr?
c. What is the pH after addition of 85.0 mg of NaOH?

49. For each solution, calculate the initial and final pH after adding 0.010 mol of HCl.
MISSED THIS? *Read Section 18.2; Watch KCV 18.2B, IWE 18.2, 18.3*

a. 500.0 mL of pure water
b. 500.0 mL of a buffer solution that is 0.125 M in $HC_2H_3O_2$ and 0.115 M in $NaC_2H_3O_2$
c. 500.0 mL of a buffer solution that is 0.155 M in $C_2H_5NH_2$ and 0.145 M in $C_2H_5NH_3Cl$

50. For each solution, calculate the initial and final pH after adding 0.010 mol of NaOH.

a. 250.0 mL of pure water
b. 250.0 mL of a buffer solution that is 0.195 M in $HCHO_2$ and 0.275 M in $KCHO_2$
c. 250.0 mL of a buffer solution that is 0.255 M in $CH_3CH_2NH_2$ and 0.235 M in $CH_3CH_2NH_3Cl$

51. A 350.0-mL buffer solution is 0.150 M in HF and 0.150 M in NaF. What mass of NaOH can this buffer neutralize before the pH rises above 4.00? If the same volume of the buffer were 0.350 M in HF and 0.350 M in NaF, what mass of NaOH could be handled before the pH rises above 4.00? **MISSED THIS?** *Read Section 18.3*

52. A 100.0-mL buffer solution is 0.100 M in NH_3 and 0.125 M in NH_4Br. What mass of HCl can this buffer neutralize before the pH falls below 9.00? If the same volume of the buffer were 0.250 M in NH_3 and 0.400 M in NH_4Br, what mass of HCl could be handled before the pH fell below 9.00?

53. Determine whether or not the mixing of each pair of solutions results in a buffer. **MISSED THIS?** *Read Section 18.3*

a. 100.0 mL of 0.10 M NH_3; 100.0 mL of 0.15 M NH_4Cl
b. 50.0 mL of 0.10 M HCl; 35.0 mL of 0.150 M NaOH
c. 50.0 mL of 0.15 M HF; 20.0 mL of 0.15 M NaOH
d. 175.0 mL of 0.10 M NH_3; 150.0 mL of 0.12 M NaOH
e. 125.0 mL of 0.15 M NH_3; 150.0 mL of 0.20 M NaOH

54. Determine whether or not the mixing of each pair of solutions results in a buffer.

a. 75.0 mL of 0.10 M HF; 55.0 mL of 0.15 M NaF
b. 150.0 mL of 0.10 M HF; 135.0 mL of 0.175 M HCl
c. 165.0 mL of 0.10 M HF; 135.0 mL of 0.050 M KOH
d. 125.0 mL of 0.15 M CH_3NH_2; 120.0 mL of 0.25 M CH_3NH_3Cl
e. 105.0 mL of 0.15 M CH_3NH_2; 95.0 mL of 0.10 M HCl

55. Blood is buffered by carbonic acid and the bicarbonate ion. Normal blood plasma is 0.024 M in HCO_3^- and 0.0012 M H_2CO_3 (pK_{a_1} for H_2CO_3 at body temperature is 6.1).
MISSED THIS? *Read Sections 18.2, 18.3; Watch KCV 18.2B, IWE 18.2, 18.3*

a. What is the pH of blood plasma?
b. If the volume of blood in a normal adult is 5.0 L, what mass of HCl can be neutralized by the buffering system in blood before the pH falls below 7.0 (which would result in death)?
c. Given the volume from part (b), what mass of NaOH can be neutralized before the pH rises above 7.8?

56. The fluids within cells are buffered by $H_2PO_4^-$ and HPO_4^{2-}.

a. Calculate the ratio of HPO_4^{2-} to $H_2PO_4^-$ required to maintain a pH of 7.1 within a cell.
b. Could a buffer system employing H_3PO_4 as the weak acid and $H_2PO_4^-$ as the weak base be used as a buffer system within cells? Explain.

57. Which buffer system is the best choice to create a buffer with pH = 7.20? For the best system, calculate the ratio of the masses of the buffer components required to make the buffer.
MISSED THIS? *Read Section 18.3*

$HC_2H_3O_2/KC_2H_3O_2$	$HClO_2/KClO_2$
NH_3/NH_4Cl	$HClO/KClO$

58. Which buffer system is the best choice to create a buffer with pH = 9.00? For the best system, calculate the ratio of the masses of the buffer components required to make the buffer.

HF/KF	HNO_2/KNO_2
NH_3/NH_4Cl	$HClO/KClO$

59. A 500.0-mL buffer solution is 0.100 M in HNO_2 and 0.150 M in KNO_2. Determine if each addition would exceed the capacity of the buffer to neutralize it. **MISSED THIS?** *Read Section 18.3*

a. 250 mg NaOH
b. 350 mg KOH
c. 1.25 g HBr
d. 1.35 g HI

60. A 1.0-L buffer solution is 0.125 M in HNO_2 and 0.145 M in $NaNO_2$. Determine the concentrations of HNO_2 and $NaNO_2$ after the addition of each substance:

a. 1.5 g HCl   b. 1.5 g NaOH   c. 1.5 g HI

Titrations, pH Curves, and Indicators

61. The graphs labeled (a) and (b) show the titration curves for two equal-volume samples of monoprotic acids, one weak and one strong. Both titrations were carried out with the same concentration of strong base. **MISSED THIS?** *Read Section 18.4*

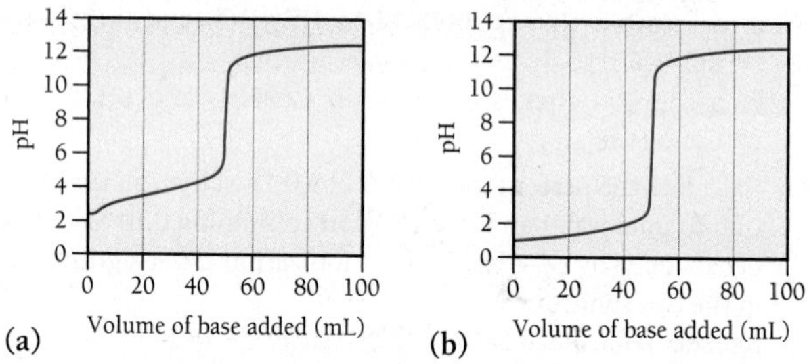

i. What is the approximate pH at the equivalence point of each curve?
ii. Which graph corresponds to the titration of the strong acid and which one to the titration of the weak acid?

62. Two 25.0-mL samples, one 0.100 M HCl and the other 0.100 M HF, are titrated with 0.200 M KOH.

a. What is the volume of added base at the equivalence point for each titration?
b. Is the pH at the equivalence point for each titration acidic, basic, or neutral?
c. Which titration curve has the lower initial pH?
d. Sketch each titration curve.

63. Two 20.0-mL samples, one 0.200 M KOH and the other 0.200 M CH_3NH_2, are titrated with 0.100 M HI.
MISSED THIS? *Read Section 18.4; Watch KCV 18.4A, 18.4B*

a. What is the volume of added acid at the equivalence point for each titration?
b. Is the pH at the equivalence point for each titration acidic, basic, or neutral?
c. Which titration curve has the lower initial pH?
d. Sketch each titration curve.

64. The graphs labeled (a) and (b) show the titration curves for two equal-volume samples of bases, one weak and one strong. Both titrations were carried out with the same concentration of strong acid.

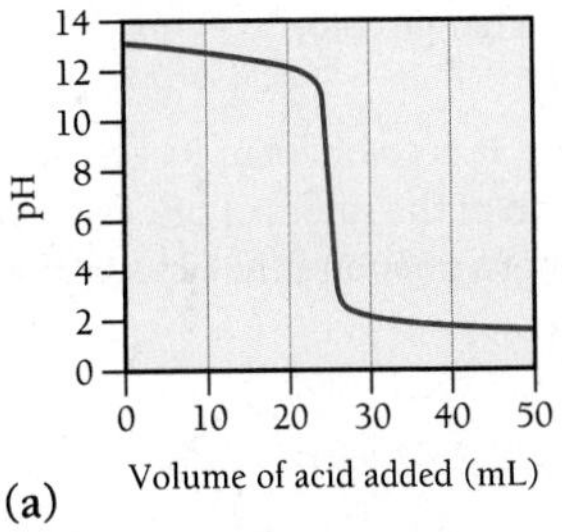

(a)

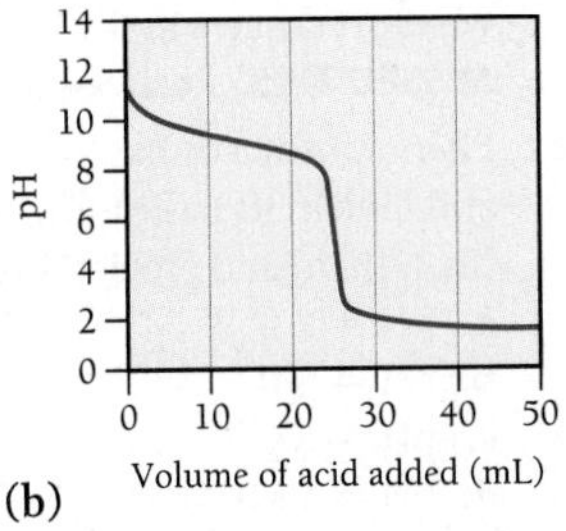

(b)

i. What is the approximate pH at the equivalence point of each curve?

ii. Which graph corresponds to the titration of the strong base and which one to the weak base?

65. Consider the curve shown here for the titration of a weak monoprotic acid with a strong base and answer each question.
MISSED THIS? *Read Section 18.4; Watch KCV 18.4B*

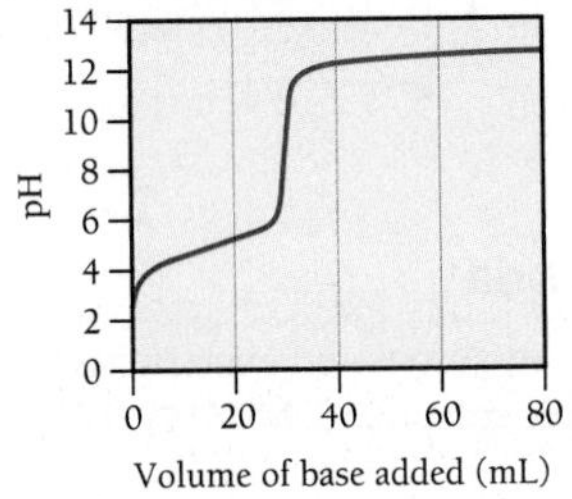

a. What is the pH and what is the volume of added base at the equivalence point?

b. At what volume of added base is the pH calculated by working an equilibrium problem based on the initial concentration and K_a of the weak acid?

c. At what volume of added base does $pH = pK_a$?

d. At what volume of added base is the pH calculated by working an equilibrium problem based on the concentration and K_b of the conjugate base?

e. Beyond what volume of added base is the pH calculated by focusing on the amount of excess strong base added?

66. Consider the curve shown here for the titration of a weak base with a strong acid and answer each question.

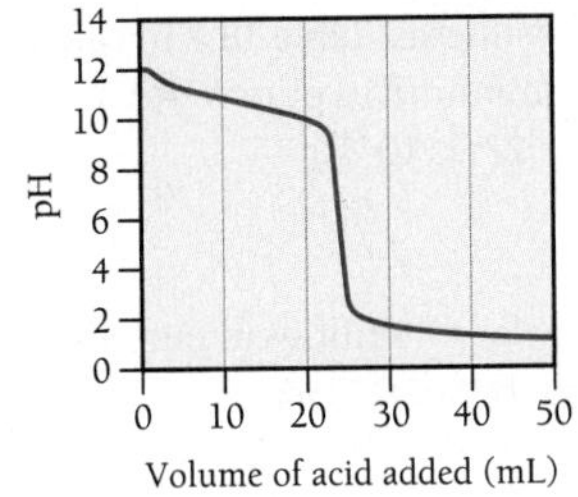

a. What is the pH and what is the volume of added acid at the equivalence point?

b. At what volume of added acid is the pH calculated by working an equilibrium problem based on the initial concentration and K_b of the weak base?

c. At what volume of added acid does $pH = 14 - pK_b$?

d. At what volume of added acid is the pH calculated by working an equilibrium problem based on the concentration and K_a of the conjugate acid?

e. Beyond what volume of added acid is the pH calculated by focusing on the amount of excess strong acid added?

67. Consider the titration of a 35.0-mL sample of 0.175 M HBr with 0.200 M KOH. Determine each quantity.
MISSED THIS? *Read Section 18.4; Watch KCV 18.4A, IWE 18.6*

a. the initial pH

b. the volume of added base required to reach the equivalence point

c. the pH at 10.0 mL of added base

d. the pH at the equivalence point

e. the pH after adding 5.0 mL of base beyond the equivalence point

68. A 20.0-mL sample of 0.125 M HNO_3 is titrated with 0.150 M NaOH. Calculate the pH for at least five different points throughout the titration curve and sketch the curve. Indicate the volume at the equivalence point on your graph.

69. Consider the titration of a 25.0-mL sample of 0.115 M RbOH with 0.100 M HCl. Determine each quantity.
MISSED THIS? *Read Section 18.4; Watch KCV 18.4A, IWE 18.6*

a. the initial pH

b. the volume of added acid required to reach the equivalence point

c. the pH at 5.0 mL of added acid

d. the pH at the equivalence point

e. the pH after adding 5.0 mL of acid beyond the equivalence point

70. A 15.0-mL sample of 0.100 M $Ba(OH)_2$ is titrated with 0.125 M HCl. Calculate the pH for at least five different points throughout the titration curve and sketch the curve. Indicate the volume at the equivalence point on your graph.

71. Consider the titration of a 20.0-mL sample of 0.105 M $HC_2H_3O_2$ with 0.125 M NaOH. Determine each quantity.
MISSED THIS? *Read Section 18.4; Watch KCV 18.4B, IWE 18.7*

a. the initial pH

b. the volume of added base required to reach the equivalence point

c. the pH at 5.0 mL of added base

d. the pH at one-half of the equivalence point

e. the pH at the equivalence point

f. the pH after adding 5.0 mL of base beyond the equivalence point

72. A 30.0-mL sample of 0.165 M propanoic acid is titrated with 0.300 M KOH. Calculate the pH at each volume of added base: 0 mL, 5 mL, 10 mL, equivalence point, one-half equivalence point, 20 mL, 25 mL. Sketch the titration curve.

73. Consider the titration of a 25.0-mL sample of 0.175 M CH_3NH_2 with 0.150 M HBr. Determine each quantity.
MISSED THIS? *Read Section 18.4; Watch KCV 18.4B, IWE 18.7*

a. the initial pH

b. the volume of added acid required to reach the equivalence point

c. the pH at 5.0 mL of added acid

d. the pH at one-half of the equivalence point

e. the pH at the equivalence point

f. the pH after adding 5.0 mL of acid beyond the equivalence point

74. A 25.0-mL sample of 0.125 M pyridine is titrated with 0.100 M HCl. Calculate the pH at each volume of added acid: 0 mL, 10 mL, 20 mL, equivalence point, one-half equivalence point, 40 mL, 50 mL. Sketch the titration curve.

75. Consider the titration curves (labeled a and b) for two weak acids, both titrated with 0.100 M NaOH.
MISSED THIS? *Read Section 18.4; Watch KCV 18.4B, IWE 18.7*

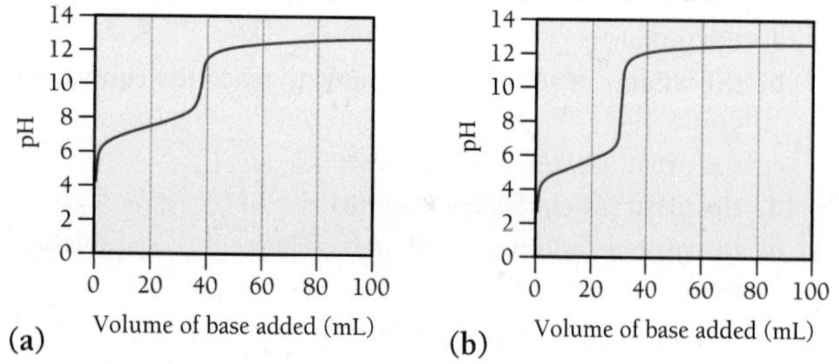

i. Which acid solution is more concentrated?
ii. Which acid has the larger K_a?

76. Consider the titration curves (labeled a and b) for two weak bases, both titrated with 0.100 M HCl.

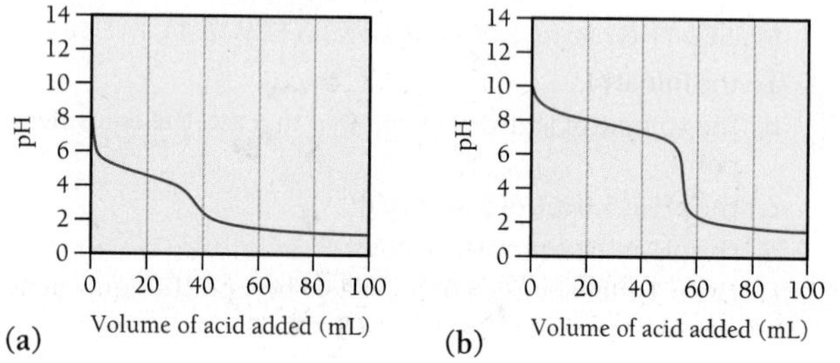

i. Which base solution is more concentrated?
ii. Which base has the larger K_b?

77. A 0.229-g sample of an unknown monoprotic acid is titrated with 0.112 M NaOH. The resulting titration curve is shown here. Determine the molar mass and pK_a of the acid.
MISSED THIS? *Read Section 18.4; Watch KCV 18.4B, IWE 18.7*

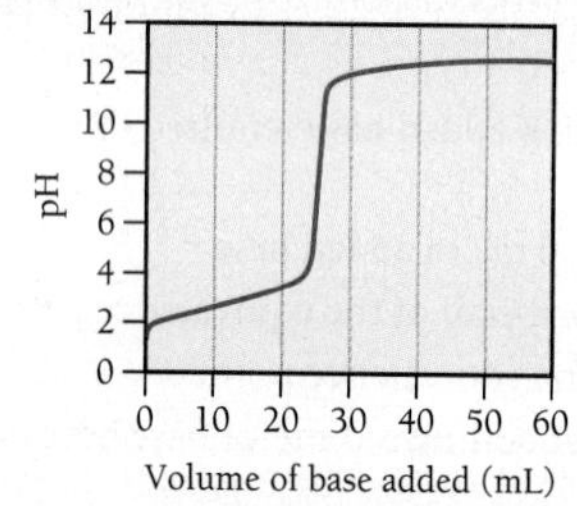

78. A 0.446-g sample of an unknown monoprotic acid is titrated with 0.105 M KOH. The resulting titration curve is shown here. Determine the molar mass and pK_a of the acid.

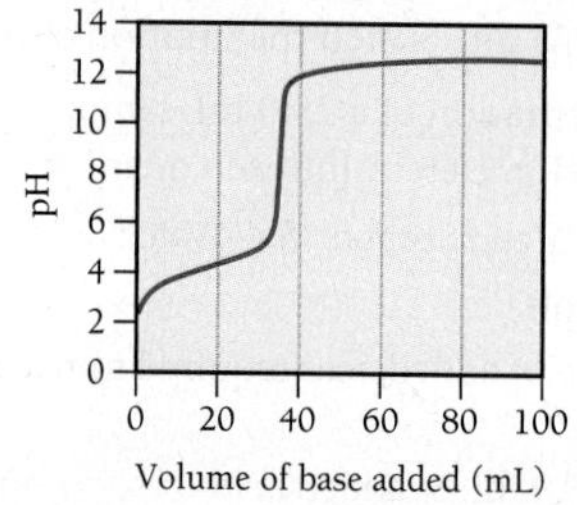

79. A 20.0-mL sample of 0.115 M sulfurous acid (H_2SO_3) solution is titrated with 0.1014 M KOH. At what added volume of base solution does each equivalence point occur?
MISSED THIS? *Read Section 18.4*

80. A 20.0-mL sample of a 0.125 M diprotic acid (H_2A) solution is titrated with 0.1019 M KOH. The acid ionization constants for the acid are $K_{a_1} = 5.2 \times 10^{-5}$ and $K_{a_2} = 3.4 \times 10^{-10}$. At what added volume of base does each equivalence point occur?

81. Methyl red has a pK_a of 5.0 and is red in its acid form and yellow in its basic form. If several drops of this indicator are placed in a 25.0-mL sample of 0.100 M HCl, what color will the solution appear? If 0.100 M NaOH is slowly added to the HCl sample, in what pH range will the indicator change color?
MISSED THIS? *Read Section 18.4*

82. Phenolphthalein has a pK_a of 9.7. It is colorless in its acid form and pink in its basic form. For each of the values of pH, calculate $[In^-]/[HIn]$ and predict the color of a phenolphthalein solution.
a. pH = 2.0
b. pH = 5.0
c. pH = 8.0
d. pH = 11.0

83. Referring to Table 18.1, pick an indicator for use in the titration of each acid with a strong base. **MISSED THIS?** *Read Section 18.4*
a. HF
b. HCl
c. HCN

84. Referring to Table 18.1, pick an indicator for use in the titration of each base with a strong acid.
a. CH_3NH_2
b. NaOH
c. $C_6H_5NH_2$

Solubility Equilibria

85. Write balanced equations and expressions for K_{sp} for the dissolution of each ionic compound. **MISSED THIS?** *Read Section 18.5*
a. $BaSO_4$
b. $PbBr_2$
c. Ag_2CrO_4

86. Write balanced equations and expressions for K_{sp} for the dissolution of each ionic compound.
a. $CaCO_3$
b. $PbCl_2$
c. AgI

87. Refer to the K_{sp} values in Table 18.2 to calculate the molar solubility of each compound in pure water.
MISSED THIS? *Read Section 18.5; Watch IWE 18.8*
a. AgBr
b. $Mg(OH)_2$
c. CaF_2

88. Refer to the K_{sp} values in Table 18.2 to calculate the molar solubility of each compound in pure water.
a. MX ($K_{sp} = 1.27 \times 10^{-36}$)
b. Ag_2CrO_4
c. $Ca(OH)_2$

89. Use the given molar solubilities in pure water to calculate K_{sp} for each compound. **MISSED THIS?** *Read Section 18.5*
a. MX; molar solubility = 3.27×10^{-11} M
b. PbF_2; molar solubility = 5.63×10^{-3} M
c. MgF_2; molar solubility = 2.65×10^{-4} M

90. Use the given molar solubilities in pure water to calculate K_{sp} for each compound.
a. $BaCrO_4$; molar solubility = 1.08×10^{-5} M
b. Ag_2SO_3; molar solubility = 1.55×10^{-5} M
c. $Pd(SCN)_2$; molar solubility = 2.22×10^{-8} M

91. Two compounds with general formulas AX and AX_2 have $K_{sp} = 1.5 \times 10^{-5}$. Which of the two compounds has the higher molar solubility?
MISSED THIS? *Read Section 18.5; Watch IWE 18.8*

92. Consider the compounds with the generic formulas listed and their corresponding molar solubilities in pure water. Which compound has the smallest value of K_{sp}?
a. AX; molar solubility $= 1.35 \times 10^{-4}$ M
b. AX_2; molar solubility $= 2.25 \times 10^{-4}$ M
c. A_2X; molar solubility $= 1.75 \times 10^{-4}$ M

93. Refer to the K_{sp} value from Table 18.2 to calculate the solubility of iron(II) hydroxide in pure water in grams per 100.0 mL of solution. **MISSED THIS?** *Read Section 18.5; Watch IWE 18.8*

94. The solubility of copper(I) chloride is 3.91 mg per 100.0 mL of solution. Calculate K_{sp} for CuCl.

95. Calculate the molar solubility of barium fluoride in each liquid or solution. **MISSED THIS?** *Read Section 18.5*
a. pure water
b. 0.10 M $Ba(NO_3)_2$
c. 0.15 M NaF

96. Calculate the molar solubility of MX ($K_{sp} = 1.27 \times 10^{-36}$) in each liquid or solution.
a. pure water
b. 0.25 M MCl_2
c. 0.20 M Na_2X

97. Calculate the molar solubility of calcium hydroxide in a solution buffered at each pH. **MISSED THIS?** *Read Section 18.5*
a. pH = 4
b. pH = 7
c. pH = 9

98. Calculate the solubility (in grams per 1.00×10^2 mL of solution) of magnesium hydroxide in a solution buffered at pH = 10. How does this compare to the solubility of $Mg(OH)_2$ in pure water?

99. Determine if each compound is more soluble in acidic solution than it is in pure water. Explain. **MISSED THIS?** *Read Section 18.5*
a. $BaCO_3$
b. CuS
c. AgCl
d. PbI_2

100. Determine if each compound is more soluble in acidic solution than it is in pure water. Explain.
a. Hg_2Br_2
b. $Mg(OH)_2$
c. $CaCO_3$
d. AgI

Precipitation and Qualitative Analysis

101. A solution containing sodium fluoride is mixed with one containing calcium nitrate to form a solution that is 0.015 M in NaF and 0.010 M in $Ca(NO_3)_2$. Does a precipitate form in the mixed solution? If so, identify the precipitate.
MISSED THIS? *Read Section 18.6; Watch IWE 18.12*

102. A solution containing potassium bromide is mixed with one containing lead acetate to form a solution that is 0.013 M in KBr and 0.0035 M in $Pb(C_2H_3O_2)_2$. Does a precipitate form in the mixed solution? If so, identify the precipitate.

103. Predict whether a precipitate will form if you mix 75.0 mL of a NaOH solution with pOH = 2.58 with 125.0 mL of a 0.018 M $MgCl_2$ solution. Identify the precipitate, if any.
MISSED THIS? *Read Section 18.6; Watch IWE 18.12*

104. Predict whether a precipitate will form if you mix 175.0 mL of a 0.0055 M KCl solution with 145.0 mL of a 0.0015 M $AgNO_3$ solution. Identify the precipitate, if any.

105. Potassium hydroxide is used to precipitate each of the cations from their respective solution. Determine the minimum concentration of KOH required for precipitation to begin in each case. **MISSED THIS?** *Read Section 18.6; Watch IWE 18.12*
a. 0.015 M $CaCl_2$
b. 0.0025 M $Fe(NO_3)_2$
c. 0.0018 M $MgBr_2$

106. Determine the minimum concentration of the precipitating agent on the right to cause precipitation of the cation from the solution on the left.
a. 0.035 M $Ba(NO_3)_2$; NaF
b. 0.085 M CaI_2; K_2SO_4
c. 0.0018 M $AgNO_3$; RbCl

107. A solution is 0.010 M in Ba^{2+} and 0.020 M in Ca^{2+}.
MISSED THIS? *Read Section 18.6; Watch IWE 18.12*
a. If sodium sulfate is used to selectively precipitate one of the cations while leaving the other cation in solution, which cation will precipitate first? What minimum concentration of Na_2SO_4 will trigger the precipitation of the cation that precipitates first?
b. What is the remaining concentration of the cation that precipitates first, when the other cation begins to precipitate?

108. A solution is 0.022 M in Fe^{2+} and 0.014 M in Mg^{2+}.
a. If potassium carbonate is used to selectively precipitate one of the cations while leaving the other cation in solution, which cation will precipitate first? What minimum concentration of K_2CO_3 will trigger the precipitation of the cation that precipitates first?
b. What is the remaining concentration of the cation that precipitates first, when the other cation begins to precipitate?

Complex Ion Equilibria

109. A solution is 1.1×10^{-3} M in $Zn(NO_3)_2$ and 0.150 M in NH_3. After the solution reaches equilibrium, what concentration of $Zn^{2+}(aq)$ remains? **MISSED THIS?** *Read Section 18.8*

110. A 120.0-mL sample of a solution that is 2.8×10^{-3} M in $AgNO_3$ is mixed with a 225.0-mL sample of a solution that is 0.10 M in NaCN. After the solution reaches equilibrium, what concentration of $Ag^+(aq)$ remains?

111. Use the appropriate values of K_{sp} and K_f to find the equilibrium constant for the reaction. **MISSED THIS?** *Read Section 18.8*

$$FeS(s) + 6\,CN^-(aq) \rightleftharpoons Fe(CN)_6^{4-}(aq) + S^{2-}(aq)$$

112. Use the appropriate values of K_{sp} and K_f to find the equilibrium constant for the reaction.

$$PbCl_2(s) + 3\,OH^-(aq) \rightleftharpoons Pb(OH)_3^-(aq) + 2\,Cl^-(aq)$$

CUMULATIVE PROBLEMS

113. A 150.0-mL solution contains 2.05 g of sodium benzoate and 2.47 g of benzoic acid. Calculate the pH of the solution.

114. A solution is made by combining 10.0 mL of 17.5 M acetic acid with 5.54 g of sodium acetate and diluting to a total volume of 1.50 L. Calculate the pH of the solution.

115. A buffer is created by combining 150.0 mL of 0.25 M $HCHO_2$ with 75.0 mL of 0.20 M NaOH. Determine the pH of the buffer.

116. A buffer is created by combining 3.55 g of NH_3 with 4.78 g of HCl and diluting to a total volume of 750.0 mL. Determine the pH of the buffer.

117. A 1.0-L buffer solution initially contains 0.25 mol of NH_3 and 0.25 mol of NH_4Cl. In order to adjust the buffer pH to 8.75, should you add NaOH or HCl to the buffer mixture? What mass of the correct reagent should you add?

118. A 250.0-mL buffer solution initially contains 0.025 mol of $HCHO_2$ and 0.025 mol of $NaCHO_2$. In order to adjust the buffer pH to 4.10, should you add NaOH or HCl to the buffer mixture? What mass of the correct reagent should you add?

119. In analytical chemistry, bases used for titrations must often be standardized; that is, their concentration must be precisely determined. Standardization of sodium hydroxide solutions can be accomplished by titrating potassium hydrogen phthalate ($KHC_8H_4O_4$), also known as KHP, with the NaOH solution to be standardized.

a. Write an equation for the reaction between NaOH and KHP.

b. The titration of 0.5527 g of KHP required 25.87 mL of an NaOH solution to reach the equivalence point. What is the concentration of the NaOH solution?

120. A 0.5224-g sample of an unknown monoprotic acid was titrated with 0.0998 M NaOH. The equivalence point of the titration occurred at 23.82 mL. Determine the molar mass of the unknown acid.

121. A 0.25-mol sample of a weak acid with an unknown pK_a was combined with 10.0 mL of 3.00 M KOH, and the resulting solution was diluted to 1.500 L. The measured pH of the solution was 3.85. What is the pK_a of the weak acid?

122. A 5.55-g sample of a weak acid with $K_a = 1.3 \times 10^{-4}$ was combined with 5.00 mL of 6.00 M NaOH, and the resulting solution was diluted to 750.0 mL. The measured pH of the solution was 4.25. What is the molar mass of the weak acid?

123. A 0.552-g sample of ascorbic acid (vitamin C) was dissolved in water to a total volume of 20.0 mL and titrated with 0.1103 M KOH. The equivalence point occurred at 28.42 mL. The pH of the solution at 10.0 mL of added base was 3.72. From this data, determine the molar mass and K_a for vitamin C.

124. Sketch the titration curve from Problem 123 by calculating the pH at the beginning of the titration, at one-half of the equivalence point, at the equivalence point, and at 5.0 mL beyond the equivalence point. Pick a suitable indicator for this titration from Table 18.1.

125. One of the main components of hard water is $CaCO_3$. When hard water evaporates, some of the $CaCO_3$ is left behind as a white mineral deposit. If a hard water solution is saturated with calcium carbonate, what volume of the solution has to evaporate to deposit 1.00×10^2 mg of $CaCO_3$?

126. Gout—a condition that results in joint swelling and pain—is caused by the formation of sodium urate ($NaC_5H_3N_4O_3$) crystals within tendons, cartilage, and ligaments. Sodium urate precipitates out of blood plasma when uric acid levels become abnormally high. This sometimes happens as a result of eating too many rich foods and consuming too much alcohol, which is why gout is sometimes referred to as the "disease of kings." If the sodium concentration in blood plasma is 0.140 M, and K_{sp} for sodium urate is 5.76×10^{-8}, what minimum concentration of urate would result in precipitation?

127. Pseudogout, a condition with symptoms similar to those of gout (see Problem 126), is caused by the formation of calcium diphosphate ($Ca_2P_2O_7$) crystals within tendons, cartilage, and ligaments. Calcium diphosphate will precipitate out of blood plasma when diphosphate levels become abnormally high. If the calcium concentration in blood plasma is 9.2 mg/dL, and K_{sp} for calcium diphosphate is 8.64×10^{-13}, what minimum concentration of diphosphate results in precipitation?

128. Calculate the solubility of silver chloride in a solution that is 0.100 M in NH_3.

129. Calculate the solubility of CuX in a solution that is 0.150 M in NaCN. K_{sp} for CuX is 1.27×10^{-36}.

130. Aniline, abbreviated ϕNH_2, where ϕ is C_6H_5, is an important organic base used in the manufacture of dyes. It has $K_b = 4.3 \times 10^{-10}$. In a certain manufacturing process, it is necessary to keep the concentration of ϕNH_3^+ (aniline's conjugate acid, the anilinium ion) below 1.0×10^{-9} M in a solution that is 0.10 M in aniline. Find the concentration of NaOH required for this process.

131. The K_b of hydroxylamine, NH_2OH, is 1.10×10^{-8}. A buffer solution is prepared by mixing 100.0 mL of a 0.36 M hydroxylamine solution with 50.0 mL of a 0.26 M HCl solution. Determine the pH of the resulting solution.

132. A 0.867-g sample of an unknown acid requires 32.2 mL of a 0.182 M barium hydroxide solution for neutralization. Assuming the acid is diprotic, calculate the molar mass of the acid.

133. A 25.0-mL volume of a sodium hydroxide solution requires 19.6 mL of a 0.189 M hydrochloric acid for neutralization. A 10.0- mL volume of a phosphoric acid solution requires 34.9 mL of the sodium hydroxide solution for complete neutralization. Calculate the concentration of the phosphoric acid solution.

134. Find the mass of sodium formate that must be dissolved in 250.0 cm^3 of a 1.4 M solution of formic acid to prepare a buffer solution with pH = 3.36.

135. What relative masses of dimethyl amine and dimethyl ammonium chloride do you need to prepare a buffer solution of pH = 10.43?

136. You are asked to prepare 2.0 L of a HCN/NaCN buffer that has a pH of 9.8 and an osmotic pressure of 1.35 atm at 298 K. What masses of HCN and NaCN should you use to prepare the buffer? (Assume complete dissociation of NaCN.)

137. What should the molar concentrations of benzoic acid and sodium benzoate be in a solution that is buffered at a pH of 4.55 and has a freezing point of −2.0 °C? (Assume complete dissociation of sodium benzoate and a density of 1.01 g/mL for the solution.)

CHALLENGE PROBLEMS

138. Derive an equation similar to the Henderson–Hasselbalch equation for a buffer composed of a weak base and its conjugate acid. Instead of relating pH to pK_a and the relative concentrations of an acid and its conjugate base (as the Henderson–Hasselbalch equation does), the equation should relate pOH to pK_b and the relative concentrations of a base and its conjugate acid.

139. Since soap and detergent action is hindered by hard water, laundry formulations usually include water softeners—called builders—designed to remove hard water ions (especially Ca^{2+} and Mg^{2+}) from the water. A common builder used in North America is sodium carbonate. Suppose that the hard water used to do laundry contains 75 ppm Ca^{2+} (reported as $CaCO_3$). What mass of Na_2CO_3 is required to remove 90.0% of these ions from 10.0 L of laundry water?

140. A 0.558-g sample of a diprotic acid with a molar mass of 255.8 g/mol is dissolved in water to a total volume of 25.0 mL. The solution is then titrated with a saturated calcium hydroxide solution.
   a. Assuming that the pK_a values for each ionization step are sufficiently different to see two equivalence points, determine the volume of added base for the first and second equivalence points.
   b. The pH after adding 25.0 mL of the base is 3.82. Find the value of K_{a_1}.
   c. The pH after adding 20.0 mL past the first equivalence point is 8.25. Find the value of K_{a_2}.

141. When excess solid $Mg(OH)_2$ is shaken with 1.00 L of 1.0 M NH_4Cl solution, the resulting saturated solution has pH = 9.00. Calculate the K_{sp} of $Mg(OH)_2$.

142. What amount of solid NaOH must be added to 1.0 L of a 0.10 M H_2CO_3 solution to produce a solution with $[H^+] = 3.2 \times 10^{-11}$ M? There is no significant volume change as the result of the addition of the solid.

143. Calculate the solubility of $Au(OH)_3$ in (a) water and (b) 1.0 M nitric acid solution ($K_{sp} = 5.5 \times 10^{-46}$).

144. Calculate the concentration of I^- in a solution obtained by shaking 0.10 M KI with an excess of AgCl(*s*).

145. What volume of 0.100 M sodium carbonate solution is required to precipitate 99% of the Mg from 1.00 L of 0.100 M magnesium nitrate solution?

146. Find the solubility of CuI in 0.40 M HCN solution. The K_{sp} of CuI is 1.1×10^{-12} and the K_f for the $Cu(CN)_2^-$ complex ion is 1×10^{24}.

147. Find the pH of a solution prepared from 1.0 L of a 0.10 M solution of $Ba(OH)_2$ and excess $Zn(OH)_2(s)$. The K_{sp} of $Zn(OH)_2$ is 3×10^{-15} and the K_f of $Zn(OH)_4^{2-}$ is 2×10^{15}.

148. What amount of HCl gas must be added to 1.00 L of a buffer solution that contains [acetic acid] = 2.0 M and [acetate] = 1.0 M in order to produce a solution with pH = 4.00?

CONCEPTUAL PROBLEMS

149. Without doing any calculations, determine if pH = pK_a, pH > pK_a, or pH < pK_a. Assume that HA is a weak monoprotic acid.
   a. 0.10 mol HA and 0.050 mol of A^- in 1.0 L of solution
   b. 0.10 mol HA and 0.150 mol of A^- in 1.0 L of solution
   c. 0.10 mol HA and 0.050 mol of OH^- in 1.0 L of solution
   d. 0.10 mol HA and 0.075 mol of OH^- in 1.0 L of solution

150. A buffer contains 0.10 mol of a weak acid and 0.20 mol of its conjugate base in 1.0 L of solution. Determine whether or not each addition exceeds the capacity of the buffer.
   a. adding 0.020 mol of NaOH
   b. adding 0.020 mol of HCl
   c. adding 0.10 mol of NaOH
   d. adding 0.010 mol of HCl

151. Consider three solutions:
   i. 0.10 M solution of a weak monoprotic acid
   ii. 0.10 M solution of strong monoprotic acid
   iii. 0.10 M solution of a weak diprotic acid

   Each solution is titrated with 0.15 M NaOH. Which quantity is the same for all three solutions?
   a. the volume required to reach the final equivalence point
   b. the volume required to reach the first equivalence point
   c. the pH at the first equivalence point
   d. the pH at one-half the first equivalence point

152. Two monoprotic acid solutions (A and B) are titrated with identical NaOH solutions. The volume to reach the equivalence point for solution A is twice the volume required to reach the equivalence point for solution B, and the pH at the equivalence point of solution A is higher than the pH at the equivalence point for solution B. Which statement is true?
   a. The acid in solution A is more concentrated than in solution B and is also a stronger acid than that in solution B.
   b. The acid in solution A is less concentrated than in solution B and is also a weaker acid than that in solution B.
   c. The acid in solution A is more concentrated than in solution B and is also a weaker acid than that in solution B.
   d. The acid in solution A is less concentrated than in solution B and is also a stronger acid than that in solution B.

153. Describe the solubility of CaF_2 in each solution compared to its solubility in water.
   a. in a 0.10 M NaCl solution
   b. in a 0.10 M NaF solution
   c. in a 0.10 M HCl solution

154. Why does the titration of a weak acid with a strong base always have a basic equivalence point?

QUESTIONS FOR GROUP WORK

Active Classroom Learning

Discuss these questions with the group and record your consensus answer.

155. Name a compound that you could add to a solution of each of the compounds to make a buffer. Explain your reasoning in complete sentences.
- a. acetic acid
- b. sodium nitrite
- c. ammonia
- d. potassium formate
- e. Na_2HPO_4 (two possible answers)

156. Derive the Henderson–Hasselbalch equation as a group. Take turns having each group member write and explain the next step in the derivation.

157. With group members acting as atoms or ions, act out the reaction that occurs when HCl is added to a buffer solution composed of $HC_2H_3O_2$ and $NaC_2H_3O_2$. Write out a script for a narrator that describes the processes that occur, including how the buffer keeps the pH approximately the same even though a strong acid is added.

158. A certain town gets its water from an underground aquifer that contains water in equilibrium with calcium carbonate limestone.
- a. What is the symbol for the equilibrium constant that describes calcium carbonate dissolving in water? What is the numerical value?
- b. Calculate the molar solubility of calcium carbonate.
- c. If an entire coffee cup of water (about 200 mL) evaporated on your desk over spring break, how many grams of calcium carbonate would be left behind?
- d. If you wanted to clean out your coffee cup, would it be better to use an acidic or a basic cleaning solution? Why?

159. Have each group member look up the K_{sp} for a different compound. Calculate the molar solubility. Do the numerical values suggest that the compound is soluble or insoluble? Compare answers with the solubility rules from Chapter 5, and have each group member present his or her findings to the group.

DATA INTERPRETATION AND ANALYSIS

Titration of an Unknown Base

160. A base is known to be one of the three listed in the table. You are given a sample of the base and asked to identify it. To do so, you dissolve 0.30 g of the base in enough water to make 25.0 mL of the basic solution. You then titrate the solution with 0.100 M HCl and record the pH as a function of the added acid resulting in the titration curve that follows. Examine the table and the titration curve and answer the questions.

Possible Bases in Sample

Base	K_b
Pyridine (C_5H_5N)	1.7×10^{-9}
Aniline ($C_6H_5NH_2$)	3.9×10^{-10}
Triethylamine ($C_6H_{15}N$)	5.6×10^{-4}

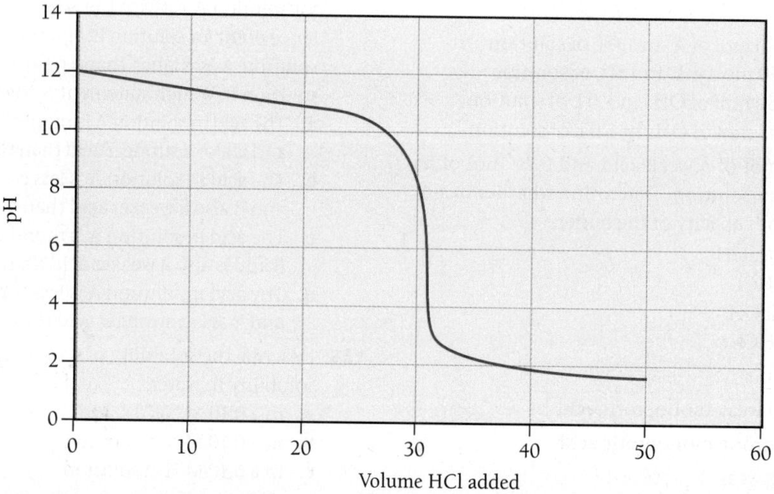

Titration Curve for 0.30 g of Unknown Base Dissolved in 25.0 mL of Solution

- a. What is the volume of added HCl at the equivalence point?
- b. What is the pH at the half-equivalence point?
- c. What is the molar mass of the unknown base?
- d. What are the pK_b and K_b of the unknown base?
- e. What is the most likely identity of the unknown base?

Cc ANSWERS TO CONCEPTUAL CONNECTIONS

Buffers

18.1 **(d)** Only this solution contains significant amounts of a weak acid and its conjugate base. (Remember that HNO_3 is a strong acid, but HNO_2 is a weak acid.)

pH of Buffer Solutions

18.2 **(a)** Since the pH of the buffer is less than the pK_a of the acid, the buffer must contain more acid than base ($[HA] > [A^-]$).

Buffering Action

18.3 **(a)** Since one HA molecule is converted to one ion of the conjugate base (A^- ion), one OH^- ion was added to the buffer solution.

Adding Acid or Base to a Buffer

18.4 **(b)** Since acid is added to the buffer, the pH will become slightly lower (slightly more acidic). Answer **(a)** reflects too large a change in pH for a buffer, and answers **(c)** and **(d)** have the pH changing in the wrong direction.

Buffer Capacity

18.5 **(a)** Adding 0.050 mol of HCl destroys the buffer because it will react with all of the NaF, leaving no conjugate base in the buffer mixture.

Titration Equivalence Point

18.6 **(d)** Because the flask contains 7 H^+ ions, the equivalence point is reached when 7 OH^- ions have been added.

Weak Acid and Strong Base Titration

18.7 **(c)** Acid A is more concentrated (it took more NaOH to reach the equivalence point), and acid B has the larger K_a (pK_a is smaller so K_a is larger).

The Half-Equivalence Point

18.8 **(c)** The pH at the half-equivalence point is the pK_a of the conjugate acid, which is equal to $14.00 - 8.75 = 5.25$.

Acid–Base Titrations

18.9 **(c)** Since the volumes and concentrations of all three acids are the same, the volume of NaOH required to reach the first equivalence point (and the only equivalence point for titrations i and iii) is the same for all three titrations.

Common Ion Effect

18.10 **(c)** The sodium nitrate solution is the only one that has no common ion with barium sulfate. The other two solutions have common ions with barium sulfate; therefore, the solubility of barium sulfate is lower in these solutions.

Selective Precipitation

18.11 **(a)** Ba^{2+} has the smallest solubility product constant and, since the stoichiometry of dissolution is the same for all three ions, it will precipitate first.

Solubility and Complex Ion Equilibria

18.12 **(c)** Only NaCN contains an anion (CN^-) that forms a complex ion with Cu^{2+} [from Table 18.3 we can see that $K_f = 1.0 \times 10^{25}$ for $Cu(CN)_4^{2-}$]. Therefore, the presence of CN^- will drive the dissolution reaction of CuS.

Die Energie der Welt ist konstant. Die Entropie der Welt strebt einem Maximum zu. (The energy of the world is constant. The entropy of the world tends towards a maximum.)

—RUDOLF CLAUSIUS (1822–1888)

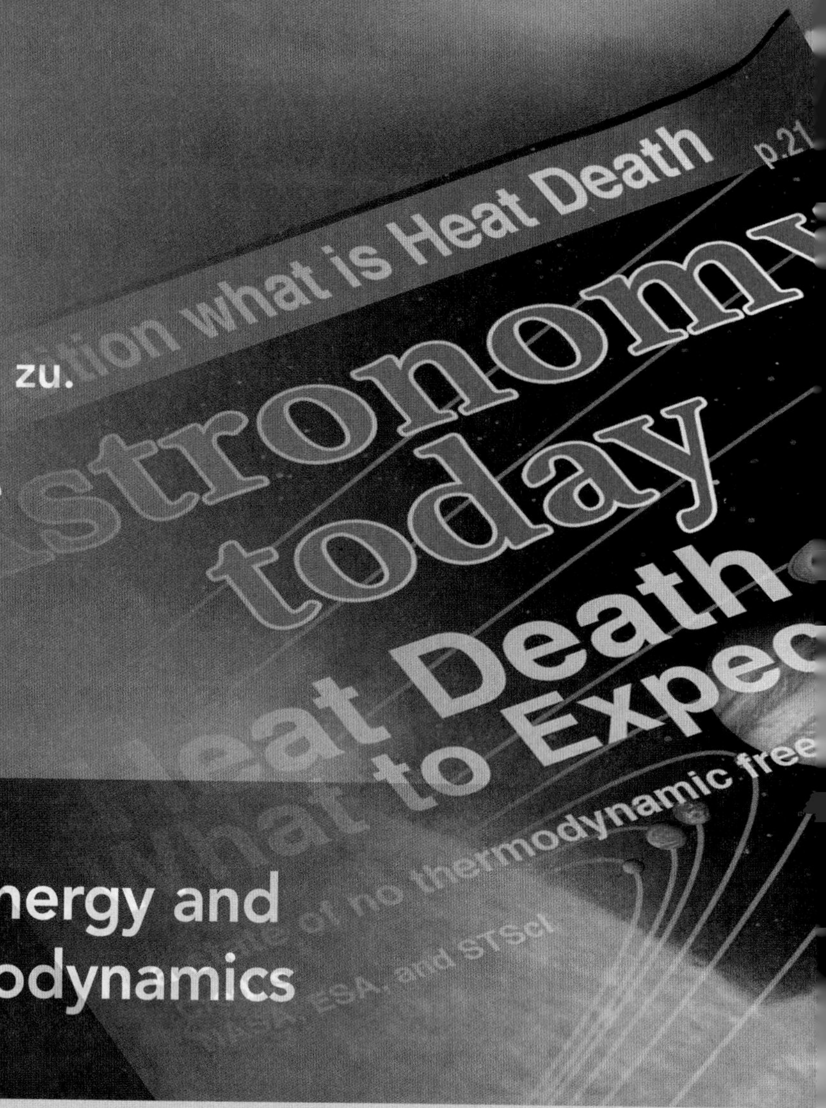

CHAPTER 19 Free Energy and Thermodynamics

Throughout this book, we have examined chemical and physical changes. We have studied how fast chemical changes occur (kinetics) and how to predict how far they will go (through the use of equilibrium constants). We have learned that acids neutralize bases and that gases expand to fill their containers. We now turn to the following question: why do these changes occur in the first place? What ultimately drives physical and chemical changes in matter? The answer may surprise you. The driving force behind chemical and physical change in the universe is a quantity called *entropy*, which is related to the dispersion (spreading out) of energy. Nature tends toward that state in which energy is spread out to the greatest extent possible. Although it does not seem obvious at first glance, the freezing of water below 0 °C, the dissolving of a solid into a solution, the neutralization of an acid by a base, and even the development of a person from an embryo all increase the entropy in the universe (they all result in greater energy dispersion). In our universe, entropy always increases.

Hot coffee cools down because of the pervasive tendency of energy to dissipate (or disperse) over time.

19.1 Cold Coffee and Dead Universes 847

19.2 Spontaneous and Nonspontaneous Processes 848

19.3 Entropy and the Second Law of Thermodynamics 850

19.4 Entropy Changes Associated with State Changes 856

19.5 Heat Transfer and Changes in the Entropy of the Surroundings 860

19.6 Gibbs Free Energy 863

19.7 Entropy Changes in Chemical Reactions: Calculating ΔS°_{rxn} 867

19.8 Free Energy Changes in Chemical Reactions: Calculating ΔG°_{rxn} 871

19.9 Free Energy Changes for Nonstandard States: The Relationship between ΔG°_{rxn} and ΔG_{rxn} 878

19.10 Free Energy and Equilibrium: Relating ΔG°_{rxn} to the Equilibrium Constant (K) 881

LEARNING OUTCOMES 886

19.1 Cold Coffee and Dead Universes

Nature hates concentrated energy. We all know this from experience. The hot coffee you just poured for yourself will be cold in 30 minutes because the concentrated thermal energy in the coffee dissipates into the surrounding room. Similarly, the concentrated energy contained in the gasoline that you just added to your car will soon dissipate into thermal energy as you drive your car to transport yourself around town. The energy in the hot coffee and the gasoline is not destroyed (recall from Chapter 7 that energy cannot be created nor destroyed). Instead it is dispersed or dissipated, changed from a concentrated form into a more spread out form. The pervasive tendency for energy to spread out or dissipate when not prevented from doing so is known as *the second law of thermodynamics*, the main topic of this chapter.

The second law of thermodynamics has profound implications, not just for the cooling off of coffee or the use of fuels, but for many other processes as well. As we will see, the second law determines the spontaneous direction of *all processes*. In other words, if you want to know if a particular process will occur (such as the cooling of coffee or the burning of fuel), you just have to determine if the process disperses or spreads out energy. If it does, the process occurs. If it does not, the process does not occur. In the cooling of coffee, we can easily tell that energy spreads out. However, for other processes, it is not so obvious. For example, the melting of ice above 0 °C disperses energy and therefore spontaneously occurs; but below 0 °C the melting of ice *does not* disperse energy and therefore does not happen. Later in this chapter, we examine why the temperature of the surroundings makes a difference.

The second law of thermodynamics is so pervasive and powerful that it predicts the fate of the universe itself. Over time, we know that the concentrated energy of the sun will disperse itself into the surroundings so that the sun burns out. Similarly, all concentrated energy in the universe will disperse so that eventually *nothing* can happen anymore. Cosmologists call this fate *heat death,* and it is the most plausible explanation for the future of our universe. However, we need not worry about either of these because the sun has several more billion years left in it, and our universe has something like 10^{100} years left before it winds down. For now, we can concentrate on understanding the second law and how it applies to predicting the spontaneity of chemical processes.

ANSWER **NOW!**

19.1 Cc Conceptual Connection

THE SECOND LAW Which process is inconsistent with the the second law of thermodynamics?

(a) The spontaneous creation of energy from nothing.
(b) The spontaneous creation of matter from nothing.
(c) The spontaneous concentration of energy from dispersed energy.

19.2 Spontaneous and Nonspontaneous Processes

A fundamental goal of thermodynamics is to predict *spontaneity*. For example, will rust spontaneously form when iron comes into contact with oxygen? Will water spontaneously decompose into hydrogen and oxygen? A **spontaneous process** is one that occurs *without ongoing outside intervention* (such as the performance of work by some external force). For example, when you drop a book in a gravitational field, it spontaneously drops to the floor. When you place a ball on a slope, it spontaneously rolls down the slope.

For simple mechanical systems, such as the dropping of a book or the rolling of a ball, predicting spontaneity is fairly intuitive. A mechanical system tends toward lowest potential energy, which is usually easy to see (at least in *simple* mechanical systems).

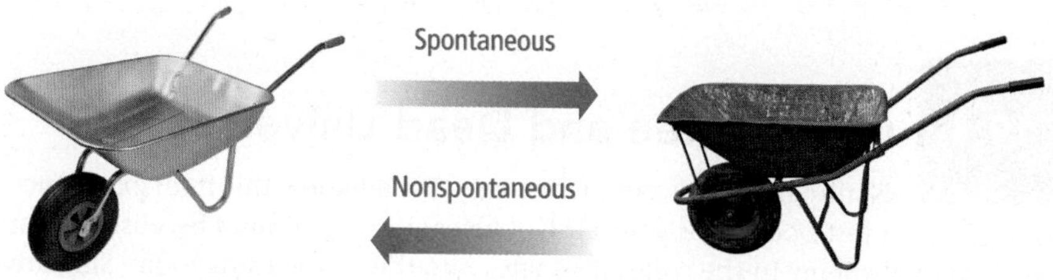

▶ Iron spontaneously rusts when it comes in contact with oxygen.

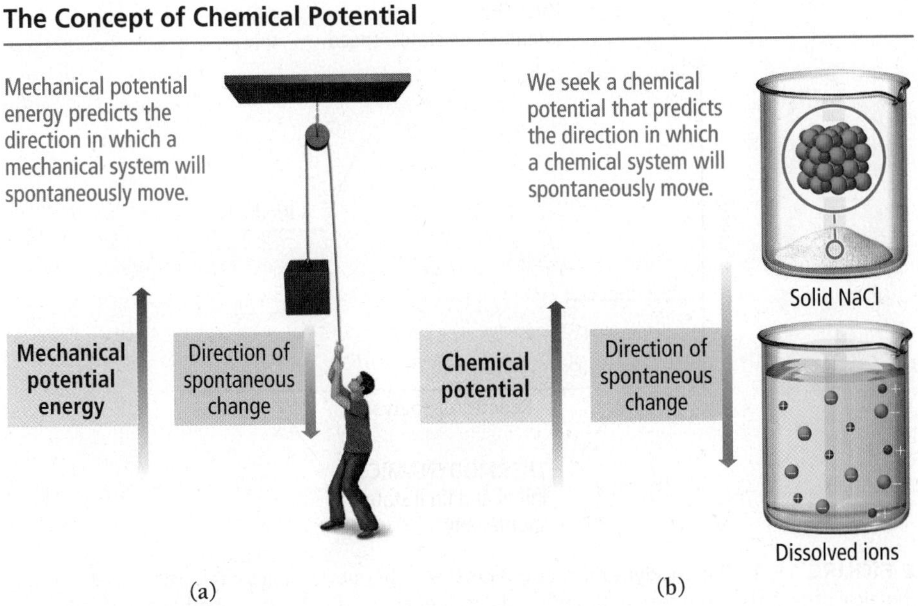

◀ **FIGURE 19.1 Mechanical Potential Energy and Chemical Potential**

However, the prediction of spontaneity for chemical systems is not so intuitively obvious. To make these predictions, we need to develop a criterion for the spontaneity of chemical systems. In other words, we need to develop a *chemical potential* that predicts the direction of a chemical system, much as mechanical potential energy predicts the direction of a mechanical system (Figure 19.1▲).

We must not confuse the *spontaneity* of a chemical reaction with the *speed* of a chemical reaction. In thermodynamics, we study the *spontaneity* of a reaction—the direction in which, and the extent to which, a chemical reaction proceeds. In kinetics, we study the *speed* of the reaction—how fast a reaction takes place (Figure 19.2►). A reaction may be thermodynamically spontaneous but kinetically slow at a given temperature. For example, the conversion of diamond to graphite is thermodynamically spontaneous. But your diamonds will not become worthless anytime soon because the process is extremely slow kinetically. Although the rate of a spontaneous process can be increased by the use of a catalyst, a nonspontaneous process cannot be made spontaneous by the use of a catalyst. Catalysts affect only the rate of a reaction, not the spontaneity.

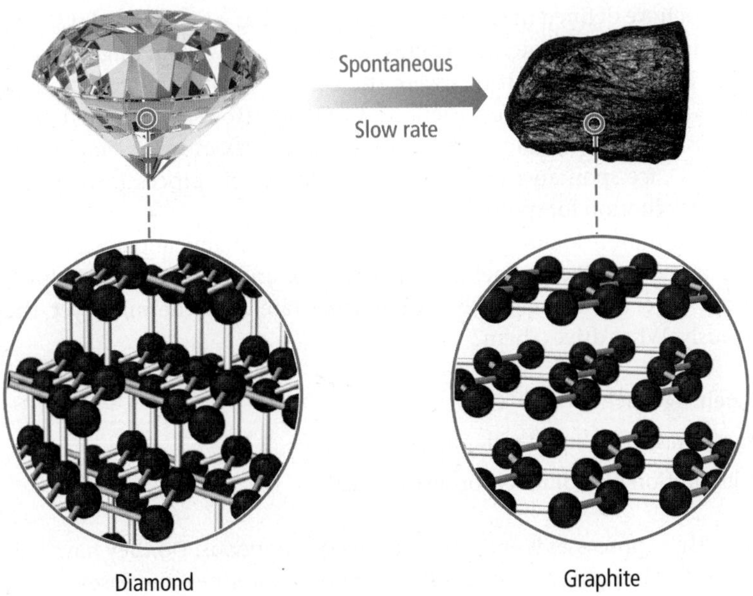

◀ Even though graphite is thermodynamically more stable than diamond, the conversion of diamond to graphite is kinetically so slow that it does not occur at any measurable rate.

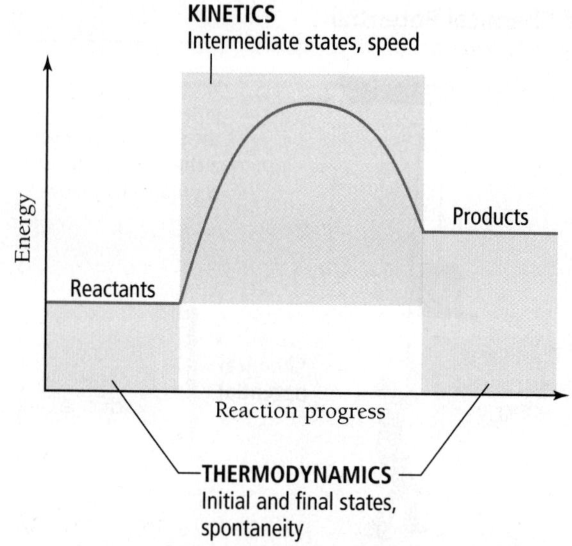

▲ **FIGURE 19.2 Thermodynamics and Kinetics** Thermodynamics deals with the relative chemical potentials of the reactants and products. It enables us to predict whether a reaction will be spontaneous and to calculate how much work it can do. Kinetics deals with the chemical potential of intermediate states and enables us to determine why a reaction is slow or fast.

One more observation about nonspontaneity—a nonspontaneous process is not *impossible*. For example, the extraction of iron metal from iron ore is a nonspontaneous process; it does not happen if the iron ore is left to itself, but that does not mean it is impossible. As we will see later in this chapter, a nonspontaneous process can be made spontaneous by coupling it to another process that is spontaneous or by supplying energy from an external source. Iron can be separated from its ore if external energy is supplied, usually by means of another reaction (that is itself highly spontaneous).

WATCH **NOW!**

KEY CONCEPT VIDEO 19.3
Entropy and the Second Law of Thermodynamics

19.3 Entropy and the Second Law of Thermodynamics

The first candidate in our search for a chemical potential might be enthalpy, which we defined in Chapter 7. Perhaps, just as a mechanical system proceeds in the direction of lowest potential energy, so a chemical system might proceed in the direction of lowest enthalpy. If this were the case, all exothermic reactions would be spontaneous and all endothermic reactions would not. However, although *most* spontaneous processes are exothermic, some spontaneous processes are *endothermic*. For example, above 0 °C, ice spontaneously melts (an endothermic process). So enthalpy must not be the sole criterion for spontaneity.

See Section 7.6 for the definition of enthalpy.

We can learn more about the driving force behind chemical processes by considering several processes (like ice melting) that involve an increase in enthalpy. The processes listed here are energetically uphill (they are endothermic), yet they occur spontaneously. What drives them?

- the melting of ice above 0 °C
- the evaporation of liquid water to gaseous water
- the dissolution of sodium chloride in water

The use of the word *disorder* here is analogous to our macroscopic notions of disorder. The definition of molecular disorder, which is covered shortly, is very specific.

Each of these processes is endothermic *and* spontaneous. Do they have anything in common? Notice that, in each process, disorder or randomness increases.

In the melting of ice, the arrangement of the water molecules changes from a highly ordered one (in ice) to a somewhat disorderly one (in liquid water).

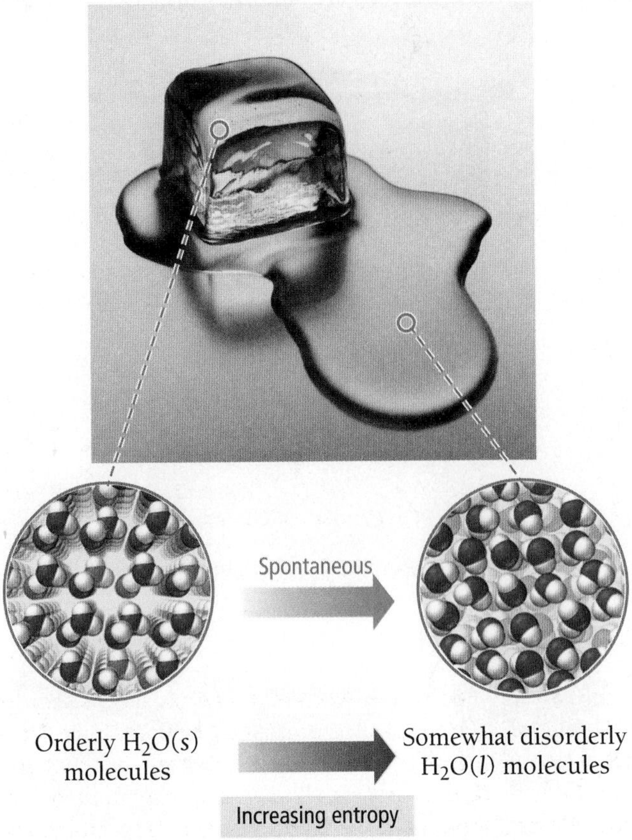

◀ When ice melts, the arrangement of water molecules changes from orderly to more disorderly.

During the evaporation of a liquid to a gas, the arrangement changes from a *somewhat* disorderly one (atoms or molecules in the liquid) to a *highly* disorderly one (atoms or molecules in the gas).

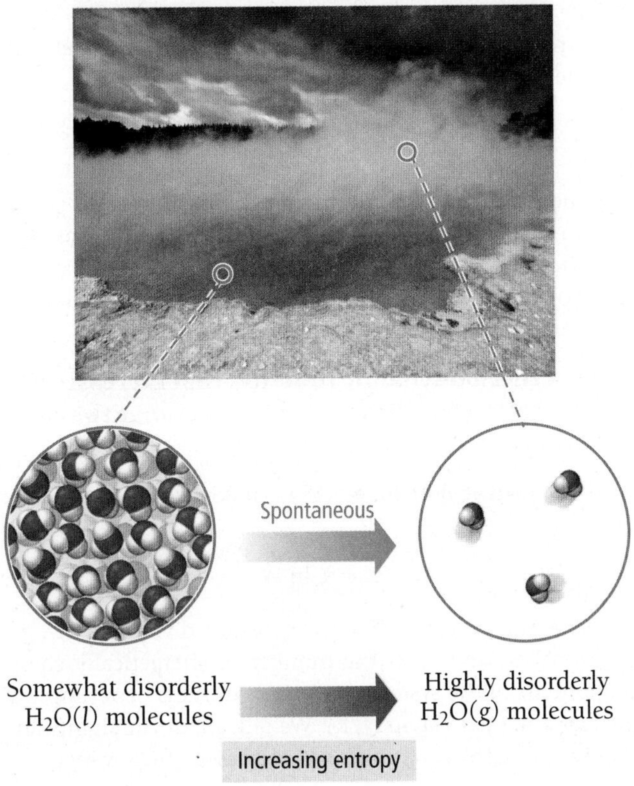

◀ When water evaporates, the arrangement of water molecules becomes still more disorderly.

In the dissolution of a salt into water, the arrangement again changes from an orderly one (in which the ions in the salt occupy regular positions in the crystal lattice) to a more disorderly one (in which the ions are randomly dispersed throughout the liquid water).

▶ When salt dissolves in water, the arrangement of the molecules and ions becomes more disorderly.

In all three of these processes, a quantity called *entropy*—related to disorder or randomness at the molecular level—increases.

Entropy

We have hit upon the criterion for spontaneity in chemical systems: entropy. Informally, we can think of entropy as disorder or randomness. But the concept of disorder or randomness on the macroscopic scale—such as the messiness of a drawer—is only *analogous* to the concept of disorder or randomness on the molecular scale. Formally, entropy, abbreviated by the symbol S, has the following definition:

Entropy (S) is a thermodynamic function that increases with the number of *energetically equivalent* ways to arrange the components of a system to achieve a particular state.

▲ Boltzmann's equation is engraved on his tombstone.

Austrian physicist Ludwig Boltzmann (1844–1906) expressed this definition mathematically as:

$$S = k \ln W$$

where k is the Boltzmann constant (the gas constant divided by Avogadro's number, $R/N_A = 1.38 \times 10^{-23}$ J/K) and W is the number of energetically equivalent ways to arrange the components of the system. Since W is unitless (it is simply a number), the units of entropy are joules per kelvin (J/K). We talk about the significance of the units shortly. As we can see from the equation, as W increases, entropy increases.

Microstates and Macrostates

The key to understanding entropy is the quantity W. What does W—the number of energetically equivalent ways to arrange the components of the system—signify? Imagine a system of particles such as a fixed amount of an ideal gas. A given set of conditions (P, V, and T) defines the *state* (or *macrostate*) of the system. As long as these conditions remain constant, the energy of the system also remains constant. However, *exactly where that energy is at any given instant is anything but constant.*

At any one instant, a particular gas particle may have a good deal of kinetic energy. However, after a very short period of time, that particle may have very little kinetic energy (because it lost its energy through collisions with other particles). The exact internal energy distribution among the particles at any one instant is sometimes referred to as a *microstate*. We can think of a microstate as a snapshot of the system at a given instant in time. The next instant, the snapshot (the microstate) changes. However, the *macrostate*—defined by P, V, and T—remains constant. A given macrostate can exist as a result of a large number of different microstates. In other words, the snapshot (or microstate) of a given macrostate is generally different from one moment to the next as the energy of the system is constantly redistributing itself among the particles of the system.

We can think of W in terms of microstates. The quantity, W, is the number of *possible* microstates that can result in a given macrostate. For example, suppose that we have two systems (call them System A and System B) and that each is composed of two particles (one blue and one red). Both systems have a total energy of 4 joules, but System A has only one energy level and System B has two:

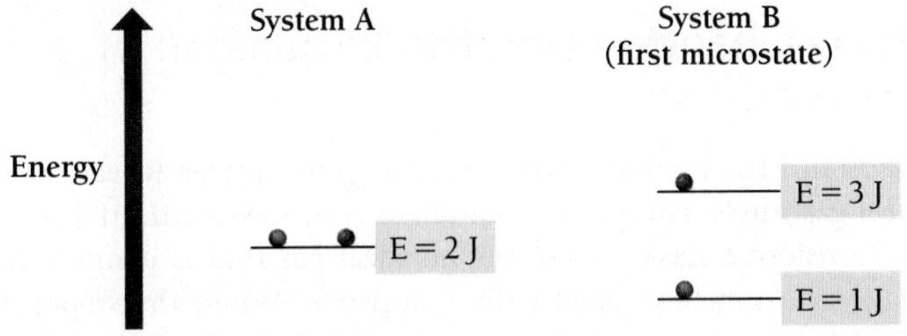

Note that each system has the same total energy, 4 J. But System A has one possible microstate because both particles must occupy the same energy level (red particle = 2 J and blue particle = 2 J), while System B has two possible microstates because the red and blue particles can occupy different energy levels (blue particle = 3 J and red particle = 1 J, or, blue particle = 1 J and red particle = 3 J).

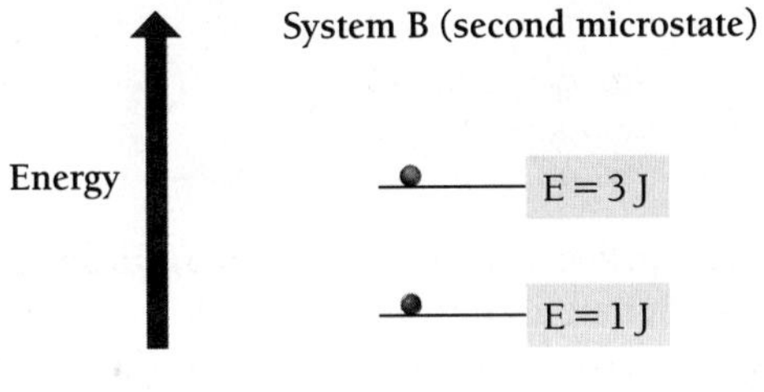

This second microstate is not possible for System A because it has only one energy level. For System A, $W = 1$, but for System B, $W = 2$. In other words, System B has more microstates that result in the same 4 J macrostate. Since W is larger for System B than for System A, System B has greater *entropy*; it has more *energetically equivalent ways to arrange the components of the system.*

We can better understand the nature of entropy by turning our attention to energy for a moment. The entropy of a state increases with the number of *energetically equivalent* ways to arrange the components of the system to achieve that particular state. This implies that *the state with the highest entropy also has the greatest dispersal of energy.*

Returning to our previous example, we see that the energy of System B is dispersed over two energy levels instead of being confined to just one. At the heart of entropy is the concept of energy dispersal or energy randomization. *A state in which a given amount of energy is more highly dispersed (or more highly randomized) has more entropy than a state in which the same energy is more highly concentrated.*

We have already alluded to the **second law of thermodynamics**; we now formally define it:

For any spontaneous process, the entropy of the *universe* increases ($\Delta S_{univ} > 0$).

The criterion for spontaneity is the entropy of the universe. Processes that increase the entropy of the universe—those that result in greater dispersal or randomization of energy—occur spontaneously. Processes that decrease the entropy of the universe do not occur spontaneously.

See the discussion of state functions in Section 7.3.

Entropy, like enthalpy, is a *state function*—its value depends only on the state of the system, not on how the system arrived at that state. Therefore, for any process, *the change in entropy is the entropy of the final state minus the entropy of the initial state*:

$$\Delta S = S_{final} - S_{initial}$$

Entropy determines the direction of chemical and physical change. *A chemical system proceeds in a direction that increases the entropy of the universe*—it proceeds in a direction that has the largest number of *energetically equivalent* ways to arrange its components.

The Entropy Change upon the Expansion of an Ideal Gas

See the discussion of work done by an expanding gas in Section 7.4.

To better understand the tendency toward greater entropy, let us examine the expansion of an ideal gas into a vacuum (a spontaneous process with no associated change in enthalpy). Consider a flask containing an ideal gas that is connected to another, evacuated, flask by a tube equipped with a stopcock. When the stopcock is opened, the gas spontaneously expands into the evacuated flask. Since the gas is expanding into a vacuum, the pressure against which it expands is zero, and therefore the work ($w = -P_{ext}\,\Delta V$) is also zero.

However, even though the total energy of the gas does not change during the expansion, the entropy does change. To picture this, consider a simplified system containing only four gas atoms:

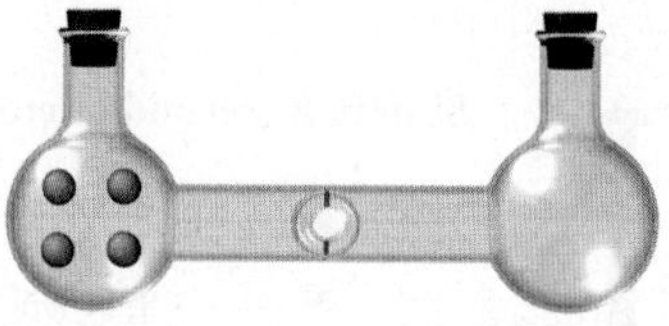

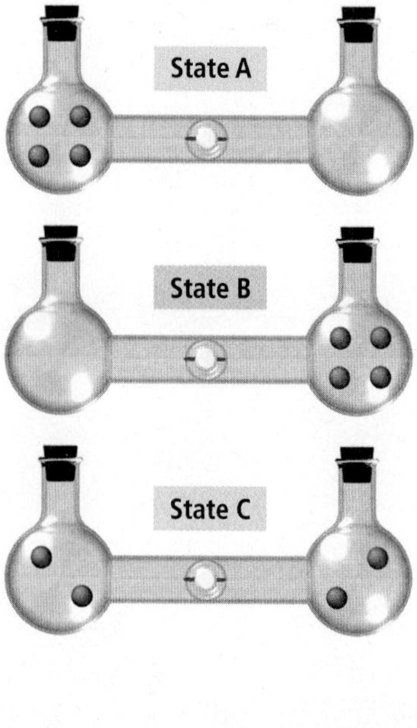

When the stopcock is opened, several possible energetically equivalent final states may result, each with the four atoms distributed in a different way. For example, there could be three atoms in the flask on the left and one in the flask on the right, or vice versa. For simplicity, we consider only the possibilities shown in the figure in the left margin, which are state A, state B, and state C. Since the energy of any one atom is the same in either flask, and since the atoms do not interact, states A, B, and C are energetically equivalent.

Now we ask the following question for each state: how many microstates give rise to the same macrostate? To keep track of the microstates, we label the atoms 1–4. Although they have different numbered labels, since the atoms are all the same, there is externally no difference between them. For states A and B, only one microstate results in the specified macrostate—atoms 1–4 on the left side or the right side, respectively:

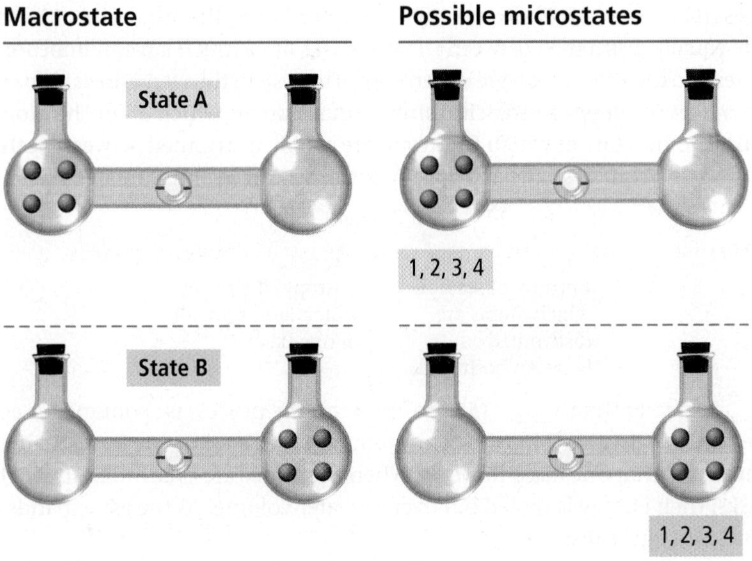

For state C, however, six different possible microstates all result in the same macrostate (two atoms on each side):

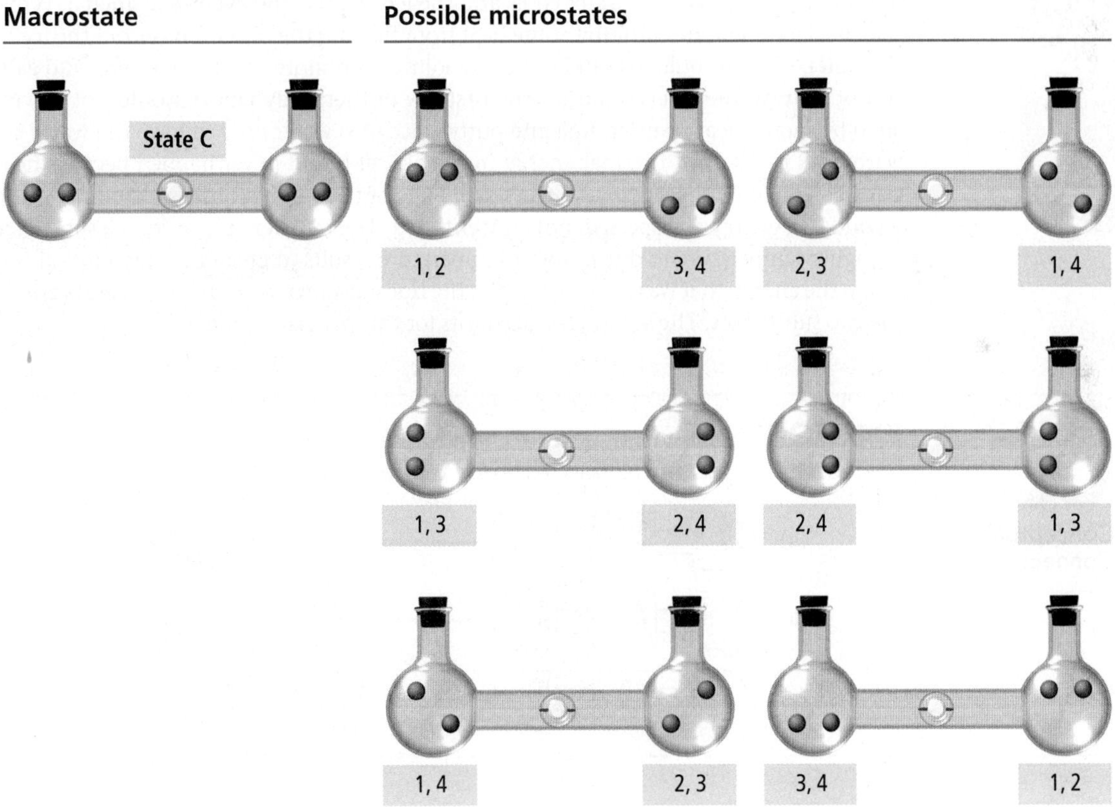

This means that if the atoms are just randomly moving between the two flasks, the statistical probability of finding the atoms in state C is six times greater than the probability of finding the atoms in state A or state B. Consequently, even for a simple system consisting of only four atoms, the atoms are most likely to be found in state C. State C has the greatest entropy—it has the greatest number of energetically equivalent ways to distribute its components.

In these drawings, the exact location of an atom within a flask is insignificant. The significant aspect is whether the atom is in the left flask or the right flask.

As the number of atoms increases, the number of microstates that leads to the atoms being equally distributed between the two flasks increases dramatically. For example, with 10 atoms, the number of microstates leading to an equal distribution of atoms between two flasks is 252, and with 20 atoms the number of microstates is 184,756. Yet, the number of microstates that leads to all of the atoms being only in the left flask (or all only in the right

For n particles, the number of ways to put r particles in one flask and $n - r$ particles in the other flask is $n!/[(n - r)!r!]$. For 10 atoms, $n = 10$ and $r = 5$.

flask) does not increase—it is always only 1. In other words, the arrangement in which the atoms are equally distributed between the two flasks has a much larger number of possible microstates and therefore much greater entropy. The system thus tends toward that state.

The *change in entropy* in transitioning from a state in which all of the atoms are in the left flask to the state in which the atoms are evenly distributed between both flasks is *positive* because the final state has a greater entropy than the initial state:

$$\Delta S = S_{\text{final}} - S_{\text{initial}}$$

Entropy of state in which atoms are distributed between both flasks

Entropy of state in which atoms are all in one flask

Since S_{final} is greater than S_{initial}, ΔS is positive and the process is spontaneous according to the second law. Notice that when the atoms are confined to one flask, their energy is also confined to that one flask; however, when the atoms are evenly distributed between both flasks, their energy is spread out over a greater volume. As the gas expands into the empty flask, energy is dispersed.

The second law explains many phenomena not explained by the first law. In Chapter 7, we learned that heat travels from a substance at higher temperature to one at lower temperature. For example, if we drop an ice cube into water, heat travels from the water to the ice cube—the water cools and the ice warms (and eventually melts). Why? The first law would not prohibit some heat from flowing the other way—from the ice to the water. The ice could lose 10 J of heat (cooling even more), and the water could gain 10 J of heat (warming even more). The first law of thermodynamics would not be violated by such a heat transfer. Imagine putting ice into water only to have the water get warmer as it absorbed thermal energy from the ice! It will never happen because heat transfer from cold to hot violates the second law of thermodynamics. According to the second law, energy is dispersed, not concentrated. The transfer of heat from a substance of higher temperature to one of lower temperature results in greater energy randomization—the energy that was concentrated in the hot substance becomes dispersed between the two substances. The second law accounts for this pervasive tendency.

ANSWER **NOW!**

19.2 Cc Conceptual Connection

ENTROPY Consider these three changes in the possible distributions of six gaseous particles within three interconnected boxes. Which change has a positive ΔS?

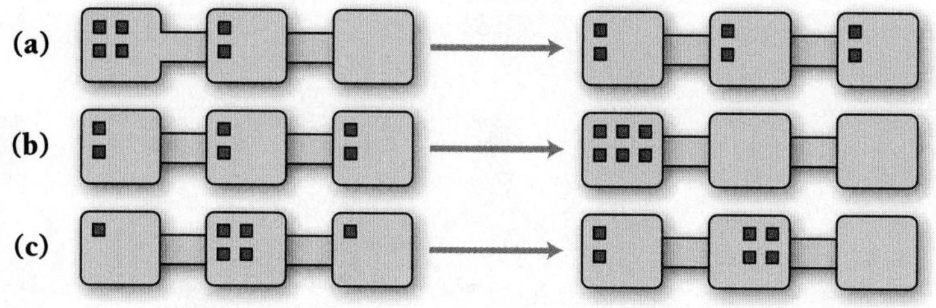

19.4 Entropy Changes Associated with State Changes

The entropy of a sample of matter *increases* as it changes state from a solid to a liquid or from a liquid to a gas (Figure 19.3▶). We first consider this idea conceptually, and then we turn to actually calculating the value of ΔS for this change. Recall that, in Chapter 7, we distinguished between a thermodynamic system and its surroundings. This distinction is useful in our discussion of entropy. For a change of state in a substance, we consider the substance to be the system. The surroundings are then the rest of the universe. Here, we focus on the entropy of the *system* undergoing the change of state (not the surroundings, which we address in Section 19.5).

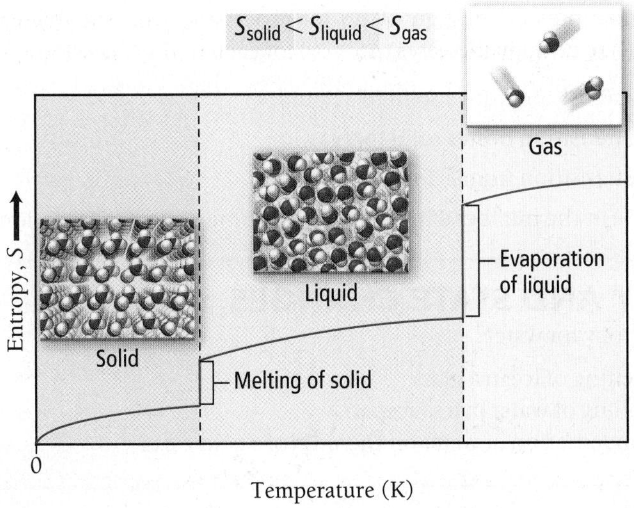

◀ **FIGURE 19.3 Entropy and State Change** Entropy increases when matter changes from a solid to a liquid and from a liquid to a gas.

Entropy and State Change: The Concept

We can informally think of the increase in entropy in going from a solid to a liquid or from a liquid to a gas by analogy with macroscopic disorder. The gaseous state is more disorderly than the liquid state, which is in turn more disorderly than the solid state. More formally, however, the differences in entropy are related to the number of energetically equivalent ways of arranging the particles in each state—there are more in the gas than in the liquid and more in the liquid than in the solid.

A gas has more energetically equivalent configurations because it has more ways to distribute its energy than a solid. The energy in a molecular solid consists largely of the vibrations between its molecules. If the same substance is in its gaseous state, however, the energy can take the form of straight-line motions of the molecules (called translational energy) and rotations of the molecules (called rotational energy). In other words, when a solid vaporizes into a gas, there are new "places" to put energy (Figure 19.4▼). The gas thus has more possible microstates (more energetically equivalent configurations) than the solid and therefore a greater entropy.

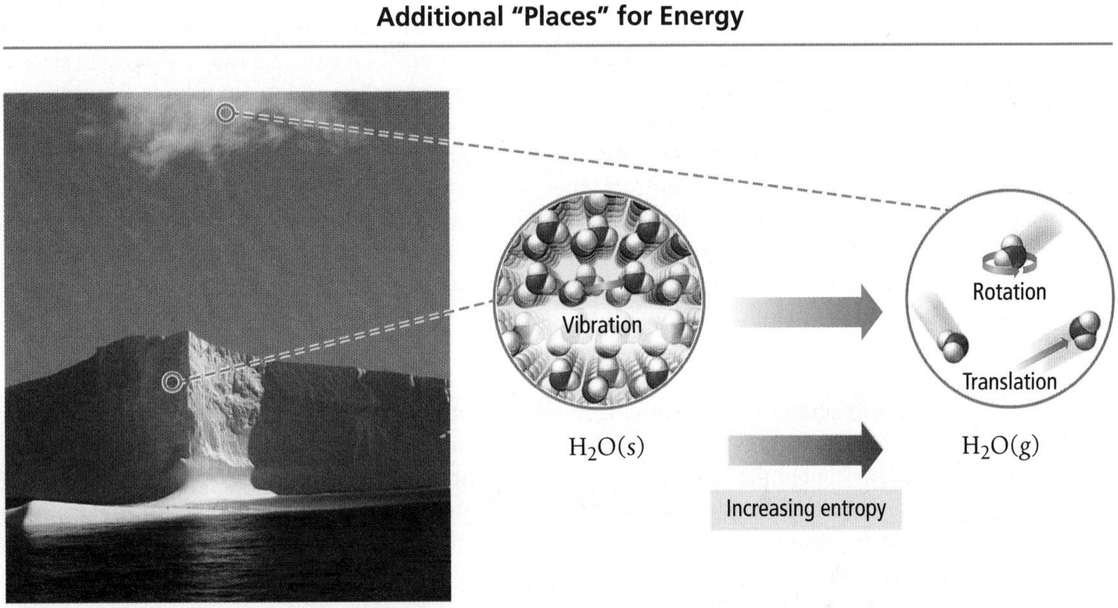

▲ **FIGURE 19.4 "Places" for Energy** In the solid state, energy is contained largely in the vibrations between molecules. In the gas state, energy can be contained in both the straight-line motion of molecules (translational energy) and the rotation of molecules (rotational energy).

We can now predict the sign of ΔS for processes involving changes of state (or phase). In general, entropy increases ($\Delta S > 0$) for each of the following:

- the phase transition from a solid to a liquid
- the phase transition from a solid to a gas
- the phase transition from a liquid to a gas
- an increase in the number of moles of a gas during a chemical reaction

ANSWER NOW!

19.3 Cc Conceptual Connection

ENTROPY AND STATE CHANGES Which process undergoes a *decrease* in entropy for water?

(a) The melting of ice in a glass
(b) The boiling of water in a saucepan
(c) The condensation of water on the sides of a cold glass

EXAMPLE 19.1 Predicting the Sign of Entropy Change

Predict the sign of ΔS for each process.

(a) $H_2O(g) \longrightarrow H_2O(l)$

(b) Solid carbon dioxide sublimes.

(c) $2\,N_2O(g) \longrightarrow 2\,N_2(g) + O_2(g)$

SOLUTION

(a) Since a gas has a greater entropy than a liquid, the entropy decreases and ΔS is negative.

(b) Since a solid has a lower entropy than a gas, the entropy increases and ΔS is positive.

(c) Since the number of moles of gas increases, the entropy increases and ΔS is positive.

FOR PRACTICE 19.1 Predict the sign of ΔS for each process.

(a) Water boils. **(b)** $I_2(g) \longrightarrow I_2(s)$ **(c)** $CaCO_3(s) \longrightarrow CaO(s) + CO_2(g)$

Entropy and State Changes: The Calculation

We have just seen how the entropy of system increases with the transition from a solid to a liquid to a gas. We can calculate the actual changes in entropy that occur in the system during these state transitions. Recall from Sections 12.5 and 12.6 that a change in state is accompanied by an exchange of heat between the system and surroundings. For example, melting and vaporization are endothermic (they absorb heat from the surroundings), while freezing and condensation are exothermic (they give off heat to the surroundings).

The definition of entropy that we introduced previously ($S = k \ln W$) shows how entropy is related to the distribution of energy among the particles that compose matter. On a macroscopic scale, we can define the change in entropy that occurs when a system exchanges a quantity of heat (q) with its surroundings at a constant temperature (T) with the following equation:

$$\Delta S = \frac{q_{\text{rev}}}{T} \quad \text{(constant temperature)} \qquad [19.1]$$

In this equation, ΔS is the entropy change of the system, q_{rev} is the heat exchanged with the surroundings in a *reversible* process (more on this to come), and T is the temperature in K. The temperature must be constant throughout the change—the process must be *isothermal.* Let's address two important concepts related to this equation, the units of entropy and reversible processes.

Units of Entropy

In Section 19.3, we saw that the units of entropy are J/K. We can now better understand these units. Entropy is a measure of energy dispersal per unit temperature and therefore has the units of energy (J) over temperature (K). For example, when a substance melts (an endothermic process), it absorbs a certain amount of energy from the surroundings. That energy becomes dispersed into the system (as the substance changes state from a solid to a liquid) and the entropy of the substance increases. The change in entropy is related to the amount of energy the substance absorbs (units of J) divided by the temperature of the substance (units of K).

Reversible Processes

A **reversible process** is one that reverses direction upon an infinitesimally small change in some property. The melting of ice when the ice and its surroundings are both at exactly 0 °C is an example of a reversible process. An infinitesimally small *removal* of heat reverses the melting and causes freezing instead. An infinitesimally small *addition* of heat causes the melting to resume. All reversible processes are in a constant state of equilibrium and represent highly idealized conditions. In contrast, the melting of ice that happens when we set an ice cube on a countertop at room temperature is *irreversible*. In this case, the countertop and the surrounding air are at 25.0 °C, and an infinitesimally small removal of heat does not reverse the melting.

We can use Equation 19.1 to calculate the change in the entropy of a system that undergoes a state change. For example, when ice melts at its melting point, the heat exchanged with the surroundings is ΔH_{fus} and the temperatue is 273 K:

$$q_{rev} = \Delta H_{fus} = 6.02\ \text{kJ/mol}$$
$$T = 273\ \text{K}$$

We substitute these quantities into Equation 19.1 to determine the change in entropy of the system when 1 mol of ice melts at its melting point:

$$\Delta S = \frac{q_{rev}}{T}$$
$$= \frac{(1\ \cancel{\text{mol}})\dfrac{6.02 \times 10^3\ \text{J}}{\cancel{\text{mol}}}}{273\ \text{K}}$$
$$= 22.1\ \text{J/K}$$

The value of ΔS is positive, as we would expect for a transition from solid to liquid.

WATCH **NOW!**
INTERACTIVE WORKED EXAMPLE 19.2

EXAMPLE 19.2 Calculating ΔS for a Change of State

Calculate the change in entropy that occurs in the system when 25.0 g of water condenses from a gas to a liquid at the normal boiling point of water (100.00 °C).

SOLUTION

Because the condensation is occurring at the boiling point of water and the temperature is constant, you can use Equation 19.1 to calculate the change in entropy of the system.	$\Delta S = \dfrac{q_{rev}}{T}$
Gather the necessary quantities. Look up the value of the enthalpy of vaporization for water at its boiling point in Table 12.7. The enthalpy of condensation is the same in value but opposite in sign.	$\Delta H_{vap} = 40.7\ \text{kJ/mol}$ $\Delta H_{condensation} = -40.7\ \text{kJ/mol}$ $T(\text{K}) = T(°\text{C}) + 273.15$
Calculate the temperature in K.	$= 100.00 + 273.15$ $= 373.15\ \text{K}$
Substitute into Equation 19.1 to calculate the change in entropy for the system.	$\Delta S = \dfrac{q_{rev}}{T}$ $= \dfrac{25.0\ \cancel{\text{g}} \times \dfrac{1\ \cancel{\text{mol}}}{18.02\ \cancel{\text{g}}} \times \left(\dfrac{-40.7 \times 10^3\ \text{J}}{\cancel{\text{mol}}}\right)}{373.15\ \text{K}}$ $= -151\ \text{J/K}$

—*Continued on the next page*

Continued—

CHECK The answer has the correct units for entropy (J/K). The answer is negative, as you would expect for the condensation of a gas to a liquid.

FOR PRACTICE 19.2 Calculate the change in entropy that occurs in the system when 10.0 g of acetone (C_3H_6O) vaporizes from a liquid to a gas at its normal boiling point (56.1 °C).

19.5 Heat Transfer and Changes in the Entropy of the Surroundings

We have now seen that the criterion for spontaneity is an increase in the entropy of the universe. However, you can probably think of several spontaneous processes in which entropy seems to decrease. For example, when water freezes at temperatures below 0 °C, the entropy of the water decreases, yet the process is spontaneous. Similarly, when water vapor in air condenses into fog on a cold night, the entropy of the water also decreases. Why are these processes spontaneous?

To answer this question, we must return to the second law: for any spontaneous process, the entropy *of the universe* increases ($\Delta S_{univ} > 0$). Even though the entropy *of the water* decreases during freezing and condensation, the entropy *of the universe* must somehow increase in order for these processes to be spontaneous. If we define the water as the system, then ΔS_{sys} is the entropy change for the water itself, ΔS_{surr} is the entropy change for the surroundings, and ΔS_{univ} is the entropy change for the universe. The entropy change for the universe is the sum of the entropy changes for the system and the surroundings:

$$\Delta S_{univ} = \Delta S_{sys} + \Delta S_{surr}$$

The second law states that the entropy of the universe must increase ($\Delta S_{univ} > 0$) for a process to be spontaneous. The entropy of the *system* can decrease ($\Delta S_{sys} < 0$) as long as the entropy of the *surroundings* increases by a greater amount ($\Delta S_{surr} > -\Delta S_{sys}$), so that the overall entropy of the *universe* undergoes a net increase.

For liquid water freezing or water vapor condensing, we know that the change in entropy for the system (ΔS_{sys}) is negative, as we discussed in Section 19.4. For ΔS_{univ} to be positive, therefore, ΔS_{surr} must be positive and greater in absolute value (or magnitude) than ΔS_{sys}, as shown graphically here:

$$\Delta S_{univ} = \Delta S_{sys} + \Delta S_{surr}$$

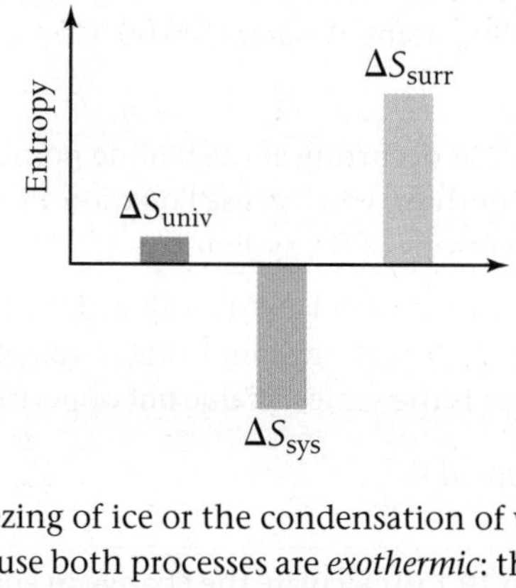

Even though (as we saw earlier) enthalpy by itself cannot determine spontaneity, the increase in the entropy of the surroundings caused by the release of heat explains why exothermic processes are so *often* spontaneous.

But why does the freezing of ice or the condensation of water increase the entropy of the surroundings? Because both processes are *exothermic*: they give off heat to the surroundings. Because we think of entropy as the dispersal or randomization of energy, *the release of heat energy by the system disperses that energy into the surroundings, increasing the entropy of the surroundings*. The freezing of water below 0 °C and the condensation of water vapor on a cold night both increase the entropy of the universe because the heat given off to the surroundings increases the entropy of the surroundings to a sufficient degree to overcome the entropy decrease in the water.

Summarizing Entropy Changes in the Surroundings:

- An exothermic process increases the entropy of the surroundings.
- An endothermic process decreases the entropy of the surroundings.

The Temperature Dependence of ΔS_{surr}

We have just seen how the freezing of water increases the entropy of the surroundings by dispersing heat energy into the surroundings. Yet we know that the freezing of water is not spontaneous at all temperatures. The freezing of water becomes *nonspontaneous* above 0 °C. Why? Because the magnitude of the increase in the entropy of the surroundings due to the dispersal of energy into the surroundings is *temperature dependent.*

The greater the temperature, the smaller the increase in entropy for a given amount of energy dispersed into the surroundings. Recall that the units of entropy are joules per kelvin: energy units divided by temperature units. As we have seen, *entropy is a measure of energy dispersal (joules) per unit temperature (kelvins).* The higher the temperature, the lower the amount of entropy for a given amount of energy dispersed. We can understand the temperature dependence of entropy changes due to heat flow with a simple analogy. Imagine that you have \$1000 to give away. If you gave the \$1000 to a millionaire, the impact on his net worth would be negligible (because he already has so much money). If you gave the same \$1000 to a poor man, however, his net worth would change substantially (because he has so little money). Similarly, if you disperse 1000 J of energy into surroundings that are hot, the entropy increase is small (because the impact of the 1000 J is small on surroundings that already contain a lot of energy). If you disperse the same 1000 J of energy into surroundings that are cold, however, the entropy increase is large (because the impact of the 1000 J is great on surroundings that contain little energy). For this same reason, the impact of the heat released to the surroundings by the freezing of water depends on the temperature of the surroundings—the higher the temperature, the smaller the impact.

We can now understand why water spontaneously freezes at low temperature but not at high temperature. For the freezing of liquid water into ice, the change in entropy of the system is negative at all temperatures:

$$\Delta S_{univ} = \Delta S_{sys} + \Delta S_{surr}$$

ΔS_{sys}: Negative

ΔS_{surr}: Positive and large at low temperature; Positive and small at high temperature

At low temperatures, on one hand, the decrease in entropy of the system is overcome by the large increase in the entropy of the surroundings (a positive quantity), resulting in a positive ΔS_{univ} and a spontaneous process. At high temperatures, on the other hand, the decrease in entropy of the system is not overcome by the increase in entropy of the surroundings (because the magnitude of the positive ΔS_{surr} is smaller at higher temperatures), resulting in a negative ΔS_{univ}; therefore, the freezing of water is not spontaneous at high temperature as shown graphically in the margin at right.

$$\Delta S_{univ} = \Delta S_{sys} + \Delta S_{surr} \quad \text{(for water freezing)}$$

Low Temperature: Spontaneous

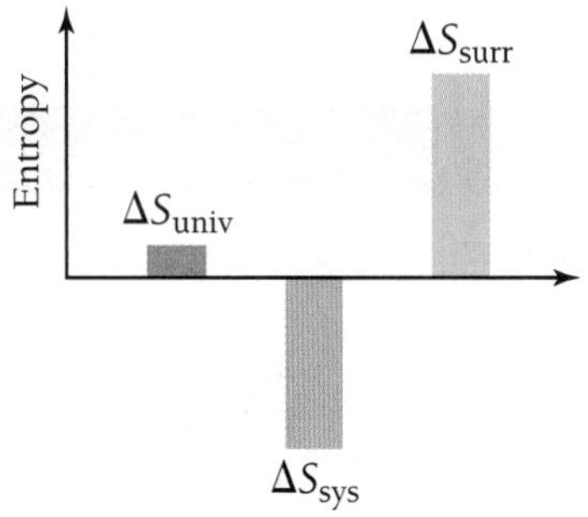

High Temperature: Nonspontaneous

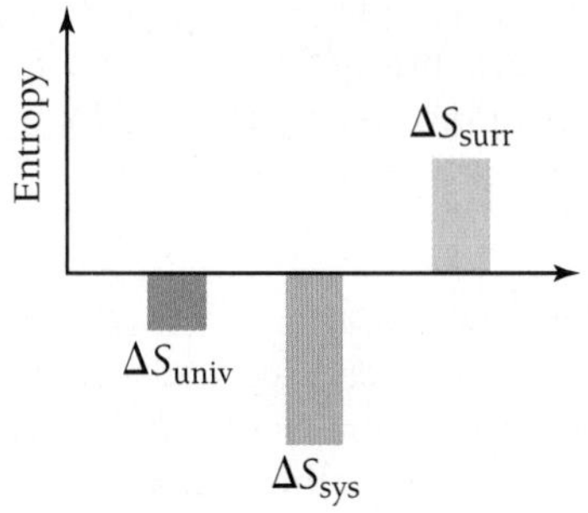

Quantifying Entropy Changes in the Surroundings

We have seen that when a system exchanges heat with the surroundings, it changes the entropy of the surroundings. In Section 19.4, we saw that, at constant temperature, we can use Equation 19.1 ($\Delta S = q_{rev}/T$)

to quantify the entropy change in the system. We can use the same equation to quantify entropy changes in the surroundings. In other words, the change in entropy of the surroundings depends on: (a) the amount of heat transferred into or out of the surroundings; and (b) the temperature of the surroundings.

Since the surroundings are usually an infinitely large bath at constant temperature, the heat transferred into or out of that bath under conditions of constant pressure (where only PV work is allowed) is simply $-\Delta H_{sys}$. The negative sign reflects that, according to the first law of thermodynamics, any heat leaving the system must go into the surroundings and vice versa ($q_{sys} = -q_{surr}$). If we incorporate this idea into Equation 19.1, we get the following equation:

$$\Delta S_{surr} = \frac{-\Delta H_{sys}}{T} \qquad \text{(constant } P, T) \qquad [19.2]$$

For any chemical or physical process occurring at constant temperature and pressure, the entropy change of the surroundings is equal to the heat dispersed into or out of the surroundings ($-\Delta H_{sys}$) divided by the temperature of the surroundings in kelvins. Notice that:

- A process that emits heat into the surroundings (ΔH_{sys} negative) *increases* the entropy of the surroundings (positive ΔS_{surr}).
- A process that absorbs heat from the surroundings (ΔH_{sys} positive) *decreases* the entropy of the surroundings (negative ΔS_{surr}).
- The magnitude of the change in entropy of the surroundings is proportional to the magnitude of ΔH_{sys}.

Equation 19.1 gives us insight into why exothermic processes have a tendency to be spontaneous at low temperatures—they increase the entropy of the surroundings. As temperature increases, however, a given negative ΔH_{sys} produces a smaller positive ΔS_{surr}; for this reason, exothermicity becomes less of a determining factor for spontaneity as temperature increases.

WATCH **NOW!**

INTERACTIVE WORKED EXAMPLE 19.3

EXAMPLE 19.3 Calculating Entropy Changes in the Surroundings

Consider the combustion of propane gas:

$$C_3H_8(g) + 5\,O_2(g) \longrightarrow 3\,CO_2(g) + 4\,H_2O(g) \qquad \Delta H_{rxn} = -2044 \text{ kJ}$$

(a) Calculate the entropy change in the surroundings when this reaction occurs at 25 °C.
(b) Determine the sign of the entropy change for the system.
(c) Determine the sign of the entropy change for the universe. Is the reaction spontaneous?

SOLUTION

(a) The entropy change of the surroundings is given by Equation 19.2. Substitute the value of ΔH_{rxn} and the temperature in kelvins and calculate ΔS_{surr}.	$T = 273 + 25 = 298\text{ K}$ $\Delta S_{surr} = \frac{-\Delta H_{rxn}}{T}$ $= \frac{-(-2044\text{ kJ})}{298\text{ K}}$ $= +6.86\text{ kJ/K}$ $= +6.86 \times 10^3\text{ J/K}$
(b) Determine the number of moles of gas on each side of the reaction. An increase in the number of moles of gas implies a positive ΔS_{sys}.	$\underbrace{C_3H_8(g) + 5\,O_2(g)}_{6\text{ mol gas}} \longrightarrow \underbrace{3\,CO_2(g) + 4\,H_2O(g)}_{7\text{ mol gas}}$ ΔS_{sys} is positive.

(c) The change in entropy of the universe is the sum of the entropy changes of the system and the surroundings. If the entropy changes of the system and surroundings are both the same sign, the entropy change for the universe also has the same sign.

$$\Delta S_{univ} = \Delta S_{sys} + \Delta S_{surr}$$

Positive Positive

Therefore, ΔS_{univ} is positive and the reaction is spontaneous.

FOR PRACTICE 19.3 Consider the reaction between nitrogen and oxygen gas to form dinitrogen monoxide:

$$2\,N_2(g) + O_2(g) \longrightarrow 2\,N_2O(g) \qquad \Delta H_{rxn} = +163.2\text{ kJ}$$

(a) Calculate the entropy change in the surroundings when this reaction occurs at 25 °C.

(b) Determine the sign of the entropy change for the system.

(c) Determine the sign of the entropy change for the universe. Is the reaction spontaneous?

FOR MORE PRACTICE 19.3 For a reaction, $\Delta H_{rxn} = -107$ kJ and $\Delta S_{rxn} = 285$ J/K. At what temperature is the change in entropy for this reaction equal to the change in entropy for the surroundings?

19.4 Cc Conceptual Connection ANSWER **NOW!**

ENTROPY AND BIOLOGICAL SYSTEMS By absorbing energy from their surroundings and synthesizing large, complex biological molecules, plants and animals tend to concentrate energy, not disperse it. How can this happen?

(a) Biological systems only appear to concentrate energy. In reality, large, complex biological molecules have more entropy than the substances from which they are composed.

(b) Biological systems can decrease their own entropy by creating more entropy in their surroundings.

(c) Biological systems are an exception to the second law of thermodynamics.

19.6 Gibbs Free Energy

Equation 19.2 establishes a relationship between the enthalpy change in a system and the entropy change in the surroundings. Recall that for any process the entropy change of the universe is the sum of the entropy change of the system and the entropy change of the surroundings:

$$\Delta S_{univ} = \Delta S_{sys} + \Delta S_{surr} \qquad [19.3]$$

Combining Equation 19.3 with Equation 19.2 gives us the following relationship at constant temperature and pressure:

$$\Delta S_{univ} = \Delta S_{sys} - \frac{\Delta H_{sys}}{T} \qquad [19.4]$$

Using Equation 19.4, we can calculate ΔS_{univ} while focusing only on the *system*. If we multiply Equation 19.4 by $-T$, we arrive at the equation:

$$\begin{aligned} -T\Delta S_{univ} &= -T\Delta S_{sys} + \cancel{T}\frac{\Delta H_{sys}}{\cancel{T}} \\ &= \Delta H_{sys} - T\Delta S_{sys} \qquad [19.5] \end{aligned}$$

If we drop the subscript *sys* (from now on ΔH and ΔS without subscripts mean ΔH_{sys} and ΔS_{sys}) we get the equation:

$$-T\Delta S_{univ} = \Delta H - T\Delta S \qquad [19.6]$$

The right-hand side of Equation 19.6 represents the change in a thermodynamic function called *Gibbs free energy*. The formal definition of **Gibbs free energy (*G*)** is:

$$G = H - TS \qquad [19.7]$$

where H is enthalpy, T is the temperature in kelvins, and S is entropy. The *change* in Gibbs free energy, symbolized by ΔG, is expressed as follows (at constant temperature):

$$\Delta G = \Delta H - T\Delta S \qquad [19.8]$$

If we combine Equations 19.6 and 19.8, we have an equation that makes clear the significance of ΔG:

$$\Delta G = -T\Delta S_{univ} \qquad \text{(constant } T, P\text{)} \qquad [19.9]$$

The change in Gibbs free energy for a process occurring at constant temperature and pressure is proportional to the negative of ΔS_{univ}. Since ΔS_{univ} is a criterion for spontaneity, ΔG is also a criterion for spontaneity (although opposite in sign). In fact, Gibbs free energy is also called *chemical potential* because it is analogous to mechanical potential energy discussed earlier. Just as mechanical systems tend toward lower potential energy, so chemical systems tend toward lower Gibbs free energy (toward lower chemical potential) (Figure 19.5▼).

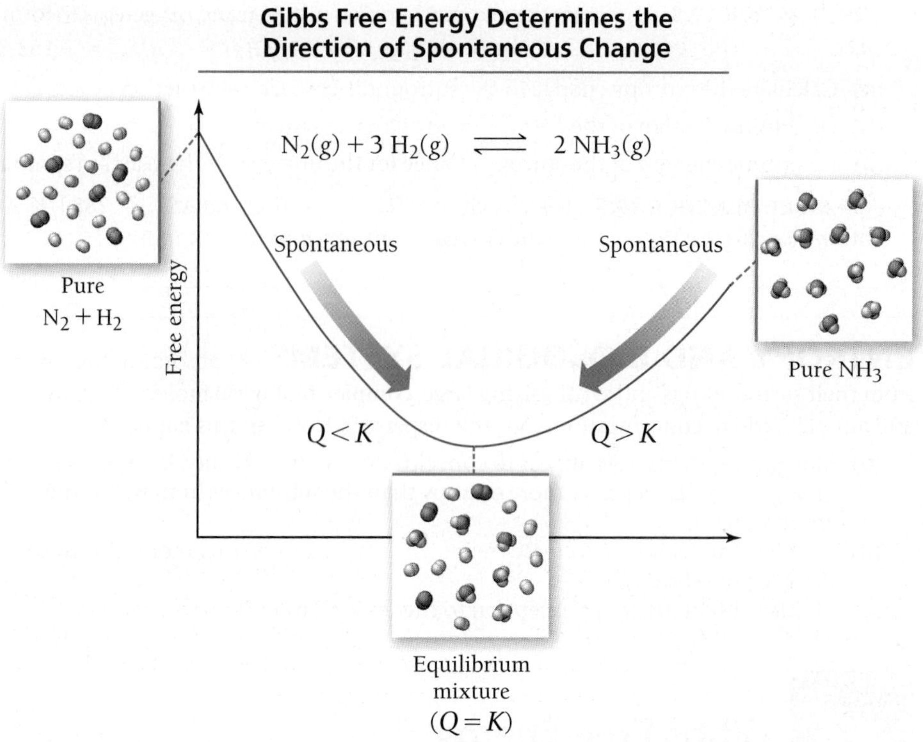

▶ **FIGURE 19.5 Gibbs Free Energy** Gibbs free energy is also called chemical potential because it determines the direction of spontaneous change for chemical systems.

Summarizing Gibbs Free Energy (at Constant Temperature and Pressure):

- ΔG is proportional to the negative of ΔS_{univ}.
- A decrease in Gibbs free energy ($\Delta G < 0$) corresponds to a spontaneous process.
- An increase in Gibbs free energy ($\Delta G > 0$) corresponds to a nonspontaneous process.

Notice that we can calculate changes in Gibbs free energy solely with reference to the system. So, to determine whether a process is spontaneous, we only have to find the change in *entropy* for the system (ΔS) and the change in *enthalpy* for the system (ΔH). We can then predict the spontaneity of the process at any temperature. In Chapter 7, we learned how to calculate changes in enthalpy (ΔH) for chemical reactions. In Section 19.7, we learn how to calculate changes in entropy (ΔS) for chemical reactions. We can then use those two quantities to calculate changes in free energy (ΔG) for chemical reactions and predict their spontaneity (Section 19.8). Before we move on to these topics, let's examine some examples that demonstrate how ΔH, ΔS, and T affect the spontaneity of chemical processes.

WATCH **NOW!**

KEY CONCEPT VIDEO 19.6
The Effect of ΔH, ΔS, and T on Reaction Spontaneity

The Effect of ΔH, ΔS, and T on Spontaneity

Case 1: ΔH Negative, ΔS Positive

If a reaction is exothermic ($\Delta H < 0$) and if the change in entropy for the reaction is positive ($\Delta S > 0$), then the change in free energy is negative at all temperatures and the reaction is spontaneous at all temperatures:

$$\Delta G = \Delta H - T\,\Delta S$$

Negative at all temperatures (ΔG) | Negative (ΔH) | Positive (ΔS)

As an example, consider the dissociation of N_2O:

$$\underset{\text{2 mol gas}}{2\,N_2O(g)} \longrightarrow \underset{\text{3 mol gas}}{2\,N_2(g) + O_2(g)} \qquad \Delta H^\circ_{rxn} = -163.2\text{ kJ}$$

The change in *enthalpy* is negative—heat is emitted, increasing the entropy of the surroundings. The change in *entropy* for the reaction is positive, which means that the entropy of the system increases. (We can see that the change in entropy is positive from the balanced equation—the number of moles of gas increases.) Since the entropy of both the system and the surroundings increases, the entropy of the universe must also increase, making the reaction spontaneous at all temperatures.

Recall from Chapter 7 that ΔH° represents the standard enthalpy change. The definition of the standard state was first given in Section 7.9 and is summarized in Section 19.7.

Case 2: ΔH Positive, ΔS Negative

If a reaction is endothermic ($\Delta H > 0$), and if the change in entropy for the reaction is negative ($\Delta S < 0$), then the change in free energy is positive at all temperatures and the reaction is nonspontaneous at all temperatures:

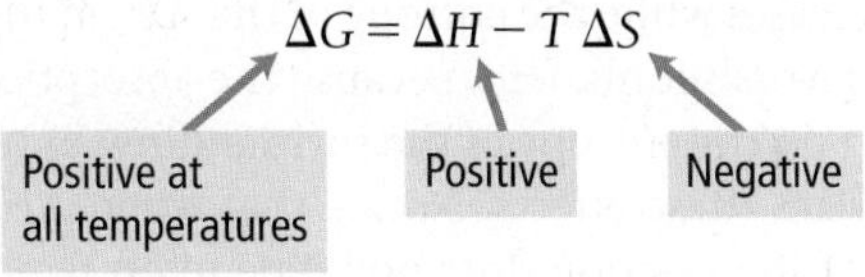

As an example, consider the formation of ozone from oxygen:

$$\underset{\text{3 mol gas}}{3\,O_2(g)} \longrightarrow \underset{\text{2 mol gas}}{2\,O_3(g)} \qquad \Delta H^\circ_{rxn} = +285.4\text{ kJ}$$

The change in *enthalpy* is positive—heat is therefore absorbed, *decreasing* the entropy of the surroundings. The change in *entropy* is negative, which means that the entropy of the system decreases. (We can see that the change in entropy is negative from the balanced equation—the number of moles of gas decreases.) Since the entropy of both the system and the surroundings decreases, the entropy of the universe must also decrease, making the reaction nonspontaneous at all temperatures.

Case 3: ΔH Negative, ΔS Negative

If a reaction is exothermic ($\Delta H < 0$) and if the change in entropy for the reaction is negative ($\Delta S < 0$), then the sign of the change in free energy depends on temperature. The reaction is spontaneous at low temperature but nonspontaneous at high temperature:

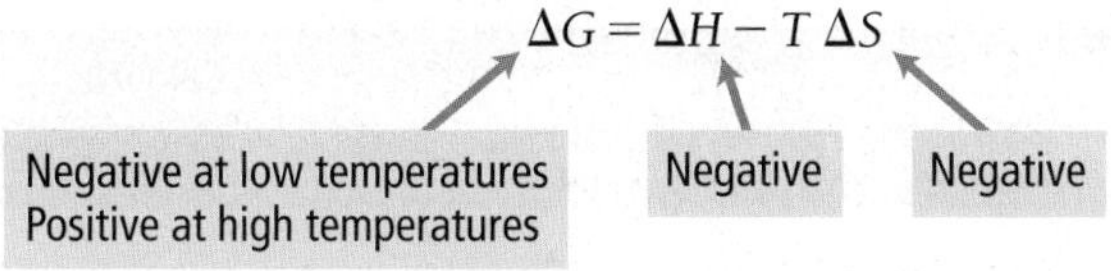

As an example, consider the freezing of liquid water to form ice:

$$H_2O(l) \longrightarrow H_2O(s) \qquad \Delta H^\circ = -6.01\text{ kJ}$$

The change in *enthalpy* is negative—heat is emitted, increasing the entropy of the surroundings. The change in *entropy* is negative, which means that the entropy of the system decreases. (We can see that the change in entropy is negative from the balanced equation—a liquid turns into a solid.)

Unlike the two previous cases, where the changes in *entropy* of the system and of the surroundings had the *same* sign, the changes here are *opposite* in sign. Therefore, the sign of the change in free energy depends on the relative magnitudes of the two changes. At a low enough temperature, the heat emitted into the surroundings causes a large entropy change in the surroundings, making the process spontaneous. At high temperature, the same amount of heat is dispersed into warmer surroundings, so the positive entropy change in the surroundings is smaller, resulting in a nonspontaneous process.

Case 4: ΔH Positive, ΔS Positive

If a reaction is endothermic ($\Delta H > 0$), and if the change in entropy for the reaction is positive ($\Delta S > 0$), then the sign of the change in free energy again depends on temperature. The reaction is nonspontaneous at low temperature but spontaneous at high temperature:

$$\Delta G = \Delta H - T\,\Delta S$$

Positive at low temperatures
Negative at high temperatures

Positive

Positive

As an example, consider the vaporizing of liquid water to gaseous water:

$$H_2O(l) \longrightarrow H_2O(g) \qquad \Delta H^\circ = +40.7 \text{ kJ (at 100 °C)}$$

The change in *enthalpy* is positive—heat is absorbed from the surroundings, so the entropy of the surroundings decreases. The change in *entropy* is positive, which means that the entropy of the system increases. (We can see that the change in entropy is positive from the balanced equation—a liquid turns into a gas.) The changes in entropy of the system and the surroundings again have opposite signs, only this time the entropy of the surroundings decreases while the entropy of the system increases. In cases such as this, high temperature favors spontaneity because the absorption of heat from the surroundings has less effect on the entropy of the surroundings as temperature increases.

Table 19.1 summarizes these effects. Notice that when ΔH and ΔS have opposite signs, the spontaneity of the reaction does not depend on temperature. *When ΔH and ΔS have the same sign, however, the spontaneity does depend on temperature.* The temperature at which the reaction changes from being spontaneous to being nonspontaneous (or vice versa) is the temperature at which ΔG changes sign, which we can find by setting $\Delta G = 0$ and solving for T, as shown in part b of Example 19.4.

TABLE 19.1 ■ The Effect of ΔH, ΔS, and T on Spontaneity

ΔH	ΔS	Low Temperature	High Temperature	Example
−	+	Spontaneous ($\Delta G < 0$)	Spontaneous ($\Delta G < 0$)	$2\,N_2O(g) \longrightarrow 2\,N_2(g) + O_2(g)$
+	−	Nonspontaneous ($\Delta G > 0$)	Nonspontaneous ($\Delta G > 0$)	$3\,O_2(g) \longrightarrow 2\,O_3(g)$
−	−	Spontaneous ($\Delta G < 0$)	Nonspontaneous ($\Delta G > 0$)	$H_2O(l) \longrightarrow H_2O(s)$
+	+	Nonspontaneous ($\Delta G > 0$)	Spontaneous ($\Delta G < 0$)	$H_2O(l) \longrightarrow H_2O(g)$

WATCH **NOW!**

INTERACTIVE WORKED EXAMPLE 19.4

EXAMPLE 19.4 Calculating Gibbs Free Energy Changes and Predicting Spontaneity from ΔH and ΔS

Consider the reaction for the decomposition of carbon tetrachloride gas:

$$CCl_4(g) \longrightarrow C(s, \text{graphite}) + 2\,Cl_2(g) \qquad \Delta H = +95.7 \text{ kJ}; \ \Delta S = +142.2 \text{ J/K}$$

(a) Calculate ΔG at 25 °C and determine whether the reaction is spontaneous.

(b) If the reaction is not spontaneous at 25 °C, determine at what temperature (if any) the reaction becomes spontaneous.

SOLUTION

(a) Use Equation 19.8 to calculate ΔG from the given values of ΔH and ΔS. The temperature must be in kelvins. *Be sure to express both ΔH and ΔS in the same units (usually joules).*	$T = 273 + 25 = 298 \text{ K}$ $\Delta G = \Delta H - T\Delta S$ $= 95.7 \times 10^3 \text{ J} - (298 \cancel{\text{K}})142.2 \text{ J}/\cancel{\text{K}}$ $= 95.7 \times 10^3 \text{ J} - 42.4 \times 10^3 \text{ J}$ $= +53.3 \times 10^3 \text{ J}$ The reaction is not spontaneous.
(b) Since ΔS is positive, ΔG becomes more negative with increasing temperature. To determine the temperature at which the reaction becomes spontaneous, use Equation 19.8 to find the temperature at which ΔG changes from positive to negative (set $\Delta G = 0$ and solve for T). The reaction is spontaneous above this temperature.	$\Delta G = \Delta H - T\Delta S$ $0 = 95.7 \times 10^3 \text{ J} - (T)142.2 \text{ J/K}$ $T = \dfrac{95.7 \times 10^3 \cancel{\text{J}}}{142.2 \cancel{\text{J}}/\text{K}}$ $= 673 \text{ K}$

FOR PRACTICE 19.4 Consider the reaction:

$$C_2H_4(g) + H_2(g) \longrightarrow C_2H_6(g) \qquad \Delta H = -137.5\ \text{kJ};\ \Delta S = -120.5\ \text{J/K}$$

Calculate ΔG at 25 °C and determine whether the reaction is spontaneous. Does ΔG become more negative or more positive as the temperature increases?

19.5 Cc Conceptual Connection ANSWER **NOW!**

ΔH, ΔS, AND ΔG Which statement is true regarding the sublimation of dry ice (solid CO_2)?

(a) ΔH is positive, ΔS is positive, and ΔG is positive at low temperatures and negative at high temperatures.
(b) ΔH is negative, ΔS is negative, and ΔG is negative at low temperatures and positive at high temperatures.
(c) ΔH is negative, ΔS is positive, and ΔG is negative at all temperatures.
(d) ΔH is positive, ΔS is negative, and ΔG is positive at all temperatures.

19.7 Entropy Changes in Chemical Reactions: Calculating ΔS°_{rxn}

WATCH **NOW!**
KEY CONCEPT VIDEO 19.7 *Standard Molar Entropies*

In Chapter 7, we learned how to calculate standard changes in enthalpy (ΔH°_{rxn}) for chemical reactions. We now turn to calculating standard changes in *entropy* for chemical reactions.

Defining Standard States and Standard Entropy Changes

Recall from Section 7.9 that the standard enthalpy change for a reaction (ΔH°_{rxn}) is the change in enthalpy for a process in which all reactants and products are in their standard states. Recall also the definition of the standard state:

- *For a Gas*: The standard state for a gas is the pure gas at a pressure of exactly 1 atm.
- *For a Liquid or Solid*: The standard state for a liquid or solid is the pure substance in its most stable form at a pressure of 1 atm and at the temperature of interest (often taken to be 25 °C).
- *For a Substance in Solution*: The standard state for a substance in solution is a concentration of 1 M.

The standard state has recently been changed to a pressure of 1 bar, which is very close to (1 atm = 1.013 bar). Both standards are now in common use.

We define the **standard entropy change for a reaction (ΔS°_{rxn})** as the change in *entropy* for a process in which all reactants and products are in their standard states. Since entropy is a function of state, the standard change in entropy is therefore the standard entropy of the products minus the standard entropy of the reactants:

$$\Delta S^\circ_{rxn} = S^\circ_{products} - S^\circ_{reactants}$$

But how do we find the standard entropies of the reactants and products? Recall from Chapter 7 that we defined *standard molar enthalpies of formation* (ΔH°_f) to use in calculating ΔH°_{rxn}. We now need to define **standard molar entropies (S°)** to use in calculating ΔS°_{rxn}.

Standard Molar Entropies (S°) and the Third Law of Thermodynamics

In Chapter 7, we defined a *relative* zero for enthalpy. To do this, we assigned a value of zero to the standard enthalpy of formation for an element in its standard state. This was necessary because absolute values of enthalpy cannot be determined. In other words, for

Perfect crystal at 0 K
W = 1 S = 0

▲ **FIGURE 19.6 Zero Entropy** A perfect crystal at 0 K has only one possible way to arrange its components.

enthalpy, there is no absolute zero against which to measure all other values; therefore, we always have to rely on enthalpy changes from an arbitrarily assigned standard (the elements in their standard states and most stable forms).

For entropy, however, *there is an absolute zero.* The absolute zero of entropy is established by the **third law of thermodynamics**, which states:

The entropy of a perfect crystal at absolute zero (0 K) is zero.

A perfect crystal at a temperature of absolute zero has only one possible way ($W = 1$) to arrange its components (Figure 19.6◀). Based on Boltzmann's definition of entropy ($S = k \ln W$), its entropy is zero ($S = k \ln 1 = 0$).

We can measure all entropy values against the absolute zero of entropy as defined by the third law. Table 19.2 lists values of standard entropies at 25 °C for selected substances. A more complete list is in Appendix IIB. Standard entropy values are listed in units of joules per mole per kelvin (J/mol · K). The units of mole in the denominator are required because *entropy is an extensive property*—it depends on the amount of the substance.

TABLE 19.2 ■ Standard Molar Entropy Values ($S°$) for Selected Substances at 298 K

Substance	$S°$(J/mol · K)	Substance	$S°$(J/mol · K)	Substance	$S°$(J/mol · K)
Gases		**Liquids**		**Solids**	
$H_2(g)$	130.7	$H_2O(l)$	70.0	$MgO(s)$	27.0
$Ar(g)$	154.8	$CH_3OH(l)$	126.8	$Fe(s)$	27.3
$CH_4(g)$	186.3	$Br_2(l)$	152.2	$Li(s)$	29.1
$H_2O(g)$	188.8	$C_6H_6(l)$	173.4	$Cu(s)$	33.2
$N_2(g)$	191.6			$Na(s)$	51.3
$NH_3(g)$	192.8			$K(s)$	64.7
$F_2(g)$	202.8			$NaCl(s)$	72.1
$O_2(g)$	205.2			$CaCO_3(s)$	91.7
$Cl_2(g)$	223.1			$FeCl_3(s)$	142.3
$C_2H_4(g)$	219.3				

At 25 °C, the standard molar entropy of any substance is the energy dispersed into one mole of that substance at 25 °C, which depends on the number of "places" to put energy within the substance. The factors that affect the number of "places" to put energy—and therefore the standard entropy—include the state of the substance, the molar mass of the substance, the particular allotrope, its molecular complexity, and its extent of dissolution. Let's examine each of these separately.

Some elements exist in two or more forms, called *allotropes*, within the same state.

Relative Standard Entropies: Gases, Liquids, and Solids

As we saw in Section 19.3, the entropy of a gas is generally greater than the entropy of a liquid, which is in turn greater than the entropy of a solid. We can see these trends in the tabulated values of standard entropies. For example, consider the relative standard entropies of liquid water and gaseous water at 25 °C:

	$S°$(J/mol · K)
$H_2O(l)$	70.0
$H_2O(g)$	188.8

Gaseous water has a much greater standard entropy because, as we discussed in Section 19.3, it has more energetically equivalent ways to arrange its components, which in turn results in greater energy dispersal at 25 °C.

Relative Standard Entropies: Molar Mass

Consider the standard entropies of the noble gases at 25 °C:

	S° (J/mol · K)	
He(g)	126.2	
Ne(g)	146.1	
Ar(g)	154.8	
Kr(g)	163.8	
Xe(g)	169.4	

The more massive the noble gas, the greater its entropy at 25 °C. A complete explanation of why entropy increases with increasing molar mass is beyond the scope of this book. Briefly, the energy states associated with the motion of heavy atoms are more closely spaced than those of lighter atoms. The more closely spaced energy states allow for greater dispersal of energy at a given temperature and therefore greater entropy. This trend is true only for elements in the same state. (The effect of a state change—from a liquid to a gas, for example—is far greater than the effect of molar mass.)

Relative Standard Entropies: Allotropes

As mentioned previously, some elements can exist in two or more forms—called *allotropes*—in the same state of matter. For example, the allotropes of carbon include diamond and graphite—both solid forms of carbon. Because the arrangement of atoms within these forms is different, their standard molar entropies are different:

	S° (J/mol · K)	
C(s, diamond)	2.4	
C(s, graphite)	5.7	

In diamond, the atoms are constrained by chemical bonds in a highly restricted three-dimensional crystal structure. In graphite, the atoms bond together in sheets, but the sheets have freedom to slide past each other. The less constrained structure of graphite results in more "places" to put energy and therefore greater entropy compared to diamond.

Relative Standard Entropies: Molecular Complexity

For a given state of matter, entropy generally increases with increasing molecular complexity. For example, consider the standard entropies of argon and nitrogen monoxide gas:

	Molar Mass (g/mol)	$S°$(J/mol · K)
Ar(*g*)	39.948	154.8
NO(*g*)	30.006	210.8

Ar has a greater molar mass than NO, yet it has less entropy at 25 °C. Why? Molecules generally have more "places" to put energy than do atoms. In a gaseous sample of argon, on one hand, the only form that energy can take is the translational motion of the atoms. In a gaseous sample of NO, on the other hand, energy can take the form of translational motion, rotational motion, and (at high enough temperatures) vibrational motions of the molecules (Figure 19.7▼). Therefore, for a given state, molecules generally have a greater entropy than free atoms.

▶ **FIGURE 19.7 "Places" for Energy in Gaseous NO** Energy can be contained in translational motion, rotational motion, and (at high enough temperatures) vibrational motion.

Similarly, more complex molecules generally have more entropy than simpler ones. For example, consider the standard entropies of carbon monoxide and ethene gas:

	Molar Mass (g/mol)	$S°$(J/mol · K)
CO(*g*)	28.01	197.7
C_2H_4(*g*)	28.05	219.3

These two substances have nearly the same molar mass, but the greater complexity of C_2H_4 results in a greater molar entropy. When molecular complexity and molar mass both increase (as is often the case), molar entropy also increases, as demonstrated by the oxides of nitrogen:

	$S°$(J/mol · K)
NO(*g*)	210.8
NO_2(*g*)	240.1
N_2O_4(*g*)	304.4

The increasing molecular complexity as we move down this list, as well as the increasing molar mass, results in more "places" to put energy and therefore greater entropy.

Relative Standard Entropies: Dissolution

The standard entropies for aqueous solutions are for the solution in its standard state, which is defined as having a concentration of 1 M.

The dissolution of a crystalline solid into solution usually results in an increase in entropy. For example, consider the standard entropies of solid and aqueous potassium chlorate:

	$S°$(J/mol · K)
$KClO_3$(*s*)	143.1
$KClO_3$(*aq*)	265.7

When solid potassium chlorate dissolves in water, the energy that was concentrated within the crystal becomes dispersed throughout the entire solution. The greater energy dispersal results in greater entropy.

STANDARD ENTROPIES Arrange these gases in order of increasing standard molar entropy: SO_3, Kr, Cl_2.

(a) $Kr < Cl_2 < SO_3$ **(b)** $Kr < SO_3 < Cl_2$

(c) $SO_3 < Cl_2 < Kr$ **(d)** $Cl_2 < Kr < SO_3$

19.6 Cc Conceptual Connection ANSWER **NOW!**

Calculating the Standard Entropy Change (ΔS°_{rxn}) for a Reaction

Since entropy is a state function, and since standard entropies for many common substances are tabulated, we can calculate the standard entropy change for a chemical reaction by calculating the difference in entropy between the products and the reactants. More specifically,

To calculate ΔS°_{rxn}, subtract the standard entropies of the reactants multiplied by their stoichiometric coefficients from the standard entropies of the products multiplied by their stoichiometric coefficients. In the form of an equation:

$$\Delta S^\circ_{rxn} = \sum n_p S^\circ(\text{products}) - \sum n_r S^\circ(\text{reactants}) \qquad [19.10]$$

In Equation 19.10, n_p represents the stoichiometric coefficients of the products, n_r represents the stoichiometric coefficients of the reactants, and S° represents the standard entropies. Keep in mind when using this equation that, *unlike enthalpies of formation, which are zero for elements in their standard states, standard entropies are always nonzero at* 25 °C. Example 19.5 demonstrates the application of Equation 19.10.

WATCH **NOW!**
INTERACTIVE WORKED EXAMPLE 19.5

EXAMPLE 19.5 Calculating Standard Entropy Changes (ΔS°_{rxn})

Calculate ΔS°_{rxn} for the balanced chemical equation:

$$4\,NH_3(g) + 5\,O_2(g) \longrightarrow 4\,NO(g) + 6\,H_2O(g)$$

SOLUTION

Begin by looking up the standard entropy for each reactant and product in Appendix IIB. Always note the correct state—(g), (l), (aq), or (s)—for each reactant and product.

Reactant or product	S°(in J/mol·K)
$NH_3(g)$	192.8
$O_2(g)$	205.2
$NO(g)$	210.8
$H_2O(g)$	188.8

Calculate ΔS°_{rxn} by substituting the appropriate values into Equation 19.10. Remember to include the stoichiometric coefficients in your calculation.

$$\begin{aligned}\Delta S^\circ_{rxn} &= \sum n_p S^\circ(\text{products}) - \sum n_r S^\circ(\text{reactants})\\ &= [4(S^\circ_{NO(g)}) + 6(S^\circ_{H_2O(g)})] - [4(S^\circ_{NH_3(g)}) + 5(S^\circ_{O_2(g)})]\\ &= [4(210.8\,J/K) + 6(188.8\,J/K)] - [4(192.8\,J/K) + 5(205.2\,J/K)]\\ &= 1976.0\,J/K - 1797.2\,J/K = 178.8\,J/K\end{aligned}$$

CHECK Notice that ΔS°_{rxn} is positive, as you would expect for a reaction in which the number of moles of gas increases.

FOR PRACTICE 19.5 Calculate ΔS°_{rxn} for the balanced chemical equation:

$$2\,H_2S(g) + 3\,O_2(g) \longrightarrow 2\,H_2O(g) + 2\,SO_2(g)$$

19.8 Free Energy Changes in Chemical Reactions: Calculating ΔG°_{rxn}

In the previous section, we learned how to calculate the standard change in entropy for a chemical reaction (ΔS°_{rxn}). However, the criterion for spontaneity at standard conditions is the **standard change in free energy (ΔG°_{rxn})**. In this section, we examine three methods to calculate the standard change in free energy for a reaction (ΔG°_{rxn}). In the first method, we calculate ΔH°_{rxn} and ΔS°_{rxn} from tabulated values of ΔH°_f and S°, and then use the relationship $\Delta G^\circ_{rxn} = \Delta H^\circ_{rxn} - T\Delta S^\circ_{rxn}$ to calculate ΔG°_{rxn}. In the second method, we use tabulated values of free energies of formation to calculate ΔG°_{rxn} directly. In the third method, we determine the free energy change for a stepwise reaction from the free energy changes of each of the steps. At the end of this section, we discuss what is "free" about free energy. Remember that ΔG°_{rxn} is extremely useful because it tells us about the spontaneity of a process at standard conditions. The more negative ΔG°_{rxn} is, the more spontaneous the process (the further it will go toward products to reach equilibrium).

Calculating Standard Free Energy Changes with $\Delta G^\circ_{rxn} = \Delta H^\circ_{rxn} - T\Delta S^\circ_{rxn}$

In Chapter 7 (Section 7.9), we used tabulated values of standard enthalpies of formation to calculate ΔH°_{rxn}. In the previous section of this chapter, we used tabulated values of standard entropies to calculate ΔS°_{rxn}. We can use these calculated values of ΔH°_{rxn} and ΔS°_{rxn} to determine the standard free energy change for a reaction by using the equation:

$$\Delta G^\circ_{rxn} = \Delta H^\circ_{rxn} - T\Delta S^\circ_{rxn} \qquad [19.11]$$

Since tabulated values of standard enthalpies of formation (ΔH°_f) and standard entropies (S°) are usually applicable at 25 °C, the equation should (strictly speaking) be valid only when $T = 298$ K (25 °C). However, the changes in ΔH°_{rxn} and ΔS°_{rxn} over a limited temperature range are small when compared to the changes in the value of the temperature itself. Therefore, we can use Equation 19.11 to estimate changes in free energy at temperatures other than 25 °C.

WATCH **NOW!**

INTERACTIVE WORKED EXAMPLE 19.6

EXAMPLE 19.6 Calculating the Standard Change in Free Energy for a Reaction Using $\Delta G^\circ_{rxn} = \Delta H^\circ_{rxn} - T\Delta S^\circ_{rxn}$

One of the possible initial steps in the formation of acid rain is the oxidation of the pollutant SO_2 to SO_3 by the reaction:

$$SO_2(g) + \tfrac{1}{2}O_2(g) \longrightarrow SO_3(g)$$

Calculate ΔG°_{rxn} at 25 °C and determine whether the reaction is spontaneous.

SOLUTION

Begin by looking up (in Appendix IIB) the standard enthalpy of formation and the standard entropy for each reactant and product.

Reactant or product	ΔH°_f (kJ/mol)	S°(J/mol·K)
$SO_2(g)$	−296.8	248.2
$O_2(g)$	0	205.2
$SO_3(g)$	−395.7	256.8

Calculate ΔH°_{rxn} using Equation 7.15.

$$\begin{aligned}\Delta H^\circ_{rxn} &= \sum n_p \Delta H^\circ_f(\text{products}) - \sum n_r \Delta H^\circ_f(\text{reactants}) \\ &= [\Delta H^\circ_{f,\,SO_3(g)}] - [\Delta H^\circ_{f,\,SO_2(g)} + \tfrac{1}{2}(\Delta H^\circ_{f,\,O_2(g)})] \\ &= -395.7\text{ kJ} - (-296.8\text{ kJ} + 0.0\text{ kJ}) = -98.9\text{ kJ}\end{aligned}$$

Calculate ΔS°_{rxn} using Equation 19.10.

$$\begin{aligned}\Delta S^\circ_{rxn} &= \sum n_p S^\circ(\text{products}) - \sum n_r S^\circ(\text{reactants}) \\ &= [S^\circ_{SO_3(g)}] - [S^\circ_{SO_2(g)} + \tfrac{1}{2}(S^\circ_{O_2(g)})] \\ &= 256.8\text{ J/K} - [248.2\text{ J/K} + \tfrac{1}{2}(205.2\text{ J/K})] = -94.0\text{ J/K}\end{aligned}$$

Calculate ΔG°_{rxn} using the calculated values of ΔH°_{rxn} and ΔS°_{rxn} and Equation 19.11. Convert the temperature to kelvins.

$$T = 25 + 273 = 298\text{ K}$$

$$\begin{aligned}\Delta G^\circ_{rxn} &= \Delta H^\circ_{rxn} - T\Delta S^\circ_{rxn} \\ &= -98.9 \times 10^3\text{ J} - 298\text{ K}(-94.0\text{ J/K}) \\ &= -70.9 \times 10^3\text{ J} = -70.9\text{ kJ}\end{aligned}$$

The reaction is spontaneous at this temperature because ΔG°_{rxn} is negative.

FOR PRACTICE 19.6 Consider the oxidation of NO to NO_2:

$$NO(g) + \tfrac{1}{2}O_2(g) \longrightarrow NO_2(g)$$

Calculate ΔG°_{rxn} at 25 °C and determine whether the reaction is spontaneous at standard conditions.

EXAMPLE 19.7 Estimating the Standard Change in Free Energy for a Reaction at a Temperature Other Than 25 °C Using $\Delta G^\circ_{rxn} = \Delta H^\circ_{rxn} - T\Delta S^\circ_{rxn}$

For the reaction in Example 19.6, estimate the value of ΔG°_{rxn} at 125 °C. Is the reaction more or less spontaneous at this elevated temperature? That is, is the value of ΔG°_{rxn} more negative (more spontaneous) or more positive (less spontaneous)?

SOLUTION

Estimate ΔG°_{rxn} at the new temperature using the calculated values of ΔH°_{rxn} and ΔS°_{rxn} from Example 19.6. For T, convert the given temperature to kelvins. Make sure to use the same units for ΔH°_{rxn} and ΔS°_{rxn} (usually joules).

$$T = 125 + 273 = 398 \text{ K}$$

$$\begin{aligned}\Delta G^\circ_{rxn} &= \Delta H^\circ_{rxn} - T\Delta S^\circ_{rxn}\\ &= -98.9 \times 10^3 \text{ J} - 398 \cancel{\text{K}}(-94.0 \text{ J}/\cancel{\text{K}})\\ &= -61.5 \times 10^3 \text{ J}\\ &= -61.5 \text{ kJ}\end{aligned}$$

Since the value of ΔG°_{rxn} at this elevated temperature is less negative (or more positive) than the value of ΔG°_{rxn} at 25 °C (which is −70.9 kJ), the reaction is less spontaneous.

FOR PRACTICE 19.7 For the reaction in For Practice 19.6, calculate the value of −70.9 kJ, at −55 °C. Is the reaction more spontaneous (more negative ΔG°_{rxn}) or less spontaneous (more positive ΔG°_{rxn}) at the lower temperature?

Calculating ΔG°_{rxn} with Tabulated Values of Free Energies of Formation

Because ΔG°_{rxn} is the *change* in free energy for a chemical reaction—the difference in free energy between the products and the reactants—and because free energy is a state function, we can calculate ΔG°_{rxn} by subtracting the free energies of the reactants of the reaction from the free energies of the products of the reaction. Also, since we are interested only in *changes* in free energy (and not in absolute values of free energy), we are free to define the *zero* of free energy as conveniently as possible. By analogy with our definition of enthalpies of formation, we define the **free energy of formation (ΔG°_f)** as follows:

> **The free energy of formation (ΔG°_f) is the change in free energy when 1 mol of a compound in its standard state forms from its constituent elements in their standard states. The free energy of formation of pure elements in their standard states is zero.**

We can measure all changes in free energy relative to pure elements in their standard states. To calculate ΔG°_{rxn}, we subtract the free energies of formation of the reactants multiplied by their stoichiometric coefficients from the free energies of formation of the products multiplied by their stoichiometric coefficients. In the form of an equation:

$$\Delta G^\circ_{rxn} = \sum n_p \Delta G^\circ_f(\text{products}) - \sum n_r \Delta G^\circ_f(\text{reactants}) \quad [19.12]$$

In Equation 19.12, n_p represents the stoichiometric coefficients of the products, n_r represents the stoichiometric coefficients of the reactants, and ΔG°_f represents the standard free energies of formation.

Table 19.3 lists ΔG°_f values for selected substances. You can find a more complete list in Appendix IIB. Notice that, by definition, *elements* have standard free energies of formation of zero. Notice also that most *compounds* have negative standard free energies of formation. This means that those compounds spontaneously form from their elements in their standard states. Compounds with positive free energies of formation do not spontaneously form from their elements and are therefore less common.

Example 19.8 demonstrates the calculation of ΔG°_{rxn} from ΔG°_f values. This method of calculating ΔG°_{rxn} works only at the temperature for which the free energies of formation are tabulated, namely, 25 °C. To estimate ΔG°_{rxn} at other temperatures we must use $\Delta G^\circ_{rxn} = \Delta H^\circ_{rxn} - T\Delta S^\circ_{rxn}$, as demonstrated previously.

TABLE 19.3 ■ Standard Molar Free Energies of Formation ΔG_f° for Selected Substances at 298 K

Substance	ΔG_f° (kJ/mol)	Substance	ΔG_f° (kJ/mol)
$H_2(g)$	0	$CH_4(g)$	−50.5
$O_2(g)$	0	$H_2O(g)$	−228.6
$N_2(g)$	0	$H_2O(l)$	−237.1
C(s, graphite)	0	$NH_3(g)$	−16.4
C(s, diamond)	2.900	NO(g)	+87.6
CO(g)	−137.2	$NO_2(g)$	+51.3
$CO_2(g)$	−394.4	NaCl(s)	−384.1

EXAMPLE 19.8 Calculating ΔG°_{rxn} from Standard Free Energies of Formation

Ozone in the lower atmosphere is a pollutant that can form by the following reaction involving the oxidation of unburned hydrocarbons:

$$CH_4(g) + 8\,O_2(g) \longrightarrow CO_2(g) + 2\,H_2O(g) + 4\,O_3(g)$$

Use the standard free energies of formation to determine ΔG°_{rxn} for this reaction at 25 °C.

SOLUTION

Begin by looking up (in Appendix IIB) the standard free energies of formation for each reactant and product. Remember that the standard free energy of formation of a pure element in its standard state is zero.

Reactant or product	ΔG_f° (in kJ/mol)
$CH_4(g)$	−50.5
$O_2(g)$	0.0
$CO_2(g)$	−394.4
$H_2O(g)$	−228.6
$O_3(g)$	163.2

Calculate ΔG°_{rxn} by substituting into Equation 19.12.

$$\begin{aligned}\Delta G^\circ_{rxn} &= \sum n_p \Delta G_f^\circ(\text{products}) - \sum n_r \Delta G_f^\circ(\text{reactants})\\ &= [\Delta G^\circ_{f,\,CO_2(g)} + 2(\Delta G^\circ_{f,\,H_2O(g)}) + 4(\Delta G^\circ_{f,\,O_3(g)})] - [\Delta G^\circ_{f,\,CH_4(g)} + 8(\Delta G^\circ_{f,\,O_2(g)})]\\ &= [-394.4\text{ kJ} + 2(-228.6\text{ kJ}) + 4(163.2\text{ kJ})] - [-50.5\text{ kJ} + 8(0.0\text{ kJ})]\\ &= -198.8\text{ kJ} + 50.5\text{ kJ}\\ &= -148.3\text{ kJ}\end{aligned}$$

FOR PRACTICE 19.8 One of the reactions that occurs within a catalytic converter in the exhaust pipe of a car is the simultaneous oxidation of carbon monoxide and reduction of NO (both of which are harmful pollutants):

$$2\,CO(g) + 2\,NO(g) \longrightarrow 2\,CO_2(g) + N_2(g)$$

Use standard free energies of formation to determine ΔG°_{rxn} for this reaction at 25 °C. Is the reaction spontaneous at standard conditions?

FOR MORE PRACTICE 19.8 In For Practice 19.8, you calculated ΔG°_{rxn} for the simultaneous oxidation of carbon monoxide and reduction of NO using standard free energies of formation. Calculate ΔG°_{rxn} for that reaction again at 25 °C, only this time use $\Delta G^\circ_{rxn} = \Delta H^\circ_{rxn} - T\Delta S^\circ_{rxn}$. How do the two values compare? Use your results to calculate ΔG°_{rxn} at 500.0 K and explain why you could not calculate ΔG°_{rxn} at 500.0 K using tabulated standard free energies of formation.

CHEMISTRY IN YOUR DAY | Making a Nonspontaneous Process Spontaneous

A process that is nonspontaneous can be made spontaneous by coupling it with another process that is highly spontaneous. For example, hydrogen gas is a potential future fuel because it can be used in a fuel cell (a type of battery in which the reactants are constantly supplied—see Chapter 20) to generate electricity. The main problem with switching to hydrogen is securing a source. Where can we get the huge amounts of hydrogen gas that would be needed to meet our world's energy needs?

Earth's oceans and lakes, of course, contain vast amounts of hydrogen. But that hydrogen is locked up in water molecules, and the decomposition of water into hydrogen and oxygen has a positive ΔG°_{rxn} and is therefore nonspontaneous:

$$H_2O(g) \longrightarrow H_2(g) + \tfrac{1}{2}O_2(g) \quad \Delta G^\circ_{rxn} = +228.6 \text{ kJ}$$

To obtain hydrogen from water, we need to find another reaction with a highly negative ΔG°_{rxn} that can couple with the decomposition reaction to give an overall reaction with a negative ΔG°_{rxn}. For example, the oxidation of carbon monoxide to carbon dioxide has a large negative ΔG°_{rxn} and is highly spontaneous:

$$CO(g) + \tfrac{1}{2}O_2(g) \longrightarrow CO_2(g) \quad \Delta G^\circ_{rxn} = -257.2 \text{ kJ}$$

If we add the two reactions together, we get a negative ΔG°_{rxn}:

Nonspontaneous

$$H_2O(g) \longrightarrow H_2(g) + \cancel{\tfrac{1}{2}O_2(g)} \quad \Delta G^\circ_{rxn} = +228.6 \text{ kJ}$$

$$CO(g) + \cancel{\tfrac{1}{2}O_2(g)} \longrightarrow CO_2(g) \quad \Delta G^\circ_{rxn} = -257.2 \text{ kJ}$$

$$H_2O(g) + CO(g) \longrightarrow H_2(g) + CO_2(g) \quad \Delta G^\circ_{rxn} = -28.6 \text{ kJ}$$

Spontaneous

The reaction between water and carbon monoxide is thus a spontaneous way to generate hydrogen gas.

The coupling of nonspontaneous reactions with highly spontaneous ones is also important in biological systems. The synthesis reactions that create the complex biological molecules (such as proteins and DNA) needed by living organisms, for example, are themselves nonspontaneous. Living systems grow and reproduce by coupling these nonspontaneous reactions to highly spontaneous ones. The main spontaneous reaction that ultimately drives the nonspontaneous ones is the metabolism of food. The oxidation of glucose, for example, is highly spontaneous:

$$C_6H_{12}O_6(s) + 6\,O_2(g) \longrightarrow 6\,CO_2(g) + 6\,H_2O(l)$$
$$\Delta G^\circ_{rxn} = -2880 \text{ kJ}$$

Spontaneous reactions such as these ultimately drive the nonspontaneous reactions necessary to sustain life.

Calculating ΔG°_{rxn} for a Stepwise Reaction from the Changes in Free Energy for Each of the Steps

Recall from Section 7.8 that because enthalpy is a state function, we can calculate ΔH°_{rxn} for a stepwise reaction from the sum of the changes in enthalpy for each step (according to Hess's law). Since free energy is also a state function, the same relationships that we covered in Chapter 7 for enthalpy also apply to free energy:

1. If a chemical equation is multiplied by some factor, then ΔG_{rxn} is also multiplied by the same factor.
2. If a chemical equation is reversed, then ΔG_{rxn} changes sign.
3. If a chemical equation can be expressed as the sum of a series of steps, then ΔG_{rxn} for the overall equation is the sum of the free energies of reactions for each step.

Example 19.9 illustrates the use of these relationships to calculate ΔG°_{rxn} for a stepwise reaction.

EXAMPLE 19.9 Calculating ΔG°_{rxn} for a Stepwise Reaction

Find ΔG°_{rxn} for the reaction:

$$3\,C(s) + 4\,H_2(g) \longrightarrow C_3H_8(g)$$

Use the following reactions with known ΔG°_{rxn} values:

$$C_3H_8(g) + 5\,O_2(g) \longrightarrow 3\,CO_2(g) + 4\,H_2O(g) \quad \Delta G^\circ_{rxn} = -2074 \text{ kJ}$$
$$C(s) + O_2(g) \longrightarrow CO_2(g) \quad \Delta G^\circ_{rxn} = -394.4 \text{ kJ}$$
$$2\,H_2(g) + O_2(g) \longrightarrow 2\,H_2O(g) \quad \Delta G^\circ_{rxn} = -457.1 \text{ kJ}$$

—*Continued on the next page*

Continued—

SOLUTION

To work this problem, you need to manipulate the given reactions with known values of ΔG°_{rxn} in such a way as to get the reactants of interest on the left, the products of interest on the right, and other species to cancel.

Since the first reaction has C_3H_8 as a reactant, and the reaction of interest has C_3H_8 as a product, reverse the first reaction and change the sign of ΔG°_{rxn}.	$3\,CO_2(g) + 4\,H_2O(g) \longrightarrow C_3H_8(g) + 5\,O_2(g) \quad \Delta G^\circ_{rxn} = +2074\text{ kJ}$
The second reaction has C as a reactant and CO_2 as a product, as required in the reaction of interest. However, the coefficient for C is 1, and in the reaction of interest, the coefficient for C is 3. Therefore, multiply this equation and its ΔG°_{rxn} by 3.	$3 \times [C(s) + O_2(g) \longrightarrow CO_2(g)] \quad \Delta G^\circ_{rxn} = 3 \times (-394.4\text{ kJ}) = -1183\text{ kJ}$
In the third reaction $H_2(g)$ is a reactant, as required. However, the coefficient for H_2 is 2, and in the reaction of interest, the coefficient for H_2 is 4. Multiply this reaction and its ΔG°_{rxn} by 2.	$2 \times [2\,H_2(g) + O_2(g) \longrightarrow 2\,H_2O(g)] \quad \Delta G^\circ_{rxn} = 2 \times (-457.1\text{ kJ}) = -914.2$
Lastly, rewrite the three reactions after multiplying through by the indicated factors and show how they sum to the reaction of interest. ΔG°_{rxn} for the reaction of interest is then the sum of the ΔG's for the steps.	$\cancel{3\,CO_2(g)} + \cancel{4\,H_2O(g)} \longrightarrow C_3H_8(g) + \cancel{5\,O_2(g)} \quad \Delta G^\circ_{rxn} = +2074\text{ kJ}$ $3\,C(s) + \cancel{3\,O_2(g)} \longrightarrow \cancel{3\,CO_2(g)} \quad \Delta G^\circ_{rxn} = -1183\text{ kJ}$ $4\,H_2(g) + \cancel{2\,O_2(g)} \longrightarrow \cancel{4\,H_2O(g)} \quad \Delta G^\circ_{rxn} = -914.2\text{ kJ}$ $3\,C(s) + 4\,H_2(g) \longrightarrow C_3H_8(g) \quad \Delta G^\circ_{rxn} = -23\text{ kJ}$

FOR PRACTICE 19.9 Find ΔG°_{rxn} for the reaction:

$$N_2O(g) + NO_2(g) \longrightarrow 3\,NO(g)$$

Use the following reactions with known ΔG°_{rxn} values:

$$2\,NO(g) + O_2(g) \longrightarrow 2\,NO_2(g) \qquad \Delta G^\circ_{rxn} = -71.2\text{ kJ}$$
$$N_2(g) + O_2(g) \longrightarrow 2\,NO(g) \qquad \Delta G^\circ_{rxn} = +175.2\text{ kJ}$$
$$2\,N_2O(g) \longrightarrow 2\,N_2(g) + O_2(g) \qquad \Delta G^\circ_{rxn} = -207.4\text{ kJ}$$

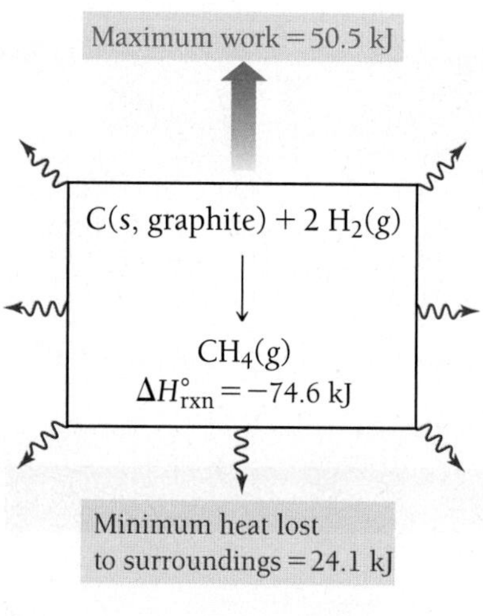

▲ **FIGURE 19.8 Free Energy** Although the reaction produces 74.6 kJ of heat, only a maximum of 50.5 kJ is available to do work. The rest of the energy is lost to the surroundings.

Why Free Energy Is "Free"

We often want to use the energy released by a chemical reaction to do work. For example, in an automobile engine, we use the energy released by the combustion of gasoline to move the car forward. The change in free energy of a chemical reaction represents the maximum amount of energy available, or *free*, to do work (if ΔG°_{rxn} is negative).

For many reactions, the change in free energy is less than the change in enthalpy for the reaction. Consider the reaction between carbon and hydrogen occurring at 25 °C:

$$C(s, \text{graphite}) + 2\,H_2(g) \longrightarrow CH_4(g)$$
$$\Delta H^\circ_{rxn} = -74.6\text{ kJ}$$
$$\Delta S^\circ_{rxn} = -80.8\text{ J/K}$$
$$\Delta G^\circ_{rxn} = -50.5\text{ kJ}$$

The reaction is exothermic and gives off 74.6 kJ of heat energy. However, the maximum amount of energy available for useful work is only 50.5 kJ (Figure 19.8◀). Why? We can see that the change in entropy of the *system* is negative. Nevertheless, the reaction is spontaneous. This is possible only if some of the emitted heat goes to increase the entropy of the surroundings by an amount sufficient to make the change in entropy of the *universe* positive. The amount of energy available to do work (the free energy) is what remains after accounting for the heat that must be lost to the surroundings.

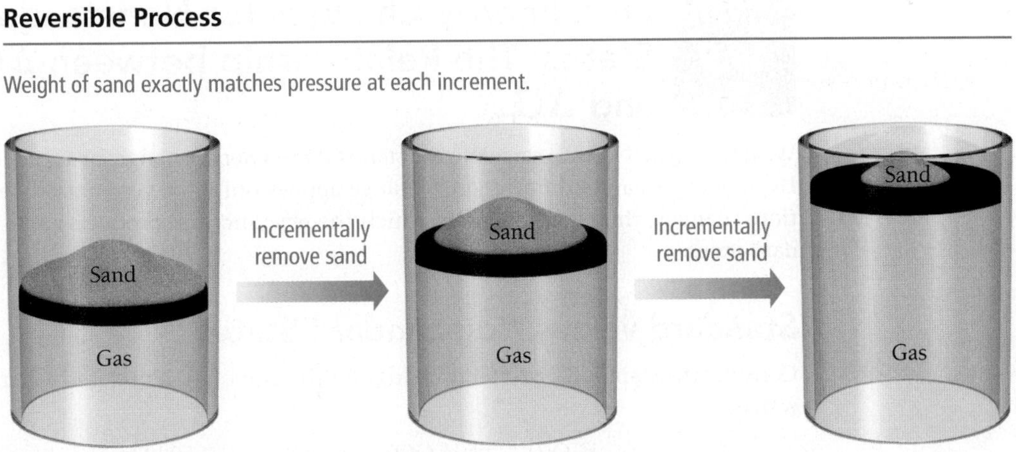

▲ **FIGURE 19.9 A Reversible Process** In a reversible process, the free energy is drawn out in infinitesimally small increments that exactly match the amount of energy that the process is producing in that increment. In this case, grains of sand are removed one at a time, resulting in a series of small expansions in which the weight of sand almost exactly matches the pressure of the expanding gas. This process is close to reversible—each sand grain would need to have an infinitesimally small mass for the process to be fully reversible.

The change in free energy for a chemical reaction represents a *theoretical limit* as to how much work can be done by the reaction. In a *real* reaction, the amount of energy available to do work is even *less* than ΔG°_{rxn} because additional energy is lost to the surroundings as heat. The only reactions that reach the theoretical limit are reversible reactions (see Section 19.4 for the definition of reversible processes). A reversible chemical reaction occurs infinitesimally slowly, and the free energy is drawn out in infinitesimally small increments that exactly match the amount of energy that the reaction is producing during that increment (Figure 19.9▲).

Applying the definition of reversibility from Section 19.4, a reversible chemical reaction is one that changes direction upon an infinitesimally small change in a variable (such as temperature or pressure) related to the reaction.

All real reactions are irreversible and therefore do not achieve the theoretical limit of available free energy. For example, consider the discharging of a battery. A battery contains chemical reactants configured in such a way that, upon spontaneous reaction, they produce an electrical current. We can harness the free energy released by the reaction to do work. For example, an electric motor can be wired to the battery. Flowing electrical current makes the motor turn (Figure 19.10▶).

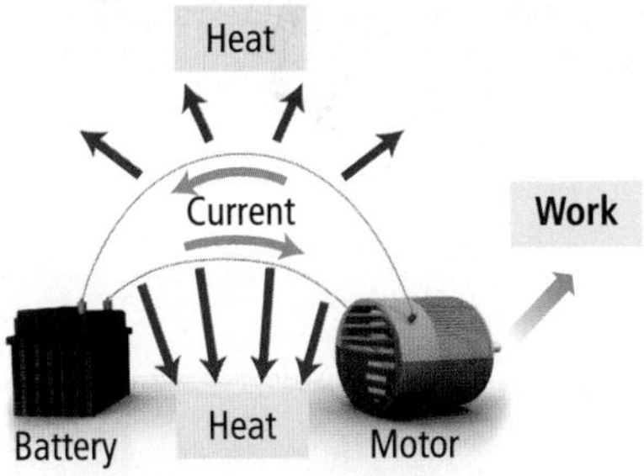

▲ **FIGURE 19.10 Energy Loss in a Battery** When current is drawn from a battery to do work, some energy is lost as heat due to resistance in the wire. Consequently, the quantity of energy required to recharge the battery will be more than the quantity of work done.

Because of the resistance in the wire, the flowing electrical current also produces some heat, which is lost to the surroundings and is not available to do work. The amount of free energy lost as heat can be decreased by slowing down the rate of current flow. The slower the rate of current flow, the less free energy is lost as heat and the more is available to do work. However, only in the theoretical case of infinitesimally slow current flow is the maximum amount of work (equal to ΔG°_{rxn}) done. Any real rate of current flow results in some loss of energy as heat. This lost energy is sometimes called the "heat tax," a loss of energy that must necessarily occur in any energy exchange. Recharging the battery necessarily requires more energy than is obtained as work because some of the energy is lost as heat. In other words, during discharging and recharging, the battery has gone through a cycle in which it returns to its original (charged) state. However, the surroundings have gained some heat during the process, and the entropy of the surroundings has increased (which makes the process spontaneous). Any real (or irreversible) cyclical process such as this suffers the same fate—the system may return to its original state, but the surroundings do not, resulting in the permanent dispersal of energy to the surroundings.

If the change in free energy of a chemical reaction is positive, then ΔG°_{rxn} represents *the minimum amount of energy required to make the reaction occur*. Again, ΔG°_{rxn} represents a theoretical limit. Making a real nonspontaneous reaction occur always requires more energy than the theoretical limit.

19.9 Free Energy Changes for Nonstandard States: The Relationship between ΔG°_{rxn} and ΔG_{rxn}

We have learned how to calculate the *standard* free energy change for a reaction (ΔG°_{rxn}). However, the standard free energy change applies only to a very narrow set of conditions, namely, those conditions in which the reactants and products are in their standard states.

Standard versus Nonstandard States

Consider the standard free energy change for the evaporation of liquid water to gaseous water:

$$H_2O(l) \rightleftharpoons H_2O(g) \qquad \Delta G^\circ_{rxn} = +8.59\ \text{kJ/mol}$$

▲ Spilled water spontaneously evaporates even though ΔG° for the vaporization of water is positive. Why?

The standard free energy change for this process is positive, so the process is nonspontaneous. But you know that if you spill water onto the floor under ordinary conditions, it spontaneously evaporates. Why? *Because under ordinary conditions the reactants and products are not in their standard states* and ΔG°_{rxn} applies only when the reactants and product are in their standard states, sometimes called *standard conditions*. For a gas (such as the water vapor in the reaction just given), the standard state is that the pure gas is present at a partial pressure of 1 atmosphere. In a flask containing liquid water and water vapor in its standard state ($P_{H_2O} = 1$ atm) at 25 °C the water does not vaporize. In fact, since ΔG°_{rxn} is negative for the reverse reaction, the reaction spontaneously occurs in reverse—water vapor condenses.

In open air under ordinary circumstances, the partial pressure of water vapor is much less than 1 atm. The state of the water vapor is not its standard state, and therefore the value of ΔG°_{rxn} does not apply. For the nonstandard state, we must calculate ΔG_{rxn} (as opposed to ΔG°_{rxn}) to predict spontaneity.

The Free Energy Change of a Reaction under Nonstandard Conditions

We can calculate the **free energy change of a reaction under nonstandard conditions (ΔG_{rxn})** from ΔG°_{rxn} using the relationship:

$$\Delta G_{rxn} = \Delta G^\circ_{rxn} + RT \ln Q \qquad [19.13]$$

where Q is the reaction quotient (defined in Section 16.7), T is the temperature in kelvins, and R is the gas constant in the appropriate units (8.314 J/mol · K).

In Equation 19.13 and all subsequent thermodynamic equations, we use Q_p for reactions involving gases, and we use Q_c for reactions involving substances dissolved in solution. We can demonstrate the use of this equation by applying it to the liquid–vapor water equilibrium under several different conditions, as shown in Figure 19.11▶. Note that by the law of mass action, for this equilibrium, $Q = P_{H_2O}$ (where the pressure is expressed in atmospheres):

$$H_2O(l) \longrightarrow H_2O(g) \qquad Q = P_{H_2O}$$

Standard Conditions

Under standard conditions, $P_{H_2O} = 1$ atm and therefore $Q = 1$. Substituting, we get the equation:

$$\begin{aligned} \Delta G_{rxn} &= \Delta G^\circ_{rxn} + RT \ln Q \\ &= +8.59\ \text{kJ/mol} + RT \ln(1) \\ &= +8.59\ \text{kJ/mol} \end{aligned}$$

Free Energy Change for the Vaporization of Water

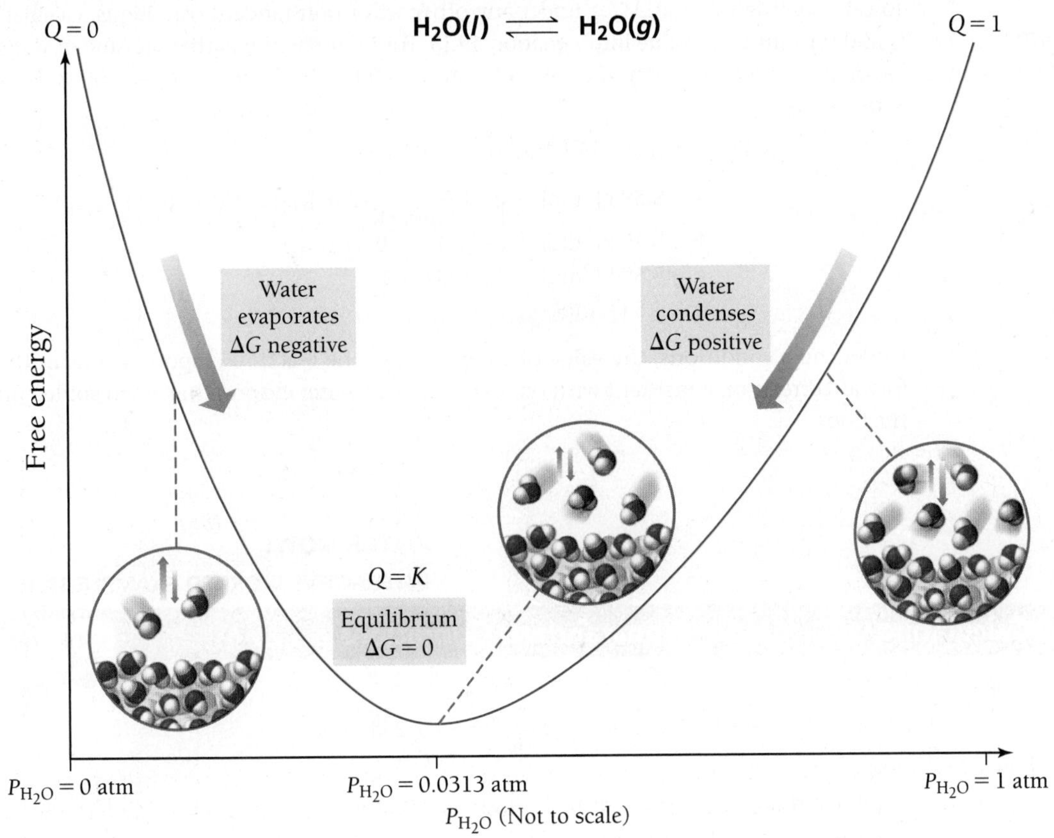

▲ **FIGURE 19.11 Free Energy versus Pressure for Water** The free energy change for the vaporization of water is a function of pressure.

Under standard conditions, Q is always equal to 1, and since $\ln(1) = 0$, the value of ΔG_{rxn} is therefore equal to ΔG°_{rxn}, as expected. For the liquid–vapor water equilibrium, because $\Delta G^\circ_{rxn} > 0$, the reaction is not spontaneous in the forward direction but is spontaneous in the reverse direction. As stated previously, under standard conditions water vapor condenses into liquid water.

Equilibrium Conditions

At 25.00 °C, liquid water is in equilibrium with water vapor at a pressure of 0.0313 atm; therefore, $Q = K_p = 0.0313$. Substituting:

$$\begin{aligned}\Delta G_{rxn} &= \Delta G^\circ_{rxn} + RT\ln(0.0313)\\ &= +8.59\text{ kJ/mol} + 8.314\frac{\text{J}}{\text{mol}\cdot\text{K}}(298.15\text{ K})\ln(0.0313)\\ &= +8.59\text{ kJ/mol} + (-8.59\times10^{3}\text{ J/mol})\\ &= +8.59\text{ kJ/mol} - 8.59\text{ kJ/mol}\\ &= 0\end{aligned}$$

Under equilibrium conditions, the value of $RT\ln Q$ is always equal in magnitude but opposite in sign to the value of ΔG°_{rxn}. Therefore, the value of ΔG_{rxn} is zero. Because $\Delta G_{rxn} = 0$, the reaction is not spontaneous in either direction, as expected for a reaction at equilibrium.

Other Nonstandard Conditions

A water partial pressure of 5.00×10^{-3} atm corresponds to a relative humidity of 16% at 25 °C.

To calculate the value of ΔG_{rxn} under any other set of nonstandard conditions, calculate Q and substitute the value into Equation 19.13. For example, the partial pressure of water vapor in the air on a dry (nonhumid) day is 5.00×10^{-3} atm, so $Q = 5.00 \times 10^{-3}$. Substituting:

$$\begin{aligned}\Delta G_{\text{rxn}} &= \Delta G^\circ_{\text{rxn}} + RT\ln(5.00 \times 10^{-3})\\ &= +8.59\text{ kJ/mol} + 8.314\frac{\text{J}}{\text{mol}\cdot\cancel{\text{K}}}(298\ \cancel{\text{K}})\ln(5.00 \times 10^{-3})\\ &= +8.59\text{ kJ/mol} + (-13.1 \times 10^3\text{ J/mol})\\ &= +8.59\text{ kJ/mol} - 13.1\text{ kJ/mol}\\ &= -4.5\text{ kJ/mol}\end{aligned}$$

Under these conditions, the value of $\Delta G_{\text{rxn}} < 0$, so the reaction is spontaneous in the forward direction, consistent with our experience of water evaporating when spilled on the floor.

WATCH **NOW!**

INTERACTIVE WORKED EXAMPLE 19.10

EXAMPLE 19.10 Calculating ΔG_{rxn} under Nonstandard Conditions

Consider the reaction at 298 K:

$$2\,NO(g) + O_2(g) \longrightarrow 2\,NO_2(g) \qquad \Delta G^\circ_{\text{rxn}} = -71.2\text{ kJ}$$

Calculate ΔG_{rxn} under these conditions:

$$P_{NO} = 0.100\text{ atm}; \quad P_{O_2} = 0.100\text{ atm}; \quad P_{NO_2} = 2.00\text{ atm}$$

Is the reaction more or less spontaneous under these conditions than under standard conditions?

SOLUTION

Use the law of mass action to calculate Q.

$$Q = \frac{(P_{NO_2})^2}{(P_{NO})^2 P_{O_2}} = \frac{(2.00)^2}{(0.100)^2(0.100)} = 4.00 \times 10^3$$

Substitute Q, T, and $\Delta G^\circ_{\text{rxn}}$ into Equation 19.13 to calculate ΔG_{rxn}. (Since the units of R include joules, write $\Delta G^\circ_{\text{rxn}}$ in joules.)

$$\begin{aligned}\Delta G_{\text{rxn}} &= \Delta G^\circ_{\text{rxn}} + RT\ln Q\\ &= -71.2 \times 10^3\text{ J} + 8.314\frac{\text{J}}{\text{mol}\cdot\cancel{\text{K}}}(298\ \cancel{\text{K}})\ln(4.00 \times 10^3)\\ &= -71.2 \times 10^3\text{ J} + 20.5 \times 10^3\text{ J}\\ &= -50.7 \times 10^3\text{ J}\\ &= -50.7\text{ kJ}\end{aligned}$$

The reaction is spontaneous under these conditions but less spontaneous than it would be under standard conditions (because ΔG_{rxn} is less negative than $\Delta G^\circ_{\text{rxn}}$).

CHECK The calculated result is consistent with what you would expect based on Le Châtelier's principle; increasing the concentration of the products and decreasing the concentration of the reactants relative to standard conditions should make the reaction less spontaneous than it was under standard conditions.

FOR PRACTICE 19.10 Consider the reaction at 298 K:

$$2\,H_2S(g) + SO_2(g) \longrightarrow 3\,S(s,\text{ rhombic}) + 2\,H_2O(g) \quad \Delta G^\circ_{\text{rxn}} = -102\text{ kJ}$$

Calculate ΔG_{rxn} under these conditions:

$$P_{H_2S} = 2.00\text{ atm}; \quad P_{SO_2} = 1.50\text{ atm}; \quad P_{H_2O} = 0.0100\text{ atm}$$

Is the reaction more or less spontaneous under these conditions than under standard conditions?

19.7 Cc Conceptual Connection ANSWER NOW!

FREE ENERGY CHANGES AND LE CHÂTELIER'S PRINCIPLE According to Le Châtelier's principle and the dependence of free energy on reactant and product concentrations, which statement is true? (Assume that both reactants and products are gaseous.)

(a) A high concentration of reactants relative to products results in a more spontaneous reaction than one in which the reactants and products are in their standard states.

(b) A high concentration of products relative to reactants results in a more spontaneous reaction than one in which the reactants and products are in their standard states.

(c) A reaction in which the reactants are in standard states, but in which no products have formed, has a ΔG_{rxn} that is more positive than ΔG°_{rxn}.

19.10 Free Energy and Equilibrium: Relating ΔG°_{rxn} to the Equilibrium Constant (K)

We have discussed throughout this chapter that ΔG°_{rxn} determines the spontaneity of a reaction when the reactants and products are in their standard states. In Chapter 16, we learned that the equilibrium constant (K) determines how far a reaction goes toward products, a measure of spontaneity. Therefore, as you might expect, the standard free energy change of a reaction and the equilibrium constant are related—the equilibrium constant becomes larger as the standard free energy change becomes more negative. In other words, if, on the one hand, the reactants in a particular reaction undergo a large *negative* free energy change as they become products, then the reaction has a large equilibrium constant, with products strongly favored at equilibrium. If, on the other hand, the reactants in a particular reaction undergo a large *positive* free energy change as they become products, then the reaction has a small equilibrium constant, with reactants strongly favored at equilibrium.

The Relationship between ΔG°_{rxn} and K

We can derive a relationship between ΔG°_{rxn} and K from Equation 19.13. We know that at equilibrium $Q = K$ and $\Delta G_{rxn} = 0$. Making these substitutions:

$$\Delta G_{rxn} = \Delta G^\circ_{rxn} + RT \ln Q$$

$$0 = \Delta G^\circ_{rxn} + RT \ln K$$

$$\Delta G^\circ_{rxn} = -RT \ln K \qquad [19.14]$$

In Equation 19.14 and all subsequent thermodynamic equations, we use K_p for reactions involving gases, and we use K_c for reactions involving substances dissolved in solution.

We can better understand the relationship between ΔG°_{rxn} and K by considering the following ranges of values for K, as summarized in Figure 19.12►:

The relationship between ΔG°_{rxn} and K is logarithmic—small changes in ΔG°_{rxn} have a large effect on K.

- When $K < 1$, $\ln K$ is negative and ΔG°_{rxn} is positive. Under standard conditions (when $Q = 1$), the reaction is spontaneous in the reverse direction.
- When $K > 1$, $\ln K$ is positive and ΔG°_{rxn} is negative. Under standard conditions (when $Q = 1$), the reaction is spontaneous in the forward direction.
- When $K = 1$, $\ln K$ is zero and ΔG°_{rxn} is zero. The reaction happens to be at equilibrium under standard conditions.

Free Energy and the Equilibrium Constant

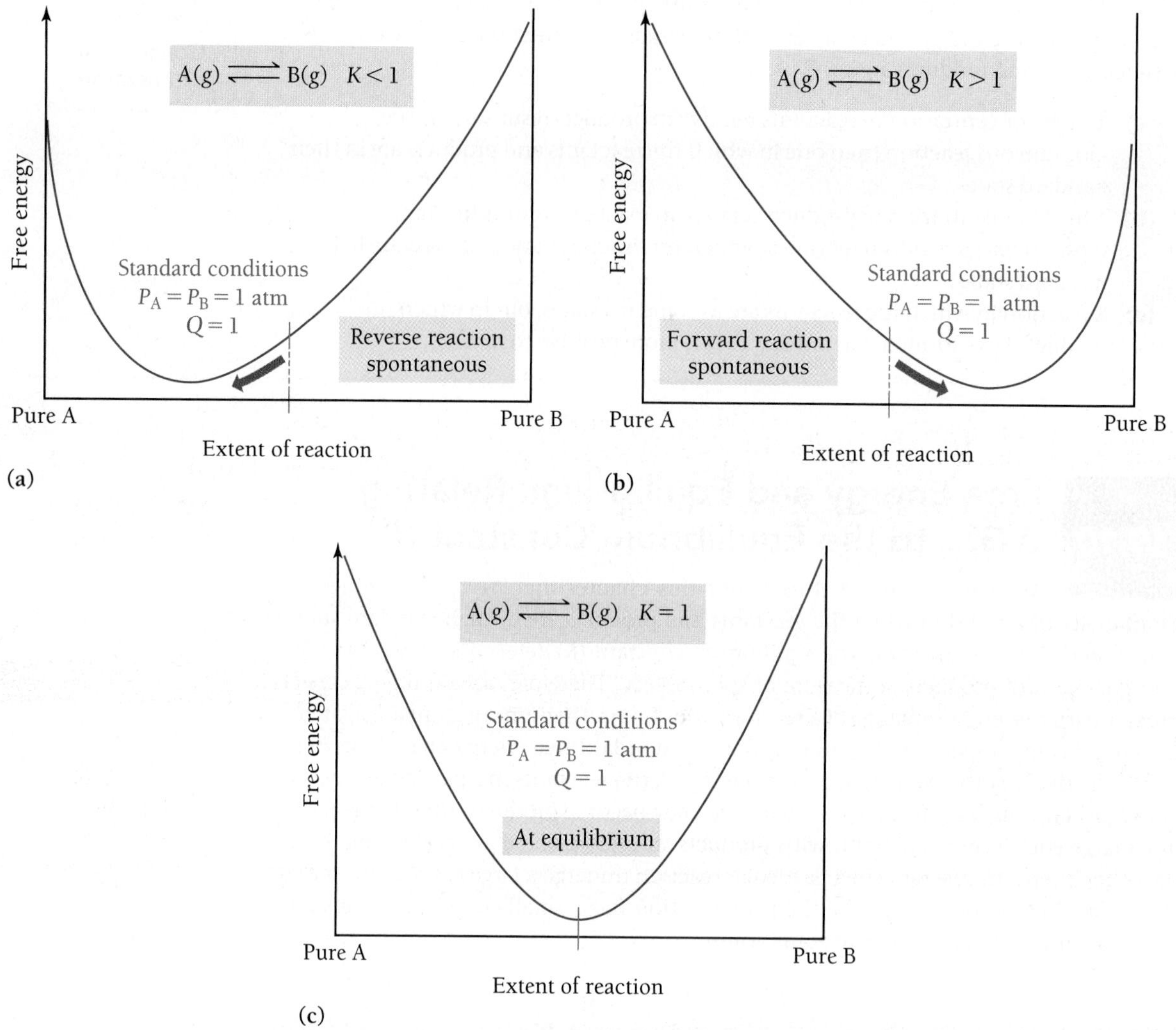

▲ **FIGURE 19.12 Free Energy and the Equilibrium Constant** **(a)** Free energy curve for a reaction with a small equilibrium constant. **(b)** Free energy curve for a reaction with a large equilibrium constant. **(c)** Free energy curve for a reaction in which $K = 1$.

WATCH **NOW!**
INTERACTIVE WORKED EXAMPLE 19.11

EXAMPLE 19.11 The Equilibrium Constant and ΔG°_{rxn}

Use tabulated free energies of formation to calculate the equilibrium constant for the reaction at 298 K:

$$N_2O_4(g) \rightleftharpoons 2\,NO_2(g)$$

SOLUTION

Look up (in Appendix IIB) the standard free energies of formation for each reactant and product.

Reactant or product	ΔG°_f (in kJ/mol)
$N_2O_4(g)$	99.8
$NO_2(g)$	51.3

Calculate ΔG°_{rxn} by substituting into Equation 19.12.

$$\begin{aligned}\Delta G^\circ_{rxn} &= \sum n_p \Delta G^\circ_f(\text{products}) - \sum n_r \Delta G^\circ_f(\text{reactants})\\ &= 2[\Delta G^\circ_{f,\,NO_2(g)}] - \Delta G^\circ_{f,\,N_2O_4(g)}\\ &= 2(51.3\text{ kJ}) - 99.8\text{ kJ}\\ &= 2.8\text{ kJ}\end{aligned}$$

Calculate K from ΔG°_{rxn} by solving Equation 19.14 for K and substituting the values of ΔG°_{rxn} and temperature.

$$\Delta G^\circ_{rxn} = -RT \ln K$$

$$\ln K = \frac{-\Delta G^\circ_{rxn}}{RT} = \frac{-2.8 \times 10^3 \, \cancel{J}/\cancel{mol}}{8.314 \frac{\cancel{J}}{\cancel{mol} \cdot \cancel{K}} (298 \, \cancel{K})} = -1.13$$

$$K = e^{-1.13} = 0.32$$

FOR PRACTICE 19.11 Calculate ΔG°_{rxn} at 298 K for the reaction:

$$I_2(g) + Cl_2(g) \rightleftharpoons 2\,ICl(g) \quad K_p = 81.9$$

K AND ΔG°_{rxn} The reaction $A(g) \rightleftharpoons B(g)$ has an equilibrium constant that is less than one. What can you conclude about ΔG°_{rxn} for the reaction?

(a) $\Delta G^\circ_{rxn} = 0$ **(b)** $\Delta G^\circ_{rxn} < 0$ **(c)** $\Delta G^\circ_{rxn} > 0$

19.8 Cc Conceptual Connection

ANSWER **NOW!**

THE CONDITIONS OF SPONTANEITY A reaction is spontaneous under a certain set of conditions. What can you conclude about ΔG_{rxn} and Q?

(a) $\Delta G_{rxn} < 0, Q > K$ **(b)** $\Delta G_{rxn} < 0, Q < K$

(c) $\Delta G_{rxn} > 0, Q < K$ **(d)** $\Delta G_{rxn} > 0, Q > K$

19.9 Cc Conceptual Connection

ANSWER **NOW!**

The Temperature Dependence of the Equilibrium Constant

We now have an equation that relates the standard free energy change for a reaction (ΔG°_{rxn}) to the equilibrium constant for a reaction (K):

$$\Delta G^\circ_{rxn} = -RT \ln K \quad [19.15]$$

We also have an equation for how the free energy change for a reaction (ΔG°_{rxn}) depends on temperature (T):

$$\Delta G^\circ_{rxn} = \Delta H^\circ_{rxn} - T\Delta S^\circ_{rxn} \quad [19.16]$$

We can combine these two equations to obtain an equation for how the equilibrium constant depends on temperature. Combining Equations 19.15 and 19.16, we arrive at:

$$-RT \ln K = \Delta H^\circ_{rxn} - T\Delta S^\circ_{rxn} \quad [19.17]$$

We can then divide both sides of Equation 19.17 by the quantity RT:

$$-\ln K = \frac{\Delta H^\circ_{rxn}}{RT} - \frac{\cancel{T}\Delta S^\circ_{rxn}}{R\cancel{T}}$$

Canceling and rearranging, we get this important result:

$$\ln K = -\frac{\Delta H^\circ_{rxn}}{R}\left(\frac{1}{T}\right) + \frac{\Delta S^\circ_{rxn}}{R} \quad [19.18]$$

$$y = mx + b$$

Equation 19.18 is in the form of a straight line. A plot of the natural log of the equilibrium constant ($\ln K$) versus the inverse of the temperature in kelvins ($1/T$) yields a straight line with a slope of $-\Delta H^\circ_{rxn}/R$ and a y-intercept of $-\Delta S^\circ_{rxn}/R$. Such a plot is useful for obtaining thermodynamic data (namely, ΔH°_{rxn} and ΔS°_{rxn}) from measurements of K as a function of temperature. However, since ΔH°_{rxn} and ΔS°_{rxn} can themselves be slightly temperature dependent, this analysis works only over a relatively limited temperature range.

The equation can also be expressed in a two-point form:

$$\ln \frac{K_2}{K_1} = -\frac{\Delta H^\circ_{rxn}}{R}\left(\frac{1}{T_2} - \frac{1}{T_1}\right) \quad [19.19]$$

We can use this equation to find ΔH°_{rxn} from a measurement of the equilibrium constant at two different temperatures or to find the equilibrium constant at some other temperature if we know the equilibrium constant at a given temperature and ΔH°_{rxn}.

QUIZ YOURSELF **NOW!**

Self-Assessment Quiz

Q1. Which reaction is most likely to have a positive ΔS_{sys}?
MISSED THIS? *Read Section 19.4*

a) $SiO_2(s) + 3\,C(s) \longrightarrow SiC(s) + 2\,CO(g)$
b) $6\,CO_2(g) + 6\,H_2O(g) \longrightarrow C_6H_{12}O_6(s) + 6\,O_2(g)$
c) $CO(g) + Cl_2(g) \longrightarrow COCl_2(g)$
d) $3\,NO_2(g) + H_2O(l) \longrightarrow 2\,HNO_3(l) + NO(g)$

Q2. The sign of ΔH_{rxn} and ΔS_{rxn} for several different reactions are given. In which case is the reaction spontaneous at all temperatures?
MISSED THIS? *Read Section 19.5; Watch IWE 19.3*

a) $\Delta H_{rxn} < 0$; $\Delta S_{rxn} < 0$
b) $\Delta H_{rxn} > 0$; $\Delta S_{rxn} > 0$
c) $\Delta H_{rxn} < 0$; $\Delta S_{rxn} > 0$
d) $\Delta H_{rxn} > 0$; $\Delta S_{rxn} < 0$

Q3. Arrange the gases—F_2, Ar, and CH_3F—in order of increasing standard molar entropy (S°) at 298 K.
MISSED THIS? *Read Section 19.7; Watch KCV 19.7*

a) $F_2 < Ar < CH_3F$
b) $CH_3F < F_2 < Ar$
c) $CH_3F < Ar < F_2$
d) $Ar < F_2 < CH_3F$

Q4. Calculate the change in entropy that occurs in the system when 1.00 mol of methanol (CH_3OH) vaporizes from a liquid to a gas at its boiling point (64.6 °C). For methanol, $\Delta H_{vap} = 35.21$ kJ/mol.
MISSED THIS? *Read Section 19.4; Watch IWE 19.2*

a) 104 J/K b) −104 J/K c) 545 J/K d) −545 J/K

Q5. A reaction has a $\Delta H_{rxn} = 54.2$ kJ. Calculate the change in entropy for the surroundings (ΔS_{surr}) for the reaction at 25.0 °C. (Assume constant pressure and temperature.)
MISSED THIS? *Read Section 19.5; Watch IWE 19.3*

a) 2.17×10^3 J/K
b) -2.17×10^3 J/K
c) −182 J/K
d) 182 J/K

Q6. A reaction has $\Delta H^\circ_{rxn} = -255$ kJ and $\Delta S^\circ_{rxn} = 211$ J/K. Calculate ΔG°_{rxn} at 55 °C.
MISSED THIS? *Read Section 19.6; Watch KCV 19.6, IWE 19.4*

a) 11.9×10^3 kJ
b) 69.5×10^3 kJ
c) −267 kJ
d) −324 kJ

Q7. Use standard entropies to calculate ΔS°_{rxn} for the balanced chemical equation:
MISSED THIS? *Read Section 19.7; Watch KCV 19.7, IWE 19.5*

$$2\,PCl_3(l) + O_2(g) \longrightarrow 2\,POCl_3(l)$$

Substance	S° (J/mol · K)
$POCl_3(l)$	222.5
$POCl_3(g)$	325.5
$PCl_3(l)$	217.1
$PCl_3(g)$	311.8
$O_2(g)$	205.2

a) −194.4 J/K
b) −199.8 J/K
c) 10.8 J/K
d) 1084.4 J/K

Q8. Use standard free energies of formation to calculate ΔG°_{rxn} for the balanced chemical equation:
MISSED THIS? *Read Section 19.8*

$$Mg(s) + N_2O(g) \longrightarrow MgO(s) + N_2(g)$$

Substance	ΔG°_{rxn} (kJ/mol)
$N_2O(g)$	103.7
$MgO(s)$	−569.3

a) 673.0 kJ b) −673.0 kJ c) −465.6 kJ d) 465.6 kJ

Q9. Find ΔG°_{rxn} for the reaction $2\,A + B \longrightarrow 2\,C$ from the given data. **MISSED THIS?** *Read Section 19.8*

$A \longrightarrow B$ $\quad \Delta G^\circ_{rxn} = 128$ kJ
$C \longrightarrow 2\,B$ $\quad \Delta G^\circ_{rxn} = 455$ kJ
$A \longrightarrow C$ $\quad \Delta G^\circ_{rxn} = -182$ kJ

a) −401 kJ b) 509 kJ c) 401 kJ d) −509 kJ

Q10. The given reaction has a $\Delta G^\circ_{rxn} = 9.4$ kJ at 25 °C. Find ΔG_{rxn} when $P_{NO_2} = 0.115$ atm and $P_{NO} = 9.7$ atm at 25 °C.
MISSED THIS? *Read Section 19.9; Watch IWE 19.10*

$$3\,NO_2(g) + H_2O(l) \longrightarrow 2\,HNO_3(l) + NO(g)$$

a) −12.3 kJ
b) 21.7×10^3 kJ
c) 31.1 kJ
d) 18.8 kJ

Q11. The reaction $A(g) \rightleftharpoons B(g)$ has an equilibrium constant of $K_p = 2.3 \times 10^{-5}$. What can you conclude about the sign of ΔG°_{rxn} for the reaction? **MISSED THIS?** *Read Section 19.10*

a) $\Delta G^\circ_{rxn} = 0$
b) ΔG°_{rxn} is negative
c) ΔG°_{rxn} is positive
d) Nothing can be concluded about the sign of ΔG°_{rxn} for the reaction.

Q12. A reaction has an equilibrium constant of $K_p = 0.018$ at 25 °C. Find ΔG°_{rxn} for the reaction at this temperature.
MISSED THIS? *Read Section 19.10; Watch IWE 19.11*

a) −835 J b) −4.32 kJ c) −9.95 kJ d) 9.95 kJ

Q13. Which distribution of six particles into three interconnected boxes has the highest entropy?
MISSED THIS? *Read Section 19.3; Watch KCV 19.3*

a) 

b) 

c) 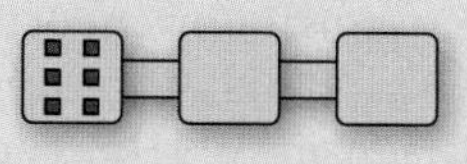

d) 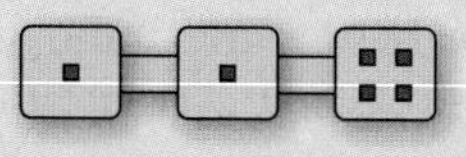

Q14. Which process results in the increase in entropy of the universe?
MISSED THIS? *Read Section 19.3; Watch KCV 19.3*

a) the cooling of a hot cup of coffee in room temperature air
b) the evaporation of water from a desk at room temperature
c) the melting of snow above 0 °C
d) all of the above

Q15. Under which set of conditions is ΔG_{rxn} for the reaction $A(g) \longrightarrow B(g)$ most likely to be negative?
MISSED THIS? *Read Section 19.9*

a) $P_A = 10.0$ atm; $P_B = 10.0$ atm
b) $P_A = 10.0$ atm; $P_B = 0.010$ atm
c) $P_A = 0.010$ atm; $P_B = 10.0$ atm
d) $P_A = 0.010$ atm; $P_B = 0.010$ atm

Q16. Which statement is true for the freezing of liquid water below 0 °C?
MISSED THIS? *Read Section 19.6; Watch KCV 19.6*

a) ΔH is positive; ΔS is negative; ΔG is negative
b) ΔH is negative; ΔS is negative; ΔG is negative
c) ΔH is positive; ΔS is positive; ΔG is positive
d) ΔH is positive; ΔS is negative; ΔG is positive

Answers: **1.** (a) **2.** (c) **3.** (d) **4.** (a) **5.** (c) **6.** (d) **7.** (a) **8.** (b) **9.** (d) **10.** (c) **11.** (c) **12.** (d) **13.** (b) **14.** (d) **15.** (b) **16.** (b)

CHAPTER 19 IN REVIEW

TERMS

Section 19.2
spontaneous process (848)

Section 19.3
entropy (S) (852)
second law of thermodynamics (854)

Section 19.4
reversible process (859)

Section 19.6
Gibbs free energy (G) (863)

Section 19.7
standard entropy change for a reaction (ΔS°_{rxn}) (867)
standard molar entropies (S°) (867)
third law of thermodynamics (868)

Section 19.8
standard change in free energy (ΔG°_{rxn}) (872)
free energy of formation (ΔG°_f) (873)

Section 19.9
free energy change of a reaction under nonstandard conditions (ΔG_{rxn}) (878)

CONCEPTS

Spontaneous and Nonspontaneous Processes (19.2)

- Both spontaneous and nonspontaneous processes can occur, but only spontaneous processes can take place without outside intervention.
- Thermodynamics is the study of the *spontaneity* of reactions, *not* to be confused with kinetics, the study of the *rate* of reactions.

Entropy and the Second Law of Thermodynamics (19.3)

- The second law of thermodynamics states that for *any* spontaneous process, the entropy of the universe increases.
- Entropy (S) is proportional to the number of energetically equivalent ways in which the components of a system can be arranged and is a measure of energy dispersal per unit temperature.

The Entropy Changes Associated with Changes of State (19.4)

- The entropy of a substance increases as it changes state from a solid to a liquid and when it changes from a liquid to a gas.
- The change in entropy for a system undergoing a reversible change in state is $\Delta S = q_{rev}/T$.

Heat Transfer and Changes in the Entropy of the Surroundings (19.5)

- For a process to be spontaneous, the total entropy of the universe (system plus surroundings) must increase.
- The entropy of the surroundings increases when the change in *enthalpy* of the system (ΔH_{sys}) is negative (i.e., for exothermic reactions).
- The change in entropy of the surroundings for a given ΔH_{sys} depends inversely on temperature—the greater the temperature, the smaller the magnitude of ΔS_{surr}.

Gibbs Free Energy (19.6)

- Gibbs free energy, G, is a thermodynamic function that is proportional to the negative of the change in the entropy of the universe. A negative ΔG represents a spontaneous reaction, and a positive ΔG represents a nonspontaneous reaction.
- We can calculate the value of ΔG for a reaction from the values of ΔH and ΔS for the *system* using the equation $\Delta G = \Delta H - T\Delta S$.

Entropy Changes in Chemical Reactions: Calculating ΔS°_{rxn} (19.7)

- We calculate the standard change in entropy for a reaction similarly to the way we calculate the standard change in enthalpy for a reaction: by subtracting the sum of the standard entropies of the reactants multiplied by their stoichiometric coefficients from the sum of the standard entropies of the products multiplied by their stoichiometric coefficients.

- Standard entropies are *absolute*; an entropy of zero is established by the third law of thermodynamics as the entropy of a perfect crystal at absolute zero.
- The entropy of a substance at a given temperature depends on factors that affect the number of energetically equivalent arrangements of the substance; these include the state, size, and molecular complexity of the substance.

Free Energy Changes in Chemical Reactions: Calculating ΔG°_{rxn} (19.8)

- There are three ways to calculate ΔG°_{rxn}: (1) from ΔH° and ΔS°, (2) from free energies of formation (only at 25 °C), and (3) from the ΔG°'s of reactions that sum to the reaction of interest.
- The magnitude of a negative ΔG°_{rxn} represents the theoretical amount of energy available to do work, while a positive ΔG°_{rxn} represents the minimum amount of energy required to make a nonspontaneous process occur.

Free Energy Changes for Nonstandard States: The Relationship between ΔG°_{rxn} and ΔG_{rxn} (19.9)

- The value of ΔG°_{rxn} applies only to standard conditions, and most real conditions are not standard.
- Under nonstandard conditions, we can calculate ΔG_{rxn} from the equation $\Delta G_{rxn} = \Delta G^\circ_{rxn} + RT \ln Q$.

Free Energy and Equilibrium: Relating ΔG°_{rxn} to the Equilibrium Constant (*K*) (19.10)

- Under standard conditions, the free energy change for a reaction is directly proportional to the negative of the natural log of the equilibrium constant, *K*; the more negative the free energy change (i.e., the more spontaneous the reaction), the larger the equilibrium constant.
- We can use the temperature dependence of ΔG°_{rxn}, as given by $\Delta G^\circ = \Delta H^\circ - T\Delta S^\circ$, to derive an equation for the temperature dependence of the equilibrium constant.

EQUATIONS AND RELATIONSHIPS

The Definition of Entropy (**19.3**)

$$S = k \ln W \quad k = 1.38 \times 10^{-23}\ \text{J/K}$$

Change in Entropy (**19.3, 19.4**)

$$\Delta S = S_{final} - S_{intial}$$

$$\Delta S = q_{rev}/T \quad \text{(Isothermal, reversible process)}$$

Change in the Entropy of the Universe (**19.5**)

$$\Delta S_{univ} = \Delta S_{sys} + \Delta S_{surr}$$

Change in the Entropy of the Surroundings (**19.5**)

$$\Delta S_{surr} = \frac{-\Delta H_{sys}}{T} \quad \text{(constant}\ T,\ P)$$

Change in Gibbs Free Energy (**19.6**)

$$\Delta G = \Delta H - T\Delta S$$

The Relationship between Spontaneity and ΔH, ΔS, and T (**19.6**)

ΔH	ΔS	Low Temperature	High Temperature
−	+	Spontaneous	Spontaneous
+	−	Nonspontaneous	Nonspontaneous
−	−	Spontaneous	Nonspontaneous
+	+	Nonspontaneous	Spontaneous

Standard Change in Entropy (**19.7**)

$$\Delta S^\circ_{rxn} = \sum n_p S^\circ(\text{products}) - \sum n_r S^\circ(\text{reactants})$$

Methods for Calculating the Free Energy of Formation (ΔG°_{rxn}) (**19.8**)

1. $\Delta G^\circ_{rxn} = \Delta H^\circ_{rxn} - T\Delta S^\circ_{rxn}$
2. $\Delta G^\circ_{rxn} = \sum n_p \Delta G^\circ_f(\text{products}) - \sum n_r \Delta G^\circ_f(\text{reactants})$
3. $\Delta G^\circ_{rxn(overall)} = \Delta G^\circ_{rxn(step\ 1)} + \Delta G^\circ_{rxn(step\ 2)} + \Delta G^\circ_{rxn(step\ 3)} + \ldots$

The Relationship between ΔG°_{rxn} and ΔG_{rxn} (**19.9**)

$$\Delta G_{rxn} = \Delta G^\circ_{rxn} + RT \ln Q \qquad R = 8.314\ \text{J/mol} \cdot \text{K}$$

The Relationship between ΔG°_{rxn} and K (**19.10**)

$$\Delta G^\circ_{rxn} = -RT \ln K$$

The Temperature Dependence of the Equilibrium Constant (**19.10**)

$$\ln K = -\frac{\Delta H^\circ_{rxn}}{R}\left(\frac{1}{T}\right) + \frac{\Delta S^\circ_{rxn}}{R}$$

$$\ln \frac{K_2}{K_1} = -\frac{\Delta H^\circ_{rxn}}{R}\left(\frac{1}{T_2} - \frac{1}{T_1}\right)$$

LEARNING OUTCOMES

Chapter Objectives	Assessment
Identify spontaneous and nonspontaneous processes (**19.2**)	Exercises 27–28
Analyze systems of particles and reactions in terms of entropy change (**19.3**)	Example 19.1 **For Practice** 19.1 **Exercises** 29–30
Calculate the entropy change for a change in state (**19.4**)	Example 19.2 **For Practice** 19.2 **Exercises** 31–34

Calculate entropy changes in the system (ΔS_{sys}), the surroundings (ΔS_{surr}), and the universe (ΔS_{univ}) (**19.5**)	Example 19.3 **For Practice** 19.3 **For More Practice** 19.3 **Exercises** 35–42
Analyze reaction spontaneity using Gibbs free energy change (ΔG), ΔH, and ΔS (**19.6**)	Example 19.4 **For Practice** 19.4 **Exercises** 43–47
Calculate the standard entropy change for a reaction (ΔS°_{rxn}) (**19.7**)	Example 19.5 **For Practice** 19.5 **Exercises** 48–58
Analyze reaction spontaneity using standard Gibbs free energy change (ΔG°_{rxn}), ΔH°_{rxn}, and ΔS°_{rxn} (**19.8**)	Examples 19.6, 19.7 **For Practice** 19.6, 19.7 **Exercises** 59–62
Calculate ΔG°_{rxn} using free energies of formation (ΔG°_f) (**19.8**)	Example 19.8 **For Practice** 19.8 **For More Practice** 19.8 **Exercises** 63–66
Calculate ΔG°_{rxn} for a stepwise reaction (**19.8**)	Example 19.9 **For Practice** 19.9 **Exercises** 67–68
Calculate ΔG_{rxn} for nonstandard conditions (**19.9**)	Example 19.10 **For Practice** 19.10 **Exercises** 69–72
Perform ΔG°_{rxn} calculations using equilibrium constants (K) (**19.10**)	Example 19.11 **For Practice** 19.11 **Exercises** 73–82

EXERCISES

Mastering Chemistry provides end-of-chapter exercises, feedback-enriched tutorial problems, animations, and interactive activities to encourage problem-solving practice and deeper understanding of key concepts and topics.

REVIEW QUESTIONS

1. What is the first law of thermodynamics, and how does it relate to energy use?

2. What is nature's heat tax, and how does it relate to energy use?

3. What is a perpetual motion machine? Can such a machine exist given the laws of thermodynamics?

4. Is it more efficient to heat your home with a natural gas furnace or an electric furnace? Explain.

5. What is a spontaneous process? Provide an example.

6. Explain the difference between the spontaneity of a reaction (which depends on thermodynamics) and the speed at which the reaction occurs (which depends on kinetics). Can a catalyst make a nonspontaneous reaction spontaneous?

7. What is the precise definition of entropy? What is the significance of entropy being a state function?

8. Why does the entropy of a gas increase when it expands into a vacuum?

9. Explain the difference between macrostates (external arrangements of particles) and microstates (internal arrangements of particles).

10. Based on its fundamental definition, explain why entropy is a measure of energy dispersion.

11. State the second law of thermodynamics. How does the second law explain why heat travels from a substance at higher temperature to one at lower temperature?

12. What happens to the entropy of a sample of matter when it changes state from a solid to a liquid? From a liquid to a gas?

13. Explain why water spontaneously freezes to form ice below 0 °C even though the entropy of the water decreases during the state transition. Why is the freezing of water not spontaneous above 0 °C?

14. Why do exothermic processes tend to be spontaneous at low temperatures? Why does their tendency toward spontaneity decrease with increasing temperature?

15. What is the significance of the change in Gibbs free energy (ΔG) for a reaction?

16. Predict the spontaneity of a reaction (and the temperature dependence of the spontaneity) for each possible combination of signs for ΔH and ΔS (for the system).

a. ΔH negative, ΔS positive **b.** ΔH positive, ΔS negative
c. ΔH negative, ΔS negative **d.** ΔH positive, ΔS positive

17. State the third law of thermodynamics and explain its significance.

18. Why is the standard entropy of a substance in the gas state greater than its standard entropy in the liquid state?

19. How does the standard entropy of a substance depend on its molar mass? On its molecular complexity?

20. How can you calculate the standard entropy change for a reaction from tables of standard entropies?

21. What are three different methods to calculate ΔG° for a reaction? Which method would you choose to calculate ΔG° for a reaction at a temperature other than 25 °C?

22. Why is free energy "free"?

23. Explain the difference between ΔG° and ΔG.

24. Why does water spilled on the floor evaporate even though ΔG° for the evaporation process is positive at room temperature?

25. How do you calculate the change in free energy for a reaction under nonstandard conditions?

26. How does the value of ΔG° for a reaction relate to the equilibrium constant for the reaction? What does a negative ΔG° for a reaction imply about K for the reaction? A positive ΔG°?

PROBLEMS BY TOPIC

Entropy, the Second Law of Thermodynamics, and the Direction of Spontaneous Change

27. Which of these processes is spontaneous?
MISSED THIS? *Read Section 19.2*
a. the combustion of natural gas
b. the extraction of iron metal from iron ore
c. a hot drink cooling to room temperature
d. drawing heat energy from the ocean's surface to power a ship

28. Which of these processes are nonspontaneous? Are the nonspontaneous processes impossible?
a. a bike going up a hill
b. a meteor falling to Earth
c. obtaining hydrogen gas from liquid water
d. a ball rolling down a hill

29. Two systems, each composed of two particles represented by circles, have 20 J of total energy. Which system, A or B, has the greater entropy? Why? **MISSED THIS?** *Read Section 19.3*

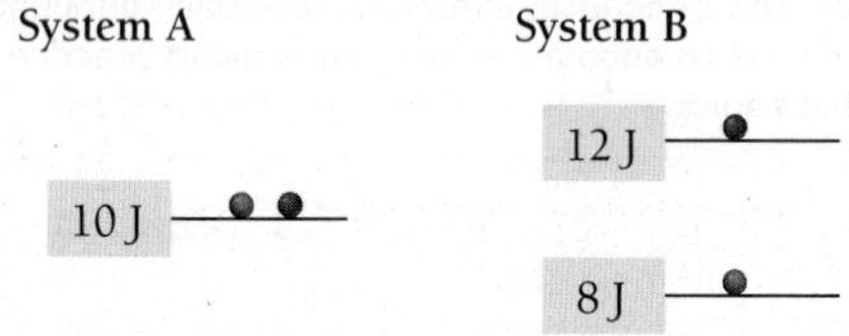

30. Two systems, each composed of three particles represented by circles, have 30 J of total energy. In how many energetically equivalent ways can you distribute the particles in each system? Which system has greater entropy?

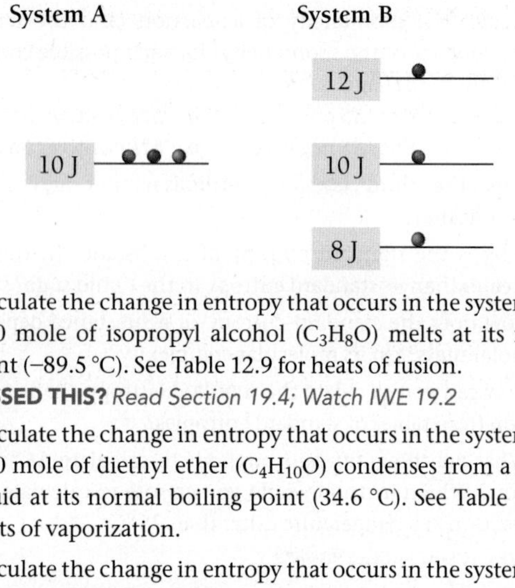

31. Calculate the change in entropy that occurs in the system when 1.00 mole of isopropyl alcohol (C_3H_8O) melts at its melting point (−89.5 °C). See Table 12.9 for heats of fusion.
MISSED THIS? *Read Section 19.4; Watch IWE 19.2*

32. Calculate the change in entropy that occurs in the system when 1.00 mole of diethyl ether ($C_4H_{10}O$) condenses from a gas to a liquid at its normal boiling point (34.6 °C). See Table 12.7 for heats of vaporization.

33. Calculate the change in entropy that occurs in the system when 45.0 g of acetone (C_3H_6O) freezes at its melting point (−94.8 °C). See Table 12.9 for heats of fusion.
MISSED THIS? *Read Section 19.4; Watch IWE 19.2*

34. Calculate the change in entropy that occurs in the system when 55.0 g of water vaporizes from a liquid to a gas at its boiling point (100.0 °C). See Table 12.7 for heats of vaporization.

35. Without doing any calculations, determine the sign of ΔS_{sys} for each chemical reaction. **MISSED THIS?** *Read Section 19.4*
a. $2\,KClO_3(s) \longrightarrow 2\,KCl(s) + 3\,O_2(g)$
b. $CH_2{=}CH_2(g) + H_2(g) \longrightarrow CH_3CH_3(g)$
c. $Na(s) + 1/2\,Cl_2(g) \longrightarrow NaCl(s)$
d. $N_2(g) + 3\,H_2(g) \longrightarrow 2\,NH_3(g)$

36. Without doing any calculations, determine the sign of ΔS_{sys} for each chemical reaction.
a. $Mg(s) + Cl_2(g) \longrightarrow MgCl_2(s)$
b. $2\,H_2S(g) + 3\,O_2(g) \longrightarrow 2\,H_2O(g) + 2\,SO_2(g)$
c. $2\,O_3(g) \longrightarrow 3\,O_2(g)$
d. $HCl(g) + NH_3(g) \longrightarrow NH_4Cl(s)$

37. Without doing any calculations, determine the signs of ΔS_{sys} and ΔS_{surr} for each chemical reaction. In addition, predict under what temperatures (all temperatures, low temperatures, or high temperatures), if any, the reaction is spontaneous.
MISSED THIS? *Read Sections 19.4, 19.5; Watch IWE 19.3*
a. $C_3H_8(g) + 5\,O_2(g) \longrightarrow 3\,CO_2(g) + 4\,H_2O(g)$ $\quad \Delta H^\circ_{rxn} = -2044$ kJ
b. $N_2(g) + O_2(g) \longrightarrow 2\,NO(g)$ $\quad \Delta H^\circ_{rxn} = +182.6$ kJ
c. $2\,N_2(g) + O_2(g) \longrightarrow 2\,N_2O(g)$ $\quad \Delta H^\circ_{rxn} = +163.2$ kJ
d. $4\,NH_3(g) + 5\,O_2(g) \longrightarrow 4\,NO(g) + 6\,H_2O(g)$ $\quad \Delta H^\circ_{rxn} = -906$ kJ

38. Without doing any calculations, determine the signs of ΔS_{sys} and ΔS_{surr} for each chemical reaction. In addition, predict under what temperatures (all temperatures, low temperatures, or high temperatures), if any, the reaction is spontaneous.
a. $2\,CO(g) + O_2(g) \longrightarrow 2\,CO_2(g)$ $\quad \Delta H^\circ_{rxn} = -566.0$ kJ
b. $2\,NO_2(g) \longrightarrow 2\,NO(g) + O_2(g)$ $\quad \Delta H^\circ_{rxn} = +113.1$ kJ
c. $2\,H_2(g) + O_2(g) \longrightarrow 2\,H_2O(g)$ $\quad \Delta H^\circ_{rxn} = -483.6$ kJ
d. $CO_2(g) \longrightarrow C(s) + O_2(g)$ $\quad \Delta H^\circ_{rxn} = +393.5$ kJ

39. Calculate ΔS_{surr} at the indicated temperature for each reaction.
MISSED THIS? *Read Section 19.5; Watch IWE 19.3*
a. $\Delta H^\circ_{rxn} = -385$ kJ; 298 K
b. $\Delta H^\circ_{rxn} = -385$ kJ; 77 K
c. $\Delta H^\circ_{rxn} = +114$ kJ; 298 K
d. $\Delta H^\circ_{rxn} = +114$ kJ; 77 K

40. A reaction has $\Delta H^\circ_{rxn} = -112$ kJ and $\Delta S^\circ_{rxn} = 354$ J/K. At what temperature is the change in entropy for the reaction equal to the change in entropy for the surroundings?

41. Given the values of ΔH°_{rxn}, ΔS°_{rxn}, and T, determine ΔS_{univ} and predict whether or not each reaction is spontaneous. (Assume that all reactants and products are in their standard states.) **MISSED THIS?** *Read Section 19.5; Watch IWE 19.3*
a. $\Delta H^\circ_{rxn} = +115$ kJ; $\Delta S^\circ_{rxn} = -263$ J/K; $T = 298$ K
b. $\Delta H^\circ_{rxn} = -115$ kJ; $\Delta S^\circ_{rxn} = +263$ J/K; $T = 298$ K
c. $\Delta H^\circ_{rxn} = -115$ kJ; $\Delta S^\circ_{rxn} = -263$ J/K; $T = 298$ K
d. $\Delta H^\circ_{rxn} = -115$ kJ; $\Delta S^\circ_{rxn} = -263$ J/K; $T = 615$ K

42. Given the values of ΔH_{rxn}, and T, determine ΔS_{rxn}, and predict whether or not each reaction is spontaneous. (Assume that all reactants and products are in their standard states.)
a. $\Delta H^\circ_{rxn} = -95$ kJ; $\Delta S^\circ_{rxn} = -157$ J/K; $T = 298$ K
b. $\Delta H^\circ_{rxn} = -95$ kJ; $\Delta S^\circ_{rxn} = -157$ J/K; $T = 855$ K
c. $\Delta H^\circ_{rxn} = +95$ kJ; $\Delta S^\circ_{rxn} = -157$ J/K; $T = 298$ K
d. $\Delta H^\circ_{rxn} = -95$ kJ; $\Delta S^\circ_{rxn} = +157$ J/K; $T = 398$ K

Standard Entropy Changes and Gibbs Free Energy

43. Calculate the change in Gibbs free energy for each of the sets of ΔH_{rxn}, ΔS_{rxn}, and T given in Problem 41. Predict whether or not each reaction is spontaneous at the temperature indicated. (Assume that all reactants and products are in their standard states.)
MISSED THIS? *Read Section 19.6; Watch KCV 19.6, IWE 19.4*

44. Calculate the change in Gibbs free energy for each of the sets of ΔH_{rxn}, ΔS_{rxn}, and T given in Problem 42. Predict whether or not each reaction is spontaneous at the temperature indicated. (Assume that all reactants and products are in their standard states.)

45. Calculate the free energy change for this reaction at 25 °C. Is the reaction spontaneous? (Assume that all reactants and products are in their standard states.)
MISSED THIS? *Read Section 19.6; Watch KCV 19.6, IWE 19.4*

$$C_3H_8(g) + 5\,O_2(g) \longrightarrow 3\,CO_2(g) + 4\,H_2O(g)$$
$$\Delta H^\circ_{rxn} = -2217\text{ kJ};\ \Delta S^\circ_{rxn} = 101.1\text{ J/K}$$

46. Calculate the free energy change for this reaction at 25 °C. Is the reaction spontaneous? (Assume that all reactants and products are in their standard states.)

$$2\,Ca(s) + O_2(g) \longrightarrow 2\,CaO(s)$$
$$\Delta H^\circ_{rxn} = -1269.8\text{ kJ};\ \Delta S^\circ_{rxn} = -364.6\text{ J/K}$$

47. Fill in the blanks in the table. Both ΔH and ΔS refer to the system.
MISSED THIS? *Read Section 19.6; Watch KCV 19.6*

ΔH	ΔS	ΔG	Low Temperature	High Temperature
−	+	−	Spontaneous	______
−	−	Temperature dependent	______	______
+	+	______	______	Spontaneous
______	−	______	Nonspontaneous	Nonspontaneous

48. Predict the conditions (high temperature, low temperature, all temperatures, or no temperatures) under which each reaction is spontaneous.
a. $H_2O(g) \longrightarrow H_2O(l)$
b. $CO_2(s) \longrightarrow CO_2(g)$
c. $H_2(g) \longrightarrow 2\,H(g)$
d. $2\,NO_2(g) \longrightarrow 2\,NO(g) + O_2(g)$ (endothermic)

49. How does the molar entropy of a substance change with increasing temperature?
MISSED THIS? *Read Section 19.7; Watch KCV 19.7*

50. What is the molar entropy of a pure crystal at 0 K? What is the significance of the answer to this question?

51. For each pair of substances, choose the one that you expect to have the higher standard molar entropy (S°) at 25 °C. Explain your choices. **MISSED THIS?** *Read Section 19.7; Watch KCV 19.7*
a. $CO(g)$; $CO_2(g)$
b. $CH_3OH(l)$; $CH_3OH(g)$
c. $Ar(g)$; $CO_2(g)$
d. $CH_4(g)$; $SiH_4(g)$
e. $NO_2(g)$; $CH_3CH_2CH_3(g)$
f. $NaBr(s)$; $NaBr(aq)$

52. For each pair of substances, choose the one that you expect to have the higher standard molar entropy (S°) at 25 °C. Explain your choices.
a. $NaNO_3(s)$; $NaNO_3(aq)$
b. $CH_4(g)$; $CH_3CH_3(g)$
c. $Br_2(l)$; $Br_2(g)$
d. $Br_2(g)$; $F_2(g)$
e. $PCl_3(g)$; $PCl_5(g)$
f. $CH_3CH_2CH_2CH_3(g)$; $SO_2(g)$

53. Rank each set of substances in order of increasing standard molar entropy (S°). Explain your reasoning.
MISSED THIS? *Read Section 19.7; Watch KCV 19.7*
a. $NH_3(g)$; $Ne(g)$; $SO_2(g)$; $CH_3CH_2OH(g)$; $He(g)$
b. $H_2O(s)$; $H_2O(l)$; $H_2O(g)$
c. $CH_4(g)$; $CF_4(g)$; $CCl_4(g)$

54. Rank each set of substances in order of increasing standard molar entropy (S°). Explain your reasoning.
a. $I_2(g)$; $F_2(g)$; $Br_2(g)$; $Cl_2(g)$
b. $H_2O(g)$; $H_2O_2(g)$; $H_2S(g)$
c. $C(s,\text{ graphite})$; $C(s,\text{ diamond})$; $C(s,\text{ amorphous})$

55. Use data from Appendix IIB to calculate ΔS°_{rxn} for each of the reactions. In each case, try to rationalize the sign of ΔS°_{rxn}.
MISSED THIS? *Read Section 19.7; Watch IWE 19.5*
a. $C_2H_4(g) + H_2(g) \longrightarrow C_2H_6(g)$
b. $C(s) + H_2O(g) \longrightarrow CO(g) + H_2(g)$
c. $CO(g) + H_2O(g) \longrightarrow H_2(g) + CO_2(g)$
d. $2\,H_2S(g) + 3\,O_2(g) \longrightarrow 2\,H_2O(l) + 2\,SO_2(g)$

56. Use data from Appendix IIB to calculate ΔS°_{rxn} for each of the reactions. In each case, try to rationalize the sign of ΔS°_{rxn}.
a. $3\,NO_2(g) + H_2O(l) \longrightarrow 2\,HNO_3(aq) + NO(g)$
b. $Cr_2O_3(s) + 3\,CO(g) \longrightarrow 2\,Cr(s) + 3\,CO_2(g)$
c. $SO_2(g) + \frac{1}{2}O_2(g) \longrightarrow SO_3(g)$
d. $N_2O_4(g) + 4\,H_2(g) \longrightarrow N_2(g) + 4\,H_2O(g)$

57. Find ΔS° for the formation of $CH_2Cl_2(g)$ from its gaseous elements in their standard states. Rationalize the sign of ΔS°.
MISSED THIS? *Read Section 19.7; Watch IWE 19.5*

58. Find ΔS° for the reaction between nitrogen gas and fluorine gas to form nitrogen trifluoride gas. Rationalize the sign of ΔS°.

59. Methanol (CH_3OH) burns in oxygen to form carbon dioxide and water. Write a balanced equation for the combustion of liquid methanol and calculate ΔH°_{rxn}, ΔS°_{rxn}, and ΔG°_{rxn} at 25 °C. Is the combustion of methanol spontaneous?
MISSED THIS? *Read Section 19.8; Watch IWE 19.6*

60. In photosynthesis, plants form glucose ($C_6H_{12}O_6$) and oxygen from carbon dioxide and water. Write a balanced equation for photosynthesis and calculate ΔH°_{rxn}, ΔS°_{rxn}, and ΔG°_{rxn} at 25 °C. Is photosynthesis spontaneous?

61. For each reaction, calculate ΔH°_{rxn}, ΔS°_{rxn}, and ΔG°_{rxn} at 25 °C and state whether or not the reaction is spontaneous. If the reaction is not spontaneous, would a change in temperature make it spontaneous? If so, should the temperature be raised or lowered from 25 °C? **MISSED THIS?** *Read Section 19.8; Watch IWE 19.6*
a. $N_2O_4(g) \longrightarrow 2\,NO_2(g)$
b. $NH_4Cl(s) \longrightarrow HCl(g) + NH_3(g)$
c. $3\,H_2(g) + Fe_2O_3(s) \longrightarrow 2\,Fe(s) + 3\,H_2O(g)$
d. $N_2(g) + 3\,H_2(g) \longrightarrow 2\,NH_3(g)$

62. For each reaction, calculate ΔH°_{rxn}, ΔS°_{rxn}, and ΔG°_{rxn} at 25 °C and state whether or not the reaction is spontaneous. If the reaction is not spontaneous, would a change in temperature make it spontaneous? If so, should the temperature be raised or lowered from 25 °C?
a. $2\,CH_4(g) \longrightarrow C_2H_6(g) + H_2(g)$
b. $2\,NH_3(g) \longrightarrow N_2H_4(g) + H_2(g)$
c. $N_2(g) + O_2(g) \longrightarrow 2\,NO(g)$
d. $2\,KClO_3(s) \longrightarrow 2\,KCl(s) + 3\,O_2(g)$

63. Use standard free energies of formation to calculate ΔG° at 25 °C for each reaction in Problem 61. How do the values of ΔG° calculated this way compare to those calculated from ΔH° and ΔS°? Which of the two methods could be used to determine how ΔG° changes with temperature?
MISSED THIS? *Read Section 19.8*

64. Use standard free energies of formation to calculate ΔG° at 25 °C for each reaction in Problem 62. How well do the values of ΔG° calculated this way compare to those calculated from ΔH° and ΔS°? Which of the two methods could be used to determine how ΔG° changes with temperature?

65. Consider the reaction:
MISSED THIS? *Read Section 19.8; Watch IWE 19.6*

$$2\,NO(g) + O_2(g) \longrightarrow 2\,NO_2(g)$$

Estimate ΔG° for this reaction at each temperature and predict whether or not the reaction is spontaneous. (Assume that ΔH° and ΔS° do not change too much within the given temperature range.)
a. 298 K b. 715 K c. 855 K

66. Consider the reaction:

$$CaCO_3(s) \longrightarrow CaO(s) + CO_2(g)$$

Estimate ΔG° for this reaction at each temperature and predict whether or not the reaction is spontaneous. (Assume that ΔH° and ΔS° do not change too much within the given temperature range.)
a. 298 K b. 1055 K c. 1455 K

67. Determine ΔG° for the reaction:
MISSED THIS? *Read Section 19.8*

$$Fe_2O_3(s) + 3\,CO(g) \longrightarrow 2\,Fe(s) + 3\,CO_2(g)$$

Use the following reactions with known ΔG°_{rxn} values:

$$2\,Fe(s) + \tfrac{3}{2}O_2(g) \longrightarrow Fe_2O_3(s) \qquad \Delta G^\circ_{rxn} = -742.2\text{ kJ}$$
$$CO(g) + \tfrac{1}{2}O_2(g) \longrightarrow CO_2(g) \qquad \Delta G^\circ_{rxn} = -257.2\text{ kJ}$$

68. Calculate ΔG°_{rxn} for the reaction:

$$CaCO_3(s) \longrightarrow CaO(s) + CO_2(g)$$

Use the following reactions and given ΔG°_{rxn} values:

$$Ca(s) + CO_2(g) + \tfrac{1}{2}O_2(g) \longrightarrow CaCO_3(s) \quad \Delta G^\circ_{rxn} = -734.4\text{ kJ}$$
$$2\,Ca(s) + O_2(g) \longrightarrow 2\,CaO(s) \qquad \Delta G^\circ_{rxn} = -1206.6\text{ kJ}$$

Free Energy Changes, Nonstandard Conditions, and the Equilibrium Constant

69. Consider the sublimation of iodine at 25.0 °C:
MISSED THIS? *Read Section 19.9; Watch IWE 19.10*

$$I_2(s) \longrightarrow I_2(g)$$

a. Find ΔG°_{rxn} at 25.0 °C.
b. Find ΔG_{rxn} at 25.0 °C under the following nonstandard conditions:
i. $P_{I_2} = 1.00$ mmHg
ii. $P_{I_2} = 0.100$ mmHg
c. Explain why iodine spontaneously sublimes in open air at 25.0 °C.

70. Consider the evaporation of methanol at 25.0 °C:

$$CH_3OH(l) \longrightarrow CH_3OH(g)$$

a. Find ΔG°_r at 25.0 °C.
b. Find ΔG_r at 25.0 °C under the following nonstandard conditions:
i. $P_{CH_3OH} = 150.0$ mmHg
ii. $P_{CH_3OH} = 100.0$ mmHg
iii. $P_{CH_3OH} = 10.0$ mmHg
c. Explain why methanol spontaneously evaporates in open air at 25.0 °C.

71. Consider the reaction:
MISSED THIS? *Read Section 19.9; Watch IWE 19.10*

$$CH_3OH(g) \rightleftharpoons CO(g) + 2\,H_2(g)$$

Calculate ΔG for this reaction at 25 °C under the following conditions:
i. $P_{CH_3OH} = 0.855$ atm
ii. $P_{CO} = 0.125$ atm
iii. $P_{H_2} = 0.183$ atm

72. Consider the reaction:

$$CO_2(g) + CCl_4(g) \rightleftharpoons 2\,COCl_2(g)$$

Calculate ΔG for this reaction at 25 °C under the following conditions:
i. $P_{CO_2} = 0.112$ atm
ii. $P_{CCl_4} = 0.174$ atm
iii. $P_{COCl_2} = 0.744$ atm

73. Use data from Appendix IIB to calculate the equilibrium constants at 25 °C for each reaction.
MISSED THIS? *Read Section 19.10; Watch IWE 19.11*
a. $2\,CO(g) + O_2(g) \rightleftharpoons 2\,CO_2(g)$
b. $2\,H_2S(g) \rightleftharpoons 2\,H_2(g) + S_2(g)$

74. Use data from Appendix IIB to calculate the equilibrium constants at 25 °C for each reaction. ΔG°_f for BrCl(g) is −1.0 kJ/mol.
a. $2\,NO_2(g) \rightleftharpoons N_2O_4(g)$
b. $Br_2(g) + Cl_2(g) \rightleftharpoons 2\,BrCl(g)$

75. Consider the reaction:
MISSED THIS? *Read Sections 19.9, 19.10; Watch IWE 19.10, 19.11*

$$CO(g) + 2\,H_2(g) \rightleftharpoons CH_3OH(g)$$
$$K_p = 2.26 \times 10^4 \text{ at } 25\text{ °C}$$

Calculate ΔG_{rxn} for the reaction at 25 °C under each of the following conditions:
a. standard conditions
b. at equilibrium
c. $P_{CH_3OH} = 1.0$ atm; $P_{CO} = P_{H_2} = 0.010$ atm

76. Consider the reaction:

$$I_2(g) + Cl_2(g) \rightleftharpoons 2\,ICl(g)$$
$$K_p = 81.9 \text{ at } 25\text{ °C}$$

Calculate ΔG_{rxn} for the reaction at 25 °C under each of the following conditions:
a. standard conditions
b. at equilibrium
c. $P_{ICl} = 2.55$ atm; $P_{I_2} = 0.325$ atm; $P_{Cl_2} = 0.221$ atm

77. Estimate the value of the equilibrium constant at 525 K for each reaction in Problem 73.
MISSED THIS? *Read Sections 19.8, 19.10; Watch IWE 19.11*

78. Estimate the value of the equilibrium constant at 655 K for each reaction in Problem 74. (ΔH°_f for BrCl is 14.6 kJ/mol.)

79. Consider the reaction: **MISSED THIS?** *Read Section 19.10*

$$H_2(g) + I_2(g) \rightleftharpoons 2\,HI(g)$$

The following data show the equilibrium constant for this reaction measured at several different temperatures. Use the data to find ΔH°_{rxn} and ΔS°_{rxn} for the reaction.

Temperature	K_p
150 K	1.4×10^{-6}
175 K	4.6×10^{-4}
200 K	3.6×10^{-2}
225 K	1.1
250 K	15.5

80. Consider the reaction:

$$2\,NO(g) + O_2(g) \rightleftharpoons 2\,NO_2(g)$$

The following data show the equilibrium constant for this reaction measured at several different temperatures. Use the data to find ΔH°_{rxn} and ΔS°_{rxn} for the reaction.

Temperature	K_p
170 K	3.8×10^{-3}
180 K	0.34
190 K	18.4
200 K	681

81. The change in enthalpy (ΔH°_{rxn}) for a reaction is -25.8 kJ/mol. The equilibrium constant for the reaction is 1.4×10^3 at 298 K. What is the equilibrium constant for the reaction at 655 K?
MISSED THIS? *Read Section 19.10*

82. A reaction has an equilibrium constant of 8.5×10^3 at 298 K. At 755 K, the equilibrium constant is 0.65. Find ΔH°_{rxn} for the reaction.

CUMULATIVE PROBLEMS

83. Determine the sign of ΔS_{sys} for each process.
a. water boiling
b. water freezing
c.

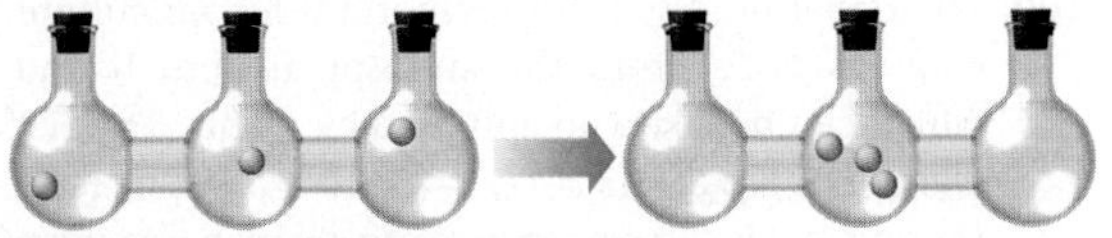

84. Determine the sign of ΔS_{sys} for each process.
a. dry ice subliming
b. dew forming
c.

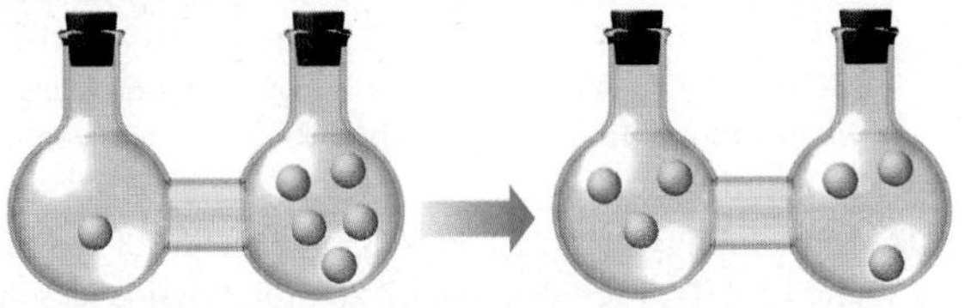

85. Our atmosphere is composed primarily of nitrogen and oxygen, which coexist at 25 °C without reacting to any significant extent. However, the two gases can react to form nitrogen monoxide according to the reaction:

$$N_2(g) + O_2(g) \rightleftharpoons 2\,NO(g)$$

a. Calculate ΔG° and K_p for this reaction at 298 K. Is the reaction spontaneous?
b. Estimate ΔG° at 2000 K. Does the reaction become more spontaneous as temperature increases?

86. Nitrogen dioxide, a pollutant in the atmosphere, can combine with water to form nitric acid. One of the possible reactions is shown here. Calculate ΔG° and K_p for this reaction at 25 °C and comment on the spontaneity of the reaction.

$$3\,NO_2(g) + H_2O(l) \longrightarrow 2\,HNO_3(aq) + NO(g)$$

87. Ethene (C_2H_4) can be halogenated by the reaction:

$$C_2H_4(g) + X_2(g) \rightleftharpoons C_2H_4X_2(g)$$

where X_2 can be Cl_2, Br_2, or I_2. Use the thermodynamic data given to calculate ΔH°, ΔS°, ΔG°, and K_p for the halogenation reaction by each of the three halogens at 25 °C. Which reaction is most spontaneous? Least spontaneous? What is the main factor responsible for the difference in the spontaneity of the three reactions? Does higher temperature make the reactions more spontaneous or less spontaneous?

Compound	ΔH°_f (kJ/mol)	S° (J/mol · K)
$C_2H_4Cl_2(g)$	-129.7	308.0
$C_2H_4Br_2(g)$	$+38.3$	330.6
$C_2H_4I_2(g)$	$+66.5$	347.8

88. H_2 reacts with the halogens (X_2) according to the reaction:

$$H_2(g) + X_2(g) \rightleftharpoons 2\,HX(g)$$

where X_2 can be Cl_2, Br_2, or I_2. Use the thermodynamic data in Appendix IIB to calculate ΔH°, ΔS°, ΔG°, and K_p for the reaction between hydrogen and each of the three halogens. Which reaction is most spontaneous? Least spontaneous? What is the main factor responsible for the difference in the spontaneity of the three reactions? Does higher temperature make the reactions more spontaneous or less spontaneous?

89. Consider this reaction occurring at 298 K:

$$N_2O(g) + NO_2(g) \rightleftharpoons 3\,NO(g)$$

a. Show that the reaction is not spontaneous under standard conditions by calculating ΔG°_{rxn}.
b. If a reaction mixture contains only N_2O and NO_2 at partial pressures of 1.0 atm each, the reaction will be spontaneous until some NO forms in the mixture. What maximum partial pressure of NO builds up before the reaction ceases to be spontaneous?
c. Can the reaction be made more spontaneous by an increase or decrease in temperature? If so, what temperature is required to make the reaction spontaneous under standard conditions?

90. Consider this reaction occurring at 298 K:

$$BaCO_3(s) \rightleftharpoons BaO(s) + CO_2(g)$$

a. Show that the reaction is not spontaneous under standard conditions by calculating ΔG°_{rxn}.
b. If $BaCO_3$ is placed in an evacuated flask, what is the partial pressure of CO_2 when the reaction reaches equilibrium?
c. Can the reaction be made more spontaneous by an increase or decrease in temperature? If so, at what temperature is the partial pressure of carbon dioxide 1.0 atm?

91. Living organisms use energy from the metabolism of food to create an energy-rich molecule called adenosine triphosphate (ATP). The ATP acts as an energy source for a variety of reactions that the living organism must carry out to survive. ATP provides energy through its hydrolysis, which can be symbolized as follows:

$$ATP(aq) + H_2O(l) \longrightarrow ADP(aq) + P_i(aq) \quad \Delta G^\circ_{rxn} = -30.5\text{ kJ}$$

where ADP represents adenosine diphosphate and P_i represents an inorganic phosphate group (such as HPO_4^{2-}).
a. Calculate the equilibrium constant, K, for the given reaction at 298 K.
b. The free energy obtained from the oxidation (reaction with oxygen) of glucose ($C_6H_{12}O_6$) to form carbon dioxide and water can be used to re-form ATP by driving the given reaction in reverse. Calculate the standard free energy change for the oxidation of glucose and estimate the maximum number of moles of ATP that can be formed by the oxidation of one mole of glucose.

92. The standard free energy change for the hydrolysis of ATP was given in Problem 91. In a particular cell, the concentrations of ATP, ADP, and P_i are 0.0031 M, 0.0014 M, and 0.0048 M, respectively. Calculate the free energy change for the hydrolysis of ATP under these conditions. (Assume a temperature of 298 K.)

93. These reactions are important in catalytic converters in automobiles. Calculate $\Delta G°$ for each at 298 K. Predict the effect of increasing temperature on the magnitude of $\Delta G°$.

a. $2\,CO(g) + 2\,NO(g) \longrightarrow N_2(g) + 2\,CO_2(g)$
b. $5\,H_2(g) + 2\,NO(g) \longrightarrow 2\,NH_3(g) + 2\,H_2O(g)$
c. $2\,H_2(g) + 2\,NO(g) \longrightarrow N_2(g) + 2\,H_2O(g)$
d. $2\,NH_3(g) + 2\,O_2(g) \longrightarrow N_2O(g) + 3\,H_2O(g)$

94. Calculate $\Delta G°$ at 298 K for these reactions and predict the effect on $\Delta G°$ of lowering the temperature.

a. $NH_3(g) + HBr(g) \longrightarrow NH_4Br(s)$
b. $CaCO_3(s) \longrightarrow CaO(s) + CO_2(g)$
c. $CH_4(g) + 3\,Cl_2(g) \longrightarrow CHCl_3(g) + 3\,HCl(g)$
($\Delta G_f°$ for $CHCl_3(g)$ is −70.4 kJ/mol.)

95. All the oxides of nitrogen have positive values of $\Delta G_f°$ at 298 K, but only one common oxide of nitrogen has a positive $\Delta S_f°$. Identify that oxide of nitrogen without reference to thermodynamic data and explain.

96. The values of $\Delta G_f°$ for the hydrogen halides become less negative with increasing atomic number. The $\Delta G_f°$ of HI is slightly positive. However, the trend in $\Delta S_f°$ is to become more positive with increasing atomic number. Explain.

97. Consider the reaction $X_2(g) \longrightarrow 2\,X(g)$. When a vessel initially containing 755 torr of X_2 comes to equilibrium at 298 K, the equilibrium partial pressure of X is 103 torr. The same reaction is repeated with an initial partial pressure of 748 torr of X_2 at 755 K; the equilibrium partial pressure of X is 532 torr. Find $\Delta H°$ for the reaction.

98. Dinitrogen tetroxide decomposes to nitrogen dioxide:

$$N_2O_4(g) \longrightarrow 2\,NO_2(g) \quad \Delta H°_{rxn} = 55.3\text{ kJ}$$

At 298 K, a reaction vessel initially contains 0.100 atm of N_2O_4. When equilibrium is reached, 58% of the N_2O_4 has decomposed to NO_2. What percentage of N_2O_4 decomposes at 388 K? Assume that the initial pressure of N_2O_4 is the same (0.100 atm).

99. Indicate and explain the sign of ΔS_{univ} for each process.

a. $2\,H_2(g) + O_2(g) \longrightarrow 2\,H_2O(l)$ at 298 K
b. the electrolysis of $H_2O(l)$ to $H_2(g)$ and $O_2(g)$ at 298 K
c. the growth of an oak tree from a little acorn

100. The Haber process is very important for agriculture because it converts $N_2(g)$ from the atmosphere into bound nitrogen, which can be taken up and used by plants. The Haber process reaction is $N_2(g) + 3\,H_2(g) \rightleftharpoons 2\,NH_3(g)$. The reaction is exothermic but is carried out at relatively high temperatures. Why?

101. A metal salt with the formula MCl_2 crystallizes from water to form a solid with the composition $MCl_2 \cdot 6\,H_2O$. The equilibrium vapor pressure of water above this solid at 298 K is 18.3 mmHg. What is the value of ΔG for the reaction $MCl_2 \cdot 6\,H_2O(s) \rightleftharpoons MCl_2(s) + 6\,H_2O(g)$ when the pressure of water vapor is 18.3 mmHg? When the pressure of water vapor is 760 mmHg?

102. The solubility of AgCl(s) in water at 25 °C is 1.33×10^{-5} mol/L and its $\Delta H°$ of solution is 65.7 kJ/mol. What is its solubility at 50.0 °C?

CHALLENGE PROBLEMS

103. Review the box in this chapter entitled *Chemistry in Your Day: Making a Nonspontaneous Process Spontaneous.* The hydrolysis of ATP, shown in Problem 91, is often used to drive nonspontaneous processes—such as muscle contraction and protein synthesis—in living organisms. The nonspontaneous process to be driven must be coupled to the ATP hydrolysis reaction. For example, suppose the nonspontaneous process is $A + B \longrightarrow AB$ ($\Delta G°$ positive). The coupling of a nonspontaneous reaction such as this one to the hydrolysis of ATP is often accomplished by the mechanism:

$$A + ATP + H_2O \longrightarrow A{-}P_i + ADP$$
$$A{-}P_i + B \longrightarrow AB + P_i$$
$$\overline{A + B + ATP + H_2O \longrightarrow AB + ADP + P_i}$$

As long as $\Delta G°_{rxn}$ for the nonspontaneous reaction is less than 30.5 kJ, the reaction can be made spontaneous by coupling in this way to the hydrolysis of ATP. Suppose that ATP is to drive the reaction between glutamate and ammonia to form glutamine:

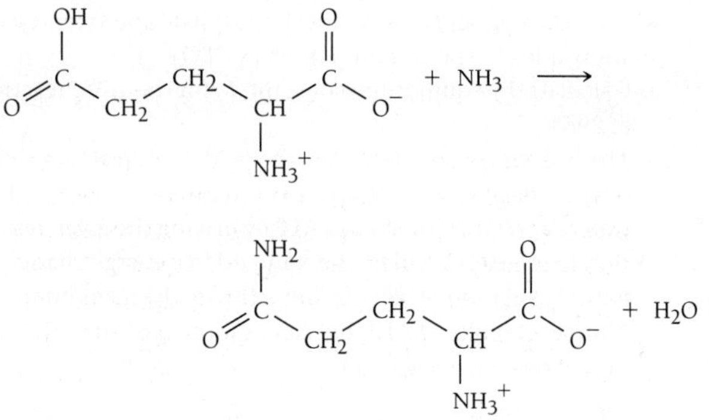

a. Calculate K for the reaction between glutamate and ammonia. (The standard free energy change for the reaction is +14.2 kJ/mol. Assume a temperature of 298 K.)
b. Write a set of reactions such as those given showing how the glutamate and ammonia reaction can couple with the hydrolysis of ATP. What are $\Delta G°_{rxn}$ and K for the coupled reaction?

104. Calculate the entropy of each state and rank the states in order of increasing entropy.

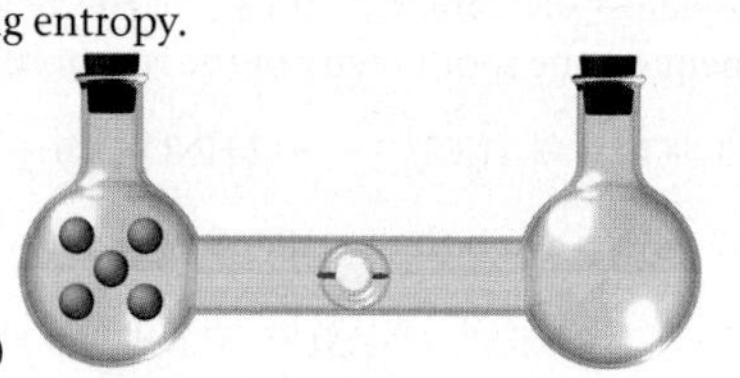
(a)

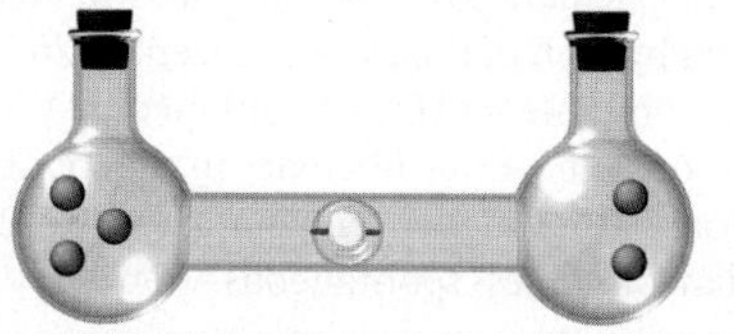
(b)

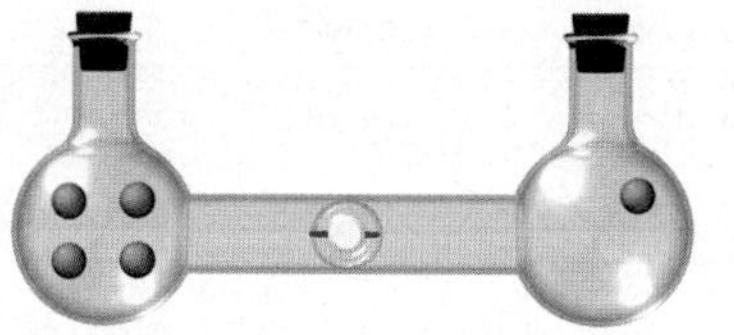
(c)

105. Suppose we redefine the standard state as $P = 2$ atm. Find the new standard ΔG_f° values of each substance.

a. $HCl(g)$ b. $N_2O(g)$ c. $H(g)$

Explain the results in terms of the relative entropies of reactants and products of each reaction.

106. The ΔG for the freezing of $H_2O(l)$ at $-10\,°C$ is -210 J/mol, and the heat of fusion of ice at this temperature is 5610 J/mol. Find the entropy change of the universe when 1 mol of water freezes at $-10\,°C$.

107. Consider the reaction that occurs during the Haber process:

$$N_2(g) + 3\,H_2(g) \longrightarrow 2\,NH_3(g)$$

The equilibrium constant is 3.9×10^5 at 300 K and 1.2×10^{-1} at 500 K. Calculate ΔH°_{rxn} and ΔS°_{rxn} for this reaction.

108. The salt ammonium nitrate can follow three modes of decomposition: (a) to $HNO_3(g)$ and $NH_3(g)$, (b) to $N_2O(g)$ and $H_2O(g)$, and (c) to $N_2(g)$, $O_2(g)$, and $H_2O(g)$. Calculate ΔG°_{rxn} for each mode of decomposition at 298 K. Explain in light of these results how it is still possible to use ammonium nitrate as a fertilizer and identify the precautions that should be taken when it is used.

109. Given the data, calculate ΔS_{vap} for each of the first four liquids. ($\Delta S_{vap} = \Delta H_{vap}/T$, where T is in K)

Compound	Name	BP (°C)	ΔH_{vap} (kJ/mol) at BP
$C_4H_{10}O$	Diethyl ether	34.6	26.5
C_3H_6O	Acetone	56.1	29.1
C_6H_6O	Benzene	79.8	30.8
$CHCl_3$	Chloroform	60.8	29.4
C_2H_5OH	Ethanol	77.8	38.6
H_2O	Water	100	40.7

All four values should be close to each other. Predict whether the last two liquids in the table have ΔS_{vap} in this same range. If not, predict whether it is larger or smaller and explain. Verify your prediction.

CONCEPTUAL PROBLEMS

110. Which is more efficient, a butane lighter or an electric lighter (such as the ones traditionally found on the dashboard of automobiles)? Explain.

111. Which statement is true?

a. A spontaneous reaction is always a fast reaction.
b. A spontaneous reaction is always a slow reaction.
c. The spontaneity of a reaction is not necessarily related to the speed of a reaction.

112. Which process is necessarily driven by an increase in the entropy of the surroundings?

a. the condensation of water
b. the sublimation of dry ice
c. the freezing of water

113. Consider the changes in the distribution of nine particles into three interconnected boxes shown here. Which has the most negative ΔS?

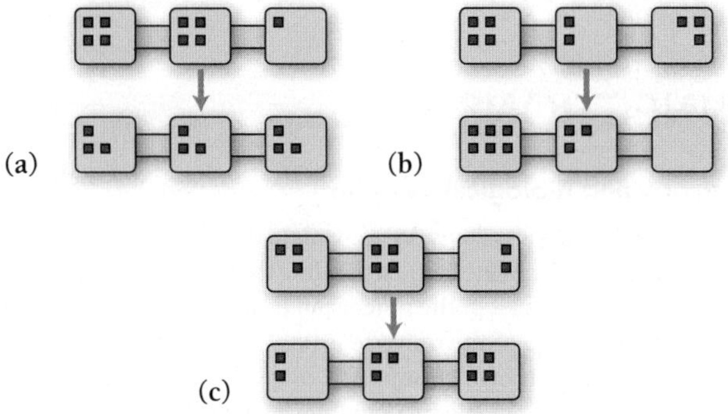

114. Which statement is true?

a. A reaction in which the entropy of the system increases can be spontaneous only if it is exothermic.
b. A reaction in which the entropy of the system increases can be spontaneous only if it is endothermic.
c. A reaction in which the entropy of the system decreases can be spontaneous only if it is exothermic.

115. Which process is spontaneous at 298 K?

a. $H_2O(l) \longrightarrow H_2O(g, 1\text{ atm})$
b. $H_2O(l) \longrightarrow H_2O(g, 0.10\text{ atm})$
c. $H_2O(l) \longrightarrow H_2O(g, 0.010\text{ atm})$

116. The free energy change of the reaction $A(g) \longrightarrow B(g)$ is zero under certain conditions. The *standard* free energy change of the reaction is -42.5 kJ. Which statement must be true about the reaction?

a. The concentration of the product is greater than the concentration of the reactant.
b. The reaction is at equilibrium.
c. The concentration of the reactant is greater than the concentration of the product.

117. The reaction $A(g) \rightleftharpoons B(g)$ has an equilibrium constant of 5.8 and under certain conditions has $Q = 336$. What can you conclude about the sign of ΔG°_{rxn} and ΔG_{rxn} for this reaction under these conditions?

QUESTIONS FOR GROUP WORK

Active Classroom Learning

Discuss these questions with the group and record your consensus answer.

118. Imagine that you roll two dice. Write down all the possible rolls that sum to 2. Write all the possible rolls that sum to 12. Write all the possible rolls that sum to 7. Which configuration has the greatest entropy: 2, 12, or 7?

119. If you roll 1 million dice, what will be the average of all the dice? If there is a room with 1 million dice and they all have a 1 on the top face, and there is an earthquake strong enough to roll dice around, what is the likelihood that after the earthquake all the top faces will sum to 1 million? To 6 million? How does this thought experiment illustrate the second law of thermodynamics?

120. Not all processes in which the system increases in entropy are spontaneous. How can this observation be consistent with the second law? Provide an example and explain your answer in complete sentences.

121. Have each group member look up ΔH_f° and S° for one substance in the reaction: $3\,O_2(g) + 6\,H_2(g) + 6\,C(s, \text{graphite}) \longrightarrow C_6H_{12}O_6(s, \text{glucose})$. What is ΔH° for this reaction? What is ΔS°? When is ΔH_f° for a substance equal to zero? When is S° for a substance equal to zero?

122. Calculate ΔG° at 25 °C for the reaction in the previous question. Is this reaction spontaneous under standard conditions? How do you know? What is the determining factor: the change in energy or the change in entropy or both? Explain.

DATA INTERPRETATION AND ANALYSIS

Thermodynamic Functions for Borax

123. Borax, sodium tetraborate decahydrate, is an important mineral found in dry lakebeds in California. It is used to make soap and glass, and it is also used as a preservative. You can use the values of K_{sp} of borax at different temperatures to determine ΔH°, ΔS°, and ΔG° for the dissolution of borax:

$$\underset{\text{(Borax)}}{Na_2B_4O_5(OH)_4 \cdot 8\,H_2O(s)} \longrightarrow 2\,Na^+(aq) + \underset{\text{(Borate)}}{B_4O_5(OH)_4^{2-}(aq)} + 8\,H_2O(l)$$

The relationship:

$$\ln(K_{sp}) = \frac{-\Delta H^\circ}{RT} + \frac{\Delta S^\circ}{R}$$

has the form of a linear equation $y = mx + b$, where y is the $\ln K_{sp}$ and x is $1/T$. The slope is equal to $(-\Delta H^\circ/R)$ and the y-intercept is $\Delta S^\circ/R$, where R is the gas constant, 8.314 J/K mol. If you measure K_{sp} at several different temperatures, you can plot the ln$K$ versus $1/T$ (T in Kelvin), as shown here.

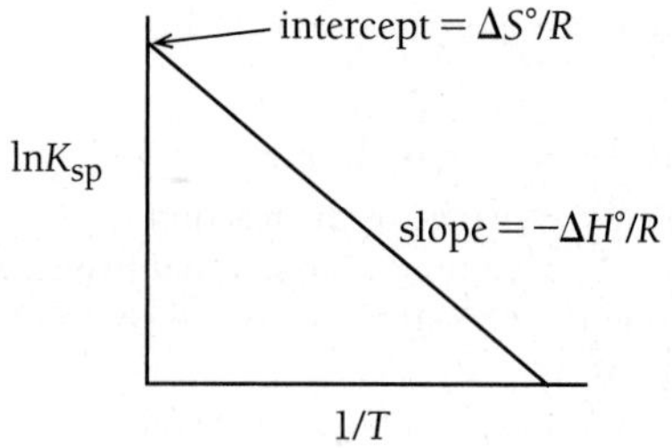

▲ Plot of lnK_{sp} versus $1/T$ where the Units of Temperature Are in Kelvin

Knowing the values of ΔH° and ΔS° at a specific temperature allows the calculation of the change in Gibbs free energy for the reaction: $\Delta G^\circ = \Delta H^\circ - T\Delta S^\circ$.

The following table lists K_{sp} values for the dissolution of borax at several different temperatures (°C).

K_{sp} Values for the Dissolution of Borax at Several Different Temperatures (°C)

Temperature (°C)	K_{sp}
40.0	0.041
45.0	0.083
50.0	0.264
55.0	0.486
60.0	0.552

a. Plot a graph of lnK_{sp} versus $1/T$ (T in Kelvin) and find the best-fitting line.
b. Determine ΔH°. Is this process endothermic or exothermic?
c. Determine ΔS°.
d. Determine ΔG°.
e. Sketch a graph of ln$K$ versus $1/T$ for an exothermic process.

Cc ANSWERS TO CONCEPTUAL CONNECTIONS

The Second Law

19.1 **(c)** The second law states that energy spontaneously disperses itself. The spontaneous concentration of energy (in a closed system) is inconsistent with the second law.

Entropy

19.2 **(a)** The more spread out the particles are between the three boxes, the greater the entropy. Therefore, the entropy change is positive only in scheme **(a)**.

Entropy and State Changes

19.3 **(c)** The condensation of water is a phase transition from gas to liquid, so entropy decreases.

Entropy and Biological Systems

19.4 **(b)** Biological systems do not violate the second law of thermodynamics. The key to understanding this concept is realizing that entropy changes in the system can be negative as long as the entropy change of the universe is positive. Biological systems can decrease their own entropy, but only at the expense of creating more entropy in the surroundings (which they do primarily by emitting the heat they generate by their metabolic processes). Thus, for any biological process, ΔS_{univ} is positive.

ΔH, ΔS, and ΔG

19.5 **(a)** Sublimation is endothermic (it requires energy to overcome the intermolecular forces that hold solid carbon dioxide together), so ΔH is positive. The number of moles of gas increases when the solid turns into a gas, so the entropy of the carbon dioxide increases and ΔS is positive. Since $\Delta G = \Delta H - T\Delta S$, ΔG is positive at low temperature and negative at high temperature.

Standard Entropies

19.6 **(a)** Kr $<$ Cl_2 $<$ SO_3. Because krypton is a monoatomic gas, it has the least entropy. Because SO_3 is the most complex molecule, it has the most entropy. The molar masses of the three gases vary slightly, but not enough to overcome the differences in molecular complexity.

Free Energy Changes and Le Châtelier's Principle

19.7 **(a)** A high concentration of reactants relative to products will lead to $Q < 1$, making the term $RT \ln Q$ in Equation 19.14 negative. ΔG_{rxn} is more negative than ΔG°_{rxn}, and the reaction is more spontaneous.

K and ΔG°_{rxn}

19.8 **(c)** Since the equilibrium constant is less than 1, the reaction proceeds toward reactants under standard conditions (when $Q = 1$). Therefore, ΔG°_{rxn} is positive.

The Conditions of Spontaneity

19.9 **(b)** $\Delta G_{rxn} < 0, Q < K$ If a reaction is spontaneous, then ΔG_{rxn} is negative and Q must be less than K (because a spontaneous reaction proceeds toward products).

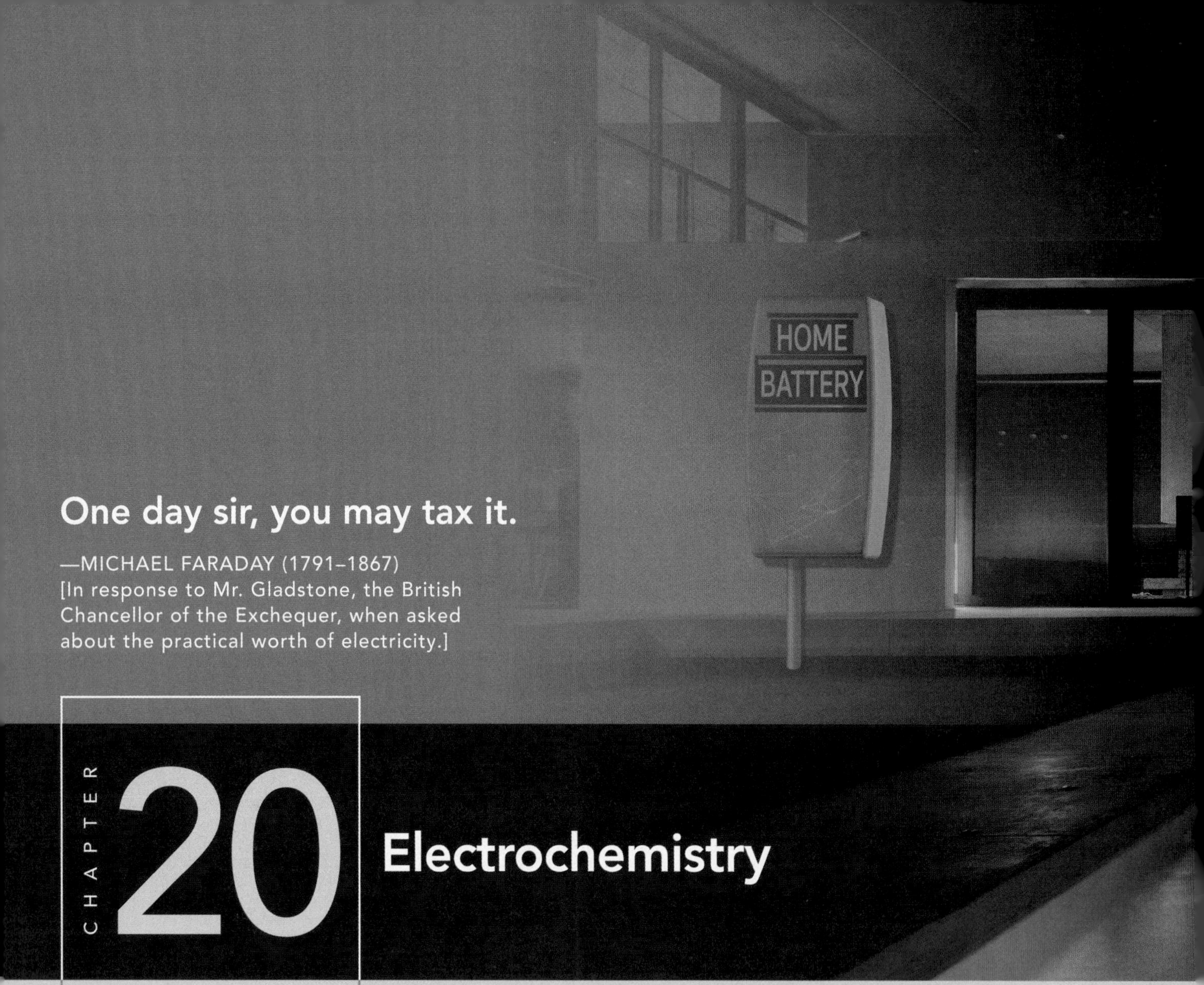

One day sir, you may tax it.

—MICHAEL FARADAY (1791–1867)
[In response to Mr. Gladstone, the British Chancellor of the Exchequer, when asked about the practical worth of electricity.]

CHAPTER 20 Electrochemistry

This chapter's opening quote from Michael Faraday illustrates an important aspect of basic research (research for the sake of understanding how nature works). The Chancellor of the Exchequer (the British cabinet minister responsible for all financial matters) wanted to know how Michael Faraday's apparently esoteric investigations of electricity would ever be useful to the empire. Faraday responded in a way that the chancellor would understand—he pointed out the eventual financial payoff. Today electricity is a fundamental form of energy, powering our entire economy. Although basic research does not always lead to useful applications, much of the technology our society relies on has grown out of basic research. The history of modern science shows that we must first understand nature (the goal of basic research) before we can harness its power. In this chapter, we discuss oxidation–reduction reactions (first introduced in Chapter 5) and how we can exploit them to generate electricity. The applications range from the batteries that power flashlights to the fuel cells that may one day power our homes and automobiles.

The house shown in this image is completely powered by batteries that are recharged with solar cells, removing the need to connect to the electrical grid. With rapid advances in battery technology, houses like this could become commonplace.

20.1 Lightning and Batteries 897

20.2 Balancing Oxidation–Reduction Equations 898

20.3 Voltaic (or Galvanic) Cells: Generating Electricity from Spontaneous Chemical Reactions 901

20.4 Standard Electrode Potentials 905

20.5 Cell Potential, Free Energy, and the Equilibrium Constant 913

20.6 Cell Potential and Concentration 917

20.7 Batteries: Using Chemistry to Generate Electricity 922

20.8 Electrolysis: Driving Nonspontaneous Chemical Reactions with Electricity 926

20.9 Corrosion: Undesirable Redox Reactions 933

LEARNING OUTCOMES 938

20.1 Lightning and Batteries

Lightning dramatically demonstrates the power of the flow of electrical charge. Many of the same principles, though in a much more controlled environment, are at work in a battery. The driving force for both lightning and the battery is the same, and we have encountered it before: Electrons flow *away* from negative charge and toward *positive* charge.

▲ Cloud-to-ground lightning

In a thundercloud, violent air currents cause water droplets and ice particles to collide. The collisions knock electrons off of molecules, creating positive and negative charges. The positive charges accumulate on small ice crystals that travel to the top of the thundercloud on rising air currents. The wet slushy bottom of the thundercloud becomes negatively charged. The resulting charge separation exists until a conductive path can form between the bottom of the cloud (negatively charged) and the top of the cloud (positively charged). The conductive path forms when the charge separation is so great that a channel of ionized air develops. This channel acts like a conductive wire, allowing a massive amount of charge to flow through it in order to equalize the charge separation. The massive flow of electrical charge is lightning.

Most lightning occurs within the thundercloud itself or from one thundercloud to another. However, if the thundercloud gets close enough to the ground, the earth underneath the cloud develops a positive charge in response to the negative charge at the base of the cloud. The channel of ionized air can then form between the cloud and the ground, resulting in the flow of charge from the base of the cloud to the earth in what is called cloud-to-ground lightning. Cloud-to-ground lightning is visible and dramatic to observers on the ground.

Batteries operate on many of the same principles that are at work in lightning. A battery is composed of substances that have different affinities for electrons. The substances are separated so that one end of the battery develops a positive charge and the other end develops a negative charge. The charge separation exists until a conductive path connects the two ends, providing a path through which charge can flow. A metal wire with an electrical load can provide such a path. When the wire is connected, electrons flow from the negative end of the battery—through the wire and through the electrical load—to the positive end. As the electrons flow through the electrical load, they can do electrical work, such as run a refrigerator or air conditioner. Battery technology has advanced dramatically in recent years, and you can now run your entire home from a bank of batteries such as the Tesla Powerwall. These batteries can recharge from solar cells, making it completely possible to live off the traditional electrical grid.

20.2 Balancing Oxidation–Reduction Equations

Recall from Section 5.9 that *oxidation* is the loss of electrons, and *reduction* is the gain of electrons. Recall also that we can identify oxidation–reduction reactions through changes in oxidation states: *oxidation corresponds to an increase in oxidation state, and reduction corresponds to a decrease in oxidation state*. For example, consider the following reaction between calcium and water:

Review Section 5.9 on assigning oxidation states.

$$\underset{0}{Ca(s)} + 2\,\underset{+1\ -2}{H_2O(l)} \longrightarrow \underset{+2\ -2\ +1}{Ca(OH)_2(aq)} + \underset{0}{H_2(g)}$$

Oxidation: Ca (0 → +2); Reduction: H (+1 → 0)

Because calcium increases in oxidation state from 0 to +2, it is oxidized. Because hydrogen decreases in oxidation state from +1 to 0, it is reduced.

Balancing redox reactions can be more complicated than balancing other types of reactions because both the mass (or number of each type of atom) and the *charge* must be balanced. We can balance redox reactions occurring in aqueous solutions with a special procedure called the *half-reaction method of balancing*. In this procedure, we break down the overall equation into two half-reactions: one for oxidation and one for reduction. We then balance the half-reactions individually and add them together. The steps differ slightly for reactions occurring in acidic and in basic solution. Examples 20.1 and 20.2 demonstrate the method for an acidic solution, and Example 20.3 demonstrates the method for a basic solution.

WATCH **NOW!**

INTERACTIVE WORKED EXAMPLE VIDEO 20.2

HOW TO: Balance Aqueous Redox Equations in Acidic Solution Using the Half-Reaction Method **GENERAL PROCEDURE**	**EXAMPLE 20.1** **Half-Reaction Method of Balancing Aqueous Redox Equations in Acidic Solution** Balance the redox equation: $Al(s) + Cu^{2+}(aq) \longrightarrow Al^{3+}(aq) + Cu(s)$	**EXAMPLE 20.2** **Half-Reaction Method of Balancing Aqueous Redox Equations in Acidic Solution** Balance the redox equation: $Fe^{2+}(aq) + MnO_4^{-}(aq) \longrightarrow Fe^{3+}(aq) + Mn^{2+}(aq)$
Step 1 *Assign oxidation states* to all atoms and identify the substances being oxidized and reduced.	$Al(s) + Cu^{2+}(aq) \longrightarrow Al^{3+}(aq) + Cu(s)$ Oxidation states: 0, +2, +3, 0 Reduction: Cu (+2 → 0) Oxidation: Al (0 → +3)	$Fe^{2+}(aq) + MnO_4^{-}(aq) \longrightarrow Fe^{3+}(aq) + Mn^{2+}(aq)$ Oxidation states: +2, +7 −2, +3, +2 Reduction: Mn (+7 → +2) Oxidation: Fe (+2 → +3)
Step 2 *Separate the overall reaction into two half-reactions*: one for oxidation and one for reduction.	***Oxidation:*** $Al(s) \longrightarrow Al^{3+}(aq)$ ***Reduction:*** $Cu^{2+}(aq) \longrightarrow Cu(s)$	***Oxidation:*** $Fe^{2+}(aq) \longrightarrow Fe^{3+}(aq)$ ***Reduction:*** $MnO_4^{-}(aq) \longrightarrow Mn^{2+}(aq)$
Step 3 *Balance each half-reaction with respect to mass* in the following order: • Balance all elements other than H and O. • Balance O by adding H_2O. • Balance H by adding H^+.	All elements are balanced, so proceed to the next step.	All elements other than H and O are balanced, so proceed to balance H and O. $Fe^{2+}(aq) \longrightarrow Fe^{3+}(aq)$ $MnO_4^{-}(aq) \longrightarrow Mn^{2+}(aq) + 4\,H_2O(l)$ $8\,H^+(aq) + MnO_4^{-}(aq) \longrightarrow Mn^{2+}(aq) + 4\,H_2O(l)$
Step 4 *Balance each half-reaction with respect to charge* by adding electrons. (Make the sum of the charges on both sides of the equation equal by adding as many electrons as necessary.)	$Al(s) \longrightarrow Al^{3+}(aq) + 3\,e^-$ $2\,e^- + Cu^{2+}(aq) \longrightarrow Cu(s)$	$Fe^{2+}(aq) \longrightarrow Fe^{3+}(aq) + 1\,e^-$ $5\,e^- + 8\,H^+(aq) + MnO_4^{-}(aq) \longrightarrow Mn^{2+}(aq) + 4\,H_2O(l)$
Step 5 *Make the number of electrons in both half-reactions equal* by multiplying one or both half-reactions by a small whole number.	$2[Al(s) \longrightarrow Al^{3+}(aq) + 3\,e^-]$ $2\,Al(s) \longrightarrow 2\,Al^{3+}(aq) + 6\,e^-$ $3[2\,e^- + Cu^{2+}(aq) \longrightarrow Cu(s)]$ $6\,e^- + 3\,Cu^{2+}(aq) \longrightarrow 3\,Cu(s)$	$5[Fe^{2+}(aq) \longrightarrow Fe^{3+}(aq) + 1\,e^-]$ $5\,Fe^{2+}(aq) \longrightarrow 5\,Fe^{3+}(aq) + 5\,e^-$ $5\,e^- + 8\,H^+(aq) + MnO_4^{-}(aq) \longrightarrow Mn^{2+}(aq) + 4\,H_2O(l)$
Step 6 *Add the two half-reactions together*, canceling electrons and other species as necessary.	$2\,Al(s) \longrightarrow 2\,Al^{3+}(aq) + \cancel{6\,e^-}$ $\cancel{6\,e^-} + 3\,Cu^{2+}(aq) \longrightarrow 3\,Cu(s)$ ——— $2\,Al(s) + 3\,Cu^{2+}(aq) \longrightarrow 2\,Al^{3+}(aq) + 3\,Cu(s)$	$5\,Fe^{2+}(aq) \longrightarrow 5\,Fe^{3+}(aq) + \cancel{5\,e^-}$ $\cancel{5\,e^-} + 8\,H^+(aq) + MnO_4^{-}(aq) \longrightarrow Mn^{2+}(aq) + 4\,H_2O(l)$ ——— $5\,Fe^{2+}(aq) + 8\,H^+(aq) + MnO_4^{-}(aq) \longrightarrow 5\,Fe^{3+}(aq) + Mn^{2+}(aq) + 4\,H_2O(l)$

—Continued on the next page

Continued—

Step 7 *Verify that the reaction is balanced* with respect to both mass and charge.

Reactants	Products
2 Al	2 Al
3 Cu	3 Cu
+6 charge	+6 charge

Reactants	Products
5 Fe	5 Fe
8 H	8 H
1 Mn	1 Mn
4 O	4 O
+17 charge	+17 charge

FOR PRACTICE 20.1 Balance the redox reaction in acidic solution:

$$H^+(aq) + Cr(s) \longrightarrow H_2(g) + Cr^{2+}(aq)$$

FOR PRACTICE 20.2 Balance the redox reaction in acidic solution:

$$Cu(s) + NO_3^-(aq) \longrightarrow Cu^{2+}(aq) + NO_2(g)$$

When a redox reaction occurs in basic solution, we balance the reaction in a similar manner, except that we add an additional step to neutralize any H^+ with OH^-. The H^+ and the OH^- combine to form H_2O as shown in Example 20.3.

WATCH **NOW!**

INTERACTIVE WORKED EXAMPLE 20.3

EXAMPLE 20.3 Balancing Redox Reactions Occurring in Basic Solution

Balance the equation occurring in basic solution:

$$I^-(aq) + MnO_4^-(aq) \longrightarrow I_2(aq) + MnO_2(s)$$

SOLUTION

To balance redox reactions occurring in basic solution, follow the half-reaction method outlined in Examples 20.1 and 20.2, but add an extra step to neutralize the acid with OH^- as shown in step 3.

1. Assign oxidation states.

$$\underset{-1}{I^-(aq)} + \underset{+7\ -2}{MnO_4^-(aq)} \longrightarrow \underset{0}{I_2(aq)} + \underset{+4\ -2}{MnO_2(s)}$$

Reduction: Mn (+7 → +4)
Oxidation: I (−1 → 0)

2. Separate the overall reaction into two half-reactions.

Oxidation: $I^-(aq) \longrightarrow I_2(aq)$

Reduction: $MnO_4^-(aq) \longrightarrow MnO_2(s)$

3. Balance each half-reaction with respect to mass.

- Balance all elements other than H and O.

$$\begin{cases} 2\,I^-(aq) \longrightarrow I_2(aq) \\ MnO_4^-(aq) \longrightarrow MnO_2(s) \end{cases}$$

- Balance O by adding H_2O.

$$\begin{cases} 2\,I^-(aq) \longrightarrow I_2(aq) \\ MnO_4^-(aq) \longrightarrow MnO_2(s) + 2\,H_2O(l) \end{cases}$$

- Balance H by adding H^+.

$$\begin{cases} 2\,I^-(aq) \longrightarrow I_2(aq) \\ 4\,H^+(aq) + MnO_4^-(aq) \longrightarrow MnO_2(s) + 2\,H_2O(l) \end{cases}$$

- Neutralize H^+ by adding enough OH^- to neutralize each H^+. Add the same number of OH^- ions to each side of the equation.

$$\begin{cases} 2\,I^-(aq) \longrightarrow I_2(aq) \\ \underbrace{4\,H^+(aq) + 4\,OH^-(aq)}_{4\,H_2O(l)} + MnO_4^-(aq) \longrightarrow MnO_2(s) + 2\,H_2O(l) + 4\,OH^-(aq) \end{cases}$$

4. Balance each half-reaction with respect to charge.

$$2\,I^-(aq) \longrightarrow I_2(aq) + 2\,e^-$$

$$4\,H_2O(l) + MnO_4^-(aq) + 3\,e^- \longrightarrow MnO_2(s) + 2\,H_2O(l) + 4\,OH^-(aq)$$

5. Make the number of electrons in both half-reactions equal.

$$3[2\,I^-(aq) \longrightarrow I_2(aq) + 2\,e^-]$$

$$6\,I^-(aq) \longrightarrow 3\,I_2(aq) + 6\,e^-$$

$$2[4\,H_2O(l) + MnO_4^-(aq) + 3\,e^- \longrightarrow MnO_2(s) + 2\,H_2O(l) + 4\,OH^-(aq)]$$

$$8\,H_2O(l) + 2\,MnO_4^-(aq) + 6\,e^- \longrightarrow 2\,MnO_2(s) + 4\,H_2O(l) + 8\,OH^-(aq)$$

6. Add the half-reactions together.

$$6\,I^-(aq) \longrightarrow 3\,I_2(aq) + \cancel{6\,e^-}$$

$$4\cancel{8}\,H_2O(l) + 2\,MnO_4^-(aq) + \cancel{6\,e^-} \longrightarrow 2\,MnO_2(s) + \cancel{4\,H_2O(l)} + 8\,OH^-(aq)$$

$$6\,I^-(aq) + 4\,H_2O(l) + 2\,MnO_4^-(aq) \longrightarrow 3\,I_2(aq) + 2\,MnO_2(s) + 8\,OH^-(aq)$$

7. Verify that the reaction is balanced.

Reactants	Products
6 I	6 I
8 H	8 H
2 Mn	2 Mn
12 O	12 O
−8 charge	−8 charge

FOR PRACTICE 20.3 Balance the following redox reaction occurring in basic solution:

$$ClO^-(aq) + Cr(OH)_4^-(aq) \longrightarrow CrO_4^{2-}(aq) + Cl^-(aq)$$

20.3 Voltaic (or Galvanic) Cells: Generating Electricity from Spontaneous Chemical Reactions

WATCH **NOW!**

KEY CONCEPT VIDEO 20.3
Voltaic Cells

Electrical current is the flow of electric charge. Electrons flowing through a wire or ions flowing through a solution both constitute electrical current. Since redox reactions involve the transfer of electrons from one substance to another, these reactions have the potential to generate electrical current, as we discussed in Section 20.1.

For example, consider the spontaneous redox reaction:

$$Zn(s) + Cu^{2+}(aq) \longrightarrow Zn^{2+}(aq) + Cu(s)$$

When Zn metal is placed in a Cu^{2+} solution, the greater tendency of zinc to lose electrons results in Zn being oxidized and Cu^{2+} being reduced. Electrons are transferred directly from the Zn to the Cu^{2+} (Figure 20.1▶). Although the actual process is more complicated, we can imagine that—on the atomic scale—a zinc atom within the zinc metal transfers two electrons to a copper ion in solution. The zinc atom then becomes a zinc ion dissolved in the solution. The copper ion accepts the two electrons and is deposited on the zinc as solid copper.

Suppose we were to separate the zinc atoms and copper ions and force the electron transfer to occur another way—not directly from the zinc atom to the copper ion, but through a wire connecting the two half-reactions. The flowing electrons would constitute an electrical current and could be used to do electrical work.

▶ **FIGURE 20.1 A Spontaneous Oxidation–Reduction Reaction** When zinc is immersed in a solution containing copper ions, the zinc atoms transfer electrons to the copper ions. The zinc atoms are oxidized and dissolve in the solution. The copper ions are reduced and are deposited on the electrode.

A Spontaneous Redox Reaction: Zn + Cu^{2+}

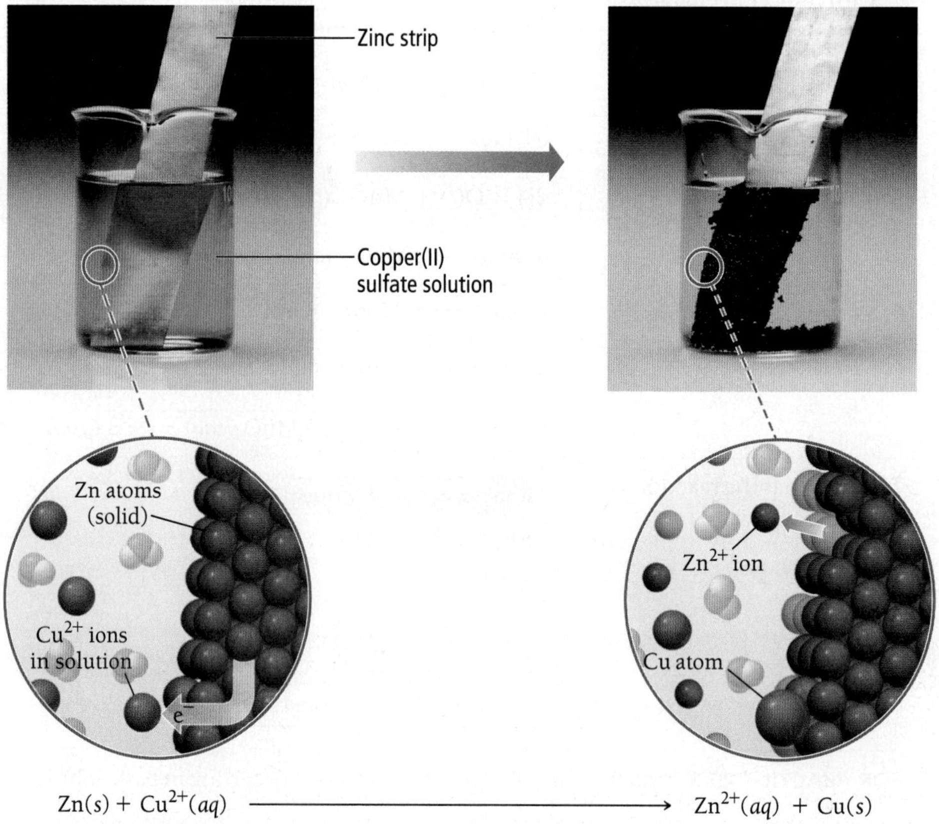

The Voltaic Cell

The generation of electricity through redox reactions is carried out in a device called an **electrochemical cell**. A **voltaic (or galvanic) cell** is an electrochemical cell that *produces* electrical current from a *spontaneous* chemical reaction. A second type of electrochemical cell, called an **electrolytic cell**, *consumes* electrical current-to drive a *nonspontaneous* chemical reaction. We discuss voltaic cells in this section and electrolytic cells in Section 20.8.

In the voltaic cell in Figure 20.2▶, a solid strip of zinc is placed in a $Zn(NO_3)_2$ solution to form a **half-cell**. A solid strip of copper placed in a $Cu(NO_3)_2$ solution forms a second half-cell. The strips act as **electrodes**, conductive surfaces through which electrons can enter or leave the half-cells. Each metal strip reaches equilibrium with its ions in solution according to these half-reactions:

$$Zn(s) \rightleftharpoons Zn^{2+}(aq) + 2\,e^-$$

$$Cu(s) \rightleftharpoons Cu^{2+}(aq) + 2\,e^-$$

The *continual* flow of electrical current in a voltaic cell requires a pathway by which counterions can flow to neutralize charge buildup; this is discussed later.

The idea that one electrode in a voltaic cell becomes more negatively charged relative to the other electrode due to differences in ionization tendencies is central to understanding how a voltaic cell works.

However, the position of these equilibria is not the same for both metals. As we have just seen, the zinc has a greater tendency to ionize than the copper, so the zinc half-reaction lies further to the right. As a result, the zinc electrode becomes negatively charged relative to the copper electrode.

If the two half-cells are connected by a wire running from the zinc—through a lightbulb or other electrical device—to the copper, electrons spontaneously flow from the zinc electrode (which is more negatively charged, and therefore, repels electrons) to the copper electrode. As the electrons flow away from the zinc electrode, the Zn/Zn^{2+} equilibrium shifts to the right (according to Le Châtelier's principle) and oxidation occurs. As electrons flow to the copper electrode, the Cu/Cu^{2+} equilibrium shifts to the left, and reduction occurs. The flowing electrons constitute an electrical current that lights the bulb.

A Voltaic Cell

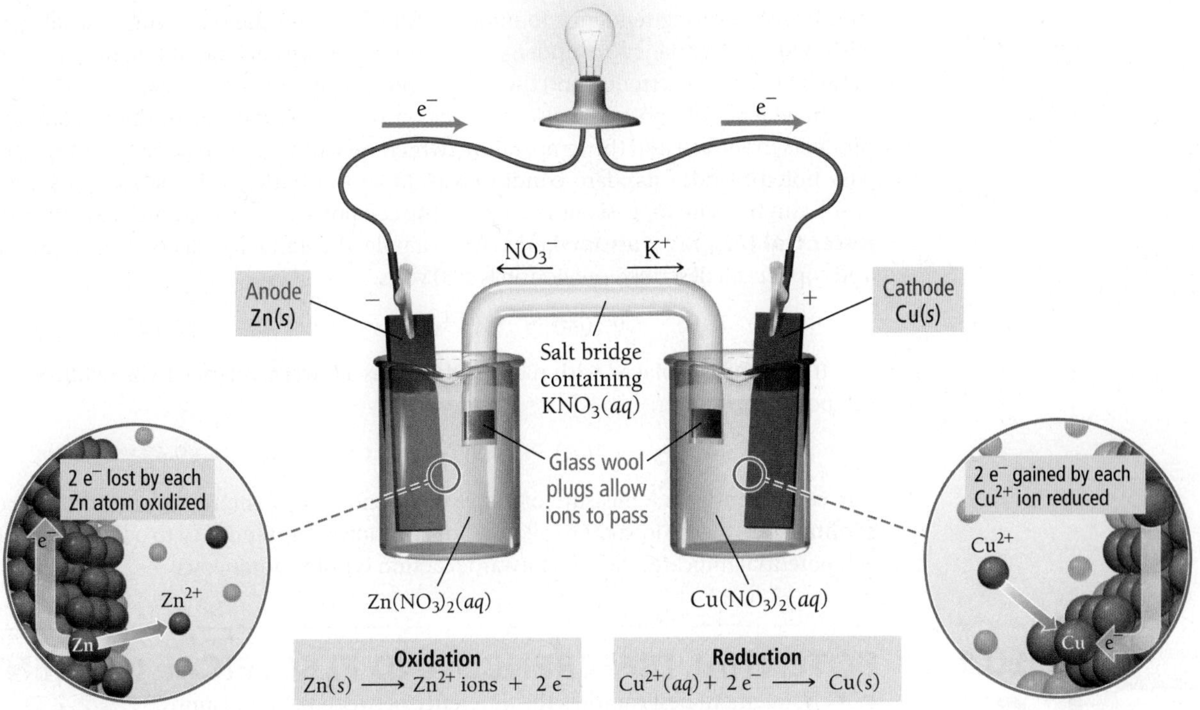

▲ **FIGURE 20.2 A Voltaic Cell** The tendency of zinc to transfer electrons to copper results in a flow of electrons through the wire that lights the bulb. The movement of electrons from the zinc anode to the copper cathode creates a positive charge buildup at the zinc half-cell and a negative charge buildup at the copper half-cell. The flow of ions within the salt bridge neutralizes this charge buildup, allowing the reaction to continue.

Current and Potential Difference

We can understand electrical current and why it flows by analogy with water current in a stream (Figure 20.3▶). The *rate of electrons flowing* through a wire is analogous to the *rate of water moving* through a stream. Electrical current is measured in units of **amperes (A)**, also called amps. One ampere represents the flow of one coulomb (a measure of electrical charge) per second:

The ampere is often abbreviated as *amp*.

$$1\text{ A} = 1\text{ C/s}$$

Because an electron has a charge of 1.602×10^{-19} C, 1 A corresponds to the flow of 6.242×10^{18} electrons per second.

The *driving force* for electrical current is analogous to the driving force for water current. Water current is driven by a difference in gravitational potential energy (caused by a gravitational field). Streams flow downhill, from higher to lower potential energy. Electrical current is also driven by a difference in potential energy (caused by an electric field resulting from the charge difference on the two electrodes) called **potential difference.** *Potential difference is a measure of the difference in potential energy (usually in joules) per unit of charge (coulombs).* The SI unit of potential difference is the **volt (V)**, which is equal to one joule per coulomb:

$$1\text{ V} = 1\text{ J/C}$$

In other words, a potential difference of one volt indicates that a charge of one coulomb experiences an energy difference of one joule between the two electrodes.

A large potential difference corresponds to a large difference in charge between the two electrodes, and therefore, a strong tendency for electron flow (analogous to a steeply descending streambed). Potential difference, since it gives rise to the force that results in the motion of electrons, is also referred to as **electromotive force (emf)**.

▲ **FIGURE 20.3 An Analogy for Electrical Current** Just as water flows downhill in response to a difference in gravitational potential energy, electrons flow through a conductor in response to an electrical potential difference, creating an electrical current.

In a voltaic cell, the potential difference between the two electrodes is the **cell potential (E_{cell})** or **cell emf**. The cell potential depends on the relative tendencies of the reactants to undergo oxidation and reduction. Combining the oxidation of a substance with a strong tendency to undergo oxidation and the reduction of a substance with a strong tendency to undergo reduction produces a large difference in charge between the two electrodes, and therefore, a high positive cell potential.

In general, cell potential also depends on the concentrations of the reactants and products in the cell and the temperature (which we will assume to be 25 °C unless otherwise noted). Under standard conditions (1 M concentration for reactants in solution and 1 atm pressure for gaseous reactants), the cell potential is called the **standard cell potential (E°_{cell})** or **standard emf**. For example, the standard cell potential in the zinc and copper cell described previously is 1.10 volts:

$$Zn(s) + Cu^{2+}(aq) \longrightarrow Zn^{2+}(aq) + Cu(s) \qquad E^{\circ}_{cell} = +1.10\text{ V}$$

If the zinc is replaced with nickel (which has a lower tendency to be oxidized), the cell potential is lower:

$$Ni(s) + Cu^{2+}(aq) \longrightarrow Ni^{2+}(aq) + Cu(s) \qquad E^{\circ}_{cell} = +0.62\text{ V}$$

The cell potential is a measure of the overall tendency of the redox reaction to occur spontaneously—the lower the cell potential, the lower the tendency to occur. A negative cell potential indicates that the forward reaction is not spontaneous.

ANSWER NOW!

20.1 Cc Conceptual Connection

POTENTIAL DIFFERENCE AND ELECTRICAL CURRENT

Which statement best captures the difference between volts and amps?

(a) The volt is a unit that quantifies the difference in electrical potential energy, and the amp is a unit that quantifies the flow of electrical current.

(b) The amp is a unit that quantifies the difference in electrical potential energy, and the volt is a unit that quantifies the flow of electrical current.

(c) The volt and amp are two different units used to measure the same thing, the flow of electrical current.

Anode, Cathode, and Salt Bridge

In all electrochemical cells, we call the electrode where oxidation occurs the **anode** and the electrode where reduction occurs the **cathode**. In a voltaic cell, the anode is the more negatively charged electrode, and we label it with a negative (–) sign. The cathode of a voltaic cell is the more positively charged electrode, and we label it with a (+) sign. Electrons flow from the anode to the cathode (from negative to positive) through the wires connecting the electrodes.

Note that the anode and cathode need not actually be negatively and positively charged, respectively. The anode is the electrode with the relatively *more* negative (or less positive) charge.

As electrons flow out of the anode, positive ions (Zn^{2+} in the preceding example) form in the oxidation half-cell, resulting in a buildup of *positive charge* in the *solution*. As electrons flow into the cathode, positive ions (Cu^{2+} in the preceding example) are reduced at the reduction half-cell, resulting in a buildup of *negative charge* in the *solution*.

If the movement of electrons from anode to cathode were the only flow of charge, the buildup of the opposite charge in the solution would stop electron flow almost immediately. The cell needs a pathway by which counterions can flow between the half-cells without the solutions in the half-cells totally mixing. One such pathway is a **salt bridge**, an inverted, U-shaped tube that contains a strong electrolyte such as KNO_3 and connects the two half-cells (see Figure 20.2). The electrolyte is usually suspended in a gel and held within the tube by permeable stoppers. The salt bridge allows a flow of ions that neutralizes the charge buildup in the solution. *The negative ions within the salt bridge flow to neutralize the accumulation of positive charge at the anode, and the positive ions flow to neutralize the accumulation of negative charge at the cathode.* In other words, the salt bridge completes the circuit, allowing electrical current to flow.

VOLTAIC CELLS In a voltaic cell, in which direction do electrons flow?

(a) from higher potential energy to lower potential energy
(b) from the cathode to the anode
(c) from lower potential energy to higher potential energy

20.2 Cc Conceptual Connection

ANSWER NOW!

Electrochemical Cell Notation

We represent electrochemical cells with a compact notation called a *cell diagram* or *line notation*. For example, we represent the electrochemical cell discussed previously in which Zn is oxidized to Zn^{2+} and Cu^{2+} is reduced to Cu as follows:

$$Zn(s)\,|\,Zn^{2+}(aq)\,||\,Cu^{2+}(aq)\,|\,Cu(aq)$$

In this representation,

- the oxidation half-reaction is on the left and the reduction is on the right. A double vertical line, indicating the salt bridge, separates the two half-reactions.
- substances in different phases are separated by a single vertical line, which represents the boundary between the phases.
- for some redox reactions, the reactants and products of one or both of the half-reactions may be in the same phase. In these cases (as shown in the example below), we separate the reactants and products from each other with a comma in the line diagram. Such cells use an inert electrode, such as platinum (Pt) or graphite, as the anode or cathode (or both).

Consider the redox reaction in which Fe(*s*) is oxidized and $MnO_4^-(aq)$ is reduced:

$$5\,Fe(s) + 2\,MnO_4^-(aq) + 16\,H^+(aq) \longrightarrow 5\,Fe^{2+}(aq) + 2\,Mn^{2+}(aq) + 8\,H_2O(s)$$

The half-reactions for this overall reaction are:

Oxidation: $Fe(s) \longrightarrow Fe^{2+}(aq) + 2\,e^-$

Reduction: $MnO_4^-(aq) + 5\,e^- + 8\,H^+(aq) \longrightarrow Mn^{2+}(aq) + 4\,H_2O(l)$

Notice that in the reduction half-reaction the principal species are all in the aqueous phase. In this case, the electron transfer needs an electrode on which to occur. An inert platinum electrode is employed, and the electron transfer takes place at its surface. Using line notation, we represent the electrochemical cell corresponding to the above reaction as:

$$Fe(s)\,|\,Fe^{2+}(aq)\,||\,MnO_4^-(aq), H^+(aq), Mn^{2+}(aq)\,|\,Pt(s)$$

The Pt(*s*) on the far right indicates that an inert platinum electrode acts as the cathode in this reaction, as depicted in Figure 20.4►.

20.4 Standard Electrode Potentials

WATCH NOW!
KEY CONCEPT VIDEO 20.4
Standard Electrode Potentials

As we have just seen, the standard cell potential (E°_{cell}) for an electrochemical cell depends on the specific half-reactions occurring in the half-cells and is a measure of the potential energy difference (per unit charge) between the two electrodes. We can think of the electrode in each half-cell as having its own individual potential, called the **standard electrode potential**. The overall standard cell potential (E°_{cell}) is the difference between the two standard electrode potentials.

We can better understand this idea with an analogy. Consider two water tanks with different water levels connected by a common pipe, as shown in Figure 20.5►. The water in each tank has its own level and corresponding potential energy. When the tanks are connected, water flows from the tank with the higher level (higher potential energy) to the tank with a lower water level (lower potential energy). Similarly, each half-cell in an electrochemical cell has its own charge and corresponding electrode potential. *When the cells are connected, electrons flow from the electrode with more negative charge (greater potential energy) to the electrode with less negative charge (less potential energy).*

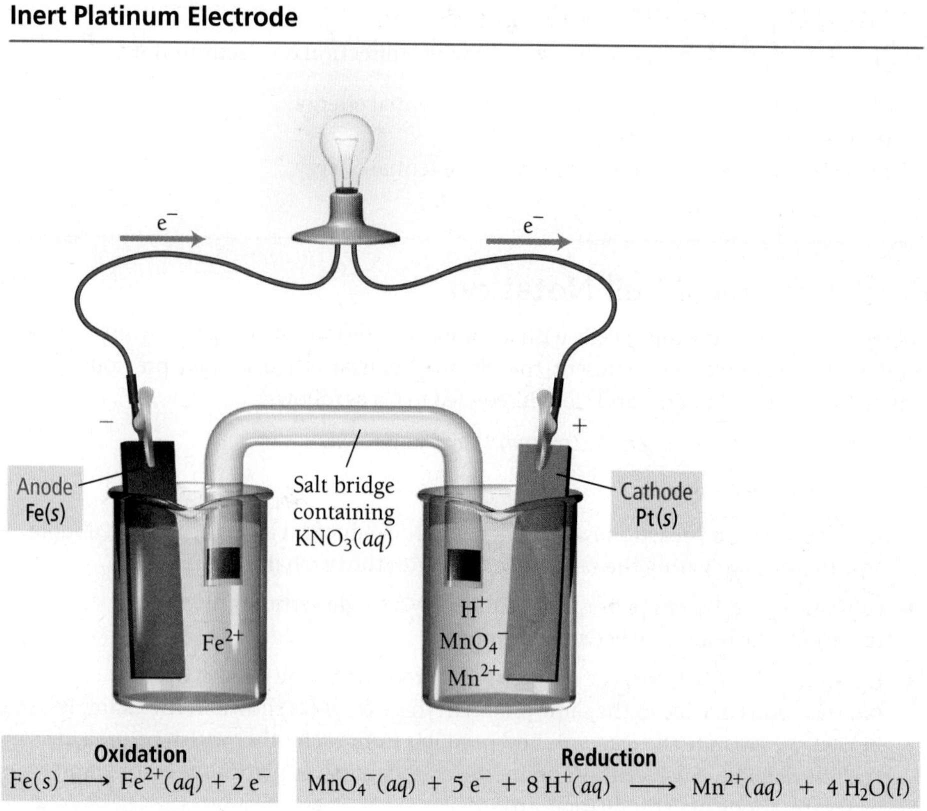

▶ **FIGURE 20.4 Inert Platinum Electrode** When the participants in a half-reaction are all in the aqueous phase, a conductive surface is needed for electron transfer to take place. In such cases, an inert electrode of graphite or platinum is often used. In this electrochemical cell, an iron strip acts as the anode and a platinum strip acts as the cathode. Iron is oxidized at the anode, and MnO_4^- is reduced at the cathode.

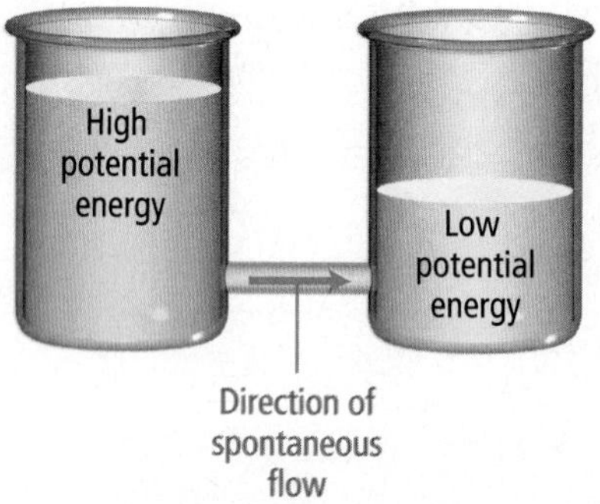

▲ **FIGURE 20.5 An Analogy for Electrode Potential**

One limitation of this analogy is that, unlike the water level in a tank, we cannot measure the electrode potential in a half-cell directly—we can only measure the overall potential that occurs when two half-cells are combined in a whole cell. However, we can arbitrarily assign a potential of zero to the electrode in a *particular* type of half-cell and then measure all other electrode potentials relative to that zero.

The half-cell electrode that is normally chosen to have a potential of zero is the **standard hydrogen electrode (SHE)**. This half-cell consists of an inert platinum electrode immersed in 1 M HCl with hydrogen gas at 1 atm bubbling through the solution, as shown in Figure 20.6▶. When the SHE acts as the cathode, the following half-reaction occurs:

$$2\,H^+(aq) + 2\,e^- \longrightarrow H_2(g) \quad E^\circ_{cathode} = 0.00\ V$$

If we connect the standard hydrogen electrode to an electrode in another half-cell of interest, we can measure the potential difference (or voltage) between the two electrodes. Because we assigned the standard hydrogen electrode zero voltage, we can now determine the electrode potential of the other half-cell.

For example, consider the electrochemical cell in Figure 20.7▶. In this electrochemical cell, Zn is oxidized to Zn^{2+} and H^+ is reduced to H_2 under standard conditions (all solutions are 1 M in concentration, and all gases are 1 atm in pressure) and at 25 °C.

Standard Hydrogen Electrode (SHE)

We arbitrarily assign the SHE an electrode potential of zero. All other electrode potentials are then measured relative to the SHE.

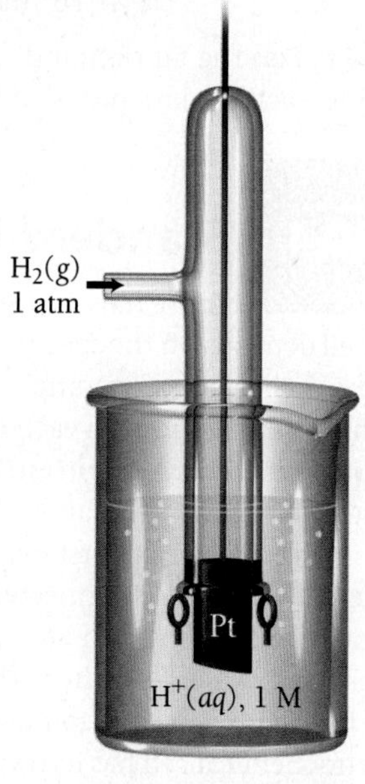

▲ **FIGURE 20.6 The Standard Hydrogen Electrode**

Measuring Half-Cell Potential with the SHE

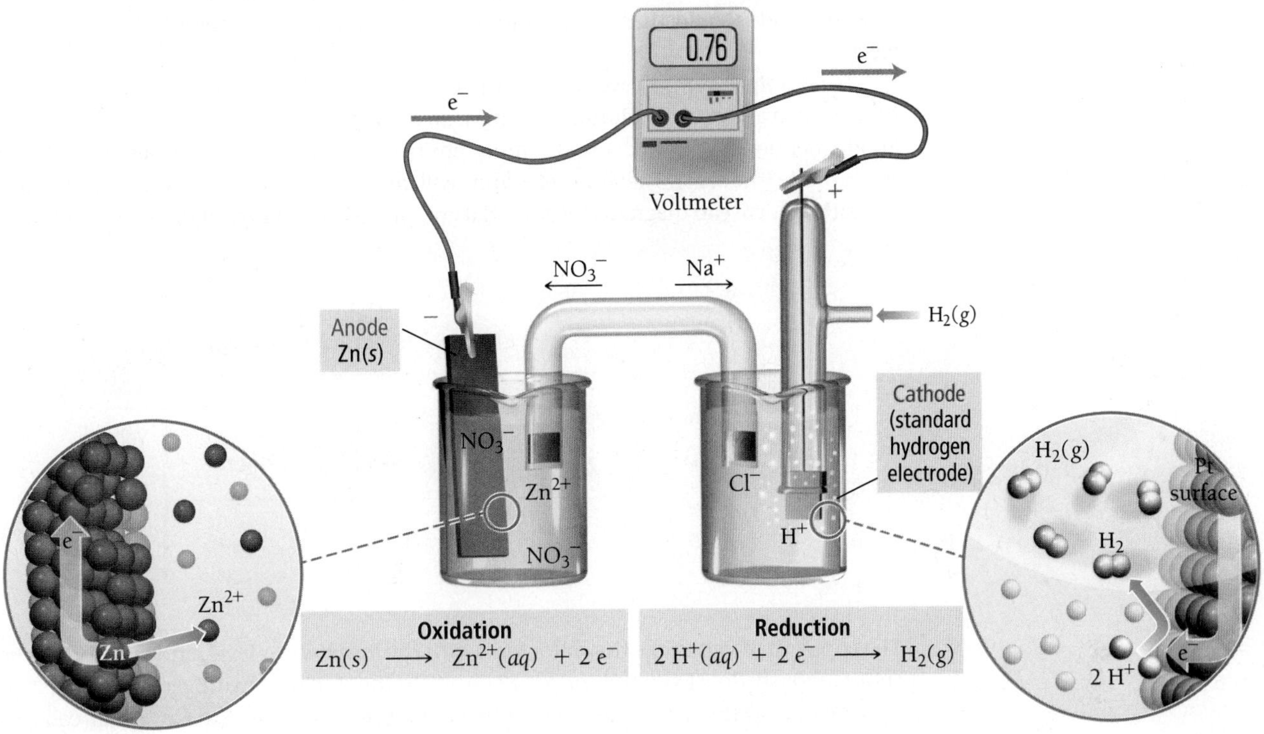

▲ **FIGURE 20.7 Measuring Electrode Potential** Because the electrode potential of the SHE is zero, the electrode potential for the oxidation of Zn is equal to the cell potential.

Electrons travel from the anode (where oxidation occurs) to the cathode (where reduction occurs), so we define E°_{cell} as *the difference in voltage between the cathode (final state) and the anode (initial state)*:

$$\begin{aligned} E^\circ_{cell} &= E^\circ_{final} - E^\circ_{initial} \\ &= E^\circ_{cathode} - E^\circ_{anode} \end{aligned}$$

The measured cell potential for this cell is +0.76 V. The anode (in this case, Zn/Zn^{2+}) is at a more negative voltage (higher potential energy) than the cathode (in this case, the SHE). Therefore, electrons spontaneously flow from the anode to the cathode. We can diagram the potential energy and the voltage as follows:

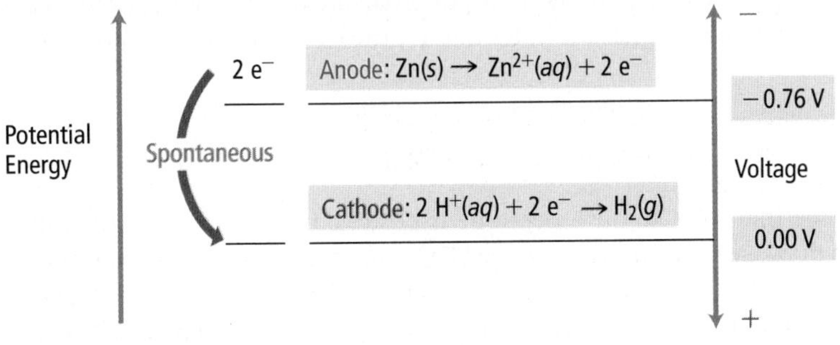

Referring back to our water tank analogy, the zinc half-cell is like the water tank with the higher water level, and electrons therefore flow from the zinc electrode to the standard hydrogen electrode.

Because we assigned the SHE a potential of zero (0.00 V), we can determine the electrode potential for the Zn/Zn^{2+} half-cell (the anode) from the measured cell potential (E°_{cell}):

$$\begin{aligned} E^\circ_{cell} &= E^\circ_{cathode} - E^\circ_{anode} \\ 0.76\ \text{V} &= 0.00\ \text{V} - E^\circ_{anode} \\ E^\circ_{anode} &= -0.76\ \text{V} \end{aligned}$$

The potential for the Zn/Zn^{2+} electrode is *negative*. The negative potential indicates that an electron at the Zn/Zn^{2+} electrode has greater potential energy than it does at the SHE. *Remember that the more negative the electrode potential is, the greater the potential energy of an electron at that electrode (because negative charge repels electrons).*

What happens if we connect an electrode in which the electron has *more positive* potential (than the standard hydrogen electrode) to the standard hydrogen electrode? That electrode would then have a more *positive* voltage (lower potential energy for an electron).

For example, suppose we connect the standard hydrogen electrode to a Cu electrode immersed in a 1 M Cu^{2+} solution. The measured cell potential for this cell is −0.34 V. The anode (defined as Cu/Cu^{2+}) is at a more positive voltage (lower potential energy) than the cathode (the SHE). Therefore, electrons will *not* spontaneously flow from the anode to the cathode. We can diagram the potential energy and the voltage of this cell as follows:

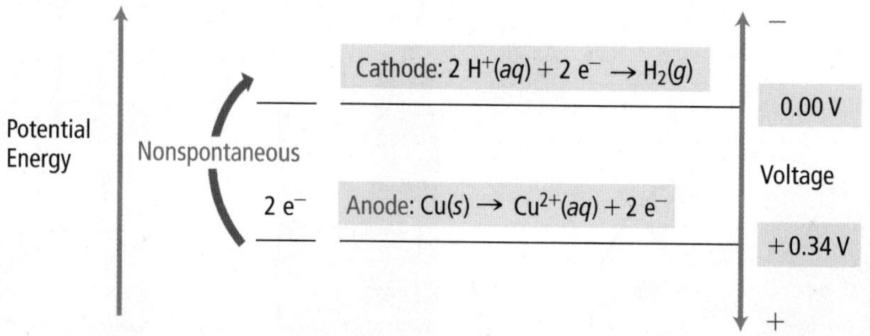

The copper half-cell is like the water tank with the lower water level, and electrons *do not* spontaneously flow from the copper electrode to the standard hydrogen electrode.

We can again determine the electrode potential for the Cu/Cu^{2+} half-cell (the anode) from the measured cell potential:

$$E^\circ_{cell} = E^\circ_{cathode} - E^\circ_{anode}$$

$$-0.34\ V = 0.00\ V - E^\circ_{anode}$$

$$E^\circ_{anode} = +0.34\ V$$

The potential for the Cu/Cu^{2+} electrode is *positive*. The positive potential indicates that an electron at the Cu/Cu^{2+} electrode has *lower* potential energy than it does at the SHE. The more positive the electrode potential, the lower the potential energy of an electron at that electrode (because positive charge attracts electrons).

By convention, standard electrode potentials are written for *reduction* half-reactions. We write the standard electrode potentials for the two half-reactions just discussed as:

$$Cu^{2+}(aq) + 2\,e^- \longrightarrow Cu(s) \qquad E^\circ = +0.34\ V$$

$$Zn^{2+}(aq) + 2\,e^- \longrightarrow Zn(s) \qquad E^\circ = -0.76\ V$$

We can see that the Cu/Cu^{2+} electrode is positive relative to the SHE (and therefore, tends to draw electrons *away* from the SHE) and that the Zn/Zn^{2+} electrode is negative relative to the SHE (and therefore, tends to repel electrons toward the SHE). Table 20.1 lists the standard electrode potentials for a number of common half-reactions.

Summarizing Standard Electrode Potentials:

- The electrode potential of the standard hydrogen electrode (SHE) is exactly zero.
- The electrode in any half-cell with a greater tendency to undergo reduction is positively charged relative to the SHE and therefore has a positive E°.
- The electrode in any half-cell with a lesser tendency to undergo reduction (or greater tendency to undergo oxidation) is negatively charged relative to the SHE and therefore has a negative E°.
- The cell potential of any electrochemical cell (E°_{cell}) is the difference between the electrode potentials of the cathode and the anode ($E^\circ_{cell} = E^\circ_{cat} - E^\circ_{an}$).
- E°_{cell} is positive for spontaneous reactions and negative for nonspontaneous reactions.

Multiplying a half-reaction by some constant to balance a redox reaction *does not* affect the value of E° for the half-reaction.

TABLE 20.1 Standard Electrode Potentials at 25 °C

High tendency towards reduction

Low tendency towards oxidation

Reduction Half-Reaction		$E°$(V)
$F_2(g) + 2\,e^-$	$\longrightarrow 2\,F^-(aq)$	2.87
$H_2O_2(aq) + 2\,H^+(aq) + 2\,e^-$	$\longrightarrow 2\,H_2O(l)$	1.78
$PbO_2(s) + 4\,H^+(aq) + SO_4^{2-}(aq) + 2\,e^-$	$\longrightarrow PbSO_4(s) + 2\,H_2O(l)$	1.69
$MnO_4^-(aq) + 4\,H^+(aq) + 3\,e^-$	$\longrightarrow MnO_2(s) + 2\,H_2O(l)$	1.68
$MnO_4^-(aq) + 8\,H^+(aq) + 5\,e^-$	$\longrightarrow Mn^{2+}(aq) + 4\,H_2O(l)$	1.51
$Au^{3+}(aq) + 3\,e^-$	$\longrightarrow Au(s)$	1.50
$PbO_2(s) + 4\,H^+(aq) + 2\,e^-$	$\longrightarrow Pb^{2+}(aq) + 2\,H_2O(l)$	1.46
$Cl_2(g) + 2\,e^-$	$\longrightarrow 2\,Cl^-(aq)$	1.36
$Cr_2O_7^{2-}(aq) + 14\,H^+(aq) + 6\,e^-$	$\longrightarrow 2\,Cr^{3+}(aq) + 7\,H_2O(l)$	1.33
$O_2(g) + 4\,H^+(aq) + 4\,e^-$	$\longrightarrow 2\,H_2O(l)$	1.23
$MnO_2(s) + 4\,H^+(aq) + 2\,e^-$	$\longrightarrow Mn^{2+}(aq) + 2\,H_2O(l)$	1.21
$IO_3^-(aq) + 6\,H^+(aq) + 5\,e^-$	$\longrightarrow \frac{1}{2}I_2(aq) + 3\,H_2O(l)$	1.20
$Br_2(l) + 2\,e^-$	$\longrightarrow 2\,Br^-(aq)$	1.09
$VO_2^+(aq) + 2\,H^+(aq) + e^-$	$\longrightarrow VO^{2+}(aq) + H_2O(l)$	1.00
$NO_3^-(aq) + 4\,H^+(aq) + 3\,e^-$	$\longrightarrow NO(g) + 2\,H_2O(l)$	0.96
$ClO_2(g) + e^-$	$\longrightarrow ClO_2^-(aq)$	0.95
$Ag^+(aq) + e^-$	$\longrightarrow Ag(s)$	0.80
$Fe^{3+}(aq) + e^-$	$\longrightarrow Fe^{2+}(aq)$	0.77
$O_2(g) + 2\,H^+(aq) + 2\,e^-$	$\longrightarrow H_2O_2(aq)$	0.70
$MnO_4^-(aq) + e^-$	$\longrightarrow MnO_4^{2-}(aq)$	0.56
$I_2(s) + 2\,e^-$	$\longrightarrow 2\,I^-(aq)$	0.54
$Cu^+(aq) + e^-$	$\longrightarrow Cu(s)$	0.52
$O_2(g) + 2\,H_2O(l) + 4\,e^-$	$\longrightarrow 4\,OH^-(aq)$	0.40
$Cu^{2+}(aq) + 2\,e^-$	$\longrightarrow Cu(s)$	0.34
$SO_4^{2-}(aq) + 4\,H^+(aq) + 2\,e^-$	$\longrightarrow H_2SO_3(aq) + H_2O(l)$	0.20
$Cu^{2+}(aq) + e^-$	$\longrightarrow Cu^+(aq)$	0.16
$Sn^{4+}(aq) + 2\,e^-$	$\longrightarrow Sn^{2+}(aq)$	0.15
$2\,H^+(aq) + 2\,e^-$	$\longrightarrow H_2(g)$	0
$Fe^{3+}(aq) + 3\,e^-$	$\longrightarrow Fe(s)$	−0.036
$Pb^{2+}(aq) + 2\,e^-$	$\longrightarrow Pb(s)$	−0.13
$Sn^{2+}(aq) + 2\,e^-$	$\longrightarrow Sn(s)$	−0.14
$Ni^{2+}(aq) + 2\,e^-$	$\longrightarrow Ni(s)$	−0.23
$Cd^{2+}(aq) + 2\,e^-$	$\longrightarrow Cd(s)$	−0.40
$Fe^{2+}(aq) + 2\,e^-$	$\longrightarrow Fe(s)$	−0.45
$Cr^{3+}(aq) + e^-$	$\longrightarrow Cr^{2+}(aq)$	−0.50
$Cr^{3+}(aq) + 3\,e^-$	$\longrightarrow Cr(s)$	−0.73
$Zn^{2+}(aq) + 2\,e^-$	$\longrightarrow Zn(s)$	−0.76
$2\,H_2O(l) + 2\,e^-$	$\longrightarrow H_2(g) + 2\,OH^-(aq)$	−0.83
$Mn^{2+}(aq) + 2\,e^-$	$\longrightarrow Mn(s)$	−1.18
$Al^{3+}(aq) + 3\,e^-$	$\longrightarrow Al(s)$	−1.66
$Mg^{2+}(aq) + 2\,e^-$	$\longrightarrow Mg(s)$	−2.37
$Na^+(aq) + e^-$	$\longrightarrow Na(s)$	−2.71
$Ca^{2+}(aq) + 2\,e^-$	$\longrightarrow Ca(s)$	−2.76
$Ba^{2+}(aq) + 2\,e^-$	$\longrightarrow Ba(s)$	−2.90
$K^+(aq) + e^-$	$\longrightarrow K(s)$	−2.92
$Li^+(aq) + e^-$	$\longrightarrow Li(s)$	−3.04

Low tendency towards reduction

High tendency towards oxidation

Example 20.4 illustrates how to calculate the potential of an electrochemical cell from the standard electrode potentials of the half-reactions.

WATCH **NOW!**

INTERACTIVE WORKED EXAMPLE 20.4

EXAMPLE 20.4 Calculating Standard Potentials for Electrochemical Cells from Standard Electrode Potentials of the Half-Reactions

Use tabulated standard electrode potentials to calculate the standard cell potential for the following reaction occurring in an electrochemical cell at 25 °C. (The equation is balanced.)

$$Al(s) + NO_3^-(aq) + 4\,H^+(aq) \longrightarrow Al^{3+}(aq) + NO(g) + 2\,H_2O(l)$$

SOLUTION

Begin by separating the reaction into oxidation and reduction half-reactions. (In this case, you can readily see that Al(*s*) is oxidized. In cases where it is not so apparent, you may want to assign oxidation states to determine the correct half-reactions.)

Oxidation: $Al(s) \longrightarrow Al^{3+}(aq) + 3\,e^-$

Reduction: $NO_3^-(aq) + 4\,H^+(aq) + 3\,e^- \longrightarrow NO(g) + 2\,H_2O(l)$

Look up the standard electrode potentials for each half-reaction in Table 20.1. Add the half-cell reactions together to obtain the overall redox equation. Calculate the standard cell potential by subtracting the electrode potential of the anode from the electrode potential of the cathode.

Oxidation (Anode): $Al(s) \longrightarrow Al^{3+}(aq) + \cancel{3\,e^-} \qquad E° = -1.66\text{ V}$

Reduction (Cathode): $NO_3^-(aq) + 4\,H^+(aq) + \cancel{3\,e^-} \longrightarrow NO(g) + 2\,H_2O(l) \qquad E° = 0.96\text{ V}$

$$Al(s) + NO_3^-(aq) + 4\,H^+(aq) \longrightarrow Al^{3+}(aq) + NO(g) + 2\,H_2O(l)$$

$$\begin{aligned} E°_{cell} &= E°_{cat} - E°_{an} \\ &= 0.96\text{ V} - (-1.66\text{ V}) \\ &= 2.62\text{ V} \end{aligned}$$

FOR PRACTICE 20.4 Use tabulated standard electrode potentials to calculate the standard cell potential for the following reaction occurring in an electrochemical cell at 25 °C. (The equation is balanced.)

$$3\,Pb^{2+}(aq) + 2\,Cr(s) \longrightarrow 3\,Pb(s) + 2\,Cr^{3+}(aq)$$

ANSWER **NOW!**

20.3 Cc Conceptual Connection

STANDARD ELECTRODE POTENTIALS An electrode has a negative electrode potential. Which statement is correct regarding the potential energy of an electron at this electrode?

(a) An electron at this electrode has a lower potential energy than it has at a standard hydrogen electrode.

(b) An electron at this electrode has a higher potential energy than it has at a standard hydrogen electrode.

(c) An electron at this electrode has the same potential energy as it has at a standard hydrogen electrode.

Predicting the Spontaneous Direction of an Oxidation–Reduction Reaction

To determine the spontaneous direction of an oxidation–reduction reaction, we examine the electrode potentials of the two relevant half-reactions in Table 20.1. The half-reaction with the more *negative* electrode potential tends to lose electrons and therefore tends to undergo oxidation. (Remember that negative charge repels electrons.) The half-reaction having the more *positive* electrode potential tends to gain electrons, and therefore, undergo reduction. (Remember that positive charge attracts electrons.)

For example, consider the two reduction half-reactions:

$$Ni^{2+}(aq) + 2\,e^- \longrightarrow Ni(s) \qquad E° = -0.23\ V$$

$$Mn^{2+}(aq) + 2\,e^- \longrightarrow Mn(s) \qquad E° = -1.18\ V$$

Because the manganese half-reaction has a more negative electrode potential, it repels electrons and proceeds in the reverse direction (oxidation). Because the nickel half-reaction has the more positive (or less negative) electrode potential, it attracts electrons and proceeds in the forward direction.

We can confirm this by calculating the standard electrode potential for manganese acting as the anode (oxidation) and nickel acting as the cathode (reduction):

Oxidation (Anode):	$Mn(s) \longrightarrow Mn^{2+}(aq) + \cancel{2\,e^-}$	$E° = -1.18\ V$
Reduction (Cathode):	$Ni^{2+}(aq) + \cancel{2\,e^-} \longrightarrow Ni(s)$	$E° = -0.23\ V$
	$Ni^{2+}(aq) + Mn(s) \longrightarrow Ni(s) + Mn^{2+}(aq)$	$E°_{cell} = E°_{cat} - E°_{an}$
		$= -0.23\ V - (-1.18\ V)$
		$= 0.95\ V$

The following mnemonics (NIO and PIR) help to predict the spontaneous direction of redox reactions:
N.I.O.—More **N**egative **I**s **O**xidation
P.I.R.—More **P**ositive **I**s **R**eduction

The overall cell potential is positive, indicating a spontaneous reaction. Consider the electrochemical cell corresponding to this spontaneous redox reaction in Figure 20.8▼. We draw the manganese half-cell on the left as the anode and the nickel half-cell on the right as the cathode. Electrons flow from the anode to the cathode.

Another way to predict the spontaneity of a redox reaction is to note the relative positions of the two half-reactions in Table 20.1. The table lists half-reactions in order of *decreasing* electrode potential, so the half-reactions near the top of the table—those having large *positive* electrode potentials—attract electrons, and therefore, tend to occur in the forward direction. Half-reactions near the bottom of the table—those having large *negative* electrode potentials—repel electrons, and therefore, tend to occur in the reverse direction. In other words, as we move down Table 20.1, the half-reactions become less likely to occur in the forward direction and more likely to occur in the reverse direction. As a result, *any reduction half-reaction listed is spontaneous when paired with the reverse of a half-reaction that appears below it in* Table 20.1.

For example, if we return to our two previous half-reactions involving manganese and nickel, we can see that the manganese half-reaction is below the nickel half-reaction in Table 20.1:

$$Ni^{2+}(aq) + 2\,e^- \longrightarrow Ni(s) \qquad E° = -0.23\ V$$

$$Mn^{2+}(aq) + 2\,e^- \longrightarrow Mn(s) \qquad E° = -1.18\ V$$

Therefore, the nickel reaction occurs in the forward direction (reduction), and the manganese reaction occurs in the reverse direction (oxidation).

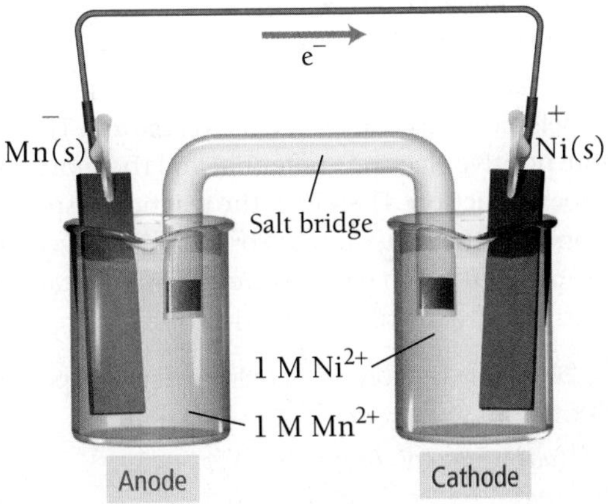

◀ **FIGURE 20.8 Mn/Ni²⁺ Electrochemical Cell** The reduction of Mn^{2+} is listed below the reduction of Ni^{2+} in Table 20.1, so the reduction of Ni^{2+} is spontaneous when paired with the oxidation of Mn.

Recall from Section 5.9 that an *oxidizing agent* causes the oxidation of another substance (and is itself reduced) and that a *reducing agent* causes the reduction of another substance (and is itself oxidized).

Summarizing the Prediction of Spontaneous Direction for Redox Reactions:

- The half-reaction with the more *positive* electrode potential attracts electrons more strongly and undergoes reduction. (Substances listed at the top of Table 20.1 tend to undergo reduction; they are good oxidizing agents.)
- The half-reaction with the more *negative* electrode potential repels electrons more strongly and undergoes oxidation. (Substances listed near the bottom of Table 20.1 tend to undergo oxidation; they are good reducing agents.)
- Any reduction reaction in Table 20.1 is spontaneous when paired with the *reverse* of any of the reactions listed below it on the table.

EXAMPLE 20.5 Predicting Spontaneous Redox Reactions and Sketching Electrochemical Cells

Without calculating E°_{cell}, predict whether each of the redox reactions is spontaneous. If the reaction is spontaneous as written, make a sketch of the electrochemical cell in which the reaction could occur. If the reaction is not spontaneous as written, write an equation for the spontaneous direction in which the reaction would occur and sketch the electrochemical cell in which the spontaneous reaction would occur. In your sketches, make sure to label the anode (which should be drawn on the left), the cathode, and the direction of electron flow.

(a) $Fe(s) + Mg^{2+}(aq) \longrightarrow Fe^{2+}(aq) + Mg(s)$

(b) $Fe(s) + Pb^{2+}(aq) \longrightarrow Fe^{2+}(aq) + Pb(s)$

SOLUTION

(a) $Fe(s) + Mg^{2+}(aq) \longrightarrow Fe^{2+}(aq) + Mg(s)$

This reaction involves the reduction of Mg^{2+}:

$$Mg^{2+}(aq) + 2\,e^- \longrightarrow Mg(s) \qquad E^\circ = -2.37\text{ V}$$

and the oxidation of Fe:

$$Fe(s) \longrightarrow Fe^{2+}(aq) + 2\,e^- \qquad E^\circ = -0.45\text{ V}$$

However, the magnesium half-reaction has the more negative electrode potential and therefore repels electrons more strongly and undergoes oxidation. The iron half-reaction has the more positive electrode potential and therefore attracts electrons more strongly and undergoes reduction. So the reaction as written is *not* spontaneous. (The reaction pairs the reduction of Mg^{2+} with the reverse of a half-reaction *above it* in Table 20.1—such pairings are not spontaneous.)

However, the reverse reaction is spontaneous:

$$Fe^{2+}(aq) + Mg(s) \longrightarrow Fe(s) + Mg^{2+}(aq)$$

The corresponding electrochemical cell is shown in Figure 20.9◀.

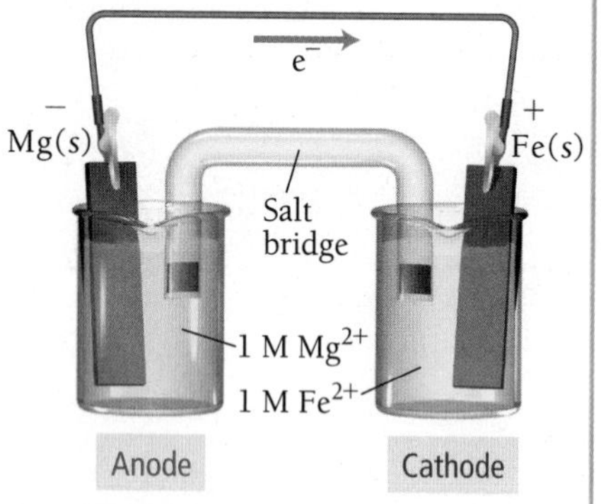

▲ **FIGURE 20.9 Mg/Fe²⁺ Electrochemical Cell**

(b) $Fe(s) + Pb^{2+}(aq) \longrightarrow Fe^{2+}(aq) + Pb(s)$

This reaction involves the reduction of Pb^{2+}:

$$Pb^{2+}(aq) + 2\,e^- \longrightarrow Pb(s) \qquad E^\circ = -0.13\text{ V}$$

and the oxidation of iron:

$$Fe(s) \longrightarrow Fe^{2+}(aq) + 2\,e^- \qquad E^\circ = -0.45\text{ V}$$

The iron half-reaction has the more negative electrode potential and therefore repels electrons and undergoes oxidation. The lead half-reaction has the more positive electrode potential and therefore attracts electrons and undergoes reduction. Therefore, the reaction *is* spontaneous as written. (The reaction pairs the reduction of Pb^{2+} with the reverse of a half-reaction *below it* in Table 20.1—such pairings are always spontaneous.) The corresponding electrochemical cell is shown in Figure 20.10◀.

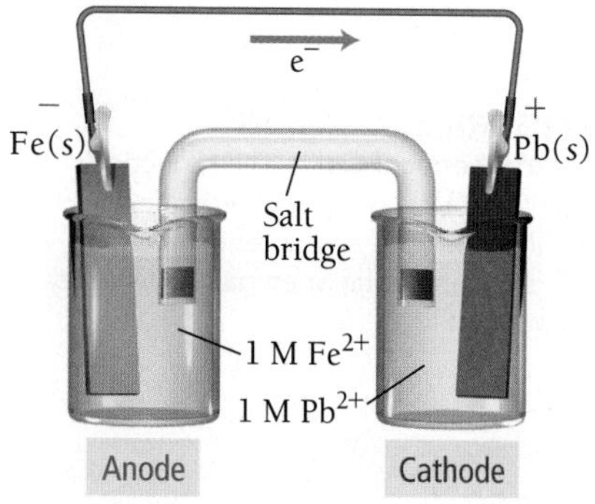

▲ **FIGURE 20.10 Fe/Pb²⁺ Electrochemical Cell**

FOR PRACTICE 20.5 Are the following redox reactions spontaneous under standard conditions?

(a) $Zn(s) + Ni^{2+}(aq) \longrightarrow Zn^{2+}(aq) + Ni(s)$

(b) $Zn(s) + Ca^{2+}(aq) \longrightarrow Zn^{2+}(aq) + Ca(s)$

SELECTIVE OXIDATION A solution contains both NaI and NaBr. Which oxidizing agent could you add to the solution to selectively oxidize $I^-(aq)$ but not $Br^-(aq)$?

(a) Cl_2 **(b)** H_2O_2 **(c)** $CuCl_2$ **(d)** HNO_3

20.4 Cc Conceptual Connection — ANSWER NOW!

Predicting Whether a Metal Will Dissolve in Acid

In Chapter 17, we learned that acids dissolve metals. Most acids dissolve metals by the reduction of H^+ ions to hydrogen gas and the corresponding oxidation of the metal to its ion. For example, if solid Zn is dropped into hydrochloric acid, the following reaction occurs:

$$\begin{array}{rcl} 2\,H^+(aq) + \cancel{2e^-} & \longrightarrow & H_2(g) \\ Zn(s) & \longrightarrow & Zn^{2+}(aq) + \cancel{2e^-} \\ \hline Zn(s) + 2\,H^+(aq) & \longrightarrow & Zn^{2+}(aq) + H_2(g) \end{array}$$

$Zn(s) + 2\,H^+(aq) \longrightarrow Zn^{2+}(aq) + H_2(g)$

▲ When zinc is immersed in hydrochloric acid, the zinc is oxidized, forming ions that become solvated in the solution. Hydrogen ions are reduced, forming bubbles of hydrogen gas.

We observe the reaction as the dissolving of the zinc and the bubbling of hydrogen gas. The zinc is oxidized and the H^+ ions are reduced. Notice that this reaction involves the pairing of a reduction half-reaction (the reduction of H^+) with the reverse of a half-reaction that falls below it in Table 20.1. Therefore, this reaction is spontaneous. What happens, however, if we pair the reduction of H^+ with the oxidation of Cu? The reaction is not spontaneous because it involves pairing the reduction of H^+ with the reverse of a half-reaction that is listed *above it* in the table. Consequently, copper does not react with H^+ and does not dissolve in acids such as HCl. In general, *metals whose reduction half-reactions are listed below the reduction of* H^+ *to* H_2 *in Table 20.1 dissolve in acids, while metals listed above it do not.*

An important exception to this rule is nitric acid (HNO_3), which can oxidize metals through the reduction half-reaction:

$$NO_3^-(aq) + 4\,H^+(aq) + 3\,e^- \longrightarrow NO(g) + 2\,H_2O(l) \quad E^\circ = 0.96\text{ V}$$

Since this half-reaction is above the reduction of H^+ in Table 20.1, HNO_3 can oxidize metals (such as copper) that can't be oxidized by HCl.

METALS DISSOLVING IN ACIDS Which metal dissolves in HNO_3 but not in HCl?

(a) Fe **(b)** Au **(c)** Ag

20.5 Cc Conceptual Connection — ANSWER NOW!

20.5 Cell Potential, Free Energy, and the Equilibrium Constant

WATCH NOW!
KEY CONCEPT VIDEO 20.5
Cell Potential, Free Energy, and the Equilibrium Constant

We have seen that a positive standard cell potential (E°_{cell}) corresponds to a spontaneous oxidation–reduction reaction. And we know (from Chapter 19) that the spontaneity of a reaction is determined by the sign of ΔG°. Therefore, E°_{cell} and ΔG° must be related. We also know from Section 19.10 that ΔG° for a reaction is related to the equilibrium constant (K) for the reaction. Since E°_{cell} and ΔG° are related, then E°_{cell} and K must also be related.

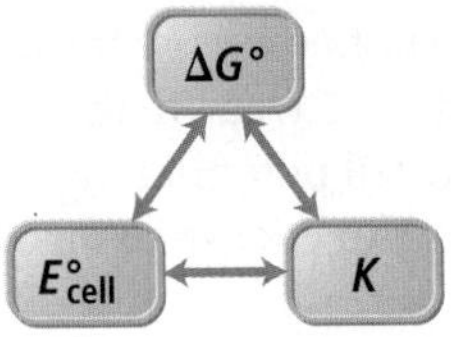

Before we look at the nature of each of these relationships in detail, let's consider the following generalizations.

For a spontaneous redox reaction (one that proceeds in the forward direction when all reactants and products are in their standard states):

- ΔG° is negative (<0)
- E°_{cell} is positive (>0)
- $K > 1$

For a nonspontaneous reaction (one that proceeds in the reverse direction when all reactants and products are in their standard states):

- ΔG° is positive (>0)
- E°_{cell} is negative (<0)
- $K < 1$

The Relationship between ΔG° and E°_{cell}

We can derive a relationship between ΔG° and E°_{cell} by briefly returning to the definition of potential difference from Section 20.3—a potential difference is a measure of the difference of potential energy per unit charge (q):

Maximum work (w_{max})

$$E = \frac{\text{potential energy difference (in J)}}{\text{charge (in C)}}$$

Charge (q)

Since the potential energy difference represents the maximum amount of work that can be done by the system on the surroundings, we can write:

$$w_{max} = -qE^\circ_{cell} \qquad [20.1]$$

The negative sign follows the convention used throughout this book that work done by the system on the surroundings is negative.

We can quantify the charge (q) that flows in an electrochemical reaction by using **Faraday's constant (*F*)**, which represents the charge in coulombs of 1 mol of electrons:

$$F = \frac{96{,}485 \text{ C}}{\text{mol e}^-}$$

The total charge is $q = nF$, where n is the number of moles of electrons from the balanced chemical equation and F is Faraday's constant. Substituting $q = nF$ into Equation 20.1:

$$\begin{aligned} w_{max} &= -qE^\circ_{cell} \\ &= -nFE^\circ_{cell} \end{aligned} \qquad [20.2]$$

Finally, recall from Chapter 19 that the standard change in free energy for a chemical reaction (ΔG°) represents the maximum amount of work that can be done by the reaction. Therefore, $w_{max} = \Delta G^\circ$. Making this substitution into Equation 20.2, we arrive at the following important result:

$$\Delta G^\circ = -nFE^\circ_{cell} \qquad [20.3]$$

where ΔG° is the standard change in free energy for an electrochemical reaction, n is the number of moles of electrons transferred in the balanced equation, F is Faraday's constant, and E°_{cell} is the standard cell potential. Example 20.6 shows how to apply this equation to calculate the standard free energy change for an electrochemical cell.

WATCH **NOW!**

INTERACTIVE WORKED EXAMPLE 20.6

EXAMPLE 20.6 Relating ΔG° and E°_{cell}

Use the tabulated electrode potentials to calculate ΔG° for the reaction:

$$I_2(s) + 2\,Br^-(aq) \longrightarrow 2\,I^-(aq) + Br_2(l)$$

Is the reaction spontaneous?

SORT You are given a redox reaction and asked to find ΔG°.

GIVEN: $I_2(s) + 2\,Br^-(aq) \longrightarrow 2\,I^-(aq) + Br_2(l)$

FIND: ΔG°

STRATEGIZE Refer to the values of electrode potentials in Table 20.1 to calculate E°_{cell}. Then use Equation 20.3 to calculate ΔG° from E°_{cell}.

CONCEPTUAL PLAN

$E^\circ_{an}, E^\circ_{cat} \longrightarrow E^\circ_{cell}$

$E^\circ_{cell} \longrightarrow \Delta G^\circ$

$\Delta G^\circ = -nFE^\circ_{cell}$

SOLVE Separate the reaction into oxidation and reduction half-reactions and find the standard electrode potentials for each. Determine E°_{cell} by subtracting E_{an} from E_{cat}.

SOLUTION

Oxidation (Anode): $2\,Br^-(aq) \longrightarrow Br_2(l) + 2\,e^-$ $\quad E^\circ = 1.09\ V$

Reduction (Cathode): $I_2(s) + 2\,e^- \longrightarrow 2\,I^-(aq)$ $\quad E^\circ = 0.54\ V$

$I_2(s) + 2\,Br^-(aq) \longrightarrow 2\,I^-(aq) + Br_2(l)$ $\quad E^\circ_{cell} = E^\circ_{cat} - E^\circ_{an} = -0.55\ V$

Calculate ΔG° from E°_{cell}. The value of n (the number of moles of electrons) corresponds to the number of electrons that are canceled in the half-reactions. Remember that 1 V = 1 J/C.

$$\Delta G^\circ = -nFE^\circ_{cell}$$
$$= -2\ \cancel{mol\ e^-}\left(\frac{96{,}485\ \cancel{C}}{\cancel{mol\ e^-}}\right)\left(-0.55\frac{J}{\cancel{C}}\right)$$
$$= +1.1 \times 10^5\ J$$

Since ΔG° is positive, the reaction is not spontaneous under standard conditions.

CHECK The answer is in the correct units (joules) and seems reasonable in magnitude ($\approx$110 kJ). You have seen (in Chapter 19) that values of ΔG° typically range from plus or minus tens to hundreds of kilojoules. The sign is positive, as expected for a reaction in which E°_{cell} is negative.

FOR PRACTICE 20.6 Use tabulated electrode potentials to calculate ΔG° for the reaction.

$$2\,Na(s) + 2\,H_2O(l) \longrightarrow H_2(g) + 2\,OH^-(aq) + 2\,Na^+(aq)$$

Is the reaction spontaneous?

20.6 Cc Conceptual Connection — ANSWER **NOW!**

PERIODIC TRENDS AND THE DIRECTION OF SPONTANEITY FOR REDOX REACTIONS Consider the result of Example 20.6. The calculation revealed that the reaction is not spontaneous. Based on conceptual reasoning, which of the following best explains why I_2 does not oxidize Br^-?

(a) Br is more electronegative than I; therefore, you do not expect Br^- to give up an electron to I_2.

(b) I is more electronegative than Br; therefore, you do not expect I_2 to give up an electron to Br^-.

(c) Br^- is in solution and I_2 is a solid. Solids do not gain electrons from substances in solution.

The Relationship between E°_{cell} and K

We can derive a relationship between the standard cell potential (E°_{cell}) and the equilibrium constant for the redox reaction occurring in the cell (K) by returning to the relationship between ΔG° and K that we learned in Chapter 19. Recall from Section 19.10 that:

$$\Delta G^\circ = -RT\ln K \qquad [20.4]$$

By setting Equations 20.3 and 20.4 equal to each other, we get:

$$-nFE^\circ_{cell} = -RT\ln K$$

$$E^\circ_{cell} = \frac{RT}{nF}\ln K \qquad [20.5]$$

Equation 20.5 is usually simplified for use at 25 °C by making the following substitutions:

$$R = 8.314\frac{\text{J}}{\text{mol}\cdot\text{K}};\ T = 298.15\ \text{K};\ F = \left(\frac{96{,}485\ \text{C}}{\text{mol e}^-}\right);\ \text{and}\ \ln K = 2.303\log K$$

Substituting into Equation 20.5, we get the following important result:

$$E^\circ_{cell} = \frac{0.0592\ \text{V}}{n}\log K \qquad [20.6]$$

where E°_{cell} is the standard cell potential, n is the number of moles of electrons transferred in the redox reaction, and K is the equilibrium constant for the balanced redox reaction at 25 °C. Example 20.7 demonstrates how to use Equation 20.6.

EXAMPLE 20.7 Relating E°_{cell} and K

Use the tabulated electrode potentials to calculate K for the oxidation of copper by H^+ (at 25 °C):

$$Cu(s) + 2\,H^+(aq) \longrightarrow Cu^{2+}(aq) + H_2(g)$$

SORT You are given a redox reaction and asked to find K.

GIVEN: $Cu(s) + 2\,H^+(aq) \longrightarrow Cu^{2+}(aq) + H_2(g)$

FIND: K

STRATEGIZE Refer to the values of electrode potentials in Table 20.1 to calculate E°_{cell}. Then use Equation 20.6 to calculate K from E°_{cell}.

CONCEPTUAL PLAN

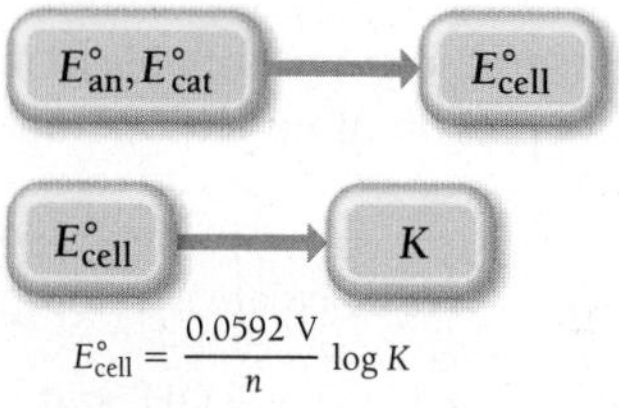

SOLVE Separate the reaction into oxidation and reduction half-reactions and find the standard electrode potentials for each. Find E°_{cell} by subtracting E_{an} from E_{cat}.

SOLUTION

Oxidation (Anode): $Cu(s) \longrightarrow Cu^{2+}(aq) + 2e^-$ $\qquad E^\circ = 0.34\ \text{V}$

Reduction (Cathode): $2\,H^+(aq) + 2e^- \longrightarrow H_2(g)$ $\qquad E^\circ = 0.00\ \text{V}$

$Cu(s) + 2\,H^+(aq) \longrightarrow Cu^{2+}(aq) + H_2(g)$ $\qquad E^\circ_{cell} = E^\circ_{cat} - E^\circ_{an}$

$= -0.34\ \text{V}$

Calculate K from E°_{cell}. The value of n (the number of moles of electrons) corresponds to the number of electrons that are canceled in the half-reactions.

$$E^\circ_{cell} = \frac{0.0592\ \text{V}}{n}\log K$$

$$\log K = E^\circ_{cell}\frac{n}{0.0592\ \text{V}}$$

$$\log K = -0.34\ \text{V}\frac{2}{0.0592\ \text{V}} = -11.4\underline{8}6$$

$$K = 10^{-11.4\underline{8}6} = 3.3 \times 10^{-12}$$

CHECK The answer has no units, as expected for an equilibrium constant. The magnitude of the answer is small, indicating that the reaction lies far to the left at equilibrium, as expected for a reaction in which E°_{cell} is negative.

FOR PRACTICE 20.7 Use the tabulated electrode potentials to calculate K for the oxidation of iron by H^+ (at 25 °C):

$$2\,Fe(s) + 6\,H^+(aq) \longrightarrow 2\,Fe^{3+}(aq) + 3\,H_2(g)$$

Notice that the fundamental quantity in the given relationships is the standard change in free energy (ΔG°). From that quantity, we can calculate both E°_{cell} and K. The relationship between these three quantities is summarized with the following diagram:

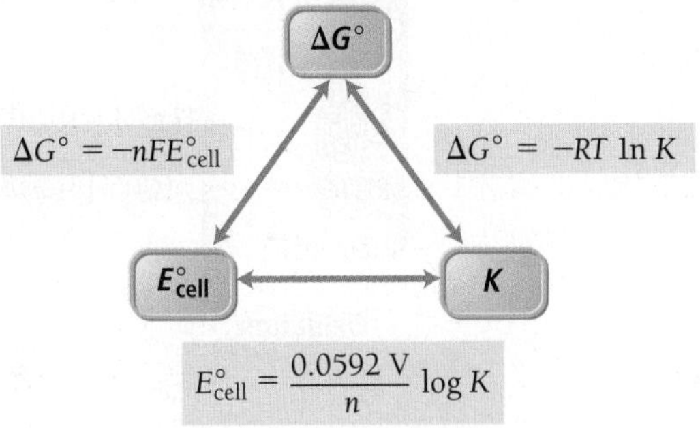

RELATING K, ΔG°_{rxn}, AND E°_{cell} A redox reaction has an equilibrium constant of $K = 1.2 \times 10^3$. Which statement is true regarding ΔG°_{rxn} and E°_{cell} for this reaction?

20.7 Cc Conceptual Connection — ANSWER **NOW!**

(a) E°_{cell} is positive and ΔG°_{rxn} is positive.
(b) E°_{cell} is negative and ΔG°_{rxn} is negative.
(c) E°_{cell} is positive and ΔG°_{rxn} is negative.
(d) E°_{cell} is negative and ΔG°_{rxn} is positive.

20.6 Cell Potential and Concentration

We have learned how to find E°_{cell} under standard conditions. For example, we know that when $[Cu^{2+}] = 1$ M and $[Zn^{2+}] = 1$ M, the following reaction produces a potential of 1.10 V:

$$Zn(s) + Cu^{2+}(aq, 1\,M) \longrightarrow Zn^{2+}(aq, 1\,M) + Cu(s) \qquad E^\circ_{cell} = 1.10\,V$$

However, what if $[Cu^{2+}] > 1$ M and $[Zn^{2+}] < 1$ M? For example, how would the cell potential for the following conditions be different from the potential under standard conditions?

$$Zn(s) + Cu^{2+}(aq, 2\,M) \longrightarrow Zn^{2+}(aq, 0.010\,M) + Cu(s) \qquad E_{cell} = ?$$

Since the concentration of a reactant is greater than standard onditions and since the concentration of product is less than standard conditions, we can use Le Châtelier's principle to predict that the reaction has an even stronger tendency to occur in the forward direction and that E_{cell} is therefore greater than +1.10 V (Figure 20.11▶).

Cell Potential under Nonstandard Conditions: The Nernst Equation

We can derive an exact relationship between E_{cell} (under nonstandard conditions) and E°_{cell} by considering the relationship between the change in free energy (ΔG) and the *standard* change in free energy (ΔG°) from Section 19.9:

$$\Delta G = \Delta G^\circ + RT \ln Q \qquad [20.7]$$

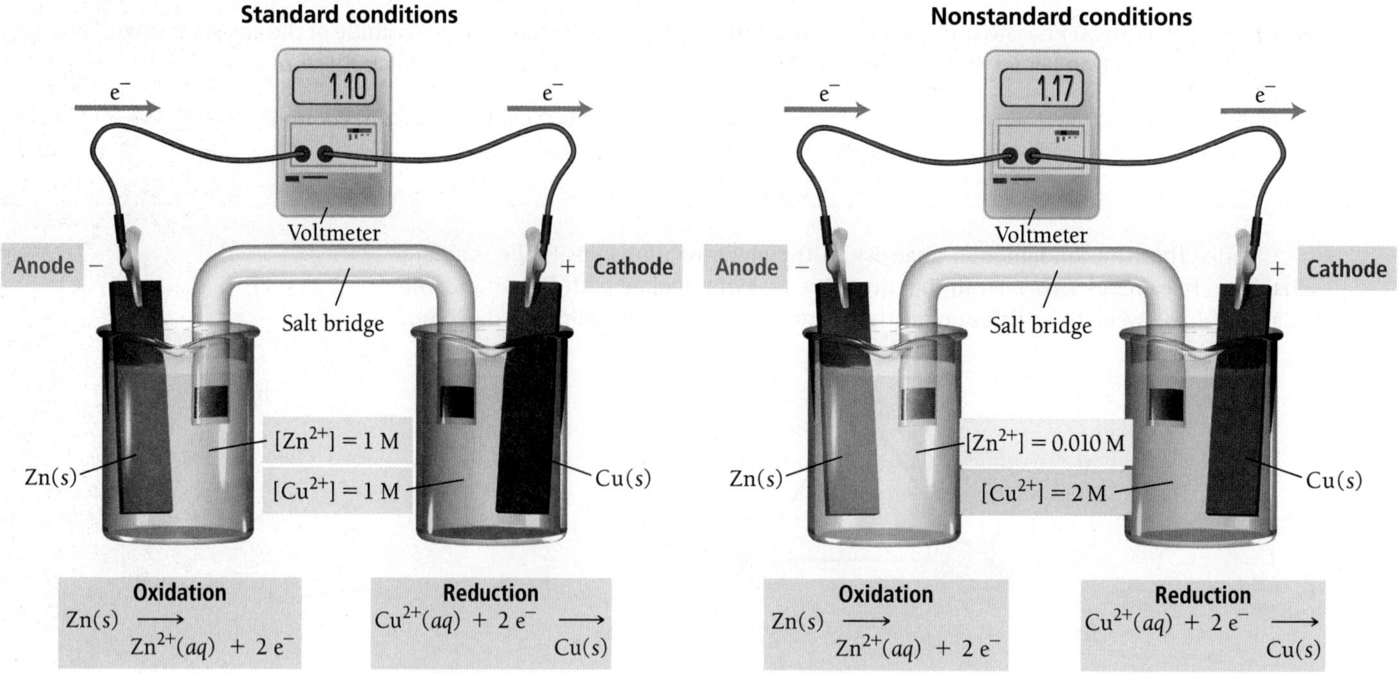

▲ **FIGURE 20.11 Cell Potential and Concentration** This figure compares the Zn/Cu^{2+} electrochemical cell under standard and nonstandard conditions. In this case, the nonstandard conditions consist of a higher Cu^{2+} concentration ($[Cu^{2+}] > 1$ M) at the cathode and a lower Zn^{2+} concentration at the anode ($[Zn^{2+}] < 1$ M). According to Le Châtelier's principle, the forward reaction has a greater tendency to occur, resulting in a greater overall cell potential than the cell potential under standard conditions.

where R is the gas constant ($8.314\,\text{J/mol}\cdot\text{K}$), T is the temperature in kelvins, and Q is the reaction quotient corresponding to the nonstandard conditions. Since we know the relationship between ΔG and E_{cell} (Equation 20.3), we can substitute into Equation 20.7:

$$\Delta G = \Delta G^\circ + RT \ln Q$$

$$-nFE_{\text{cell}} = -nFE^\circ_{\text{cell}} + RT \ln Q$$

We then divide each side by $-nF$ to arrive at:

$$E_{\text{cell}} = E^\circ_{\text{cell}} - \frac{RT}{nF} \ln Q \qquad [20.8]$$

As we have seen, R and F are constants; at $T = 25\,°\text{C}$, $\frac{RT}{nF} \ln Q = \frac{0.0592\text{ V}}{n} \log Q$.

Substituting into Equation 20.8, we arrive at the **Nernst equation**:

$$E_{\text{cell}} = E^\circ_{\text{cell}} - \frac{0.0592\text{ V}}{n} \log Q \qquad [20.9]$$

where E_{cell} is the cell potential in volts, E°_{cell} is the *standard* cell potential in volts, n is the number of moles of electrons transferred in the redox reaction, and Q is the reaction quotient. Notice that, under standard conditions, $Q = 1$, and (since $\log 1 = 0$) $E_{\text{cell}} = E^\circ_{\text{cell}}$, as expected. Example 20.8 shows how to calculate the cell potential under nonstandard conditions.

EXAMPLE 20.8 Calculating E_{cell} under Nonstandard Conditions

Determine the cell potential for an electrochemical cell based on the following two half-reactions:

Oxidation: $Cu(s) \longrightarrow Cu^{2+}(aq, 0.010\ M) + 2\ e^-$

Reduction: $MnO_4^-(aq, 2.0\ M) + 4\ H^+(aq, 1.0\ M) + 3\ e^- \longrightarrow MnO_2(s) + 2\ H_2O(l)$

SORT You are given the half-reactions for a redox reaction and the concentrations of the aqueous reactants and products. You are asked to find the cell potential.

GIVEN: $[MnO_4^-] = 2.0\ M$; $[H^+] = 1.0\ M$; $[Cu^{2+}] = 0.010\ M$

FIND: E_{cell}

STRATEGIZE Use the tabulated values of electrode potentials to calculate E°_{cell}. Then use Equation 20.9 to calculate E_{cell}.

CONCEPTUAL PLAN

$E^\circ_{an}, E^\circ_{cat} \longrightarrow E^\circ_{cell}$

$E^\circ_{cell}, [MnO_4^-], [H^+], [Cu^{2+}] \longrightarrow E_{cell}$

$$E_{cell} = E^\circ_{cell} - \frac{0.0592\ V}{n} \log Q$$

SOLVE Write the oxidation and reduction half-reactions, multiplying by the appropriate coefficients to cancel the electrons. Find the standard electrode potentials for each half-reaction. Find E°_{cell}.

SOLUTION

Oxidation (Anode): $3[Cu(s) \longrightarrow Cu^{2+}(aq) + 2\cancel{e^-}]$ $\quad E^\circ = 0.34\ V$

Reduction (Cathode): $2[MnO_4^-(aq) + 4\ H^+(aq) + 3\cancel{e^-} \longrightarrow MnO_2(s) + 2\ H_2O(l)]$ $\quad E^\circ = 1.68\ V$

$$3\ Cu(s) + 2\ MnO_4^-(aq) + 8\ H^+(aq) \longrightarrow 3\ Cu^{2+}(aq) + 2\ MnO_2(s) + 4\ H_2O(l)$$

$$E^\circ_{cell} = E^\circ_{cat} - E^\circ_{an} = 1.34\ V$$

Calculate E_{cell} from E°_{cell}. The value of n (the number of moles of electrons) corresponds to the number of electrons (six in this case) canceled in the half-reactions. Determine Q based on the overall balanced equation and the given concentrations of the reactants and products. (Note that pure liquid water, solid MnO_2, and solid copper are omitted from the expression for Q.)

$$E_{cell} = E^\circ_{cell} - \frac{0.0592\ V}{n} \log Q$$

$$= E^\circ_{cell} - \frac{0.0592\ V}{n} \log \frac{[Cu^{2+}]^3}{[MnO_4^-]^2[H^+]^8}$$

$$= 1.34\ V - \frac{0.0592\ V}{6} \log \frac{(0.010)^3}{(2.0)^2(1.0)^8}$$

$$= 1.34\ V - (-0.065\ V)$$

$$= 1.41\ V$$

CHECK The answer has the correct units (V). The value of E_{cell} is larger than E°_{cell}, as expected based on Le Châtelier's principle because one of the aqueous reactants has a concentration greater than standard conditions and the one aqueous product has a concentration less than standard conditions. Therefore, the reaction has a greater tendency to proceed toward products and a greater cell potential.

FOR PRACTICE 20.8 Determine the cell potential of an electrochemical cell based on the following two half-reactions:

Oxidation: $Ni(s) \longrightarrow Ni^{2+}(aq, 2.0\ M) + 2\ e^-$

Reduction: $VO_2^+(aq, 0.010\ M) + 2\ H^+(aq, 1.0\ M) + e^- \longrightarrow VO^{2+}(aq, 2.0\ M) + H_2O(l)$

From Equation 20.9, we can conclude the following:

- When a redox reaction within a voltaic cell occurs under standard conditions, $Q = 1$; therefore, $E_{cell} = E^\circ_{cell}$.

$$\begin{aligned} E_{cell} &= E^\circ_{cell} - \frac{0.0592\ \text{V}}{n} \log Q \\ &= E^\circ_{cell} - \frac{0.0592\ \text{V}}{n} \log 1 \\ &= E^\circ_{cell} \end{aligned}$$

$\log 1 = 0$

- When a redox reaction within a voltaic cell occurs under conditions in which $Q < 1$, the greater concentration of reactants relative to products drives the reaction to the right, resulting in $E_{cell} > E^\circ_{cell}$.
- When a redox reaction within an electrochemical cell occurs under conditions in which $Q > 1$, the greater concentration of products relative to reactants drives the reaction to the left, resulting in $E_{cell} < E^\circ_{cell}$.
- When a redox reaction reaches equilibrium, $Q = K$. The redox reaction has no tendency to occur in either direction and $E_{cell} = 0$:

$$\begin{aligned} E_{cell} &= E^\circ_{cell} - \frac{0.0592\ \text{V}}{n} \log Q \\ &= E^\circ_{cell} - \frac{0.0592\ \text{V}}{n} \log K \\ &= E^\circ_{cell} - E^\circ_{cell} \\ &= 0 \end{aligned}$$

E°_{cell} (see Equation 20.6)

This last point explains why batteries do not last forever—as the reactants are depleted, the reaction proceeds toward equilibrium and the potential tends toward zero.

ANSWER **NOW!**

20.8 Cc Conceptual Connection

RELATING Q, K, E_{cell}, AND E°_{cell} In an electrochemical cell, $Q = 0.0010$ and $K = 0.10$. What can you conclude about E_{cell} and E°_{cell}?

(a) E_{cell} is positive and E°_{cell} is negative.
(b) E_{cell} is negative and E°_{cell} is positive.
(c) Both E_{cell} and E°_{cell} are positive.
(d) Both E_{cell} and E°_{cell} are negative.

Concentration Cells

Since cell potential depends not only on the half-reactions occurring in the cell, but also on the *concentrations* of the reactants and products in those half-reactions, we can construct a voltaic cell in which both half-reactions are the same, but in which *a difference in concentration drives the current flow*. For example, consider the electrochemical cell shown in Figure 20.12▶, in which copper is oxidized at the anode and copper ions are reduced at the cathode. The second part of Figure 20.12 depicts this cell under nonstandard conditions, with $[Cu^{2+}] = 2.0\ \text{M}$ in one half-cell and $[Cu^{2+}] = 0.010\ \text{M}$ in the other:

$$Cu(s) + Cu^{2+}(aq, 2.0\ \text{M}) \longrightarrow Cu^{2+}(aq, 0.010\ \text{M}) + Cu(s)$$

A Concentration Cell

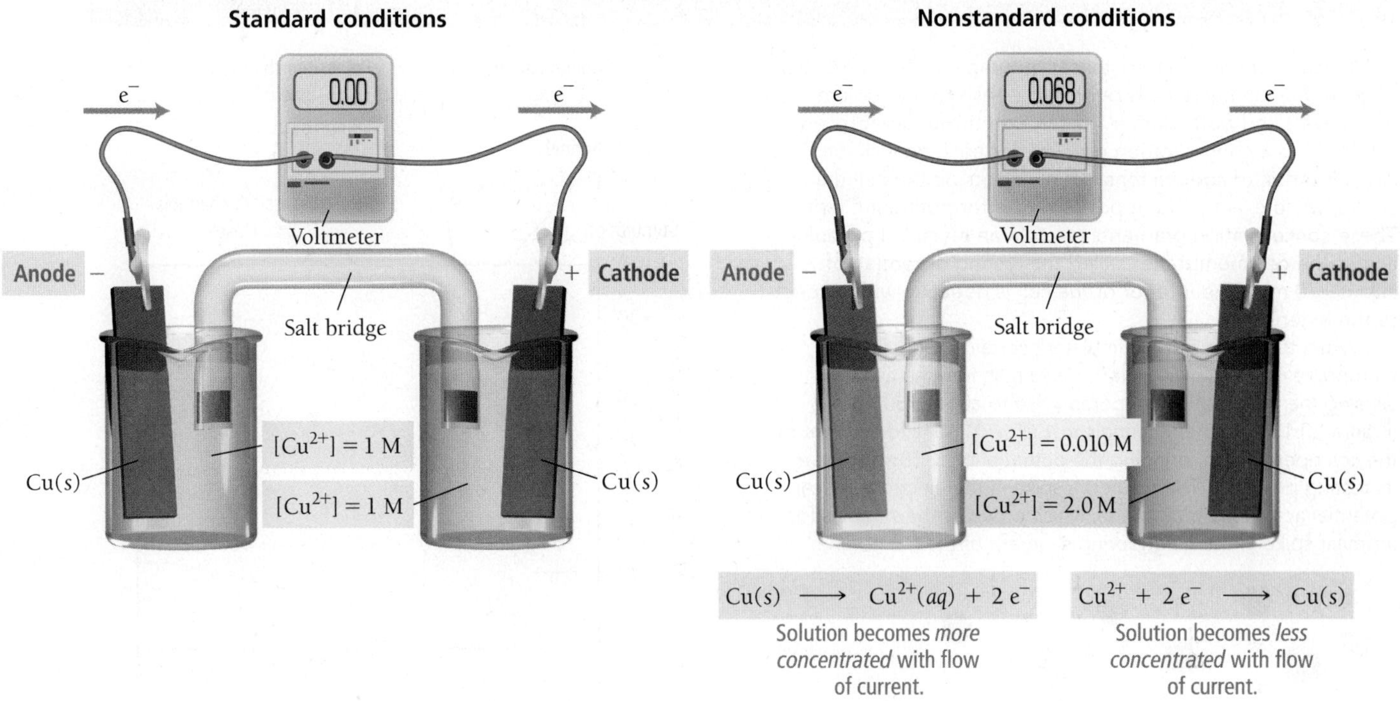

▲ **FIGURE 20.12 Cu/Cu^{2+} Concentration Cell** If two half-cells have the same Cu^{2+} concentration, the cell potential is zero. If one half-cell has a greater Cu^{2+} concentration than the other, a spontaneous reaction occurs. In the reaction, Cu^{2+} ions in the more concentrated cell are reduced (to solid copper), while Cu^{2+} ions in the more dilute cell are formed (from solid copper). The concentration of copper ions in the two half-cells tends toward equality.

The half-reactions are identical, and the *standard* cell potential is therefore zero:

Reduction (Cathode):	$Cu^{2+}(aq) + \cancel{2e^-} \longrightarrow Cu(s)$	$E° = 0.34\ V$
Oxidation (Anode):	$Cu(s) \longrightarrow Cu^{2+}(aq) + \cancel{2e^-}$	$E° = 0.34\ V$
	$Cu^{2+}(aq) + Cu(s) \longrightarrow Cu(s) + Cu^{2+}(aq)$	$E°_{cell} = E°_{cat} - E°_{an} = +0.00\ V$

Because of the different concentrations in the two half-cells, the cell potential must be calculated using the Nernst equation:

$$E_{cell} = E°_{cell} - \frac{0.0592\ V}{2} \log \frac{0.010}{2.0}$$

$$= 0.000\ V + 0.068\ V$$

$$= 0.068\ V$$

The cell produces a potential of 0.068 V. *Electrons spontaneously flow from the half-cell with the lower copper ion concentration to the half-cell with the higher copper ion concentration.* We can imagine a concentration cell in the same way we think about any concentration gradient. If we mix a concentrated solution of Cu^{2+} with a dilute solution, the Cu^{2+} ions flow from the concentrated solution to the dilute one. Similarly, in a concentration cell, the transfer of electrons *from* the dilute half-cell results in the formation of Cu^{2+} ions in the dilute half-cell. The electrons flow to the concentrated cell, where they react with Cu^{2+} ions and reduce them to Cu(*s*). Therefore, *the flow of electrons has the effect of increasing the concentration of Cu^{2+} in the dilute cell and decreasing the concentration of Cu^{2+} in the concentrated half-cell.*

CHEMISTRY AND MEDICINE | Concentration Cells in Human Nerve Cells

Recall from Section 9.1 that tiny pumps in the membranes of human nerve cells pump ions—especially sodium (Na^+) and potassium (K^+)—through those membranes, establishing a concentration gradient for each type of ion. The concentration of sodium ions is higher outside the cell than within, while exactly the opposite is true for potassium ions. These concentration gradients result in an electrical potential across the cell membrane, called the resting potential, of about −70 mV. (The interior of the cell is negative with respect to the exterior.)

When the nerve cell is stimulated, certain channels in the membrane open, allowing Na^+ ions to rush into the cell and causing the potential to temporarily rise to about +30 mV (Figure 20.13▼). Other channels that allow K^+ ions to rush out of the cell open in turn, bringing the potential back down to near its resting potential. The result is a spike in the electrochemical potential across the membrane, which provides the stimulus for a similar spike in the neighboring segment of the membrane (Figure 20.14▲). In this way, an electrical signal moves down the length of a nerve cell.

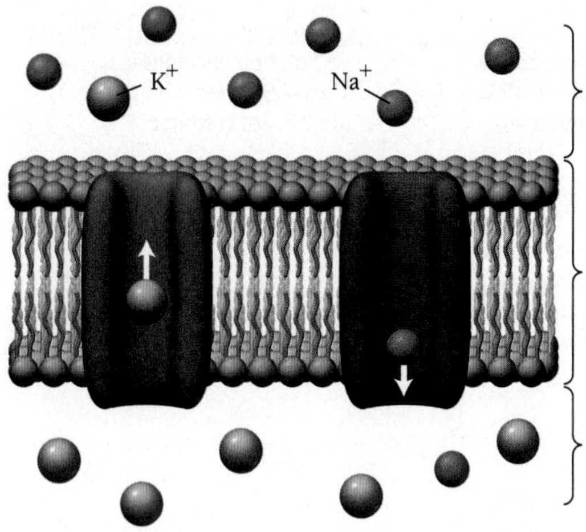

▲ **FIGURE 20.13 Concentration Changes in Nerve Cells**

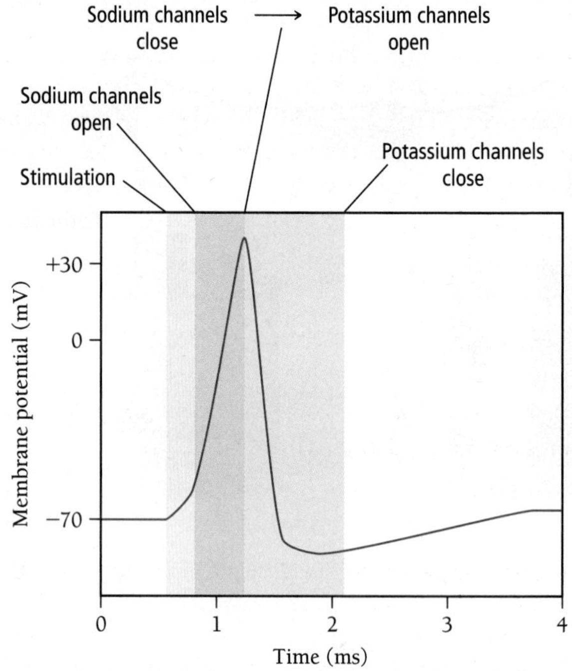

▲ **FIGURE 20.14 Potential Changes across the Nerve Cell Membrane** The changes in ion concentrations that take place when a nerve cell is stimulated result in a spike in the electrochemical potential across the membrane.

When the electrical signal reaches the end of the nerve cell, it triggers the release of a chemical neurotransmitter, which travels to the neighboring nerve cell and stimulates the same kind of electrochemical spike. In this way, neural signals travel throughout the brain and nervous system.

20.7 Batteries: Using Chemistry to Generate Electricity

We have seen that we can combine the electron-losing tendency of one substance with the electron-gaining tendency of another to create electrical current in a voltaic cell. Batteries are voltaic cells conveniently packaged to act as portable sources of electricity. The actual oxidation and reduction reactions vary depending on the particular type of battery. In this section, we examine several different types.

Dry-Cell Batteries

Common batteries, such as the kind in a flashlight, are called **dry-cell batteries** because they do not contain large amounts of liquid water. There are several familiar types of dry-cell batteries. The most inexpensive are composed of a zinc case that acts as the anode (Figure 20.15(a)▶). The zinc is oxidized according to the reaction:

Oxidation (Anode): $Zn(s) \longrightarrow Zn^{2+}(aq) + 2\,e^-$

The cathode is a carbon rod immersed in a moist paste of MnO_2 that also contains NH_4Cl. The MnO_2 is reduced to Mn_2O_3 according to the reaction:

$$\textbf{\textit{Reduction (Cathode):}}\quad 2\,MnO_2(s) + 2\,NH_4^+(aq) + 2\,e^- \longrightarrow Mn_2O_3(s) + 2\,NH_3(g) + H_2O(l)$$

These two half-reactions produce a voltage of about 1.5 V. Two or more of these batteries can be connected in series (cathode-to-anode connection) to produce higher voltages.

The more common **alkaline batteries** (Figure 20.15(b)▶) employ slightly different half-reactions in a basic medium (therefore the name alkaline). In an alkaline battery, the zinc is oxidized in a basic environment:

$$\textbf{\textit{Oxidation (Anode):}}\quad Zn(s) + \cancel{2\,OH^-}(aq) \longrightarrow Zn(OH)_2(s) + \cancel{2e^-}$$
$$\textbf{\textit{Reduction (Cathode):}}\quad 2\,MnO_2(s) + 2\,H_2O(l) + \cancel{2e^-} \longrightarrow 2\,MnO(OH)(s) + \cancel{2\,OH^-}(aq)$$
$$\textbf{\textit{Overall reaction:}}\quad Zn(s) + 2\,MnO_2(s) + 2\,H_2O(l) \longrightarrow Zn(OH)_2(s) + 2\,MnO(OH)(s)$$

Alkaline batteries have a longer working life and a longer shelf life than their nonalkaline counterparts.

Lead–Acid Storage Batteries

The batteries in most automobiles are **lead-acid storage batteries**. These batteries consist of six electrochemical cells wired in series (Figure 20.16▼). Each cell produces 2 V for a total of 12 V. Each cell contains a porous lead anode where oxidation occurs and a lead(IV) oxide cathode where reduction occurs according to the reactions:

$$\textbf{\textit{Oxidation (Anode):}}\quad Pb(s) + HSO_4^-(aq) \longrightarrow PbSO_4(s) + \cancel{H^+}(aq) + \cancel{2e^-}$$
$$\textbf{\textit{Reduction (Cathode):}}\quad PbO_2(s) + HSO_4^-(aq) + 2\,\cancel{3}\,H^+(aq) + \cancel{2e^-} \longrightarrow PbO_4(s) + 2\,H_2O(l)$$
$$\textbf{\textit{Overall reaction:}}\quad Pb(s) + PbO_2(s) + 2\,HSO_4^-(aq) + 2\,H^+(aq) \longrightarrow 2\,PbSO_4(s) + 2\,H_2O(l)$$

Both the anode and the cathode are immersed in sulfuric acid (H_2SO_4). As electrical current is drawn from the battery, both electrodes become coated with $PbSO_4(s)$. If the battery is run for a long time without recharging, too much $PbSO_4(s)$ develops on the surface of the electrodes and the battery goes dead. The lead–acid storage battery can be recharged by an electrical current (which must come from an external source such as an alternator in a car). The current causes the preceding reaction to occur in reverse, converting the $PbSO_4(s)$ back to $Pb(s)$ and $PbSO_4(s)$.

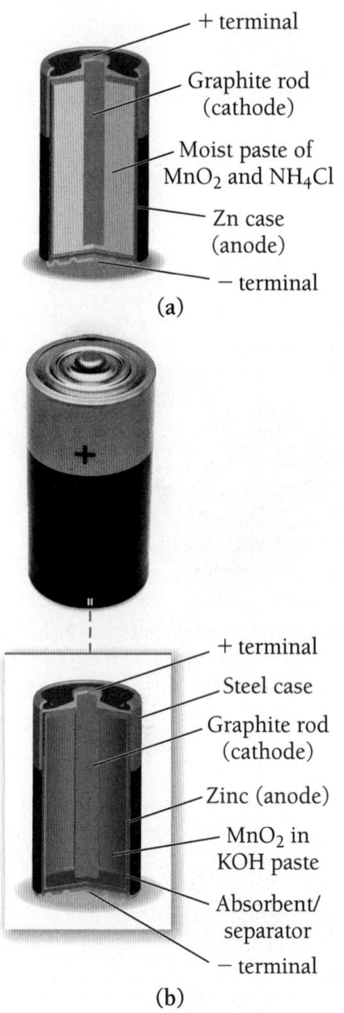

▲ **FIGURE 20.15 Dry-Cell Battery** **(a)** In a common dry-cell battery, the zinc case acts as the anode and a graphite rod immersed in a moist, slightly acidic paste of MnO_2 and NH_4Cl acts as the cathode. **(b)** Longer-lived alkaline batteries employ a graphite cathode immersed in a paste of MnO_2 and a base.

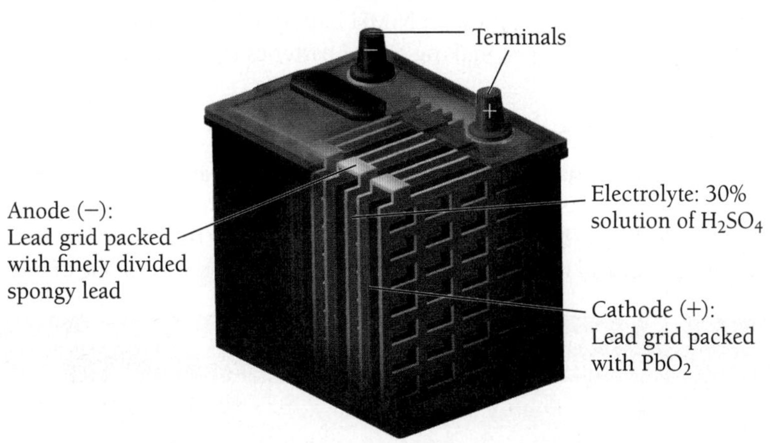

▲ **FIGURE 20.16 Lead–Acid Storage Battery** A lead–acid storage battery consists of six cells wired in series. Each cell contains a porous lead anode and a lead oxide cathode, both immersed in sulfuric acid.

Other Rechargeable Batteries

The ubiquity of power electronic products such as laptops and smartphones, as well as the growth in popularity of hybrid electric vehicles, drives the need for efficient, long-lasting, rechargeable batteries. The most common types include the **nickel–cadmium (NiCad) battery**, the **nickel–metal hydride (NiMH) battery**, and the **lithium ion battery**.

The Nickel–Cadmium (NiCad) Battery

Nickel–cadmium batteries consist of a solid cadmium anode and a NiO(OH)(*s*) cathode. The electrolyte is usually KOH(*aq*). During operation, the cadmium is oxidized and the NiO(OH) is reduced according to the equations:

Oxidation (Anode): $Cd(s) + 2\,OH^-(aq) \longrightarrow Cd(OH)_2(s) + 2\,e^-$

Reduction (Cathode): $2\,NiO(OH)(s) + 2\,H_2O(l) + 2\,e^- \longrightarrow 2\,Ni(OH)_2(s) + 2\,OH^-(aq)$

▲ Several types of batteries, including NiCad, NiMH, and lithium ion batteries, are recharged by chargers that use household current.

The overall reaction produces about 1.30 V. As current is drawn from the NiCad battery, solid cadmium hydroxide accumulates on the anode and solid nickel(II) hydroxide accumulates on the cathode. But if current is run in the opposite direction, the reactants can be regenerated from the products. A common problem in recharging NiCad and other rechargeable batteries is knowing when to stop. Once all of the products of the reaction are converted back to reactants, the charging process should ideally terminate. If charging does not stop, the electrical current drives other, usually unwanted, reactions such as the electrolysis of water to form hydrogen and oxygen gas. These reactions typically damage the battery and may sometimes even cause an explosion. Consequently, most commercial battery chargers have sensors that measure when the charging is complete. These sensors rely on the small changes in voltage or increases in temperature that occur once the products have all been converted back to reactants.

The Nickel–Metal Hydride (NiMH) Battery

Although NiCad batteries were the standard rechargeable battery for many years, they are being replaced by other types of rechargeable batteries, in part because of the toxicity of cadmium and the resulting disposal problems. One of these replacements is the nickel–metal hydride or NiMH battery. The NiMH battery employs the same cathode reaction as the NiCad battery, but it uses a different anode reaction. In the anode of a NiMH battery, hydrogen atoms held in a metal alloy are oxidized. If we let M represent the metal alloy, we can write the half-reactions as follows:

Oxidation (Anode): $M \cdot H(s) + OH^-(aq) \longrightarrow M(s) + H_2O(l) + e^-$

Reduction (Cathode): $NiO(OH)(s) + H_2O(l) + e^- \longrightarrow Ni(OH)_2(s) + OH^-(aq)$

In addition to being more environmentally friendly than NiCad batteries, NiMH batteries also have a greater energy density (energy content per unit battery mass), as we can see in Table 20.2. In some cases, an NiMH battery can carry twice the energy of a NiCad battery of the same mass, making NiMH batteries the most common choice for hybrid electric vehicles.

The Lithium Ion Battery

The newest and most expensive common type of rechargeable battery is the lithium ion battery. Since lithium is the least dense metal (0.53 g/cm^3), lithium batteries have high-energy densities (see Table 20.2). The lithium battery works differently than the other batteries we have examined so far, and the details of its operation are beyond the scope of our current

TABLE 20.2 ■ Energy Density and Overcharge Tolerance of Several Rechargeable Batteries

Battery Type	Energy Density (W · h/kg)	Overcharge Tolerance
NiCad	45–80	Moderate
NiMH	60–120	Low
Li ion	110–160	Low
Pb storage	30–50	High

discussion. Briefly, we can describe operation of the lithium battery as being due primarily to the motion of lithium ions from the anode to the cathode. The anode is composed of graphite into which lithium ions are incorporated between layers of carbon atoms. Upon discharge, the lithium ions spontaneously migrate to the cathode, which consists of a lithium transition metal oxide such as $LiCoO_2$ or $LiMn_2O_4$. The transition metal is reduced during this process. Upon recharging, the transition metal is oxidized, forcing the lithium to migrate back into the graphite (Figure 20.17►). The flow of lithium ions from the anode to the cathode causes a corresponding flow of electrons in the external circuit. Lithium ion batteries are commonly used in applications where light weight and high-energy density are important. These include smartphones, laptop computers, and digital cameras.

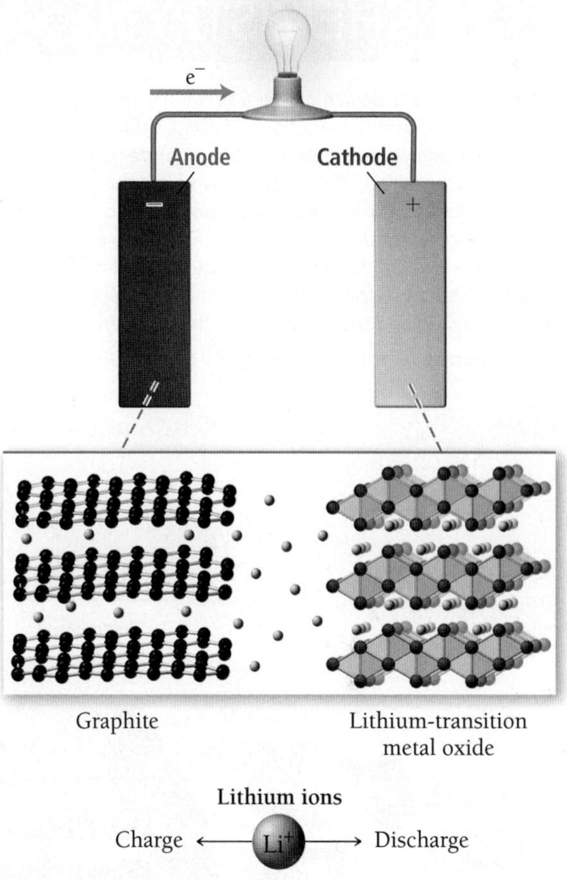

▲ **FIGURE 20.17 Lithium Ion Battery** In the lithium ion battery, the spontaneous flow of lithium ions from the graphite anode to the lithium transition metal oxide cathode causes a corresponding flow of electrons in the external circuit.

Fuel Cells

Fuel cells may one day replace—or at least work in combination with—centralized power grid electricity. In addition, vehicles powered by fuel cells may one day usurp vehicles powered by internal combustion engines. Fuel cells are like batteries; the key difference is that a battery is self-contained, while in a fuel cell the reactants need to be constantly replenished from an external source. With use, normal batteries lose their ability to generate voltage because the reactants become depleted as electrical current is drawn from the battery. In a **fuel cell**, the reactants—the fuel provided from an external source—constantly flow through the battery, generating electrical current as they undergo a redox reaction.

The most common fuel cell is the hydrogen–oxygen fuel cell (Figure 20.18▼). In this cell, hydrogen gas flows past the anode (a screen coated with platinum catalyst) and undergoes oxidation:

Oxidation (Anode): $2\,H_2(g) + 4\,OH^-(aq) \longrightarrow 4\,H_2O(l) + 4\,e^-$

Hydrogen–Oxygen Fuel Cell

In this fuel cell, hydrogen and oxygen combine to form water.

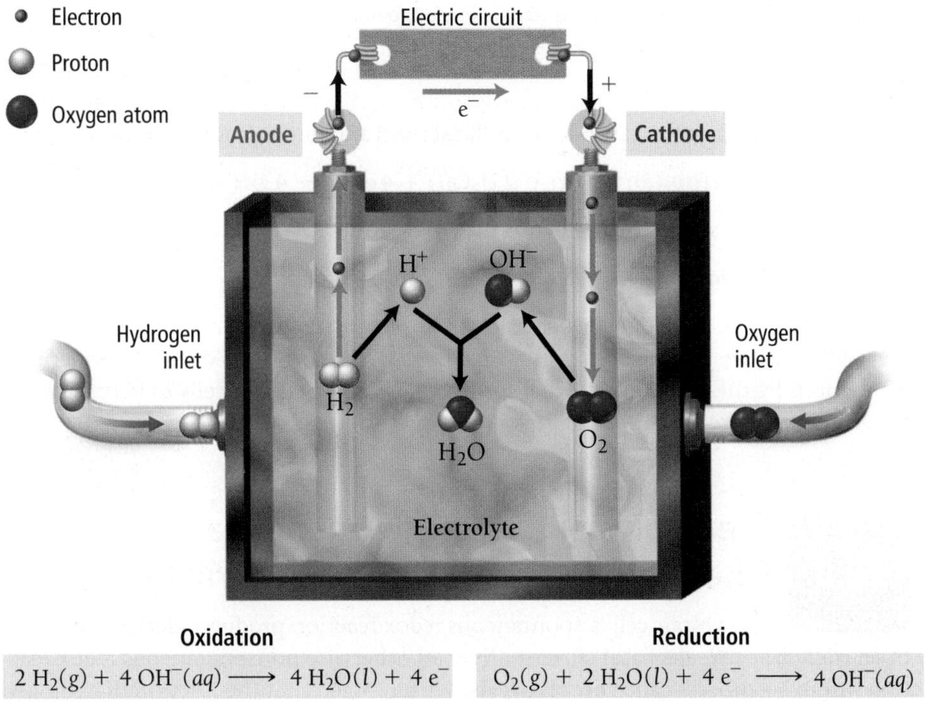

◄ **FIGURE 20.18 Hydrogen–Oxygen Fuel Cell**

CHEMISTRY IN YOUR DAY | The Fuel-Cell Breathalyzer

Police use a device called a breathalyzer to measure the amount of ethyl alcohol (CH_3CH_2OH) in the bloodstream of a person suspected of driving under the influence of alcohol (Figure 20.19▼). Breathalyzers work because the quantity of ethyl alcohol in the breath is proportional to the quantity of ethyl alcohol in the bloodstream. One type of breathalyzer employs a fuel cell to measure the quantity of alcohol in the breath. When a suspect blows into the breathalyzer, ethyl alcohol is oxidized to acetic acid at the anode:

Oxidation (Anode): $\underset{\text{ethyl alcohol}}{CH_3CH_2OH(g)} + 4\,OH^-(aq) \longrightarrow \underset{\text{acetic acid}}{HC_2H_3O_2(g)} + 3\,H_2O(l) + 4\,e^-$

At the cathode, oxygen is reduced:

Reduction (Cathode): $O_2(g) + 2\,H_2O(l) + 4\,e^- \longrightarrow 4\,OH^-(aq)$

The overall reaction is the oxidation of ethyl alcohol to acetic acid and water:

Overall: $CH_3CH_2OH(g) + O_2(g) \longrightarrow HC_2H_3O_2(g) + H_2O(l)$

The magnitude of electrical current produced depends on the quantity of alcohol in the breath. A higher current results from a higher blood alcohol level. When calibrated correctly, the fuel-cell breathalyzer can precisely measure the blood alcohol level of a suspected drunk driver.

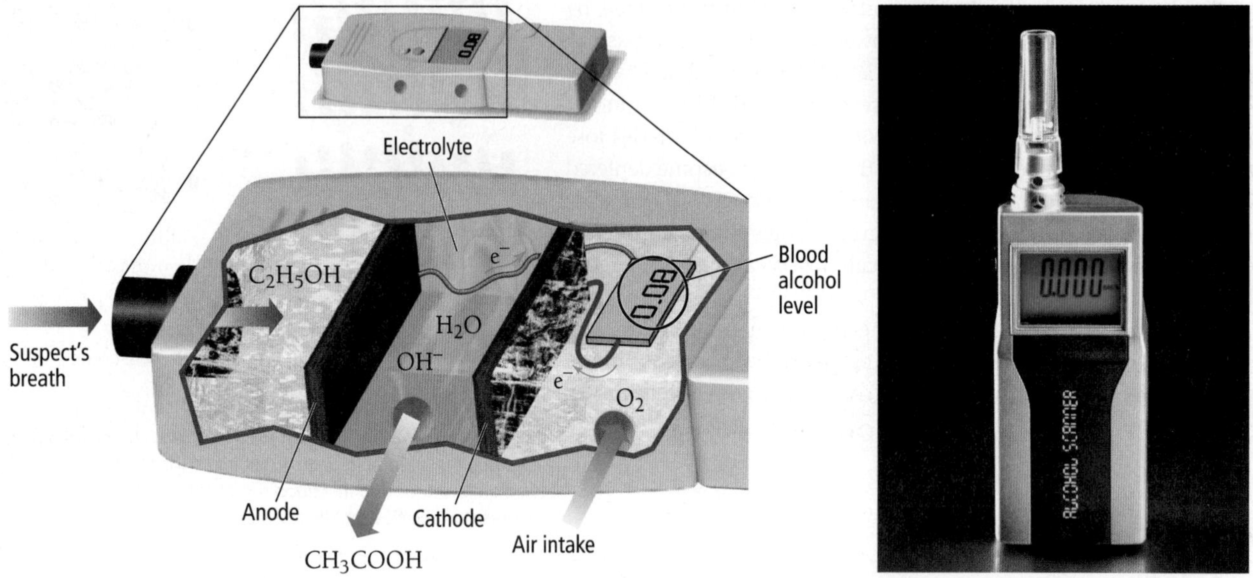

▲ **FIGURE 20.19 Fuel-Cell Breathalyzer** The fuel-cell breathalyzer works by oxidizing ethyl alcohol in the breath to acetic acid. The electrical current that is produced is proportional to the concentration of ethyl alcohol in the breath.

Oxygen gas flows past the cathode (a similar screen) and undergoes reduction:

Reduction (Cathode): $O_2(g) + 2\,H_2O(l) + 4\,e^- \longrightarrow 4\,OH^-(aq)$

The half-reactions sum to the following overall reaction:

Overall reaction: $2\,H_2(g) + O_2(g) \longrightarrow 2\,H_2O(l)$

Notice that the only product is water. In the space shuttle program, hydrogen–oxygen fuel cells consume hydrogen to provide electricity and astronauts drink the water that is produced by the reaction. In order for hydrogen-powered fuel cells to become more widely used, a more readily available source of hydrogen must be developed.

20.8 Electrolysis: Driving Nonspontaneous Chemical Reactions with Electricity

In a voltaic cell, a spontaneous redox reaction produces electrical current. In an *electrolytic cell*, electrical current drives an otherwise nonspontaneous redox reaction through a process called **electrolysis**. We have seen that the reaction of hydrogen with oxygen to form water is spontaneous and can be used to produce an electrical current in a fuel cell. Conversely, by *supplying* electrical current, we can cause the reverse reaction to occur, separating water into hydrogen and oxygen (Figure 20.20▼):

$2\,H_2(g) + O_2(g) \longrightarrow 2\,H_2O(l)$ (spontaneous—produces electrical current; occurs in a voltaic cell)

$2\,H_2O(l) \longrightarrow 2\,H_2(g) + O_2(g)$ (nonspontaneous—consumes electrical current; occurs in an electrolytic cell)

Recall from Section 20.7 that one of the problems associated with the widespread adoption of hydrogen fuel cells is the scarcity of hydrogen. Where will the hydrogen to power these fuel cells come from? One possible solution is to obtain hydrogen from water through solar-powered electrolysis. A solar-powered electrolytic cell can produce hydrogen from water when the sun is shining. The hydrogen made in this way could be converted back to water to generate electricity and could also be used to power fuel-cell vehicles.

Electrolysis also has numerous other applications. For example, most metals are found in Earth's crust as metal oxides. Converting an oxide to a pure metal requires that the metal be reduced, a nonspontaneous process. Electrolysis can be used to produce these metals. Thus, sodium is produced by the electrolysis of molten sodium chloride (discussed in the following subsection).

Electrolysis is also used to plate metals onto other metals. For example, silver can be plated onto a less expensive metal using the electrolytic cell shown in Figure 20.21▼. In this cell, a silver electrode is placed in a solution containing silver ions. An electrical current causes the oxidation of silver at the anode (replenishing the silver ions in solution) and the reduction of silver ions at the cathode (coating the less expensive metal with solid silver):

Oxidation (Anode): $Ag(s) \longrightarrow Ag^+(aq) + e^-$

Reduction (Cathode): $Ag^+(aq) + e^- \longrightarrow Ag(s)$

Since the standard cell potential of the reaction is zero, the reaction is not spontaneous under standard conditions. An external power source can be used to drive current flow and cause the reaction to occur.

Electrolysis of Water

Electrical current can decompose water into hydrogen and oxygen gas.

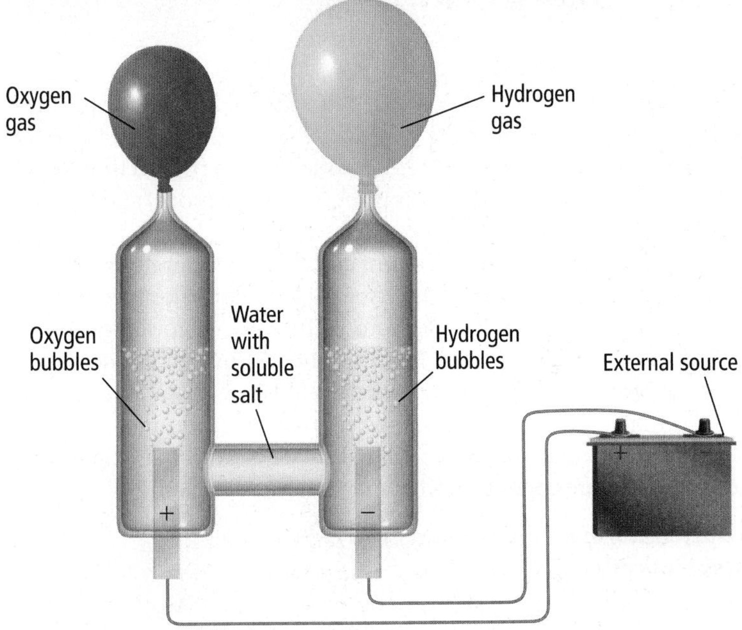

Anode	Cathode
$2\,H_2O(l) \longrightarrow O_2(g) + 4\,H^+(aq) + 4\,e^-$	$2\,H_2O(l) + 2\,e^- \longrightarrow H_2(g) + 2\,OH^-(aq)$

▲ **FIGURE 20.20 Electrolysis of Water**

Electrolytic Cell for Silver Plating

Silver can be plated from a solution of silver ions onto metallic objects in an electrolytic cell.

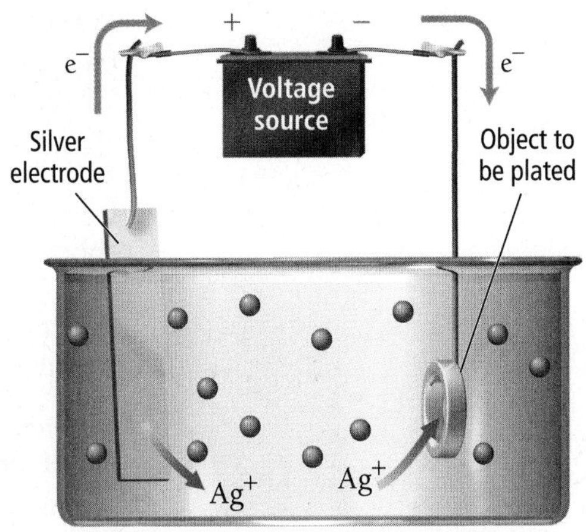

Anode	Cathode
$Ag(s) \longrightarrow Ag^+(aq) + e^-$	$Ag^+(aq) + e^- \longrightarrow Ag(s)$

▲ **FIGURE 20.21 Silver Plating**

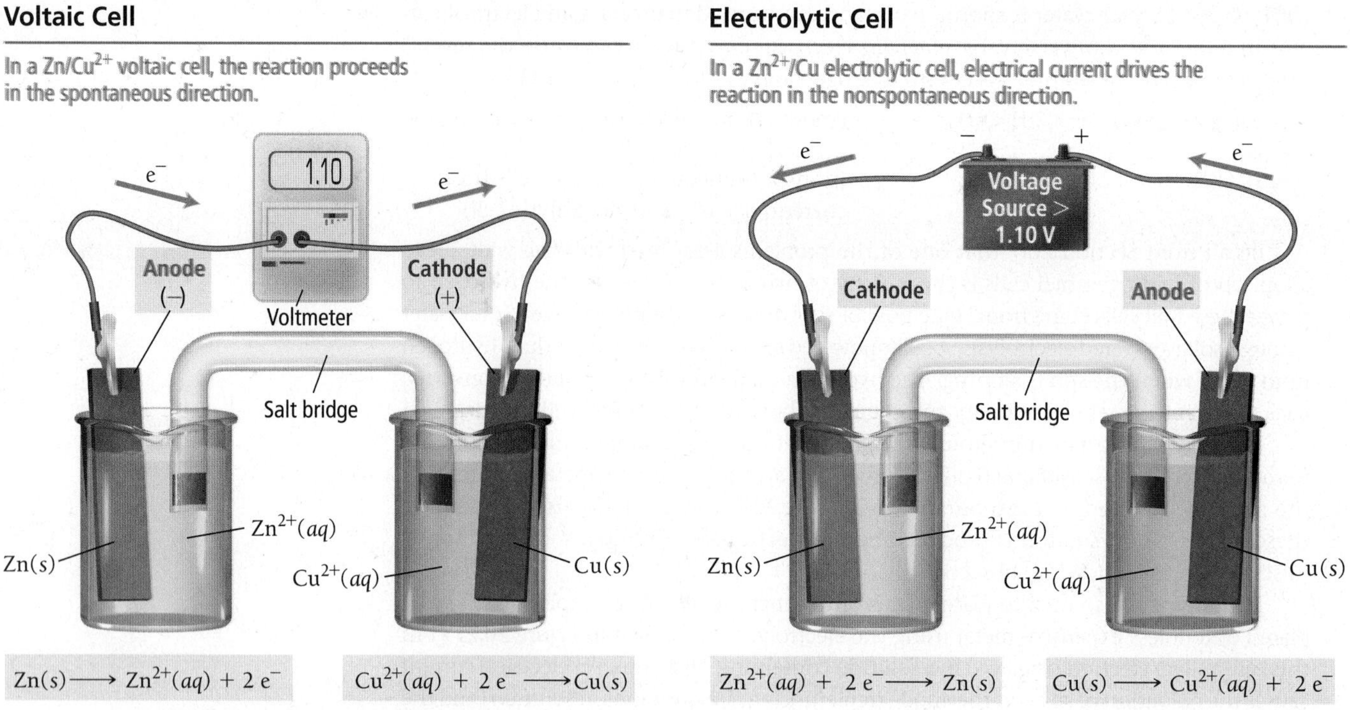

▲ **FIGURE 20.22** Voltaic versus Electrolytic Cells

The voltage required to cause electrolysis depends on the specific half-reactions. For example, we have seen that the oxidation of zinc and the reduction of Cu^{2+} produce a voltage of 1.10 V under standard conditions:

Reduction (Cathode):	$Cu^{2+}(aq) + 2\cancel{e^-} \longrightarrow Cu(s)$	$E° = 0.34\text{ V}$
Oxidation (Anode):	$Zn(s) \longrightarrow Zn^{2+}(aq) + 2\cancel{e^-}$	$E° = -0.76\text{ V}$
	$Cu^{2+}(aq) + Zn(s) \longrightarrow Cu(s) + Zn^{2+}(aq)$	$E°_{cell} = E°_{cat} - E°_{an}$
		$= +1.10\text{ V}$

If a power source producing *more than 1.10 V* is inserted into the Zn/Cu^{2+} voltaic cell, electrons can be forced to flow in the opposite direction, causing the reduction of Zn^{2+} and the oxidation of Cu, as shown in Figure 20.22▲. Notice that in the electrolytic cell, the anode has become the cathode (oxidation always occurs at the anode) and the cathode has become the anode.

In a *voltaic cell*, the anode is the source of electrons and is therefore labeled with a negative charge. The cathode draws electrons and is therefore labeled with a positive charge. In an *electrolytic cell*, however, the source of the electrons is the external power source. The external power source must *draw electrons away* from the anode; thus, the anode must be connected to the positive terminal of the battery (as shown in Figure 20.22). Similarly, the power source drives electrons toward the cathode (where they are used in reduction), so the cathode must be connected to the *negative* terminal of the battery. The charge labels (+ and −) on an electrolytic cell are opposite of what they are in a voltaic cell.

Summarizing Characteristics of Electrochemical Cell Types:

In all electrochemical cells:

- Oxidation occurs at the anode.
- Reduction occurs at the cathode.

In voltaic cells:

- The anode is the source of electrons and has a negative charge (anode −).
- The cathode draws electrons and has a positive charge (cathode +).

In electrolytic cells:

- Electrons are drawn away from the anode, which must be connected to the positive terminal of the external power source (anode +).
- Electrons are forced to the cathode, which must be connected to the negative terminal of the power source (cathode −).

VOLTAIC AND ELECTROLYTIC CELLS Which statement is true for both electrolytic and voltaic cells?

(a) The cell spontaneously produces a positive voltage.
(b) Electrons flow from the anode to the cathode.
(c) Oxidation occurs at the cathode.

20.9 Cc Conceptual Connection ANSWER NOW!

Predicting the Products of Electrolysis

Predicting the products of an electrolysis reaction is in some cases relatively straightforward and in other cases more complex. We cover the simpler cases first and follow with the more complex ones.

Pure Molten Salts

Consider the electrolysis of a molten salt such as sodium chloride, shown in Figure 20.23►. Na^+ and Cl^- are the only species present in the cell. The chloride ion cannot be further reduced (−1 is its lowest oxidation state), so it must be oxidized. The sodium ion cannot be further oxidized (+1 is its highest oxidation state), so it must be reduced. Thus, we can write the half-reactions:

Oxidation (Anode): $2\,Cl^-(l) \longrightarrow Cl_2(g) + \cancel{2\,e^-}$

Reduction (Cathode): $2\,Na^+(l) + \cancel{2\,e^-} \longrightarrow 2\,Na(s)$

$$2\,Na^+(l) + 2\,Cl^-(l) \longrightarrow 2\,Na(s) + Cl_2(g)$$

Although the reaction as written is not spontaneous, it can be driven to occur in an electrolytic cell by an external power source.

We can generalize as follows:

- In the electrolysis of a pure molten salt, the anion is oxidized and the cation is reduced.

Electrolysis of a Molten Salt

In the electrolysis of a pure molten salt, the anion (in this case) is oxidized and the cation (in this case) is reduced.

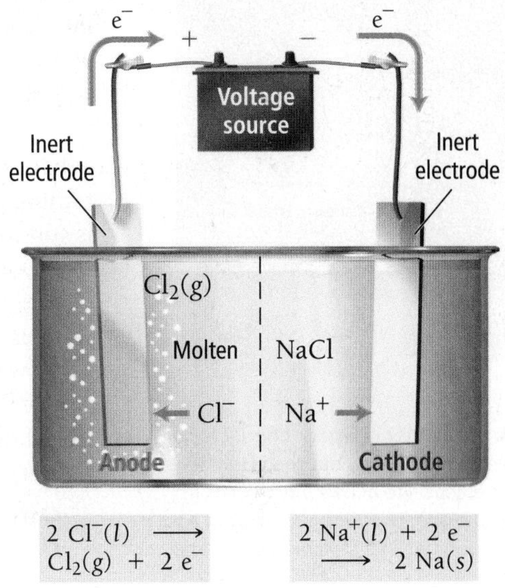

▲ **FIGURE 20.23 Electrolysis of Molten NaCl**

Mixtures of Cations or Anions

What if a molten salt contains more than one anion or cation? For example, suppose our electrolysis cell contains both NaCl and KCl. Which of the two cations is reduced at the cathode? In order to answer this question, we must determine which of the two cations is more easily reduced.

Although the values of electrode potentials for aqueous solutions given in Table 20.1 do not apply to molten salts, the relative ordering of the electrode potentials does reflect the relative ease with which the metal cations are reduced. We can see from the table that the reduction of Na^+ is listed *above* the reduction of K^+; that is, Na^+ has a more positive electrode potential:

$$Na^+(aq) + e^- \longrightarrow Na(s) \quad E° = -2.71\text{ V} \quad \text{(for aqueous solution)}$$
$$K^+(aq) + e^- \longrightarrow K(s) \quad E° = -2.92\text{ V} \quad \text{(for aqueous solution)}$$

Throughout this discussion, "more positive" means the same thing as "less negative."

Therefore, Na^+ is easier to reduce than K^+. Consequently, in a mixture of NaCl and KCl, Na^+ has a greater tendency to be reduced at the cathode.

Similarly, what if a mixture of molten salts contained more than one anion? For example, in a mixture of NaBr and NaCl, which of the two anions is oxidized at the cathode? The answer is similar: the anion that is more easily oxidized (the one with the more negative electrode potential):

$$2\,Cl^-(aq) \longrightarrow Cl_2(g) + 2\,e^- \quad E° = 1.36\text{ V} \quad \text{(for aqueous solution)}$$
$$2\,Br^-(aq) \longrightarrow Br_2(l) + 2\,e^- \quad E° = 1.09\text{ V} \quad \text{(for aqueous solution)}$$

Throughout this discussion, "more negative" means the same thing as "less positive."

Since the electrode potential for the bromine half-reaction is more negative, electrons are more easily extracted from it. The bromide ion is therefore oxidized at the anode.

We can generalize as follows:

- The cation that is most easily reduced (the one with the more positive electrode potential) is reduced first.
- The anion that is most easily oxidized (the one with the more negative electrode potential) is oxidized first.

Remember NIO and PIR:
N.I.O.—More **N**egative **I**s **O**xidation
P.I.R.—More **P**ositive **I**s **R**eduction

Aqueous Solutions

Electrolysis in an aqueous solution is complicated by the possibility of the electrolysis of water itself. Recall that water can be either oxidized or reduced according to the following half-reactions:

Oxidation (Anode): $2\,H_2O(l) \longrightarrow O_2(g) + 4\,H^+(aq) + 4\,e^-$ $\quad E° = 1.23\text{ V (standard conditions)}$
$E = 0.82\text{ V}([H^+] = 10^{-7}\text{ M})$

Reduction (Cathode): $2\,H_2O(l) + 2\,e^- \longrightarrow H_2(g) + 2\,OH^-(aq)$ $\quad E° = -0.83\text{ V (standard conditions)}$
$E = -0.41\text{ V}([OH^-] = 10^{-7}\text{ M})$

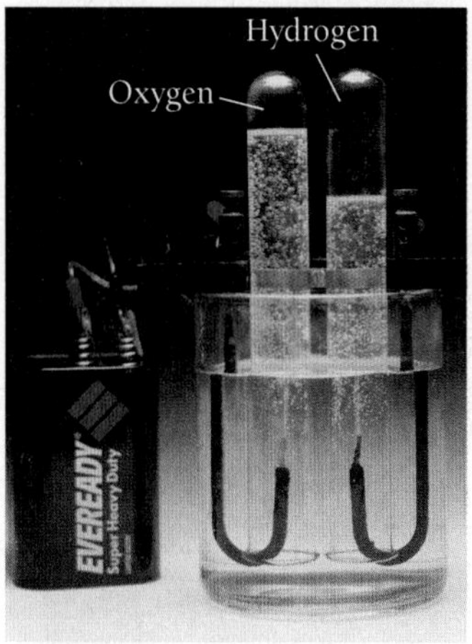

▲ Pure water is a poor conductor of electrical current, but the addition of an electrolyte allows electrolysis to take place, producing hydrogen and oxygen gas in a stoichiometric ratio.

The electrode potentials under standard conditions are shown to the right of each half-reaction. However, in pure water at room temperature, the concentrations of H^+ and OH^- are not standard. The electrode potentials for $[H^+] = 10^{-7}$ M and $[OH^-] = 10^{-7}$ M are shown in blue. Using those electrode potentials, we can calculate E_{cell} for the electrolysis of water as follows:

$$E_{cell} = E_{cat} - E_{an} = -0.41\text{ V} - 0.82\text{ V} = -1.23\text{ V}$$

When a battery with a potential of several volts is connected to an electrolysis cell containing pure water, no reaction occurs because the concentration of ions in pure water is too low to conduct any significant electrical current. When an electrolyte such as Na_2SO_4 is added to the water, however, electrolysis occurs readily.

In any aqueous solution in which electrolysis is to take place, the electrolysis of water is also possible. For example, consider the electrolysis of a sodium iodide solution, as shown in Figure 20.24▼. For the electrolysis of *molten* NaI, we can readily predict that I^- is oxidized at the anode and that Na^+ is reduced at the cathode. In an aqueous solution, however, two different oxidation half-reactions are possible at the anode, the oxidation of I^- and the oxidation of water:

Oxidation: $2\,I^-(aq) \longrightarrow I_2(aq) + 2\,e^-$ $\quad E° = 0.54\text{ V}$
Oxidation: $2\,H_2O(l) \longrightarrow O_2(g) + 4\,H^+(aq) + 4\,e^-$ $\quad E = 0.82\text{ V }([H^+] = 10^{-7}\text{ M})$

Similarly, two different reduction half-reactions are possible at the cathode, the reduction of Na^+ and the reduction of water:

Reduction: $2\,Na^+(aq) + 2\,e^- \longrightarrow 2\,Na(s)$ $\quad E° = -2.71\text{ V}$
Reduction: $2\,H_2O(l) + 2\,e^- \longrightarrow H_2(g) + 2\,OH^-(aq)$
$E = -0.41\text{ V }([OH^-] = 10^{-7}\text{ M})$

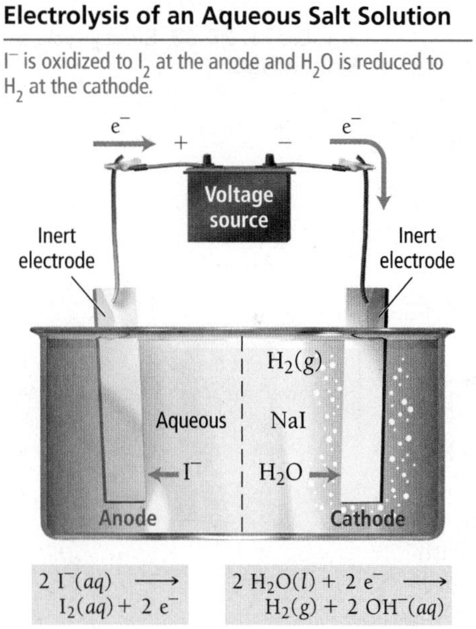

▲ **FIGURE 20.24 Electrolysis of Aqueous NaI** In this cell, the sodium ions are not reduced because their electrode potential is more negative than the electrode potential of water.

How do we know which reactions actually occur? In both cases, the answer is the same: *the half-reaction that occurs more easily*. For oxidation, the half-reaction with the more negative electrode potential is the easier one from which to extract electrons. In this case, therefore, the iodide ion is oxidized at the anode. For reduction, the half-reaction with the more positive electrode potential is the one that accepts electrons more easily. In this case, therefore, water is reduced at the cathode. Notice that Na^+ cannot be reduced in an aqueous solution—water is reduced before Na^+.

We can make the following generalization:

- The cations of active metals—those that are not easily reduced, such as Li^+, K^+, Na^+, Mg^{2+}, Ca^{2+}, and Al^{3+}—cannot be reduced from aqueous solutions by electrolysis because water is reduced at a lower voltage.

The Electrolysis of Aqueous Sodium Chloride and Overvoltage

An additional complication that we must consider when predicting the products of electrolysis is *overvoltage*—an additional voltage that must be applied in order to make some nonspontaneous reactions occur.

We can demonstrate this concept by considering the electrolysis of a sodium chloride solution, shown in Figure 20.25▶. In order to predict the product of the electrolysis, we consider the two possible oxidation half-reactions:

Oxidation: $2\,Cl^-(aq) \longrightarrow Cl_2(g) + 2\,e^-$ $\qquad E° = 1.36\ V$

Oxidation: $2\,H_2O(l) \longrightarrow O_2(g) + 4\,H^+(aq) + 4\,e^-$

$E = 0.82\ V\ ([H^+] = 10^{-7}\ M)$

and the two possible reduction half-reactions:

Reduction: $2\,Na^+(aq) + 2\,e^- \longrightarrow 2\,Na(s)$ $\qquad E° = -2.71\ V$

Reduction: $2\,H_2O(l) + 2\,e^- \longrightarrow H_2(g) + 2\,OH^-(aq)$

$E = -0.41\ V\ ([OH^-] = 10^{-7}\ M)$

Since the oxidation of water has a more negative electrode potential than the oxidation of Cl^-, we would initially predict that it would be easier to remove electrons from water, and thus water should be oxidized at the anode. Similarly, since the reduction of water has a more positive electrode potential than the reduction of Na^+, we would expect that it would be easier to get water to accept electrons, so water should be reduced at the cathode. In other words, we initially predict that a sodium chloride solution would simply result in the electrolysis of water, producing oxygen gas at the anode and hydrogen gas at the cathode. If we construct such a cell, however, we find that, although hydrogen gas is indeed formed at the cathode (as predicted), oxygen gas is *not* formed at the anode—chlorine gas is formed instead. Why? The answer is that even though the electrode potential for the oxidation of water is 0.82 V, the reaction actually requires a voltage greater than 0.82 V in order to occur. (The reasons for this behavior are related to kinetic factors that are beyond the scope of our current discussion.) This additional voltage, the *overvoltage*, increases the voltage required for the oxidation of water to about 1.4 V. The result is that the chloride ion oxidizes more easily than water and $Cl_2(g)$ is observed at the anode.

The Effect of Overvoltage on the Electrolysis of Aqueous NaCl

Because of overvoltage, the anode reaction of this cell is the oxidation of Cl^- to Cl_2 gas (rather than the oxidation of water to H^+ and O_2 gas).

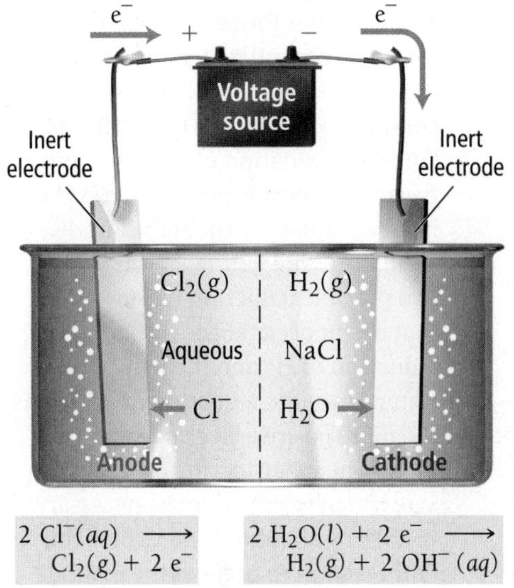

▲ **FIGURE 20.25 Electrolysis of Aqueous NaCl: The Effect of Overvoltage**

EXAMPLE 20.9 Predicting the Products of Electrolysis Reactions

Predict the half-reaction occurring at the anode and the half-reaction occurring at the cathode for electrolysis for each reaction.

(a) a mixture of molten $AlBr_3$ and $MgBr_2$

(b) an aqueous solution of LiI

SOLUTION

(a) In the electrolysis of a molten salt, the anion is oxidized and the cation is reduced. However, this mixture contains two cations. Start by writing the possible oxidation and reduction half-reactions that might occur. Because Br^- is the only anion, write the equation for its oxidation, which occurs at the anode.
At the cathode, both the reduction of Al^{3+} and the reduction of Mg^{2+} are possible. The one that actually occurs is the one that occurs more easily.
Since the reduction of Al^{3+} has a more positive electrode potential in aqueous solution, this ion is more easily reduced. Therefore, the reduction of Al^{3+} occurs at the cathode.

Oxidation: $2\,Br^-(l) \longrightarrow Br_2(g) + 2\,e^-$

Reduction: $Al^{3+}(l) + 3\,e^- \longrightarrow Al(s)$ $\quad E° = -1.66\ V$ (for aqueous solution)

$Mg^{2+}(l) + 2\,e^- \longrightarrow Mg(s)$ $\quad E° = -2.37\ V$ (for aqueous solution)

Reduction that actually occurs (more positive potential)

—Continued on the next page

Continued—

(b) Since LiI is in an aqueous solution, two different oxidation half-reactions are possible at the anode, the oxidation of I^- and the oxidation of water. Write half-reactions for each including the electrode potential. Remember to use the electrode potential of water under conditions in which $[H^+] = 10^{-7}$ M. Since the oxidation of I^- has the more negative electrode potential, it is the half-reaction to occur at the anode. Similarly, write half-reactions for the two possible reduction half-reactions that might occur at the cathode, the reduction of Li^+ and the reduction of water. Since the reduction of water has the more positive electrode potential (even when considering overvoltage, which would raise the necessary voltage by about 0.4–0.6 V), it is the half-reaction to occur at the cathode.

Oxidation that actually occurs (more negative potential)

Oxidation:

$$2\,I^-(aq) \longrightarrow I_2(l) + 2\,e^- \qquad E° = 0.54\text{ V}$$

Oxidation:

$$2\,H_2O(l) \longrightarrow O_2(g) + 4\,H^+(aq) + 4\,e^- \qquad E° = 0.82\text{ V} \quad ([H^+] = 10^{-7}\text{ M})$$

Reduction:

$$2\,Li^+(aq) + 2\,e^- \longrightarrow 2\,Li(s) \qquad E° = -3.04\text{ V}$$

Reduction:

$$2\,H_2O(l) + 2\,e^- \longrightarrow H_2(g) + 2\,OH^-(aq) \qquad E = -0.41\text{ V} \quad ([OH^-] = 10^{-7}\text{ M})$$

Reduction that actually occurs (more positive potential)

FOR PRACTICE 20.9 Predict the half-reactions occurring at the anode and the cathode for the electrolysis of aqueous Na_2SO_4.

Electrolytic Cell for Copper Plating

In this cell, copper ions are plated onto other metals.

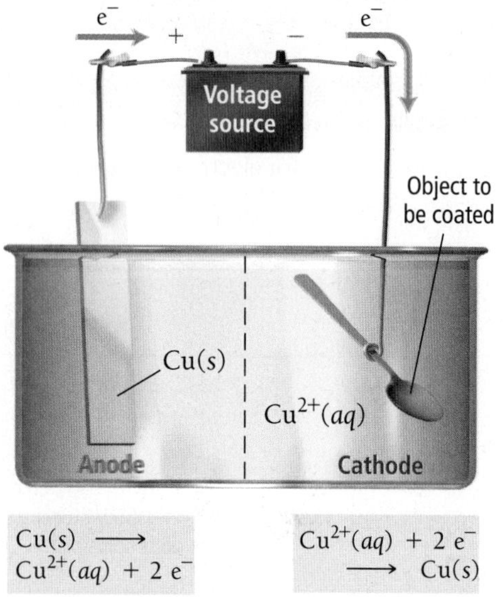

▲ **FIGURE 20.26 Electrolytic Cell for Copper Plating** In this cell, it takes two moles of electrons to plate one mole of copper atoms.

Stoichiometry of Electrolysis

In an electrolytic cell, electrical current is used to drive a particular chemical reaction. In a sense, the electrons act as a reactant and therefore have a stoichiometric relationship with the other reactants and products. Unlike ordinary reactants, for which we usually measure quantity as mass, for electrons we measure quantity as charge.

For example, consider an electrolytic cell used to coat copper onto metals, as shown in Figure 20.26◀. The half-reaction by which copper is deposited onto the metal is:

$$Cu^{2+}(aq) + 2\,e^- \longrightarrow Cu(s)$$

For every 2 mol of electrons that flow through the cell, 1 mol of solid copper is plated. We can write the stoichiometric relationship:

$$2\text{ mol } e^- : 1\text{ mol } Cu(s)$$

We can determine the number of moles of electrons that have flowed in a given electrolysis cell by measuring the total charge that has flowed through the cell, which in turn depends on the *magnitude* of the current and on the *time* that the current runs. Recall from Section 20.3 that the unit of current is the ampere:

$$1\text{ A} = 1\frac{\text{C}}{\text{s}}$$

If we multiply the amount of current (in A) flowing through the cell by the time (in s) that the current flowed, we find the total charge that passed through the cell in that time:

$$\text{Current}\left(\frac{\text{C}}{\cancel{\text{s}}}\right) \times \text{time}(\cancel{\text{s}}) = \text{charge}(\text{C})$$

The relationship between charge and the number of moles of electrons is given by Faraday's constant, which, as we saw previously, corresponds to the charge in coulombs of 1 mol of electrons:

$$F = \frac{96{,}485\text{ C}}{\text{mol } e^-}$$

These relationships can be used to solve problems involving the stoichiometry of electrolytic cells, as demonstrated in Example 20.10.

20.10 Cc Conceptual Connection ANSWER NOW!

ELECTROLYSIS Silver plating uses the reaction $Ag^+(aq) + e^- \longrightarrow Ag(s)$. How many moles of electrons must pass through an electrolytic cell for silver plating in order to plate 3 moles of Ag?

(a) 1 mole e^- **(b)** 2 mole e^- **(c)** 3 mole e^- **(d)** 4 mole e^-

EXAMPLE 20.10 Stoichiometry of Electrolysis

Gold can be plated out of a solution containing Au^{3+} according to the half-reaction:

$$Au^{3+}(aq) + 3\,e^- \longrightarrow Au(s)$$

What mass of gold (in grams) is plated by a 25-minute flow of 5.5 A current?

SORT You are given the half-reaction for the plating of gold, which shows the stoichiometric relationship between moles of electrons and moles of gold. You are also given the current and duration. You must find the mass of gold that will be deposited in that time.

GIVEN: 3 mol e^- : 1 mol Au
5.5 amps
25 min

FIND: g Au

STRATEGIZE You need to find the amount of gold, which is related stoichiometrically to the number of electrons that have flowed through the cell. Begin with time in minutes and convert to seconds. Then, because current is a measure of charge per unit time, use the given current and the time to find the number of coulombs. Use Faraday's constant to calculate the number of moles of electrons and the stoichiometry of the reaction to find the number of moles of gold. Finally, use the molar mass of gold to convert to mass of gold.

CONCEPTUAL PLAN

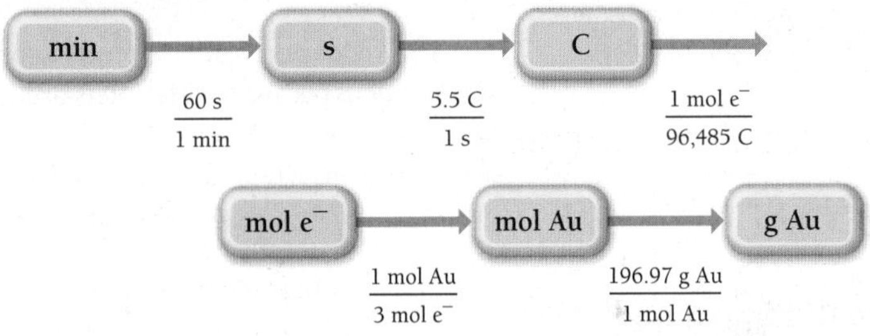

SOLVE Follow the conceptual plan to solve the problem, canceling units to arrive at the mass of gold.

SOLUTION

$$25\ \cancel{\text{min}} \times \frac{60\ \cancel{\text{s}}}{1\ \cancel{\text{min}}} \times \frac{5.5\ \cancel{\text{C}}}{1\ \cancel{\text{s}}} \times \frac{1\ \cancel{\text{mol e}^-}}{96{,}485\ \cancel{\text{C}}} \times \frac{1\ \cancel{\text{mol Au}}}{3\ \cancel{\text{mol e}^-}} \times \frac{196.97\ \text{g Au}}{1\ \cancel{\text{mol Au}}} = 5.6\ \text{g Au}$$

CHECK The answer has the correct units (g Au). The magnitude of the answer is reasonable if you consider that 10 amps of current for 1 hour is the equivalent of about 1/3 mol of electrons (check for yourself), which would produce 1/9 mol (or about 20 g) of gold.

FOR PRACTICE 20.10 Silver can be plated out of a solution containing Ag^+ according to the half-reaction:

$$Ag^+(aq) + e^- \longrightarrow Ag(s)$$

How much time (in minutes) does it take to plate 12 g of silver using a current of 3.0 A?

20.9 Corrosion: Undesirable Redox Reactions

Corrosion is the (usually) gradual, nearly always undesired, oxidation of metals that are exposed to oxidizing agents in the environment. From Table 20.1, we can see that the reduction of oxygen in the presence of water has an electrode potential of +0.40 V:

$$O_2(g) + 2\,H_2O(l) + 4\,e^- \longrightarrow 4\,OH^-(aq) \qquad E^\circ = +0.40\ \text{V}$$

▲ A metal must usually be reduced to extract it from its ore. In corrosion, the metal is oxidized back to its more natural state.

▲ Aluminum is stable because its oxide forms a protective film over the underlying metal, preventing further oxidation.

In the presence of acid, the reduction of oxygen has an even more positive electrode potential of +1.23 V:

$$O_2(g) + 4\,H^+(aq) + 4\,e^- \longrightarrow 2\,H_2O(l) \qquad E^\circ = +1.23\text{ V}$$

The reduction of oxygen, therefore, has a strong tendency to occur and can bring about the oxidation of other substances, especially metals. Notice that the half-reactions for the reduction of most metal ions are listed *below* the half-reactions for the reduction of oxygen in Table 20.1. Consequently, the oxidation (or corrosion) of those metals is spontaneous when paired with the reduction of oxygen. Corrosion is the opposite of the process by which metals are extracted from their ores. In extraction, the free metal is reduced out from its ore. In corrosion, the metal is oxidized.

Corrosion of Iron

Given the ease with which metals oxidize in the presence of oxygen, acid, and water, why are metals used so frequently as building materials in the first place? Many metals form oxides that coat the surface of the metal and prevent further corrosion. For example, bare aluminum metal, with an electrode potential of −1.66 V, is quickly oxidized in the presence of oxygen. However, the oxide that forms at the surface of aluminum is Al_2O_3. In its crystalline form, Al_2O_3 is sapphire, a highly inert and structurally solid substance. The Al_2O_3 coating acts to protect the underlying aluminum metal, preventing further corrosion.

The oxides of iron, in contrast, are not structurally stable, and they tend to flake away from the underlying metal, exposing it to further corrosion. A significant part of the iron produced each year is used to replace rusted iron. Rusting is a redox reaction in which iron is oxidized according to the following half-reaction:

$$Fe(s) \longrightarrow Fe^{2+}(aq) + 2\,e^- \qquad E^\circ = -0.45\text{ V}$$

This oxidation reaction tends to occur at defects on the surface of the iron—known as *anodic regions* because oxidation is occurring at these locations—as shown in Figure 20.27▼. The electrons produced at the anodic region travel through the metal to areas called *cathodic regions* where they react with oxygen and H^+ ions dissolved in moisture:

$$O_2(g) + 4\,H^+(aq) + 4\,e^- \longrightarrow 2\,H_2O(l) \qquad E^\circ = +1.23\text{ V}$$

The Rusting of Iron

The oxidation of iron occurs at anodic regions on the metal surface. The iron ions migrate to cathodic regions, where they react with oxygen and water to form rust.

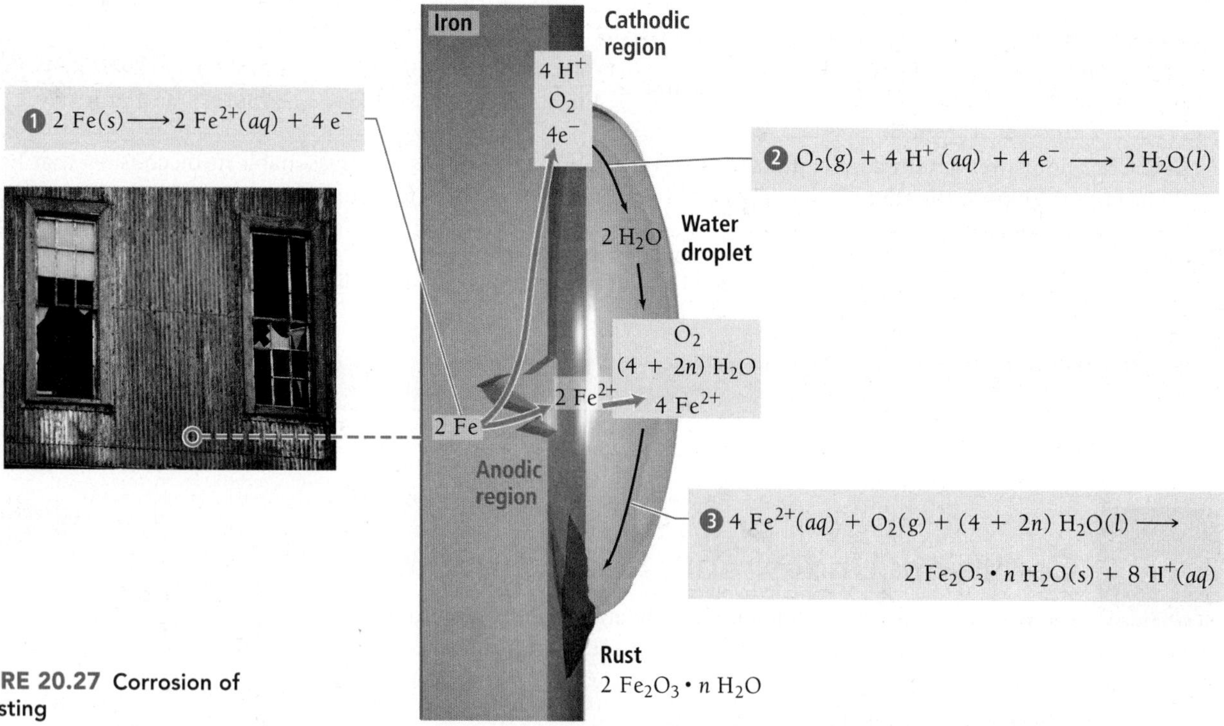

► **FIGURE 20.27 Corrosion of Iron: Rusting**

(The H^+ ions come from carbonic acid, which naturally forms in water from carbon dioxide in air.) The overall reaction has a cell potential of +1.68 V and is highly spontaneous:

$$2\,Fe(s) + O_2(g) + 4\,H^+(aq) \longrightarrow 2\,H_2O(l) + 2\,Fe^{2+}(aq) \qquad E^\circ_{cell} = +1.68\text{ V}$$

The Fe^{2+} ions formed in the anodic regions can migrate through moisture on the surface of the iron to cathodic regions, where they are further oxidized by reaction with more oxygen:

$$4\,Fe^{2+}(aq) + O_2(g) + (4 + 2n)\,H_2O(l) \longrightarrow \underset{\text{rust}}{2\,Fe_2O_3 \cdot nH_2O(s)} + 8\,H^+(aq)$$

Rust is a hydrated form of iron(III) oxide whose exact composition depends on the conditions under which it forms.

Consider each of the following important aspects of the formation of rust:

- *Moisture must be present for rusting to occur.* The presence of water is necessary because water is a reactant in the last reaction and because charge (either electrons or ions) must be free to flow between the anodic and cathodic regions.
- *Additional electrolytes promote rusting.* The presence of an electrolyte (such as sodium chloride) on the surface of iron promotes rusting because it enhances current flow. This is why cars rust so quickly in cold climates where roads are salted, or in coastal areas where seawater mist is present.
- *The presence of acids promotes rusting.* Because H^+ ions are involved in the reduction of oxygen, lower pH enhances the cathodic reaction and leads to faster rusting.

Preventing the Corrosion of Iron

Preventing the rusting of iron is a major industry. The most obvious way to prevent rust is to keep iron dry. Without water, the redox reaction cannot occur. Another way to prevent rust is to coat iron with a substance that is impervious to water. Cars, for example, are painted and sealed to prevent rust. A scratch in the paint can lead to rusting of the underlying iron.

▲ In galvanized nails, a layer of zinc prevents the underlying iron from rusting. The zinc oxidizes in place of the iron, forming a protective layer of zinc oxide.

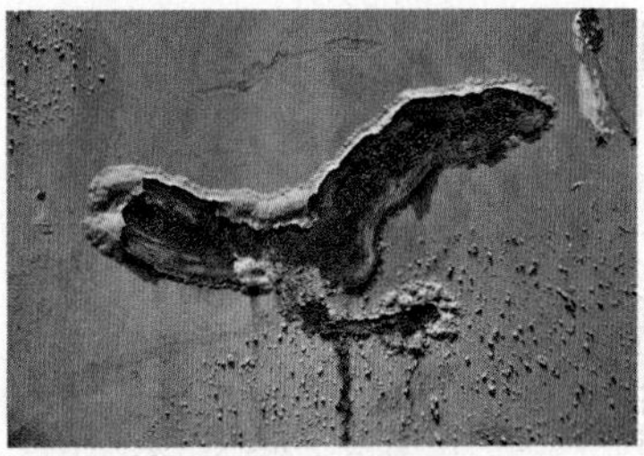

▲ A scratch in paint often allows the underlying iron to rust.

Rust can also be prevented by placing a *sacrificial electrode* in electrical contact with the iron. The sacrificial electrode must be composed of a metal that oxidizes more easily than iron (that is, it must be below iron in Table 20.1). The sacrificial electrode oxidizes in place of the iron (just as the more easily oxidizable species in a mixture is the one to oxidize), protecting the iron from oxidation. A related way to protect iron from rusting is to coat it with a metal that oxidizes more easily than iron. Galvanized nails, for example, are coated with a thin layer of zinc. Since zinc has a more negative electrode potential than iron, it will oxidize in place of the underlying iron (just as a sacrificial electrode does). The oxide of zinc is not crumbly and remains on the nails as a protective coating.

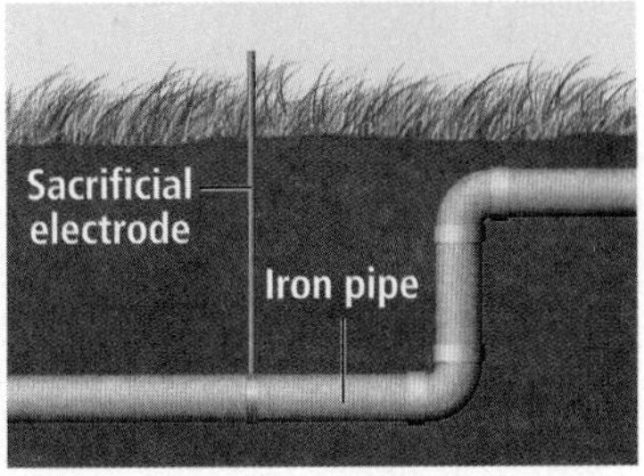

▲ If a metal more active than iron, such as magnesium or aluminum, is in electrical contact with iron, the metal rather than the iron will be oxidized. This principle underlies the use of sacrificial electrodes to prevent the corrosion of iron.

SACRIFICIAL ELECTRODES Which of these metals does not act as a sacrificial electrode for iron?

(a) Cu **(b)** Mg **(c)** Zn **(d)** Mn

20.11 Cc Conceptual Connection

ANSWER NOW!

QUIZ YOURSELF **NOW!**

Self-Assessment Quiz

Q1. Balance the redox reaction equation (occurring in acidic solution) and choose the correct coefficients for each reactant and product.
MISSED THIS? Read Section 20.2; Watch KCV 20.2, IWE 20.2

$\_VO_2^+(aq) + \_Sn(s) + \_H^+(aq) \longrightarrow \_VO^{2+}(aq) + \_Sn^{2+}(aq) + \_H_2O(l)$

a) 2,1,4 ⟶ 2,1,2
b) 1,1,2 ⟶ 1,1,1
c) 2,1,2 ⟶ 2,1,1
d) 2,1,2 ⟶ 2,1,2

Q2. Which statement is true for voltaic cells?
MISSED THIS? Read Section 20.3

a) Electrons flow from the anode to the cathode.
b) Electrons flow from the more negatively charged electrode to the more positively charged electrode.
c) Electrons flow from higher potential energy to lower potential energy.
d) All of the above are true.

Q3. Use Table 20.1 to calculate E°_{cell} for the reaction.
MISSED THIS? Read Section 20.4; Watch KCV 20.4, IWE 20.4

$2\,ClO_2(g) + Pb(s) \longrightarrow 2\,ClO_2^-(aq) + Pb^{2+}(aq)$

a) 1.77 V
b) 2.03 V
c) 0.82 V
d) 1.08 V

Q4. Use Table 20.1 to determine which statement is true of the voltaic cell pictured here.
MISSED THIS? Read Section 20.4; Watch KCV 20.4

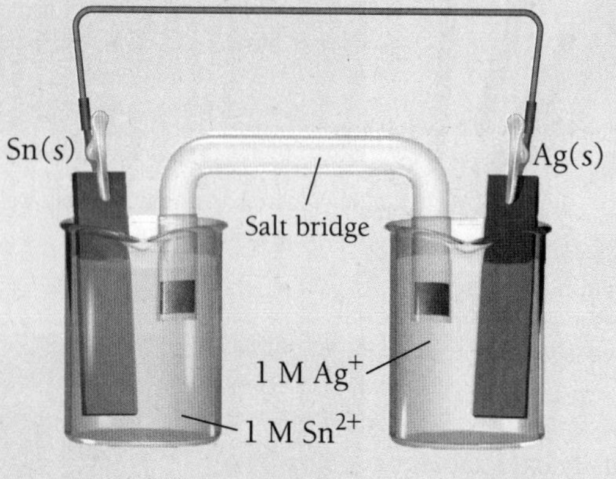

a) Sn is the anode; Ag is the cathode; electrons flow from left to right.
b) Sn is the cathode; Ag is the anode; electrons flow from left to right.
c) Sn is the anode; Ag is the cathode; electrons flow from right to left.
d) Sn is the cathode; Ag is the anode; electrons flow from right to left.

Q5. Use Table 20.1 to determine which metal *does not* dissolve in hydrochloric acid (HCl). *MISSED THIS? Read Section 20.4*

a) Zn
b) Cd
c) Cu
d) Fe

Q6. The Zn/Zn^{2+} electrode has a standard electrode potential of $E^\circ = -0.76$ V. How does the relative potential energy of an electron at the Zn/Zn^{2+} electrode compare to the potential energy of an electron at the standard hydrogen electrode?
MISSED THIS? Read Section 20.4; Watch KCV 20.4

a) An electron at the Zn/Zn^{2+} electrode has a higher potential energy than an electron at the standard hydrogen electrode.
b) An electron at the Zn/Zn^{2+} electrode has a lower potential energy than an electron at the standard hydrogen electrode.
c) An electron at the Zn/Zn^{2+} electrode has the same potential energy as an electron at the standard hydrogen electrode.
d) Nothing can be concluded about the relative potential energy of an electron at the standard electrode potential.

Q7. Use Table 20.1 to calculate ΔG° for the reaction.
MISSED THIS? Read Section 20.5; Watch KCV 20.5, IWE 20.6

$2\,MnO_4^-(aq) + Cd(s) \longrightarrow 2\,MnO_4^{2-}(aq) + Cd^{2+}(aq)$

a) +30.9 kJ
b) −30.9 kJ
c) −185 kJ
d) +185 kJ

Q8. A redox reaction has an $E^\circ_{cell} = -0.56$ V. What can you conclude about the equilibrium constant (K) for the reaction?
MISSED THIS? Read Section 20.5; Watch KCV 20.5

a) $K < 1$
b) $K > 1$
c) $K = 0$
d) Nothing can be concluded about K from E°_{cell}.

Q9. Find E_{cell} for an electrochemical cell based on the following reaction with $[MnO_4^-] = 2.0$ M, $[H^+] = 1.0$ M, and $[Ag^+] = 0.010$ M. E°_{cell} for the reaction is +0.88 V.
MISSED THIS? Read Section 20.6

$MnO_4^-(aq) + 4\,H^+(aq) + 3\,Ag(s) \longrightarrow MnO_2(s) + 2\,H_2O(l) + 3\,Ag^+(aq)$

a) 0.83 V
b) 1.00 V
c) 0.76 V
d) 0.93 V

Q10. In an electrochemical cell, $Q = 0.010$ and $K = 855$. What can you conclude about E_{cell} and E°_{cell}?
MISSED THIS? Read Section 20.6

a) E_{cell} is positive and E°_{cell} is negative.
b) E_{cell} is negative and E°_{cell} is positive.
c) E_{cell} and E°_{cell} are both negative.
d) E_{cell} and E°_{cell} are both positive.

Q11. Which reaction occurs at the *anode* of a lead storage battery?
MISSED THIS? Read Section 20.7

a) $Zn(s) + 2\,OH^-(aq) \longrightarrow Zn(OH)_2(s) + 2\,e^-$
b) $PbO_2(s) + HSO_4^-(aq) + 3\,H^+(aq) + 2\,e^- \longrightarrow PbSO_4(s) + 2\,H_2O(l)$
c) $Pb(s) + HSO_4^-(aq) \longrightarrow PbSO_4(s) + H^+(aq) + 2\,e^-$
d) $O_2(g) + 2\,H_2O(l) + 4\,e^- \longrightarrow 4\,OH^-(aq)$

Q12. Which reaction could be used to generate electricity in a voltaic electrochemical cell?
MISSED THIS? Read Section 20.4; Watch KCV 20.4

a) $Pb^{2+}(aq) + Mg(s) \longrightarrow Mg^{2+}(aq) + Pb(s)$
b) $Zn^{2+}(aq) + Sn(s) \longrightarrow Sn^{2+}(aq) + Zn(s)$
c) $NaCl(aq) + AgNO_3(aq) \longrightarrow AgCl(s) + NaNO_3(aq)$
d) None of the above

Q13. Which reaction occurs at the cathode of an electrolytic cell containing a mixture of molten KCl and $ZnCl_2$?
MISSED THIS? Read Section 20.8

a) $K(s) \longrightarrow K^+(l) + e^-$
b) $K^+(l) + e^- \longrightarrow K(s)$
c) $Zn^{2+}(l) + 2\,e^- \longrightarrow Zn(s)$
d) $2\,Cl^-(l) \longrightarrow Cl_2(g) + 2\,e^-$

Q14. Copper is plated onto the cathode of an electrolytic cell containing $CuCl_2(aq)$. How long does it take to plate 111 mg of copper with a current of 3.8 A?
MISSED THIS? Read Section 20.8

a) 1.3×10^3 s b) 44 s c) 89 s d) 22 s

Q15. Which metal can be used as a sacrificial electrode to prevent the rusting of an iron pipe? MISSED THIS? Read Section 20.9

a) Au b) Ag c) Cu d) Mn

Answers: 1. (a) **2.** (d) **3.** (d) **4.** (a) **5.** (c) **6.** (a) **7.** (c) **8.** (a) **9.** (b) **10.** (d) **11.** (c) **12.** (a) **13.** (c) **14.** (c) **15.** (d)

CHAPTER 20 IN REVIEW

TERMS

Section 20.3
- electrical current (901)
- electrochemical cell (902)
- voltaic (galvanic) cell (902)
- electrolytic cell (902)
- half-cell (902)
- electrode (902)
- ampere (A) (903)
- potential difference (903)
- volt (V) (903)
- electromotive force (emf) (903)
- cell potential (cell emf) (E_{cell}) (904)
- standard cell potential (standard emf) (E°_{cell}) (904)
- anode (904)
- cathode (904)
- salt bridge (904)

Section 20.4
- standard electrode potential (905)
- standard hydrogen electrode (SHE) (906)

Section 20.5
- Faraday's constant (F) (914)

Section 20.6
- Nernst equation (918)

Section 20.7
- dry-cell battery (922)
- alkaline battery (923)
- lead–acid storage battery (923)
- nickel–cadmium (NiCad) battery (924)
- nickel–metal hydride (NiMH) battery (924)
- lithium ion battery (924)
- fuel cell (925)

Section 20.8
- electrolysis (926)

Section 20.9
- corrosion (933)

CONCEPTS

Pulling the Plug on the Power Grid (20.1)

- Oxidation–reduction reactions are reactions in which electrons are transferred from one reactant to another.
- In the most common form of fuel cell, an electrical current is created as hydrogen is oxidized and oxygen is reduced; water is the only product.

Balancing Oxidation–Reduction Equations (20.2)

- Oxidation is the loss of electrons and corresponds to an increase in oxidation state; reduction is the gain of electrons and corresponds to a decrease in oxidation state.
- We can balance redox reactions using the half-reaction method, in which the oxidation and reduction reactions are balanced separately and then added. This method differs slightly for redox reactions in acidic and in basic solutions.

Voltaic (or Galvanic) Cells: Generating Electricity from Spontaneous Chemical Reactions (20.3)

- A voltaic electrochemical cell separates the reactants of a spontaneous redox reaction into two half-cells that are connected by a wire and a means to exchange ions so that electricity is generated.
- In an electrochemical cell, the electrode where oxidation occurs is the anode and the electrode where reduction occurs is the cathode; electrons flow from the anode to the cathode.
- The rate of electrons flowing through a wire is measured in amperes (A), and the cell potential is measured in volts (V).
- A salt bridge allows ions to flow between the half-cell solutions and prevent the buildup of charge.
- The cell diagram or line notation symbolizes electrochemical cells concisely by separating the components of the reaction using lines or commas.

Standard Electrode Potentials (20.4)

- The electrode potentials of half-cells are measured in relation to that of a standard hydrogen electrode, which is assigned an electrode potential of zero under standard conditions (solution concentrations of 1 M, gas pressures of 1 atm, and a temperature of 25 °C).
- A species with a highly positive E° has a strong tendency to attract electrons and undergo reduction (and is therefore an excellent oxidizing agent).
- A species with a highly negative E° has a strong tendency to repel electrons and undergo oxidation (and is therefore an excellent reducing agent).

Cell Potential, Free Energy, and the Equilibrium Constant (20.5)

- In a spontaneous reaction, E°_{cell} is positive, the change in free energy (ΔG°) is negative, and the equilibrium constant (K) is greater than 1.
- In a nonspontaneous reaction, E°_{cell} is negative, ΔG° is positive, and K is less than 1.
- Because E°_{cell}, ΔG°, and K all relate to spontaneity, we can derive equations relating all three quantities.

Cell Potential and Concentration (20.6)

- The standard cell potential (E°_{cell}) is related to the cell potential (E_{cell}) by the Nernst equation, $E_{cell} = E^\circ_{cell} - (0.0592\ \text{V}/n) \log Q$.
- As shown by the Nernst equation, E_{cell} is related to the reaction quotient (Q); E_{cell} equals zero when Q equals K.
- In a concentration cell, the reactions at both electrodes are identical and electrons flow because of a difference in concentration. Nerve cells are a biological example of concentration cells.

Batteries: Using Chemistry to Generate Electricity (20.7)

- Batteries are packaged voltaic cells.
- Dry-cell batteries, including alkaline batteries, do not contain large amounts of water.
- The reactions in rechargeable batteries, such as lead–acid storage, nickel–cadmium, nickel–metal hydride, and lithium ion batteries, can be reversed.
- Fuel cells are similar to batteries except that fuel-cell reactants must be continually replenished from an external source.

Electrolysis: Driving Nonspontaneous Chemical Reactions with Electricity (20.8)

- An electrolytic electrochemical cell differs from a voltaic cell in that (1) an electrical charge is used to drive the reaction, and (2) although the anode is still the site of oxidation and the cathode the site of reduction, they are represented with signs opposite those of a voltaic cell (anode +, cathode –).
- In electrolysis reactions, the anion is oxidized; if there is more than one anion, the anion with the more negative $E°$ is oxidized.
- We can use stoichiometry to calculate the quantity of reactants consumed or products produced in an electrolytic cell.

Corrosion: Undesirable Redox Reactions (20.9)

- Corrosion is the undesired oxidation of metal by environmental oxidizing agents.
- When some metals, such as aluminum, oxidize, they form a stable compound that prevents further oxidation. Iron, in contrast, does not form a structurally stable compound when oxidized, and therefore, rust flakes off and exposes more iron to corrosion.
- Iron corrosion can be prevented by protecting iron from water, minimizing the presence of electrolytes and acids, or using a sacrificial electrode.

EQUATIONS AND RELATIONSHIPS

Definition of an Ampere (20.3)

$$1\text{ A} = 1\text{ C/s}$$

Definition of a Volt (20.3)

$$1\text{ V} = 1\text{ J/s}$$

Standard Hydrogen Electrode (20.4)

$$2\,H^+(aq) + 2\,e^- \longrightarrow H_2(g) \quad E° = 0.00\text{ V}$$

Equation for Cell Potential (20.4)

$$E°_{cell} = E°_{cathode} - E°_{anode}$$

Relating $\Delta G°$ and $E°_{cell}$ (20.5)

$$\Delta G° = -nFE°_{cell} \qquad F = \frac{96{,}485\text{ C}}{\text{mol e}^-}$$

Relating $E°_{cell}$ and K (20.5)

$$E°_{cell} = \frac{0.0592\text{ V}}{n}\log K \qquad (\text{at } 25\text{ °C})$$

The Nernst Equation (20.6)

$$E_{cell} = E°_{cell} - \frac{0.0592\text{ V}}{n}\log Q \qquad (\text{at } 25\text{ °C})$$

LEARNING OUTCOMES

Chapter Objectives	Assessment
Balance acidic solution redox equations using the half-reaction method (20.2)	Examples 20.1, 20.2 **For Practice** 20.1, 20.2 **Exercises** 37–40
Balance basic solution redox equations using the half-reaction method (20.2)	Example 20.3 **For Practice** 20.3 **Exercises** 41–42
Identify the parts of a voltaic cell (20.3)	**Exercises** 43–44
Represent electrochemical cells using cell diagram notation (20.3)	**Exercises** 49–52
Calculate standard cell potentials ($E°_{cell}$) for electrochemical cells (20.4)	Example 20.4 **For Practice** 20.4 **Exercises** 45–48, 61–62
Predict the spontaneity of redox reactions (20.4)	Example 20.5 **For Practice** 20.5 **Exercises** 53–54, 61–62
Identify solutions that can selectively oxidize metals and metal ions (20.4)	**Exercises** 55–60, 63–64
Calculate standard free energy changes ($\Delta G°$) for electrochemical reactions from standard cell potentials ($E°_{cell}$) (20.5)	Example 20.6 **For Practice** 20.6 **Exercises** 65–66
Perform calculations involving $\Delta G°$, $E°_{cell}$, and K for electrochemical reactions (20.5)	Example 20.7 **For Practice** 20.7 **Exercises** 67–72, 103–104
Analyze cell potentials under nonstandard conditions (20.6)	Example 20.8 **For Practice** 20.8 **Exercises** 73–82
Analyze batteries in terms of mass components, redox reactions, and standard cell potentials (20.7)	**Exercises** 83–86
Analyze electrolytic cells in terms of component parts, reactions, voltages, and direction of electron flow (20.8)	**Exercises** 89–90, 97–98
Analyze molten-salt electrolysis reactions in terms of products and half-reactions (20.8)	**Exercises** 91–94
Analyze aqueous-solution electrolysis reactions in terms of products and half-reactions (20.8)	Example 20.9 **For Practice** 20.9 **Exercises** 95–96
Perform stoichiometric calculations for electrolysis reactions (20.8)	Example 20.10 **For Practice** 20.10 **Exercises** 99–102
Predict metals that act as sacrificial electrodes for iron (20.9)	**Exercises** 87–88

EXERCISES

Mastering Chemistry provides end-of-chapter exercises, feedback-enriched tutorial problems, animations, and interactive activities to encourage problem-solving practice and deeper understanding of key concepts and topics.

REVIEW QUESTIONS

1. In electrochemistry, spontaneous redox reactions are used for what purpose?

2. In electrochemistry, what kind of reaction can be driven by electricity?

3. Give the basic definitions of oxidation and reduction and explain the basic procedure for balancing redox reactions.

4. Explain the difference between a voltaic (or galvanic) electrochemical cell and an electrolytic cell.

5. What reaction (oxidation or reduction) occurs at the anode of a voltaic cell? What is the sign of the anode? Do electrons flow toward or away from the anode?

6. What reaction (oxidation or reduction) occurs at the cathode of a voltaic cell? What is the sign of the cathode? Do electrons flow toward or away from the cathode?

7. Explain the purpose of a salt bridge in an electrochemical cell.

8. What unit is used to measure the magnitude of electrical current? What unit is used to measure the magnitude of a potential difference? Explain how electrical current and potential difference differ.

9. What is the definition of the standard cell potential (E°_{cell})? What does a large positive standard cell potential imply about the spontaneity of the redox reaction occurring in the cell? What does a negative standard cell potential imply about the reaction?

10. Describe the basic features of a cell diagram (or line notation) for an electrochemical cell.

11. Why do some electrochemical cells employ inert electrodes such as platinum?

12. Describe the standard hydrogen electrode (SHE) and explain its use in determining standard electrode potentials.

13. How is the cell potential of an electrochemical cell (E°_{cell}) related to the potentials of the half-cells?

14. Does a large positive electrode potential indicate a strong oxidizing agent or a strong reducing agent? What about a large negative electrode potential?

15. Is a spontaneous redox reaction obtained by pairing any reduction half-reaction with one listed above it or with one listed below it in Table 20.1?

16. How can Table 20.1 be used to predict whether or not a metal will dissolve in HCl? In HNO_3?

17. Explain why E°_{cell}, ΔG°_{rxn}, and K are all interrelated.

18. Does a redox reaction with a small equilibrium constant ($K < 1$) have a positive or a negative E°_{cell}? Does it have a positive or a negative ΔG°_{rxn}?

19. How does E_{cell} depend on the concentrations of the reactants and products in the redox reaction occurring in the cell? What effect does increasing the concentration of a reactant have on E_{cell}? Increasing the concentration of a product?

20. Use the Nernst equation to show that $E_{cell} = E^\circ_{cell}$ under standard conditions.

21. What is a concentration electrochemical cell?

22. What are the anode and cathode reactions in a common dry-cell battery? In an alkaline battery?

23. What are the anode and cathode reactions in a lead–acid storage battery? What happens when the battery is recharged?

24. What are the three common types of portable rechargeable batteries, and how does each one work?

25. What is a fuel cell? What is the most common type of fuel cell, and what reactions occur at its anode and cathode?

26. Explain how a fuel-cell breathalyzer works.

27. List some applications of electrolysis.

28. The anode of an electrolytic cell must be connected to which terminal—positive or negative—of the power source?

29. What species is oxidized, and what species is reduced in the electrolysis of a pure molten salt?

30. If an electrolytic cell contains a mixture of species that can be oxidized, how do you determine which species will actually be oxidized? If it contains a mixture of species that can be reduced, how do you determine which one will actually be reduced?

31. Why does the electrolysis of an aqueous sodium chloride solution produce hydrogen gas at the cathode?

32. What is overvoltage in an electrochemical cell? Why is it important?

33. How is the amount of current flowing through an electrolytic cell related to the amount of product produced in the redox reaction?

34. What is corrosion? Why is corrosion only a problem for some metals (such as iron)?

35. Explain the role of each of the following in promoting corrosion: moisture, electrolytes, and acids.

36. How can the corrosion of iron be prevented?

PROBLEMS BY TOPIC

Balancing Redox Reactions

37. Balance each redox reaction occurring in acidic aqueous solution.
MISSED THIS? *Read Section 20.2; Watch KCV 20.2, IWE 20.2*

a. $K(s) + Cr^{3+}(aq) \longrightarrow Cr(s) + K^+(aq)$

b. $Al(s) + Fe^{2+}(aq) \longrightarrow Al^{3+}(aq) + Fe(s)$

c. $BrO_3^-(aq) + N_2H_4(g) \longrightarrow Br^-(aq) + N_2(g)$

38. Balance each redox reaction occurring in acidic aqueous solution.

a. $Zn(s) + Sn^{2+}(aq) \longrightarrow Zn^{2+}(aq) + Sn(s)$

b. $Mg(s) + Cr^{3+}(aq) \longrightarrow Mg^{2+}(aq) + Cr(s)$

c. $MnO_4^-(aq) + Al(s) \longrightarrow Mn^{2+}(aq) + Al^{3+}(aq)$

39. Balance each redox reaction occurring in acidic aqueous solution.
MISSED THIS? *Read Section 20.2; Watch KCV 20.2, IWE 20.2*

a. $PbO_2(s) + I^-(aq) \longrightarrow Pb^{2+}(aq) + I_2(s)$

b. $SO_3^{2-}(aq) + MnO_4^-(aq) \longrightarrow SO_4^{2-}(aq) + Mn^{2+}(aq)$

c. $S_2O_3^{2-}(aq) + Cl_2(g) \longrightarrow SO_4^{2-}(aq) + Cl^-(aq)$

40. Balance each redox reaction occurring in acidic aqueous solution.

a. $I^-(aq) + NO_2^-(aq) \longrightarrow I_2(s) + NO(g)$

b. $ClO_4^-(aq) + Cl^-(aq) \longrightarrow ClO_3^-(aq) + Cl_2(g)$

c. $NO_3^-(aq) + Sn^{2+}(aq) \longrightarrow Sn^{4+}(aq) + NO(g)$

41. Balance each redox reaction occurring in basic aqueous solution.
MISSED THIS? *Read Section 20.2; Watch KCV 20.2, IWE 20.3*
a. $H_2O_2(aq) + ClO_2(aq) \longrightarrow ClO_2^-(aq) + O_2(g)$
b. $Al(s) + MnO_4^-(aq) \longrightarrow MnO_2(s) + Al(OH)_4^-(aq)$
c. $Cl_2(g) \longrightarrow Cl^-(aq) + ClO^-(aq)$

42. Balance each redox reaction occurring in basic aqueous solution.
a. $MnO_4^-(aq) + Br^-(aq) \longrightarrow MnO_2(s) + BrO_3^-(aq)$
b. $Ag(s) + CN^-(aq) + O_2(g) \longrightarrow Ag(CN)_2^-(aq)$
c. $NO_2^-(aq) + Al(s) \longrightarrow NH_3(g) + AlO_2^-(aq)$

Voltaic Cells, Standard Cell Potentials, and Direction of Spontaneity

43. Sketch a voltaic cell for each redox reaction. Label the anode and cathode and indicate the half-reaction that occurs at each electrode and the species present in each solution. Also indicate the direction of electron flow. **MISSED THIS?** *Read Section 20.3*
a. $2\,Ag^+(aq) + Pb(s) \longrightarrow 2\,Ag(s) + Pb^{2+}(aq)$
b. $2\,ClO_2(g) + 2\,I^-(aq) \longrightarrow 2\,ClO_2^-(aq) + I_2(s)$
c. $O_2(g) + 4\,H^+(aq) + 2\,Zn(s) \longrightarrow 2\,H_2O(l) + 2\,Zn^{2+}(aq)$

44. Sketch a voltaic cell for each redox reaction. Label the anode and cathode and indicate the half-reaction that occurs at each electrode and the species present in each solution. Also indicate the direction of electron flow.
a. $Ni^{2+}(aq) + Mg(s) \longrightarrow Ni(s) + Mg^{2+}(aq)$
b. $2\,H^+(aq) + Fe(s) \longrightarrow H_2(g) + Fe^{2+}(aq)$
c. $2\,NO_3^-(aq) + 8\,H^+(aq) + 3\,Cu(s) \longrightarrow 2\,NO(g) + 4\,H_2O(l) + 3\,Cu^{2+}(aq)$

45. Calculate the standard cell potential for each of the electrochemical cells in Problem 43.
MISSED THIS? *Read Section 20.4; Watch KCV 20.4, IWE 20.4*

46. Calculate the standard cell potential for each of the electrochemical cells in Problem 44.

47. Consider the voltaic cell:
MISSED THIS? *Read Sections 20.3, 20.4; Watch KCV 20.4, IWE 20.4*

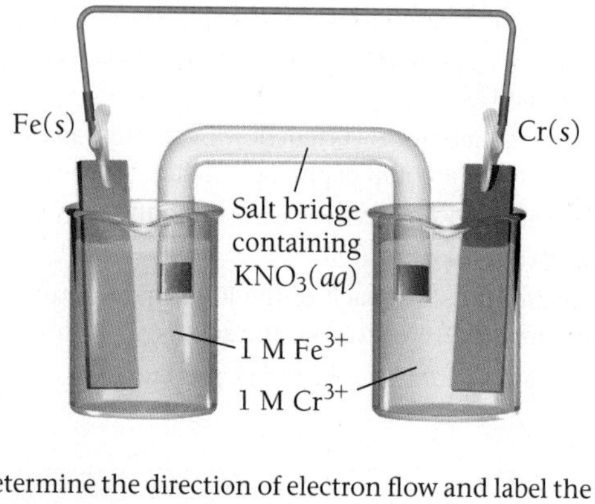

a. Determine the direction of electron flow and label the anode and the cathode.
b. Write a balanced equation for the overall reaction and calculate E°_{cell}.
c. Label each electrode as negative or positive.
d. Indicate the direction of anion and cation flow in the salt bridge.

48. Consider the voltaic cell:
a. Determine the direction of electron flow and label the anode and the cathode.
b. Write a balanced equation for the overall reaction and calculate E°_{cell}.
c. Label each electrode as negative or positive.
d. Indicate the direction of anion and cation flow in the salt bridge.

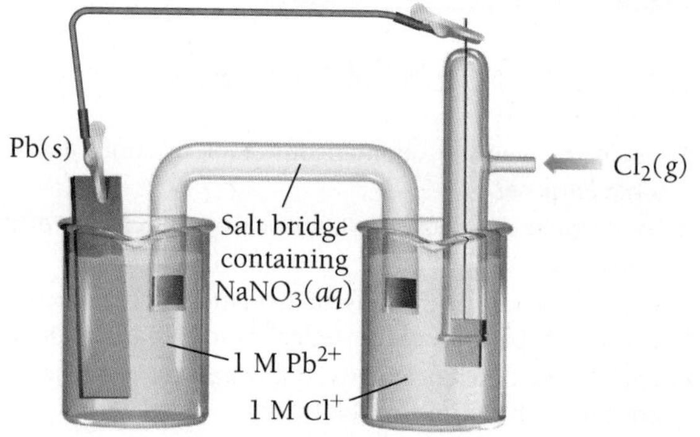

49. Use line notation to represent each electrochemical cell in Problem 43. **MISSED THIS?** *Read Section 20.3*

50. Use line notation to represent each electrochemical cell in Problem 44.

51. Make a sketch of the voltaic cell represented by the line notation. Write the overall balanced equation for the reaction and calculate E°_{cell}. **MISSED THIS?** *Read Section 20.3*

$$Sn(s)\,|\,Sn^{2+}(aq)\,\|\,NO(g)\,|\,NO_3^-(aq), H^+(aq)\,|\,Pt(s)$$

52. Make a sketch of the voltaic cell represented by the line notation. Write the overall balanced equation for the reaction and calculate E°_{cell}.

$$Mn(s)\,|\,Mn^{2+}(aq)\,\|\,ClO_2^-(aq)\,|\,ClO_2(g)\,|\,Pt(s)$$

53. Determine whether or not each redox reaction occurs spontaneously in the forward direction.
MISSED THIS? *Read Section 20.4; Watch KCV 20.4*
a. $Ni(s) + Zn^{2+}(aq) \longrightarrow Ni^{2+}(aq) + Zn(s)$
b. $Ni(s) + Pb^{2+}(aq) \longrightarrow Ni^{2+}(aq) + Pb(s)$
c. $Al(s) + 3\,Ag^+(aq) \longrightarrow Al^{3+}(aq) + 3\,Ag(s)$
d. $Pb(s) + Mn^{2+}(aq) \longrightarrow Pb^{2+}(aq) + Mn(s)$

54. Determine whether or not each redox reaction occurs spontaneously in the forward direction.
a. $Ca^{2+}(aq) + Zn(s) \longrightarrow Ca(s) + Zn^{2+}(aq)$
b. $2\,Ag^+(aq) + Ni(s) \longrightarrow 2\,Ag(s) + Ni^{2+}(aq)$
c. $Fe(s) + Mn^{2+}(aq) \longrightarrow Fe^{2+}(aq) + Mn(s)$
d. $2\,Al(s) + 3\,Pb^{2+}(aq) \longrightarrow 2\,Al^{3+}(aq) + 3\,Pb(s)$

55. Which metal could you use to reduce Mn^{2+} ions but not Mg^{2+} ions? **MISSED THIS?** *Read Section 20.4; Watch KCV 20.4*

56. Which metal can be oxidized with an Sn^{2+} solution but not with an Fe^{2+} solution?

57. Determine whether or not each metal dissolves in 1 M HCl. For those metals that do dissolve, write a balanced redox reaction showing what happens when the metal dissolves.
MISSED THIS? *Read Section 20.4; Watch KCV 20.4*
a. Al b. Ag c. Pb

58. Determine whether or not each metal dissolves in 1 M HCl. For those metals that do dissolve, write a balanced redox reaction showing what happens when the metal dissolves.
a. Cu b. Fe c. Au

59. Determine whether or not each metal dissolves in 1 M HNO_3. For those metals that do dissolve, write a balanced redox reaction showing what happens when the metal dissolves.
MISSED THIS? *Read Section 20.4; Watch KCV 20.4*
a. Cu
b. Au

60. Determine whether or not each metal dissolves in 1 M HIO_3. For those metals that do dissolve, write a balanced redox equation for the reaction that occurs.
a. Au
b. Cr

61. Calculate E°_{cell} for each balanced redox reaction and determine if the reaction is spontaneous as written.
MISSED THIS? *Read Section 20.4; Watch KCV 20.4, IWE 20.4*
a. $2\,Cu(s) + Mn^{2+}(aq) \longrightarrow 2\,Cu^+(aq) + Mn(s)$
b. $MnO_2(aq) + 4\,H^+(aq) + Zn(s) \longrightarrow Mn^{2+}(aq) + 2\,H_2O(l) + Zn^{2+}(aq)$
c. $Cl_2(g) + 2\,F^-(aq) \longrightarrow F_2(g) + 2\,Cl^-(aq)$

62. Calculate E°_{cell} for each balanced redox reaction and determine if the reaction is spontaneous as written.
a. $O_2(g) + 2\,H_2O(l) + 4\,Ag(s) \longrightarrow 4\,OH^-(aq) + 4\,Ag^+(aq)$
b. $Br_2(l) + 2\,I^-(aq) \longrightarrow 2\,Br^-(aq) + I_2(s)$
c. $PbO_2(s) + 4\,H^+(aq) + Sn(s) \longrightarrow Pb^{2+}(aq) + 2\,H_2O(l) + Sn^{2+}(aq)$

63. Which metal cation is the best oxidizing agent?
MISSED THIS? *Read Section 20.4; Watch KCV 20.4*
a. Pb^{2+} b. Cr^{3+} c. Fe^{2+} d. Sn^{2+}

64. Which metal is the best reducing agent?
a. Mn b. Al c. Ni d. Cr

Cell Potential, Free Energy, and the Equilibrium Constant

65. Use tabulated electrode potentials to calculate ΔG°_{rxn} for each reaction at 25 °C.
MISSED THIS? *Read Section 20.5; Watch KCV 20.5, IWE 20.6*
a. $Pb^{2+}(aq) + Mg(s) \longrightarrow Pb(s) + Mg^{2+}(aq)$
b. $Br_2(l) + 2\,Cl^-(aq) \longrightarrow 2\,Br^-(aq) + Cl_2(g)$
c. $MnO_2(s) + 4\,H^+(aq) + Cu(s) \longrightarrow Mn^{2+}(aq) + 2\,H_2O(l) + Cu^{2+}(aq)$

66. Use tabulated electrode potentials to calculate ΔG°_{rxn} for each reaction at 25 °C.
a. $2\,Fe^{3+}(aq) + 3\,Sn(s) \longrightarrow 2\,Fe(s) + 3\,Sn^{2+}(aq)$
b. $O_2(g) + 2\,H_2O(l) + 2\,Cu(s) \longrightarrow 4\,OH^-(aq) + 2\,Cu^{2+}(aq)$
c. $Br_2(l) + 2\,I^-(aq) \longrightarrow 2\,Br^-(aq) + I_2(s)$

67. Calculate the equilibrium constant for each of the reactions in Problem 65. **MISSED THIS?** *Read Section 20.5; Watch KCV 20.5*

68. Calculate the equilibrium constant for each of the reactions in Problem 66.

69. Calculate the equilibrium constant for the reaction between $Ni^{2+}(aq)$ and Cd(s) (at 25 °C).
MISSED THIS? *Read Section 20.5; Watch KCV 20.5*

70. Calculate the equilibrium constant for the reaction between $Fe^{2+}(aq)$ and Zn(s) (at 25 °C).

71. Calculate ΔG°_{rxn} and E°_{cell} for a redox reaction with $n = 2$ that has an equilibrium constant of $K = 25$ (at 25 °C).
MISSED THIS? *Read Section 20.5; Watch KCV 20.5*

72. Calculate ΔG°_{rxn} and E°_{cell} for a redox reaction with $n = 3$ that has an equilibrium constant of $K = 0.050$ (at 25 °C).

Nonstandard Conditions and the Nernst Equation

73. A voltaic cell employs the following redox reaction:
MISSED THIS? *Read Section 20.6*

$$Sn^{2+}(aq) + Mn(s) \longrightarrow Sn(s) + Mn^{2+}(aq)$$

Calculate the cell potential at 25 °C under each set of conditions.
a. standard conditions
b. $[Sn^{2+}] = 0.0100$ M; $[Mn^{2+}] = 2.00$ M
c. $[Sn^{2+}] = 2.00$ M; $[Mn^{2+}] = 0.0100$ M

74. A voltaic cell employs the redox reaction:

$$2\,Fe^{3+}(aq) + 3\,Mg(s) \longrightarrow 2\,Fe(s) + 3\,Mg^{2+}(aq)$$

Calculate the cell potential at 25 °C under each set of conditions.
a. standard conditions
b. $[Fe^{3+}] = 1.0 \times 10^{-3}$ M; $[Mg^{2+}] = 2.50$ M
c. $[Fe^{3+}] = 2.00$ M; $[Mg^{2+}] = 1.5 \times 10^{-3}$ M

75. An electrochemical cell is based on these two half-reactions:
MISSED THIS? *Read Section 20.6*

Ox: $Pb(s) \longrightarrow Pb^{2+}(aq, 0.10\ M) + 2\,e^-$

Red: $MnO_4^-(aq, 1.50\ M) + 4\,H^+(aq, 2.0\ M) + 3\,e^- \longrightarrow MnO_2(s) + 2\,H_2O(l)$

Calculate the cell potential at 25 °C.

76. An electrochemical cell is based on these two half-reactions:

Ox: $Sn(s) \longrightarrow Sn^{2+}(aq, 2.00\ M) + 2\,e^-$

Red: $ClO_2(g, 0.100\ atm) + e^- \longrightarrow ClO_2^-(aq, 2.00\ M)$

Calculate the cell potential at 25 °C.

77. A voltaic cell consists of a Zn/Zn^{2+} half-cell and a Ni/Ni^{2+} half-cell at 25 °C. The initial concentrations of Ni^{2+} and Zn^{2+} are 1.50 M and 0.100 M, respectively.
MISSED THIS? *Read Section 20.6*
a. What is the initial cell potential?
b. What is the cell potential when the concentration of Ni^{2+} has fallen to 0.500 M?
c. What are the concentrations of Ni^{2+} and Zn^{2+} when the cell potential falls to 0.45 V?

78. A voltaic cell consists of a Pb/Pb^{2+} half-cell and a Cu/Cu^{2+} half-cell at 25 °C. The initial concentrations of Pb^{2+} and Cu^{2+} are 0.0500 M and 1.50 M, respectively.
a. What is the initial cell potential?
b. What is the cell potential when the concentration of Cu^{2+} has fallen to 0.200 M?
c. What are the concentrations of Pb^{2+} and Cu^{2+} when the cell potential falls to 0.35 V?

79. Make a sketch of a concentration cell employing two Zn/Zn^{2+} half-cells. The concentration of Zn^{2+} in one of the half-cells is 2.0 M, and the concentration in the other half-cell is 1.0×10^{-3} M. Label the anode and the cathode and indicate the half-reaction occurring at each electrode. Also indicate the direction of electron flow.
MISSED THIS? *Read Section 20.6*

80. Consider the concentration cell:

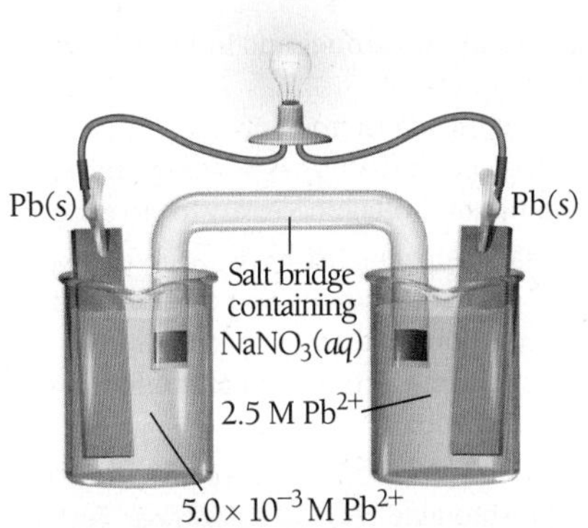

a. Label the anode and cathode.
b. Indicate the direction of electron flow.
c. Indicate what happens to the concentration of Pb^{2+} in each half-cell.

81. A concentration cell consists of two Sn/Sn^{2+} half-cells. The cell has a potential of 0.10 V at 25 °C. What is the ratio of the Sn^{2+} concentrations in the two half-cells?
MISSED THIS? *Read Section 20.6*

82. A Cu/Cu^{2+} concentration cell has a voltage of 0.22 V at 25 °C. The concentration of Cu^{2+} in one of the half-cells is 1.5×10^{-3} M. What is the concentration of Cu^{2+} in the other half-cell? (Assume the concentration in the unknown cell is the *lower* of the two concentrations.)

Batteries, Fuel Cells, and Corrosion

83. Determine the optimum mass ratio of Zn to MnO_2 in an alkaline battery. **MISSED THIS?** *Read Section 20.7*

84. What mass of lead sulfate is formed in a lead–acid storage battery when 1.00 g of Pb undergoes oxidation?

85. Refer to the tabulated values of ΔG_f° in Appendix IIB to calculate E_{cell}° for a fuel cell that employs the reaction between methane gas (CH_4) and oxygen to form carbon dioxide and gaseous water. **MISSED THIS?** *Read Sections 20.5, 20.7; Watch IWE 20.6*

86. Refer to the tabulated values of ΔG_f° in Appendix IIB to calculate E_{cell}° for the fuel-cell breathalyzer, which employs the following reaction. (ΔG_f° for $HC_2H_3O_2(g) = -374.2$ kJ/mol.)

$$CH_3CH_2OH(g) + O_2(g) \longrightarrow HC_2H_3O_2(g) + H_2O(g)$$

87. Determine whether or not each metal, if coated onto iron, would prevent the corrosion of iron.
MISSED THIS? *Read Section 20.9*

a. Zn   b. Sn   c. Mn

88. Determine whether or not each metal, if coated onto iron, would prevent the corrosion of iron.

a. Mg   b. Cr   c. Cu

Electrolytic Cells and Electrolysis

89. Consider the electrolytic cell: **MISSED THIS?** *Read Section 20.8*

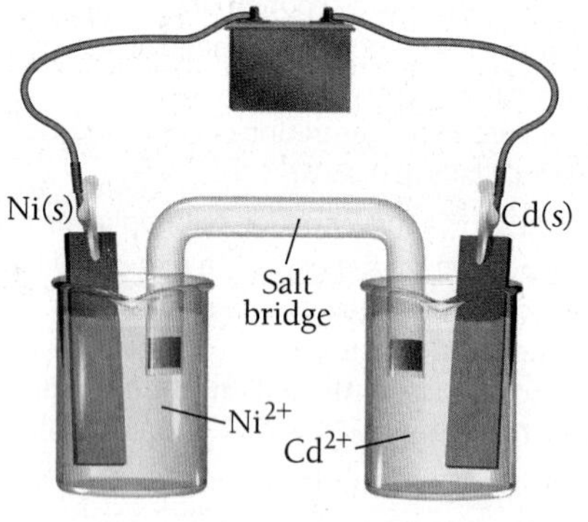

a. Label the anode and the cathode and indicate the half-reactions occurring at each.

b. Indicate the direction of electron flow.

c. Label the terminals on the battery as positive or negative and calculate the minimum voltage necessary to drive the reaction.

90. Draw an electrolytic cell in which Mn^{2+} is reduced to Mn and Sn is oxidized to Sn^{2+}. Label the anode and cathode, indicate the direction of electron flow, and write an equation for the half-reaction occurring at each electrode. What minimum voltage is necessary to drive the reaction?

91. Write equations for the half-reactions that occur in the electrolysis of molten potassium bromide. **MISSED THIS?** *Read Section 20.8*

92. What products are obtained in the electrolysis of molten NaI?

93. Write equations for the half-reactions that occur in the electrolysis of a mixture of molten potassium bromide and molten lithium bromide. **MISSED THIS?** *Read Section 20.8*

94. What products are obtained in the electrolysis of a molten mixture of KI and KBr?

95. Write equations for the half-reactions that occur at the anode and cathode for the electrolysis of each aqueous solution. **MISSED THIS?** *Read Section 20.8*

a. $NaBr(aq)$ b. $PbI_2(aq)$ c. $Na_2SO_4(aq)$

96. Write equations for the half-reactions that occur at the anode and cathode for the electrolysis of each aqueous solution.

a. $Ni(NO_3)_2(aq)$ b. $KCl(aq)$ c. $CuBr_2(aq)$

97. Make a sketch of an electrolysis cell that electroplates copper onto other metal surfaces. Label the anode and the cathode and indicate the reactions that occur at each.
MISSED THIS? *Read Section 20.8*

98. Make a sketch of an electrolysis cell that electroplates nickel onto other metal surfaces. Label the anode and the cathode and indicate the reactions that occur at each.

99. Copper can be electroplated at the cathode of an electrolysis cell by the half-reaction: **MISSED THIS?** *Read Section 20.8*

$$Cu^{2+}(aq) + 2\,e^- \longrightarrow Cu(s)$$

How much time would it take for 325 mg of copper to be plated at a current of 5.6 A?

100. Silver can be electroplated at the cathode of an electrolysis cell by the half-reaction:

$$Ag^+(aq) + e^- \longrightarrow Ag(s)$$

What mass of silver would plate onto the cathode if a current of 6.8 A flowed through the cell for 72 min?

101. A major source of sodium metal is the electrolysis of molten sodium chloride. What magnitude of current produces 1.0 kg of sodium metal in 1 hour? **MISSED THIS?** *Read Section 20.8*

102. What mass of aluminum metal can be produced per hour in the electrolysis of a molten aluminum salt by a current of 25 A?

103. Consider the reaction shown here occurring at 25 °C.
MISSED THIS? *Read Section 20.5, Watch KCV 20.5, IWE 20.6*

$$A(s) + B^{2+}(aq) \longrightarrow A^{2+}(aq) + B(s) \quad \Delta G_{rxn}^\circ = -14.0 \text{ kJ}$$

Determine the value of E_{cell}° and K for the reaction and complete the table.

$[B^{2+}]$	$[A^{2+}]$	Q	E_{cell}	ΔG_{rxn}
1.00	1.00			
1.00	1.00×10^{-4}			
1.0×10^{-4}	1.0			
3.54×10^{-3}	1.0			

104. Consider the reaction shown here occurring at 25 °C.

$$Cr(s) + Cd^{2+}(aq) \longrightarrow Cr^{2+}(aq) + Cd(s)$$

Determine E_{cell}°, K, and ΔG_{rxn}° for the reaction and complete the table.

$[Cd^{2+}]$	$[Cr^{2+}]$	Q	E_{cell}	ΔG_{rxn}
1.00	1.00			
1.00	1.00×10^{-5}			
1.00×10^{-5}	1.00			
4.18×10^{-4}	1.00			

CUMULATIVE PROBLEMS

105. Consider the unbalanced redox reaction:

$$MnO_4^-(aq) + Zn(s) \longrightarrow Mn^{2+}(aq) + Zn^{2+}(aq)$$

Balance the equation and determine the volume of a 0.500 M $KMnO_4$ solution required to completely react with 2.85 g of Zn.

106. Consider the unbalanced redox reaction:

$$Cr_2O_7^{2-}(aq) + Cu(s) \longrightarrow Cr^{3+}(aq) + Cu^{2+}(aq)$$

Balance the equation and determine the volume of a 0.850 M $K_2Cr_2O_7$ solution required to completely react with 5.25 g of Cu.

107. Consider the molecular views of an Al strip and Cu^{2+} solution. Draw a similar sketch showing what happens to the atoms and ions after the Al strip is submerged in the solution for a few minutes.

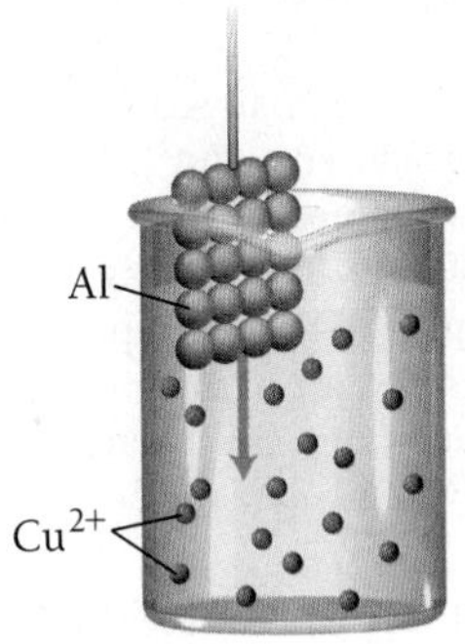

108. Consider the molecular view of an electrochemical cell involving the overall reaction:

$$Zn(s) + Ni^{2+}(aq) \longrightarrow Zn^{2+}(aq) + Ni(s)$$

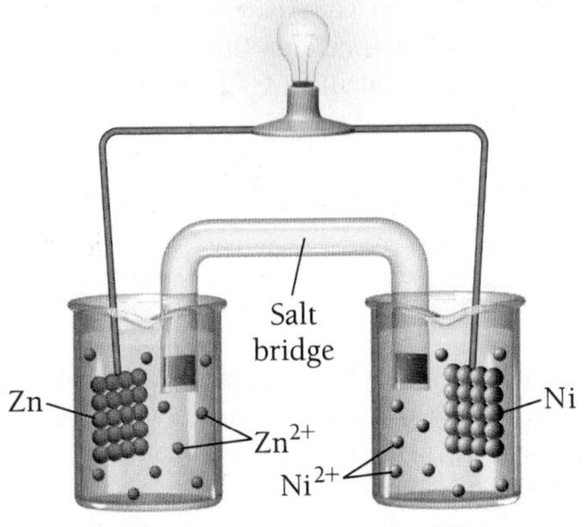

Draw a similar sketch of the cell after it has generated a substantial amount of electrical current.

109. Determine whether HI can dissolve each metal sample. If it can, write a balanced chemical reaction showing how the metal dissolves in HI and determine the minimum volume of 3.5 M HI required to completely dissolve the sample.

a. 2.15 g Al b. 4.85 g Cu c. 2.42 g Ag

110. Determine if HNO_3 can dissolve each metal sample. If it can, write a balanced chemical reaction showing how the metal dissolves in HNO_3 and determine the minimum volume of 6.0 M HNO_3 required to completely dissolve the sample.

a. 5.90 g Au b. 2.55 g Cu c. 4.83 g Sn

111. The cell potential of this electrochemical cell depends on the pH of the solution in the anode half-cell.

$$Pt(s)\,|\,H_2(g, 1\text{ atm})\,|\,H^+(aq, ?\text{ M})\,\|\,Cu^{2+}(aq, 1.0\text{ M})\,|\,Cu(s)$$

What is the pH of the solution if E_{cell} is 355 mV?

112. The cell potential of this electrochemical cell depends on the gold concentration in the cathode half-cell.

$$Pt(s)\,|\,H_2(g, 1.0\text{ atm})\,|\,H^+(aq, 1.0\text{ M})\,\|\,Au^{3+}(aq, ?\text{ M})\,|\,Au(s)$$

What is the concentration of Au^{3+} in the solution if E_{cell} is 1.22 V?

113. A friend wants you to invest in a new battery she has designed that produces 24 V in a single voltaic cell. Why should you be wary of investing in such a battery?

114. What voltage can theoretically be achieved in a battery in which lithium metal is oxidized and fluorine gas is reduced? Why might such a battery be difficult to produce?

115. A battery relies on the oxidation of magnesium and the reduction of Cu^{2+}. The initial concentrations of Mg^{2+} and Cu^{2+} are 1.0×10^{-4} M and 1.5 M, respectively, in 1.0-liter half-cells.

a. What is the initial voltage of the battery?

b. What is the voltage of the battery after delivering 5.0 A for 8.0 h?

c. How long can the battery deliver 5.0 A before going dead?

116. A rechargeable battery is constructed based on a concentration cell constructed of two Ag/Ag^+ half-cells. The volume of each half-cell is 2.0 L, and the concentrations of Ag^+ in the half-cells are 1.25 M and 1.0×10^{-3} M.

a. How long can this battery deliver 2.5 A of current before it goes dead?

b. What mass of silver is plated onto the cathode by running at 3.5 A for 5.5 h?

c. Upon recharging, how long would it take to redissolve 1.00×10^2 g of silver at a charging current of 10.0 amps?

117. If a water electrolysis cell operates at a current of 7.8 A, how long will it take to generate 25.0 L of hydrogen gas at a pressure of 25.0 atm and a temperature of 25 °C?

118. When a suspected drunk driver blows 188 mL of his breath through the fuel-cell breathalyzer described in Section 20.7, the breathalyzer produces an average of 324 mA of current for 10 s. Assuming a pressure of 1.0 atm and a temperature of 25 °C, what percent (by volume) of the driver's breath is ethanol?

119. The K_{sp} of CuI is 1.1×10^{-12}. Find E_{cell} for the cell:

$$Cu(s)\,|\,CuI(s)\,|\,I^-(aq)(1.0\text{ M})\,\|\,Cu^+(aq)(1.0\text{ M})\,|\,Cu(s)$$

120. The K_{sp} of $Zn(OH)_2$ is 1.8×10^{-14}. Find E_{cell} for the half-reaction:

$$Zn(OH)_2(s) + 2\,e^- \rightleftharpoons Zn(s) + 2\,OH^-(aq)$$

121. Calculate ΔG°_{rxn} and K for each reaction.

a. The disproportionation of $Mn^{2+}(aq)$ to $Mn(s)$ and $MnO_2(s)$ in acid solution at 25 °C.

b. The disproportionation of $MnO_2(s)$ to $Mn^{2+}(aq)$ and $MnO_4^-(aq)$ in acid solution at 25 °C.

122. Calculate ΔG°_{rxn} and K for each reaction.

a. The reaction of $Cr^{2+}(aq)$ with $Cr_2O_7^{2-}(aq)$ in acid solution to form $Cr^{3+}(aq)$.

b. The reaction of $Cr^{3+}(aq)$ and $Cr(s)$ to form $Cr^{2+}(aq)$. [The electrode potential of $Cr^{2+}(aq)$ to $Cr(s)$ is –0.91 V.]

123. The molar mass of a metal (M) is 50.9 g/mol; it forms a chloride of unknown composition. Electrolysis of a sample of the molten chloride with a current of 6.42 A for 23.6 minutes produces 1.20 g of M at the cathode. Determine the empirical formula of the chloride.

124. A metal forms the fluoride MF_3. Electrolysis of the molten fluoride by a current of 3.86 A for 16.2 minutes deposits 1.25 g of the metal. Calculate the molar mass of the metal.

125. A sample of impure tin of mass 0.535 g is dissolved in strong acid to give a solution of Sn^{2+}. The solution is then titrated with a 0.0448 M solution of NO_3^-, which is reduced to $NO(g)$. The equivalence point is reached upon the addition of 0.0344 L of the NO_3^- solution. Find the percent by mass of tin in the original sample, assuming that it contains no other reducing agents.

126. A 0.0251-L sample of a solution of Cu^+ requires 0.0322 L of 0.129 M $KMnO_4$ solution to reach the equivalence point. The products of the reaction are Cu^{2+} and Mn^{2+}. What is the concentration of the Cu^{2+} solution?

127. A current of 11.3 A is applied to 1.25 L of a solution of 0.552 M HBr converting some of the H^+ to $H_2(g)$, which bubbles out of solution. What is the pH of the solution after 73 minutes?

128. A 215-mL sample of a 0.500 M NaCl solution with an initial pH of 7.00 is subjected to electrolysis. After 15.0 minutes, a 10.0-mL portion (or aliquot) of the solution was removed from the cell and titrated with 0.100 M HCl solution. The endpoint in the titration was reached upon addition of 22.8 mL of HCl. Assuming constant current, what was the current (in A) running through the cell?

129. An $MnO_2(s)/Mn^{2+}(aq)$ electrode in which the pH is 10.24 is prepared. Find the $[Mn^{2+}]$ necessary to lower the potential of the half-cell to 0.00 V (at 25 °C).

130. To what pH should you adjust a standard hydrogen electrode to get an electrode potential of −0.122 V? (Assume that the partial pressure of hydrogen gas remains at 1 atm.)

CHALLENGE PROBLEMS

131. Suppose a hydrogen–oxygen fuel-cell generator produces electricity for a house. Use the balanced redox reactions and the standard cell potential to predict the volume of hydrogen gas (at STP) required each month to generate the electricity. Assume the home uses 1.2×10^3 kWh of electricity per month.

132. A voltaic cell designed to measure $[Cu^{2+}]$ is constructed of a standard hydrogen electrode and a copper metal electrode in the Cu^{2+} solution of interest. If you want to construct a calibration curve for how the cell potential varies with the concentration of copper(II), what do you plot in order to obtain a straight line? What is the slope of the line?

133. The surface area of an object to be gold plated is 49.8 cm^2, and the density of gold is 19.3 g/cm^3. A current of 3.25 A is applied to a solution that contains gold in the +3 oxidation state. Calculate the time required to deposit an even layer of gold 1.00×10^{-3} cm thick on the object.

134. To electrodeposit all the Cu and Cd from a solution of $CuSO_4$ and $CdSO_4$ required 1.20 F of electricity ($1\ F = 1\ mol\ e^-$). The mixture of Cu and Cd that was deposited had a mass of 50.36 g. What mass of $CuSO_4$ was present in the original mixture?

135. Sodium oxalate, $Na_2C_2O_4$, in solution is oxidized to $CO_2(g)$ by MnO_4^-, which is reduced to Mn^{2+}. A 50.1-mL volume of a solution of MnO_4^- is required to titrate a 0.339-g sample of sodium oxalate. This solution of MnO_4^- is used to analyze uranium-containing samples. A 4.62-g sample of a uranium-containing material requires 32.5 mL of the solution for titration. The oxidation of the uranium can be represented by the change $UO^{2+} \longrightarrow UO_2^{2+}$. Calculate the percentage of uranium in the sample.

136. Three electrolytic cells are connected in a series. The electrolytes in the cells are aqueous copper(II) sulfate, gold(III) sulfate, and silver nitrate. A current of 2.33 A is applied, and after some time 1.74 g Cu is deposited. How long was the current applied? What mass of gold and silver was deposited?

137. The cell $Pt(s)|Cu^+(1\ M), Cu^{2+}(1\ M)||Cu^+(1\ M)|Cu(s)$ has $E° = 0.364$ V. The cell $Cu(s)|Cu^{2+}(1\ M)||Cu^+(1\ M)|Cu(s)$ has $E° = 0.182$ V. Write the cell reaction for each cell and explain the differences in $E°$. Calculate $\Delta G°$ for each cell reaction to help explain these differences.

CONCEPTUAL PROBLEMS

138. An electrochemical cell has a positive standard cell potential but a negative cell potential. Which statement is true for the cell?

a. $K > 1; Q > K$ b. $K < 1; Q > K$
c. $K > 1; Q < K$ d. $K < 1; Q < K$

139. Which oxidizing agent will oxidize Br^- but not Cl^-?

a. $K_2Cr_2O_7$ (in acid) b. $KMnO_4$ (in acid)
c. HNO_3

140. A redox reaction employed in an electrochemical cell has a negative $\Delta G°_{rxn}$. Which statement is true?

a. $E°_{cell}$ is positive; $K < 1$
b. $E°_{cell}$ is positive; $K > 1$
c. $E°_{cell}$ is negative; $K > 1$
d. $E°_{cell}$ is negative; $K < 1$

141. A redox reaction has an equilibrium constant of $K = 0.055$. What is true of $\Delta G°_{rxn}$ and $E°_{cell}$ for this reaction?

QUESTIONS FOR GROUP WORK

Active Classroom Learning

Discuss these questions with the group and record your consensus answer.

142. Balance the redox reactions by following the steps in the text. Rotate through the group, having each group member do the next step in the process and explain that step to the rest of the group.

a. $I_2(s) + Fe(s) \longrightarrow FeI_2(s)$
b. $Cl_2(g) + H_2O_2(aq) \longrightarrow Cl^-(aq) + O_2(g)$ (acidic)
c. $Hg^{2+}(aq) + H_2(g) \longrightarrow Hg(l) + H_2O(l)$ (basic)
d. $CH_3OH(l) + O_2(g) \longrightarrow CO_2(g) + H_2O(l)$ (acidic)

143. Have each group member select a half-reaction from Table 20.1. Each member should calculate the standard cell potential of an electrochemical cell formed between each member's half-reaction and the half-reaction of each of the other group members. For each pair of half-reactions, write the overall balanced chemical reaction that will be spontaneous.

144. Calculate $\Delta G°$ and K for each reaction the group created in Question 143. For one of the reactions, explain how the sign or magnitude of each quantity ($E°_{cell}$, $\Delta G°$, and K) is consistent with the fact that the reaction is spontaneous in the direction written.

145. Design a device that uses an electrochemical cell to determine the amount of Cu^{2+} in a sample of water. Describe, in detail, the construction and the theory of operation of your device. If you are able to measure voltage with one-millivolt accuracy, what will the uncertainty in your measured concentration be?

146. Using a library or the Internet, research a fuel cell that uses methanol for fuel. What is the reaction at the anode? What is the reaction at the cathode? What is the overall reaction? What is the standard cell potential? How many kWh can it generate from 1 L (0.792 kg) of methanol?

DATA INTERPRETATION AND ANALYSIS

Measuring Concentration with Voltage

147. In this chapter, you have seen that the voltage of an electrochemical cell is sensitive to the concentrations of the reactants and products in the cell. As a result, electrochemical cells can be used to measure the concentrations of certain species in solution. For example, the voltage of an electrochemical cell based on the reaction $H_2(g) + Cu^{2+}(aq) \longrightarrow 2\,H^+(aq) + Cu(s)$ is sensitive to both the Cu^{2+} concentration and the H^+ concentration in solution. If the H^+ concentration is held constant, then the voltage only depends on the Cu^{2+} concentration, and we can use the cell to measure the Cu^{2+} concentration in an unknown solution. The tabulated data shows the measured voltage in the hydrogen/copper electrochemical cell just discussed for several different Cu^{2+} concentrations. Examine the data and answer the questions that follow.

$[Cu^{2+}]$	Voltage (V)	$[Cu^{2+}]$	Voltage (V)
0.100	0.310	0.500	0.331
0.200	0.319	0.700	0.335
0.300	0.325	1.00	0.340
0.400	0.328		

a. Construct a graph of the measured voltage versus the copper concentration. Is the graph linear?

b. Determine how you might manipulate the data to produce a linear graph. (*Hint*: See the Nernst equation.)

c. Reconstruct a graph of the data using the method to produce a linear graph from part b. Determine the slope and *y*-intercept of the best-fitting line to the points in your graph. Could you have predicted the slope and intercept from the Nernst equation?

d. The voltage of two unknown solutions are measured and recorded. Use the slope and intercept from part c to determine the Cu^{2+} concentrations of the unknown solutions.

Unknown Cu^{2+} Solution	Voltage (V)
i	0.303
ii	0.338

Cc ANSWERS TO CONCEPTUAL CONNECTIONS

Potential Difference and Electrical Current

20.1 **(a)** The volt is a unit of potential difference, the difference in potential energy and the amp is a unit of electrical current, the flow of electrical charge.

Voltaic Cells

20.2 **(a)** Electrons are negatively charged and therefore flow away from the more negatively charged electrode and toward the more positively charged electrode.

Standard Electrode Potentials

20.3 **(b)** A negative electrode potential indicates that an electron at that electrode has greater potential energy than it has at a standard hydrogen electrode.

Selective Oxidation

20.4 **(d)** The reduction of HNO_3 is below the reduction of Br_2 and above the reduction of I_2 in Table 20.1. Since any reduction half-reaction is spontaneous when paired with the reverse of a half-reaction below it in the table, the reduction of HNO_3 is spontaneous when paired with the oxidation of I^- but is not spontaneous when paired with the oxidation of Br^-.

Metals Dissolving in Acids

20.5 **(c)** Ag falls above the half-reaction for the reduction of H^+ but below the half-reaction for the reduction of NO_3^- in Table 20.1.

Periodic Trends and the Direction of Spontaneity for Redox Reactions

20.6 **(a)** Br is more electronegative than I. If the two atoms were in competition for the electron, the electron would go to the more electronegative atom (Br). Therefore, I_2 does not spontaneously gain electrons from Br^-.

Relating K, ΔG°_{rxn}, and E°_{cell}

20.7 **(c)** Since $K > 1$, the reaction is spontaneous under standard conditions (when $Q = 1$, the reaction proceeds toward the products). Therefore, E°_{cell} is positive and ΔG°_{rxn} is negative.

Relating Q, K, E_{cell}, and E°_{cell}

20.8 **(a)** Since $K > 1$, E°_{cell} is negative (under standard conditions, the reaction is not spontaneous). Since $Q < K$, E_{cell} is positive (the reaction is spontaneous under the nonstandard conditions of the cell).

Voltaic and Electrolytic Cels

20.9 **(b)** Since oxidation always occurs at the anode, electrons flow away from the anode and toward the cathode (where reduction occurs).

Electrolysis

20.10 **(c)** The stoichiometry of the reaction shows that 1 mole of silver plates for every 1 mole of electrons; therefore 3 moles of electrons are required to plate 3 moles of silver.

Sacrificial Electrodes

20.11 **(a)** Cu. The electrode potential for Fe is more negative than that of Cu. Therefore, Fe oxidizes more easily than Cu.

I am among those who think that science has great beauty. A scientist in his laboratory is not only a technician; he is also a child placed before natural phenomena which impress him like a fairy tale.

—MARIE CURIE (1867–1934)

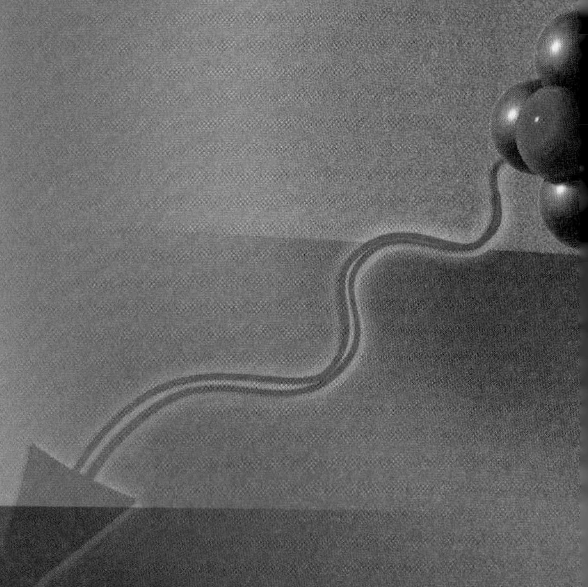

CHAPTER 21

Radioactivity and Nuclear Chemistry

In this chapter, we examine radioactivity and nuclear chemistry, both of which involve changes within the *nuclei* of atoms. Unlike ordinary chemical processes, in which elements retain their identity, nuclear processes often result in one element changing into another, frequently emitting tremendous amounts of energy. Radioactivity has numerous applications, including the diagnosis and treatment of medical conditions such as cancer, thyroid disease, abnormal kidney and bladder function, and heart disease. Naturally occurring radioactivity allows us to estimate the age of fossils, rocks, and ancient artifacts. And radioactivity, perhaps most famously, led to the discovery of nuclear fission, used for electricity generation and nuclear weapons.

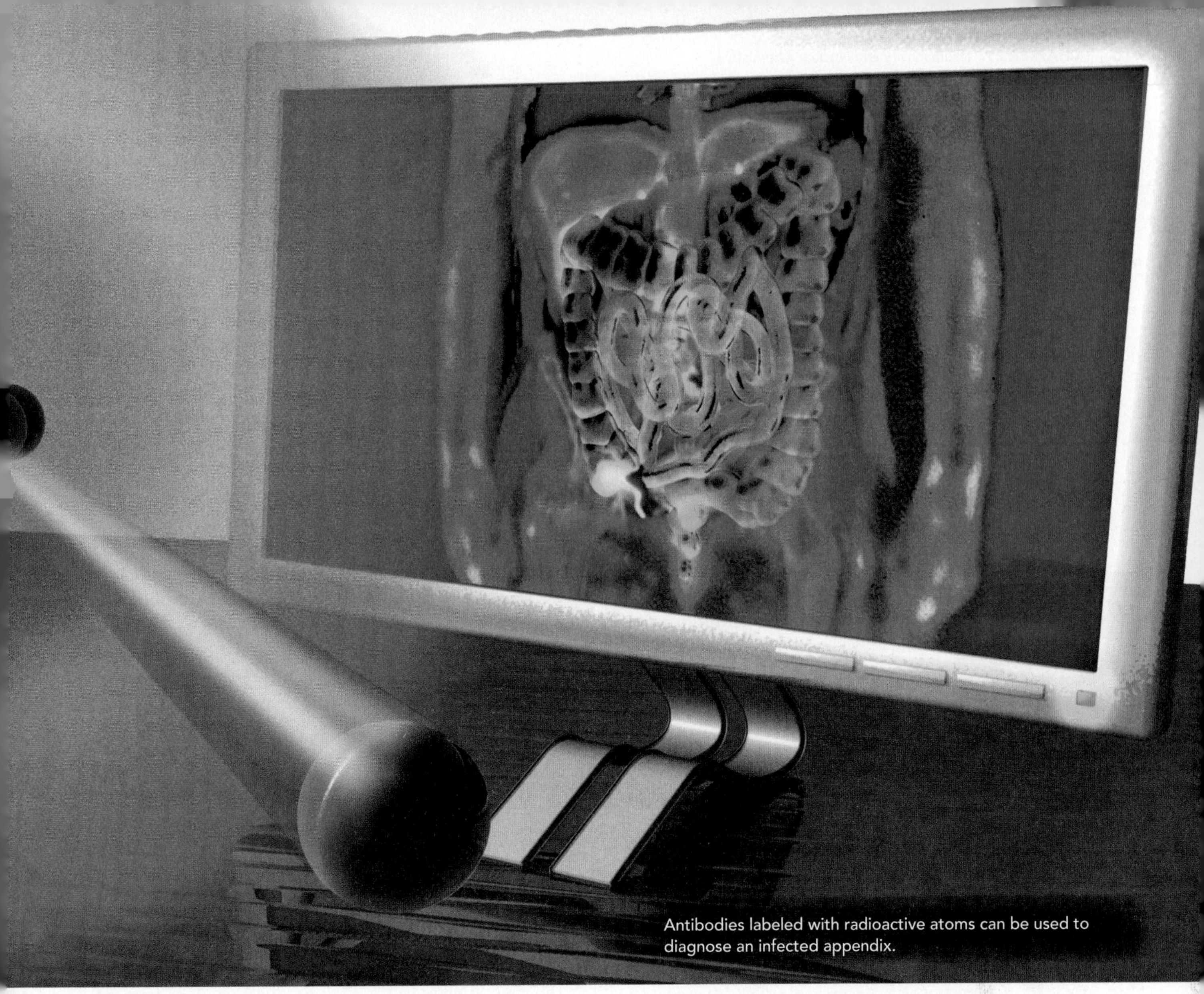

Antibodies labeled with radioactive atoms can be used to diagnose an infected appendix.

21.1 Diagnosing Appendicitis 947

21.2 The Discovery of Radioactivity 948

21.3 Types of Radioactivity 949

21.4 The Valley of Stability: Predicting the Type of Radioactivity 954

21.5 Detecting Radioactivity 957

21.6 The Kinetics of Radioactive Decay and Radiometric Dating 958

21.7 The Discovery of Fission: The Atomic Bomb and Nuclear Power 965

21.8 Converting Mass to Energy: Mass Defect and Nuclear Binding Energy 969

21.9 Nuclear Fusion: The Power of the Sun 971

21.10 Nuclear Transmutation and Transuranium Elements 972

21.11 The Effects of Radiation on Life 974

21.12 Radioactivity in Medicine and Other Applications 976

LEARNING OUTCOMES 981

21.1 Diagnosing Appendicitis

One morning a few years ago I awoke with a dull pain on the lower right side of my abdomen that was worse by early afternoon. Since pain in this area can indicate appendicitis (inflammation of the appendix), and since I know that appendicitis can be dangerous if left untreated, I went to the hospital emergency room. The doctor who examined me recommended a simple blood test to determine my white blood cell count. Patients with appendicitis usually have a high white blood cell count because the body is trying to fight the infection. In my case, the test was negative—I had a normal white blood cell count.

Although my symptoms were consistent with appendicitis, the negative blood test clouded the diagnosis. The doctor said that I could elect to have my appendix removed anyway (even though it might be healthy) or I could submit to another test that might confirm the appendicitis. I chose the additional test, which involved *nuclear medicine*, an area of medical practice that employs *radioactivity* to diagnose and treat disease. **Radioactivity** is the emission of subatomic particles or high-energy electromagnetic radiation by the nuclei of certain atoms. Such atoms are said to be **radioactive**. Most radioactive emissions can pass through many types of matter (such as skin and muscle, in this case).

During the test, antibodies—naturally occurring molecules that fight infection—were labeled with radioactive atoms and then injected into my bloodstream. Because antibodies attack infection, they migrate to areas of the body where infection is present. If my appendix was indeed infected, the antibodies would accumulate there. I waited about an hour, and then a technician took me to a room and laid me on a table. She inserted a photographic film in a panel above me and removed the covering that prevents exposure of the film. Radioactivity is invisible to the eye, but it exposes photographic film. If my appendix had been infected, it would have (by then) contained a high concentration of the radioactively labeled antibodies. The antibodies would emit radiation and expose the film. The test, however, was negative. No radioactivity was emanating from my appendix. After several hours, the pain in my abdomen subsided and I went home. I never did find out what caused the pain.

▲ The greenish light emitted from glow-in-the-dark toys is phosphorescence.

21.2 The Discovery of Radioactivity

Radioactivity was first observed in 1896 by a French scientist named Antoine-Henri Becquerel (1852–1908). Becquerel was interested in the newly discovered X-rays (see Chapter 8), which were a hot topic of physics research in his time. He hypothesized that X-rays were emitted in conjunction with **phosphorescence**, the long-lived *emission* of light that sometimes follows the absorption of light by certain atoms and molecules. Phosphorescence is probably most familiar to you as the *glow* in glow-in-the-dark products (such as toys or stickers). After such a product is exposed to light, it reemits some of that light, usually at slightly longer wavelengths. If you turn off the room lights or put the glow-in-the-dark product in the dark, you see the greenish glow of the emitted light. Becquerel hypothesized that this visible greenish glow was associated with the emission of X-rays (which are invisible).

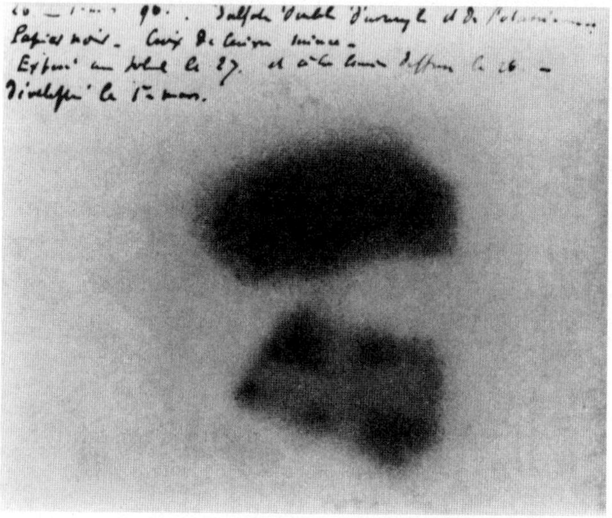

▲ **FIGURE 21.1 The Discovery of Radioactivity** This photographic plate (with Becquerel's original comments at top) played a key role in the discovery of radioactivity. Becquerel placed a uranium-containing compound on the plate (which was wrapped in black cloth to shield it from visible light). The plate was darkened by some unknown form of penetrating radiation that was produced continuously, independently of phosphorescence.

To test his hypothesis, Becquerel placed crystals—composed of potassium uranyl sulfate, a compound known to phosphoresce—on top of a photographic plate wrapped in black cloth. He then exposed the crystals to sunlight. He knew the crystals had phosphoresced because he could see the emitted light when he brought them back into the dark. If the crystals had also emitted X-rays, the X-rays would have passed through the black cloth and exposed the underlying photographic plate. Becquerel performed the experiment several times and always got the same result—the photographic plate showed a dark exposure spot where the crystals had been (Figure 21.1◀). Becquerel believed his hypothesis was correct and presented the results—that phosphorescence and X-rays were linked—to the French Academy of Sciences.

Becquerel later retracted his results, however, when he discovered that a photographic plate with the same crystals showed a dark exposure spot even when the plate and the crystals were stored in a drawer and not exposed to sunlight. Becquerel realized that the crystals themselves were constantly emitting something that exposed the photographic plate, regardless of whether or not they phosphoresced. Becquerel concluded that it was the uranium within the crystals that was the source of the emissions, and he named the emissions *uranic rays*.

Soon after Becquerel's discovery, a young graduate student named Marie Sklodowska Curie (1867–1934) (one of the first women in France to pursue doctoral work) decided to study uranic rays for her doctoral thesis. Her first task was to determine whether any other substances besides uranium (the heaviest known element at the time) emitted these rays. In her search, Curie discovered two new elements, both of which also emitted uranic rays. Curie named one of her newly discovered elements polonium, after her home country of Poland. The other element she named radium, because of its high level of radioactivity. Radium is so radioactive that it gently glows in the dark and emits significant amounts of heat. Since it was clear that these rays were not unique to uranium, Curie changed the name of uranic rays to radioactivity. In 1903, Curie and her husband, Pierre Curie, as well as Becquerel were all awarded the Nobel Prize in physics for the discovery of radioactivity. In 1911, Curie received a second Nobel Prize, this time in chemistry, for her discovery of the two new elements.

▲ Marie Curie, one of the first women in France to pursue a doctoral degree, was twice awarded the Nobel Prize, in 1903 and 1911. She is seen here with her daughters, in about 1905. Irène (right) became a distinguished nuclear physicist in her own right, winning a Nobel Prize in 1935. Eve (left) wrote a highly acclaimed biography of her mother.

21.3 Types of Radioactivity

While Curie focused her work on discovering the different kinds of radioactive elements, Ernest Rutherford and others focused on characterizing the radioactivity itself. These scientists found that the emissions are produced by the nuclei of radioactive atoms. Such nuclei are unstable and spontaneously decompose, emitting small pieces of themselves to gain stability. These fragments are the radioactivity that Becquerel and Curie detected. Natural radioactivity can be categorized into several different types, including *alpha* (α) *decay*, *beta* (β) *decay*, *gamma* (γ) *ray emission*, and *positron emission*. In addition, some unstable atomic nuclei can attain greater stability by absorbing electrons from one of the atoms' own orbitals, a process called *electron capture*.

WATCH NOW!

KEY CONCEPT VIDEO 21.3
Types of Radioactivity

Element 96 is named curium in honor of Marie Curie and her contributions to our understanding of radioactivity.

In order to understand these different types of radioactivity, we must briefly review the notation for symbolizing isotopes from Section 2.6. Recall that we can represent any isotope with the following notation:

Mass number → $^{A}_{Z}X$ ← Chemical symbol
Atomic number ↗

Mass number (A) = the sum of the number of protons and number of neutrons in the nucleus

Atomic number (Z) = the number of protons in the nucleus

Since A represents the sum of the number of protons and neutrons, and since Z represents the number of protons, the number of neutrons in the nucleus (N) is $A - Z$.

$$N = A - Z$$

↑ Number of neutrons

▲ Radium, discovered by Marie Curie, is so radioactive that it glows visibly and emits heat.

For example, the symbol $^{21}_{10}\text{Ne}$ represents the neon isotope containing 10 protons and 11 neutrons. The symbol $^{20}_{10}\text{Ne}$ represents the neon isotope containing 10 protons and 10 neutrons. Remember that most elements have several different isotopes. When we are discussing nuclear properties, we often refer to a particular isotope (or species) of an element as a **nuclide**.

We represent the main subatomic particles—protons, neutrons, and electrons—with similar notation.

Proton symbol $^{1}_{1}\text{p}$ — The 1 in the lower left corner of the proton symbol represents 1 proton.

Neutron symbol $^{1}_{0}\text{n}$ — The 0 in the lower left corner of the neutron symbol represents 0 protons.

Electron symbol $^{0}_{-1}\text{e}$ — The −1 in the lower left corner of the electron symbol is a bit different from the other atomic numbers, but it will make sense to you when we see it in the context of nuclear decay a bit later in this section.

ANSWER NOW!

21.1 Cc Conceptual Connection

SYMBOLIZING ISOTOPES How many protons and neutrons are there in the isotope $^{27}_{13}\text{Al}$?

(a) 27 neutrons; 13 protons
(b) 13 neutrons; 27 protons
(c) 13 neutrons; 14 protons
(d) 14 neutrons; 13 protons

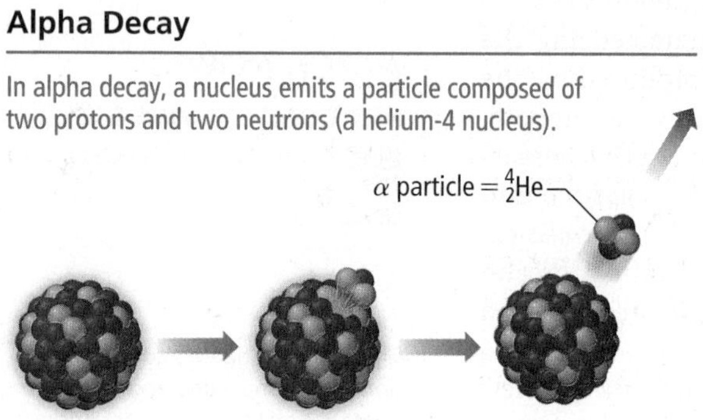

▲ **FIGURE 21.2 Alpha Decay**

Alpha (α) Decay

Alpha (α) decay occurs when an unstable nucleus emits a particle composed of two protons and two neutrons (Figure 21.2◄). Since two protons and two neutrons combined are identical to a helium-4 nucleus, the symbol for alpha radiation is the symbol for helium-4:

Alpha (α) particle $^{4}_{2}\text{He}$ 

When an element emits an alpha particle, the number of protons in its nucleus changes, transforming the element into a different element. We symbolize this phenomenon with a **nuclear equation**, an equation that represents nuclear processes such as radioactivity. For example, the nuclear equation for the alpha decay of uranium-238 is:

Parent nuclide → $^{238}_{92}\text{U}$; Daughter nuclide → $^{234}_{90}\text{Th}$

$$^{238}_{92}\text{U} \longrightarrow \, ^{234}_{90}\text{Th} + \, ^{4}_{2}\text{He}$$

As we discuss in Section 21.4, nuclei are unstable when they are too large or when they contain an unbalanced ratio of neutrons to protons.

The original atom is the *parent nuclide*, and the product of the decay is the *daughter nuclide*. In this case, uranium-238 (the parent nuclide) becomes thorium-234 (the daughter nuclide). Unlike a chemical reaction, in which elements retain their identities, in a nuclear reaction elements often change their identities. Like a chemical equation, however, a nuclear equation must be balanced. *The sum of the atomic numbers on both sides of a nuclear equation must be equal, and the sum of the mass numbers on both sides must also be equal:*

In nuclear chemistry, we are primarily interested in changes within the nucleus; therefore, the 2+ charge that we would normally write for a helium nucleus is omitted for an alpha particle.

$$^{238}_{92}\text{U} \longrightarrow \, ^{234}_{90}\text{Th} + \, ^{4}_{2}\text{He}$$

Reactants	Products
Sum of mass numbers = 238	Sum of mass numbers = 234 + 4 = 238
Sum of atomic numbers = 92	Sum of atomic numbers = 90 + 2 = 92

We can deduce the identity and symbol of the daughter nuclide in any alpha decay from the mass and atomic number of the parent nuclide. During alpha decay, the mass number decreases by 4 and the atomic number decreases by 2, as shown in Example 21.1.

WATCH **NOW!**

INTERACTIVE WORKED EXAMPLE 21.1

EXAMPLE 21.1 Writing Nuclear Equations for Alpha Decay

Write the nuclear equation for the alpha decay of Ra-224.

SOLUTION

Begin with the symbol for Ra-224 on the left side of the equation and the symbol for an alpha particle on the right side.	${}^{224}_{88}\mathrm{Ra} \longrightarrow {}^{?}_{?}? + {}^{4}_{2}\mathrm{He}$
Equalize the sum of the mass numbers and the sum of the atomic numbers on both sides of the equation by writing the appropriate mass number and atomic number for the unknown daughter nuclide.	${}^{224}_{88}\mathrm{Ra} \longrightarrow {}^{220}_{86}? + {}^{4}_{2}\mathrm{He}$
Refer to the periodic table to determine the identity of the unknown daughter nuclide from its atomic number and write its symbol. Since the atomic number is 86, the daughter nuclide is radon (Rn).	${}^{224}_{88}\mathrm{Ra} \longrightarrow {}^{220}_{86}\mathrm{Rn} + {}^{4}_{2}\mathrm{He}$

FOR PRACTICE 21.1 Write the nuclear equation for the alpha decay of Po-216.

Alpha radiation is the 18-wheeler truck of radioactivity. The alpha particle is by far the most massive of all particles commonly emitted by radioactive nuclei. Consequently, alpha radiation has the most potential to interact with and damage other molecules, including biological ones. Highly energetic radiation interacts with other molecules and atoms by ionizing them. When radiation ionizes molecules within the cells of living organisms, the cells can usually repair the damage. However, in some cases the cells can die or begin to reproduce abnormally. The ability of radiation to ionize other molecules and atoms is called its **ionizing power**. Of all types of radioactivity, alpha radiation has the highest ionizing power.

However, alpha particles, because of their large size, have the lowest **penetrating power**—the ability to penetrate matter. (Imagine a semi trying to get through a traffic jam.) In order for radiation to damage important molecules within living cells, it must penetrate into the cell. Alpha radiation does not easily penetrate into cells because it can be stopped by a sheet of paper, by clothing, or even by air. Consequently, a low-level alpha emitter that remains outside the body is relatively safe. However, consuming large amounts of an alpha emitter can be dangerous because the alpha particles then have direct access to the molecules that compose organs and tissues.

Beta (β) Decay

Beta (β) decay occurs when an unstable nucleus emits an electron (Figure 21.3►). How does a nucleus, which contains only protons and neutrons, emit an electron? In some unstable nuclei, a neutron changes into a proton and emits an electron:

Beta decay Neutron $\longrightarrow$ proton + emitted electron

The symbol for a beta (β) particle in a nuclear equation is:

Beta (β) particle ${}^{0}_{-1}\mathrm{e}$

We represent beta decay with this nuclear equation:

$${}^{1}_{0}\mathrm{n} \longrightarrow {}^{1}_{1}\mathrm{p} + {}^{0}_{-1}\mathrm{e}$$

The −1 reflects the charge of the electron, which is equivalent to an atomic number of −1 in a nuclear equation. When an atom emits a beta particle, its atomic number increases by 1 because it then has an additional proton. For example, the nuclear equation for the beta decay of radium-228 is:

$${}^{228}_{88}\mathrm{Ra} \longrightarrow {}^{228}_{89}\mathrm{Ac} + {}^{0}_{-1}\mathrm{e}$$

Notice that the nuclear equation is balanced—the sum of the mass numbers on both sides is equal, and the sum of the atomic numbers on both sides is equal.

Beta Decay

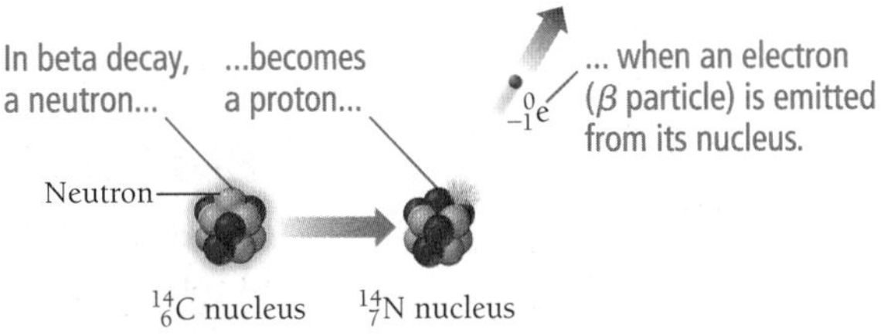

▲ **FIGURE 21.3 Beta Decay**

This kind of beta radiation is also called beta minus (β^-) radiation due to its negative charge.

Beta radiation is the sport utility vehicle (SUV) of radioactivity. Beta particles are much less massive than alpha particles and consequently have a lower ionizing power. However, because of their smaller size, beta particles have a higher penetrating power and only something as substantive as a sheet of metal or a thick piece of wood stops them. Consequently, a beta emitter outside of the body poses a higher risk than an alpha emitter. If ingested, however, the beta emitter does less damage than an alpha emitter.

Gamma (γ) Ray Emission

See Section 8.2 for a review of electromagnetic radiation.

Gamma (γ) ray emission is significantly different from alpha or beta radiation. Gamma radiation is a form of *electromagnetic* radiation (see Section 8.2). Gamma rays are high-energy (short-wavelength) photons. The symbol for a gamma ray is:

Gamma (γ) ray $\quad {}^{0}_{0}\gamma$

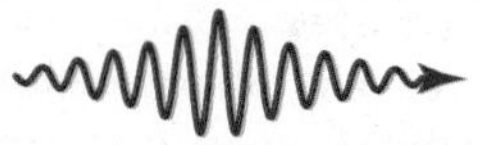

A gamma ray has no charge and no mass. When a gamma-ray photon is emitted from a radioactive atom, it does not change the mass number or the atomic number of the element. Gamma rays are usually emitted from nuclei in excited states or in conjunction with other types of radiation. For example, the alpha emission of U-238 (discussed previously) is also accompanied by the emission of a gamma ray:

$$^{238}_{92}\text{U} \longrightarrow {}^{234}_{90}\text{Th} + {}^{4}_{2}\text{He} + {}^{0}_{0}\gamma$$

The emission of gamma rays in conjunction with other types of radiation is so common that it is often left out of nuclear equations. Nuclear chemists simply understand that the gamma rays are emitted along with the other types of decay. However, in some instances, there can be a delay between the initial decay and the subsequent emission of gamma ray. The initial decay leaves the daughter nucleus in *metastable* state (an unstable state that can exist for a prolonged period of time). The daughter then emits a gamma particle at a later time. For example, technetium-99 has a gamma-emitting metastable state:

$$^{99\text{m}}_{43}\text{Tc} \longrightarrow {}^{99}_{43}\text{Tc} + {}^{0}_{0}\gamma$$

The m next to the mass number stands for metastable.

Gamma rays are the motorcycles of radioactivity. They have the lowest ionizing power but the highest penetrating power. (Imagine a motorcycle zipping through a traffic jam.) Shielding gamma rays requires several inches of lead or thick slabs of concrete.

ANSWER NOW!

21.2 Cc Conceptual Connection

PENETRATING POWER If the room next door contains an alpha emitter, a beta emitter, and a gamma emitter, all with similar activities, which particles are you most likely to detect in the room you are in?

(a) alpha particles **(b)** beta particles **(c)** gamma particles

Positron Emission

Positron emission occurs when an unstable nucleus emits a positron (Figure 21.4◀). A **positron** is the *antiparticle* of the electron; it has the same mass as an electron but the opposite charge. If a positron collides with an electron, the two particles annihilate each other, releasing energy in the form of gamma rays. In positron emission, a proton is converted into a neutron and emits a positron:

Positron emission $\quad$ Proton $\longrightarrow$ neutron + emitted positron

The symbol for a positron in a nuclear equation is:

Positron $\quad {}^{0}_{+1}\text{e}$

We represent positron emission with this nuclear equation:

$$^{1}_{1}\text{p} \longrightarrow {}^{1}_{0}\text{n} + {}^{0}_{+1}\text{e}$$

Positron Emission

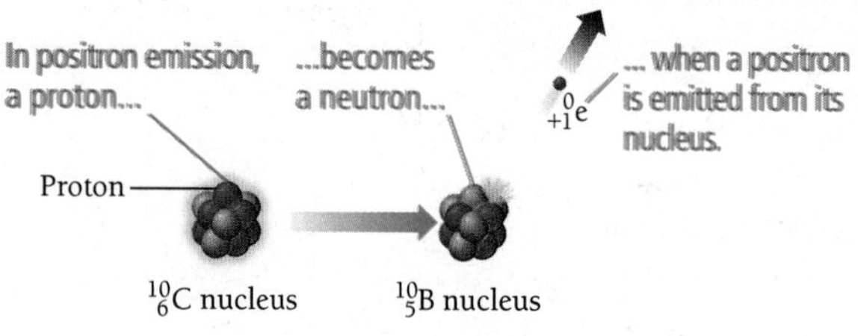

▲ **FIGURE 21.4 Positron Emission**

When an atom emits a positron, its atomic number *decreases* by 1 because it has one less proton after emission. Consider the nuclear equation for the positron emission of phosphorus-30 as an example:

$$^{30}_{15}\text{P} \longrightarrow {}^{30}_{14}\text{Si} + {}^{0}_{+1}\text{e}$$

Positron emission can be thought of as a type of beta emission and is sometimes referred to as beta plus emission (β^+).

We can determine the identity and symbol of the daughter nuclide in any positron emission in a manner similar to that used for alpha and beta decay, as shown in Example 21.2. Positrons are similar to beta particles in their ionizing and penetrating power.

Electron Capture

Unlike the forms of radioactive decay that we have discussed so far, electron capture involves a particle being *absorbed by* rather than *emitted from* an unstable nucleus. **Electron capture** occurs when a nucleus assimilates an electron from an inner orbital of its electron cloud. Like positron emission, the net effect of electron capture is the conversion of a proton into a neutron:

Electron capture Proton + electron ⟶ neutron

We represent electron capture with this nuclear equation:

$$^{1}_{1}\text{p} + {}^{0}_{-1}\text{e} \longrightarrow {}^{1}_{0}\text{n}$$

When an atom undergoes electron capture, its atomic number decreases by 1 because it has one less proton. For example, when Ru-92 undergoes electron capture, its atomic number changes from 44 to 43:

$$^{92}_{44}\text{Ru} + {}^{0}_{-1}\text{e} \longrightarrow {}^{92}_{43}\text{Tc}$$

Table 21.1 summarizes the different kinds of radiation.

WATCH **NOW!**

INTERACTIVE WORKED EXAMPLE 21.2

EXAMPLE 21.2 Writing Nuclear Equations for Beta Decay, Positron Emission, and Electron Capture

Write the nuclear equation for each type of decay.

(a) beta decay in Bk-249 **(b)** positron emission in O-15 **(c)** electron capture in I-111

SOLUTION

(a) In beta decay, the atomic number *increases* by 1 and the mass number remains unchanged. The daughter nuclide is element number 98, californium.	$^{249}_{97}\text{Bk} \longrightarrow {}^{249}_{98}? + {}^{0}_{-1}\text{e}$ $^{249}_{97}\text{Bk} \longrightarrow {}^{249}_{98}\text{Cf} + {}^{0}_{-1}\text{e}$
(b) In positron emission, the atomic number *decreases* by 1 and the mass number remains unchanged. The daughter nuclide is element number 7, nitrogen.	$^{15}_{8}\text{O} \longrightarrow {}^{15}_{7}? + {}^{0}_{+1}\text{e}$ $^{15}_{8}\text{O} \longrightarrow {}^{15}_{7}\text{N} + {}^{0}_{+1}\text{e}$
(c) In electron capture, the atomic number also *decreases* by 1 and the mass number remains unchanged. The daughter nuclide is element number 52, tellurium.	$^{111}_{53}\text{I} + {}^{0}_{-1}\text{e} \longrightarrow {}^{111}_{52}?$ $^{111}_{53}\text{I} + {}^{0}_{-1}\text{e} \longrightarrow {}^{111}_{52}\text{Te}$

FOR PRACTICE 21.2

(a) Write three nuclear equations to represent the nuclear decay sequence that begins with the alpha decay of U-235 followed by a beta decay of the daughter nuclide and then another alpha decay.

(b) Write the nuclear equation for the positron emission of Na-22.

(c) Write the nuclear equation for electron capture in Kr-76.

FOR MORE PRACTICE 21.2 Potassium-40 can decay to produce Ar-40. What is the method of decay? Write the nuclear equation for this decay.

TABLE 21.1 ■ Modes of Radioactive Decay

Decay Mode	Process	Change in: *A*	*Z*	*N/Z**	Example
α	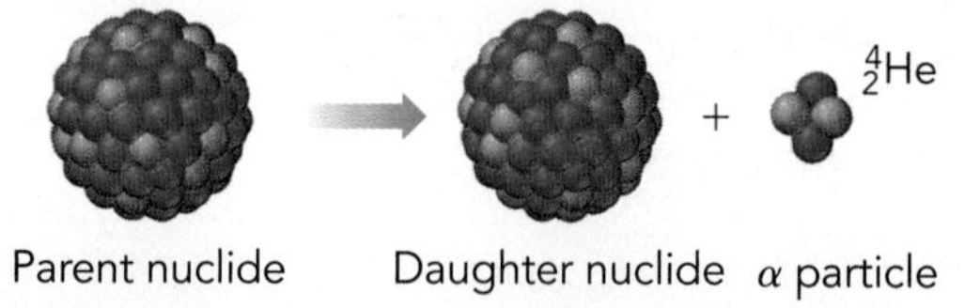	−4	−2	Increase	$^{238}_{92}U \longrightarrow ^{234}_{90}Th + ^{4}_{2}He$
β	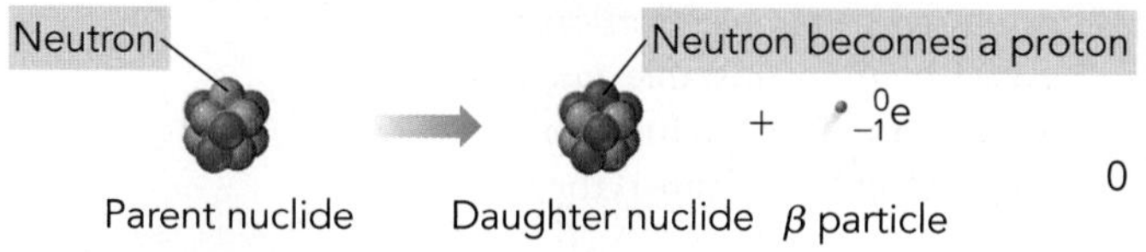	0	+1	Decrease	$^{228}_{88}Ra \longrightarrow ^{228}_{89}Ac + ^{0}_{-1}e$
γ	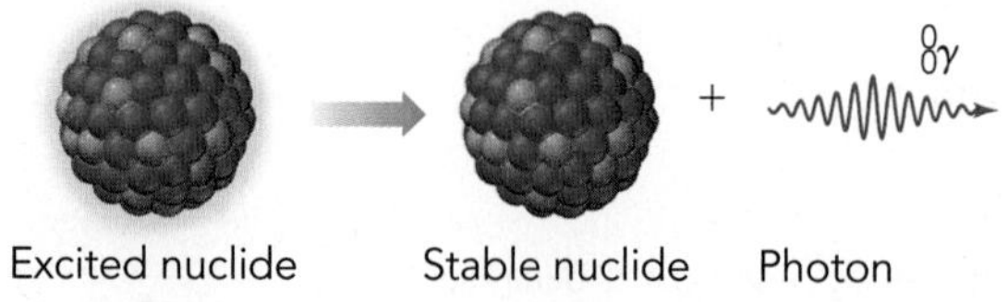	0	0	None	$^{99m}_{43}Tc \longrightarrow ^{99}_{43}Tc + ^{0}_{0}\gamma$
Positron emission	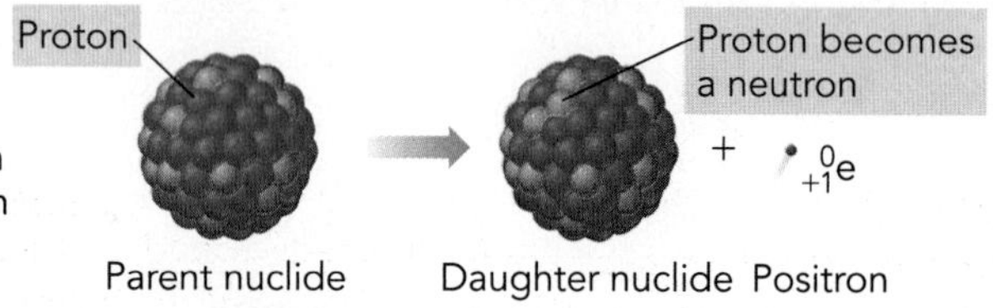	0	−1	Increase	$^{30}_{15}P \longrightarrow ^{30}_{14}Si + ^{0}_{+1}e$
Electron capture	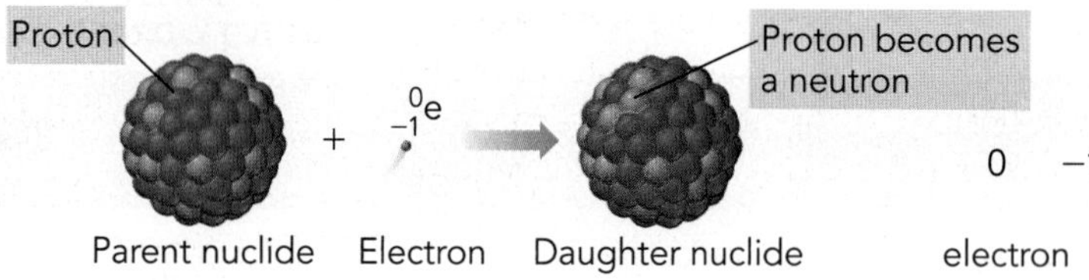	0	−1	Increase	$^{92}_{44}Ru + ^{0}_{-1}e \longrightarrow ^{92}_{43}Tc$

* Neutron-to-proton ratio

ANSWER **NOW!**

21.3 Cc Conceptual Connection

ALPHA AND BETA DECAY Consider the graphical representation of a series of decays shown here.

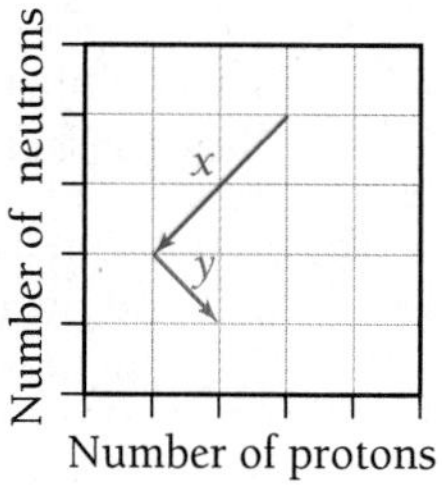

The arrow labeled *x* and the arrow labeled *y* each correspond to what kind of decay?

(a) *x* corresponds to alpha decay and *y* corresponds to positron emission.
(b) *x* corresponds to positron emission and *y* corresponds to alpha decay.
(c) *x* corresponds to alpha decay and *y* corresponds to beta decay.
(d) *x* corresponds to beta decay and *y* corresponds to alpha decay.

21.4 The Valley of Stability: Predicting the Type of Radioactivity

So far, we have described various different types of radioactivity. But we have not discussed what causes a particular nuclide to be radioactive in the first place. And why do some nuclides decay via alpha decay, while others decay via beta decay or positron emission? The answers to these questions are not simple, but we can get a basic idea of the factors that influence the stability of the nucleus and the nature of its decay.

A nucleus is a collection of protons (positively charged) and neutrons (uncharged). We know that positively charged particles such as protons repel one another. So what binds the nucleus together? A fundamental force of physics known as the **strong force** binds the nucleus together. All **nucleons**—protons and neutrons—are attracted to one another by the strong force. However, the strong force acts only at very short distances. We can think of the stability of a nucleus as a balance between the *repulsive* coloumbic force among protons and the *attractive* strong force among all nucleons. The neutrons in a nucleus, therefore, play an important role in stabilizing the nucleus because they attract other nucleons (through the strong force) but lack the repulsive force associated with positive charge.

It might seem that adding more neutrons would *always* lead to greater stability, so that the more neutrons the better. This is not the case, however, because protons and neutrons occupy energy levels in a nucleus that are similar to those occupied by electrons in an atom. As you add more neutrons, the neutrons must occupy increasingly higher-energy levels within the nucleus. At some point, the energy payback from the strong force is not enough to compensate for the high-energy state that the neutrons must occupy.

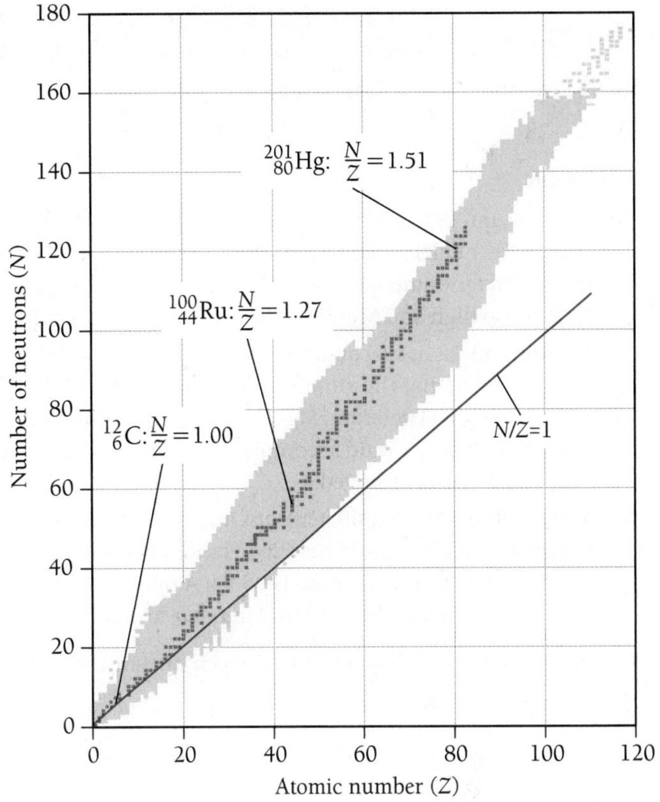

▲ **FIGURE 21.5 Stable and Unstable Nuclei** A plot of *N* (the number of neutrons) versus *Z* (the number of protons) for all known nuclei. The green dots represent stable nuclei, and the yellow dots represent unstable nuclei. A nucleus with an *N*/*Z* ratio that is too high tends to undergo beta decay. A nucleus with an *N*/*Z* ratio that is too low tends to undergo positron emission or electron capture.

An important number in determining nuclear stability is the *ratio* of neutrons to protons (N/Z). Figure 21.5▶ is a plot of the number of neutrons versus the number of protons for all known nuclei. The yellow dots represent unstable nuclei, and the green dots represent stable ones. The region of the graph with the green dots (stable nuclei) is known as the *valley* (or *island*) *of stability*. Notice that for the lighter elements, the N/Z ratio of stable nuclei is about 1 (equal numbers of neutrons and protons). For example, the most abundant isotope of carbon ($Z = 6$) is carbon-12, which contains six protons and six neutrons. However, beyond about $Z = 20$, the N/Z ratio of stable nuclei begins to get larger. For example, at $Z = 44$ stable nuclei have N/Z ratios of about 1.275 and at $Z = 80$, the N/Z ratio reaches about 1.5. Above $Z = 83$, stable nuclei do not exist—bismuth ($Z = 83$) is the heaviest element with stable (nonradioactive) isotopes.

The type of radioactivity emitted by a nuclide depends in part on the N/Z ratio.

N/Z too high: Nuclides that lie above the valley of stability have too many neutrons and tend to convert neutrons to protons via beta decay. The process of undergoing beta decay moves the nuclide down in the plot in Figure 21.5 and closer to (or into) the valley of stability.

N/Z too low: Nuclides that lie below the valley of stability have too many protons and tend to convert protons to neutrons via positron emission or electron capture. This moves the nuclide up in the plot in Figure 21.5 and closer to (or into) the valley of stability.

One way to decide whether a particular nuclide has an N/Z that is too high, too low, or about right is to consult Figure 21.5. Those nuclides that lie within the valley of stability are stable. Alternatively, we can also compare the mass number of the nuclide to the atomic mass listed in the periodic table for the corresponding element. The atomic mass is an average of the masses of the most stable nuclides for an element and thus represents an N/Z that is about right. For example, suppose we want to evaluate N/Z for Ru-112. Ruthenium has an atomic mass of 101.07, so we know that the nuclide with a mass number of 112 contains too many neutrons and therefore has an N/Z that is too high. The following example demonstrates how to apply these considerations in predicting the mode of decay for a nucleus.

EXAMPLE 21.3 Predicting the Type of Radioactive Decay

Predict whether each nuclide is more likely to decay via beta decay or positron emission.

(a) Mg-28 **(b)** Mg-22 **(c)** Mo-102

SOLUTION

(a) Magnesium-28 has 16 neutrons and 12 protons, so $N/Z = 1.33$. However, for $Z = 12$, you can see from Figure 21.5 that stable nuclei should have an N/Z of about 1. Alternatively, you can see from the periodic table that the atomic mass of magnesium is 24.31. Therefore, a nuclide with a mass number of 28 is too heavy to be stable because the N/Z ratio is too high and Mg-28 undergoes *beta decay*, resulting in the conversion of a neutron to a proton.

(b) Magnesium-22 has 10 neutrons and 12 protons, so $N/Z = 0.83$ (too low). Alternatively, you can see from the periodic table that the atomic mass of magnesium is 24.31. A nuclide with a mass number of 22 is too light; the N/Z ratio is too low. Therefore, Mg-22 undergoes *positron emission*, resulting in the conversion of a proton to a neutron. (Electron capture would accomplish the same thing as positron emission, but in Mg-22, positron emission is the only decay mode observed.)

(c) Molybdenum-102 has 60 neutrons and 42 protons, so $N/Z = 1.43$. However, for $Z = 42$, you can see from Figure 21.5 that stable nuclei should have N/Z ratios of about 1.3. Alternatively, you can see from the periodic table that the atomic mass of molybdenum is 95.94. A nuclide with a mass number of 102 is too heavy to be stable; the N/Z ratio is too high. Therefore, Mo-102 undergoes *beta decay*, resulting in the conversion of a neutron to a proton.

FOR PRACTICE 21.3 Predict whether each nuclide is more likely to decay via beta decay or positron emission.

(a) Pb-192 **(b)** Pb-212 **(c)** Xe-114

Magic Numbers

TABLE 21.2 ■ Number of Stable Nuclides with Even and Odd Numbers of Nucleons

Z	N	Number of Nuclides
Even	Even	157
Even	Odd	53
Odd	Even	50
Odd	Odd	5

In addition to the N/Z ratio, the *actual number* of protons and neutrons also affects the stability of the nucleus. Table 21.2 shows the number of nuclei with different possible combinations of even or odd nucleons. Notice that a large number of stable nuclides have both an even number of protons and an even number of neutrons. Only five stable nuclides have an odd and odd combination.

The reason for this is that nucleons occupy energy levels within the nucleus much as electrons occupy energy levels within an atom. Just as atoms with certain numbers of electrons are uniquely stable (in particular, the number of electrons associated with the noble gases: 2, 10, 18, 36, 54, etc.), so atoms with certain numbers of nucleons (N or $Z = 2, 8, 20, 28, 50, 82$, and $N = 126$) are uniquely stable. These numbers are referred to as **magic numbers**. Nuclei containing a magic number of protons or neutrons are particularly stable. Since the magic numbers are even, this accounts in part for the abundance of stable nuclides with even numbers of nucleons. Moreover, nucleons also have a tendency to pair (much as electrons pair). This tendency and the resulting stability of paired nucleons also contribute to the abundance of stable nuclides with even numbers of nucleons.

Radioactive Decay Series

Atoms with $Z > 83$ are radioactive and decay in one or more steps involving primarily alpha and beta decay (with some gamma decay to carry away excess energy). For example, uranium (atomic number 92) is the heaviest naturally occurring element. Its most common isotope is U-238, an alpha emitter that decays to Th-234:

$$^{238}_{92}\text{U} \longrightarrow {}^{234}_{90}\text{Th} + {}^{4}_{2}\text{He}$$

The daughter nuclide, Th-234, is itself radioactive—it is a beta emitter that decays to Pa-234:

$$^{234}_{90}\text{Th} \longrightarrow {}^{234}_{91}\text{Pa} + {}^{0}_{-1}\text{e}$$

Protactinium-234 is also radioactive, decaying to U-234 via beta emission. Radioactive decay continues until a stable nuclide, Pb-206, is reached. Figure 21.6▶ illustrates the entire uranium-238 decay series.

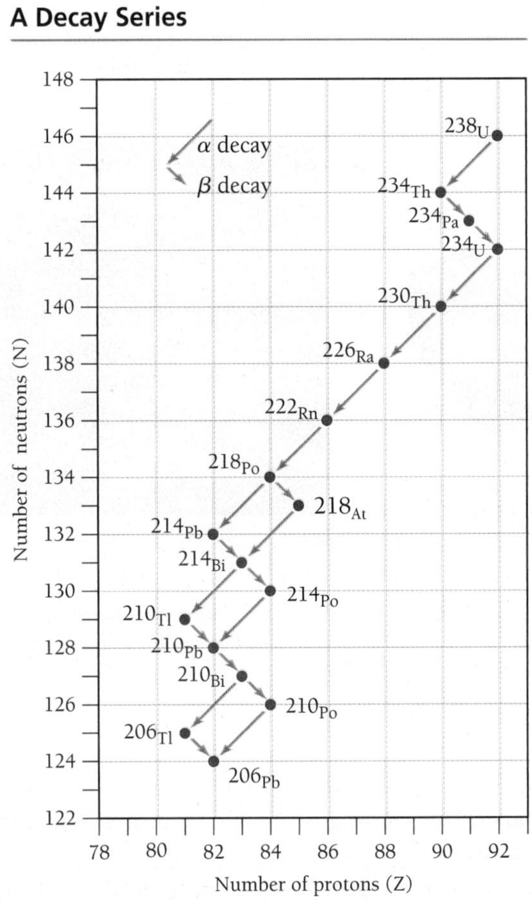

◀ **FIGURE 21.6 The Uranium-238 Radioactive Decay Series** Uranium-238 decays via a series of steps ending in Pb-206, a stable element. Each diagonal line to the left represents an alpha decay, and each diagonal line to the right represents a beta decay.

PREDICTING TYPE OF RADIOACTIVE DECAY A nuclide has a mass number of 116. The atomic mass of the element listed in the periodic table is 102.9. Will the element undergo beta decay or positron emission?

(a) beta decay
(b) positron emission

21.4 Cc Conceptual Connection

ANSWER NOW!

21.5 Detecting Radioactivity

The particles emitted by radioactive nuclei are very energetic and therefore can be readily detected. In a radiation detector, the particles are detected through their interactions with atoms or molecules. The most common radiation detectors are **thermoluminescent dosimeters** (Figure 21.7▶), which are issued to people working with or near radioactive substances. These dosimeters contain crystals of salts such as calcium fluoride that are excited by the ionizing radiation. The excited electrons are trapped by impurities that are intentionally introduced into the crystals. When the crystals are heated, the electrons relax to their ground state, emitting light. The amount of light emitted is proportional to the radiation exposure. These dosimeters are collected and processed regularly as a way to monitor a person's exposure. We discuss the effects and measurement of exposure in more detail in Section 21.11.

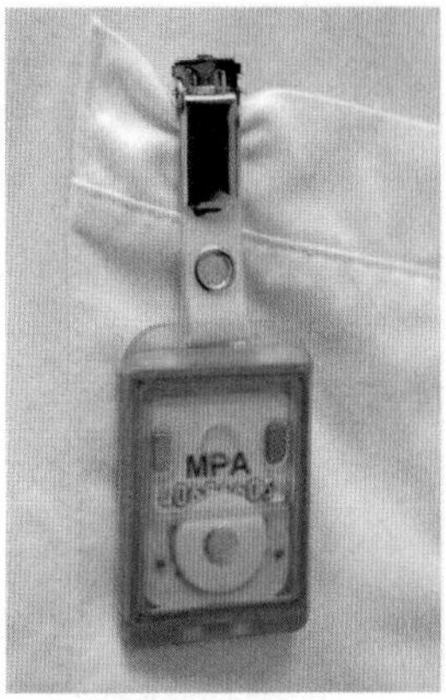

▲ **FIGURE 21.7 Thermoluminescent Dosimeter** A thermoluminescent dosimeter contains crystals that when heated emit light in proportion to radiation exposure.

Radioactivity can be instantly detected with devices such as a **Geiger-Müller counter** (Figure 21.8▶, on the next page). In this instrument (commonly referred to as a Geiger counter), particles emitted by radioactive nuclei pass through an argon-filled chamber. The energetic particles create a trail of ionized argon atoms. High voltage applied between a wire within the chamber and the chamber walls causes these newly formed ions to produce an electrical signal that can be displayed on a meter or turned

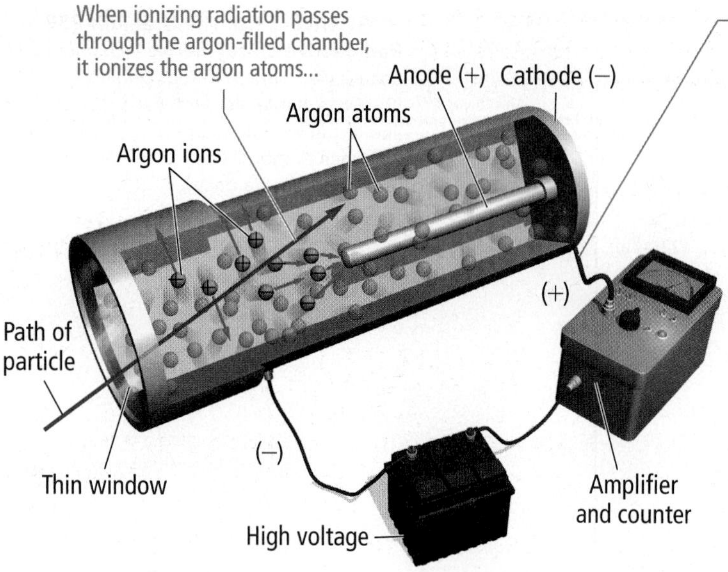

▲ **FIGURE 21.8 Geiger–Müller Counter** When ionizing radiation passes through the argon-filled chamber, it ionizes the argon atoms, giving rise to a brief, tiny pulse of electrical current that is transduced onto a meter or into an audible click.

into an audible click. Each click corresponds to a radioactive particle passing through the argon gas chamber. This clicking is the stereotypical sound most people associate with a radiation detector.

A second type of device commonly used to detect radiation instantly is a **scintillation counter**. In a scintillation counter, radioactive emissions pass through a material (such as NaI or CsI) that emits ultraviolet or visible light in response to excitation by high-energy photons. The photons excite the atoms to a higher-energy state. The atoms release this energy as light, which is detected and turned into an electrical signal that is read on a meter.

21.6 The Kinetics of Radioactive Decay and Radiometric Dating

Radioactivity is a natural component of our environment. The ground beneath you most likely contains radioactive atoms that emit radiation. The food you eat contains a residual quantity of radioactive atoms that are absorbed into your body fluids and incorporated into tissues. Small amounts of radiation from space make it through our atmosphere to constantly bombard Earth. Humans and other living organisms have evolved in this environment and have adapted to survive in it.

One reason for the radioactivity in our environment is the instability of all atomic nuclei beyond atomic number 83 (bismuth). Every element with more than 83 protons in its nucleus is unstable and therefore radioactive. In addition, some isotopes of elements with fewer than 83 protons are also unstable and radioactive. Radioactive nuclides *persist* in our environment because new radioactive nuclides are constantly being formed and because many of the existing ones decay away only very slowly.

You may find it useful to review the discussion of first-order kinetics in Section 15.3.

All radioactive nuclei decay via first-order kinetics, so the rate of decay in a particular sample is directly proportional to the number of nuclei present as indicated in the equation:

$$\text{Rate} = kN$$

where N is the number of radioactive nuclei and k is the rate constant. Different radioactive nuclides decay into their daughter nuclides with different rate constants. Some nuclides decay quickly (large rate constant), while others decay slowly (small rate constant).

The time it takes for one-half of the parent nuclides in a radioactive sample to decay to the daughter nuclides is the *half-life* and is identical to the concept of half-life for chemical reactions that we discussed in Chapter 15. Thus, the relationship between the half-life of a nuclide and its rate constant is given by the same expression (Equation 15.19) that we derived for a first-order reaction in Section 15.4:

$$t_{1/2} = \frac{0.693}{k} \qquad [21.1]$$

Nuclides that decay quickly have short half-lives and large rate constants—they are considered very active (many decay events per unit time). Nuclides that decay slowly have long half-lives and are less active (fewer decay events per unit time). For example, thorium-232 is an alpha emitter with a half-life of 1.4×10^{10} years, or 14 billion years. A sample of Th-232 containing 1 million atoms decays to $^1/_2$ million atoms in 14 billion years and then to $^1/_4$ million in another 14 billion years and so on. Notice that a radioactive sample does *not* decay to *zero* atoms in two half-lives—we can't add two half-lives together to get a "whole" life. The amount that remains after one half-life is always one-half of what was present at the start. The amount that remains after two half-lives is one-quarter of what was present at the start, and so on.

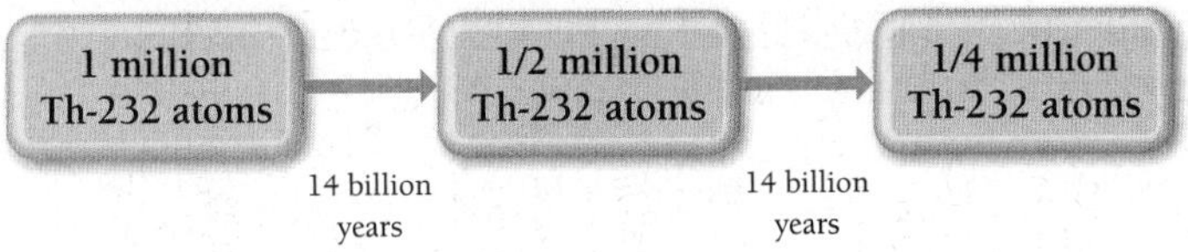

Some nuclides have very short half-lives. For example, radon-220 has a half-life of approximately 1 minute (Figure 21.9▼). A 1-million-atom sample of radon-220 decays to $^1/_4$ million radon-220 atoms in just two minutes and to approximately 1000 atoms in 10 minutes. Table 21.3 lists several nuclides and their half-lives.

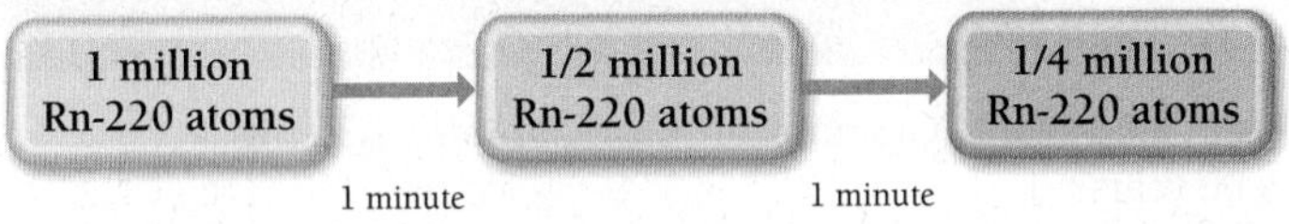

TABLE 21.3 ■ Selected Nuclides and Their Half-Lives

Nuclide	Half-Life	Type of Decay
$^{232}_{90}Th$	1.4×10^{10} yr	Alpha
$^{238}_{92}U$	4.5×10^{9} yr	Alpha
$^{14}_{6}C$	5715 yr	Beta
$^{220}_{86}Rn$	55.6 s	Alpha
$^{219}_{90}Th$	1.05×10^{-6} s	Alpha

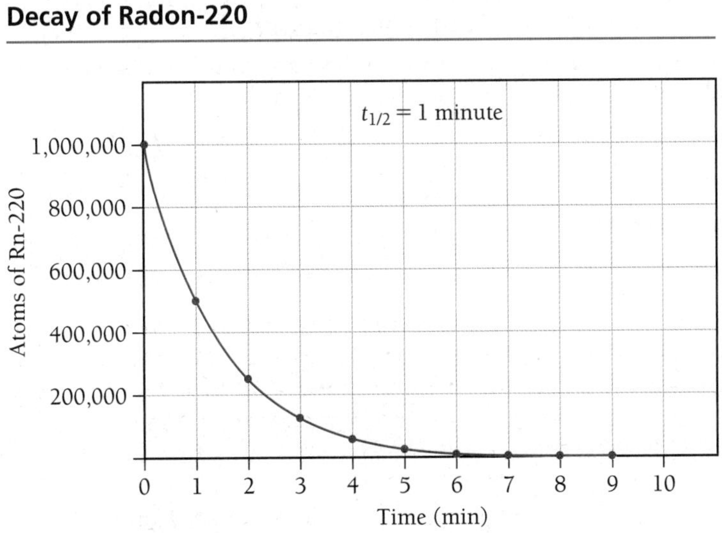

▲ **FIGURE 21.9 The Decay of Radon-220** Radon-220 decays with a half-life of approximately 1 minute.

ANSWER **NOW!**

21.5 Cc Conceptual Connection

HALF-LIFE Consider this graph representing the decay of a radioactive nuclide.

What is the half-life of the nuclide?

(a) 625 years

(b) 1250 years

(c) 2500 years

(d) 3125 years

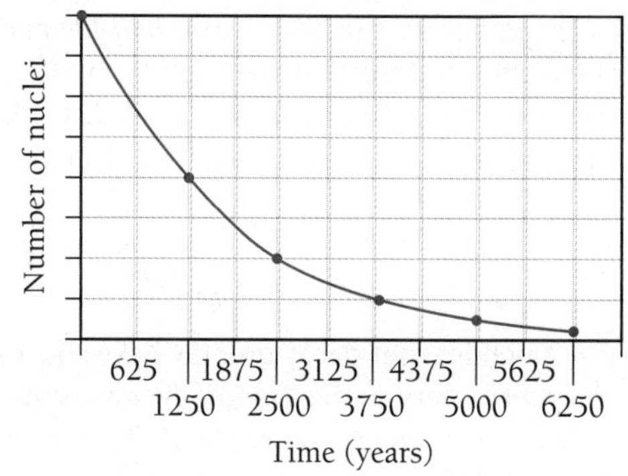

The Integrated Rate Law

Recall from Chapter 15 that for first-order chemical reactions, the concentration of a reactant as a function of time is given by the integrated rate law:

$$\ln\frac{[A]_t}{[A]_0} = -kt \qquad [21.2]$$

Because nuclear decay follows first-order kinetics, we can substitute the number of nuclei for concentration to arrive at the equation:

$$\ln\frac{N_t}{N_0} = -kt \qquad [21.3]$$

where N_t is the number of radioactive nuclei at time t and N_0 is the initial number of radioactive nuclei. Example 21.4 demonstrates the use of this equation.

WATCH **NOW!**

INTERACTIVE WORKED EXAMPLE 21.4

EXAMPLE 21.4 Radioactive Decay Kinetics

Plutonium-236 is an alpha emitter with a half-life of 2.86 years. If a sample initially contains 1.35 mg of Pu-236, what mass of Pu-236 is present after 5.00 years?

SORT You are given the initial mass of Pu-236 in a sample and asked to find the mass after 5.00 years.	**GIVEN:** $m_{\text{Pu-236}}(\text{initial}) = 1.35\text{ mg}$; $t = 5.00\text{ yr}$; $t_{1/2} = 2.86\text{ yr}$ **FIND:** $m_{\text{Pu-236}}(\text{final})$
STRATEGIZE Use the integrated rate law (Equation 21.3) to solve this problem. You must determine the value of the rate constant (k) from the half-life expression (Equation 21.1).	**CONCEPTUAL PLAN** $t_{1/2} \rightarrow k$ $t_{1/2} = \frac{0.693}{k}$
Use the value of the rate constant, the initial mass of Pu-236, and the time along with integrated rate law to find the final mass of Pu-236. Since the mass of the Pu-236 ($m_{\text{Pu-236}}$) is directly proportional to the number of atoms (N), and since the integrated rate law contains the ratio (N_t/N_0), you can substitute the initial and final masses for the initial and final number of atoms.	$k, m_{\text{Pu-236}}(\text{initial}), t \rightarrow m_{\text{Pu-236}}(\text{final})$ $\ln\frac{N_t}{N_0} = -kt$
SOLVE Follow your plan. Begin by determining the rate constant from the half-life.	**SOLUTION** $t_{1/2} = \frac{0.693}{k}$ $k = \frac{0.693}{t_{1/2}} = \frac{0.693}{2.86\text{ yr}}$ $= 0.24\underline{2}3/\text{yr}$

Solve the integrated rate law for N_t and substitute the values of the rate constant, the initial mass of Pu-236, and the time into the solved equation. Calculate the final mass of Pu-236.

$$\ln\frac{N_t}{N_0} = -kt$$

$$\frac{N_t}{N_0} = e^{-kt}$$

$$N_t = N_0 e^{-kt}$$

$$N_t = 1.35\text{ mg}\,[e^{-(0.2423/\text{yr})(5.00\text{ yr})}]$$

$$N_t = 0.402\text{ mg}$$

CHECK The units of the answer (mg) are correct. The magnitude of the answer (0.402 mg) is about one-third of the original mass (1.35 mg), which seems reasonable given that the amount of time is between one and two half-lives. (One half-life would result in one-half of the original mass, and two half-lives would result in one-fourth of the original mass.)

FOR PRACTICE 21.4 How long will it take for the 1.35 mg sample of Pu-236 in Example 21.4 to decay to 0.100 mg?

Since radioactivity is a first-order process, the rate of decay is linearly proportional to the number of nuclei in the sample. Therefore, the initial rate of decay (rate_0) and the rate of decay at time t (rate_t) can also be used in the integrated rate law:

$$\text{Rate}_t = kN_t \qquad \text{Rate}_0 = kN_0$$

$$\frac{N_t}{N_0} = \frac{\text{rate}_t/k}{\text{rate}_0/k} = \frac{\text{rate}_t}{\text{rate}_0}$$

Substituting into Equation 21.3, we get the following result:

$$\ln\frac{\text{rate}_t}{\text{rate}_0} = -kt \qquad [21.4]$$

We can use Equation 21.4 to predict how the rate of decay of a radioactive sample will change with time or how much time has passed based on how the rate has changed (see examples later in this section).

The radioactive isotopes in our environment and their predictable decay with time can therefore be used to estimate the age of rocks or artifacts containing those isotopes. The technique is known as **radiometric dating**, and we examine two different types individually.

HALF-LIFE AND THE AMOUNT OF RADIOACTIVE SAMPLE A sample initially contains 1.6 moles of a radioactive isotope. How much of the sample remains after four half-lives?

(a) 0.0 mol **(b)** 0.10 mol **(c)** 0.20 mol **(d)** 0.40 mol

21.6 Cc Conceptual Connection

ANSWER NOW!

Radiocarbon Dating: Using Radioactivity to Measure the Age of Fossils and Artifacts

Archaeologists, geologists, anthropologists, and other scientists use **radiocarbon dating**, a technique devised in 1949 by Willard Libby (1908–1980) at the University of Chicago, to estimate the ages of fossils and artifacts. For example, in 1947, young shepherds searching for a stray goat near the Dead Sea (east of Jerusalem) entered a cave and discovered ancient scrolls that had been stuffed into jars. These scrolls—now named the Dead Sea Scrolls—are 2000-year-old texts of the Hebrew Bible, predating other previously discovered manuscripts by almost a thousand years.

▲ The Dead Sea Scrolls are 2000-year-old biblical manuscripts. Their age was determined by radiocarbon dating.

The Dead Sea Scrolls, like other ancient artifacts, contain a radioactive signature that reveals their age. This signature results from the presence of carbon-14 (which is radioactive) in the environment. Carbon-14 is constantly formed in the upper atmosphere by the neutron bombardment of nitrogen:

$${}^{14}_{7}\text{N} + {}^{1}_{0}\text{n} \longrightarrow {}^{14}_{6}\text{C} + {}^{1}_{1}\text{H}$$

Libby received the Nobel Prize in 1960 for the development of radiocarbon dating.

After it forms, carbon-14 decays back to nitrogen by beta emission with a half-life of 5715 years:

$$^{14}_{6}\text{C} \longrightarrow {}^{14}_{7}\text{N} + {}^{0}_{-1}\text{e} \quad t_{1/2} = 5715 \text{ yr}$$

A steady state is a set of conditions that results in constant concentrations of the relevant species.

The continuous formation of carbon-14 in the atmosphere and its continuous decay to nitrogen-14 produce a nearly constant steady-state amount of atmospheric carbon-14. The atmospheric carbon-14 is oxidized to carbon dioxide and incorporated into plants by photosynthesis. The C-14 then makes its way up the food chain and ultimately into all living organisms. As a result, the tissues in all living plants, animals, and humans contain the same ratio of carbon-14 to carbon-12 (^{14}C : ^{12}C) as that found in the atmosphere. When a living organism dies, however, it stops incorporating new carbon-14 into its tissues. The ^{14}C : ^{12}C ratio then begins to decrease with a half-life of 5715 years.

Because many artifacts, including the Dead Sea Scrolls, are made from materials that were once living—such as papyrus, wood, or other plant and animal derivatives—the ^{14}C : ^{12}C ratio in these artifacts indicates their age. For example, suppose an ancient artifact has a ^{14}C : ^{12}C ratio that is 25% of that found in living organisms. How old is the artifact? Because it contains one-quarter as much carbon-14 as a living organism, it is two half-lives or 11,430 years old. The maximum age that can be estimated from carbon-14 dating is about 50,000 years—beyond that, the amount of carbon-14 is too low to measure accurately.

We can check the accuracy of carbon-14 dating against objects whose ages are known from historical sources. These kinds of comparisons reveal that ages obtained from C-14 dating deviate from the actual ages by up to about 5%. For a 6000-year-old object, that is an error of about 300 years. The reason for the deviations is the variance of atmospheric C-14 levels over time.

▲ Western bristlecone pine trees can live up to 5000 years; scientists can precisely determine the age of a tree by counting the annual rings in its trunk. In this way, the trees can calibrate the time scale for radiocarbon dating.

In order to make C-14 dating more accurate, scientists have studied the carbon-14 content of western bristlecone pine trees, which can live up to 5000 years. The tree trunks of the pines contain growth rings corresponding to each year of the tree's life, and the wood laid down in each ring incorporates carbon derived from the carbon dioxide in the atmosphere at that time. The rings thus provide a historical record of the atmospheric carbon-14 content. In addition, the rings of living trees can be correlated with the rings of dead trees (if the lifetimes of the trees overlap), allowing the record to be extended back about 11,000 years. Using the data from the bristlecone pine, we can correct the 5% deviations from historical dates. In this way, the known ages of bristlecone pine trees are used to calibrate C-14 dating, resulting in more accurate results.

ANSWER **NOW!**

21.7 Cc Conceptual Connection

RADIOCARBON DATING An ancient bone contains 1/8 of the amount of carbon-14 found in living organisms. How old is the bone?

(a) 5,715 years (one C-14 half-life)
(b) 11,430 years (two C-14 half-lives)
(c) 17,145 years (three C-14 half-lives)
(d) 22,860 years (four C-14 half-lives)

WATCH **NOW!**

INTERACTIVE WORKED EXAMPLE 21.5

EXAMPLE 21.5 Radiocarbon Dating

A skull believed to belong to an ancient human being has a carbon-14 decay rate of 4.50 disintegrations per minute per gram of carbon (4.50 dis/min · g C). If living organisms have a decay rate of 15.3 dis/min · g C, how old is the skull? (The decay rate is directly proportional to the amount of carbon-14 present.)

SORT You are given the current rate of decay for the skull and the assumed initial rate. You are asked to find the age of the skull, which is the time that passed in order for the rate to have reached its current value.	**GIVEN:** $\text{rate}_t = 4.50 \text{ dis/min} \cdot \text{g C}$; $\text{rate}_0 = 15.3 \text{ dis/min} \cdot \text{g C}$; **FIND:** t
STRATEGIZE Use the expression for half-life (Equation 21.1) to find the rate constant (k) from the half-life for C-14, which is 5715 years (Table 21.3).	**CONCEPTUAL PLAN** $t_{1/2} \rightarrow k$; $t_{1/2} = \dfrac{0.693}{k}$

Use the value of the rate constant and the initial and current rates to find t from the integrated rate law (Equation 21.4).	k, rate_t, rate_0 → t $\ln\frac{\text{rate}_t}{\text{rate}_0} = -kt$
SOLVE Begin by finding the rate constant from the half-life.	**SOLUTION** $t_{1/2} = \frac{0.693}{k}$ $k = \frac{0.693}{t_{1/2}} = \frac{0.693}{5715\ \text{yr}}$ $= 1.2\underline{1}3 \times 10^{-4}/\text{yr}$
Substitute the rate constant and the initial and current rates into the integrated rate law and solve for t.	$\ln\frac{\text{rate}_t}{\text{rate}_0} = -kt$ $t = -\frac{\ln\frac{\text{rate}_t}{\text{rate}_0}}{k} = -\frac{\ln\frac{4.50\ \cancel{\text{dis/min}\cdot\text{g C}}}{15.3\ \cancel{\text{dis/min}\cdot\text{g C}}}}{1.2\underline{1}3 \times 10^{-4}/\text{yr}}$ $= 1.0 \times 10^4\ \text{yr}$

CHECK The units of the answer (yr) are correct. The magnitude of the answer is about 10,000 years, which is a little less than two half-lives. This value is reasonable given that two half-lives would result in a decay rate of about 3.8 dis/min · g C.

FOR PRACTICE 21.5 A researcher claims that an ancient scroll originated from Greek scholars in about 500 B.C. Its carbon-14 decay rate is 89% of that found in living organisms. How old is the scroll, and could it be authentic?

CHEMISTRY IN YOUR DAY | Radiocarbon Dating and the Shroud of Turin

The Shroud of Turin—kept in the cathedral of Turin in Italy—is a linen cloth bearing a mysterious image. Many people have interpreted the image as that of a man who appears to have been crucified. The image becomes clearer if the shroud is photographed and viewed as a negative. Some claim that the shroud is the original burial cloth of Jesus, miraculously imprinted with his image. In 1988, the Roman Catholic Church chose three independent laboratories to perform radiocarbon dating on the shroud. The laboratories took samples of the cloth and measured the carbon-14 content. The three independent laboratories all arrived at similar results—the shroud was made from linen originating in about A.D. 1325. Although some have disputed the results (and continue to do so), and although no scientific test is 100% reliable, newspapers around the world announced that the Shroud did not date back to biblical times.

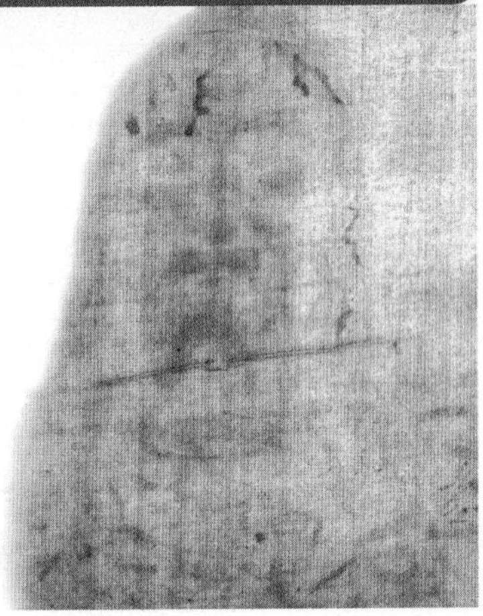

▶ The linen cloth known as the Shroud of Turin bears the image of a man believed by some to be Jesus.

Uranium/Lead Dating

Radiocarbon dating can only measure the ages of objects that were once living and that are relatively young (<50,000 years). Other radiometric dating techniques can measure the ages of prehistoric objects that were never alive. The most dependable technique relies on the ratio of uranium-238 to lead-206 within igneous rocks (rocks of volcanic origin). This technique measures the time that has passed since the rock solidified (at which point the "radiometric clock" is reset).

Because U-238 decays into Pb-206 with a half-life of 4.5×10^9 years, the relative amounts of U-238 and Pb-206 in a uranium-containing rock reveal its age. For example, if a rock originally contained U-238 and currently contains equal amounts of U-238 and Pb-206, it is 4.5 billion years old, assuming that the rock did not contain any Pb-206 when it was formed. The latter assumption can be tested because the lead that results from the decay of uranium has a different isotopic composition than the lead that was deposited in rocks at the time of their formation. Example 21.6 shows how we can use the relative amounts of Pb-206 and U-238 to estimate a rock's age.

EXAMPLE 21.6 Using Uranium/Lead Dating to Estimate the Age of a Rock

A meteor contains 0.556 g of Pb-206 to every 1.00 g of U-238. Assuming that the meteor did not contain any Pb-206 at the time of its formation, determine the age of the meteor. Uranium-238 decays to lead-206 with a half-life of 4.5 billion years.

SORT You are given the current masses of Pb-206 and U-238 in a rock and asked to find its age. You are also given the half-life of U-238.

GIVEN: $m_{\text{U-238}} = 1.00\text{ g}$; $m_{\text{Pb-206}} = 0.556\text{ g}$; $t_{1/2} = 4.5 \times 10^9\text{ yr}$

FIND: t

STRATEGIZE Use the integrated rate law (Equation 21.3) to solve this problem. To do so, first determine the value of the rate constant (k) from the half-life expression (Equation 21.1).

CONCEPTUAL PLAN

$$t_{1/2} \longrightarrow k \qquad t_{1/2} = \frac{0.693}{k}$$

Before substituting into the integrated rate law, you need the ratio of the current amount of U-238 to the original amount (N_t/N_0). The current mass of uranium is simply 1.00 g. The initial mass includes the current mass (1.00 g) plus the mass that has decayed into lead-206, which you can determine from the current mass of Pb-206.

$$\text{g Pb-206} \xrightarrow{\frac{1\text{ mol Pb}}{206\text{ g Pb}}} \text{mol Pb-206} \xrightarrow{\frac{1\text{ mol U}}{1\text{ mol Pb}}} \text{mol U-238} \xrightarrow{\frac{238\text{ g U}}{1\text{ mol U}}} \text{g U-238}$$

Use the value of the rate constant and the initial and current amounts of U-238 and the integrated rate law to find t.

$$k, N_t, N_0 \longrightarrow t \qquad \ln\frac{N_t}{N_0} = -kt$$

SOLVE Follow your plan. Begin by finding the rate constant from the half-life.

SOLUTION

$$t_{1/2} = \frac{0.693}{k}$$

$$k = \frac{0.693}{t_{1/2}} = \frac{0.693}{4.5 \times 10^9\text{ yr}}$$

$$= 1.54 \times 10^{-10}/\text{yr}$$

Determine the mass in grams of U-238 required to form the given mass of Pb-206.

$$0.556\ \cancel{\text{g Pb-206}} \times \frac{\cancel{1\text{ mol Pb-206}}}{206\ \cancel{\text{g Pb-206}}} \times \frac{\cancel{1\text{ mol U-238}}}{\cancel{1\text{mol Pb-206}}} \times \frac{238\text{ g U-238}}{\cancel{1\text{ mol U-238}}}$$

$$= 0.6424\text{ g U-238}$$

Substitute the rate constant and the initial and current masses of U-238 into the integrated rate law and solve for t. (The initial mass of U-238 is the sum of the current mass and the mass required to form the given mass of Pb-206.)

$$\ln\frac{N_t}{N_0} = -kt$$

$$t = -\frac{\ln\frac{N_t}{N_0}}{k} = -\frac{\ln\frac{1.00\ \cancel{\text{g}}}{1.00\ \cancel{\text{g}} + 0.6424\ \cancel{\text{g}}}}{1.54 \times 10^{-10}/\text{yr}}$$

$$= 3.2 \times 10^9\text{ yr}$$

CHECK The units of the answer (yr) are correct. The magnitude of the answer is about 3.2 billion years, which is less than one half-life. This value is reasonable given that less than half of the uranium in the meteor has decayed into lead.

FOR PRACTICE 21.6 A rock contains a Pb-206 to U-238 mass ratio of 0.145 : 1.00. Assuming that the rock did not contain any Pb-206 at the time of its formation, determine its age.

The Age of Earth

The uranium/lead radiometric dating technique as well as other radiometric dating techniques (such as the decay of potassium-40 to argon-40) have been widely used to measure the ages of rocks on Earth and have produced highly consistent results. Rocks with ages greater than 3.5 billion years have been found on every continent. The oldest rocks have an age of approximately 4.0 billion years, establishing a lower limit for Earth's age (Earth is at least as old as its oldest rocks). The ages of about 70 meteorites that have struck Earth have also been extensively studied and have been found to be about 4.5 billion years old. Since the meteorites were formed at the same time as our solar system (which includes Earth), the best estimate for Earth's age is therefore about 4.5 billion years. That age is consistent with the estimated age of our universe—about 13.8 billion years.

The age of the universe is estimated from its expansion rate, which can be measured by examining changes in the wavelength of light from distant galaxies.

21.7 The Discovery of Fission: The Atomic Bomb and Nuclear Power

In the mid-1930s, Enrico Fermi (1901–1954), an Italian physicist, attempted to synthesize a new element by bombarding uranium—the heaviest known element at that time—with neutrons. Fermi speculated that if a neutron could be incorporated into the nucleus of a uranium atom, the nucleus might undergo beta decay, converting a neutron into a proton. If that happened, a new element, with atomic number 93, would be synthesized for the first time. The nuclear equation for the process is shown here:

The element with atomic number 100 is named fermium in honor of Enrico Fermi.

$$^{238}_{92}\text{U} + {}^{1}_{0}\text{n} \longrightarrow {}^{239}_{92}\text{U} \longrightarrow {}^{239}_{93}\text{X} + {}^{0}_{-1}\text{e}$$

Neutron — Newly synthesized element

Fermi performed the experiment and detected the emission of beta particles. However, his results were inconclusive. Had he synthesized a new element? Fermi never chemically examined the products to determine their composition and therefore could not say with certainty that he had.

Three researchers in Germany—Lise Meitner (1878–1968), Fritz Strassmann (1902–1980), and Otto Hahn (1879–1968)—repeated Fermi's experiments and then performed careful chemical analysis of the products. What they found in the products—several elements *lighter* than uranium—would change the world forever. On January 6, 1939, Meitner, Strassmann, and Hahn reported that the neutron bombardment of uranium resulted in **nuclear fission**—the splitting of the uranium atom. The nucleus of the neutron-bombarded uranium atom was split into barium, krypton, and other smaller products. They also determined that the process emits enormous amounts of energy. A nuclear equation for a fission reaction, showing how uranium breaks apart into the daughter nuclides, is shown here:

The element with atomic number 109 is named meitnerium in honor of Lise Meitner.

$$^{235}_{92}\text{U} + {}^{1}_{0}\text{n} \longrightarrow {}^{140}_{56}\text{Ba} + {}^{93}_{36}\text{Kr} + 3\,{}^{1}_{0}\text{n} + \text{energy}$$

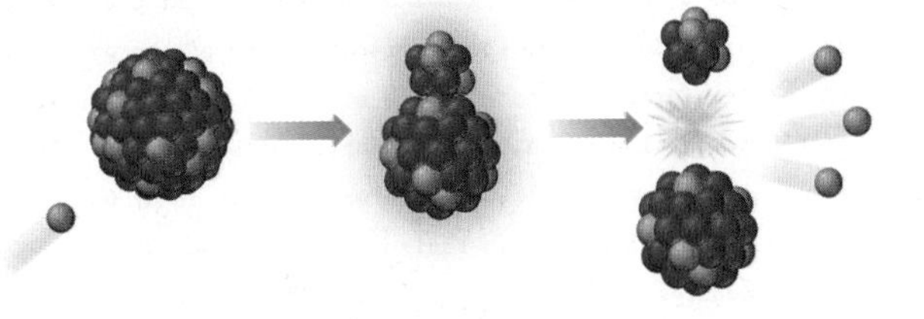

Notice that the initial uranium atom is the U-235 isotope, which constitutes less than 1% of all naturally occurring uranium. U-238, the most abundant uranium isotope, does not undergo fission. Notice also that the process produces three neutrons, which have the potential to initiate fission in three other U-235 atoms.

Scientists quickly realized that a sample rich in U-235 could undergo a **chain reaction** in which neutrons produced by the fission of one uranium nucleus would induce fission in other uranium nuclei (Figure 21.10▶). This self-amplifying reaction is capable of producing an enormous amount of energy. This is the energy that is harnessed in an atomic bomb. However, to make a bomb, a **critical mass** of U-235—enough U-235 to produce a self-sustaining reaction—is necessary.

▲ Lise Meitner in Otto Hahn's Berlin laboratory. Together with Hahn and Fritz Strassmann, Meitner determined that U-235 could undergo nuclear fission.

The Manhattan Project

Fearing that Nazi Germany would develop a bomb based on nuclear fission, several U.S. scientists persuaded Albert Einstein, the most famous scientist of the time, to write a letter

▶ FIGURE 21.10 A Self-Amplifying Chain Reaction The fission of one U-235 nucleus emits neutrons that can then initiate fission in other U-235 nuclei, resulting in a chain reaction that releases enormous amounts of energy.

Fission Chain Reaction

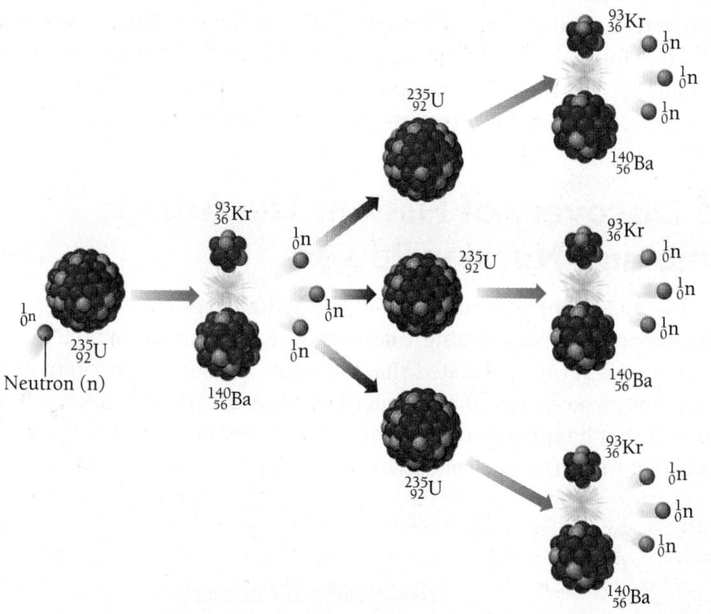

to President Franklin Roosevelt warning of this possibility. Einstein wrote, ". . . and it is conceivable—though much less certain—that extremely powerful bombs of a new type may thus be constructed. A single bomb of this type, carried by boat and exploded in a port, might very well destroy the whole port together with some of the surrounding territory."

▶ Einstein's letter (part of which is shown here) encouraged Franklin Roosevelt to fund research for a fission bomb.

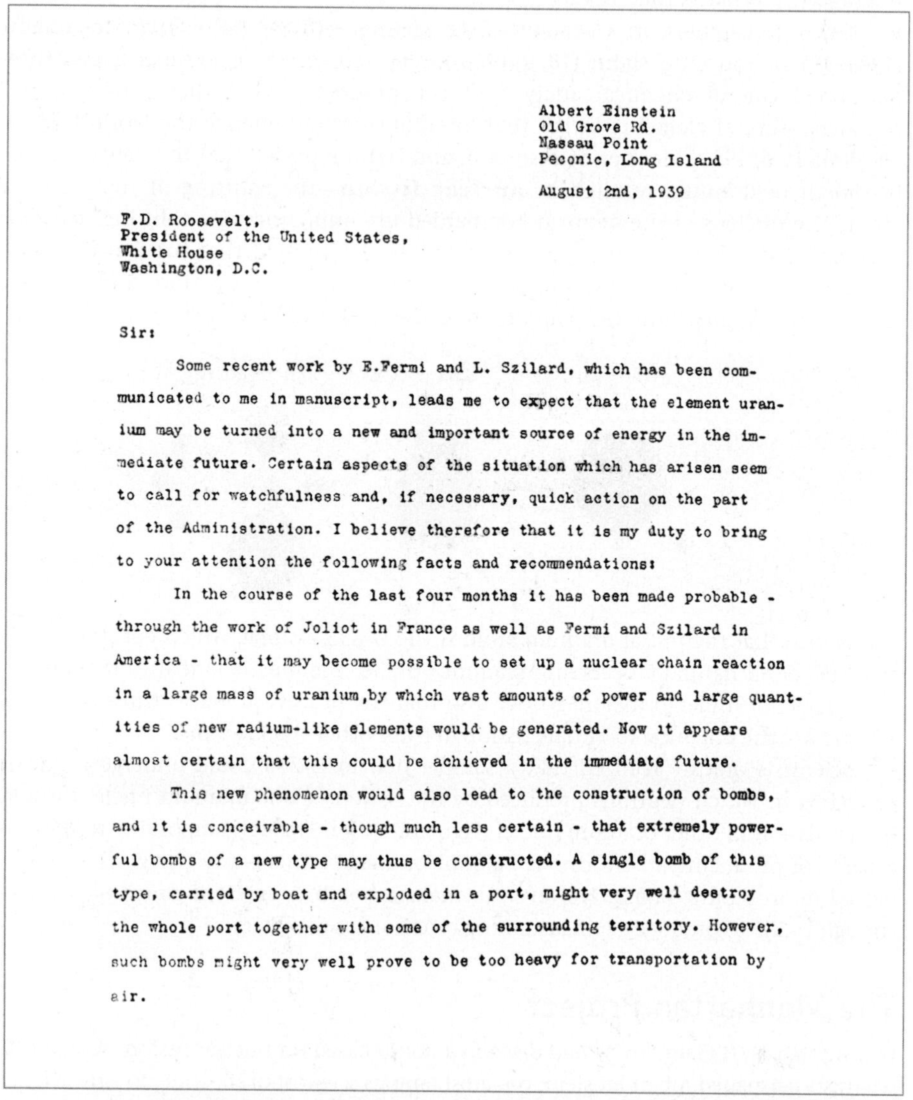

Albert Einstein
Old Grove Rd.
Nassau Point
Peconic, Long Island

August 2nd, 1939

F.D. Roosevelt,
President of the United States,
White House
Washington, D.C.

Sir:

Some recent work by E.Fermi and L. Szilard, which has been communicated to me in manuscript, leads me to expect that the element uranium may be turned into a new and important source of energy in the immediate future. Certain aspects of the situation which has arisen seem to call for watchfulness and, if necessary, quick action on the part of the Administration. I believe therefore that it is my duty to bring to your attention the following facts and recommendations:

In the course of the last four months it has been made probable - through the work of Joliot in France as well as Fermi and Szilard in America - that it may become possible to set up a nuclear chain reaction in a large mass of uranium,by which vast amounts of power and large quantities of new radium-like elements would be generated. Now it appears almost certain that this could be achieved in the immediate future.

This new phenomenon would also lead to the construction of bombs, and it is conceivable - though much less certain - that extremely powerful bombs of a new type may thus be constructed. A single bomb of this type, carried by boat and exploded in a port, might very well destroy the whole port together with some of the surrounding territory. However, such bombs might very well prove to be too heavy for transportation by air.

Einstein's letter helped persuade Roosevelt, and in 1941 he assembled the resources to begin the costliest scientific project ever attempted. The top-secret endeavor was called the *Manhattan Project*, and its primary goal was to build an atomic bomb before the Germans did. Physicist J. R. Oppenheimer (1904–1967) led the project at a high-security research facility in Los Alamos, New Mexico. Four years later, on July 16, 1945, the United States detonated the world's first nuclear weapon at a test site in New Mexico. The first atomic bomb exploded with a force equivalent to 18,000 tons of dynamite. Ironically, the Germans—who had *not* made a successful nuclear bomb—had already been defeated by this time. Instead, the United States used the atomic bomb on Japan. One bomb was dropped on Hiroshima and a second bomb was dropped on Nagasaki. Together, the bombs killed approximately 200,000 people and led to Japan's surrender.

▲ On July 16, 1945, in the New Mexico desert, the world's first atomic bomb was detonated. It had the power of 18,000 tons of dynamite.

Nuclear Power: Using Fission to Generate Electricity

Nuclear reactions, such as fission, generate enormous amounts of energy. In a nuclear bomb, the energy is released all at once. The energy can also be released more slowly and used for peaceful purposes such as electricity generation. In the United States, nuclear fission generates about 20% of electricity. In some other countries, nuclear fission generates as much as 70% of electricity. To get an idea of the amount of energy released during fission, imagine a hypothetical nuclear-powered car. Suppose the fuel for such a car was a uranium cylinder about the size of a pencil. How often would you have to refuel the car? The energy content of the uranium cylinder is equivalent to about 1000 twenty-gallon tanks of gasoline. If you refuel your gasoline-powered car once a week, your nuclear-powered car could go 1000 weeks—almost 20 years—before refueling.

Similarly, a nuclear-powered electricity generation plant can produce a lot of electricity from a small amount of fuel. Such plants exploit the heat created by fission, using it to boil water and make steam, which then turns the turbine on a generator to produce electricity (Figure 21.11▼). The fission reaction occurs in the nuclear core of the

Nuclear Reactor

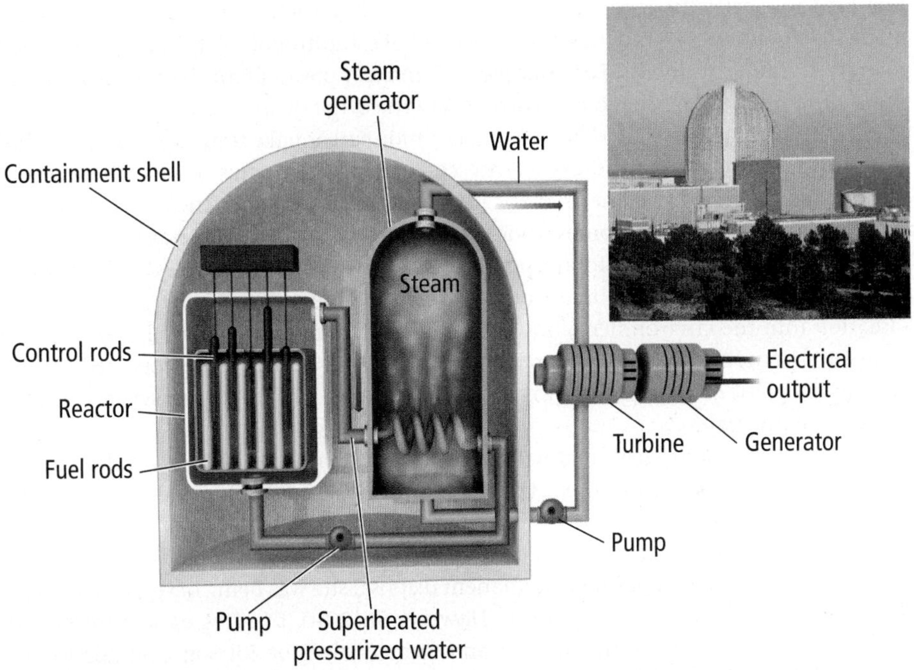

▲ **FIGURE 21.11 A Nuclear Reactor** The fission of U-235 in the core of a nuclear power plant generates heat that creates steam and turns a turbine on an electrical generator. Control rods are raised or lowered to control the fission reaction. (Note that the water carrying heat away from the reactor core is contained within its own pipes and does not come into direct contact with the steam that drives the turbines.)

power plant. The core consists of uranium fuel rods—enriched to about 3.5% U-235—interspersed between retractable neutron-absorbing control rods. When the control rods are retracted from the fuel rod assembly, the chain reaction can occur. When the control rods are fully inserted into the fuel assembly, however, they absorb the neutrons that would otherwise induce fission, shutting down the chain reaction. By retracting or inserting the control rods, the operator increases or decreases the rate of fission. In this way, the fission reaction is controlled to produce the right amount of heat needed for electricity generation. In case of a power failure, the control rods automatically drop into the fuel rod assembly, shutting down the fission reaction.

A typical nuclear power plant generates enough electricity for a city of about one million people and uses about 50 kg of fuel per day. In contrast, a coal-burning power plant uses about 2,000,000 kg of fuel to generate the same amount of electricity. Furthermore, a nuclear power plant generates no air pollution and no greenhouse gases. A coal-burning power plant emits pollutants such as carbon monoxide, nitrogen oxides, and sulfur oxides. Coal-burning power plants also emit carbon dioxide, a greenhouse gas.

▲ In 1986, the reactor core at Chernobyl (in what is now Ukraine) overheated, exploded, and destroyed part of the containment structure. The release of radioactive nuclides into the environment forced the government to relocate over 335,000 people.

Reactor cores in the United States are not made of graphite and cannot burn in the way that the Chernobyl core did.

Problems with Nuclear Power

Nuclear power generation, however, is not without problems. Foremost among them is the danger of nuclear accidents. In spite of safety precautions, the fission reaction occurring in a nuclear power plant can overheat. The most famous examples of this occurred in Chernobyl, in the former Soviet Union, on April 26, 1986, and at the Fukushima Daiichi Nuclear Power Plant in Japan in March of 2011.

In the Chernobyl incident, operators of the plant were performing an experiment designed to reduce maintenance costs. In order to perform the experiment, they had to disable many of the safety features of the reactor core. The experiment failed with disastrous results. The nuclear core, composed partly of graphite, overheated and began to burn. The accident caused 31 immediate deaths and produced a fire that scattered radioactive debris into the atmosphere, making much of the surrounding land (within about a 32-kilometer radius) uninhabitable. As bad as the accident was, however, it was not a nuclear detonation. A nuclear power plant *cannot* become a nuclear bomb. The uranium fuel used in electricity generation is not sufficiently enriched in U-235 to produce a nuclear detonation. U.S. nuclear power plants have additional safety features designed to prevent similar accidents. For example, U.S. nuclear power plants have large containment structures to contain radioactive debris in the event of an accident.

In the 2011 Japanese accident, a 9.0 magnitude earthquake triggered a tsunami that flooded the coastal plant and caused the cooling system pumps to fail. Three of the nuclear cores within the plant dramatically overheated and experienced a partial meltdown (in which the fuel becomes so hot that it melts). The accident was intensified by the loss of water in the fuel storage ponds (pools of water normally used to keep spent fuel cool), which caused the fuel stored in the ponds to also overheat. The release of radiation into the environment, however, while significant, was much lower in Japan than at Chernobyl. In fact, no radioactivity-related deaths were reported at the Fukushima plant or the surrounding area. The cleanup of the site, however, will continue for many years.

A second problem associated with nuclear power is waste disposal. Although the amount of nuclear fuel used in electricity generation is small compared to other fuels, some of the products of the reaction are radioactive and have long half-lives. What do we do with this waste? Currently, in the United States, nuclear waste is stored on site at the nuclear power plants. A single permanent disposal site was being developed in Yucca Mountain, Nevada, to store U.S. waste. However, in 2010, the Obama administration halted the development of this project and formed the Blue Ribbon Commission on America's Nuclear Future to explore alternatives. The committee has made several important recommendations. These include the development of both a temporary above-ground storage facility and a permanent underground facility. However, the committee has not made any decisions regarding Yucca Mountain as a potential site for the storage facility.

21.8 Converting Mass to Energy: Mass Defect and Nuclear Binding Energy

Nuclear fission produces large amounts of energy. But where does the energy come from? We can answer this question by carefully examining the masses of the reactants and products in the fission equation from Section 21.7:

$$^{235}_{92}\text{U} + ^{1}_{0}\text{n} \longrightarrow ^{140}_{56}\text{Ba} + ^{93}_{36}\text{Kr} + 3\,^{1}_{0}\text{n}$$

Mass Reactants		Mass Products	
$^{235}_{92}\text{U}$	235.04392 amu	$^{140}_{56}\text{Ba}$	139.910581 amu
$^{1}_{0}\text{n}$	1.00866 amu	$^{93}_{36}\text{Kr}$	92.931130 amu
		$3\,^{1}_{0}\text{n}$	3(1.00866) amu
Total	**236.05258 amu**		**235.86769 amu**

Notice that the products of the nuclear reaction have *less mass* than the reactants. The missing mass is converted to energy. In Chapter 1, we learned that matter is conserved in chemical reactions. In nuclear reactions matter can be converted to energy. The relationship between the amount of matter that is lost and the amount of energy formed is given by Einstein's famous equation relating the two quantities:

In a chemical reaction, there are also mass changes associated with the emission or absorption of energy. Because the energy involved in chemical reactions is so much smaller than that of nuclear reactions, however, these mass changes are completely negligible.

$$E = mc^2$$

where E is the energy produced, m is the mass lost, and c is the speed of light.

For example, in the fission reaction just shown, we calculate the quantity of energy produced as follows:

$$\begin{aligned}\text{Mass lost } (m) &= 236.05258\text{ amu} - 235.86769\text{ amu}\\ &= 0.18489\,\cancel{\text{amu}} \times \frac{1.66054 \times 10^{-27}\text{ kg}}{1\,\cancel{\text{amu}}}\\ &= 3.0702 \times 10^{-28}\text{ kg}\end{aligned}$$

$$\begin{aligned}\text{Energy produced } (E) &= mc^2\\ &= 3.0702 \times 10^{-28}\text{ kg}\,(2.9979 \times 10^{8}\text{ m/s})^2\\ &= 2.7593 \times 10^{-11}\text{ J}\end{aligned}$$

The result (2.7593×10^{-11}J) is the energy produced when one nucleus of U-235 undergoes fission. This may not seem like much energy, but it is only the energy produced by the fission of a *single* nucleus. We can also calculate the energy produced *per mole* of U-235 to compare it to a chemical reaction:

$$2.7593 \times 10^{-11}\frac{\text{J}}{\cancel{\text{U-235 atom}}} \times \frac{6.0221 \times 10^{23}\,\cancel{\text{U-235 atoms}}}{1\text{ mol U-235}} = 1.6617 \times 10^{13}\text{ J/mol U-235}$$

The energy produced by the fission of 1 mol of U-235 is about 17 billion kJ. In contrast, a highly exothermic chemical reaction produces 1000 kJ per mole of reactant. Fission produces over a million times more energy per mole than chemical processes.

Mass Defect and Nuclear Binding Energy

We can examine the formation of a stable nucleus from its component particles as a nuclear reaction in which mass is converted to energy. For example, consider the formation of helium-4 from its components:

$$2\,^{1}_{1}\text{H} + 2\,^{1}_{0}\text{n} \longrightarrow ^{4}_{2}\text{He}$$

The electrons are contained on the left side in the two $^{1}_{1}\text{H}$ and on the right side in $^{4}_{2}\text{He}$. If you write the equation using only two protons on the left ($^{1}_{1}\text{p}$), you must also add two electrons to the left.

Mass Reactants		Mass Products	
$2\,^{1}_{1}\text{H}$	2(1.00783) amu	$^{4}_{2}\text{He}$	4.00260 amu
$2\,^{1}_{0}\text{n}$	2(1.00866) amu		
Total	**4.03298 amu**		**4.00260 amu**

A helium-4 atom has less mass than the sum of the masses of its separate components. This difference in mass, known as the **mass defect**, exists in all stable nuclei. The energy corresponding to the mass defect—obtained by substituting the mass defect into the equation $E = mc^2$—is the **nuclear binding energy**, the amount of energy required to break apart the nucleus into its component nucleons.

An electron volt is defined as the kinetic energy of an electron that has been accelerated through a potential difference of 1 V.

Although chemists often report energies in joules, nuclear physicists often use the electron volt (eV) or megaelectron volt (MeV): 1 MeV $= 1.602 \times 10^{-13}$ J. Unlike energy in joules, which is typically reported per mole, energy in electron volts is reported per nucleus. A particularly useful conversion for calculating and reporting nuclear binding energies is the relationship between amu (mass units) and MeV (energy units):

$$1 \text{ amu} = 931.5 \text{ MeV}$$

A mass defect of 1 amu, when substituted into the equation $E = mc^2$, gives an energy of 931.5 MeV. Using this conversion factor, we can readily calculate the binding energy of the helium nucleus:

$$\text{Mass defect} = 4.03298 \text{ amu} - 4.00260 \text{ amu}$$
$$= 0.03038 \text{ amu}$$

$$\text{Nuclear binding energy} = 0.03038 \cancel{\text{amu}} \times \frac{931.5 \text{ MeV}}{1 \cancel{\text{amu}}}$$
$$= 28.30 \text{ MeV}$$

The binding energy of the helium nucleus is 28.30 MeV. In order to compare the binding energy of one nucleus to that of another, we calculate the *binding energy per nucleon*, which is the nuclear binding energy of a nuclide divided by the number of nucleons in the nuclide. For helium-4, we calculate the binding energy per nucleon as follows:

$$\text{Binding energy per nucleon} = \frac{28.30 \text{ MeV}}{4 \text{ nucleons}}$$
$$= 7.075 \text{ MeV per nucleon}$$

We can calculate the binding energy per nucleon for other nuclides in the same way. For example, the nuclear binding energy of carbon-12 is 7.680 MeV per nucleon. Since the binding energy per nucleon of carbon-12 is greater than that of helium-4, we conclude that the carbon-12 nuclide is more *stable* (it has lower potential energy).

EXAMPLE 21.7 Mass Defect and Nuclear Binding Energy

Calculate the mass defect and nuclear binding energy per nucleon (in MeV) for C-16, a radioactive isotope of carbon with a mass of 16.014701 amu.

SOLUTION

Calculate the mass defect as the difference between the mass of one C-16 atom and the sum of the masses of six hydrogen atoms and 10 neutrons.	$\text{Mass defect} = 6(\text{mass } ^1_1\text{H}) + 10(\text{mass } ^1_0\text{n}) - \text{mass } ^{16}_{6}\text{C}$ $= 6(1.00783 \text{ amu}) + 10(1.00866 \text{ amu}) - 16.014701 \text{ amu}$ $= 0.118879 \text{ amu}$
Calculate the nuclear binding energy by converting the mass defect (in amu) into MeV. (Use 1 amu = 931.5 MeV.)	$0.118879 \cancel{\text{amu}} \times \frac{931.5 \text{ MeV}}{\cancel{\text{amu}}} = 110.74 \text{ MeV}$
Determine the nuclear binding energy per nucleon by dividing by the number of nucleons in the nucleus.	$\text{Nuclear binding energy per nucleon} = \frac{110.74 \text{ MeV}}{16 \text{ nucleons}}$ $= 6.921 \text{ MeV/nucleon}$

FOR PRACTICE 21.7 Calculate the mass defect and nuclear binding energy per nucleon (in MeV) for U-238, which has a mass of 238.050784 amu.

The Nuclear Binding Energy Curve

Figure 21.12▼ shows the binding energy per nucleon plotted as a function of mass number (A). The binding energy per nucleon is relatively low for small mass numbers and increases until about $A = 60$, where it reaches a maximum. Nuclides with mass numbers of about 60, therefore, are among the most stable. Beyond $A = 60$, the binding energy per nucleon decreases again. Figure 21.12 illustrates why nuclear fission is a highly exothermic process. When a heavy nucleus, such as U-235, breaks up into smaller nuclei, such as Ba-140 and Kr-93, the binding energy per nucleon increases. This is analogous to a chemical reaction in which weak bonds break and strong bonds form. In both cases, the process is exothermic. Figure 21.12 also reveals that the *combining* of two lighter nuclei (below $A = 60$) to form a heavier nucleus is exothermic as well. This process is called *nuclear fusion*, which we discuss in the next section of this chapter.

The Curve of Binding Energy

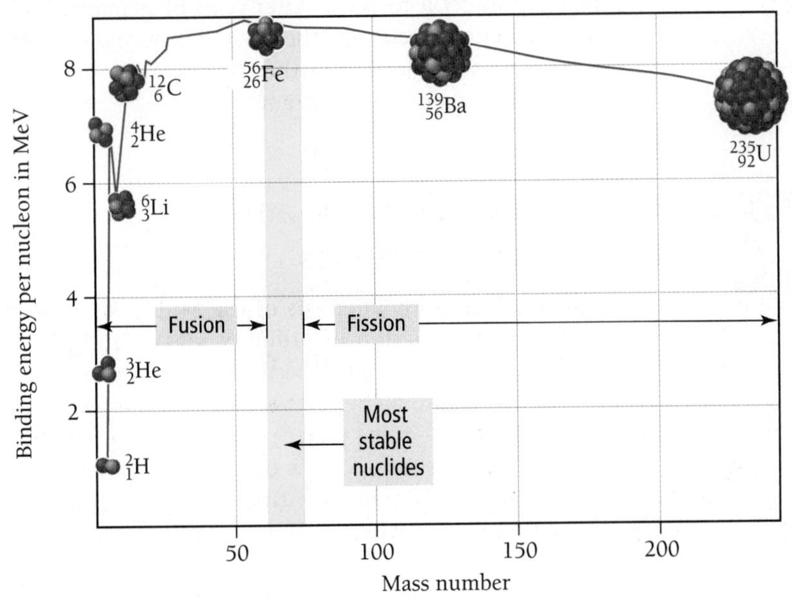

◀ **FIGURE 21.12 Nuclear Binding Energy per Nucleon** The nuclear binding energy per nucleon (a measure of the stability of a nucleus) reaches a maximum at Fe-56. Energy can be obtained either by breaking a heavy nucleus up into lighter ones (fission) or by combining lighter nuclei into heavier ones (fusion).

21.9 Nuclear Fusion: The Power of the Sun

Nuclear fission is the *splitting* of a heavy nucleus to form two or more lighter ones. **Nuclear fusion**, by contrast, is the *combination* of two light nuclei to form a heavier one. Both fusion and fission emit large amounts of energy because, as we have just seen, they both form daughter nuclides with greater binding energies per nucleon than the parent nuclides. Nuclear fusion is the energy source of stars, including our sun. In stars, hydrogen atoms fuse together to form helium atoms, emitting energy in the process.

Nuclear fusion is also the basis of hydrogen bombs. A modern hydrogen bomb has up to 1000 times the explosive force of the first atomic bombs. These bombs employ the fusion reaction shown here:

$$^{2}_{1}H + ^{3}_{1}H \longrightarrow ^{4}_{2}He + ^{1}_{0}n$$

In this reaction, deuterium (the isotope of hydrogen with one neutron) and tritium (the isotope of hydrogen with two neutrons) combine to form helium-4 and a neutron (Figure 21.13▶). Because fusion reactions require two positively charged nuclei (which repel each other) to fuse together, extremely high temperatures are required.

Deuterium-Tritium Fusion Reaction

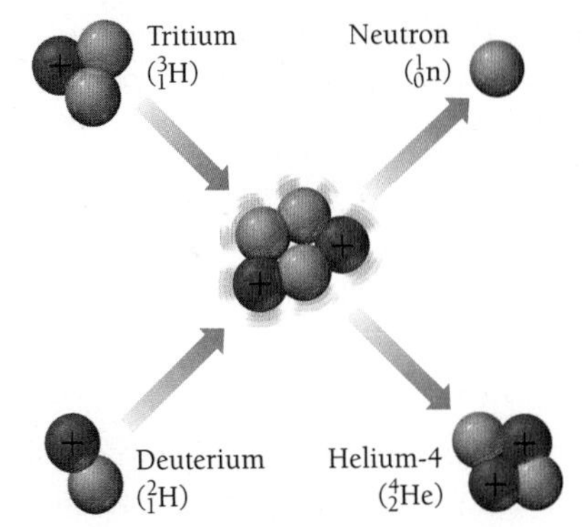

▲ **FIGURE 21.13 A Nuclear Fusion Reaction** In this reaction, two heavy isotopes of hydrogen, deuterium (hydrogen-2) and tritium (hydrogen-3), fuse to form helium-4 and a neutron.

Tokamak Fusion Reactor

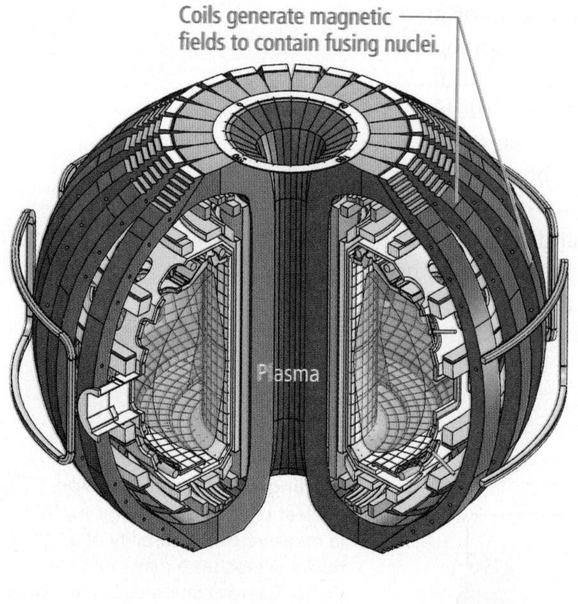

▲ **FIGURE 21.14 Tokamak Fusion Reactor** A tokamak uses powerful magnetic fields to confine nuclear fuel at the enormous temperatures needed for fusion. The high temperatures produce a *plasma*, a state of matter in which some fraction of the atoms is ionized.

In a hydrogen bomb, a small fission bomb is detonated first, creating temperatures and pressures high enough for fusion to proceed.

Nuclear fusion has been intensely investigated as a way to produce electricity. Because of the higher-energy density—fusion provides about ten times more energy per gram of fuel than does fission—and because the products of the reaction are less problematic than those of fission, fusion holds promise as a future energy source. However, despite concerted efforts, the generation of electricity by fusion remains elusive. One of the main problems is the high temperature required for fusion to occur—no material can withstand those temperatures. Using powerful magnetic fields or laser beams, scientists have succeeded in compressing and heating nuclei to the point where fusion has been initiated and even sustained for brief periods of time (Figure 21.14◀). To date, however, the amount of energy generated by fusion reactions has been less than the amount required to get it to occur. After years of spending billions of dollars on fusion research, the U.S. Congress has reduced funding for these projects. Whether fusion will ever be a viable energy source remains uncertain.

21.10 Nuclear Transmutation and Transuranium Elements

One of the goals of the early chemists of the Middle Ages, who were known as *alchemists*, was the transformation of ordinary metals into gold. Many alchemists hoped to turn low-cost metals, such as lead or tin, into precious metals, and in this way become wealthy. These alchemists were never successful because their attempts were merely chemical—they mixed different metals together or tried to get them to react with other substances in order to turn them into gold. In a chemical reaction, an element retains its identity, so a less valuable metal—such as lead—always remains lead, even when it forms a compound with another element.

▲ The Joliot-Curies won the 1935 Nobel Prize in chemistry for their work on nuclear transmutation.

Nuclear reactions, in contrast to chemical reactions, result in the transformation of one element into another, a process known as **transmutation**. We have already seen how this occurs in radioactive decay, in fission, and in fusion. In addition, other nuclear reactions that transmute elements are possible. For example, in 1919 Ernest Rutherford bombarded nitrogen-17 with alpha particles to form oxygen:

$$^{14}_{7}\text{N} + ^{4}_{2}\text{He} \longrightarrow ^{17}_{8}\text{O} + ^{1}_{1}\text{H}$$

Irène Joliot-Curie (daughter of Marie Curie) and her husband Frédéric bombarded aluminum-27 with alpha particles to form phosphorus:

$$^{27}_{13}\text{Al} + ^{4}_{2}\text{He} \longrightarrow ^{30}_{15}\text{P} + ^{1}_{0}\text{n}$$

In the 1930s, scientists began building devices that accelerate particles to high velocities, opening the door to even more possibilities. These devices are generally of two types, the **linear accelerator** and the **cyclotron**.

In a single-stage linear accelerator, a charged particle such as a proton is accelerated in an evacuated tube. The accelerating force is provided by a potential difference (or voltage) between the ends of the tube. In multistage linear accelerators, such as the Stanford Linear Accelerator (SLAC) at Stanford University, a series of tubes of increasing length are connected to a source of alternating voltage, as shown in Figure 21.15▶. The voltage alternates in such a way that, as a positively charged particle leaves a particular tube, that tube becomes positively charged, repelling the particle to the next tube. At the same

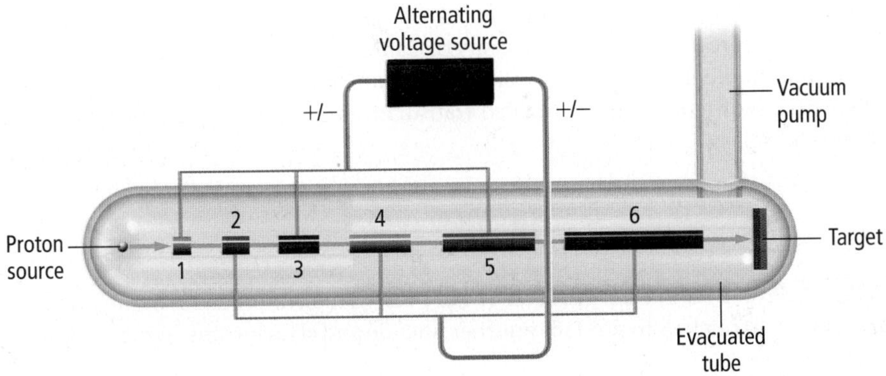

◀ **FIGURE 21.15 The Linear Accelerator** In a multistage linear accelerator, the charge on successive tubes is rapidly alternated in such a way that as a positively charged particle leaves a particular tube, that tube becomes positively charged, repelling the particle toward the next tube. At the same time, the tube that the particle is now approaching becomes negatively charged, pulling the particle toward it. This process repeats through a number of tubes until the particle has been accelerated to a high velocity.

time, the tube that the particle is now approaching becomes negatively charged, pulling the particle toward it. This continues throughout the linear accelerator, allowing the particle to be accelerated to velocities up to 90% of the speed of light. When particles of this speed collide with a target, they produce a shower of subatomic particles that can be studied. For example, researchers using the Stanford Linear Accelerator were awarded the 1990 Nobel Prize in physics for discovering evidence that protons and neutrons were composed of still smaller subatomic particles called *quarks*.

In a cyclotron, a similarly alternating voltage is used to accelerate a charged particle, only this time the alternating voltage is applied between the two semicircular halves of the cyclotron (Figure 21.16▼). A charged particle originally in the middle of the two semicircles is accelerated back and forth between them. Additional magnets cause the particle to move in a spiral path. As the charged particle spirals out from the center, it gains speed and eventually exits the cyclotron aimed at the target.

▲ The Stanford Linear Accelerator (top) is located at Stanford University in California. The Fermi National Accelerator Laboratory complex in Batavia, Illinois (bottom), includes two cyclotrons in a figure-8 configuration.

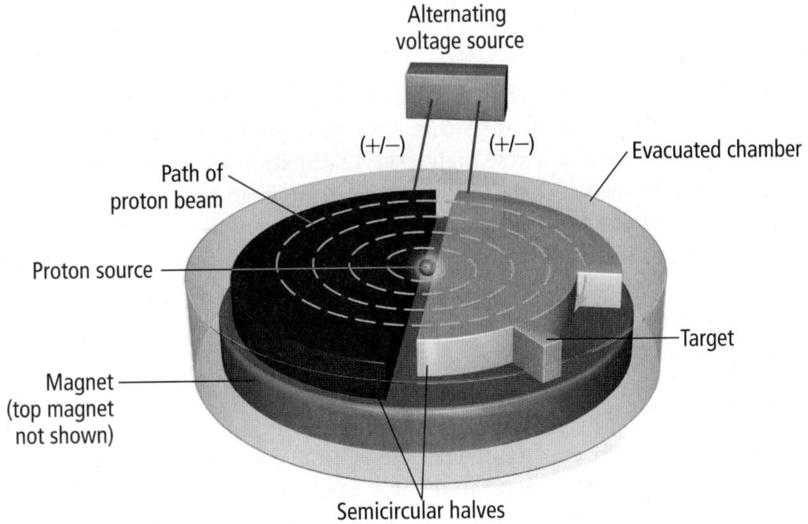

▲ **FIGURE 21.16 The Cyclotron** In a cyclotron, two semicircular D-shaped structures are subjected to an alternating voltage. A charged particle, starting from a point between the two, is accelerated back and forth between them, while additional magnets cause the particle to move in a spiral path.

With linear accelerators or cyclotrons, all sorts of nuclear transmutations can be achieved. In this way, scientists have made nuclides that don't normally exist in nature. For example, uranium-238 can be made to collide with carbon-12 to form an element with atomic number 98:

$$^{238}_{92}\text{U} + {}^{12}_{6}\text{C} \longrightarrow {}^{244}_{98}\text{Cf} + 6\,{}^{1}_{0}\text{n}$$

Most synthetic elements are unstable and have very short half-lives. Some exist for only fractions of a second after they are made.

This element was named californium (Cf) because it was first produced (by a slightly different nuclear reaction) at the University of California, Berkeley. Many other nuclides with atomic numbers larger than that of uranium have been synthesized since the 1940s. These synthetic elements—called transuranium elements—have been added to the periodic table.

ANSWER **NOW!**

21.8
Cc
Conceptual Connection

NUCLEAR TRANSFORMATIONS Californium-252 is bombarded with a boron-10 nucleus to produce another nuclide and six neutrons. Which nuclide forms?

(a) lawrencium-262
(b) lawrencium-256
(c) californium-246
(d) neptunium-236

21.11 The Effects of Radiation on Life

As we discussed in Section 21.2, the energy associated with radioactivity can ionize molecules. When radiation ionizes important molecules in living cells, problems can develop. The ingestion of radioactive materials—especially alpha and beta emitters—is particularly dangerous because the radioactivity once inside the body can do additional damage. The effects of radiation can be divided into three different types, which we discuss in this section: acute radiation damage, increased cancer risk, and genetic effects.

Acute Radiation Damage

Acute radiation damage results from exposure to large amounts of radiation in a short period of time. The main sources of this kind of exposure are nuclear bombs and exposed nuclear reactor cores. These high levels of radiation kill large numbers of cells. Rapidly dividing cells, such as those in the immune system and the intestinal lining, are most susceptible to radiation. Consequently, people exposed to high levels of radiation have weakened immune systems and a lowered ability to absorb nutrients from food. In milder cases, recovery is possible with time. In more extreme cases, death results, often from infection.

Increased Cancer Risk

We explain DNA in more detail in Chapter 23.

Lower doses of radiation over extended periods of time can increase cancer risk. Radiation increases cancer risk because it can damage DNA, the molecules in cells that carry instructions for cell growth and replication. When the DNA within a cell is damaged, the cell normally dies. Occasionally, however, changes in DNA cause cells to grow abnormally and to become cancerous. These cancerous cells grow into tumors that can spread and, in some cases, cause death. Cancer risk increases with increasing radiation exposure. However, cancer is so prevalent and has so many convoluted causes that determining an exact threshold for increased cancer risk from radiation exposure is difficult.

Genetic Defects

Another possible result of radiation exposure is genetic defects in future generations. If radiation damages the DNA of reproductive cells—such as eggs or sperm—then the offspring that develop from those cells may have genetic abnormalities. Genetic defects of this type have been observed in laboratory animals exposed to high levels of radiation. However, such genetic defects—with a clear causal connection to radiation exposure—have yet to be verified in humans, even in studies of Hiroshima survivors.

Measuring Radiation Exposure and Dose

We can measure radiation exposure in a number of different ways. One method is to measure **exposure**, the number of decay events to which a person is exposed. The unit used for this type of exposure measurement is the *curie* (Ci), defined as 3.7×10^{10} decay events per second. A person exposed to a curie of radiation from an alpha emitter is bombarded by 3.7×10^{10} alpha particles per second. However, recall that different kinds of radiation produce different effects. For example, we know that alpha radiation has a much greater ionizing power than beta radiation. Consequently, a certain number of alpha decays occurring within a person's body (due to the ingestion of an alpha emitter) do more damage than the same number of beta decays. If the alpha emitter and beta emitter are external to the body, however, the radiation from the alpha emitter is largely stopped by clothing or the skin (due to the low penetrating power of alpha radiation), whereas the radiation from the beta emitter penetrates the skin and causes more damage. Consequently, the curie is not an effective measure of how much biological tissue damage the radiation actually does.

A better way to assess radiation exposure is to measure radiation **dose**, the amount of energy actually absorbed by body tissue. The units used for this type of exposure measurement are the *gray* (Gy), which corresponds to 1 J of energy absorbed per kilogram of body tissue, and the *rad* (for *r*adiation *a*bsorbed *d*ose), which corresponds to 0.01 Gy:

$$1 \text{ gray (Gy)} = 1 \text{ J/kg body tissue}$$
$$1 \text{ rad} = 0.01 \text{ J/kg body tissue}$$

Although these units measure the actual energy absorbed by bodily tissues, they still do not account for the amount of damage to biological molecules caused by that energy absorption, which differs from one type of radiation to another and from one type of biological tissue to another. For example, when a gamma ray passes through biological tissue, the energy absorbed is spread out over the long distance that the radiation travels through the body, resulting in a low ionization density within the tissue. When an alpha particle passes through biological tissue, in contrast, the energy is absorbed over a much shorter distance, resulting in a much higher ionization density. The higher ionization density results in greater damage, even though the amount of energy absorbed by the tissue might be the same.

Consequently, a correction factor, called the **biological effectiveness factor**, or **RBE** (for *R*elative *B*iological *E*ffectiveness), is usually multiplied by the dose in rads to obtain the dose in a unit called the **rem** for *r*oentgen *e*quivalent *m*an:

A *roentgen* is defined as the amount of radiation that produces 2.58×10^{-1} C of charge per kg of air.

$$\text{Dose in rads} \times \text{biological effectiveness factor} = \text{dose in rems}$$

The biological effectiveness factor for alpha radiation, for example, is much higher than that for gamma radiation.

On average, each adult is exposed to approximately 310 mrem of radiation per year from natural sources, shown in Table 21.4. The majority of this exposure comes from radon, one of the products in the uranium decay series. As we can see from Table 21.4, however, some medical procedures also involve exposure levels similar to those received from natural sources. The increased use of computed tomography (CT) scans over the last decade—which have associated exposures of 200–1600 mrem—has raised some concerns about the overuse of that technology in medicine.

The SI unit that corresponds to the rem is the sievert (Sv). However, the rem is still commonly used in the United States. The conversion factor is 1 rem = 0.01 Sv.

It takes much more than the average natural radiation dose or the dose from a medical diagnostic procedure to produce significant health effects in humans. The first measurable effect, a decreased white blood cell count, occurs at instantaneous exposures of approximately 20 rem (Table 21.5). Exposures of 100 rem produce a definite increase in cancer risk, and exposures of over 500 rem often result in death.

TABLE 21.4 ■ Radiation Dose by Source for Persons Living in the United States

Source	Dose
Natural Radiation	
A 5-hour jet airplane ride	2.5 mrem/trip (0.5 mrem/hr at 39,000 feet) (whole body dose)
Cosmic radiation from outer space	27 mrem/yr (whole body dose)
Terrestrial radiation	28 mrem/yr (whole body dose)
Natural radionuclides in the body	35 mrem/yr (whole body dose)
Radon gas	200 mrem/yr (lung dose)
Diagnostic Medical Procedures	
Chest X-ray	8 mrem (whole body dose)
Dental X-rays (panoramic)	30 mrem (skin dose)
Dental X-rays (two bitewings)	80 mrem (skin dose)
Mammogram	138 mrem per image
Barium enema (X-ray portion only)	406 mrem (bone marrow dose)
Upper gastrointestinal tract test	244 mrem (X-ray portion only) (bone marrow dose)
Thallium heart scan	500 mrem (whole body dose)
Computed tomography (CT) head	200 mrem (whole body dose)
Computed tomography (CT) abdomen and pelvis	1000 mrem (whole body dose)
Consumer Products	
Building materials	3.5 mrem/yr (whole body dose)
Luminous watches (H-3 and Pm-147)	0.04–0.1 mrem/yr (whole body dose)
Tobacco products (to smokers of 30 cigarettes per day)	16,000 mrem/yr (bronchial epithelial dose)

Source: Department of Health and Human Services, National Institutes of Health.

TABLE 21.5 ■ Effects of Instantaneous Radiation Exposure

Approximate Dose (rem)	Probable Outcome
20–100	Decreased white blood cell count; possible increase in cancer risk
100–400	Radiation sickness including vomiting and diarrhea; skin lesions; increase in cancer risk
500	Death (often within 2 months)
1000	Death (often within 2 weeks)
2000	Death (within hours)

ANSWER NOW!

21.9 Cc Conceptual Connection

RADIATION DOSE Suppose a person ingests equal amounts of two nuclides, both of which are beta emitters (of roughly equal energy). Nuclide A has a half-life of 8.5 hours and Nuclide B has a half-life of 15.0 hours. Both nuclides are eliminated from the body within 24 hours of ingestion. Which of the two nuclides produces the greater radiation dose?

(a) Nuclide A **(b)** Nuclide B
(c) Both nuclides produce the same radiation dose.

21.12 Radioactivity in Medicine and Other Applications

Radioactivity is often perceived as dangerous; however, it is also immensely useful to physicians in the diagnosis and treatment of disease and has numerous other valuable applications. The use of radioactivity in medicine can be broadly divided into *diagnostic techniques* (which diagnose disease) and *therapeutic techniques* (which treat disease).

Diagnosis in Medicine

The use of radioactivity in diagnosis usually involves a **radiotracer**, a radioactive nuclide attached to a compound or introduced into a mixture in order to track the movement of the compound or mixture within the body. Tracers are useful in the diagnosis of disease because of two main factors: (1) the sensitivity with which radioactivity can be detected, and (2) the identical chemical behavior of a radioactive nucleus and its nonradioactive counterpart. For example, the thyroid gland naturally concentrates iodine. When a patient is given small amounts of iodine-131 (a radioactive isotope of iodine), the radioactive iodine accumulates in the thyroid, just as nonradioactive iodine does. However, the radioactive iodine emits radiation, which can be detected with great sensitivity and used to measure the rate of iodine uptake by the thyroid, and thus to image the gland.

Because different radiotracers are taken up preferentially by different organs or tissues, various radiotracers are used to monitor metabolic activity and image a variety of organs and structures, including the kidneys, heart, brain, gallbladder, bones, and arteries, as shown in Table 21.6. Radiotracers can also be employed to locate infections or cancers within the body. To locate an infection, antibodies are labeled (or tagged) with a radioactive nuclide, such as technetium-99m (where "m" means metastable), and administered to the patient. The tagged antibodies aggregate at the infected site, as described in Section 21.1. Cancerous tumors can be detected because they naturally concentrate phosphorus. When a patient is given phosphorus-32 (a radioactive isotope of phosphorus) or a phosphate compound incorporating another radioactive isotope such as Tc-99m, the tumors concentrate the radioactive substance and become sources of radioactivity that can be detected (Figure 21.17▲).

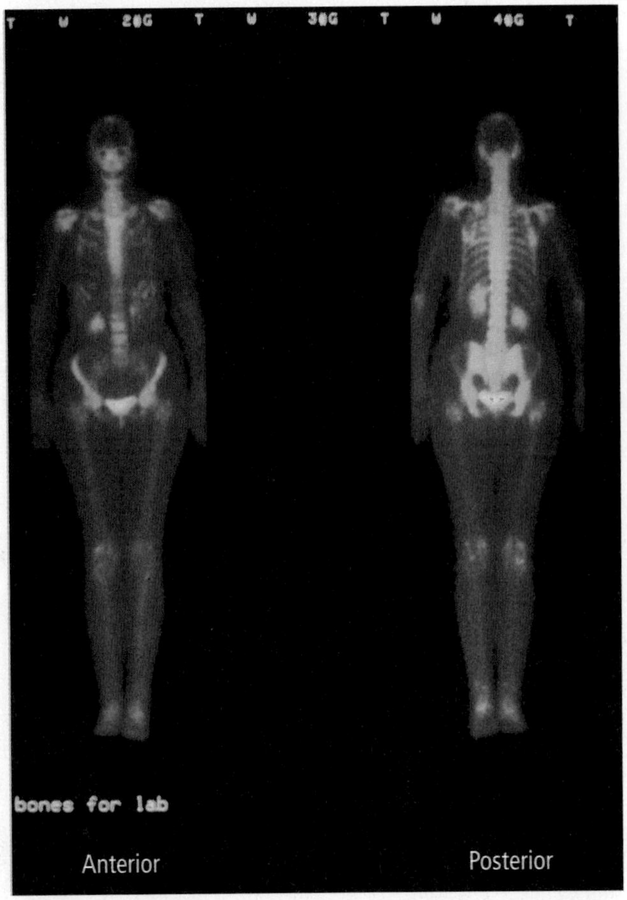

▲ **FIGURE 21.17 A Bone Scan** These images, front and rear views of the human body, were created by the gamma ray emissions of Tc-99m. Such scans are used to locate cancer that has metastasized (spread) to the bones from a primary tumor elsewhere.

A specialized imaging technique known as **positron emission tomography (PET)** employs positron-emitting nuclides, such as fluorine-18, synthesized in cyclotrons. The fluorine-18 is attached to a metabolically active substance such as glucose and administered to the patient. As the glucose travels through the bloodstream and to the heart and brain, it carries the radioactive fluorine, which decays with a half-life of just under two hours. When a fluorine-18 nuclide decays, it emits a positron that immediately combines with any nearby electrons. Since a positron and an electron are antiparticles, they annihilate one other, producing two gamma rays that travel in exactly opposing directions. The gamma rays can be detected by an array of detectors that can

TABLE 21.6 ■ Common Radiotracers

Nuclide	Type of Emission	Half-Life	Body Part Studied
Technetium-99m	Gamma (primarily)	6.01 hours	Various organs, bones
Iodine-131	Beta	8.0 days	Thyroid
Iron-59	Beta	44.5 days	Blood, spleen
Thallium-201	Electron capture	3.05 days	Heart
Fluorine-18	Positron emission	1.83 hours	PET studies of heart, brain
Phosphorus-32	Beta	14.3 days	Tumors in various organs

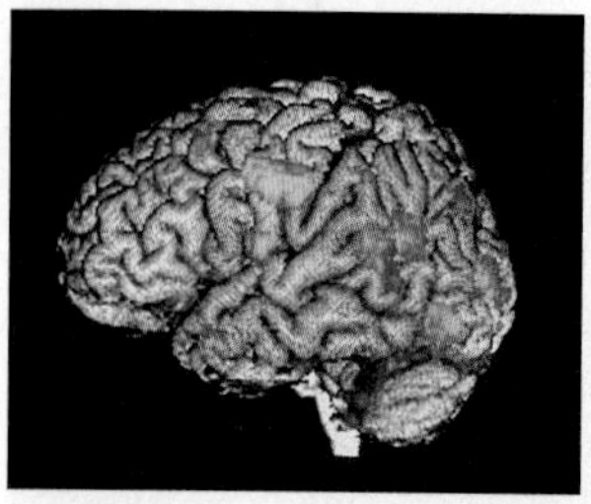

▲ **FIGURE 21.18 A PET Scan** The colored areas indicate regions of high metabolic activity in the brain of a schizophrenic patient experiencing hallucinations.

locate the point of origin of the rays with great accuracy. The result is a set of highly detailed images that show both the rate of glucose metabolism and structural features of the imaged organ (Figure 21.18◀).

Radiotherapy in Medicine

Because radiation kills cells and is particularly effective at killing rapidly dividing cells, it is often used as a therapy for cancer (cancer cells reproduce much faster than normal cells). Medical technicians focus high-energy photons on internal tumors to kill them. The photon beam is usually moved in a circular path around the tumor (Figure 21.19▼), maximizing the exposure of the tumor while minimizing the exposure of the surrounding healthy tissue. Nonetheless, cancer patients receiving such treatment usually develop the symptoms of radiation sickness, which include vomiting, skin burns, and hair loss.

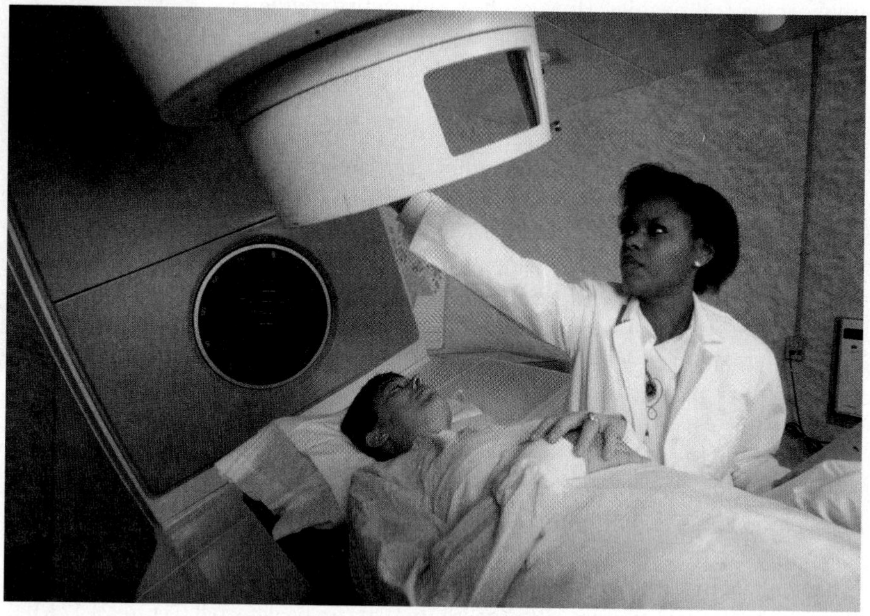

► **FIGURE 21.19 Radiotherapy for Cancer** This treatment involves exposing a malignant tumor to gamma rays generated by nuclides such as cobalt-60. The beam is moved in a circular pattern around the tumor to maximize exposure of the tumor to radiation while minimizing the exposure of healthy tissues.

You may wonder why radiation—which is known to cause cancer—is also used to treat cancer. The answer lies in risk analysis. A cancer patient is normally exposed to radiation doses of about 100 rem. Such a dose increases cancer risk by about 1%. However, if the patient has a 100% chance of dying from the cancer that he already has, such a risk becomes acceptable, especially since there is a significant chance of curing the cancer.

Other Applications

Radioactivity is often used to kill microorganisms. For example, physicians use radiation to sterilize medical devices that are to be surgically implanted. The radiation kills bacteria that might otherwise lead to infection. Similarly, radiation is used to kill bacteria and parasites in foods. Like the pasteurization of milk, the irradiation of foods makes them safer to consume and gives them a longer shelf life (Figure 21.20◀). The irradiation of raw meat and poultry kills *E. coli* and *Salmonella*, bacteria that can lead to serious illness and even death when consumed. The irradiation of food does not, however, make the food itself radioactive, nor does it decrease the nutritional value of the food. In the United States, the irradiation of many different types of foods—including beef, poultry, potatoes, flour, and fruit—has been approved by the U.S. Food and Drug Administration (FDA) and the U.S. Department of Agriculture (USDA).

▲ **FIGURE 21.20 Irradiation of Food** Irradiation kills microbes that cause food to decay, allowing for longer and safer storage. The food is not made radioactive, and its properties are unchanged in the process. These strawberries were picked at the same time, but those on the bottom were irradiated before storage.

Radioactivity is also used to control harmful insect populations. For example, fruit flies can be raised in large numbers in captivity and sterilized with radiation. When these fruit flies are released, they mate with wild fruit flies but do not produce offspring. The efforts of the wild fruit flies, which might otherwise lead to reproduction, are wasted, and the next generation of flies is smaller than it would otherwise have been. Similar strategies have been employed to control the populations of disease-carrying mosquitoes.

QUIZ YOURSELF **NOW!**

Self-Assessment Quiz

Q1. Which daughter nuclide forms when polonium-214 undergoes alpha decay?
MISSED THIS? *Read Section 21.3; Watch KCV 21.3, IWE 21.1*

a) $^{218}_{86}Rn$ b) $^{214}_{85}At$ c) $^{214}_{83}Bi$ d) $^{210}_{82}Pb$

Q2. Which nuclear equation accurately represents the beta decay of Xe-133?
MISSED THIS? *Read Section 21.3; Watch KCV 21.3, IWE 21.2*

a) $^{133}_{54}Xe \longrightarrow ^{133}_{55}Cs + ^{0}_{-1}e$
b) $^{133}_{54}Xe \longrightarrow ^{133}_{53}I + ^{0}_{+1}e$
c) $^{133}_{54}Xe + ^{0}_{-1}e \longrightarrow ^{133}_{53}I$
d) $^{133}_{54}Xe \longrightarrow ^{129}_{52}Cs + ^{4}_{2}He$

Q3. Which nuclide is most likely to undergo beta decay?
MISSED THIS? *Read Section 21.4*

a) Si-22 b) Rb-91 c) Ar-35 d) Co-52

Q4. Which form of radioactive decay would you be most likely to detect if it were happening in the room next to the one you are currently in? **MISSED THIS?** *Read Section 21.3; Watch KCV 21.3*

a) alpha b) beta
c) gamma d) positron emission

Q5. The chart shows the mass of a decaying nuclide versus time. What is the half-life of the decay?
MISSED THIS? *Read Section 21.6*

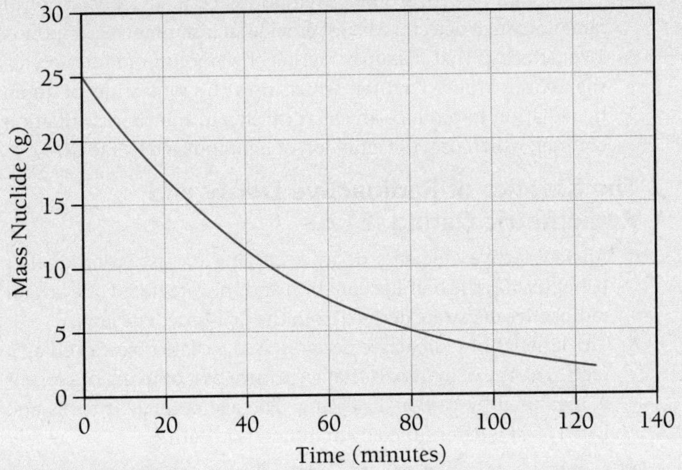

a) 15 min b) 25 min
c) 35 min d) 70 min

Q6. Iron-59 is a beta emitter with a half-life of 44.5 days. If a sample initially contains 132 mg of iron-59, how much iron-59 is left in the sample after 265 days?
MISSED THIS? *Read Section 21.6; Watch IWE 21.4*

a) 0.00 mg
b) 2.13 mg
c) 33.2 mg
d) 66.0 mg

Q7. An artifact has a carbon-14 decay rate of 8.55 disintegrations per minute per gram of carbon (8.55 dis/min · g C). Living organisms have carbon-14 decay rate of 15.3 dis/min · g C. How old is the artifact? (The half-life of carbon-14 is 5715 yr.)
MISSED THIS? *Read Section 21.6; Watch IWE 21.5*

a) 4.81×10^3 yr
b) 2.10×10^3 yr
c) 3.20×10^3 yr
d) 1.21×10^{-4} yr

Q8. An igneous rock contains a Pb-206/U-238 mass ratio of 0.372. How old is the rock? (U-238 decays into Pb-206 with a half-life of 4.5×10^9 yr.) **MISSED THIS?** *Read Section 21.6*

a) 4.50×10^9 yr
b) 6.42×10^9 yr
c) 2.05×10^9 yr
d) 2.32×10^9 yr

Q9. Calculate the nuclear binding energy per nucleon for cobalt-59, the only stable isotope of cobalt. The mass of cobalt-59 is 58.933198 amu. (The mass of $^{1}_{1}H$ is 1.00783 amu, and the mass of a neutron is 1.00866 amu.)
MISSED THIS? *Read Section 21.8*

a) 517.3 MeV
b) 8.768 MeV
c) 19.16 MeV
d) 1.011×10^{-5} MeV

Q10. Which problem is not associated with nuclear power generation? **MISSED THIS?** *Read Section 21.9*

a) danger of overheated nuclear core
b) waste disposal
c) global warming
d) none of the above (All of the above are problems associated with nuclear power generation.)

Answers: **1.** (d) **2.** (a) **3.** (b) **4.** (c) **5.** (c) **6.** (b) **7.** (a) **8.** (d) **9.** (b) **10.** (c)

CHAPTER 21 IN REVIEW

TERMS

Section 21.1
radioactivity (948)
radioactive (948)

Section 21.2
phosphorescence (948)

Section 21.3
nuclide (949)
alpha (α) decay (950)
alpha (α) particle (950)
nuclear equation (950)
ionizing power (951)
penetrating power (951)
beta (β) decay (951)
beta (β) particle (951)
gamma (γ) ray emission (952)
gamma (γ) ray (952)
positron emission (952)
positron (952)
electron capture (953)

Section 21.4
strong force (955)
nucleons (955)
magic numbers (956)

Section 21.5
thermoluminescent dosimeter (957)
Geiger–Müller counter (957)
scintillation counter (958)

Section 21.6
radiometric dating (961)
radiocarbon dating (961)

Section 21.7
nuclear fission (965)
chain reaction (965)
critical mass (965)

Section 21.8
mass defect (970)
nuclear binding energy (970)

Section 21.9
nuclear fusion (971)

Section 21.10
transmutation (972)
linear accelerator (972)
cyclotron (972)

Section 21.11
exposure (975)
dose (975)
biological effectiveness factor (RBE) (975)
rem (975)

Section 21.12
radiotracer (977)
positron emission tomography (PET) (977)

CONCEPTS

Diagnosing Appendicitis (21.1)

- Radioactivity is the emission of subatomic particles or energetic electromagnetic radiation by the nuclei of certain atoms.
- Because some radioactive emissions can pass through matter, radioactivity is useful in medicine and many other areas of study.

The Discovery of Radioactivity (21.2)

- Radioactivity was discovered by Antoine-Henri Becquerel when he found that uranium causes a photographic exposure in the absence of light.
- Marie Sklodowska Curie later determined that this phenomenon was not unique to uranium, and she began calling the rays that produced the exposure radioactivity. Curie also discovered two new elements, polonium and radium.

Types of Radioactivity (21.3)

- The major types of natural radioactivity are alpha (α) decay, beta (β) decay, gamma (γ) ray emission, and positron emission.
- Alpha radiation is helium nuclei. Beta particles are electrons. Gamma rays are electromagnetic radiation of very high energy. Positrons are the antiparticles of electrons.
- A nucleus may absorb one of its orbital electrons in a process called electron capture.
- We can represent each radioactive process with a nuclear equation that illustrates how the parent nuclide changes into the daughter nuclide. In a nuclear equation, although the specific types of atoms may not balance, the atomic numbers and mass numbers must.
- Each type of radioactivity has a different ionizing and penetrating power. These values are inversely related; a particle with a higher ionizing power has a lower penetrating power. Alpha particles are the most massive and they have the highest ionizing power, followed by beta particles and positrons, which are equivalent in their ionizing power. Gamma rays have the lowest ionizing power.

The Valley of Stability: Predicting the Type of Radioactivity (21.4)

- The stability of a nucleus, and therefore the probability that it will undergo radioactive decay, depends largely on two factors. The first is the ratio of neutrons to protons (N/Z) because neutrons provide a strong force that overcomes the electromagnetic repulsions between the positive protons. This ratio is one for smaller elements but becomes greater than one for larger elements. The second factor related to nuclei stability is a concept known as magic numbers; certain numbers of nucleons are more stable than others.

Detecting Radioactivity (21.5)

- Radiation detectors determine the quantity of radioactivity in an area or sample.
- Thermoluminescent dosimeters employ salt crystals for detection of radiation; such detectors do not provide an instantaneous response.
- Two detectors that instantly register the amount of radiation are the Geiger–Müller counter, which uses the ionization of argon by radiation to produce an electrical signal, and the scintillation counter, which uses the emission of light induced by radiation.

The Kinetics of Radioactive Decay and Radiometric Dating (21.6)

- All radioactive elements decay according to first-order kinetics (Chapter 15); the half-life equation and the integrated rate law for radioactive decay are derived from the first-order rate laws.
- The kinetics of radioactive decay is used to date objects and artifacts. The age of materials that were once part of living organisms is measured by carbon-14 dating. The age of ancient rocks and Earth itself is determined by uranium/lead dating.

The Discovery of Fission: The Atomic Bomb and Nuclear Power (21.7)

- Fission is the splitting of an atom, such as uranium-235, into two atoms of lesser atomic weight.
- Because the fission of one uranium-235 atom releases enormous amounts of energy and produces neutrons that can split other uranium-235 atoms, the energy from these collective reactions can be harnessed in an atomic bomb or nuclear reactor.
- Nuclear power produces no air pollution and requires little mass to release lots of energy; however, there is always a danger of accidents, and it is difficult to dispose of nuclear waste.

Converting Mass to Energy: Mass Defect and Nuclear Binding Energy (21.8)

- In a nuclear fission reaction, mass is converted into energy.
- The difference in mass between a nuclide and the individual protons and neutrons that compose it is the mass defect, and the corresponding energy, calculated from Einstein's equation $E = mc^2$, is the nuclear binding energy.
- The stability of a nucleus is determined by the binding energy per nucleon, which increases up to mass number 60 and then decreases.

Nuclear Fusion: The Power of the Sun (21.9)

- Stars produce their energy by the process that is the opposite of fission: nuclear fusion, the combination of two light nuclei to form a heavier one.
- Modern nuclear weapons employ fusion. Although fusion has been examined as a possible method to produce electricity, experiments with hydrogen fusion have thus far been more costly than productive.

Nuclear Transmutation and Transuranium Elements (21.10)

- Nuclear transmutation, the changing of one element to another element, was used to create the transuranium elements, elements with atomic numbers greater than that of uranium.
- Two devices are most commonly used to accelerate particles to the high speeds necessary for transmutation reactions: the linear accelerator and the cyclotron. Both use alternating voltage to propel particles by electromagnetic forces.

The Effects of Radiation on Life (21.11)

- The effects of radiation can be grouped into three categories. Acute radiation damage is caused by a large exposure to radiation for a short period of time. Lower radiation exposures may result in increased cancer risk because of damage to DNA. Genetic defects are caused by damage to the DNA of reproductive cells.
- The most effective unit of measurement for the amount of radiation absorbed is the rem, which takes into account the different penetrating and ionizing powers of the various types of radiation.

Radioactivity in Medicine (21.12)

- Radioactivity is central to the diagnosis of medical problems by means of radiotracers and positron emission tomography (PET). Both of these techniques can provide data about the appearance and metabolic activity of an organ, or help locate a tumor.
- Radiation is also used to treat cancer because it kills cells. Radiation can kill bacteria in foods and control harmful insect populations.

EQUATIONS AND RELATIONSHIPS

The First-Order Rate Law (21.6)

$$\text{Rate} = kN$$

The Half-Life Equation (21.6)

$$t_{1/2} = \frac{0.693}{k} \quad k = \text{rate constant}$$

The Integrated Rate Law (21.6)

$$\ln \frac{N_t}{N_0} = -kt \quad N_t = \text{number of radioactive nuclei at time } t$$

$$N_0 = \text{initial number of radioactive nuclei}$$

Einstein's Energy–Mass Equation (21.8)

$$E = mc^2$$

LEARNING OUTCOMES

Chapter Objectives	Assessment
Write nuclear equations for alpha decay (21.3)	Example 21.1 **For Practice** 21.1 **Exercises** 31–36
Write nuclear equations for beta decay, gamma emission, positron decay, and electron capture (21.3)	Example 21.2 **For Practice** 21.2 **For More Practice** 21.2 **Exercises** 31–36
Predict the type of radioactive decay (21.4)	Example 21.3 **For Practice** 21.3 **Exercises** 37–44
Perform radioactive decay calculations (21.6)	Example 21.4 **For Practice** 21.4 **Exercises** 45–50
Perform radiometric carbon dating calculations (21.6)	Example 21.5 **For Practice** 21.5 **Exercises** 51–54
Perform radiometric uranium/lead dating calculations (21.6)	Example 21.6 **For Practice** 21.6 **Exercises** 55–56
Predict the products of neutron-induced fission reactions (21.7)	**Exercises** 57–64
Perform mass-energy calculations for nuclear fission (21.8)	Example 21.7 **For Practice** 21.7 **Exercises** 65–70
Perform mass-energy calculations for nuclear fusion (21.9)	**Exercises** 71–72
Determine the amount of energy absorbed from the decay of radioactive material (21.11)	**Exercises** 73–76

EXERCISES

Mastering Chemistry provides end-of-chapter exercises, feedback-enriched tutorial problems, animations, and interactive activities to encourage problem-solving practice and deeper understanding of key concepts and topics.

REVIEW QUESTIONS

1. What is radioactivity? Who discovered it? How was it discovered?
2. Explain Marie Curie's role in the discovery of radioactivity.
3. Define *A*, *Z*, and *X* in the following notation used to specify a nuclide: ${}^{A}_{Z}X$.
4. Use the notation from Question 3 to write symbols for a proton, a neutron, and an electron.
5. What is an alpha particle? What happens to the mass number and atomic number of a nuclide that emits an alpha particle?
6. What is a beta particle? What happens to the mass number and atomic number of a nuclide that emits a beta particle?
7. What is a gamma ray? What happens to the mass number and atomic number of a nuclide that emits a gamma ray?
8. What is a positron? What happens to the mass number and atomic number of a nuclide that emits a positron?
9. Describe the process of electron capture. What happens to the mass number and atomic number of a nuclide that undergoes electron capture?
10. Rank alpha particles, beta particles, positrons, and gamma rays in terms of: (a) increasing ionizing power; (b) increasing penetrating power.
11. Explain why the ratio of neutrons to protons (N/Z) is important in determining nuclear stability. How can you use the N/Z ratio of a nuclide to predict the kind of radioactive decay that it might undergo?
12. What are magic numbers? How are they important in determining the stability of a nuclide?
13. Describe the basic way that each device detects radioactivity: (a) thermoluminescent dosimeter; (b) Geiger–Müller counter; and (c) scintillation counter.
14. Explain the concept of half-life with respect to radioactive nuclides. What rate law is characteristic of radioactivity?
15. Explain the main concepts behind the technique of radiocarbon dating. How can radiocarbon dating be corrected for changes in atmospheric concentrations of C-14? What range of ages can be reliably determined by C-14 dating?
16. How is the uranium to lead ratio in a rock used to estimate its age? How does this dating technique provide an estimate for Earth's age? How old is Earth according to this dating method?
17. Describe fission. Include the concepts of chain reaction and critical mass in your description. How and by whom was fission discovered? Explain how fission can be used to generate electricity.
18. What was the Manhattan Project? Briefly describe its development and culmination.
19. Describe the advantages and disadvantages of using fission to generate electricity.
20. The products of a nuclear reaction usually have a different mass than the reactants. Why?
21. Explain the concepts of mass defect and nuclear binding energy. At what mass number does the nuclear binding energy per nucleon peak? What is the significance of this?
22. What is fusion? Why can fusion and fission both produce energy? Explain.
23. What are some of the problems associated with using fusion to generate electricity?
24. Explain transmutation and provide one or two examples.
25. How does a linear accelerator work? For what purpose is it used?
26. Explain the basic principles of cyclotron function.
27. How does radiation affect living organisms?
28. Explain why different kinds of radiation affect biological tissues differently, even though the amount of radiation exposure may be the same.
29. Explain the significance of the biological effectiveness factor in measuring radiation exposure. What types of radiation would you expect to have the highest biological effectiveness factor?
30. Describe some of the medical uses, both in diagnosis and in treatment of disease, of radioactivity.

PROBLEMS BY TOPIC

Radioactive Decay and Nuclide Stability

31. Write a nuclear equation for the indicated decay of each nuclide.
MISSED THIS? *Read Section 21.3; Watch KCV 21.3, IWE 21.1, 21.2*
a. U-234 (alpha)
b. Th-230 (alpha)
c. Pb-214 (beta)
d. N-13 (positron emission)
e. Cr-51 (electron capture)
32. Write a nuclear equation for the indicated decay of each nuclide.
a. Po-210 (alpha)
b. Ac-227 (beta)
c. Tl-207 (beta)
d. O-15 (positron emission)
e. Pd-103 (electron capture)
33. Write a partial decay series for Th-232 undergoing the sequential decays: $\alpha, \beta, \beta, \alpha$.
MISSED THIS? *Read Section 21.3; Watch KCV 21.3, IWE 21.1, 21.2*
34. Write a partial decay series for Rn-220 undergoing the sequential decays: $\alpha, \alpha, \beta, \beta$.
35. Fill in the missing particles in each nuclear equation.
MISSED THIS? *Read Section 21.3; Watch KCV 21.3, IWE 21.1, 21.2*
a. $\_\_\_\_ \longrightarrow {}^{217}_{85}At + {}^{4}_{2}He$
b. ${}^{241}_{94}Pu \longrightarrow {}^{241}_{95}Am + \_\_\_\_$
c. ${}^{19}_{11}Ne \longrightarrow {}^{19}_{10}Ne + \_\_\_\_$
d. ${}^{75}_{34}Se + \_\_\_\_ \longrightarrow {}^{75}_{33}As$
36. Fill in the missing particles in each nuclear equation.
a. ${}^{241}_{95}Am \longrightarrow {}^{237}_{93}Np + \_\_\_\_$
b. $\_\_\_\_ \longrightarrow {}^{233}_{92}U + {}^{0}_{-1}e$
c. ${}^{237}_{93}Np \longrightarrow \_\_\_\_ + {}^{4}_{2}He$
d. ${}^{75}_{35}Br \longrightarrow \_\_\_\_ + {}^{0}_{+1}e$

37. Determine whether or not each nuclide is likely to be stable. State your reasons. **MISSED THIS?** *Read Section 21.4*
a. Mg-26 b. Ne-25
c. Co-51 d. Te-124

38. Determine whether or not each nuclide is likely to be stable. State your reasons.
a. Ti-48 b. Cr-63
c. Sn-102 d. Y-88

39. The first six elements of the first transition series have the following number of stable isotopes:
MISSED THIS? *Read Section 21.4*

Element	Number of Stable Isotopes
Sc	1
Ti	5
V	1
Cr	3
Mn	1
Fe	4

Explain why Sc, V, and Mn each have only one stable isotope while the other elements have several.

40. Neon and magnesium each have three stable isotopes while sodium and aluminum each have only one. Explain why this might be so.

41. Predict a likely mode of decay for each unstable nuclide.
MISSED THIS? *Read Section 21.4*
a. Mo-109 b. Ru-90
c. P-27 d. Sn-100

42. Predict a likely mode of decay for each unstable nuclide.
a. Sb-132 b. Te-139
c. Fr-202d. Ba-123

43. Which nuclide in each pair would you expect to have the longer half-life? **MISSED THIS?** *Read Section 21.4*
a. Cs-113 or Cs-125
b. Fe-62 or Fe-70

44. Which nuclide in each pair would you expect to have the longer half-life?
a. Cs-149 or Cs-139
b. Fe-45 or Fe-52

The Kinetics of Radioactive Decay and Radiometric Dating

45. One of the nuclides in spent nuclear fuel is U-235, an alpha emitter with a half-life of 703 million years. How long will it take for the amount of U-235 to reach 10.0% of its initial amount?
MISSED THIS? *Read Section 21.6; Watch IWE 21.4*

46. A patient is given 0.050 μg of technetium-99m, a radioactive isotope with a half-life of about 6.0 hours. How long does it take for the radioactive isotope to decay to $1.0 \times 10^{-3} \mu g$? (Assume no excretion of the nuclide from the body.)

47. A radioactive sample contains 1.55 g of an isotope with a half-life of 3.8 days. What mass of the isotope remains after 5.5 days?
MISSED THIS? *Read Section 21.6; Watch IWE 21.4*

48. At 8:00 A.M., a patient receives a 1.5-μg dose of I-131 to treat thyroid cancer. If the nuclide has a half-life of eight days, what mass of the nuclide remains in the patient at 5:00 P.M. the next day? (Assume no excretion of the nuclide from the body.)

49. A sample of F-18 has an initial decay rate of 1.5×10^5/s. How long will it take for the decay rate to fall to 2.5×10^3/s? (F-18 has a half-life of 1.83 hours.)
MISSED THIS? *Read Section 21.6; Watch IWE 21.4*

50. A sample of Tl-201 has an initial decay rate of 5.88×10^4/s. How long will it take for the decay rate to fall to 287/s? (Tl-201 has a half-life of 3.042 days.)

51. A wooden boat discovered just south of the Great Pyramid in Egypt has a carbon-14/carbon-12 ratio that is 72.5% of that found in living organisms. How old is the boat?
MISSED THIS? *Read Section 21.6; Watch IWE 21.5*

52. A layer of peat beneath the glacial sediments of the last ice age has a carbon-14/carbon-12 ratio that is 22.8% of that found in living organisms. How long ago was this ice age?

53. An ancient skull has a carbon-14 decay rate of 0.85 disintegration per minute per gram of carbon (0.85 dis/min · g C). How old is the skull? (Assume that living organisms have a carbon-14 decay rate of 15.3 dis/min · g C and that carbon-14 has a half-life of 5715 yr.)
MISSED THIS? *Read Section 21.6; Watch IWE 21.5*

54. A mammoth skeleton has a carbon-14 decay rate of 0.48 disintegration per minute per gram of carbon (0.48 dis/min · g C). When did the mammoth live? (Assume that living organisms have a carbon-14 decay rate of 15.3 dis/min · g C and that carbon-14 has a half-life of 5715 yr.)

55. A rock from Australia contains 0.438 g of Pb-206 to every 1.00 g of U-238.Assuming that the rock did not contain any Pb-206 at the time of its formation, how old is the rock?
MISSED THIS? *Read Section 21.6*

56. A meteor has a Pb-206:U-238 mass ratio of 0.855:1.00. What is the age of the meteor? (Assume that the meteor did not contain any Pb-206 at the time of its formation.)

Fission, Fusion, and Transmutation

57. Write the nuclear reaction for the neutron-induced fission of U-235 to form Xe-144 and Sr-90. How many neutrons are produced in the reaction? **MISSED THIS?** *Read Section 21.7*

58. Write the nuclear reaction for the neutron-induced fission of U-235 to produce Te-137 and Zr-97. How many neutrons are produced in the reaction?

59. Write the nuclear equation for the fusion of two H-2 atoms to form He-3 and one neutron. **MISSED THIS?** *Read Section 21.9*

60. Write the nuclear equation for the fusion of H-3 with H-1 to form He-4.

61. A breeder nuclear reactor is a reactor in which nonfissionable (nonfissile) U-238 is converted into fissionable (fissile) Pu-239. The process involves bombardment of U-238 by neutrons to form U-239, which then undergoes two sequential beta decays. Write nuclear equations for this process.
MISSED THIS? *Read Sections 21.3, 21.7; Watch KCV 21.3, IWE 21.2*

62. Write the series of nuclear equations to represent the bombardment of Al-27 with a neutron to form a product that subsequently undergoes a beta decay.

63. Rutherfordium-257 was synthesized by bombarding Cf-249 with C-12. Write the nuclear equation for this reaction.
MISSED THIS? *Read Section 21.10*

64. Element 107, now named bohrium, was synthesized by German researchers by colliding bismuth-209 with chromium-54 to form a bohrium isotope and one neutron. Write the nuclear equation to represent this reaction.

Energetics of Nuclear Reactions, Mass Defect, and Nuclear Binding Energy

65. If 1.0 g of matter is converted to energy, how much energy is formed? **MISSED THIS?** *Read Section 21.8*

66. A typical home uses approximately 1.0×10^3 kWh of energy per month. If the energy came from a nuclear reaction, what mass would have to be converted to energy per year to meet the energy needs of the home?

67. Calculate the mass defect and nuclear binding energy per nucleon of each nuclide. **MISSED THIS?** *Read Section 21.8*

a. O-16 (atomic mass = 15.994915 amu)
b. Ni-58 (atomic mass = 57.935346 amu)
c. Xe-129 (atomic mass = 128.904780 amu)

68. Calculate the mass defect and nuclear binding energy per nucleon of each nuclide.

a. Li-7 (atomic mass = 7.016003 amu)
b. Ti-48 (atomic mass = 47.947947 amu)
c. Ag-107 (atomic mass = 106.905092 amu)

69. Calculate the quantity of energy produced per gram of U-235 (atomic mass = 235.043922 amu) for the neutron-induced fission of U-235 to form Xe-144 (atomic mass = 143.9385 amu) and Sr-90 (atomic mass = 89.907738 amu) (discussed in Problem 57). **MISSED THIS?** *Read Section 21.8*

70. Calculate the quantity of energy produced per mole of U-235 (atomic mass = 235.043922 amu) for the neutron-induced fission of U-235 to produce Te-137 (atomic mass = 136.9253 amu) and Zr-97 (atomic mass = 96.910950 amu) (discussed in Problem 58).

71. Calculate the quantity of energy produced per gram of reactant for the fusion of two H-2 (atomic mass = 2.014102 amu) atoms to form He-3 (atomic mass = 3.016029 amu) and one neutron (discussed in Problem 59). **MISSED THIS?** *Read Section 21.8*

72. Calculate the quantity of energy produced per gram of reactant for the fusion of H-3 (atomic mass = 3.016049 amu) with H-1 (atomic mass = 1.007825 amu) to form He-4 (atomic mass = 4.002603 amu) (discussed in Problem 60).

Effects and Applications of Radioactivity

73. A 75-kg human has a dose of 32.8 rad of radiation. How much energy is absorbed by the person's body? Compare this energy to the amount of energy absorbed by the person's body if he or she jumped from a chair to the floor (assume that the chair is 0.50 m from the ground and that all of the energy from the fall is absorbed by the person). **MISSED THIS?** *Read Section 21.11*

74. If a 55-gram laboratory mouse has a dose of 20.5 rad of radiation, how much energy is absorbed by the mouse's body?

75. PET studies require fluorine-18, which is produced in a cyclotron and decays with a half-life of 1.83 hours. Assuming that the F-18 can be transported at 60.0 miles/hour, how close must the hospital be to the cyclotron if 65% of the F-18 produced makes it to the hospital?
MISSED THIS? *Read Sections 21.6, 21.11; Watch IWE 21.4*

76. Suppose a patient is given 1.55 μg of I-131, a beta emitter with a half-life of 8.0 days. Assuming that none of the I-131 is eliminated from the person's body in the first 4.0 hours of treatment, what is the exposure (in Ci) during those first four hours?

CUMULATIVE PROBLEMS

77. Complete each nuclear equation and calculate the energy change (in J/mol of reactant) associated with each (Be-9 = 9.012182 amu, Bi-209 = 208.980384 amu, He-4 = 4.002603 amu, Li-6 = 6.015122 amu, Ni-64 = 63.927969 amu, Rg-272 = 272.1535 amu, Ta-179 = 178.94593 amu, and W-179 = 178.94707 amu).

a. $\_\_\_ + {}^{9}_{4}\text{Be} \longrightarrow {}^{6}_{3}\text{Li} + {}^{4}_{2}\text{He}$
b. ${}^{209}_{83}\text{Bi} + {}^{64}_{28}\text{Ni} \longrightarrow {}^{272}_{111}\text{Rg} + \_\_\_$
c. ${}^{179}_{74}\text{W} + \_\_\_ \longrightarrow {}^{179}_{73}\text{Ta}$

78. Complete each nuclear equation and calculate the energy change (in J/mol of reactant) associated with each (Al-27 = 26.981538 amu, Am-241 = 241.056822 amu, He-4 = 4.002603 amu, Np-237 = 237.048166 amu, P-30 = 29.981801 amu, S-32 = 31.972071 amu, and Si-29 = 28.976495 amu).

a. ${}^{27}_{13}\text{Al} + {}^{4}_{2}\text{He} \longrightarrow {}^{30}_{15}\text{P} + \_\_\_$
b. ${}^{32}_{16}\text{S} + \_\_\_ \longrightarrow {}^{29}_{14}\text{Si} + {}^{4}_{2}\text{He}$
c. ${}^{241}_{95}\text{Am} \longrightarrow {}^{237}_{93}\text{Np} + \_\_\_$

79. Write the nuclear equation for the most likely mode of decay for each unstable nuclide.

a. Ru-114
b. Ra-216
c. Zn-58
d. Ne-31

80. Write the nuclear equation for the most likely mode of decay for each unstable nuclide.

a. Kr-74
b. Th-221
c. Ar-44
d. Nb-85

81. Bismuth-210 is a beta emitter with a half-life of 5.0 days. If a sample contains 1.2 g of Bi-210 (atomic mass = 209.984105 amu), how many beta emissions occur in 13.5 days? If a person's body intercepts 5.5% of those emissions, to what amount of radiation (in Ci) is the person exposed?

82. Polonium-218 is an alpha emitter with a half-life of 3.0 minutes. If a sample contains 55 mg of Po-218 (atomic mass = 218.008965 amu), how many alpha emissions occur in 25.0 minutes? If the polonium is ingested by a person, to what amount of radiation (in Ci) is the person exposed?

83. Radium-226 (atomic mass = 226.025402 amu) decays to radon-224 (a radioactive gas) with a half-life of 1.6×10^3 years. What volume of radon gas (at 25.0 °C and 1.0 atm) does 25.0 g of radium produce in 5.0 days? (Report your answer to two significant digits.)

84. In one of the neutron-induced fission reactions of U-235 (atomic mass = 235.043922 amu), the products are Ba-140 and Kr-93 (a radioactive gas). What volume of Kr-93 (at 25.0 °C and 1.0 atm) is produced when 1.00 g of U-235 undergoes this fission reaction?

85. When a positron and an electron annihilate one another, the resulting mass is completely converted to energy. Calculate the energy associated with this process in kJ/mol.

86. A typical nuclear reactor produces about 1.0 MW of power per day. What is the minimum rate of mass loss required to produce this much energy?

87. Find the binding energy in an atom of ^{3}He, which has a mass of 3.016030 amu.

88. The overall hydrogen burning reaction in stars can be represented as the conversion of four protons to one α particle. Use the data for the mass of H-1 and He-4 to calculate the energy released by this process.

89. The nuclide ^{247}Es can be made by bombardment of ^{238}U in a reaction that emits five neutrons. Identify the bombarding particle.

90. The nuclide ^{6}Li reacts with ^{2}H to form two identical particles. Identify the particles.

91. The half-life of ^{238}U is 4.5×10^{9} yr. A sample of rock of mass 1.6 g produces 29 dis/s. Assuming all the radioactivity is due to ^{238}U, find the percent by mass of ^{238}U in the rock.

92. The half-life of ^{232}Th is 1.4×10^{10} yr. Find the number of disintegrations per hour emitted by 1.0 mol of ^{232}Th.

93. A 1.50-L gas sample at 745 mm Hg and 25.0 °C contains 3.55% radon-220 by volume. Radon-220 is an alpha emitter with a half-life of 55.6 s. How many alpha particles are emitted by the gas sample in 5.00 minutes?

94. A 228-mL sample of an aqueous solution contains 2.35% $MgCl_2$ by mass. Exactly one-half of the magnesium ions are Mg-28, a beta emitter with a half-life of 21 hours. What is the decay rate of Mg-28 in the solution after 4.00 days? (Assume a density of 1.02 g/mL for the solution.)

95. When a positron and an electron collide and annihilate each other, two photons of equal energy are produced. Find the wavelength of these photons.

96. The half-life of ^{235}U, an alpha emitter, is 7.1×10^{8} yr. Calculate the number of alpha particles emitted by 1.0 mg of this nuclide in 1.0 minute.

97. Given that the energy released in the fusion of two deuterons to a ^{3}He and a neutron is 3.3 MeV, and in the fusion to tritium and a proton it is 4.0 MeV, calculate the energy change for the process $^{3}He + {}^{1}n \longrightarrow {}^{3}H + {}^{1}p$. Suggest an explanation for why this process occurs at much lower temperatures than either of the first two.

98. The nuclide ^{18}F decays by both electron capture and β^{+} decay. Find the difference in the energy released by these two processes. The atomic masses are $^{18}F = 18.000950$ and $^{18}O = 17.9991598$.

CHALLENGE PROBLEMS

99. The space shuttle carries about 72,500 kg of solid aluminum fuel, which is oxidized with ammonium perchlorate according to the reaction shown here:

$$10\,Al(s) + 6\,NH_4ClO_4(s) \longrightarrow 4\,Al_2O_3(s) + 2\,AlCl_3(s) + 12\,H_2O(g) + 3\,N_2(g)$$

The space shuttle also carries about 608,000 kg of oxygen (which reacts with hydrogen to form gaseous water).

a. Assuming that aluminum and oxygen are the limiting reactants, determine the total energy produced by these fuels. (ΔH_f° for solid ammonium perchlorate is −295 kJ/mol.)

b. Suppose that a future space shuttle is powered by matter–antimatter annihilation. The matter could be normal hydrogen (containing a proton and an electron), and the antimatter could be antihydrogen (containing an antiproton and a positron). What mass of antimatter is required to produce the energy equivalent of the aluminum and oxygen fuel currently carried on the space shuttle?

100. Suppose that an 85.0-gram laboratory animal ingests 10.0 mg of a substance that contained 2.55% by mass Pu-239, an alpha emitter with a half-life of 24,110 years.

a. What is the animal's initial radiation exposure in curies?

b. If all of the energy from the emitted alpha particles is absorbed by the animal's tissues, and if the energy of each emission is 7.77×10^{-12} J, what is the dose in rads to the animal in the first 4.0 hours following the ingestion of the radioactive material? Assuming a biological effectiveness factor of 20, what is the 4.0-hour dose in rems?

101. In addition to the natural radioactive decay series that begins with U-238 and ends with Pb-206, there are natural radioactive decay series that begin with U-235 and Th-232. Both of these series end with nuclides of Pb. Predict the likely end product of each series and the number of α decay steps that occur.

102. The hydride of an unstable nuclide of a Group IIA metal, $MH_2(s)$, decays by α-emission. A 0.025-mol sample of the hydride is placed in an evacuated 2.0 L container at 298 K. After 82 minutes, the pressure in the container is 0.55 atm. Find the half-life of the nuclide.

103. The nuclide ^{38}Cl decays by beta emission with a half-life of 37.2 min. A sample of 0.40 mol of $H^{38}Cl$ is placed in a 6.24-L container. After 74.4 min the pressure is 1650 mmHg. What is the temperature of the container?

104. When $^{10}BF_3$ is bombarded with neutrons, the boron-10 undergoes an α decay, but the F is unaffected. A 0.20-mol sample of $^{10}BF_3$ contained in a 3.0-L container at 298 K is bombarded with neutrons until half of the $^{10}BF_3$ has reacted. What is the pressure in the container at 298 K?

CONCEPTUAL PROBLEMS

105. Closely examine the diagram representing the beta decay of fluorine-21 and draw in the missing nucleus.

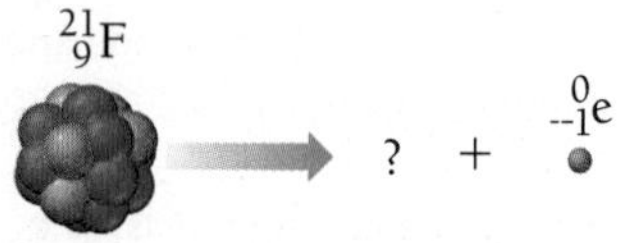

106. Approximately how many half-lives must pass for the amount of radioactivity in a substance to decrease to below 1% of its initial level?

107. A person is exposed for three days to identical amounts of two different nuclides that emit positrons of roughly equal energy. The half-life of nuclide A is 18.5 days, and the half-life of nuclide B is 255 days. Which of the two nuclides poses the greater health risk?

108. Identical amounts of two different nuclides, an alpha emitter and a gamma emitter, with roughly equal half-lives are spilled in a building adjacent to your bedroom. Which of the two nuclides is likely to pose the greater health threat to you while you sleep in your bed? If you accidentally wander into the building and ingest equal amounts of the two nuclides, which of the two is likely to pose the greater health threat?

109. Drugstores in many areas now carry tablets, under such trade names as Iosat and NoRad, designed to be taken in the event of an accident at a nuclear power plant or a terrorist attack that releases radioactive material. These tablets contain potassium iodide (KI). Can you explain the nature of the protection that they provide? (*Hint:* See the label in the photo.)

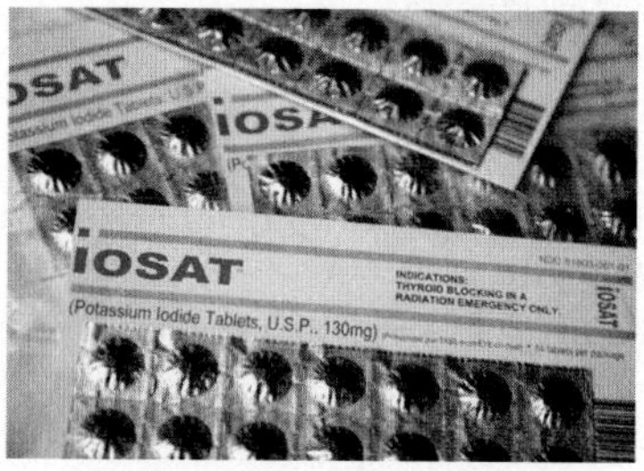

QUESTIONS FOR GROUP WORK

Active Classroom Learning

Discuss these questions with the group and record your consensus answer.

110. Complete the table of particles involved in radioactive decay.

Particle Name	Symbol	Mass Number	Atomic Number or Charge
alpha particle	$^{4}_{2}$He		
	$^{0}_{-1}$e		−1
gamma ray	$^{0}_{0}\gamma$		
positron		0	
	$^{1}_{0}$n	1	
proton	$^{1}_{1}$p		

111. Have each group member study a different mode of radioactive decay (alpha, beta, gamma, positron emission, or electron capture) and present it to the group. Each presentation should include a description of the process, a description of how the atomic and mass numbers change, and at least one specific example. Presentations should also address the questions: What do all nuclear reactions have in common, and how do they differ from each other?

112. Two students are discussing whether or not the total mass changes during a nuclear reaction. The first student insists that mass is conserved. The second student says that mass is converted into energy. Explain the context in which each student is correct and how that fact is applied to solve problems.

113. Write all the balanced nuclear equations for each step of the nuclear decay sequence that starts with U-238 and ends with U-234. Refer to Figure 21.6 for the decay processes involved.

114. Radon-220 undergoes alpha decay with a half-life of 55.6 s. Assume there are 16,000 atoms present initially and make a table showing how many atoms will be present at 0 s, 55.6 s, 111.2 s, 166.8 s, 222.4 s, and 278.0 s (all multiples of the half-life). Now calculate how many atoms will be present at 50 s, 100 s, and 200 s (not multiples of the half-life). Make a graph with number of atoms present on the *y*-axis and total time on the *x*-axis.

DATA INTERPRETATION AND ANALYSIS

Decay of Technetium-99m

115. A common isotope used in medical imaging is technetium-99m, which emits gamma rays.

$$^{99m}_{43}\text{Tc} \longrightarrow ^{99}_{43}\text{Tc} + ^{0}_{0}\gamma$$

A sample initially containing 0.500 mg of technetium-99m is monitored as a function of time. Based on its rate of gamma ray emission, a graph, showing the mass of active technetium-99m as a function of time, is prepared. Study the graph and answer the questions that follow.

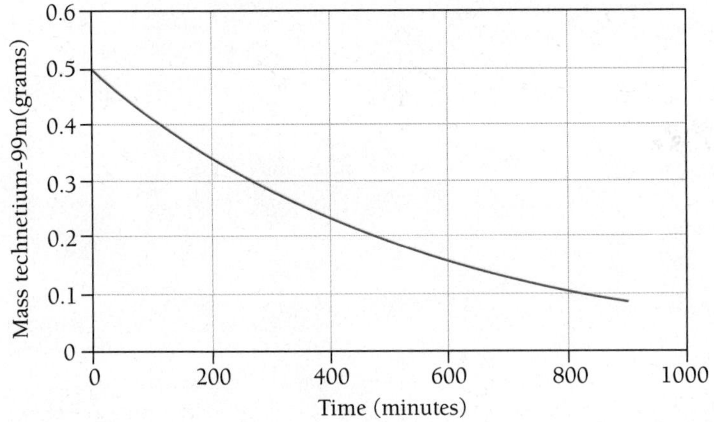

▲ **Mass of technitium-99m as a function of time**

a. What is the mass of technetium-99m present at 200 minutes? At 400 minutes?

b. What is the half-life of technetium-99m in minutes? In hours?

c. If a patient is given a 2.0-μg dose of technetium-99m, how much of it is left in the patient's body after 10 hours? (For this problem, assume that the technetium-99m is not biologically removed from the body.)

Cc ANSWERS TO CONCEPTUAL CONNECTIONS

Symbolizing Isotopes

21.1 **(d)** The number on the upper left is the mass number, which is equal to the sum of the number of protons and neutrons. The number on the lower left is the atomic number, which is equal to the number of protons. Therefore, the number of neutrons is equal to the number on the upper left (27) minus the number on lower left (13), which equals 14.

Penetrating Power

21.2 **(c)** Gamma particles have the highest penetrating power, so they are most likely to penetrate through the wall and into the room.

Alpha and Beta Decay

21.3 **(c)** The arrow labeled *x* represents a decrease of two neutrons and two protons, indicative of alpha decay. The arrow labeled *y* represents a decrease of one neutron and an increase of one proton, indicative of beta decay.

Predicting Type of Radioactive Decay

21.4 **(a)** The nuclide has a mass number that is larger than the atomic mass of the element; therefore, it has too many neutrons relative to protons and it will undergo beta decay, decreasing the number of neutrons and increasing the number of protons.

Half-Life

21.5 **(b)** The half-life is the time it takes for the number of nuclei to decay to one-half of their original number.

Half-Life and the Amount of Radioactive Sample

21.6 **(b)** 0.10 mol. The sample loses one-half of the number of moles per half-life; over the course of four half-lives, the amount falls to 0.10 mol.

Radiocarbon Dating

21.7 **(c)** After three C-14 half-lives, the amount of C-14 falls to 1/8 of that found in living organisms.

Nuclear Transformations

21.8 **(b)** Lawrencium-256. The mass numbers on both sides of the equation must be equal (262), and the atomic numbers must also be equal (103); therefore, the nuclear equation is:

$$^{252}_{98}\text{Cf} + ^{10}_{5}\text{B} \longrightarrow ^{256}_{103}\text{Lr} + 6\,^{1}_{0}\text{n}.$$

Radiation Exposure

21.9 **(a)** Nuclide A. Because Nuclide A has a shorter half-life, more of the nuclides will decay, and therefore produce radiation, before they exit the body.

Organic chemistry just now is enough to drive one mad. It gives one the impression of a primeval, tropical forest full of the most remarkable things. . . .

—FRIEDRICH WÖHLER (1800–1882)

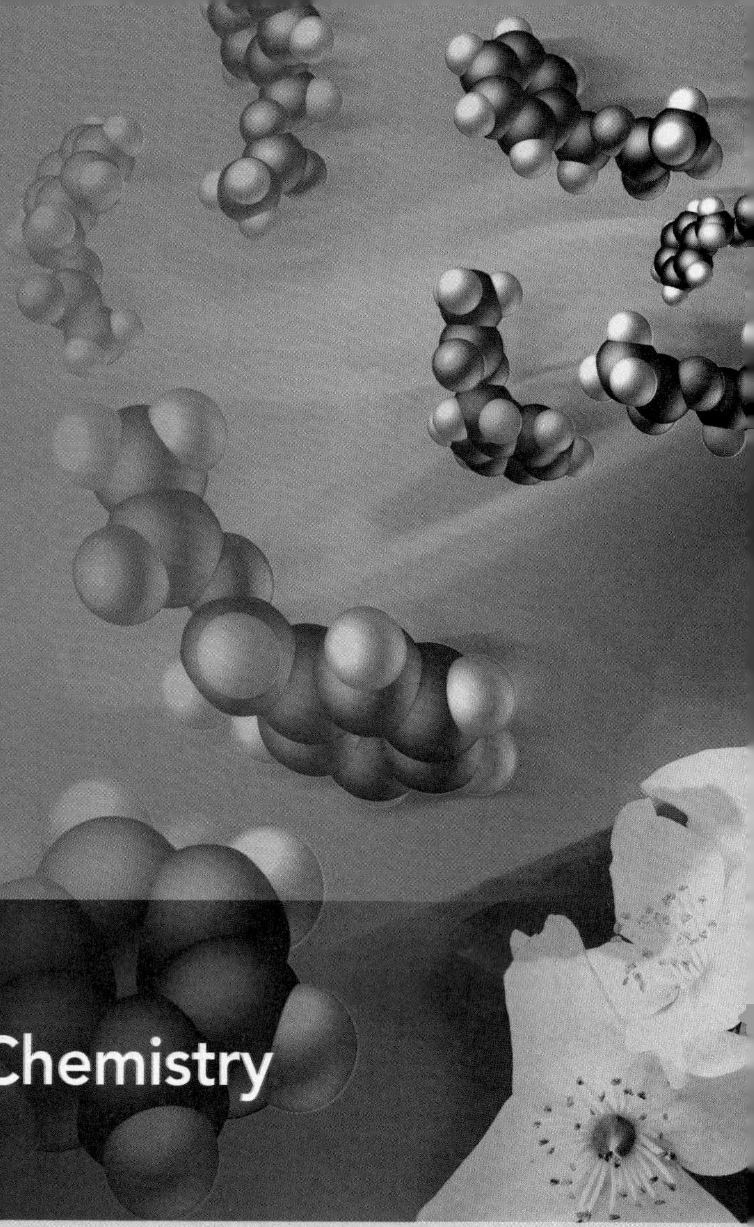

CHAPTER 22 Organic Chemistry

Organic chemistry is the study of carbon-containing compounds. Carbon is unique in the sheer number of compounds that it forms. Millions of organic compounds are known, and researchers discover new ones every day. Carbon is also unique in the *diversity* of compounds that it forms. In most cases, a fixed number of carbon atoms can combine with a fixed number of atoms of another element to form many different compounds. For example, 10 carbon atoms and 22 hydrogen atoms form 75 distinctly different compounds. With carbon as the backbone, nature is able to take the same combination of atoms and bond them together in slightly different ways to produce a huge variety of substances. It is not surprising that life is based on the chemistry of carbon because life needs diversity to exist, and organic chemistry is nothing if not diverse. In this chapter, we peer into Friedrich Wöhler's "primeval tropical forest" and discover the most remarkable things.

A common ingredient in women's perfume is benzyl acetate ($C_9H_{10}O_2$), an organic compound (pictured here) derived from flowers such as jasmine. Benzyl acetate has a fresh, floral fragrance.

22.1 Fragrances and Odors 989
22.2 Carbon: Why It Is Unique 990
22.3 Hydrocarbons: Compounds Containing Only Carbon and Hydrogen 992
22.4 Alkanes: Saturated Hydrocarbons 998
22.5 Alkenes and Alkynes 1002
22.6 Hydrocarbon Reactions 1007
22.7 Aromatic Hydrocarbons 1010
22.8 Functional Groups 1013
22.9 Alcohols 1014
22.10 Aldehydes and Ketones 1016
22.11 Carboxylic Acids and Esters 1019
22.12 Ethers 1021
22.13 Amines 1022
LEARNING OUTCOMES 1026

22.1 Fragrances and Odors

Have you ever ridden an elevator with someone wearing too much perfume? Or found yourself too close to a skunk? Or caught a whiff of rotting fish? What causes these fragrances and odors? When we inhale certain molecules called odorants, they bind with olfactory receptors in our noses. This interaction sends a nerve signal to the brain that we experience as a smell. Some smells, such as that of perfume, are pleasant (when not overdone). Other smells, such as that of the skunk or rotting fish,

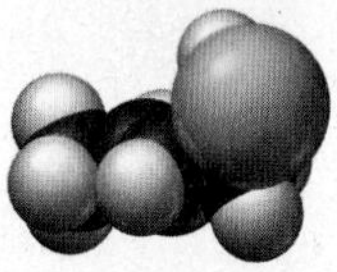

$CH_3CH{=}CHCH_2SH$

2-Butene-1-thiol

CH_3 (on the second carbon)

$CH_3CHCH_2CH_2SH$

3-Methyl-1-butanethiol

▲ The smell of skunk is due primarily to the molecules shown here.

are unpleasant. Our sense of smell helps us identify food, people, and other organisms, and it alerts us to dangers such as polluted air or spoiled food. Smell (olfaction) is one way we probe the environment around us.

Odorants, if they are to reach our noses, must be volatile. However, many volatile substances have no scent at all. Nitrogen, oxygen, water, and carbon dioxide molecules, for example, are constantly passing through our noses, yet they produce no smell because they do not bind to olfactory receptors. Most common smells are caused by **organic molecules**, molecules containing carbon combined with several other elements, such as hydrogen, nitrogen, oxygen, and sulfur. Organic molecules are responsible for the smells of roses, vanilla, cinnamon, almond, jasmine, body odor, and rotting fish. When you wander into a rose garden, you experience the sweet smell caused in part by geraniol, an organic compound emitted by roses. Women's perfumes commonly contain benzyl acetate, a floral-smelling compound common in flowers such as jasmine. Men's colognes often contain patchouli alcohol, an earthy-smelling organic compound extracted from the patchouli plant. If you have been in the vicinity of skunk spray (or have been unfortunate enough to be sprayed yourself), you are familiar with the unpleasant smell of 2-butene-1-thiol and 3-methyl-1-butanethiol, two particularly odoriferous compounds present in the secretion that skunks use to defend themselves.

The study of compounds containing carbon combined with one or more of the elements mentioned previously (hydrogen, nitrogen, oxygen, and sulfur), including their properties and their reactions, is **organic chemistry**. Besides composing much of what we smell, organic compounds are prevalent in foods, drugs, petroleum products, and pesticides. Organic chemistry is also the basis for living organisms. Life has evolved based on carbon-containing compounds, making organic chemistry of utmost importance to any person interested in understanding living organisms.

22.2 Carbon: Why It Is Unique

Why did life evolve based on the chemistry of carbon? Why is life not based on some other element? The answer may not be simple, but we do know that life—in order to exist—must entail complexity, and carbon chemistry is clearly complex. The number of compounds containing carbon is greater than the number of compounds containing all of the other elements combined. The reasons for carbon's unique and versatile behavior include its ability to form four covalent bonds, its ability to form double and triple bonds, and its tendency to *catenate* (that is, to form chains).

Carbon's Tendency to Form Four Covalent Bonds

Carbon—with its four valence electrons—forms four covalent bonds. Consider the Lewis structure and space-filling models of two simple carbon compounds, methane and ethane:

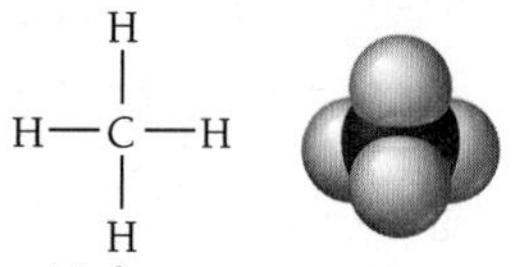

Methane

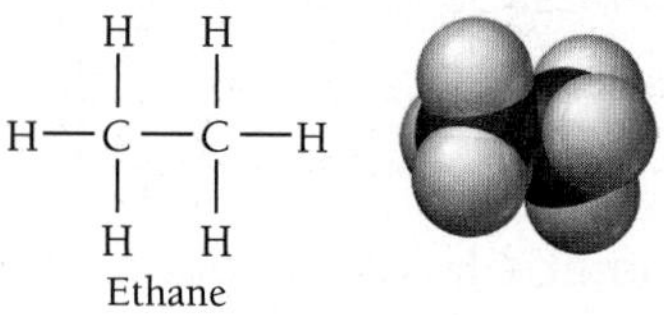

Ethane

The geometry about a carbon atom forming four single bonds is tetrahedral, as shown in the figure for methane. Carbon's ability to form four bonds, and to form those bonds with a number of different elements, results in the potential to form many different compounds. As you learn to draw structures for organic compounds, always remember to draw carbon with four bonds.

Carbon's Ability to Form Double and Triple Bonds

Carbon atoms also form double bonds (trigonal planar geometry) and triple bonds (linear geometry), adding even more diversity to the number of compounds that carbon forms. Consider the Lewis structure and space-filling models of the carbon compounds ethene and ethyne:

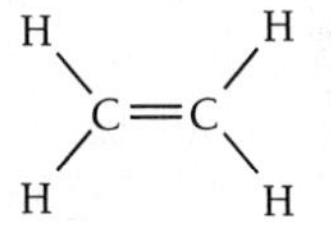
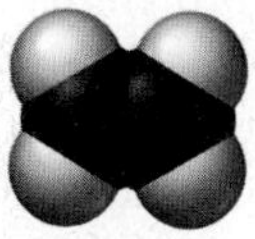

Ethene

H—C≡C—H

Ethyne

In contrast, silicon (the element in the periodic table with properties closest to that of carbon) does not readily form double or triple bonds because the greater size of silicon atoms results in a Si—Si bond that is too long for much overlap between nonhybridized *p* orbitals.

CHEMISTRY IN YOUR DAY | Vitalism and the Perceived Differences between Organic and Inorganic Compounds

By the end of the eighteenth century, chemists had learned that compounds could be broadly categorized as either organic or inorganic. Organic compounds come from living things, whereas inorganic compounds come from the nonliving things on Earth. Sugar—obtained from sugarcane or the sugar beet—is a common example of an organic compound. Salt—mined from the ground or extracted from ocean water—is a common example of an inorganic compound.

Organic and inorganic compounds are different, not only in their origin, but also in their properties. Organic compounds are easily decomposed. Sugar, for example, readily decomposes into carbon and water when heated. (Think of the last time you burned something sugary in a pan or in the oven.) Inorganic compounds are more difficult to decompose. Salt decomposes only when heated to very high temperatures.

Even more curious to these early chemists was their inability to synthesize a single organic compound in the laboratory. Although they were able to synthesize many inorganic compounds, despite concerted efforts, they were not able to synthesize any organic compounds.

The origin and properties of organic compounds led early chemists to postulate that organic compounds were unique to living organisms. They hypothesized that living organisms contained a *vital force*—a mystical or supernatural power—that allowed them to produce organic compounds. They thought that producing an organic compound outside of a living organism was impossible because the vital force was not present. This belief—which became known as *vitalism*—explained why no chemist had succeeded in synthesizing an organic compound in the laboratory.

An experiment performed in 1828 by German chemist Friedrich Wöhler (1800–1882) marked the beginning of the end of vitalism. Wöhler heated ammonium cyanate (an inorganic compound) and formed urea (an organic compound):

$$\underset{\text{ammonium cyanate}}{NH_4OCN} \xrightarrow{\text{heat}} \underset{\text{urea}}{H_2NCONH_2}$$

Urea was a known organic compound that had previously been isolated only from urine. Although it was not realized at the time, Wöhler's simple experiment was a key step in opening all of life to scientific investigation. He showed that the compounds composing living organisms—like all compounds—follow scientific laws and can be studied and understood. Today, known organic compounds number in the millions, and modern organic chemistry is a vast field that produces substances as diverse as drugs, petroleum products, and plastics.

Friedrich Wöhler

▶ The synthesis of urea in 1828 by German chemist Friedrich Wöhler marked the beginning of the end for vitalism.

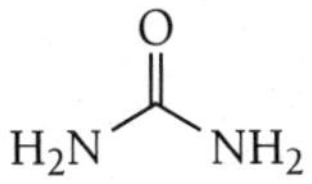

Urea

Carbon's Tendency to Catenate

Carbon, more than any other element, can bond to itself to form chain, branched, and ring structures as we can see in propane, isobutane, and cyclohexane:

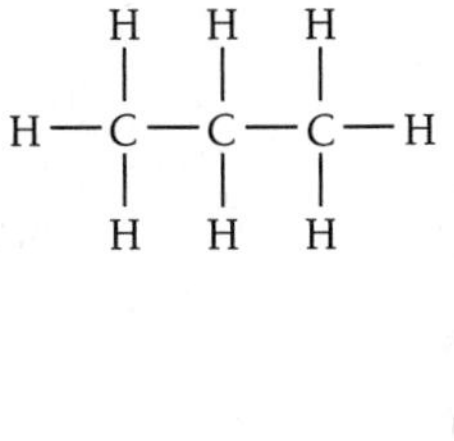

Propane

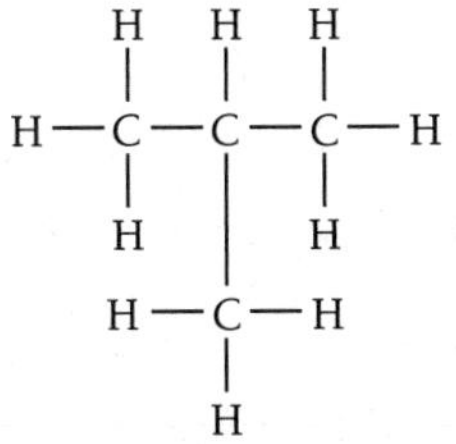

Isobutane

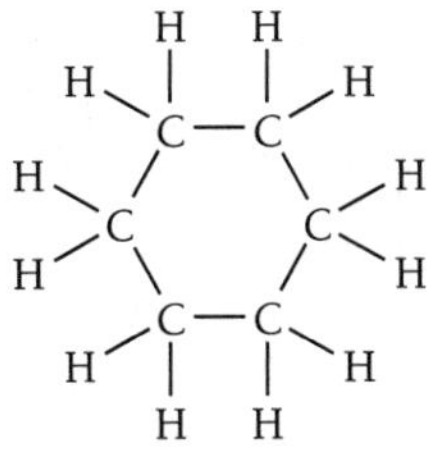

Cyclohexane

Although other elements can form chains, none surpasses carbon at this ability. Silicon, for example, can form chains with itself. However, silicon's affinity for oxygen (the Si—O bond is stronger than the Si—Si bond) coupled with the prevalence of oxygen in our atmosphere means that silicon-silicon chains are readily oxidized to form silicates (the silicon-oxygen compounds that compose a significant proportion of minerals). By contrast, the C—C bond (347 kJ/mol) and the C—O bond (359 kJ/mol) are nearly the same strength, allowing carbon chains to exist relatively peacefully in an oxygen-rich environment.

22.3 Hydrocarbons: Compounds Containing Only Carbon and Hydrogen

Hydrocarbons—compounds that contain only carbon and hydrogen—are the simplest organic compounds. However, because of the uniqueness of carbon, many different kinds of hydrocarbons exist. We use hydrocarbons primarily as fuels. Candle wax, oil, gasoline, liquid petroleum (LP) gas, and natural gas are all composed of hydrocarbons. Hydrocarbons are also the starting materials in the synthesis of many different consumer products, including fabrics, soaps, dyes, cosmetics, drugs, plastic, and rubber.

As shown in Figure 22.1▼, we classify hydrocarbons into four different types: **alkanes**, **alkenes**, **alkynes**, and **aromatic hydrocarbons**. We differentiate alkanes, alkenes, and alkynes—also called **aliphatic hydrocarbons**—based on the kinds of bonds between carbon atoms. (We discuss aromatic hydrocarbons in detail in Section 22.7.) As Table 22.1 illustrates, alkanes have only single bonds between carbon atoms, alkenes have a double bond, and alkynes have a triple bond.

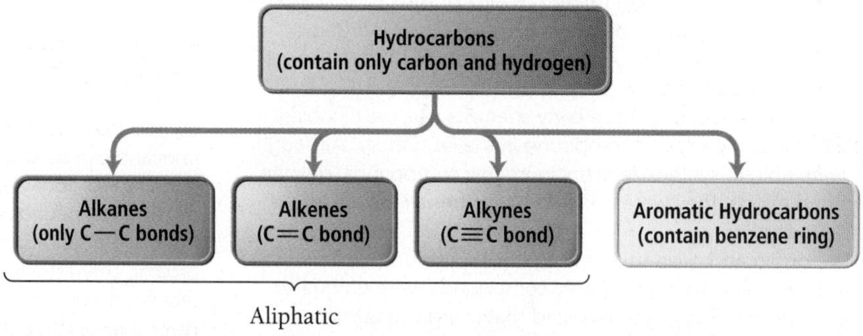

▶ **FIGURE 22.1 Four Types of Hydrocarbons**

TABLE 22.1 ■ Alkanes, Alkenes, Alkynes

Type of Hydrocarbon	Type of Bonds	Generic Formula*	Example
Alkanes	All single	C_nH_{2n+2}	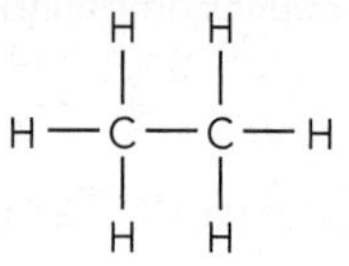 Ethane
Alkenes	One (or more) double	C_nH_{2n}	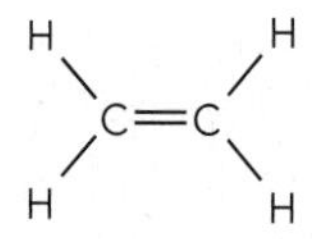 Ethene
Alkynes	One (or more) triple	C_nH_{2n-2}	 Ethyne

* *n* is the number of carbon atoms. These formulas apply only to noncyclic structures containing no more than one multiple bond.

Drawing Hydrocarbon Structures

Throughout this book, we have relied primarily on molecular formulas as the simplest way to represent compounds. In organic chemistry, molecular formulas are insufficient because, as we have already discussed, the same atoms can bond together in different ways to form different compounds. For example, consider an alkane with four carbon atoms and 10 hydrogen atoms. Two different structures, named butane and isobutane, are possible:

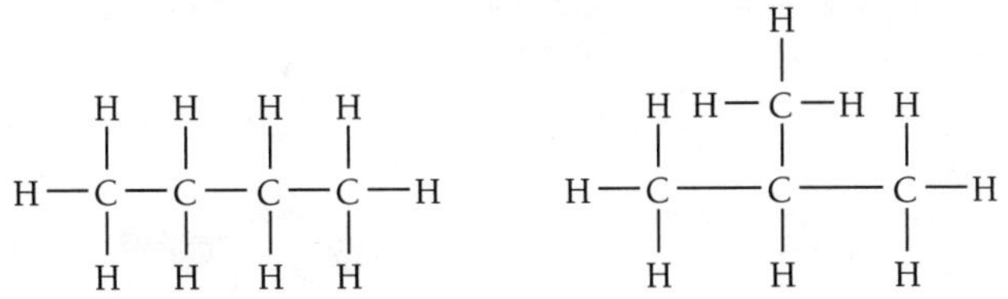

Butane Isobutane

Butane and isobutane are **structural isomers**, molecules with the same molecular formula but different structures. Because of their different structures, they have different properties—indeed, they are different compounds. Isomerism is ubiquitous in organic chemistry. Butane has two structural isomers. Pentane (C_5H_{12}) has three, hexane (C_6H_{14}) has five, and decane ($C_{10}H_{22}$) has 75!

We represent the structure of a particular hydrocarbon with a **structural formula**, a formula that shows not only the numbers of each kind of atoms, but also how the atoms are bonded. Organic chemists use several different kinds of structural formulas. For example, we can represent butane and isobutane in each of the following ways:

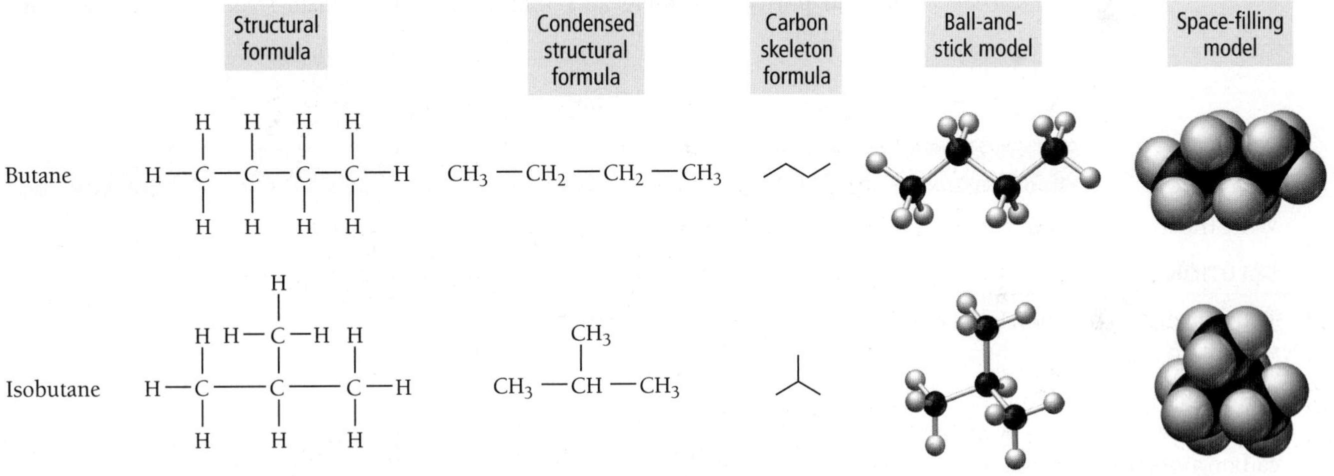

The structural formula shows all of the carbon and hydrogen atoms in the molecule and how they are bonded. The *condensed structural formula* groups the hydrogen atoms with the carbon atom to which they are bonded. Condensed structural formulas may show some of the bonds (as the previous examples do) or none at all. We can also write the condensed structural formula for butane as $CH_3CH_2CH_2CH_3$. The *carbon skeleton formula* (also called a line formula) shows the carbon–carbon bonds only as lines. Each end or bend of a line represents a carbon atom bonded to as many hydrogen atoms as necessary to form a total of four bonds. Carbon skeleton formulas allow us to draw complex structures quickly.

A carbon skeleton formula is called a *line* formula because it uses lines to represent a molecule.

Note that structural formulas are generally not three-dimensional representations of molecules—as space-filling or ball-and-stick models are—but rather two-dimensional representations that show how atoms are bonded together. As such, the most important feature of a structural formula is the *connectivity* of the atoms, not the exact way the formula is drawn. For example, consider the two condensed structural formulas for butane and the corresponding space-filling models below them as shown on the right. Since rotation about single bonds is relatively unhindered at room temperature, the two structural formulas are identical, even though they are drawn differently.

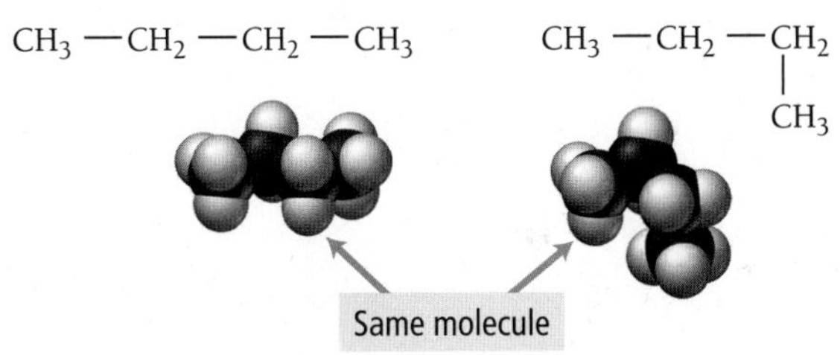

We represent double and triple bonds in structural formulas with double or triple lines. For example, we draw the structural formulas for C_3H_6 (propene) and C_3H_4 (propyne) as follows:

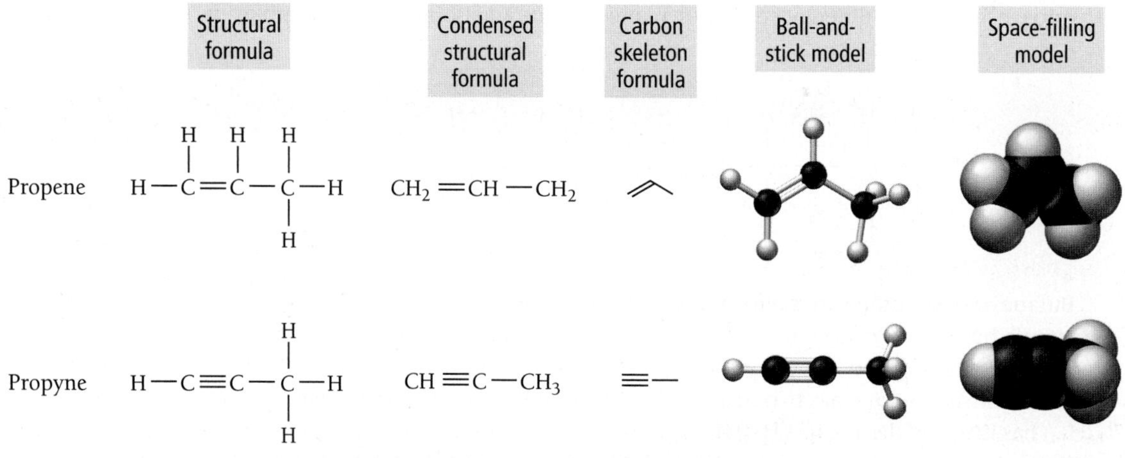

The kind of structural formula we use depends on how much information we want to portray. Example 22.1 illustrates how to write structural formulas for a compound.

EXAMPLE 22.1 Writing Structural Formulas for Hydrocarbons

Write the structural formulas and carbon skeleton formulas for the five isomers of C_6H_{14} (hexane).

SOLUTION

To begin, draw the carbon backbone of the straight-chain isomer.	C—C—C—C—C—C
Next, determine the carbon backbone structure of the other isomers by arranging the carbon atoms in four other unique ways.	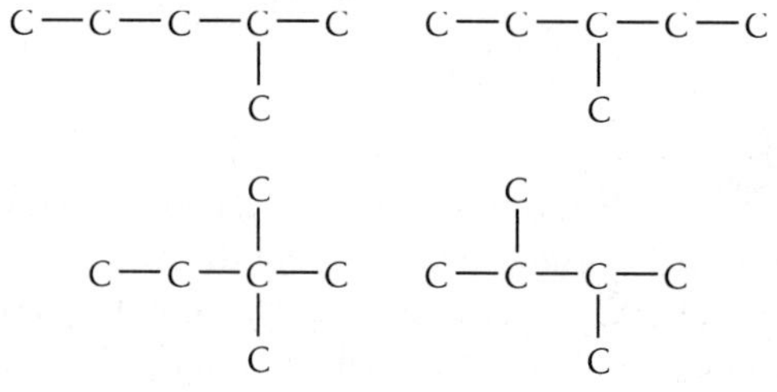
Fill in all the hydrogen atoms so that each carbon forms four bonds.	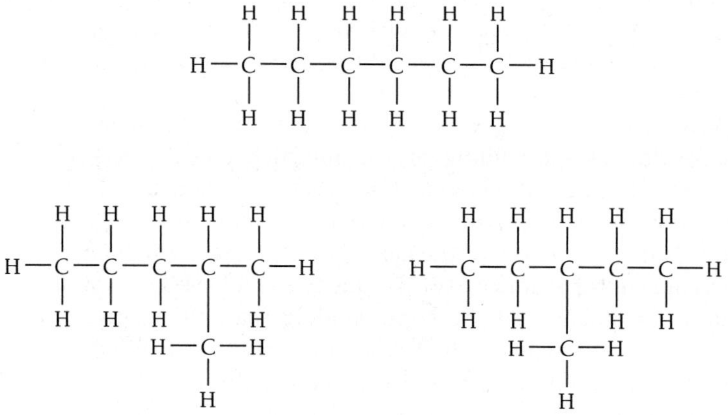

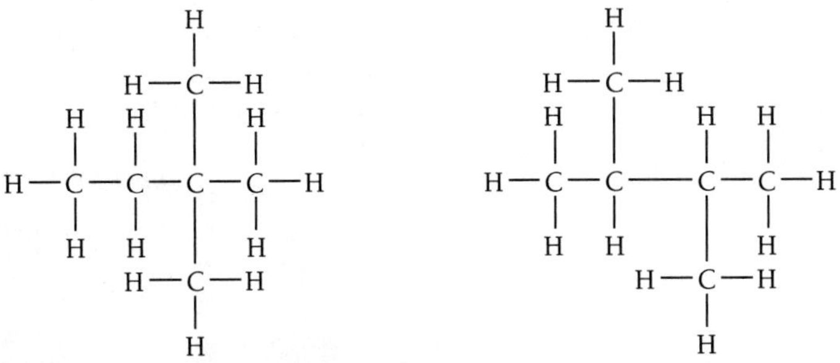

Write the carbon skeleton formulas by using lines to represent each carbon–carbon bond. Remember that each end and each bend represent a carbon atom.

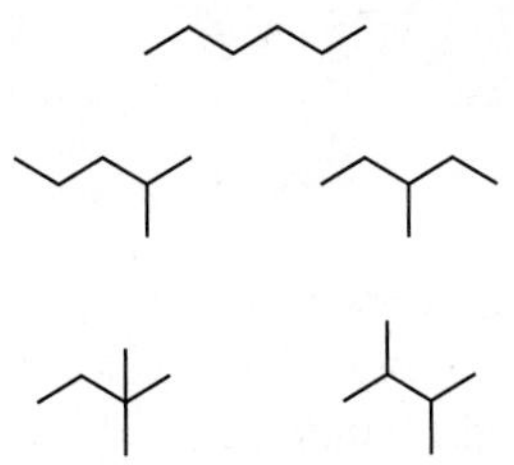

FOR PRACTICE 22.1 Write the structural formulas and carbon skeleton formulas for the three isomers of C_5H_{12} (pentane).

22.1 Cc Conceptual Connection

ANSWER **NOW!**

ORGANIC STRUCTURES Which structure is an *isomer* of the molecule shown here (and not just the same structure)?

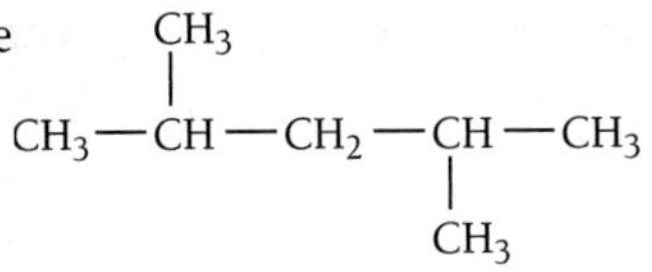

(a) 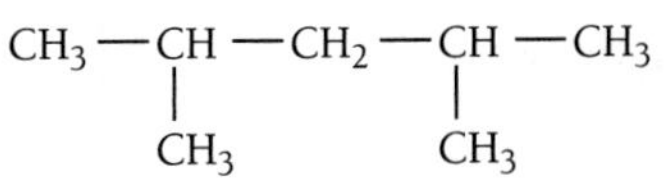

(b) 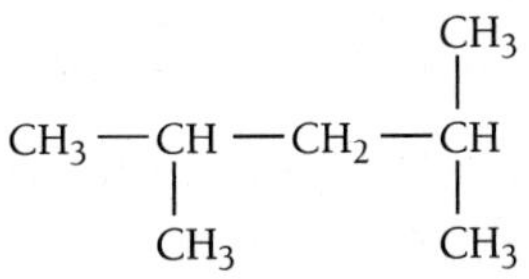

(c) 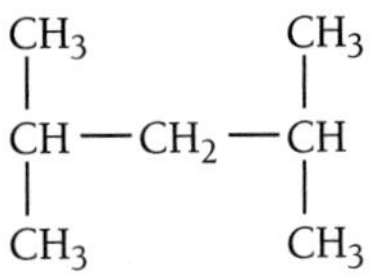

(d) 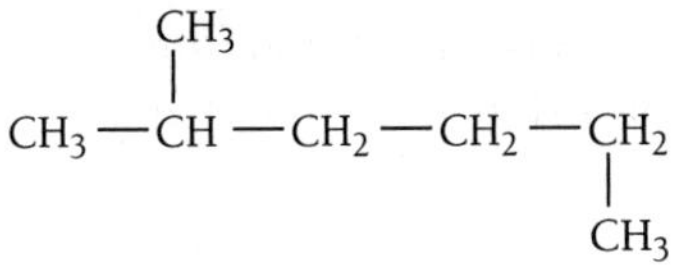

Stereoisomerism and Optical Isomerism

Stereoisomers are molecules in which the atoms have the same connectivity but a different spatial arrangement. We categorize stereoisomers into two types: geometric (or cis–trans) isomers and optical isomers. We discuss geometric isomers in Section 22.5. **Optical isomers** are two molecules that are nonsuperimposable mirror images of one another. Consider the molecule shown here with its mirror image:

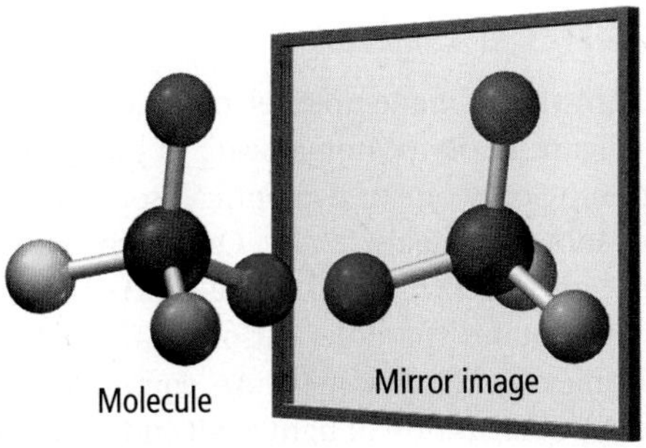

The molecule cannot be superimposed onto its mirror image. If we swing the mirror image around to try to superimpose the two, we find that there is no way to get all four substituent atoms to align together. (A substituent is an atom or group of atoms that is substituted for a hydrogen atom in an organic compound.)

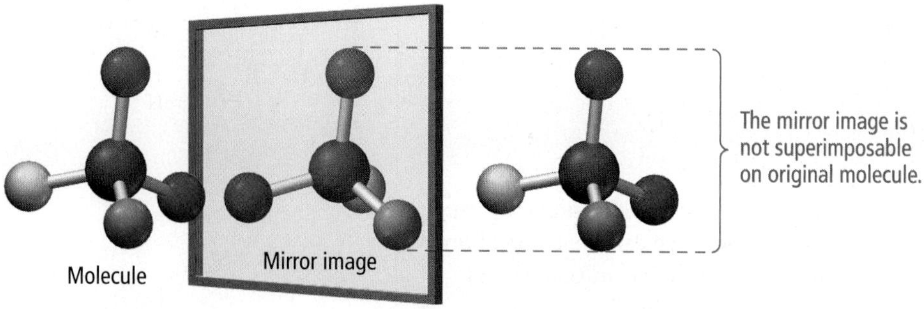

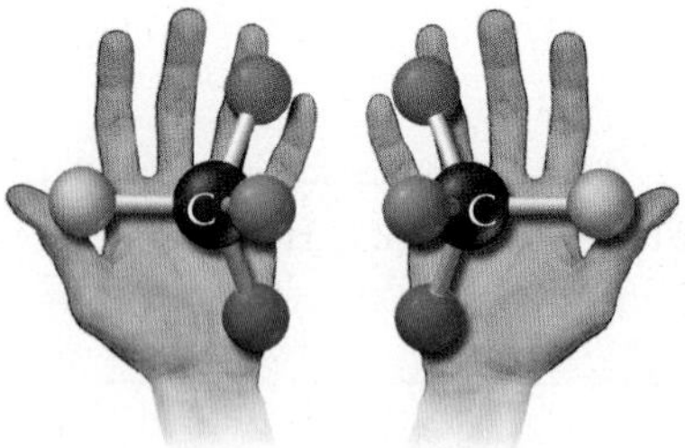

▲ **FIGURE 22.2 Mirror Images** The left and right hands are nonsuperimposable mirror images, just as is the case for optical isomers.

Optical isomers are similar to your right and left hands (Figure 22.2◀). The two are mirror images of one another, but you cannot superimpose one on the other. For this reason, a right-handed glove does not fit on your left hand and vice versa.

Any carbon atom with four different substituents in a tetrahedral arrangement exhibits optical isomerism. Consider 3-methylhexane:

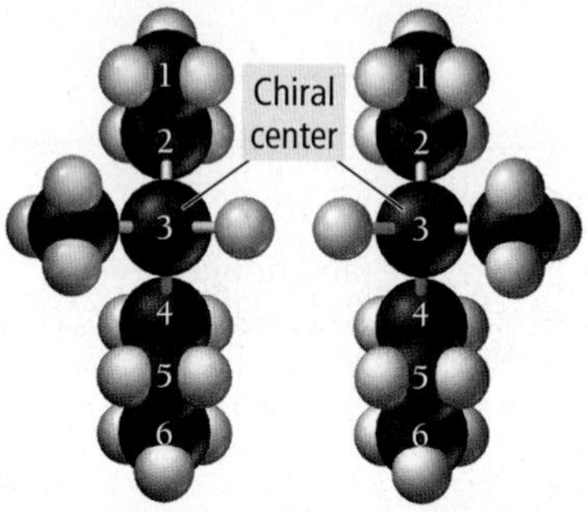

Optical isomers of 3-methylhexane

The molecules shown here are nonsuperimposable mirror images and are optical isomers of one other.

Optical isomers are also called **enantiomers**. Any molecule, such as 3-methylhexane, that exhibits optical isomerism is said to be **chiral**, from the Greek word *cheir*, which means "hand." Optical isomerism is important, not only to organic chemistry, but also to biology and biochemistry. Most biological molecules are chiral and usually only one or the other enantiomer is active in biological systems. For example, glucose, the primary fuel of cells, is chiral. Only one of the enantiomers of glucose has that familiar sweet taste, and only that enantiomer can fuel cellular functioning; the other enantiomer is not even metabolized by the body.

Some of the physical and chemical properties of enantiomers are indistinguishable from one another. For example, both of the optical isomers of 3-methylhexane have identical freezing points, melting points, and densities. However, the properties of enantiomers differ from one another in two important ways: (1) in the direction in which they rotate polarized light and (2) in their chemical behavior in a chiral environment.

Rotation of Polarized Light

Plane-polarized light is light that is made up of electric field waves that oscillate in only one plane as shown in Figure 22.3▶. When a beam of plane-polarized light is directed through a sample containing only one of two optical isomers, the plane of polarization of the light is rotated as shown in Figure 22.4▶. One of the two optical isomers rotates the polarization of the light clockwise and is the **dextrorotatory** isomer (or the *d* isomer). The other isomer rotates the polarization of the light counterclockwise and is the **levorotatory** isomer (or the *l* isomer). An equimolar mixture of both optical isomers does not rotate the polarization of light at all and is called a **racemic mixture.**

Dextrorotatory means turning clockwise or to the right. *Levorotatory* means turning counterclockwise or to the left.

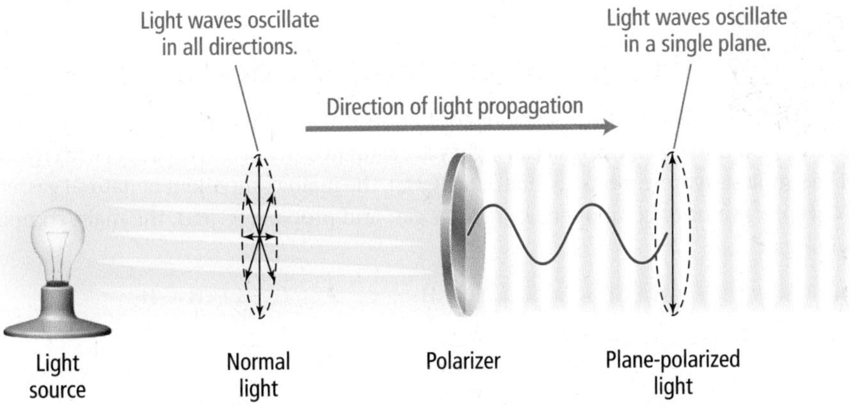

◀ **FIGURE 22.3 Plane-Polarized Light** The electric field of plane-polarized light oscillates in one plane.

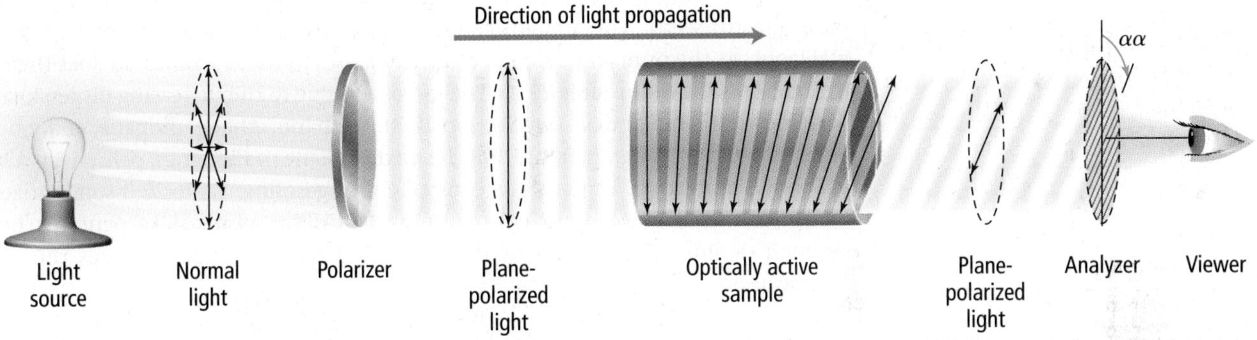

▲ **FIGURE 22.4 Rotation of Plane-Polarized Light** Plane-polarized light rotates as it passes through a sample containing only one of two optical isomers.

Chemical Behavior in a Chiral Environment

Optical isomers also exhibit different chemical behavior when they are in a chiral environment (a chiral environment is one that is not superimposable on its mirror image). Enzymes are large biological molecules that catalyze reactions in living organisms and provide chiral environments. Consider the following simplified picture of two enantiomers in a chiral environment:

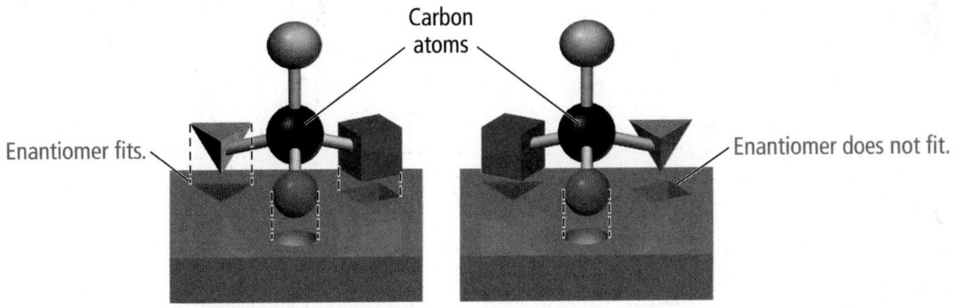

One of the enantiomers fits the template, but the other does not, no matter how it is rotated. In this way, an enzyme is able to catalyze the reaction of one enantiomer because that particular enantiomer fits the "template." As we have already seen, most biological molecules are chiral, and usually only one or the other enantiomer is active in biological systems.

OPTICAL ISOMERS Which molecule exhibits optical isomerism?

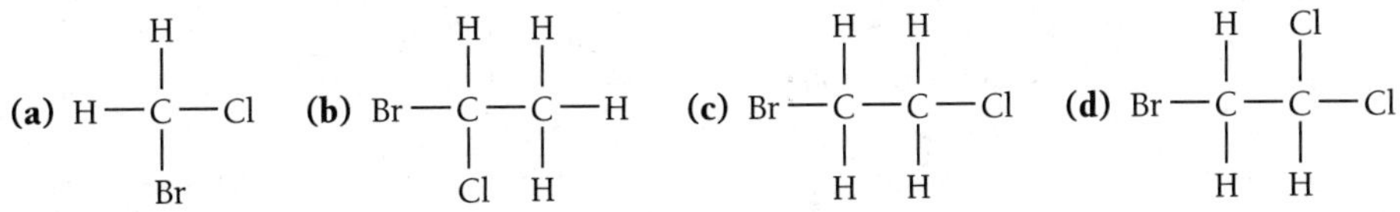

22.2 Cc Conceptual Connection

ANSWER NOW!

22.4 Alkanes: Saturated Hydrocarbons

Alkanes (hydrocarbons containing only single bonds) are often referred to as **saturated hydrocarbons** because they are saturated (loaded to capacity) with hydrogen. The simplest hydrocarbons are methane (CH_4), the main component of natural gas; ethane (C_2H_6), a minority component in natural gas; and propane (C_3H_8), the main component of LP gas:

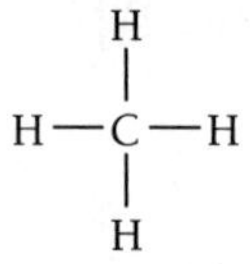

Methane

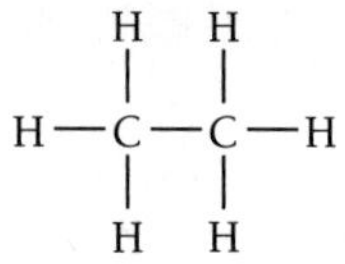

Ethane

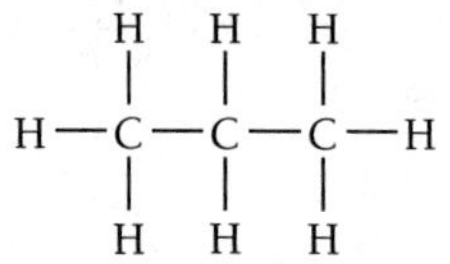

Propane

Alkanes containing four or more carbon atoms may be straight or branched (as we have already seen). The straight-chain isomers are often called normal alkanes, or *n*-alkanes. As the number of carbon atoms increases in the *n*-alkanes, so does their boiling point (as shown in Table 22.2). The increase is due to the increasing dispersion force with increasing molar mass (see Section 12.3). Methane, ethane, propane, and *n*-butane are all gases at room temperature, but the next *n*-alkane in the series, pentane, is a liquid at room temperature. Pentane is a component of gasoline. Table 22.3 summarizes the *n*-alkanes through decane, which contains 10 carbon atoms. Like pentane, hexane through decane are all components of gasoline. Table 22.4 summarizes the uses of hydrocarbons.

TABLE 22.2 ■ *n*-Alkane Boiling Points

n-Alkane	Boiling Point (°C)
Methane	−161.5
Ethane	−88.6
Propane	−42.1
n-Butane	−0.5
n-Pentane	36.0
n-Hexane	68.7
n-Heptane	98.5
n-Octane	125.6

TABLE 22.3 ■ *n*-Alkanes

n	Name	Molecular Formula C_nH_{2n+2}	Structural Formula	Condensed Structural Formula
1	Methane	CH_4	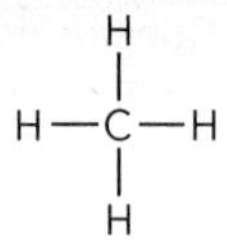	CH_4
2	Ethane	C_2H_6	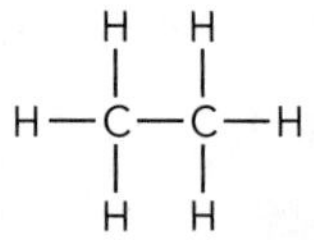	CH_3CH_3
3	Propane	C_3H_8	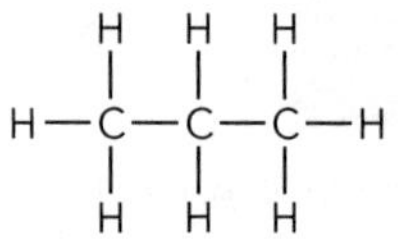	$CH_3CH_2CH_3$
4	*n*-Butane	C_4H_{10}	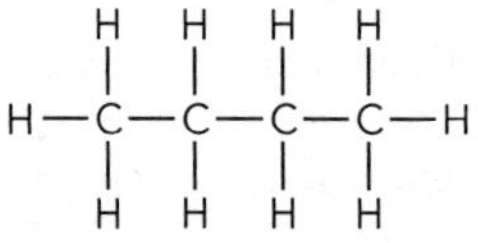	$CH_3CH_2CH_2CH_3$
5	*n*-Pentane	C_5H_{12}	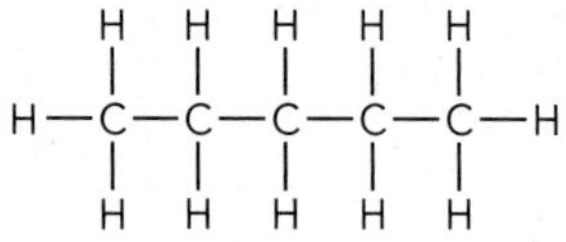	$CH_3CH_2CH_2CH_2CH_3$

6	*n*-Hexane	C_6H_{14}	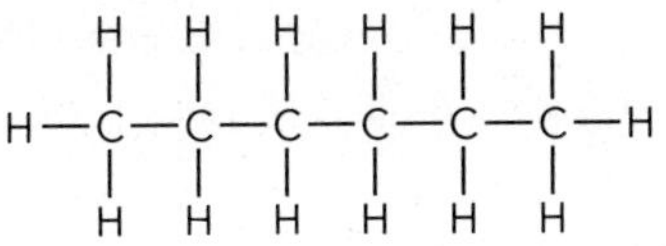	$CH_3CH_2CH_2CH_2CH_2CH_3$
7	*n*-Heptane	C_7H_{16}	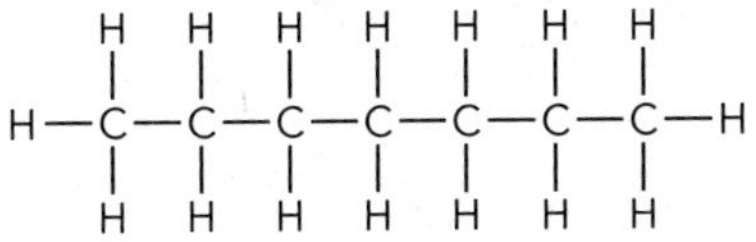	$CH_3CH_2CH_2CH_2CH_2CH_2CH_3$
8	*n*-Octane	C_8H_{18}	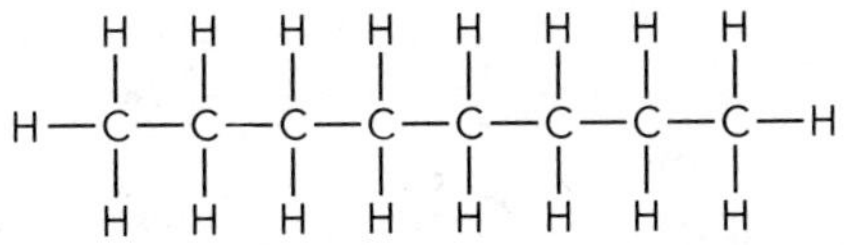	$CH_3CH_2CH_2CH_2CH_2CH_2CH_2CH_3$
9	*n*-Nonane	C_9H_{20}	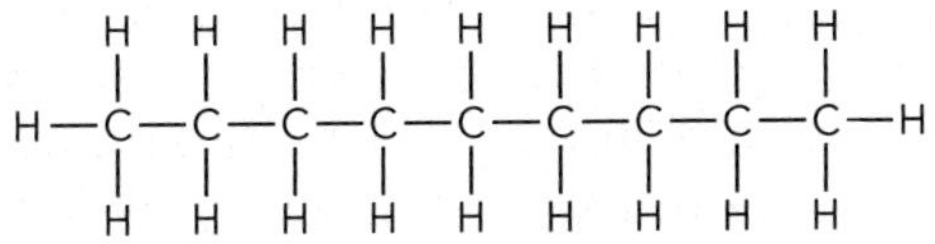	$CH_3CH_2CH_2CH_2CH_2CH_2CH_2CH_2CH_3$
10	*n*-Decane	$C_{10}H_{22}$	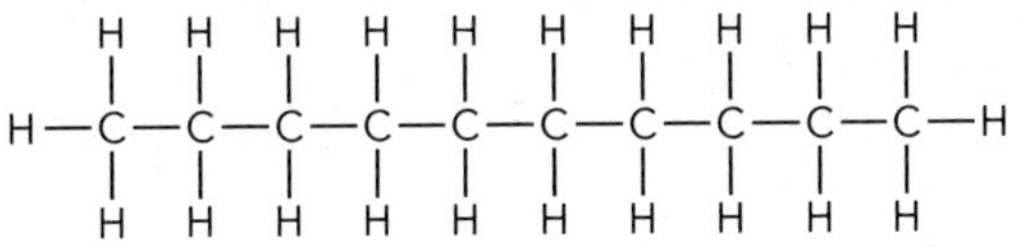	$CH_3CH_2CH_2CH_2CH_2CH_2CH_2CH_2CH_2CH_3$

TABLE 22.4 ■ Uses of Hydrocarbons

Number of Carbon Atoms	State	Major Uses
1–4	Gas	Heating fuel, cooking fuel
5–7	Low-boiling liquids	Solvents, gasoline
6–18	Liquids	Gasoline
12–24	Liquids	Jet fuel, portable-stove fuel
18–50	High-boiling liquids	Diesel fuel, lubricants, heating oil
50+	Solids	Petroleum jelly, paraffin wax

Naming Alkanes

Many organic compounds have common names that we can learn only through familiarity. Because of the sheer number of organic compounds, however, we need a systematic method of nomenclature. In this book, we adopt the nomenclature system recommended by the IUPAC (International Union of Pure and Applied Chemistry), which is used throughout the world. In this system, the longest continuous chain of carbon atoms—called the base chain—determines the base name of the compound. The root of the base name depends on the number of carbon atoms in the base chain, as shown in Table 22.5. Base names for alkanes always have the ending *-ane*. Groups of carbon atoms branching off the base chain are alkyl groups and are named as substituents. Remember that a *substituent* is an atom or group of atoms that has been substituted for a hydrogen atom in an organic compound. Common alkyl groups are shown in Table 22.6.

TABLE 22.5 ■ Prefixes for Base Names of Alkane Chains

Number of Carbon Atoms	Prefix
1	meth-
2	eth-
3	prop-
4	but-
5	pent-
6	hex-
7	hept-
8	oct-
9	non-
10	dec-

TABLE 22.6 ■ Common Alkyl Groups

Condensed Structural Formula	Name	Condensed Structural Formula	Name
$—CH_3$	Methyl	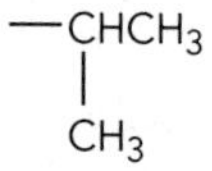	Isopropyl
$—CH_2CH_3$	Ethyl	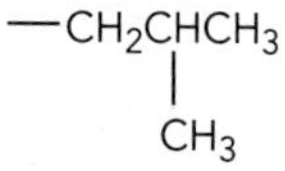	Isobutyl
$—CH_2CH_2CH_3$	Propyl	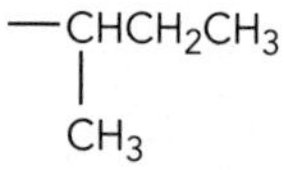	*sec*-Butyl
$—CH_2CH_2CH_2CH_3$	Butyl	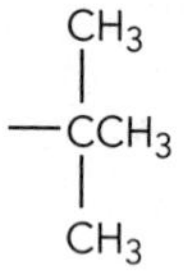	*tert*-Butyl

The procedure in Examples 22.2 and 22.3 will allow you to systematically name many alkanes. The procedure is in the left column and two examples of applying the procedure are in the center and right columns.

WATCH **NOW!**

INTERACTIVE WORKED EXAMPLE VIDEO 22.3

HOW TO: *Name Alkanes*

EXAMPLE 22.2

Naming Alkanes

Name this alkane:

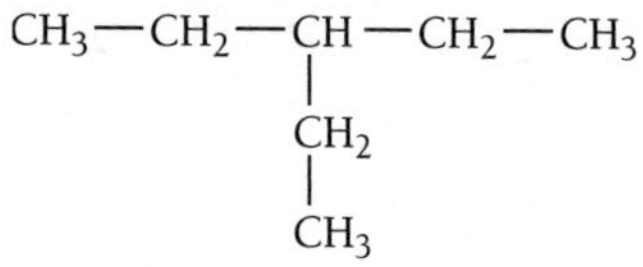

EXAMPLE 22.3

Naming Alkanes

Name this alkane:

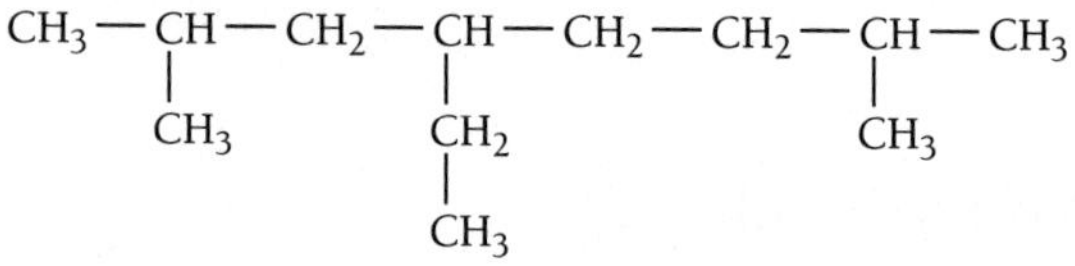

1. Count the number of carbon atoms in the longest continuous carbon chain to determine the base name of the compound. Locate the prefix corresponding to this number of atoms in Table 22.5 and add the ending *-ane* to form the base name.

SOLUTION (Example 22.2)

This compound has five carbon atoms in its longest continuous chain.

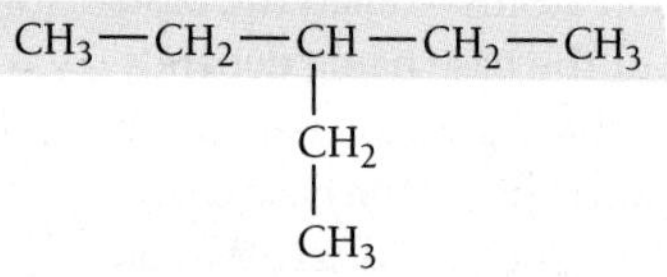

The correct prefix from Table 22.5 is *pent-*. The base name is pentane.

SOLUTION (Example 22.3)

This compound has eight carbon atoms in its longest continuous chain.

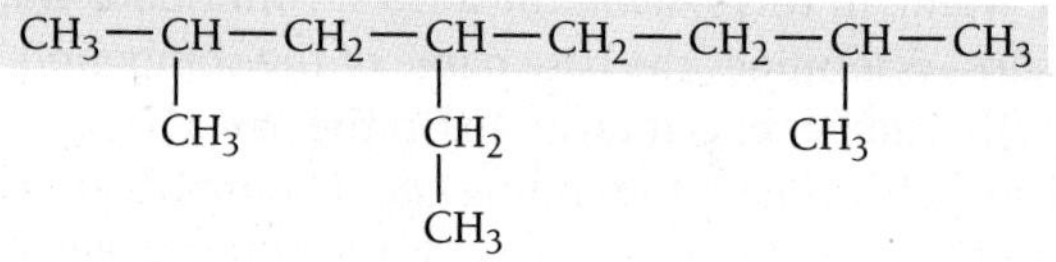

The correct prefix from Table 22.5 is *oct-*. The base name is octane.

2. Consider every branch from the base chain to be a substituent. Name each substituent according to Table 22.6.	This compound has one substituent named *ethyl.* 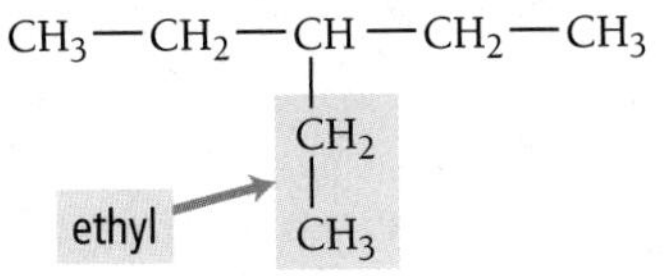	This compound has one substituent named *ethyl* and two named *methyl.* 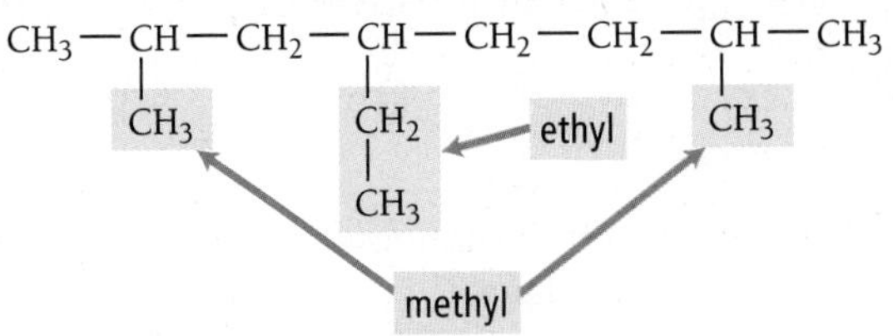
3. Beginning with the end closest to the branching, number the base chain and assign a number to each substituent. (If two substituents occur at equal distances from each end, go to the next substituent to determine from which end to start numbering.)	Number the base chain as follows: 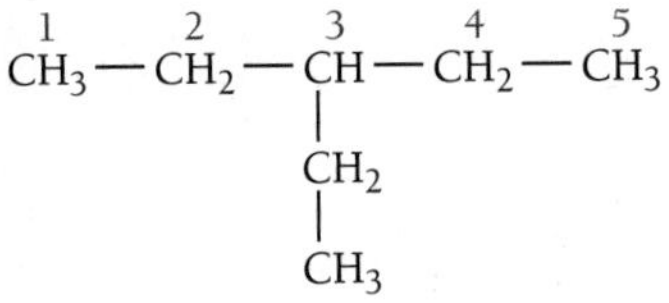 Assign the number 3 to the ethyl substituent.	Number the base chain as follows: 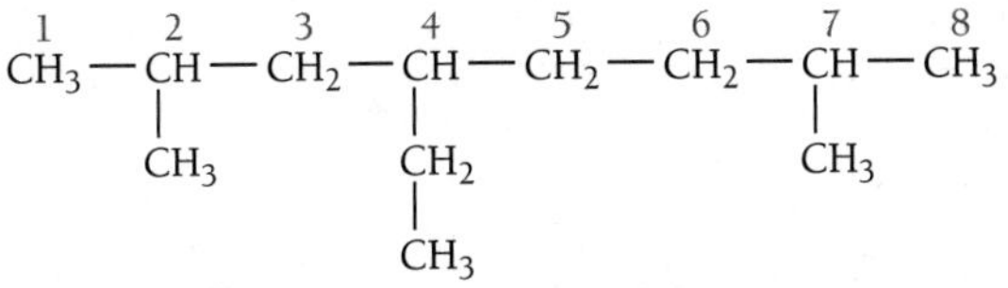 Assign the number 4 to the ethyl substituent and the numbers 2 and 7 to the two methyl substituents.
4. Write the name of the compound in the following format: (substituent number)-(substituent name)(base name). If there are two or more substituents, give each one a number and list them alphabetically with hyphens between words and numbers.	The name of the compound is: 3-ethylpentane	The basic form of the name of the compound is: 4-ethyl-2,7-methyloctane List ethyl before methyl because substituents are listed in alphabetical order.
5. If a compound has two or more identical substituents, indicate the number of identical substituents with the prefix *di-* (2), *tri-* (3), or *tetra-* (4) before the substituent's name. Separate the numbers indicating the positions of the substituents relative to each other with a comma. Do not take the prefixes into account when alphabetizing.	Does not apply to this compound.	This compound has two methyl substituents; therefore, the name of the compound is: 4-ethyl-2,7-dimethyloctane
	FOR PRACTICE 22.2 Name this alkane: 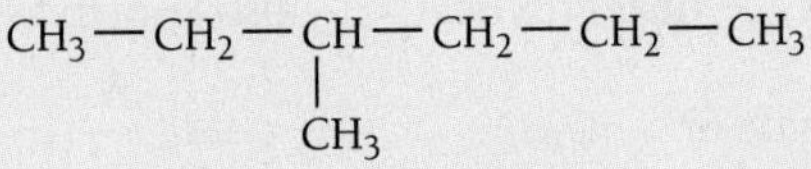	**FOR PRACTICE 22.3** Name this alkane: 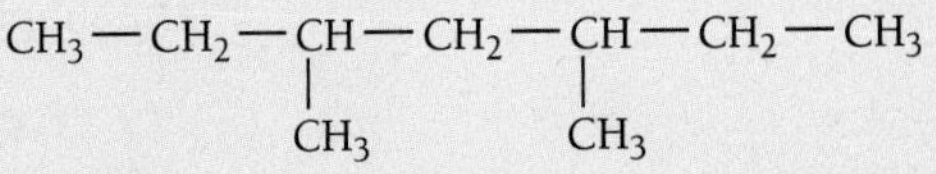

EXAMPLE 22.4 Naming Alkanes

Name this alkane: $CH_3—CH(CH_3)—CH_2—CH(CH_3)—CH_3$

SOLUTION

1. The longest continuous carbon chain has five atoms. Therefore, the base name is pentane.	$CH_3—CH(CH_3)—CH_2—CH(CH_3)—CH_3$
2. This compound has two substituents, both of which are named methyl.	$CH_3—CH(CH_3)—CH_2—CH(CH_3)—CH_3$ (both CH_3 branches labeled: methyl)
3. Since both substituents are equidistant from the ends, it does not matter from which end you start numbering.	$\overset{1}{CH_3}—\overset{2}{CH}(CH_3)—\overset{3}{CH_2}—\overset{4}{CH}(CH_3)—\overset{5}{CH_3}$
4,5. Use the general form for the name: (substituent number)-(substituent name)(base name) Because this compound contains two identical substituents, step 5 from the naming procedure applies and you use the prefix *di*-. Indicate the position of each substituent with a number separated by a comma.	2,4-dimethylpentane

FOR PRACTICE 22.4 Name this alkane: $CH_3—CH(CH_3)—CH_2—CH(CH_3)—CH(CH_3)—CH_3$

22.5 Alkenes and Alkynes

The general formulas shown here for alkenes and alkynes assume only one multiple bond.

Alkenes are hydrocarbons containing at least one double bond between carbon atoms. Alkynes contain at least one triple bond. Because of the double or triple bond, alkenes and alkynes have fewer hydrogen atoms than the corresponding alkanes and are therefore called **unsaturated hydrocarbons** because they are not loaded to capacity with hydrogen. Recall that noncyclic alkenes have the formula C_nH_{2n} and noncyclic alkynes have the formula C_nH_{2n-2}. The simplest alkene is ethene (C_2H_4), also called ethylene:

	Formula	Structural formula	Space-filling model
Ethene or ethylene	C_2H_4	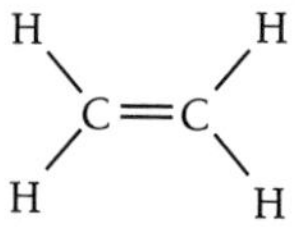	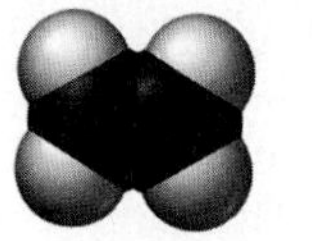

The geometry about each carbon atom in ethene is trigonal planar (see Example 11.8 for the valence bond model of ethene), making ethene a flat, rigid molecule. Ethene is a ripening agent in fruit such as bananas. When a banana within a cluster of bananas begins to ripen, it emits ethene. The ethene then causes other bananas in the cluster to ripen. Banana farmers usually pick bananas green for ease of shipping. When the bananas arrive at their destination, the fruit is often "gassed" with ethene to initiate ripening. Table 22.7 lists the names and structures of several other alkenes. Most of them do not have familiar uses except their presence as minority components in fuels.

The simplest alkyne is ethyne, C_2H_2, also known as acetylene:

	Formula	Structural formula	Space-filling model
Ethyne or acetylene	C_2H_2	$H—C≡C—H$	

TABLE 22.7 ■ Alkenes

n	Name	Molecular Formula C_nH_{2n}	Structural Formula	Condensed Structural Formula
2	Ethene	C_2H_4	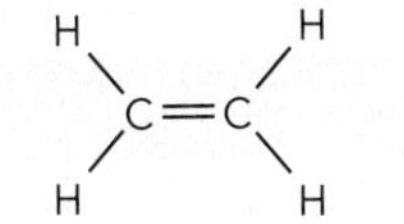	$CH_2{=}CH_2$
3	Propene	C_3H_6	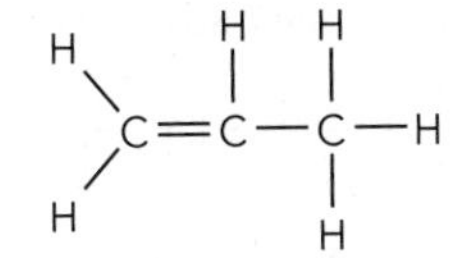	$CH_2{=}CHCH_2$
4	1-Butene*	C_4H_8	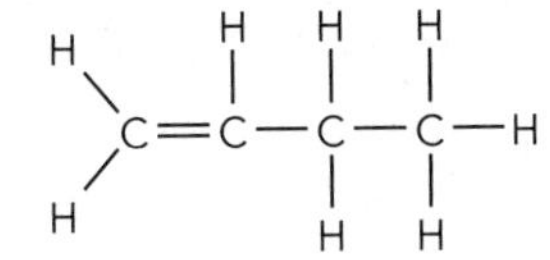	$CH_2{=}CHCH_2CH_3$
5	1-Pentene*	C_5H_{10}	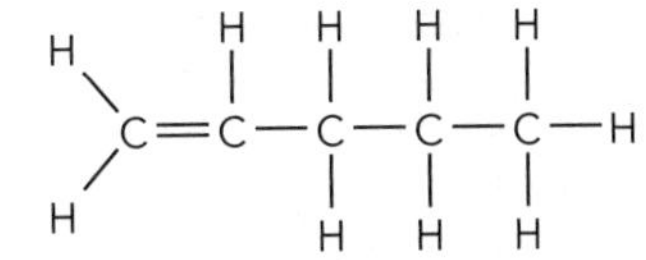	$CH_2{=}CHCH_2CH_2CH_3$
6	1-Hexene*	C_6H_{12}	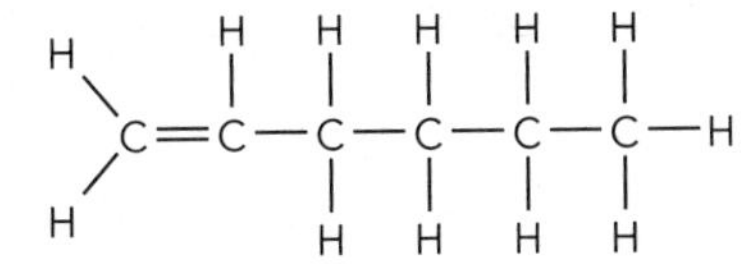	$CH_2{=}CHCH_2CH_2CH_2CH_3$

* These alkenes have one or more isomers depending on the position of the double bond. The isomers shown here have the double bond in the 1 position, meaning the first carbon–carbon bond of the chain.

The geometry about each carbon atom in ethyne is linear, making ethyne a linear molecule. Ethyne (or acetylene) is commonly used as fuel for welding torches. Table 22.8 shows the names and structures of several other alkynes. Like alkenes, the alkynes do not have familiar uses other than their presence as minority components of gasoline.

ALKANES, ALKENES, AND ALKYNES The formulas of three noncyclic hydrocarbons are listed below. Which of these is an alkene?

(a) C_4H_{10} **(b)** C_3H_4 **(c)** C_5H_{10}

22.3 Cc Conceptual Connection

ANSWER **NOW!**

▲ Welding torches burn ethyne in pure oxygen to produce the very hot flame needed for melting metals.

Naming Alkenes and Alkynes

We name alkenes and alkynes in the same way we name alkanes with the following exceptions:

- The base chain is the longest continuous carbon chain *that contains the double or triple bond.*
- The base name has the ending *-ene* for alkenes and *-yne* for alkynes.
- We number the base chain to give the double or triple bond the lowest possible number.
- We insert a number indicating the position of the double or triple bond (lowest possible number) just before the base name.

For example, the alkene and alkyne shown here are 2-methyl-2-pentene and 1-butyne:

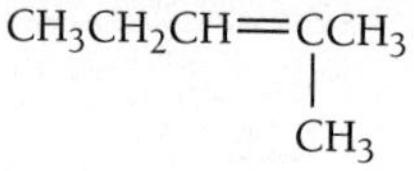
2-Methyl-2-pentene

$CH{\equiv}CCH_2CH_3$
1-Butyne

TABLE 22.8 ■ Alkynes

n	Name	Molecular Formula C_nH_{2n-2}	Structural Formula	Condensed Structural Formula
2	Ethyne	C_2H_2	H—C≡C—H	$CH{\equiv}CH$
3	Propyne	C_3H_4	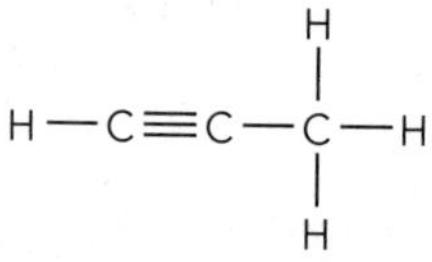	$CH{\equiv}CCH_3$
4	1-Butyne*	C_4H_6	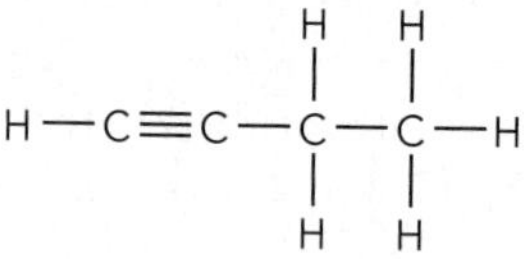	$CH{\equiv}CCH_2CH_3$
5	1-Pentyne*	C_5H_8	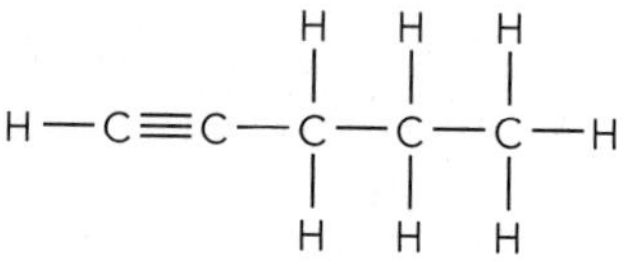	$CH{\equiv}CCH_2CH_2CH_3$
6	1-Hexyne*	C_6H_{10}	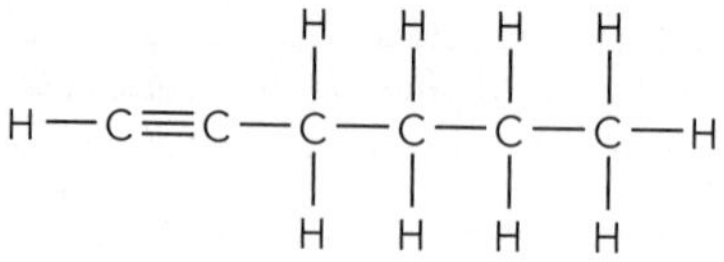	$CH{\equiv}CCH_2CH_2CH_2CH_3$

* These alkynes have one or more isomers depending on the position of the triple bond. The isomers shown here have the triple bond in the 1 position, meaning the first carbon–carbon bond of the chain.

EXAMPLE 22.5 Naming Alkenes and Alkynes

Name each compound.

(a) 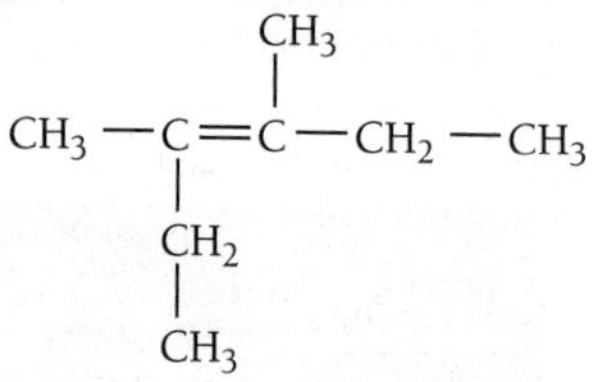

(b) 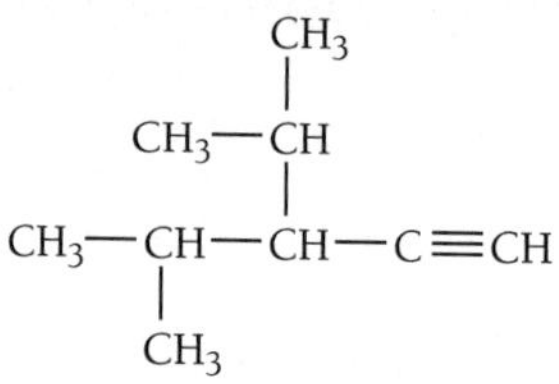

SOLUTION

(a) 1. The longest continuous carbon chain containing the double bond has six carbon atoms. The base name is therefore *hexene*.

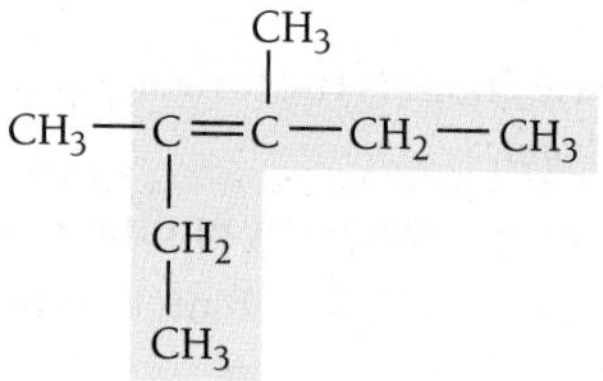

2. The two substituents are both methyl.

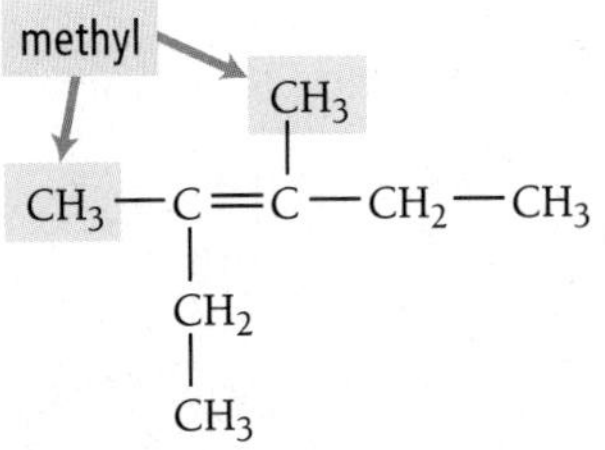

3. One of the exceptions listed previously states that, in naming alkenes, you should number the chain so that the *double bond* has the lowest number. In this case, the double bond is equidistant from the ends. Assign the double bond the number 3. The two methyl groups are then at positions 3 and 4.

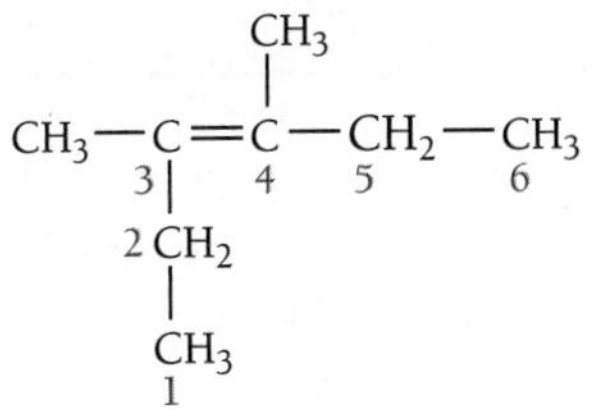

4, 5. Use the general form for the name:
(substituent number)-(substituent name)(base name)
Because this compound contains two identical substituents, step 5 of the naming procedure applies. Use the prefix *di-*. In addition, indicate the position of each substituent with a number separated by a comma. Because this compound is an alkene, specify the position of the double bond, isolated by hyphens, just before the base name.

3,4-dimethyl-3-hexene

(b) 1. The longest continuous carbon chain containing the triple bond is five carbon atoms long; therefore, the base name is *pentyne*.

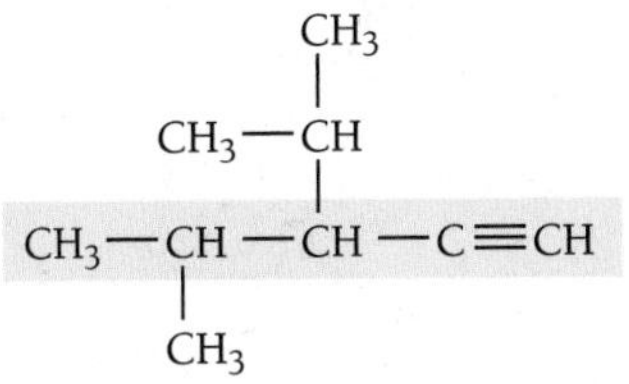

2. There are two substituents; one is a methyl group and the other an isopropyl group.

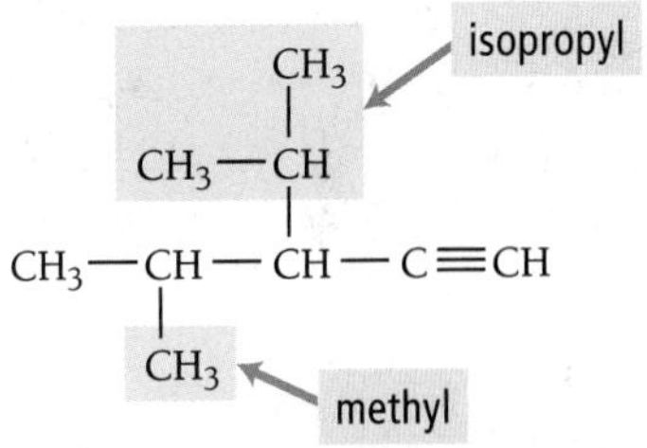

3. Number the base chain, giving the triple bond the lowest number (1). Assign the isopropyl and methyl groups the numbers 3 and 4, respectively.

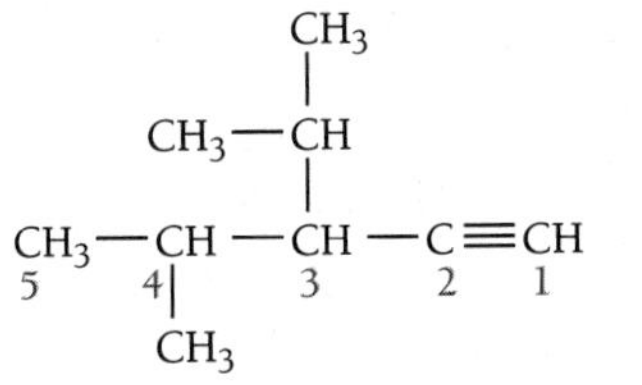

4. Use the general form for the name:
(substituent number)-(substituent name)(base name)
Since there are two substituents, list both of them in alphabetical order. Because this compound is an alkyne, specify the position of the triple bond with a number isolated by hyphens just before the base name.

3-isopropyl-4-methyl-1-pentyne

—*Continued on the next page*

Continued—

FOR PRACTICE 22.5 Name each compound.

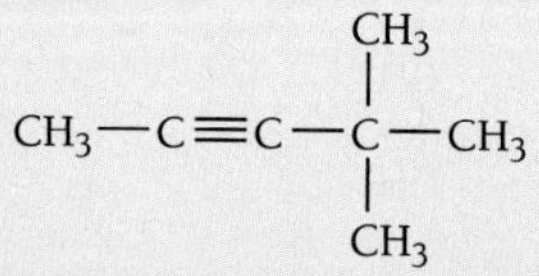

(a)

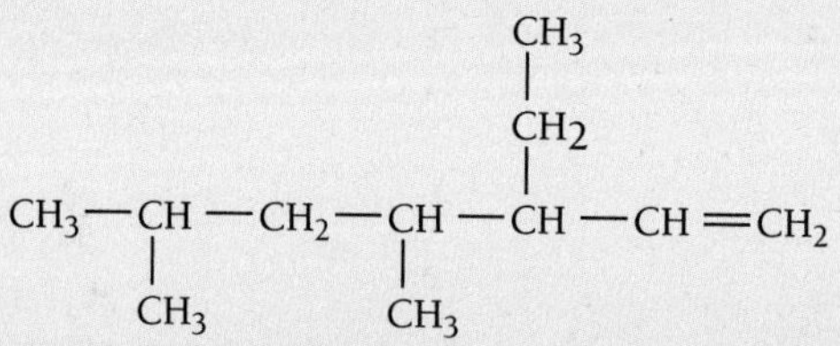

(b)

Geometric (Cis–Trans) Isomerism in Alkenes

A major difference between a single bond and a double bond is the degree to which rotation occurs about the bond. As discussed in Section 11.7, rotation about a double bond is highly restricted due to the overlap between unhybridized *p* orbitals on the adjacent carbon atoms.

Consider the difference between 1,2-dichloroethane and 1,2-dichloroethene:

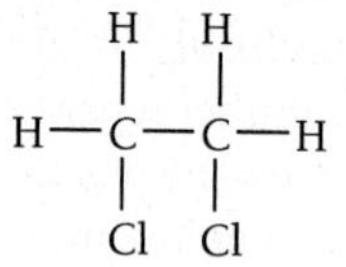

1,2-Dichloroethane

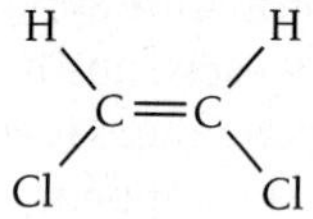

1,2-Dichloroethene

The hybridization of the carbon atoms in 1,2-dichloroethane is sp^3, resulting in relatively free rotation about the sigma single bond. Consequently, the two structures are identical at room temperature because they quickly interconvert:

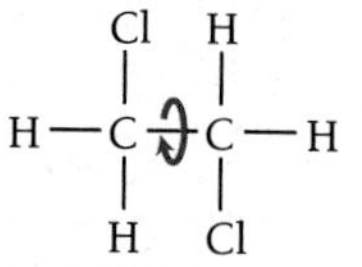

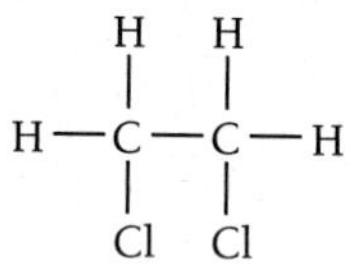

In contrast, rotation about the double bond (sigma + pi) in 1,2-dichloroethene is restricted, so at room temperature, 1,2-dichloroethene exists in two isomeric forms:

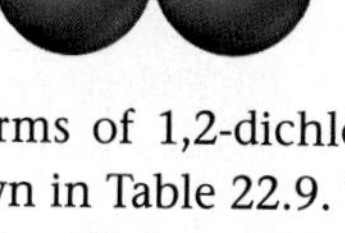

cis-1,2-Dichloroethene

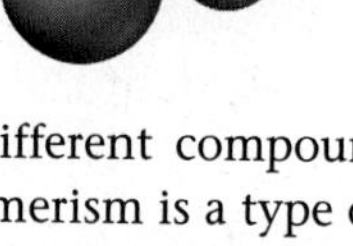

trans-1,2-Dichloroethene

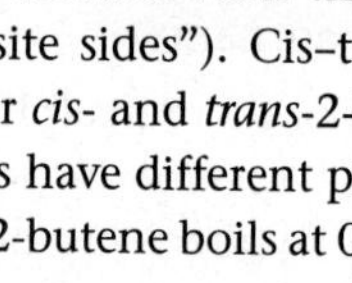

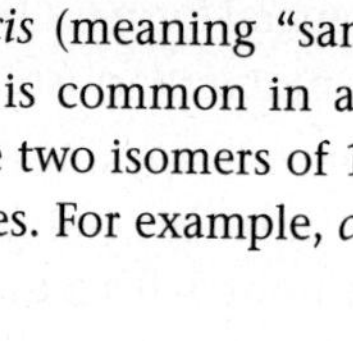

These two forms of 1,2-dichloroethene are different compounds with different properties as shown in Table 22.9. This kind of isomerism is a type of stereoisomerism (see Section 22.3) called **geometric** (or **cis–trans**) **isomerism**. We distinguish between the two isomers with the designations *cis* (meaning "same side") and *trans* (meaning "opposite sides"). Cis–trans isomerism is common in alkenes. As another example, consider *cis*- and *trans*-2-butene. Like the two isomers of 1,2-dichloroethene, these two isomers have different physical properties. For example, *cis*-2-butene boils at 3.7 °C, and *trans*-2-butene boils at 0.9 °C:

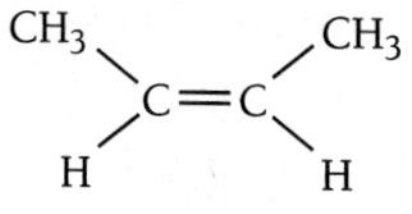

cis-2-Butene

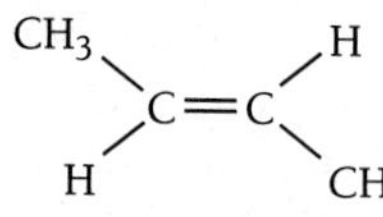

trans-2-Butene

TABLE 22.9 ■ Physical Properties of *cis*- and *trans*-1,2-Dichloroethene

Name	Structure	Space-filling Model	Density (g/mL)	Melting Point (°C)	Boiling Point (°C)
cis-1,2-Dichloroethene	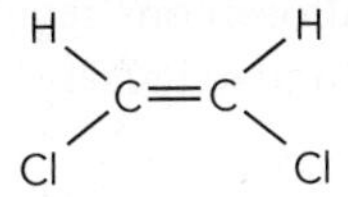	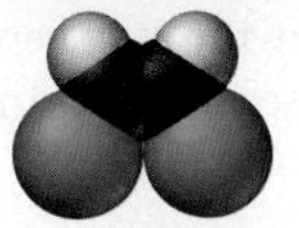	1.284	−80.5	60.1
trans-1,2-Dichloroethene	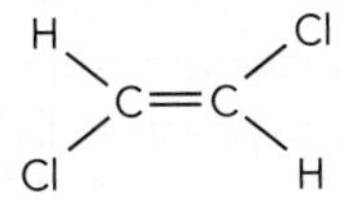	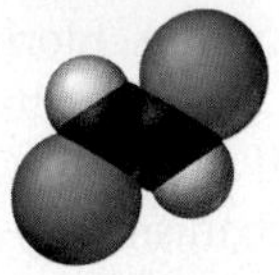	1.257	−49.4	47.5

22.6 Hydrocarbon Reactions

One of the most common hydrocarbon reactions is combustion, the burning of hydrocarbons in the presence of oxygen. Hydrocarbon combustion reactions are highly exothermic and are commonly used to warm homes and buildings, to generate electricity, and to power the engines of cars, ships, and airplanes. It is not an exaggeration to say that hydrocarbon combustion makes our current way of life possible. Approximately 90% of energy produced in the United States is generated by hydrocarbon combustion.

Alkanes, alkenes, and alkynes all undergo combustion. In a combustion reaction, the hydrocarbon reacts with oxygen to form carbon dioxide and water:

$$CH_3CH_2CH_3(g) + 5\,O_2(g) \longrightarrow 3\,CO_2(g) + 4\,H_2O(g) \quad \text{Alkane combustion}$$
$$CH_2{=}CHCH_2CH_3(g) + 6\,O_2(g) \longrightarrow 4\,CO_2(g) + 4\,H_2O(g) \quad \text{Alkene combustion}$$
$$CH{\equiv}CCH_3(g) + 4\,O_2(g) \longrightarrow 3\,CO_2(g) + 2\,H_2O(g) \quad \text{Alkyne combustion}$$

Reactions of Alkanes

In addition to combustion reactions, alkanes also undergo *substitution* reactions, in which one or more hydrogen atoms on an alkane are replaced by one or more other atoms. The most common substitution reaction is halogen substitution (also referred to as halogenation). For example, methane can react with chlorine gas in the presence of heat or light to form chloromethane:

$$\underset{\text{Methane}}{CH_4(g)} + \underset{\text{Chlorine}}{Cl_2(g)} \xrightarrow{\text{heat or light}} \underset{\text{Chloromethane}}{CH_3Cl(g)} + HCl(g)$$

Ethane reacts with chlorine gas to form chloroethane:

$$\underset{\text{Ethane}}{CH_3CH_3(g)} + \underset{\text{Chlorine}}{Cl_2(g)} \xrightarrow{\text{heat or light}} \underset{\text{Chloromethane}}{CH_3CH_2Cl(g)} + HCl(g)$$

Multiple halogenation reactions can occur because halogens can replace more than one of the hydrogen atoms on an alkane. For example, chloromethane can react with chlorine, and the product of that reaction can react again (and so on):

$$\underset{\text{Chloromethane}}{CH_3Cl(g)} + \underset{\text{Chlorine}}{Cl_2(g)} \xrightarrow{\text{heat or light}} \underset{\text{Dichloromethane (also known as methylene chloride)}}{CH_2Cl_2(g)} + HCl(g)$$

$$\underset{\text{Dichloromethane}}{CH_2Cl_2(g)} + \underset{\text{Chlorine}}{Cl_2(g)} \xrightarrow{\text{heat or light}} \underset{\text{Trichloromethane (also known as chloroform)}}{CHCl_3(g)} + HCl(g)$$

$$\underset{\text{Trichloromethane}}{CHCl_3(g)} + \underset{\text{Chlorine}}{Cl_2(g)} \xrightarrow{\text{heat or light}} \underset{\text{Tetrachloromethane (also known as carbon tetrachloride)}}{CCl_4(g)} + HCl(g)$$

The general form for halogen substitution reactions is:

$$\underset{\text{Alkane}}{R{-}H} + \underset{\text{Halogen}}{X_2} \xrightarrow{\text{heat or light}} \underset{\text{Haloalkane}}{R{-}X} + \underset{\text{Hydrogen halide}}{HX}$$

Notice that the halogenation of hydrocarbons requires initiation with heat or light, which causes the chlorine–chlorine bond to break:

$$Cl{-}Cl \xrightarrow{\text{heat or light}} Cl\cdot + Cl\cdot$$

The resulting chlorine atoms are *free radicals* (see Section 10.9), as the dot that represents each chlorine atom's unpaired electron indicates. Chlorine radicals are highly reactive and attack the C—H bond in hydrocarbons. The subsequent reaction proceeds by this mechanism:

$$Cl\cdot + R{-}H \longrightarrow R\cdot + HCl$$
$$R\cdot + Cl_2 \longrightarrow R{-}Cl + Cl\cdot$$

Notice that a chlorine free radical is produced as a product of the last step. This free radical can go on to react again, unless it encounters another chlorine free radical, in which case it reacts with it to re-form Cl_2.

Reactions of Alkenes and Alkynes

Alkenes and alkynes undergo addition reactions in which molecules add across (on either side of) the multiple bond. For example, ethene reacts with chlorine gas to form dichloroethane:

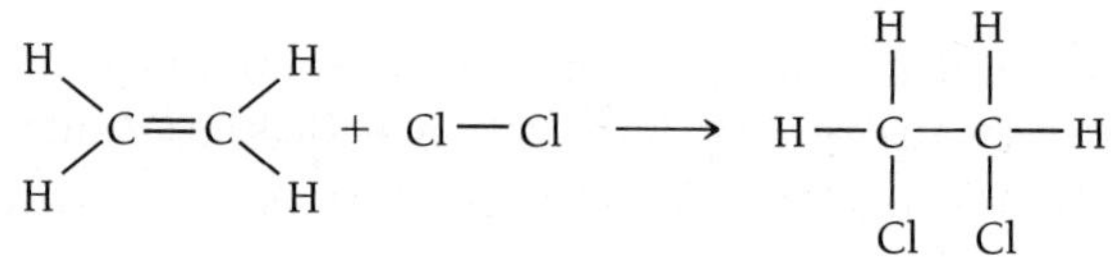

The addition of chlorine converts the carbon–carbon double bond into a single bond because each carbon atom bonds to a chlorine atom.

We often indicate the presence of a catalyst by adding a label over the reaction arrow.

Alkenes and alkynes can also add hydrogen in hydrogenation reactions. For example, in the presence of an appropriate catalyst, propene reacts with hydrogen gas to form propane:

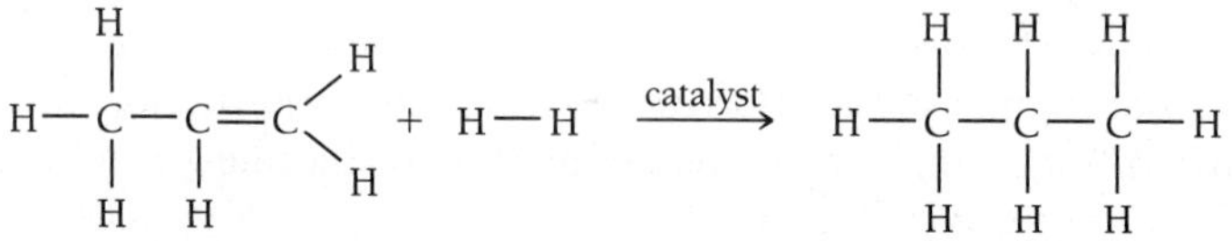

Hydrogenation reactions convert unsaturated hydrocarbons into saturated hydrocarbons. For example, hydrogenation reactions convert unsaturated vegetable oils into saturated fats. Most vegetable oils are unsaturated because their carbon chains contain double bonds. The double bonds put bends into the carbon chains that result in less efficient packing of molecules; thus vegetable oils are liquids at room temperature, while saturated fats are solids at room temperature. When food manufacturers add hydrogen to the double bonds of vegetable oil, the unsaturated fat is converted into a saturated fat, turning the liquid oil into a solid at room temperature. The words "partially hydrogenated vegetable oil" on a label indicate a food product that contains saturated fats made via hydrogenation reactions. Most food manufacturers have stopped using these fats because the process also introduces *trans-fats* into the mix, which have been shown to contribute to health problems such as heart disease.

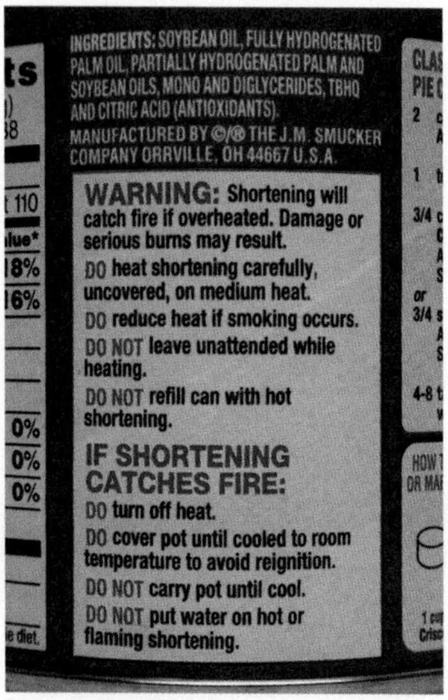

▲ Partially hydrogenated vegetable oil is a saturated fat that is made by hydrogenating unsaturated fats.

Alkenes can also add unsymmetrical reagents across the double bond. For example, ethene reacts with hydrogen chloride to form chloroethane:

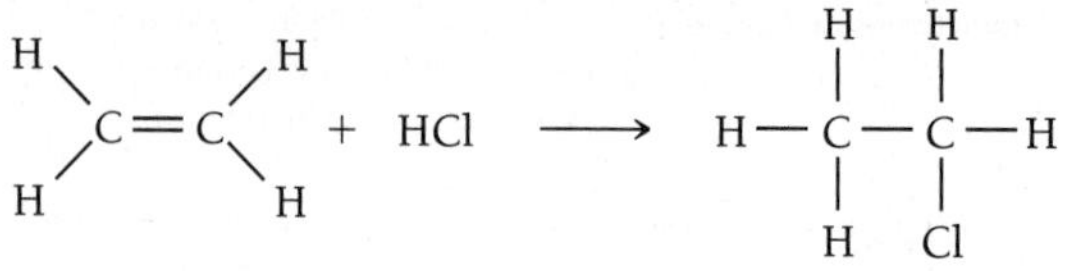

Chloroethane

If the alkene itself is also unsymmetrical, then the addition of an unsymmetrical reagent leads to the potential for two different products. For example, when HCl reacts with propene, two products are possible:

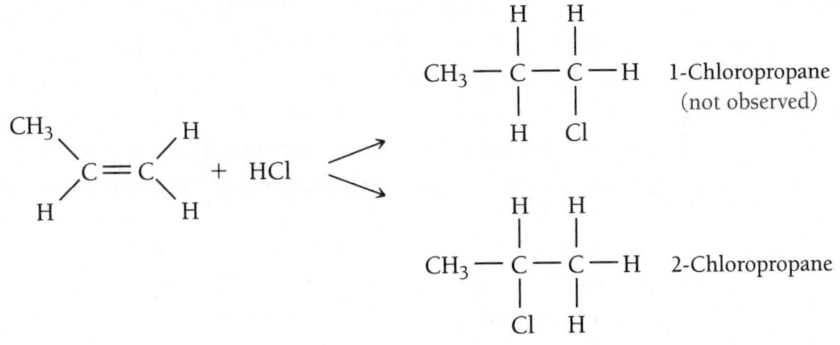

When this reaction is carried out in the lab, however, only the 2-chloropropane forms. We can predict the product of the addition of an unsymmetrical reagent to an unsymmetrical alkene with Markovnikov's rule, which states the following:

When a polar reagent is added to an unsymmetrical alkene, the positive end (the least electronegative part) of the reagent adds to the carbon atom that has the most hydrogen atoms.

In most reactions of this type, the positive end of the reagent is hydrogen; therefore, the hydrogen atom bonds to the carbon atom that already contains the most hydrogen atoms.

EXAMPLE 22.6 Alkene Addition Reactions

Determine the products of each reaction.

(a) $CH_3CH_2CH{=}CH_2 + Br_2 \longrightarrow$ **(b)** $CH_3CH_2CH{=}CH_2 + HBr \longrightarrow$

(a) The reaction of 1-butene with bromine is an example of a symmetric addition. The bromine adds across the double bond, and each carbon forms a single bond to a bromine atom.

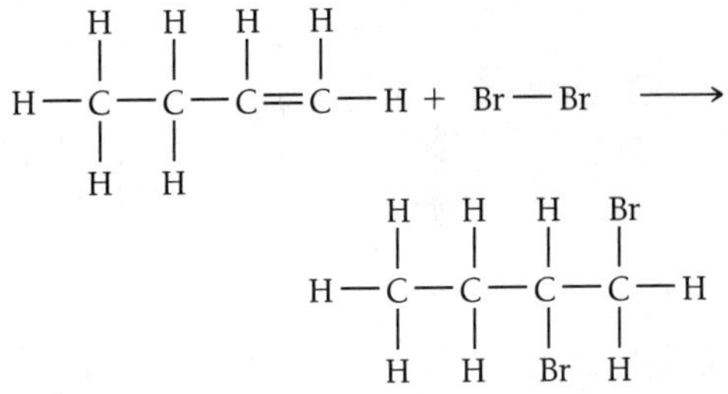

(b) The reaction of 1-butene with hydrogen bromide is an example of an unsymmetrical addition. Apply Markovnikov's rule to determine which carbon the hydrogen bonds with and which carbon the bromine atom bonds with. Markovnikov's rule predicts that the hydrogen bonds to the end carbon in this case.

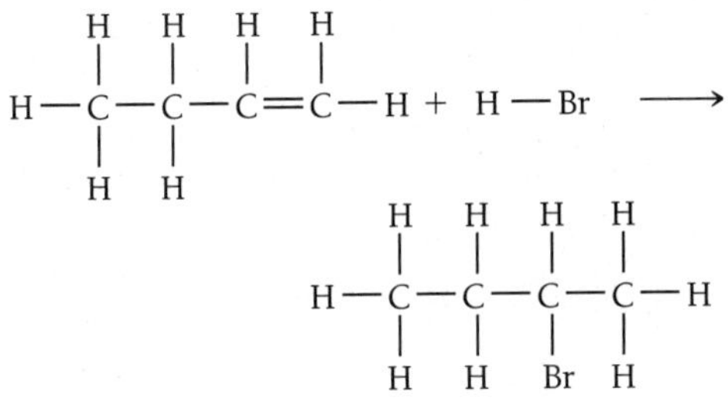

FOR PRACTICE 22.6 Determine the products of each reaction.

(a) 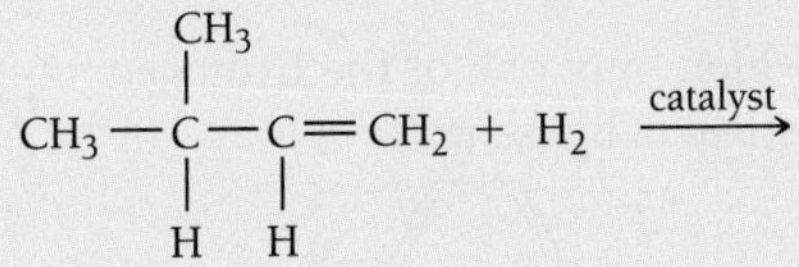

(b) 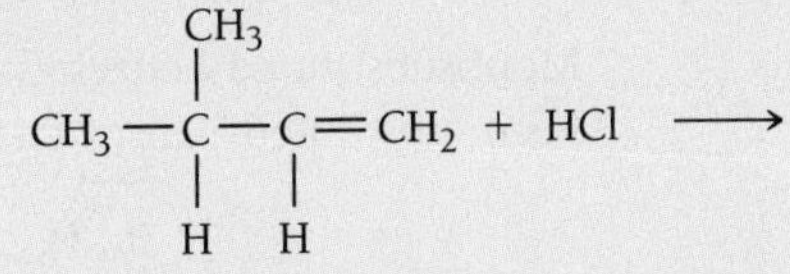

22.7 Aromatic Hydrocarbons

As you might imagine, determining the structure of organic compounds has not always been easy. During the mid-1800s chemists were working to determine the structure of a particularly stable organic compound named benzene (C_6H_6). In 1865, Friedrich August Kekulé (1829–1896) had a dream in which he envisioned chains of carbon atoms as snakes. The snakes danced before him, and one of them twisted around and bit its tail. Based on that vision, Kekulé proposed the following structure for benzene:

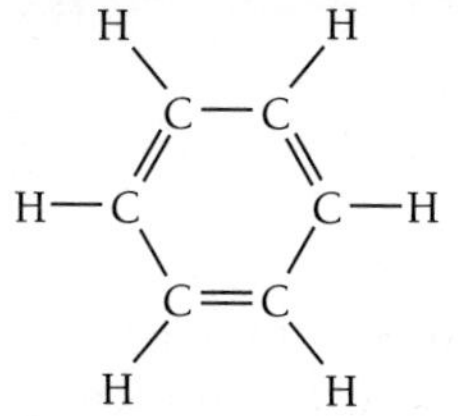

This structure has alternating single and double bonds. When we examine the carbon–carbon bond lengths in benzene, however, we find that all the bonds are the same length, which indicates that the following resonance structures are a more accurate representation of benzene:

Recall from Section 10.8 that the actual structure of a molecule represented by resonance structures is intermediate between the two resonance structures and is called a *resonance hybrid*.

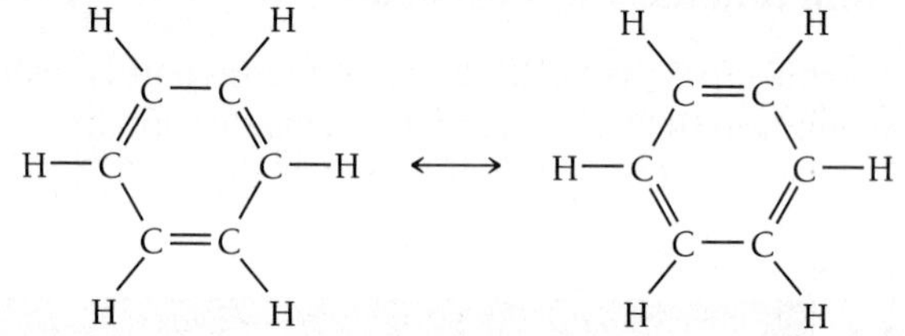

The true structure of benzene is a hybrid of the two resonance structures. We often represent benzene with the following carbon skeletal formula (or line formula):

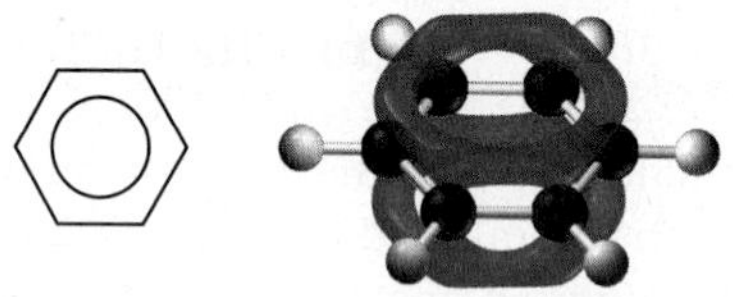

The ring represents the delocalized π electrons that occupy the molecular orbital shown superimposed on the ball-and-stick model. When drawing benzene rings, either by themselves or as parts of other compounds, organic chemists use either this diagram or just one of the resonance structures with alternating double bonds. Both representations indicate the same thing—a benzene ring.

The benzene ring structure occurs in many organic compounds. An atom or group of atoms can be substituted for one or more of the six hydrogen atoms on the ring to form compounds referred to as substituted benzenes, such as chlorobenzene and phenol:

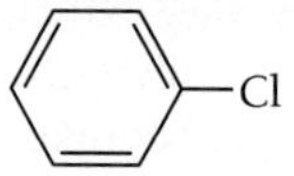

Chlorobenzene

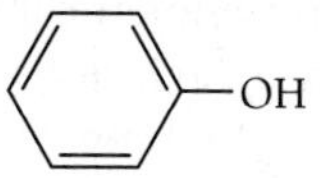

Phenol

Because many compounds containing benzene rings have pleasant aromas, benzene rings are also called *aromatic rings*, and compounds containing them are called *aromatic compounds*. Aromatic compounds are responsible for the pleasant smells of cinnamon, vanilla, and jasmine.

Naming Aromatic Hydrocarbons

Monosubstituted benzenes—benzenes in which only one of the hydrogen atoms has been substituted—are often named as derivatives of benzene:

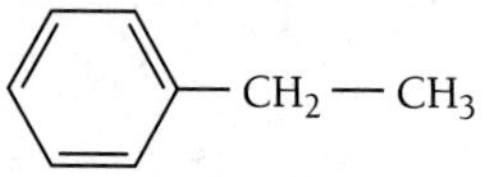

Ethylbenzene

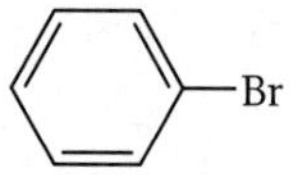

Bromobenzene

These names take the general form:

(name of substituent)benzene

However, many monosubstituted benzenes have names that can only be learned through familiarity. Some common ones are shown here:

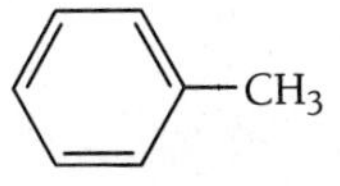

Toluene

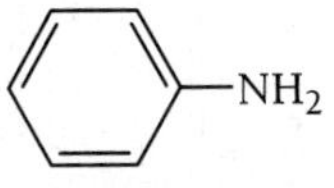

Aniline

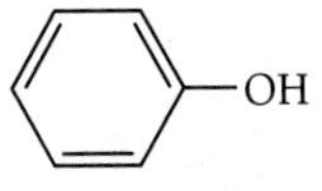

Phenol

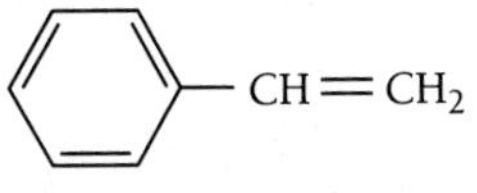

Styrene

Some substituted benzenes, especially those with large substituents, are named by treating the benzene ring as the substituent. In these cases, the benzene substituent is referred to as a **phenyl group**:

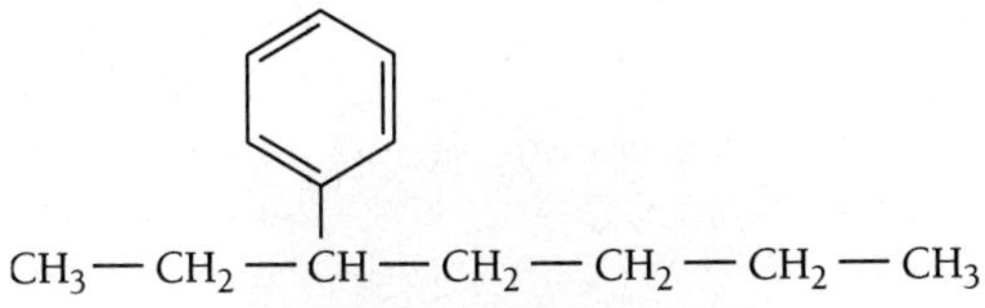

3-Phenylheptane

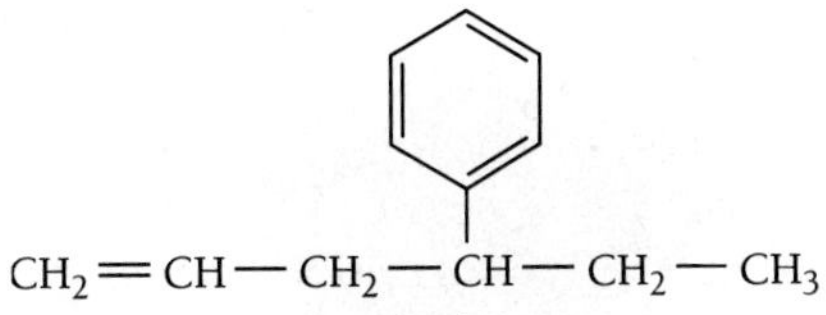

4-Phenyl-1-hexene

Disubstituted benzenes—benzenes in which two hydrogen atoms have been substituted—are numbered, and the substituents are listed alphabetically. We determine the order of numbering on the ring by the alphabetical order of the substituents:

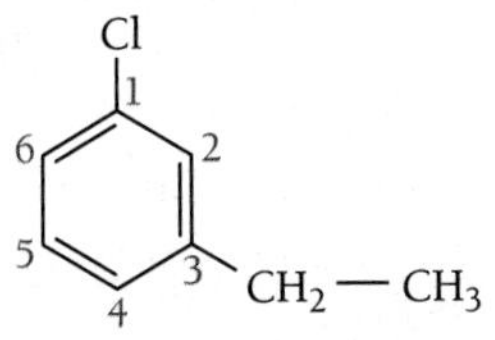

1-Chloro-3-ethylbenzene

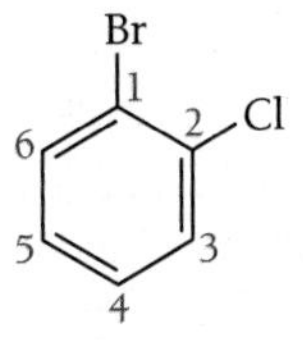

1-Bromo-2-chlorobenzene

When the two substituents are identical, we use the prefix *di-*:

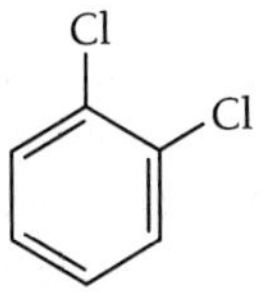

1,2-Dichlorobenzene

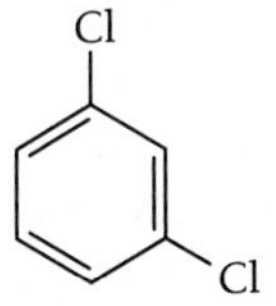

1,3-Dichlorobenzene

1,4-Dichlorobenzene

Also in common use, in place of numbering, are the prefixes *ortho* (1,2 disubstituted), *meta* (1,3 disubstituted), and *para* (1,4 disubstituted):

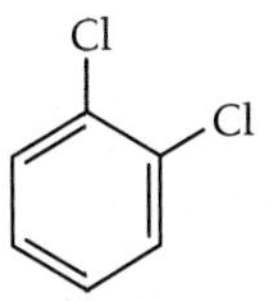

ortho-Dichlorobenzene
or
o-Dichlorobenzene

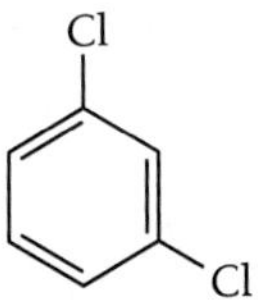

meta-Dichlorobenzene
or
m-Dichlorobenzene

para-Dichlorobenzene
or
p-Dichlorobenzene

Compounds containing fused aromatic rings are called polycyclic aromatic hydrocarbons. Some common examples (shown in Figure 22.5▶) include naphthalene, the substance that composes mothballs, and pyrene, a carcinogen found in cigarette smoke.

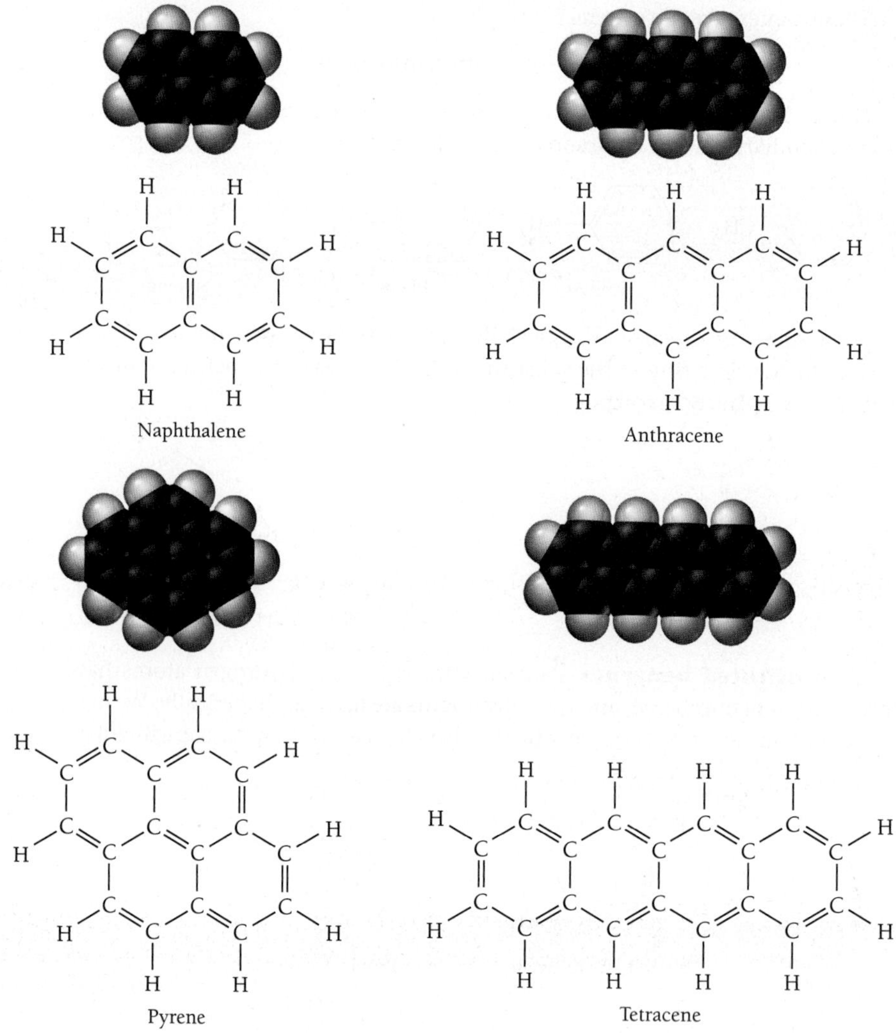

▶ **FIGURE 22.5 Polycyclic Aromatic Compounds** The structures of some common polycyclic aromatic compounds contain fused rings.

Reactions of Aromatic Compounds

We might expect benzene to react similarly to the alkenes, readily undergoing addition reactions across its double bonds. However, because of electron delocalization around the ring and the resulting greater stability, benzene does not typically undergo addition reactions. Instead, benzene undergoes substitution reactions in which the hydrogen atoms are replaced by other atoms or groups of atoms as shown in the following examples:

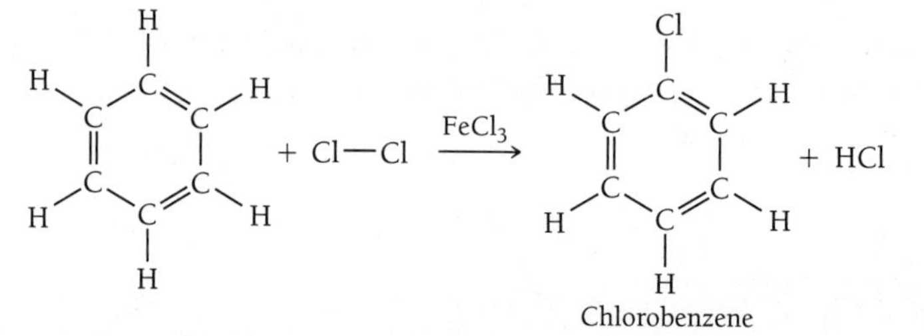

The substances shown over the arrows are catalysts needed to increase the rate of the reaction.

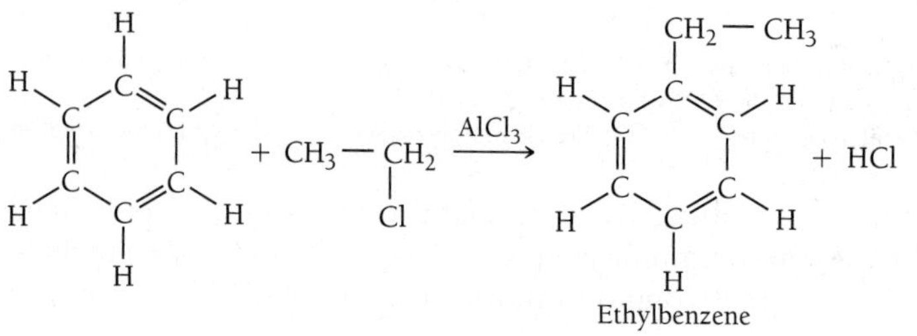

22.8 Functional Groups

Most other families of organic compounds are hydrocarbons with a *functional group*—a characteristic atom or group of atoms—inserted into the hydrocarbon. A group of organic compounds that all have the same functional group is a *family*. For example, the members of the family of alcohols each have an —OH functional group and the general formula R—OH, where R represents a hydrocarbon group. (That is, we refer to the hydrocarbon group as an "R group.") Some specific examples include methanol and isopropyl alcohol (the main component of rubbing alcohol):

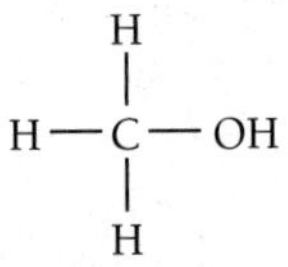

Methanol

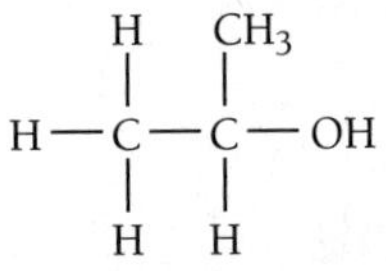

Isopropyl alcohol

The presence of a functional group in a hydrocarbon alters the properties of the compound significantly. For example, methane is a nonpolar gas. By contrast, methanol—methane with an —OH group substituted for one of the hydrogen atoms—is a polar, hydrogen-bonded liquid at room temperature. Although each member of a family is unique and different, their common functional group causes some similarities in both their physical and chemical properties. Table 22.10 lists some common functional groups, their general formulas, and an example of each.

TABLE 22.10 ■ Some Common Functional Groups

Family	General Formula*	Condensed General Formula	Example	Name
Alcohols	R—OH	ROH	CH_3CH_2OH	Ethanol (ethyl alcohol)
Ethers	R—O—R	ROR	CH_3OCH_3	Dimethyl ether
Aldehydes	R—C(=O)—H	RCHO	CH_3—C(=O)—H	Ethanal (acetaldehyde)
Ketones	R—C(=O)—R	RCOR	CH_3—C(=O)—CH_3	Propanone (acetone)
Carboxylic acids	R—C(=O)—OH	RCOOH	CH_3—C(=O)—OH	Ethanoic acid (acetic acid)
Esters	R—C(=O)—OR	RCOOR	CH_3—C(=O)—OCH_3	Methyl acetate
Amines	R—N(R)—R	R_3N	CH_3CH_2—N(H)—H	Ethylamine

22.9 Alcohols

As we discussed in Section 22.8, **alcohols** are organic compounds containing the —OH functional group, or **hydroxyl group**, and they have the general formula R—OH. In addition to methanol and isopropyl alcohol, ethanol and 1-butanol (shown here) are also common alcohols:

CH_3-CH_2-OH

Ethanol

$CH_3-CH_2-CH_2-CH_2-OH$

1-Butanol

Naming Alcohols

The names of alcohols are like the names of alkanes with the following differences:

- The base chain is the longest continuous carbon chain that contains the —OH functional group.
- The base name has the ending *-ol*.
- We number the base chain to assign the —OH group the lowest possible number.
- We insert a number indicating the position of the —OH group just before the base name. For example:

$CH_3CH_2CH_2CH(OH)CH_3$

2-Pentanol

$CH_2(OH)-CH_2-CH(CH_3)-CH_3$

3-Methyl-1-butanol

About Alcohols

The familiar alcohol in alcoholic beverages, ethanol, is most commonly formed by the yeast fermentation of sugars, such as glucose, from fruits and grains:

$$\underset{\text{Glucose}}{C_6H_{12}O_6} \xrightarrow{\text{yeast}} 2\ \underset{\text{Ethanol}}{CH_3CH_2OH} + 2\ CO_2$$

Alcoholic beverages contain ethanol, water, and a few other components that impart flavor and color. Beer usually contains 3–6% ethanol. Wine contains about 12–14% ethanol, and spirits—beverages like whiskey, rum, or tequila—range from 40% to 80% ethanol, depending on their *proof*. The proof of an alcoholic beverage is twice the percentage of its ethanol content, so an 80-proof whiskey contains 40% ethanol. Ethanol is used as a gasoline additive because it increases the octane rating of gasoline and fosters its complete combustion, reducing the levels of certain pollutants such as carbon monoxide and the precursors of ozone.

Isopropyl alcohol (or 2-propanol) is available at any drugstore under the name of rubbing alcohol. It is commonly used as a disinfectant for wounds and to sterilize medical instruments. Isopropyl alcohol should never be consumed internally, as it is highly toxic. Four ounces of isopropyl alcohol can cause death. A third common alcohol is methanol, also called wood alcohol. Methanol is commonly used as a laboratory solvent and as a fuel additive. Like isopropyl alcohol, methanol is toxic and should never be consumed.

Alcohol Reactions

Alcohols undergo a number of reactions including substitution, elimination (or dehydration), and oxidation. Alcohols also react with active metals to form strong bases.

Substitution

Alcohols react with acids such as HBr to form halogenated hydrocarbons:

$$ROH + HBr \longrightarrow R{-}Br + H_2O$$

In these reactions, the halogen replaces the hydroxyl group on the alcohol. For example, ethanol reacts with hydrobromic acid to form bromoethane and water:

$$CH_3CH_2OH + HBr \longrightarrow CH_3CH_2Br + H_2O$$

Elimination (or Dehydration)

In the presence of concentrated acids such as H_2SO_4, alcohols react and eliminate water, forming an alkene. For example, ethanol eliminates water to form ethene according to the reaction:

$$\underset{\displaystyle H}{\underset{|}{CH_2}}{-}\underset{\displaystyle OH}{\underset{|}{CH_2}} \xrightarrow{H_2SO_2} CH_2{=}CH_2 + H_2O$$

Oxidation

In organic chemistry, we think of oxidation and reduction in terms of the changes to the carbon atoms in the molecule. Thus, oxidation is the gaining of oxygen or the losing of hydrogen by a carbon atom. Reduction is the loss of oxygen or the gaining of hydrogen by a carbon atom. We can draw a series showing relative states of oxidation:

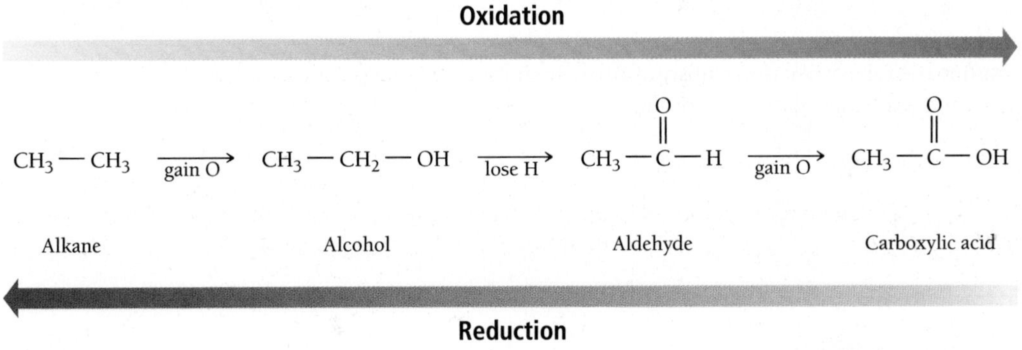

In this view, an alcohol is a partially oxidized hydrocarbon; it can be further oxidized to form an aldehyde or carboxylic acid, or it can be reduced to form a hydrocarbon (but this is rare). For example, ethanol can be oxidized to acetic acid according to the reaction:

$$CH_3CH_2OH \xrightarrow[H_2SO_4]{Na_2Cr_2O_7} CH_3COOH$$

Reaction with Active Metals

Alcohols react with active metals, such as sodium, much as water does. For example, methanol reacts with sodium to form *sodium methoxide* and hydrogen gas:

$$CH_3OH + Na \longrightarrow \underset{\text{Sodium methoxide}}{CH_3ONa} + \tfrac{1}{2}H_2$$

The reaction of *water* with sodium produces *sodium hydroxide* and hydrogen gas:

$$H_2O + Na \longrightarrow NaOH + \tfrac{1}{2}H_2$$

In both cases, a strong base forms (OH^- for water and CH_3O^- for methanol).

EXAMPLE 22.7 Alcohol Reactions

Determine the type of reaction (substitution, dehydration, oxidation, or reaction with an active metal) that occurs in each case, and write formulas for the products.

(a) 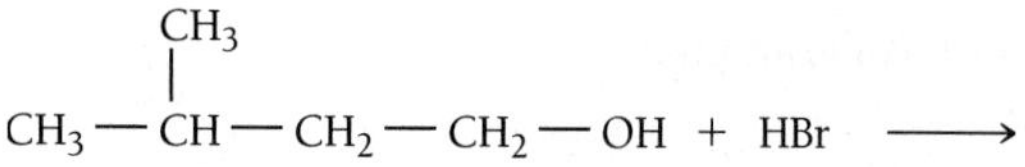

(b) 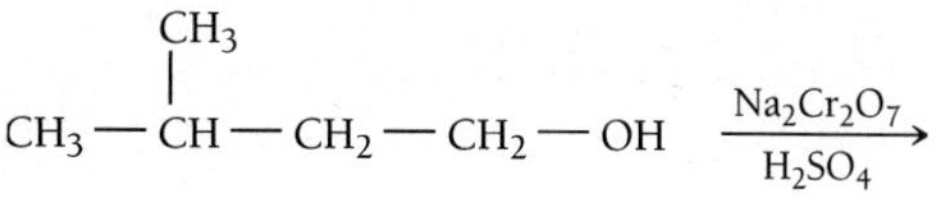

SOLUTION

(a) An alcohol reacting with an acid is an example of a *substitution reaction*. The product of the substitution reaction is a halogenated hydrocarbon and water.

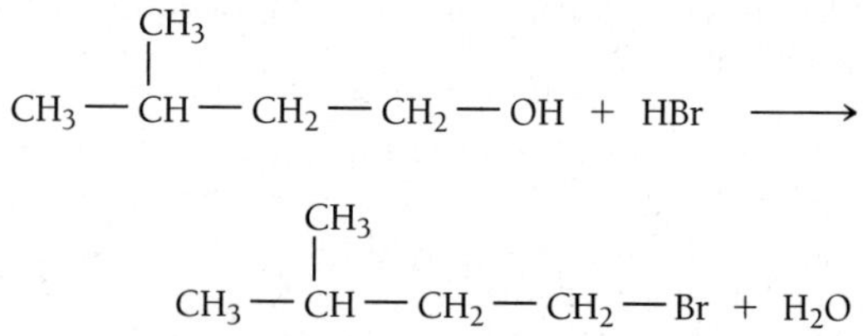

(b) An alcohol in solution with sodium dichromate and acid undergoes an *oxidation reaction*. The product of the oxidation reaction is a carboxylic acid functional group. (We discuss carboxylic acid functional groups in detail in Section 22.11.)

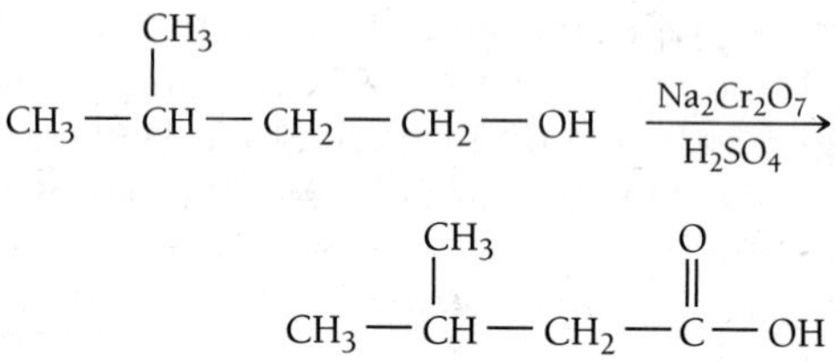

FOR PRACTICE 22.7 Determine the type of reaction (substitution, dehydration, oxidation, or reaction with an active metal) that occurs in each case, and write formulas for the products.

(a) $CH_3CH_2OH + Na \longrightarrow$

(b) 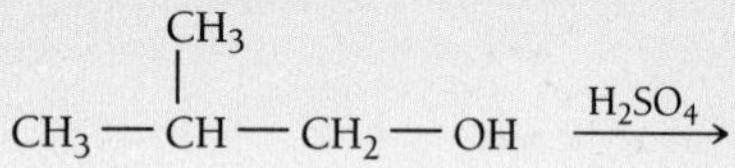

22.10 Aldehydes and Ketones

Aldehydes and **ketones** have the following general formulas:

The condensed structural formula for aldehydes is RCHO and that for ketones is RCOR.

Aldehyde Ketone

The functional group for both aldehydes and ketones is the **carbonyl group**:

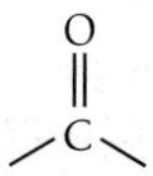

Ketones have an R group attached to both sides of the carbonyl, while aldehydes have one R group and a hydrogen atom. (An exception is formaldehyde, which is an aldehyde with two H atoms bonded to the carbonyl group.)

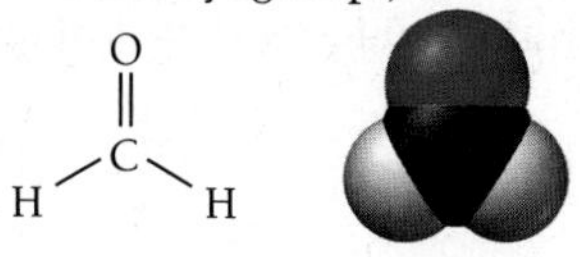

Formaldehyde or methanal

Other common aldehydes and ketones are shown in Figure 22.6▼.

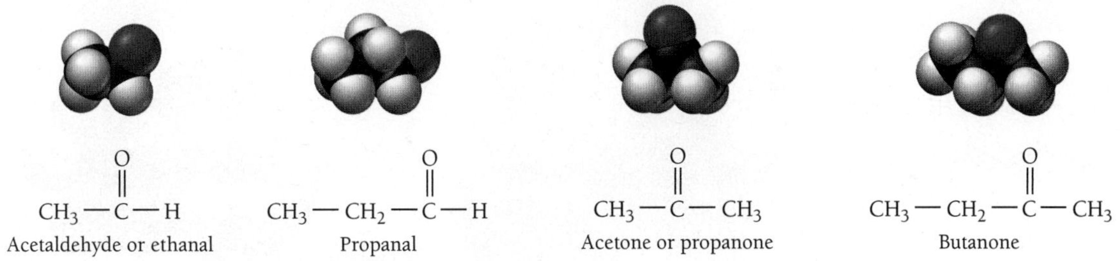

▲ **FIGURE 22.6 Common Aldehydes and Ketones**

Naming Aldehydes and Ketones

Many aldehydes and ketones have common names that we can learn only by becoming familiar with them, but we can systematically name simple aldehydes according to the number of carbon atoms in the longest continuous carbon chain that contains the carbonyl group. We form the base name from the name of the corresponding alkane by dropping the *-e* and adding the ending *-al*:

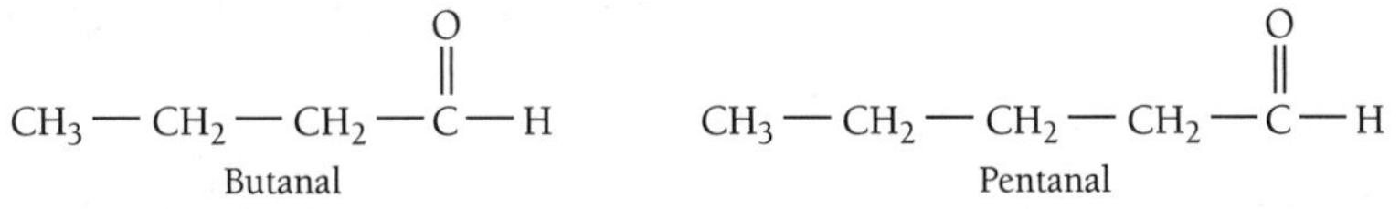

We name simple ketones according to the longest continuous carbon chain containing the carbonyl group, forming the base name from the name of the corresponding alkane by dropping the letter *-e* and adding the ending *-one*. For ketones, we number the chain to give the carbonyl group the lowest possible number:

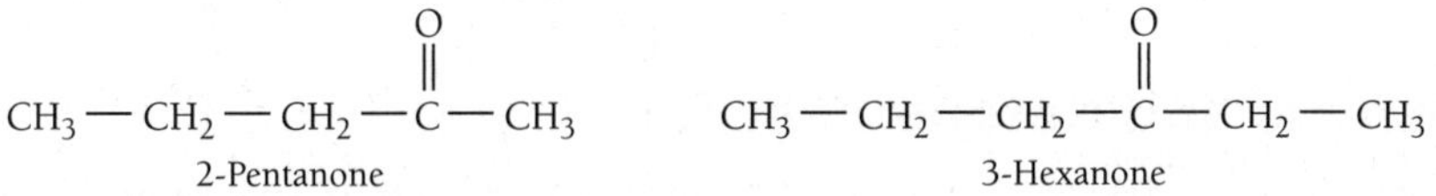

About Aldehydes and Ketones

The most familiar aldehyde is probably formaldehyde, shown earlier in this section. Formaldehyde is a gas with a pungent odor. It is often mixed with water to make formalin, a preservative and disinfectant. Formaldehyde is also found in wood smoke, which is one reason that smoking is an effective method of food preservation—the formaldehyde kills bacteria. Aromatic aldehydes, those that also contain an aromatic ring, have pleasant aromas. For example, vanillin causes the smell of vanilla, cinnamaldehyde is the sweet-smelling component of cinnamon, and benzaldehyde accounts for the smell of almonds (Figure 22.7▼):

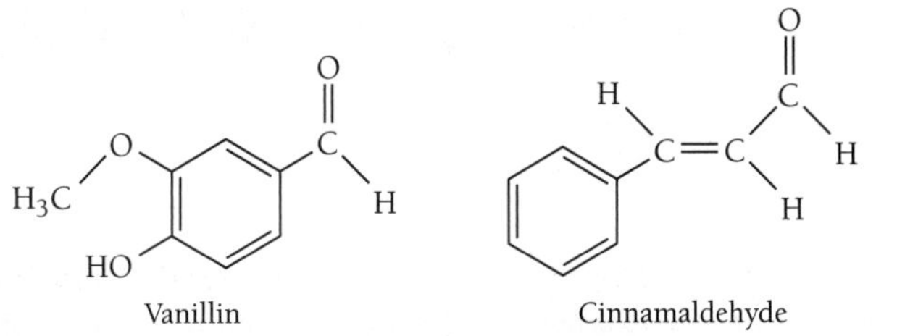

▲ **FIGURE 22.7 The Nutty Aroma of Almonds** Benzaldehyde is partly responsible for the smell of almonds.

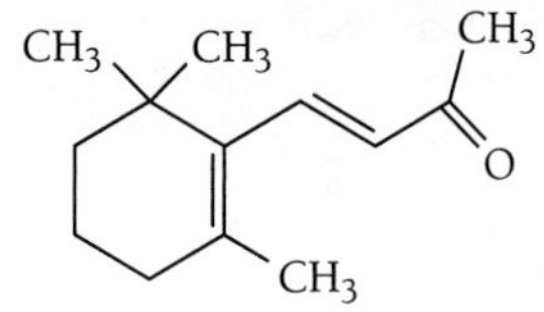

Ionone

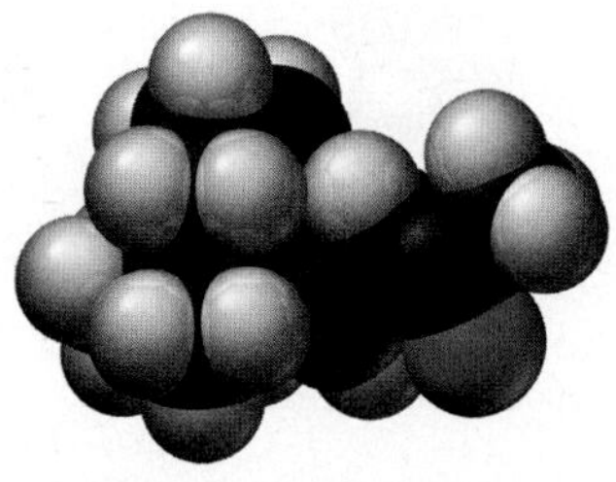

▲ **FIGURE 22.8 The Fragrance of Raspberries** Ionone is partly responsible for the smell of raspberries.

The most familiar ketone is acetone, the main component of nail polish remover. Other ketones have more pleasant aromas. For example, carvone is largely responsible for the smell of spearmint, 2-heptanone (among other compounds) for the smell of cloves, and ionone for the smell of raspberries (Figure 22.8▲):

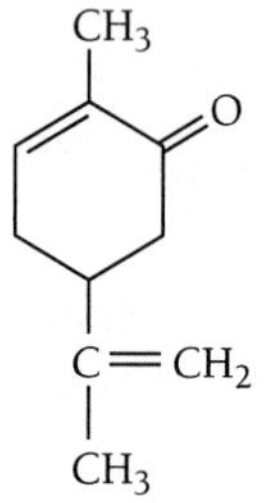

Carvone

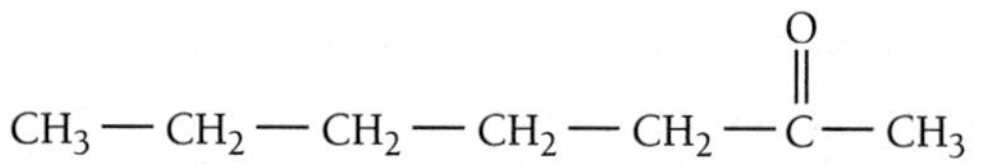

2-Heptanone

Aldehyde and Ketone Reactions

Aldehydes and ketones can be formed by the *oxidation* of alcohols. For example, ethanol can be oxidized to ethanal, and 2-propanol can be oxidized to 2-propanone (or acetone):

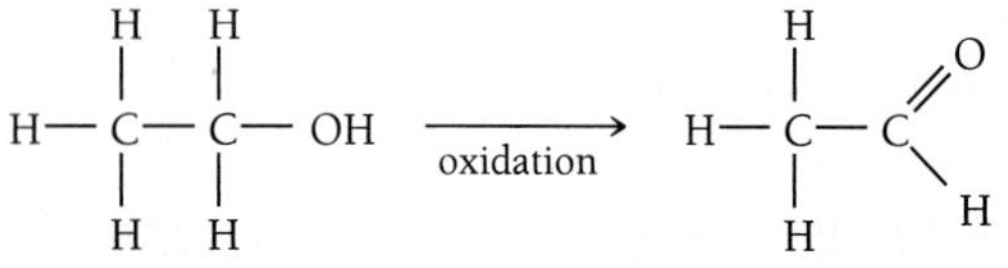

Ethanol Ethanal

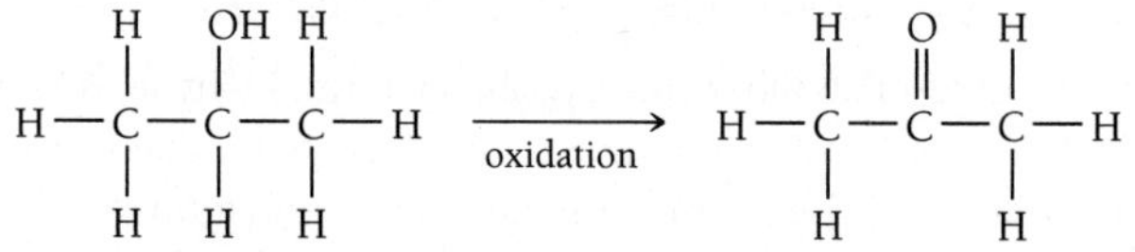

2-Propanol 2-Propanone

In the reverse reaction, an aldehyde or ketone is reduced to an alcohol. For example, 2-butanone can be reduced to 2-butanol in the presence of a reducing agent:

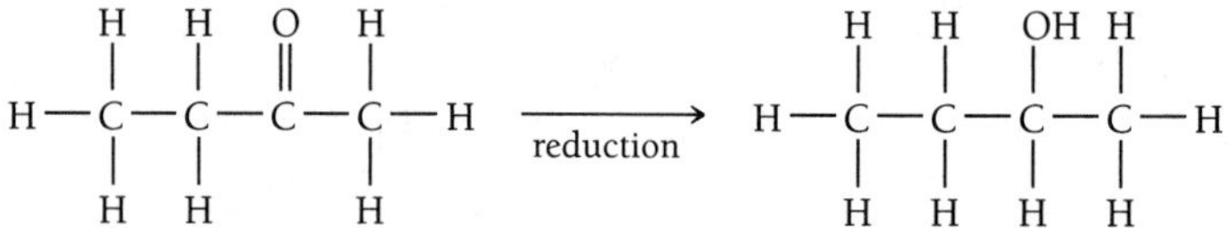

2-Butanone 2-Butanol

The carbonyl group in aldehydes and ketones is unsaturated, much like the double bond in an alkene. Because of this feature, the most common reactions of aldehydes and ketones are **addition reactions**. However, in contrast to the carbon–carbon double bond in alkenes, which is nonpolar, the double bond in the carbonyl group is highly polar (Figure 22.9▶). Consequently, additions across the double bond result in the more electronegative part of the reagent bonding to the carbon atom and the less electronegative part (often hydrogen) bonding to the oxygen atom. For example, HCN adds across the carbonyl double bond in formaldehyde:

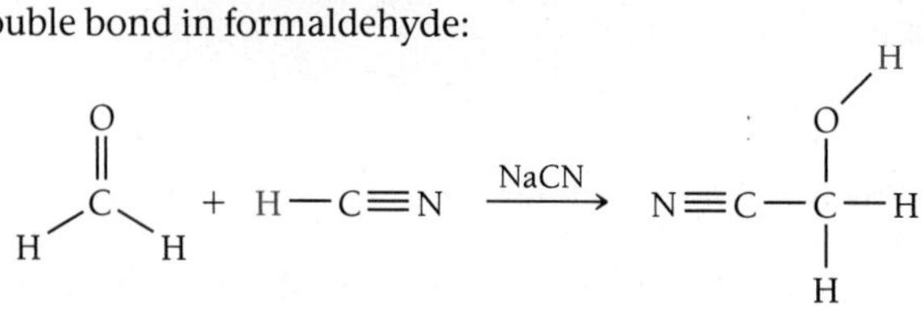

Formaldehyde Acetaldehyde Acetone

▲ **FIGURE 22.9 Charge Density Plots of the Carbonyl Group** The carbonyl group is highly polar, as shown in these plots of electrostatic potential.

22.11 Carboxylic Acids and Esters

Carboxylic acids and **esters** have the general formulas:

$$R-\overset{\overset{\displaystyle O}{\|}}{C}-OH \qquad\qquad R-\overset{\overset{\displaystyle O}{\|}}{C}-OR$$

Carboxylic acid Ester

The condensed structural formula for carboxylic acids is RCOOH; for esters it is RCOOR.

Figure 22.10▶ shows the structures of some common carboxylic acids and esters.

$$CH_3-\overset{\overset{\displaystyle O}{\|}}{C}-OH$$

Ethanoic acid or acetic acid

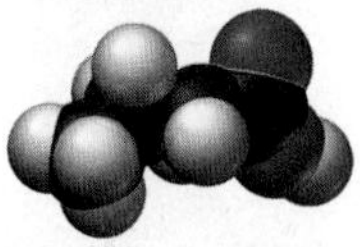

$$CH_3-CH_2-CH_2-\overset{\overset{\displaystyle O}{\|}}{C}-OH$$

Butanoic acid

$$CH_3-CH_2-CH_2-\overset{\overset{\displaystyle O}{\|}}{C}-O-CH_3$$

Methyl butanoate

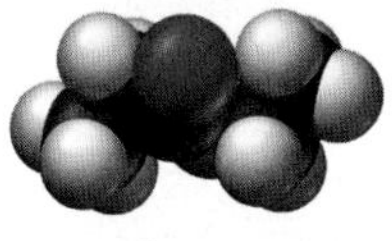

$$CH_3-CH_2-\overset{\overset{\displaystyle O}{\|}}{C}-O-CH_2-CH_3$$

Ethyl propanoate

▲ **FIGURE 22.10 Common Carboxylic Acids and Esters**

Naming Carboxylic Acids and Esters

We systematically name carboxylic acids according to the number of carbon atoms in the longest chain containing the —COOH functional group. We form the base name by dropping the *-e* from the name of the corresponding alkane and adding the ending *-oic acid*:

$$CH_3-CH_2-\overset{\overset{\displaystyle O}{\|}}{C}-OH \qquad\qquad CH_3-CH_2-CH_2-CH_2-\overset{\overset{\displaystyle O}{\|}}{C}-OH$$

Propanoic acid Pentanoic acid

We name esters as if they were derived from a carboxylic acid by replacing the H on the OH with an alkyl group. The R group from the parent acid forms the base name of the compound. We change the *-ic* on the name of the corresponding carboxylic acid to *-ate*, and drop *acid*, naming the R group that replaced the H on the carboxylic acid as an alkyl group with the ending *-yl*, as shown in the following examples:

$$CH_3-CH_2-\overset{\overset{\displaystyle O}{\|}}{C}-OH \qquad\qquad CH_3-CH_2-CH_2-CH_2-\overset{\overset{\displaystyle O}{\|}}{C}-OH$$

Propanoic acid Pentanoic acid

$$CH_3-CH_2-\overset{\overset{\displaystyle O}{\|}}{C}-OCH_3 \qquad\qquad CH_3-CH_2-CH_2-CH_2-\overset{\overset{\displaystyle O}{\|}}{C}-OCH_2CH_3$$

Methyl propanoate Ethyl pentanoate

About Carboxylic Acids and Esters

Like all acids, carboxylic acids taste sour. The most familiar carboxylic acid is ethanoic acid, better known by its common name, acetic acid. Acetic acid is the active ingredient in vinegar. It can form by the oxidation of ethanol, which is why wines left open to air become sour. Some yeasts and bacteria also form acetic acid when they metabolize sugars in bread dough. These are added to bread dough to make sourdough bread. Other common carboxylic acids include methanoic acid (formic acid), present in bee

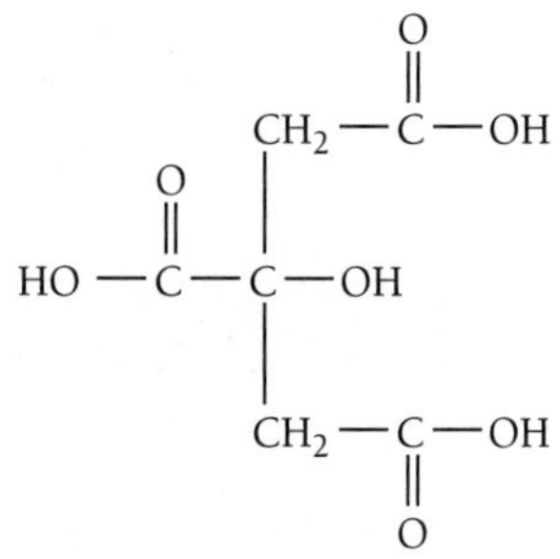

Citric acid

▲ **FIGURE 22.11 The Tart Taste of Limes** Citric acid is partly responsible for the sour taste of limes.

stings and ant bites; lactic acid, which collects in muscles after intense exercise causing soreness; and citric acid, found in limes, lemons, and oranges (Figure 22.11▲):

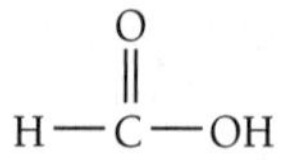

Formic or methanoic acid

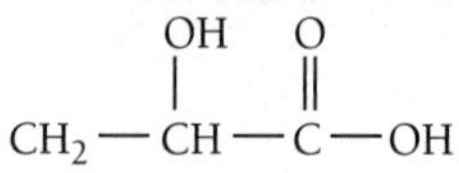

Lactic acid

Esters are best known for their sweet smells. Methyl butanoate is largely responsible for the smell and taste of apples, and ethyl butanoate is partly responsible for the smell and taste of pineapples (see Figure 22.12▼):

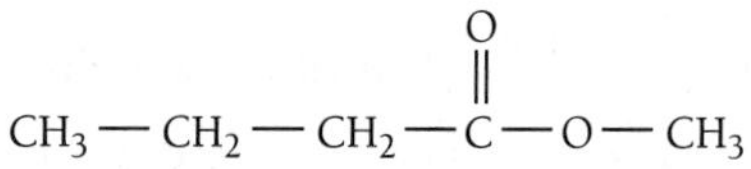

Methyl butanoate

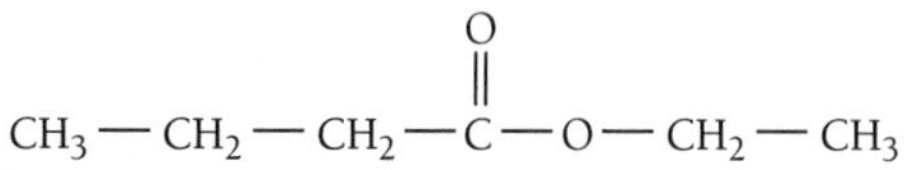

Ethyl butanoate

▲ **FIGURE 22.12 The Aroma of Pineapple** Ethyl butanoate is partly responsible for the aroma of pineapples.

Carboxylic Acid and Ester Reactions

Carboxylic acids act as weak acids in solution:

$$RCOOH(aq) + H_2O(l) \rightleftharpoons H_3O^+(aq) + RCOO^-(aq)$$

Like all acids, carboxylic acids react with strong bases via neutralization reactions. For example, propanoic acid reacts with sodium hydroxide to form sodium propanoate and water:

$$CH_3CH_2COOH(aq) + NaOH(aq) \longrightarrow CH_3CH_2COO^-Na^+(aq) + HOH(l)$$

A carboxylic acid reacts with an alcohol to form an ester via a **condensation reaction**, a reaction in which two (or more) organic compounds join, often with the loss of water (or some other small molecule):

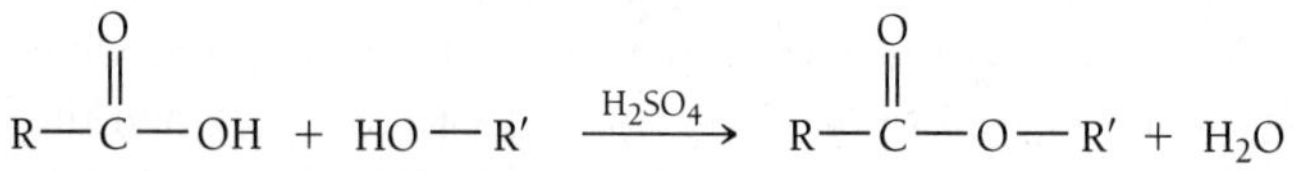

Acid Alcohol Ester Water

An important example of this reaction is the formation of acetylsalicylic acid (aspirin) from ethanoic acid (acetic acid) and salicylic acid (originally obtained from the bark of the willow tree):

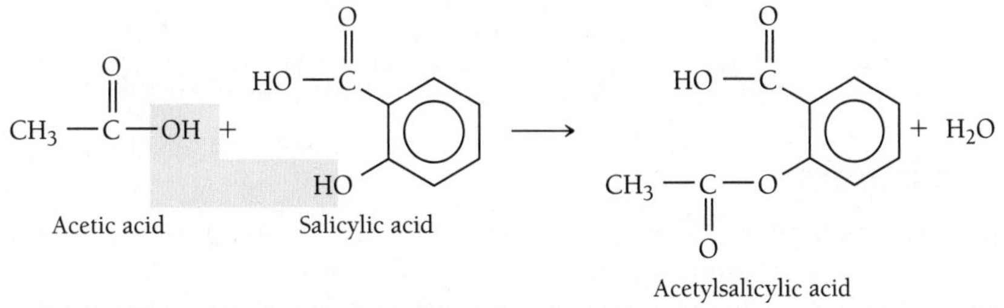

If we subject a carboxylic acid to high temperatures, it undergoes a condensation reaction with itself to form an acid anhydride (anhydride means "without water"):

$$\text{RCOOH}(aq) + \text{HOOCR}(aq) \longrightarrow \underset{\text{Acid anhydride}}{\text{RCOOOCR}(aq)} + \text{HOH}(aq)$$

We can add water to an acid anhydride to reverse the reaction just shown and regenerate the carboxylic acid molecules.

OXIDATION Arrange the compounds from least oxidized to most oxidized.

22.4 Cc Conceptual Connection — ANSWER **NOW!**

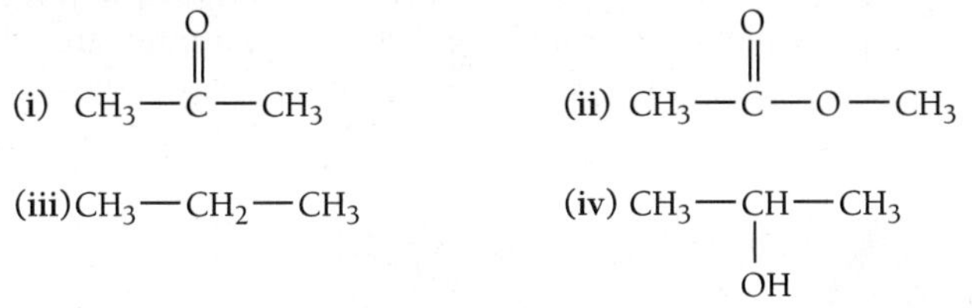

(a) iii < i < iv < ii
(b) ii < i < iv < iii
(c) iii < iv < i < ii
(d) ii < iv < i < iii

22.12 Ethers

Ethers are organic compounds with the general formula ROR. The two R groups may be identical or they may be different. Some common ethers are shown in Figure 22.13▼.

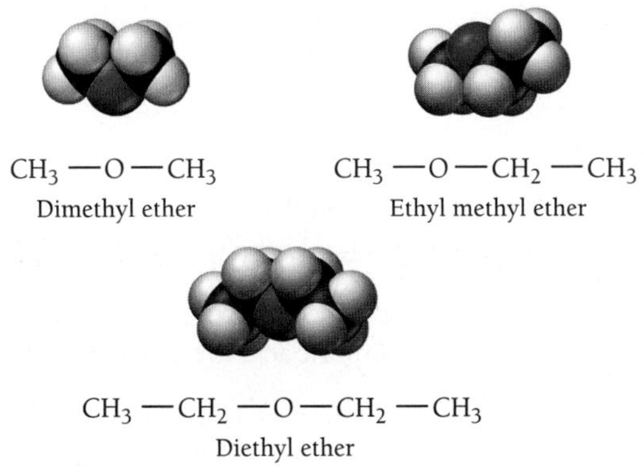

▲ **FIGURE 22.13 Ethers**

Naming Ethers

Common names for ethers have the format:

(R group 1) (R group 2) ether

If the two R groups differ, we use each of their names in alphabetical order. If the two R groups are the same, we use the prefix *di-*. Some examples include:

$$H_3C-CH_2-CH_2-O-CH_2-CH_2-CH_3$$

Dipropyl ether

$$H_3C-CH_2-O-CH_2-CH_2-CH_3$$

Ethyl propyl ether

About Ethers

The most common ether is diethyl ether. Diethyl ether is a useful laboratory solvent because it can dissolve many organic compounds and it has a low boiling point (34.6 °C). The low boiling point allows for easy removal of the solvent. Diethyl ether was used as a general anesthetic for many years. When inhaled, diethyl ether depresses the central nervous system, causing unconsciousness and insensitivity to pain. Its use as an anesthetic, however, has decreased in recent years because other compounds have the same anesthetic effect with fewer side effects (such as nausea).

22.13 Amines

The simplest nitrogen-containing compound is ammonia (NH_3). **Amines** are organic compounds containing nitrogen that are derived from ammonia with one or more of the hydrogen atoms replaced by alkyl groups. Like ammonia, amines are weak bases. We systematically name amines according to the hydrocarbon groups attached to the nitrogen and assign the ending *-amine*:

$$CH_3-CH_2-\underset{\displaystyle H}{\underset{|}{N}}-H$$

Ethylamine

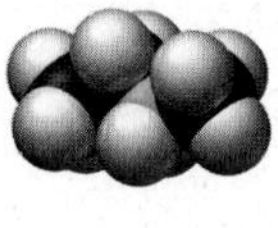

$$CH_3-CH_2-\underset{\displaystyle CH_3}{\underset{|}{N}}-H$$

Ethylmethylamine

Amines are most commonly known for their awful odors. When a living organism dies, the bacteria that feast on its proteins emit amines. For example, trimethylamine causes the smell of rotten fish, and cadaverine causes the smell of decaying animal flesh:

$$CH_3-\overset{\displaystyle CH_3}{\overset{|}{N}}-CH_3$$

Trimethylamine

$$NH_2-CH_2-CH_2-CH_2-CH_2-CH_2-NH_2$$

Cadaverine

Amine Reactions

Just as carboxylic acids act as weak acids, so amines act as weak bases:

$$RNH_2(aq) + H_2O(l) \rightleftharpoons RNH_3^+(aq) + OH^-(aq)$$

Like all bases, amines react with strong acids to form salts called ammonium salts. For example, methylamine reacts with hydrochloric acid to form methylammonium chloride:

$$CH_3NH_2(aq) + HCl(aq) \longrightarrow CH_3NH_3^+Cl^-(aq)$$

Methylammonium chloride

An important amine reaction that we will see again in Chapter 23 is the condensation reaction between a carboxylic acid and an amine to form an amide:

$$CH_3COOH(aq) + HNHR(aq) \longrightarrow CH_3CONHR(aq) + HOH(l)$$

This reaction is responsible for the formation of proteins from amino acids (see Section 23.4).

Self-Assessment Quiz

Q1. Which property of carbon is related to its ability to form a large number of compounds? **MISSED THIS?** *Read Section 22.2*

a) its tendency to form four covalent bonds
b) its ability to form double and triple bonds
c) its tendency to catenate
d) all of the above

Q2. What is the correct formula for the alkane (noncyclical) containing eight carbon atoms?
MISSED THIS? *Read Section 22.3*

a) C_8H_{16} b) C_8H_{18} c) C_8H_{14} d) C_8H_8

Q3. Which structure is not an isomer of $CH_3CH_2CH_2CH_2CH_3$?
Missed This? *Read Section 22.3*

a) 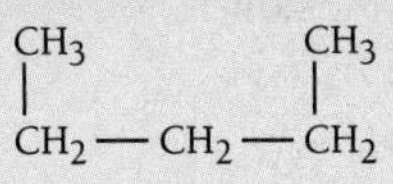

b) 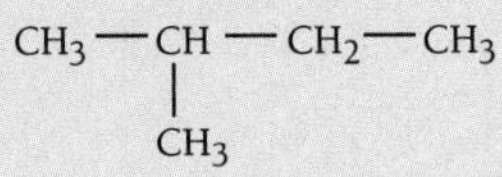

c) 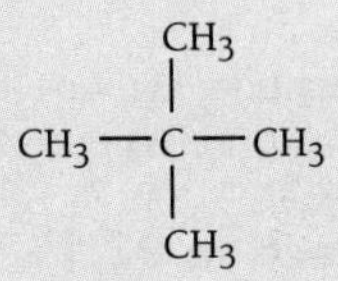

d) None of the above (all are isomers).

Q4. Which structure can exhibit optical isomerism?
MISSED THIS? *Read Section 22.3*

a) 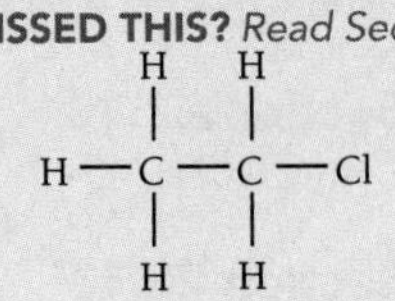

c) 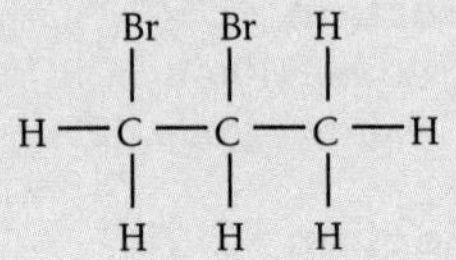

b) 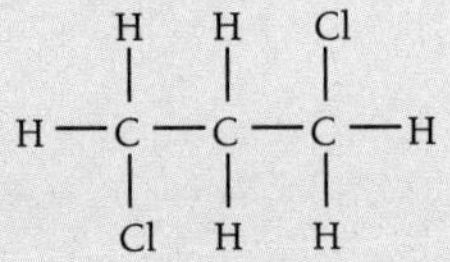

d) 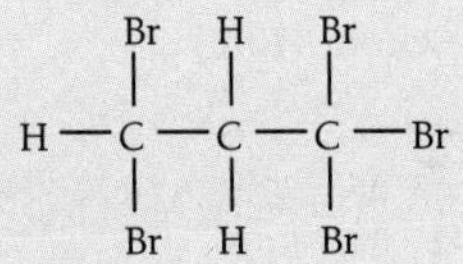

Q5. Name the compound:
MISSED THIS? *Read Section 22.4; Watch IWE 22.3*

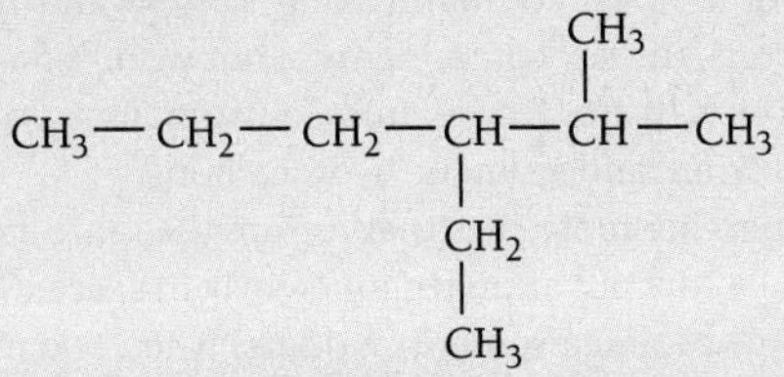

a) 4-ethyl-5-methylhexane
b) 3-ethyl-2-methylhexane
c) 3-ethyl-2-methylnonane
d) 4-methyl-5-ethylhexane

Q6. Name the compound:
MISSED THIS? *Read Section 22.5*

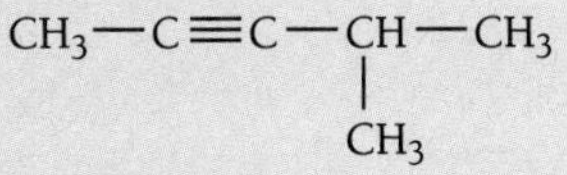

a) 4-methyl-2-pentyne
b) 2-methyl-3-pentyne
c) 2-methyl-3-hexyne
d) 4-methyl-2-hexyne

Q7. Determine the product of the reaction:
MISSED THIS? *Read Section 22.6*

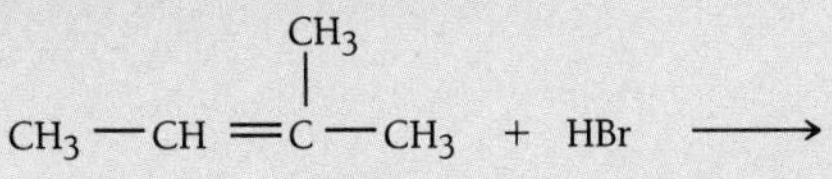

a) 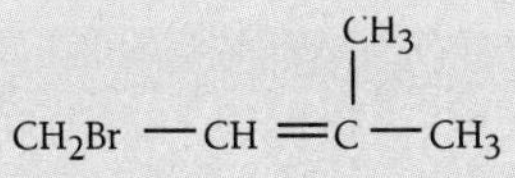

b) 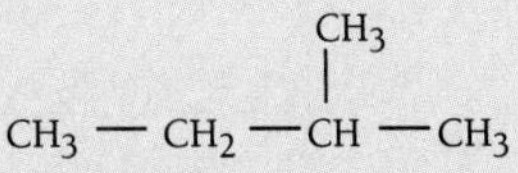

c) 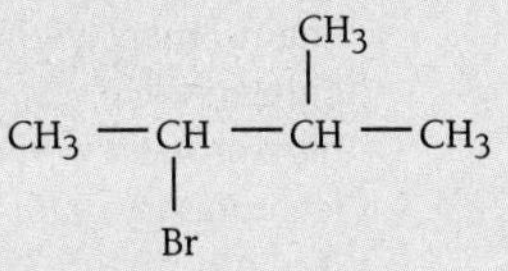

d) 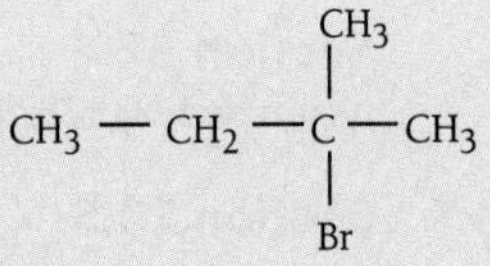

Q8. Determine the product of the reaction:
MISSED THIS? *Read Section 22.9*

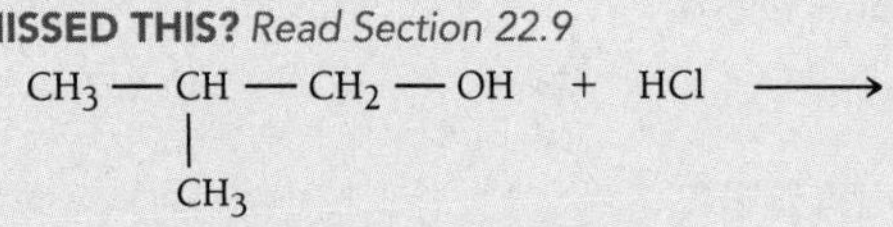

a) 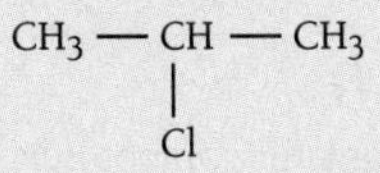

b) 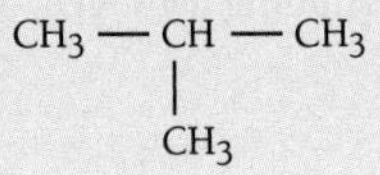

c) 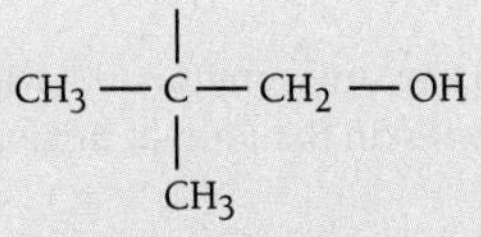

d) 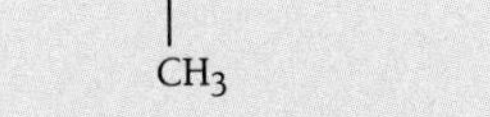

—Continued on the next page

Continued—

Q9. Which compound is an ester? **MISSED THIS?** *Read Section 22.8*

a) $CH_3-CH_2-O-CH_3$

b) $CH_3-CH_2-\overset{\displaystyle O}{\overset{\|}{C}}-OH$

c) $CH_3-\overset{\displaystyle O}{\overset{\|}{C}}-CH_3$

d) $CH_3-\overset{\displaystyle O}{\overset{\|}{C}}-O-CH_2CH_3$

Q10. Which compound is most likely to have a foul odor? **MISSED THIS?** *Read Section 22.8*

a) $CH_3-\overset{\displaystyle O}{\overset{\|}{C}}-O-CH_3$

b) $CH_3-CH_2-NH_2$

c) $CH_3-CH_2-O-CH_3$

d) $CH_3-CH_2-CH_2-OH$

Answers: **1.** (d) **2.** (b) **3.** (a) **4.** (c) **5.** (b) **6.** (a) **7.** (d) **8.** (d) **9.** (d) **10.** (b)

CHAPTER 22 IN REVIEW

TERMS

Section 22.1
organic molecule (990)
organic chemistry (990)

Section 22.3
alkane (992)
alkene (992)
alkyne (992)
aromatic hydrocarbon (992)
aliphatic hydrocarbon (992)
structural isomers (993)
structural formula (993)
stereoisomers (995)
optical isomers (995)
enantiomers (996)
chiral (996)
dextrorotatory (996)
levorotatory (996)
racemic mixture (996)

Section 22.4
saturated hydrocarbon (998)

Section 22.5
unsaturated hydrocarbon (1002)
geometric (cis–trans) isomerism (1006)

Section 22.7
phenyl group (1011)
disubstituted benzene (1011)

Section 22.9
alcohol (1014)
hydroxyl group (1014)

Section 22.10
aldehyde (1016)
ketone (1016)
carbonyl group (1016)
addition reaction (1018)

Section 22.11
carboxylic acid (1019)
esters (1019)
condensation reaction (1020)

Section 22.12
ether (1021)

Section 22.13
amine (1022)

CONCEPTS

Fragrances and Odors (22.1)

- Organic chemistry is the study of organic compounds, which contain carbon (and other elements including hydrogen, oxygen, and nitrogen).

Carbon (22.2)

- Carbon forms more compounds than all the other elements combined.
- Carbon's four valence electrons (in conjunction with its size) allow carbon to form four bonds (in the form of single, double, or triple bonds).
- Carbon also has the capacity to catenate, to form long chains, because of the strength of the carbon–carbon bond.

Hydrocarbons (22.3)

- Organic compounds containing only carbon and hydrogen are hydrocarbons, the key components of our world's fuels.
- We categorize hydrocarbons into four different types: alkanes, alkenes, alkynes, and aromatic hydrocarbons.
- Stereoisomers are molecules that feature the same atoms bonded in the same order but arranged differently in space. Optical isomerism, a type of stereoisomerism, occurs when two molecules are nonsuperimposable mirror images of one another.

Alkanes (22.4)

- Alkanes are saturated hydrocarbons—they contain only single bonds and are therefore represented by the generic formula C_nH_{2n+2}. Alkane names always end in *-ane*.

Alkenes and Alkynes (22.5)

- Alkenes and alkynes are unsaturated hydrocarbons—they contain double bonds (alkenes) or triple bonds (alkynes) and are represented by the generic formulas C_nH_{2n} and C_nH_{2n-2}, respectively.
- Alkene names end in *-ene* and alkynes end in *-yne*.
- Because rotation about a double bond is severely restricted, geometric (or cis–trans) isomerism occurs in alkenes.

Hydrocarbon Reactions (22.6)

- The most common hydrocarbon reaction is probably combustion, in which hydrocarbons react with oxygen to form carbon dioxide and water; this reaction is exothermic and is used to provide most of our society's energy.
- Alkanes can also undergo substitution reactions, where heat or light causes another atom, commonly a halogen such as bromine, to be substituted for a hydrogen atom.
- Unsaturated hydrocarbons undergo addition reactions. If the addition reaction is between two unsymmetrical molecules, Markovnikov's rule predicts that the positive end of the polar reagent adds to the carbon with the most hydrogen atoms.

Aromatic Hydrocarbons (22.7)

- Aromatic hydrocarbons contain six-membered benzene rings represented with alternating single and double bonds that become equivalent through resonance. These compounds are called aromatic because they often produce pleasant fragrances.
- Because of the stability of the aromatic ring, benzene is more stable than a straight-chain alkene, and it undergoes substitution rather than addition reactions.

Functional Groups (22.8)

- Characteristic groups of atoms, such as hydroxyl (—OH), are functional groups. Molecules that contain the same functional group have similar chemical and physical properties and are referred to as families.

Alcohols (22.9)

- The family of alcohols contains the —OH group and is named with the suffix *-ol*.
- Alcohols are commonly used in gasoline, in alcoholic beverages, and in sterilization procedures.
- Alcohols undergo substitution reactions, in which a substituent such as a halogen replaces the hydroxyl group.
- Alcohols undergo elimination reactions, in which water is eliminated across a bond to form an alkene, and oxidation or reduction reactions.
- Alcohols also react with active metals to form alkoxide ions and hydrogen gas.

Aldehydes and Ketones (22.10)

- Aldehydes and ketones both contain a carbonyl group (a carbon atom double-bonded to oxygen).
- In aldehydes, the carbonyl group is at the end of a carbon chain, while in ketones it is between two other carbon atoms.
- Aldehydes are named with the suffix *-al* and ketones with the suffix *-one*.
- A carbonyl can be formed by the oxidation of an alcohol or reverted to an alcohol by reduction.
- Like alkenes, carbonyls undergo addition reactions; however, because the carbon–oxygen bond is highly polar, the electronegative component of the reagent always adds to the carbon atom, and the less electronegative part adds to the oxygen.

Carboxylic Acids and Esters (22.11)

- Carboxylic acids contain a carbonyl group and a hydroxide on the same carbon and are named with the suffix *-oic acid*.
- Esters contain a carbonyl group bonded to an oxygen atom that is in turn bonded to an R group; they are named with the suffix *-oate*.
- Carboxylic acids taste sour, such as acetic acid in vinegar, while esters smell sweet.
- Carboxylic acids react as weak acids but can also form esters through condensation reactions with alcohols.

Ethers (22.12)

- The family of ethers contains an oxygen atom between two R groups.
- Ethers are named with the ending *-yl ether*.

Amines (22.13)

- Amines are organic compounds that contain nitrogen and are named with the suffix *-amine*.
- They are known for their terrible odors; the smell of decaying animal flesh is produced by cadaverine.
- Amines act as weak bases and produce a salt when mixed with a strong acid.
- The combination of an amine with a carboxylic acid leads to a condensation reaction; in our bodies, this reaction produces proteins from amino acids.

EQUATIONS AND RELATIONSHIPS

Halogen Substitution Reactions in Alkanes (22.6)

$$\underset{\text{Alkane}}{R{-}H} + \underset{\text{Halogen}}{X_2} \xrightarrow{\text{heat or light}} \underset{\text{Haloalkane}}{R{-}X} + \underset{\text{Hydrogen halide}}{HX}$$

Addition Reactions in Alkenes (22.6)

$$R{-}C = C{-}R + X_2 \longrightarrow R{-}CX - CX{-}R$$

Common Functional Groups (**22.8**)

Family	General Formula	Condensed General Formula	Example	Name
Alcohols	R—OH	ROH	CH_3CH_2OH	Ethanol (ethyl alcohol)
Ethers	R—O—R	ROR	CH_3OCH_3	Dimethyl ether
Aldehydes	R—C(=O)—H	RCHO	H_3C—C(=O)—H	Ethanal (acetaldehyde)
Ketones	R—C(=O)—R	RCOR	H_3C—C(=O)—CH_3	Propanone (acetone)
Carboxylic acids	R—C(=O)—OH	RCOOH	H_3C—C(=O)—OH	Acetic acid
Esters	R—C(=O)—OR	RCOOR	H_3C—C(=O)—OCH_3	Methyl acetate
Amines	R—N(R)—R	R_3N	H_3CH_2C—N(H)—H	Ethylamine

Alcohol Reactions (**22.9**)

Substitution $ROH + HBr \longrightarrow R{-}Br + H_2O$

Oxidation $R{-}CH_2{-}CH_2(OH) \xrightarrow[H_2SO_4]{Na_2Cr_2O_7} R{-}CH_2{-}C(=O){-}OH$

Alcohol → Aldehyde

Elimination $R{-}CH_2{-}CH_2(OH) \xrightarrow{H_2SO_4} R{-}CH{=}CH_2 + H_2O$

Carboxylic Acid Condensation Reactions (**22.11**)

$R{-}C(=O){-}OH + HO{-}R' \xrightarrow{H_2SO_4} R{-}C(=O){-}O{-}R' + H_2O$

Acid + Alcohol → Ester + Water

Amine Acid–Base Reactions (**22.13**)

$RNH_2(aq) + H_2O(l) \longrightarrow RNH_3^+(aq) + OH^-(aq)$

Amine–Carboxylic Acid Condensation Reactions (**22.13**)

$CH_3COOH(aq) + HNHR(aq) \longrightarrow CH_3CONHR(aq) + H_2O(l)$

LEARNING OUTCOMES

Chapter Objectives	Assessment
Identify structural properties of hydrocarbons (**22.3**)	Example 22.1 **For Practice 22.1** **Exercises 33–40**
Write structural formulas and names for alkanes (**22.4**)	Examples 22.2, 22.3, 22.4 **For Practice 22.2, 22.3, 22.4** **Exercises 41–44**
Write structural formulas and names for alkenes and alkynes (**22.5**)	Example 22.5 **For Practice 22.5** **Exercises 49–56**
Write reactions for alkanes, alkenes, and alkynes (**22.6**)	Example 22.6 **For Practice 22.6** **Exercises 45–48, 57–60**
Write structural formulas and names for aromatic hydrocarbons (**22.7**)	**Exercises 61–68**
Write reactions for aromatic hydrocarbons (**22.7**)	**Exercises 69–70**
Write structural formulas and names for alcohols (**22.9**)	**Exercises 71–72**
Write reactions for alcohols (**22.9**)	Example 22.7 **For Practice 22.7** **Exercises 73–74**
Write structural formulas and names for aldehydes and ketones (**22.10**)	**Exercises 75–76**
Write reactions for aldehydes and ketones (**22.10**)	**Exercises 77–78**
Write structural formulas and names for carboxylic acids and esters (**22.11**)	**Exercises 79–80**
Write reactions for carboxylic acids and esters (**22.11**)	**Exercises 81–82**
Write structural formulas and names for ethers (**22.12**)	**Exercises 83–84**
Write structural formulas and names for amines (**22.13**)	**Exercises 85–86**
Write reactions for amines (**22.13**)	**Exercises 87–88**

EXERCISES

Mastering Chemistry provides end-of-chapter exercises, feedback-enriched tutorial problems, animations, and interactive activities to encourage problem-solving practice and deeper understanding of key concepts and topics.

REVIEW QUESTIONS

1. What kinds of molecules often trigger our sense of smell?

2. What is organic chemistry?

3. What is unique about carbon and carbon-based compounds? Why did life evolve around carbon?

4. Why does carbon form such a large diversity of compounds?

5. Why does silicon exhibit less diversity of compounds than carbon does?

6. Describe the geometry and hybridization about a carbon atom that forms

a. four single bonds.
b. two single bonds and one double bond.
c. one single bond and one triple bond.

7. What are hydrocarbons? What are their main uses?

8. What are the main classifications of hydrocarbons? What are their generic molecular formulas?

9. Explain the differences between a structural formula, a condensed structural formula, a carbon skeleton formula, a ball-and-stick model, and a space-filling model.

10. What are structural isomers? How do the properties of structural isomers differ from one another?

11. What are optical isomers? How do the properties of optical isomers differ from one another?

12. Define each term related to optical isomerism: enantiomers, chiral, dextrorotatory, levorotatory, racemic mixture.

13. What is the difference between saturated and unsaturated hydrocarbons?

14. What are the key differences in the way that alkanes, alkenes, and alkynes are named?

15. Explain geometric isomerism in alkenes. How do the properties of geometric isomers differ from one another?

16. Describe and provide an example of a hydrocarbon combustion reaction.

17. What kinds of reactions are common to alkanes? List an example of each.

18. Describe each kind of reaction.

a. substitution reaction
b. addition reaction
c. elimination reaction

19. What kinds of reactions are common to alkenes? Give an example of each.

20. Explain Markovnikov's rule and give an example of a reaction to which it applies.

21. What is the structure of benzene? What are the different ways in which this structure is represented?

22. What kinds of reactions are common to aromatic compounds? Provide an example of each.

23. What is a functional group? List some examples.

24. What is the generic structure of alcohols? Write the structures of two specific alcohols.

25. Explain oxidation and reduction with respect to organic compounds.

26. What kinds of reactions are common to alcohols? Provide an example of each.

27. What are the generic structures for aldehydes and ketones? Write a structure for a specific aldehyde and ketone.

28. What kinds of reactions are common to aldehydes and ketones? List an example of each.

29. What are the generic structures for carboxylic acids and esters? Write a structure for a specific carboxylic acid and ester.

30. What kinds of reactions are common to carboxylic acids and esters? Provide an example of each.

31. What is the generic structure of ethers? Write the structures of two specific ethers.

32. What is the generic structure of amines? Write the structures of two specific amines.

PROBLEMS BY TOPIC

Hydrocarbons

33. Based on the molecular formula, determine whether each compound is an alkane, alkene, or alkyne. (Assume that the hydrocarbons are noncyclical and there is no more than one multiple bond.) **MISSED THIS?** *Read Section 22.3*

a. C_5H_{12} b. C_3H_6 c. C_7H_{12} d. $C_{11}H_{22}$

34. Based on the molecular formula, determine whether each compound is an alkane, alkene, or alkyne. (Assume that the hydrocarbons are noncyclical and there is no more than one multiple bond.)

a. C_8H_{16} b. C_4H_6 c. C_7H_{16} d. C_2H_2

35. Write structural formulas for each of the nine structural isomers of heptane. **MISSED THIS?** *Read Section 22.3*

36. Write structural formulas for any 6 of the 18 structural isomers of octane.

37. Determine whether each compound exhibits optical isomerism. **MISSED THIS?** *Read Section 22.3*

a. CCl_4

b. 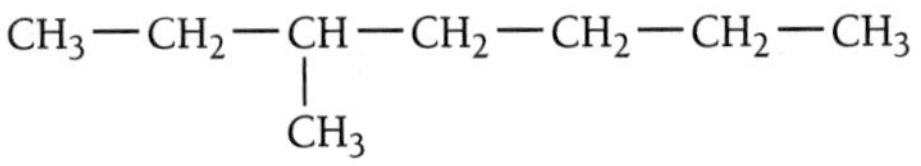

c. 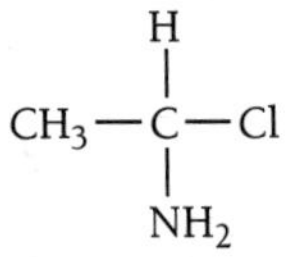

d. $CH_3CHClCH_3$

38. Determine whether each compound exhibits optical isomerism.

a. $CH_3CH_2CHClCH_3$ b. $CH_3CCl_2CH_3$

c. 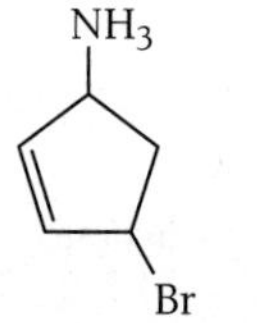

d. 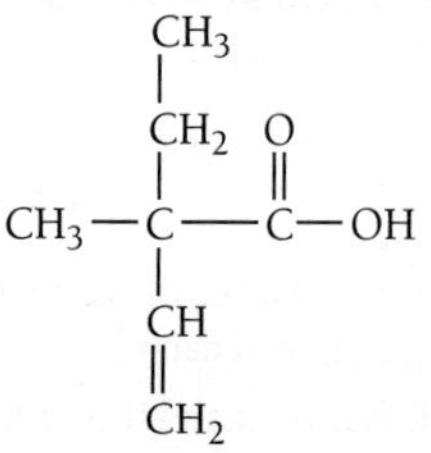

39. Determine whether the molecules in each pair are the same or enantiomers. **MISSED THIS?** *Read Section 22.3*

a. 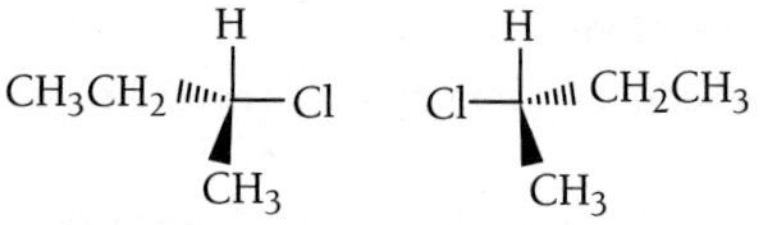

b. 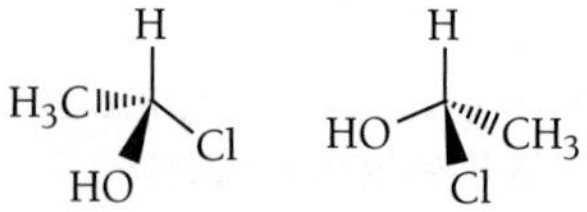

c. 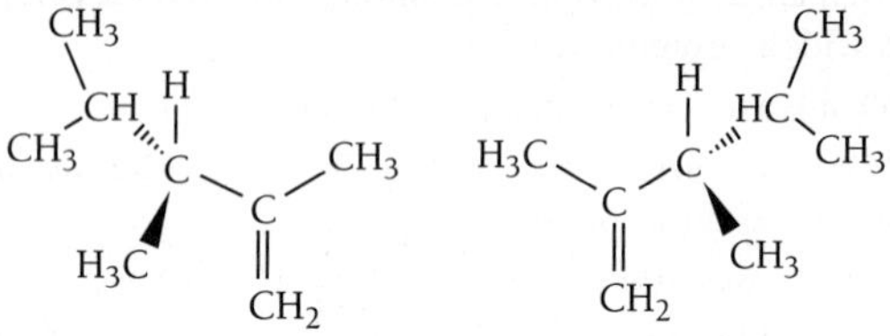

40. Determine whether the molecules in each pair are the same or enantiomers.

a. 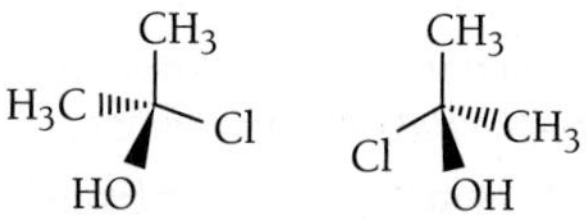

b. 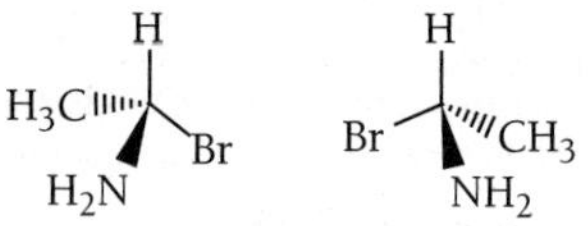

c. 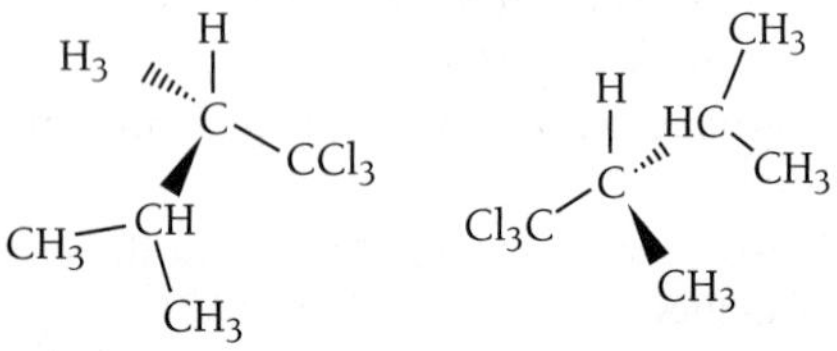

Alkanes

41. Name each alkane.
MISSED THIS? *Read Section 22.4; Watch IWE 22.3*

a. $CH_3-CH_2-CH_2-CH_2-CH_3$

b. 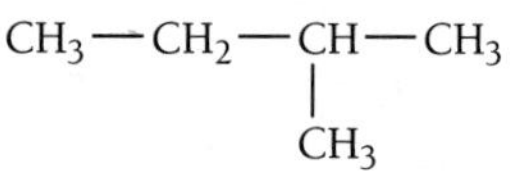

c. 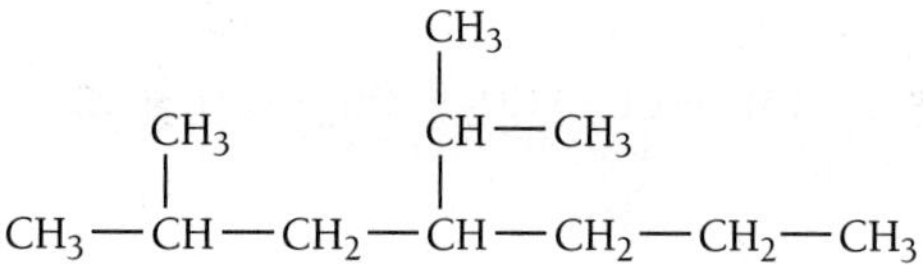

d. 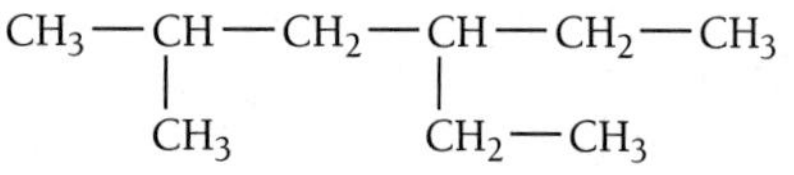

42. Name each alkane.

a. 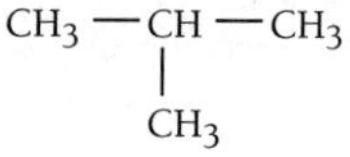

b. 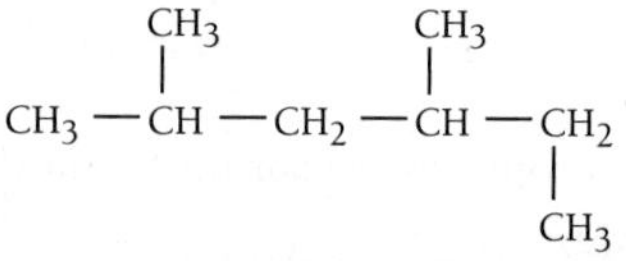

c. 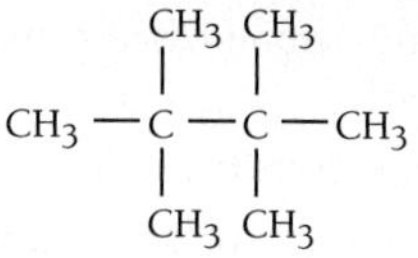

d. 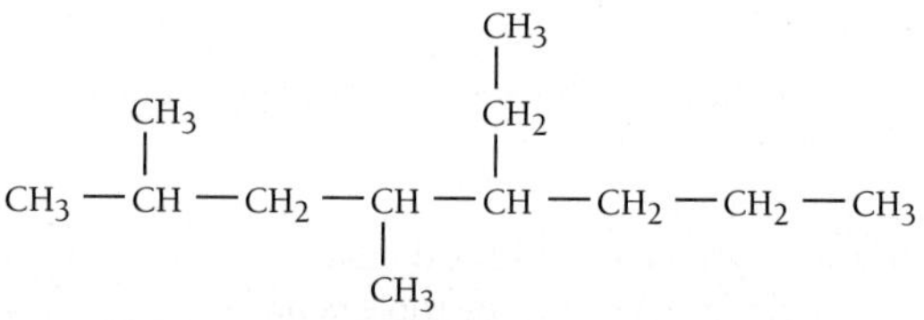

43. Draw a structure for each alkane.
MISSED THIS? *Read Section 22.4; Watch IWE 22.3*

a. 3-ethylhexane
b. 3-ethyl-3-methylpentane
c. 2,3-dimethylbutane
d. 4,7-diethyl-2,2-dimethylnonane

44. Draw a structure for each alkane.

a. 2,2-dimethylpentane
b. 3-isopropylheptane
c. 4-ethyl-2,2-dimethylhexane
d. 4,4-diethyloctane

45. Complete and balance each hydrocarbon combustion reaction.
MISSED THIS? *Read Section 22.6*

a. $CH_3CH_2CH_3 + O_2 \longrightarrow$
b. $CH_3CH_2CH{\equiv}CH_2 + O_2 \longrightarrow$
c. $CH{\equiv}CH + O_2 \longrightarrow$

46. Complete and balance each hydrocarbon combustion reaction.

a. $CH_3CH_2CH_2CH_3 + O_2 \longrightarrow$
b. $CH_2{=}CHCH_3 + O_2 \longrightarrow$
c. $CH{\equiv}CCH_2CH_3 + O_2 \longrightarrow$

47. List all the possible products for each alkane substitution reaction. (Assume monosubstitution.)
MISSED THIS? *Read Section 22.6*

a. $CH_3CH_3 + Br_2 \longrightarrow$
b. $CH_3CH_2CH_3 + Cl_2 \longrightarrow$
c. $CH_2Cl_2 + Br_2 \longrightarrow$
d. 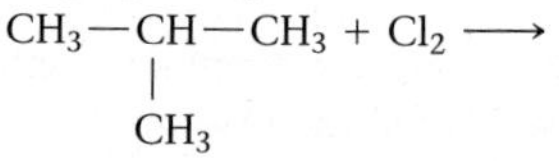

48. List all the possible products for each alkane substitution reaction. (Assume monosubstitution.)

a. $CH_4 + Cl_2 \longrightarrow$
b. $CH_3CH_2Br + Br_2 \longrightarrow$
c. $CH_3CH_2CH_2CH_3 + Cl_2 \longrightarrow$
d. $CH_3CHBr_2 + Br_2 \longrightarrow$

Alkenes and Alkynes

49. Write structural formulas for each of the possible isomers of *n*-hexene that are formed by moving the position of the double bond. **MISSED THIS?** *Read Section 22.5*

50. Write structural formulas for each of the possible isomers of *n*-pentyne that are formed by moving the position of the triple bond.

51. Name each alkene. **MISSED THIS?** *Read Section 22.5*

a. $CH_2{=}CH{-}CH_2{-}CH_3$

b. 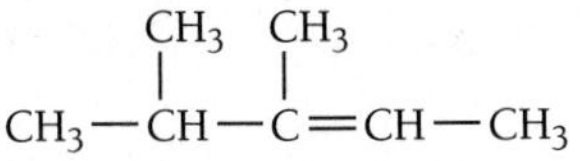

c. 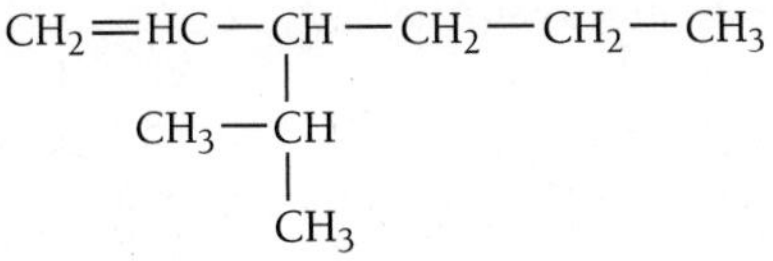

d. 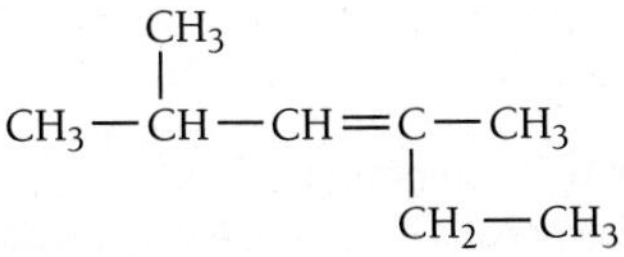

52. Name each alkene.

a. $CH_3{-}CH_2{-}CH{=}CH{-}CH_2{-}CH_3$

b. 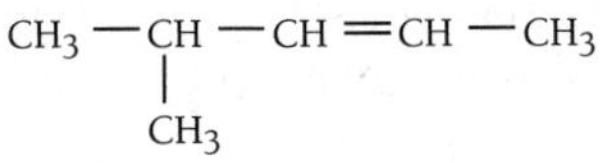

c. 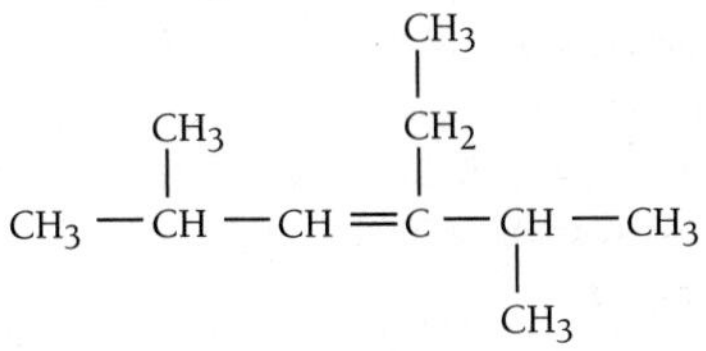

d. 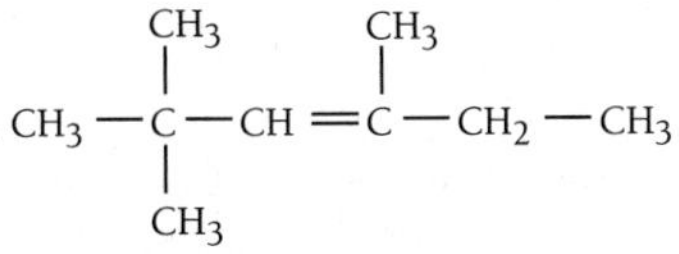

53. Name each alkyne. **MISSED THIS?** *Read Section 22.5*

a. $CH_3{-}C{\equiv}C{-}CH_3$

b. 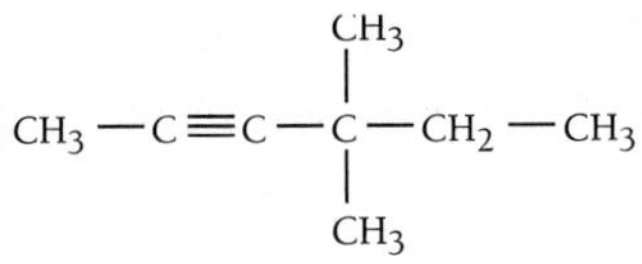

c. 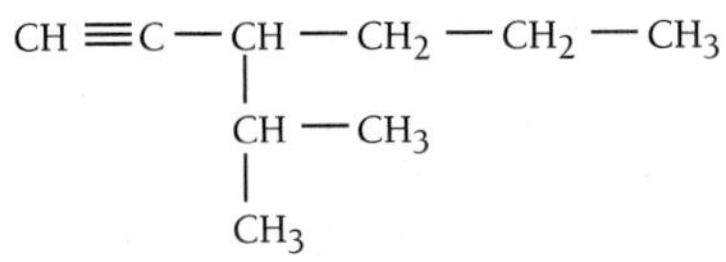

d. 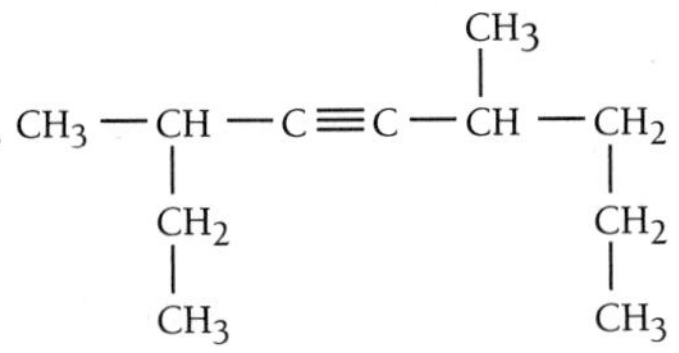

54. Name each alkyne.

a. 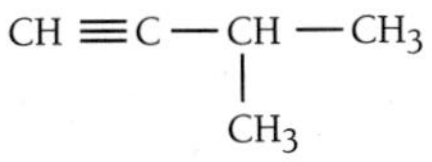

b. 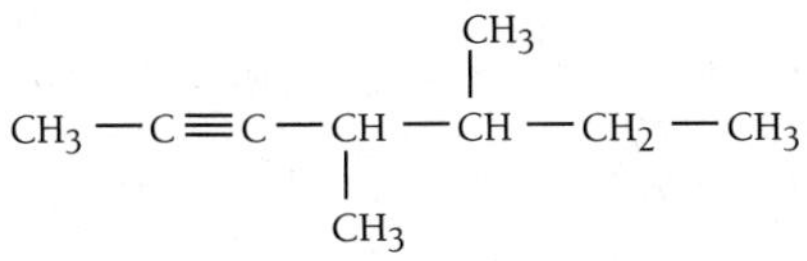

c. 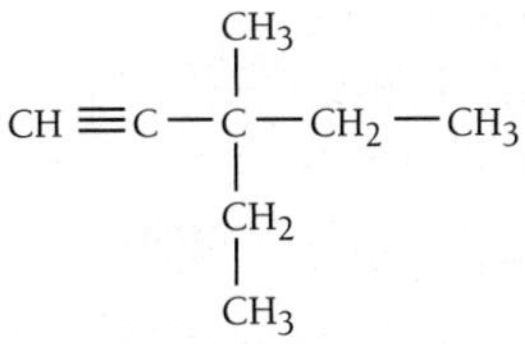

d. 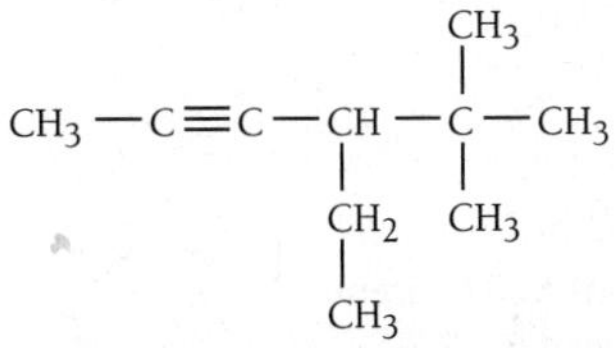

55. Draw the correct structure for each compound. **MISSED THIS?** *Read Section 22.5*

a. 4-octyne
b. 3-nonene
c. 3,3-dimethyl-1-pentyne
d. 5-ethyl-3,6-dimethyl-2-heptene

56. Draw the correct structure for each compound.

a. 2-hexene
b. 1-heptyne
c. 4,4-dimethyl-2-hexene
d. 3-ethyl-4-methyl-2-pentene

57. List the products of each alkene addition reaction. **MISSED THIS?** *Read Section 22.6*

a. $CH_3{-}CH{=}CH{-}CH_3 + Cl_2 \longrightarrow$

b. 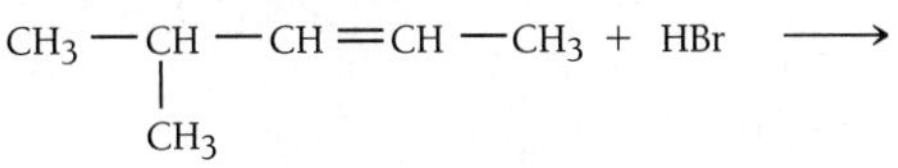

c. $CH_3{-}CH_2{-}CH{=}CH{-}CH_3 + Br_2 \longrightarrow$

d. 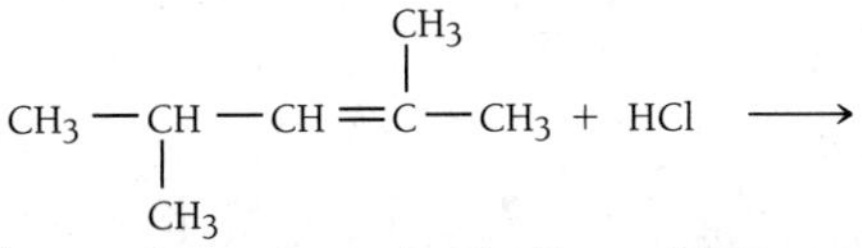

58. What are the products of each alkene addition reaction?

a. 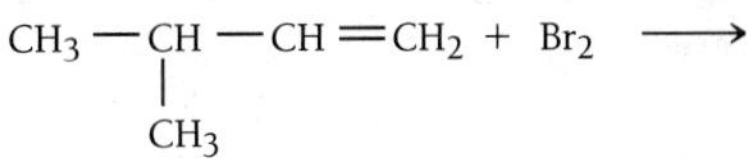

b. $CH_2{=}CH{-}CH_3 + Cl_2 \longrightarrow$

c. 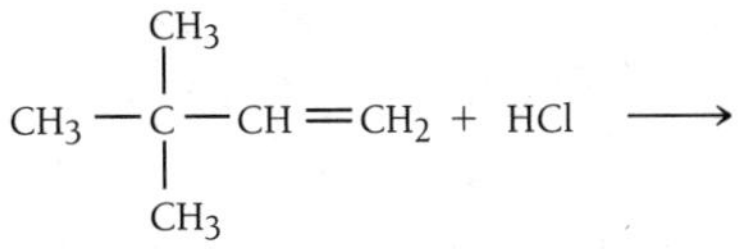

d. 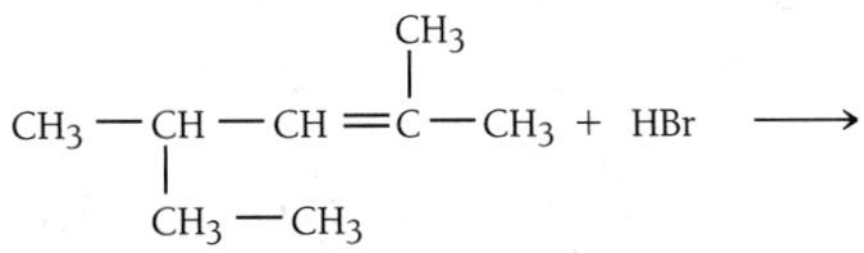

59. Complete each hydrogenation reaction. **MISSED THIS?** *Read Section 22.6*

a. $CH_2{=}CH{-}CH_3 + H_2 \xrightarrow{\text{catalyst}}$

b. 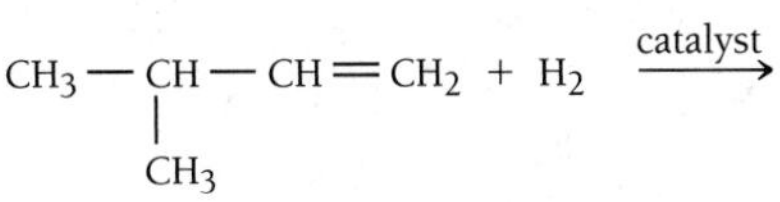

c. 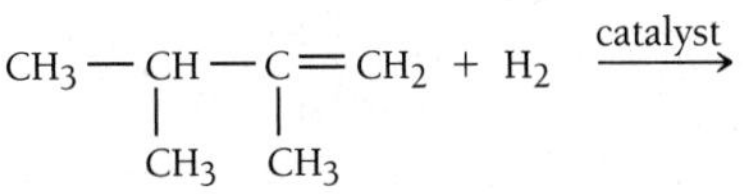

60. Complete each hydrogenation reaction.

a. $CH_3-CH_2-CH=CH_2 + H_2 \xrightarrow{\text{catalyst}}$

b. 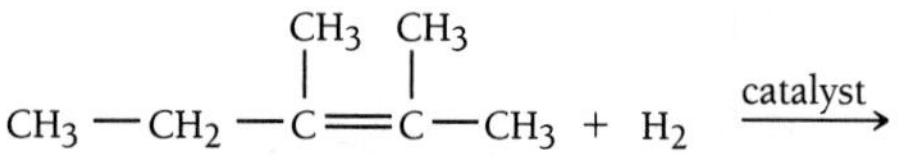

c. 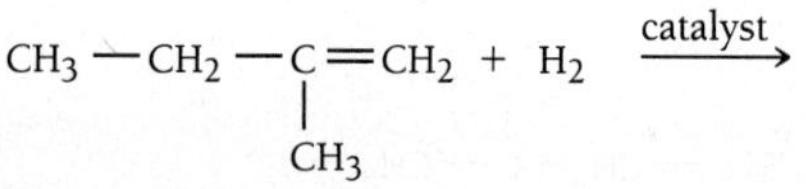

Aromatic Hydrocarbons

61. Name each monosubstituted benzene.
MISSED THIS? *Read Section 22.7*

a. 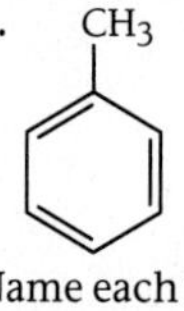
b. 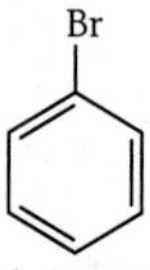
c. 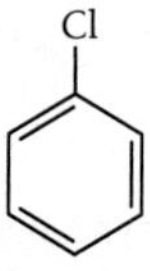

62. Name each monosubstituted benzene.

a. 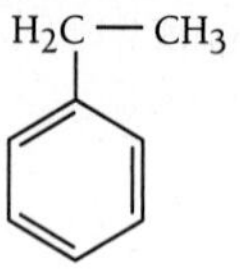
b. 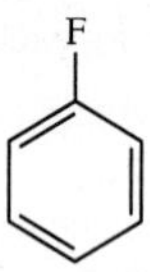
c. 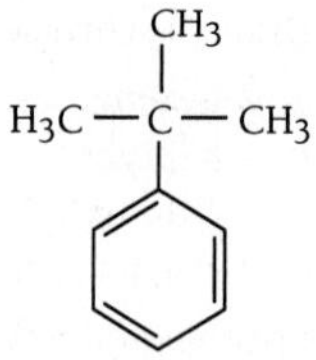

63. Name each compound in which the benzene ring is best treated as a substituent. **MISSED THIS?** *Read Section 22.7*

a. 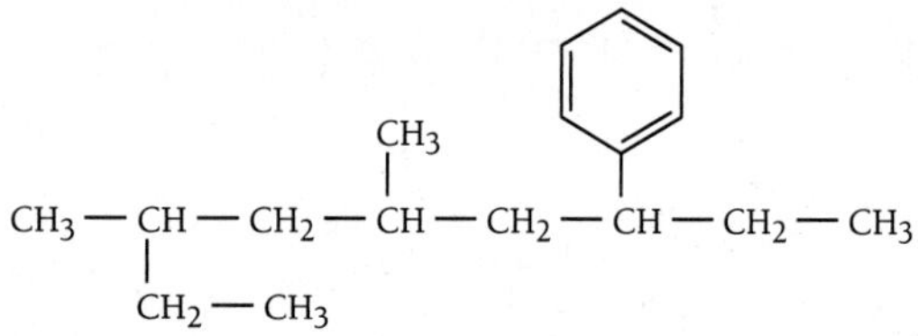

b. 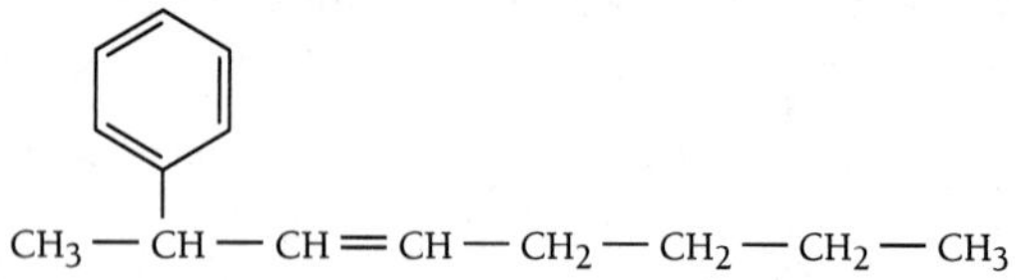

c. 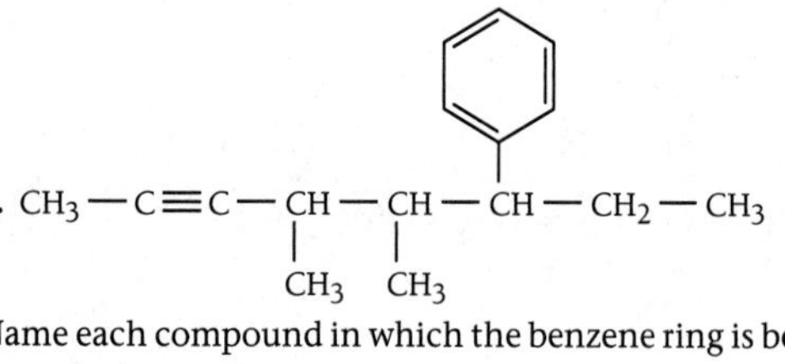

64. Name each compound in which the benzene ring is best treated as a substituent.

a. 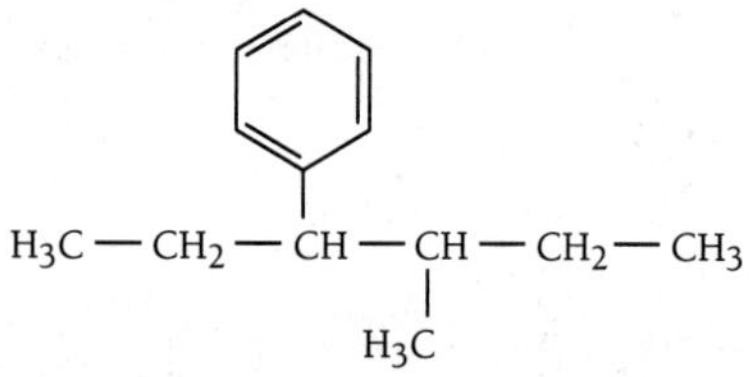

b. 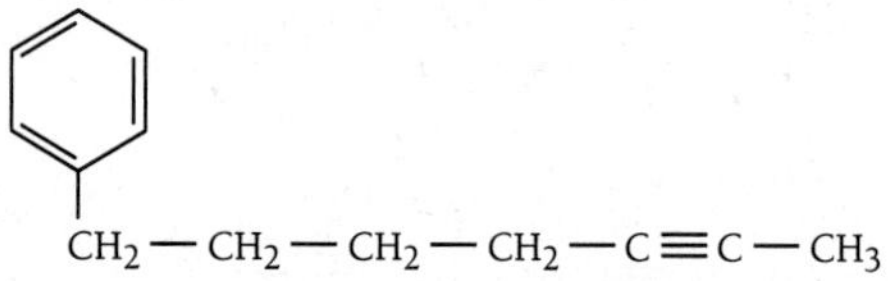

c. 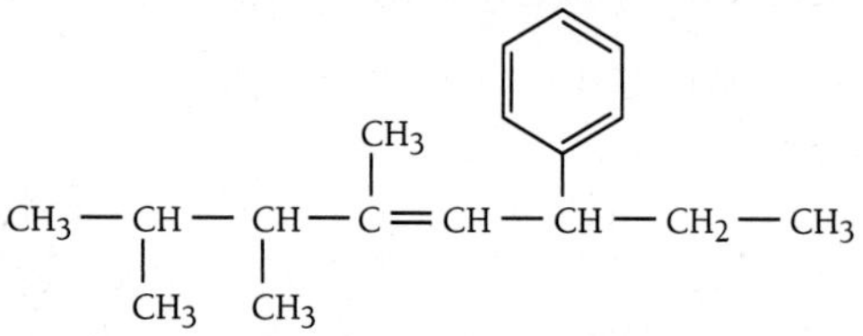

65. Name each disubstituted benzene.
MISSED THIS? *Read Section 22.7*

a. 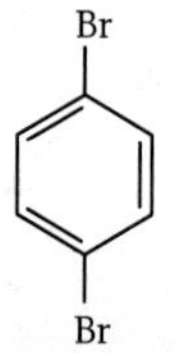
b. 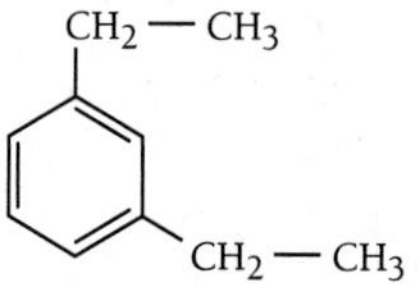
c. 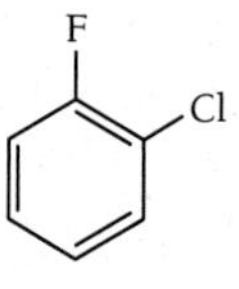

66. Name each disubstituted benzene.

a. 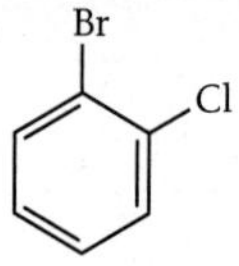
b. 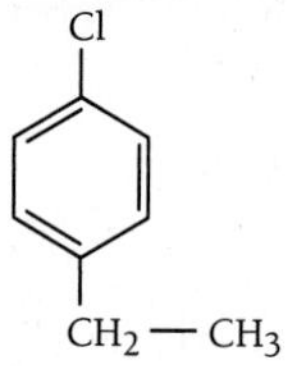
c. 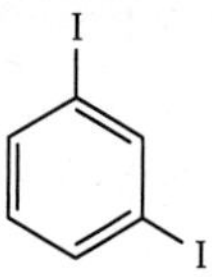

67. Draw the structure for each compound.
MISSED THIS? *Read Section 22.7*

a. isopropylbenzene
b. *meta*-dibromobenzene
c. 1-chloro-4-methylbenzene

68. Draw the structure for each compound.

a. ethylbenzene
b. 1-iodo-2-methylbenzene
c. *para*-diethylbenzene

69. What are the products of each aromatic substitution reaction?
MISSED THIS? *Read Section 22.7*

a. 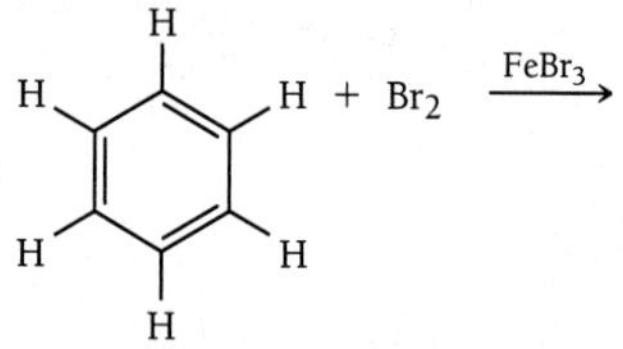

b. 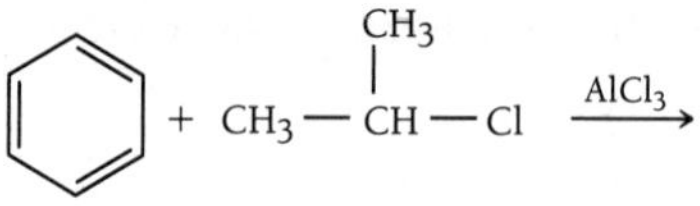

70. What are the products of each aromatic substitution reaction?

a. 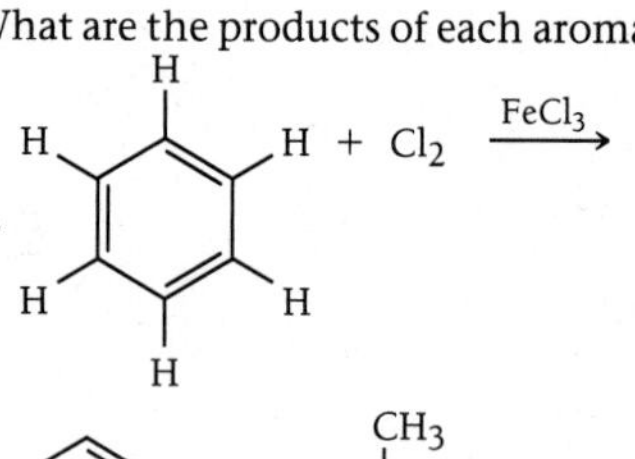

b. 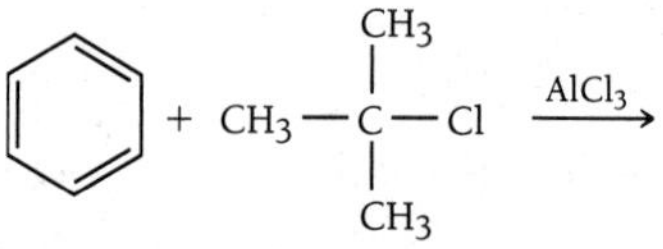

Alcohols

71. Name each alcohol. **MISSED THIS?** *Read Section 22.9*

a. $CH_3-CH_2-CH_2-OH$

b. 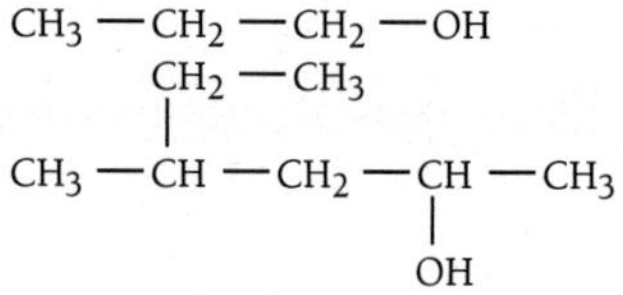

c. 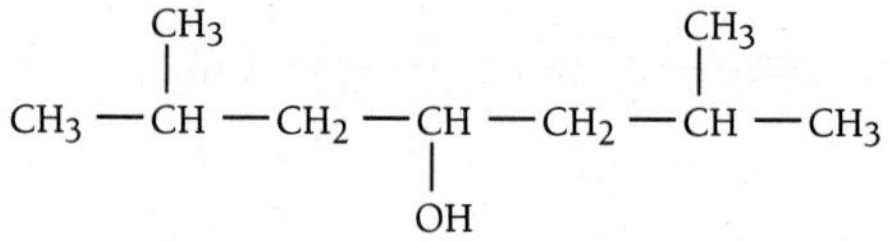

d. 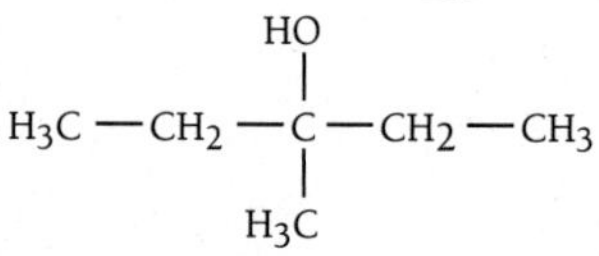

92. Name each compound.

a. 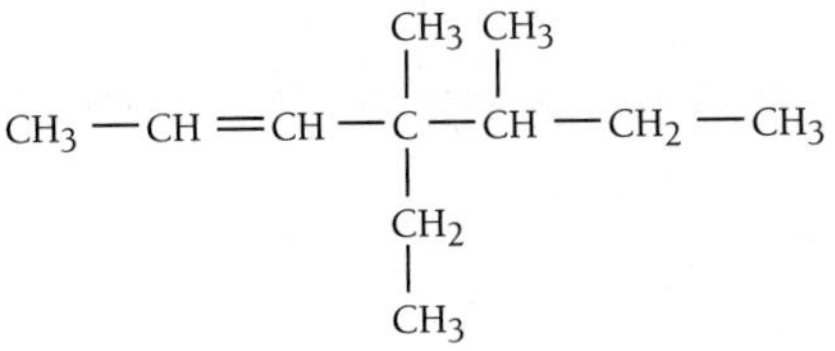

b. 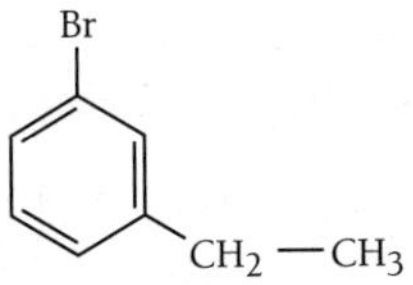

c. 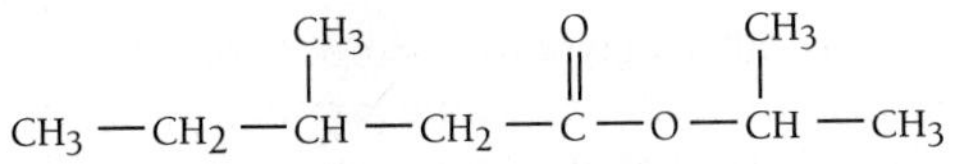

d. 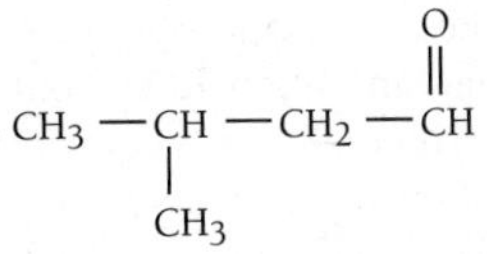

93. Determine whether the two structures are isomers or the same molecule drawn in two different ways.

a. 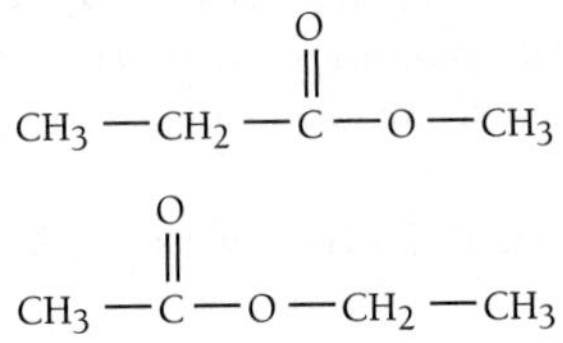

b. 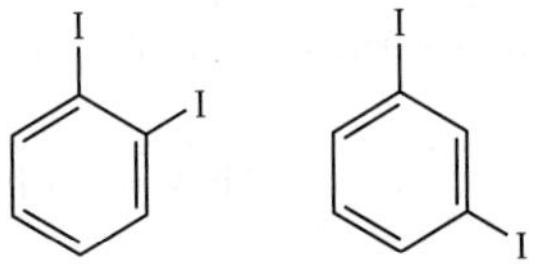

c. 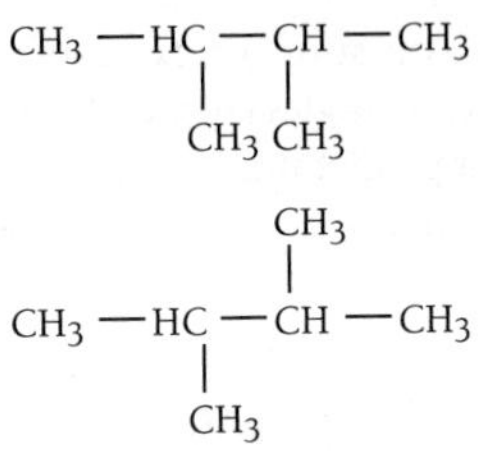

94. Determine whether the two structures are isomers or the same molecule drawn two different ways.

a. 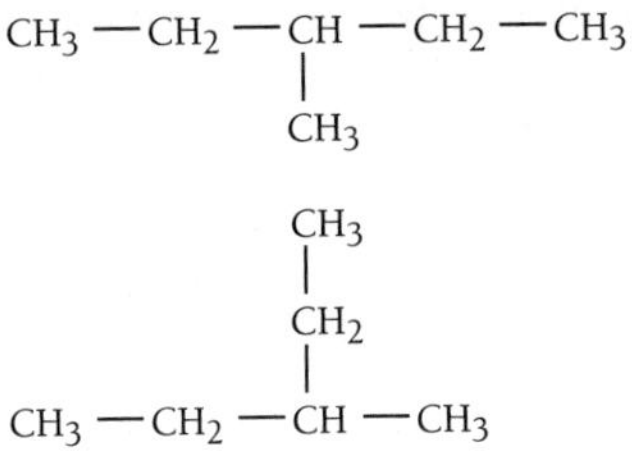

b. 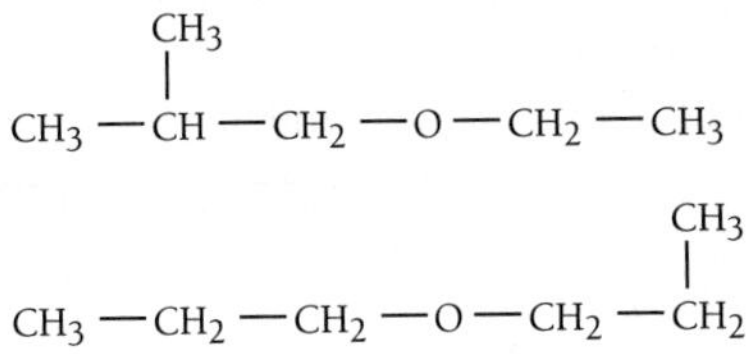

c. 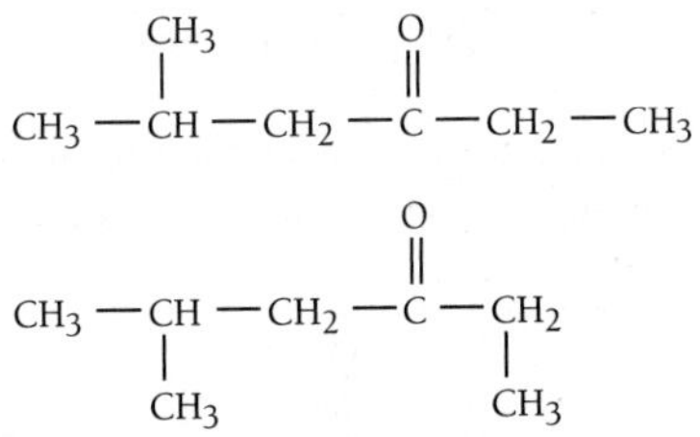

95. What minimum amount of hydrogen gas, in grams, is required to completely hydrogenate 15.5 kg of 2-butene?

96. How many kilograms of CO_2 does the complete combustion of 3.8 kg of *n*-octane produce?

97. Classify each organic reaction as combustion, alkane substitution, alkene addition or hydrogenation, aromatic substitution, or alcohol substitution, elimination, or oxidation.

a. $2\ CH_3CH{=}CH_2 + 9\ O_2 \longrightarrow 6\ CO_2 + 6\ H_2O$

b. $CH_3CH_2CH_3 + Cl_2 \longrightarrow CH_3CH_2CH_2Cl + HCl$

c. 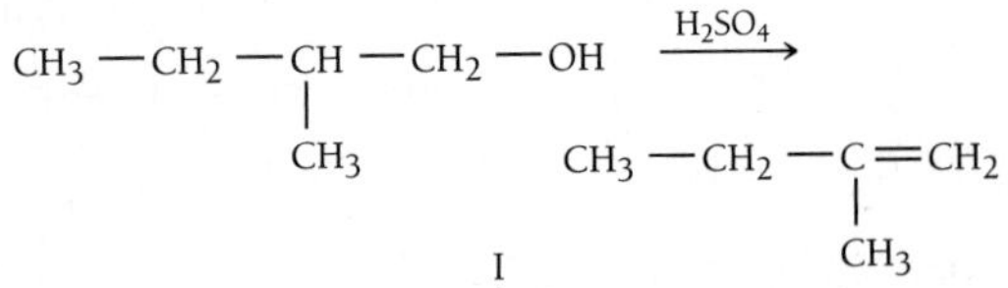

d. 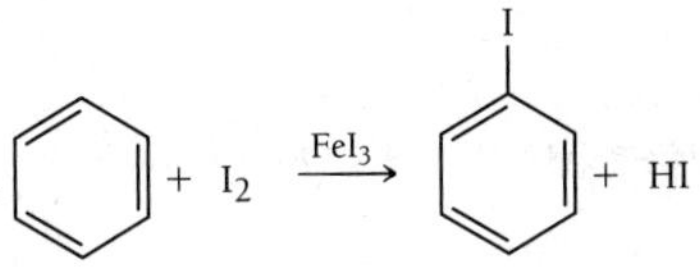

98. Determine the products of each reaction.

a. 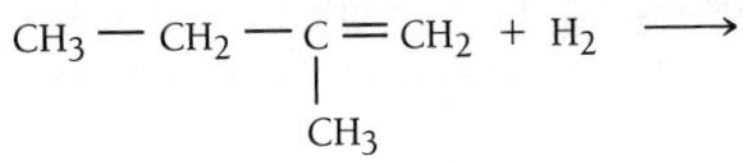

b. $CH_3-CH_2-CH_2-CH_2-OH + HCl \longrightarrow$

c. 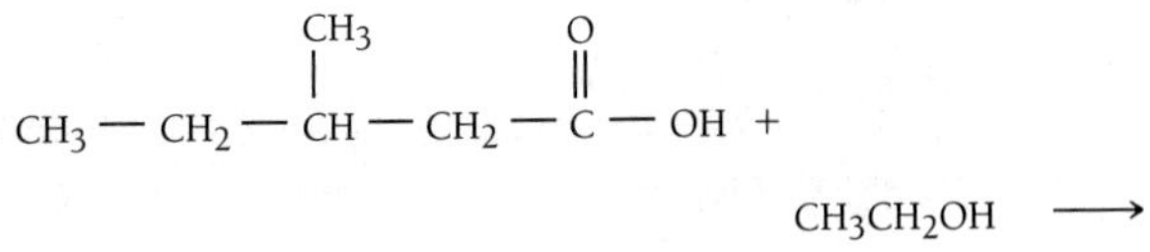

d. 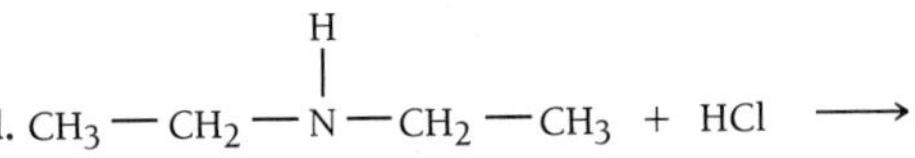

99. Draw the structure that corresponds to each name and indicate which structures can exist as stereoisomers.

a. 3-methyl-1-pentene b. 3,5-dimethyl-2-hexene
c. 3-propyl-2-hexene

100. Identify the two compounds that display stereoisomerism and draw their structures.

a. 3-methyl-3-pentanol b. 2-methyl-2-pentanol
c. 3-methyl-2-pentanol d. 2-methyl-3-pentanol
e. 2,4-dimethyl-3-pentanol

101. There are 11 structures (ignoring stereoisomerism) with the formula C_4H_8O that have no carbon branches. Draw the structures and identify the functional groups in each.

102. There are eight structures with the formula C_3H_7NO in which the O is part of a carbonyl group. Draw the structures and identify the functional groups in each.

103. Explain why carboxylic acids are much stronger acids than alcohols.

104. The hydrogen at C-1 of 1-butyne is much more acidic than the one at C-1 in 1-butene. Explain.

CHALLENGE PROBLEMS

105. Determine the one or two steps it takes to get from the starting material to the product using the reactions found in this chapter.

a. 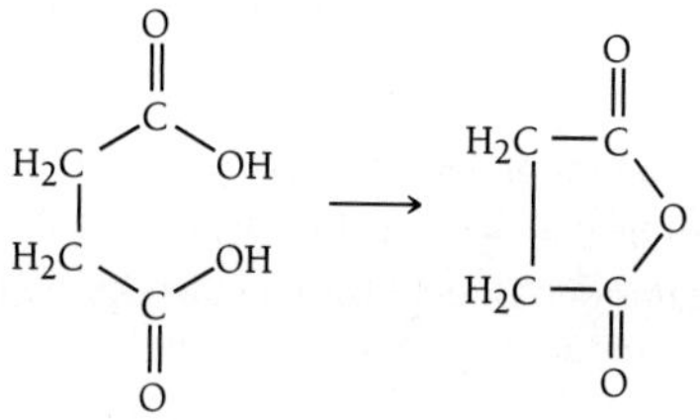

b. 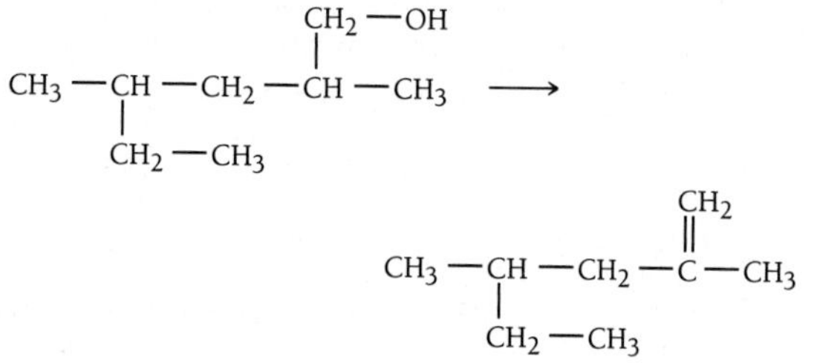

c. 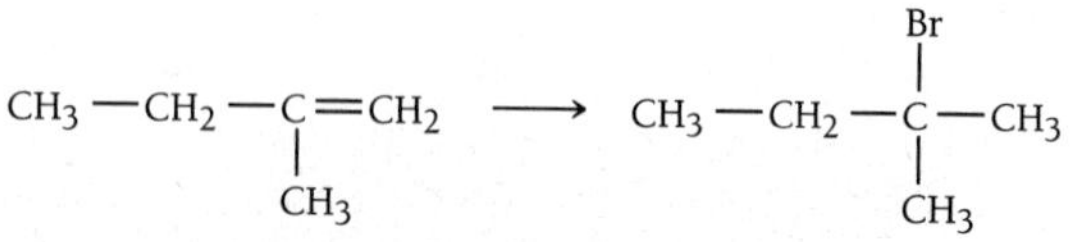

106. Given the following synthesis of ethyl 3-chloro-3-methylbutanoate, fill in the missing intermediates or reactants.

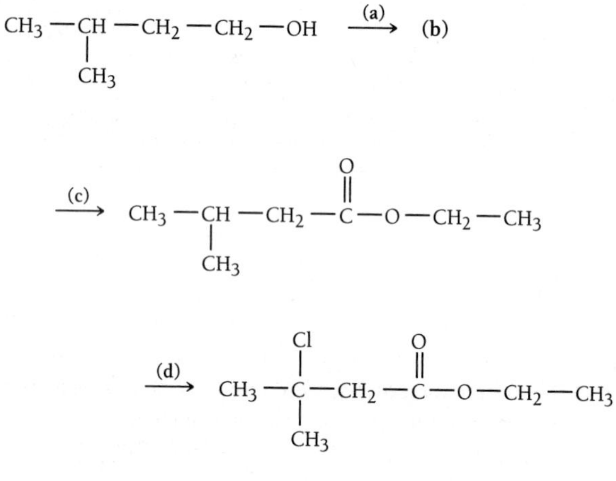

107. For the chlorination of propane, the two isomers shown here are possible.

$CH_3CH_2CH_3 + Cl_2 \longrightarrow$

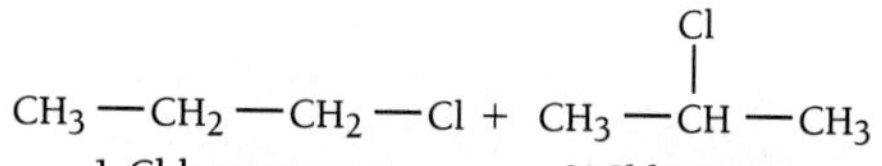

1-Chloropropane 2-Chloropropane

Propane has six hydrogen atoms on terminal carbon atoms—called primary (1°) hydrogen atoms—and two hydrogen atoms on the interior carbon atom—called secondary (2°) hydrogen atoms.

a. If the two different types of hydrogen atoms were equally reactive, what ratio of 1-chloropropane to 2-chloropropane would we expect as monochlorination products?

b. The result of a reaction yields 55% 2-chloropropane and 45% 1-chloropropane. What can we conclude about the relative reactivity of the two different kinds of hydrogen atoms? Determine a ratio of the reactivity of one type of hydrogen atom to the other.

108. There are two isomers of C_4H_{10}. Suppose that each isomer is treated with Cl_2 and the products that have the composition $C_4H_8Cl_2$ are isolated. Find the number of different products that form from each of the original C_4H_{10} compounds. Do not consider optical isomerism.

109. Identify the compounds formed in the previous problem that are chiral.

110. Nitromethane has the formula CH_3NO_2, with the N bonded to the C and without O—O bonds. Draw its two most important contributing structures.

a. What is the hybridization of the C, and how many hybrid orbitals are in the molecule?

b. What is the shortest bond?

c. Between which two atoms is the strongest bond found?

d. Predict whether the HCH bond angles are greater or less than 109.5° and justify your prediction.

111. Free radical fluorination of methane is uncontrollably violent, and free radical iodination of methane is a very poor reaction. Explain these observations in light of bond energies.

112. There are two compounds with the formula C_3H_6, one of which does not have a multiple bond. Draw its structure and explain why it is much less stable than the isomer with the double bond.

113. Consider molecules that have two carbons and two chlorines. Draw the structures of three of these with no dipole moment and two with a dipole moment.

CONCEPTUAL PROBLEMS

114. Pick the more oxidized structure in each pair.

a. 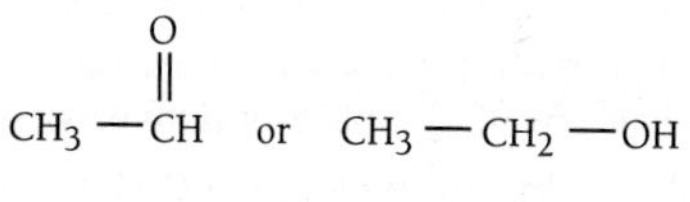

b. $CH_3—CH_2—OH$ or $CH_3—CH_3$

c. 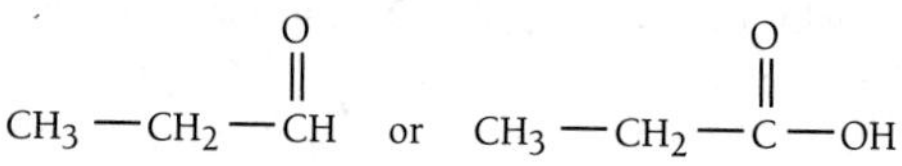

115. Draw the structure and name a compound with the formula C_8H_{18} that forms only one product with the formula $C_8H_{17}Br$ when it is treated with Br_2.

116. Determine whether each structure is chiral.

a. 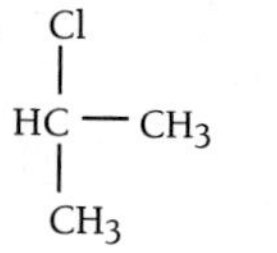

b. 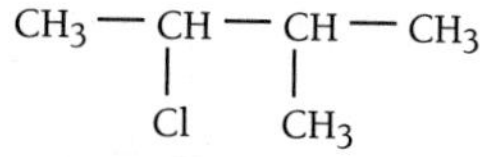

c. $CH_3—CH_2—OH$

d. 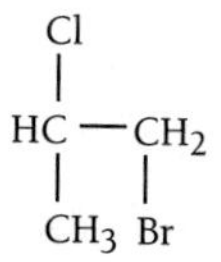

QUESTIONS FOR GROUP WORK

Active Classroom Learning

Discuss these questions with the group and record your consensus answer.

117. Have each group member select a different functional group. Individually, draw and name a compound containing your functional group. Pass your drawing to the group member on your right and your compound name to the group member on your left. Name the compound for the drawing you received and draw the compound whose name you received.

118. Using complete sentences, compare and contrast each of the following. Mention at least two similarities and two differences for each.

a. salt and sugar
b. methane and 3-methylheptane
c. aldehydes and ketones

119. The octane rating for gasoline is a measurement of how readily a fuel combusts compared to 2,2,4-trimethylpentane, an isomer of octane.

a. Draw 2,2,4-trimethylpentane and verify that it is an isomer of octane.
b. Draw four other isomers of octane.
c. Select one of the isomers and draw it so that it looks different on the page, but is still the exact same compound.
d. Name the isomer you drew in part c.
e. Define "isomer" using a complete sentence.

120. Working individually, have each group member select from the chapter a reaction characteristic of a particular organic functional group. Individually, write out your reaction with one of the following left as a blank: one reactant, one product, or reaction conditions. Pass your reaction to the group member on your right. Have group members fill in the blank of the reaction they receive.

DATA INTERPRETATION AND ANALYSIS

Preparation of Fruit-Scented Esters

121. Ester compounds often have a sweet, pleasant odor. Many characteristic fruit scents are largely due to the natural presence of one or more ester compounds. As such, artificial scents for foods are often composed of complex mixtures of various esters. The exact identities and ratios of ingredients that compose particular scents are closely guarded secrets in the food and fragrance industry.

Suppose that you are a chemist working for a company that is creating a new line of air fresheners. The company is considering three scents: apple, pear, and pineapple. The project manager has asked you to prepare the ester compounds that are largely responsible for these scents. The carbon skeleton formulas for these ester compounds are shown in Figure a.

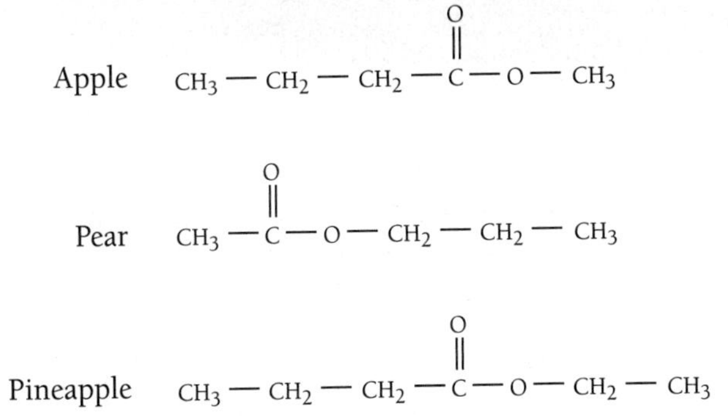

▲ **FIGURE A Structures of Ester Compounds Responsible for Various Fruit Scents**

To prepare these esters, you have been given the alcohols listed in Table a and an adequate supply of all other necessary reagents, solvents, equipment, and the like.

TABLE A ■ Molar Mass, Density, and Cost of Alcohol Compounds for Ester Compound Preparation

Reagent	Molar mass (g/mol)	Density (g/mL)	Cost, per 1.00 L
methanol	32.04	0.79	$46.20
ethanol	46.07	0.79	$112.00
1-propanol	60.10	0.80	$72.70
1-butanol	74.12	0.81	$72.60

Use the information provided in the figure and the table to answer the following questions:

a. Provide a name for each ester that you will prepare.
b. Draw the structure of each alcohol listed in Table A.
c. Determine the procedure you will use to prepare each ester, using the reactions found in this chapter. (*Hint*: Recall that esters are derived from a carboxylic acid and an alcohol.)
d. Calculate the cost to prepare 100.0 g of each ester. Which one will be the most expensive to prepare? Which ester will be the least expensive? (Consider only the cost of the alcohols in Table a and disregard the costs of other reagents. Assume 100% yield for all reactions.)

Cc ANSWERS TO CONCEPTUAL CONNECTIONS

Organic Structures

22.1 **(d)** The others are simply the same structure drawn in slightly different ways.

Optical Isomers

22.2 **(b)** This structure is the only one that contains a carbon atom (the one on the left) with four different substituent groups attached (a Br atom, a Cl atom, an H atom, and a CH_3 group).

Alkanes, Alkenes, and Alkynes

22.3 **(c)** Since the formula is C_5H_{10}, it follows the general formula for alkenes, C_nH_{2n}, with $n = 5$.

Oxidation

22.4 **(c)** The oxidation state of a carbon atom increases as the number of oxygen atoms bonded to it increases and decreases as the number of hydrogen atoms bonded to it increases.

We've discovered the secret of life.

—FRANCIS H. C. CRICK (1916–2004)

CHAPTER 23 Biochemistry

In Chapter 22, we examined organic chemistry and discussed the different types of organic compounds and their structures and chemistry. In this chapter, we turn to biochemical compounds, those organic compounds important in living organisms. Biochemistry—the area of study at the interface between chemistry and biology that strives to understand living organisms at the molecular level—exploded in the second half of the twentieth century. That explosion began with the discovery of the structure of DNA in 1953 by James D. Watson and Francis H. C. Crick and continues to this day, most recently marked by the 2003 completion of the Human Genome Project, which succeeded in mapping the 3 billion base pairs within the DNA of humans. The benefits of biochemistry to humankind are numerous, ranging from a better understanding of illnesses and better drugs to cure them to a better understanding of ourselves and our origins.

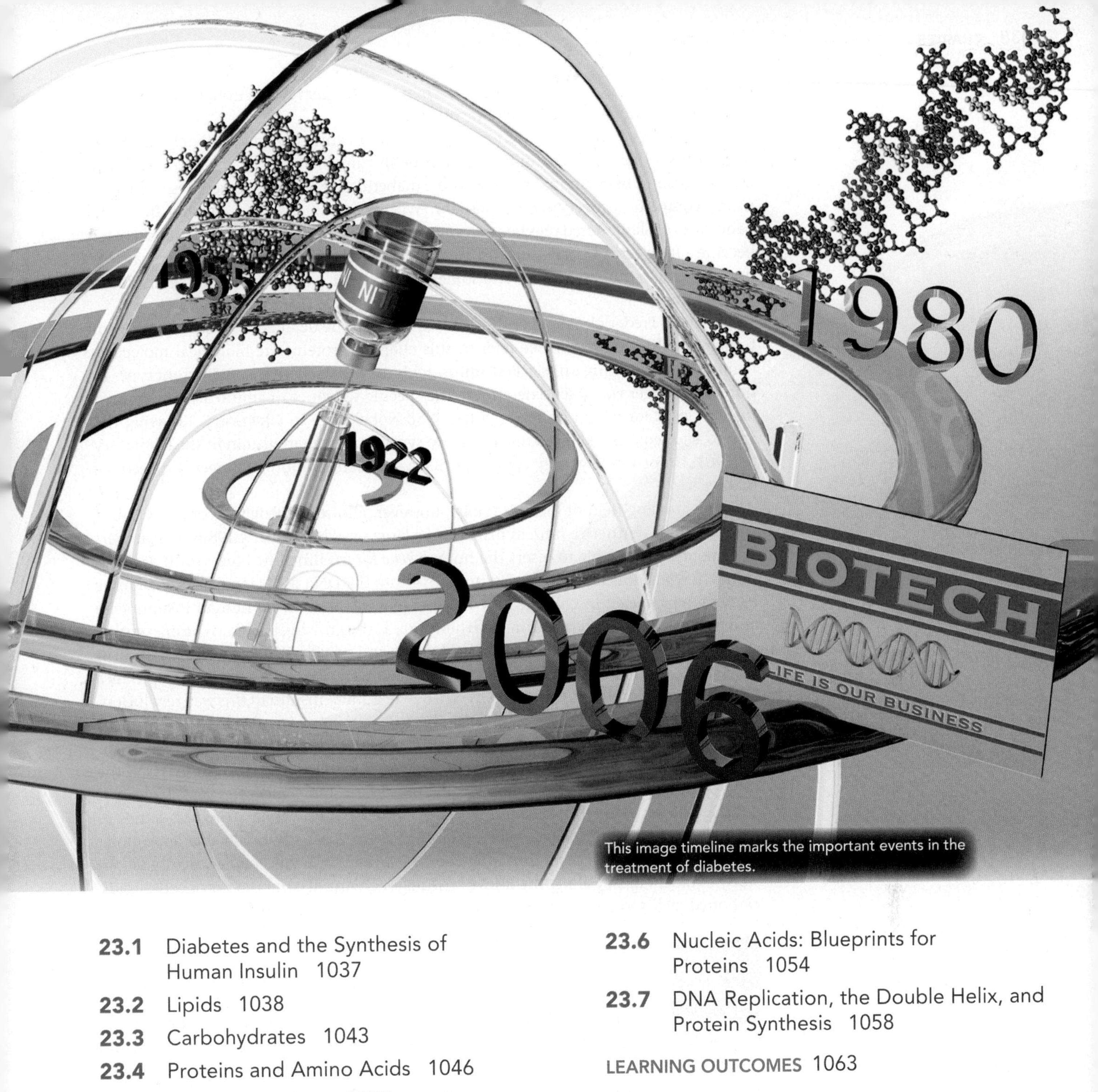

This image timeline marks the important events in the treatment of diabetes.

23.1 Diabetes and the Synthesis of Human Insulin 1037
23.2 Lipids 1038
23.3 Carbohydrates 1043
23.4 Proteins and Amino Acids 1046
23.5 Protein Structure 1050
23.6 Nucleic Acids: Blueprints for Proteins 1054
23.7 DNA Replication, the Double Helix, and Protein Synthesis 1058
LEARNING OUTCOMES 1063

23.1 Diabetes and the Synthesis of Human Insulin

Diabetes afflicts over 16 million people in the United States alone. Today, it is a chronic but generally manageable ailment; at the beginning of the twentieth century, however, diabetes was often fatal. The most dangerous form, type 1 diabetes, develops when the pancreas does not make enough *insulin*, a protein that promotes the absorption of glucose from the blood into cells, where glucose is used for energy. Consequently, people with diabetes have high blood-sugar levels that can lead to a number of complications, including heart disease, blindness, and kidney failure. Before 1922, the only option diabetics had was to control their blood-sugar levels through diet, but this was often not enough to overcome the disease.

Important advances throughout the twentieth century dramatically changed the prognosis for diabetics. The initial breakthrough came in 1922, when researchers first injected insulin from animal sources into a diabetic. The insulin worked, resulting in a nearly complete recovery for the patient. Within a year, insulin harvested from the pancreases of slaughtered pigs became widely available, and, for many patients, diabetes became a long-term manageable disease. However, insulin taken from pigs and cattle is not identical to human insulin, and some patients do not tolerate the animal insulin as well as others.

In 1955, Frederick Sanger (1918–2013) discovered the detailed chemical structure of human insulin. As we will see later in this chapter, proteins are biological molecules composed of repeating units called amino acids (of which there are 20 different types in humans). Sanger was able to determine the specific sequence of amino acids in human insulin, work for which he received the 1958 Nobel Prize in Chemistry. Knowing the amino acid sequence allowed researchers to synthesize human insulin in the laboratory by 1963. Unfortunately, they could not make sufficient amounts to meet the needs of diabetics.

The growing field of biotechnology, however, allowed a fledgling company called Genentech to synthesize human insulin on a large scale by the early 1980s. Researchers at Genentech were able to insert the human *gene* for insulin—the blueprint that determines how insulin is synthesized in humans—into the DNA of bacterial cells. When the bacteria reproduced in culture, they made copies of the inserted human insulin gene and passed it on to their offspring. Furthermore, as the growing bacterial culture synthesized the bacterial proteins that it needed to grow and survive, it also synthesized human insulin. In other words, researchers at Genentech were able to get bacteria to produce human insulin for them! The ability to synthesize human insulin in this way revolutionized the treatment of diabetes, resulting in better health and extended lives for hundreds of millions of people who suffer from this disease.

The study of the chemistry occurring in living organisms is **biochemistry**, the topic of this chapter. Many biologically important molecules are very large and complex—they are *macromolecules*. However, understanding their structures is not as difficult as you might imagine because most of them consist of much smaller, simpler components linked together into long chains (*polymers*). In this chapter, we divide our study of biochemistry along the lines of the major chemical components of cells: lipids, carbohydrates, proteins, and nucleic acids.

23.2 Lipids

Lipids are the chemical components of the cell that are insoluble in water but soluble in nonpolar solvents. Fatty acids, fats, oils, phospholipids, glycolipids, and steroids are all lipids. Their insolubility in water makes it possible for lipids to compose the structural components of cell membranes, which separate the aqueous interior of the cell from its aqueous environment in the body. Lipids also play a role in long-term energy storage and insulation.

Fatty Acids

One type of lipid is the **fatty acid**, a carboxylic acid (see Section 22.11) with a long hydrocarbon tail. The general structure for a fatty acid contains the carboxylic acid group:

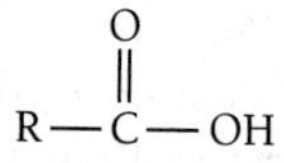

Fatty acid general structure

The R on the left side of the structure represents a hydrocarbon chain containing 3 to 19 carbon atoms. Fatty acids differ only in their R group.

Myristic acid, found in butterfat and in coconut oil, has the R group $CH_3(CH_2)_{12}$. Myristic acid is a *saturated* fatty acid: its carbon chain has no double bonds:

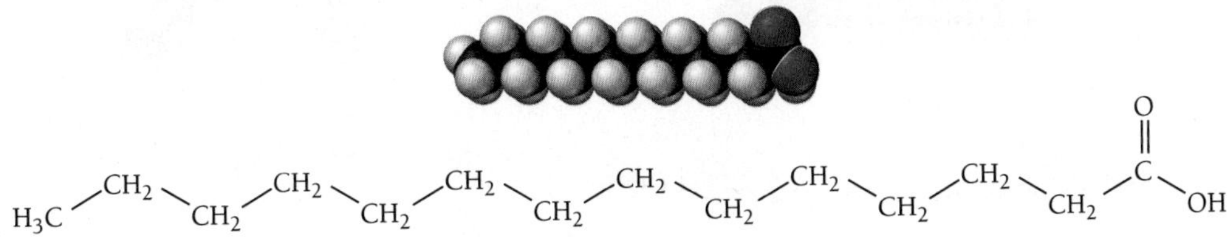

Myristic acid

Other fatty acids—called *monounsaturated* or *polyunsaturated* fatty acids—have one or more double bonds in their carbon chains. For example, oleic acid—found in olive oil, peanut oil, and human fat—is a monounsaturated fatty acid:

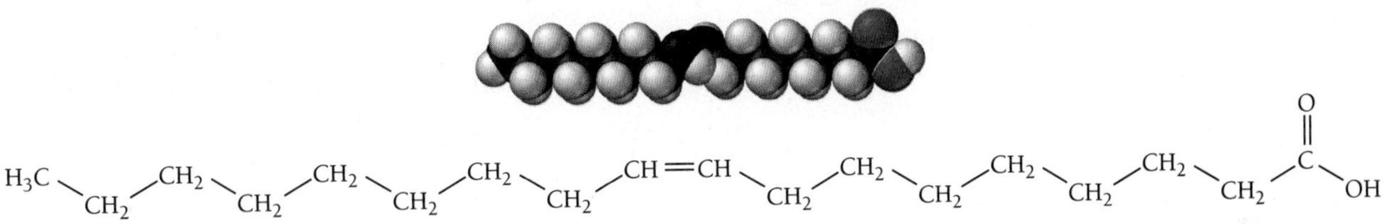

Oleic acid

The long hydrocarbon tails of fatty acids make them insoluble in water. Table 23.1 lists several fatty acids, some common sources for each, and their melting points. Notice that the melting points of the fatty acids *increase* as their carbon chain lengths increase. The longer the chains, the greater the dispersion forces between adjacent molecules in the solid state, and the higher the melting point. Notice also that the melting points *decrease* with the presence of double bonds. For example, stearic acid and oleic acid have the same number of carbon atoms, but stearic acid melts at 70 °C and oleic acid melts at 4 °C. The double bond puts a "kink" in the carbon chain that makes it more difficult for neighboring molecules to interact over the entire length of the chain (Figure 23.1▶), thus lowering the melting point.

Dispersion forces are discussed in Section 12.3.

TABLE 23.1 ■ Fatty Acids

Saturated Fatty Acids

Name	Number of Carbons	mp (°C)	Structure	Sources
Butyric acid	4	−7.9	$CH_3CH_2CH_2COOH$	Milk fat
Capric acid	10	31	$CH_3(CH_2)_8COOH$	Milk fat, whale oil
Myristic acid	14	59	$CH_3(CH_2)_{12}COOH$	Butterfat, coconut oil
Palmitic acid	16	64	$CH_3(CH_2)_{14}COOH$	Beef fat, butterfat
Stearic acid	18	70	$CH_3(CH_2)_{16}COOH$	Beef fat, butterfat

Unsaturated Fatty Acids

Name	Number of Carbons	Number of Double Bonds	mp (°C)	Structure	Sources
Oleic acid	18	1	4	$CH_3(CH_2)_7CH{=}CH(CH_2)_7COOH$	Olive oil, peanut oil
Linoleic acid	18	2	−5	$CH_3(CH_2)_4(CH{=}CHCH_2)_2(CH_2)_6COOH$	Linseed oil, corn oil
Linolenic acid	18	3	−11	$CH_3CH_2(CH{=}CHCH_2)_3(CH_2)_6COOH$	Linseed oil, corn oil

The Effect of Unsaturation

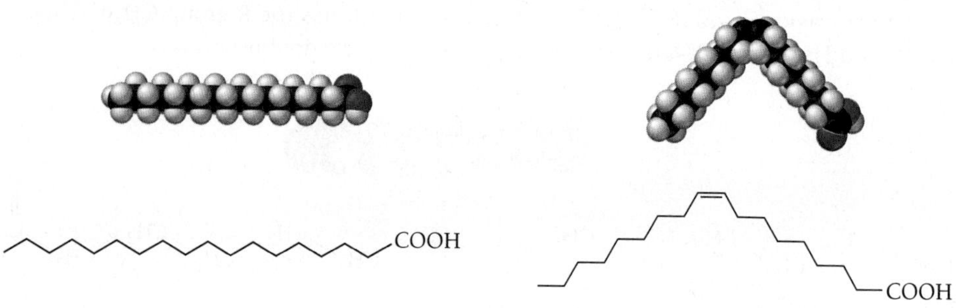

Stearic acid, mp 70 °C

Oleic acid, mp 4 °C

▲ **FIGURE 23.1 The Effect of Unsaturation** A double bond results in a bend in the carbon chain of a fatty acid or fat. The bend makes it more difficult for neighboring molecules to interact over the entire length of the carbon chain, thus lowering the melting point.

Fats and Oils

Fats and oils are **triglycerides**, triesters composed of glycerol with three fatty acids attached. Triglycerides form when a glycerol molecule reacts with three fatty acids:

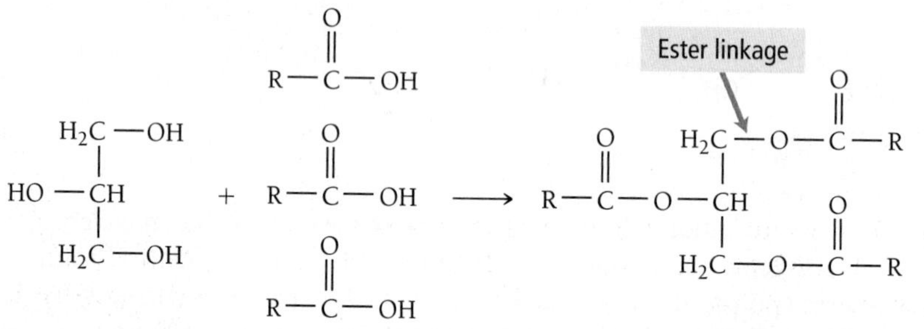

Glycerol 3 Fatty acids Triglyceride

We discussed the general structure of esters in Section 21.11.

The bonds that join the glycerol to the fatty acids are called **ester linkages**. For example, tristearin—the main component of beef fat—forms from the reaction of glycerol and three stearic acid molecules (Figure 23.2▼). If the fatty acids in a triglyceride are saturated, the triglyceride is a **saturated fat** and tends to be solid at room temperature. Triglycerides from warm-blooded animals (for example, lard from pigs) are generally saturated.

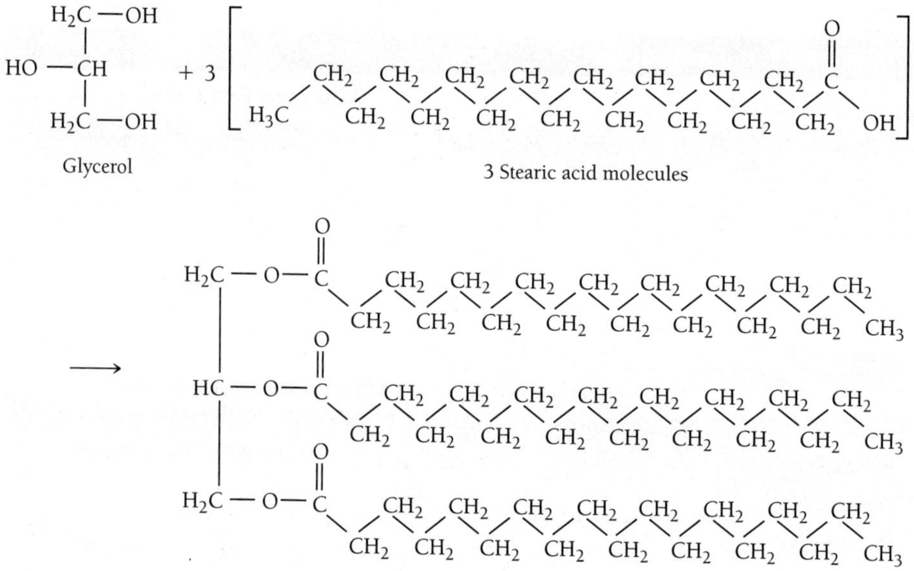

Tristearin

▲ **FIGURE 23.2 The Formation of Tristearin** The reaction between glycerol and stearic acid forms tristearin.

Tristearin: A Saturated Fat

Tristearin is a triglyceride found in lard; it is a saturated fat.

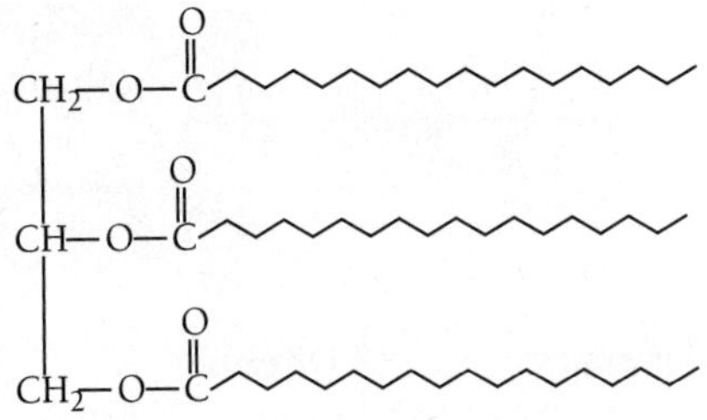

Tristearin, mp 72 °C

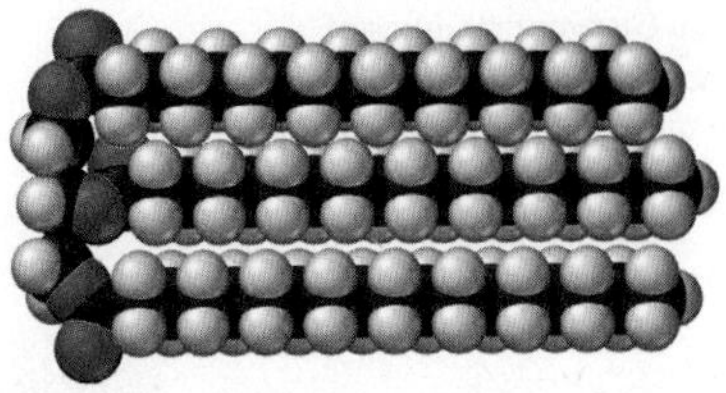

If the fatty acids in a triglyceride are unsaturated, the triglyceride is an **unsaturated fat**, or an oil, and tends to be liquid at room temperature. Triglycerides from plants (olive oil, corn oil, canola oil, etc.) or from cold-blooded animals (fish oil) are generally unsaturated.

Most of the fats and oils in our diet are triglycerides. During digestion, triglycerides are broken down into fatty acids, glycerol, monoglycerides, and diglycerides. These products pass through the intestinal wall and reassemble into triglycerides before they are absorbed into the blood. This process is slower than the digestion of other food types, and for this reason eating fats and oils gives a lasting feeling of fullness.

Triolein: A Monounsaturated Fat

Triolein is a triglyceride found in olive oil; it is a monounsaturated fat.

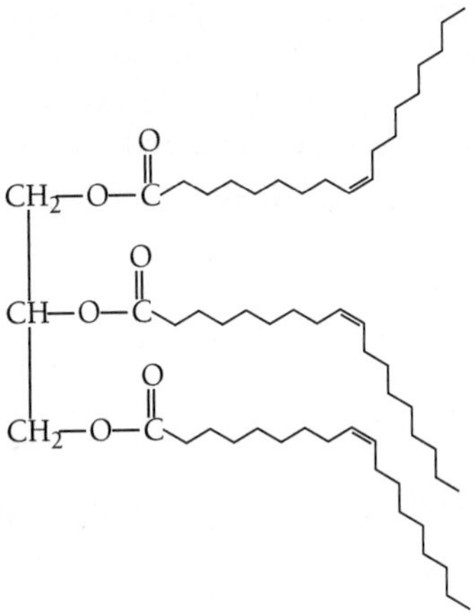

Triolein, mp −4 °C

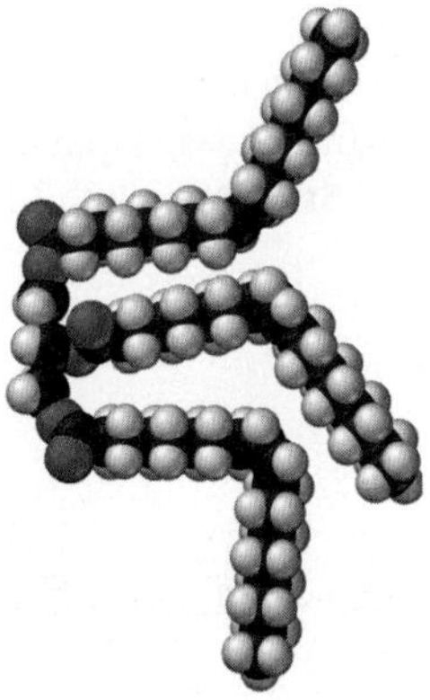

The effect of fats and oils on health has been widely debated. Some diets call for a drastic reduction of our daily intake of fats and oils, whereas others actually call for an *increase* in fats and oils. The U.S. Food and Drug Administration (FDA) recommends moderate consumption of fats and oils, less than 30% of total caloric intake.

Other Lipids

Additional lipids found in cells include phospholipids, glycolipids, and steroids. **Phospholipids** have the same basic structure as triglycerides, except that one of the fatty acid groups is replaced with a phosphate group. Unlike a fatty acid, which is nonpolar, the phosphate group is polar. A phospholipid molecule therefore has a polar region and a nonpolar region. Consider the structure of phosphatidylcholine, a phospholipid found in the cell membranes of higher animals (Figure 23.3▶). The polar part of the molecule is *hydrophilic* (has a strong affinity for water), while the nonpolar part is *hydrophobic* (is repelled by water).

Glycolipids have similar structures and properties. The nonpolar section of a glycolipid is composed of a fatty acid chain and a hydrocarbon chain. The polar section is a

▶ FIGURE 23.3 Phosphatidylcholine Phosphatidylcholine is a phospholipid. The structure is similar to a triglyceride except that one of the fatty acid groups is replaced with a phosphate group.

Phosphatidylcholine: A Phospholipid

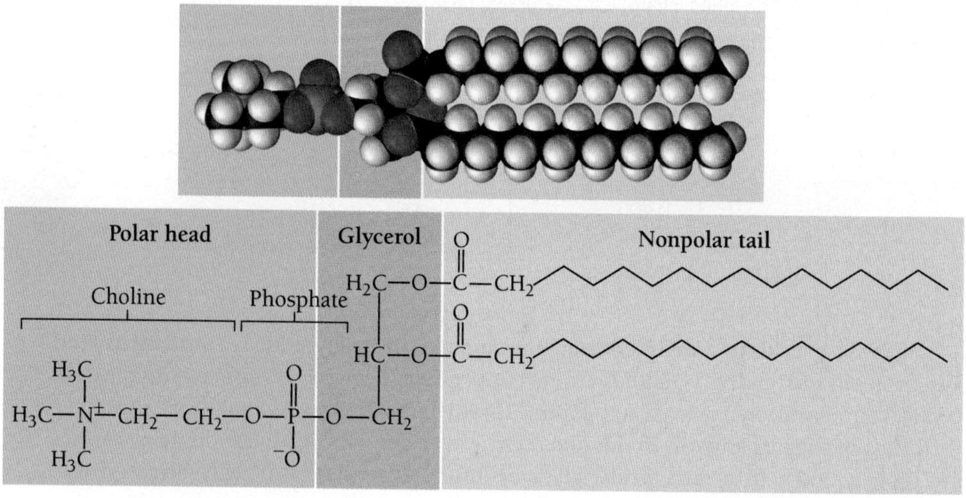

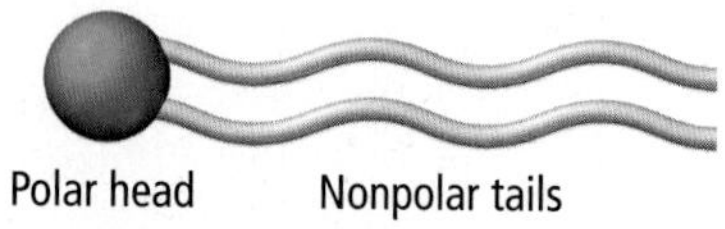

▲ FIGURE 23.4 Schematic for Phospholipid or Glycolipid We represent a phospholipid or a glycolipid as a circle (the polar part of the molecule) with two long tails (the nonpolar part of the molecule).

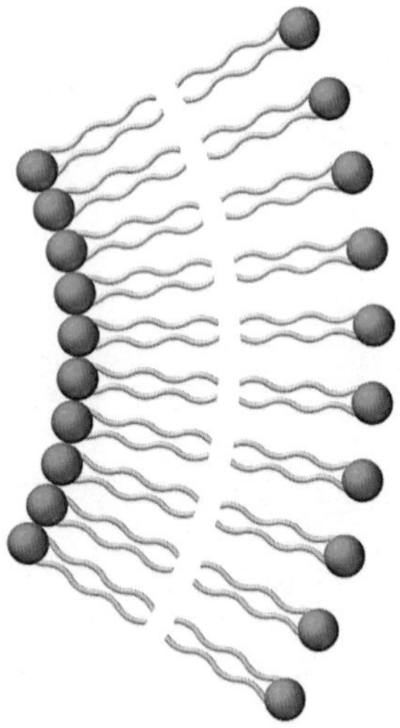

▲ FIGURE 23.5 Lipid Bilayer Lipid bilayers are composed of phospholipids or glycolipids arranged in a structure that encapsulates cells and many cellular structures.

sugar molecule such as glucose. We often portray phospholipids or glycolipids schematically as a circle with two long tails (Figure 23.4◀). The circle represents the polar, hydrophilic part of the molecule, and the tails represent the nonpolar, hydrophobic parts. Phospholipids and glycolipids are key components of cell membranes; the polar parts interact with the aqueous environments inside and outside the cell, and the nonpolar parts interact with each other, forming a double-layered structure called a **lipid bilayer** (Figure 23.5◀). Lipid bilayers encapsulate cells and many cellular structures.

Steroids are lipids with a four-ring structure:

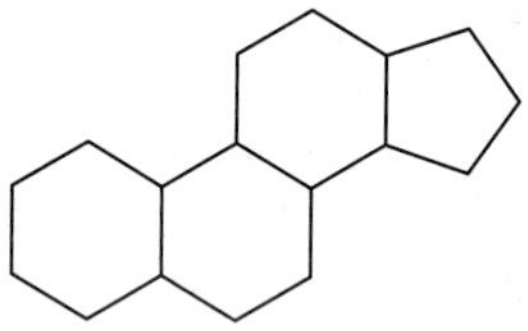

Cholesterol, testosterone, and β-estradiol are common steroids:

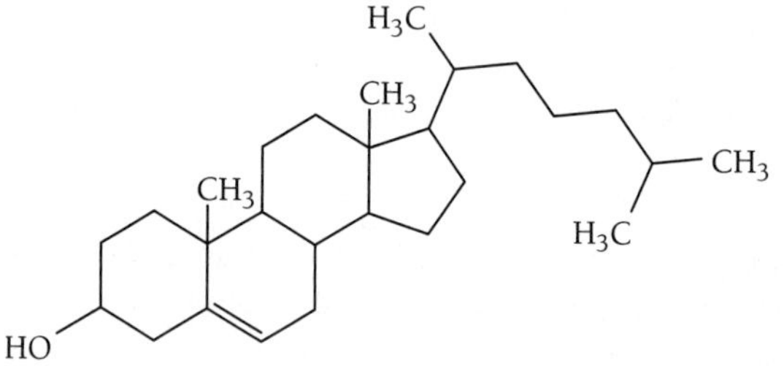

Cholesterol

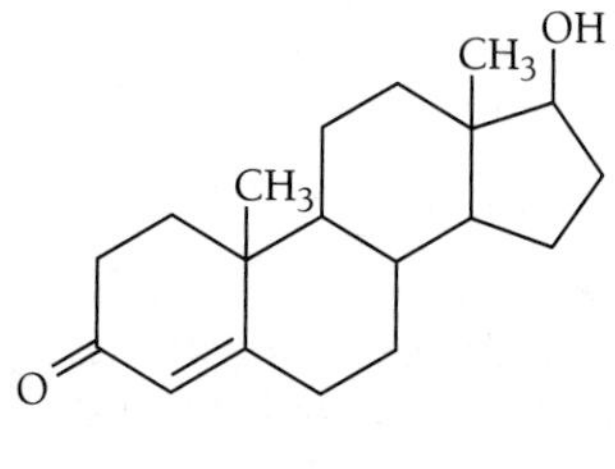

Testosterone

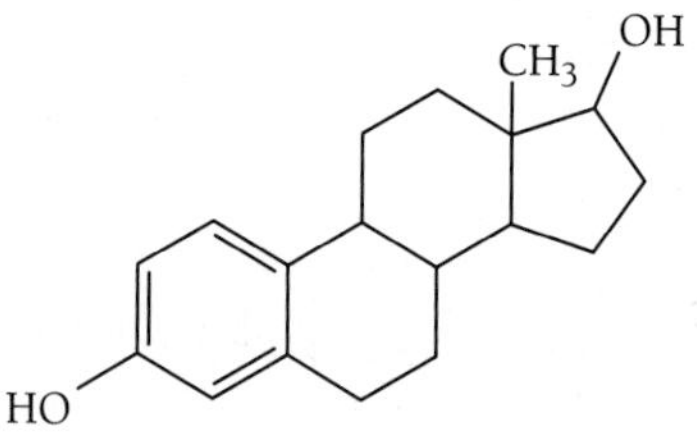

β-Estradiol

Hormones are chemical messengers that are released by cells in one part of the body and cause an effect in cells in another part of the body.

Although cholesterol has a bad reputation, it serves many important functions in the body. Like phospholipids and glycolipids, cholesterol is part of cell membranes. Cholesterol also serves as a starting material (or precursor) for the body's synthesis of other steroids such as testosterone, a principal male hormone, and β-estradiol, a principal female hormone.

LIPIDS Which type of lipid is most common in our diet?

(a) phospholipids **(b)** triglycerides
(c) glycolipids **(d)** steroids

23.1 Cc Conceptual Connection

ANSWER **NOW!**

23.3 Carbohydrates

Carbohydrates are responsible for short-term storage of energy in living organisms, and they make up the main structural components of plants. Carbohydrates—as their name, which means carbon and water, implies—often have the general formula $(CH_2O)_n$. Structurally, we identify **carbohydrates** as polyhydroxy aldehydes or ketones. For example, glucose, with the formula $C_6H_{12}O_6$, has the following structure:

The name should not be taken literally—the hydrogen and oxygen in carbohydrates do not bond together in the same way that they bond in water.

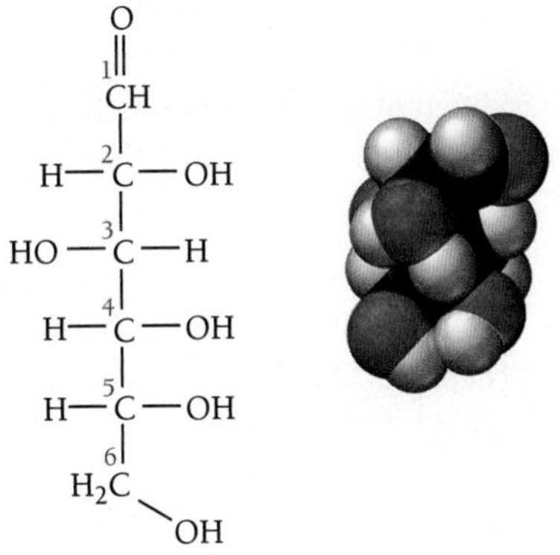

Glucose

Glucose is a six-carbon aldehyde (that is, it contains the —CHO group) with —OH groups on five of the six carbon atoms. The many —OH groups make glucose soluble in water (and therefore in blood), which is crucial to glucose's role as the primary fuel of cells. Glucose is easily transported in the bloodstream and is soluble within the aqueous interior of a cell. We broadly classify carbohydrates as simple carbohydrates (or simple sugars) and complex carbohydrates.

Recall from Section 22.10 that aldehydes have the general structure RCHO and ketones have the general structure RCOR.

Simple Carbohydrates: Monosaccharides and Disaccharides

3-carbon sugar: triose
4-carbon sugar: tetrose
5-carbon sugar: pentose
6-carbon sugar: hexose
7-carbon sugar: heptose
8-carbon sugar: octose

Monosaccharides—meaning "one sugar"—are the simplest carbohydrates. Monosaccharides contain between three and eight carbon atoms and have only one aldehyde or ketone functional group. The general names for monosaccharides begin with a prefix that indicates the number of carbon atoms, followed by the suffix *-ose*. The most common carbohydrates in living organisms are pentoses and hexoses.

Glucose, the structure of which we saw previously, is an example of a **hexose**, a six-carbon sugar. Glucose is also an example of an **aldose**, a sugar with an aldehyde group. Often, we combine these two ways of designating sugars; glucose is an *aldohexose* (*aldo-* indicates that it is an aldehyde; *-hex-* indicates that it has six carbon atoms; and *-ose* indicates that it is a carbohydrate).

Another common carbohydrate is fructose, a polyhydroxy *ketone* with the structure shown in the margin. Glucose and fructose are structural isomers—they both have the same formula ($C_6H_{12}O_6$), but they have different structures. Fructose is a **ketose**, a sugar that is a ketone. Since fructose has six carbon atoms, it is a *ketohexose*. Fructose, often called fruit sugar, is in many fruits and vegetables and is a major component of honey.

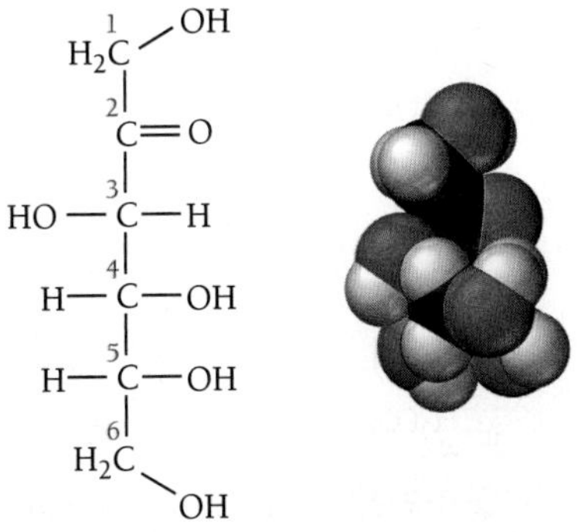

Fructose

EXAMPLE 23.1 Carbohydrates and Optical Isomerism

Closely examine the structure of glucose shown here. Does glucose exhibit optical isomerism (discussed in Section 22.3)? If so, which carbon atoms are chiral?

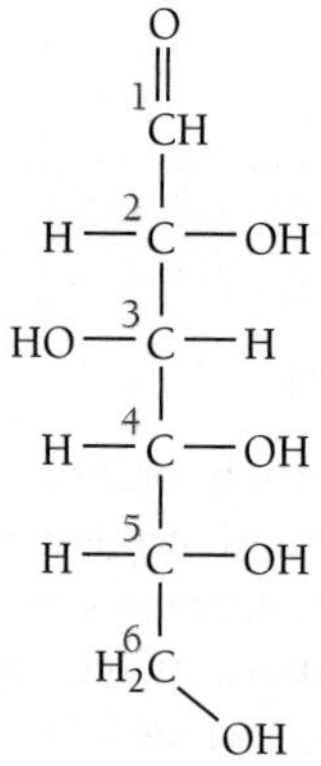

Glucose

SOLUTION

Any carbon atom with four different substituents attached to it is chiral. Glucose has four chiral carbon atoms (labeled 2, 3, 4, and 5) and therefore exhibits optical isomerism.

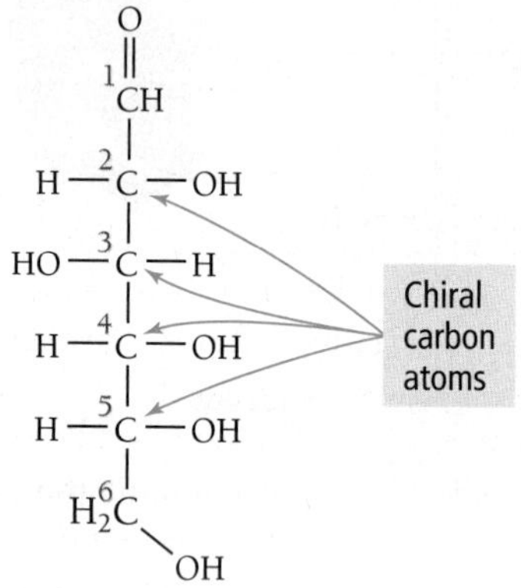

Glucose

Variations in the positions of the —OH and —H groups on these carbon atoms result in a number of different possible isomers for glucose. For example, switching the relative positions of the —OH and —H group on the carbon atom closest to the carbonyl group results in mannose, an optical isomer of glucose.

FOR PRACTICE 23.1 Examine the structure of fructose (p. 1043). Does fructose exhibit optical isomerism? How many of the carbon atoms in fructose are chiral?

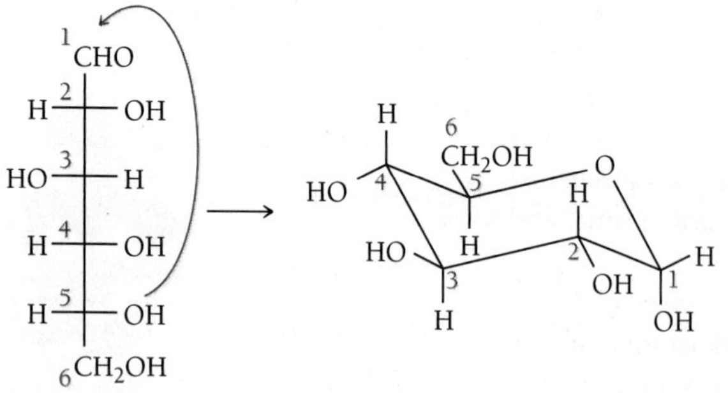

▲ FIGURE 23.6 Intramolecular Reaction of Glucose to Form a Ring The alcohol group on C5 in glucose reacts with the carbonyl group (C1) to form a closed ring.

Most five- and six-carbon monosaccharides undergo intramolecular reactions that convert their straight carbon chain into a ring. For example, in glucose, the alcohol group on C5 reacts with the carbonyl group (C1), as shown in Figure 23.6◄, to form the ring structure shown here:

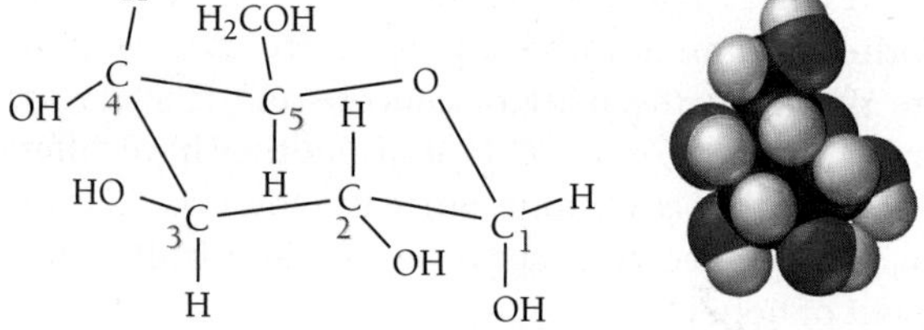

In a glucose solution, the vast majority of the molecules are in ring form. However, the molecules in ring form exist in equilibrium with a small fraction in the open-chain form. Other common monosaccharides, in their ring form, include fructose (discussed previously in its straight-chain form) and galactose shown at the right.

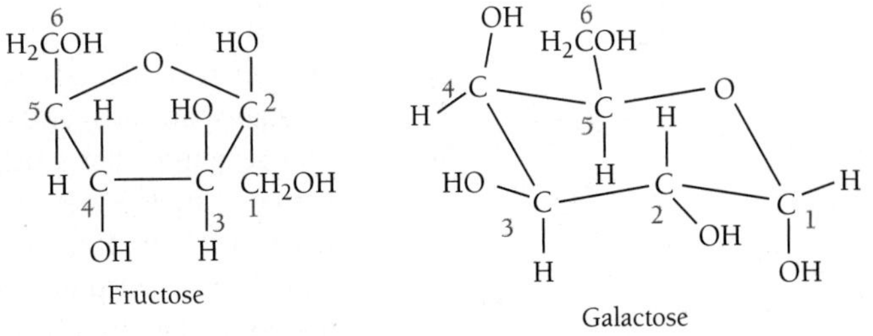

Galactose, also known as brain sugar, is a hexose usually found combined with other monosaccharides in disaccharides such as lactose (see next paragraph). Galactose also occurs within the brain and nervous system of most animals. Galactose and glucose differ only in the stereochemistry at C4. Notice that in galactose the —OH group is roughly perpendicular to the plane of the ring, while in glucose it is roughly in the same plane as the ring.

Two monosaccharides can link together via a **glycosidic linkage** to form a **disaccharide**, a carbohydrate that can be decomposed into two simpler sugars. For example, glucose and fructose join to form sucrose, commonly known as table sugar (Figure 23.7▶). When we eat disaccharides, the link between individual monosaccharides is broken during digestion by **hydrolysis**, the splitting of a chemical bond with water that results in the addition of H and OH to the products. The resultant monosaccharides readily pass through the intestinal wall and enter the bloodstream to become fuel for cells.

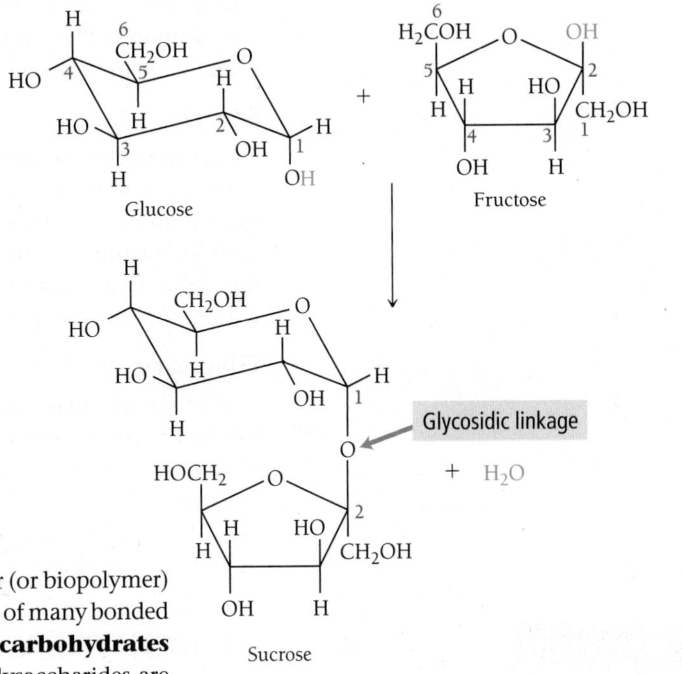

▲ **FIGURE 23.7 Formation of a Glycosidic Linkage** Glucose and fructose can join, eliminating water and forming a glycosidic linkage that results in the disaccharide sucrose, commonly known as table sugar.

Complex Carbohydrates

Monosaccharides can also link to form a type of natural polymer (or biopolymer) called a **polysaccharide**, a long, chain-like molecule composed of many bonded monosaccharide units. Polysaccharides are known as **complex carbohydrates** because of their long chains of sugars. The most common polysaccharides are *cellulose*, *starch*, and *glycogen*, all three of which are composed of repeating glucose units. The main difference among them lies in the way the units are bonded to each other. In cellulose, the oxygen atoms are roughly parallel with the planes of the rings. This is referred to as a β-glycosidic linkage. In starch and glycogen, the oxygen atoms joining neighboring glucose units point down relative to the planes of the rings. This is an α-glycosidic linkage:

Cellulose

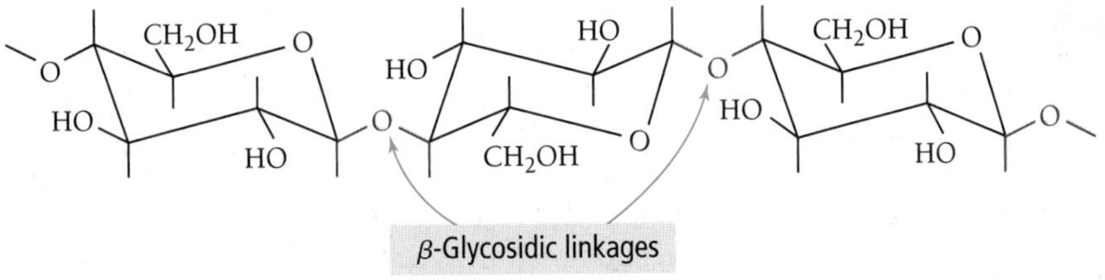

Starch

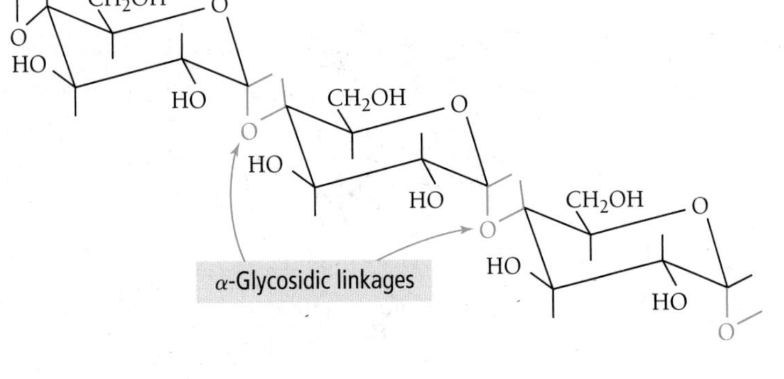

◀ The primary difference between starch and cellulose is in the way the units are bonded together.

Cellulose

The main structural component of plants, **cellulose**, is the most abundant organic substance on Earth and consists of glucose units bonded together by β-glycosidic linkages. This structure allows neighboring cellulose molecules to form multiple hydrogen bonds with one another, resulting in the rigid and structurally stable properties we associate with wood and fiber. Humans lack the enzyme required to digest cellulose. When we eat cellulose (usually called fiber when it is present in foods), it passes right through our intestines, providing bulk to stools and preventing constipation. In contrast, some bacteria have the enzyme required to metabolize cellulose into its component glucose units. These bacteria are common in the guts of termites and ruminants such as cows, allowing them to extract caloric content from cellulose.

Starch

The main energy storage medium for plants is **starch**, the soft, pliable substance abundant in potatoes and grains. Starch is composed of two slightly different polysaccharides, *amylose* and *amylopectin*. Both are made up of glucose units bonded together by α-glycosidic linkages, but amylopectin contains branches in the chains. When animals digest starch, the link between individual glucose units is broken by hydrolysis, allowing glucose molecules to pass through the intestinal wall and into the bloodstream.

Glycogen

The structure of **glycogen** is similar to that of amylopectin, but the chain is even more highly branched. Animals use glycogen to store glucose in the muscles. Glycogen's highly branched structure leaves many end groups that can be quickly hydrolyzed to meet energy needs. When muscles become depleted of glycogen, muscle movement and exercise become much more difficult. Marathon runners often "hit the wall" at about mile 20 because they have depleted most of the glycogen from their muscles.

ANSWER **NOW!**

23.2 **Cc** Conceptual Connection

CARBOHYDRATES Which type of carbohydrate functions as the main structural material in plants?

(a) glucose **(b)** glycogen
(c) sucrose **(d)** cellulose

23.4 Proteins and Amino Acids

Proteins are the workhorse molecules in living organisms; they are involved in virtually every facet of cell structure and function. For example, most of the chemical reactions that occur in living organisms are enabled by **enzymes**, proteins that act as catalysts in biochemical reactions. Without enzymes, life would be impossible. Proteins are also the structural elements of muscle, skin, and cartilage. They transport oxygen in the blood, act as antibodies to fight disease, and function as hormones to regulate metabolic processes. Proteins reign supreme as the working molecules of life. Table 23.2 summarizes the functions of some of the important classes of proteins and lists examples of each.

TABLE 23.2 ■ Protein Functions

Class of Protein	Primary Function	Example
Structural proteins	Compose structures within living organisms	Collagen (skin, tendon, cartilage), keratin (hair, fingernails)
Enzymes	Catalyze and control biochemical reactions	DNA polymerase (involved in replication of DNA)
Hormones	Regulate metabolic processes	Insulin (regulates glucose metabolism)
Transport proteins	Transport substances from one place to another	Hemoglobin (transports oxygen)
Storage proteins	Provide source of essential nutrients	Casein (protein in mammalian milk)
Contractile and motile proteins	Mediate motion and muscle contraction	Actin and myosin (provide muscle contraction)
Protective proteins	Protect and defend cells	Antibodies (neutralize infectious agents)

Amino Acids: The Building Blocks of Proteins

Proteins are polymers of amino acids. Each **amino acid** molecule consists of a carbon atom—called the α-carbon—bonded to four different groups: an amine group, an R group (also called a side chain), a carboxylic acid group, and a hydrogen atom:

In a protein, the presence of an R group does not necessarily indicate a pure alkyl group. See Table 23.3 for possible R groups.

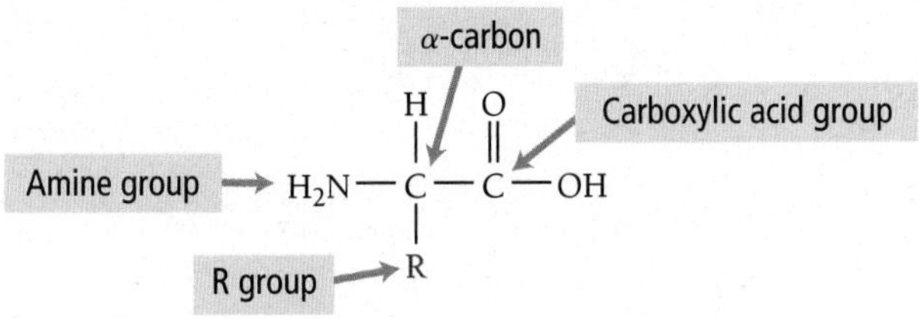

Amino acid general structure

Amino acids differ from each other in their R groups. For example, the R group in alanine is a methyl group (CH_3):

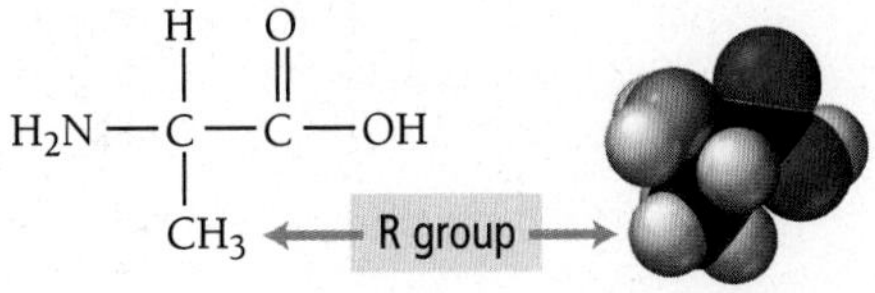

Alanine

Other amino acids are glycine (R = H), phenylalanine (R = $CH_2C_6H_5$), serine (R = CH_2OH), aspartic acid (R = CH_2COOH), and lysine (R = $CH_2CH_2CH_2CH_2NH_2$):

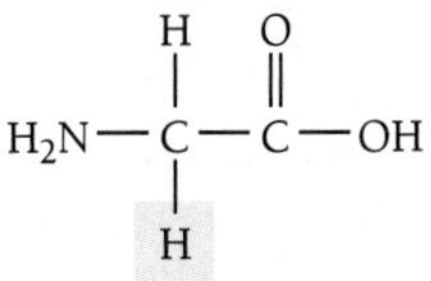

Glycine

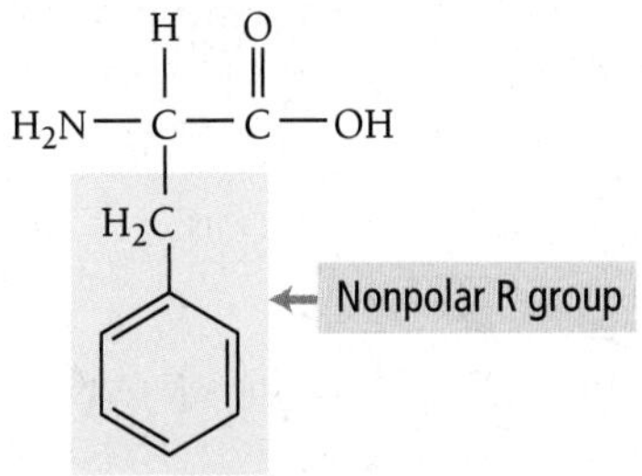

Phenylalanine

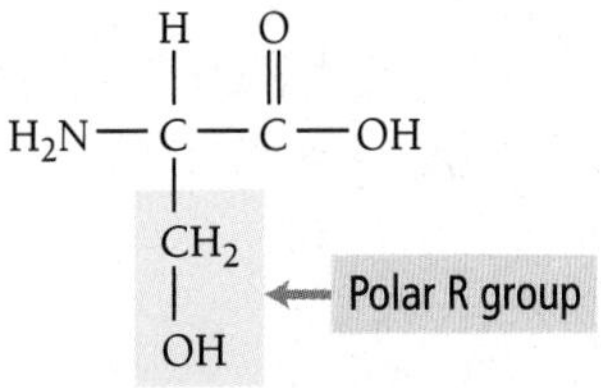

Serine

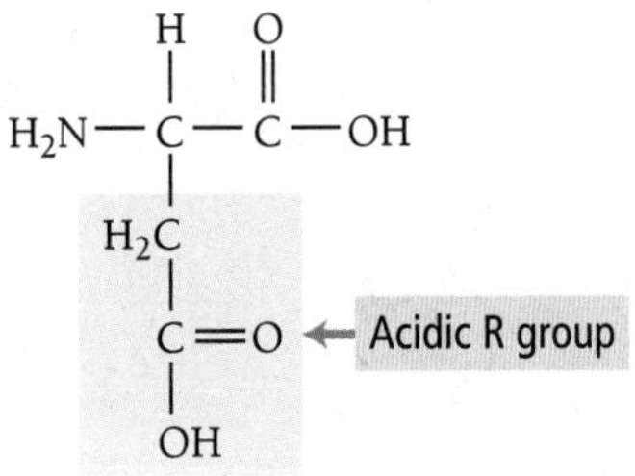

Aspartic acid

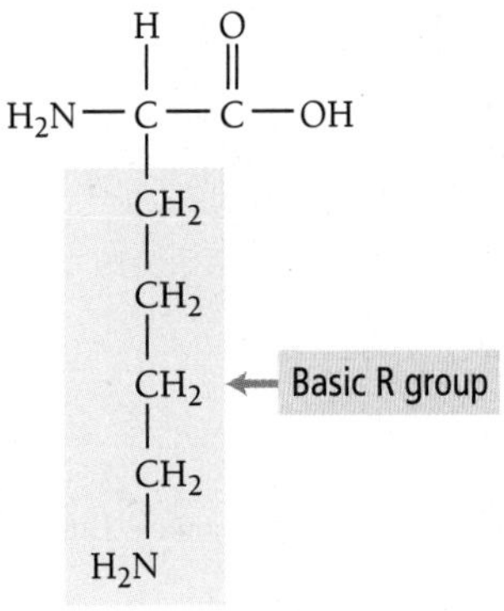

Lysine

The R groups, or side chains, differ chemically. For example, phenylalanine has a large nonpolar R group, whereas serine has a polar one. Aspartic acid has an acidic R group, whereas lysine, since it contains nitrogen, has a basic one. When amino acids are strung together to make a protein, the chemical properties of the R groups determine the structure and properties of the protein. Table 23.3 shows the most common amino acids in proteins and their three-letter abbreviations. The diversity of amino acids creates the possibility for an even larger diversity of proteins.

TABLE 23.3 ■ Common Amino Acids

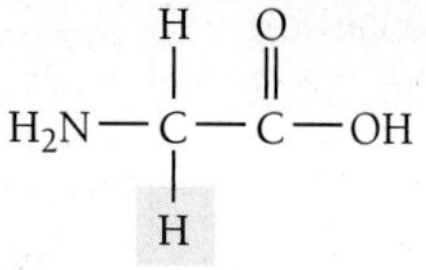

Glycine (Gly)

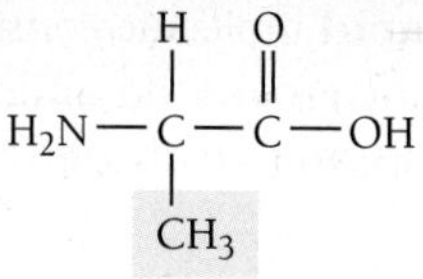

Alanine (Ala)

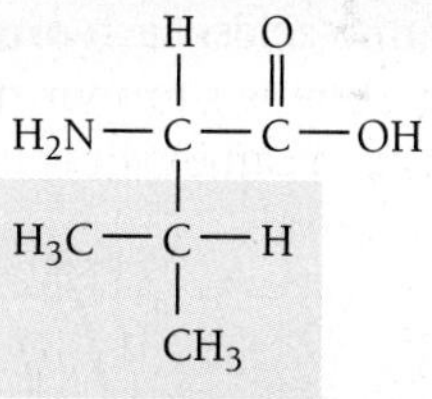

Valine (Val)

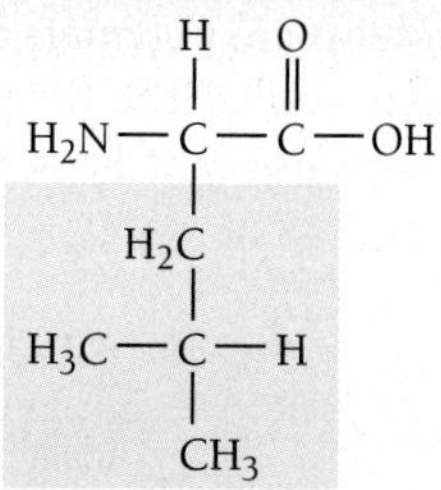

Leucine (Leu)

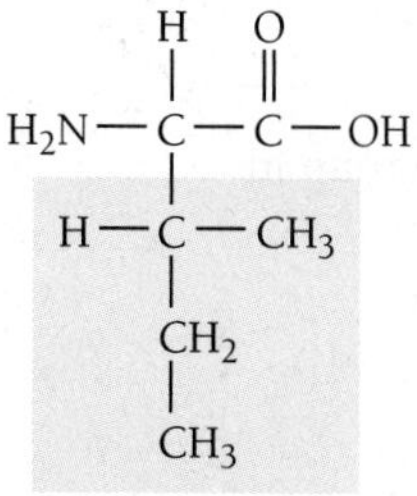

Isoleucine (Ile)

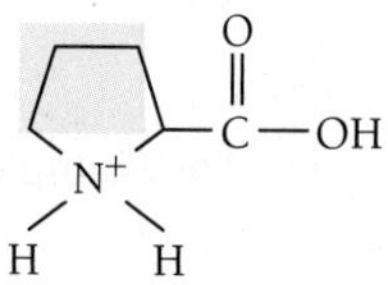

Proline (Pro)

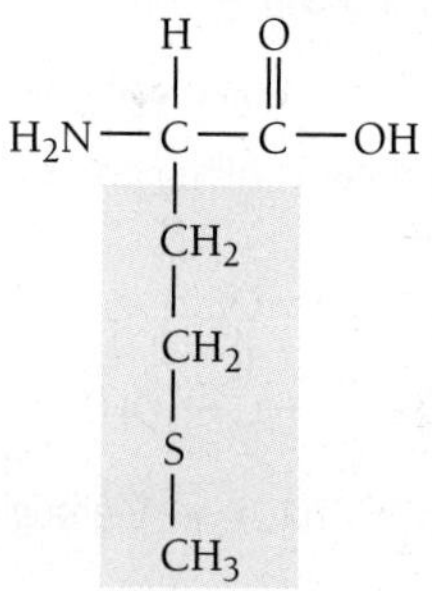

Methionine (Met)

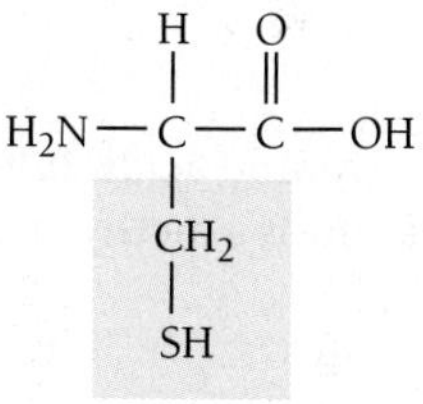

Cysteine (Cys)

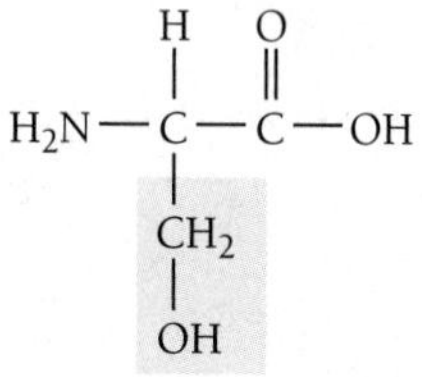

Serine (Ser)

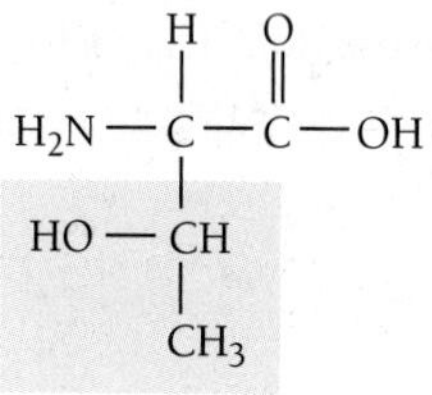

Threonine (Thr)

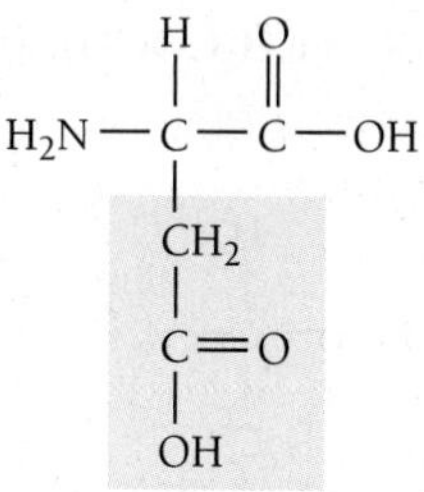

Aspartic acid (Asp)

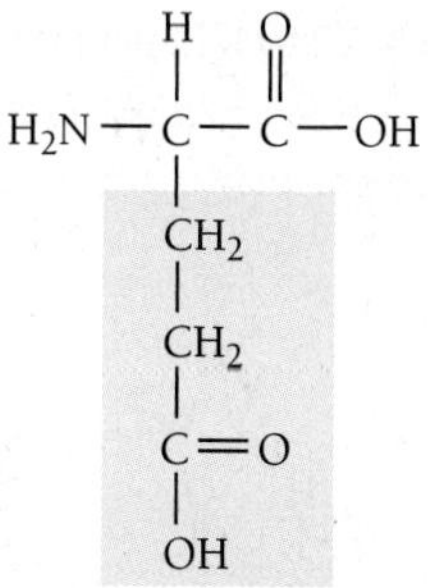

Glutamic acid (Glu)

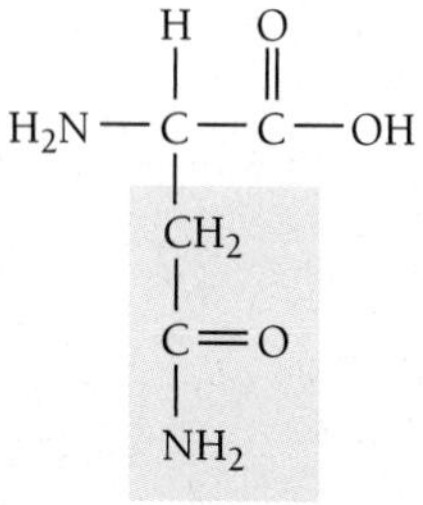

Asparagine (Asn)

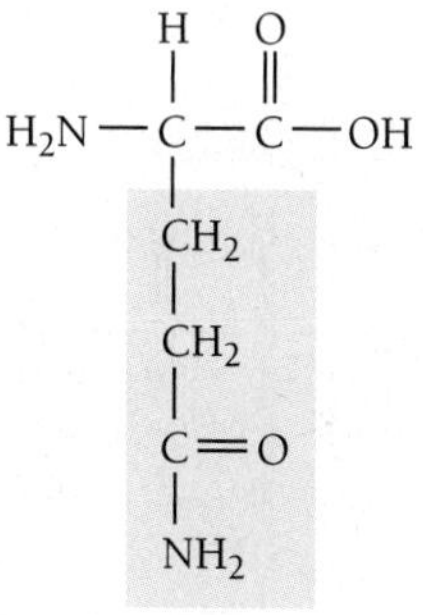

Glutamine (Gln)

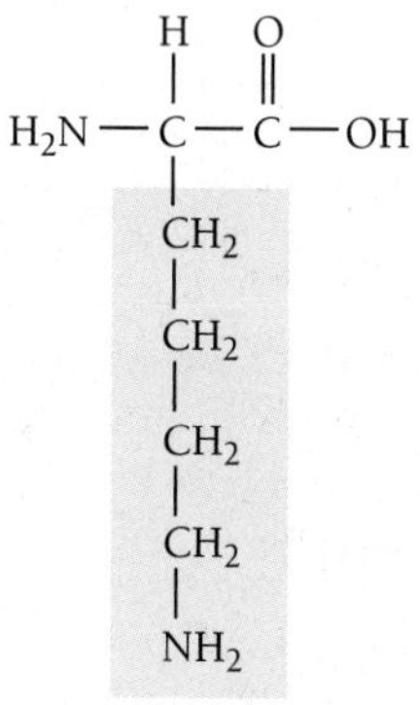

Lysine (Lys)

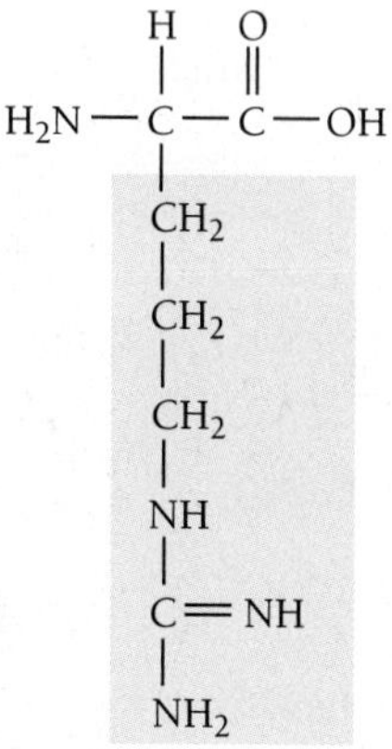

Arginine (Arg)

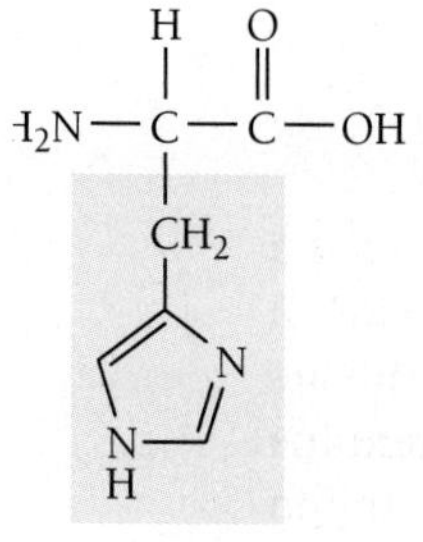

Histidine (His)

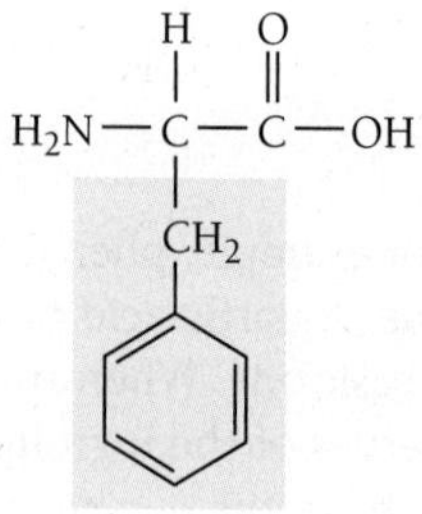

Phenylalanine (Phe)

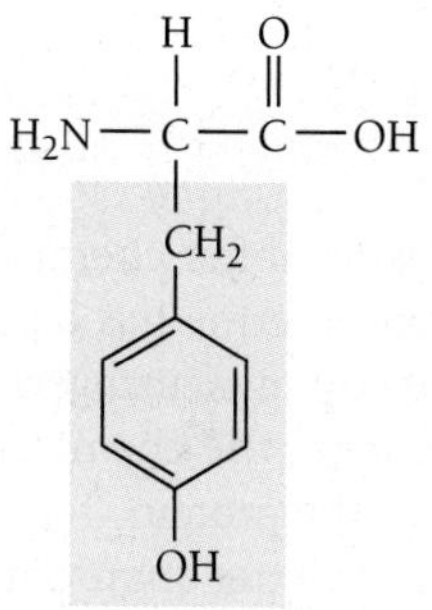

Tyrosine (Tyr)

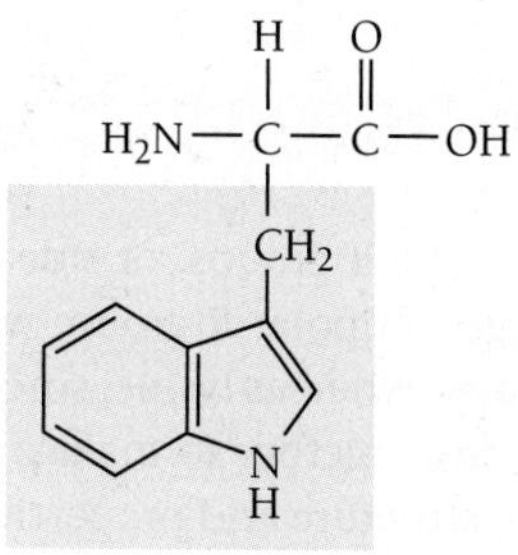

Tryptophan (Trp)

Because all amino acids (except glycine) contain four different groups attached to a tetrahedral carbon (the α-carbon), all amino acids (except glycine) are chiral about that carbon. The amino acids that compose naturally occurring proteins are the L-enantiomers, and they are called L-amino acids. Why life on Earth is based on this enantiomer over the other is an interesting question that remains to be answered. (It seems just as likely that life could have used the D-enantiomer.)

Although we usually write the structures of amino acids as neutral, their actual structure is ionic and depends on pH. In general, amino acids undergo an intramolecular acid–base reaction and form a *dipolar ion*, or *zwitterion*:

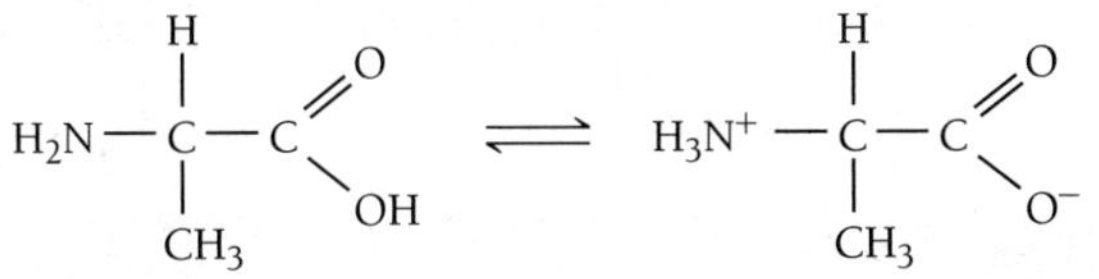

Dipolar ion

At room temperature this equilibrium lies far to the right. Since one side of the dipolar ion is positively charged and the other negatively charged, amino acids are highly polar and soluble in water. They also have fairly high melting points (usually >200 °C). In addition, the intramolecular acid–base reaction makes amino acids less acidic and less basic than most carboxylic acids and amines, respectively.

Peptide Bonding between Amino Acids

Amino acids link together through the reaction of the amine end of one amino acid with the carboxylic end of another:

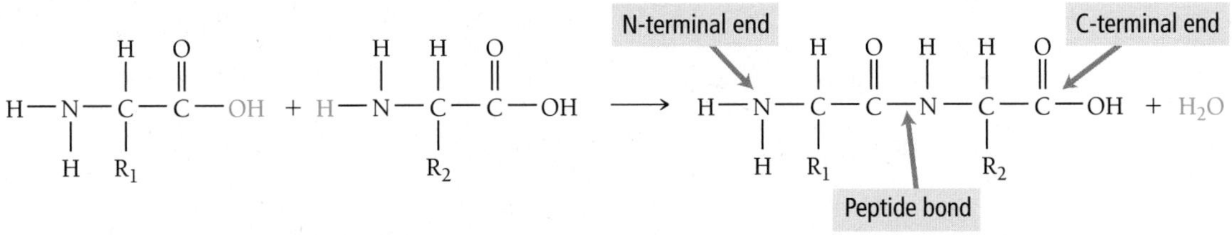

The resulting bond is a **peptide bond**, and the resulting molecule—two amino acids linked together—is a **dipeptide**. When two or more amino acids link in this way, the molecule they form has two distinct ends: an amino terminal (or N-terminal end) and a carboxyl terminal (or C-terminal end). A *tripeptide* is three amino acids joined by peptide bonds; a *tetrapeptide* is four; and so on. Short chains of amino acids are called *oligopeptides* generally, and longer chains (more than 20) are called **polypeptides**. Functional proteins usually contain one or more polypeptide chains, with each chain consisting of hundreds or even thousands of amino acids joined by peptide bonds.

The formation of a peptide bond is an example of a condensation reaction (see Section 22.11).

EXAMPLE 23.2 Peptide Bonds

Show the reaction by which valine, cysteine, and phenylalanine (in that order) link via peptide bonds. Designate valine as N-terminal and label the N-terminal and C-terminal ends in the resulting tripeptide.

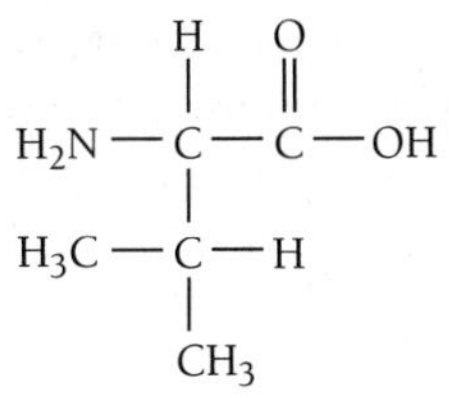

Valine

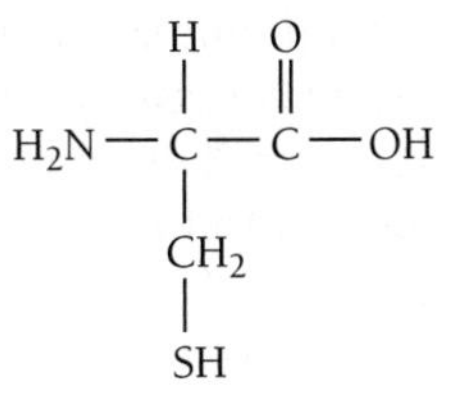

Cysteine

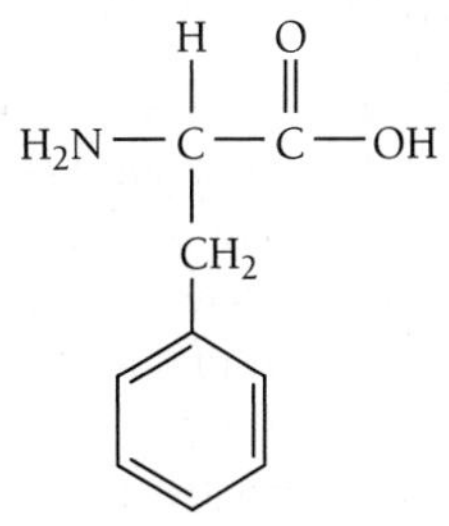

Phenylalanine

—*Continued on the next page*

Continued—

SOLUTION

Peptide bonds form when the carboxylic end of one amino acid reacts with the amine end of another amino acid.

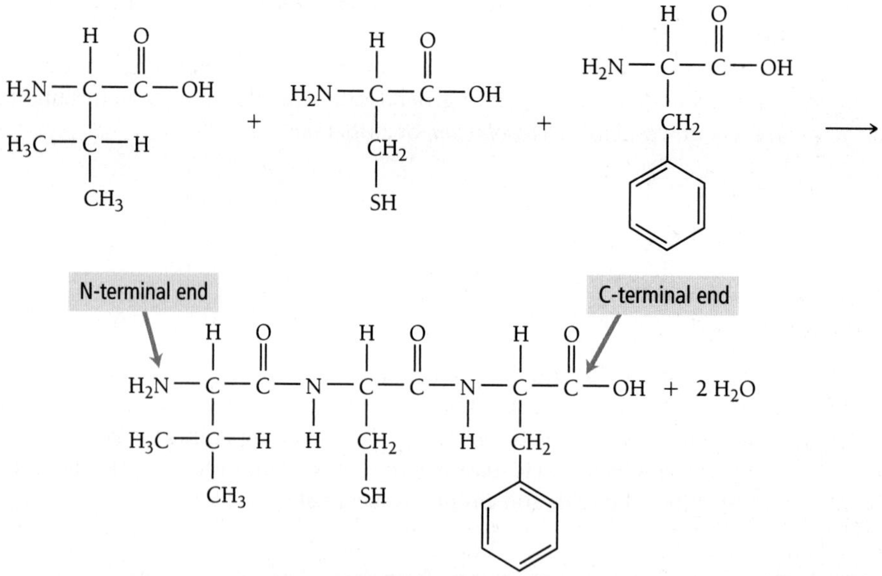

FOR PRACTICE 23.2 Show the reaction by which alanine, threonine, and serine (in that order) link via peptide bonds. Designate alanine as the N-terminal and label the N-terminal and C-terminal ends in the resulting tripeptide.

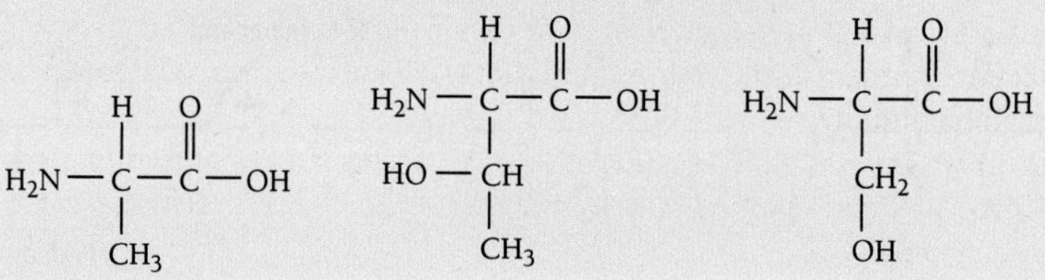

Alanine Threonine Serine

ANSWER **NOW!**

23.3 Cc Conceptual Connection

PEPTIDES How many different tripeptides can form from the three amino acids listed here? (The amino acids are indicated using the three-letter amino acid abbreviations from Table 23.3.)

Ser, Ala, Gly

(a) 1 **(b)** 3 **(c)** 6 **(d)** 12

23.5 Protein Structure

A protein's structure is critical to its function. For example, recall from Section 23.1 that insulin is a protein that promotes the absorption of glucose out of the blood and into muscle cells where the glucose is needed for energy. Insulin recognizes muscle cells because muscle cell surfaces contain *insulin receptors*, molecules that fit a specific portion of the insulin protein. If insulin were a different shape, it would not latch onto insulin receptors on muscle cells and could not do its job. Thus, the shape or *conformation* of a protein is crucial to its function.

We can broadly classify proteins into two main structural categories: fibrous proteins and globular proteins (Figure 23.8▶). **Fibrous proteins** tend to have relatively

Fibrous and Globular Proteins

Fibrous proteins tend to have relatively simple linear structures.

Globular proteins tend to have more complex three-dimensional structures that are roughly spherical in shape.

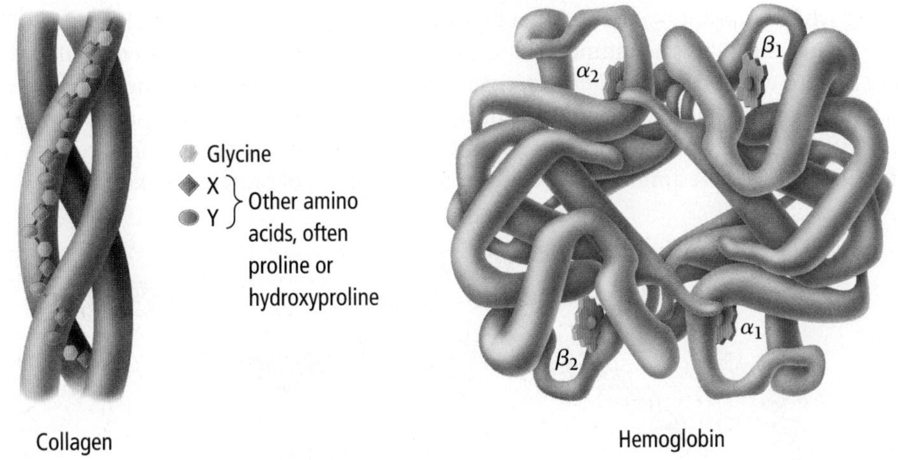

◀ **FIGURE 23.8 Fibrous and Globular Proteins**

simple linear structures and are insoluble in aqueous solutions. They serve primarily structural functions within living organisms. Collagen and keratin, for example, are both fibrous proteins (see Table 23.2). **Globular proteins** tend to have more complex structures but are often roughly spherical in overall shape. Globular proteins are generally structured so that polar side chains on amino acids are oriented toward the exterior of the protein, while nonpolar side chains are oriented toward the interior of the protein. Consequently, globular proteins tend to be soluble in water, but they maintain a nonpolar environment within the protein that excludes water. Hemoglobin and insulin are both globular proteins.

Protein structure is analyzed at four levels: primary structure, secondary structure, tertiary structure, and quaternary structure (Figure 23.9▼). We examine each of these categories separately.

Levels of Protein Structure

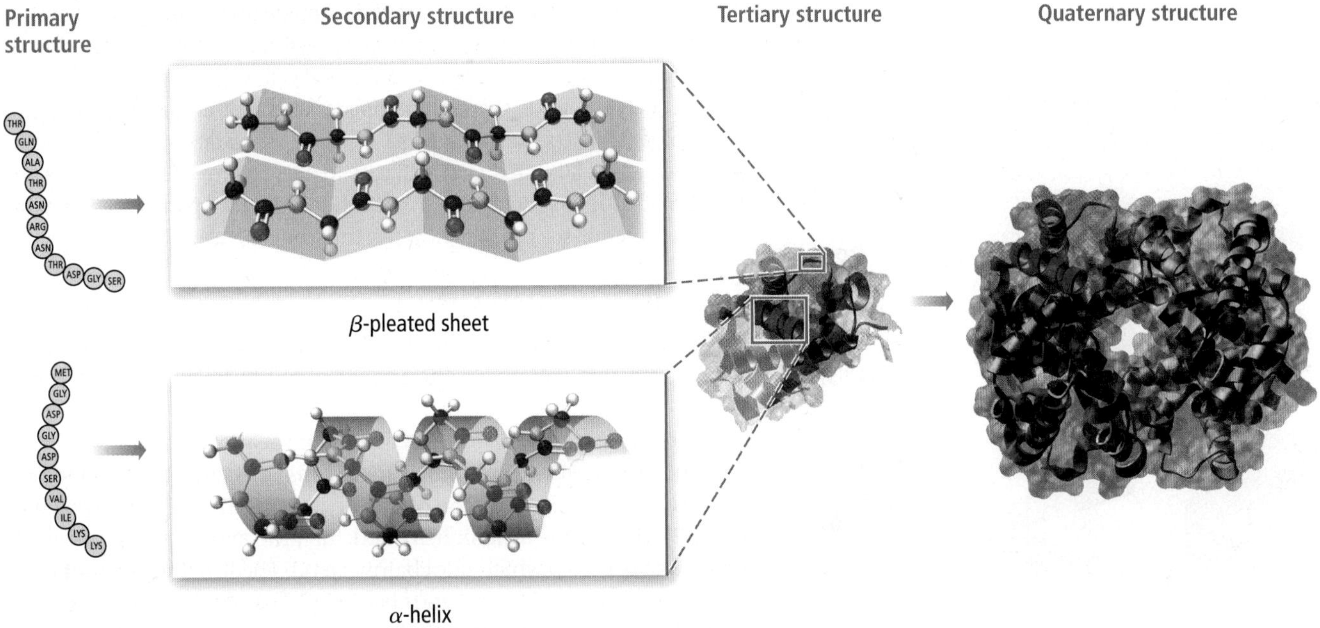

▲ **FIGURE 23.9 Levels of Protein Structure** Protein structure is analyzed at four levels: primary, secondary, tertiary, and quaternary.

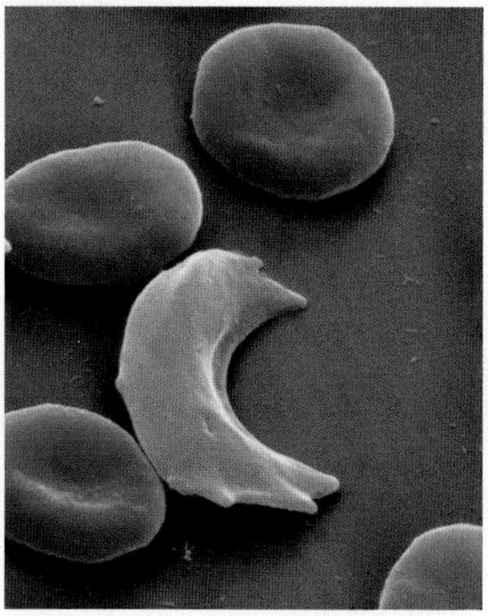

▲ The genetic disease known as sickle-cell anemia results in red blood cells with a sickle shape. These cells impede circulation of blood, causing damage to major organs.

Primary Structure

The **primary structure** of a protein is the sequence of amino acids in its chain(s). Primary structure, which determines the other three kinds of structure, is maintained by the covalent peptide bonds between individual amino acids. The primary structure of egg-white lysozyme—a protein that helps fight infection—is shown in Figure 23.10▼. The figure illustrates the amino acid sequence, the N-terminal and C-terminal ends, and the presence of *disulfide linkages*, covalent cross-links between cysteine amino acids in the polymer. We discuss disulfide linkages in more detail later in the section on tertiary structure. Researchers determined the first amino acid sequences for proteins in the 1950s. Today, the amino acid sequences for thousands of proteins are known.

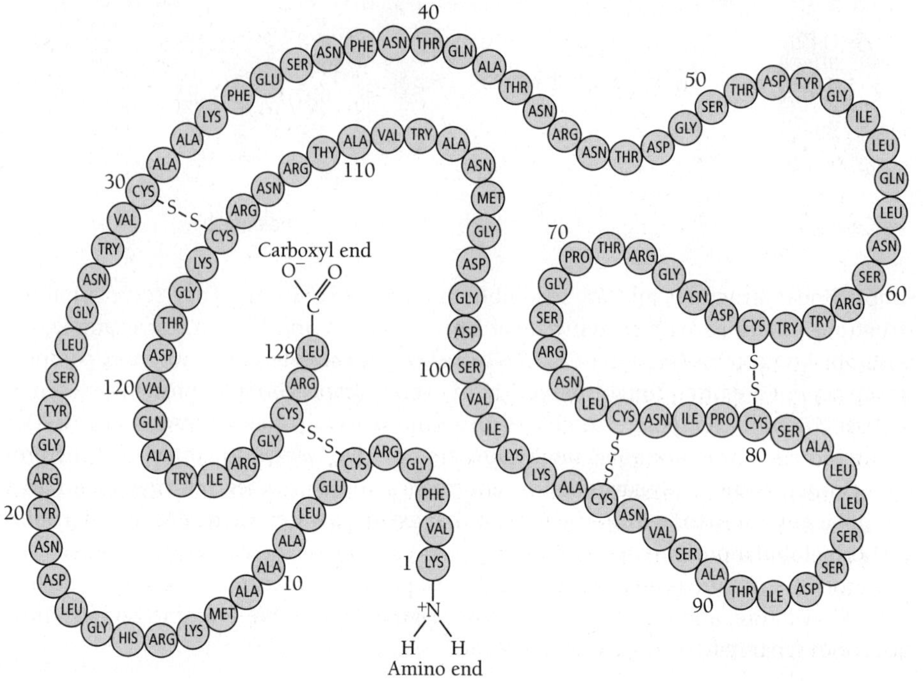

▶ **FIGURE 23.10 Primary Structure of Egg-White Lysozyme** Primary structure refers to the sequence of amino acids in a protein.

Changes in the amino acid sequence of a protein, even minor ones, can destroy the function of a protein. Hemoglobin, as we saw in Chapter 16, is a protein that transports oxygen in the blood. It is composed of four polypeptide chains made up of a total of 574 amino acid units. If valine is replaced by glutamic acid in just one position on two of these chains, the disease known as sickle-cell anemia results. The red blood cells of people with sickle-cell anemia take on a sickle shape that impedes circulation, causing damage to major organs. In the past, sickle-cell anemia was fatal, often resulting in death before age 30—all due to a change in a few atoms of two amino acids out of 574. Modern therapies have extended the life span of people with sickle-cell anemia so that they now live into their 40s and 50s.

α-Helix protein structure

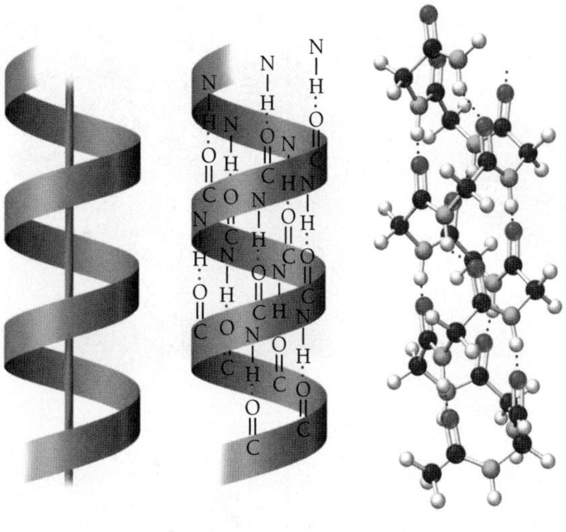

▲ **FIGURE 23.11 The α-Helix Structure** The α-helix is an example of secondary protein structure.

Secondary Structure

The **secondary structure** of a protein refers to certain regular periodic or repeating patterns in the arrangement of protein chains. Secondary structure is maintained by interactions between amino acids that are fairly close together in the linear sequence of the protein chain or that are adjacent to each other on neighboring chains or chains that fold back on themselves. The most common of these patterns is the ***α*-helix**, shown in Figure 23.11◀. In the α-helix-helix structure, the amino acid chain wraps into a tight coil from which side chains extend. The structure is maintained by hydrogen-bonding interactions between NH and CO groups along the peptide backbone of the protein. Some proteins—such as keratin, which composes human hair—have the α-helix pattern throughout their entire chain. Other proteins have very little or no α-helix pattern in their chain.

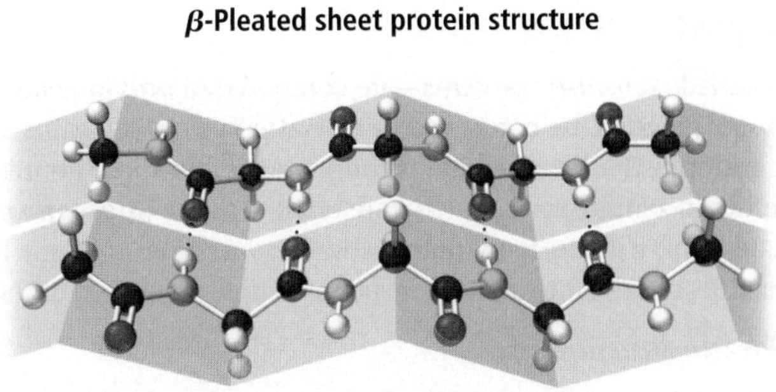

◀ **FIGURE 23.12 The β-Pleated Sheet Structure** The β-pleated sheet is a secondary protein structure.

A second common pattern in the secondary structure of proteins is the **β-pleated sheet** (Figure 23.12▲). In this structure, the chain is extended (as opposed to coiled) and forms a zigzag pattern. The peptide backbones of neighboring chains interact with one another through hydrogen bonding to form zigzag-shaped sheets. Some proteins—such as silk—have the β-pleated sheet structure throughout their entire chains. Since the protein chains in the β-pleated sheet are fully extended, silk is inelastic. Many proteins have some sections that are β-pleated sheet, other sections that are α-helical, and still other sections that have less regular patterns referred to as **random coils**.

Tertiary Structure

The **tertiary structure** of a protein consists of the large-scale bends and folds resulting from interactions between the R groups of amino acids that are separated by large distances in the linear sequence of the protein chain. These interactions, shown in Figure 23.13▼, include hydrogen bonding, disulfide linkages (covalent bonds between cysteine amino acids), hydrophobic interactions (attractions between large, nonpolar side chains), and salt bridges (acid–base interactions between acidic and basic side chains). Fibrous proteins generally lack tertiary structure; they simply extend in a long continuous chain with some secondary structure. Globular proteins, by contrast, fold in on themselves, forming complex globular shapes rich in tertiary structure.

Interactions That Maintain Tertiary Structure

The tertiary structure of a protein is maintained by interactions between the R groups of amino acids that are separated by large distances in the linear sequence of the protein chain.

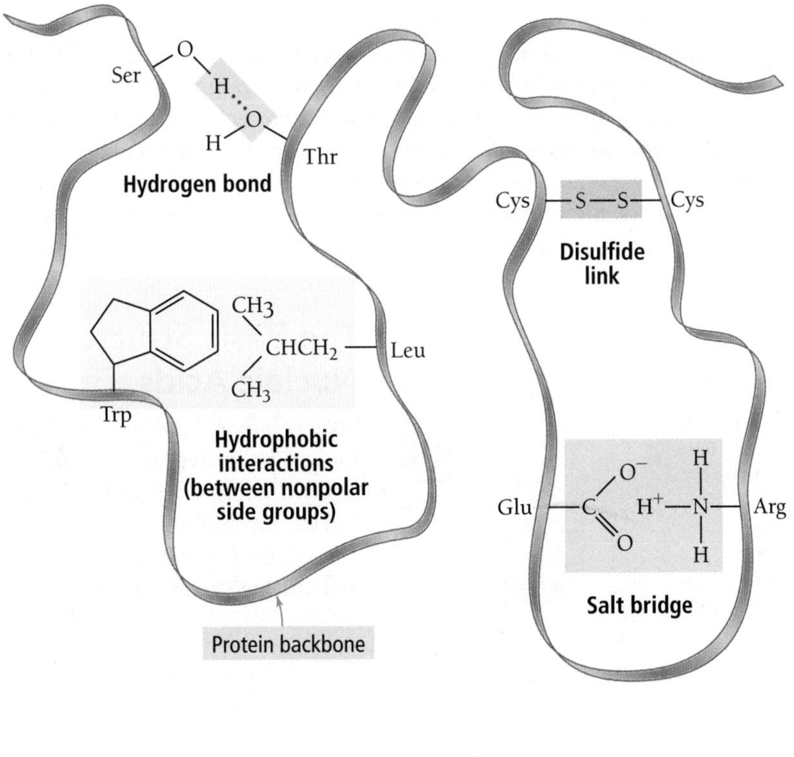

◀ **FIGURE 23.13 Interactions within Proteins**

Quaternary Structure

Some proteins—called *monomeric* proteins—are composed of only one polypeptide chain. However, *multimeric* proteins are composed of several polypeptide chains, called subunits. We just saw, for example, that hemoglobin is composed of four such subunits. The way that subunits fit together in a multimeric protein is referred to as the **quaternary structure** of the protein. Quaternary structure is maintained by the same types of interactions that maintain tertiary structure, but the interactions are between amino acids on different subunits.

Summarizing Protein Structure:

- Primary structure is the amino acid sequence. It is maintained by the peptide bonds that hold amino acids together.
- Secondary structure refers to the repeating patterns in the arrangement of protein chains. These are maintained by interactions between the peptide backbones of amino acids that are close together in the chain sequence or adjacent to each other on neighboring chains. Secondary structure is characteristic of fibrous proteins, but globular proteins also frequently feature regions of α-helix, β-pleated sheet, and random coil secondary structure.
- Tertiary structure refers to the large-scale twists and folds of globular proteins. These are maintained by interactions between the R groups of amino acids that are separated by long distances in the chain sequence.
- Quaternary structure refers to the arrangement of subunits in proteins that have more than one polypeptide chain. Quaternary structure is maintained by interactions between amino acids on different subunits.

ANSWER **NOW!**

23.4 Cc Conceptual Connection

PROTEIN STRUCTURE What level of protein structure is maintained by peptide bonds?

(a) Primary **(b)** Secondary **(c)** Tertiary **(d)** Quaternary

23.6 Nucleic Acids: Blueprints for Proteins

We have seen that the amino acid sequence in a protein determines that protein's structure and function. If the amino acid sequence is incorrect, the protein is unlikely to function properly. How do cells in living organisms synthesize the many thousands of different required proteins, each with the correct amino acid sequence? The answer lies in **nucleic acids**, molecules that serve as blueprints for protein synthesis. Nucleic acids employ a chemical code to specify the correct amino acid sequences for proteins. Nucleic acids are broadly divided into two types: deoxyribonucleic acid, or DNA, which exists primarily in the nucleus of the cell; and ribonucleic acid, or RNA, which exists throughout the cell.

DNA: Basic Structure

DNA is composed of repeating units called nucleotides. Each nucleotide consists of a phosphate group, a sugar, and a base.

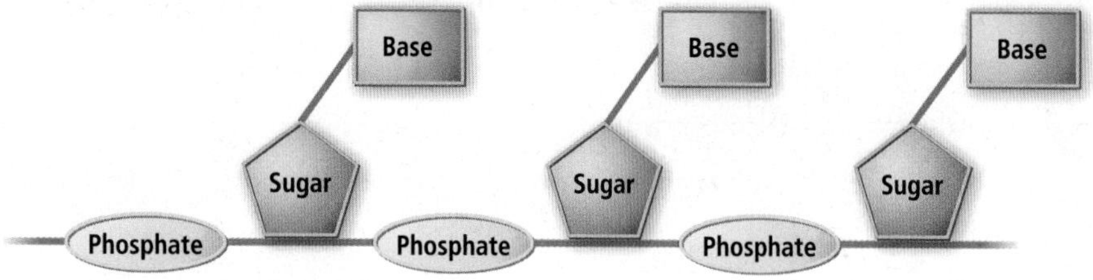

▲ **FIGURE 23.14 DNA Structure**

The Basic Structure of Nucleic Acids

Like proteins, nucleic acids are polymers. The individual units composing nucleic acids are **nucleotides**. Each nucleotide has three parts: a sugar, a base, and a phosphate group that serves as a link between sugars (Figure 23.14◀).

Sugars

In DNA, the sugar is deoxyribose, whereas in RNA the sugar is ribose:

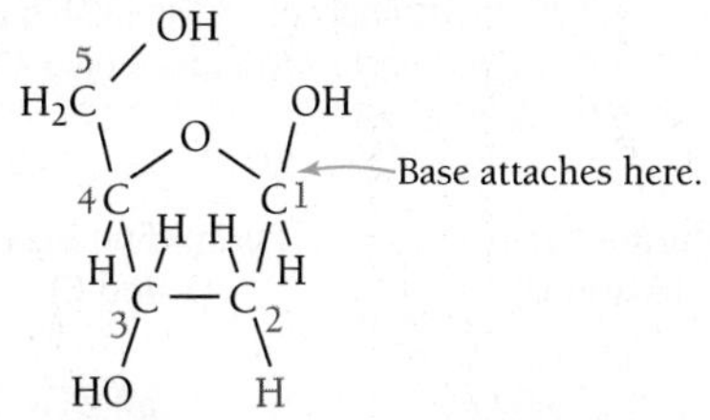

Deoxyribose

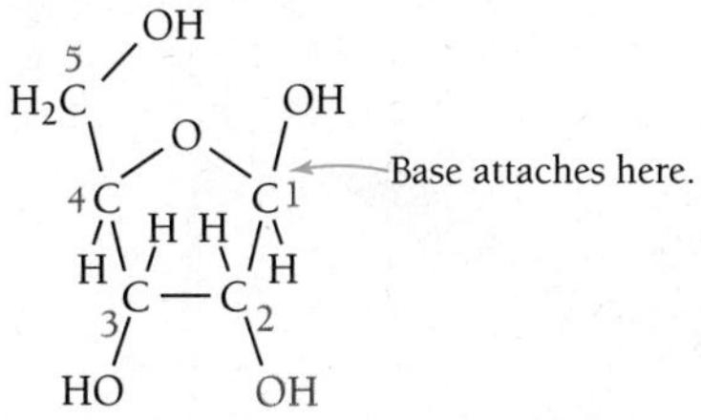

Ribose

The base attaches to the sugar at C1, and the phosphate attaches to the sugar at C3 and C5. When a base is attached to the sugar, the numbers of the carbon atoms in the sugar ring are primed to distinguish them from the carbon atoms on the bases (which are not primed). For example, C5 becomes C5′ and C3 becomes C3′.

Bases

Every nucleotide in DNA has the same sugar, but each nucleotide has just one of four different bases. In DNA, the four bases are adenine (A), cytosine (C), guanine (G), and thymine (T). Each of these bases bonds to the sugar via the nitrogen atom circled in the illustrations shown here:

Purine Bases

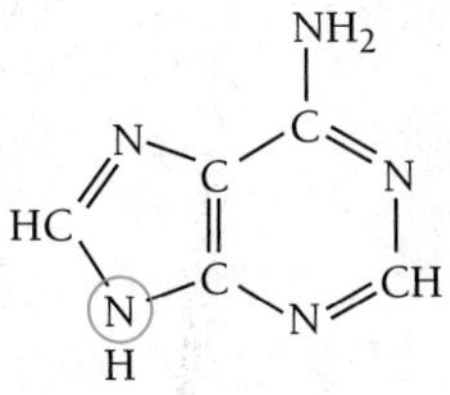

Adenine

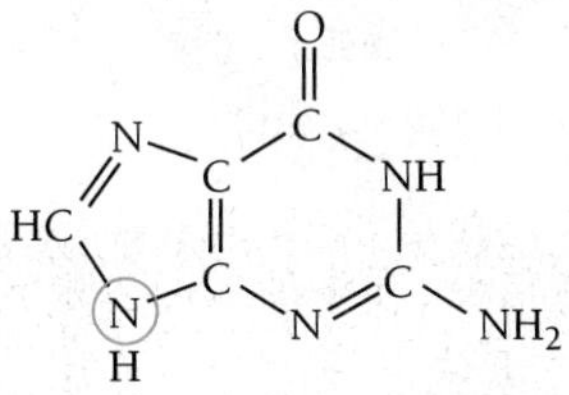

Guanine

Pyrimidine Bases

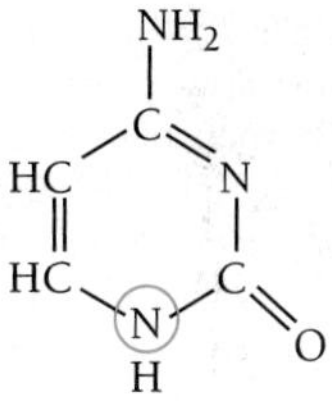

Cytosine

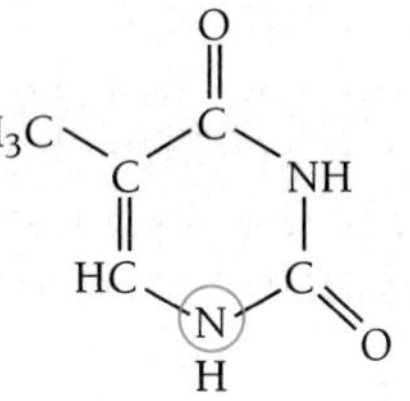

Thymine

Adenine and guanine are called *purine* bases because they resemble the bicyclic compound purine. Cytosine and thymine are called *pyrimidine* bases because they resemble the monocyclic compound pyrimidine:

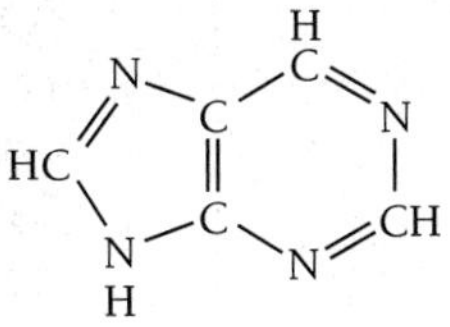

Purine

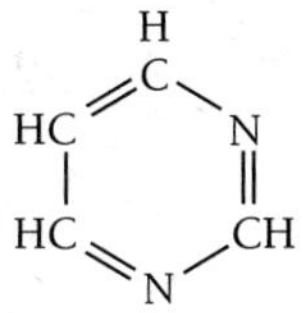

Pyrimidine

In RNA, the base uracil (U), also a pyridimine base, replaces thymine. Uracil and thymine differ only in a methyl ($-CH_3$) group:

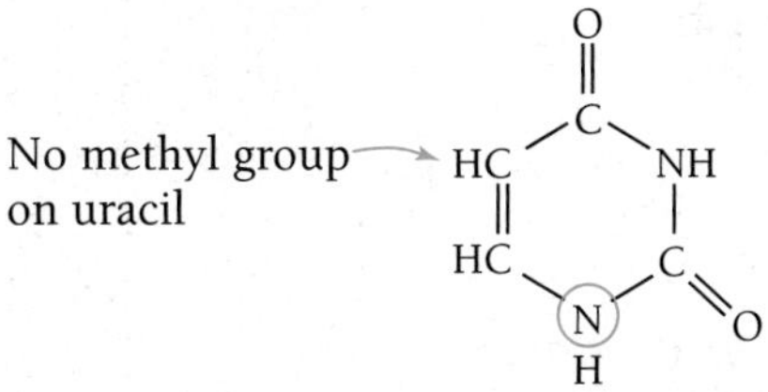

Uracil

Base Pairing in DNA

The bases in nucleic acids are complementary.

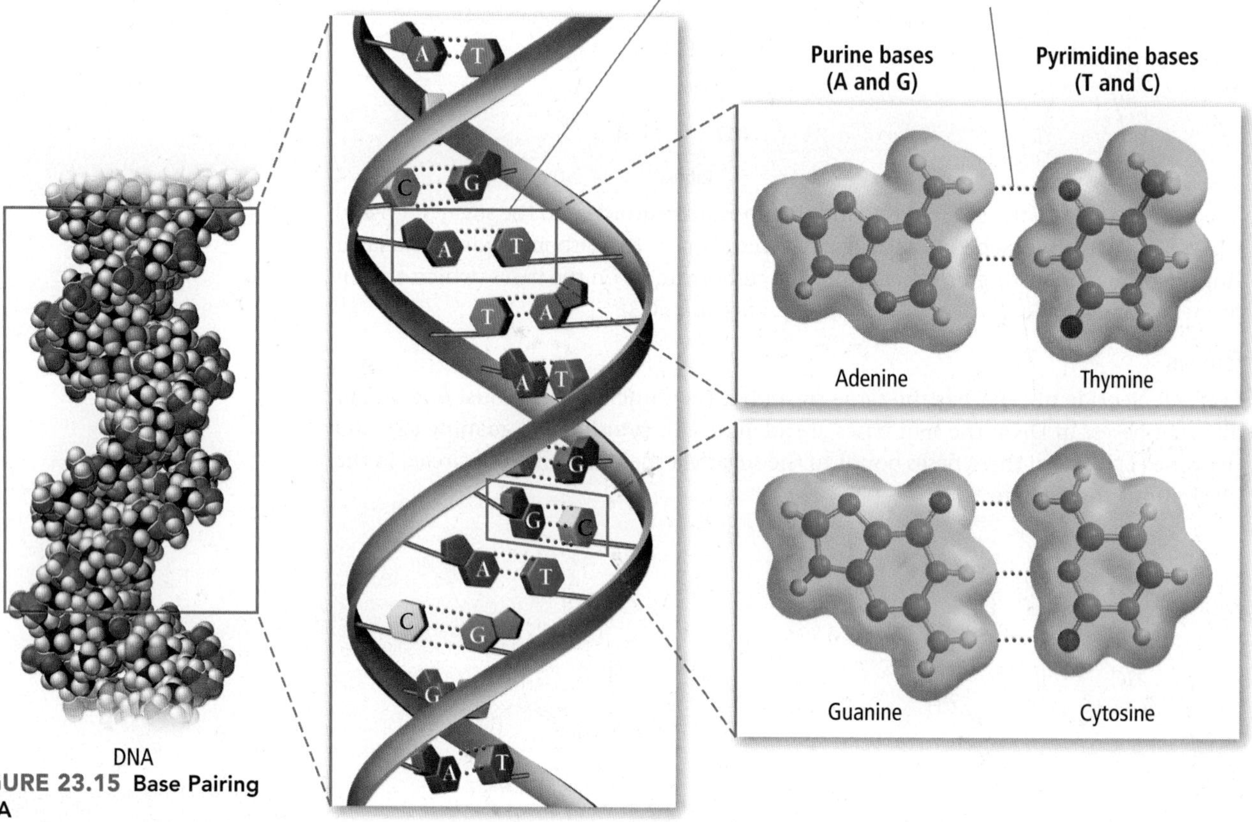

▲ **FIGURE 23.15 Base Pairing in DNA**

The bases in nucleic acids are **complementary**—that is, each one precisely pairs with another base. Each pyrimidine base pairs with only one purine base via specific hydrogen bonds that occur between the two bases. More specifically, guanine pairs only with cytosine through three hydrogen bonds, and adenine pairs only with thymine through two hydrogen bonds as shown in Figure 23.15▲. In other words, guanine is complementary to cytosine and adenine is complementary to thymine. This base pairing is central to DNA replication, as we discuss in Section 23.7.

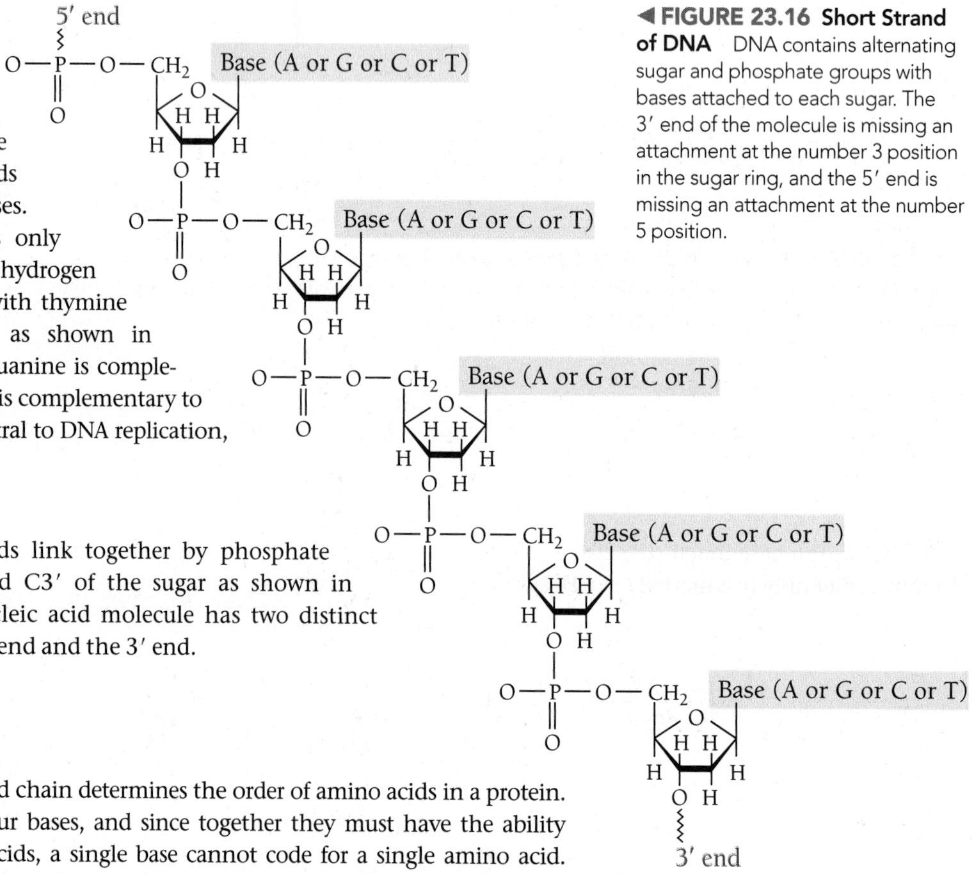

◀ **FIGURE 23.16 Short Strand of DNA** DNA contains alternating sugar and phosphate groups with bases attached to each sugar. The 3′ end of the molecule is missing an attachment at the number 3 position in the sugar ring, and the 5′ end is missing an attachment at the number 5 position.

Phosphate Links

The sugar units in nucleic acids link together by phosphate groups, which bind to C5′ and C3′ of the sugar as shown in Figure 23.16▶. Note that a nucleic acid molecule has two distinct ends, which we refer to as the 5′ end and the 3′ end.

The Genetic Code

The order of bases in a nucleic acid chain determines the order of amino acids in a protein. However, since there are only four bases, and since together they must have the ability to code for 20 different amino acids, a single base cannot code for a single amino acid.

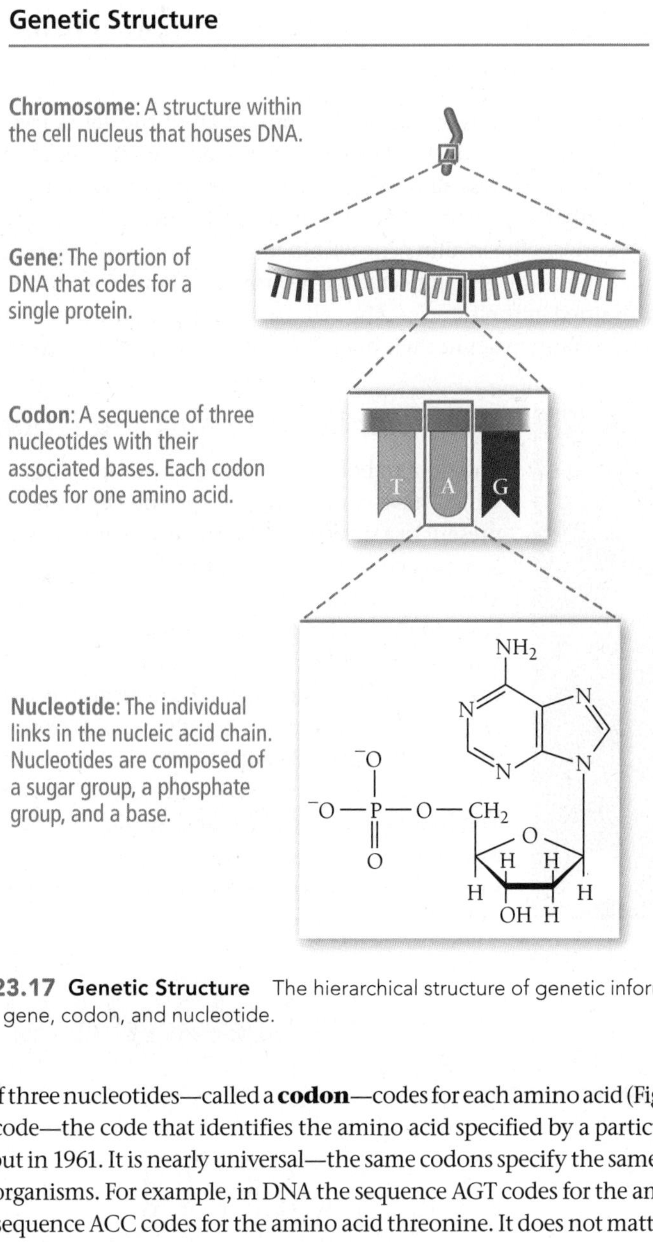

▲ **FIGURE 23.17 Genetic Structure** The hierarchical structure of genetic information is chromosome, gene, codon, and nucleotide.

A sequence of three nucleotides—called a **codon**—codes for each amino acid (Figure 23.17▲). The genetic code—the code that identifies the amino acid specified by a particular codon—was worked out in 1961. It is nearly universal—the same codons specify the same amino acids in nearly all organisms. For example, in DNA the sequence AGT codes for the amino acid serine, and the sequence ACC codes for the amino acid threonine. It does not matter if the DNA is in a rat, a bacterium, or a human—the code is the same.

A **gene** is a sequence of codons within a DNA molecule that codes for a single protein. Since proteins vary in size from a few dozen to thousands of amino acids, genes vary in length from dozens to thousands of codons. For example, egg-white lysozyme (see Figure 23.10) is composed of 129 amino acids. So the lysozyme gene contains 129 codons—one for each amino acid in the lysozyme protein. Each codon is like a three-letter word that specifies one amino acid. String the correct number of codons together in the correct sequence, and you have a gene, the instructions for the amino acid sequence in a protein. Genes are contained in structures called **chromosomes** (Figure 23.18►). A human cell generally contains 46 chromosomes in its nucleus.

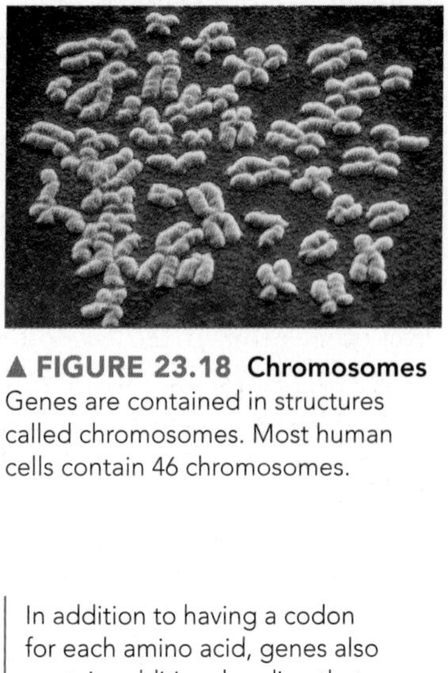

▲ **FIGURE 23.18 Chromosomes** Genes are contained in structures called chromosomes. Most human cells contain 46 chromosomes.

In addition to having a codon for each amino acid, genes also contain additional coding that signals, for example, where the gene begins and where it ends.

THE GENETIC CODE Assuming you have four different bases, how many amino acids can you code for with two-base sequences?

(a) 2 **(b)** 4 **(c)** 16 **(d)** 64

23.5 Cc Conceptual Connection

ANSWER **NOW!**

23.7 DNA Replication, the Double Helix, and Protein Synthesis

Most of the cells in our bodies contain all of the genes required to make all of the proteins that we need—the DNA within any one cell is *complete*. However, any particular cell does not express all those genes; it does not synthesize all those proteins. Cells synthesize only the proteins that are important to their function. For example, a pancreatic cell expresses the insulin gene within its nucleus to synthesize insulin. Pancreatic cells do not express the gene for keratin (the protein in hair), even though the keratin gene is also contained in their nuclei. The cells in our scalp, in contrast, which also have both insulin and keratin genes in their nuclei, synthesize keratin but not insulin.

▲ **FIGURE 23.19 Watson and Crick** James Watson and Francis Crick discovered the structure of DNA, including the double helix and the pairing of complementary bases.

DNA Replication and the Double Helix

The human body contains on the order of 10^{13} cells, most of which have complete copies of the DNA that originally was present in a single cell (the fertilized egg). When a cell divides, it makes complete copies of its DNA for each daughter cell. The ability of DNA to copy itself is related to its structure, discovered in 1953 by James D. Watson and Francis H. C. Crick. Watson and Crick, aided by evidence from X-ray diffraction photos (see Section 13.2), determined that DNA exists as two complementary strands wound around each other in a double helix (Figure 23.19◀). The strands are antiparallel, so one runs $3' \longrightarrow 5'$ while the other runs $5' \longrightarrow 3'$. The bases on each DNA strand are directed toward the interior of the helix, where they hydrogen-bond to their complementary bases on the other strand. For example, if a section of DNA contains the bases:

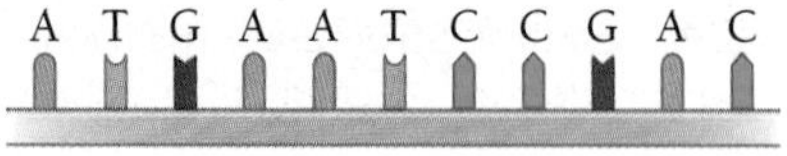

the complementary strand has the sequence:

As we saw earlier, A pairs only with T, and C pairs only with G. The two complementary strands are tightly wrapped into a helical coil, the famous DNA double helix structure (Figure 23.20▼).

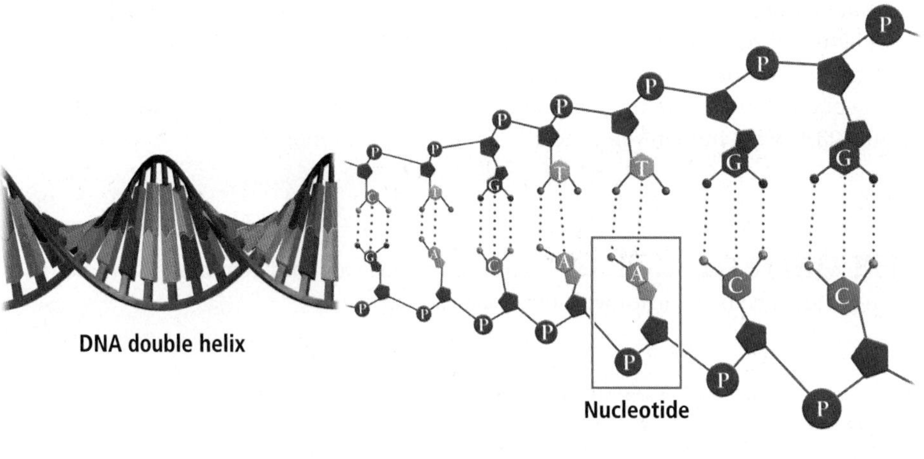

► **FIGURE 23.20 DNA Double Helix** Two complementary strands of DNA wrap around one another to form a double helix.

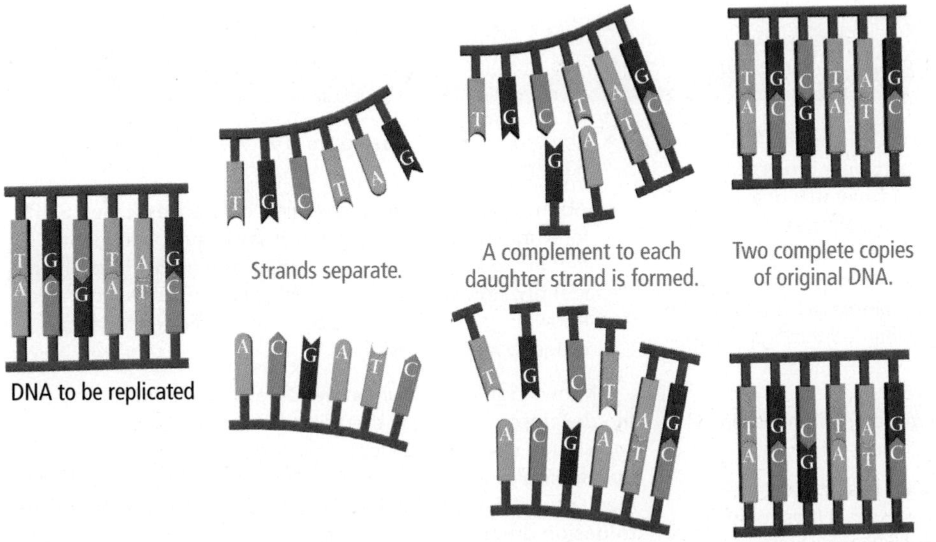

◀ **FIGURE 23.21 DNA Replication** When a cell is about to divide, its DNA unwinds. With the help of the enzyme DNA polymerase, a complement to each daughter strand is formed, resulting in two complete copies of the original DNA.

When a cell is about to divide, the DNA unwinds and the hydrogen bonds joining the complementary bases break (Figure 23.21▲), forming two daughter strands. With the help of the enzyme DNA polymerase, a complement to each daughter strand—with the correct complementary bases in the correct sequence—forms. The hydrogen bonds between the old strands and the newly complementary strands then re-form, resulting in two complete copies of the original DNA, one for each daughter cell.

Protein Synthesis

Living organisms must continually synthesize thousands of proteins to survive, each when it is needed and in the quantities required. When a cell needs to make a particular protein, the gene—the section of the DNA that codes for that particular protein—unravels. Complementary copies of that gene are then synthesized (or transcribed) as single strands of *messenger RNA* (or mRNA). The mRNA moves out of the cell's nucleus to structures in the cytoplasm called *ribosomes*.

At the ribosome, protein synthesis occurs. The ribosome (which has a large subunit and a small subunit) moves along the mRNA chain that codes for the protein, "reading" the sequence of codons. At each codon, the specified amino acid is brought into place, and a peptide bond forms with the previous amino acid (Figure 23.22▼). As the ribosome moves along the mRNA, the protein forms. All of this is orchestrated by enzymes that catalyze the necessary reactions.

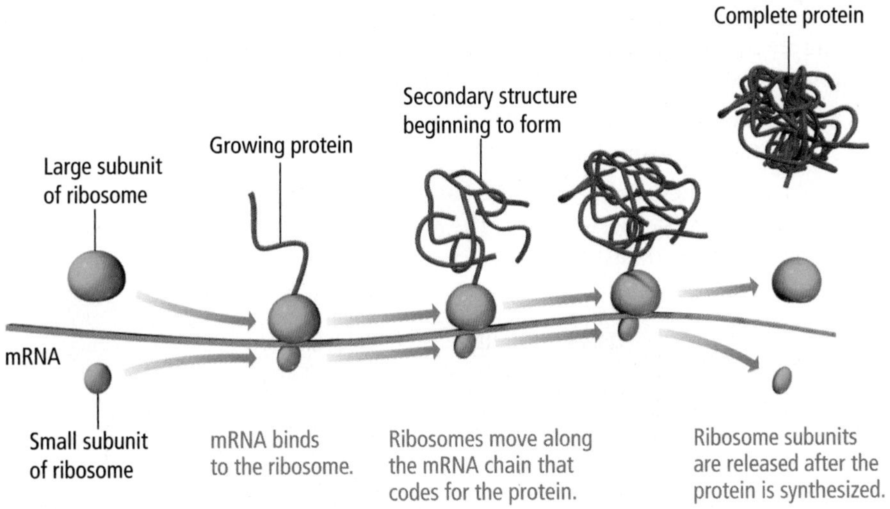

▲ **FIGURE 23.22 Protein Synthesis** A ribosome moves along a strand of mRNA, joining amino acids to form a protein.

CHEMISTRY AND MEDICINE | The Human Genome Project

In 1990, the U.S. Department of Energy (DOE) and the National Institutes of Health (NIH) embarked on a 15-year project to map the human genome, all of the genetic material of a human being. Over 2500 researchers from 18 countries contributed to this research, which has been referred to as the Mount Everest of biology. An initial draft of the map was completed in 2001, and the final draft was completed in 2003. Here, we highlight some of what has been learned through this massive undertaking.

- The human genome contains 3165 million nucleotide base pairs.
- The average gene contains about 3000 base pairs. The largest gene is for the protein dystrophin (dystrophin deficiency is the root cause of muscular dystrophy); it contains 2.4 million base pairs.
- The human genome contains about 30,000 genes. The function of over half of these is still unknown. Before the Human Genome Project, researchers had estimated that humans had about 100,000 genes. The number of genes in humans is not much larger than the number found in many simpler organisms. For example, the number of genes in a roundworm is nearly 20,000. Whatever makes humans unique, it is not the number of genes in our genome.
- Less than 2% of human DNA actually consists of genes. These genes are aggregated in seemingly random areas within the genome, with vast expanses of noncoding DNA between the coding regions. This stands in contrast to other organisms, which tend to have more uniform distribution of genes throughout their genome.
- The order of DNA base pairs is 99.9% identical in all humans.
- About 1.4 million single base-pair differences (called SNPs for single-nucleotide polymorphisms) have been identified in the human genome. Understanding SNPs can help identify individuals who are susceptible to certain diseases. Knowledge of SNPs may also allow physicians to tailor drugs to match individuals.

Knowledge of the human genome is expected to lead to the development of new therapies in several ways. First, knowledge of genes can lead to smart drug design. Instead of developing drugs by trial and error (the current procedure for many drugs), knowledge of a specific gene will allow scientists to design drugs to carry out a specific function related to that gene or its protein product. Second, human genes themselves can provide the blueprint for the production of certain types of drugs, either in the laboratory or by other organisms. For example, in Section 23.1 we discussed how insulin is made by inserting the insulin gene into bacteria, which then synthesize the needed drug. Intriguingly, it may even be possible to replace abnormal or missing genes in the cells of diseased patients. Such gene therapies are still in the early stages of development, but they may eventually give us a powerful new tool for combating inherited diseases.

Although the completion of the Human Genome Project may seem like the end, it is really just the beginning. Thousands of studies in the coming years will rely on the data obtained through this endeavor.

Summarizing DNA Coding:

- DNA contains the code for the sequence of amino acids in proteins.
- A codon—three nucleotides with their bases—codes for one amino acid.
- A gene—a sequence of codons—codes for one protein.
- Genes are contained in structures called chromosomes that occur within cells. Humans have 46 chromosomes in the nuclei of their cells.
- When a human cell divides, each daughter cell receives a complete copy of the DNA—all 46 chromosomes.
- When a cell synthesizes a protein, the base sequence of the gene that codes for that protein is transferred to mRNA. The mRNA then moves to a ribosome, where the amino acids are linked in the correct sequence to synthesize the protein. The general sequence of information flow is:

$$\text{DNA} \longrightarrow \text{RNA} \longrightarrow \text{PROTEIN}$$

Self-Assessment Quiz

Q1. Which compound is a lipid?
MISSED THIS? MISSED THIS? *Read Section 23.2*

a) 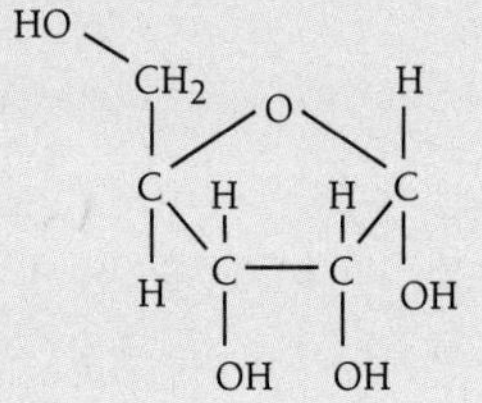

b) 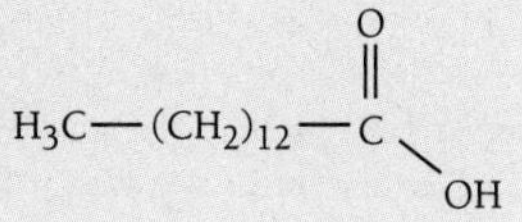

c) 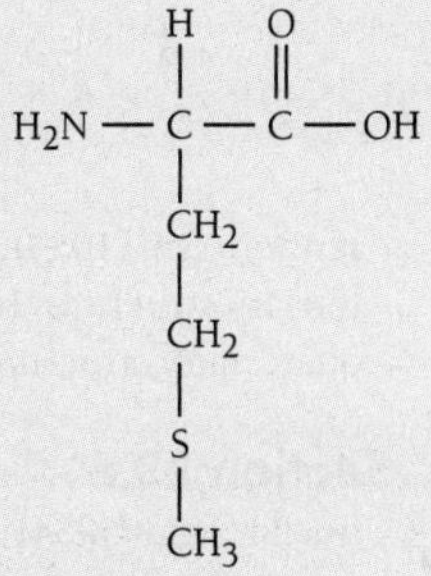

d) $H_3C-CH_2-O-CH_2-CH_3$

Q2. Which compound is a carbohydrate?
MISSED THIS? *Read Section 23.3*

a) 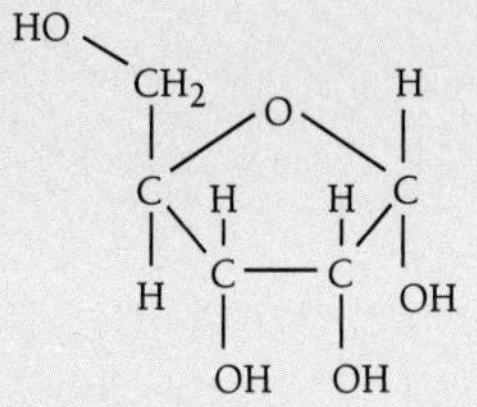

b) 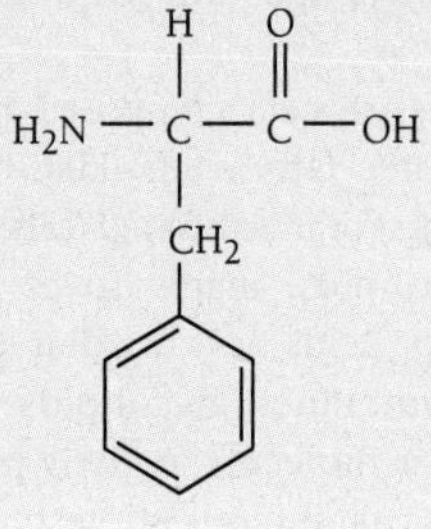

c) $H_3C-CH_2-CH_2-CH_2-CH_2-CH_2-CH_2-CH_2$

d) 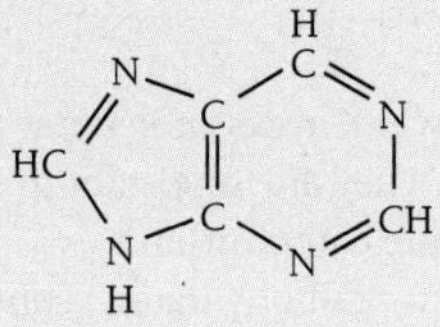

Q3. Which compound is an amino acid?
MISSED THIS? *Read Section 23.4*

a) 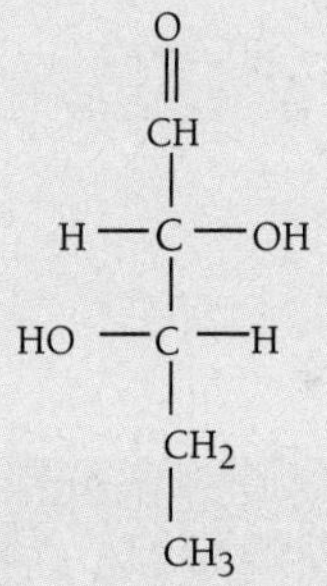

b) $H_2N-CH_2-CH_2-CH_2-CH_2-CH_2-NH_2$

c) 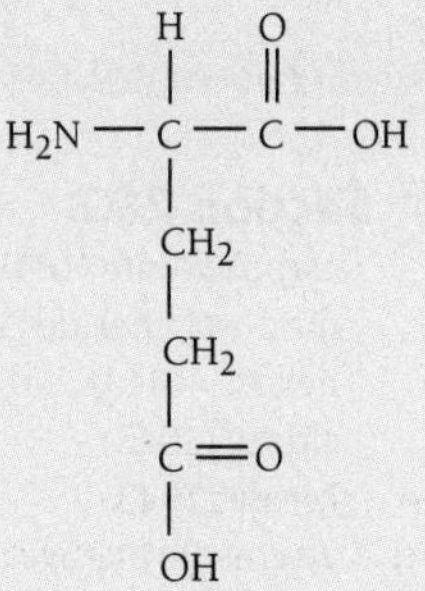

d) 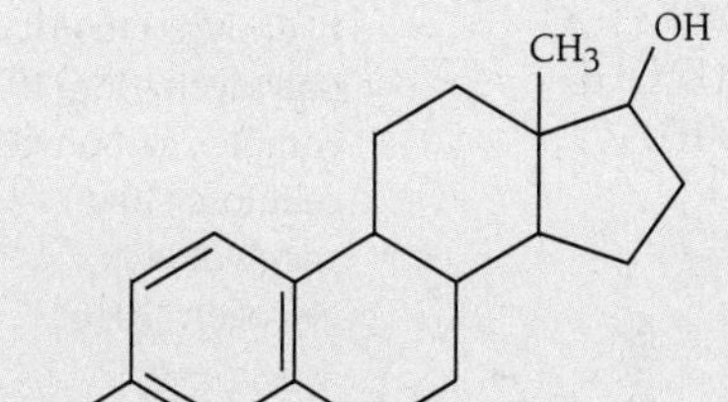

Q4. The sequence of amino acids in a protein chain is an example of which kind of protein structure?
MISSED THIS? *Read Section 23.5*

a) primary
b) secondary
c) tertiary
d) quaternary

Q5. A section of DNA contains the bases ATTCGGAA. What is the correct sequence of bases in the complementary strand?
MISSED THIS? *Read Section 23.6*

a) CGGATTCC
b) ATTCGGAA
c) AAGGCTTA
d) TAAGCCTT

Q6. A codon is a sequence within DNA that codes for what?
MISSED THIS? *Read Section 23.6*

a) an amino acid
b) a protein
c) a carbohydrate
d) a fat

Q7. Which of the functions listed is *not* attributed to proteins?
MISSED THIS? *Read Section 23.4*

a) catalyze biochemical reactions
b) transport substances from one place to another
c) mediate muscle contraction
d) none of the above (all of these functions are attributed to proteins)

—Continued on the next page

Continued—

Q8. Which is a primary function of nucleic acids?
MISSED THIS? *Read Section 23.6*

a) energy storage
b) coding the amino acid sequence for proteins
c) oxygen transport
d) regulation of metabolic processes

Q9. Peptide bonds occur in which type of biochemical compounds?
MISSED THIS? *Read Section 23.4*

a) lipids
b) carbohydrates
c) proteins
d) nucleic acids

Q10. How many nucleotides are required to code for all of the amino acids in a protein that contains 186 amino acids?
MISSED THIS? *Read Sections 23.6, 23.7*

a) 186
b) 372
c) 558
d) 1

Answers: 1. (b) **2.** (a) **3.** (c) **4.** (a) **5.** (d) **6.** (a) **7.** (d) **8.** (b) **9.** (c) **10.** (c)

CHAPTER 23 IN REVIEW

TERMS

Section 23.1
biochemistry (1038)

Section 23.2
lipid (1038)
fatty acid (1038)
triglyceride (1040)
ester linkage (1040)
saturated fat (1041)
unsaturated fat (1041)
phospholipid (1041)
glycolipid (1041)
lipid bilayer (1042)
steroid (1042)

Section 23.3
carbohydrate (1043)
monosaccharide (1043)
hexose (1043)
aldose (1043)
ketose (1043)
glycosidic linkage (1045)
disaccharide (1045)
hydrolysis (1045)
polysaccharide (1045)
complex carbohydrate (1045)
cellulose (1046)
starch (1046)
glycogen (1046)

Section 23.4
enzyme (1046)
amino acid (1047)
peptide bond (1049)
dipeptide (1049)
polypeptide (1049)

Section 23.5
fibrous protein (1050)
globular protein (1051)
primary structure (1052)
secondary structure (1052)
α-helix (1052)
β-pleated sheet (1053)
random coil (1053)
tertiary structure (1053)
quaternary structure (1054)

Section 23.6
nucleic acid (1054)
nucleotide (1054)
complementary (1056)
codon (1057)
gene (1057)
chromosome (1057)

CONCEPTS

Diabetes and the Synthesis of Human Insulin (23.1)

- Diabetes is a chronic illness that occurs when the pancreas cannot make enough insulin, a protein that promotes the absorption of glucose into cells.
- The chemical structure of insulin was discovered in 1955 by Frederick Sanger, who made it possible for insulin to be synthesized in the laboratory.
- Eventually, scientists inserted the human gene that codes for the production of insulin into bacteria, which were then able to produce enough insulin to supply diabetics.

Lipids (23.2)

- Lipids are biological chemicals that are nonpolar and, therefore, insoluble in water. In our bodies, lipids compose cell membranes, store energy, and provide insulation.
- A type of lipid called a fatty acid is a carboxylic acid with a long hydrocarbon chain. Fatty acids can be saturated, meaning they contain the maximum number of hydrogen atoms, or unsaturated, meaning they contain one or more carbon–carbon double bonds. Saturated fatty acids experience greater intermolecular forces, making them solid at room temperature, while unsaturated fatty acids are liquids.
- Fats and oils are triglycerides, triesters composed of glycerol bonded by ester linkages to three fatty acids. Like fatty acids, triglycerides can be saturated (fats) or unsaturated (oils).
- Other lipids include phospholipids, made up of a glycerol bonded to two nonpolar fatty acids and a polar phosphate group, used in animal cell membranes; glycolipids, similar to phospholipids but with a sugar molecule as their polar head; and steroids, four-ringed lipids that include cholesterol and sex hormones.

Carbohydrates (23.3)

- Carbohydrates are polyhydroxy aldehydes or ketones and generally have the formula $(CH_2O)_n$. They are important to short-term energy storage and plant structure composition.
- Monosaccharides, the simplest carbohydrates, contain three to eight carbons with one aldehyde or ketone functional group. Glucose, an example of a hexose, can exist both in a linear form and a ring form.

- Two monosaccharides combine to form a disaccharide. For example, glucose and fructose combine to form sucrose. The glycosidic linkages that connect the two monosaccharides are broken during digestion by hydrolysis.
- Polysaccharides are polymers of monosaccharides known as complex carbohydrates. They include cellulose, also called fiber, the main structural component of plants; starch, an energy storage compound found in potatoes and grains; and glycogen, a polysaccharide used by animals to store glucose in the muscles.

Proteins and Amino Acids (23.4)

- Proteins are polymers of amino acids and serve a variety of biological functions including structure composition, metabolic regulation, and muscle contraction. Enzymes are particularly important proteins that catalyze biochemical reactions in cells.
- An amino acid contains a carbon atom bonded to an amine group, a carboxylic acid group, a hydrogen atom, and an R group. There are 20 amino acids in humans, and they differ only in their R group.
- Amino acids form peptide bonds between the amine end of one amino acid with the carboxylic end of another, creating dipeptides, tripeptides, and so on, or polypeptides, large examples of which are called proteins.

Protein Structure (23.5)

- Protein structure and shape are critical to protein function.
- Proteins can be broadly divided into two structural categories. Fibrous proteins are generally linear, insoluble structures that serve structural functions. Globular proteins fold into roughly spherical conformations with nonpolar side chains oriented to the interior and polar side chains oriented to the exterior; this structure makes globular proteins soluble in water.
- Protein structure can be analyzed at four levels. The primary structure is the sequence of the amino acid chain. The secondary structure refers to certain regular repeating patterns in the arrangement of protein chains, such as α-helix and β-pleated sheet patterns. The tertiary structure refers to large-scale bends and folds due to interactions between the R groups of amino acids such as hydrogen bonding, disulfide linkages, hydrophobic interactions, and salt bridges. Quaternary structure shows the way that monomeric subunits fit together in multimeric proteins that have more than one polypeptide chain.

Nucleic Acids (23.6)

- Nucleic acids, such as DNA and RNA, are the chemical blueprints used to synthesize proteins. Nucleic acids are polymers of nucleotides, each of which is composed of a sugar, a base, and a phosphate group.
- The bases of DNA are adenine (A), cytosine (C), guanine (G), and thymine (T), which are subject to complementary pairing: each pyrimidine base combines with only one purine base.
- Phosphate links bind the C5′ carbon of one sugar with the C3′ carbon of another sugar to make the polymeric chain.
- The order of the bases in a nucleic acid chain specifies the order of amino acids in a protein.
- Each amino acid is coded by a codon, a sequence of three bases. A gene is a sequence of codons that codes for a specific protein. Genes, in turn, are contained in structures called chromosomes.

DNA Replication, the Double Helix, and Protein Synthesis (23.7)

- Though the DNA code is complete in any cell in the body, every cell does not express every gene. Cells only express the genes relevant to their function.
- DNA is composed of two complementary strands wound around each other in a double helix. The strands are antiparallel; the bases of each strand face the interior and hydrogen-bond to their complements on the other strand.
- In order to replicate, a DNA strand divides and an enzyme called DNA polymerase creates the complement of each of the divided strands, thereby making two copies of the original DNA molecule.
- To synthesize proteins, the section of DNA that codes for that gene unravels. Messenger RNA (mRNA) is synthesized as a copy of the gene. The mRNA joins with ribosomes, structures that "read" the mRNA code and synthesize the correct sequence of amino acids.

LEARNING OUTCOMES

Chapter Objectives	Assessment
Identify the structural properties of lipids (23.2)	Exercises 31–36
Identify the structural properties of carbohydrates (23.3)	Exercises 37–40
Draw structures for carbohydrates (23.3)	Example 23.1 **For Practice** 23.1 **Exercises** 41–48
Describe the basic structure and function of proteins and amino acids (23.4)	Exercises 49–52
Draw structures for amino acids joined by peptide bonds (23.4)	Example 23.2 **For Practice** 23.2 **Exercises** 53–58
Analyze proteins in terms of primary, secondary, tertiary, and quaternary structure (23.5)	Exercises 59–62
Identify the structural properties of nucleic acids (23.6)	Exercises 63–70

EXERCISES

Mastering Chemistry provides end-of-chapter exercises, feedback-enriched tutorial problems, animations, and interactive activities to encourage problem-solving practice and deeper understanding of key concepts and topics.

REVIEW QUESTIONS

1. What is biochemistry? What significant advances in biochemistry have helped diabetics?

2. What is a lipid? What roles do lipids play in living organisms?

3. What is a fatty acid? Draw the general structure of a fatty acid.

4. What effect do double bonds have within the hydrocarbon chain of a fatty acid?

5. What are triglycerides? Draw a general structure of a triglyceride.

6. Explain the difference, in terms of both structure and properties, between a saturated fat and an unsaturated fat.

7. Describe the basic structure of phospholipids and glycolipids. What functions do these lipids have in living organisms?

8. What is a steroid? List some functions of steroids.

9. What are carbohydrates? What role do they play in living organisms?

10. How do monosaccharides and disaccharides differ? Aldoses and ketoses?

11. How do simple and complex carbohydrates differ?

12. How do cellulose, starch, and glycogen differ? Describe the function of each.

13. What roles do proteins play in living organisms? List specific examples.

14. Describe the basic structure of an amino acid. How are amino acids linked together to form proteins?

15. How do the properties of the R groups in amino acids relate to the properties of proteins?

16. Why are amino acids chiral?

17. Draw the structure of a neutral amino acid and its dipolar ion.

18. Draw the structure of any two amino acids, showing how they link together to form a dipeptide.

19. Why is protein structure important?

20. How do fibrous proteins and globular proteins differ?

21. Describe the various levels of protein structure (primary, secondary, tertiary, and quaternary).

22. What types of interactions or bonds maintain each of the structures listed in the previous problem?

23. Describe the secondary structures known as α-helix and β-pleated sheet.

24. What is the function of nucleic acids in living organisms?

25. What is the general structure of a nucleic acid?

26. The bases in nucleic acids are *complementary*. What does this mean?

27. What is a codon? A gene? A chromosome?

28. Do most cells contain complete copies of an organism's DNA? Do most cells express all of the genes contained in their DNA?

29. Explain the mechanism by which DNA is replicated.

30. Explain the mechanism by which proteins are synthesized from the information contained within DNA.

PROBLEMS BY TOPIC

Lipids

31. Determine whether or not each molecule is a lipid. If the molecule is a lipid, indicate the kind of lipid. If it is a fatty acid or a triglyceride, classify it as saturated or unsaturated.
MISSED THIS? *Read Section 23.2*

a. $CH_3-CH_2-CH_2-CH_2-CH_2-CH_2-CH_2-CH_2-CH_2-CH_3$

b. 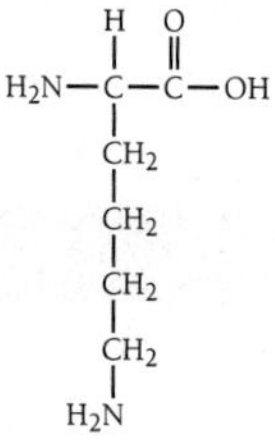

c. 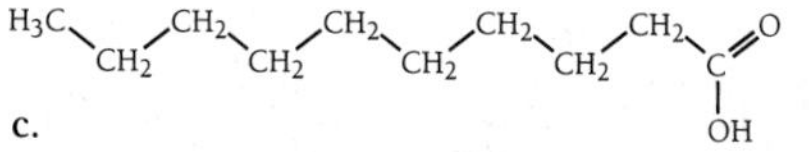

d. 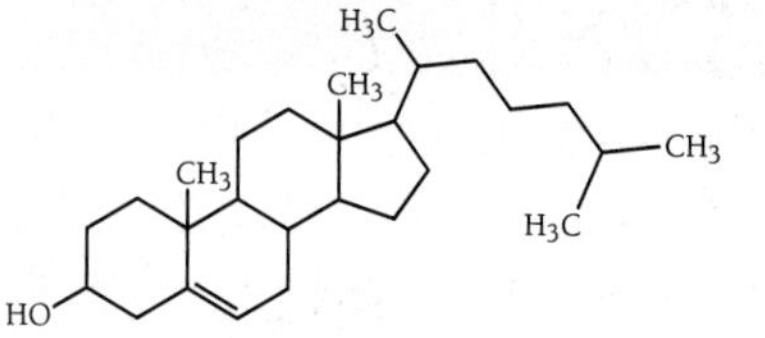

32. Determine whether or not each molecule is a lipid. If the molecule is a lipid, state the kind of lipid. If it is a fatty acid or a triglyceride, classify it as saturated or unsaturated.

a. 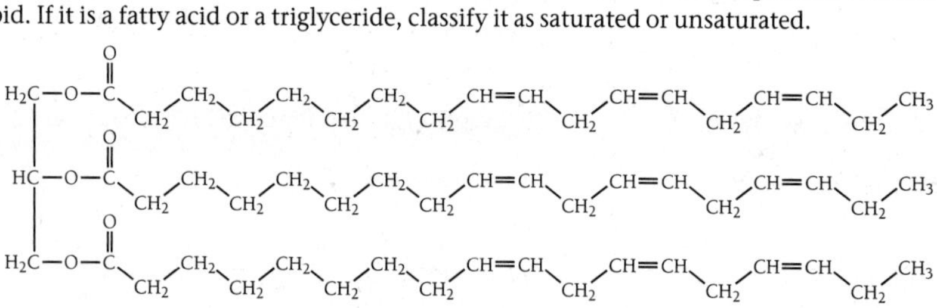

b. $CH_3-CH_2-CH_2-CH_2-CH_2-CH_2-CH_2-CH_2-CH_2-CH_2-CH_2-CH_3$

c. 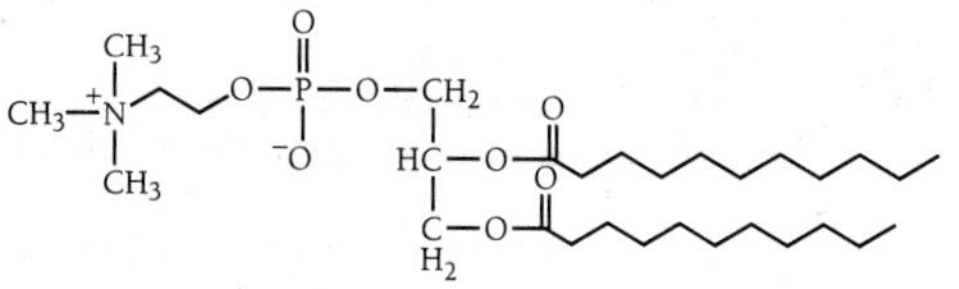

d. 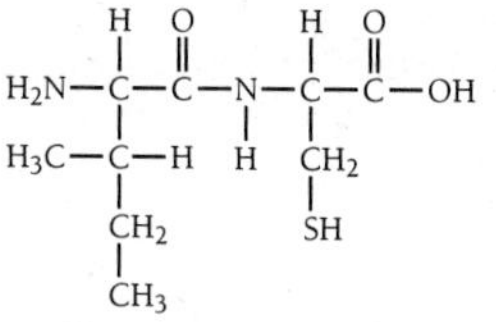

33. Determine whether or not each molecule is a fatty acid. If it is a fatty acid, classify it as saturated, monounsaturated, or polyunsaturated.
MISSED THIS? *Read Section 23.2*

a. 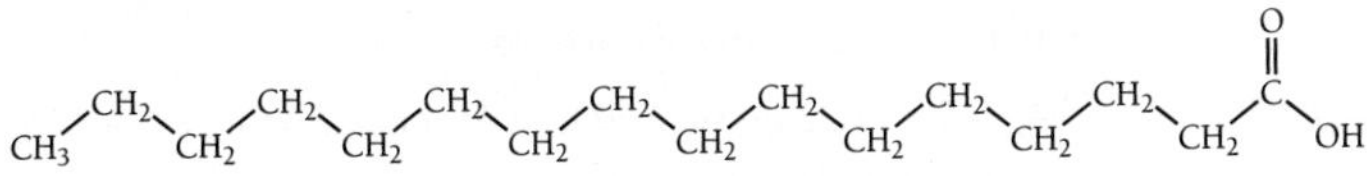

b. 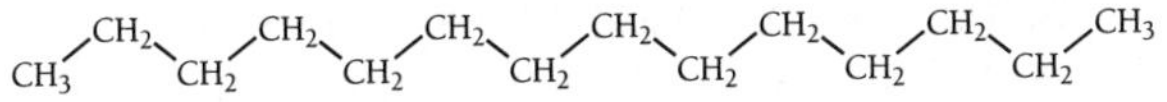

c. 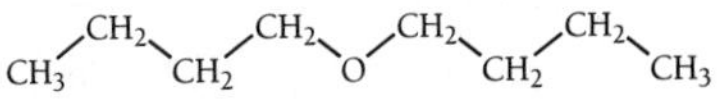

d. 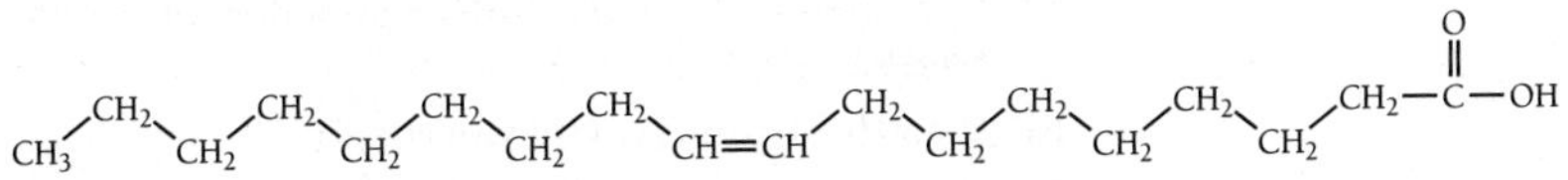

34. Which fatty acid is most likely to be a solid at room temperature?

a. 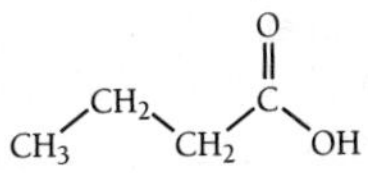

b. 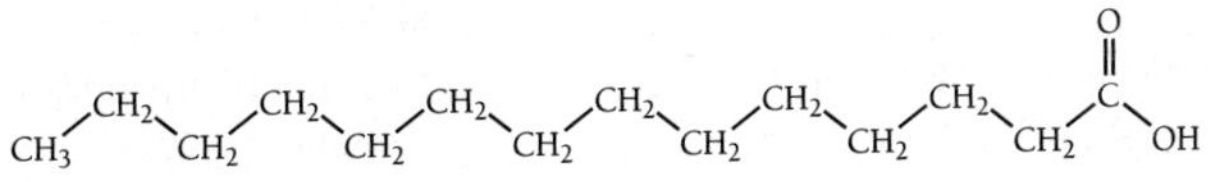

c. 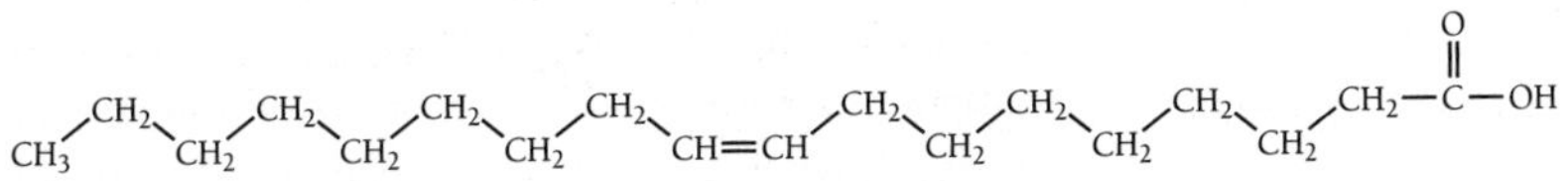

d. 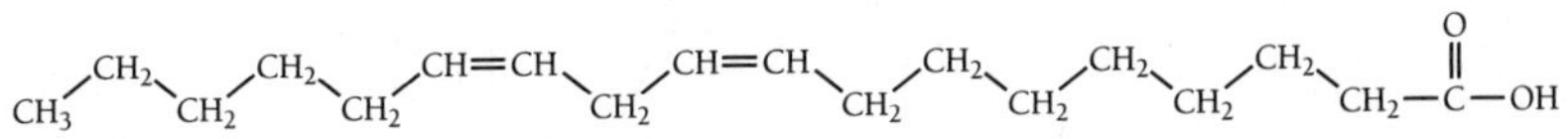

35. Draw structures showing the reaction of glycerol with linoleic acid to form the triglyceride trilinolean. Would you expect this triglyceride to be a fat or an oil? **MISSED THIS?** *Read Section 23.2*

36. Draw structures showing the reaction of glycerol with myristic acid to form the triglyceride trimyristin. Would you expect this triglyceride to be a fat or an oil?

Carbohydrates

37. Determine whether or not each structure is a carbohydrate. If the molecule is a carbohydrate, classify it as a monosaccharide, disaccharide, or trisaccharide. **MISSED THIS?** *Read Section 23.3*

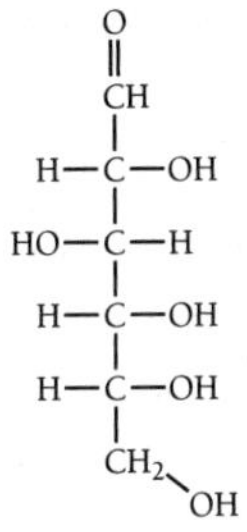
a.

b. 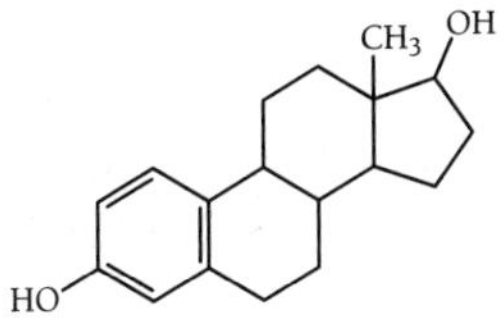

c. 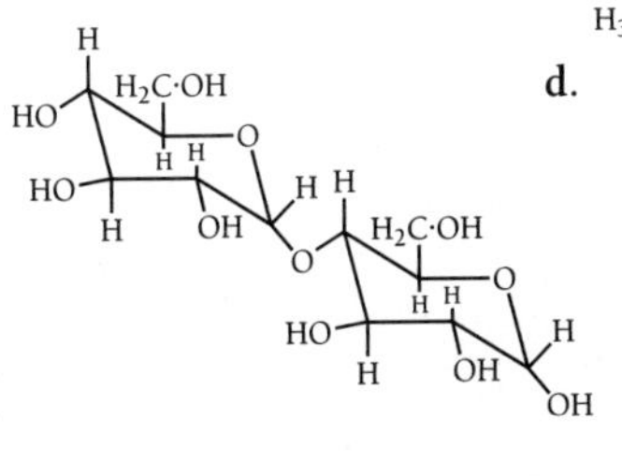

d. 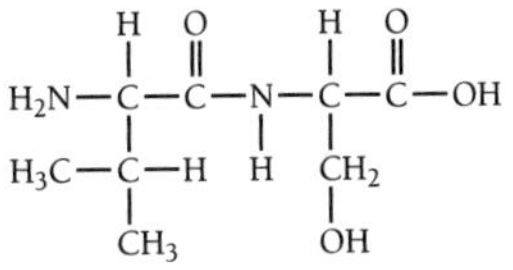

38. Determine whether or not each structure is a carbohydrate. If the molecule is a carbohydrate, classify it as a monosaccharide, disaccharide, or trisaccharide.

a. 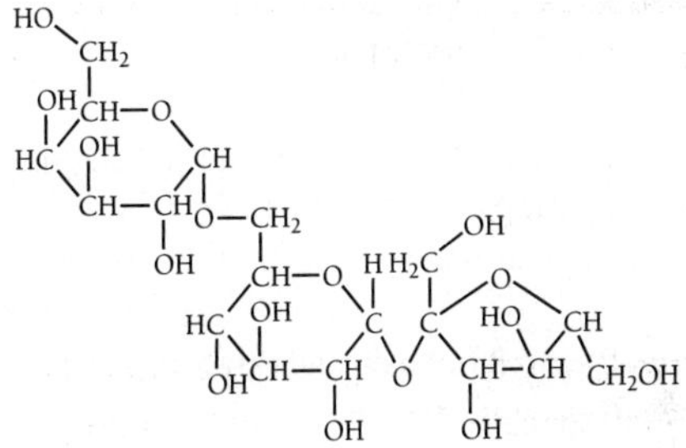

b. 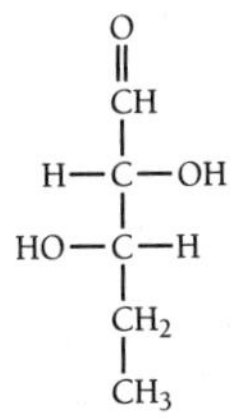

c. 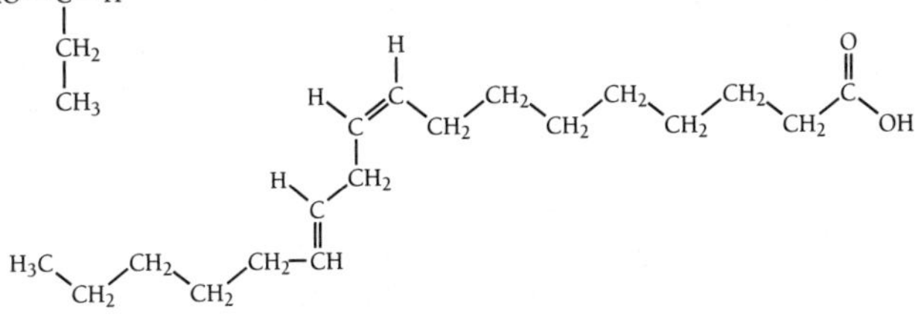

d. 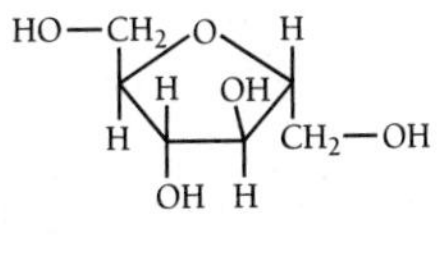

39. Classify each saccharide as an aldose or a ketose. Also classify each as a triose, tetrose, pentose, and so on.
MISSED THIS? *Read Section 23.3*

a. 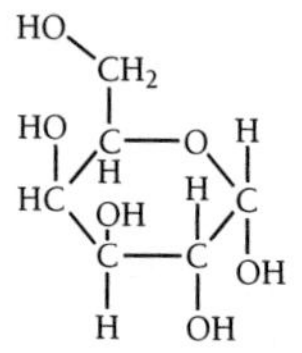

b. 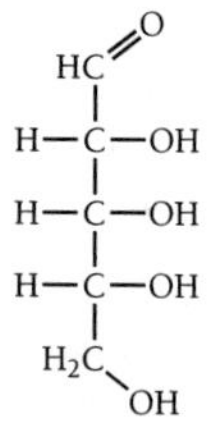

c. 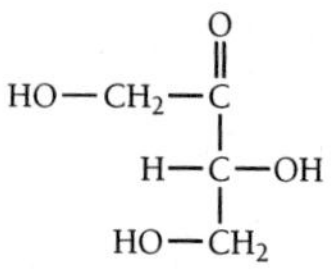

d. 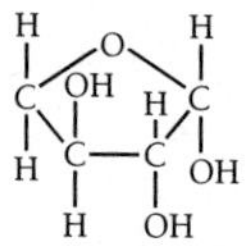

40. Classify each saccharide as an aldose or a ketose. Also classify each as a triose, tetrose, pentose, and so on.

a. 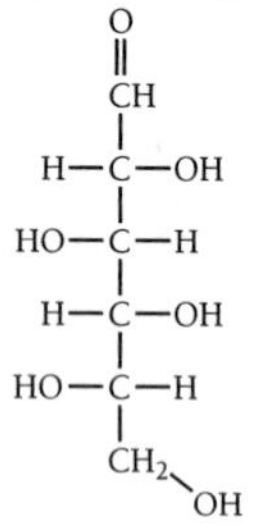

b. 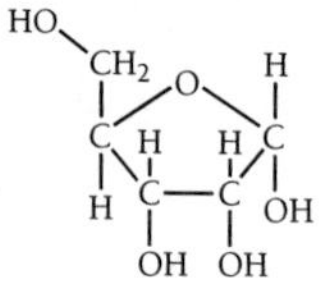

c. 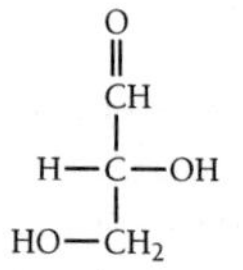

d. 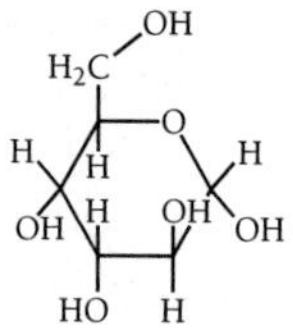

41. How many chiral carbon atoms are in each of the structures in Problem 39? **MISSED THIS?** *Read Section 23.3*

42. How many chiral carbon atoms are in each of the structures in Problem 40?

43. Draw structures for the straight-chain and ring forms of glucose. **MISSED THIS?** *Read Section 23.3*

44. Draw structures for the straight-chain and ring forms of fructose.

45. Draw the products that result from the hydrolysis of the carbohydrate pictured on the right. **MISSED THIS?** *Read Section 23.3*

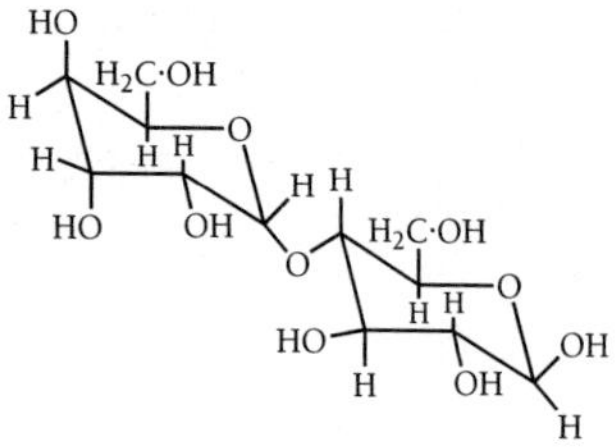

46. Draw the products that result from the hydrolysis of the carbohydrate pictured on the right.

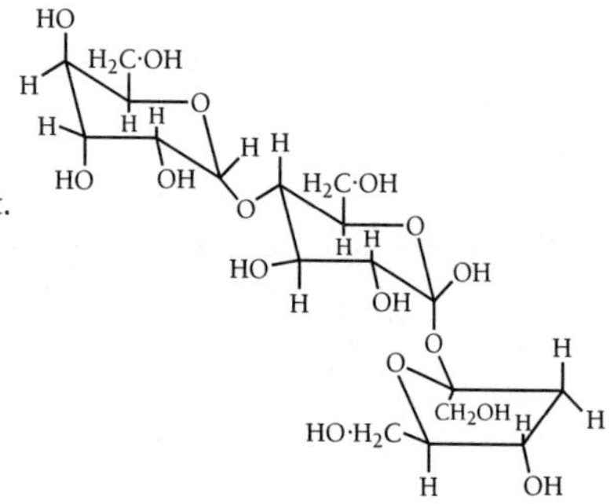

47. Draw the structure of sucrose. Label the glucose and fructose rings in this disaccharide. **MISSED THIS?** *Read Section 23.3*

48. Lactose is a disaccharide of glucose and galactose. Draw the structure of lactose.

Amino Acids and Proteins

49. Draw each amino acid in its dipolar ion form.
MISSED THIS? *Read Section 23.4*
a. Thr b. Ala c. Leu d. Lys

50. Draw each amino acid in its dipolar ion form.
a. Val b. Phe c. Tyr d. Cys

51. Draw the structures of the two enantiomers of alanine.
MISSED THIS? *Read Section 23.4*

52. Draw the structures of the two enantiomers of cysteine.

53. How many different tripeptides can form from serine, glycine, and cysteine? List the amino acid sequence of each one.
MISSED THIS? *Read Section 23.4*

54. How many dipeptides can form from leucine and serine? List the amino acid sequence for each one.

55. Draw the reaction by which serine and tyrosine form a peptide bond. **MISSED THIS?** *Read Section 23.4*

56. Draw the reaction by which valine and asparagine form a peptide bond.

57. Draw a structure for each tripeptide.
MISSED THIS? *Read Section 23.4*
a. Gln-Met-Cys b. Ser-Leu-Cys c. Cys-Leu-Ser

58. Draw a structure for each tetrapeptide.
a. Ser-Ala-Leu-Cys b. Gln-Met-Cys-Gly c. Gly-Cys-Met-Gln

59. A phenylalanine amino acid on a protein strand undergoes hydrophobic interactions with another phenylalanine amino acid that is 26 amino acid units away. The resulting fold in the protein is an example of which kind of structure? (primary, secondary, tertiary, or quaternary)
MISSED THIS? *Read Section 23.5*

60. An amino acid on a protein strand forms a hydrogen bond to another amino acid that is four amino acid units away. The next amino acid on the chain does the same, hydrogen-bonding to an amino acid that is four amino acids away from it. This pattern repeats itself over a significant part of the protein chain. The resulting pattern in the protein is an example of which kind of structure? (primary, secondary, tertiary, or quaternary)

61. The amino acid sequence in one section of a protein is shown here. It represents which kind of structure? (primary, secondary, tertiary, or quaternary) **MISSED THIS?** *Read Section 23.5*

-Lys-Glu-Thr-Ala-Ala-Ala-Lys-Phe-Glu-

62. A dimeric protein is composed of two individual chains of amino acids. The way these two chains fit together is an example of which kind of structure? (primary, secondary, tertiary, or quaternary)

Nucleic Acids

63. Determine whether or not each structure is a nucleotide. For each nucleotide, identify the base as A, T, C, or G.
MISSED THIS? *Read Section 23.6*

a. 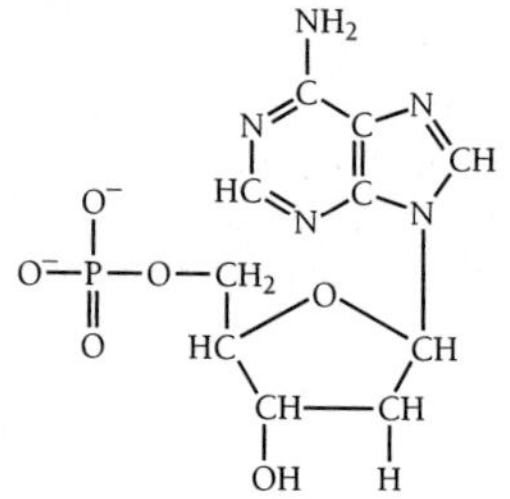

b. 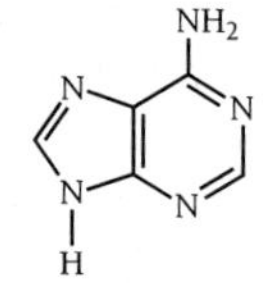

c. 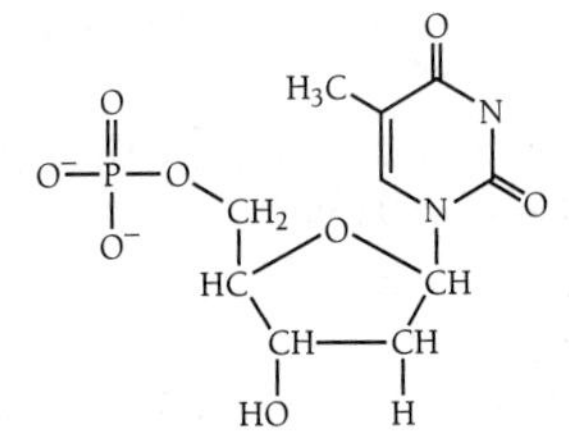

d. 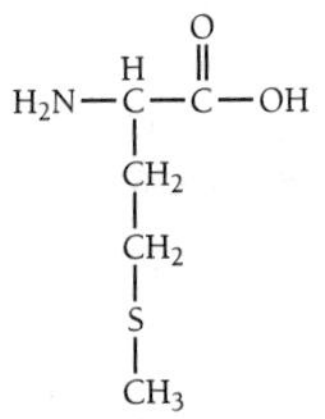

64. Determine whether or not each structure is a nucleotide. For each nucleotide, identify the base as A, T, C, or G.

a. 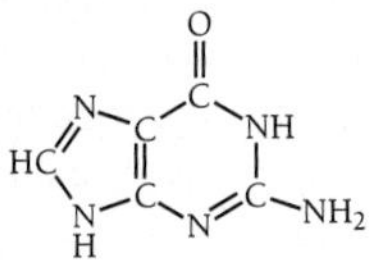

b. 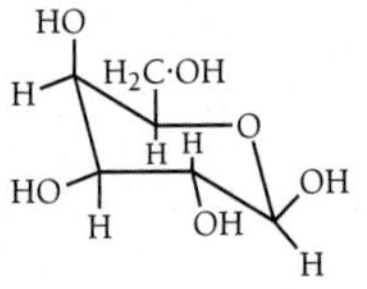

c. 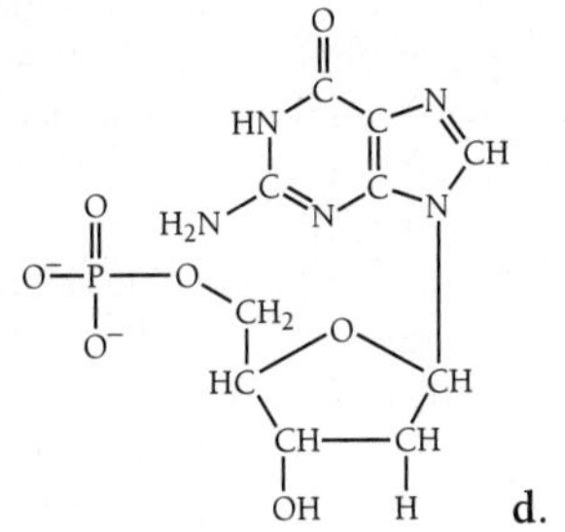

d. 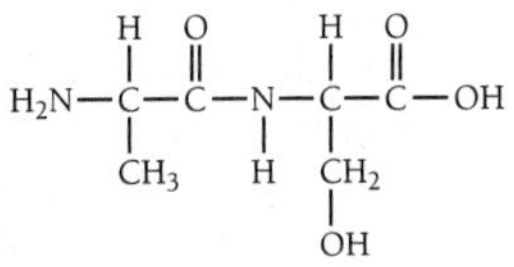

65. Draw the structures of the two purine bases in nucleic acids. **MISSED THIS?** *Read Section 23.6*

66. Draw the structures of the three pyrimidine bases in nucleic acids.

67. Draw the DNA strand that is complementary to the DNA strand shown here. **MISSED THIS?** *Read Section 23.7*

T G T A C G C

68. Draw the DNA strand that is complementary to the DNA strand shown here.

A T G A C T G

69. A monomeric protein contains 154 amino acids. How many codons code for these amino acids? How many nucleotides? **MISSED THIS?** *Read Sections 23.6, 23.7*

70. A dimeric protein contains 142 amino acids in one strand and 148 in the other. How many codons code for these amino acids? How many nucleotides?

CUMULATIVE PROBLEMS

71. Determine the class of biochemical compound that contains each type of linkage.

a. peptide bonds
b. glycosidic linkage
c. ester linkage

72. Name the type of polymer associated with each monomer.

a. nucleotide
b. amino acid
c. saccharide

73. What is the difference between a codon and a nucleotide? A codon and a gene?

74. What is the difference between a fatty acid and a triglyceride? A triglyceride and a phospholipid?

75. The amino acid alanine has the condensed structural formula shown here:

$$NH_2CH(CH_3)COOH$$

Determine the VSEPR geometry about each internal atom and make a three-dimensional sketch of the molecule.

76. The amino acid serine has the condensed structural formula shown here:

$$NH_2CH(CH_2OH)COOH$$

Determine the VSEPR geometry about each internal atom and make a three-dimensional sketch of the molecule.

77. Which amino acids in Table 23.3 are most likely to be involved in hydrophobic interactions?

78. Sickle-cell anemia is caused by a genetic defect that substitutes valine for glutamic acid at one position in two of the four chains of the hemoglobin protein. The result is a decrease in the water solubility of hemoglobin. Examine the structures of valine and glutamic acid and explain why this occurs.

79. Determining the amino acid sequence in a protein usually involves treating the protein with various reagents that break up the protein into smaller fragments that can be individually sequenced. Treating a particular 11-amino acid polypeptide with one reagent produced the fragments:

Ala-Leu-Phe-Gly-Asn-Lys   Trp-Glu-Cys   Gly-Arg

Treating the same polypeptide with a different reagent produced the fragments:

Glu-Cys   Gly-Asn-Lys-Trp   Gly-Arg-Ala-Leu-Phe

What is the amino acid sequence of the polypeptide?

80. Treating a particular polypeptide with one reagent (as described in the previous problem) produced the fragments:

Gly-Glu-Ser-Lys   Trp-Arg   Leu-Thr-Ala-Trp

Treating the same polypeptide with a different reagent produced the fragments:

Gly-Glu   Thr-Ala-Trp   Ser-Lys-Trp-Arg-Leu

What is the amino acid sequence of the polypeptide?

81. Naturally occurring D-glucose is one of a pair of enantiomers. Its mirror image is L-glucose. Draw the two cyclic six-membered isomers of L-glucose that differ in the configuration around C1 and indicate which is α and which is β.

82. Calculate the mass percent of phosphorus in a strand of DNA that consists of equal amounts of each of the four N-bases.

83. The double helical structure of DNA disrupts on heating but re-forms on cooling. Use thermodynamic reasoning to account for these observations.

84. From the structural formula of cholesterol shown on page 1042, determine (a) the composition and (b) the number of chiral centers.

CHALLENGE PROBLEMS

85. One way to fight viral infections is to prevent a virus from replicating its DNA. Without DNA replication, the virus cannot multiply. Some viral drug therapies cause the introduction of *fake* nucleotides into cells. When the virus uses one of these fake nucleotides in an attempt to replicate its DNA, the fake nucleotide doesn't work and viral DNA replication is halted. For example, azidothymidine (AZT), a drug used to fight the human immunodeficiency virus (HIV) that causes AIDS, results in the introduction of the following fake thymine-containing nucleotide into cells. Examine the structures of the real nucleotide and the AZT fake nucleotide. Propose a mechanism for how this fake nucleotide might halt DNA replication.

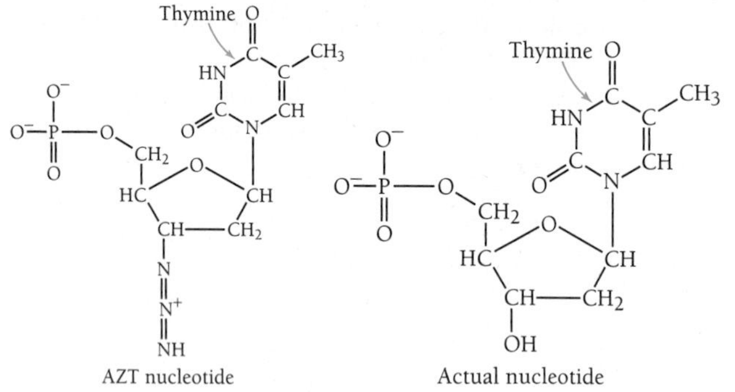

86. Draw each molecule and identify the chiral centers within them.

a. ribose

b. galactose

c. 5-deoxyribose (*Hint:* The 5 indicates that the oxygen is removed from the 5th carbon.)

87. Glucose transport across the red blood cell membranes (erythrocyte membrane) is a well-studied system. One laboratory project obtained the data shown here for glucose transport.

$[\text{Glucose}]_{\text{outside}}$ (mM)	Rate of Glucose Entry (μM/min)
0.5	12
1.0	19
2.0	27
3.0	32
4.0	35

The kinetics of glucose transport through the membrane follows the Michaelis–Menten equation:

$$V_0 = \frac{V_{\max}[\text{glucose}]}{K_t + [\text{glucose}]}$$

V_0 = rate of glucose entry

$V_{\max}$ = maximum rate (the point at which addition of glucose has no effect on the rate)

K_t = transport constant

The Michaelis–Menten equation can be rearranged so that a plot $1/V_0$ versus $1/[\text{glucose}]$ produces a straight line. Rearrange the equation and plot the data in order to determine K_t and $V_{\max}$ for glucose transport across the erythrocyte membrane.

88. Eukaryotic DNA is equipped with special ends called telomers. Telomers are made up of hexanucleotide sequences that repeat at the ends of the DNA. For example, human DNA features repeating AGGGTT sequences. Functionally, telomers protect the ends of chromosomes from being treated as a broken piece of DNA in need of repair. Interestingly, telomers are cut off each time the DNA is replicated, indicating a possible cellular clock that allows only a certain number of cellular replications. Telomerase is the enzyme that catalyzes the synthesis of telomers. Telomerase is present in limited quantities within certain cells such as fetal tissue, adult male germ cells, and stem cells. It is also found in over 85% of tumor cells. Researchers speculate that the telomerase activity may be linked to cancer. Propose an explanation for why telomerase activity could be associated with cancer and speculate on ways in which cancer treatments in the future may capitalize on research on this enzyme.

89. Write the major equilibrium that is established in a solution of glycine at pH = 2 and at pH = 10. The pK_a of the COOH group is 2.3, and the pK_a of the NH_3^+ group is 9.6. Determine the relative concentrations of each member of the relevant conjugate acid–base pair at pH = 2 and pH = 10. Calculate the pH at which glycine is neutral.

CONCEPTUAL PROBLEMS

90. How many different tetrapeptides can form from four different amino acids?

91. Could the genetic code have been based on just three bases and three-base codons? Explain why or why not. (Assume that the code must accommodate 20 different amino acids.)

92. The genetic code is random, which means that a particular codon could have coded for a different amino acid. The genetic code is also nearly universal, meaning that it is the same code in nearly all organisms (and in the few where it differs, it does so only slightly). If scientists ever find life on another planet, they will be curious to know its genetic code. What would a completely different genetic code indicate about the origin of the life-forms? What would a genetic code identical to terrestrial life indicate?

QUESTIONS FOR GROUP WORK

Active Classroom Learning

Discuss these questions with the group and record your consensus answer.

93. Compare and contrast cornstarch with cotton balls, which are made of almost pure cellulose. Include at least three ways in which they are similar and three ways in which they are different. Mention aspects you have observed in daily life and aspects on the molecular scale.

94. With group members acting as atoms, molecules, or molecular fragments, act out the formation of a peptide bond.

95. Describe how a common object or toy (e.g., a train, building blocks, or beads on a string) could represent a protein. Describe how amino acids and peptide bonds are represented in your analogy. Also describe the representation of primary, secondary, tertiary, and quaternary structure in your analogy.

96. Use the tabulated key to decipher the mRNA encoded message. Group members may split up the message and decode separate parts, but each part must be decoded by at least two group members (to prevent errors). Describe how the process your group uses to decode the message is significant for biochemistry.

Codon	Amino Acid	Codon	Amino Acid	Codon	Amino Acid	Codon	Amino Acid
UUC	A	ACU	H	GAC	O	GGC	V
CUA	B	GCG	I	GAA	P	UGA	W
AUU	C	UAC	J	UGU	Q	UAA	X
AUG	D	CAU	K	UGG	R	UAG	Y
GUC	E	CAG	L	CGC	S	GGU	Z
UCC	F	AAC	M	AGU	T		
CCG	G	AAG	N	AGG	U		

CUAGCGGACAUUACUGUCAACGCGCGCAGUUGGUAGGCGCGC
UUCAACUUCGGUGCGAAGCCG!

97. Working individually, draw an accurate structure for one of the following (don't tell other group members which one you choose): a monosaccharide, a disaccharide, a polysaccharide, a fatty acid, a triglyceride, a steroid, an amino acid, or a dipeptide. After each group member has completed drawing a structure, take turns showing your structure to the group. How many group members can correctly identify the structure you drew? How many of your group members' structures can you correctly identify?

DATA INTERPRETATION AND ANALYSIS

Digestion of Lactose by the Lactase Enzyme

98. Lactose is a disaccharide sugar present in milk. Lactose is composed of two monosaccharides, galactose and glucose, that are joined together by a β-glycosidic bond. The β-glycosidic bond forms between the hydroxyl group on C-1 of galactose and C-4 of glucose.

When lactose is digested, the glycosidic bond between galactose and glucose is hydrolyzed. The enzyme responsible for hydrolyzing lactose is *lactase*, which is found in the small intestine. Millions of people lack sufficient levels of lactase, and as a result, they experience lactose intolerance. If lactose is not hydrolyzed, it remains in the intestines. Bacteria in the gut ferment the lactose, causing many unpleasant symptoms such as indigestion, cramping, and gas. Fortunately, commercial preparations can enable lactose-intolerant individuals to consume and digest milk products without discomfort.

Use the information provided to answer the following questions:

a. Draw the structure of lactose. (The structures of galactose and glucose are shown on page 1045 with their carbon numbering scheme.)

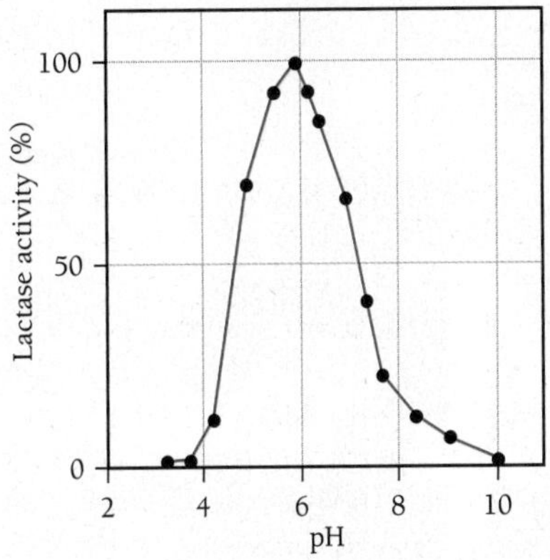

◀ Digestion of Lactose by the Lactase Enzyme [Source: *European Journal of Biochemistry*, Vol. 114, p. 653–661 (1981).]

b. Lactase enzyme activity, like most enzymes, is sensitive to pH. The figure above illustrates how lactase activity is affected by the pH of a solution. Based on the data in Figure a, what can you conclude about the pH of the small intestine?

c. A glutamic acid in the active site of lactase is suspected to be involved in the catalytic mechanism. Draw the structure of the glutamic acid side chain in the ionization state that likely exists when lactase is most catalytically active.

Cc ANSWERS TO CONCEPTUAL CONNECTIONS

Lipids

23.1 **(b)** Triglycerides compose a significant part of our diet because they compose fats and oils such as lard and olive oil.

Carbohydrates

23.2 **(d)** Cellulose functions as the main structural material in plants.

Peptides

23.3 **(c)** Six possible tripeptides can form from these three amino acids. They are (1) Ser-Gly-Ala; (2) Gly-Ala-Ser; (3) Ala-Ser-Gly; (4) Ala-Gly-Ser; (5) Ser-Ala-Gly; and (6) Gly-Ser-Ala. Notice that bonding the amino acids in reverse order results in a different molecule because the N-terminal and the C-terminal ends reside on different amino acids. For example, in Ser-Gly-Ala, the N-terminal amino acid is Ser (conventionally drawn on the left) and the C-terminal side is Ala. In Ala-Gly-Ser, in contrast, the N-terminal amino acid is Ala and the C-terminal one is Ser.

Protein Structure

23.4 **(a)** Primary structure refers to the order of amino acids in the protein chain and is maintained by peptide bonds between the amino acids.

The Genetic Code

23.5 **(c)** The number of unique two-base sequences of four bases is $4^2 = 16$. A two-base system could code for 16 amino acids.

What one learns in chemistry is that Nature wrote all the rules of structuring; man does not invent chemical structuring rules; he only discovers the rules. All the chemist can do is find out what Nature permits, and any substances that are thus developed or discovered are inherently natural.

—R. BUCKMINSTER FULLER (1895–1983)

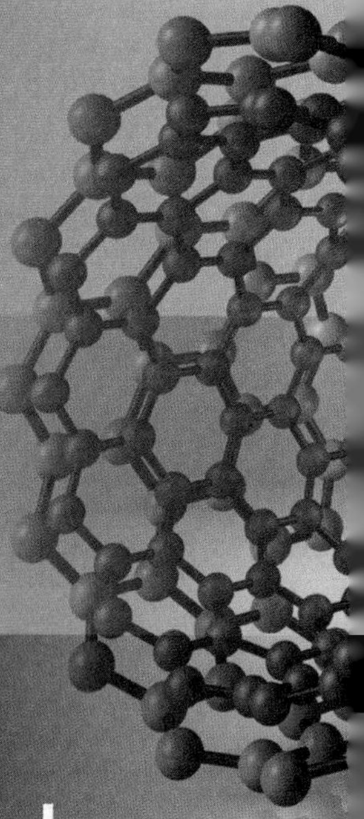

CHAPTER 24 Chemistry of the Nonmetals

In these last few chapters, we explore the descriptive chemistry of the nonmetals and metals. These descriptions are part of a branch of chemistry called inorganic chemistry. We begin our exploration of descriptive inorganic chemistry by looking at the chemistry of some of the main-group elements. The main-group elements are grouped together because their valence electrons occupy only *s* or *p* orbitals; however, their properties vary greatly. The main-group elements include metals, nonmetals, and metalloids and they may be solids, liquids, or gases at room temperature. This great diversity of properties, bonding, and structures of all the main-group elements cannot be adequately described in a single chapter. Therefore, this chapter focuses on only a few main-group elements (silicon, boron, carbon, nitrogen, phosphorus, oxygen, sulfur, and the halogens) and their compounds in an effort to illustrate the diversity within the group.

24.1 Insulated Nanowires 1071

24.2 The Main-Group Elements: Bonding and Properties 1072

24.3 Silicates: The Most Abundant Matter in Earth's Crust 1074

24.4 Boron and Its Remarkable Structures 1078

24.5 Carbon, Carbides, and Carbonates 1081

24.6 Nitrogen and Phosphorus: Essential Elements for Life 1085

24.7 Oxygen 1091

24.8 Sulfur: A Dangerous but Useful Element 1093

24.9 Halogens: Reactive Elements with High Electronegativity 1097

LEARNING OUTCOMES 1103

24.1 Insulated Nanowires

In 1991, scientists discovered carbon nanotubes, the long, thin, hollow cylinders of carbon atoms that we discussed in Section 13.6. In the late 1990s, scientists discovered that they could make similar tubes from boron nitride. Boron nitride contains BN units that are isoelectronic (having the same number of electrons) with carbon in the sense that each BN unit contains eight valence electrons, or four per atom (just like carbon). The size and electronegativity of a carbon atom are also almost equal to the average of those properties for a boron atom and a nitrogen atom (Table 24.1). As a result, BN forms a number of structures that are similar to those formed by carbon, including nanotubes.

TABLE 24.1 ■ Properties of Boron Nitride and Carbon

Element	Atomic Radius (pm)	Ionization Energy (kJ/mol)	Electronegativity
B	85	800	2
BN	77.5 average	1101 average	2.5 average
N	70	1402	3
C	77	1086	2.5

An important difference between boron nitride nanotubes and carbon nanotubes is their conductivity. Carbon nanotubes conduct electrical current, but boron nitride tubes act as insulators. In 2003, scientists were able to combine these two sorts of nanotubes into one structure: a conducting carbon nanotube with an insulating boron nitride sheath, shown in Figure 24.1◄. The result is an insulated conducting wire that is 100,000 times thinner than a human hair. Such thin wires may someday be used in computers and other electronic devices, allowing these devices to continue to become smaller and more efficient.

The more we learn about the structures and reactivities of known materials, the better equipped we are to discover new materials and applications. Even though it may seem that most inorganic compounds have already been discovered and analyzed, new materials, with immense impacts on our society, are constantly being discovered. As Buckminster Fuller stated in this chapter's opening quote, we continue to find "what Nature permits." In some cases, what nature permits turns out to be extremely useful to society.

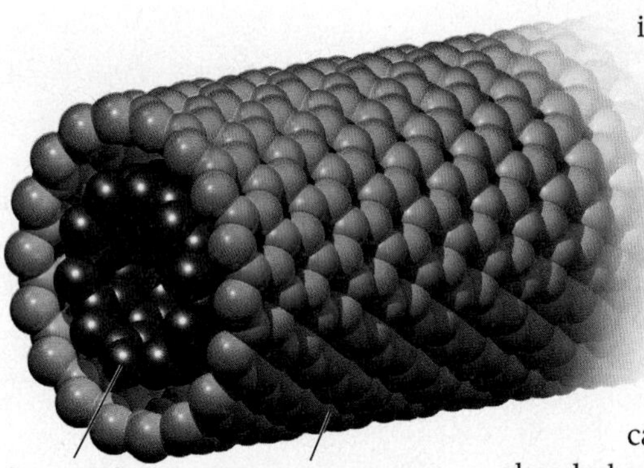

▲ **FIGURE 24.1 Boron Nitride Nanotube** The model represents an insulating BN nanotube filled with a conducting carbon nanotube.

24.2 The Main-Group Elements: Bonding and Properties

We identify the **main-group elements** by their electron configurations. In this chapter, we focus on groups 3A–7A, the major part of the *p* block in the periodic table. The *p* orbitals fill incrementally across any row of this section of the periodic table; they contain from one electron (in group 3A) to five electrons (in group 7A). The physical properties of the elements, such as atomic size and electronegativity, also change across each period, and this affects their reactivity and the types of compounds they form.

	1A	2A	3B	4B	5B	6B	7B	8B	8B	8B	1B	2B	3A	4A	5A	6A	7A	8A
1	1 H																	2 He
2	3 Li	4 Be											5 B	6 C	7 N	8 O	9 F	10 Ne
3	11 Na	12 Mg											13 Al	14 Si	15 P	16 S	17 Cl	18 Ar
4	19 K	20 Ca	21 Sc	22 Ti	23 V	24 Cr	25 Mn	26 Fe	27 Co	28 Ni	29 Cu	30 Zn	31 Ga	32 Ge	33 As	34 Se	35 Br	36 Kr
5	37 Rb	38 Sr	39 Y	40 Zr	41 Nb	42 Mo	43 Tc	44 Ru	45 Rh	46 Pd	47 Ag	48 Cd	49 In	50 Sn	51 Sb	52 Te	53 I	54 Xe
6	55 Cs	56 Ba	57 La	72 Hf	73 Ta	74 W	75 Re	76 Os	77 Ir	78 Pt	79 Au	80 Hg	81 Tl	82 Pb	83 Bi	84 Po	85 At	86 Rn
7	87 Fr	88 Ra	89 Ac	104 Rf	105 Db	106 Sg	107 Bh	108 Hs	109 Mt	110 Ds	111 Rg	112 Cn	113 Nh	114 Fl	115 Mc	116 Lv	117 Ts	118 Og

Recall from Section 9.6 that the effective nuclear charge of the main-group elements becomes greater as we move to the right across any row in the periodic table. This increasing effective charge results in smaller radii, increasing electronegativity, and increasing ionization energy as we move to the right across the periods. Consequently, as we have seen since the early chapters of this book, the nonmetals on the right side of the periodic table (those toward the right of the *p* block) tend to form anions in ionic compounds. They are easily reduced, gaining electrons to completely fill their *p* orbitals and attain noble gas electron configurations. These elements act in reactions as *oxidizing agents*—they oxidize other substances while they are themselves reduced. The smallest halogens and the elements in the oxygen group are the strongest oxidizing agents in the *p* block.

Elements near the center of the *p* block have fewer *p* electrons and do not usually fill the *p* orbitals by forming anions; instead they share electrons, forming covalent bonds. We see this type of reactivity in the vast array of molecular compounds formed by the smaller elements in the carbon and nitrogen groups. The main-group elements on the far left of the *p* block have only one *p* electron and form cations in ionic compounds and electron-deficient species (species with an incomplete octet) in covalent compounds.

Notice that as we move to the right across any row in the *p* block, the type of bonding changes as the elements become less metallic. Recall from Section 9.8 that metallic character increases as we go down each column. The diagonal group of metalloid elements stretching from boron to astatine divides the main-group elements: to the left of this diagonal, the elements are metals that form cations and metallic compounds; to the right, the elements are nonmetals that form anions and covalent compounds.

The vast range in elemental properties, from those of metallic elements such as thallium and lead that have very low electronegativities of 1.8 and 1.9 (respectively) to those of the nonmetallic elements such as oxygen and fluorine that have the highest electronegativities of 3.5 and 4.0 (respectively), results in the great chemical diversity of the elements in the *p* block. These elements include metals, alloys, simple covalent compounds, enormous covalent network compounds, simple binary ionic compounds, and complex chain and layered ionic compounds.

Major Divisions of the Periodic Table

Metals | Metalloids | Nonmetals

	1A 1	2A 2	3B 3	4B 4	5B 5	6B 6	7B 7	8B 8	8B 9	8B 10	1B 11	2B 12	3A 13	4A 14	5A 15	6A 16	7A 17	8A 18
1	1 H																	2 He
2	3 Li	4 Be											5 B	6 C	7 N	8 O	9 F	10 Ne
3	11 Na	12 Mg											13 Al	14 Si	15 P	16 S	17 Cl	18 Ar
4	19 K	20 Ca	21 Sc	22 Ti	23 V	24 Cr	25 Mn	26 Fe	27 Co	28 Ni	29 Cu	30 Zn	31 Ga	32 Ge	33 As	34 Se	35 Br	36 Kr
5	37 Rb	38 Sr	39 Y	40 Zr	41 Nb	42 Mo	43 Tc	44 Ru	45 Rh	46 Pd	47 Ag	48 Cd	49 In	50 Sn	51 Sb	52 Te	53 I	54 Xe
6	55 Cs	56 Ba	57 La	72 Hf	73 Ta	74 W	75 Re	76 Os	77 Ir	78 Pt	79 Au	80 Hg	81 Tl	82 Pb	83 Bi	84 Po	85 At	86 Rn
7	87 Fr	88 Ra	89 Ac	104 Rf	105 Db	106 Sg	107 Bh	108 Hs	109 Mt	110 Ds	111 Rg	112 Cn	113 Nh	114 Fl	115 Mc	116 Lv	117* Ts	118 Og

Lanthanides	58 Ce	59 Pr	60 Nd	61 Pm	62 Sm	63 Eu	64 Gd	65 Tb	66 Dy	67 Ho	68 Er	69 Tm	70 Yb	71 Lu
Actinides	90 Th	91 Pa	92 U	93 Np	94 Pu	95 Am	96 Cm	97 Bk	98 Cf	99 Es	100 Fm	101 Md	102 No	103 Lr

ANSWER **NOW!**

24.1 Cc Conceptual Connection

***p*-BLOCK ELEMENTS** Which element is a *p*-block element?

(a) Ca **(b)** S
(c) Ag **(d)** U

24.3 Silicates: The Most Abundant Matter in Earth's Crust

The most abundant elements in Earth's crust are oxygen (45–50% by mass) and silicon (about 28% by mass). The few other elements that individually comprise more than 1% of the crust's mass are aluminum, iron, calcium, magnesium, sodium, and potassium (Figure 24.2▼), and most of these are found in silicon and oxygen compounds. In order to understand the matter on Earth's surface, we must understand silicon and oxygen compounds.

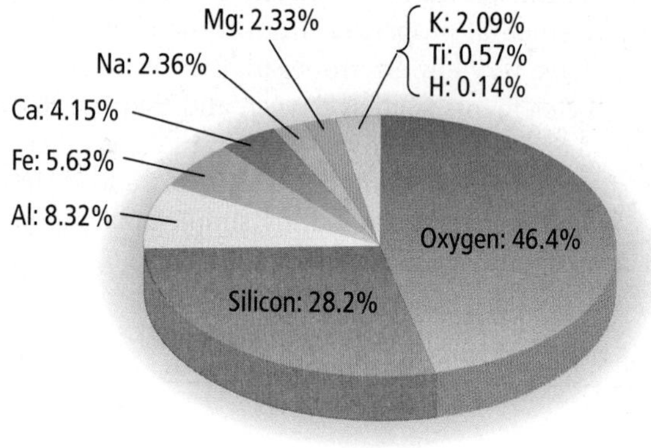

▶ **FIGURE 24.2 Major Elements in Earth's Crust** The major components of Earth's crust are oxygen and silicon. Only a few other elements compose more than 1% of the crust each.

A rock is a heterogeneous mixture that may contain one or more minerals.

Silicates are covalent atomic solids (see Section 13.6) that contain silicon, oxygen, and various metal atoms. Rocks, clays, and soils contain silicates. Their great diversity illustrates a theme that we have encountered since Chapter 1 of this book: the properties of substances are determined by their atomic and molecular structures. The structures of silicates determine their properties—and since these structures are varied, their properties are also varied. Some silicates form strong three-dimensional materials, whereas others break into sheets, and still others are highly fibrous. Let's examine several of these structures more closely.

Quartz

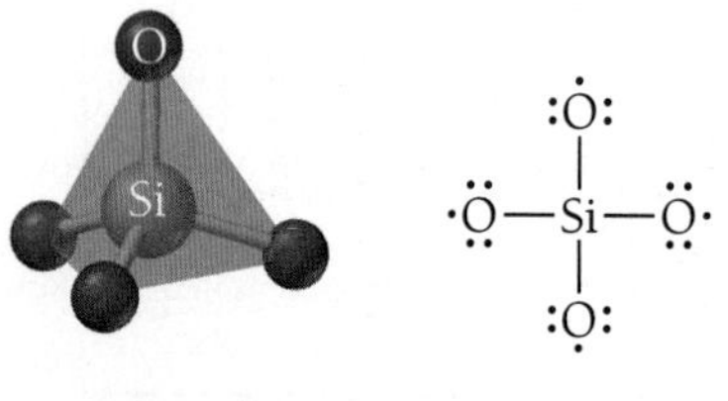

▲ **FIGURE 24.3 SiO_4 Tetrahedron** In a SiO_4 tetrahedron, silicon occupies the center of the tetrahedron, and one oxygen atom occupies each corner.

Recall from Chapter 13 that silicon and oxygen form a network covalent structure in which a silicon atom bonds to four oxygen atoms, forming a tetrahedral shape with the silicon atom in the middle and the four oxygen atoms at the corners of the tetrahedron (Figure 24.3◀). As we examined in Chapter 13, the silicon atom bonds to each oxygen atom with a single covalent sigma bond. Recall that the silicon atom in this structure bonds to four oxygen atoms and obtains a complete octet. However, each oxygen atom is one electron short of an octet, so each O atom forms a second covalent bond to a different Si atom, forming the three-dimensional structure of **quartz**. Quartz has a formula unit of SiO_2 and is generally called **silica**. Each Si atom is in a tetrahedron surrounded by four O atoms, and each O atom acts as a bridge connecting the corners of two tetrahedrons (Figure 24.4▶).

Aluminosilicates

Aluminosilicates are a family of compounds in which aluminum atoms substitute for silicon atoms in some of the lattice sites of the silica structure. Since the aluminum ion has only three valence electrons (in contrast to the four valence electrons of silicon), a SiO_2 unit becomes AlO_2^- upon substitution of aluminum. The negative charge is balanced by a positive counterion. A common group of aluminosilicates is the feldspars. The mineral albite is a feldspar. A **mineral** is a homogeneous, crystalline substance that naturally occurs in the Earth's crust. In albite, one-fourth of the Si atoms are replaced by Al atoms. Na^+ ions provide the necessary balancing positive charge. The formula for albite is $Na(AlSi_3O_8)$, but it may be written as $Na(AlO_2)(SiO_2)_3$ to illustrate the substitution of Al for Si.

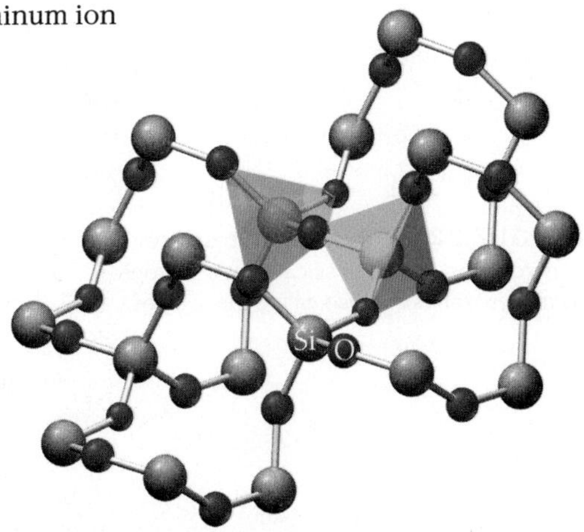

▶ **FIGURE 24.4 Structure of Quartz** In the quartz structure, each Si atom is in a tetrahedron surrounded by four O atoms, and each O atom is a bridge connecting the corners of two tetrahedrons.

EXAMPLE 24.1 Determining the Composition of an Aluminosilicate

Write the formula for anorthite, a crystal in which Al atoms substitute for one-half of the Si atoms and the charge is balanced by Ca^{2+} ions.

SOLUTION

The AlO_2^- unit substitutes for one-half of the SiO_2 units; therefore, the formula has equal numbers of AlO_2^- and SiO_2 units. You must balance every AlO_2^- ion in the formula by a corresponding positive charge. Since Ca^{2+} has a 2+ charge, it can balance two AlO_2^- units. Thus, the formula for anorthite is $Ca(Al_2Si_2O_8)$ or $Ca(AlO_2)_2(SiO_2)_2$.

FOR PRACTICE 24.1 Orthoclase is a crystal in which Al^{3+} substitutes for one-fourth of the Si^{4+} ions. K^+ ions balance the charge. Write the formula for orthoclase.

Individual Silicate Units, Silicate Chains, and Silicate Sheets

In many silicate compounds, the oxygen atoms are not connected to two silicon atoms to form the neutral compound that is found in quartz. Instead, the oxygen atoms gain electrons from metal atoms and form polyatomic anions, such as SiO_4^{4-}. The positively charged metal ions then bond to the negatively charged silicon oxide. In these minerals, the SiO_4 tetrahedrons occur singly, in chains, or in sheets.

When a tetrahedron occurs singly (not bonded to other tetrahedrons), it forms the SiO_4^{4-} polyatomic anion (which has four extra electrons that satisfy the octet rule for the four oxygen atoms). These types of silicates are **orthosilicates** (or nesosilicates) and require cations that have a total charge of 4+ to neutralize the negative charge. The cations can be of a single metal, such as Zn^{2+} in Zn_2SiO_4 (the mineral willemite), or they can be a mixture of different metals, such as the family of crystals called olivines $[(Mg,Fe)_2SiO_4]$ where the Mg^{2+} and Fe^{2+} ions can exist in variable proportions, providing a total charge of 4+. All of these compounds are held together by ionic bonding between the metal cations and SiO_4^{4-} polyatomic anions.

The silicate tetrahedrons can also form structures called **pyrosilicates** (or sorosilicates) in which two tetrahedrons share one corner (Figure 24.5▶), forming the disilicate ion, which has the formula $Si_2O_7^{6-}$. This group requires cations that balance the 6− charge on $Si_2O_7^{6-}$. Again, these cations can be the same metal ions or a mixture of different metal ions. For example, in the mineral hardystonite ($Ca_2ZnSi_2O_7$), two Ca^{2+} ions and one Zn^{2+} ion provide the 6+ charge.

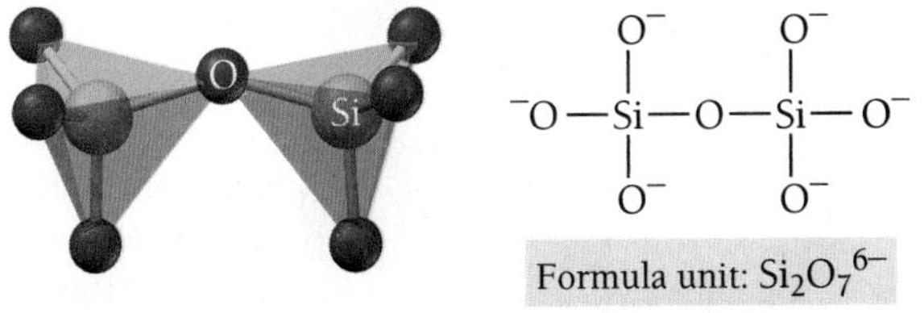

▲ **FIGURE 24.5 Pyrosilicate Structure** In pyrosilicates, the silicate tetrahedrons share one corner, forming $Si_2O_7^{6-}$ units. Pyrosilicates are also called sorosilicates.

The silicon tetrahedron also forms structures called **pyroxenes** (or inosilicates) in which many of the tetrahedrons bond together creating chains (Figure 24.6▼). The formula unit for these chains is the SiO_3^{2-} unit, and the repeating unit in the structure is two formula units ($Si_2O_6^{4-}$). Two of the oxygen atoms are bonded to two silicon atoms (and thus to two other tetrahedrons) at two of the four corners of each tetrahedron. The silicate chains are held together by ionic bonding to metal cations, which lie between the chains. For example, in the crystal diopside, $CaMg(SiO_3)_2$, Ca^{2+} and Mg^{2+} ions bond with the silicate chains.

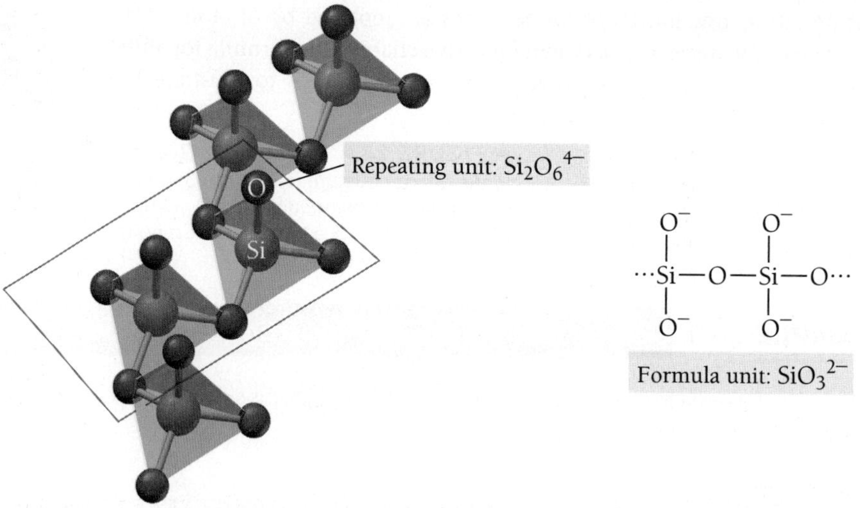

► **FIGURE 24.6 Pyroxene Structure** In pyroxenes, chains of silicate tetrahedrons form. Pyroxenes are also called inosilicates.

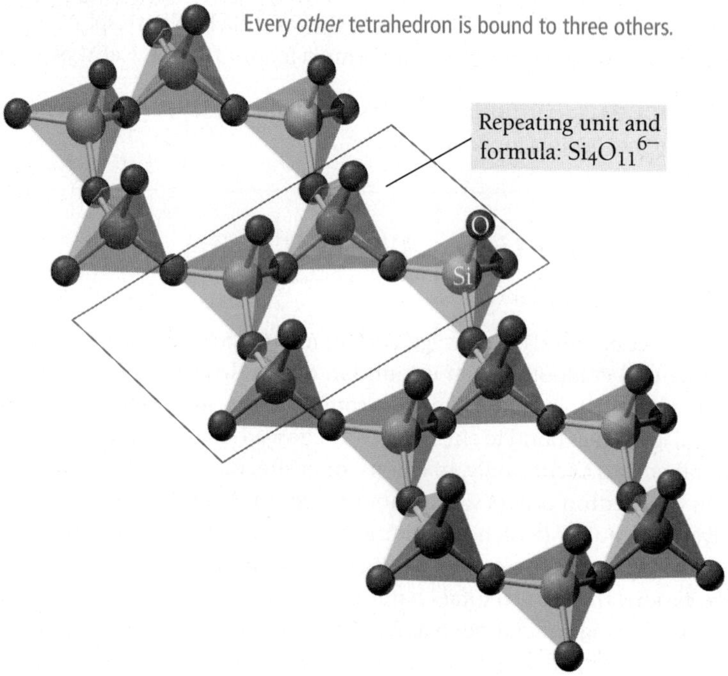

▲ **FIGURE 24.7 Amphibole Structure** Amphiboles contain double chains of silica tetrahedrons.

▲ The fibrous texture of asbestos results from the silicate double chains of the amphibole structure.

▲ The flaky texture of mica is due to silicate sheets of the phyllosilicate structure.

Some silicate structures have *double chains* in which half of the tetrahedrons of one chain are bonded to tetrahedrons in another chain through oxygen atoms. The minerals with double silicate chains are called amphiboles, and the repeating unit in the crystal is $Si_4O_{11}^{6-}$ (Figure 24.7▲). Half of the tetrahedrons are bonded by two of the four corner O atoms, and half of the tetrahedrons are bonded by three of the four corners, joining the two chains together. The bonding within the double chains is very strong, but the bonding between the double chains is not so strong. This structure often results in fibrous minerals such as asbestos. An example of an asbestos-type mineral is tremolite,

$Ca_2(OH)_2Mg_5(Si_4O_{11})_2$. In this crystal, hydroxide ions bonded to some of the metal cations help balance the charge between the cations and the anionic silicate chains.

When three of the four oxygen atoms are bonded between the silicate tetrahedrons, the sheet structure shown in Figure 24.8▶ results. These compounds are called phyllosilicates and have a formula unit of $Si_2O_5^{2-}$. Sheets of tetrahedral silicates are bonded together by metal cations that lie between the sheets. For example, the mineral *talc*, $Mg_3(Si_2O_5)_2(OH)_2$, is a phyllosilicate. The weak interactions between silicate sheets give talc its slippery feel (this is similar to the way the weak interactions between sheets of carbon atoms give graphite its slippery feel). Table 24.2 summarizes the different kinds of silicate structures.

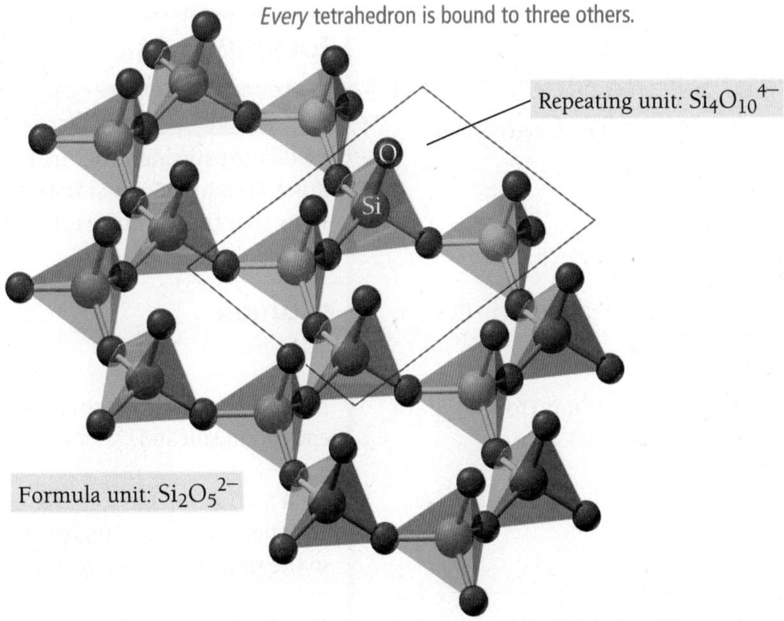

▲ **FIGURE 24.8 Phyllosilicate Structure** In phyllosilicates, three of the four oxygens are bonded to two silicon atoms, forming sheets of silica tetrahedrons.

TABLE 24.2 ■ Types of Silicate Structures

Tetrahedrons	Shared Vertices	Formula Unit	Si : O Ratio	Class Name	Example
Single tetrahedron	0	SiO_4^{4-}	1 : 4	Orthosilicates, nesosilicates	Olivine, Mg_2SiO_4
Double tetrahedron	1	$Si_2O_7^{6-}$	2 : 7	Pyrosilicates, sorosilicates	Hardystonite, $Ca_2ZnSi_2O_7$
Single chain	2	SiO_3^{2-}	1 : 3	Pyroxenes, inosilicates	Jadeite, $NaAl(SiO_3)_2$
Double chain	2 and 3	$Si_4O_{11}^{6-}$	4 : 11	Amphiboles	Tremolite, $Ca_2(OH)_2Mg_5(Si_4O_{11})_2$
Sheet	3	$Si_2O_5^{2-}$	2 : 5	Phyllosilicates	Talc, $Mg_3(Si_2O_5)_2(OH)_2$
Network covalent	4	SiO_2	1 : 2	Silicas, tectosilicates	Quartz, SiO_2
Network covalent	4	$AlSi_3O_8^-$ or $Al_2Si_2O_8^{2-}$	Variable	Feldspars	Albite, $NaAlSi_3O_8$

EXAMPLE 24.2 Composition and Charge Balance of Silicates

The silicate chrysotile is an amphibole with the formula $Mg_6Si_4O_{11}(OH)_x$. Use charge balancing to calculate the value of x in the formula.

SOLUTION

The silicate unit for amphiboles is $Si_4O_{11}^{6-}$. The formula has six Mg^{2+} ions for a total charge of 12+. To balance, you need to add another 6− charge to the 6− charge for the silicate. Therefore, add six OH^- ions to the formula for chrysotile, giving a formula of $Mg_6Si_4O_{11}(OH)_6$.

FOR PRACTICE 24.2 Use charge balancing to calculate how many hydroxide ions there are in the formula of the mineral pyrophyllite, $Al_2(Si_2O_5)_2(OH)_x$.

HOW TO: *Predict Types of Silicate Structure and Account for Charge Balance*	**EXAMPLE 24.3** **Predicting Silicate Structures** Predict the silicate structure for the mineral spudomene, $LiAlSi_2O_6$, and show that the formula is charge neutral.	**EXAMPLE 24.4** **Predicting Silicate Structures** Predict the silicate structure for the mineral thortveitite, $Sc_2Si_2O_7$, and show that the formula is charge neutral.
Determine the ratio of Si to O in the formula.	**SOLUTION** $Si:O = 1:3$	**SOLUTION** $Si:O = 2:7$
Match the Si : O ratio to the type of silicate in Table 24.2.	A 1 : 3 ratio is a single chain, a pyroxene (or inosilicate).	A 2 : 7 ratio is a double tetrahedron, a pyrosilicate (or sorosilicate).
Determine the total anion charge.	Each SiO_3 group has a charge of 2−, and there are two groups per formula, so the total anion charge is 4−.	Each Si_2O_7 group has a charge of 6−, and there is one group per formula, so the total anion charge is 6−.
Determine the total cation charge and show that it matches the total anion charge.	The Li^+ cation has a 1+ charge, and the Al^{3+} cation has a 3+ charge for a total of 4+, which matches the anion charge.	Each scandium cation has a charge of 3+ for a total of 6+, which matches the anion charge.
	FOR PRACTICE 24.3 Predict the silicate structure for the mineral phenakite, Be_2SiO_4, and show that the formula is charge neutral.	**FOR PRACTICE 24.4** Predict the silicate structure for the mineral diopside, $CaMgSi_2O_6$, and show that the formula is charge neutral.

24.4 Boron and Its Remarkable Structures

The group 3A elements each have a filled *s* sublevel and one electron in the *p* sublevel. This electron configuration prevents these main-group elements, especially boron, from easily attaining a full octet. Most of the elements in group 3A are metals; however, because of its small size and higher electronegativity, boron behaves as a semimetal. These characteristics endow boron with some special properties and result in a wide array of structures not common to most elements.

Elemental Boron

The structure of elemental boron is complex. Boron has at least five different allotropes (different structures with the same elemental composition). The structure of each allotrope is based on an icosahedron (Figure 24.9◀), a geometrical shape that contains 20 triangular faces joined at 12 vertices and that is very roughly spherical. Twelve boron atoms occupy the 12 vertices. Each different allotrope connects the icosahedrons in different ways. They all have boron atoms outside the icosahedrons that connect the icosahedrons.

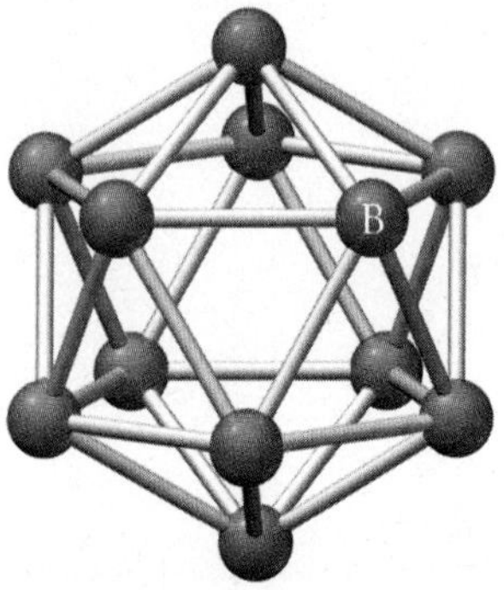

▲ **FIGURE 24.9 B_{12} Icosahedron** An icosahedron contains 20 triangular faces that are connected at 12 vertices. Elemental boron forms several different structures, each based on the basic icosahedral unit.

Boron is rare in Earth's crust, making up less than 0.001% by mass. Yet because it is highly concentrated at various deposits around the world, it can be mined in large quantities. The largest deposit occurs at a mine in Boron, California, which has operated continuously for over 135 years. Naturally occurring boron always occurs in compounds, and it is almost always bonded to oxygen. Among the major sources of boron are the sodium borates, which include borax, $Na_2[B_4O_5(OH)_4] \cdot 8\,H_2O$, and kernite, $Na_2[B_4O_6(OH)_2] \cdot 3\,H_2O$. Another major source of boron is calcium borate, or colemanite, $Ca_2B_6O_{11} \cdot 5\,H_2O$. In all of these compounds, boron is bonded in polyatomic anions.

The primary use for boron today is in glass manufacture. Recall from Section 13.7 that adding boron oxide to silicon oxide glass alters the thermal expansion of the glass, which is important for glassware intended for heating. When glass is heated, the outer edge of the glass warms and expands more quickly than the inner edge, creating stress that can result in cracking. Adding boron oxide to glass reduces its thermal expansion, allowing the glass (called borosilicate glass or Pyrex) to be heated without cracking.

Elemental boron is also used in the nuclear energy industry. Boron readily absorbs neutrons and is used in the control rods of nuclear reactors. When the nuclear reaction needs to be slowed down, the rods are inserted into the reactor to absorb the neutrons (see Section 21.7).

Boron–Halogen Compounds: Trihalides

Boron forms many covalently bonded compounds in which boron atoms bond to each other. In some ways, these compounds are similar to those in which carbon covalently bonds to itself; however, the structures are different because boron is less electronegative and has only three valence electrons. Recall from earlier in this section that elemental boron has a tendency to form polyhedral cluster structures. Boron also tends to form electron-deficient compounds (compounds in which boron lacks an octet).

Boron halides have the general formula BX_3 and have a trigonal planar structure:

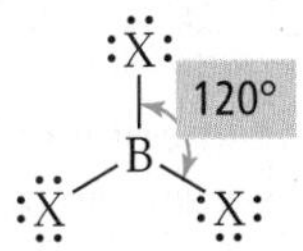

The bonds in the boron trihalides are stronger and shorter than a typical single bond, which we can explain using valence bond theory and hybridization. The boron atom uses sp^2 hybridized orbitals to form sigma bonds with the three halogen atoms. Because boron's three valence electrons are used to form the sigma bonds, the third p orbital of boron is an empty orbital that is perpendicular to the trigonal plane of the molecule. Each halogen atom has a filled p orbital, also perpendicular to the trigonal plane of the molecule. The empty p orbital on the boron atom can overlap with the full p orbitals on the halogens, forming a coordinate-covalent-type second bond. In BCl_3, for example, the boron and chlorine are joined by bonds resembling a double bond. Like normal double bonds, the boron–chlorine bond is shorter and stronger than a single bond.

The boron trihalides are strong Lewis acids. For example, BF_3 reacts with NH_3 according to the following Lewis acid–base reaction:

$$BF_3(g) + :NH_3(g) \longrightarrow F_3B:NH_3(s)$$

Boron trihalides act as Lewis acids in many organic reactions, such as those in which alcohols or acids are converted into esters. In water, the trihalides hydrolyze to form acidic solutions according to these reactions:

$$BF_3 + H_2O \longrightarrow BF_3 \cdot H_2O \longrightarrow BF_3OH^-(aq) + H^+(aq)$$

$$4\ BF_3 + 3\ H_2O \longrightarrow 3\ H^+ + 3\ BF_4^-(aq) + B(OH)_3(aq)$$

$$BCl_3 + 3\ H_2O \longrightarrow B(OH)_3(aq) + 3\ H^+(aq) + 3\ Cl^-(aq)$$

Boron–Oxygen Compounds

Boron forms very strong bonds with oxygen in structures that contain trigonal BO_3 structures. The formula for the crystalline structure of boron and oxygen is B_2O_3. In this compound, the trigonal BO_3 structures hook together to form interlocking B_6O_6 hexagonal rings (Figure 24.10▶). Each hexagonal ring has a boron atom at each of its six corners and an oxygen atom in the middle of each of the six sides. The compound B_2O_3 melts at 450 °C. If the molten B_2O_3 cools quickly, it forms a glass (an amorphous solid). The glass still contains many interlocking B_6O_6 hexagonal rings but lacks the long-range order of the crystal. Molten boron oxide dissolves many metal oxides and silicon oxide to form glasses of many different compositions.

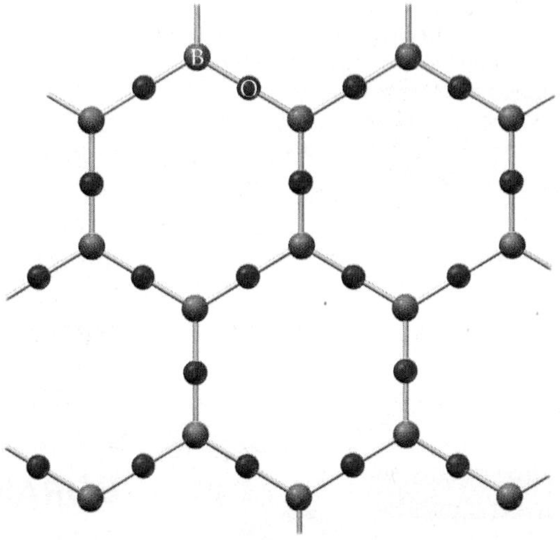

▲ **FIGURE 24.10 B_2O_3 Structure** Crystalline B_2O_3 consists of BO_3 trigonal structures that form hexagonal rings of B_6O_6.

Boron–Hydrogen Compounds: Boranes

Compounds composed of boron and hydrogen, called **boranes**, form many unique cluster, cagelike, and netlike structures. The ***closo*-boranes** have the formula $B_nH_n^{2-}$ and form fully closed polyhedrons with triangular sides; Figure 24.11▼ shows two of these structures. A boron atom, with an attached hydrogen atom, occupies each of the vertices in the polyhedrons. The *closo*-borane with the formula $B_{12}H_{12}^{2-}$ forms the full icosohedral shape that elemental boron does, but it includes added hydrogen atoms.

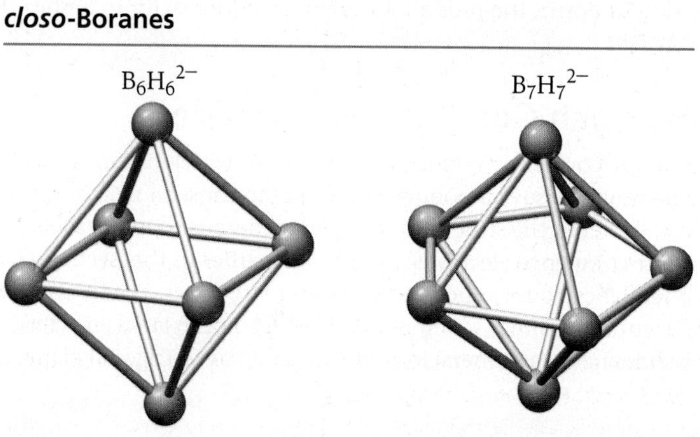

▶ **FIGURE 24.11 *closo*-Borane Structures** *closo*-Borane structures form closed polyhedrons with triangular faces. In this figure, each sphere represents a BH unit. $B_6H_6^{2-}$ has an octahedral (square bipyramidal) shape. $B_7H_7^{2-}$ has a pentagonal bipyramidal shape.

If the borane polyhedron is missing one or more boron atoms, extra hydrogen atoms attach to the structure to make the borane neutral. Researchers have identified over 35 structurally different neutral boranes, ranging from B_2H_6 to $B_{20}H_{26}$. We classify these neutral boranes on the basis of their different chemical formulas. The ***nido*-boranes**, named from the Latin word for *nest*, have the formula B_nH_{n+4}. They consist of a cage of boron atoms missing one corner. The ***arachno*-boranes**, named from the Greek word for *spiderweb*, have the formula B_nH_{n+6}. They consist of a cage of boron atoms that is missing two or three corners. Figure 24.12▼ shows examples of a *nido*- and an *arachno*-borane.

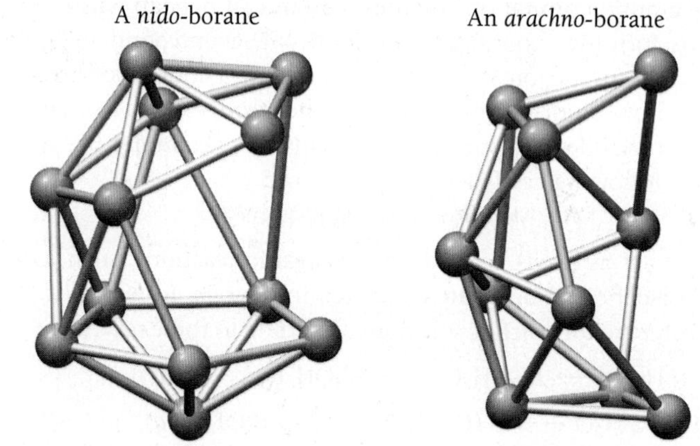

▶ **FIGURE 24.12 *nido*- and *arachno*-Boranes** The *nido*-borane structure forms a cage missing one boron atom from a corner. The *arachno*-borane structure forms a web missing more than one boron from a corner.

Boranes not only form interesting structures, but they are also valuable as catalysts in organic reactions. For example, adding an alkene to a diborane forms an alkane bonded to the boron atom. The alkane can be cleaved (split) from the boron, resulting in a net hydrogenation reaction such as the one shown here that can be carried out under mild (lower temperature) conditions:

$$B_2H_6(g) + 6\,CH_2{=}CHCH_3(g) \longrightarrow 2\,B(CH_2CH_2CH_3)_3(l)$$

ANSWER NOW!

24.2 Cc Conceptual Connection

BORANES Which species is most likely to be an example of a *nido*-borane?

(a) $B_{10}H_{14}$

(b) $B_8H_8^{2-}$

(c) B_4H_{10}

24.5 Carbon, Carbides, and Carbonates

The group 4A elements exhibit the most versatile bonding of all elements. As we saw in Chapters 13 and 22, carbon has the ability to bond with other carbon atoms and with a few other elements to form a great variety of organic compounds. These compounds are the molecules of life, which we examined in Chapter 23. The different forms of elemental crystalline carbon were covered in Chapter 13 (see Section 13.6). Here we focus on amorphous carbon and those compounds of carbon that are known as *inorganic* (rather than organic).

Amorphous Carbon

Carbon occurs naturally in noncrystalline forms. Noncrystalline **coal** forms from the decomposition of ancient plant material that has been buried for millions of years, during which time it undergoes a process called carbonization. The carbonization reaction, which occurs under high pressure in the presence of water and the absence of air, removes most of the hydrogen and oxygen (which are lost as volatile gases such as methane and water) from the original organic compounds that composed the plant. The resulting coal contains a mixture of various hydrocarbons and carbon-rich particles. It is extensively mined and employed as an energy source throughout the world. Coal types are classified by the amount of carbon and other elements that they contain, as shown in Table 24.3.

Among the types of coal listed in Table 24.3, anthracite has the highest carbon content and consequently yields the most energy per mass when burned. Bituminous coal also contains a relatively high amount of carbon but has in addition high levels of sulfur, which results in increased formation of sulfur oxides when bituminous coal is burned. Sulfur oxides are the pollutants that create acid rain (see Sections 3.6 and 17.12).

Heating coal in the absence of air forms a solid called **coke** that is composed mainly of carbon and ash. Coke is used in the steel industry for the reduction of iron ore to iron. In a blast furnace, the carbon in the coke is oxidized to form carbon monoxide, which reduces the iron in iron(III) oxide according to these reactions:

$$O_2(g) + \underset{\text{coke}}{C(s)} \longrightarrow CO_2(g)$$

$$CO_2(g) + \underset{\text{coke}}{C(s)} \longrightarrow 2\,CO(g)$$

$$Fe_2O_3(s) + 3\,CO(g) \longrightarrow 2\,Fe(s) + 3\,CO_2(g)$$

Heating wood in the absence of air produces **charcoal**. Like coal, charcoal contains a high amount of amorphous free carbon and is a common fuel for outdoor cooking grills. Charcoal retains the general overall shape of the original wood, but the process creates many voids, resulting in a much lower density. The voids within charcoal create a high surface area that makes the charcoal useful for filtration. The impurities in a liquid or gas adsorb (or stick) on the charcoal surface as the liquid or gas flows through the pores in the charcoal.

Very fine carbon particles with high surface areas are called **activated carbon**, or *activated charcoal*. The large surface area of the particles, greater than $10^3\ m^2/g$, makes activated carbon particles extremely efficient at adsorbing other molecules onto their surfaces. Activated carbon is made by heating amorphous carbon in steam, which breaks the grains into smaller sizes and removes any other materials adsorbed on the surface. Activated carbon is used to filter impurities from gas and as a decolorizing agent, removing impurities that discolor organic products such as sugar or wheat flour.

TABLE 24.3 ■ Approximate Composition of the Main Types of Coal

Type of Coal	Free C (mol %)	Total C (mol %)	H (mol %)	O (mol %)	S (mol %)
Lignite	22	71	4	23	1
Bituminous	60	80	6	8	5
Anthracite	88	93	3	3	1

▲ Automobile tires are black because of the carbon black that is added to strengthen the tires and maintain flexibility.

Soot is an amorphous form of carbon that forms during the incomplete combustion of hydrocarbons; its presence is indicated by blue or black smoke. Toxic carbon monoxide also forms in the process:

$$H_xC_y(s) + O_2(g) \longrightarrow H_2O(g) + CO_2(g) + CO(g) + \underset{\text{soot}}{C(s)}$$

Carbon black, a fine, powdered form of carbon, is a component of soot. Each day, over a million tons of carbon black, a strengthener for rubber tires, is used in manufacturing. The black color of automobile tires is due to the several kilograms of carbon black within each tire, accounting for over 25% of the mass of the typical tire.

Carbides

Binary compounds composed of carbon combined with less electronegative elements are **carbides**. We classify carbides into three general categories: ionic, covalent, and metallic. All types of carbides have some shared properties; they are extremely hard materials with high melting points.

Ionic Carbides

Compounds composed of carbon and a low-electronegativity metal such as an alkali metal or an alkaline earth metal are **ionic carbides**. Most ionic carbides contain the dicarbide ion, C_2^{2-}, commonly called the *acetylide ion*. For example, calcium carbide has the formula CaC_2 and a structure similar to that of NaCl (Figure 24.13▼).

Calcium carbide forms by the reaction of calcium oxide with coke in an electric furnace:

$$CaO(s) + 3\,C(s) \longrightarrow CaC_2(s) + CO(g)$$

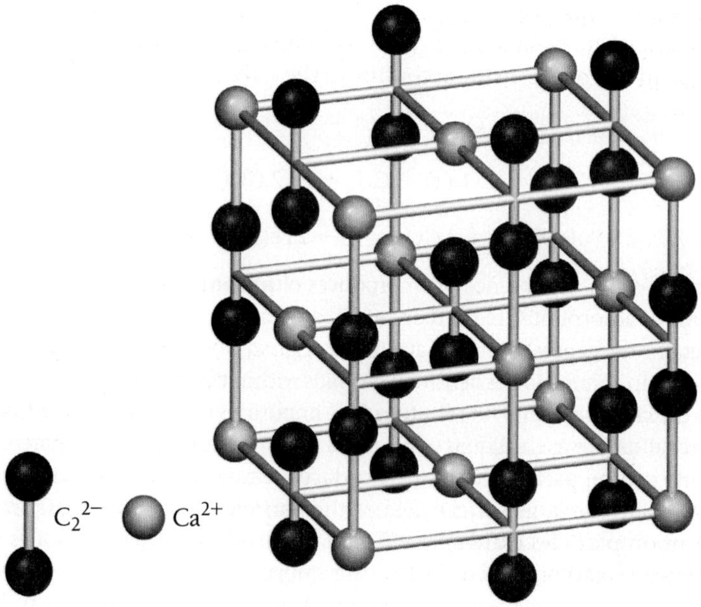

▶ **FIGURE 24.13 Calcium Carbide Structure** In the NaCl-type structure for CaC_2, the dicarbide ions are in the positions of the chloride ions, making the structure slightly noncubic.

Ionic carbides react with water, forming acetylene. For example, sodium carbide reacts with water according to the reaction shown here:

$$Na_2C_2(s) + 2\,H_2O(l) \longrightarrow 2\,NaOH(aq) + C_2H_2(g)$$

In the past, calcium carbide was used as a source of acetylene (which is highly flammable) for lighting. The solid CaC_2 reacts with water, releasing acetylene gas, which was burned in applications such as automobile headlights and lamps for mines. Transporting solid calcium carbide was more convenient and safer than transporting the flammable gas.

CARBIDE FORMULAS What is the correct formula for potassium carbide?

(a) KC_2

(b) K_2C_2

(c) K_2C

24.3 Cc Conceptual Connection

ANSWER **NOW!**

Covalent Carbides

Compounds composed of carbon and low-electronegativity *nonmetals* or *metalloids* are **covalent carbides**. The most important covalent carbide is silicon carbide (SiC), a very hard material. Over 500,000 tons of silicon carbide are produced annually, mostly for use as an abrasive material in the cutting and polishing of metals. In a process analogous to the formation of calcium carbide, silicon carbide forms by the reaction of silicon oxide with coke at high temperatures:

$$SiO_2(s) + 3\,C(s) \longrightarrow SiC(s) + 2\,CO(g)$$

A gem-quality form of SiC, called *moissanite*, has also been developed. Moissanite is described as being more brilliant than all other gems, including diamonds. Yet moissanite costs much less than diamond and is consequently sold as a diamond substitute (like the more common diamond substitute cubic zirconia, ZrO_2). Moissanite was first identified in small particles at the Diablo Canyon meteorite impact crater in Arizona and is sometimes advertised as "a gift from the stars."

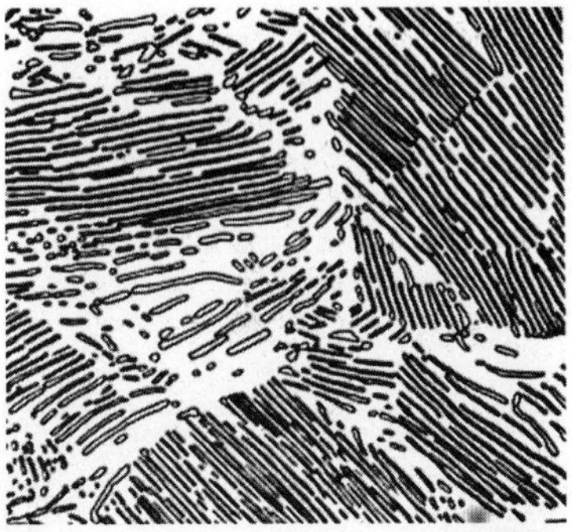

2500×

▲ This micrograph shows cementite (dark regions) in steel.

Metallic Carbides

Compounds composed of carbon and metals that have a metallic lattice with holes small enough to fit carbon atoms are **metallic carbides**. Metallic carbides retain many metallic properties, such as high electrical conductivity, but they are stronger, harder, and less malleable than their corresponding metals. Adding carbon to steel, for example, increases its hardness by forming regions of cementite (Fe_3C) in the steel matrix. Tungsten carbide (WC) is a metallic carbide used in cutting tools.

Carbon Oxides

Carbon forms two stable oxides, carbon monoxide and carbon dioxide. Earth's atmosphere contains about 0.04% carbon dioxide by volume. Plants use atmospheric carbon dioxide to produce sugars during photosynthesis:

$$6\,CO_2(g) + 6\,H_2O(g) \longrightarrow C_6H_{12}O_6(s) + 6\,O_2(g)$$

Carbon dioxide returns to the atmosphere via animal respiration, plant and animal decay, and (in modern history) fossil fuel combustion. Because carbon dioxide is highly soluble in water, the oceans of the world act as a reservoir for CO_2, keeping the amount of CO_2 in the atmosphere generally stable. As we saw in Section 7.10, however, the increase in the combustion of fossil fuels in the last century has increased the amount of CO_2 in the atmosphere by about 38%.

Recall from Section 12.8 that CO_2 has a triple point at −57 °C and 5.1 atm. At atmospheric pressure, therefore, the liquid phase of CO_2 does not exist. Solid carbon dioxide sublimes directly to the gas phase when heated, which is why solid CO_2 is called "dry ice."

Carbon monoxide (CO) is a colorless, odorless, and tasteless gas. The boiling point of carbon monoxide is −192 °C at atmospheric pressure, and CO is only very slightly soluble in water. Carbon monoxide is toxic because it interferes with the ability of hemoglobin to bind oxygen. Unlike carbon dioxide, which is very stable, carbon monoxide is relatively reactive and can be used as a reducing agent.

For example, carbon monoxide reacts with oxygen and metal oxides to form carbon dioxide:

$$2\,CO(g) + O_2(g) \longrightarrow 2\,CO_2(g)$$
$$CO(g) + CuO(s) \longrightarrow CO_2(g) + Cu(s)$$

Carbon monoxide also reduces many nonmetals, producing compounds with the reduced form of the nonmetal:

$$CO(g) + Cl_2(g) \longrightarrow COCl_2(g)$$
$$CO(g) + S(s) \longrightarrow COS(g)$$

The product of the first reaction listed is phosgene ($COCl_2$), also known as carbonyl chloride, a poisonous gas that was used in World War I as a chemical weapon. Phosgene is now an important industrial chemical used in the production of polycarbonates. The product of the second reaction, carbonyl sulfide (COS), is a fungicide (a substance that kills fungi).

Carbonates

When carbon dioxide dissolves in water, it forms carbonic acid (H_2CO_3). As a weak acid, carbonic acid partially ionizes into hydrogen carbonate (or bicarbonate) and carbonate:

$$CO_2(aq) + H_2O(l) \rightleftharpoons \underset{\text{carbonic acid}}{H_2CO_3(aq)}$$

$$H_2CO_3(aq) \rightleftharpoons H^+(aq) + \underset{\text{hydrogen carbonate}}{HCO_3^-(aq)} \rightleftharpoons 2\,H^+(aq) + \underset{\text{carbonate}}{CO_3^{2-}(aq)}$$

Recall from Section 14.4 that the solubility of carbon dioxide, like that of other gases, increases with increasing pressure. Carbon dioxide under high pressure carbonates soft drinks. Under most conditions, less than 0.5% of the dissolved carbon dioxide reacts with water to form carbonic acid. This leaves most of the carbon dioxide as dissolved gas molecules, so the soft drink does not acquire much of a sour acidic taste.

The hydrated crystal of sodium carbonate, $Na_2CO_3 \cdot 10\,H_2O$, is known as **washing soda**. Heating washing soda releases the waters of hydration, forming the stable anhydrous sodium carbonate, Na_2CO_3. All of the alkali metal ions form stable carbonates that remain stable even when heated. The carbonates all make basic solutions when added to water because the carbonate ions readily ionize water (as described more fully in Section 17.8):

$$Na_2CO_3(s) \longrightarrow 2\,Na^+(aq) + CO_3^{2-}(aq)$$
$$CO_3^{2-}(aq) + H_2O(l) \longrightarrow HCO_3^-(aq) + OH^-(aq)$$

Sodium bicarbonate ($NaHCO_3$) is *baking soda*. When heated, baking soda gives off carbon dioxide gas, which is why its use in baking helps raise dough:

$$2\,NaHCO_3(s) \longrightarrow Na_2CO_3(s) + H_2O(l) + CO_2(g)$$

Baking *powder* is a mixture of $NaHCO_3$ and an acid. The two components of the mixture are kept from reacting by a starch filler. When water is added to the mixture, however, the two components dissolve and react, producing the carbon dioxide that forms pockets of gas in baked products. You can perform a simple test to determine if baking powder is still good (that is, whether the acid has not already slowly reacted with the sodium bicarbonate) by pouring some boiling water over a small sample of the baking powder. If the hot water produces bubbles, then the baking powder is still active. Alka-Seltzer is another common consumer product that employs sodium bicarbonate, in this case mixed with citric acid and aspirin. When immersed in water, the acid and carbonate react to produce carbon dioxide, creating the familiar fizz.

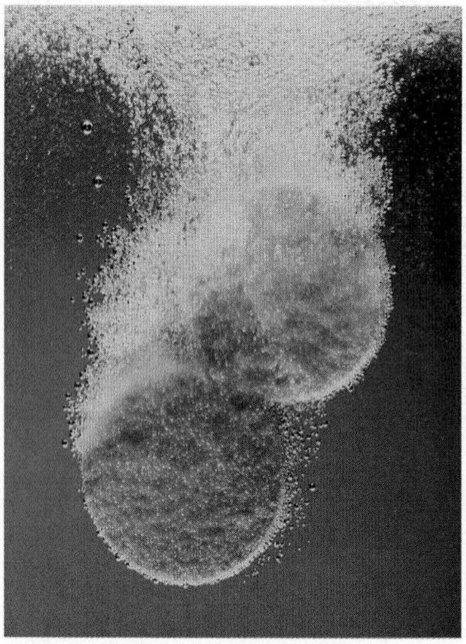

▲ Alka-Seltzer™ contains sodium bicarbonate mixed with citric acid and aspirin. When put in water, the acid and carbonate react.

ANSWER **NOW!**

24.4 Cc Conceptual Connection

CARBONATE SOLUBILITY As we saw in Chapter 5, the carbonates of metal ions other than group 1A are insoluble in water. Which action would increase their solubility?

(a) adding acid to the solution
(b) adding base to the solution
(c) increasing the amount of the solid carbonate in the solution

24.6 Nitrogen and Phosphorus: Essential Elements for Life

The group 5A elements range from nonmetallic nitrogen and phosphorus to metallic bismuth. Both nitrogen and phosphorus are nonmetals; they do not conduct electricity, and they form acidic oxides. Both have s^2p^3 electron configurations, and yet their chemical properties are very different. Phosphorus is much larger and less electronegative; it also has *d* orbitals available for bonding.

Elemental Nitrogen and Phosphorus

Nitrogen was identified in 1772 and phosphorus in 1669. Elemental nitrogen is a diatomic gas that composes about 78% of Earth's atmosphere by volume (see Section 6.6). To obtain elemental nitrogen, air is cooled below −196 °C, which causes it to liquefy. When the liquid air is warmed slightly, the nitrogen boils off, leaving liquid oxygen (which boils at the higher temperature of −183 °C). Passing the vaporized gas over hot copper metal purifies the nitrogen by removing residual oxygen (which reacts with the copper to form CuO). Nitrogen gas can also be separated from the other atmospheric gases by passing air through certain silicate materials called *zeolites,* which have channels of just the right diameter to separate gas molecules of different size. Some mineral sources for nitrogen are saltpeter (KNO_3) and Chile saltpeter ($NaNO_3$).

As we first saw in Section 10.5, nitrogen molecules have a triple bond between the two N atoms. The strength of the triple bond makes N_2 very stable, and attempts to break the bond have not been commercially successful. When nitrogen gas is heated with oxygen or hydrogen, nitric oxide (NO) or ammonia (NH_3), respectively, form with low yields. When nitrogen gas is heated with active metals, metal nitrides form. Aside from this, however, nitrogen gas is relatively unreactive.

The stability of elemental nitrogen makes it useful in creating a protective atmosphere to prevent oxidation in many industrial processes. For example, industrial furnaces employ a nitrogen atmosphere to anneal (hold at elevated temperature below the melting point) products made of metal, and chemical reactions sensitive to oxygen are carried out in a nitrogen atmosphere. Nitrogen is also used to preserve a variety of foods.

Elemental phosphorus was first isolated by accident from urine when Henning Brand (1630–1710), a physician and alchemist from Hamburg, Germany, was distilling urine in an ill-informed attempt to obtain gold from the golden liquid. The elemental form of phosphorus that Brand obtained instead was a white, waxy, flammable solid called **white phosphorus**. White phosphorus is highly toxic to humans. For over a hundred years, urine was the main source for elemental phosphorus. Today, however, phosphorus is obtained from a calcium phosphate mineral called apatite, [$Ca_3(PO_4)_2$]. The mineral is heated with sand and coke in an electric furnace:

$$\underset{\text{apatite}}{2\,Ca_3(PO_4)_2(s)} + \underset{\text{sand}}{6\,SiO_2(s)} + \underset{\text{coke}}{10\,C(s)} \longrightarrow \underset{\text{white phosphorus}}{P_4(g)} + 6\,CaSiO_3(l) + 10\,CO(g)$$

White phosphorus consists of P_4 molecules in a tetrahedral shape, with the phosphorus atoms at the corners of the tetrahedron (Figure 24.14▶). The bond angles between the three P atoms on any one face of the tetrahedron are small (60°) and strained, making the P_4 molecule unstable and reactive. White phosphorus spontaneously burns in air; it is normally stored under water to prevent contact with air.

When heated to about 300 °C in the absence of air, white phosphorus slightly changes its structure to a different allotrope called **red phosphorus**, which is amorphous. The general structure of red phosphorus is similar to that of white phosphorus, except that one of the bonds between two phosphorus atoms in the tetrahedron is broken (Figure 24.15▶). The two phosphorus atoms link to other phosphorus atoms, making chains that vary in structure.

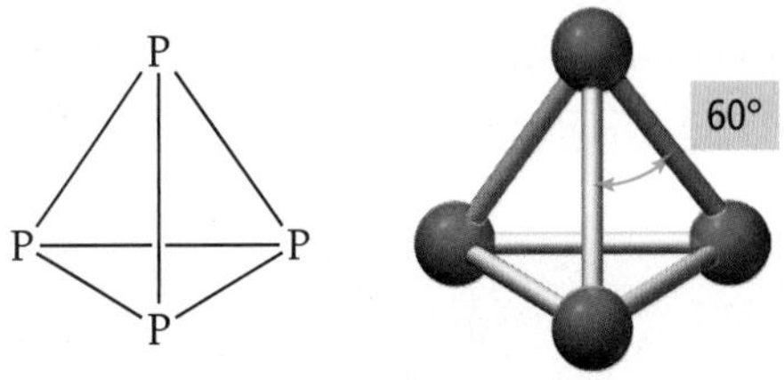

▲ **FIGURE 24.14 White Phosphorus** The small bond angle of 60° between the phosphorus atoms at the corners of the tetrahedron puts a great strain on the structure and makes the P_4 molecule unstable.

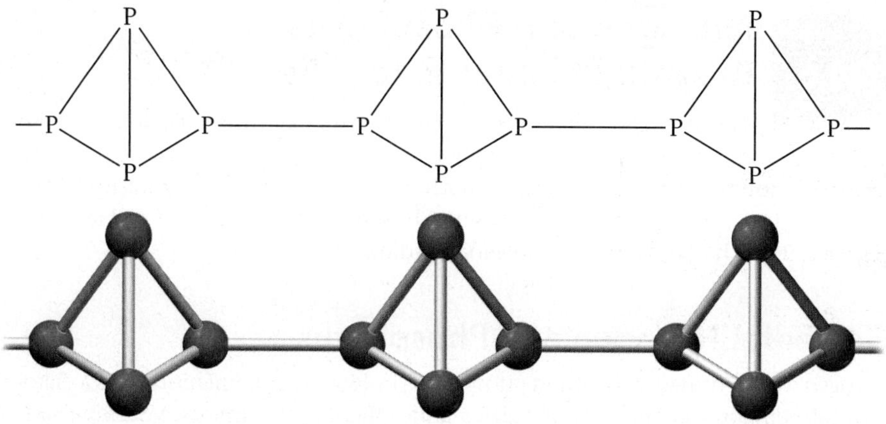

▶ **FIGURE 24.15 Red Phosphorus** Red phosphorus consists of chains of phosphorus atoms that form amorphous structures.

Red phosphorus is neither as reactive nor as toxic as white phosphorus, and even though it is also flammable, it can be stored in air. Red phosphorus is used commercially in applications such as match heads. Rubbing a match head onto a surface produces enough heat (through friction) to ignite the phosphorus. Most strike-anywhere matches feature the phosphorus compound tetraphosphorus trisulfide (P_4S_3) and an oxidizing agent, potassium chlorate ($KClO_3$).

A third allotrope of phosphorus is **black phosphorus**. Black phosphorus is obtained by heating white phosphorus under pressure. This form of phosphorus is the most thermodynamically stable form and therefore the least reactive. Black phosphorus has a layered structure similar to that of graphite.

TABLE 24.4 ■ Oxidation States of Various Nitrogen Compounds

Nitrogen-Containing Compound	Oxidation State
NH_3	−3
N_2H_4	−2
H_2NOH	−1
HN_3	$-\frac{1}{3}$
N_2	0
N_2O	+1
NO	+2
N_2O_3, NF_3	+3
NO_2, N_2O_4	+4
N_2O_5, HNO_3	+5

Nitrogen Compounds

Nitrogen, with a valence electron configuration of $2s^22p^3$, can gain three electrons or lose five electrons to obtain an octet. Nitrogen forms many covalent compounds with oxidation states from −3 to +5, as shown in Table 24.4.

Nitrogen Hydrides

The most common nitrogen hydride is **ammonia** (NH_3), the strong-smelling compound in which nitrogen displays its lowest oxidation state (−3). Ammonia is important to humans because it reacts with sulfuric acid (or phosphoric acid) to produce ammonium salts for fertilizers:

$$2\,NH_3(g) + H_2SO_4(aq) \longrightarrow (NH_4)_2SO_4(aq)$$

For hundreds of years, natural biological materials such as animal manure were used as nitrogen-containing fertilizers. In the 1800s, however, the nitrogen-bearing nitrate mineral $NaNO_3$ was discovered in Chile (and named Chile saltpeter). This nitrate mineral became an important source of fertilizer and made the country of Chile very wealthy. However, because Chile saltpeter was a limited source, chemists were continually striving to develop a new source.

The obvious *unlimited* source of nitrogen is the atmosphere, but the strong triple bond in elemental nitrogen renders it unusable by plants. In order to be used as fertilizer, elemental nitrogen has to be *fixed*, which means that it has to be converted into a nitrogen-containing compound such as NH_3. However, the direct reaction of nitrogen gas with hydrogen gas to form ammonia is very slow and produces low yields of ammonia under normal conditions:

$$N_2(g) + 3\,H_2(g) \rightleftharpoons 2\,NH_3(g)$$

In the early 1900s, German chemist Fritz Haber studied the equilibrium conditions for this reaction and showed that high pressures and lower temperatures favored the product. Carrying out the reaction at a higher pressure and using a catalyst to increase the reaction rate, the industrial process for producing ammonia from nitrogen gas and hydrogen gas—now called the **Haber-Bosch process**—became practical by the mid-1930s. This process is the main industrial process for making ammonia and fixing nitrogen for many uses, including fertilizers and explosives.

Hydrazine (N_2H_4) is another nitrogen and hydrogen compound in which nitrogen has a negative oxidation state (−2). Hydrazine is the nitrogen analog of hydrogen peroxide; it has a bond between nitrogen atoms that is similar to the bond between oxygen atoms in hydrogen peroxide (Figure 24.16▼). Hydrazine, like hydrogen peroxide, is a colorless liquid. However, while hydrogen peroxide is a powerful oxidizing agent, hydrazine is a powerful reducing agent, as shown in the following reactions:

$$\underset{-2\ +1}{N_2H_4(l)} + \underset{+1\ -1}{2\,H_2O_2(l)} \longrightarrow \underset{0}{N_2(g)} + \underset{+1\ -2}{4\,H_2O(g)}$$

Reduction (O: −1 → −2); Oxidation (N: −2 → 0)

$$\underset{-2\ +1}{N_2H_4(aq)} + \underset{0}{2\,I_2(aq)} \longrightarrow \underset{0}{N_2(g)} + \underset{+1\ -1}{4\,HI(aq)}$$

Reduction (I: 0 → −1); Oxidation (N: −2 → 0)

$$\underset{-2\ +1}{N_2H_4(aq)} + \underset{+2}{2\,Pb^{2+}(aq)} \longrightarrow \underset{0}{N_2(g)} + \underset{0}{2\,Pb(s)} + \underset{+1}{4\,H^+(aq)}$$

Reduction (Pb: +2 → 0); Oxidation (N: −2 → 0)

The oxidation state of each atom appears directly below its symbol. Notice that in each reaction, nitrogen is oxidized and causes the reduction of the other reactant.

Hydrogen azide (HN_3) is a nitrogen and hydrogen compound with a higher nitrogen-to-hydrogen ratio than ammonia or hydrazine. Ammonia and hydrazine are both basic:

$$N_2H_4(aq) + H_2O(l) \longrightarrow N_2H_5^+(aq) + OH^-(aq)$$
$$NH_3(aq) + H_2O(l) \longrightarrow NH_4^+(aq) + OH^-(aq)$$

Hydrogen azide, by contrast, is acidic, ionizing in water to form the azide ion (N_3^-):

$$HN_3(aq) + H_2O(l) \longrightarrow H_3O^+(aq) + N_3^-(aq)$$

Hydrogen azide is thermodynamically unstable compared to its constituent elements and reacts explosively to produce hydrogen and nitrogen gas:

$$2\,HN_3(l) \longrightarrow H_2(g) + 3\,N_2(g)$$

The sodium azide salt is a stable solid at room temperature, but at elevated temperatures, or with a spark, it quickly forms elemental sodium and nitrogen gas:

$$2\,NaN_3(s) \longrightarrow 2\,Na(l) + 3\,N_2(g)$$

The large volume of N_2 gas that forms from a small volume of $NaN_3(s)$ is the basis for airbags in automobiles. However, pure sodium azide also forms liquid sodium, which is dangerous because of its high reactivity. Therefore, other components, such as KNO_3 and SiO_2 are added to the mixture in airbags to react with the liquid sodium:

$$10\,Na(l) + 2\,KNO_3(s) \longrightarrow K_2O(s) + 5\,Na_2O(s) + N_2(g)$$
$$2\,K_2O(s) + SiO_2(s) \longrightarrow K_4SiO_4(s)$$
$$2\,Na_2O(s) + SiO_2(s) \longrightarrow Na_4SiO_4(s)$$

The overall reaction produces the large volume of nitrogen gas required to fill an automobile airbag quickly, along with harmless potassium and sodium silicates.

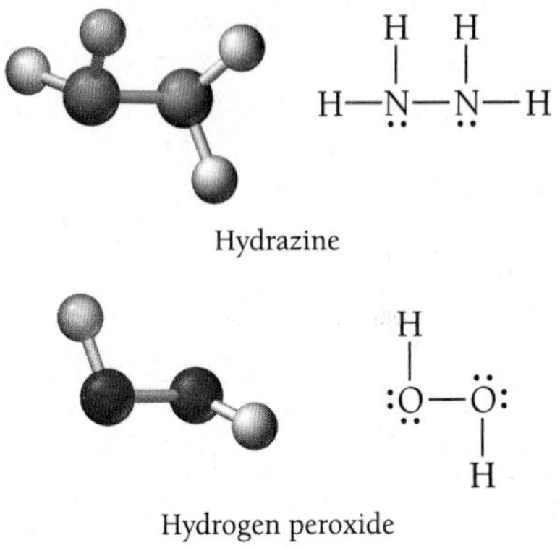

▲ **FIGURE 24.16 Hydrazine and Hydrogen Peroxide** Hydrazine forms a structure similar to hydrogen peroxide with an N—N bond in the place of the O—O bond.

Nitrogen Oxides

Under certain conditions, especially high temperatures, nitrogen is oxidized by oxygen to form a number of different oxides. For example, during lightning storms, nitrogen monoxide (NO) gas forms in the upper atmosphere:

$$N_2(g) + O_2(g) \xrightarrow{\text{lighting}} 2\,NO(g)$$

Other nitrogen oxides, such as nitrogen dioxide and dinitrogen trioxide, form from the further oxidation of nitrogen monoxide:

$$2\,NO(g) + O_2(g) \longrightarrow 2\,NO_2(g)$$
$$NO(g) + NO_2(g) \longrightarrow N_2O_3(l)$$

All nitrogen oxides are thermodynamically unstable and eventually decompose into their constituent elements or react to form more stable compounds. However, many of these reactions are kinetically slow, so some nitrogen oxides persist for long periods of time.

The most important nitrogen oxide, because of its significance in biological systems, is probably nitrogen monoxide (NO), also called nitric oxide. In 1987, nitrogen monoxide was named molecule of the year by the journal *Science* because of several discoveries related to its biological functions. For example, NO helps control blood pressure through blood vessel dilation, it is important in memory and digestion, and it plays major roles in inducing male erections and female uterine contractions. The ability to adjust NO levels is a key role of the medications that treat erectile dysfunction (such as Viagra).

Earlier in this section, we learned that lightning forms NO in the atmosphere. In Sections 3.6 and 17.12 we saw that NO and NO_2, formed as by-products of fossil fuel combustion, are among the important precursors of acid rain. Nitrogen monoxide and nitrogen dioxide are both reactive free radicals (they contain unpaired electrons). At low temperature, two NO_2 molecules dimerize to form N_2O_4, pairing their two lone electrons. If N_2O_4 is heated, it decomposes back to NO_2. Consequently, the equilibrium between NO_2 and N_2O_4 is highly temperature-dependent, as we saw in Section 16.9:

$$\underset{\text{colorless}}{N_2O_4(g)} \xrightarrow{\text{heat}} \underset{\text{reddish brown}}{2\,NO_2(g)}$$

Dinitrogen monoxide (N_2O), also called nitrous oxide, is a good oxidizing agent. It can support the combustion of active metals:

$$Mg(s) + N_2O(g) \longrightarrow MgO(s) + N_2(g)$$

Dinitrogen monoxide is unstable when heated, decomposing into nitrogen and oxygen gas:

$$2\,N_2O(g) \xrightarrow{\text{heat}} 2\,N_2(g) + O_2(g)$$

Dinitrogen monoxide (often referred to as "nitrous" or laughing gas) is used as an anesthetic by dentists and to pressurize food dispensers (such as whipped-cream dispensers). Commercially, N_2O is produced by the decomposition of ammonium nitrate:

$$NH_4NO_3(aq) \xrightarrow{\text{heat}} N_2O(g) + 2\,H_2O(l)$$

Nitric Acid, Nitrates, and Nitrides

Nitric acid is an important commercial product of nitrogen. In an electric furnace, nitric acid forms from nitrogen and oxygen gas:

$$2\,N_2(g) + 5\,O_2(g) + 2\,H_2O(g) \longrightarrow 4\,HNO_3(g)$$

This reaction is thermodynamically favored, but it is kinetically slow. (What would happen to our atmosphere if this reaction were thermodynamically *and* kinetically favored?) Because of the slow speed of this reaction, a more efficient process, called the **Ostwald process**, is used to commercially produce nitric acid.

The first step of the Ostwald process involves passing ammonia gas over hot metal gauze at 600–700 °C to form NO gas. The gauze is made of metals such as platinum and rhodium, which are good catalysts for this reaction:

$$4\,NH_3(g) + 5\,O_2(g) \xrightarrow{\text{catalyst}} 4\,NO(g) + 6\,H_2O(g)$$

Next, additional oxygen is added to oxidize the NO to NO_2 gas, which is then passed through a water spray to form nitric acid:

$$3\,NO_2(g) + H_2O(l) \longrightarrow 2\,HNO_3(aq) + NO(g)$$

These steps are similar to the natural process that forms acid rain from NO and NO_2 gas in the atmosphere. The NO gas made during this last step can be recycled back to form more NO_2 and eventually more HNO_3.

Nitric acid is a strong acid that completely ionizes in water. Concentrated nitric acid is 70% nitric acid by mass, or 16 M. A small fraction of the HNO_3 in a bottle of concentrated nitric acid will react with water to form NO_2, a reddish brown gas that, in small amounts, gives the acid its characteristic pale yellow color:

$$4\,HNO_3(aq) \longrightarrow 4\,NO_2(g) + O_2(g) + 2\,H_2O(l)$$

The main commercial uses of nitric acid are in the production of fertilizers and explosives. Over a million tons of ammonium nitrate fertilizer is produced annually by the reaction between ammonia and nitric acid:

$$NH_3(g) + HNO_3(aq) \longrightarrow NH_4NO_3(aq)$$

Besides being a good fertilizer, ammonium nitrate and some other nitrates are also good explosives. Ammonium nitrate explodes according to the following reaction:

$$2\,NH_4NO_3(s) \xrightarrow{\text{heat}} 2\,N_2O(g) + 4\,H_2O(g) \longrightarrow 2\,N_2(g) + O_2(g) + 4\,H_2O(g)$$

Metal nitrates are responsible for the various colors seen in fireworks displays. The different metal ions emit different colors as the nitrate explodes in air. For example, copper(II) nitrate produces a green-colored light according to the reaction:

$$2\,Cu(NO_3)_2(g) \xrightarrow{\text{heat}} 2\,CuO(s) + 4\,NO_2(g) + O_2(g) + \text{green light}$$

As we learned in Chapter 5, nitrates are very soluble in water. For reactions that need soluble metal cations, a nitrate compound is a good source for the cation without interference from the anion.

Nitrites are compounds containing the nitrite ion (NO_2^-). Sodium nitrite is used as a food preservative because it kills *Clostridium botulinum* bacteria, the cause of botulism, and because it keeps meat from discoloring when the meat is exposed to air. Consumers have voiced concerns over this practice, both because it hides the true age of the meat and because the nitrites can react with amines in the meat to form compounds called nitrosamines, which are suspected cancer-causing agents. However, no evidence exists to support the idea that nitrites at levels currently used in meats increase cancer risk in humans.

Phosphorus Compounds

Phosphorus has a valence electron configuration of $3s^23p^3$, similar to that of nitrogen. Phosphorus also forms many compounds, with oxidation states ranging from −3 through +5. The most stable compounds have the +5 oxidation state.

Phosphine

Phosphine (PH_3) is a colorless, poisonous gas that smells like decaying fish. In phosphine, phosphorus has an oxidation state of −3. Since phosphorus is less electronegative than nitrogen, phosphine is less polar than ammonia. Phosphine forms from the hydrolysis of metal phosphides:

$$Ca_3P_2(s) + 6\,H_2O(l) \longrightarrow 2\,PH_3(g) + 3\,Ca(OH)_2(aq)$$

The disproportionation of white phosphorus in a basic solution can also produce phosphine:

$$2\,P_4(s) + 3\,OH^-(aq) + 9\,H_2O(l) \longrightarrow 5\,PH_3(g) + 3\,H_2PO_4^-(aq)$$

Disproportionation is a reaction in which an element is both reduced and oxidized during the same reaction. In this equation the phosphorus in P_4 is both oxidized and reduced. Phosphorus has an oxidation number of 0 in P_4 and is reduced to −3 in PH_3 and oxidized to +5 in $H_2PO_4^-$.

When heated, phosphine decomposes to phosphorus and hydrogen:

$$4\,PH_3(g) \longrightarrow P_4(s) + 6\,H_2(g)$$

Like ammonia, phosphine can form phosphonium compounds such as PH_4Cl and PH_4I. Unlike ammonia, phosphine is not basic in aqueous solution.

Phosphorus Halides

When phosphorus reacts with the halogens, it forms phosphorus halides, the most important of which generally have the formulas PX_3 and PX_5:

$$P_4(s) + 6\,Cl_2(g) \longrightarrow 4\,PCl_3(l)$$

$$P_4(s) + 10\,Cl_2(g) \longrightarrow 4\,PCl_5(s) \quad \text{(with excess chlorine)}$$

Phosphorus halides react with water to form phosphoric acid and the corresponding hydrogen halide. For example, PCl_3 reacts with water:

$$PCl_3(l) + 3\,H_2O(l) \longrightarrow H_3PO_4(aq) + 3\,HCl(aq)$$

Reaction of PCl_3 with oxygen at room temperature forms phosphorus oxychloride:

$$2\,PCl_3(l) + O_2(g) \longrightarrow 2\,POCl_3(l)$$

Other phosphorus oxyhalides form as a result of the reactions of $POCl_3$ with metal fluorides or iodides:

$$POCl_3(l) + 3\,NaI(s) \longrightarrow POI_3(g) + 3\,NaCl(s)$$

The phosphorus halides and oxyhalides are important compounds in organic chemistry and serve as starting materials for the production of many phosphorus-containing compounds. Many of the key compounds in pesticides, oil additives, fire retardants for clothing, and surfactants (agents that act at surfaces), for example, are commercially made from phosphorus oxyhalides.

Phosphorus Oxides

White phosphorus reacts directly with oxygen to form phosphorus oxides, as in the reaction shown here:

$$P_4(s) + 5\,O_2(g) \longrightarrow P_4O_{10}(g)$$

The product depends on the amount of oxygen. Tetraphosphorus hexaoxide, $P_4O_6(s)$, forms when oxygen is limited, and tetraphosphorus decaoxide, $P_4O_{10}(s)$, forms when greater amounts of oxygen are available.

Phosphorus oxides form interesting cage structures (Figure 24.17▼). We can visualize the P_4O_6 structure as a tetrahedron with a phosphorus atom at each of the vertices and an oxygen atom between each pair of phosphorus atoms. The P_4O_{10} structure has four additional oxygen atoms bonded to each phosphorus atom at the vertices of each tetrahedron.

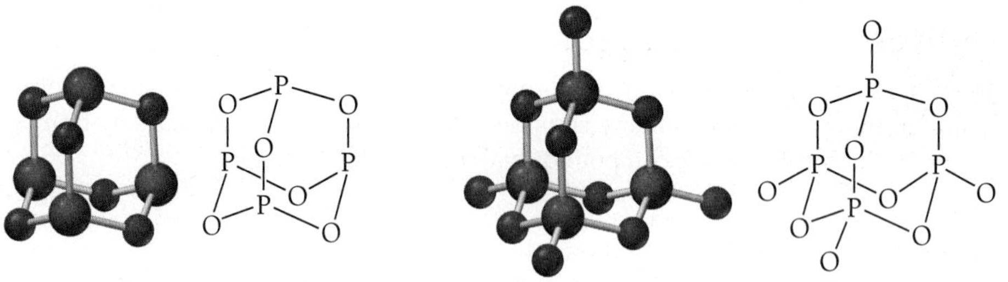

P_4O_6 P_4O_{10}

▶ **FIGURE 24.17 Tetraphosphorus Hexaoxide and Decaoxide, P_4O_6 and P_4O_{10}** The P_4O_6 structure has the P atoms at the corners of a tetrahedron and the O atoms on the edges. The P_4O_{10} structure has O atoms also bonded to the P atoms at the corners.

Phosphoric Acid and Phosphates

Phosphoric acid and phosphates are among the most important phosphorus-containing compounds. Phosphoric acid is a colorless solid that melts at 42 °C. Concentrated phosphoric acid is 85% phosphoric acid by mass, or 14.7 M. Phosphoric acid is produced from the oxidation of white phosphorus to tetraphosphorus decaoxide (see previous reaction), which is then reacted with water:

$$P_4O_{10}(s) + 6\,H_2O(l) \longrightarrow 4\,H_3PO_4(aq)$$

This method produces a very pure phosphoric acid. A less pure product forms from the reaction of calcium phosphate (a mineral source of phosphate) with concentrated sulfuric acid:

$$Ca_3(PO_4)_2(s) + 3\,H_2SO_4(aq) \longrightarrow 3\,CaSO_4(s) + 2\,H_3PO_4(aq)$$

One direct use of phosphoric acid is rust removal. In steel production, thick steel slabs must be heated and rolled into thinner ones. During this process, the hot steel is exposed to air, which oxidizes the surface. To remove this rust, the thin steel sheets pass through phosphoric or hydrochloric acid baths, which dissolve the rust from the metal.

A major use of phosphoric acid is fertilizer production. In the past, phosphorus-containing materials such as fish, bones, and bat guano were used as fertilizer. Sulfuric acid decomposes bones to make phosphorus compounds that are more readily taken up by plants. Today many different phosphorus compounds have been developed specifically as fertilizers for various types of plants.

Detergent manufacturers use sodium phosphate compounds as additives. Compounds such as sodium pyrophosphate ($Na_4P_2O_7$) and sodium tripolyphosphate ($Na_5P_3O_{10}$) remove metal ions such as Ca^{2+} and Mg^{2+} from hard water, increasing the effectiveness of the detergent and preventing scum rings on sinks and tubs. However, phosphate compounds in detergents are being replaced by other compounds because of ecological problems—primarily the overfertilization of algae in bodies of water—associated with the phosphates.

Phosphoric acid and phosphates are also important chemicals in the food industry. Phosphoric acid is a soft drink additive. At a low concentration, phosphoric acid is nontoxic and adds a tart, acidic taste to soft drinks. It also prevents bacterial growth in the soda. Table 24.5 summarizes the uses of phosphates in the food industry.

TABLE 24.5 ■ Uses of Phosphates in the Food Industry

Phosphoric acid, H_3PO_4	Flavor agent in soda, yeast nutrient
Sodium dihydrogen phosphate (also sodium phosphate monobasic), NaH_2PO_4	Emulsifier, pH buffering agent
Sodium hydrogen phosphate (also sodium phosphate dibasic), Na_2HPO_4	Baking powder, fermentation auxiliary
Sodium hexametaphosphate, $(NaPO_3)_6$	Preservative, pH buffering agent
Sodium trimetaphosphate, $(NaPO_3)_3$	Starch modifier, juice dispersant
Iron(III) pyrophosphate nonahydrate, $Fe_4(P_2O_7)_3 \cdot 9\ H_2O$	Nutritional supplement
Sodium monofluorophosphate, Na_2PO_3F	Fluoride source for toothpaste
Pyrophosphate, $P_2O_7^{4-}$	Tartar control for toothpaste

24.7 Oxygen

The group 6A elements have an s^2p^4 valence electron configuration and a strong attraction for electrons. They obtain a full octet by gaining only two more electrons. Because of its small size, oxygen is a much stronger oxidizing agent than the rest of the group 6A elements. Oxygen has the second highest electronegativity of any element (3.5), while the rest of the 6A elements range from 2.5 to 2.0. Because of its high abundance (almost half the mass of Earth's crust is composed of oxygen) and its high reactivity, oxygen occurs in many common compounds, including metal oxides, carbonates, silicates, hydrates, and water. Oxygen is also critical for life; the oxidation of biomolecules by oxygen provides energy for most living systems on Earth.

Elemental Oxygen

Oxygen exists naturally as a colorless, odorless, diatomic, nonpolar gas. It condenses to a pale blue liquid at −183 °C. Oxygen is slightly soluble in water (0.04 g in 1 L or 0.001 M at 25 °C). This rather low concentration of oxygen is enough to support life in aquatic environments. A few types of living systems that dwell deep in the ocean near vents that exude sulfur-containing fumes base their life processes on sulfur chemistry rather than oxygen chemistry.

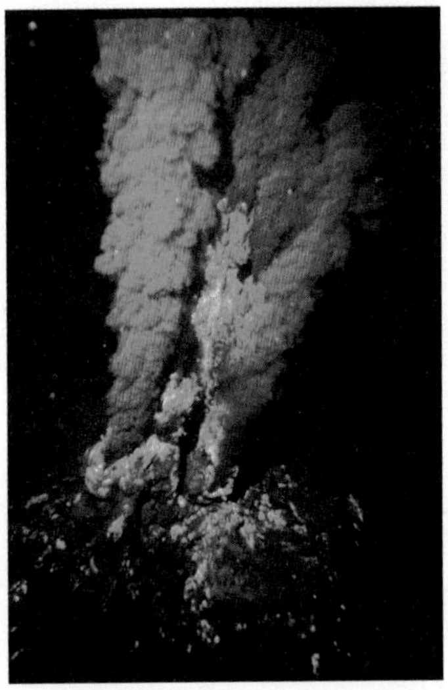

▲ Black smokers are vents found under the ocean that provide energy based on sulfur chemistry for life dwelling near the vents.

Today, about 21% of Earth's atmosphere is composed of O_2, but this was not always the case. Earth's early atmosphere was reducing (rather than oxidizing) and contained hydrogen, methane, ammonia, and carbon dioxide. About 2.7 billion years ago, cyanobacteria (blue-green algae) began to convert the carbon dioxide and water to oxygen by photosynthesis. It took hundreds of millions of years to reach the current oxygen levels.

Joseph Priestley (1733–1804), an English scientist and minister, is credited with discovering oxygen. In 1774, he isolated oxygen by focusing sunlight on mercury(II) oxide and collecting the gas that was released as the red powder oxide formed liquid mercury. He tested the gas by using it to make a candle burn more brightly. He carried out a number of experiments with oxygen over the years, including bravely breathing his newfound gas. Antoine Lavoisier (1743–1794) is credited with recognizing that oxygen is necessary for combustion. He described combustion as the reaction of a substance with oxygen (and not the loss of a substance). These discoveries and explanations were important steps in the development of modern chemistry.

Oxygen is one of the most abundantly produced industrial chemicals. The major production method is the *fractionation* of air. Fractionation involves cooling air until its components liquefy. Then the air is warmed, and components such as N_2 and Ar are separated out, leaving oxygen behind. Most commercial oxygen is stored and transported as a gas in tanks under high pressure. Another method for the production of oxygen is the electrolysis of water. Passing an electric current through water containing a small amount of an electrolyte produces hydrogen gas at the cathode and oxygen gas at the anode (see Section 20.8). Because of the large amount of electricity needed, however, electrolysis is not a cost-efficient method for oxygen production:

$$2\,H_2O(l) \xrightarrow{\text{electrical current}} 2\,H_2(g) + O_2(g)$$

In the laboratory, oxygen can be produced by heating and decomposing metal oxides and other oxygen-containing compounds. The oxides of mercury, silver, and gold lose all their oxygen when heated, while the oxides of other metals, such as barium, lose only some of their oxygen:

$$2\,HgO(s) \xrightarrow{\text{heat}} 2\,Hg(l) + O_2(g)$$

$$2\,BaO_2(s) \xrightarrow{\text{heat}} 2\,BaO(s) + O_2(g)$$

Metal nitrates and chlorates also yield oxygen when heated. A catalyst, such as manganese oxide or iron oxide, can make these reactions very fast and dangerous:

$$2\,NaNO_3(s) \xrightarrow{\text{heat}} 2\,NaNO_2(s) + O_2(g)$$

$$2\,KClO_3(s) \xrightarrow[\text{heat}]{\text{catalyst}} 2\,KCl\,(s) + 3\,O_2(g)$$

Uses for Oxygen

The greatest industrial use for oxygen is the enrichment of the air in a blast furnace for the conversion of high-carbon iron to steel. Large quantities of oxygen are also used in oxyhydrogen or oxyacetylene torches for the cutting of metals. In addition, oxygen is used to create artificial air for use underwater, during high-altitude travel, and in safety equipment.

Oxygen plays an important role in the treatment of a number of medical conditions, such as acute and chronic lung diseases and heart disorders. Generally, patients use masks or nasal catheters to receive oxygen from a tank of compressed oxygen. However, portable oxygen concentrators have been developed that use molecular sieves to separate and concentrate oxygen from air. Hyperbaric oxygen therapy is the application of high oxygen levels to patients with skin wounds, such as those with skin grafts or hard-to-heal wounds associated with diabetes. The high oxygen level kills anaerobic bacteria that can infect such wounds.

Oxides

As a strong oxidizing agent, oxygen reacts with most other elements to form oxides. We classify oxides according to the oxidation state of oxygen in the oxide (Table 24.6). The type of oxide that forms depends on the size and charge of the metal. Regular oxides are more stable for the smaller ions with a higher charge. Superoxides are more stable for the larger ions with a smaller charge.

TABLE 24.6 ■ Types of Oxides

Class	Ion	Oxidation State of O	Example
Oxide	O^{2-}	−2	Li_2O, MgO
Peroxide	O_2^{2-}	−1	Na_2O_2, BaO_2
Superoxide	O_2^{-}	$-\frac{1}{2}$	RbO_2, CsO_2

Oxygen also reacts with many nonmetals to form covalent compounds. Many of these nonmetals form several different binary oxides. For example, we have already seen that carbon forms CO and CO_2 and that nitrogen forms N_2O, NO, N_2O_3, NO_2, N_2O_4, and N_2O_5.

OXIDES Which compound is a superoxide?

(a) K_2O

(b) K_2O_2

(c) KO_2

24.5 Cc Conceptual Connection

ANSWER **NOW!**

Ozone

Ozone (O_3), an allotrope of oxygen, is a toxic blue diamagnetic gas with a strong odor. People can detect the smell at levels as low as 0.01 ppm, and the odor is often noticed in electrical storms or near electrical equipment because the gas forms from O_2 by an electrical discharge. Ozone is denser than O_2 and condenses to a deep blue liquid at −112 °C. Ozone is naturally made by the irradiation of O_2 with ultraviolet light in the upper atmosphere:

$$3\,O_2(g) \xrightarrow{\text{UV radiation}} 2\,O_3(g)$$

Ozone is also produced by passing O_2 gas through an electric field. The volume of gas decreases as the O_2 is converted to O_3. Ozone is produced industrially by the electrolysis of cold concentrated sulfuric acid.

Thermodynamically unstable, ozone decomposes spontaneously to oxygen:

$$2\,O_3(g) \longrightarrow 3\,O_2(g)$$

Ozone is used commercially as a strong oxidizing agent. For example, ozone can oxidize NO_2 to N_2O_5 or PbS to $PbSO_4$:

$$2\,NO_2(g) + O_3(g) \longrightarrow N_2O_5(g) + O_2(g)$$

$$PbS(s) + 4\,O_3(g) \longrightarrow PbSO_4(s) + 4\,O_2(g)$$

Ozone kills bacteria and is an environmentally safe replacement for chlorine in water-purification plants because the only by-product is O_2. However, since ozone naturally decomposes, it must constantly be replenished—an economic drawback that limits its use.

The air we breathe contains ozone because it forms as a by-product of fossil fuel combustion. Since it is a strong oxidizing agent, it is a harmful substance. In the lower atmosphere, ozone damages the lungs and skin, stings the eyes, and damages most plant and animal tissues. Ozone also reacts with many types of plastic and rubber materials, causing them to become brittle and to crack.

As we also saw in Section 7.10, the layer of ozone in the upper atmosphere plays an important role in the absorption of harmful ultraviolet radiation from the sun. It absorbs the UV radiation and breaks apart to O_2 and O. This oxygen atom will often react with another O_2 molecule to re-form as ozone. During this cycle, each ozone molecule absorbs many ultraviolet photons. Recall from Section 3.9 that the ozone layer has been depleted by chlorofluorocarbons (CFCs). However, legislation has banned CFCs in the hope that their reduction will help the ozone layer to recover.

24.8 Sulfur: A Dangerous but Useful Element

Like oxygen, sulfur is a nonmetal that belongs to the 6A family. However, sulfur's 3*p* orbitals extend farther out from the nucleus than do oxygen's 2*p* orbitals. Consequently, sulfur is larger and is a much weaker oxidizing agent than oxygen. Unlike oxygen, which forms compounds with *only* negative oxidation states, sulfur forms compounds with both negative and positive oxidation states. Sulfur, selenium, and tellurium generally form covalent compounds with +4 or +6 oxidation states, forming anions only when bonding with highly electropositive metals. Sulfur is also much less abundant than oxygen, yet it still composes about 0.06% of the mass of Earth's crust.

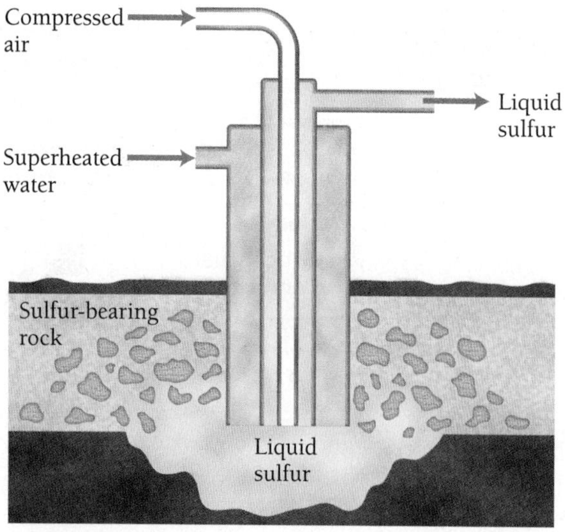

▲ **FIGURE 24.18 The Frasch Process** The Frasch process extracts molten sulfur from the ground by forcing superheated water into beds of deposited solid sulfur.

Elemental Sulfur

Elemental sulfur occurs in a few natural deposits, mostly deep underground in the Gulf Coast area of the United States and in eastern Europe. These deposits are believed to have formed as a by-product of anaerobic bacteria that decomposed sulfur-containing minerals over many years. The **Frasch process**, which allows us to recover sulfur from the earth, is diagrammed in Figure 24.18◀. Superheated water and compressed air are forced down long pipes into the sulfur deposits. The hot water melts the sulfur, which is pushed up to the surface along with the hot water through a third pipe. Some sulfur deposits also occur at Earth's surface—often in hot springs—where volcanic activity has made the sulfur accessible (Figure 24.19▼).

Sulfur has several allotropes; the most common naturally occurring allotrope of sulfur is composed of an S_8 ring structure called cyclooctasulfur. Most of the different allotropes have ring structures with rings ranging in size from S_6 to S_{20}. When heated above its melting point of 112 °C, cyclooctasulfur forms a straw-yellow liquid with low viscosity. Above 150 °C, the rings begin to break, and the sulfur becomes a darker, more viscous liquid as the broken rings entangle one another. The color is darkest at 180 °C when the liquid becomes very viscous and pours very slowly, as can be seen in the accompanying photo. Above this temperature, however, the intermolecular forces between the S_8 chains weaken, and the liquid becomes less viscous again. If the hot liquid is poured into cold water, the sulfur will quench into an amorphous solid (Figure 24.20▼). Initially, this amorphous material is flexible like a plastic, but it hardens into a brittle solid.

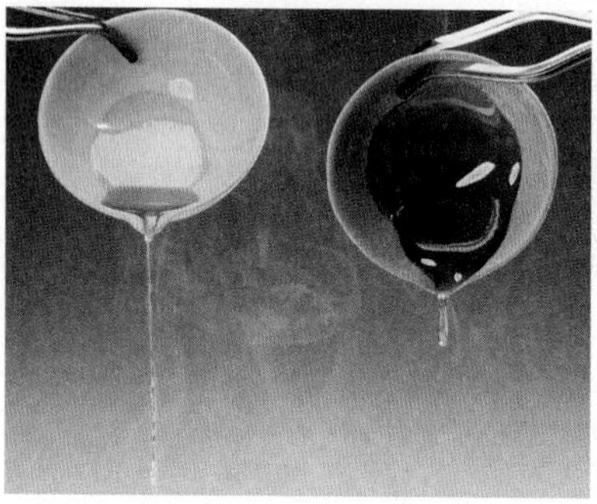

▲ Molten sulfur below 150 °C (left) and nearing 180 °C (right).

The Frasch process, while important, provides less than one-third of the world's sulfur; sulfur is a by-product of a number of other industrial processes and is thus recovered from them. For example, dihydrogen monosulfide (H_2S), which is commonly called hydrogen sulfide, is a component of natural gas. The H_2S is separated from the other components by passing the gas through organic solvents such as ethanolamine. The H_2S dissolves in the organic solvent:

$$\underset{\text{ethanolamine}}{HOC_2H_4NH_2(l)} + H_2S(g) \longrightarrow HOC_2H_4NH_3^+(\text{solvent}) + HS^-(\text{solute})$$

▲ **FIGURE 24.19 Sulfur Deposits** Some sulfur deposits can also be found at Earth's surface where volcanic activity has brought the element to the surface.

▲ **FIGURE 24.20 Quenching Liquid Sulfur** When hot liquid sulfur is poured into cold water, the sulfur quenches into an amorphous solid.

The H_2S is recovered and oxidized to elemental sulfur through a two-step process—the **Claus process**—that accounts for over 50% of all sulfur produced:

$$2\,H_2S(g) + 3\,O_2(g) \longrightarrow 2\,SO_2(g) + 2\,H_2O(g)$$

$$4\,H_2S(g) + 2\,SO_2(g) \longrightarrow 6\,S(s) + 4\,H_2O(g)$$

The third major source of sulfur production is metal sulfide minerals, such as the mineral iron(II) disulfide (also known as iron pyrite). Roasting iron pyrite in the absence of air causes the sulfur to disproportionate (react with itself) to form iron(II) sulfide and elemental sulfur:

$$2\,FeS_2(s) \xrightarrow{\text{heat}} 2\,FeS(s) + S_2(g)$$

Alternatively, the metal sulfide can be roasted in air to oxidize the metal sulfide. The sulfur is then removed as sulfur dioxide:

$$2\,ZnS(s) + 3\,O_2(g) \longrightarrow 2\,ZnO(s) + 2\,SO_2(g)$$

Hydrogen Sulfide and Metal Sulfides

Hydrogen sulfide, a component of natural gas, is toxic and forms by the reactions of anaerobic bacteria on organic substances. Rotting vegetation and bogs are natural sources of H_2S for the atmosphere. Fortunately, we can detect the odor of H_2S (a rotten egg smell) at concentrations as low as 0.02 ppm, which pose no threat to our health. Levels as low as 10 ppm can cause nausea, and 100 ppm can cause death. The smell of H_2S becomes more difficult to detect at high levels because H_2S also has an anesthetic effect that dulls the sense of smell. Consequently, the sudden onset of strong H_2S odor is a reason to move quickly to fresh air.

It might initially seem that hydrogen sulfide (H_2S) would share chemical properties with water (H_2O), but it does not. Water has a larger bond angle (104.5°) than hydrogen sulfide (92.5°) and is much more polar. Because of its polarity, water forms strong hydrogen bonds, whereas hydrogen sulfide does not. In addition, the O—H bond is much stronger than the S—H bond. These differences result in a far lower boiling point and greater reactivity for hydrogen sulfide compared to water. Water is a stable molecule in the presence of air and oxygen. Hydrogen sulfide burns in air, reacting with oxygen to form elemental sulfur or sulfur oxides.

EXAMPLE 24.5 Balancing of and Assigning Oxidation States to Sulfur Reactions

Write a balanced equation for the reaction of O_2 and H_2S to form elemental S (in the form of S_8). Identify the change of the oxidation state for S.

SOLUTION

Write the skeletal equation. The products are elemental S_8 and H_2O.	$H_2S(g) + O_2(g) \longrightarrow H_2O(g) + S_8(s)$
Since hydrogen is initially balanced, balance S first, followed by H and O.	$8\,H_2S(g) + 4\,O_2(g) \longrightarrow 8\,H_2O(g) + S_8(s)$
Assign oxidation states to each element (see Section 5.9).	$\underset{+1\ -2}{8\,H_2S(g)} + \underset{0}{4\,O_2(g)} \longrightarrow \underset{+1\ -2}{8\,H_2O(g)} + \underset{0}{S_8(s)}$ Oxidation (S: −2 → 0) The oxidation state of S changes from −2 in H_2S to 0 in S_8; therefore, S is oxidized.

FOR PRACTICE 24.5 Write a balanced equation for the reaction of oxygen with H_2S to form SO_2. Identify the change of the oxidation state for S.

TABLE 24.7 ■ Common Metal Sulfides

Sulfide	Formula	Common Name	K_{sp} (at 25 °C)
Iron(II) disulfide	FeS_2	Pyrite	3.72×10^{-19}
Zinc sulfide	ZnS	Sphalerite	2.0×10^{-25}
Lead(II) sulfide	PbS	Galena	9.04×10^{-29}
Mercury(II) sulfide	HgS	Cinnabar	1.6×10^{-54}

Hydrogen sulfide forms from the reactions of metal sulfides with hydrochloric acid:

$$FeS(s) + 2\,HCl(aq) \longrightarrow FeCl_2(s) + H_2S(g)$$

Only a few of the metal sulfides, those with group 1A and 2A metals and Al, are very soluble in water. Some common metal sulfides and their solubility product constants are listed in Table 24.7. The low solubility of these sulfides allows the use of H_2S as a good analytical method to determine whether metal ions are present in a solution. Sodium sulfide is used to precipitate toxic metals from industrial waste sources.

Metal sulfides have a number of industrial uses, mostly because they are toxic to bacteria. For example, SeS_2 is a shampoo additive that kills bacteria and controls dandruff, and As_2S_3 kills parasites.

Sulfur Dioxide

Sulfur dioxide is another toxic sulfur compound. Under standard conditions, it is a colorless, dense gas that has an acidic taste. The acidic taste results from the reaction of the gas with the water in your mouth:

$$SO_2(g) + H_2O(l) \longrightarrow H_2SO_3(aq)$$

Sulfur dioxide forms naturally during volcanic activity when sulfides oxidize in the high volcanic temperatures. Sulfur dioxide is also a pollutant that forms during many industrial processes, such as coal and oil combustion and metal extraction. As we have seen, when the sulfur dioxide is emitted into the air, it reacts with oxygen and water to produce acid rain:

$$2\,SO_2(g) + 2\,H_2O(g) + O_2(g) \longrightarrow 2\,H_2SO_4(aq)$$

Sulfuric acid as a pollutant is destructive to plants, animals, and human-made structures (see Section 17.12).

To prevent the release of SO_2 into the atmosphere, industrial processes "scrub" their emissions to remove the SO_2. The exhaust gas flows through stacks lined with calcium carbonate that, when heated, capture sulfur oxides in the form of calcium sulfate dust:

$$CaCO_3(s) \xrightarrow{\text{heat}} CaO(s) + CO_2(g)$$

$$2\,CaO(s) + 2\,SO_2(g) + O_2(g) \longrightarrow 2\,CaSO_4(s)$$

The $CaSO_4$ dust is collected and disposed of. New uses for the tons of waste $CaSO_4$, such as discarded fireproof insulation, are needed.

One use for SO_2 capitalizes on its toxicity. Food producers spray fruits and other vegetation with a solution containing SO_2 to kill mold and preserve the fruit. As a result, the fruits and vegetables can be shipped throughout the world, making it possible for inhabitants of the Northern Hemisphere to enjoy summer fruits (from the Southern Hemisphere) in the winter.

Sulfuric Acid

The most important use of sulfur and its compounds is the production of sulfuric acid. In fact, sulfuric acid is the most abundantly produced chemical in the world because it is a strong acid, a strong oxidizing agent, and a good dehydrating agent. It is also plentiful and inexpensive. Sulfuric acid is used in fertilizers, color dyes, petrochemicals, paints, plastics, explosives, battery, steel, and detergent industries, to name just a few.

Pure H_2SO_4 melts at 10.4 °C and boils at 337 °C. At room temperature, it is an oily, dense liquid. Sulfuric acid reacts vigorously and exothermically with water. Pure or concentrated H_2SO_4 must be added to water slowly to avoid rapid heating, boiling, and splattering:

$$H_2SO_4(l) \xrightarrow{H_2O(l)} H_2SO_4(aq) \quad \text{highly exothermic}$$

The strong attraction between sulfuric acid and water makes sulfuric acid a very strong dehydrating agent. As shown in Figure 24.21▶, its affinity for water is strong enough to decompose some organic materials, such as sucrose:

$$C_{12}H_{22}O_{11}(s) + H_2SO_4(l) \longrightarrow 12\,C(s) + 11\,H_2O(g) + H_2SO_4(aq)$$

Sulfuric acid is produced industrially by a method known as the **contact process**, developed in the early twentieth century. In this method, elemental sulfur is first heated in air to form SO_2 gas, which is then heated in contact with a V_2O_5 catalyst to form SO_3 gas:

$$S(g) + O_2(g) \xrightarrow{\text{heat}} SO_2(g)$$

$$2\,SO_2(g) + O_2(g) \xrightarrow{V_2O_5\text{ catalyst}} 2\,SO_3(g)$$

The SO_3 gas is absorbed into concentrated sulfuric acid, producing a dense form of sulfuric acid called oleum, $H_2S_2O_7$, which produces H_2SO_4 when dissolved in water:

$$SO_3(g) + H_2SO_4(l) \longrightarrow H_2S_2O_7(l)$$

$$H_2S_2O_7(l) + H_2O(l) \longrightarrow 2\,H_2SO_4(aq)$$

As we have already seen, sulfuric acid is used in fertilizer production, which consumes a significant amount of the sulfuric acid produced.

▲ **FIGURE 24.21 Dehydration of Sucrose** Sulfuric acid dehydrates sucrose by removing the hydrogen and oxygen as water molecules and leaving carbon behind. The porous carbon foam forms because the reaction is very exothermic.

24.9 Halogens: Reactive Elements with High Electronegativity

The halogens are all one electron short of a noble gas electron configuration. They are the most electronegative elements in their respective periods and are therefore very reactive. They do not naturally occur in their elemental form. The source of most of the halogens (except fluorine) is the dissolved salts present in seawater. The major sources for fluorine are several different minerals, including fluorspar (CaF_2) and fluoroapatite [$Ca_{10}F_2(PO_4)_6$].

We have already seen some of the properties of the halogens, especially those that exhibit periodic trends, in Section 9.9. For example, the atomic radius of the halogens increases regularly from fluorine to iodine, as shown in Table 24.8. Due partly to its small size, fluorine has the highest electronegativity of all elements and is always found in oxidation states of −1 or 0. The other halogens can be found with oxidation states ranging from −1 to +7. The positive oxidation states occur when a halogen bonds to more electronegative elements such as fluorine or oxygen.

TABLE 24.8 ■ Selected Properties of the Halogens

Element	Melting Point (°C)	Boiling Point (°C)	Atomic Radius (pm)	Electronegativity
Fluorine	−219	−188	72	4.0
Chlorine	−101	−34	99	3.0
Bromine	−7	60	113	2.8
Iodine	114	185	133	2.5

EXAMPLE 24.6 Determining the Oxidation State of Halogens in Compounds

Calculate the oxidation state of Cl in each compound.

(a) ClO_3^- **(b)** HClO **(c)** Cl_2

SOLUTION

(a) For ClO_3^-, each O atom has an oxidation state of −2 for a total of −6 for all three O atoms. Therefore, the Cl atom has to have an oxidation state of +5 for the sum of the oxidation states to equal the charge of the ion $(5 - 6 = -1)$.

(b) For HClO, the O atom has an oxidation state of −2, and the H atom has an oxidation state of +1. Therefore, the Cl atom has to have an oxidation state of +1 to have a neutral charge $(1 + 1 - 2 = 0)$.

(c) For Cl_2, the Cl atoms are in their elemental state, so they have an oxidation state of 0.

FOR PRACTICE 24.6 Calculate the oxidation state of Cl in ClO_4^- and Cl^-.

Elemental Fluorine and Hydrofluoric Acid

Fluorine is the most reactive element and forms binary compounds with all elements except He, Ne, and Ar. Fluorine even forms compounds with some of the noble gases, producing compounds such as XeF_2, XeF_6, and $XeOF_4$. The high reactivity of fluorine is related to several factors. First, the F—F bond is among the weakest halogen–halogen bonds, as shown in Table 24.9. In order for a halogen to react with other substances, the halogen–halogen bond must break. The energy required to break that bond is small for F_2, so the resulting reaction is more exothermic. Second, the small size of fluorine results in a high lattice energy for the ionic compounds that it forms. The high lattice energy means the compounds are very stable.

TABLE 24.9 ■ Comparison of Halogen X—X Bond Energy

Halogen	F—F	Cl—Cl	Br—Br	I—I
Bond energy (kJ/mol)	159	243	193	151

The high reactivity of fluorine is illustrated by its ability to burn (or quickly oxidize) many substances, such as iron and sulfur, that do not readily burn with oxygen:

$$Fe(s) + F_2(g) \longrightarrow FeF_2(s)$$
$$S(s) + 3\,F_2(g) \longrightarrow SF_6(g)$$

Fluorine gas even reacts with asbestos and glass, two materials commonly used as containers for reactive substances. Consequently, fluorine is normally held in metal containers made of iron, copper, or nickel. These metals also initially react with fluorine, but then a thin layer of the product coats the surface of the metal, protecting the underlying metal from further reaction.

Elemental fluorine is produced from the electrolysis of hydrofluoric acid, forming F_2 and H_2 gases:

Oxidation: $$2\,F^-(g) \longrightarrow F_2(g) + 2\,e^-$$

Reduction: $$2\,H^+(g) + 2\,e^- \longrightarrow H_2(g)$$

Gaseous hydrogen fluoride can be obtained from the reaction of the mineral fluorspar (CaF_2) with sulfuric acid:

$$CaF_2(s) + H_2SO_4(l) \longrightarrow 2HF(g) + CaSO_4(s)$$

In its solid form, HF has a crystal structure that contains zigzag chains of alternating H and F atoms. In aqueous solutions, HF is a weak acid ($K_a = 3.5 \times 10^{-4}$ for HF at 298 K). Like all anions in aqueous solution, the F^- ions from ionized HF are solvated by water molecules. However, the F^- ions can also associate with other HF molecules to form HF_2^-.

$$F^-(aq) + HF(aq) \longrightarrow HF_2^-(aq)$$

The structure of HF_2^-, shown here, is unique because it contains a bridging hydrogen atom (a hydrogen atom that essentially forms two bonds):

Hydrofluoric acid is a strong oxidizing agent and reacts with glass according to the following reactions:

$$SiO_2(s) + 4\,HF(aq) \longrightarrow SiF_4(g) + 2\,H_2O(l)$$

or:

$$SiO_2(s) + 6\,HF(aq) \longrightarrow SiF_6^{2-}(aq) + 2\,H^+(aq) + 2\,H_2O(l)$$

As a result, hydrofluoric acid cannot be held in a glass container and is generally stored in plastic. The ability of HF to react with glass makes it useful in etching glass. The parts of the glass to be etched are left exposed, and the rest of the surface is masked with a nonreactive substance such as plastic. The surface is then exposed to hydrofluoric acid and the non-masked glass etches away, leaving the desired pattern. Hydrofluoric acid is particularly dangerous because it quickly penetrates into tissues, damaging internal organs and bones. Direct exposure of just 2% of body surface area to concentrated hydrofluoric acid can be fatal.

Elemental Chlorine

Historically, the primary source for chlorine has been seawater. Electrolysis of NaCl in seawater produces Cl_2 gas and H_2 gas:

$$2\,NaCl(aq) + 2\,H_2O(l) \xrightarrow{\text{electricity}} Cl_2(g) + 2\,NaOH(aq) + H_2(g)$$

Today, much Cl_2 gas is produced and collected as a by-product of the various metal processing methods, such as in the reduction of metal chlorides to form metals:

$$MgCl_2(l) \xrightarrow{\text{electricity}} Mg(s) + Cl_2(g)$$

Halogen Compounds

Halogens form ionic compounds with most metals, they form covalent compounds with many nonmetals, and they can bond with other halogens to form interhalogen compounds. Here we look at some of the compounds halogens form.

Interhalogen Compounds

Covalent compounds composed of two different halogens are known as **interhalogen compounds** or *interhalides*. The general formula of these compounds is AB_n, where A is the larger halogen, B is the smaller halogen, and n is 1, 3, 5, or 7. The smaller halogens surround the larger halogen in the AB_3 compounds. The only known AB_5 compounds contain fluorine as the smaller halogen (because the other halogens are too large for five of them to fit around another halogen). The compound IF_7 is the only known interhalogen compound with $n = 7$. The large size of the iodine atom allows seven small fluorine atoms to surround it. The interhalides can be formed by reacting the elemental halogens with one another. Interhalide polyatomic ions, such as ICl_2^+ and ICl_4^-, also exist.

EXAMPLE 24.7 Formation of Interhalogen Compounds

Write the balanced equation for the formation of ClF_3 gas from the elemental halogens.

SOLUTION

The unbalanced reaction is:

$$Cl_2(g) + F_2(g) \longrightarrow ClF_3(g)$$

At least two ClF_3 molecules form from each Cl_2 molecule; therefore, add a 2 before ClF_3 and then a 3 before F_2. The balanced equation is:

$$Cl_2(g) + 3\,F_2(g) \longrightarrow 2\,ClF_3(g)$$

FOR PRACTICE 24.7 Write a balanced equation for the formation of IF_5 gas from the elemental halogens.

The geometry of the interhalides can be predicted from the valence shell electron pair repulsion model (VSEPR). Because the halogens do not form double or triple bonds, the shapes of these compounds are relatively straightforward to determine, as shown in Examples 24.8 and 24.9.

HOW TO: Determine the Shape of Interhalogen Compounds	EXAMPLE 24.8 Molecular Shapes of Interhalogen Compounds	EXAMPLE 24.9 Molecular Shapes of Interhalogen Compounds
	Determine the molecular geometry of IBr_2^-.	Determine the molecular geometry of IF_7.
Identify the central atom.	**SOLUTION** I	**SOLUTION** I
Draw the Lewis structure (see Section 10.5).	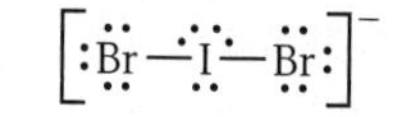	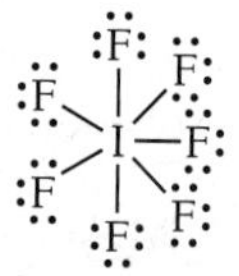
Count the number of bonds and lone pairs on the central atom.	The I atom has two bonds and three lone pairs for a total of five electron groups.	The I atom has seven bonds on the central atom for a total of seven electron groups.
Determine the electron geometry from the number of electron groups (see Section 11.4).	With five electron groups, the electron geometry is *trigonal bipyramidal.*	With seven electron groups, the electron geometry is *pentagonal bipyramidal.*
Determine the molecular shape from the number of bonds and lone pairs.	With two bonds the molecular geometry is *linear* because the three lone pairs occupy equatorial positions. 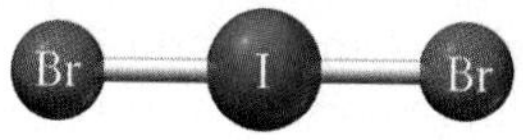	With seven bonds, the molecular geometry is also *pentagonal bipyramidal.* 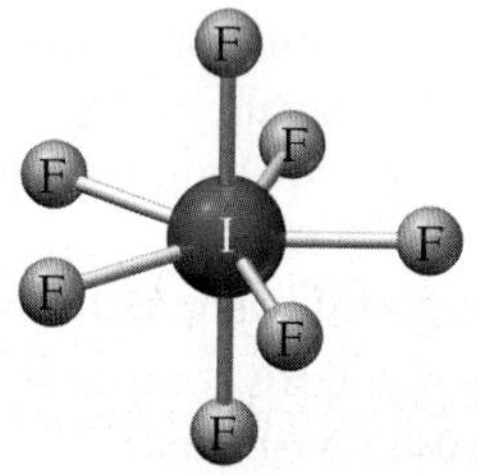
	FOR PRACTICE 24.8 Determine the electron geometry and molecular geometry of ICl_2^+.	**FOR PRACTICE 24.9** Determine the electron geometry and molecular geometry of BrF_5.

The only industrially useful interhalide is ClF_3, employed in the nuclear energy industry to produce $UF_6(g)$, which is used to separate ^{235}U (<1% of naturally occurring uranium) from ^{238}U. Uranium ores react with gaseous hydrogen fluoride to form $UF_4(s)$, which reacts with $ClF_3(g)$ to form the gaseous uranium compound:

$$UO_2(s) + 4\,HF(g) \longrightarrow UF_4(s) + 2\,H_2O(g)$$

$$UF_4(s) + ClF_3(g) \longrightarrow UF_6(g) + ClF(g)$$

Because of the difference in mass between the two isotopes, $^{238}UF_6$ effuses more slowly than $^{235}UF_6$ (see Section 6.9 for a description of effusion). The mixture of gases is allowed to flow through barriers with very small pores. Since $^{235}UF_6$ effuses more quickly, the initial flow of gas that exits the pores is enriched in $^{235}UF_6$. By repeating the process, the two isotopes can be nearly completely separated.

Halogen Oxides

Most halogen oxides are unstable, and many are explosive. A unique halogen oxide is OF_2; oxygen usually has a negative oxidation state in its compounds but has a +2 oxidation state in OF_2 (due to the high electronegativity of fluorine).

A number of different chlorine oxides are known, including Cl_2O, ClO_2, Cl_2O_6, and Cl_2O_7. Chlorine dioxide is a powerful oxidizing agent used to bleach flour and wood pulp (to make white paper). Because ClO_2 is explosive, the gas is diluted with CO_2 or N_2 for safety. Some water treatment plants use ClO_2 for water disinfection in place of Cl_2. ClO_2 is produced by the oxidation of sodium chlorite with Cl_2 or by the reduction of sodium chlorate with hydrochloric acid:

$$2\,NaClO_2(aq) + Cl_2(g) \longrightarrow 2\,NaCl(aq) + 2\,ClO_2(g)$$

$$2\,NaClO_3(aq) + 4\,HCl(aq) \longrightarrow 2\,ClO_2(g) + Cl_2(g) + 2\,H_2O(l) + 2\,NaCl(aq)$$

EXAMPLE 24.10 Identifying Changes in Oxidation States

Identify the change of oxidation state for Cl in the production of chlorine dioxide from sodium chlorite. Identify the oxidizing agent and the reducing agent.

SOLUTION

First determine the oxidation state of Cl in each compound.

$$\underset{+1\;+3\;-2}{2\,NaClO_2(aq)} + \underset{0}{Cl_2(g)} \longrightarrow \underset{+1\;-1}{2\,NaCl(aq)} + \underset{+4\;-2}{2\,ClO_2(g)}$$

The Cl in the $NaClO_2$ was oxidized from +3 to +4 by the oxidizing agent Cl_2, which was reduced from 0 to −1 by the reducing agent $NaClO_2$.

FOR PRACTICE 24.10 Identify the change of oxidation state for Cl in the production of chlorine dioxide from sodium chlorate. Identify the oxidizing agent and the reducing agent.

QUIZ YOURSELF **NOW!**

Self-Assessment Quiz

Q1. An aluminosilicate is composed of a crystal in which Al atoms substitute for three-fourths of the Si atoms in the silica structure. The negative charge of the AlO_2^- groups is balanced by Na^+ ions. What is the formula of the aluminosilicate? **MISSED THIS?** *Read Section 24.3*

a) $Na(AlSi_3O_8)$ b) $Na_2(Al_2Si_2O_8)$
c) $Na_3(Al_3SiO_8)$ d) $NaSiO_2$

Q2. Use charge balance to determine x in the formula for the sorosilicate bertrandite, $Be_4Si_2O_7(OH)_x$. **MISSED THIS?** *Read Section 24.3*

a) 1 b) 2 c) 3 d) 4

Q3. Which element is important in the manufacturing of glassware intended for heating? **MISSED THIS?** *Read Section 24.4*

a) carbon b) nitrogen
c) phosphorus d) boron

Q4. Fertilizers commonly contain compounds of which element? **MISSED THIS?** *Read Section 24.6*

a) nitrogen b) aluminum
c) fluorine d) boron

Q5. What is the oxidation state of bromine in the compound $NaBrO_3$? **MISSED THIS?** *Read Section 24.9*

a) +2 b) −3 c) −4 d) +5

Q6. What is the molecular geometry of ICl_4^-? **MISSED THIS?** *Read Section 24.9*

a) tetrahedral b) square planar
c) octahedral d) seesaw

Q7. Which element is oxidized in the reaction? **MISSED THIS?** *Read Section 24.7*

$$2\,CaO(s) + 2\,SO_2(g) + O_2(g) \longrightarrow 2\,CaSO_4(s)$$

a) Ca b) O c) S
d) None of the above (no element is oxidized in the reaction)

Q8. Which carbon oxide does not exist? **MISSED THIS?** *Read Section 24.5*

a) CO b) CO_2 c) CO_3^{2-} d) CO_4

Q9. Which element is extracted from the ground primarily in its elemental form? **MISSED THIS?** *Read Section 24.8*

a) boron b) phosphorus
c) sulfur d) fluorine

Q10. Which substance forms when carbon dioxide dissolves in water? **MISSED THIS?** *Read Section 24.5*

a) CO b) H_2CO c) CH_4 d) H_2CO_3

Answers: **1.** (c) **2.** (b) **3.** (d) **4.** (a) **5.** (d) **6.** (b) **7.** (c) **8.** (d) **9.** (c) **10.** (d)

CHAPTER 24 IN REVIEW

TERMS

Section 24.2
main-group elements (1072)

Section 24.3
silicates (1074)
quartz (1074)
silica (1074)
aluminosilicates (1075)
mineral (1075)
orthosilicates (1075)
pyrosilicates (1075)
pyroxenes (1076)

Section 24.4
boranes (1080)
closo-boranes (1080)
nido-boranes (1080)
arachno-boranes (1080)

Section 24.5
coal (1081)
coke (1081)
charcoal (1081)
activated carbon (1081)
soot (1082)
carbon black (1082)
carbides (1082)
ionic carbides (1082)
covalent carbides (1083)
metallic carbides (1083)
washing soda (1084)

Section 24.6
white phosphorus (1085)
red phosphorus (1085)
black phosphorus (1086)
ammonia (1086)
Haber–Bosch process (1086)
hydrazine (1087)
hydrogen azide (1087)
Ostwald process (1088)
phosphine (1089)

Section 24.7
ozone (1093)

Section 24.8
Frasch process (1094)
Claus process (1095)
contact process (1097)

Section 24.9
interhalogen compounds (1099)

CONCEPTS

Bonding and Properties (24.2)

- Main-group elements are defined by their electron configurations and their location on the periodic table.
- The properties of the main-group elements show great diversity. Metals, nonmetals, and metalloids are all found among the main-group elements.
- Some main-group elements form covalent bonds, while others form ionic bonds.

The Most Common Matter: Silicates (24.3)

- Silicates (found in rocks, clays, and soils) are covalent atomic solids that contain silicon, oxygen, and various metal atoms.
- Silicate structures consist of four oxygen atoms bonded to silicon, forming a negatively charged polyatomic anion with a tetrahedral shape. Various metal ions within the structure balance the charge of the compound.
- The SiO_4 tetrahedrons can link to form chains, double chains, sheets, or even extended three-dimensional structures.
- The properties of the silicates depend on the connections between the silicate tetrahedrons. Because of the wide variety of combinations of tetrahedron connections and the many different metal ions that fit within the structure, an enormous variety of different silicate minerals exist in nature, making the silicate materials the most common structures found on Earth.

Boron (24.4)

- Because of its small size and high electronegativity, boron behaves as a metalloid.
- The structure of elemental boron consists of icosahedron structures bonded together in various ways.
- Boron tends to form electron-deficient compounds.
- Compounds of boron and hydrogen form cluster compounds resembling spheres, cages, and nets.

Carbon (24.5)

- Organic chemistry is based on the chemistry of carbon, and carbon is also very important in many inorganic compounds and applications. Important types of amorphous elemental carbon include carbon black and coke.
- Important types of inorganic carbon compounds include carbides and carbonates. Carbon can form carbides with metallic, covalent, or ionic properties.
- Carbon and its oxygen compounds are intimately involved in the functions of life.

Nitrogen and Phosphorus (24.6)

- Nitrogen and phosphorus have been known for over 200 years; both form compounds, with oxidation numbers ranging from −3 up to +5.
- Both nitrogen and phosphorus compounds are critical for plant growth; their most important use is as fertilizers. The strong triple bond between nitrogen atoms in N_2 makes nitrogen from the atmosphere inaccessible to most plants, so ingenious chemical processes have been devised to make nitrogen compounds that are more available to plants.

Oxygen (24.7)

- Oxygen is the most common element on Earth. It is found in the atmosphere as the elemental gas and as many oxide gases.
- Oxygen is found in ocean water and in Earth's crust as silicate and oxide compounds. Oxygen is a strong oxidizing agent and forms compounds with $-\frac{1}{2}$, −1, or −2 oxidation states.
- Ozone, O_3, is a helpful molecule in the upper atmosphere, where it absorbs harmful ultraviolet radiation, but it is a harmful molecule at Earth's surface.

Sulfur (24.8)

- More sulfuric acid is produced than any other chemical; most of it is used to make fertilizers. Other uses take advantage of its strong oxidation and dehydration properties.
- Elemental sulfur has several allotropes ranging from ring structures to chain structures and amorphous materials, depending on temperature.

Halogens (24.9)

- The halogens are the most electronegative elements, so they are always found as compounds, usually ionic. When the halogens bond with other electronegative elements, however, they can form covalent compounds.
- Fluorine has special chemical properties because it is the most electronegative element and is very small, making it a very strong oxidizing agent.
- Interhalogen compounds are formed between two halogens, with the larger halogen as the central atom of the structure.

LEARNING OUTCOMES

Chapter Objectives	Assessment
Analyze silicates in terms of composition, charge balance, and type (24.3)	Examples 24.1–24.4 **For Practice** 24.1–24.4 **Exercises** 15–24
Analyze boron-containing compounds in terms of structure and properties (24.4)	**Exercises** 25–32
Analyze carbon-containing compounds in terms of structure and properties (24.5)	**Exercises** 33–38
Predict the products of reactions involving carbon-containing compounds (24.5)	**Exercises** 39–42
Analyze phosphorus- and nitrogen-containing compounds in terms of structure and properties (24.6)	**Exercises** 43–50, 53–58
Predict the products of reactions involving nitrogen- and phosphorus-containing compounds (24.6)	**Exercises** 51–52, 59–60
Analyze oxygen-containing compounds in terms of structure and properties (24.7)	**Exercises** 61–64
Analyze sulfur-containing compounds in terms of structure and properties (24.8)	Example 24.5 **For Practice** 24.5 **Exercises** 65–68
Predict the products for reactions involving sulfur-containing compounds (24.8)	**Exercises** 69–70
Analyze halogen-containing compounds in terms of structure and properties (24.9)	Examples 24.6–24.10 **For Practice** 24.6–24.10 **Exercises** 71–72
Predict the products of reactions involving halogen-containing compounds (24.9)	**Exercises** 73–76

EXERCISES

Mastering Chemistry provides end-of-chapter exercises, feedback-enriched tutorial problems, animations, and interactive activities to encourage problem-solving practice and deeper understanding of key concepts and topics.

REVIEW QUESTIONS

1. Why does BN form compounds similar to those formed by elemental carbon?

2. What is the main characteristic that determines whether or not an element is a main-group element?

3. Does the metallic characteristic of a main-group element increase or decrease as we move down a family? Explain why.

4. Why does silicon form only single bonds with oxygen but carbon, which is in the same family as silicon, forms double bonds with oxygen in many compounds?

5. What is the difference between a rock and a mineral?

6. Briefly define each term.
a. orthosilicate b. amphibole c. pyroxene
d. pyrosilicate e. feldspar

7. Why is boron oxide often added to silica glass?

8. Why does boron form electron-deficient bonds? Provide an example.

9. Explain why solid CO_2 is referred to as dry ice.

10. Nitric acid and phosphoric acid are two major chemical products of the chemical industry. Describe some of their uses.

11. What is the typical concentration of oxygen in dry air?

12. Describe how nitrogen can be separated from the other components of air.

13. Earth's atmosphere originally did not contain oxygen. Explain how the atmosphere gained oxygen.

14. Name a benefit, a hazard, and a useful commercial application of ozone.

PROBLEMS BY TOPIC

Silicates: The Most Abundant Matter in Earth's Crust

15. Silicon bonds to oxygen to form a tetrahedral shape in both the network covalent silica compound, SiO_2, and in ionic silicate compounds. What is the oxidation state of Si in each of these structures? **MISSED THIS?** *Read Section 24.3*
a. silica compound, SiO_2 b. orthosilicates, SiO_4^{4-}
c. pyrosilicates, $Si_2O_7^{6-}$

16. What is the oxidation state of Si in each of these structures?
a. pyroxenes, SiO_3^{2-} b. amphiboles, $Si_4O_{11}^{6-}$
c. phyllosilicates, $Si_2O_5^{2-}$

17. In the orthosilicate garnet, the formula unit has three SiO_4^{4-} units and is balanced by Ca^{2+} and Al^{3+} cations. Determine the formula unit of garnet. **MISSED THIS?** *Read Section 24.3*

18. In the pyroxene kanoite, the formula unit has two SiO_3^{2-} units and is balanced by manganese and magnesium ions. Determine the formula unit of kanoite. Assume that the oxidation state of Mn is +2.

19. Kaolin is a clay material that is a phyllosilicate. Use charge balancing to determine how many hydroxide ions are in the formula for kaolin, $Al_2Si_2O_5(OH)_x$. **MISSED THIS?** *Read Section 24.3*

20. Tremolite is a double-chain silicate in the amphibole class. Use charge balancing to determine how many hydroxide ions are in the formula for tremolite, $Ca_2Mg_5Si_8O_{22}(OH)_x$.

21. How are the silica tetrahedrons linked for $ZrSiO_4$? Which class of silicates does this compound belong to?
MISSED THIS? *Read Section 24.3*

22. How are the silica tetrahedrons linked for $CaSiO_3$? Which class of silicates does this compound belong to?

23. Predict the structure and give the charges on the cations in one of the minerals in the hornblende family, $Ca_2Mg_4FeSi_7AlO_{22}(OH)_2$.
MISSED THIS? *Read Section 24.3*

24. Predict the structure and label the charges on the cations in the mineral hedenbergite, $CaFeSi_2O_6$.

Boron and Its Remarkable Structures

25. A major source of boron is the mineral kernite, $Na_2[B_4O_5(OH)_4] \cdot 3H_2O$. Calculate how many grams of boron can be produced from 1.0×10^3 kg of a kernite-bearing ore if the ore contains 0.98% kernite by mass and the process has a 65% yield. **MISSED THIS?** *Read Section 24.4*

26. An uncommon mineral of boron is ulexite, $NaCaB_5O_9 \cdot 8H_2O$. How many grams of boron can be produced from 5.00×10^2 kg of ulexite-bearing ore if the ore contains 0.032% ulexite by mass and the process has an 88% yield?

27. Explain why the bond angles in BCl_3 and NCl_3 are different. **MISSED THIS?** *Read Section 24.4*

28. Explain why the bond between B and Cl in the molecule BCl_3 is shorter than would be expected for a single B—Cl bond.

29. Predict the number of vertices and faces on each *closo*-borane. **MISSED THIS?** *Read Section 24.4*

a. $B_6H_6^{2-}$ b. $B_{12}H_{12}^{2-}$

30. Predict the number of vertices and faces on each *closo*-borane.

a. $B_4H_4^{2-}$ b. $B_9H_9^{2-}$

31. Describe the differences among a *closo*-borane, a *nido*-borane, and an *arachno*-borane. **MISSED THIS?** *Read Section 24.4*

32. Describe how boron is used in the nuclear industry.

Carbon, Carbides, and Carbonates

33. Describe the difference between regular charcoal and activated charcoal. **MISSED THIS?** *Read Section 24.5*

34. Explain why the structure of charcoal allows carbon to act as a good filter while the diamond structure does not.

35. Describe the difference between an ionic carbide and a covalent carbide. Which types of atoms will form these carbides with carbon? **MISSED THIS?** *Read Section 24.5*

36. Silicon carbide is produced by heating silicone polymers, forming methane gas, hydrogen gas, and silicon carbide. Balance the reaction of heating $[(CH_3)_2Si]_8$ to form silicon carbide.

37. Referring to the phase diagram in Section 12.8, describe what happens to the phase of CO_2 during each process. **MISSED THIS?** *Read Section 24.5*

a. reducing the pressure on solid CO_2 that is at −80 °C
b. decreasing the temperature on CO_2 gas that is held at a pressure of 20 atm
c. increasing the temperature on solid CO_2 that is held at a pressure of 0.8 atm

38. Referring to the phase diagram in Section 12.8, describe what happens to the phase of CO_2 during each process:

a. reducing the temperature from the critical point
b. increasing the pressure on CO_2 gas that is held at a temperature of −50 °C
c. increasing the temperature on solid CO_2 that is held at a pressure of 20 atm

39. Predict the products for each reaction and write a balanced equation. **MISSED THIS?** *Read Section 24.5*

a. $CO(g) + CuO(s)$ b. $SiO_2(s) + C(s)$ c. $S(s) + CO(g)$

40. Predict the products for each reaction and write a balanced equation.

a. $CO(g) + Cl_2(g)$ b. $CO_2(g) + Mg(s)$ c. $S(s) + C(s)$

41. Give the oxidation state for carbon in: **MISSED THIS?** *Read Section 24.5*

a. CO b. CO_2 c. C_3O_2

42. Write a balanced reaction for the gas release reaction of Alka-Seltzer, sodium bicarbonate with citric acid, $C_6H_8O_7$. (The acid is a triprotic acid and consists of a chain of three carbon atoms, each with a carboxylic acid group, COOH.)

Nitrogen and Phosphorus: Essential Elements for Life

43. Explain the process of fixing nitrogen. **MISSED THIS?** *Read Section 24.6*

44. Explain why the diatomic nitrogen atom is unusable by most plants. Where do plants get nitrogen?

45. Describe the differences in the allotropes of white and red phosphorus. Explain why red phosphorus is more stable. **MISSED THIS?** *Read Section 24.6*

46. Describe how red and black phosphorus are made from white phosphorus.

47. Saltpeter and Chile saltpeter are two important mineral sources for nitrogen. Calculate the mass percent of nitrogen in each mineral. **MISSED THIS?** *Read Section 24.6*

48. Apatite is a main mineral source for the production of phosphorus. Calculate the atomic and mass percent of P in the mineral apatite.

49. Referring to the tables in Appendix IIB, determine whether or not hydrogen azide is stable at room temperature compared to its elements, H_2 and N_2. Is hydrogen azide stable at any temperature? **MISSED THIS?** *Read Section 24.6*

50. Referring to the tables in Appendix IIB, determine if dinitrogen monoxide is stable at room temperature compared to its elements, O_2 and N_2. Is dinitrogen monoxide stable at any temperature?

51. Predict the products for each reaction and write a balanced equation. **MISSED THIS?** *Read Section 24.6*

a. $NH_4NO_3(aq)$ + heat
b. $NO_2(g) + H_2O(l)$
c. $PCl_3(l) + O_2(g)$

52. Predict the products for each reaction and write a balanced equation.

a. $NO(g) + NO_2(g)$ b. heating PH_3 c. $P_4(s) + 5\,O_2(g)$

53. Rank the nitrogen ions from the one with N in the highest oxidation state to the one with N in the lowest. **MISSED THIS?** *Read Section 24.6*

$$N_3^-, N_2H_5^+, NO_3^-, NH_4^+, NO_2^-$$

54. Determine the oxidation state of N in the compounds in the reaction for the formation of nitric acid. Identify the oxidizing agent and the reducing agent.

$$3\,NO_2(g) + H_2O(l) \longrightarrow 2\,HNO_3(l) + NO(g)$$

55. Draw the Lewis structures for the phosphorus halides PCl_3 and PCl_5. Describe their VSEPR shape. **MISSED THIS?** *Read Section 24.6*

56. Dinitrogen pentoxide is an ionic compound formed from the ions NO_2^+ and NO_3^-. Give the oxidation state of N in each ion and the VSEPR shape for each of the ions.

57. Ammonium carbonate is produced from the reaction of urea, $CO(NH_2)_2$ with water. Write a balanced equation for this reaction and determine how much urea is needed to produce 23 g of ammonium carbonate. **MISSED THIS?** *Read Section 24.6*

58. Explain why phosphine, PH_3, is less polar than ammonia.

59. Reacting oxygen with white phosphorus can form either P_4O_6 or P_4O_{10}. State the conditions that determine which product forms. **MISSED THIS?** *Read Section 24.6*

60. P_4O_{10} is one of the most effective drying agents, having the ability to extract water from other molecules. The P_4O_{10} forms phosphoric acid. Write balanced reactions for the reaction of P_4O_{10} with:

a. HNO_3, forming N_2O_5 b. H_2SO_4, forming SO_3

Oxygen

61. Name the major source of the element oxygen and describe how it is produced. **MISSED THIS?** *Read Section 24.7*

62. Explain why either greatly decreasing or increasing the percentage of oxygen in the atmosphere is dangerous.

63. Identify each compound as an oxide, peroxide, or superoxide. **MISSED THIS?** *Read Section 24.7*
a. LiO_2 b. CaO c. K_2O_2

64. Identify each compound as an oxide, peroxide, or superoxide.
a. MgO b. Na_2O_2 c. CsO_2

Sulfur: A Dangerous but Useful Element

65. Explain why the viscosity of liquid sulfur increases with increasing temperature initially, but then decreases upon further increases in temperature. **MISSED THIS?** *Read Section 24.8*

66. Sulfur dioxide is a toxic sulfur compound. List one natural source and one industrial source that produce SO_2.

67. Calculate the maximum mass (in grams) of each metal sulfide that will dissolve in 1.0 L of a solution that is 5.00×10^{-5} M in Na_2S. **MISSED THIS?** *Read Section 24.8*
a. PbS b. ZnS

68. A coal source contains 1.1% sulfur by mass. If 2.0×10^4 kg of coal is burned and forms oxides, calculate the mass of $CaSO_4(s)$ that is produced from "scrubbing" the SO_2 pollutant out of the exhaust gas. Assume that all of the sulfur in the coal is converted to calcium sulfate.

69. Write the equation for roasting iron pyrite in the absence of air to form elemental sulfur. Calculate the volume of S_2 gas that can be produced from roasting 5.5 kg of iron pyrite. Assume that all of the sulfur in the iron pyrite is converted to S_2 gas. (Assume STP to calculate the gas volume.)
MISSED THIS? *Read Section 24.8*

70. Write an overall reaction from the two steps in the Claus process. Calculate the volume of H_2S gas needed to produce 1.0 kg of S(*s*). (Assume STP to calculate the gas volume.)

Halogens

71. Determine the oxidation state of Xe and give the VSEPR structure for each compound. **MISSED THIS?** *Read Section 24.9*
a. XeF_2 b. XeF_6 c. $XeOF_4$

72. Describe the shape of each halogen compound.
a. BrF_4^- b. IF_3 c. BrO_2^- d. ClO_4^-

73. When chlorine is bubbled through a colorless aqueous solution containing bromide ions, the solution turns red and the chlorine is reduced. Write a balanced equation for this reaction and identify the oxidizing and reducing agent.
MISSED THIS? *Read Section 24.9*

74. Carbon tetrachloride is produced by passing chlorine gas over carbon disulfide in the presence of a catalyst. The reaction also produces S_2Cl_2. Write the balanced reaction and identify which element is oxidized and which element is reduced.

75. If 55 g of $SiO_2(s)$ glass is placed into 111 L of 0.032 M HF, is there enough HF to dissolve all of the glass? Determine which substance is the limiting reagent and calculate how much of the other reagent is left if the reaction proceeds to completion.
MISSED THIS? *Read Section 24.9*

76. Describe the difference in the types of bonds (single, double, triple) and the shapes of the following two iodine ions: ICl_4^- and IO_4^-.

CUMULATIVE PROBLEMS

77. From the compositions of lignite and bituminous coal, calculate the mass of sulfuric acid that could potentially form as acid rain from burning 1.00×10^2 kg of each type of coal.

78. Calculate the volume of CO_2 released from heating and decomposing 88 g of sodium bicarbonate. (Assume standard pressure and temperature.)

79. All of the halogens form oxoacids. The perhalic acids have the general formula of HXO_4. Explain why $HClO_4$ is a much stronger acid than HIO_4.

80. The halogens form oxoacids with different amounts of oxygen. Explain why $HClO_4$ is a stronger acid than $HClO_2$.

81. Determine the ratio of effusion rates of HCl compared to each gas.
a. Cl_2 b. HF c. HI

82. Calculate the ratio of effusion rates for each pair of gases.
a. $^{238}UF_6$ and ClF b. $^{238}UF_6$ and $^{235}UF_6$

83. Sodium peroxide is a very powerful oxidizing agent. Balance the reaction of sodium peroxide with elemental iron to give sodium oxide and Fe_3O_4.

84. Sulfur dioxide is a reducing agent. When it is bubbled through an aqueous solution containing Br_2, a red-colored solution, it reduces the bromine to colorless bromide ions and forms sulfuric acid. Write a balanced equation for this reaction and identify the oxidizing and reducing agent.

85. Using the molecular orbital model for a diatomic molecule, explain the different bond lengths for the ions of oxygen. Also state which ion is diamagnetic.

Ion	O—O Bond Length (pm)
O_2^+	112
O_2	121
O_2^-	133
O_2^{2-}	149

86. The *closo*-borane with the formula $B_6H_6^{2-}$ has the six B atoms at vertices, forming an octahedron structure with eight faces. The formula for the number of sides is $2n - 4$, where n is the number of boron atoms. Determine the number of vertices and faces for each *closo*-borane.
a. $B_4H_4^{2-}$ b. $B_{12}H_{12}^{2-}$

87. Find the amount (in moles) of C—C bonds that must be broken when 1.0 mole of C(*g*) is formed from C(diamond). Calculate the ΔH of sublimation of diamond from the data in Appendix II, Table B. Then do the calculation using the C—C bond energy in Table 10.3. Suggest a reason for the difference between the two values.

88. Breathing air that contains 0.13% CO by volume for 30 minutes will cause death. CO can form by incomplete combustion of carbon-containing compounds. Calculate the minimum volume of octane (C_8H_{18}, a component of gasoline, which has a density of 0.70 g/mL) that must burn to produce this composition of CO in a garage of volume 40 m^3 at 298 K and 1.0 atm.

89. Given that the ΔH_f° of 1 M H_2SO_3 is −633 kJ, use the data in Appendix II, Table B to calculate the ΔH° for the formation of a 1 M solution of SO_2 in water from $SO_2(g)$.

90. Use the data in Appendix II, Table B to calculate ΔH° for the formation of a 1 M solution of H_2SO_4 from $SO_3(g)$.

CHALLENGE PROBLEMS

91. Calculate the standard enthalpy of reaction for reducing the different forms of iron oxide to iron metal and CO_2 from the reaction of the oxide with CO. Identify which reaction is the most exothermic per mole of iron and explain why.
    a. Fe_3O_4
    b. FeO
    c. Fe_2O_3

92. Balance the equation for the production of acetylene (C_2H_2) from the reaction of calcium carbide with water. If the acetylene is burned to form water and carbon dioxide, how many kilojoules of energy are produced from the complete reaction of 18 g of calcium carbide?

93. Carbon suboxide, C_3O_2, is a linear molecule with the two oxygen atoms at the end and double bonds between each carbon and oxygen atom.
    a. Draw the Lewis structure for C_3O_2.
    b. State the type of hybridization of each carbon atom.
    c. Calculate the heat of reaction for the reaction of carbon suboxide with water to form malonic acid ($HO_2CCH_2CO_2H$). *Hint:* Each end of malonic acid has a carbon double bonded to an oxygen and to a hydroxide.

94. Calcium carbonate is insoluble in water. Yet, it dissolves in an acidic solution. Calculate the standard enthalpy, entropy, and Gibbs free energy change for the reaction between solid calcium carbonate and hydrochloric acid. What drives the reaction, the enthalpy change or the entropy change?

95. When hydrazine is dissolved in water, it acts like a base.

$$N_2H_4(aq) + H_2O(l) \rightleftharpoons N_2H_5^+(aq) + OH^-(aq) \qquad K_{b_1} = 8.5 \times 10^{-7}$$

$$N_2H_5^+(aq) + H_2O(l) \rightleftharpoons N_2H_6^{2+}(aq) + OH^-(aq) \qquad K_{b_2} = 8.9 \times 10^{-16}$$

    a. Calculate the K_b for the overall reaction of hydrazine forming $N_2H_6^{2+}$.
    b. Calculate K_{a_1} for $N_2H_5^+$.
    c. Calculate the concentration of hydrazine and both cations in a solution buffered at a pH of 8.5 for a solution that was made by dissolving 0.012 mol of hydrazine in 1 L of water.

96. Solid fuel in the booster rockets for spacecraft consists of aluminum powder as the fuel and ammonium perchlorate as the oxidizing agent.

$$3\,NH_4ClO_4(s) + 3\,Al(s) \longrightarrow Al_2O_3(s) + AlCl_3(s) + 6\,H_2O(g) + 3\,NO(g)$$

If a rocket launch burns 2.200×10^3 kg of aluminum, calculate the energy produced in joules. Calculate the volume of the gas produced, assuming it was cooled back to 298 K at 1 atm. The standard enthalpy of formation of solid ammonium perchlorate is −295.3 kJ/mol.

97. Two known compounds have the formula $H_2N_2O_2$. One of them is a weak acid and one is a weak base. The acid, called hyponitrous acid, has two O—H bonds. The base, called nitramide, has no O—H bonds. Draw Lewis structures for these compounds. Predict whether the acid is stronger or weaker than nitrous acid and whether the base is stronger or weaker than ammonia.

CONCEPTUAL PROBLEMS

98. Explain why fine particles of activated charcoal can absorb more (as a filter) than large briquettes of charcoal.

99. The two major components of the atmosphere are the diatomic molecules of nitrogen and oxygen. Explain why pure nitrogen is used as a protective atmosphere in the laboratory and pure oxygen is much more reactive.

100. Explain why nitrogen can form compounds with many different oxidation numbers.

101. Describe how sodium dihydrogen phosphate can be used as a pH buffering agent.

102. Explain why H_2S has a different bond angle and is much more reactive than H_2O.

103. Explain why fluorine is found only with the oxidation state of −1 or 0, while the other halogens are found in compounds with other oxidation states.

104. Why do some substances burn in fluorine gas even if they do not burn in oxygen gas?

105. Explain why SO_2 is used as a reducing agent but SO_3 is not.

106. Explain why the interhalogen molecule $BrCl_3$ exists but $ClBr_3$ does not.

QUESTIONS FOR GROUP WORK

Active Classroom Learning

Discuss these questions with the group and record your consensus answer.

107. Have each group member select a different element from this list: B, C, N, O, and F. Have all group members look up the following values for their elements: valence electron configuration, covalent atomic radius, effective nuclear charge, first ionization energy, and Pauling electronegativity. All members should compare the values for their elements with those of the group. Repeat with O, S, Se, Te, and Po. Account for the trends you see by referring to quantum-mechanical shells. Note and provide a tentative explanation for any exceptions to trends you observe.

108. Provide a detailed chemical description of your birthstone or favorite gem. If two members of the group share a birthstone, have one select another gem, so that no two group members work with the same gem. Is your gem a silicate? What type? Share your findings with your group. Does your group agree on which gem has the most interesting structure?

109. As a group, create a single schematic drawing of a factory that uses the Haber–Bosch process and the Ostwald process to make NH_4NO_3 fertilizer. The factory may only take in $N_2(g)$, $H_2(g)$, and $O_2(g)$. Pass your diagram around the group and have each group member add one step in the process. Where might the factory obtain H_2?

110. Ask each group member to work individually to write out two or three reactions from one section of the chapter. Replace the symbol for the element that is the topic of that section with a blank or an X. Take turns playing "identify the mystery element" as follows. One person shares his or her reactions (with the blanks) with the group. The person to the right of the person sharing tries to identify the missing element. If that person can't, the group member to the right tries. Continue until either the element has been identified or all group members have had a chance. The next round starts with the person who

was first to guess the element sharing reactions with the group. Continue until all have shared reactions and all reactions have been correctly identified.

111. Working individually, find a sentence in the chapter that uniquely describes a particular main-group compound. As in the previous question, take turns reading your sentences to the group saying "blank" in place of the name of the compound and giving group members a chance to identify the compound.

DATA INTERPRETATION AND ANALYSIS

Hydrogen Sulfide in Well Water

112. Hydrogen sulfide (H_2S) smells like rotten eggs; its smell can be detected at concentrations as low as 0.02 ppm. Well water, which is drawn from underground depths of 30–250 meters (100–800 feet), is sometimes contaminated with hydrogen sulfide. The contamination arises from bacterial decomposition of sulfur-containing organic and inorganic matter present in the oxygen-deficient underground environment. Some H_2S gas dissolves in the water that is pumped for drinking supplies, where it is detected by taste at concentrations as low as 0.05 ppm. Municipalities remove H_2S to improve water taste and to prevent the accumulation of toxic H_2S gas within the system.

The first table that follows lists hydrogen sulfide solubility in water when the partial pressure of hydrogen sulfide is 1.00 atm. The second table lists solubility product constant data for common metal sulfides.

Hydrogen Sulfide Solubility in Water (Partial Pressure of Hydrogen Sulfide = 1.00 atm)

Temperature, °C	Mole fraction of hydrogen sulfide in water
15	2.335×10^{-3}
20	2.075×10^{-3}
25	1.85×10^{-3}
30	1.66×10^{-3}
35	1.51×10^{-3}

[Source: *CRC Handbook of Chemistry and Physics*, 85th Edition]

Solubility Product Constant Data of Common Metal Sulfides

Sulfide	K_{sp} at 25 °C
copper(II) sulfide	6×10^{-37}
iron(II) sulfide	6×10^{-19}
lead(II) sulfide	9.04×10^{-29}
zinc sulfide	2.0×10^{-25}

Use the information provided in the tables to answer the following questions:

a. What can you conclude about the temperature dependence of H_2S solubility in water?

b. Suppose that water analysis indicates that your well's water contains 1.8 mg H_2S per liter of well water. Using Henry's law (Chapter 14) and the data in the first table, calculate the partial pressure of H_2S, in atm, that exists above your well water at 25 °C. (Assume the well water is in a closed container).

c. Air containing H_2S at 20 ppm (by volume) and below is considered safe to breathe. Is the air above the solution in part b safe to breathe? (The total pressure is 1.00 atm.)

d. A water technician recommends that you treat your well water with hydrogen peroxide, H_2O_2, in order to convert H_2S to sulfate (which does not have an offensive odor or taste), according to the following unbalanced reaction:

$$H_2O_2(aq) + H_2S(aq) \longrightarrow SO_4^{2-}(aq) + H^+(aq) + H_2O(l)$$

What volume of a 3.0% by mass solution of hydrogen peroxide is required to treat 955 liters of your well water? (Assume that no other species are present to react with the H_2O_2 and that the density of the hydrogen peroxide solution is 1.0 g/mL.)

e. Hydrogen sulfide is a weak diprotic acid that ionizes in water to form hydrogen sulfide (HS^-) and sulfide (S^{2-}). Sulfide dissolved in water can be precipitated as an insoluble metal sulfide, according to the following reaction:

$$M^{2+}(aq) + S^{2-}(aq) \longrightarrow MS(s)$$

Which metal in the second table most effectively removes hydrogen sulfide from water?

f. What volume, in mL, of a 0.500 M solution of the metal ion you chose in part e is required to remove the hydrogen sulfide present in 955 liters of your well water (from part b)?

g. What mass, in grams, of the metal sulfide (from part f) precipitates? (Assume 100% yield.)

Cc ANSWERS TO CONCEPTUAL CONNECTIONS

p-Block Elements

24.1 **(b)** Sulfur is a *p*-block element because it falls in column 6A. Columns 3A to 8A are all part of the *p*-block.

Boranes

24.2 **(a)** *Nido*-boranes have the general formula B_nH_{n+4}.

Carbide Formulas

24.3 **(c)** The charge of the potassium ion is 1+ and that of the carbide ion is 2–, so the charge-neutral formula is K_2C_2.

Carbonate Solubility

24.4 **(a)** Since the carbonate ion is basic, adding acid to the solution drives the dissolution reaction to the right because the acid reacts with the carbonate ion. (Recall from Section 18.5 that the solubility of an ionic compound with a basic anion increases with increasing acidity.)

Oxides

24.5 **(c)** The oxidation state of oxygen in K_2O_2 is $-\frac{1}{2}$, so this compound is a superoxide.

The metals are not presented immediately to the hand of man . . . but they are, for the most part, buried in darkness, in the bowels of the earth, where they are so much disguised, by combination and mixture with other substances, that they often appear entirely unlike themselves.

—WILLIAM HENRY (1774–1836)

CHAPTER 25 Metals and Metallurgy

If you look around your house, classroom, or neighborhood, much of what you see is made of metal or at least has some metal parts. Can you imagine life without metals? Without metals, we would have no skyscrapers, which need the rigid framework of steel beams; no automobiles, which need metal engines and bodies; and no electricity, which needs copper and aluminum wire for transmission. Metallurgy is both a very old and a very new science. We find the roots of metallurgy in the distant past, when our primitive ancestors began to search for and process metals. Of the three prehistoric ages of humankind—the Stone Age, the Bronze Age, and the Iron Age—two are named after our quest for metals. But we do not commonly find metals as elements on Earth; instead we find them in compounds, often scattered within other compounds. The mining, separating, and refining of the vast array of metals is a fairly new science. Many modern metals were not available even as recently as 200 years ago. In the middle of the nineteenth century, gold was cheaper than aluminum because aluminum was so difficult to refine, and titanium, which is important in the aerospace industry, could not even be manufactured. In this chapter, we cover the area of chemistry known as metallurgy.

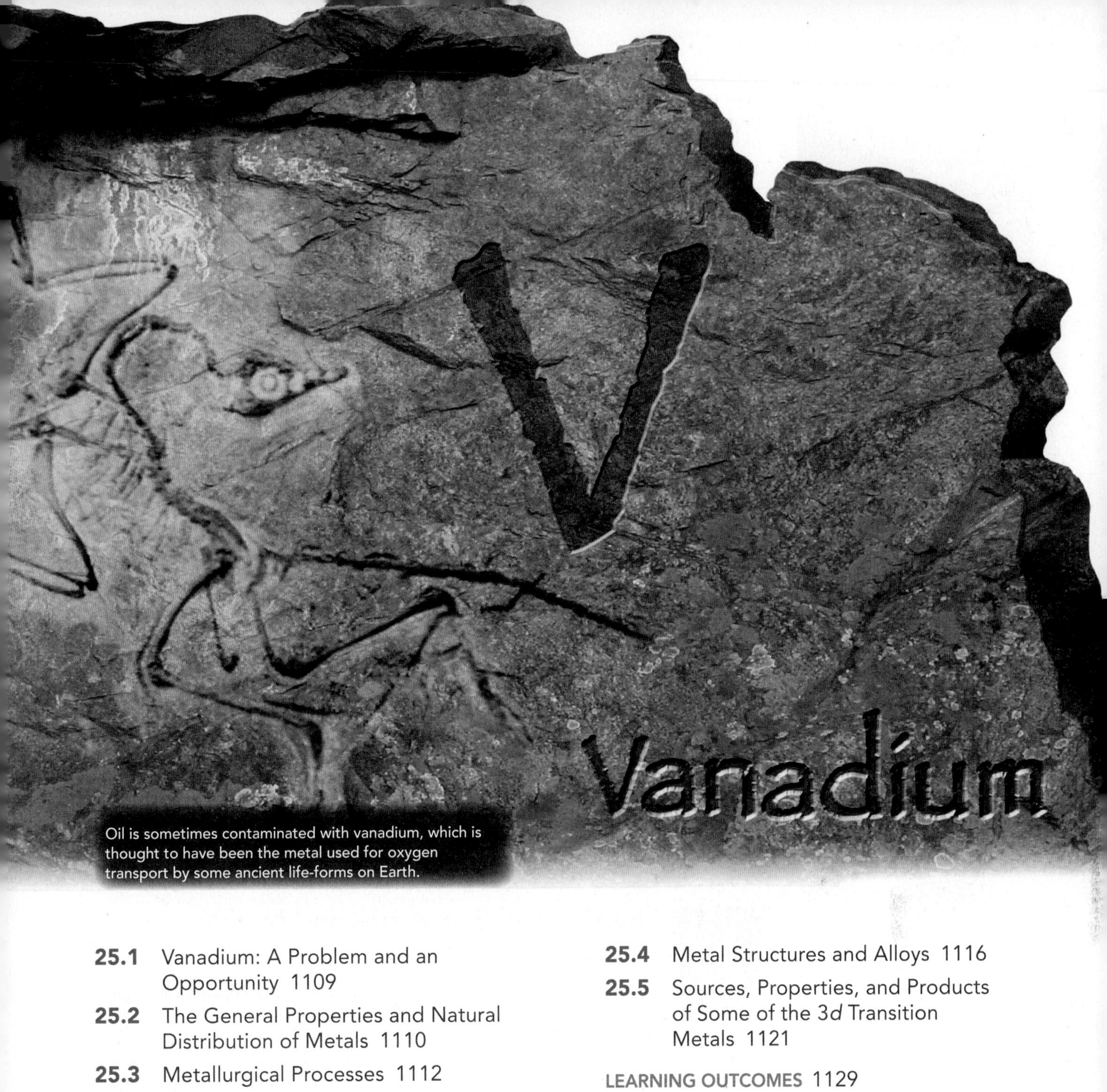

Oil is sometimes contaminated with vanadium, which is thought to have been the metal used for oxygen transport by some ancient life-forms on Earth.

25.1 Vanadium: A Problem and an Opportunity 1109
25.2 The General Properties and Natural Distribution of Metals 1110
25.3 Metallurgical Processes 1112
25.4 Metal Structures and Alloys 1116
25.5 Sources, Properties, and Products of Some of the 3*d* Transition Metals 1121
LEARNING OUTCOMES 1129

25.1 Vanadium: A Problem and an Opportunity

Companies often seek help from university researchers to solve specific technical problems. In one case, representatives of an oil company sought help from a university's chemistry and engineering departments to address vanadium contamination in oil. Because vanadium is toxic, the U.S. government regulates the quantity of vanadium that can be emitted by industrial processes, and oil companies have to figure out environmentally acceptable ways to remove the vanadium from the oil.

Vanadium is a rare element, making up only about 0.015% of Earth's crust (by mass). It is a soft white metal with high ductility and malleability, which means that it can be easily drawn into narrow wires or rolled into thin sheets. Because of the

▲ Vanadium is a soft white metal.

high reactivity of pure vanadium, this element occurs naturally within compounds (not in its elemental form). However, vanadium compounds are not normally found in the rocks or soils near oil fields, so why does this rare, reactive metal occur in oil? The answer lies in the biology of ancient life-forms. Most modern animals use iron in hemoglobin to transport oxygen through their bloodstreams (see Section 16.1), and a few (such as lobsters) use copper for this function. It appears that some extinct animals used vanadium. Even today, one group of simple marine organisms, the tunicates or sea squirts, are believed to employ vanadium compounds for oxygen transport. The source of vanadium in some crude oil may be the very animals from which the oil was formed.

During refining, crude oil is heated to carry out the reactions that form the different petroleum products. If some of the vanadium-containing oil burns during heating, the vanadium forms vanadate compounds, ionic compounds with vanadium oxide polyatomic ions such as VO_4^{3-} and VO_3^{-}. These compounds, which have low melting points, can dissolve the protective oxide coatings on stainless steel containers, causing the steel to corrode and ruining the containers in which the oil is stored. If the vanadium compounds are not removed from the oil before storage, the customer inherits the problem. In addition, vanadium and many of its compounds are toxic, so oil companies cannot simply dump the extracted vanadium compounds into the environment.

The presence of vanadium in crude oil may, however, turn out to be profitable for the oil companies. If an economical method could be found to recover vanadium from oil, then oil could become a major source of vanadium, a valuable metal with several important industrial uses, including the production of iron alloys and sulfuric acid.

The recovery of vanadium from oil involves metallurgy, the topic of this chapter. **Metallurgy** includes all the processes associated with mining, separating, and refining metals and the subsequent production of pure metals and mixtures of metals called *alloys* (which we define in Section 25.4). In this chapter, we explore the general properties and natural distribution of metals; several different categories of metallurgical processes, including pyrometallurgy, hydrometallurgy, electrometallurgy, and powder metallurgy; the structures and alloys formed by metals; and the metallic products and applications for several selected materials.

25.2 The General Properties and Natural Distribution of Metals

Metals share several common properties. All metals are opaque (we cannot see through them), and they are good conductors of heat and electricity. They generally have high malleability (the capacity to be bent or hammered into desired forms) and ductility (the capacity to be drawn into wires). We can explain these properties by the bonding theories that we have already examined for metals: the electron sea model and band theory. In the electron sea model, discussed in Section 10.11, each metal atom within a metal sample donates one or more electrons to an *electron sea*, which flows within the metal. In band theory, discussed in Section 13.8, the atomic orbitals of the metal atoms are combined, forming *bands* that are delocalized over the entire crystalline solid; electrons move freely within these bands. The mobile electrons in both of these models endow metals with many of their shared properties.

Each metal, however, is also unique, and even their shared properties may vary within a range. For example, some metals, such as copper, silver, and aluminum, have much higher thermal and electrical conductivities than do other metals. Table 25.1 lists the thermal conductivity and electrical resistivity (a low resistivity corresponds to a high conductivity) of a few metals. Notice that both properties can vary by factors of 10 or more. Most metals are very strong, malleable, and ductile. But lead is a soft, weak metal, and chromium is a brittle metal that will not bend without breaking. When we think about the shared properties of metals, we must allow for a range of properties as well as some unique ones.

TABLE 25.1 ■ Thermal Conductivity and Electrical Resistivity of Several Metals

Metal	Thermal Conductivity (W/cm · K)	Electrical Resistivity ($\mu\Omega \cdot$ cm)
Ag, silver	4.29	1.59
Cu, copper	4.01	1.67
Fe, iron	0.804	9.71
V, vanadium	0.307	24.8

Over 75% of the elements in the periodic table are metals, yet metals make up only about 25% of the mass of Earth's crust (see Figure 24.2 for the composition of Earth's crust). Earth's core is thought to be composed of iron and nickel, but because the core is so far from the surface, these metals are not accessible. The most abundant metal on Earth is aluminum, a main-group metal. Several alkali and alkaline earth metals (calcium, sodium, potassium, and magnesium) make up more than 1% of Earth's crust. Iron, which makes up about 5% of the crust, is the only transition metal that accounts for more than 0.1% of the crust. Of the first-row transition metals, titanium, chromium, iron, nickel, copper, and zinc are all plentiful enough to be important industrial materials.

▲ Gold is one of the few metals that can be found as an element in nature, often in veins like the one shown here.

Only a few metals occur naturally as elements, including nickel, copper, palladium, silver, platinum, and gold. Because of their low reactivity, these metals are often called the *noble metals*. They are usually concentrated within mountainous or volcanic regions in small, isolated veins within a rock matrix.

▲ Most NaCl salt is produced by trapping ocean water in shallow basins and letting the water evaporate.

Most of the rest of the metals occur naturally in positive oxidation states within mineral deposits. **Minerals** (as we saw in Chapter 24) are homogeneous, naturally occurring, crystalline inorganic solids. A rock that contains a high concentration of a specific mineral is called an **ore**. Metallurgical processes separate useful minerals from other, unusable material in the ore.

The main sources for the alkali metals are chloride minerals, such as halite (sodium chloride) and sylvite (potassium chloride). Halite occurs in large deposits in sites that were once ancient oceans, or it can be precipitated by evaporating ocean water. The main source for some other metals are oxide minerals, such as hematite (Fe_2O_3), rutile (TiO_2), and cassiterite (SnO_2). The ores containing these minerals are unevenly distributed throughout Earth. For example, North America has large deposits of hematite but no substantial deposits of cassiterite. Sulfides are the most important minerals for many metals, such as galena (PbS), cinnabar (HgS), sphalerite (ZnS), and molybdenite (MoS_2).

The main mineral source for some other metals can be complex. For example, the primary *mineral* sources for vanadium are vanadinite [$Pb_5(VO_4)_3Cl$] and carnotite [$K_2(UO_2)_2(VO_4)_2 \cdot 3\,H_2O$], which is also a main mineral source for uranium. Vanadium, as we have seen, is also found in crude oil. No specific minerals contain the metal radium. Yet radium sometimes substitutes for uranium within uranium-containing minerals. The small amount of radium that replaces uranium in carnotite is the major source of radium. Tantalum and niobium, named after the Greek god Tantalus and his daughter Niobe, always occur together in mixed deposits of columbite [$Fe(NbO_3)_2$] and tantalite [$Fe(TaO_3)_2$]. The minerals are mined together, and the elements are later separated by recrystallization (see Section 14.4).

METALS Which statement about metals is generally false?

(a) Most metals occur naturally as pure elements in the earth's crust.
(b) Most metals have high electrical conductivity.
(c) Most metals are opaque (you cannot see through them).
(d) Most metals are malleable.

25.1 Cc Conceptual Connection

ANSWER **NOW!**

25.3 Metallurgical Processes

Mined ores are first physically *separated* into their metal-containing and nonmetal-containing components. Then, the elemental metal is extracted from the compounds in which it is found, a process called **extractive metallurgy**. In this section, we look at several metallurgical processes, including pyrometallurgy, hydrometallurgy, electrometallurgy, and powder metallurgy. After separation and extraction, the metal is **refined**; refining is the process in which the crude material is purified.

Separation

The first step in processing metal-containing ores is crushing the ore into smaller particles. The particles that contain the minerals are then separated from the undesired material, called **gangue** (pronounced "gang"), usually by physical methods. For example, in some cases, a cyclone of wind is used to lift the gangue away from the metal-containing particles, as shown in Figure 25.1▼. If the minerals are magnetic, magnets can separate the minerals. Electrostatic forces can also separate polar minerals from nonpolar gangue.

Sometimes solutions separate the minerals from the gangue, as shown in Figure 25.2▼. A *wetting agent* (or detergent) that preferentially attaches to the mineral surfaces is added to a mixture of the mined material and water. Air is blown through the mixture, forming bubbles and a froth. Because they are attached to the wetting agent, the minerals segregate into the froth, where they can be collected. The gangue separates into the solution.

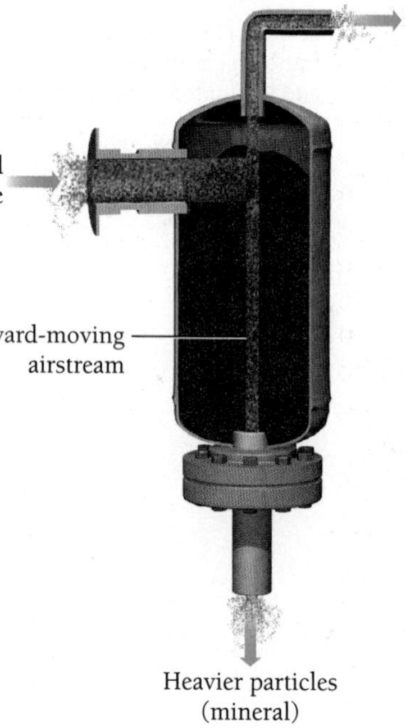

▲ **FIGURE 25.1 Separation by Air** An industrial cyclone separates the crushed light particles of gangue from the heavier metal-bearing particles.

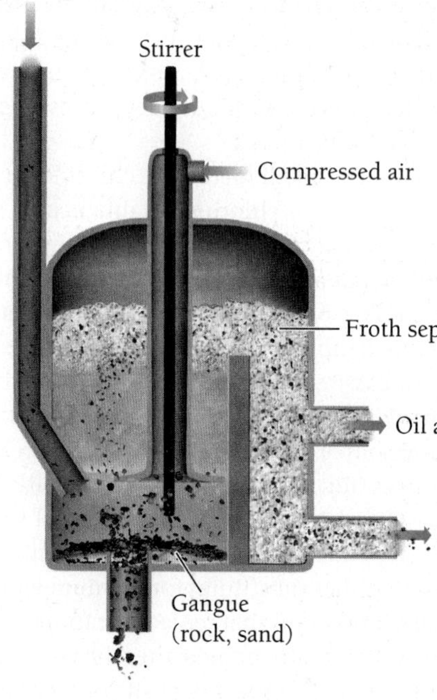

▲ **FIGURE 25.2 Separation by Using a Solution** A wetting agent helps the minerals attach to the froth in a bubbled solution. The minerals in the froth are separated from the gangue remaining in the solution.

Pyrometallurgy

Pyrometallurgy contains the Greek stem *pyro*, meaning fire or heat.

Once the mineral is separated from the gangue, the elemental metal is extracted from the mineral. Several different techniques can achieve this separation. In **pyrometallurgy**, heat is employed to extract a metal from its mineral. Different heating conditions have different effects on the mineral.

Calcination is the heating of an ore in order to decompose it and drive off a volatile product. For example, when carbonate minerals are heated, carbon dioxide is driven off, as shown in these examples:

$$PbCO_3(s) \xrightarrow{\text{heat}} PbO(s) + CO_2(g)$$

$$4\ FeCO_3(s) + O_2(g) \xrightarrow{\text{heat}} 2\ Fe_2O_3(s) + 4\ CO_2(g)$$

Many minerals occur in a hydrated form (that is, they contain water). Calcination can also drive off water:

Hydrated compounds are discussed in Section 3.5.

$$Fe_2O_3 \cdot 2\ Fe(OH)_3(s) \xrightarrow{\text{heat}} 2\ Fe_2O_3(s) + 3\ H_2O(g)$$

Heating that causes a chemical reaction between the furnace atmosphere (the gases in the furnace) and the mineral is called **roasting**. Roasting is particularly important in processing sulfide ores. The ores are heated in the presence of oxygen, converting the sulfide into an oxide and emitting sulfur dioxide. For example, the roasting of lead(II) sulfide occurs by the reaction:

$$2\ PbS(s) + 3\ O_2(g) \xrightarrow{\text{heat}} 2\ PbO(s) + 2\ SO_2(g)$$

In some cases, especially with the less active metals such as mercury, roasting the sulfide produces the pure metal:

$$HgS(s) + O_2(g) \xrightarrow{\text{heat}} Hg(g) + SO_2(g)$$

When roasting forms a liquid product, which makes separation easier, it is called **smelting**. Consider, for example, the smelting of zinc oxide:

$$ZnO(s) + C(s) \xrightarrow{\text{heat}} Zn(l) + CO(g)$$

The gaseous carbon monoxide separates from the liquid zinc, allowing the metal to be readily recovered. In some cases, a flux must be added to the mixture during smelting to help separate the two materials. The **flux** is a material that will react with the gangue to form a substance with a low melting point. For example, oxides of silicon within gangue can be liquefied by reaction with calcium carbonate according to the reaction:

$$\underset{\text{gangue}}{SiO_2(s)} + \underset{\text{flux}}{CaCO_3(s)} \longrightarrow CO_2(g) + \underset{\text{slag}}{CaSiO_3(l)}$$

The waste liquid solution that forms from the flux and gangue is usually a silicate material called a **slag**. The liquid metal and the liquid slag have different densities, and therefore separate. Holes tapped at different heights into the side of the container holding the liquid metal and slag allow the more dense liquid to flow out of the lower tap holes and the less dense liquid to flow out of the higher tap holes.

Hydrometallurgy

The use of an aqueous solution to extract metals from their ores is **hydrometallurgy**. A hydrometallurgy process is used to obtain gold. Gold occurs in its elemental state, but often as very small particles mixed with other substances. The gold can be separated out of the mixture by selectively dissolving it into solution, a process called **leaching**. In this process, solid gold reacts with sodium cyanide to form a soluble gold complex:

$$4\ Au(s) + 8\ CN^-(aq) + O_2(g) + 2\ H_2O(l) \longrightarrow 4\ Au(CN)_2^-(aq) + 4\ OH^-(aq)$$

The impurities are filtered out of the solution, and the gold is reduced back to elemental gold with a reactive metal such as zinc:

$$2\ Au(CN)_2^-(aq) + Zn(s) \longrightarrow Zn(CN)_4^{2-}(aq) + 2\ Au(s)$$

Leaching has been practiced for many years and often results in the contamination of streams and rivers with cyanide. New alternatives using the thiosulfate ion ($S_2O_3^-$) are being investigated to replace leaching.

Different acid, base, and salt solutions are sometimes used to selectively separate out metal-bearing minerals. For example, sulfuric acid is used to separate the copper and iron from the mineral chalcopyrite, $CuFeS_2$, and a sodium chloride solution is used to separate the lead from the insoluble mineral anglesite, $PbSO_4$:

$$2\,CuFeS_2(s) + H_2SO_4(aq) + 4\,O_2(g) \longrightarrow 2\,CuSO_4(aq) + Fe_2O_3(s) + 3\,S(s) + H_2O(l)$$
$$PbSO_4(s) + 4\,NaCl(aq) \longrightarrow Na_2[PbCl_4](aq) + Na_2SO_4(aq)$$

Hydrometallurgy is often more economical than pyrometallurgy because of the high energy costs associated with the elevated temperatures needed for calcination and roasting.

Electrometallurgy

See Section 20.8 for a description of electrolysis.

In **electrometallurgy**, electrolysis is used to produce metals from their compounds. For example, the *Hall process* is an electrometallurgical process crucial to aluminum production. The main source of aluminum is bauxite, $Al_2O_3 \cdot n\,H_2O$. A hydrometallurgical process, the *Bayer process*, separates bauxite from the iron and silicon dioxide with which it is usually found. In this process, the bauxite is heated in a concentrated aqueous NaOH solution under high pressure. The aluminum oxide dissolves, leaving the other oxides behind in solid form:

$$Al_2O_3 \cdot n\,H_2O(s) + 2\,OH^-(aq) + 2\,H_2O(l) \longrightarrow 2\,Al(OH)_4^-(aq)$$

The basic aluminum solution is separated from the oxide solids, and then the aluminum oxide is precipitated out of solution by neutralizing it (recall the pH dependence of the solubility of $Al(OH)_3$ from Section 18.8). Calcination of the precipitate at temperatures greater than 1000 °C yields anhydrous alumina (Al_2O_3). Electrolysis is then used to reduce the aluminum out of the aluminum oxide. Because Al_2O_3 melts at such a high temperature (greater than 2000 °C), however, the electrolysis is not carried out on molten Al_2O_3. Instead, in the Hall process the Al_2O_3 is dissolved into molten cryolite (Na_3AlF_6), and graphite rods are used as electrodes to carry out the electrolysis in the liquid mixture (Figure 25.3▼). The carbon that composes the graphite electrodes is oxidized by the dissolved oxygen ions in the molten salt and converted to carbon dioxide. The aluminum ions dissolved in the molten salt reduce to molten aluminum, which sinks down to the bottom of the cell and is removed:

Oxidation: $C(s) + 2\,O^{2-}(\text{dissolved}) \longrightarrow CO_2(g) + 4\,e^-$

Reduction: $3\,e^- + Al^{3+}(\text{dissolved}) \longrightarrow Al(l)$

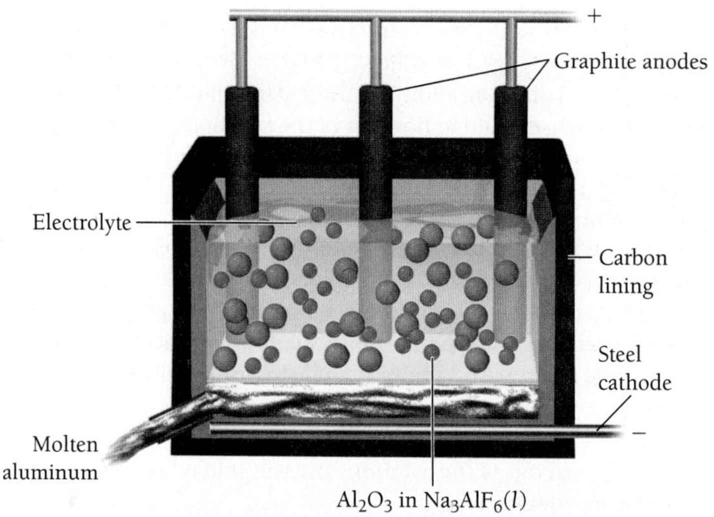

▶ **FIGURE 25.3 The Hall Process** The Hall process produces aluminum metal by reducing the aluminum ions in alumina. Graphite electrodes act as reducing agents. Dissolved oxygen ions in the molten cryolite oxidize the carbon in the graphite electrodes to form carbon dioxide.

Another important example of metallurgy is the refinement of copper. The most abundant copper source is the mineral chalcopyrite, $CuFeS_2$. First, the chalcopyrite is converted to CuS by roasting. During this process, the iron also forms oxides and sulfides. Silica is added to form an iron silicate slag, which is then removed. The remaining copper(II) sulfide reacts with oxygen to form sulfur dioxide gas and copper metal, but the metal is not very pure. Electrolysis is employed to refine the copper.

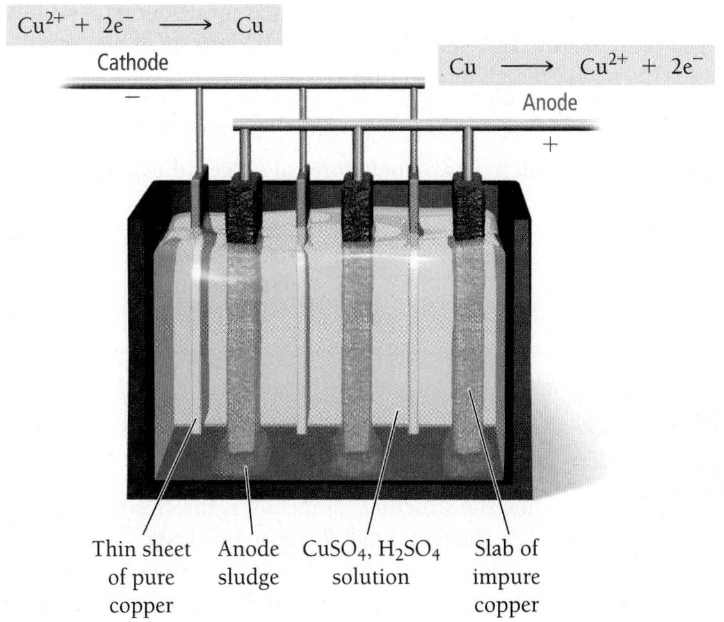

◀ **FIGURE 25.4 Copper Electrolysis Cell** Copper is refined by electrolysis. The impure copper is oxidized at the anode and then reduced to form pure metal on the cathode. Many precious metals collect in the sludge at the bottom of the electrolysis cell.

In the electrolysis cell used to refine copper, both the anode and the cathode are made of copper (Figure 25.4▲). The anode is the impure copper (that needs to be refined), and the cathode is a thin sheet of pure copper. As the current flows through the cell, the copper from the anode oxidizes and dissolves in a copper sulfate solution. It then plates out as pure copper on the cathode. The impurities in the copper anode separate from the copper during electrolysis because, even though the more active metals also oxidize from the anode, they stay in solution and do not plate out on the cathode. The less active metals do not oxidize at all and simply fall to the bottom of the cell as the copper is dissolved from the anode. The sludge at the bottom of the electrolysis cell contains many precious metals, including gold and silver. About one-quarter of the silver produced in the United States is from the impurities recovered from the refinement of copper.

Powder Metallurgy

Powder metallurgy, first developed in the 1920s, is used to make metallic components from powdered metal. In powder metallurgy, micron-sized metal particles are pressed together under high pressures to form the desired component. The component is then heated (*sintered*). The sintering process occurs below the melting point of the powder but at a temperature high enough to fuse the metal particles together, strengthening the metal and increasing its density.

▲ These metal products were all made by powder metallurgy.

Originally, iron powder from mill scrap was used in powder metallurgy. The scrap was primarily iron oxide that would fall off the steel as it was being milled. The iron oxide dust was heated in a hydrogen atmosphere to reduce the oxide to iron particles. Manufacturers called the powdered metal *iron sponge* because numerous holes form in the particles when the oxygen escapes.

In the 1960s, the A. O. Smith Company in the United States introduced a new method for the development of powdered metal, called water atomization. In this method, the pure metal is melted and a small stream of the liquid is allowed to flow from the bottom of the container of molten metal. A high-pressure blast of cold water hits the stream of metal, breaking it into small droplets that quickly solidify. Powdered metal particles made in this way are smoother and more dense than the sponge powder particles from oxide scrap. In addition to powdered iron metal, many copper, bronze, carbide, and brass parts are made with powder metallurgical processes.

Powder metallurgy offers several advantages over traditional casting or milling of metal. For example, waste is almost eliminated because the part can be pressed directly into the desired shape. Intricate teeth on gears and multiple holes can be designed into the press, and therefore do not have to be machined after production. Making cast metal objects from metals with high melting points, such as molybdenum and tungsten, can be difficult because of the high temperatures necessary to melt the metal. Using the powder avoids the need for high temperatures.

ANSWER **NOW!**

25.2 Cc Conceptual Connection

METALLURGY Which type of metallurgical process uses electrolysis to extract a metal from its ore?

(a) pyrometallurgy
(b) hydrometallurgy
(c) powder metallurgy
(d) electrometallurgy

25.4 Metal Structures and Alloys

We can describe the structures of metals as the closest packing of spheres, first discussed in Section 13.3. Elemental metals generally crystallize in one of the basic types of crystal lattices, including face-centered cubic, body-centered cubic, and hexagonal closest packed. The crystal structure of a metal may change, however, as a function of temperature and pressure. Table 25.2 lists the crystal structures for the 3*d* transition metals.

TABLE 25.2 ■ The Crystal Structures of the 3*d* Elements

Metal	Natural Crystal Structure at Room Temperature and Atmospheric Pressure	Other Crystal Structures at Different Temperatures and Pressures
Sc	Hexagonal closest packed	Face-centered cubic, body-centered cubic
Ti	Hexagonal closest packed	Body-centered cubic above 882 °C
V	Body-centered cubic	
Cr	Body-centered cubic	Hexagonal closest packed
Mn	Alpha complex body-centered cubic form	Beta simple cubic form above 727 °C Face-centered cubic above 1095 °C Body-centered cubic above 1133 °C
Fe	Body-centered cubic	Face-centered cubic above 909 °C Body-centered cubic above 1403 °C
Co	Hexagonal closest packed	Face-centered cubic above 420 °C
Ni	Face-centered cubic	
Cu	Face-centered cubic	
Zn	Hexagonal closest packed	

Alloys

An **alloy** is a metallic material that contains more than one element. Some alloys are simply solid solutions, whereas others are specific compounds with definite ratios of the component elements. Alloys have metallic properties, but they can consist of either two or more metals or a metal and a nonmetal. We broadly classify alloys as substitutional or interstitial. In a **substitutional alloy**, one metal atom substitutes for another in the crystal structure. The crystal structure may either stay the same upon the substitution, or it may change to accommodate the differences between the atoms. In an **interstitial alloy**, small, usually nonmetallic atoms fit in between the metallic atoms of a crystal. The alloy maintains its metallic properties with these interstitial atoms in the structure.

Substitutional Alloys

For two metals to form a substitutional alloy, the radii of the two metal atoms must be similar, usually within 15% of each other. For example, the atomic radii of copper and nickel are both 135 pm, and both of the elements form the face-centered cubic structure. Therefore, either metal can easily replace the other in the metal crystal structure.

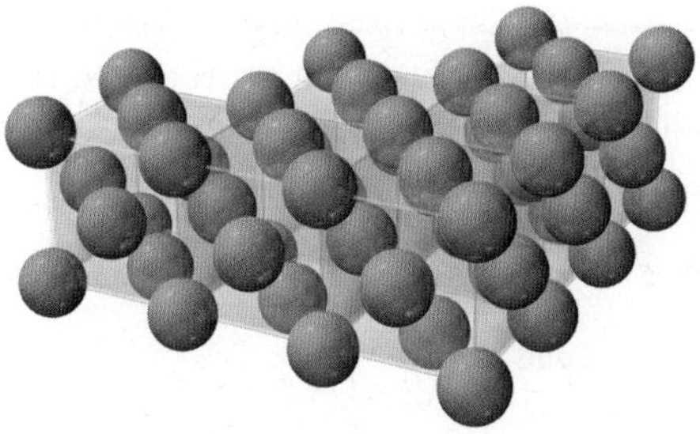

▲ Copper crystallizes in the face-centered structure shown here.

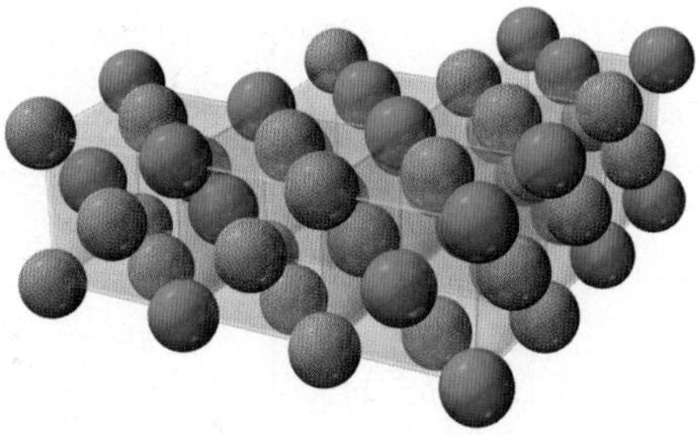

▲ In a nickel and copper alloy, nickel atoms substitute for some of the copper atoms.

Figure 25.5▶ is a phase diagram for a copper and nickel alloy. This phase diagram, called a *binary* phase diagram, is different from the diagrams that we discussed in Section 12.8, which show the phases of a pure substance at different pressures and temperatures. This diagram shows the different phases for a mixture at different *compositions* and temperatures. The *x*-axis indicates the composition (in this case, the mole percent of nickel in the alloy, with the left side representing pure copper and the right side representing pure nickel). The *y*-axis indicates the temperature.

Pure copper melts at 1084 °C, as indicated by the change from solid to liquid at 0% nickel. Pure nickel melts at 1455 °C, as indicated by the change from solid to liquid at 100% nickel. The area on the diagram above the line connecting the melting points of copper and nickel represents a liquid solution of the two metals. The area below that line represents a solid solution of the two metals. Any ratios of copper and nickel can form the face-centered cubic structure.

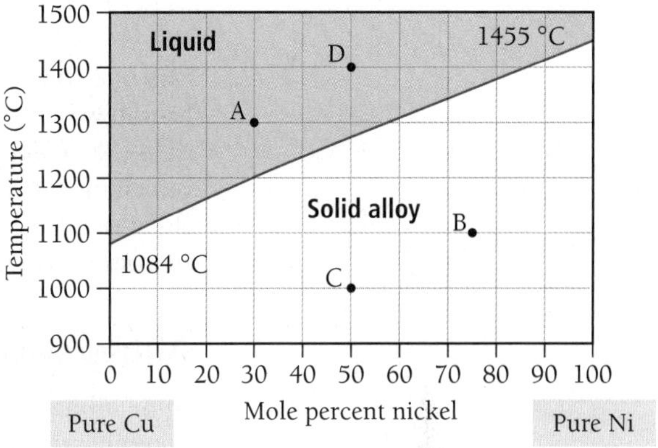

▲ **FIGURE 25.5 Cu–Ni Phase Diagram** Because copper and nickel have similar crystal structures and similar size, together they can form a solid solution. A solution forms at all compositions from pure copper to pure nickel.

HOW TO: *Interpret a Binary Phase Diagram*	**EXAMPLE 25.1** **Determining Alloy Compositions from a Phase Diagram** Determine the composition and phase present at point A on Figure 25.5.	**EXAMPLE 25.2** **Determining Alloy Compositions from a Phase Diagram** Determine the composition and phase present at point B on Figure 25.5.
Locate the temperature and composition of the alloy on the binary phase diagram in Figure 25.5.	Point A represents 30 mol% Ni at 1300 °C.	Point B represents 75 mol% Ni at 1100 °C.
Identify the phase.	The point is above the melting point line, so the phase is liquid.	The point is below the melting point line, so the phase is solid.
Identify the amount of copper and nickel in the phase.	This liquid phase is made up of 30 mol% Ni, so it is 70 mol% Cu.	This solid phase is made up of 75 mol% Ni, so it is 25 mol% Cu.
	FOR PRACTICE 25.1 Determine the composition and phase present at point C on Figure 25.5.	**FOR PRACTICE 25.2** Determine the composition and phase present at point D on Figure 25.5.

The phase diagrams of some alloys are more complex. Consider the phase diagram for chromium and vanadium in Figure 25.6▶. Both Cr and V form the body-centered cubic crystal, and the atoms are similar in size. Yet this phase diagram reveals an important difference between this alloy and the Cu and Ni alloy: the melting temperature does not

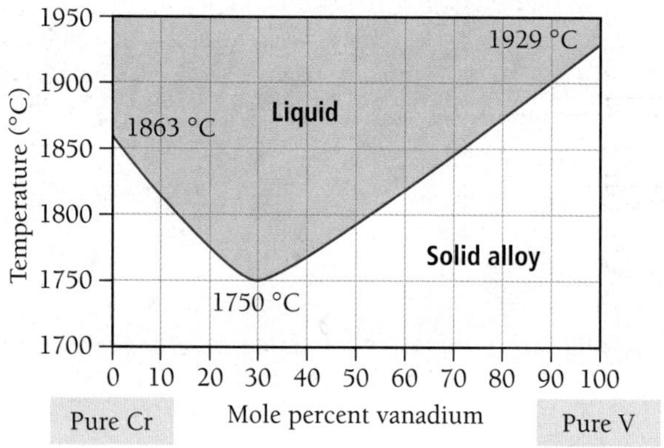

▶ **FIGURE 25.6 Cr–V Phase Diagram** In a binary phase diagram of two metals that form a solid solution, an intermediate composition can have either the highest or lowest melting point. In the chromium and vanadium phase diagram an intermediate composition has the lowest melting point.

vary in a uniform way from the lower melting point of Cr to the higher melting point of V. Instead we see that the alloys with intermediate compositions melt at lower temperatures than either pure metal. The lowest melting point is 1750 °C at a composition of 30 mol % vanadium. Solid compositions that melt at temperatures lower than either of the pure metals, as well as compositions that melt at temperatures higher than either of the two metals, are common in these types of alloys.

Alloys with Limited Solubility

Some alloys are composed of metals that each have different crystal structures. For example, nickel crystallizes in the face-centered cubic structure and chromium in the body-centered cubic structure. Because of their different structures, these two metals do not form a miscible solid solution at all compositions. At some intermediate composition, the structure has to change from that of one of the metals to that of the other. Figure 25.7◀ is the nickel and chromium phase diagram from 700 °C to 1900 °C. Notice that the diagram has two different solid phases: face-centered cubic and body-centered cubic. From pure nickel (0 mol % chromium) to about 40–50 mol % chromium, the structure is face-centered cubic. In this structure, Cr atoms substitute for Ni atoms in the face-centered cubic structure of nickel. However, beyond a certain percentage of chromium (which depends on temperature), that structure is no longer stable. At 700 °C about 40 mol % Cr can fit in the crystal, and at 1200 °C about 50 mol % Cr can fit in. Adding additional Cr beyond these points results in a different phase.

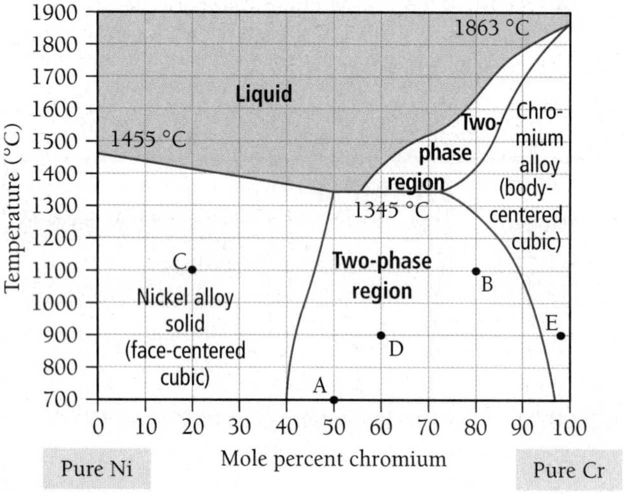

▲ **FIGURE 25.7 Cr–Ni Phase Diagram** Because chromium and nickel form solids with crystal structures that differ from each other, an alloy mixture of the two metals does not form a solid solution at all compositions. A two-phase region exists at compositions between the possible compositions of the two different structures. In the two-phase region, both crystal structures coexist in equilibrium.

At the other end of the diagram (nearly pure chromium) and at 700 °C, only a small amount of nickel can be substituted into the body-centered cubic structure of the chromium. As the temperature rises to 1300 °C, however, about 20 mol % nickel can be accommodated into the chromium structure. The region in between the two phases is called a **two-phase region**. At these compositions, the two phases (nickel-rich face-centered cubic and chromium-rich body-centered cubic) exist together. The amount of each phase depends upon the composition of the alloy.

We can determine the composition and relative amounts of the two different phases that coexist in a two-phase region from a phase diagram. Point A on Figure 25.7 in the Cr–Ni phase diagram represents 50% composition at 700 °C, and both phases are present. Some of the Cr atoms have substituted into the nickel-rich face-centered cubic structure, but there is too much Cr to all fit into the crystal. The leftover Cr atoms form the chromium-rich body-centered cubic structure with a small number of Ni atoms in the crystal.

The two crystals that exist at point A are (1) the nickel-rich face-centered cubic structure with 40 mol % Cr; and (2) the chromium-rich body-centered cubic structure with 5 mol % Ni. The 50% composition on the phase diagram has just slightly more Cr atoms than can fit into the nickel structure. Thus, most of the crystals in the two-phase region are the nickel-rich face-centered cubic structure with only a small amount of the chromium-rich body-centered cubic structure, as determined by a method called the *lever rule*. The **lever rule** states that in a two-phase region, whichever phase is closer to the composition of the alloy is the more abundant phase. In this example, the 50 mol % Cr composition on the phase diagram is closer to the 40 mol % Cr composition of the nickel-rich face-centered cubic phase than the 95 mol % Cr composition of the chromium-rich body-centered cubic phase, so more face-centered cubic crystals are present than body-centered cubic crystals.

HOW TO: *Interpret the Phases and Compositions in a Binary Phase Diagram as Described by the Lever Rule*	EXAMPLE 25.3 **Alloy Compositions in a Solid Solution with Limited Solubility** Determine the composition, relative amounts, and phases present at point B on Figure 25.7.	EXAMPLE 25.4 **Alloy Compositions in a Solid Solution with Limited Solubility** Determine the composition, relative amounts, and phases present at point C on Figure 25.7.
Locate the temperature and composition of the alloy on the binary phase diagram.	Point B represents 80 mol % Cr at 1100 °C.	Point C represents 20 mol % Cr at 1100 °C.
Identify the phases.	Point B is located in the two-phase region, consisting of the nickel-rich face-centered cubic structure and the chromium-rich body-centered cubic structure.	Point C is located in the one-phase region of the nickel-rich face-centered cubic structure.
Identify the amount of Ni and Cr in the phases.	The nickel-rich face-centered cubic structure has 45 mol % Cr and 55 mol % Ni, and the chromium-rich body-centered cubic structure has 90 mol % Cr and 10 mol % Ni.	The nickel-rich face-centered cubic structure at this point has 20 mol % Cr and 80 mol % Ni.
Identify the relative amounts of the phases.	At a composition of 80 mol % Cr, the composition is closer to the Cr-rich body-centered cubic phase, so there is more of this phase than there is of the Ni-rich face-centered cubic phase.	There is only one phase. It is 100 mol % of the Ni face-centered cubic phase.
	FOR PRACTICE 25.3 Determine the composition, relative amounts, and phases present at point D on Figure 25.7.	**FOR PRACTICE 25.4** Determine the composition, relative amounts, and phases present at point E on Figure 25.7.

Interstitial Alloys

Recall that in contrast to substitutional alloys, where one metal atom substitutes for another in the lattice, interstitial alloys contain atoms of one kind that fit into the holes, or interstitial sites, of the crystal structure of the other metal. In metals with the interstitial elements hydrogen, boron, nitrogen, or carbon, the alloy that results retains its metallic properties.

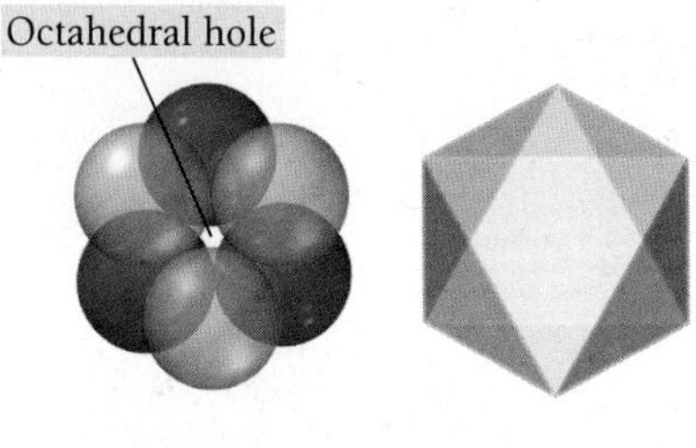

▲ **FIGURE 25.8 Octahedral Holes in Closest-Packed Crystals** Octahedral holes are found in a closest-packed structure. In the closest-packed structure, the octahedral hole is surrounded by six atoms.

Closest-packed crystal structures have two different types of holes between the atoms in the crystalline lattice. An **octahedral hole**, shown in Figure 25.8◀, exists in the middle of six atoms on two adjacent closest-packed sheets of metal atoms. The hole is located directly above the center of three closest-packed metal atoms in one sheet and below the three metal atoms in the adjacent sheet. This configuration of metal atoms is identical to a regular octahedral configuration that consists of four atoms in a square plane with one atom above and one atom below the square.

We can calculate the size of an octahedral hole by determining the size of a hole on a square of four atoms in a plane (Figure 25.9◀). Any of the four corners of the square is the 90° angle of a right triangle formed from the adjacent two sides and the diagonal line that runs across the center of the square. According to the Pythagorean theorem, the length of the diagonal line (c) is related to the length of the sides (a and b) as follows:

$$c^2 = a^2 + b^2 \qquad [25.1]$$

If we let r_m equal the metal atom radius, the lengths of the sides are $2r_m$. We can then substitute $2r_m$ for both a and b:

$$c^2 = (2r_m)^2 + (2r_m)^2$$
$$c^2 = 8r_m^2$$
$$c = 2.828r_m \qquad [25.2]$$

We can see from Figure 25.9 that the length of the diagonal (c) is twice the radius of the atoms plus twice the radius of the hole:

$$c = 2r_m + 2r_{hole} \qquad [25.3]$$

Combining Equations 25.2 and 25.3, we get the important result:

$$2.828r_m = 2r_m + 2r_{hole}$$
$$0.828r_m = 2r_{hole}$$
$$r_{hole} = 0.414r_m \qquad [25.4]$$

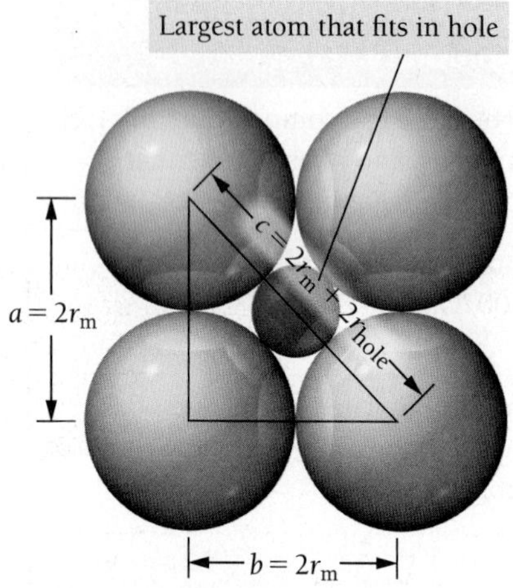

▲ **FIGURE 25.9 A Different View of an Octahedral Hole** An octahedral hole can be viewed as the area in the middle of a square plane of atoms, with one additional atom above the hole and one additional atom below the hole, accounting for the six close atoms. The diagonal of the square is equal to the radius of the two corner atoms plus the diameter of the hole. The Pythagorean theorem relates the length of the diagonal to the lengths of the sides of the square.

The octahedral hole, surrounded by six metal atoms, has a radius that is 41.4% of the metal atom radius. By contrast, the hole in the center of a cube in the *simple cubic* structure has a radius that is 73% of the metal atom radius. The *number* of octahedral holes in a closest-packed structure is equal to the number of metal atoms.

The second type of interstitial hole in a closest-packed structure is a **tetrahedral hole** (first introduced in Section 13.5), which forms directly above the center point of three closest-packed metal atoms in one plane and below a fourth metal atom located directly above the center point in the adjacent plane (Figure 25.10▼). The number of tetrahedral holes in a closest-packed structure is equal to *twice* the number of metal atoms. Because this hole is surrounded by only four atoms, the hole is smaller than the octahedral interstitial hole. We can apply geometric considerations similar to those used previously for the octahedral hole to determine that the tetrahedral hole has a radius that is 23% of the metal atom radius.

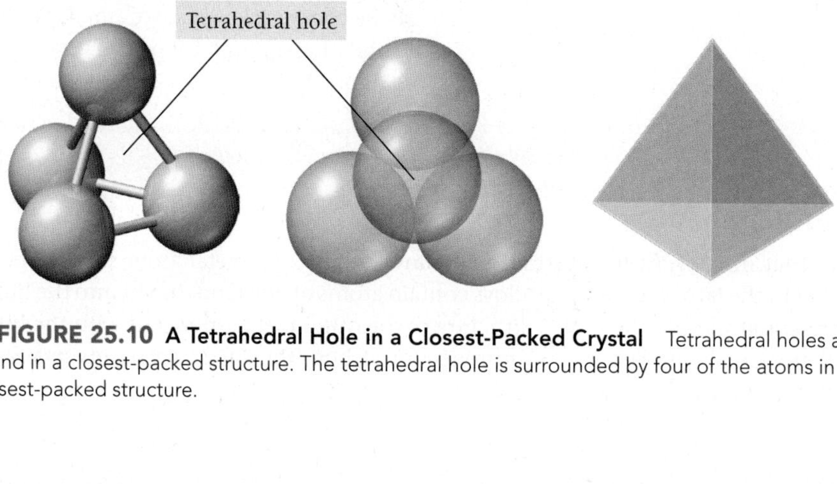

▲ **FIGURE 25.10 A Tetrahedral Hole in a Closest-Packed Crystal** Tetrahedral holes are found in a closest-packed structure. The tetrahedral hole is surrounded by four of the atoms in the closest-packed structure.

TABLE 25.3 ■ Formulas of Several Interstitial Alloys

Compound	Type of Interstitial Hole Occupied	Fraction of Holes Occupied	Formula
Titanium carbide	Octahedral	All	TiC
Molybdenum nitride	Octahedral	One-half	Mo_2N
Tungsten nitride	Octahedral	One-half	W_2N
Manganese nitride	Octahedral	One-quarter	Mn_4N
Palladium hydride	Tetrahedral	One-quarter	Pd_2H
Titanium hydride	Tetrahedral	All	TiH_2

Interstitial alloys form when small nonmetallic atoms fit within the octahedral or tetrahedral holes of the crystalline lattice of the metal. The formulas for these alloys depend both on the type of hole occupied by the nonmetallic atom and on the fraction of holes occupied. For example, titanium and carbon form an alloy with a closest-packed structure for titanium in which all of the octahedral holes are filled with carbon atoms. Since the number of octahedral holes in a closest-packed structure is equal to the number of atoms in the structure, the ratio of carbon atoms to titanium atoms is 1:1 and the corresponding formula is TiC. In the compound formed between molybdenum and nitrogen, by contrast, only one-half of the octahedral holes in the closest-packed structure of Mo are filled with N. Therefore, the formula for this compound is Mo_2N. Table 25.3 lists the formulas and relative number of holes filled for several different interstitial alloys.

INTERSTITIAL ALLOYS An interstitial alloy contains a nonmetal (X) that occupies one-eighth of the tetrahedral holes of the cubic closest-packed structure of the metal (M). What is its formula?

(a) MX **(b)** M_2X **(c)** MX_2 **(d)** M_4X

25.3 Cc Conceptual Connection

ANSWER **NOW!**

25.5 Sources, Properties, and Products of Some of the 3*d* Transition Metals

In this section, we examine major sources, interesting properties, and important products of several of the 3*d* transition metals, specifically, titanium, chromium, manganese, cobalt, copper, nickel, and zinc. We also survey the different metallurgical methods used to separate and refine them. The variety of uses for these metals reflects their varied structures and properties.

Titanium

Titanium is the ninth most abundant element in Earth's crust and the fourth most abundant metal. Titanium was discovered in 1791, but the pure metal was not isolated until 1910. The principal minerals of titanium are rutile (TiO_2) and ilmenite ($FeTiO_3$). Another source of titanium is coal ash, the residue from burned coal. Black shiny ilmenite is found in granite deposits along the North Atlantic coast, often within silica sand. The mineral ilmenite is magnetic due to the presence of Fe^{2+} ions, so it can be separated with a magnet from the nonmagnetic silica. The separated mineral is heated in the presence of carbon under an atmosphere of chlorine gas, forming $TiCl_4$, a volatile gas that can be isolated:

$$FeTiO_3(s) + 3\,Cl_2(g) + 3\,C(s) \longrightarrow 3\,CO(g) + FeCl_2(s) + TiCl_4(g)$$

The $TiCl_4$ gas is reacted with hot magnesium metal turnings (shaved pieces of magnesium), forming elemental titanium—a solid sponge material:

$$TiCl_4(g) + 2\,Mg(s) \longrightarrow 2\,MgCl_2(l) + Ti(s)$$

Titanium is very reactive, readily oxidizing in the presence of oxygen and even nitrogen. Consequently, the elemental titanium is **arc-melted**—a method in which the solid metal is melted with an arc (an electrical discharge) from a high-voltage electric source in a controlled atmosphere to prevent oxidation—and then collected in a water-cooled copper pot. Because of titanium's high reactivity, any further processing must be done in a protective atmosphere of an inert gas, such as Ar, to prevent oxidation.

Despite its reactivity, solid titanium is highly resistant to corrosion in air, acid, and seawater because it quickly reacts with oxygen to form an oxide that coats the surface, preventing further oxidation of the underlying metal. Consequently, titanium is often used in the production of ship components such as propeller shafts and rigging. Titanium is also very strong and light; it is stronger than steel and less than half as dense. It is denser than aluminum but twice as strong. For these reasons, titanium is used in the airline industry for the production of jet engine parts. When titanium is alloyed with 5% aluminum and trace amounts of Fe, Cr, and Mo, the resulting metal retains its strength under higher temperatures.

The most common use of titanium, however, is as titanium(IV) oxide (TiO_2), which forms a clear crystal but a brilliant white powder. Most white paints include TiO_2, which is far less toxic than PbO_2, which was used in older paints. Titanium(IV) oxide is made by reacting sulfuric acid with ilmenite, which dissolves the titanium into solution:

$$FeTiO_3(s) + 3\,H_2SO_4(l) \longrightarrow FeSO_4(aq) + Ti(SO_4)_2(aq) + 3\,H_2O(l)$$

Neutralizing the solution with a strong base forms titanium(IV) oxide:

$$Ti^{4+}(aq) + 4\,OH^-(aq) \longrightarrow TiO_2(s) + 2\,H_2O(l)$$

Calcination of the oxide dries it to form TiO_2 rutile crystals. Large rutile crystals are sometimes used as gems because they resemble diamonds.

Chromium

The name *chromium* comes from the Greek root *chroma*, which means color. The different compounds of chromium are brightly colored (Table 25.4; Figure 25.11◀). The main ore source of chromium is chromite, $FeCr_2O_4$. No appreciable sources of chromium ores exist in the United States. Chromium metal is produced by reducing chromium ore with aluminum:

$$3\,FeCr_2O_4(s) + 8\,Al(s) \longrightarrow 4\,Al_2O_3(s) + 6\,Cr(s) + 3\,Fe(s)$$

Metallic chromium is a white, hard, lustrous, and brittle metal. The metal readily dissolves in acids such as hydrochloric acid and sulfuric acid, but it does not dissolve in concentrated nitric acid (because nitric acid forms an oxide on the surface of the chromium that resists further reaction). The primary use of chromium is in the production of steel alloys called *stainless steels*. Reducing chromite with carbon produces ferrochrome, an alloy that is added to steel:

$$FeCr_2O_4(s) + 4\,C(g) \xrightarrow{\text{heat}} Fe_xCr_y(s) + 4\,CO(g)$$

▲ **FIGURE 25.11 Chromium Compounds** Chromium compounds tend to be brightly colored.

TABLE 25.4 ■ The Colors of Various Chromium Compounds

Compound	Color
Chromates (CrO_4^{2-})	Yellow
Chromium(II) iodide	Red-brown
Chromium(III) iodide	Green-black
Chromium(II) chloride	White
Chromium(III) chloride	Violet
Dichromates ($Cr_2O_7^{2-}$)	Orange
Chromium(III) oxide	Deep green
Chrome alum	Purple
Chromium(VI) oxychloride (CrO_2Cl_2)	Dark red
Chromium(II) acetate	Red

The chromium reacts with any oxygen in the steel to protect the iron from rusting. Chromium compounds were also used extensively in metal coatings, such as paints, because the chromium helps to rustproof the underlying metal. They are also used in wood preservatives because these compounds kill many of the bacteria and molds that rot wood. Chromium compounds are finding less use today, however, because of their toxicity and potential carcinogenicity. Nonetheless, because of their great corrosion resistance, chromate coatings are still used on large outdoor steel structures such as bridges, and chromate paints are used to mark streets (on the pavement) and on street signs.

Because chromium has the electron configuration $[Ar]4s^1 3d^5$, with six orbitals available for bonding, it can have oxidation states from +1 to +6. Low-oxidation-state chromium exists primarily as the *cation* in salt compounds such as $Cr(NO_3)_3$ and $CrCl_3$. High-oxidation-state chromium occurs within the polyatomic *anions* of salts. The most important compounds with chromium in the +6 oxidation state are the chromates and dichromates. In an acidic solution (below pH 6), the orange-red dichromate ion $Cr_2O_7^{2-}$ is more stable. In more basic solutions (above pH 6), the yellow chromate ion CrO_4^{2-} dominates. Adding acid to a solution containing the chromate ion produces the dichromate ion:

$$2\,H^+(aq) + 2\,CrO_4^{2-}(aq) \longrightarrow Cr_2O_7^{2-}(aq) + H_2O(l)$$

The chromate ion has a tetrahedral arrangement of oxygen atoms around a chromium atom. The dichromate ion has one bridging oxygen between the two tetrahedrons surrounding the chromium ions:

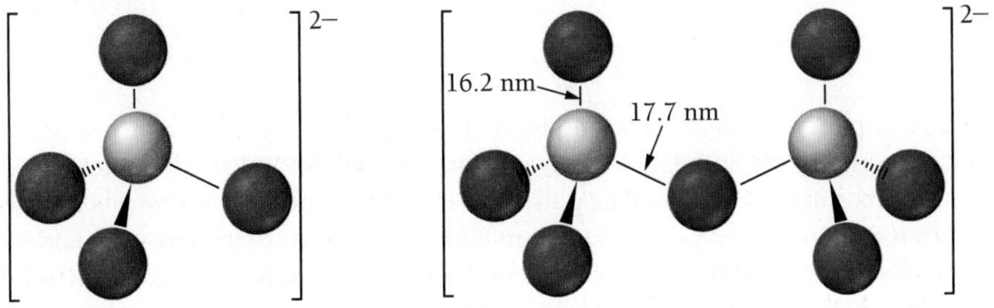

Chromate (CrO_4^{2-}) Dichromate ($Cr_2O_7^{2-}$)

The high-oxidation-state chromates and dichromates are very strong oxidizing agents (that is, they are easily reduced). Consequently, they are used as coatings on other metal surfaces to prevent oxidation. The chromates react with the atoms on the surface of the other metals, forming a strongly bonded gel-like film. The film is nonmetallic and bonds very effectively with paint and resins that are applied over the film. We can see evidence of the oxidizing power of dichromate in the ability of ammonium dichromate to sustain combustion without any additional oxygen. Once ignited, ammonium dichromate burns with visible flames, giving off a smoke of green chromium(III) oxide dust:

▲ Ammonium dichromate does not require additional oxygen to burn.

$$(NH_4)_2Cr_2O_7(s) \xrightarrow{\text{heat}} 4\,H_2O(g) + N_2(g) + Cr_2O_3(s)$$

Manganese

Manganese, with the electron configuration $[Ar]4s^2 3d^5$, exhibits a wide range of oxidation states, from +1 to +7. The most common natural sources of manganese are pyrolusite (MnO_2), hausmannite (Mn_3O_4), and rhodochrosite ($MnCO_3$) minerals. Calcination of rhodochrosite produces manganese(IV) oxide:

$$MnCO_3(s) + {}^1\!/_2 O_2(g) \xrightarrow{\text{heat}} MnO_2(s) + CO_2(g)$$

The manganese(IV) oxide or pyrolusite minerals can react with active metals such as Al or Na to produce the elemental metal:

$$3\,MnO_2(s) + 4\,Al(s) \longrightarrow 3\,Mn(s) + 2\,Al_2O_3(s)$$

Pyrolusite, however, is often found as an impure mineral, containing mixtures of MnO and Fe_2O_3. Heating the mineral in the presence of carbon can reduce the mineral, forming an alloy of manganese and iron called ferromanganese:

$$MnO_2(s) + MnO(s) + Fe_2O_3(s) + n\,C(s) \longrightarrow Mn_xFe_yC_z(s) + n\,CO(g)$$

Ferromanganese generally contains about 5–6% carbon and is used as an alloying material in steel production. Manganese is added to steel alloys to change the physical properties of the steel. For example, manganese makes the steel easier to deform at high temperatures. Adding manganese to steel helps the rolling and forging steps of steel production. Steel alloys containing about 12% manganese are used in military armor and industrial applications such as bulldozer blades. Manganese also strengthens copper, aluminum, and magnesium alloys.

Manganese is a reactive metal that dissolves in most acids. When heated in the presence of air, it forms the various manganese oxides, including MnO, Mn_3O_4, and MnO_2. When heated in pure oxygen, the high-oxidation-state oxide Mn_2O_7 also forms. At high-oxidation states, the manganese compounds are good oxidizing agents. Dissolving MnO_2 into a solution of hydrochloric acid oxidizes the chloride and produces chlorine gas:

$$MnO_2(s) + 4\,HCl(aq) \longrightarrow Cl_2(g) + 2\,H_2O(l) + MnCl_2(aq)$$

The permanganate ion (MnO_4^-) has an oxidation state of +7 for Mn and is also an important oxidizing agent. The permanganate ion can even oxidize hydrogen peroxide, which is itself used as an oxidizing agent:

$$2\,MnO_4^-(aq) + 3\,H_2O_2(aq) + 2\,H^+(aq) \longrightarrow 2\,MnO_2(s) + 3\,O_2(g) + 4\,H_2O(g)$$

The compound MnO_2 is a glass additive. By itself, MnO_2 is either a brown or black crystal, depending on the degree of hydration. Yet, when added to a silica glass, it imparts a pink color to the glass. The pink color is useful because it counteracts the green color often seen in glass, which is due to small concentrations of impure iron oxides. In other words, MnO_2 is added to glass to "decolorize" it. Old manganese-containing glass that has been exposed to UV light for over 100 years develops a slight purple tint. This purple color is due to the oxidation of MnO_2 to Mn(VII) oxides.

Cobalt

Cobalt ore is often found within the ores of other metals, such as iron, nickel, lead, and silver. Cobalt's most common ores are sulfide minerals, such as cobaltite (CoAsS), which is collected as a by-product in the extraction processes of the other metal ores. No large deposits of cobalt ores occur in the United States, but surveys indicate that there are cobalt-rich deposits in the Pacific Ocean near the Hawaiian Islands.

Cobalt, like iron and nickel, is **ferromagnetic** and is important in the production of magnets. The atoms in ferromagnetic materials contain unpaired electrons like the paramagnetic materials described in Section 9.7. In ferromagnetic materials, however, these electrons can all align with their spins oriented in the same direction, creating a permanent magnetic field.

Magnets are increasingly important in industrial and military applications. In the United States, concerns have arisen over the lack of domestic sources of cobalt for these applications. New and stronger magnetic materials that do not require cobalt have been developed, but these require neodymium, which is found mostly in China.

Cobalt is also an important additive for high-strength steels. Carbaloy, a mixture composed primarily of cobalt metal with grains of tungsten carbide, is a very tough material. The strength of the cobalt and the hardness of the carbides make carbaloy a good material for industrial cutting and abrasion. Cobalt also forms many compounds with brilliant blue colors and is used in making pigments and inks. Cobalt compounds are essential for health because cobalt is the metal in vitamin B_{12}, which prevents anemia.

Copper

Copper, which can be found in its elemental form, was one of the first elements to be isolated and used by humans—copper products have been known for over 10,000 years. Ancient civilizations used copper to form tools. The earliest known artifacts produced by the smelting of copper are at a site in Tepe Yahya, Iran, dating from about 3800 B.C.E. The discovery of **bronze**, a copper and tin alloy, improved tool making because copper's bronze alloys are stronger, and they resist wear and corrosion better than pure copper.

The most important copper ores are chalcopyrite ($CuFeS_2$) and malachite [$Cu_2(OH)_2CO_3$]. Copper ores often occur near deposits of elemental copper, providing early humans with an easy way to locate copper ores. The electrometallurgical production of pure copper from chalcopyrite is described in Section 25.3.

The high natural abundance and generally high concentration of copper and copper ores make copper an economical choice for many industrial applications. Today over 40% of copper products are made from recycled copper. The ease and low cost of recycling copper have allowed copper to remain an important industrial metal.

The high conductivity of copper is second only to that of silver, making copper the most important metal for electrical wires. Along with iron in steel, copper is now among the most widely used metals; it is used in electrical motors and devices, the electrical wiring that snakes through the walls of houses, and the electrical transmission network linking power sources to homes and industries all over the world. Because of its high heat conductivity, copper is also used as a heat exchange material—for example, in car radiators. In addition, copper is used to make pipes for water distribution. Copper pipes can be readily connected to each other with watertight seals by soldering. Copper displaced lead for use as water pipes because of the toxicity of lead. Today, because of its lower price and lighter weight, plastic is used for many water pipes.

▲ Copper is used in a variety of applications.

Copper has a distinctive reddish color that can be polished to a beautiful metallic luster; it has been used in architecture, as a decorative metal in jewelry, and as a material for sculpture. Copper composes the decorative sheathings on many domes and rooftop art works. When exposed to the atmosphere and rain, copper can oxidize, forming a number of different compounds, such as malachite and brochanite ($Cu_4SO_4(OH)_6$), which have beautiful blue or green colors. Copper roofing shingles can be purchased as polished copper sheets or as sheets that have already been oxidized and exhibit a beautiful weathered *patina* (a coating that comes with age and use). Chemical compounds speed up the aging process and produce the desired patina, which takes 20 or more years to develop naturally.

Even though copper has many useful properties, it is not a very strong metal; therefore, alloys of copper with improved strength have been developed. Bronze was one of the first alloys ever produced. This alloy of copper and tin has been used for thousands of years because it could be made even in the low heat of a Stone Age campfire. **Brass**, another widely used alloy, contains copper and zinc. Many brass and bronze alloys also contain other metals to achieve certain physical properties. Some of the most important applications of bronze and brass are for plumbing fixtures, bearings, and art decorations. In addition, the tendency of brass and bronze alloys (unlike those of iron) not to spark when struck makes them useful in applications where sparks could be dangerous.

▲ Copper wiring is used to conduct electricity in wires.

Nickel

Most of the world's nickel comes from deposits in Ontario, Canada. These deposits are believed to have formed from a meteorite impact (most meteorites have high nickel content). The nickel occurs as a sulfide compound mixed with copper and iron sulfides. To produce nickel, sulfides are roasted in air to form metal oxides, and then they are reduced to the elemental metals with carbon. The metal mixture is heated in the presence of carbon monoxide, forming nickel carbonyl, which has a boiling point of 43 °C and can be collected as a gas:

$$Ni(s) + 4\,CO(g) \xrightarrow{\text{heat}} Ni(CO)_4(g)$$

When the nickel carbonyl is heated past 200 °C, it decomposes back to nickel metal and carbon monoxide. This method of refining nickel is the *Mond process*.

Nickel metal is fairly unreactive and resistant to corrosion, characteristics that it shares with platinum and palladium. Consequently, nickel is used as an alloying metal in the production of stainless steels. Many nickel alloys are used for applications where corrosion resistance is important. For example, the alloy Monel contains 72% Ni, 25% Cu, and 3% Fe and is resistant to reaction with most chemicals. Monel does not react even with fluorine gas at room temperature. Nickel–steel alloys are used for armor plates, and elemental nickel is often plated onto other metals as a protective coating.

Zinc

Elemental zinc was officially discovered in Europe in 1746 when calamine (zinc silicate) was reduced with charcoal to produce the metal. However, zinc had been used for many hundreds of years before this discovery because zinc ores and copper ores were used to form copper–zinc brass alloys. The main sources of zinc are ores composed of sphalerite (ZnS), smithsonite ($ZnCO_3$), and an oxide mixture of zinc, iron, and manganese called franklinite. These ores are roasted to form the oxides of the metals and then reduced with carbon to produce the elemental metals.

▲ Zinc phosphate adheres strongly to steel surfaces, forming rough crystals onto which other coatings, such as paint, can be applied.

Zinc combines with many different metals to form useful alloys. As we have discussed, the combination of zinc and copper produces the brass family of alloys. The combination of zinc and nickel with copper produces alloys with a silver color called *German* or *silver brass*. Zinc is also used in solder alloys with low melting points.

Galvanizing a steel object (such as a nail) involves dipping the object into a molten bath of zinc. The zinc, which is more reactive than the iron in steel, preferentially oxidizes, forming a tough protective coating. Zinc compounds are also used to coat steel before applying other coatings. The zinc compounds, such as zinc phosphate, adhere strongly to the steel surface, forming rough crystals onto which other coatings, such as paint, adhere very well. If a painted steel surface is scratched, the underlying exposed metal is susceptible to rust, but the added zinc ions prevent this by migrating toward the defect and forming a protective zinc oxide coating.

Zinc and zinc compounds have generally been considered safe. Zinc additives in coatings have replaced many of the chromium and lead additives (both of which are toxic) that were previously used. Today, however, even zinc additives in coatings are being studied for environmental hazards. In Europe, all substances that contain zinc compounds must be labeled as potential polluters of environmental water. More environmentally safe organic compounds have been developed to replace the metallic anticorrosion additives, but these compounds are more expensive to produce. Opportunities abound for chemists to develop needed products that are both environmentally safe and economically viable.

QUIZ YOURSELF **NOW!**

Self-Assessment Quiz

Q1. Which metal is naturally found in its elemental state?
MISSED THIS? *Read Section 25.2*

a) gold
b) titanium
c) chromium
d) iron

Q2. Which reaction is an example of pyrometallurgy?
MISSED THIS? *Read Section 25.3*

a) $Ti^{4+}(aq) + 4\,OH^-(aq) \rightarrow TiO_2(s) + 2\,H_2O(l)$
b) $2\,MnCO_3(s) + O_2(g) \xrightarrow{heat} 2\,MnO_2(s) + 2\,CO_2(g)$
c) $Ni(s) + 4\,CO(g) \longrightarrow Ni(CO)_4(g)$
d) $3\,MnO_2(s) + 4\,Al(s) \longrightarrow 3\,Mn(s) + 2\,Al_2O_3(s)$

Q3. Based on the data shown here, which pair of metals is likely to form a substitutional alloy?
MISSED THIS? *Read Section 25.4*

Metal	Atomic Radius	Crystal Structure
Sc	162 pm	Hexagonal Closest packed
W	135 pm	Body-centered cubic
Cu	128 pm	Face-centered cubic
Cr	128 pm	Body-centered cubic

a) Sc and W
b) Cu and Cr
c) Cu and Sc
d) Cr and W

Q4. Two metals, A and B, form a substitutional alloy with the binary phase diagram shown here. What is the melting point of the alloy at a composition that is 75% A and 25% B? **MISSED THIS?** *Read Section 25.4*

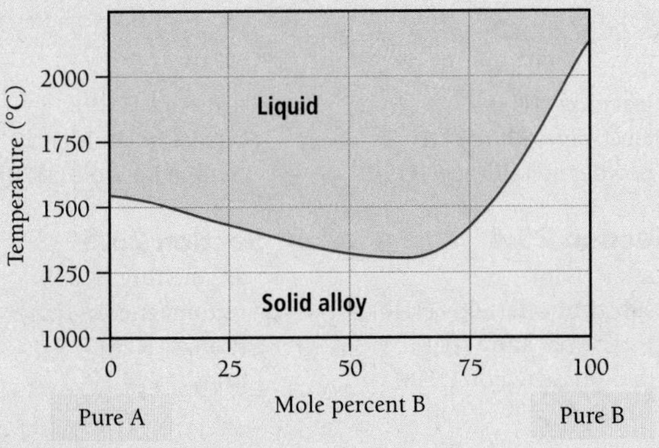

a) 1000 °C
b) 1300 °C
c) 1450 °C
d) 2000 °C

Q5. Two metals, A and B, form a substitutional alloy with the binary phase diagram shown here. Determine the composition and relative amounts of the two phases present at 50% composition and 1500 °C. **MISSED THIS?** *Read Section 25.4*

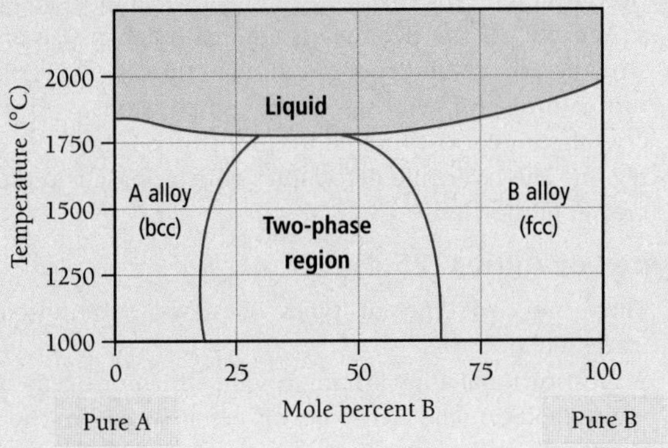

a) The A-rich bcc phase is 80% A and 20% B; the B-rich fcc phase is 37% A and 63% B; the mixture contains more of the A-rich fcc phase.
b) The A-rich bcc phase is 20% A and 80% B; the B-rich fcc phase is 63% A and 37% B; the mixture contains more of the B-rich fcc phase.
c) The A-rich bcc phase is 50% A and 50% B; the B-rich fcc phase is 50% A and 50% B; the mixture contains equal amounts of both phases.
d) The A-rich bcc phase is 80% A and 20% B; the B-rich fcc phase is 37% A and 63% B; the mixture contains more of the B-rich fcc phase.

Q6. An interstitial alloy contains a nonmetal (X) that occupies one-fourth of the octahedral holes in the closest-packed lattice of the metal (M). What is the formula for the alloy? **MISSED THIS?** *Read Section 25.4*

a) M_4X
b) MX_4
c) M_2X
d) MX_2

Q7. Which metal is commonly used to make electrical wires? **MISSED THIS?** *Read Section 25.5*

a) zinc
b) cobalt
c) manganese
d) copper

Q8. Which metal is commonly used to make parts for aircraft engines? **MISSED THIS?** *Read Section 25.5*

a) zinc
b) titanium
c) nickel
d) silver

Q9. Calculate the mass percent of chromium in the mineral chromite ($FeCr_2O_4$). **MISSED THIS?** *Read Section 3.9*

a) 83.97%
b) 46.46%
c) 86.78%
d) 36.13%

Q10. What is a common use for zinc? **MISSED THIS?** *Read Section 25.5*

a) galvanization of steel
b) lightweight aircraft parts
c) paint pigments
d) production of magnets

Answers: 1. (a) **2.** (b) **3.** (d) **4.** (c) **5.** (d) **6.** (a) **7.** (d) **8.** (b) **9.** (b) **10.** (a)

CHAPTER 25 IN REVIEW

TERMS

Section 25.1
metallurgy (1110)

Section 25.2
minerals (1111)
ore (1111)

Section 25.3
extractive metallurgy (1112)
refining (1112)
gangue (1112)
pyrometallurgy (1112)
calcination (1113)
roasting (1113)
smelting (1113)
flux (1113)
slag (1113)
hydrometallurgy (1113)
leaching (1113)
electrometallurgy (1114)
powder metallurgy (1115)

Section 25.4
alloy (1116)
substitutional alloy (1116)
interstitial alloy (1116)
two-phase region (1118)
lever rule (1119)
octahedral hole (1120)
tetrahedral hole (1120)

Section 25.5
arc-melting (1122)
ferromagnetic (1124)
bronze (1125)
brass (1125)

CONCEPTS

General Properties (25.2)

- Metals have many common physical properties, such as high conductivity of electricity and heat and high malleability and ductility. These properties vary among the different metals.

Natural Distribution of Metals (25.2)

- Metals are unevenly distributed throughout Earth's crust. All the metals together compose about 25% of the mass of Earth's crust, but just a few key metals are abundant enough to each individually compose more than 1% of the crust.
- Few metals exist naturally in their elemental state; most are found in ores, rocks that contain a high concentration of metal-containing minerals.
- Most metal-containing minerals are oxides, sulfides, chlorides, carbonates, or more complex compounds.

Metallurgical Processes (25.3)

- To be useful, metals have to be separated from the gangue, the unusable part of the ores, reduced to elemental metals and refined to be more pure.
- Extractive metallurgy is the general term for the processes, such as pyrometallurgy, hydrometallurgy, and electrometallurgy, that separate metal from ore.
- A method of forming metal components from micron-sized metal particles is powder metallurgy.

Phase Diagrams (25.4)

- Elemental metals tend to crystallize in three crystalline structures: face-centered cubic, body-centered cubic, and hexagonal closest packed.
- When two types of metal atoms bond together, they form an alloy.
- A binary phase diagram is a graphical representation of the phases and crystal types of alloys present at different compositions and temperatures.
- If the two metals in an alloy are similar in size and have the same crystal structure, they tend to form a miscible solid solution, which means that they can form an alloy at any composition ratio. If the two metals are dissimilar in size or crystal structure, the solubility of one atom in the other's crystal structure is often limited. At certain compositions, two different crystals can coexist in equilibrium; this is called a two-phase region. The lever rule determines which phase is present in a greater proportion.

Types of Alloys (25.4)

- There are two different types of alloys, substitutional and interstitial.
- A substitutional alloy is a mixture in which one type of metal atom replaces another type of metal atom in the crystal structure.
- In an interstitial alloy, one type of atom (either a metal or nonmetal) fits into the holes within the crystal structure of the metal. Interstitial alloys can be made with different atoms filling different fractions of the different types of holes.

EQUATIONS AND RELATIONSHIPS

Lever Rule (**25.4**)

In a two-phase region on a phase diagram, two different crystal structures coexist in equilibrium. Whichever phase has a composition closer to the overall composition of the alloy is the phase present in the larger relative amount.

LEARNING OUTCOMES

Chapter Objectives	Assessment
Describe metals in terms of their properties, abundance, and natural distribution on Earth (**25.2**)	Exercises 15–20
Describe common metallurgical processes (**25.3**)	Exercises 21–30
Analyze alloys in terms of composition, relative amounts, and phases present (**25.4**)	Examples 25.1, 25.2, 25.3, 25.4 **For Practice** 25.1, 25.2, 25.3, 25.4 Exercises 31–38
Determine the composition of an interstitial alloy from the occupancy of the interstitial holes (**25.4**)	Exercises 39–42
Describe common 3*d* transition metals in terms of sources, properties, and products (**25.5**)	Exercises 43–58

EXERCISES

Mastering Chemistry provides end-of-chapter exercises, feedback-enriched tutorial problems, animations, and interactive activities to encourage problem-solving practice and deeper understanding of key concepts and topics.

REVIEW QUESTIONS

1. Why is vanadium present in oil from some sources?

2. List three categories of metallurgical processes.

3. Why is Ni not considered a common metal, even though it composes over 2% of the total mass of Earth and only Fe and Mg have a higher percent composition of Earth's total mass?

4. Metal elements are found in both minerals and ores. Describe the difference between a mineral and an ore.

5. Ores contain minerals and gangue. Describe the difference between a mineral and gangue.

6. Calcination, roasting, and smelting are three pyrometallurgical processes. Compare and contrast the processes.

7. What compound has been historically used to leach gold from gold ores? Why is this process being discontinued?

8. Name three advantages of making metal components from the powder metallurgical process.

9. Describe the difference between body-centered cubic and face-centered cubic structures.

10. Describe the difference between a substitutional alloy and an interstitial alloy.

11. Why was copper one of the first metals that humans used?

12. Describe why bronze was one of the first alloys that humans used.

13. Both brass and bronze contain copper. Describe the difference between these two alloys.

14. List the properties of copper that make it appropriate for electric wires and the properties that make it appropriate for water pipes.

PROBLEMS BY TOPIC

The General Properties and Natural Distribution of Metals

15. Describe three typical properties of metals.
MISSED THIS? *Read Section 25.2*

16. Describe whether each property is generally higher or lower for metals compared to nonmetals.

a. thermal conductivity
b. electrical resistivity
c. transparency
d. ductility

17. List four metal elements that each individually compose more than 1% of Earth's crust. **MISSED THIS?** *Read Section 25.2*

18. List four metals that occur as elements in their natural state in Earth's crust.

19. List the name and formula of one important mineral source for each of these metals: Fe, Hg, V, and Nb.
MISSED THIS? *Read Section 25.2*

20. List the name and formula of one important mineral source for each of these metals: Ti, Zn, U, and Ta.

Metallurgical Processes

21. Two ores of magnesium are $MgCO_3$ and $Mg(OH)_2$. Write balanced equations for the calcination of these two minerals to form MgO.
MISSED THIS? *Read Section 25.3*

22. Two ores of copper are CuO and CuS. Write balanced equations for the roasting of CuO with C to form Cu metal and the roasting of CuS with O_2 to form CuO.

23. Give the definition of a flux and identify the flux in the reaction.
MISSED THIS? *Read Section 25.3*

$$SiO(s) + MgO(s) \longrightarrow MgSiO_3(l)$$

24. Give the definition of a slag and identify the slag in the reaction.

$$SiO_2(s) + MgO(s) \longrightarrow MgSiO_3(l)$$

25. Provide a general description of how hydrometallurgy is used to extract metals from ores. **MISSED THIS?** *Read Section 25.3*

26. Provide a general description of how electrometallurgy is used to extract metals from ores.

27. How is Al_2O_3 separated from other oxides using the Bayer process? What soluble form of aluminum forms from Al_2O_3 during the Bayer process? **MISSED THIS?** *Read Section 25.3*

28. When copper is purified using an electrochemical cell, which electrode has the pure copper and which electrode has the impure copper? Explain how gold is obtained from this process.

29. Describe the difference between sponge-powdered iron and water-atomized powdered iron. **MISSED THIS?** *Read Section 25.3*

30. Describe the difference in the processing of sponge-powdered iron and water-atomized powdered iron.

Metal Structures and Alloys

31. Determine the composition of each vanadium alloy. **MISSED THIS?** *Read Section 25.4*

a. One-half of the V atoms are replaced by Cr atoms.
b. One-fourth of the V atoms are replaced by Fe atoms.
c. One-fourth of the V atoms are replaced by Cr atoms, and one-fourth of the V atoms are replaced by Fe atoms.

32. Determine the composition of each cobalt alloy.

a. One-third of the Co atoms are replaced by Zn atoms.
b. One-eighth of the Co atoms are replaced by Ti atoms.
c. One-third of the Co atoms are replaced by Zn atoms, and one-sixth of the Co atoms are replaced by Ti atoms.

33. Referring to Table 25.2, explain why you might expect Cr and Fe to form miscible alloys. **MISSED THIS?** *Read Section 25.4*

34. Referring to Table 25.2, explain why you might expect Co and Cu to not form miscible alloys.

35. Determine the composition and phases present at points A and B on the Cr–Fe phase diagram. **MISSED THIS?** *Read Section 25.4*

Cr–Fe

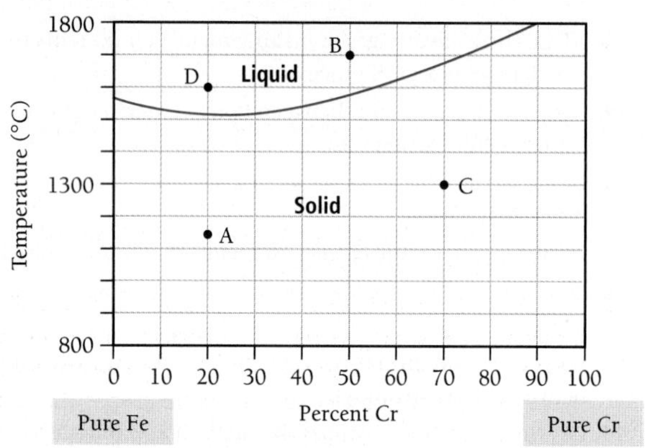

36. Determine the composition and phase present at points C and D on the Cr–Fe phase diagram (see Problem 35 for diagram).

37. Determine the composition, relative amounts, and phases present at points A and B on the Co–Cu phase diagram. **MISSED THIS?** *Read Section 25.4*

Co–Cu

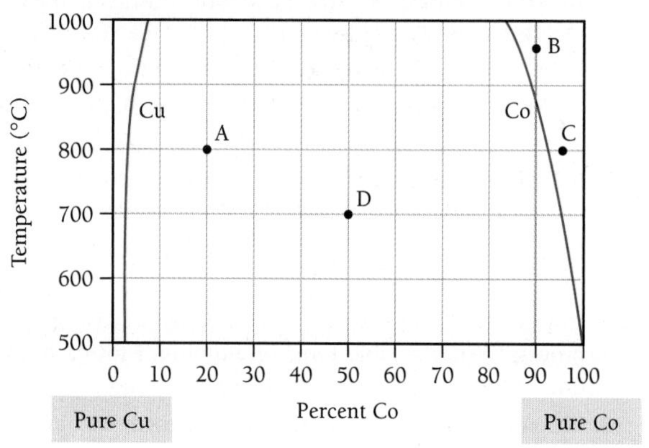

38. Determine the composition, relative amounts, and phases present at points C and D on the Co–Cu phase diagram (see Problem 37 for phase diagram).

39. The elements Mn and Si are added to steel to improve its properties in electric motors, and some C is often found as a detrimental impurity. Which of these elements fills interstitial holes in the Fe lattice, and which substitutes for the Fe in the lattice? **MISSED THIS?** *Read Section 25.4*

40. The elements Si and P are added to steel to improve its properties in electric motors, and some N is often found as a detrimental impurity. Which of these elements fills interstitial holes in the Fe lattice, and which substitutes for the Fe in the lattice?

41. Determine the formula for each interstitial alloy. **MISSED THIS?** *Read Section 25.4*

a. Nitrogen occupies one-half of the octahedral sites of a closest-packed Mo structure.
b. Hydrogen occupies all of the tetrahedral sites of a Cr closest-packed structure.

42. Determine the formula for each interstitial alloy.

a. Nitrogen occupies one-fourth of the octahedral sites of a closest-packed Fe structure.
b. Hydrogen occupies one-half of the tetrahedral sites of a Ti closest-packed structure.

Sources, Properties, and Products of Some of the 3*d* Transition Metals

43. Identify the metal found in each mineral. **MISSED THIS?** *Read Section 25.5*

a. sphalerite b. malachite c. hausmannite

44. Name at least one important mineral that is a source for each metal.

a. Fe b. Co c. Cr

45. Calculate the heat of reaction (ΔH°_{rxn}) for the calcination of rhodochrosite. (ΔH°_f for rhodochrosite is -894.1 kJ/ mol.) **MISSED THIS?** *Read Section 25.5*

46. The extraction of Mn from pyrolusite with aluminum produces pure Mn metal and Al_2O_3. Calculate the heat of reaction (ΔH°_{rxn}).

47. Describe the effects of adding Cr to steel and give a use for chromium–steel alloys. **MISSED THIS?** *Read Section 25.5*

48. Describe the effects of adding Mn to steel and give a use for manganese–steel alloys.

49. Calculate the mole percent and mass percent of Ti in the minerals rutile and ilmenite. **MISSED THIS?** *Read Sections 25.5, 3.9*

50. Calculate the mole percent and mass percent of Mn in the minerals pyrolusite and rhodochrosite.

51. Why is it important to use an inert atmosphere to surround the metal when arc-melting titanium? **MISSED THIS?** *Read Section 25.5*

52. Titanium is a very reactive metal. Explain why titanium has a high corrosion resistance to seawater and can be used for the production of ship components.

53. Which compound of Ti is the most important industrial product of titanium metal? Describe an application for this compound. **MISSED THIS?** *Read Section 25.5*

54. Describe how Zn is used to protect the surface of steel products. What is the name of this process?

55. Describe the Bayer process. **MISSED THIS?** *Read Section 25.5*

56. Describe the Mond process.

57. Which metals are found in carbaloy steel? **MISSED THIS?** *Read Section 25.5*

58. Which metals are found in Monel steel?

CUMULATIVE PROBLEMS

59. After 2.0×10^4 kg of an ore that contains 0.051% ilmenite is mined, the percent yield from extracting and refining the metals from the mineral is 87% for the iron and 63% for the titanium. Calculate the mass of iron and titanium produced from the ore.

60. Calculate the mass of aluminum metal that is needed to produce Cr metal from 5.00×10^2 g of chromite. Calculate how many grams of Cr metal are produced from 5.00×10^2 g of chromite.

61. How many lattice atoms surround a tetrahedral hole and an octahedral hole in a closest-packed structure? Describe which hole site is larger and explain why.

62. Explain why the crystal structure and atomic size of the two elements are important factors in a two-component phase diagram.

63. Why does Mn form compounds with higher oxidation states than Cr?

64. Why is MnO_2 added to silica glass?

65. Co, Fe, and Ni are ferromagnetic. What is the difference between ferromagnetic and paramagnetic?

66. Is the chromate ion or dichromate ion more stable in an acidic solution? Which ion has a higher Cr : O ratio? Which ion has a higher oxidation state for Cr?

67. The first ionization energies of iron, cobalt, nickel, and the first three platinum metals are all about the same, but the first ionization energies of osmium, iridium, and platinum are substantially greater. Suggest an explanation for this observation.

68. Although both the group IA and IB metals have a half-filled *s* subshell, the IB metals have markedly higher first ionization energies, densities, and melting points, and markedly lower second and third ionization energies than the corresponding IA metals. Explain these observations.

CHALLENGE PROBLEMS

69. Iron powder is placed into a tall cylinder-shaped die and pressed from the top and bottom to make a cylinder-shaped pressed part with a height of 5.62 cm and a radius of 4.00 cm. The density of the iron powder before it was pressed was 2.41 g/mL. The density of a pressed iron part is 6.85 g/mL. The density of pure solid iron is 7.78 g/mL.
    a. Calculate the original height of the powder before it was pressed.
    b. Calculate the theoretical height of the pressed component if it could be pressed to the same density of pure iron.
    c. What percentage of the pressed iron part is composed of voids between the iron particles?

70. When a part is made by pressing together powdered metal, no metal is wasted. In contrast, metal is typically scrapped after a metal part is cut from a solid metal plate. If a circular part with a diameter of 10.0 cm is made from an original shape of a square with a side length of 10.0 cm, calculate the percentage of the metal that is thrown away as scrap. If the circular shape also has a circular hole with a diameter of 6.0 cm, calculate the percentage of the metal that is thrown away as scrap.

71. Hydrogen can be in both the octahedral and tetrahedral holes for lanthanum. Determine the percentage of the holes that are filled if the formula is $LaH_{2.76}$.

72. Tin exists in two allotropic forms. Gray tin has a diamond structure, and white tin has a close-packed structure. Predict which allotrope is (a) denser, (b) a conductor of electricity. Predict the valence electronic configuration of tin in each allotrope.

73. Find the equilibrium constant at 298 K for the reaction.

$$[Ag(CN)_2]^-(aq) + Cu(s) \rightleftharpoons [Cu(CN)_2]^-(aq) + Ag(s)$$

The K_f for $[Cu(CN)_2]^- = 1.0 \times 10^{24}$ and the rest of the data needed are in Appendix II.

74. Find the equilibrium constant at 298 K for the reaction.

$$2\,[Cu(NH_3)_2]^+(aq) \rightleftharpoons [Cu(NH_3)_4]^{2+}(aq) + Cu(s)$$

The K_f for $[Cu(NH_3)_2]^+ = 6.3 \times 10^{10}$ and the rest of the data needed are in Appendix II.

75. Propose a chemical procedure to extract cobalt from the mineral cobaltite, CoAsS. What are some of the hazards of such a procedure?

CONCEPTUAL PROBLEMS

76. Why are metals such as Ni and Co economical to mine and use in industrial processes, even though they have a very low natural abundance in Earth's crust?

77. Explain why metals such as Au and Ag are found in their elemental states in nature, but metals like Na and Ca are always found in compounds in nature.

78. What allows some pairs of metals to form alloys that have the same structure at any composition, while other pairs of metals form alloys with structures that depend on the relative composition of the two metals?

QUESTIONS FOR GROUP WORK

Active Classroom Learning

Discuss these questions with the group and record your consensus answer.

79. Assign each element in the first row of the transition metals, scandium through zinc, to a group member. Have each group member look up on the Internet or in a reputable chemistry reference book the electrical resistivity for his or her element(s). Agree on the units and temperature. As a group, prepare a graph of resistivity versus atomic number. What is the general trend in resistivity as the atomic number increases? What atomic properties might account for this trend? Are there any notable exceptions?

80. Create a table comparing and contrasting pyrometallurgy, hydrometallurgy, and electrometallurgy. Include a definition, an application or two, and any relevant notes for each type of metallurgy. Once your table is complete, pass it around your group asking each group member to read one cell from your table. Have other group members take turns trying to identify the type of metallurgy from the fact that is read aloud.

81. Would you expect an alloy of iron and vanadium to be substitutional or interstitial? Explain your choice. Create a phase diagram for the binary alloy of iron and vanadium based on the tabulated data provided.

% V	Melting Point
0	1530
20	1480
40	1470
60	1560
80	1720
100	1900

82. Assign each group member a different interstitial alloy from Table 25.3. Each group member should look up a few interesting facts for his or her alloy, including how it is used. Present findings, along with a description of each alloy's structure, to the group.

83. Working individually, create a fill-in-the-blank question by rewriting a characteristic sentence or chemical reaction from Section 25.5, but leaving out the name of the metal focused on in the content selected. Take turns sharing questions with the rest of the group. Take turns in the group trying to fill in the blank with the correct metal.

DATA INTERPRETATION AND ANALYSIS

Soldering with Tin–Lead Alloys

84. Alloys of tin and lead are common solders. A *solder* is a metal alloy that melts at a relatively low temperature and connects two or more metal pieces. The technique of soldering is commonly used by plumbers to fuse copper water pipes and by electricians to affix electrical components to printed circuit boards. The table that follows lists tensile strength and hardness data for pure tin, pure lead, and two tin–lead alloys. *Tensile strength* is the maximum stress a stretched material can withstand before breaking. *Hardness* on the Brinell Scale is a measure of a substance's resistance to indentation when subjected to impact by a steel ball (the higher the number, the greater the hardness).

Strength and Hardness of Tin, Lead, and Tin–Lead Alloys

Substance	Tensile Strength, MPa	Hardness (Brinell Scale)
Pure tin	13.2	4
Pure lead	12.3	4
63% tin–37% lead (mass%)	51.5	17
50% tin–50% lead (mass%)	41.2	14

The tin–lead phase diagram in the graph that follows contains a *eutectic point*—a point on the phase diagram representing the lowest melting point. The eutectic composition has a sharp

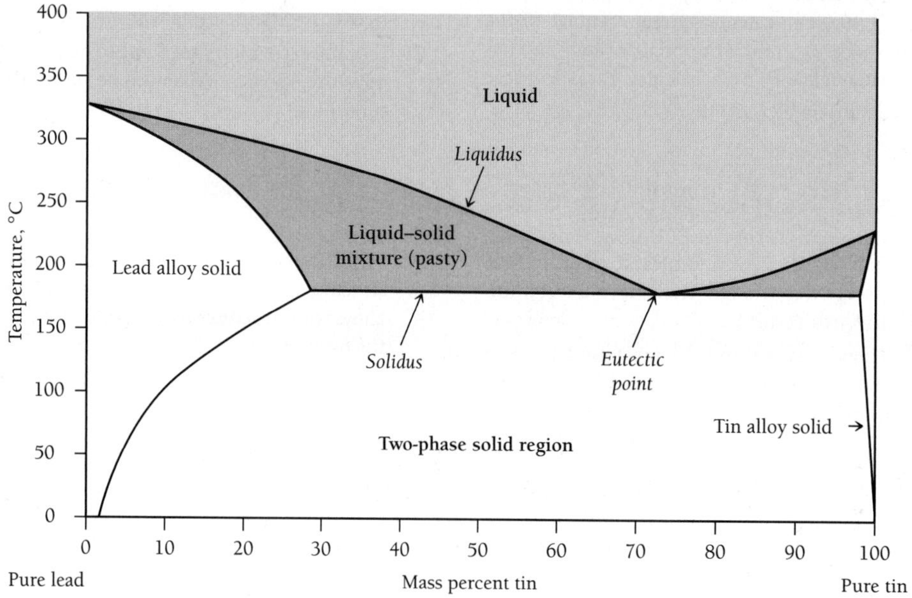

Tin–Lead Phase Diagram

melting transition. All other compositions of tin–lead melt over a range of temperatures, beginning at the *solidus* line (the line separating the solid phase and the liquid–solid region) and ending at the *liquidus* line (the line separating the liquid phase and the liquid–solid region). Between these lines, a mixture of liquid and solid exists. This mixture is described as "pasty" because it can be worked into an optimal shape around the connection point of the two base metal pieces.

Use the information provided to answer the following questions:

a. Based on the data provided in the table, explain why tin–lead alloys are better solders than pure tin or pure lead.

b. Based on the phase diagram shown, do tin and lead form a miscible solid solution at all compositions?

c. According to the phase diagram, what are the melting points of pure tin and pure lead?

d. What composition of tin and lead constitutes a eutectic mixture, and what is the melting point of the eutectic mixture?

e. Why is a 63% tin/37% lead (mass %) alloy commonly used for electrical soldering projects?

f. What is the melting range of a 50% tin/50% lead (mass %) alloy?

Cc ANSWERS TO CONCEPTUAL CONNECTIONS

Metals

25.1 **(a)** Although some metals occur naturally as pure elements in Earth's crust, most metals occur as compounds known as minerals.

Metallurgy

25.2 **(d)** Electrometallurgy uses electrolysis to extract a metal from its ore.

Interstitial Alloys

25.3 **(d)** Since the ratio of tetrahedral holes to metal atoms is 2:1 and since only one-eighth of the holes are occupied, the formula must contain four metals to every one nonmetal atom.

"Chemistry must become the astronomy of the molecular world."

—ALFRED WERNER (1866–1919)

CHAPTER 26 Transition Metals and Coordination Compounds

In this chapter, we examine the chemistry of the transition metals and an important class of transition metal compounds called coordination compounds. We will see that coordination compounds form all of the types of isomers that we have studied so far, as well as some new types. In our examination of the transition metals, we draw on much of what we learned in Chapters 8 and 9 about electronic structure and periodicity. We also briefly revisit valence bond theory to understand bonding in coordination compounds, but we quickly shift to a different theory—called crystal field theory—that better explains many of the properties of these compounds. Transition metals and coordination compounds are important, not only because of their interesting chemistry, but because of their numerous applications. Coordination compounds are the basis for a number of therapeutic drugs, chemical sensors, and coloring agents. In addition, many biological molecules contain transition metals that bond in ways that are similar to coordination compounds.
For example, the oxygen-carrying site on hemoglobin is an iron ion bonded partly to an amino acid in the hemoglobin molecule and partly to a flat molecule called a porphyrin. An oxygen molecule reversibly bonds to the iron and is transported throughout the body by blood flow.

The color of ruby is caused by a splitting of the *d*-orbital energy levels in Cr^{3+} by the host crystal.

26.1 The Colors of Rubies and Emeralds 1135
26.2 Properties of Transition Metals 1136
26.3 Coordination Compounds 1140
26.4 Structure and Isomerization 1145
26.5 Bonding in Coordination Compounds 1150
26.6 Applications of Coordination Compounds 1155
LEARNING OUTCOMES 1160

26.1 The Colors of Rubies and Emeralds

Rubies are deep red and emeralds are brilliant green, yet the color of both gemstones is caused by the same ion, Cr^{3+}. The difference lies in the crystal that hosts the ion. Rubies are crystals of aluminum oxide (Al_2O_3) in which about 1% of the Al^{3+} ions are replaced by Cr^{3+} ions. Emeralds, by contrast, are crystals of beryllium aluminum silicate [$Be_3Al_2(SiO_3)_6$] in which a similar percentage of the Al^{3+} ions is replaced by Cr^{3+}. The embedded Cr^{3+} ion is red in the aluminum oxide crystal but green in the beryllium aluminum silicate crystal. Why?

▲ **Ruby and Emerald** The red color of ruby and the green color of emerald are both caused by Cr^{3+}.

The answer to this question lies in the effect that the host crystal has on the energies of the atomic orbitals in Cr^{3+}. Atoms in the crystal create an electric field around the ion—called the *crystal field*—that splits the five normally degenerate *d* orbitals into two or more levels. The color of each gemstone is caused by electron transitions between these levels. In rubies, the crystal field is stronger (and the corresponding splitting of the *d* orbitals greater) than it is in emeralds. Recall from Chapter 8 that the color of a substance depends on the colors *absorbed* by that substance, which in turn depends on the energy differences between the orbitals involved in the absorption. The greater splitting in ruby results in a greater energy difference between the *d* orbitals of Cr^{3+}, and consequently the absorption of a different color of light than in emerald.

The colors of several other gemstones are also caused by the splitting of the *d* orbitals in transition metal ions embedded within host crystals. For example, the red in garnet, which has $Mg_3Al_2(SiO_4)_3$ as a host crystal, and the yellow-green of peridot, which has Mg_2SiO_4 as a host crystal are both caused by electron transitions between *d* orbitals in Fe^{2+}. Similarly, the blue in turquoise, which has $[Al_6(PO_4)_4(OH)_8 \cdot 4\,H_2O]^{2-}$ as a host crystal, is due to transitions between the *d* orbitals in Cu^{2+}.

In this chapter, we examine the properties of the transition metals and their ions more closely. We also examine the properties of coordination compounds in some detail. We first discussed this common type of transition metal compound in Chapter 18 (see Section 18.8). In a coordination compound, bonds to a central metal ion split the *d* orbitals much as they are split in the crystals of gemstones. The theory that explains the splitting and the corresponding colors is **crystal field theory**, which we also explore in this chapter.

▲ **Garnet, Peridot, and Turquoise** The red in garnet and the yellow-green of peridot are both caused by Fe^{2+}. The blue of turquoise is caused by Cu^{2+}.

26.2 Properties of Transition Metals

Transition metals, the elements in the *d* block of the periodic table, are a study in similarities and differences. When we compare their properties with the varied properties of the main-group elements, they seem markedly similar. For example, almost all transition metals have moderate to high densities, good electrical conductivity, high melting points, and moderate to extreme hardness. Their similar properties are related to their similar electron configurations: they all have electrons in *d* orbitals that can be involved in metallic bonding. In spite of their similarities, however, each element is also unique, and the transition metals exhibit a wide variety of chemical behavior. Before we examine some of their periodic properties, let's review the electron configurations of these elements, first discussed in Chapter 9.

Electron Configurations

Recall from Section 9.4 that, as we move to the right across a row of transition elements, electrons are added to $(n - 1)d$ orbitals (where n is the row number in the periodic table and also the quantum number of the highest occupied principal level). For example, as we move across the fourth-period transition metals, electrons are added to the $3d$ orbitals, as Table 26.1 shows.

In general, the ground state electron configurations for the transition elements are

rows 1 and 2: [noble gas] $ns^2(n - 1)d^x$

rows 3 and 4: [noble gas] $ns^2(n - 2)f^{14}(n - 1)d^x$

where x ranges from 1 to 10. Recall from Section 9.4, however, that because the ns and $(n - 1)d$ sublevels are close in energy, many exceptions occur. For example, in the first transition series of the d block, the outer configuration is $4s^2 3d^x$ with two exceptions: Cr is $4s^1 3d^5$ and Cu is $4s^1 3d^{10}$. This behavior is related to the closely spaced $3d$ and $4s$ energy levels and the stability associated with a half-filled or completely filled d sublevel.

Recall from Section 9.7 that the transition metals form ions by losing electrons from the ns orbital *before* losing electrons from the $(n - 1)d$ orbitals. For example, Fe^{2+} has an electron configuration of [Ar] $3d^6$ because it has lost both of the $4s$ electrons to form the 2+ charge. Examples 26.1 and 26.2 review the steps in writing electron configurations for transition metals and their ions.

TABLE 26.1 ■ First-Row Transition Metal Orbital Occupancy

	4s	3d				
Sc	↑↓	↑				
Ti	↑↓	↑	↑			
V	↑↓	↑	↑	↑		
Cr	↑	↑	↑	↑	↑	↑
Mn	↑↓	↑	↑	↑	↑	↑
Fe	↑↓	↑↓	↑	↑	↑	↑
Co	↑↓	↑↓	↑↓	↑	↑	↑
Ni	↑↓	↑↓	↑↓	↑↓	↑	↑
Cu	↑	↑↓	↑↓	↑↓	↑↓	↑↓
Zn	↑↓	↑↓	↑↓	↑↓	↑↓	↑↓

HOW TO: *Write Electron Configurations*	**EXAMPLE 26.1** **Writing Electron Configurations for Transition Metals** Write the ground state electron configuration for Zr.	**EXAMPLE 26.2** **Writing Electron Configurations for Transition Metals** Write the ground state electron configuration for Co^{3+}.
Identify the noble gas that precedes the element and write it in square brackets.	**SOLUTION** [Kr]	**SOLUTION** [Ar]
Count down the periods to determine the outer principal quantum level—this is the quantum level for the s orbital. Subtract one to obtain the quantum level for the d orbital. If the element is in the third or fourth transition series, include $(n - 2)f^{14}$ electrons in the configuration.	Zr is in the fifth period, so the orbitals used are: [Kr] $5s4d$	Co is in the fourth period, so the orbitals used are: [Ar] $4s3d$
Count across the row to see how many electrons are in the neutral atom and fill the orbitals accordingly.	Zr has four more electrons than Kr. [Kr] $5s^2 4d^2$	Co has nine more electrons than Ar. [Ar] $4s^2 3d^7$
For an ion, remove the required number of electrons, first from the s and then from the d orbitals.		Co^{3+} has three fewer electrons than the Co atom. [Ar] $4s^0 3d^6$ or [Ar] $3d^6$
	FOR PRACTICE 26.1 Write the ground state electron configuration for Os.	**FOR PRACTICE 26.2** Write the ground state electron configuration for Nb^{2+}.

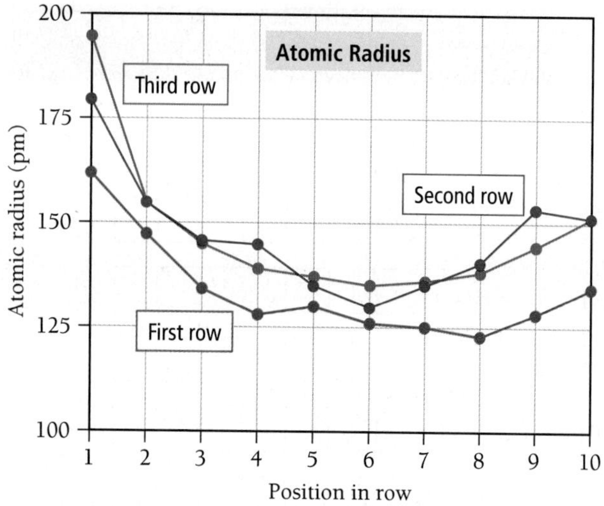

▲ **FIGURE 26.1 Trends in Atomic Radius** With the exception of a decrease in radius from the first to the second element, there is only a small variation in atomic radius across a row. There is a small and expected increase in radius from the first to the second transition row but virtually no difference in radius from the second to the third.

Atomic Size

As we discussed in Section 9.6, for main-group elements, the size of atoms decreases across a period and increases down a column. For transition metals, however, there is little variation in size across a row (other than for the first two elements in each transition metal row, such as Sc and Ti in the first row), as Figure 26.1◀ illustrates. The reason for the difference is that, across a row of transition elements, the number of electrons in the outermost principal energy level (highest n value) is nearly constant. As another proton is added to the nucleus with each successive element, another electron is added as well, but the electron goes into an $n - 1$ orbital. The number of outermost electrons thus stays the same, and the electrons experience a roughly constant effective nuclear charge as we move across the row, keeping the radii approximately constant.

Looking down a group, we see a small but expected increase in size from the first transition metal row to the second, but the size of elements in the third row is about the same as it is for those in the second row. This pattern is also different from that of the main-group elements, especially when we consider that in any given column, the third transition row has 32 more electrons than the second row. The reason that the third transition row elements are not larger is because 14 of the 32 electrons are in a $(n - 2)f$ sublevel, and while electrons in f orbitals are in lower principal quantum levels, they are not very effective at shielding the outer electrons from nuclear charge. Consequently, the outer electrons are held more tightly by the nucleus, offsetting the typical increase in size between the periods—an effect called the **lanthanide contraction**.

ANSWER **NOW!**

26.1 Cc Conceptual Connection

ATOMIC SIZE Which element has the larger atomic radius, Fe or W?

(a) Fe
(b) W

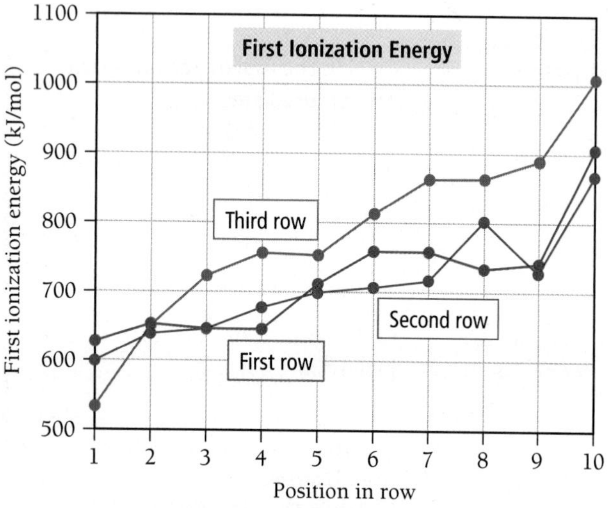

▲ **FIGURE 26.2 Trends in First Ionization Energy** First ionization energy generally increases across a row, following the main-group trend. However, in contrast to the main-group trend, the third transition row has a higher ionization energy than the first and second rows.

Ionization Energy

The first ionization energies of transition elements follow the expected main-group periodic trend and slowly increase across a row (Figure 26.2◀), but the increase is smaller than for main-group elements. As we move down a group, we see that the third transition row generally has a higher ionization energy than do the first two rows, a trend counter to that observed in the main-group elements. In the transition elements the charge of the nucleus increases substantially from one row to the next, but there is only a small increase in atomic size between the first and second rows, and no increase in size between the second and third row. The outer electrons are therefore held more tightly in the third transition row than in the first two rows.

Electronegativity

The electronegativity values of the transition metals, like their ionization energies, follow the main-group trend and slowly increase across a row, as shown in Figure 26.3▼. The increase is smaller than the increase that occurs in the main-group elements, but we expect that given the similarity in the sizes of the atoms. The trend in electronegativity values down a group (or column) is another example of the transition metals behaving differently from the main-group elements. The electronegativity values generally increase from the first transition row to the second, but there is no further increase for the third row. In the main-group elements, in contrast, we see a *decrease* in electronegativity as we move down a group. The difference is again caused by the relatively small change in atomic size as we move down a column for the transition elements, accompanied by a large increase in nuclear charge. One of the heaviest metals, gold (Au), is also the most electronegative metal. Its electronegativity value (EN = 2.4) is even higher than that of some nonmetals (EN of P is 2.1), and compounds of an Au^- ion have been observed.

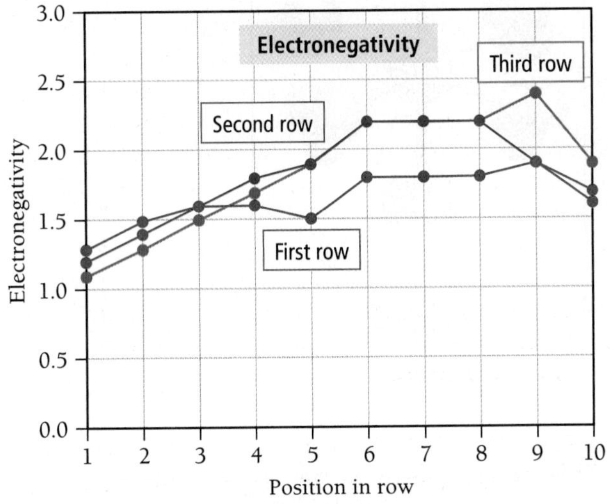

◀ **FIGURE 26.3 Trends in Electronegativity** The electronegativity of the transition elements generally increases across a row, following the main-group trend. However, in contrast to the main-group trend, electronegativity increases from the first transition row to the second. There is little electronegativity difference between the second and third transition rows.

Oxidation States

Unlike main-group metals, which tend to exhibit only one oxidation state, the transition metals often exhibit a variety of oxidation states (Figure 26.4▼). The highest oxidation state for a transition metal is +7 for manganese (Mn). The electron configuration of manganese in this oxidation state corresponds to the loss of all the electrons in the 4*s* and 3*d* orbitals, leaving a noble gas electron configuration ([Ar]). This is the same configuration we see for all of the highest oxidation states of the elements to the left of Mn. To the right of manganese, the oxidation states are all lower, mostly +2 or +3. A +2 oxidation state for a transition metal is not surprising, as 4*s* electrons are readily lost.

Metals in high oxidation states, such as +7, exist only when the metal is bound to a highly electronegative element such as oxygen; they do not exist as bare ions.

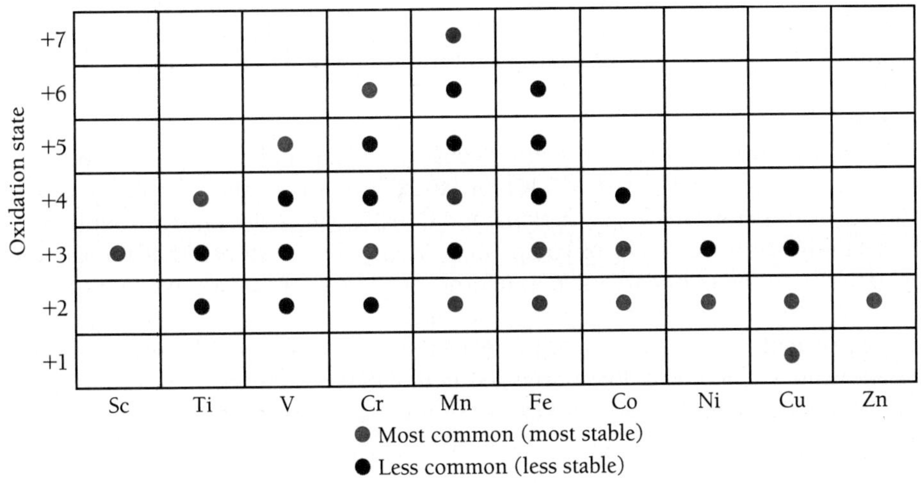

◀ **FIGURE 26.4 First-Row Transition Metal Oxidation States** The transition metals exhibit many more oxidation states than the main-group elements. These oxidation states range from +7 to +1.

26.3 Coordination Compounds

We discussed at the end of Chapter 18 that transition metals tend to form *complex ions*. A **complex ion** contains a central metal ion bound to one or more *ligands*. A **ligand** is a Lewis base (or electron pair donor) that forms a bond with the metal. When a complex ion combines with one or more *counterions* (ions of opposite charge that are not acting as ligands), the resulting neutral compound is a **coordination compound**.

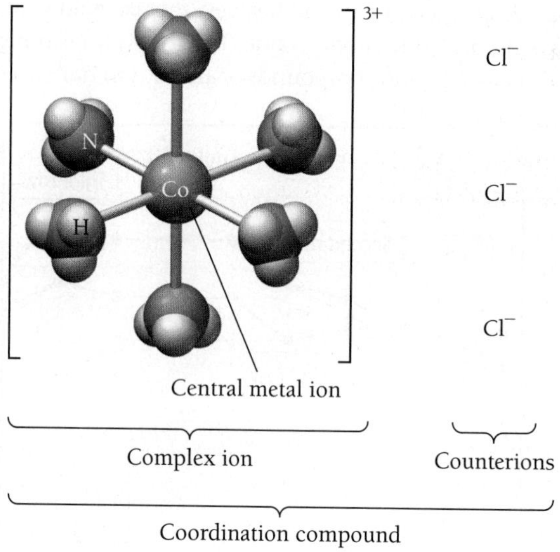

▲ **Complex Ion and Coordination Compound** A coordination compound contains a complex ion and corresponding counterions. The complex ion contains a central metal atom coordinated to several ligands. The compound shown here is $[Co(NH_3)_6]Cl_3$.

The first coordination compounds were discovered in the early eighteenth century, but their nature was not understood until nearly 200 years later. Swiss chemist Alfred Werner (1866–1919) studied coordination compounds extensively—especially a series of cobalt(III) compounds with ammonia. The formulas for these compounds were then written as $CoCl_3 \cdot 6\,NH_3$, $CoCl_3 \cdot 5\,NH_3$, and $CoCl_3 \cdot 4\,NH_3$. In 1893, Werner proposed that the central metal ion has two types of interactions that he named **primary valence** and **secondary valence**. The primary valence is the oxidation state on the central metal atom, and the secondary valence is the number of molecules or ions directly bound to the metal atom, called the **coordination number**. In $CoCl_3 \cdot 6\,NH_3$ the primary valence is +3, and it was discovered that the ammonia molecules are directly bound to the central cobalt, giving a coordination number of 6. Today we write the formula of this compound as $[Co(NH_3)_6]Cl_3$ to better represent the coordination compound as the combination of a complex ion, $Co(NH_3)_6^{3+}$, and three Cl^- counterions.

We write the formulas of the other cobalt(III) compounds studied by Werner as $[Co(NH_3)_5Cl]Cl_2$ and $[Co(NH_3)_4Cl_2]Cl$. In these two cases, the complex ions are $Co(NH_3)_5Cl^{2+}$ (with two Cl^- counterions) and $Co(NH_3)_4Cl_2^+$ (with one Cl^- counterion), respectively. With this series of compounds, Werner demonstrated that the Cl^- can replace NH_3 in the secondary valence. In other words, Cl^- can act as a counterion, or it can bond directly to the metal as part of the complex ion.

The complex ion itself contains the metal ion in the center and the ligands—which can be neutral molecules or ions—arranged around it. We can think of the metal–ligand complex as a Lewis acid–base adduct (see Section 17.11) because the bond is formed when the ligand donates a pair of electrons to an empty orbital on the metal. For example, consider the reaction between the silver ion and ammonia:

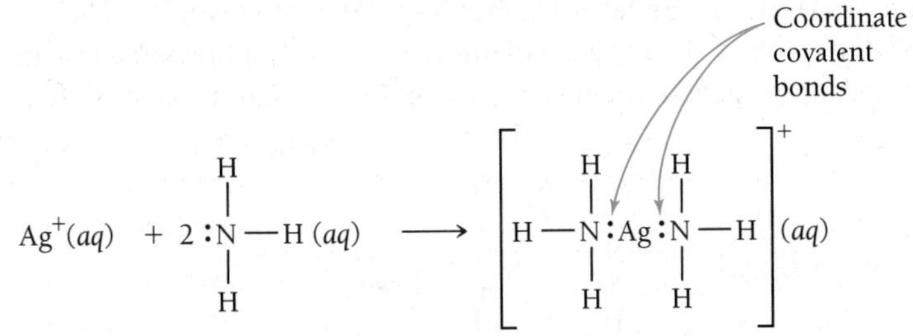

Lewis acid Lewis base Lewis acid–base adduct

A bond of this type, which we first encountered in Section 11.6, is often referred to as a **coordinate covalent bond**. Ligands are therefore good Lewis bases and have at least one pair of electrons to donate to, and bond with, the central metal ion. Table 26.2 contains a number of common ligands.

TABLE 26.2 ■ Common Ligands

Name	Lewis diagram
Water	$H-\ddot{\underset{..}{O}}-H$
Ammonia	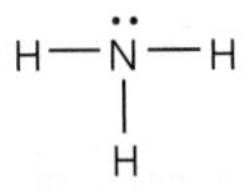
Chloride ion	$[:\ddot{\underset{..}{Cl}}:]^-$
Carbon monoxide	$:C\equiv O:$
Cyanide ion	$[:C\equiv N:]^-$
Thiocyanate ion	$[:\ddot{\underset{..}{S}}=C=\ddot{N}:]^-$
Oxalate ion (ox)	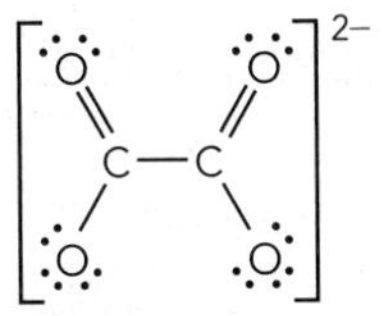
Ethylenediamine (en)	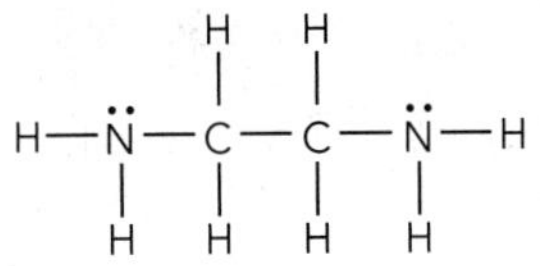
Ethylenediaminetetraacetate (EDTA)	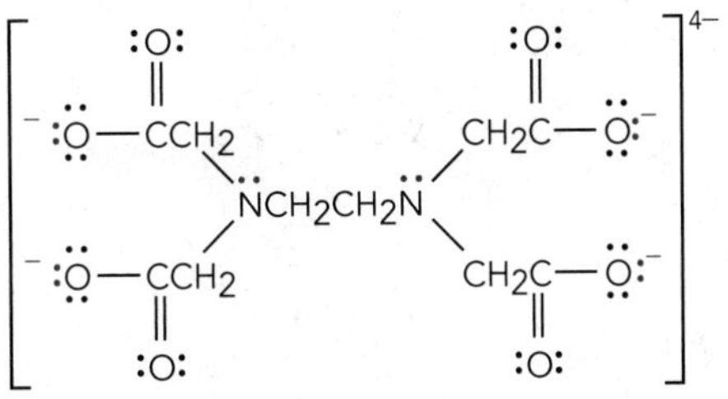

Ligands that donate only one electron pair to the central metal are **monodentate**. Some ligands have the ability to donate two pairs of electrons (from two different atoms) to the metal; these are **bidentate**. Examples of bidentate ligands include the oxalate ion (abbreviated ox) and the ethylenediamine molecule (abbreviated en) shown here. The ethylenediamine ligand bonded to Co^{3+} is shown in Figure 26.5(a)▼.

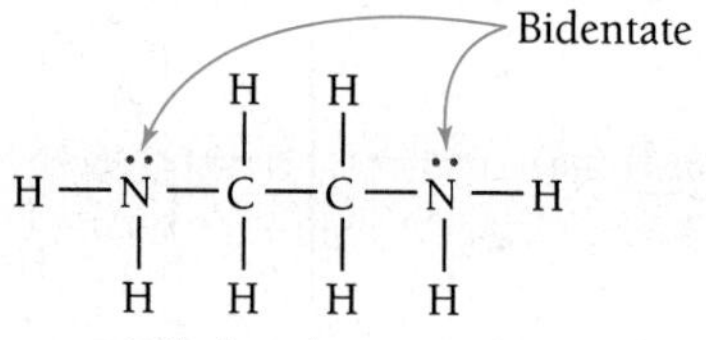

Some ligands, called **polydentate** ligands, can donate even more than two electron pairs (from more than two atoms) to the metal. The most common polydentate ligand is the ethylenediaminetetraacetate ion ($EDTA^{4-}$) shown here:

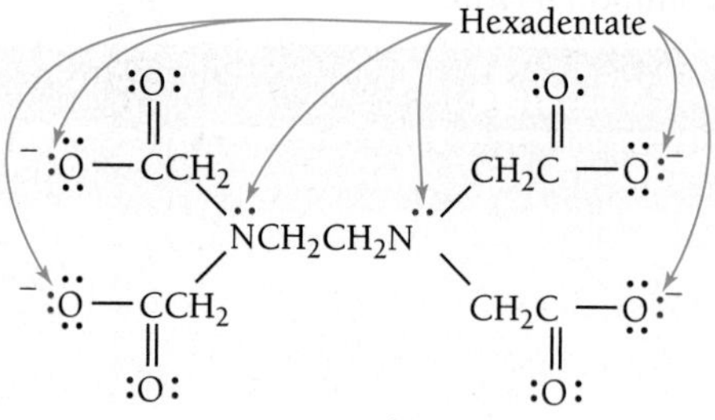

The EDTA ligand wraps itself completely around the metal, donating up to six pairs of electrons (Figure 26.5(b)▼). A complex ion that contains either a bidentate or polydentate ligand is a **chelate** (pronounced "key-late"), and the coordinating ligand is known as a **chelating agent**.

A survey of many coordination compounds shows that coordination numbers can vary from as low as 2 to as high as 12. The most common coordination numbers are 6, as occurs in $[Co(NH_3)_6]^{3+}$, and 4, as occurs in $[PdCl_4]^{2-}$. Coordination numbers greater than 6 are rarely observed for the first-row transition metals. Typically, only 1+ metal ions have a coordination number as low as 2, as occurs in $[Ag(NH_3)_2]^+$. Odd coordination numbers exist, but they are rare.

▶ **FIGURE 26.5 Bidentate and Polydentate Ligands Coordinated to Co(III)** **(a)** Ethylenediamine is a bidentate ligand; **(b)** EDTA is a hexadentate ligand.

Bidentate and Polydentate Ligands Coordinated to Co(III)

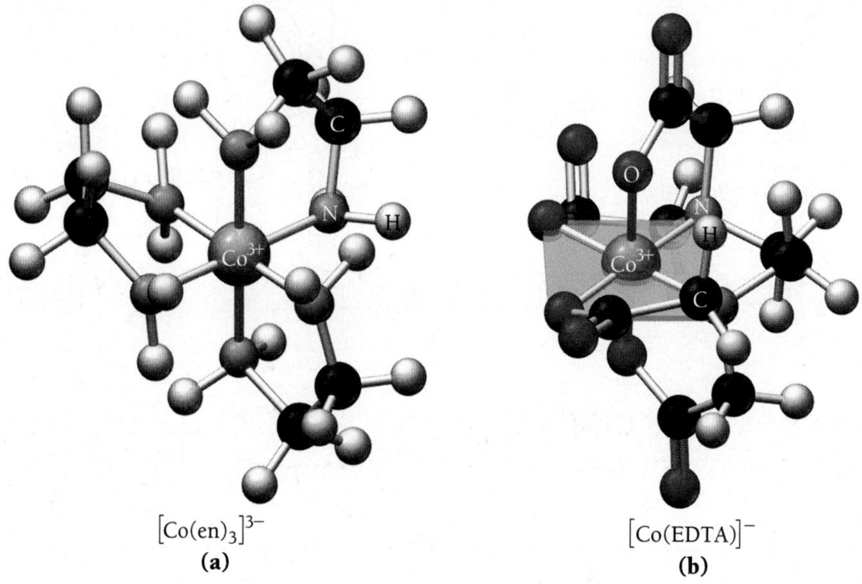

The common geometries of complex ions, shown in Table 26.3, depend in part on their coordination number. A coordination number of 2 results in a linear geometry, and a coordination number of 6 results in an octahedral geometry. A coordination number of 4 can have either a tetrahedral geometry or a square planar geometry, depending on the number of *d* electrons in the metal ion. Metal ions with a d^8 electron configuration (such as $[PdCl_4]^{2-}$) exhibit square planar geometry, and metal ions with a d^{10} electron configuration (such as $[Zn(NH_3)_4]^{2+}$) exhibit tetrahedral geometry.

TABLE 26.3 ■ Common Geometrics of Complex Ions

Coordination Number	Shape	Model	Example
2	Linear	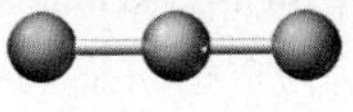	$[Ag(NH_3)_2]^+$
4	Square planar	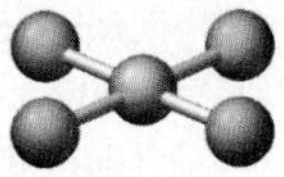	$[PdCl_4]^{2-}$
4	Tetrahedral	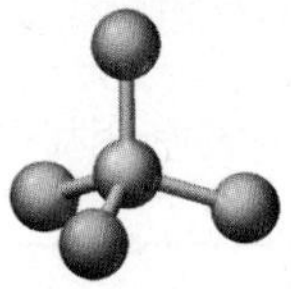	$[Zn(NH_3)_4]^{2+}$
6	Octahedral	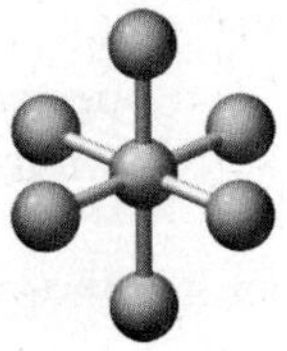	$[Fe(H_2O)_6]^{3+}$

Naming Coordination Compounds

To name coordination compounds, we follow a series of general rules based on the system originally proposed by Werner. As with all ionic compounds (see Section 3.5), the name of the cation goes before the name of the anion.

Guidelines for Naming Complex Ions	Examples
1. Name the ligands.	
■ Name neutral ligands as molecules with the following notable exceptions:	$NH_2CH_2CH_2NH_2$ is ethylenediamine.
H_2O (aqua)	H_2O is aqua.
NH_3 (ammine)	
CO (carbonyl)	
■ Name anionic ligands with the name of the ion plus an ending modified as follows:	
-ide becomes -o	Cl^- is chloro.
-ate becomes -ato	SO_4^{2-} is sulfato.
-ite becomes -ito	SO_3^{2-} is sulfito.
Table 26.4 lists the names of some common ligands.	
2. List the names of the ligands in alphabetical order before the name of the metal cation.	Ammine (NH_3) is listed before chloro (Cl^-), which is listed before nitrito (NO_2^-).

—Continued on the next page

Guidelines for Naming Complex Ions	Examples
3. Use a prefix to indicate the number of ligands (when there is more than one of a particular type): *di-* (2), *tri-* (3), *tetra-* (4), *penta-* (5), or *hexa-* (6). If the name of the ligand already contains a prefix, such as ethylenediamine, place parentheses around the ligand name and use *bis-* (2), *tris-* (3), or *tetrakis-* (4) to indicate the number. Prefixes do not affect the order in which you list the ligands.	Trichloro indicates three Cl^- ligands. Tetraammine indicates four NH_3 ligands. Tris(ethylenediamine) indicates three ethylenediamine ligands.
4. Name the metal. **a.** When the complex ion is a cation, use the name of the metal followed by the oxidation state written with a Roman numeral.	In cations: Co^{3+} is cobalt(III). Pt^{2+} is platinum(II). Cu^+ is copper(I).
b. If the complex ion is an anion, drop the ending of the metal and add *–ate* followed by the oxidation state written with a Roman numeral. Some metals use the Latin root with the *-ate* ending. Table 26.5 lists the names for some common metals in anionic complexes.	In anions: Co^{3+} is cobaltate(III). Pt^{2+} is platinate(II). Cu^+ is cuprate(I).
5. Write the entire name of the complex ion by listing the ligands first followed by the metal.	$[Pt(NH_3)_2Cl_4]^{2-}$ is diamminetetrachloroplatinate(II). $[Co(NH_3)_6]^{3+}$ is hexaamminecobalt(III).

TABLE 26.4 ■ Names and Formulas of Common Ligands

Ligand	Name in Complex Ion
Anions	
Bromide, Br^-	Bromo
Chloride, Cl^-	Chloro
Hydroxide, OH^-	Hydroxo
Cyanide, CN^-	Cyano
Nitrite, NO_2^-	Nitro
Oxalate, $C_2O_4^{2-}$ (ox)	Oxalato
Ethylenediaminetetraacetate ($EDTA^{4-}$)	Ethylenediaminetetraacetato
Neutral molecules	
Water, H_2O	Aqua
Ammonia, NH_3	Ammine
Carbon monoxide, CO	Carbonyl
Ethylenediamine (en)	Ethylenediamine

TABLE 26.5 ■ Names of Common Metals When Found in Anionic Complex Ions

Metal	Name in Anionic Complex
Chromium	Chromate
Cobalt	Cobaltate
Copper	Cuprate
Gold	Aurate
Iron	Ferrate
Lead	Plumbate
Manganese	Manganate
Molybdenum	Molybdate
Nickel	Nickelate
Platinum	Platinate
Silver	Argentate
Tin	Stannate
Zinc	Zincate

When we write the *formula* of a complex ion, we write the symbol for the metal first, followed by neutral molecules and then anions. If there is more than one anion or neutral molecule acting as a ligand, we list them in alphabetical order based on the chemical symbol.

HOW TO: *Name Coordination Compounds*	**EXAMPLE 26.3** **Naming Coordination Compounds** Name the following compound: $[Cr(H_2O)_5Cl]Cl_2$.	**EXAMPLE 26.4** **Naming Coordination Compounds** Name the following compound: $K_3[Fe(CN)_6]$.
Identify the cation and anion and first name the simple ion (i.e., not the complex one).	**SOLUTION** $[Cr(H_2O)_5Cl]^{2+}$ is a complex cation. Cl^- is chloride.	**SOLUTION** K^+ is potassium. $[Fe(CN)_6]^{3-}$ is a complex anion.
Give each ligand a name and list them in alphabetical order.	H_2O is aqua. Cl^- is chloro.	CN^- is cyano.
Name the metal ion.	Cr^{3+} is chromium(III).	Fe^{3+} is ferrate(III) because the complex is anionic.
Name the complex ion by adding prefixes to indicate the number of each ligand followed by the name of each ligand followed by the name of the metal ion.	$[Cr(H_2O)_5Cl]^{2+}$ is pentaaquachlorochromium(III).	$[Fe(CN)_6]^{3-}$ is hexacyanoferrate(III).
Name the compound by writing the name of the cation before the anion. The only space is between ion names.	$[Cr(H_2O)_5Cl]Cl_2$ is pentaaquachlorochromium(III) chloride.	$K_3[Fe(CN)_6]$ is potassium hexacyanoferrate(III).
	FOR PRACTICE 26.3 Name the following compound: $[Mn(CO)(NH_3)_5]SO_4$.	**FOR PRACTICE 26.4** Name the following compound: $Na_2[PtCl_4]$.

26.4 Structure and Isomerization

Isomerism is common in coordination compounds. We broadly divide the isomerism observed in coordination compounds into two categories. Each category has subcategories, as shown in Figure 26.6▶, on the next page. In **structural isomers**, atoms are connected to one another in different ways, whereas in **stereoisomers**, atoms are connected in the same way but the ligands have a different spatial arrangement about the metal atom.

Structural Isomerism

We subdivide the broad category of structural isomers into two types: coordination isomers and linkage isomers. **Coordination isomers** occur when a coordinated ligand exchanges places with the uncoordinated counterion. For example, two different compounds have the general formula $Co(NH_3)_5BrCl$. In one of them, the bromine coordinates to the metal and chloride is a counterion, pentaamminebromocobalt(II) chloride, $[Co(NH_3)_5Br]Cl$; in the other one, the chlorine coordinates to the metal and bromide is the counterion, pentaamminechlorocobalt(II) bromide, $[Co(NH_3)_5Cl]Br$.

Linkage isomers have ligands that can coordinate to the metal in different orientations. For example, the nitrite ion (NO_2^-) has a lone pair on the N atom as well as lone pairs on the O atoms—either of the two atoms can form coordinate covalent bonds with the metal. When the nitrite ion coordinates through the N atom, it is a *nitro* ligand and is represented as NO_2^-, but when it coordinates through the O atom, it is a *nitrito* ligand and is usually represented as ONO^-. An example of linkage isomerization can be seen in the

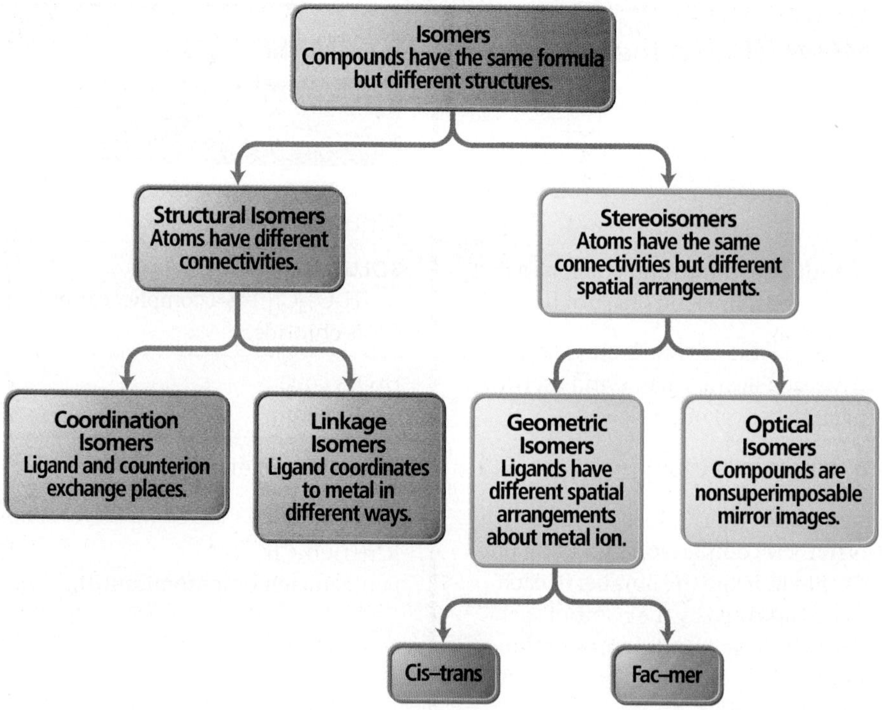

▲ **FIGURE 26.6 Types of Isomers**

yellow-orange complex ion pentaamminenitrocobalt(III), $[Co(NH_3)_5NO_2]^{2+}$, which contrasts with the red-orange complex ion pentaamminenitritocobalt(III), $[Co(NH_3)_5ONO]^{2+}$, as shown in Figure 26.7▼. Table 26.6 lists other ligands capable of linkage isomerization.

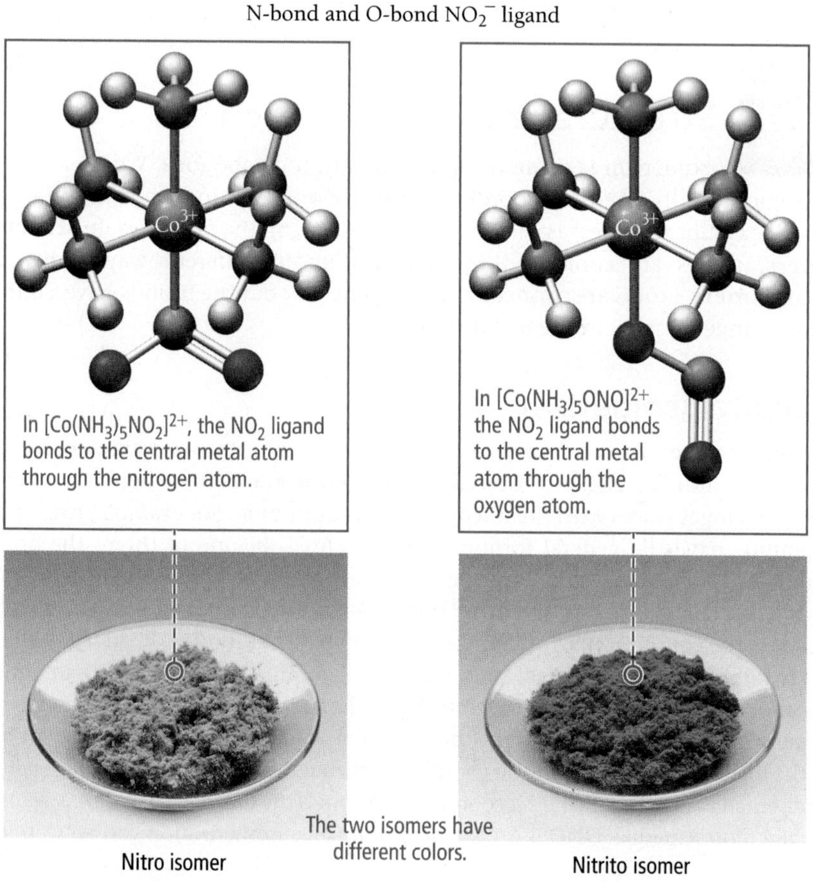

► **FIGURE 26.7 Linkage Isomers**

TABLE 26.6 ■ Ligands Capable of Linkage Isomerization

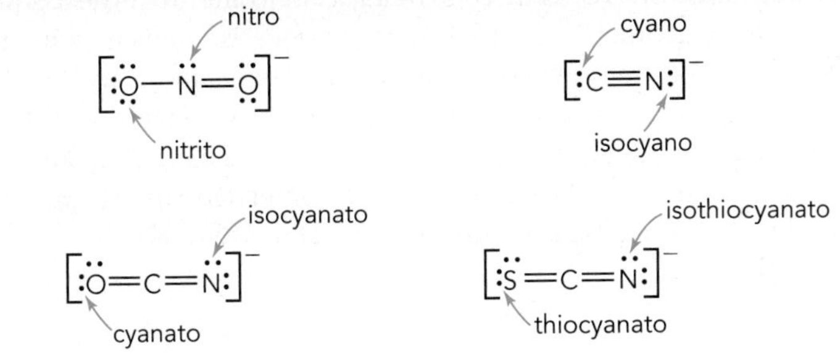

Stereoisomerism

We can also subdivide the broad category of stereoisomers into two types: geometric isomers and optical isomers. **Geometric isomers** result when the ligands bonding to the metal have a different spatial arrangement. One type of geometric isomerism, as we saw in Section 22.5, is cis–trans isomerism, which in complex ions occurs in square planar complexes of the general formula MA_2B_2 or octahedral complexes of the general formula MA_4B_2. For example, cis–trans isomerism occurs in the square planar complex $Pt(NH_3)_2Cl_2$. Figure 26.8(a)▼ shows the two distinct ways in which the ligands can be oriented around the metal. In one complex, the Cl^- ligands are next to each other on one side of the molecule—this is the cis isomer. In the other complex, the Cl^- ligands are on opposite sides of the molecule—this is the trans isomer.

Geometric isomerism also exists in the octahedral complex ion $[Co(NH_3)_4Cl_2]^+$. As shown in Figure 26.8(b)▼, the ligands arrange themselves around the metal in two ways, one with the Cl^- ligands on the same side (the cis isomer) and another with the Cl^- ligands

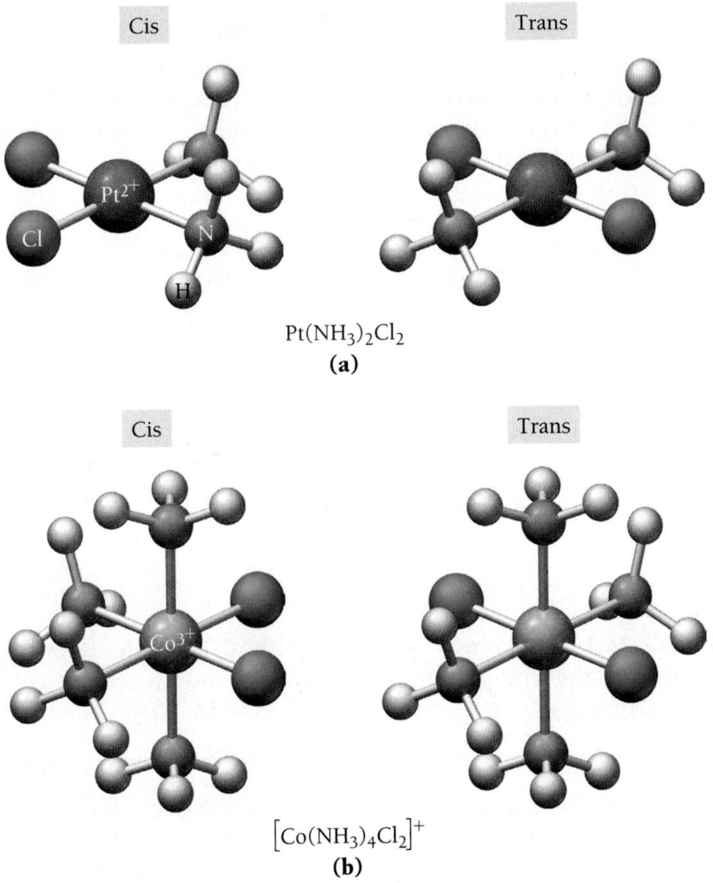

◀ **FIGURE 26.8 Cis–trans Isomerism** **(a)** Cis–trans isomerism in square planar $Pt(NH_3)_2Cl_2$. In the cis isomer, the Cl^- ligands are next to each other on one side of the molecule. In the trans isomer, the Cl^- ligands are on opposite sides of the molecule. **(b)** Cis–trans isomerism in octahedral $[Co(NH_3)_4Cl_2]^+$. In the cis isomer, the Cl^- ligands are on the same side. In the trans isomer, the Cl^- ligands are on opposite sides.

on opposite sides of the metal (the trans isomer). Note that cis–trans isomerism does not occur in tetrahedral complexes because all bond angles around the metal are 109.5°, and each corner of a tetrahedron is considered to be adjacent to all three other corners.

Another type of geometric isomerism is fac–mer isomerism, which occurs in octahedral complexes of the general formula MA_3B_3. For example, in $Co(NH_3)_3Cl_3$, the ligands arrange themselves around the metal in two ways (Figure 26.9▼). In the fac isomer, the three Cl^- ligands are all on one side of the molecule and make up one face of the octahedron (fac is short for facial). In the mer isomer, the three ligands form an arc around the middle of the octahedron (mer is short for meridional).

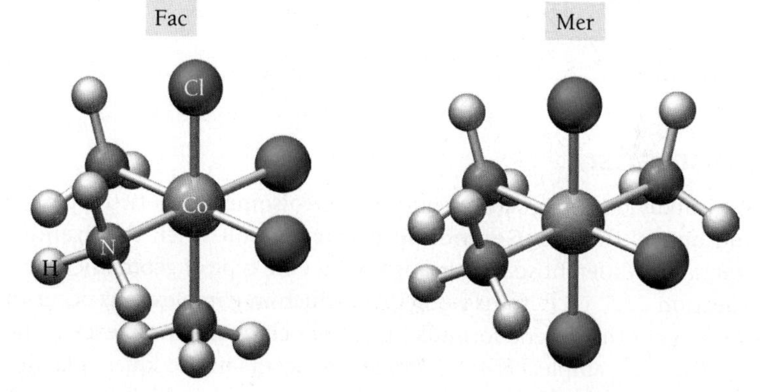

▶ **FIGURE 26.9 Fac–Mer Isomerism in $CO(NH_3)_3Cl_3$** In the fac isomer, all three Cl^- ligands are on one side of the molecule and make up one face of the octahedron. In the mer isomer, the three ligands inscribe an arc around the middle (or meridian) of the octahedron.

HOW TO: *Identify and Draw Geometric Isomers*	**EXAMPLE 26.5** **Identifying and Drawing Geometric Isomers** Draw the structures and label the type of all the isomers of $[Co(en)_2Cl_2]^+$.	**EXAMPLE 26.6** **Identifying and Drawing Geometric Isomers** Draw the structures and label the type of all the isomers of $[Ni(CN)_2Cl_2]^{2-}$.
Identify the coordination number and the geometry around the metal.	**SOLUTION** The ethylenediamine (en) ligand is bidentate, so each occupies two coordination sites. Each Cl^- is monodentate, occupying one site. The total coordination number is 6, so this must be an octahedral complex.	**SOLUTION** All the ligands are monodentate, so the total coordination number is 4. Ni^{2+} is a d^8 electronic configuration, so we expect a square planar complex.
Identify if this is cis–trans or fac–mer isomerism.	With ethylenediamine occupying four sites and Cl^- occupying two sites, it fits the general formula MA_4B_2, leading to cis–trans isomers.	Square planar complexes can only have cis–trans isomers.
Draw and label the two isomers.	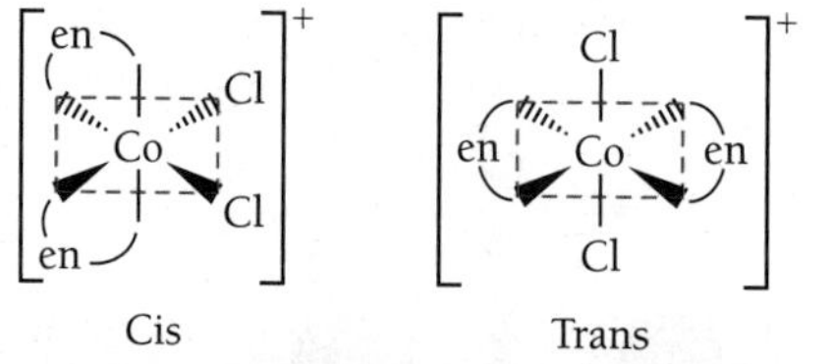	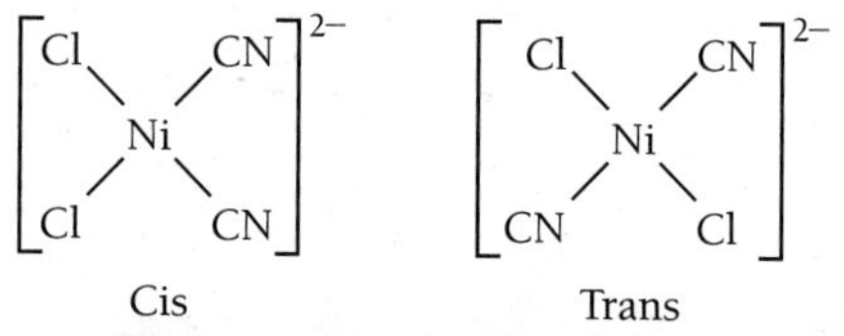
	FOR PRACTICE 26.5 Draw the structures and label the type of all the isomers of $[Cr(H_2O)_3Cl_3]^+$.	**FOR PRACTICE 26.6** Draw the structures and label the type of all the isomers of $[Co(NH_3)_2Cl_2(ox)]^-$.

The second category of stereoisomerism is optical isomerism. Recall from 21.3 that **optical isomers** are nonsuperimposable mirror images of one another. If you hold your right hand up to a mirror, the image in the mirror looks like your left hand. No matter how you rotate or flip your left hand, you cannot superimpose it on your right hand. Molecules or ions that exhibit this quality are *chiral*. The isomers are *enantiomers*, and they exhibit the property of optical activity (the rotation of polarized light). The complex ion $[Co(en)_3]^{3+}$ is nonsuperimposable on its mirror image, so it is a chiral complex (Figure 26.10▼).

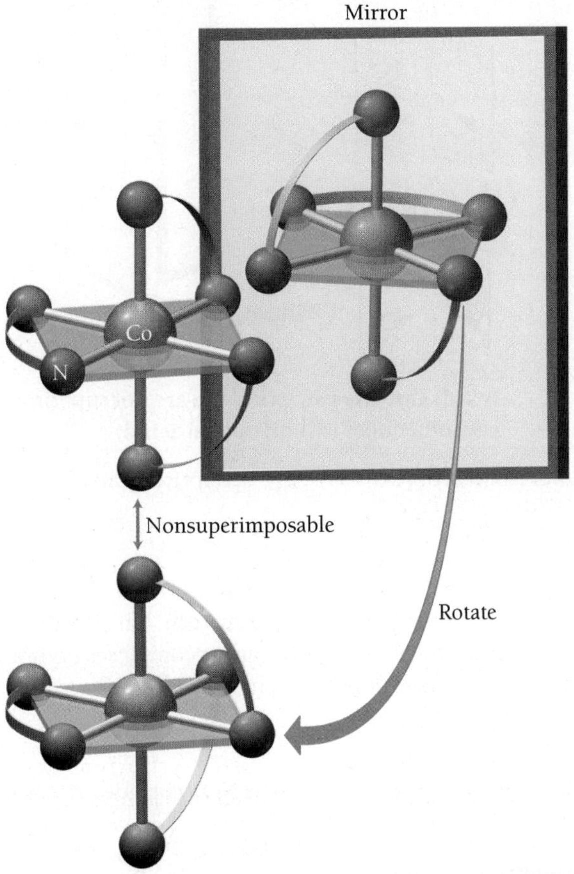

◀ **FIGURE 26.10 Optical Isomerism in $[Co(en)_3]^{3+}$** The mirror images of $[Co(en)_3]^{3+}$ are not superimposable. (The connected nitrogen atoms represent the ethylenediamine ligand.)

EXAMPLE 26.7 Recognizing and Drawing Optical Isomers

Determine whether the cis or trans isomers in Example 26.5 are optically active (demonstrate optical isomerism).

SOLUTION

Draw the trans isomer of $[Co(en)_2Cl_2]^+$ and its mirror image. Check to see if they are superimposable by rotating one isomer 180°.

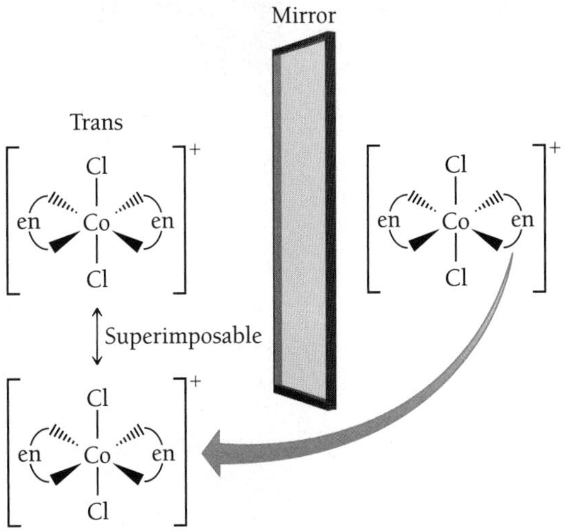

In this case the two are identical, so there is no optical activity.

—*Continued on the next page*

Continued—

Draw the cis isomer and its mirror image. Check to see if they are superimposable by rotating one isomer 180°.

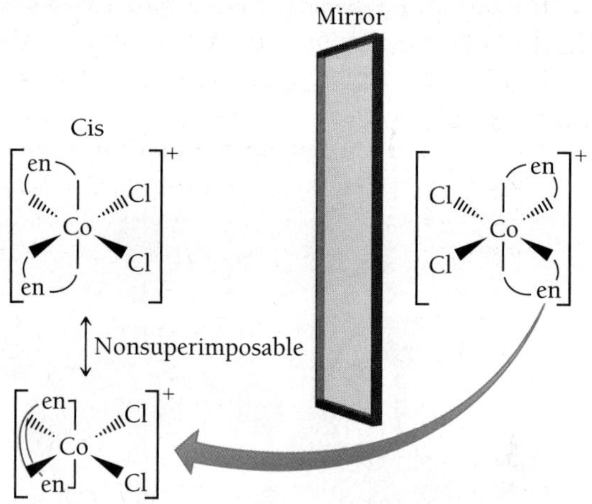

In this case the two structures are not superimposable, so the cis isomer does exhibit optical activity.

FOR PRACTICE 26.7 Determine whether the fac or mer isomers of $[Cr(H_2O)_3Cl_3]^+$ are optically active.

The previous examples demonstrate optical isomerism in octahedral complexes. Tetrahedral complexes can also exhibit optical isomerism, but only if all four coordination sites are occupied by different ligands. Square planar complexes do not normally exhibit optical isomerism as they are superimposable on their mirror images.

ANSWER **NOW!**

26.2 Cc Conceptual Connection

ISOMERISM Which type of isomerism is NOT considered structural isomerism?

(a) coordination isomerism
(b) linkage isomerism
(c) geometric isomerism

26.5 Bonding in Coordination Compounds

The bonding in complex ions and coordination compounds can be described by valence bond theory, which helps us to understand the geometries of the complex ions. However, other properties of complex ions, such as their colors and their magnetic properties, require a different model called crystal field theory. We examine both models in this section.

Valence Bond Theory

Recall from Section 11.6 that according to valence bond theory, a coordinate covalent bond is the overlap between a completely filled atomic orbital and an empty atomic orbital. In complex ions, the filled orbital is on the ligand, and the empty orbital is on the metal ion. The metal ion orbitals are hybridized according to the geometry of the complex ion. The common hybridization schemes are shown in Figure 26.11▶. An octahedral complex ion requires six empty orbitals in an octahedral arrangement on the metal ion. A full set of d^2sp^3 hybrid orbitals results in the exact orbitals needed for this geometry. A set of sp^3 hybrid orbitals results in a tetrahedral arrangement of orbitals, a set of dsp^2 hybrid orbitals results in a square planar arrangement, and a set of sp hybrid orbitals results in a linear arrangement of orbitals. In each case, the coordinate covalent bond is formed by the overlap between the orbitals on the ligands and the hybridized orbitals on the metal ion.

Crystal Field Theory

Crystal field theory (CFT) is a bonding model for transition metal complexes that helps us to understand their colors and magnetic properties. To illustrate the basic principles of CFT, we examine the central metal atom's *d* orbitals in an octahedral complex.

Geometry	Hybridization	Orbitals
Linear	*sp*	
Tetrahedral	sp^3	
Square planar	dsp^2	
Octahedral	d^2sp^3	

▲ **FIGURE 26.11 Common Hybridization Schemes in Complex Ions** We can deduce the valence bond model hybridization schemes from the geometry of the complex ion.

Octahedral Complexes

The basic premise of CFT is that complex ions form because of attractions between the electrons on the ligands and the positive charge on the metal ion. However, the electrons on the ligands also repel the electrons in the *unhybridized* metal *d* orbitals. CFT focuses on these repulsions. Figure 26.12▼ shows how the ligand positions superimpose on the *d* orbitals in an octahedral complex. Notice that the ligands in an octahedral complex are located in the same space as the lobes of the $d_{x^2-y^2}$ and d_{z^2} orbitals. The repulsions between electron pairs in the ligands and any potential electrons in the *d* orbitals result in an increase in the energies of these orbitals. In contrast, the d_{xy}, d_{xz}, and d_{yz} orbitals lie between the axes and have nodes directly on the axes, which results in less repulsion and lower energies for these three orbitals. In other words, the *d* orbitals—which are degenerate in the bare metal ion—are split into higher- and lower-energy levels because of the spatial arrangement of the ligands (Figure 26.13►, on the next page). The difference in energy between these split *d* orbitals is known as the crystal field splitting energy (Δ). The magnitude of the splitting depends on the particular complex. In **strong-field complexes**, the splitting is large, and in **weak-field complexes**, the splitting is small.

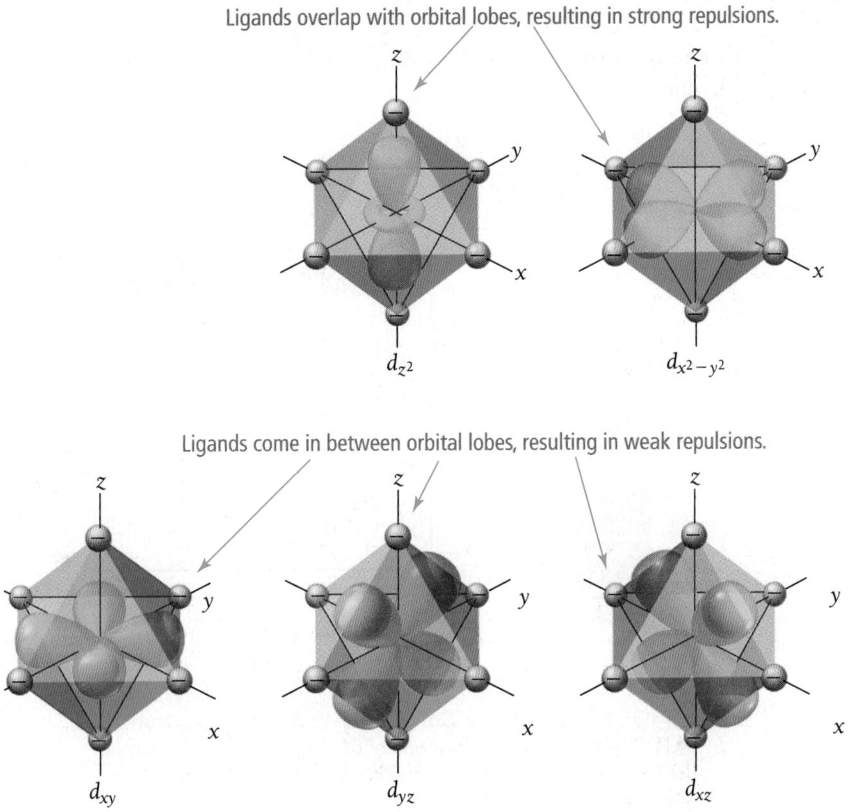

◄ **FIGURE 26.12 Relative Positions of *d* Orbitals and Ligands in an Octahedral Complex** The ligands in an octahedral complex (represented here as spheres of negative charge) interact most strongly with the d_{z^2} and $d_{x^2-y^2}$ orbitals.

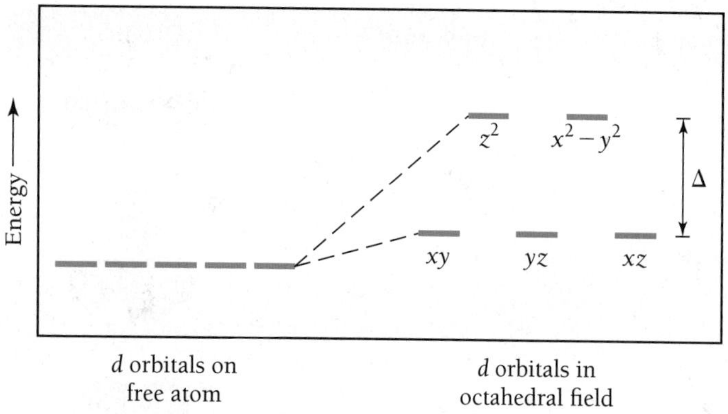

▲ **FIGURE 26.13 *d* Orbital Splitting in an Octahedral Field** The otherwise degenerate *d* orbitals are split into two energy levels by the ligands in an octahedral complex ion.

The Color of Complex Ions and Crystal Field Strength

In the opening section of this chapter, we discussed how transition metals in host crystals often show brilliant colors because of the crystal field splitting of their *d* orbitals. Solutions of complex ions display brilliant colors because of similar splittings. For example, an $[Fe(CN)_6]^{3-}$ solution is deep red, and an $[Ni(NH_3)_6]^{2+}$ solution is blue (Figure 26.14▼).

Recall from Chapter 8 that the color of an object is related to the absorption of light energy by its electrons. If a substance absorbs all of the visible wavelengths, it appears black. If it transmits (or reflects) all the wavelengths (absorbs no light), it appears colorless. A substance appears to be a particular color if it absorbs some visible light but also transmits (or reflects) the wavelengths associated with that color. A substance also appears to be a given color if it transmits (or reflects) most wavelengths but absorbs the *complementary color* on a color wheel (Figure 26.15▼). For example, a substance that absorbs green light (the complement of red) will appear red. A solution of $[Ti(H_2O)_6]^{3+}$ is purple because it absorbs strongly between 490 and 580 nm, the green-yellow region of the visible spectrum (Figure 26.16(a)▼).

The easiest way to measure the energy difference between the *d* orbitals in a complex ion is to use spectroscopy to determine the wavelength of light absorbed when an electron makes a transition from the lower-energy *d* orbitals to the higher-energy ones. With that information we can calculate the crystal field splitting energy, Δ:

$$E_{photon} = h\nu = \frac{hc}{\lambda} = \Delta$$

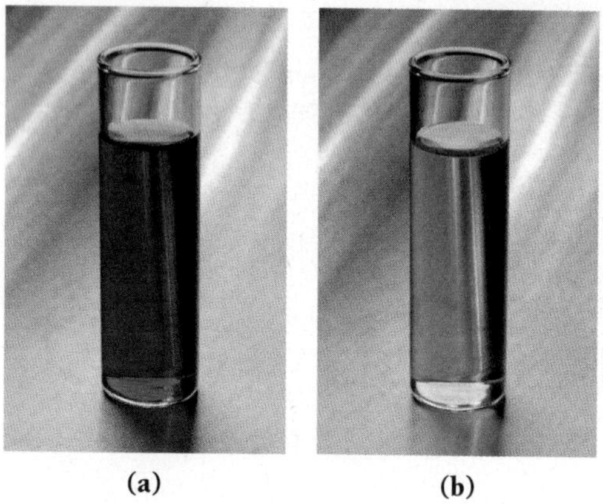

▲ **FIGURE 26.14 Colors of Complex Ions** **(a)** The complex ion $[Fe(CN)_6]^{3-}$ forms a deep red solution, and **(b)** $[Ni(NH_3)_6]^{2+}$ is blue.

Consider the $[Ti(H_2O)_6]^{3+}$ absorption spectrum shown in Figure 26.16(b)▼. The maximum absorbance is at 498 nm. Using this wavelength, we calculate Δ:

$$\Delta = \frac{hc}{\lambda} = \frac{(6.626 \times 10^{-34}\ \text{J}\cdot\text{s})(3.00 \times 10^{8}\ \text{m/s})}{(498\ \text{nm} \times 1 \times 10^{-9}\ \text{m/nm})}$$

$$\Delta = 3.99 \times 10^{-19}\ \text{J}$$

This energy corresponds to a single $[Ti(H_2O)_6]^{3+}$ ion. We can convert to kilojoules per mole:

$$\Delta = \left(3.99 \times 10^{-19}\frac{\text{J}}{\text{ion}}\right)\left(6.02 \times 10^{23}\frac{\text{ion}}{\text{mol}}\right)\left(1\frac{\text{kJ}}{1000\ \text{J}}\right) = 240\ \text{kJ/mol}$$

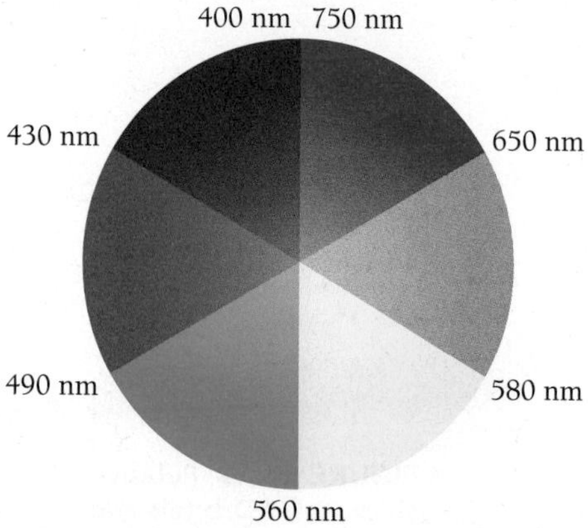

▲ **FIGURE 26.15 The Color Wheel** Colors across from one another on the color wheel are said to be complementary. A substance that absorbs a color on the wheel will appear to be its complementary color.

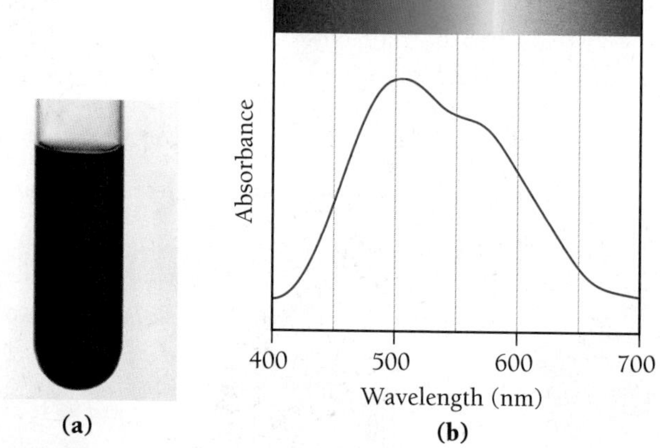

▲ **FIGURE 26.16 The Color and Absorption Spectrum of $[Ti(H_2O)_6]^{3+}$** **(a)** A solution containing $[Ti(H_2O)_6]^{3+}$ is purple. **(b)** The absorption spectrum of $[Ti(H_2O)_6]^{3+}$ extends across the green-yellow region of the spectrum.

EXAMPLE 26.8 Crystal Field Splitting Energy

The complex ion $[Cu(NH_3)_6]^{2+}$ is blue in aqueous solution. Estimate the crystal field splitting energy (in kJ/mol) for this ion.

SOLUTION

Begin by consulting the color wheel to determine approximately which wavelength is being absorbed.	Because the solution is blue, you can deduce that orange light is absorbed since orange is the complementary color to blue.
Estimate the absorbed wavelength.	The color orange ranges from 580 to 650 nm, so you can estimate the average wavelength as 615 nm.
Calculate the energy corresponding to this wavelength, using $E = hc/\lambda$. This energy corresponds to Δ.	$E = \dfrac{(6.626 \times 10^{-34}\,\text{J}\cdot\cancel{\text{s}})(3.00 \times 10^{8}\,\cancel{\text{m}}/\cancel{\text{s}})}{(615\,\cancel{\text{nm}})(1 \times 10^{-9}\,\cancel{\text{m}}/\cancel{\text{nm}})}$ $E = 3.23 \times 10^{-19}\,\text{J} = \Delta$
Convert J/ion into kJ/mol.	$E = \dfrac{(3.23 \times 10^{-19}\,\cancel{\text{J}}/\cancel{\text{ion}})(6.02 \times 10^{23}\,\cancel{\text{ion}}/\text{mol})}{(1000\,\cancel{\text{J}}/\text{kJ})}$ $\Delta = 195\,\text{kJ/mol}$

FOR PRACTICE 26.8 The complex ion $[Co(NH_3)_5NO_2]^{2+}$ is yellow. Estimate the crystal field splitting energy (in kJ/mol) for this ion.

The magnitude of the crystal field splitting in a complex ion—and, therefore whether it is a strong-field or a weak-field complex—depends in large part on the ligands attached to the central metal ion. Spectroscopic studies of various ligands attached to the same metal allow us to arrange different ligands in order of their ability to split the *d* orbitals. This list is known as the *spectrochemical series* and is arranged from ligands that result in the largest Δ to those that result in the smallest:

$$CN^- > NO_2^- > en > NH_3 > H_2O > OH^- > F^- > Cl^- > Br^- > I^-$$

large Δ small Δ

typically strong-field ligands typically weak-field ligands

Ligands that produce large values of Δ are *strong-field ligands*, and those that give small values of Δ are *weak-field ligands*.

The metal ion also has an effect on the magnitude of Δ. If we examine different metal ions with the same ligand, we find that Δ increases as the charge on the metal ion increases. The greater charge on the metal draws the ligands closer, causing greater repulsion with the *d* orbitals and therefore a larger Δ. An example of this behavior occurs in the complex ions between NH_3 (a ligand in the middle of the spectrochemical series) and the +2 or +3 oxidation states of cobalt. Hexaamminecobalt(II) ion, $[Co(NH_3)_6]^{2+}$, has a weak crystal field (small Δ) and hexaamminecobalt(III) ion, $[Co(NH_3)_6]^{3+}$, has a strong field (large Δ).

WEAK- AND STRONG-FIELD LIGANDS Two ligands, A and B, form complexes with a particular metal ion. When the metal ion complexes with ligand A, the resulting solution is red. When the metal ion complexes with ligand B, the resulting solution is yellow. Which of the two ligands produces the larger Δ?

(a) Ligand A **(b)** Ligand B

26.3 Cc Conceptual Connection

ANSWER **NOW!**

Magnetic Properties

The strength of the crystal field can affect the magnetic properties of a transition metal complex. Recall that, according to Hund's rule, electrons occupy degenerate orbitals singly as long as an empty orbital is available. When the energies of the *d* orbitals are

Recall from Section 9.7 that a paramagnetic species contains unpaired electrons and a diamagnetic one does not.

split by ligands, the lower-energy orbitals fill first. Once they are half-filled, the next electron can either: (1) pair with an electron in one of the lower-energy half-filled orbitals by overcoming the electron–electron repulsion associated with having two electrons in the same orbital; or (2) go into an empty orbital of higher energy by overcoming the energy difference between the orbitals—in this case, the crystal field splitting energy, Δ. The magnitude of Δ compared to the electron–electron repulsions determines which of these two actually occurs.

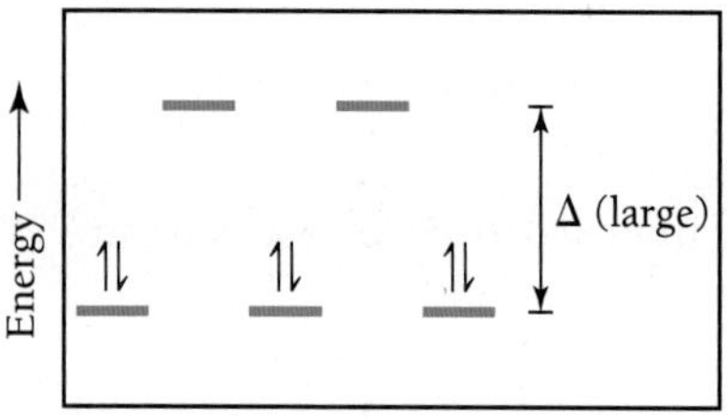

$[Fe(CN_6)]^{4-}$

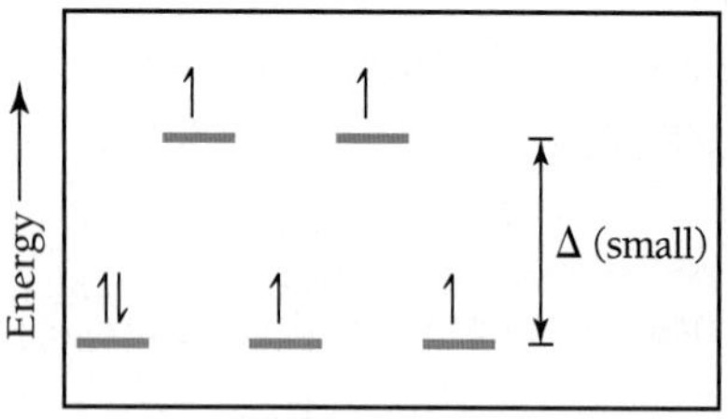

$[Fe(H_2O)_6]^{2+}$

We can compare two iron(II) complexes to see the difference in behavior under strong- and weak-field conditions. $[Fe(CN)_6]^{4-}$ is known to be diamagnetic, and $[Fe(H_2O)_6]^{2+}$ is known to be paramagnetic. Both of these complexes contain Fe^{2+}, which has an electron configuration of [Ar] $3d^6$. In the case of $[Fe(CN)_6]^{4-}$, CN^- is a strong-field ligand that generates a large Δ, so it takes more energy to occupy the higher-energy level than it does to pair the electrons in the lower-energy level. The result is that all six electrons are paired and the compound is diamagnetic, as shown in the accompanying figure in the margin.

In $[Fe(H_2O)_6]^{2+}$, H_2O is a weak-field ligand that generates a small Δ, so the electron pairing energy is greater than Δ. Consequently, the first five electrons occupy the five *d* orbitals singly and only the sixth pairs up, resulting in a paramagnetic compound with four unpaired electrons, as shown in the accompanying figure in the margin.

In general, complexes with strong-field ligands have fewer unpaired electrons relative to the free metal ion and are therefore called **low-spin complexes.** Complexes with weak-field ligands, by contrast, have the same number of unpaired electrons as the free metal ion and are **high-spin complexes.**

When we examine the orbital diagrams of the d^1 through d^{10} metal ions in octahedral complexes, we find that only d^4, d^5, d^6, and d^7 metal ions have low- and high-spin possibilities. Since there are three lower-energy *d* orbitals, the d^1, d^2, and d^3 metal ions always have unpaired electrons, independent of Δ. In the d^8, d^9, and d^{10} metal ions, the three lower-energy orbitals are completely filled, so the remaining electrons fill the two higher orbitals (as expected according to Hund's rule), also independent of Δ.

HOW TO: *Determine the Number of Unpaired Electrons in Octahedral Complexes*	**EXAMPLE 26.9** **High- and Low-Spin Octahedral Complexes** How many unpaired electrons are there in the complex ion $[CoF_6]^{3-}$?	**EXAMPLE 26.10** **High- and Low-Spin Octahedral Complexes** How many unpaired electrons are there in the complex ion $[Co(NH_3)_5NO_2]^{2+}$?
Begin by determining the charge and number of *d* electrons on the metal.	**SOLUTION** The metal is Co^{3+} and has a d^6 electronic configuration.	**SOLUTION** The metal is Co^{3+} and has a d^6 electronic configuration.
Look at the spectrochemical series to determine whether the ligand is a strong-field or a weak-field ligand.	F^- is a weak-field ligand, so Δ is relatively small.	NH_3 and NO_2^- are both strong-field ligands, so Δ is relatively large.
Decide if the complex is high- or low-spin and draw the electron configuration.	Weak-field ligands yield high-spin configurations. 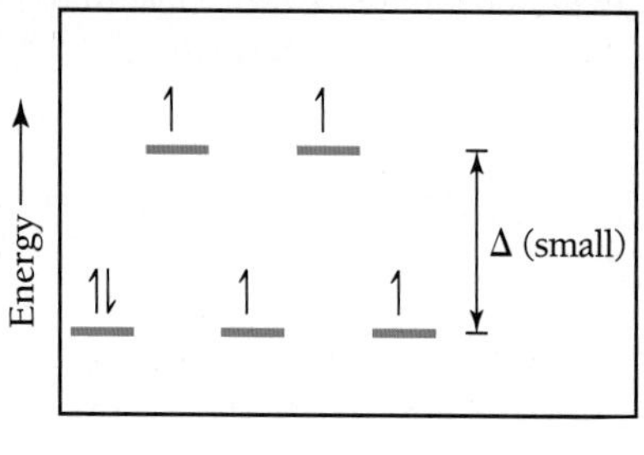	Strong-field ligands yield low-spin configurations. 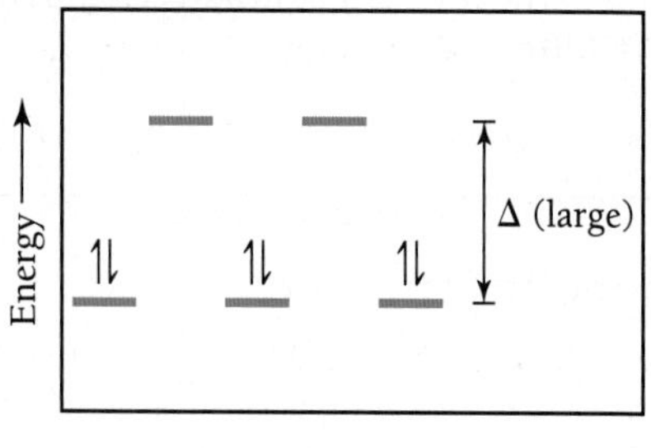

Count the unpaired electrons.	This configuration has four unpaired electrons.	This configuration has no unpaired electrons.
	FOR PRACTICE 26.9 How many unpaired electrons are there in the complex ion $[FeCl_6]^{3-}$?	**FOR PRACTICE 26.10** How many unpaired electrons are there in the complex ion $[Co(CN)_6]^{4-}$?

Tetrahedral and Square Planar Complexes

So far, we have examined the *d* orbital energy changes only for octahedral complexes, but transition metal complexes can have other geometries, such as tetrahedral and square planar. We use crystal field theory to determine the *d* orbital splitting pattern for these geometries as well. For a tetrahedral complex, the *d* orbital splitting pattern is the opposite of the octahedral splitting pattern: three *d* orbitals (d_{xy}, d_{xz}, and d_{yz}) are higher in energy, and two *d* orbitals ($d_{x^2-y^2}$ and d_{z^2}) are lower in energy (Figure 26.17▼). Almost all tetrahedral complexes are high-spin because of reduced ligand–metal interactions. The *d* orbitals in a tetrahedral complex interact with only four ligands, as opposed to six in the octahedral complex, so the value of Δ is generally smaller.

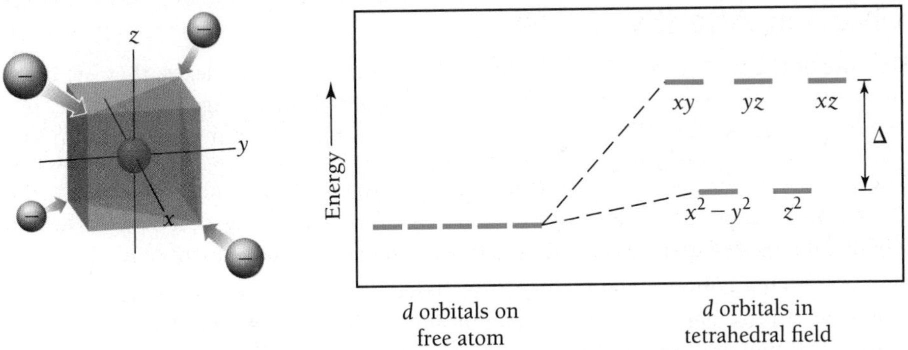

◀ **FIGURE 26.17 Splitting of *d* Orbitals by a Tetrahedral Ligand Geometry** In tetrahedral complexes, the splitting of the *d* orbitals has a pattern that is the opposite of the octahedral splitting pattern. The d_{xy}, d_{yz}, and d_{xz} orbitals are higher in energy than the d_{z^2} and $d_{x^2-y^2}$ orbitals.

A square planar complex gives us the most complex splitting pattern of the three geometries (Figure 26.18▼). As we discussed previously, square planar complexes occur in d^8 metal ions, such as Pt^{2+}, Pd^{2+}, Ir^+, or Au^{3+}, and they are low-spin in nearly all cases.

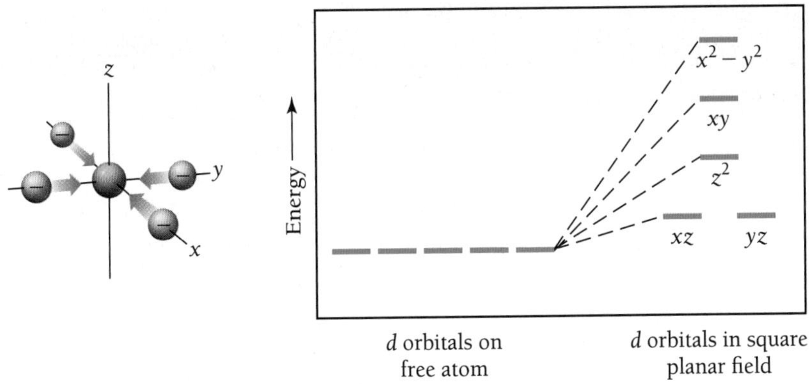

◀ **FIGURE 26.18 Splitting of *d* Orbitals by a Square Planar Ligand Geometry** Square planar complexes produce the *d* orbital energy pattern shown here.

26.6 Applications of Coordination Compounds

Coordination compounds are found in living systems, in industry, and even in household products. Recall from Chapter 25 how silver and gold metals are extracted from their respective ores using cyanide complexes and how nickel metal is extracted by forming the gaseous carbonyl complex, $Ni(CO)_4$. In this section, we describe a few additional applications of coordination compounds.

Chelating Agents

In Section 26.3, we introduced the chelating agent ethylenediaminetetraacetate ion ($EDTA^{4-}$). This ligand has lone pairs on six different donor atoms that can interact with a metal ion to form very stable metal complexes. EDTA is used to treat victims of heavy metal poisoning such as lead poisoning. The patient is given $[Ca(EDTA)]^{2-}$ and because the lead complex ($K_f = 2 \times 10^{18}$) is more stable than the calcium complex ($K_f = 4 \times 10^{10}$), the lead displaces the calcium. The body excretes the lead complex and leaves behind the calcium, which is nontoxic (and is in fact a nutrient).

(a) (b)

▲ **FIGURE 26.19 Chemical Analysis with SCN^-** **(a)** Blue indicates Co^{2+}. **(b)** Red indicates Fe^{3+}.

Chemical Analysis

Some ligands are selective in their binding, preferring specific metal ions; these ligands can be used in chemical analysis. For example, dimethylglyoxime (dmg) is used to chemically analyze a sample for Ni^{2+} or Pd^{2+}. In the presence of Ni^{2+}, an insoluble red precipitate forms, and in the presence of Pd^{2+}, an insoluble yellow precipitate forms. Similarly, the SCN^- ligand is used to test for Co^{2+} or Fe^{3+}. In the presence of Co^{2+} a blue solution forms, and in the presence of Fe^{3+} a deep red solution forms (Figure 26.19◀).

Coloring Agents

Because of the wide variety of colors found in coordination complexes, they are often used as coloring agents. For example, a commercially available agent, iron blue, is a mixture of the hexacyano complexes of iron(II) and iron(III). Iron blue is used in ink, paint, cosmetics (eye shadow), and blueprints.

Biomolecules

Living systems contain many molecules based on metal complexes. Hemoglobin (involved in oxygen transport), cytochrome c (involved in electron transport), carbonic anhydrase (involved in respiration), and chlorophyll (involved in photosynthesis) all have coordinated metal ions that are critical to their structure and function. Table 26.7 summarizes the biological significance of many of the other first-row transition metals.

TABLE 26.7 ■ Transition Metals and Some of Their Functions in the Human Body

Transition Metal	Biological Function
Chromium	Works with insulin to control utilization of glucose
Manganese	Fat and carbohydrate synthesis
Molybdenum	Involved in hemoglobin synthesis
Iron	Oxygen transport
Copper	Involved in hemoglobin synthesis
Zinc	Involved in cell reproduction and tissue growth; part of more than 70 enzymes; assists in the utilization of carbohydrate, protein, and fat

Hemoglobin and Cytochrome C

In hemoglobin and in cytochrome c, an iron complex called a heme is connected to a protein, as shown in the accompanying figure. A heme is an iron ion coordinated to a flat,

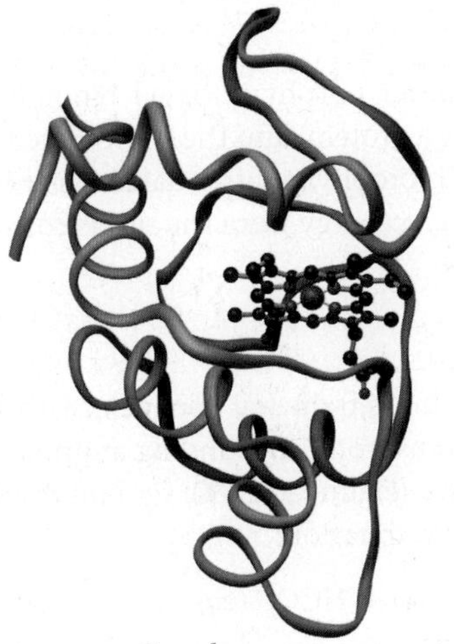

Cytochrome c

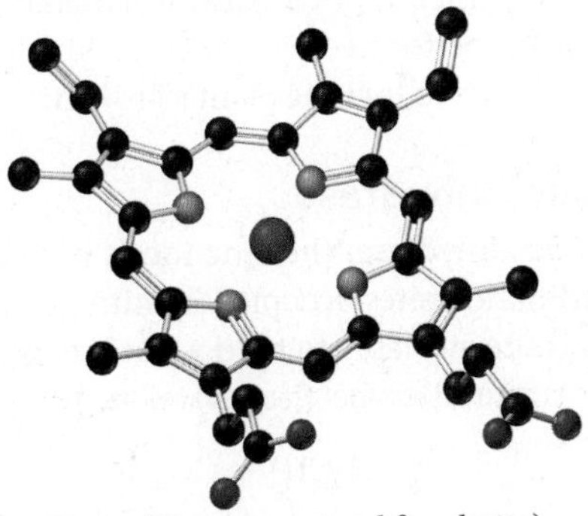

Heme (H atoms omitted for clarity)

polydentate ligand called a porphyrin (Figure 26.20▼). The porphyrin ligand has a planar ring structure with four nitrogen atoms that can coordinate to the metal ion. Different porphyrins have different substituent groups connected around the outside of the ring.

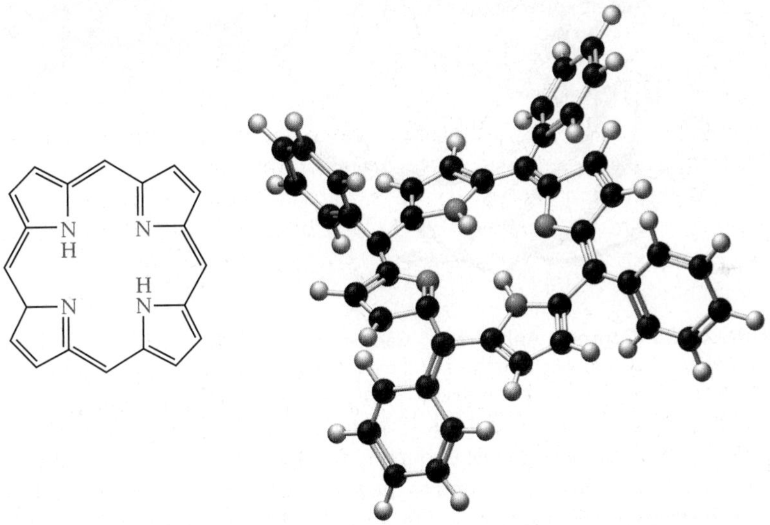

◀ **FIGURE 26.20 Porphyrin** A porphyrin has four nitrogen atoms that can coordinate to a central metal atom.

In hemoglobin, the iron complex is octahedral, with the four nitrogen atoms of the porphyrin in a square planar arrangement around the metal. A nitrogen atom from a nearby amino acid of the protein occupies the fifth coordination site, and either O_2 or H_2O occupies the last coordination site (Figure 26.21▶). In the lungs, where the oxygen content is high, the hemoglobin

Hemoglobin is discussed in Section 16.1.

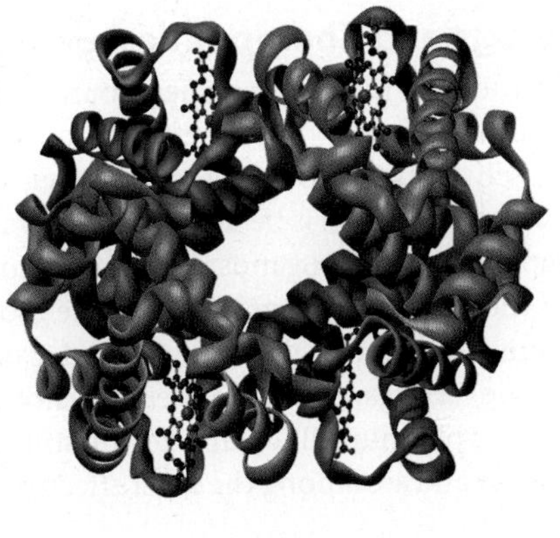

Hemoglobin

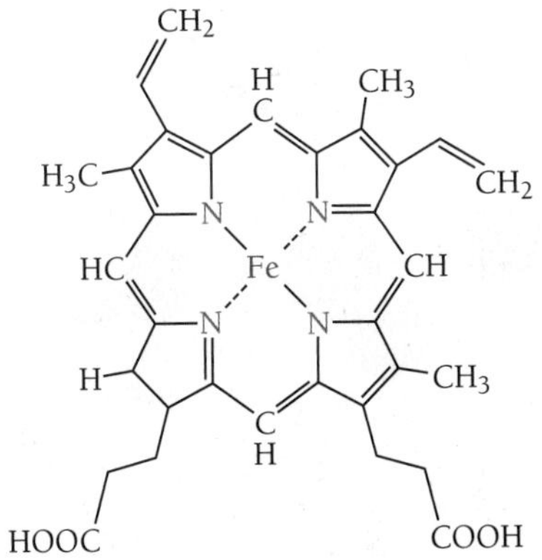

Heme structure

▶ **FIGURE 26.21 Hemoglobin** In hemoglobin, the iron complex is octahedral, with the four nitrogen atoms of the porphyrin in a square planar arrangement around the metal. A nitrogen atom from a nearby amino acid of the protein occupies the fifth coordination site, and either O_2 or H_2O occupies the last coordination site.

coordinates to an O_2 molecule. The oxygen-rich hemoglobin is carried by the bloodstream to areas throughout the body that are depleted in oxygen, where oxygen is released and replaced by a water molecule. The hemoglobin then travels back to the lungs to repeat the cycle.

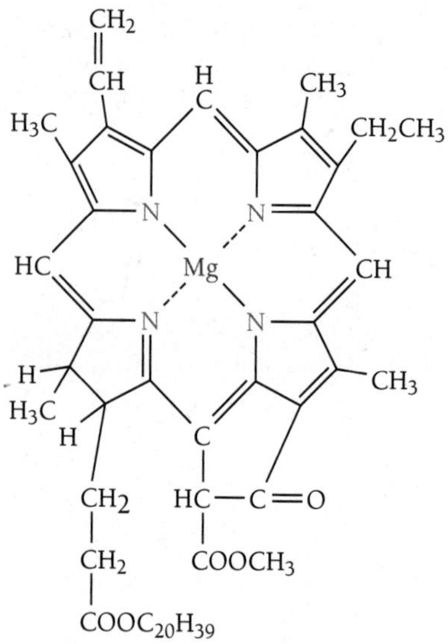

▲ FIGURE 26.22 Chlorophyll Chlorophyll, involved in photosynthesis in plants, contains magnesium coordinated to a porphyrin.

Chlorophyll

Chlorophyll, shown in Figure 26.22◀, is another porphyrin-based biomolecule. In chlorophyll the porphyrin is not surrounded by a protein, and the coordinated metal is magnesium (which is not a transition metal). Chlorophyll is essential for the photosynthesis process performed by plants, in which light energy from the sun is converted to chemical energy to fuel the plant's growth.

Carbonic Anhydrase

In carbonic anhydrase, the zinc ion is bound in a tetrahedral complex, with three of the coordination sites occupied by nitrogen atoms from surrounding amino acids and the fourth site available to bind a water molecule (Figure 26.23▼). Carbonic anhydrase catalyzes the reaction between water and CO_2 in respiration:

$$H_2O(l) + CO_2(g) \rightleftharpoons H^+(aq) + HCO_3^-(aq)$$

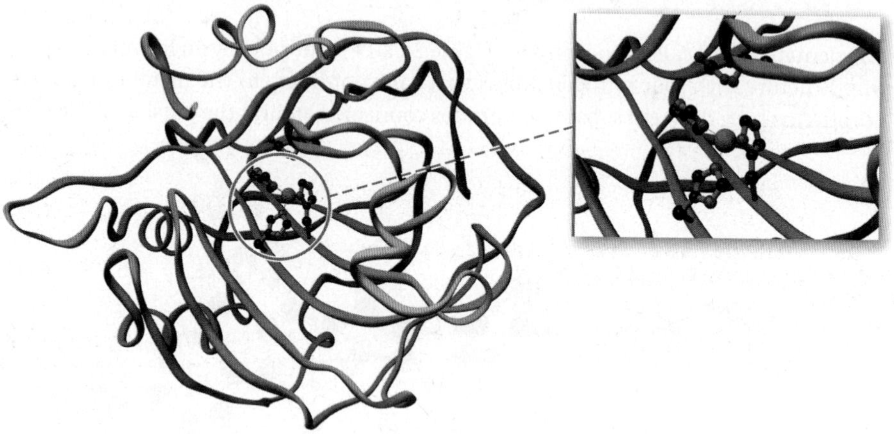

▲ FIGURE 26.23 Carbonic Anhydrase Carbonic anhydrase contains a zinc ion that is bound in a tetrahedral complex, with three of the coordination sites occupied by nitrogen atoms from surrounding amino acids. The fourth site is available to bind a water molecule.

A water molecule alone is not acidic enough to react with a CO_2 molecule at a sufficient rate. When the water molecule is bound to the zinc ion in carbonic anhydrase, the positive charge on the metal draws electron density from the O—H bond and the H_2O becomes more acidic—sufficiently so to readily lose a proton. The resulting bound OH^- easily reacts with a CO_2 molecule, and the reaction is much faster than the uncatalyzed version.

Drugs and Therapeutic Agents

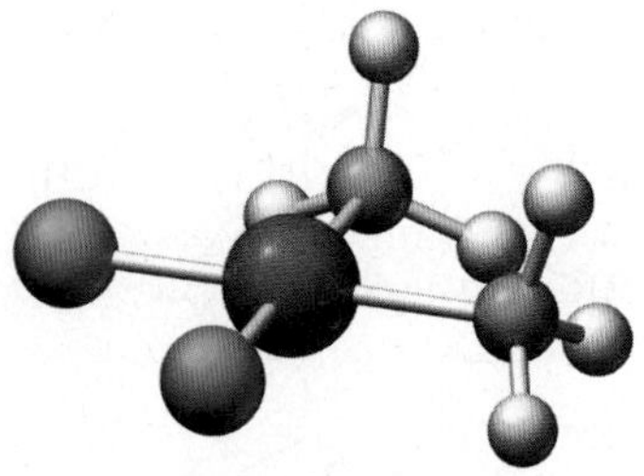

▲ FIGURE 26.24 Cisplatin Cisplatin is an effective anticancer agent.

In the mid-1960s, researchers found that the platinum(II) complex *cis*-$[Pt(NH_3)_2Cl_2]$, known as cisplatin, is an effective anticancer agent (Figure 26.24◀). Interestingly, the closely related geometric isomer *trans*-$[Pt(NH_3)_2Cl_2]$ has little or no effect on cancer tumors. Cisplatin is believed to function by attaching itself to the cancer cell's DNA and replacing the Cl^- ligands with donor atoms from the DNA strands. The cis arrangement of the Cl^- ligands corresponds to the geometry required to bind to the DNA strands. The trans isomer, though closely related, cannot bind properly because of the arrangement of the Cl^- ligands and is therefore not an effective agent. Cisplatin and other closely related platinum(II) complexes are still used today in chemotherapy for certain types of cancer and are among the most effective anticancer agents available for these cases.

Self-Assessment Quiz

Q1. What is the electron configuration of the Cu^+ ion?
MISSED THIS? *Read Section 26.2*

a) $[Ar]4s^2 3d^9$
b) $[Ar]4s^2 3d^8$
c) $[Ar]4s^1 3d^9$
d) $[Ar]4s^0 3d^{10}$

Q2. Which metal has the highest first ionization energy?
MISSED THIS? *Read Section 26.2*

a) Ti b) Mn c) Ru d) Au

Q3. What is the name of the compound $[CoCl(NH_3)_5]Cl_2$?
MISSED THIS? *Read Section 26.3*

a) pentaamminetrichlorocobalt(III) chloride
b) pentaamminechlorocobalt(III) chloride
c) pentaamminechlorocobalt(II) chloride
d) pentaamminetrichlorocobalt(II) chloride

Q4. What is the formula of hexaaquamanganese(II) sulfate?
MISSED THIS? *Read Section 26.3*

a) $[Mn(OH)_6]SO_4$
b) $[Mn(H_2O)_6]SO_4$
c) $[Mn(H_2O)_6]_2SO_4$
d) $[Mn_2(H_2O)_6]SO_4$

Q5. Which complex ion can exhibit cis-trans isomerism? Assume that M is the metal ion, A and B are ligands, and the geometry is octahedral.
MISSED THIS? *Read Section 26.4*

a) $[MA_6]^{2+}$
b) $[MA_5B]^{2+}$
c) $[MA_4B_2]^{2+}$
d) $[MA_3B_3]^{2+}$

Q6. Pick the optical isomer of the complex ion represented here:
MISSED THIS? *Read Section 26.4*

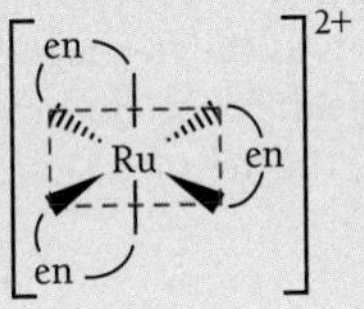

(a)
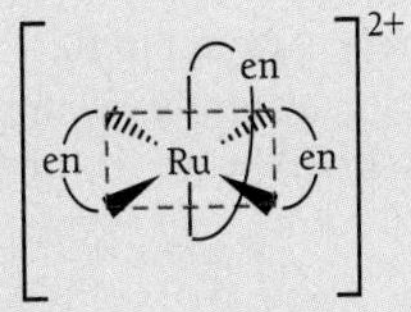

(b)
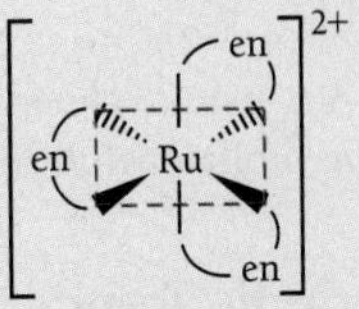

(c)
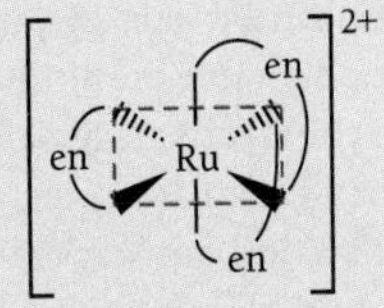

(d)
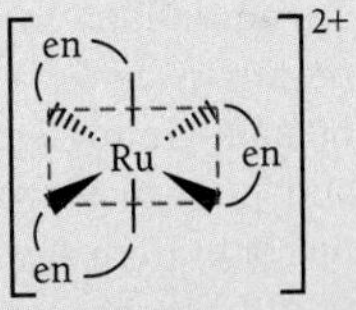

Q7. According to valence bond theory, what is the hybridization of the central metal ion in an octahedral complex ion?
MISSED THIS? *Read Section 26.5*

a) *sp* b) sp^3 c) dsp^2 d) d^2sp^3

Q8. Estimate the crystal field splitting energy (in kJ/mol) for a complex ion that is red in solution.
MISSED THIS? *Read Section 26.5*

a) 228 kJ/mol
b) 171 kJ/mol
c) 2.84×10^{-19} kJ/mol
d) 3.79×10^{-19} kJ/mol

Q9. Use crystal field theory to determine the number of unpaired electrons in the complex ion $[Fe(CN)_6]^{4-}$.
MISSED THIS? *Read Section 26.5*

a) 0 b) 2 c) 3 d) 4

Q10. Which complex ion is diamagnetic?
MISSED THIS? *Read Section 26.5*

a) $[Cr(H_2O)_4Cl_2]^+$
b) $[Fe(H_2O)_6]^{2+}$
c) $[Co(NH_3)_6]^{3+}$
d) $[CoCl_6]^{3-}$

Answers: 1. (d) **2.** (d) **3.** (b) **4.** (b) **5.** (c, d) **6.** (b) **7.** (d) **8.** (a) **9.** (a) **10.** (c)

CHAPTER 26 IN REVIEW

TERMS

Section 26.1
crystal field theory (1136)

Section 26.2
lanthanide contraction (1138)

Section 26.3
complex ion (1140)
ligand (1140)
coordination compound (1140)
primary valence (1140)
secondary valence (1140)
coordination number (1140)
coordinate covalent bond (1141)
monodentate (1142)
bidentate (1142)
polydentate (1142)
chelate (1142)
chelating agent (1142)

Section 26.4
structural isomers (1145)
stereoisomers (1145)
coordination isomers (1145)
linkage isomers (1145)
geometric isomers (1147)
optical isomers (1148)

Section 26.5
strong-field complex (1151)
weak-field complex (1151)
low-spin complex (1154)
high-spin complex (1154)

CONCEPTS

Electron Configurations (26.2)

- As we move across a row of transition elements, electrons add to the $(n-1)d$ orbitals, resulting in a general electron configuration for the first- and second-row transition elements of [noble gas] $ns^2(n-1)d^x$ and for the third and fourth rows of [noble gas] $ns^2(n-2)f^{14}(n-1)d^x$, where x ranges from 1 to 10.
- A transition element forms a cation by losing electrons from the ns orbitals before losing electrons from the $(n-1)d$ orbitals.

Periodic Trends (26.2)

- The variations in atomic size, ionization energy, and electronegativity across a row in the periodic table are similar to those of main-group elements (although the trends are less pronounced and less regular). As we move down a group, however, atomic size increases from the first row to the second but stays roughly constant from the second row to the third because of the lanthanide contraction. This contraction results in ionization energy and electronegativity trends as we move down a column that are opposite of the main-group elements.

Composition and Naming of Coordination Compounds (26.3)

- A coordination compound is composed of a complex ion and a counterion.
- A complex ion contains a central metal ion bound to one or more ligands. The number of ligands directly bound to the metal ion is the coordination number.
- The ligand forms a coordinate covalent bond to the metal ion by donating a pair of electrons to an empty orbital on the metal.
- Ligands that donate a single pair of electrons are monodentate. A ligand that donates two pairs of electrons is bidentate, and a ligand that donates more than two pairs is polydentate.
- In naming coordination compounds, we use the name of the cation followed by the name of the anion. To name a complex ion, we use the guidelines outlined in Section 26.3.

Types of Isomers (26.4)

- We broadly divide the isomerism observed in coordination compounds into two categories: structural isomers, in which atoms are connected differently to one another, and stereoisomers, in which atoms are connected in the same way but the ligands have a different spatial arrangement about the metal atom.
- Structural isomers are either coordination isomers (a coordinated ligand exchanges places with an uncoordinated counterion) or linkage isomers (a particular ligand has the ability to coordinate to the metal in different ways).
- Stereoisomers are either geometric isomers (the ligands bonded to the metal have a different spatial arrangement relative to each other, leading to cis–trans or fac–mer isomers) or optical isomers (nonsuperimposable mirror images).

Crystal Field Theory (26.5)

- Crystal field theory is a bonding model for transition metal complex ions. The model describes how the degeneracy of the d orbitals is broken by the repulsive forces between the electrons on the ligands around the metal ion and the d orbitals in the metal ion.
- The energy difference between the split d orbitals is the crystal field splitting energy (Δ). The magnitude of Δ depends in large part on the ligands bound to the metal.
- Octahedral complexes with a d^4, d^5, d^6, or d^7 metal ion can have two possible electronic configurations with different numbers of unpaired electrons. The first, called high-spin, has the same number of unpaired electrons as the free metal ion and is usually the result of a weak crystal field. The second, called low-spin, has fewer unpaired electrons than the free metal ion and is usually the result of a strong crystal field.

EQUATIONS AND RELATIONSHIPS

Crystal Field Splitting Energy (**26.5**)

$\Delta = hc/\lambda$ (where λ is the wavelength of maximum absorption)

LEARNING OUTCOMES

Chapter Objectives	Assessment
Write electron configurations for transition elements (**26.2**)	Examples 26.1, 26.2 **For Practice** 26.1, 26.2 **Exercises** 17–20
Name and write formulas for complex ions and coordination compounds (**26.3**)	Examples 26.3, 26.4 **For Practice** 26.3, 26.4 **Exercises** 21–28
Identify and draw geometric isomers (**26.4**)	Examples 26.5, 26.6 **For Practice** 26.5, 26.6 **Exercises** 29–36
Identify and draw optical isomers (**26.4**)	Example 26.7 **For Practice** 26.7 **Exercises** 37–40
Calculate crystal field splitting energy (**26.5**)	Example 26.8 **For Practice** 26.8 **Exercises** 43–46
Predict high-spin and low-spin octahedral complex ions (**26.5**)	Examples 26.9, 26.10 **For Practice** 26.9, 26.10 **Exercises** 41–42, 47–52
Describe applications of coordination compounds (**26.6**)	**Exercises** 53–56

EXERCISES

Mastering Chemistry provides end-of-chapter exercises, feedback-enriched tutorial problems, animations, and interactive activities to encourage problem-solving practice and deeper understanding of key concepts and topics.

REVIEW QUESTIONS

1. When a transition metal atom forms an ion, which electrons are lost first?
2. Explain why transition metals exhibit multiple oxidation states instead of a single oxidation state (like most of the main-group metals).
3. Why is the +2 oxidation state so common for transition metals?
4. Explain why atomic radii of elements in the third row of the transition metals are no larger than those of elements in the second row.
5. Gold is the most electronegative transition metal. Explain.
6. Briefly define each term.
   a. coordination number
   b. ligand
   c. bidentate and polydentate
   d. complex ion
   e. chelating agent
7. Using the Lewis acid–base definition, how would you categorize a ligand? How would you categorize a transition metal ion?
8. Explain the differences between each pair of isomer types.
   a. structural isomer and stereoisomer
   b. linkage isomer and coordination isomer
   c. geometric isomer and optical isomer
9. Which complex ion geometry has the potential to exhibit cis–trans isomerism: linear, tetrahedral, square planar, octahedral?
10. How can you tell whether a complex ion is optically active?
11. Explain the differences between weak-field and strong-field metal complexes.
12. Explain why compounds of Sc^{3+} are colorless, but compounds of Ti^{3+} are colored.
13. Explain why compounds of Zn^{2+} are colorless, but compounds of Cu^{2+} are often blue or green.
14. Explain the differences between high-spin and low-spin metal complexes.
15. Why are almost all tetrahedral complexes high-spin?
16. Many transition metal compounds are colored. How does crystal field theory account for this?

PROBLEMS BY TOPIC

Properties of Transition Metals

17. Write the ground state electron configuration for each atom and ion pair. **MISSED THIS?** *Read Section 26.2*
    a. Ni, Ni^{2+} b. Mn, Mn^{4+} c. Y, Y^{+} d. Ta, Ta^{2+}
18. Write the ground state electron configuration for each atom and ion pair.
    a. Zr, Zr^{2+} b. Co, Co^{2+} c. Tc, Tc^{3+} d. Os, Os^{4+}
19. Determine the highest possible oxidation state for each element. **MISSED THIS?** *Read Section 26.2*
    a. V b. Re c. Pd
20. Which first-row transition metal(s) has the following highest possible oxidation state?
    a. +3 b. +7 c. +4

Coordination Compounds

21. Determine the oxidation state and coordination number of the metal ion in each complex ion. **MISSED THIS?** *Read Section 26.3*
    a. $[Cr(H_2O)_6]^{3+}$ b. $[Co(NH_3)_3Cl_3]^{-}$
    c. $[Cu(CN)_4]^{2-}$ d. $[Ag(NH_3)_2]^{+}$
22. Determine the oxidation state and coordination number of the metal ion in each complex ion.
    a. $[Co(NH_3)_5Br]^{2+}$ b. $[Fe(CN)_6]^{4-}$
    c. $[Co(ox)_3]^{4-}$ d. $[PdCl_4]^{2-}$
23. Name each complex ion or coordination compound. **MISSED THIS?** *Read Section 26.3*
    a. $[Cr(H_2O)_6]^{3+}$ b. $[Cu(CN)_4]^{2-}$
    c. $[Fe(NH_3)_5Br]SO_4$ d. $[Co(H_2O)_4(NH_3)(OH)]Cl_2$
24. Name each complex ion or coordination compound.
    a. $[Cu(en)_2]^{2+}$ b. $[Mn(CO)_3(NO_2)_3]^{2+}$
    c. $Na[Cr(H_2O)_2(ox)_2]$ d. $[Co(en)_3][Fe(CN)_6]$
25. Write the formula for each complex ion or coordination compound. **MISSED THIS?** *Read Section 26.3*
    a. hexaamminechromium(III)
    b. potassium hexacyanoferrate(III)
    c. ethylenediaminedithiocyanatocopper(II)
    d. tetraaquaplatinum(II) hexachloroplatinate(IV)
26. Write the formula for each complex ion or coordination compound.
    a. hexaaquanickel(II) chloride
    b. pentacarbonylchloromanganese(I)
    c. ammonium diaquatetrabromovanadate(III)
    d. tris(ethylenediamine)cobalt(III) trioxalatoferrate(III)
27. Write the formula and the name of each complex ion. **MISSED THIS?** *Read Section 26.3*
    a. a complex ion with Co^{3+} as the central ion and three NH_3 molecules and three CN^- ions as ligands
    b. a complex ion with Cr^{3+} as the central ion and a coordination number of 6 with ethylenediamine ligands
28. Write the formula and the name of each complex ion or coordination compound.
    a. a complex ion with four water molecules and two ONO^- ions connected to an Fe(III) ion
    b. a coordination compound made of two complex ions: one a complex of V(III) with two ethylenediamine molecules and two Cl^- ions as ligands and the other a complex of Ni(II) having a coordination number of 4 with Cl^- ions as ligands

Structure and Isomerism

29. Draw two linkage isomers of $[Mn(NH_3)_5(NO_2)]^{2+}$.
MISSED THIS? *Read Section 26.4*

30. Draw two linkage isomers of $[PtCl_3(SCN)]^{2-}$.

31. Write the formulas and names for the coordination isomers of $[Fe(H_2O)_6]Cl_2$. **MISSED THIS?** *Read Section 26.4*

32. Write the formulas and names for the coordination isomers of $[Co(en)_3][Cr(ox)_3]$.

33. Which complexes exhibit geometric isomerism?
MISSED THIS? *Read Section 26.4*

a. $[Cr(NH_3)_5(OH)]^{2+}$
b. $[Cr(en)_2Cl_2]^{+}$
c. $[Cr(H_2O)(NH_3)_3Cl_2]^{+}$
d. $[Pt(NH_3)Cl_3]^{-}$
e. $[Pt(H_2O)_2(CN)_2]$

34. Which complexes exhibit geometric isomerism?

a. $[Co(H_2O)_2(ox)_2]^{-}$
b. $[Co(en)_3]^{3+}$
c. $[Co(H_2O)_2(NH_3)_2(ox)]^{+}$
d. $[Ni(NH_3)_2(en)]^{2+}$
e. $[Ni(CO)_2Cl_2]$

35. If W, X, Y, and Z are different monodentate ligands, how many geometric isomers are there for each ion?
MISSED THIS? *Read Section 26.4*

a. square planar $[NiWXYZ]^{2+}$
b. tetrahedral $[ZnWXYZ]^{2+}$

36. How many geometric isomers are there for each species?

a. $[Fe(CO)_3Cl_3]$
b. $[Mn(CO)_2Cl_2Br_2]^{+}$

37. Draw the structures and label the type for all the isomers of each ion. **MISSED THIS?** *Read Section 26.4*

a. $[Cr(CO)_3(NH_3)_3]^{3+}$
b. $[Pd(CO)_2(H_2O)Cl]^{+}$

38. Draw the structures and label the type for all the isomers of each species.

a. $[Fe(CO)_4Cl_2]^{+}$
b. $[Pt(en)Cl_2]$

39. Determine if either isomer of $[Cr(NH_3)_2(ox)_2]^{-}$ is optically active.
MISSED THIS? *Read Section 26.4*

40. Determine if either isomer of $[Fe(CO)_3Cl_3]$ is optically active.

Bonding in Coordination Compounds

41. Draw the octahedral crystal field splitting diagram for each metal ion. **MISSED THIS?** *Read Section 26.5*

a. Zn^{2+}
b. Fe^{3+} (high- and low-spin)
c. V^{3+}
d. Co^{2+} (high-spin)

42. Draw the octahedral crystal field splitting diagram for each metal ion.

a. Cr^{3+}
b. Cu^{2+}
c. Mn^{3+} (high- and low-spin)
d. Fe^{2+} (low-spin)

43. The $[CrCl_6]^{3-}$ ion has a maximum in its absorption spectrum at 735 nm. Calculate the crystal field splitting energy (in kJ/mol) for this ion. **MISSED THIS?** *Read Section 26.5*

44. The absorption spectrum of the complex ion $[Rh(NH_3)_6]^{3+}$ has maximum absorbance at 295 nm. Calculate the crystal field splitting energy (in kJ/mol) for this ion.

45. Three complex ions of cobalt(III), $[Co(CN)_6]^{3-}$, $[Co(NH_3)_6]^{3+}$, and $[CoF_6]^{3-}$, absorb light at wavelengths of (in no particular order) 290 nm, 440 nm, and 770 nm. Match each complex ion to the appropriate wavelength absorbed. What color would you expect each solution to be? **MISSED THIS?** *Read Section 26.5*

46. Three bottles of aqueous solutions are discovered in an abandoned lab. The solutions are green, yellow, and purple. It is known that three complex ions of chromium(III) were commonly used in that lab: $[Cr(H_2O)_6]^{3+}$, $[Cr(NH_3)_6]^{3+}$, and $[Cr(H_2O)_4Cl_2]^{+}$. Determine the likely identity of each of the colored solutions.

47. The $[Mn(NH_3)_6]^{2+}$ ion is paramagnetic with five unpaired electrons. The NH_3 ligand is usually a strong-field ligand. Is NH_3 acting as a strong-field ligand in this case?
MISSED THIS? *Read Section 26.5*

48. The complex $[Fe(H_2O)_6]^{2+}$ is paramagnetic. Is the H_2O ligand inducing a strong or weak field?

49. How many unpaired electrons would you expect for each complex ion? **MISSED THIS?** *Read Section 26.5*

a. $[RhCl_6]^{3-}$
b. $[Co(OH)_6]^{4-}$
c. *cis*-$[Fe(en)_2(NO_2)_2]^{+}$

50. How many unpaired electrons would you expect for each complex ion?

a. $[Cr(CN)_6]^{4-}$
b. $[MnF_6]^{4-}$
c. $[Ru(en)_3]^{2+}$

51. How many unpaired electrons would you expect for the complex ion $[CoCl_4]^{2-}$ if it is a tetrahedral shape?
MISSED THIS? *Read Section 26.5*

52. The complex ion $[PdCl_4]^{2-}$ is known to be diamagnetic. Use this information to determine if it is a tetrahedral or square planar structure.

Applications of Coordination Compounds

53. What structural feature do hemoglobin, cytochrome c, and chlorophyll have in common?
MISSED THIS? *Read Section 26.6*

54. Identify the central metal atom in each complex.

a. hemoglobin
b. carbonic anhydrase
c. chlorophyll
d. iron blue

55. Hemoglobin exists in two predominant forms in our bodies. One form, known as oxyhemoglobin, has O_2 bound to the iron and the other, known as deoxyhemoglobin, has a water molecule bound instead. Oxyhemoglobin is a low-spin complex that gives arterial blood its red color, and deoxyhemoglobin is a high-spin complex that gives venous blood its darker color. Explain these observations in terms of crystal field splitting. Would you categorize O_2 as a strong- or weak-field ligand? **MISSED THIS?** *Read Section 26.6*

56. Carbon monoxide and the cyanide ion are both toxic because they bind more strongly than oxygen to the iron in hemoglobin (Hb).

$$Hb + O_2 \rightleftharpoons HbO_2 \qquad K = 2 \times 10^{12}$$

$$Hb + CO \rightleftharpoons HbCO \qquad K = 1 \times 10^{14}$$

Calculate the equilibrium constant value for this reaction:

$$HbO_2 + CO \rightleftharpoons HbCO + O_2$$

Does the equilibrium favor reactants or products?

CUMULATIVE PROBLEMS

57. Recall from Chapter 9 that Cr and Cu are exceptions to the normal orbital filling, resulting in a [Ar] $4s^1 3d^x$ configuration. Write the ground state electron configuration for each species.
a. Cr, Cr^+, Cr^{2+}, Cr^{3+}
b. Cu, Cu^+, Cu^{2+}

58. Most of the second row transition metals do not follow the normal orbital filling pattern. Five of them—Nb, Mo, Ru, Rh, and Ag—have a [Kr] $5s^1 4d^x$ configuration and Pd has a [Kr] $4d^{10}$ configuration. Write the ground state electron configuration for each species.
a. Mo, Mo^+, Ag, Ag^+
b. Ru, Ru^{3+}
c. Rh, Rh^{2+}
d. Pd, Pd^+, Pd^{2+}

59. Draw the Lewis diagrams for each ligand. Indicate the lone pair(s) that may be donated to the metal. Indicate any you expect to be bidentate or polydentate.
a. NH_3 b. SCN^- c. H_2O

60. Draw the Lewis diagrams for each ligand. Indicate the lone pair(s) that may be donated to the metal. Indicate any you expect to be bidentate or polydentate.
a. CN^-
b. bipyridine (bipy), which has the following structure:

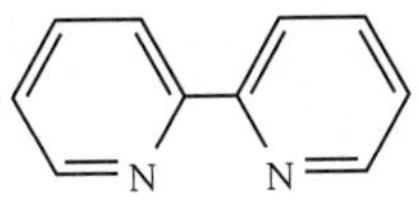

c. NO_2^-

61. List all the different formulas for an octahedral complex made from a metal (M) and three different ligands (A, B, and C). Describe any isomers for each complex.

62. Amino acids, such as glycine (gly), form complexes with the trace metal ions found in the bloodstream. Glycine, whose structure is shown here, acts as a bidentate ligand coordinating with the nitrogen atom and one of the oxygen atoms.

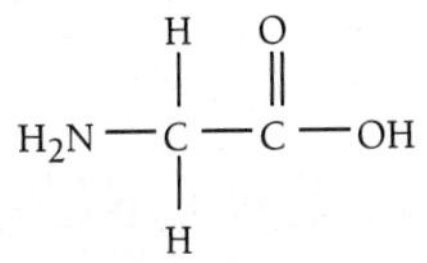

Draw all the possible isomers of:
a. square planar $[Ni(gly)_2]$
b. tetrahedral $[Zn(gly)_2]$
c. octahedral $[Fe(gly)_3]$

63. Oxalic acid solutions remove rust stains. Draw a complex ion that is likely responsible for this effect. Does it have any isomers?

64. W, X, Y, and Z are different monodentate ligands.
a. Is the square planar $[NiWXYZ]^{2+}$ optically active?
b. Is the tetrahedral $[ZnWXYZ]^{2+}$ optically active?

65. Hexacyanomanganate(III) ion is a low-spin complex. Draw the crystal field splitting diagram with electrons filled in appropriately. Is this complex paramagnetic or diamagnetic?

66. Determine the color and approximate wavelength absorbed most strongly by each solution.
a. blue solution b. red solution
c. yellow solution

67. Draw the structures of all the geometric isomers of $[Ru(H_2O)_2(NH_3)_2Cl_2]^+$. Draw the mirror images of any that are chiral.

68. A 0.32 mol amount of NH_3 is dissolved in 0.47 L of a 0.38 M silver nitrate solution. Calculate the equilibrium concentrations of all species in the solution.

CHALLENGE PROBLEMS

69. When a solution of $PtCl_2$ reacts with the ligand trimethylphosphine, $P(CH_3)_3$, two compounds are produced. The compounds share the same elemental analysis: 46.7% Pt; 17.0% Cl; 14.8% P; 17.2% C; 4.34% H. Determine the formula, draw the structure, and give the systematic name for each compound.

70. Draw a crystal field splitting diagram for a trigonal planar complex ion. Assume the plane of the molecule is perpendicular to the *z*-axis.

71. Draw a crystal field splitting diagram for a trigonal bipyramidal complex ion. Assume the axial positions are on the *z*-axis.

72. Explain why $[Ni(NH_3)_4]^{2+}$ is paramagnetic, while $[Ni(CN)_4]^{2-}$ is diamagnetic.

73. Sulfide (S^{2-}) salts are notoriously insoluble in aqueous solution.
a. Calculate the molar solubility of nickel(II) sulfide in water. $K_{sp}(NiS) = 3 \times 10^{-16}$
b. Nickel(II) ions form a complex ion in the presence of ammonia with a formation constant (K_f) of 2.0×10^8: $Ni^{2+} + 6\,NH_3 \rightleftharpoons [Ni(NH_3)_6]^{2+}$. Calculate the molar solubility of NiS in 3.0 M NH_3.
c. Explain any differences between the answers to parts **a** and **b**.

74. Calculate the solubility of $Zn(OH)_2(s)$ in 2.0 M NaOH solution. (*Hint:* You must take into account the formation of $Zn(OH)_4^{2-}$, which has a $K_f = 2 \times 10^{15}$.)

75. Halide complexes of metal M of the form $[MX_6]^{3-}$ are found to be stable in aqueous solution. But it is possible that they undergo rapid ligand exchange with water (or other ligands) that is not detectable because the complexes are less stable. This property is referred to as their *lability*. Suggest an experiment to measure the lability of these complexes that does not employ radioactive labels.

76. The K_f for $[Cu(en)_2]^{2+}$ is much larger than the one for $[Cu(NH_3)_4]^{2+}$. This difference is primarily an entropy effect. Explain why and calculate the difference between the $\Delta S°$ values at 298 K for the complete dissociation of the two complex ions. (*Hint:* The value of ΔH is about the same for both systems.)

77. When solid $Cd(OH)_2$ is added to a solution of 0.10 M NaI, some of it dissolves. Calculate the pH of the solution at equilibrium.

CONCEPTUAL PROBLEMS

78. Two ligands, A and B, both form complexes with a particular metal ion. When the metal ion complexes with ligand A, the solution is green. When the metal ion complexes with ligand B, the solution is violet. Which of the two ligands results in the larger Δ?

79. Which element has the higher ionization energy, Cu or Au?

80. The complexes of Fe^{3+} have magnetic properties that depend on whether the ligands are strong or weak field. Explain why this observation supports the idea that electrons are lost from the 4*s* orbital before the 3*d* orbitals in the transition metals.

QUESTIONS FOR GROUP WORK

Active Classroom Learning

Discuss these questions with the group and record your consensus answer.

81. Choose a row of the transition metals in the periodic table. Have each group member look up and graph (where appropriate) a separate trend for the elements in that row, choosing from electron configuration, atomic size, ionization energy, and electronegativity. Each member should present a graph to the group and describe the general trend and any notable exceptions. If possible, form new groups made up of individuals who researched the same property for different rows of the periodic table.

82. Have each group member write down the names and formulas for two coordination compounds. Taking turns, show each formula to the group and have the rest of the group name the compound, with each member contributing one step in the process. Once all group members have had their formulas named, repeat the process by showing each formula name to the group and having group members determine the correct formula.

83. Working individually, draw a pair of coordination compounds that are isomers. Take turns showing your drawings to the group and have them identify the type of isomerism and the reasons your drawing demonstrates that type of isomerism. If your group misidentifies your type of isomerism, rather than telling them the correct answer right away, point out the part of the structure that prevents it from being the type of isomerism they thought it was.

84. Divide the electron configurations d^1 through d^{10} among the group members so that every configuration is assigned to at least two group members. Working individually, draw the orbital diagram for the configurations assigned to you, including both high-spin and low-spin diagrams where possible. Present your diagrams to your group. Combine everyone's diagrams into one set for the group.

85. Working individually, review one of the applications of coordination complexes. Without referring to the text or mentioning the key words in the heading of the subsection, describe the application you reviewed. As group members each describe the application they reviewed, take turns attempting to identify the key words from the heading of the subsection they are describing.

DATA INTERPRETATION AND ANALYSIS

Qualitative Test for Fe^{3+} Ions in Solution

86. Many aqueous solutions of complex ions display brilliant colors that depend on the identities of the metal ion and ligand(s). Some ligands bind selectively to certain metal ions, producing complex ions with characteristic colors. These distinctive complex ions serve as qualitative indicators for the presence of particular metal ions. For example, Fe^{3+} is identified by the rapid formation of the intensely colored pentaaquathiocyanatoiron(III) complex ion, $[Fe(H_2O)_5SCN]^{2+}$, when thiocyanate, SCN^-, is added to a solution containing hexaaquairon(III), $[Fe(H_2O)_6]^{3+}$, according to the following chemical equation:

$$\underset{\text{pale violet}}{[Fe(H_2O)_6]^{3+}(aq)} + \underset{\text{colorless}}{SCN^-(aq)} \rightleftharpoons \underset{\text{intensely colored}}{[Fe(H_2O)_5SCN]^{2+}(aq)}$$

Examine the absorption spectrum of an aqueous solution of $[Fe(H_2O)_5SCN]^{2+}$ shown here and answer the questions that follow.

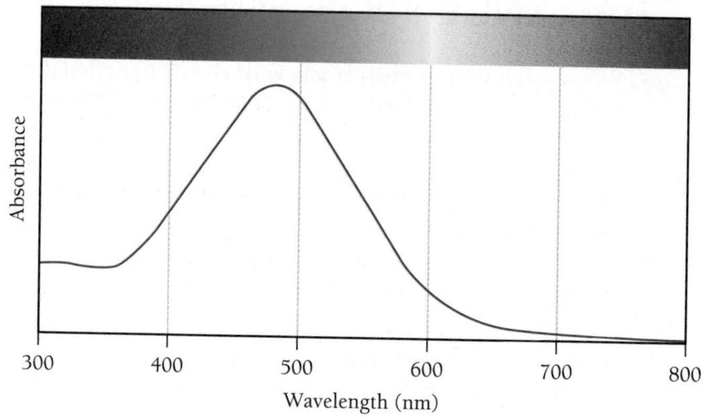

Absorption Spectrum of $[Fe(H_2O)_5SCN]^{2+}$

a. What is the color of the aqueous solution of $[Fe(H_2O)_5SCN]^{2+}$ based on the spectrum?

b. Calculate the crystal field splitting energy, Δ, of $[Fe(H_2O)_5SCN]^{2+}$, in kJ/mol.

c. The hexaaquairon(III) complex ion, $[Fe(H_2O)_6]^{3+}$, produces a pale violet aqueous solution. Is the crystal field splitting energy, Δ, of $[Fe(H_2O)_6]^{3+}$ smaller or larger than the Δ of $[Fe(H_2O)_5SCN]^{2+}$?

d. On the basis of your answers to parts b and c, compare the crystal field strengths of water and thiocyanate ligands.

e. The complex ion hexacyanoferrate(III), $[Fe(CN)_6]^{3-}$, is red in aqueous solution. What can you conclude about the relative crystal field splitting energies of $[Fe(CN)_6]^{3-}$ and $[Fe(H_2O)_5SCN]^{2+}$?

Cc ANSWERS TO CONCEPTUAL CONNECTIONS

Atomic Size

26.1 **(b)** The element W has the larger radius because it is in the third transition row and Fe is in the first. Atomic radii increase from the first to the second transition row and stay roughly constant from the second to the third.

Isomerism

26.2 **(c)** Geometric isomers are two molecules in which the atoms are bonded together in the same way, but with different overall orientations in space. Therefore, geometric isomers are *not* structural isomers.

Weak- and Strong-Field Ligands

26.3 **(b)** Ligand B forms a yellow solution, which means that the complex absorbs in the violet region. Ligand A forms a red solution, which means that the complex absorbs in the green region. Since the violet region of the electromagnetic spectrum is of shorter wavelength (higher energy) than the green region, ligand B produces a higher Δ.

APPENDIX I

Common Mathematical Operations in Chemistry

A. Scientific Notation

A number written in scientific notation consists of a **decimal part**, a number that is usually between 1 and 10, and an **exponential part**, 10 raised to an **exponent**, n:

$$1.2 \times 10^{-10}$$

Exponent (n)

Decimal part — Exponential part

Each of the following numbers is written in both scientific and decimal notation:

$$1.0 \times 10^{5} = 100{,}000 \qquad 1.0 \times 10^{-5} = 0.000010$$

$$6.7 \times 10^{3} = 6700 \qquad 6.7 \times 10^{-3} = 0.0067$$

A positive exponent (n) means 1 multiplied by 10 n times:

$$10^0 = 1$$

$$10^1 = 1 \times 10$$

$$10^2 = 1 \times 10 \times 10 = 100$$

$$10^3 = 1 \times 10 \times 10 \times 10 = 1000$$

A negative exponent ($-n$) means 1 divided by 10 n times:

$$10^{-1} = \frac{1}{10} = 0.1$$

$$10^{-2} = \frac{1}{10 \times 10} = 0.01$$

$$10^{-3} = \frac{1}{10 \times 10 \times 10} = 0.001$$

To convert a number to scientific notation, we move the decimal point to obtain a number between 1 and 10 and then multiply by 10 raised to the appropriate power. For example, to write 5983 in scientific notation, we move the decimal point to the left three places to get 5.983 (a number between 1 and 10) and then multiply by 1000 to make up for moving the decimal point:

$$5983 = 5.983 \times 1000$$

Since 1000 is 10^3, we write:

$$5983 = 5.983 \times 10^3$$

We can do this in one step by counting how many places we move the decimal point to obtain a number between 1 and 10 and then writing the decimal part multiplied by 10 raised to the number of places we moved the decimal point:

$$5983 = 5.983 \times 10^3$$

If the decimal point is moved to the left, as in the previous example, the exponent is positive. If the decimal is moved to the right, the exponent is negative:

$$0.00034 = 3.4 \times 10^{-4}$$

To express a number in scientific notation:

1. Move the decimal point to obtain a number between 1 and 10.
2. Write the result from step 1 multiplied by 10 raised to the number of places you moved the decimal point.
   - *The exponent is positive if you moved the decimal point to the left.*
   - *The exponent is negative if you moved the decimal point to the right.*

Consider the following additional examples:

$$290{,}809{,}000 = 2.90809 \times 10^8$$

$$0.000000000070\text{ m} = 7.0 \times 10^{-11}\text{ m}$$

Multiplication and Division

To multiply numbers expressed in scientific notation, multiply the decimal parts and add the exponents:

$$(A \times 10^m)(B \times 10^n) = (A \times B) \times 10^{m+n}$$

To divide numbers expressed in scientific notation, divide the decimal parts and subtract the exponent in the denominator from the exponent in the numerator:

$$\frac{(A \times 10^m)}{(B \times 10^n)} = \left(\frac{A}{B}\right) \times 10^{m-n}$$

Consider the following example involving multiplication:

$$(3.5 \times 10^4)(1.8 \times 10^6) = (3.5 \times 1.8) \times 10^{4+6}$$

$$= 6.3 \times 10^{10}$$

Consider the following example involving division:

$$\frac{(5.6 \times 10^7)}{(1.4 \times 10^3)} = \left(\frac{5.6}{1.4}\right) \times 10^{7-3}$$

$$= 4.0 \times 10^4$$

Addition and Subtraction

To add or subtract numbers expressed in scientific notation, rewrite all the numbers so that they have the same exponent, then add or subtract the decimal parts of the numbers. The exponents remained unchanged:

$$\begin{array}{r} A \times 10^n \\ \pm B \times 10^n \\ \hline (A \pm B) \times 10^n \end{array}$$

Notice that the numbers *must have* the same exponent. Consider the following example involving addition:

$$\begin{array}{r} 4.82 \times 10^7 \\ \underline{+3.4 \times 10^6} \end{array}$$

First, express both numbers with the same exponent. In this case, you rewrite the lower number and perform the addition as follows:

$$\begin{array}{r} 4.82 \times 10^7 \\ +0.34 \times 10^7 \\ \hline 5.16 \times 10^7 \end{array}$$

Consider the following example involving subtraction:

$$\begin{array}{r} 7.33 \times 10^5 \\ \underline{-1.9 \times 10^4} \end{array}$$

First, express both numbers with the same exponent. In this case, you rewrite the lower number and perform the subtraction as follows:

$$\begin{array}{r} 7.33 \times 10^5 \\ -0.19 \times 10^5 \\ \hline 7.14 \times 10^5 \end{array}$$

Powers and Roots

To raise a number written in scientific notation to a power, raise the decimal part to the power and multiply the exponent by the power:

$$\begin{aligned} (4.0 \times 10^6)^2 &= 4.0^2 \times 10^{6\times 2} \\ &= 16 \times 10^{12} \\ &= 1.6 \times 10^{13} \end{aligned}$$

To take the *n*th root of a number written in scientific notation, take the *n*th root of the decimal part and divide the exponent by the root:

$$\begin{aligned} (4.0 \times 10^6)^{1/3} &= 4.0^{1/3} \times 10^{6/3} \\ &= 1.6 \times 10^2 \end{aligned}$$

B. Logarithms

Common (or Base 10) Logarithms

The common or base 10 logarithm (abbreviated log) of a number is the exponent to which 10 must be raised to obtain that number. For example, the logarithm of 100 is 2 because 10 must be raised to the second power to get 100. Similarly, the logarithm of 1000 is 3 because 10 must be raised to the third power to get 1000. The logarithms of several multiples of 10 are shown here:

$$\log 10 = 1$$

$$\log 100 = 2$$

$$\log 1000 = 3$$

$$\log 10{,}000 = 4$$

Because $10^0 = 1$ by definition, $\log 1 = 0$.

The logarithm of a number smaller than one is negative because 10 must be raised to a negative exponent to get a number smaller than one. For example, the logarithm of 0.01 is −2 because 10 must be raised to −2 to get 0.01. Similarly, the logarithm of 0.001 is −3 because 10 must be raised to −3 to get 0.001. The logarithms of several fractional numbers are shown below:

$$\log 0.1 = -1$$

$$\log 0.01 = -2$$

$$\log 0.001 = -3$$

$$\log 0.0001 = -4$$

The logarithms of numbers that are not multiples of 10 can be computed on your calculator. See your calculator manual for specific instructions.

Inverse Logarithms

The inverse logarithm or invlog function is exactly the opposite of the logarithm function. For example, the logarithm of 100 is 2 and the inverse logarithm of 2 is 100. The logarithm function and the invlog function undo one another:

$$\log 100 = 2$$

$$\text{invlog } 2 = 100$$

$$\text{invlog}(\log 100) = 100$$

The inverse logarithm of a number is 10 rasied to that number:

$$\text{invlog } x = 10^x$$

$$\text{invlog } 3 = 10^3 = 1000$$

The inverse logarithms of numbers can be computed on your calculator. See your calculator manual for specific instructions.

Natural (or Base e) Logarithms

The natural (or base *e*) logarithm (abbreviated ln) of a number is the exponent to which *e* (which has the value of 2.71828...) must be raised to obtain that number. For example, the ln of 100 is 4.605 because *e* must be raised to 4.605 to get 100. Similarly, the ln of 10.0 is 2.303 because *e* must be raised to 2.303 to get 10.0.

The inverse natural logarithm or invln function is exactly the opposite of the ln function. For example, the natural logarithm of 100 is 4.605 and the inverse natural logarithm of 4.605 is 100. The inverse natural logarithm of a number is simply *e* raised to that number:

$$\text{invln } x = e^x$$

$$\text{invln } 3 = e^3 = 20.1$$

The invln of a number can be computed on your calculator. See your calculator manual for specific instructions.

Mathematical Operations Using Logarithms

Because logarithms are exponents, mathematical operations involving logarithms are similar to those involving exponents as follows:

$$\log(a \times b) = \log a + \log b \qquad \ln(a \times b) = \ln a + \ln b$$

$$\log \frac{a}{b} = \log a - \log b \qquad \ln \frac{a}{b} = \ln a - \ln b$$

$$\log a^n = n \log a \qquad \ln a^n = n \ln a$$

C. Quadratic Equations

A quadratic equation contains at least one term in which the variable x is raised to the second power (and no terms in which x is raised to a higher power). A quadratic equation has the following general form:

$$ax^2 + bx + c = 0$$

A quadratic equation can be solved for x using the quadratic formula:

$$x = \frac{-b \pm \sqrt{b^2 - 4ac}}{2a}$$

Quadratic equations are often encountered when solving equilibrium problems. Here we show how to use the quadratic formula to solve a quadratic equation for x:

$$3x^2 - 5x + 1 = 0 \quad (\textit{quadratic equation})$$

$$x = \frac{-b \pm \sqrt{b^2 - 4ac}}{2a}$$

$$= \frac{-(-5) \pm \sqrt{(-5)^2 - 4(3)(1)}}{2(3)}$$

$$= \frac{5 \pm 3.6}{6}$$

$$x = 1.43 \quad \text{or} \quad x = 0.233$$

As you can see, the solution to a quadratic equation usually has two values. In any real chemical system, one of the values can be eliminated because it has no physical significance. (For example, it may correspond to a negative concentration, which does not exist.)

D. Graphs

Graphs are often used to visually show the relationship between two variables. For example, in Chapter 5 we show the following relationship between the volume of a gas and its pressure:

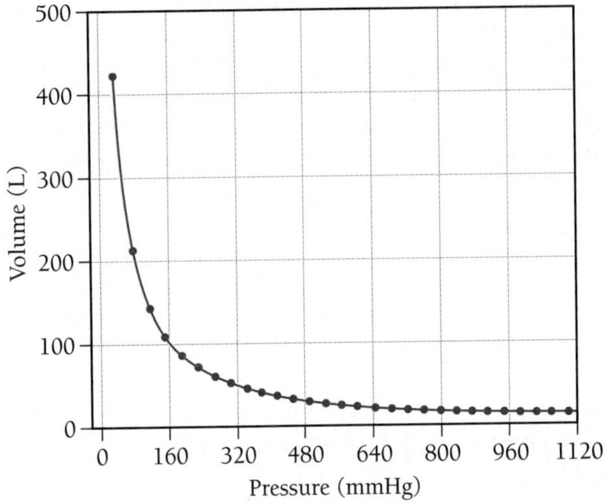

▲ **Volume versus Pressure** A plot of the volume of a gas sample—as measured in a J-tube—versus pressure. The plot shows that volume and pressure are inversely related.

The horizontal axis is the x-axis and is normally used to show the independent variable. The vertical axis is the y-axis and is normally used to show how the other variable (called the dependent variable) varies with a change in the independent variable. In this case, the graph shows that as the pressure of a gas sample increases, its volume decreases.

Many relationships in chemistry are *linear*, which means that if you change one variable by a factor of n the other variable will also change by a factor of n. For example, the volume of a gas is linearly related to the number of moles of gas. When two quantities are linearly related, a graph of one versus the other produces a straight line. For example, the graph below shows how the volume of an ideal gas sample depends on the number of moles of gas in the sample:

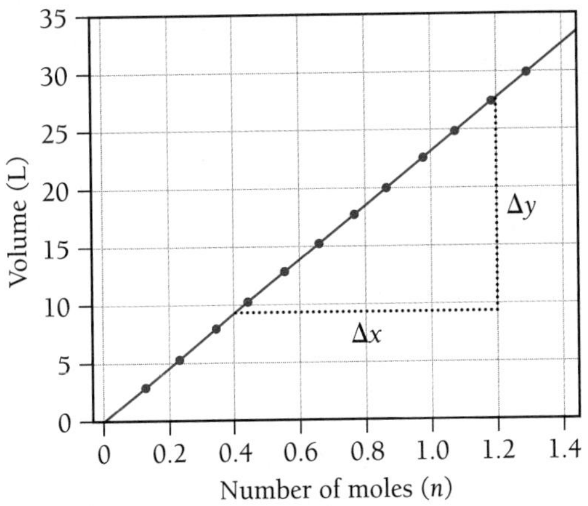

▲ **Volume versus Number of Moles** The volume of a gas sample increases linearly with the number of moles of gas in the sample.

A linear relationship between any two variables x and y can be expressed by the following equation:

$$y = mx + b$$

where m is the slope of the line and b is the y-intercept. The slope is the change in y divided by the change in x:

$$m = \frac{\Delta y}{\Delta x}$$

For the graph above, we can estimate the slope by simply estimating the changes in y and x for a given interval. For example, between $x = 0.4$ mol and 1.2 mol, $\Delta x = 0.80$ mol and we can estimate that $\Delta y = 18$ L. Therefore the slope is:

$$m = \frac{\Delta y}{\Delta x} = \frac{18\ \text{L}}{0.80\ \text{mol}} = 23\ \text{mol/L}$$

In several places in this book, logarithmic relationships between variables can be plotted in order to obtain a linear relationship. For example, the variables $[A]_t$ and t in the following equation are not linearly related, but the natural logarithm of $[A]_t$ and t are linearly related:

$$\ln[A]_t = -kt + \ln[A]_0$$

$$y = mx + b$$

A plot of $\ln[A]_t$ versus t will therefore produce a straight line with slope $= -k$ and y-intercept $= \ln[A]_0$.

APPENDIX II Useful Data

A. Atomic Colors

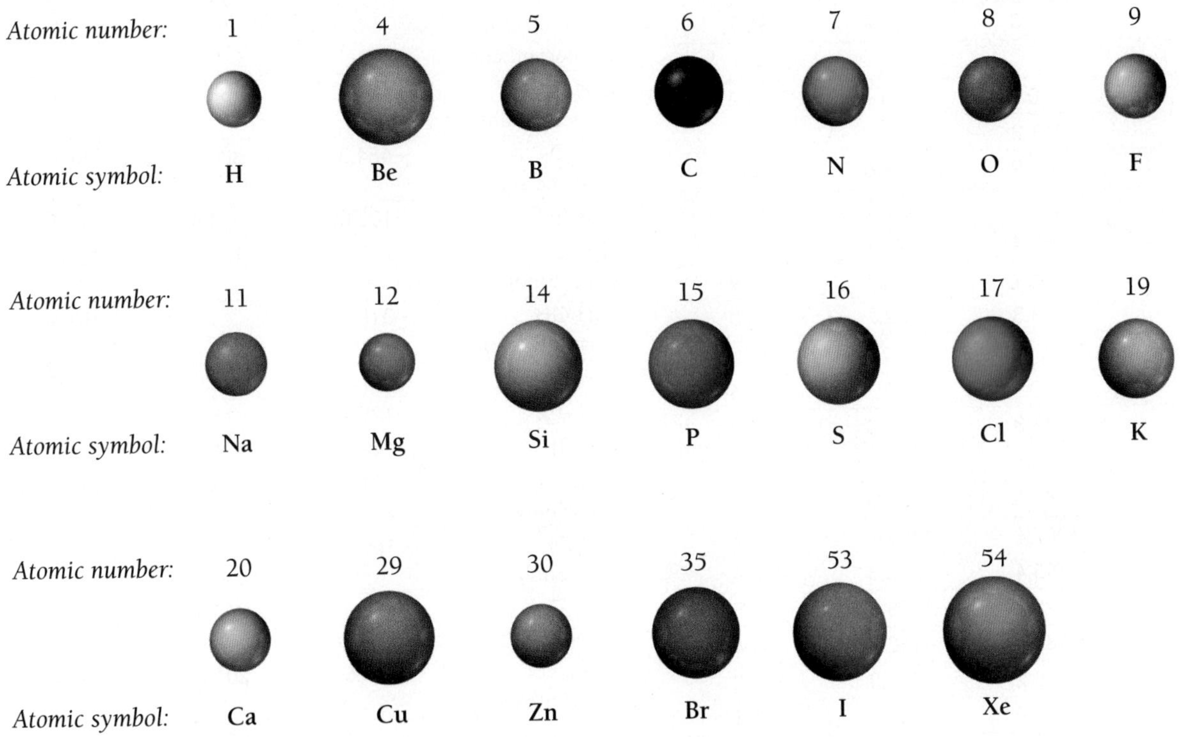

B. Standard Thermodynamic Quantities for Selected Substances at 25 °C

Substance	ΔH°_f(kJ/mol)	ΔG°_f(kJ/mol)	S°(J/mol · K)
Aluminum			
Al(*s*)	0	0	28.32
Al(*g*)	330.0	289.4	164.6
Al^{3+}(*aq*)	−538.4	−483	−325
$AlCl_3$(*s*)	−704.2	−628.8	109.3
Al_2O_3(*s*)	−1675.7	−1582.3	50.9
Barium			
Ba(*s*)	0	0	62.5
Ba(*g*)	180.0	146.0	170.2
Ba^{2+}(*aq*)	−537.6	−560.8	9.6
$BaCO_3$(*s*)	−1213.0	−1134.4	112.1
$BaCl_2$(*s*)	−855.0	−806.7	123.7
BaO(*s*)	−548.0	−520.3	72.1
$Ba(OH)_2$(*s*)	−944.7		
$BaSO_4$(*s*)	−1473.2	−1362.2	132.2

Substance	ΔH°_f(kJ/mol)	ΔG°_f(kJ/mol)	S°(J/mol · K)
Beryllium			
Be(*s*)	0	0	9.5
BeO(*s*)	−609.4	−580.1	13.8
$Be(OH)_2$(*s*)	−902.5	−815.0	45.5
Bismuth			
Bi(*s*)	0	0	56.7
$BiCl_3$(*s*)	−379.1	−315.0	177.0
Bi_2O_3(*s*)	−573.9	−493.7	151.5
Bi_2S_3(*s*)	−143.1	−140.6	200.4
Boron			
B(*s*)	0	0	5.9
B(*g*)	565.0	521.0	153.4
BCl_3(*g*)	−403.8	−388.7	290.1
BF_3(*g*)	−1136.0	−1119.4	254.4
B_2H_6(*g*)	36.4	87.6	232.1

—(*Continued on the next page*)

Substance	ΔH_f°(kJ/mol)	ΔG_f°(kJ/mol)	S°(J/mol·K)
$B_2O_3(s)$	−1273.5	−1194.3	54.0
$H_3BO_3(s)$	−1094.3	−968.9	90.0
Bromine			
$Br(g)$	111.9	82.4	175.0
$Br_2(l)$	0	0	152.2
$Br_2(g)$	30.9	3.1	245.5
$Br^-(aq)$	−121.4	−102.8	80.71
$HBr(g)$	−36.3	−53.4	198.7
Cadmium			
$Cd(s)$	0	0	51.8
$Cd(g)$	111.8	77.3	167.7
$Cd^{2+}(aq)$	−75.9	−77.6	−73.2
$CdCl_2(s)$	−391.5	−343.9	115.3
$CdO(s)$	−258.4	−228.7	54.8
$CdS(s)$	−161.9	−156.5	64.9
$CdSO_4(s)$	−933.3	−822.7	123.0
Calcium			
$Ca(s)$	0	0	41.6
$Ca(g)$	177.8	144.0	154.9
$Ca^{2+}(aq)$	−542.8	−553.6	−53.1
$CaC_2(s)$	−59.8	−64.9	70.0
$CaCO_3(s)$	−1207.6	−1129.1	91.7
$CaCl_2(s)$	−795.4	−748.8	108.4
$CaF_2(s)$	−1228.0	−1175.6	68.5
$CaH_2(s)$	−181.5	−142.5	41.4
$Ca(NO_3)_2(s)$	−938.2	−742.8	193.2
$CaO(s)$	−634.9	−603.3	38.1
$Ca(OH)_2(s)$	−985.2	−897.5	83.4
$CaSO_4(s)$	−1434.5	−1322.0	106.5
$Ca_3(PO_4)_2(s)$	−4120.8	−3884.7	236.0
Carbon			
C(s, graphite)	0	0	5.7
C(s, diamond)	1.88	2.9	2.4
$C(g)$	716.7	671.3	158.1
$CH_4(g)$	−74.6	−50.5	186.3
$CH_3Cl(g)$	−81.9	−60.2	234.6
$CH_2Cl_2(g)$	−95.4		270.2
$CH_2Cl_2(l)$	−124.2	−63.2	177.8
$CHCl_3(l)$	−134.1	−73.7	201.7
$CCl_4(g)$	−95.7	−62.3	309.7
$CCl_4(l)$	−128.2	−66.4	216.4
$CH_2O(g)$	−108.6	−102.5	218.8
CH_2O_2 (*l*, formic acid)	−425.0	−361.4	129.0
CH_3NH_2 (*g*, methylamine)	−22.5	32.7	242.9
$CH_3OH(l)$	−238.6	−166.6	126.8
$CH_3OH(g)$	−201.0	−162.3	239.9

Substance	ΔH_f°(kJ/mol)	ΔG_f°(kJ/mol)	S°(J/mol·K)
$C_2H_2(g)$	227.4	209.9	200.9
$C_2H_4(g)$	52.4	68.4	219.3
$C_2H_6(g)$	−84.68	−32.0	229.2
$C_2H_5OH(l)$	−277.6	−174.8	160.7
$C_2H_5OH(g)$	−234.8	−167.9	281.6
C_2H_3Cl (*g*, vinyl chloride)	37.2	53.6	264.0
$C_2H_4Cl_2$ (*l*, dichloroethane)	−166.8	−79.6	208.5
C_2H_4O (*g*, acetaldehyde)	−166.2	−133.0	263.8
$C_2H_4O_2$ (*l*, acetic acid)	−484.3	−389.9	159.8
$C_3H_8(g)$	−103.85	−23.4	270.3
C_3H_6O (*l*, acetone)	−248.4	−155.6	199.8
C_3H_7OH (*l*, isopropanol)	−318.1		181.1
$C_4H_{10}(l)$	−147.3	−15.0	231.0
$C_4H_{10}(g)$	−125.7	−15.71	310.0
$C_6H_6(l)$	49.1	124.5	173.4
$C_6H_5NH_2$ (*l*, aniline)	31.6	149.2	191.9
C_6H_5OH (*s*, phenol)	−165.1	−50.4	144.0
$C_6H_{12}O_6$ (*s*, glucose)	−1273.3	−910.4	212.1
$C_{10}H_8$ (*s*, naphthalene)	78.5	201.6	167.4
$C_{12}H_{22}O_{11}$ (*s*, sucrose)	−2226.1	−1544.3	360.24
$CO(g)$	−110.5	−137.2	197.7
$CO_2(g)$	−393.5	−394.4	213.8
$CO_2(aq)$	−413.8	−386.0	117.6
$CO_3^{2-}(aq)$	−677.1	−527.8	−56.9
$HCO_3^-(aq)$	−692.0	−586.8	91.2
$H_2CO_3(aq)$	−699.7	−623.2	187.4
$CN^-(aq)$	151	166	118
$HCN(l)$	108.9	125.0	112.8
$HCN(g)$	135.1	124.7	201.8
$CS_2(l)$	89.0	64.6	151.3
$CS_2(g)$	116.7	67.1	237.8
$COCl_2(g)$	−219.1	−204.9	283.5
$C_{60}(s)$	2327.0	2302.0	426.0
Cesium			
$Cs(s)$	0	0	85.2
$Cs(g)$	76.5	49.6	175.6
$Cs^+(aq)$	−258.0	−292.0	132.1
$CsBr(s)$	−400	−387	117
$CsCl(s)$	−438	−414	101.2
$CsF(s)$	−553.5	−525.5	92.8
$CsI(s)$	−342	−337	127

Substance	ΔH_f°(kJ/mol)	ΔG_f°(kJ/mol)	S°(J/mol·K)
Chlorine			
Cl(*g*)	121.3	105.3	165.2
Cl_2(*g*)	0	0	223.1
Cl^-(*aq*)	−167.1	−131.2	56.6
HCl(*g*)	−92.3	−95.3	186.9
HCl(*aq*)	−167.2	−131.2	56.5
ClO_2(*g*)	102.5	120.5	256.8
Cl_2O(*g*)	80.3	97.9	266.2
Chromium			
Cr(*s*)	0	0	23.8
Cr(*g*)	396.6	351.8	174.5
Cr^{3+}(*aq*)	−1971		
CrO_4^{2-}(*aq*)	−872.2	−717.1	44
Cr_2O_3(*s*)	−1139.7	−1058.1	81.2
$Cr_2O_7^{2-}$(*aq*)	−1476	−1279	238
Cobalt			
Co(*s*)	0	0	30.0
Co(*g*)	424.7	380.3	179.5
CoO(*s*)	−237.9	−214.2	53.0
$Co(OH)_2$(*s*)	−539.7	−454.3	79.0
Copper			
Cu(*s*)	0	0	33.2
Cu(*g*)	337.4	297.7	166.4
Cu^+(*aq*)	51.9	50.2	−26
Cu^{2+}(*aq*)	64.9	65.5	−98
CuCl(*s*)	−137.2	−119.9	86.2
$CuCl_2$(*s*)	−220.1	−175.7	108.1
CuO(*s*)	−157.3	−129.7	42.6
CuS(*s*)	−53.1	−53.6	66.5
$CuSO_4$(*s*)	−771.4	−662.2	109.2
Cu_2O(*s*)	−168.6	−146.0	93.1
Cu_2S(*s*)	−79.5	−86.2	120.9
Fluorine			
F(*g*)	79.38	62.3	158.75
F_2(*g*)	0	0	202.79
F^-(*aq*)	−335.35	−278.8	−13.8
HF(*g*)	−273.3	−275.4	173.8
Gold			
Au(*s*)	0	0	47.4
Au(*g*)	366.1	326.3	180.5
Helium			
He(*g*)	0	0	126.2
Hydrogen			
H(*g*)	218.0	203.3	114.7
H^+(*aq*)	0	0	0
H^-(*aq*)	1536.3	1517.1	108.9
H_2(*g*)	0	0	130.7

Substance	ΔH_f°(kJ/mol)	ΔG_f°(kJ/mol)	S°(J/mol·K)
Iodine			
I(*g*)	106.76	70.2	180.79
I_2(*s*)	0	0	116.14
I_2(*g*)	62.42	19.3	260.69
I^-(*aq*)	−56.78	−51.57	106.45
HI(*g*)	26.5	1.7	206.6
Iron			
Fe(*s*)	0	0	27.3
Fe(*g*)	416.3	370.7	180.5
Fe^{2+}(*aq*)	−87.9	−84.94	−113.4
Fe^{3+}(*aq*)	−47.69	−10.54	−293.3
$FeCO_3$(*s*)	−740.6	−666.7	92.9
$FeCl_2$(*s*)	−341.8	−302.3	118.0
$FeCl_3$(*s*)	−399.5	−334.0	142.3
FeO(*s*)	−272.0	−255.2	60.75
$Fe(OH)_3$(*s*)	−823.0	−696.5	106.7
FeS_2(*s*)	−178.2	−166.9	52.9
Fe_2O_3(*s*)	−824.2	−742.2	87.4
Fe_3O_4(*s*)	−1118.4	−1015.4	146.4
Lead			
Pb(*s*)	0	0	64.8
Pb(*g*)	195.2	162.2	175.4
Pb^{2+}(*aq*)	0.92	−24.4	18.5
$PbBr_2$(*s*)	−278.7	−261.9	161.5
$PbCO_3$(*s*)	−699.1	−625.5	131.0
$PbCl_2$(*s*)	−359.4	−314.1	136.0
PbI_2(*s*)	−175.5	−173.6	174.9
$Pb(NO_3)_2$(*s*)	−451.9		
PbO(*s*)	−217.3	−187.9	68.7
PbO_2(*s*)	−277.4	−217.3	68.6
PbS(*s*)	−100.4	−98.7	91.2
$PbSO_4$(*s*)	−920.0	−813.0	148.5
Lithium			
Li(*s*)	0	0	29.1
Li(*g*)	159.3	126.6	138.8
Li^+(*aq*)	−278.47	−293.3	12.24
LiBr(*s*)	−351.2	−342.0	74.3
LiCl(*s*)	−408.6	−384.4	59.3
LiF(*s*)	−616.0	−587.7	35.7
LiI(*s*)	−270.4	−270.3	86.8
$LiNO_3$(*s*)	−483.1	−381.1	90.0
LiOH(*s*)	−487.5	−441.5	42.8
Li_2O(*s*)	−597.9	−561.2	37.6
Magnesium			
Mg(*s*)	0	0	32.7
Mg(*g*)	147.1	112.5	148.6
Mg^{2+}(*aq*)	−467.0	−455.4	−137
$MgCl_2$(*s*)	−641.3	−591.8	89.6
$MgCO_3$(*s*)	−1095.8	−1012.1	65.7
MgF_2(*s*)	−1124.2	−1071.1	57.2

—(*Continued on the next page*)

Substance	ΔH_f°(kJ/mol)	ΔG_f°(kJ/mol)	S°(J/mol·K)
$MgO(s)$	−601.6	−569.3	27.0
$Mg(OH)_2(s)$	−924.5	−833.5	63.2
$MgSO_4(s)$	−1284.9	−1170.6	91.6
$Mg_3N_2(s)$	−461	−401	88
Manganese			
$Mn(s)$	0	0	32.0
$Mn(g)$	280.7	238.5	173.7
$Mn^{2+}(aq)$	−219.4	−225.6	−78.8
$MnO(s)$	−385.2	−362.9	59.7
$MnO_2(s)$	−520.0	−465.1	53.1
$MnO_4^-(aq)$	−529.9	−436.2	190.6
Mercury			
$Hg(l)$	0	0	75.9
$Hg(g)$	61.4	31.8	175.0
$Hg^{2+}(aq)$	170.21	164.4	−36.19
$Hg_2^{2+}(aq)$	166.87	153.5	65.74
$HgCl_2(s)$	−224.3	−178.6	146.0
$HgO(s)$	−90.8	−58.5	70.3
$HgS(s)$	−58.2	−50.6	82.4
$Hg_2Cl_2(s)$	−265.4	−210.7	191.6
Nickel			
$Ni(s)$	0	0	29.9
$Ni(g)$	429.7	384.5	182.2
$NiCl_2(s)$	−305.3	−259.0	97.7
$NiO(s)$	−239.7	−211.7	37.99
$NiS(s)$	−82.0	−79.5	53.0
Nitrogen			
$N(g)$	472.7	455.5	153.3
$N_2(g)$	0	0	191.6
$NF_3(g)$	−132.1	−90.6	260.8
$NH_3(g)$	−45.9	−16.4	192.8
$NH_3(aq)$	−80.29	−26.50	111.3
$NH_4^+(aq)$	−133.26	−79.31	111.17
$NH_4Br(s)$	−270.8	−175.2	113.0
$NH_4Cl(s)$	−314.4	−202.9	94.6
$NH_4CN(s)$	0.4		
$NH_4F(s)$	−464.0	−348.7	72.0
$NH_4HCO_3(s)$	−849.4	−665.9	120.9
$NH_4I(s)$	−201.4	−112.5	117.0
$NH_4NO_3(s)$	−365.6	−183.9	151.1
$NH_4NO_3(aq)$	−339.9	−190.6	259.8
$HNO_3(g)$	−133.9	−73.5	266.9
$HNO_3(aq)$	−207	−110.9	146
$NO(g)$	91.3	87.6	210.8
$NO_2(g)$	33.2	51.3	240.1
$NO_3^-(aq)$	−206.85	−110.2	146.70
$NOBr(g)$	82.2	82.4	273.7
$NOCl(g)$	51.7	66.1	261.7
$N_2H_4(l)$	50.6	149.3	121.2
$N_2H_4(g)$	95.4	159.4	238.5
$N_2O(g)$	81.6	103.7	220.0

Substance	ΔH_f°(kJ/mol)	ΔG_f°(kJ/mol)	S°(J/mol·K)
$N_2O_4(l)$	−19.5	97.5	209.2
$N_2O_4(g)$	9.16	99.8	304.4
$N_2O_5(s)$	−43.1	113.9	178.2
$N_2O_5(g)$	13.3	117.1	355.7
Oxygen			
$O(g)$	249.2	231.7	161.1
$O_2(g)$	0	0	205.2
$O_3(g)$	142.7	163.2	238.9
$OH^-(aq)$	−230.02	−157.3	−10.90
$H_2O(l)$	−285.8	−237.1	70.0
$H_2O(g)$	−241.8	−228.6	188.8
$H_2O_2(l)$	−187.8	−120.4	109.6
$H_2O_2(g)$	−136.3	−105.6	232.7
Phosphorus			
$P(s, white)$	0	0	41.1
$P(s, red)$	−17.6	−12.1	22.8
$P(g)$	316.5	280.1	163.2
$P_2(g)$	144.0	103.5	218.1
$P_4(g)$	58.9	24.4	280.0
$PCl_3(l)$	−319.7	−272.3	217.1
$PCl_3(g)$	−287.0	−267.8	311.8
$PCl_5(s)$	−443.5		
$PCl_5(g)$	−374.9	−305.0	364.6
$PF_5(g)$	−1594.4	−1520.7	300.8
$PH_3(g)$	5.4	13.5	210.2
$POCl_3(l)$	−597.1	−520.8	222.5
$POCl_3(g)$	−558.5	−512.9	325.5
$PO_4^{3-}(aq)$	−1277.4	−1018.7	−220.5
$HPO_4^{2-}(aq)$	−1292.1	−1089.2	−33.5
$H_2PO_4^-(aq)$	−1296.3	−1130.2	90.4
$H_3PO_4(s)$	−1284.4	−1124.3	110.5
$H_3PO_4(aq)$	−1288.3	−1142.6	158.2
$P_4O_6(s)$	−1640.1		
$P_4O_{10}(s)$	−2984	−2698	228.9
Platinum			
$Pt(s)$	0	0	41.6
$Pt(g)$	565.3	520.5	192.4
Potassium			
$K(s)$	0	0	64.7
$K(g)$	89.0	60.5	160.3
$K^+(aq)$	−252.14	−283.3	101.2
$KBr(s)$	−393.8	−380.7	95.9
$KCN(s)$	−113.0	−101.9	128.5
$KCl(s)$	−436.5	−408.5	82.6
$KClO_3(s)$	−397.7	−296.3	143.1
$KClO_4(s)$	−432.8	−303.1	151.0
$KF(s)$	−567.3	−537.8	66.6
$KI(s)$	−327.9	−324.9	106.3
$KNO_3(s)$	−494.6	−394.9	133.1

Substance	ΔH_f°(kJ/mol)	ΔG_f°(kJ/mol)	S°(J/mol·K)
KOH(s)	−424.6	−379.4	81.2
KOH(*aq*)	−482.4	−440.5	91.6
KO_2(s)	−284.9	−239.4	116.7
K_2CO_3(s)	−1151.0	−1063.5	155.5
K_2O(s)	−361.5	−322.1	94.14
K_2O_2(s)	−494.1	−425.1	102.1
K_2SO_4(s)	−1437.8	−1321.4	175.6
Rubidium			
Rb(s)	0	0	76.8
Rb(*g*)	80.9	53.1	170.1
Rb^+(*aq*)	−251.12	−283.1	121.75
RbBr(s)	−394.6	−381.8	110.0
RbCl(s)	−435.4	−407.8	95.9
$RbClO_3$(s)	−392.4	−292.0	152
RbF(s)	−557.7		
RbI(s)	−333.8	−328.9	118.4
Scandium			
Sc(s)	0	0	34.6
Sc(*g*)	377.8	336.0	174.8
Selenium			
Se(s, gray)	0	0	42.4
Se(*g*)	227.1	187.0	176.7
H_2Se(*g*)	29.7	15.9	219.0
Silicon			
Si(s)	0	0	18.8
Si(*g*)	450.0	405.5	168.0
$SiCl_4$(*l*)	−687.0	−619.8	239.7
SiF_4(*g*)	−1615.0	−1572.8	282.8
SiH_4(*g*)	34.3	56.9	204.6
SiO_2(s, quartz)	−910.7	−856.3	41.5
Si_2H_6(*g*)	80.3	127.3	272.7
Silver			
Ag(s)	0	0	42.6
Ag(*g*)	284.9	246.0	173.0
Ag^+(*aq*)	105.79	77.11	73.45
AgBr(s)	−100.4	−96.9	107.1
AgCl(s)	−127.0	−109.8	96.3
AgF(s)	−204.6	−185	84
AgI(s)	−61.8	−66.2	115.5
$AgNO_3$(s)	−124.4	−33.4	140.9
Ag_2O(s)	−31.1	−11.2	121.3
Ag_2S(s)	−32.6	−40.7	144.0
Ag_2SO_4(s)	−715.9	−618.4	200.4
Sodium			
Na(s)	0	0	51.3
Na(*g*)	107.5	77.0	153.7
Na^+(*aq*)	−240.34	−261.9	58.45
NaBr(s)	−361.1	−349.0	86.8
NaCl(s)	−411.2	−384.1	72.1
NaCl(*aq*)	−407.2	−393.1	115.5

Substance	ΔH_f°(kJ/mol)	ΔG_f°(kJ/mol)	S°(J/mol·K)
$NaClO_3$(s)	−365.8	−262.3	123.4
NaF(s)	−576.6	−546.3	51.1
$NaHCO_3$(s)	−950.8	−851.0	101.7
$NaHSO_4$(s)	−1125.5	−992.8	113.0
NaI(s)	−287.8	−286.1	98.5
$NaNO_3$(s)	−467.9	−367.0	116.5
$NaNO_3$(*aq*)	−447.5	−373.2	205.4
NaOH(s)	−425.8	−379.7	64.4
NaOH(*aq*)	−470.1	−419.2	48.2
NaO_2(s)	−260.2	−218.4	115.9
Na_2CO_3(s)	−1130.7	−1044.4	135.0
Na_2O(s)	−414.2	−375.5	75.1
Na_2O_2(s)	−510.9	−447.7	95.0
Na_2SO_4(s)	−1387.1	−1270.2	149.6
Na_3PO_4(s)	−1917	−1789	173.8
Strontium			
Sr(s)	0	0	55.0
Sr(*g*)	164.4	130.9	164.6
Sr^{2+}(*aq*)	−545.51	−557.3	−39
$SrCl_2$(s)	−828.9	−781.1	114.9
$SrCO_3$(s)	−1220.1	−1140.1	97.1
SrO(s)	−592.0	−561.9	54.4
$SrSO_4$(s)	−1453.1	−1340.9	117.0
Sulfur			
S(s, rhombic)	0	0	32.1
S(s, monoclinic)	0.3	0.096	32.6
S(*g*)	277.2	236.7	167.8
S_2(*g*)	128.6	79.7	228.2
S_8(*g*)	102.3	49.7	430.9
S^{2-}(*aq*)	41.8	83.7	22
SF_6(*g*)	−1220.5	−1116.5	291.5
HS^-(*aq*)	−17.7	12.4	62.0
H_2S(*g*)	−20.6	−33.4	205.8
H_2S(*aq*)	−39.4	−27.7	122
$SOCl_2$(*l*)	−245.6		
SO_2(*g*)	−296.8	−300.1	248.2
SO_3(*g*)	−395.7	−371.1	256.8
SO_4^{2-}(*aq*)	−909.3	−744.6	18.5
HSO_4^-(*aq*)	−886.5	−754.4	129.5
H_2SO_4(*l*)	−814.0	−690.0	156.9
H_2SO_4(*aq*)	−909.3	−744.6	18.5
$S_2O_3^{2-}$(*aq*)	−648.5	−522.5	67
Tin			
Sn(s, white)	0	0	51.2
Sn(s, gray)	−2.1	0.1	44.1
Sn(*g*)	301.2	266.2	168.5
$SnCl_4$(*l*)	−511.3	−440.1	258.6
$SnCl_4$(*g*)	−471.5	−432.2	365.8
SnO(s)	−280.7	−251.9	57.2
SnO_2(s)	−577.6	−515.8	49.0

—(Continued on the next page)

Substance	ΔH_f°(kJ/mol)	ΔG_f°(kJ/mol)	S°(J/mol · K)
Titanium			
Ti(*s*)	0	0	30.7
Ti(*g*)	473.0	428.4	180.3
$TiCl_4$(*l*)	−804.2	−737.2	252.3
$TiCl_4$(*g*)	−763.2	−726.3	353.2
TiO_2(*s*)	−944.0	−888.8	50.6
Tungsten			
W(*s*)	0	0	32.6
W(*g*)	849.4	807.1	174.0
WO_3(*s*)	−842.9	−764.0	75.9
Uranium			
U(*s*)	0	0	50.2
U(*g*)	533.0	488.4	199.8
UF_6(*s*)	−2197.0	−2068.5	227.6
UF_6(*g*)	−2147.4	−2063.7	377.9
UO_2(*s*)	−1085.0	−1031.8	77.0
Vanadium			
V(*s*)	0	0	28.9
V(*g*)	514.2	754.4	182.3
Zinc			
Zn(*s*)	0	0	41.6
Zn(*g*)	130.4	94.8	161.0
Zn^{2+}(*aq*)	−153.39	−147.1	−109.8
$ZnCl_2$(*s*)	−415.1	−369.4	111.5
ZnO(*s*)	−350.5	−320.5	43.7
ZnS (*s*, zinc blende)	−206.0	−201.3	57.7
$ZnSO_4$(*s*)	−982.8	−871.5	110.5

C. Aqueous Equilibrium Constants

1. Dissociation Constants for Acids at 25 °C

Name	Formula	K_{a_1}	K_{a_2}	K_{a_3}
Acetic	$HC_2H_3O_2$	1.8×10^{-5}		
Acetylsalicylic	$HC_9H_7O_4$	3.3×10^{-4}		
Adipic	$H_2C_6H_8O_4$	3.9×10^{-5}	3.9×10^{-6}	
Arsenic	H_3AsO_4	5.5×10^{-3}	1.7×10^{-7}	5.1×10^{-12}
Arsenous	H_3AsO_3	5.1×10^{-10}		
Ascorbic	$H_2C_6H_6O_6$	8.0×10^{-5}	1.6×10^{-12}	
Benzoic	$HC_7H_5O_2$	6.5×10^{-5}		
Boric	H_3BO_3	5.4×10^{-10}		
Butanoic	$HC_4H_7O_2$	1.5×10^{-5}		
Carbonic	H_2CO_3	4.3×10^{-7}	5.6×10^{-11}	
Chloroacetic	$HC_2H_2O_2Cl$	1.4×10^{-3}		
Chlorous	$HClO_2$	1.1×10^{-2}		
Citric	$H_3C_6H_5O_7$	7.4×10^{-4}	1.7×10^{-5}	4.0×10^{-7}
Cyanic	HCNO	2×10^{-4}		
Formic	$HCHO_2$	1.8×10^{-4}		
Hydrazoic	HN_3	2.5×10^{-5}		
Hydrocyanic	HCN	4.9×10^{-10}		
Hydrofluoric	HF	6.8×10^{-4}		
Hydrogen chromate ion	$HCrO_4^-$	3.0×10^{-7}		
Hydrogen peroxide	H_2O_2	2.4×10^{-12}		
Hydrogen selenate ion	$HSeO_4^-$	2.2×10^{-2}		
Hydrosulfuric	H_2S	8.9×10^{-8}	1×10^{-19}	
Hydrotelluric	H_2Te	2.3×10^{-3}	1.6×10^{-11}	
Hypobromous	HBrO	2.8×10^{-9}		
Hypochlorous	HClO	2.9×10^{-8}		
Hypoiodous	HIO	2.3×10^{-11}		
Iodic	HIO_3	1.7×10^{-1}		
Lactic	$HC_3H_5O_3$	1.4×10^{-4}		
Maleic	$H_2C_4H_2O_4$	1.2×10^{-2}	5.9×10^{-7}	
Malonic	$H_2C_3H_2O_4$	1.5×10^{-3}	2.0×10^{-6}	
Nitrous	HNO_2	4.6×10^{-4}		
Oxalic	$H_2C_2O_4$	6.0×10^{-2}	6.1×10^{-5}	
Paraperiodic	H_5IO_6	2.8×10^{-2}	5.3×10^{-9}	
Phenol	HC_6H_5O	1.3×10^{-10}		
Phosphoric	H_3PO_4	7.5×10^{-3}	6.2×10^{-8}	4.2×10^{-13}
Phosphorous	H_3PO_3	5×10^{-2}	2.0×10^{-7}	
Propanoic	$HC_3H_5O_2$	1.3×10^{-5}		
Pyruvic	$HC_3H_3O_3$	4.1×10^{-3}		
Pyrophosphoric	$H_4P_2O_7$	1.2×10^{-1}	7.9×10^{-3}	2.0×10^{-7}
Selenous	H_2SeO_3	2.4×10^{-3}	4.8×10^{-9}	
Succinic	$H_2C_4H_4O_4$	6.2×10^{-5}	2.3×10^{-6}	
Sulfuric	H_2SO_4	Strong acid	1.2×10^{-2}	
Sulfurous	H_2SO_3	1.6×10^{-2}	6.4×10^{-8}	
Tartaric	$H_2C_4H_4O_6$	1.0×10^{-3}	4.6×10^{-5}	
Trichloroacetic	$HC_2Cl_3O_2$	2.2×10^{-1}		
Trifluoroacetic acid	$HC_2F_3O_2$	3.0×10^{-1}		

2. Dissociation Constants for Hydrated Metal Ions at 25 °C

Cation	Hydrated Ion	K_a
Al^{3+}	$Al(H_2O)_6^{3+}$	1.4×10^{-5}
Be^{2+}	$Be(H_2O)_6^{2+}$	3×10^{-7}
Co^{2+}	$Co(H_2O)_6^{2+}$	1.3×10^{-9}
Cr^{3+}	$Cr(H_2O)_6^{3+}$	1.6×10^{-4}
Cu^{2+}	$Cu(H_2O)_6^{2+}$	3×10^{-8}
Fe^{2+}	$Fe(H_2O)_6^{2+}$	3.2×10^{-10}
Fe^{3+}	$Fe(H_2O)_6^{3+}$	6.3×10^{-3}
Ni^{2+}	$Ni(H_2O)_6^{2+}$	2.5×10^{-11}
Pb^{2+}	$Pb(H_2O)_6^{2+}$	3×10^{-8}
Sn^{2+}	$Sn(H_2O)_6^{2+}$	4×10^{-4}
Zn^{2+}	$Zn(H_2O)_6^{2+}$	2.5×10^{-10}

3. Dissociation Constants for Bases at 25 °C

Name	Formula	K_b
Ammonia	NH_3	1.76×10^{-5}
Aniline	$C_6H_5NH_2$	3.9×10^{-10}
Bicarbonate ion	HCO_3^-	2.3×10^{-8}
Carbonate ion	CO_3^{2-}	1.8×10^{-4}
Codeine	$C_{18}H_{21}NO_3$	1.6×10^{-6}
Diethylamine	$(C_2H_5)_2NH$	6.9×10^{-4}
Dimethylamine	$(CH_3)_2NH$	5.4×10^{-4}
Ethylamine	$C_2H_5NH_2$	5.6×10^{-4}
Ethylenediamine	$C_2H_8N_2$	8.3×10^{-5}
Hydrazine	H_2NNH_2	1.3×10^{-6}
Hydroxylamine	$HONH_2$	1.1×10^{-8}
Ketamine	$C_{13}H_{16}ClNO$	3×10^{-7}
Methylamine	CH_3NH_2	4.4×10^{-4}
Morphine	$C_{17}H_{19}NO_3$	1.6×10^{-6}
Nicotine	$C_{10}H_{14}N_2$	1.0×10^{-6}
Piperidine	$C_5H_{10}NH$	1.33×10^{-3}
Propylamine	$C_3H_7NH_2$	3.5×10^{-4}
Pyridine	C_5H_5N	1.7×10^{-9}
Strychnine	$C_{21}H_{22}N_2O_2$	1.8×10^{-6}
Triethylamine	$(C_2H_5)_3N$	5.6×10^{-4}
Trimethylamine	$(CH_3)_3N$	6.4×10^{-5}

4. Solubility Product Constants for Compounds at 25 °C

Compound	Formula	K_{sp}
Aluminum hydroxide	$Al(OH)_3$	1.3×10^{-33}
Aluminum phosphate	$AlPO_4$	9.84×10^{-21}
Barium carbonate	$BaCO_3$	2.58×10^{-9}
Barium chromate	$BaCrO_4$	1.17×10^{-10}
Barium fluoride	BaF_2	2.45×10^{-5}
Barium hydroxide	$Ba(OH)_2$	5.0×10^{-3}
Barium oxalate	BaC_2O_4	1.6×10^{-6}
Barium phosphate	$Ba_3(PO_4)_2$	6×10^{-39}
Barium sulfate	$BaSO_4$	1.07×10^{-10}
Cadmium carbonate	$CdCO_3$	1.0×10^{-12}
Cadmium hydroxide	$Cd(OH)_2$	7.2×10^{-15}
Cadmium sulfide	CdS	8×10^{-28}
Calcium carbonate	$CaCO_3$	4.96×10^{-9}
Calcium chromate	$CaCrO_4$	7.1×10^{-4}
Calcium fluoride	CaF_2	1.46×10^{-10}
Calcium hydroxide	$Ca(OH)_2$	4.68×10^{-6}
Calcium hydrogen phosphate	$CaHPO_4$	1×10^{-7}
Calcium oxalate	CaC_2O_4	2.32×10^{-9}
Calcium phosphate	$Ca_3(PO_4)_2$	2.07×10^{-33}
Calcium sulfate	$CaSO_4$	7.10×10^{-5}
Chromium(III) hydroxide	$Cr(OH)_3$	6.3×10^{-31}
Cobalt(II) carbonate	$CoCO_3$	1.0×10^{-10}
Cobalt(II) hydroxide	$Co(OH)_2$	5.92×10^{-15}
Cobalt(II) sulfide	CoS	5×10^{-22}
Copper(I) bromide	$CuBr$	6.27×10^{-9}
Copper(I) chloride	$CuCl$	1.72×10^{-7}
Copper(I) cyanide	$CuCN$	3.47×10^{-20}
Copper(II) carbonate	$CuCO_3$	2.4×10^{-10}
Copper(II) hydroxide	$Cu(OH)_2$	2.2×10^{-20}
Copper(II) phosphate	$Cu_3(PO_4)_2$	1.40×10^{-37}
Copper(II) sulfide	CuS	1.27×10^{-36}
Iron(II) carbonate	$FeCO_3$	3.07×10^{-11}

—(Continued on the next page)

Compound	Formula	K_{sp}
Iron(II) hydroxide	$Fe(OH)_2$	4.87×10^{-17}
Iron(II) sulfide	FeS	3.72×10^{-19}
Iron(III) hydroxide	$Fe(OH)_3$	2.79×10^{-39}
Lanthanum fluoride	LaF_3	2×10^{-19}
Lanthanum iodate	$La(IO_3)_3$	7.50×10^{-12}
Lead(II) bromide	$PbBr_2$	4.67×10^{-6}
Lead(II) carbonate	$PbCO_3$	7.40×10^{-14}
Lead(II) chloride	$PbCl_2$	1.17×10^{-5}
Lead(II) chromate	$PbCrO_4$	2.8×10^{-13}
Lead(II) fluoride	PbF_2	3.3×10^{-8}
Lead(II) hydroxide	$Pb(OH)_2$	1.43×10^{-20}
Lead(II) iodide	PbI_2	9.8×10^{-9}
Lead(II) phosphate	$Pb_3(PO_4)_2$	1×10^{-54}
Lead(II) sulfate	$PbSO_4$	1.82×10^{-8}
Lead(II) sulfide	PbS	9.04×10^{-29}
Magnesium carbonate	$MgCO_3$	6.82×10^{-6}
Magnesium fluoride	MgF_2	5.16×10^{-11}
Magnesium hydroxide	$Mg(OH)_2$	2.06×10^{-13}
Magnesium oxalate	MgC_2O_4	4.83×10^{-6}
Manganese(II) carbonate	$MnCO_3$	2.24×10^{-11}
Manganese(II) hydroxide	$Mn(OH)_2$	1.6×10^{-13}
Manganese(II) sulfide	MnS	2.3×10^{-13}
Mercury(I) bromide	Hg_2Br_2	6.40×10^{-23}
Mercury(I) carbonate	Hg_2CO_3	3.6×10^{-17}
Mercury(I) chloride	Hg_2Cl_2	1.43×10^{-18}
Mercury(I) chromate	Hg_2CrO_4	2×10^{-9}
Mercury(I) cyanide	$Hg_2(CN)_2$	5×10^{-40}
Mercury(I) iodide	Hg_2I_2	5.2×10^{-29}
Mercury(II) hydroxide	$Hg(OH)_2$	3.1×10^{-26}
Mercury(II) sulfide	HgS	1.6×10^{-54}
Nickel(II) carbonate	$NiCO_3$	1.42×10^{-7}
Nickel(II) hydroxide	$Ni(OH)_2$	5.48×10^{-16}
Nickel(II) sulfide	NiS	3×10^{-20}
Silver bromate	$AgBrO_3$	5.38×10^{-5}
Silver bromide	AgBr	5.35×10^{-13}
Silver carbonate	Ag_2CO_3	8.46×10^{-12}
Silver chloride	AgCl	1.77×10^{-10}
Silver chromate	Ag_2CrO_4	1.12×10^{-12}
Silver cyanide	AgCN	5.97×10^{-17}
Silver iodide	AgI	8.51×10^{-17}
Silver phosphate	Ag_3PO_4	8.89×10^{-17}
Silver sulfate	Ag_2SO_4	1.20×10^{-5}
Silver sulfide	Ag_2S	6×10^{-51}
Strontium carbonate	$SrCO_3$	5.60×10^{-10}
Strontium chromate	$SrCrO_4$	3.6×10^{-5}
Strontium phosphate	$Sr_3(PO_4)_2$	1×10^{-31}
Strontium sulfate	$SrSO_4$	3.44×10^{-7}
Tin(II) hydroxide	$Sn(OH)_2$	5.45×10^{-27}
Tin(II) sulfide	SnS	1×10^{-26}
Zinc carbonate	$ZnCO_3$	1.46×10^{-10}
Zinc hydroxide	$Zn(OH)_2$	3×10^{-17}
Zinc oxalate	ZnC_2O_4	2.7×10^{-8}
Zinc sulfide	ZnS	2×10^{-25}

5. Complex Ion Formation Constants in Water at 25 °C

Complex Ion	K_f
$[Ag(CN)_2]^-$	1×10^{21}
$[Ag(EDTA)]^{3-}$	2.1×10^{7}
$[Ag(en)_2]^+$	5.0×10^{7}
$[Ag(NH_3)_2]^+$	1.7×10^{7}
$[Ag(SCN)_4]^{3-}$	1.2×10^{10}
$[Ag(S_2O_3)_2]^{3-}$	2.8×10^{13}
$[Al(EDTA)]^-$	1.3×10^{16}
$[AlF_6]^{3-}$	7×10^{19}
$[Al(OH)_4]^-$	3×10^{33}
$[Al(ox)_3]^{3-}$	2×10^{16}
$[CdBr_4]^{2-}$	5.5×10^{3}
$[Cd(CN)_4]^{2-}$	3×10^{18}
$[CdCl_4]^{2-}$	6.3×10^{2}
$[Cd(en)_3]^{2+}$	1.2×10^{12}
$[CdI_4]^{2-}$	2×10^{6}
$[Co(EDTA)]^{2-}$	2.0×10^{16}
$[Co(EDTA)]^-$	1×10^{36}
$[Co(en)_3]^{2+}$	8.7×10^{13}
$[Co(en)_3]^{3+}$	4.9×10^{48}
$[Co(NH_3)_6]^{2+}$	1.3×10^{5}
$[Co(NH_3)_6]^{3+}$	2.3×10^{33}
$[Co(OH)_4]^{2-}$	5×10^{9}
$[Co(ox)_3]^{4-}$	5×10^{9}
$[Co(ox)_3]^{3-}$	1×10^{20}

Complex Ion	K_f
$[Co(SCN)_4]^{2-}$	1×10^3
$[Cr(EDTA)]^-$	1×10^{23}
$[Cr(OH)_4]^-$	8.0×10^{29}
$[CuCl_3]^{2-}$	5×10^5
$[Cu(CN)_4]^{2-}$	1.0×10^{25}
$[Cu(EDTA)]^{2-}$	5×10^{18}
$[Cu(en)_2]^{2+}$	1×10^{20}
$[Cu(NH_3)_4]^{2+}$	1.7×10^{13}
$[Cu(ox)_2]^{2-}$	3×10^8
$[Fe(CN)_6]^{4-}$	1.5×10^{35}
$[Fe(CN)_6]^{3-}$	2×10^{43}
$[Fe(EDTA)]^{2-}$	2.1×10^{14}
$[Fe(EDTA)]^-$	1.7×10^{24}
$[Fe(en)_3]^{2+}$	5.0×10^9
$[Fe(ox)_3]^{4-}$	1.7×10^5
$[Fe(ox)_3]^{3-}$	2×10^{20}
$[Fe(SCN)]^{2+}$	8.9×10^2
$[Hg(CN)_4]^{2-}$	1.8×10^{41}
$[HgCl_4]^{2-}$	1.1×10^{16}
$[Hg(EDTA)]^{2-}$	6.3×10^{21}
$[Hg(en)_2]^{2+}$	2×10^{23}
$[HgI_4]^{2-}$	2×10^{30}

Complex Ion	K_f
$[Hg(ox)_2]^{2-}$	9.5×10^6
$[Ni(CN)_4]^{2-}$	2×10^{31}
$[Ni(EDTA)]^{2-}$	3.6×10^{18}
$[Ni(en)_3]^{2+}$	2.1×10^{18}
$[Ni(NH_3)_6]^{2+}$	2.0×10^8
$[Ni(ox)_3]^{4-}$	3×10^8
$[PbCl_3]^-$	2.4×10^1
$[Pb(EDTA)]^{2-}$	2×10^{18}
$[PbI_4]^{2-}$	3.0×10^4
$[Pb(OH)_3]^-$	8×10^{13}
$[Pb(ox)_2]^{2-}$	3.5×10^6
$[Pb(S_2O_3)_3]^{4-}$	2.2×10^6
$[PtCl_4]^{2-}$	1×10^{16}
$[Pt(NH_3)_6]^{2+}$	2×10^{35}
$[Sn(OH)_3]^-$	3×10^{25}
$[Zn(CN)_4]^{2-}$	2.1×10^{19}
$[Zn(EDTA)]^{2-}$	3×10^{16}
$[Zn(en)_3]^{2+}$	1.3×10^{14}
$[Zn(NH_3)_4]^{2+}$	2.8×10^9
$[Zn(OH)_4]^{2-}$	2×10^{15}
$[Zn(ox)_3]^{4-}$	1.4×10^8

D. Standard Electrode Potentials at 25 °C

Half-Reaction	$E°$(V)
$F_2(g) + 2\,e^- \longrightarrow 2\,F^-(aq)$	2.87
$O_3(g) + 2\,H^+(aq) + 2\,e^- \longrightarrow O_2(g) + H_2(l)$	2.08
$Ag^{2+}(aq) + e^- \longrightarrow Ag^+(aq)$	1.98
$Co^{3+}(aq) + e^- \longrightarrow Co^{2+}(aq)$	1.82
$H_2O_2(aq) + 2\,H^+(aq) + 2\,e^- \longrightarrow 2\,H_2O(l)$	1.78
$PbO_2(s) + 4\,H^+(aq) + SO_4^{2-}aq) + 2\,e^- \longrightarrow PbSO_4(s) + 2\,H_2O(l)$	1.69
$MnO_4^-(aq) + 4\,H^+(aq) + 3\,e^- \longrightarrow MnO_2(s) + 2\,H_2O(l)$	1.68
$2\,HClO(aq) + 2\,H^+(aq) + 2\,e^- \longrightarrow Cl_2(g) + 2\,H_2O(l)$	1.61
$MnO_4^-(aq) + 8\,H^+(aq) + 5\,e^- \longrightarrow Mn^{2+}(aq) + 4\,H_2O(l)$	1.51
$Au^{3+}(aq) + 3\,e^- \longrightarrow Au(s)$	1.50
$2\,BrO_3^-(aq) + 12\,H^+(aq) + 10\,e^- \longrightarrow Br_2(l) + 6\,H_2O(l)$	1.48
$PbO_2(s) + 4\,H^+(aq) + 2\,e^- \longrightarrow Pb^{2+}(aq) + 2\,H_2O(l)$	1.46
$Cl_2(g) + 2\,e^- \longrightarrow 2\,Cl^-(aq)$	1.36

Half-Reaction	$E°$(V)
$Cr_2O_7^{2-}(aq) + 14\,H^+(aq) + 6\,e^- \longrightarrow 2\,Cr^{3+}(aq) + 7\,H_2O(l)$	1.33
$O_2(g) + 4\,H^+(aq) + 4\,e^- \longrightarrow 2\,H_2O(l)$	1.23
$MnO_2(s) + 4\,H^+(aq) + 2\,e^- \longrightarrow Mn^{2+}(aq) + 2\,H_2O(l)$	1.21
$IO_3^-(aq) + 6\,H^+(aq) + 5\,e^- \longrightarrow \frac{1}{2}\,I_2(aq) + 3\,H_2O(l)$	1.20
$Br_2(l) + 2\,e^- \longrightarrow 2\,Br^-(aq)$	1.09
$AuCl_4^-(aq) + 3\,e^- \longrightarrow Au(s) + 4\,Cl^-(aq)$	1.00
$VO_2^+(aq) + 2\,H^+(aq) + e^- \longrightarrow VO^{2+}(aq) + H_2O(l)$	1.00
$HNO_2(aq) + H^+(aq) + e^- \longrightarrow NO(g) + 2\,H_2O(l)$	0.98
$NO_3^-(aq) + 4\,H^+(aq) + 3\,e^- \longrightarrow NO(g) + 2\,H_2O(l)$	0.96
$ClO_2(g) + e^- \longrightarrow ClO_2^-(aq)$	0.95
$2\,Hg^{2+}(aq) + 2\,e^- \longrightarrow 2\,Hg_2^{2+}(aq)$	0.92
$Ag^+(aq) + e^- \longrightarrow Ag(s)$	0.80
$Hg_2^{2+}(aq) + 2\,e^- \longrightarrow 2\,Hg(l)$	0.80

—(Continued on the next page)

Half-Reaction	$E°$(V)
$Fe^{3+}(aq) + e^- \longrightarrow Fe^{2+}(aq)$	0.77
$PtCl_4^{2-}(aq) + 2\ e^- \longrightarrow Pt(s) + 4\ Cl^-(aq)$	0.76
$O_2(g) + 2\ H^+(aq) + 2\ e^- \longrightarrow H_2O_2(aq)$	0.70
$MnO_4^-(aq) + e^- \longrightarrow MnO_4^{2-}(aq)$	0.56
$I_2(s) + 2\ e^- \longrightarrow 2\ I^-(aq)$	0.54
$Cu^+(aq) + e^- \longrightarrow Cu(s)$	0.52
$O_2(g) + 2\ H_2O(l) + 4\ e^- \longrightarrow 4\ OH^-(aq)$	0.40
$Cu^{2+}(aq) + 2\ e^- \longrightarrow Cu(s)$	0.34
$BiO^+(aq) + 2\ H^+(aq) + 3\ e^- \longrightarrow Bi(s) + H_2O(l)$	0.32
$Hg_2Cl_2(s) + 2\ e^- \longrightarrow 2\ Hg(l) + 2\ Cl^-(aq)$	0.27
$AgCl(s) + e^- \longrightarrow Ag(s) + Cl^-(aq)$	0.22
$SO_4^{2-}(aq) + 4\ H^+(aq) + 2\ e^- \longrightarrow H_2SO_3(aq) + H_2O(l)$	0.20
$Cu^{2+}(aq) + e^- \longrightarrow Cu^+(aq)$	0.16
$Sn^{4+}(aq) + 2\ e^- \longrightarrow Sn^{2+}(aq)$	0.15
$S(s) + 2\ H^+(aq) + 2\ e^- \longrightarrow H_2S(g)$	0.14
$AgBr(s) + e^- \longrightarrow Ag(s) + Br^-(aq)$	0.071
$2\ H^+(aq) + 2\ e^- \longrightarrow H_2(g)$	0.00
$Fe^{3+}(aq) + 3\ e^- \longrightarrow Fe(s)$	−0.036
$Pb^{2+}(aq) + 2\ e^- \longrightarrow Pb(s)$	−0.13
$Sn^{2+}(aq) + 2\ e^- \longrightarrow Sn(s)$	−0.14
$AgI(s) + e^- \longrightarrow Ag(s) + I^-(aq)$	−0.15

Half-Reaction	$E°$(V)
$N_2(g) + 5\ H^+(aq) + 4\ e^- \longrightarrow N_2H_5^+(aq)$	−0.23
$Ni^{2+}(aq) + 2\ e^- \longrightarrow Ni(s)$	−0.23
$Co^{2+}(aq) + 2\ e^- \longrightarrow Co(s)$	−0.28
$PbSO_4(s) + 2\ e^- \longrightarrow Pb(s) + SO_4^{2-}(aq)$	−0.36
$Cd^{2+}(aq) + 2\ e^- \longrightarrow Cd(s)$	−0.40
$Fe^{2+}(aq) + 2\ e^- \longrightarrow Fe(s)$	−0.45
$2\ CO_2(g) + 2\ H^+(aq) + 2\ e^- \longrightarrow H_2C_2O_4(aq)$	−0.49
$Cr^{3+}(aq) + e^- \longrightarrow Cr^{2+}(aq)$	−0.50
$Cr^{3+}(aq) + 3\ e^- \longrightarrow Cr(s)$	−0.73
$Zn^{2+}(aq) + 2\ e^- \longrightarrow Zn(s)$	−0.76
$2\ H_2O(l) + 2\ e^- \longrightarrow H_2(g) + 2\ OH^-(aq)$	−0.83
$Mn^{2+}(aq) + 2\ e^- \longrightarrow Mn(s)$	−1.18
$Al^{3+}(aq) + 3\ e^- \longrightarrow Al(s)$	−1.66
$H_2(g) + 2\ e^- \longrightarrow 2\ H^-(aq)$	−2.23
$Mg^{2+}(aq) + 2\ e^- \longrightarrow Mg(s)$	−2.37
$La^{3+}(aq) + 3\ e^- \longrightarrow La(s)$	−2.38
$Na^+(aq) + e^- \longrightarrow Na(s)$	−2.71
$Ca^{2+}(aq) + 2\ e^- \longrightarrow Ca(s)$	−2.76
$Ba^{2+}(aq) + 2\ e^- \longrightarrow Ba(s)$	−2.90
$K^+(aq) + e^- \longrightarrow K(s)$	−2.92
$Li^+(aq) + e^- \longrightarrow Li(s)$	−3.04

E. Vapor Pressure of Water at Various Temperatures

T (°C)	P (torr)	T (°C)	P (torr)	T (°C)	P (torr)	T (°C)	P (torr)
0	4.58	21	18.65	35	42.2	92	567.0
5	6.54	22	19.83	40	55.3	94	610.9
10	9.21	23	21.07	45	71.9	96	657.6
12	10.52	24	22.38	50	92.5	98	707.3
14	11.99	25	23.76	55	118.0	100	760.0
16	13.63	26	25.21	60	149.4	102	815.9
17	14.53	27	26.74	65	187.5	104	875.1
18	15.48	28	28.35	70	233.7	106	937.9
19	16.48	29	30.04	80	355.1	108	1004.4
20	17.54	30	31.82	90	525.8	110	1074.6

APPENDIX III

Answers to Selected Exercises

Chapter 1

33. **a.** theory **b.** observation
c. law **d.** observation

35. Several answers possible

37. **a.** mixture, homogeneous
b. pure substance, compound
c. pure substance, element
d. mixture, heterogeneous

39.

Substance	Pure or Mixture	Type
Aluminum	Pure	Element
Apple juice	Mixture	Homogeneous
Hydrogen peroxide	Pure	Compound
Chicken soup	Mixture	Heterogeneous

41. **a.** pure substance, compound
b. mixture, heterogeneous
c. mixture, homogeneous
d. pure substance, element

43. physical, chemical, physical, physical, physical

45. **a.** chemical **b.** physical
c. physical **d.** chemical

47. **a.** chemical **b.** physical
c. chemical **d.** chemical

49. **a.** physical **b.** chemical **c.** physical

51. **a.** 0 °C **b.** −321 °F
c. −78.3 °F **d.** 310.2 K

53. −89.2 °C, 184.0 K

55. **a.** 1.2 nm **b.** 22 fs
c. 1.5 Gg **d.** 3.5 ML

57. **a.** 4.5×10^{-9} s **b.** 1.8×10^{-14} s
c. 1.28×10^{-10} m **d.** 3.5×10^{-5} m

59.

1245 kg	1.245×10^{6} g	1.245×10^{9} mg
515 km	5.15×10^{6} dm	5.15×10^{7} cm
122.355 s	1.22355×10^{5} ms	0.122355 ks
3.345 kJ	3.345×10^{3} J	3.345×10^{6} mJ

61. **e.** 254.998 km **f.** 2.54998×10^{-1} Mm
g. 254998×10^{3} mm **h.** 254998×10^{2} cm

63. 10,000 1 cm squares

65. no

67. 1.26 g/cm^3

69. **a.** 463 g **b.** 3.7 L

71. 201. $\times 10^{3}$ g

73. **a.** 73.7 mL **b.** 88.2 °C **c.** 647 mL

75. **a.** 1,050,501 **b.** 0.0020
c. 0.0000000000002 **d.** 0.001090

77. **a.** 3 **b.** ambiguous; without more information, assume three significant figures.
c. 3 **d.** 5
e. ambiguous; without more information, assume one significant figure.

79. **a.** not exact **b.** exact
c. not exact **d.** exact

81. **a.** 156.9 **b.** 156.8 **c.** 156.8 **d.** 156.9

83. **a.** 1.84 **b.** 0.033
c. 0.500 **d.** 34

85. **a.** 41.4 **b.** 133.5
c. 73.0 **d.** 0.42

87. **a.** 391.3 **b.** 1.1×10^{4}
c. 5.96 **d.** 5.93×10^{4}

89. 0.74 g/mL

91. **a.** 2.78×10^{4} cm^3 **b.** 1.898×10^{-3} kg
c. 1.98×10^{7} cm

93. **a.** 60.6 in **b.** 3.14×10^{3} g
c. 3.7 qt **d.** 4.29 in

95. 5.0×10^{1} min

97. 4.0×10^{1} mi/gal

99. **a.** 1.95×10^{-4} km^2 **b.** 1.95×10^{4} dm^2
c. 1.95×10^{6} cm^2

101. 0.680 mi^2

103. 0.95 mL

105. 3.1557×10^{7} s/solar year

107. **a.** extensive **b.** intensive
c. intensive **d.** intensive
e. extensive

109. −34 °F

111. $F = \text{kg}(\text{m/s}^2)$ = N (for newton), kN, pN

113. **a.** 2.2×10^{-6} **b.** 0.0159 **c.** 6.9×10^{4}

115. **a.** mass of can of gold = 1.9×10^{4} g
mass of can of sand = 3.0×10^{3} g
b. Yes, the thief sets off the trap because the can of sand is lighter than the gold cylinder.

117. 22 in^3

119. 7.6 g/cm^3

121. 3.11×10^{5} lb

123. 3.3×10^{2} km

125. 6.8×10^{-15}

127. 2.4×10^{19} km

129. 488 grams

131. 0.661 Ω

133. 0.492

135. 18.2 atm

137. $1\text{ J} = 1\text{ kg m}^2/\text{s}^2$
$m = \text{kg}, v^2 = (\text{m/s})^2\ mv = \text{kg m}^2/\text{s}^2$
$P = \text{N/m}^2 = \text{kg m/s}^2/\text{m}^2 = \text{kg/m s}^2$
$V = \text{m}^2\ PV = \text{kg m}^3/\text{m s}^2 = \text{kg m}^2/\text{s}^2$

139. 9.0×10^{1} mg CO

141. 13% increase

143. No. Since the container is sealed, the atoms and molecules can move around, but they cannot leave. If no atoms or molecules can leave, the mass must be constant.

145. 343 1 cm cubes
147. **a.** the dark block **b.** the light-colored block **c.** cannot tell
149. **a.** law **b.** theory **c.** observation **d.** law
155. **a.** 8.2% **c.** 24.4 million cubic kilometers

Chapter 2

29. 13.5 g
31. These results are not consistent with the law of definite proportions because sample 1 is composed of 11.5 parts Cl to 1 part C and sample 2 is composed of 9.05 parts Cl to 1 part C. The law of definite proportions states that a given compound always contains exactly the same proportion of elements by mass.
33. 23.8 g
35. For the law of multiple proportions to hold, the ratio of the masses of O combining with 1 g of O's in the compound should be a small whole number. 0.3369/0.168 = 2.00
37. Sample 1: 1.00 g O_2/1.00 g S; Sample 2: 1.50 g O_2/1.00 g S
Sample 2/sample 1 = 1.50/1.00 = 1.50
3 O atoms/2 O atoms = 1.5
39. **a.** not consistent
b. consistent: Dalton's atomic theory states that the atoms of a given element are identical.
c. consistent: Dalton's atomic theory states that atoms combine in simple whole-number ratios to form compounds.
d. not consistent
41. **a.** consistent: Rutherford's nuclear model states that the atom is largely empty space.
b. consistent: Rutherford's nuclear model states that most of the atom's mass is concentrated in a tiny region called the nucleus.
c. not consistent **d.** not consistent
43. -2.3×10^{-19} C
45. 9.4×10^{13} excess electrons, 8.5×10^{-17} kg
47. **a, b, c**
49. 1.83×10^{3} e^-
51. **a.** Ag-107 **b.** Ag-109 **c.** U-238 **d.** H-2
53. **a.** 7$^1_1$p and 7$^0_1$n **b.** 11$^1_1$p and 12$^0_1$n **c.** 86$^1_1$p and 136$^0_1$n **d.** 82$^1_1$p and 126$^0_1$n
55. 6 $^1_1$p and 8 $^1_0$n, $^{14}_{6}$C
57. **a.** 28$^1_1$p and 26 e^- **b.** 16$^1_1$p and 18 e^- **c.** 35$^1_1$p and 36 e^- **d.** 24$^1_1$p and 21 e^-
59. **a.** 2– **b.** 1+ **c.** 3+ **d.** 1+
61.

Symbol	Ion Formed	Number of Electrons in Ion	Number of Protons in Ion
Ca	Ca^{2+}	18	20
Be	Be^{2+}	2	4
Se	Se^{2-}	36	34
In	In^{3+}	46	49

63. **a.** potassium, metal **b.** barium, metal **c.** iodine, nonmetal **d.** oxygen, nonmetal **e.** antimony, metalloid
65. **a** and **b** are main-group elements.
67. **a.** alkali metal
b. halogen
c. alkaline earth metal
d. alkaline earth metal
e. noble gas
69. Cl and F because they are in the same group or family. Elements in the same group or family have similar chemical properties.
71.

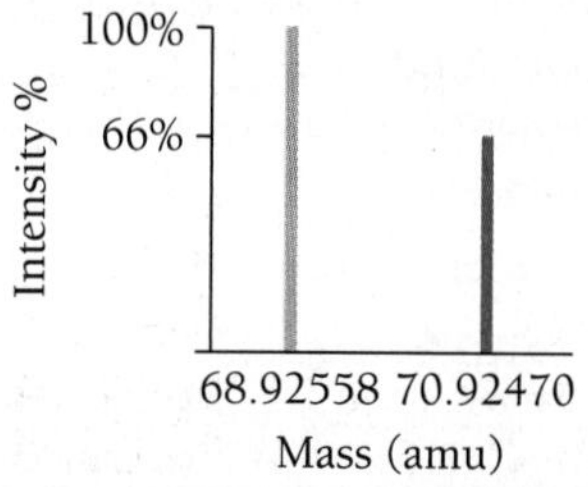

73. The fluorine-19 isotope must have a large percent abundance, which would make fluorine produce a large peak at this mass. Chlorine has two isotopes (Cl-35 and Cl-37). The atomic mass is simply the weighted average of these two, which means that there is no chlorine isotope with a mass of 35.45 amu.
75. 121.8 amu, Sb
77. Br-79 78.92, amu 50.96%
79. 152 amu
81. 3.32×10^{24} atoms
83. **a.** 0.295 mol Ar **b.** 0.0543 mol Zn **c.** 0.144 mol Ta **d.** 0.0304 mol Li
85. 2.11×10^{22} atoms
87. **a.** 1.01×10^{23} atoms **b.** 6.78×10^{21} atoms **c.** 5.39×10^{21} atoms **d.** 5.6×10^{20} atoms
89. **a.** 36 grams **b.** 0.187 grams **c.** 62 grams **d.** 3.1 grams
91. 2.6×10^{21} atoms
93. 3.239×10^{-22} g
95. 1.50 g
97. C_2O_3
99. 4.82241×10^{7} C/kg
101. 207 amu
103. ^{237}Pa, ^{238}U, ^{239}Np, ^{240}Pu, ^{235}Ac, ^{234}Ra, etc.
105.

Symbol	Z	A	#p	#e^-	#n	Charge
O	8	16	8	10	8	2–
Ca^{2+}	20	40	20	18	20	2+
Mg^{2+}	12	25	12	10	13	2+
N^{3-}	7	14	7	10	7	3–

107. $V_n = 8.2 \times 10^{-8}$ pm^3, $V_a = 1.4 \times 10^{6}$ pm^3, 5.9×10^{-12}%
109. 6.022×10^{21} dollars total, 8.6×10^{11} dollars per person, billionaires
111. 15.985 amu
113. 4.76×10^{24} atoms

115. 3.56 cm
117. Li-6 = 7.494%, Li-7 = 92.506%
119. 75.0% gold
121. 106.91 amu
123. 1.66×10^{22} gold atoms
125. 1×10^{78} atoms/universe
127. 0.423
129. 63.67 g/mol
131. 25.06 g/mol
133. Li-6 Li-7

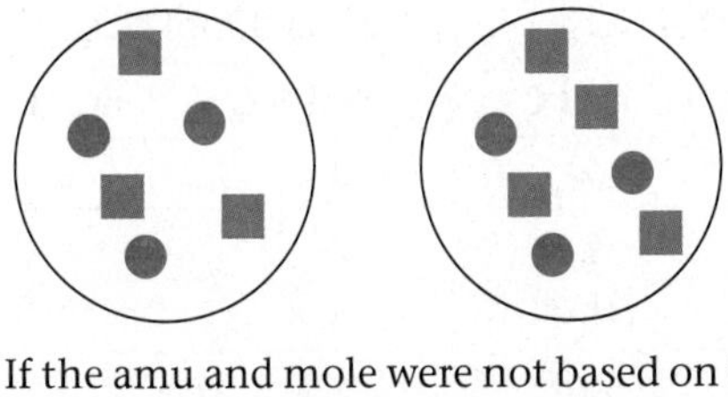

135. If the amu and mole were not based on the same isotope, the numerical values obtained for an atom of material and a mole of material would not be the same. If, for example, the mole were based on the number of particles in C-12 but the amu were changed to a fraction of the mass of an atom of Ne-20, the number of particles and the number of amu that make up one mole of material would no longer be the same. We would no longer have the relationship in which the mass of an atom in amu is numerically equal to the mass of a mole of those atoms in grams.
137. The different isotopes of the same element have the same number of protons and electrons, so the attractive forces between the nucleus and the electrons are constant and there is no difference in the radii of the isotopes. Ions, on the other hand, have a different number of electrons than the parent atom from which they are derived. Cations have fewer electrons than the parent atom. The attractive forces are greater because there is a larger positive charge in the nucleus than the negative charge in the electron cloud. So, cations are smaller than the atom they are derived from. Anions have more electrons than the parent. The electron cloud has a greater negative charge than the nucleus, so the anions have larger radii than the parent.
142. **a.** 2000, 0.24 μg/m^3; 2016, 0.017 μg/m^3
c. 2.9×10^{14} Pb atoms

Chapter 3

23. **a.** 3 Mg, 2 P, 8 O **b.** 1 Ba, 2 Cl
c. 1 Fe, 2 N, 4 O **d.** 1 Ca, 2 O, 2 H
25. **a.** NH_3 **b.** C_2H_6 **c.** SO_3
27. **a.** atomic **b.** molecular
c. atomic **d.** molecular
29. **a.** molecular **b.** ionic
c. ionic **d.** molecular
31. **a.** molecular element **b.** molecular compound
c. atomic element
33. **a.** CaO **b.** ZnS **c.** RbBr **d.** Al_2O_3
35. **a.** $Ca(OH)_2$ **b.** $CaCrO_4$
c. $Ca_3(PO_4)_2$ **d.** $Ca(CN)_2$
37. **a.** magnesium nitride **b.** potassium fluoride
c. sodium oxide **d.** lithium sulfide
e. cesium fluoride **f.** potassium iodide
39. **a.** tin(II) oxide **b.** chromium(III) sulfide
c. rubidium iodide **d.** barium bromide
41. **a.** copper(I) nitrite **b.** magnesium acetate
c. barium nitrate **d.** lead(II) acetate
43. **a.** $NaHSO_3$ **b.** $LiMnO_4$
c. $AgNO_3$ **d.** K_2SO_4
e. $RbHSO_4$ **f.** $KHCO_3$
45. **a.** cobalt(II) sulfate heptahydrate
b. $IrBr_3 \times 4\,H_2O$
c. magnesium bromate hexahydrate
d. $K_2CO_3 \times 2\,H_2O$
47. **a.** carbon monoxide **b.** nitrogen triiodide
c. silicon tetrachloride
d. tetranitrogen tetraselenide
49. **a.** PCl_3 **b.** ClO
c. S_2F_4 **d.** PF_5
51. **a.** hydroiodic acid **b.** nitric acid
c. carbonic acid
53. **a.** HF **b.** HBr **c.** H_2SO_3
55. **a.** strontium chloride **b.** tin(IV) oxide
c. diphosphorus pentasulfide
d. acetic acid
57. **a.** potassium chlorate **b.** diiodine pentoxide
c. lead(II) sulfate
59. **a.** 46.01 amu **b.** 58.12 amu
c. 180.16 amu **d.** 238.03 amu
61. **a.** 0.471 mol **b.** 0.0362 mol
c. 968 mol **d.** 0.279 mol
63. **a.** 0.554 mol **b.** 28.4 mol
c. 0.378 mol **d.** 1093 mol
65. **a.** 2.2×10^{23} molecules **b.** 7.06×10^{23} molecules
c. 4.16×10^{23} molecules **d.** 1.09×10^{23} molecules
67. **a.** 0.0790 g **b.** 0.84 g **c.** 2.992×10^{-22} g
69. 0.10 mg
71. **a.** 74.87% C **b.** 79.88% C
c. 92.24% C **d.** 37.23% C
73. NH_3: 82.27% N
$CO(NH_2)_2$: 46.65% N
NH_4NO_3: 35.00% N
$(NH_4)_2SO_4$: 21.20% N
NH_3 has the highest N content.
75. 20.8 g F
77. 196 μg KI
79. **a.** 2:1 **b.** 4:1 **c.** 6:2:1
81. **a.** 0.885 mol H **b.** 5.2 mol H
c. 29 mol H **d.** 33.7 mol H
83. **a.** 3.3 g Na **b.** 3.6 g Na
c. 1.4 g Na **d.** 1.7 g Na
85. 1.41×10^{23} F atoms
87. **a.** Ag_2O **b.** $Co_3As_2O_8$ **c.** $SeBr_4$
89. **a.** C_5H_7N **b.** $C_4H_5N_2O$
91. $C_{13}H_{18}O_2$
93. NCl_3
95. **a.** $C_{12}H_{14}N_2$ **b.** $C_6H_3Cl_3$ **c.** $C_{10}H_{20}N_2S_4$

97. CH_2
99. C_2H_4O
101. a. inorganic **b.** organic
c. organic **d.** inorganic
103. a. alkene **b.** alkane
c. alkyne **d.** alkane
105. a. $CH_3CH_2CH_3$
b. propane
c. $CH_3CH_2CH_2CH_2CH_2CH_2CH_2CH_3$
d. pentane
107. a. functionalized hydrocarbon, alcohol
b. hydrocarbon
c. functionalized hydrocarbon, ketone
d. functionalized hydrocarbon, amine
109. 1.50×10^{24} molecules EtOH
111. a. K_2CrO_4, 40.27% K, 26.78% Cr, 32.95% O
b. $Pb_3(PO_4)_2$, 76.60% Pb, 7.63% P, 15.77% O
c. H_2SO_3, 2.46% H, 39.07% S, 58.47% O
d. $CoBr_2$, 26.94% Co, 73.06% Br
113. 1.80×10^2 g Cl_2/yr
115. M = Fe
117. estradiol = $C_{18}H_{24}O_2$
119. $C_{18}H_{20}O_2$
121. 7 H_2O
123. C_6H_9BrO
125. 1.87×10^{21} atoms
127. 92.93 amu
129. $x = 1, y = 2$
131. 41.7 mg
133. 0.224 g
135. 22.0% by mass
137. 1.6×10^7 kg Cl
139. 7.8×10^3 kg rock
141. $C_5H_{10}SI$
143. X_3Y_2
145. The sphere in the molecular models represents the electron cloud of the atom. On this scale, the nucleus would be too small to see.
147. The statement is incorrect because a chemical formula is based on the ratio of atoms combined, not the ratio of grams combined. The statement should read, "The chemical formula for ammonia (NH_3) indicates that ammonia contains three hydrogen atoms to each nitrogen atom."
149. O, S, H
154. a. Yes. **c.** 50.05%

Chapter 4

13. $2\,SO_2(g) + O_2(g) + 2\,H_2O(l) \longrightarrow 2\,H_2SO_4(aq)$
15. $2\,Na(s) + 2\,H_2O(l) \longrightarrow H_2(g) + 2\,NaOH(aq)$
17. $C_{12}H_{22}O_{11}(s) + H_2O(l) \longrightarrow 4\,C_2H_5OH(aq) + 4\,CO_2(g)$
19. a. $PbS(s) + 2\,HBr(aq) \longrightarrow PbBr_2(s) + H_2S(g)$
b. $CO(g) + 3\,H_2(g) \longrightarrow CH_4(g) + H_2O(l)$
c. $4\,HCl(aq) + MnO_2(g) \longrightarrow MnCl_2(aq) + 2\,H_2O(l) + Cl_2(g)$
d. $C_5H_{12}(l) + 8\,O_2(g) \longrightarrow 5\,CO_2(g) + 6\,H_2O(g)$
21. $Na_2CO_3(aq) + CuCl_2(aq) \longrightarrow CuCO_3(s) + 2\,NaCl(aq)$
23. a. $2\,CO_2(g) + CaSiO_3(s) + H_2O(l) \longrightarrow SiO_2(s) + Ca(HCO_3)_2(aq)$
b. $2\,Co(NO_3)_3(aq) + 3\,(NH_4)_2S(aq) \longrightarrow Co_2S_3(s) + 6\,NH_4NO_3(aq)$
c. $Cu_2O(s) + C(s) \longrightarrow 2\,Cu(s) + CO(g)$
d. $H_2(g) + Cl_2(g) \longrightarrow 2\,HCl(g)$
25. $2\,C_6H_{14}(g) + 19\,O_2(g) \longrightarrow 12\,CO_2(g) + 14\,H_2O(g)$, 68 mol O_2
27. a. 5.0 mol NO_2 **b.** 14. mol NO_2
c. 0.281 mol NO_2 **d.** 53.1 mol NO_2
29.

mol SiO_2	mol C	mol SiC	mol CO
3	9	3	6
2	6	2	4
5	15	5	10
2.8	8.4	2.8	5.6
0.517	1.55	0.517	1.03

31. 9.3 g HBr, 0.12 g H_2
33. a. 5.56 g $BaCl_2$
b. 6.55 g $CaCO_3$
c. 6.09 g Mg O
d. 6.93 g Al_2O_3
35. a. Na **b.** Na **c.** Br_2 **d.** Na
37. 3 molecules Cl_2
39. a. 2 mol **b.** 7 mol **c.** 9.40 mol
41. 0.5 mol O_2
43. a. 2.5 g **b.** 31.1 g **c.** 1.16 g
45. 2.91 grams CO remaining
47. limiting reactant: Pb^{2+} theoretical yield: 34.5 g $PbCl_2$ percent yield: 85.3%
49. limiting reactant: NH_3 theoretical yield: 240.5 kg CH_4N_2O, percent yield: 70.01%
51. a. $S(s) + O_2(g) \longrightarrow SO_2(g)$
b. $2\,C_3H_6(g) + 9\,O_2(g) \longrightarrow 6\,CO_2(g) + 6\,H_2O(g)$
c. $2\,Ca(s) + O_2(g) \longrightarrow 2\,CaO(g)$
d. $C_5H_{12}S(l) + 9\,O_2(g) \longrightarrow 5\,CO_2(g) + SO_2(g) + 6\,H_2O(g)$
53. $Sr(s) + I_2(g) \longrightarrow SrI_2(s)$
55. $2\,Li(s) + 2\,H_2O(l) \longrightarrow 2\,Li^+(aq) + 2\,OH^-(aq) + H_2(g)$
57. $H_2(g) + Br_2(g) \longrightarrow 2\,HBr(g)$
59. 3.1 kg
61. limiting reactant: $C_7H_6O_3$, theoretical yield: 1.63 g $C_9H_8O_4$ percent yield: 74.8%
63. b
65. 0.333 g PH_3
67. 30.8 kg CO_2
69. 1.6 g C_2H_2
71. 2.8 mol A
73. 96.6 g Mn
75. d. 1.5 g K, 0.38 g O_2
77. a)
81. a. Experiments 1, 2, and 3
c. 2 A + 1 B **e.** 2 C

Chapter 5

21. a. 1.17 M LiCl **b.** 0.123 M $C_6H_{12}O_6$ **c.** 0.00453 M NaCl

23. a. 0.150 M NO_3^- **b.** 0.300 M NO_3^- **c.** 0.450 M NO_3^-

25. a. 1.3 mol **b.** 1.5 mol **c.** 0.211 mol

27. 37 g

29. 0.27 M

31. 6.0 L

33. 37.1 mL

35. 2.1 L

37. lead nitrate, 3.75 g, 65.3%

39. a. yes **b.** no **c.** yes **d.** no

41. a. soluble Ag^+, NO_3^-
b. soluble Pb^{2+}, $C_2H_3O_2^-$
c. soluble K^+, NO_3^-
d. soluble NH_4^+, S^{2-}

43. a. NO REACTION
b. NO REACTION
c. $CrBr_2(aq) + Na_2CO_3(aq) \longrightarrow CrCO_3(s) + 2\,NaBr(aq)$
d. $3\,NaOH(aq) + FeCl_3(aq) \longrightarrow Fe(OH)_3(s) + 3\,NaCl(aq)$

45. a. $K_2CO_3(aq) + Pb(NO_3)_2(aq) \longrightarrow PbCO_3(s) + 2\,KNO_3(aq)$
b. $Li_2SO_4(aq) + Pb(C_2H_3O_2)_2(aq) \longrightarrow PbSO_4(s) + 2\,LiC_2H_3O_2(aq)$
c. $Cu(NO_3)_2(aq) + MgS(aq) \longrightarrow CuS(s) + Mg(NO_3)_2(aq)$
d. NO REACTION

47. a. Complete:
$H^+(aq) + Cl^-(aq) + Li^+(aq) + OH^-(aq) \longrightarrow H_2O(l) + Li^+(aq) + Cl^-(aq)$
Net: $H^+(aq) + OH^-(aq) \longrightarrow H_2O(l)$
b. Complete:
$Ca^{2+}(aq) + S^{2-}(aq) + Cu^{2+}(aq) + 2\,Cl^-(aq) \longrightarrow CuS(s) + Ca^{2+}(aq) + 2\,Cl^-(aq)$
Net: $Cu^{2+}(aq) + S^{2-}(aq) \longrightarrow CuS(s)$
c. Complete:
$Na^+(aq) + OH^-(aq) + HC_2H_3O_2(aq) \longrightarrow H_2O(l) + Na^+(aq) + C_2H_3O_2^-(aq)$
Net: $OH^-(aq) + HC_2H_3O_2(aq) \longrightarrow H_2O(l) + C_2H_3O_2^-(aq)$
d. Complete:
$6\,Na^+(aq) + 2\,PO_4^{3-}(aq) + 3\,Ni^{2+}(aq) + 6\,Cl^-(aq) \longrightarrow Ni_3(PO_4)_2(s) + 6\,Na^+(aq) + 6\,Cl^-(aq)$
Net: $3\,Ni^{2+}(aq) + 2\,PO_4^{3-}(aq) \longrightarrow Ni_3(PO_4)_2(s)$

49. Complete:
$Hg_2^{2+}(aq) + 2\,NO_3^-(aq) + 2\,Na^+(aq) + 2\,Cl^-(aq) \longrightarrow Hg_2Cl_2(s) + 2\,Na^+(aq) + 2\,NO_3^-(aq)$
Net: $Hg_2^{2+}(aq) + 2\,Cl^-(aq) \longrightarrow Hg_2Cl_2(s)$

51. Molecular:
$HBr(aq) + KOH(aq) \longrightarrow H_2O(l) + KBr(aq)$
Net ionic: $H^+(aq) + OH^-(aq) \longrightarrow H_2O(l)$

53. a. $H_2SO_4(aq) + Ca(OH)_2(aq) \longrightarrow 2\,H_2O(l) + CaSO_4(s)$
b. $HClO_4(aq) + KOH(aq) \longrightarrow H_2O(l) + KClO_4(aq)$
c. $H_2SO_4(aq) + 2\,NaOH(aq) \longrightarrow 2\,H_2O(l) + Na_2SO_4(aq)$

55. a. Complete ionic:
$H^+(aq) + Br^-(aq) + Na^+(aq) + OH^-(aq) \longrightarrow H_2O(l) + Na^+(aq) + Br^-(aq)$
Net ionic: $H^+(aq)\ OH^-(aq) \longrightarrow H_2O(l)$
b. Complete ionic:
$HF(aq) + Na^+(aq) + OH^-(aq) \longrightarrow H_2O(l) + Na^+(aq) + F^-(aq)$
Net ionic:
$HF(aq) + OH^-(aq) \longrightarrow H_2O(l) + F^-(aq)$
c. Complete ionic:
$HC_2H_3O_2(aq) + Rb^+(aq) + OH^-(aq) \longrightarrow H_2O(l) + Rb^+(aq) + C_2H_3O_2^-(aq)$
Net ionic:
$HC_2H_3O_2(aq) + OH^-(aq) \longrightarrow H_2O(l) + C_2H_3O_2^-(aq)$

57. 0.1810 M $HClO_4$

59. a. $2\,HBr(aq) + NiS(s) \longrightarrow H_2S(g) + NiBr_2(aq)$
b. $NH_4I(aq) + NaOH(aq) \longrightarrow H_2O(l) + NH_3(g) + NaI(aq)$
c. $2\,HBr(aq) + Na_2S(aq) \longrightarrow H_2S(g) + 2\,NaBr(aq)$
d. $2\,HClO_4(aq) + Li_2CO_3(aq) \longrightarrow H_2O(l) + CO_2(g) + 2\,LiClO_4(aq)$

61. a. Ag: 0 **b.** Ag: +1
c. Ca: +2, F: −1 **d.** H: +1, S: −2
e. C: +4, O: −2 **f.** Cr: +6, O: −2

63. a. +2 **b.** +6 **c.** +3

65. a. redox reaction, oxidizing agent: O_2 reducing agent: Li
b. redox reaction, oxidizing agent: Fe^{2+} reducing agent: Mg
c. not a redox reaction **d.** not a redox reaction

67. b and c occur spontaneously in the forward direction.

69. Fe, Cr, Zn, Mn, Al, Mg, Na, Ca, K, Li

71. Mg

73. 3.32 M

75. 1.1 g

77. a. $2\,HCl(aq) + Hg_2(NO_3)_2(aq) \longrightarrow Hg_2Cl_2(s) + 2\,HNO_3(aq)$
b. $KHSO_3(aq) + HNO_3(aq) \longrightarrow H_2O(l) + SO_2(g) + KNO_3(aq)$
c. $2\,NH_4Cl(aq) + Pb(NO_3)_2(aq) \longrightarrow PbCl_2(s) + 2\,NH_4NO_3(aq)$
d. $2\,NH_4Cl(aq) + Ca(OH)_2(aq) \longrightarrow 2\,NH_3(g) + 2\,H_2O(g) + CaCl_2(aq)$

79. 22 g

81. 6.9 g

83. Br is the oxidizing agent, Au is the reducing agent, 38.8 g $KAuF_4$.

85. Ca^{2+} and Cu^{2+} present in the original solution.
Net ionic for first precipitate:
$Ca^{2+}(aq) + SO_4^{2-}(aq) \longrightarrow CaSO_4(s)$
Net ionic for second precipitate:
$Cu^{2+}(aq) + CO_3^{2-}(aq) \longrightarrow CuCO_3(s)$

87. 11.8 g AgI

89. 5.5% by mass

91. a. Add 4 particles of solute.
b. Add 1 L solvent.
c. Add 0.3 L solvent.
93. b.
98. a. 10.3 ppb; 3.81 ppb, 1.69 ppb
c. If the water provider used first-draw samples, they would have been required to take action. If they used 2 min flush samples, they woud not have been required to take action. Residents probably don't flush their pipes before taking water, so the first-draw technique is probably closer to actual practice.

Chapter 6

25. a. 0.832 atm **b.** 632 mmHg
c. 12.2 psi **d.** 8.43×10^4 Pa
27. a. 809.0 mmHg **b.** 1.064 atm
c. 809.0 torr **d.** 107.9 kPa
29. a. 832 mmHg **b.** 718 mmHg
31. 4.4×10^2 mmHg
33. 58.9 mL
35. 4.22 L
37. 3.0 L. The volume would not be different if the gas was argon.
39. 1.16 atm
41. 2.1 mol
43. Yes, the final gauge pressure is 43.5 psi, which exceeds the maximum rating.
45. 16.2 L
47. 286 atm, 17.5 bottles purged
49. b
51. 4.76 atm
53. 37.3 L
55. 9.43 g/L
57. 44.0 g/mol
59. 4.00 g/mol
61. $P_{tot} = 434$ torr, $mass_{N_2} = 0.437$ g, $mass_{O_2} = 0.237$ g, $mass_{He} = 0.0340$ g
63. 1.84 atm
65. $\chi_{N_2} = 0.627, \chi_{O_2} = 0.373$, $P_{N_2} = 0.687$ atm, $P_{O_2} = 0.409$ atm
67. $P_{H_2} = 0.921$ atm, $mass_{H_2} = 0.0539$ g
69. 7.47×10^{-2} g
71. 38 L
73. $V_{H_2} = 48.2$ L, $V_{CO} = 24.1$ L
75. 22.8 g NaN_3
77. 60.4%
79. F_2, 2.84 g ClF_3
81. a. yes
b. no
c. No. Even though the argon atoms are more massive than the helium atoms, both have the same kinetic energy at a given temperature. The argon atoms therefore move more slowly and so exert the same pressure as the helium atoms.
d. He
83. $F_2: u_{rms} = 442$ m/s, $KE_{avg} = 3.72 \times 10^3$ J;
$Cl_2: u_{rms} = 324$ m/s, $KE_{avg} = 3.72 \times 10^3$ J;
$Br_2: u_{rms} = 216$ m/s, $KE_{avg} = 3.72 \times 10^3$ J;
rankings: $u_{rms}: Br_2 < Cl_2 < F_2$, $KE_{avg}: Br_2 = Cl_2 = F_2$,
rate of effusion: $Br_2 < Cl_2 <$ F2
85. rate $^{238}UF_6$/rate $^{235}UF_6 = 0.99574$
87. krypton
89. A has the higher molar mass, B has the higher rate of effusion.
91. That the volume of gas particles is small compared to the space between them breaks down under conditions of high pressure. At high pressure, the particles themselves occupy a significant portion of the total gas volume.
93. 0.05826 L (ideal); 0.0708 L (V.D.W.); difference because of high pressure, at which Ne no longer acts ideally
95. 97.8%
97. 27.8 g/mol
99. C_4H_{10}
101. 4.70 L
103. $2\,HCl(aq) + K_2S(s) \longrightarrow H_2S(g) + 2\,KCl(aq)$, 0.191 g $K_2S(s)$
105. 11.7 L
107. $mass_{air} = 8.56$ g, $mass_{He} = 1.20$ g, mass difference $= 7.36$ g
109. 4.76 L/s
111. total force $= 6.15 \times 10^3$ pounds; no, the can cannot withstand this force.
113. 5.8×10^3 balloons
115. 4.0 cm
117. 77.7%
119. 0.32 gram
121. 311 K
123. 5.0 g
125. C_3H_8
127. 0.39 g Ar
129. 74.0 mmHg
131. 25% N_2H_4
133. 25%
135. $P_{CH_4} = 7.30 \times 10^{-2}$ atm, $P_{O_2} = 4.20 \times 10^{-1}$ atm, $P_{NO} = 2.79 \times 10^{-3}$ atm, $P_{CO_2} = 5.03 \times 10^{-3}$ atm, $P_{H_2O} = 5.03 \times 10^{-3}$ atm, $P_{NO_2} = 2.51 \times 10^{-2}$ atm, $P_{OH} = 1.01 \times 10^{-2}$ atm, $P_{tot} = 0.542$ atm
137. 0.42
139. Because helium is less dense than air, the balloon moves in a direction opposite the direction in which the air inside the car is moving due to the acceleration and deceleration of the car.
141. −29%
143. a. false **b.** false **c.** false **d.** true
145. four times the initial pressure
147. Although the velocity "tails" have different lengths, the average length of the tails on the helium atoms is longer than the average length of the tails on the neon atoms, which is in turn longer than the average length of the tails on the krypton atoms. The lighter the

atom, the faster the tails must move on average to have the same kinetic energy.

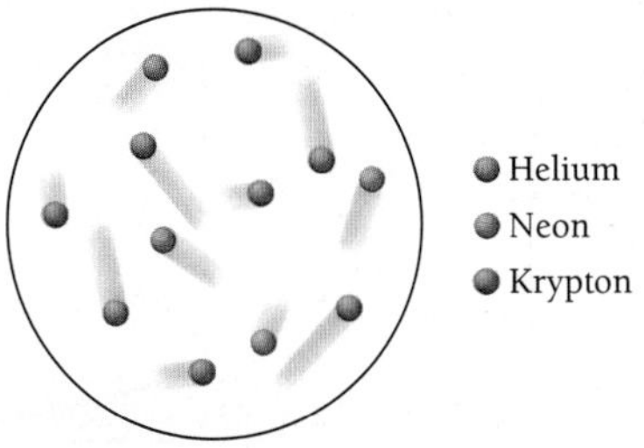

153. a. inverse relationship
c. 1.3×10^{-6} mol
e. Yes, because in these equations, 1 mole of O_3 reacts to form 1 mole of NO_2.

Chapter 7

33. a. 1.92×10^9 J **b.** 5.14×10^4 cal
c. 2.37×10^6 J **d.** 0.681 Cal
35. a. 9.987×10^6 J **b.** 9.987×10^3 kJ
c. 2.78 kWh
37. d
39. a. heat, + **b.** work, – **c.** heat, +
41. -7.27×10^2 kJ
43. 311 kJ
45. The drinks that went into cooler B had more thermal energy than the refrigerated drinks that went into cooler A. The temperature difference between the drinks in cooler B and the ice was greater than the difference between the drinks and the ice in cooler A. More thermal energy was exchanged between the drinks and the ice in cooler B, which resulted in more melting.
47. 4.7×10^5 J
49. a. 7.6×10^2 °C
b. 4.3×10^2 °C
c. 1.3×10^2 °C
d. 49 °C
51. -2.8×10^2 J
53. 489 J
55. $\Delta E = -3463$ kJ, $\Delta H = -3452$ kJ
57. a. exothermic, –
b. endothermic, +
c. exothermic, –
59. -4.30×10^3 kJ
61. 6.46×10^4 kJ
63. 1.0 kg CO_2
65. mass of silver 77.1 grams
67. final temperature 28.4 °C
69. specific heat capacity of substance A 1.10 J/g · °C
71. Measurement B corresponds to conditions of constant pressure. Measurement A corresponds to conditions of constant volume. When a fuel is burned under constant pressure, some of the energy released does work on the atmosphere by expanding against it. Less energy is manifest as heat due to this work. When a fuel is burned under constant volume, all of the energy released by the combustion reaction is evolved as heat.
73. -6.3×10^3 kJ/mol
75. -1.6×10^5 J
77. a. $-\Delta H_1$
b. $2\ \Delta H_1$
c. $-\frac{1}{2}\Delta H_1$
79. –23.9 kJ
81. –173.2 kJ
83. a. $N_2(g) + 3\,H_2(g) \longrightarrow 2\,NH_3(g)$, $\Delta H_f^\circ = -45.9$ kJ/mol
b. $C(s, \text{graphite}) + O_2(g) \longrightarrow CO_2(g)$, $\Delta H_f^\circ = -393.5$ kJ/mol
c. $2\,Fe(s) + 3/2\,O_2(g) \longrightarrow Fe_2O_3(s)$, $\Delta H_f^\circ = -824.2$ kJ/mol
d. $C(s, \text{graphite}) + 2\,H_2(g) \longrightarrow CH_4(g)$, $\Delta H_f^\circ = -74.6$ kJ/mol
85. -380.2 kJ/mol
87. a. -137.1 kJ **b.** -41.2 kJ
c. -137 kJ **d.** 290.7 kJ
89. $6\,CO_2(g) + 6\,H_2O(l) \longrightarrow C_6H_{12}O_6(s) + 6\,O_2(g)$, $\Delta H_{rxn}^\circ = 2803$ kJ
91. -113.0 kJ/mol
93. a. 5.49 g CO_2 **b.** 6.46 g CO_2
c. 6.94 g CO_2
Natural gas, $CH_4(g)$, contributes the least to global warming by producing the least $CO_2(g)$ per kJ of heat produced.
95. 2×10^{13} kg CO_2 produced per year, 150 years
97. $\Delta E = -1.7$ J, $q = -0.5$ J, $w = -1.2$ J
99. 78 g
101. $\Delta H = 6.0$ kJ/mol, 1.1×10^2 g
103. 26.1 °C
105. palmitic acid: 9.9378 Cal/g; sucrose: 3.938 Cal/g; fat contains more Cal/g than sugar.
107. $\Delta H = \Delta E + nR\Delta T$
109. 5.7 Cal/g
111. $\Delta E = 0$, $\Delta H = 0$, $q = -w = 3.0 \times 10^3$ J
113. –294 kJ/mol
115. 94.0 kJ
117. 23.9 °C
119. 7.3×10^3 g H_2SO_4
121. 7.2×10^2 g
123. 78.2 °C
125. $C_v = \frac{3}{2}R$, $C_p = \frac{5}{2}R$
127. $q = 1030$ kJ, $\Delta H = 1030$ kJ, $\Delta E = 952$ kJ, $w = -78$ kJ
129. –1292 kJ
131. d
133. a. At constant pressure, heat can be added and work can be done on the system. $\Delta E = q + w$; therefore, $q = \Delta E - w$.
135. The aluminum is cooler because it has a lower heat capacity (specific heat).
137. $q = -2418$ J, $w = -5$ kJ,
$\Delta H = -2418$ J/mol, $\Delta E = -2423$ J/mol
139. b. $\Delta H > \Delta E$
144. a. $C_3H_8(g) + 5\,O_2(g) \longrightarrow 3\,CO_2(g) + 4\,H_2O(l)$
$C_3H_8(g) + 5\,O_2(g) \longrightarrow 3\,CO_2(g) + 4\,H_2O(g)$
c. LLV because the water formed is the gaseous state; 46.3×10^3 kJ

Chapter 8

35. 499 s

37. i. d, c, b, a
ii. a, b, c, d

39. a. 4.74×10^{14} Hz
b. 5.96×10^{14} Hz
c. 5.8×10^{18} Hz

41. a. 3.14×10^{-19} J
b. 3.95×10^{-19} J
c. 3.8×10^{-15} J

43. 1.03×10^{16} photons

45. a. 79.8 kJ/mol
b. 239 kJ/mol
c. 798 kJ/mol

47.

49. 3.6×10^6 m/s

51. 5.39 nm

53. 1.1×10^{-34} m. The wavelength of a baseball is negligible with respect to its size.

55. $\Delta v = 1.04 \times 10^5$ m/s

57. 2*s*

59. a. $l = 0$
b. $l = 0, 1$
c. $l = 0, 1, 2$
d. $l = 0, 1, 2, 3$

61. c

63. See **Figures 7.25** and **7.26**. The 2*s* and 3*p* orbitals would, on average, be farther from the nucleus and have more nodes than the 1*s* and 2*p* orbitals.

65. $n = 1$

67. $2p \longrightarrow 1s$

69. a. 122 nm, UV
b. 103 nm, UV
c. 486 nm, visible
d. 434 nm, visible

71. $n = 2$

73. 344 nm

75. 6.4×10^{17} photons/s

77. 0.0547 nm

79. 91.2 nm

81. a. 4
b. 9
c. 16

83. $n=4 \longrightarrow n=3, n=5 \longrightarrow n=3, n=6 \longrightarrow n=3$, respectively

85. $4.84 \times 10^{14}\ s^{-1}$

87. 11 m

89. 6.78×10^{-3} J

91. 632 nm

93. 2.98×10^{-4} mol

95. a. $E_1 = 2.51 \times 10^{-18}$ J, $E_2 = 1.00 \times 10^{-17}$ J, $E_3 = 2.26 \times 10^{-17}$ J
b. 26.5 nm, UV; 15.8 nm, UV

97.

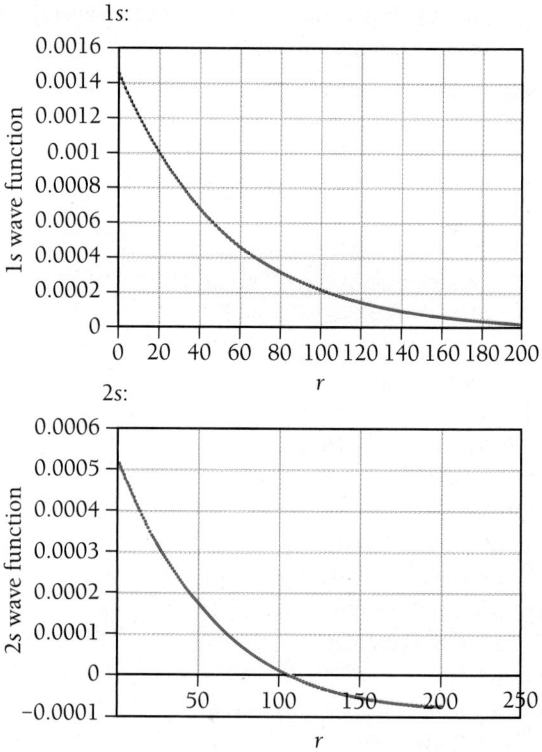

The plot for the 2*s* wave function extends below the *x*-axis. The *x*-intercept represents the radial node of the orbital.

99. 7.39×10^5 m/s

101. $\Delta E = 1.1 \times 10^{-20}$ J, 7.0×10^2 nm

103. 11 m

105. In the Bohr model, electrons exist in specific orbits encircling the atom. In the quantum-mechanical model, electrons exist in orbitals that are really probability density maps of where the electron is likely to be found. The Bohr model is inconsistent with Heisenberg's uncertainty principle.

107. a. yes **b.** no **c.** yes **d.** no

114. a. 5.93×10^{-19} J **c.** 2-EHMC
e. 1.4×10^7 J

Chapter 9

39. a. $1s^2 2s^2 2p^6 3s^2 3p^2$ **b.** $1s^2 2s^2 2p^4$
c. $1s^2 2s^2 2p^6 3s^2 3p^6 4s^1$ **d.** $1s^2 2s^2 2p^6$

41. a.

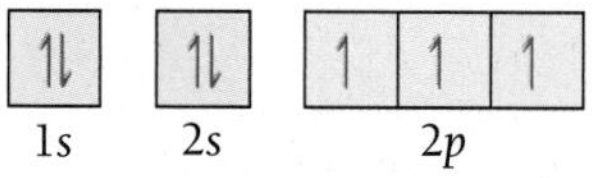

b.

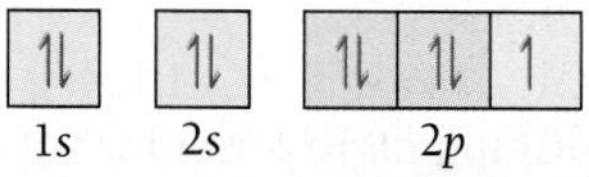

c.

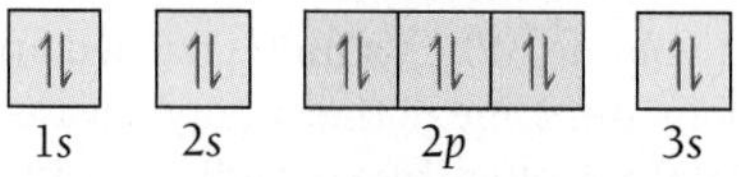

d.

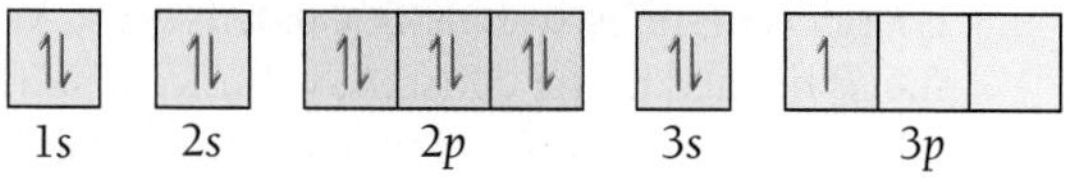

43. a. $[Ne]3s^23p^3$ **b.** $[Ar]4s^23d^{10}4p^2$
c. $[Kr]5s^24d^2$ **d.** $[Kr]5s^24d^{10}5p^5$

45. a. 1 **b.** 10 **c.** 5 **d.** 2

47. a. V, As **b.** Se **c.** V **d.** Kr

49. a. 2 **b.** 1 **c.** 10 **d.** 6

51. reactive metal: **a**, reactive nonmetal: **c**

53. c

55. The valence electrons of nitrogen will experience a greater effective nuclear charge. The valence electrons of both atoms are screened by two core electrons, but N has a greater number of protons and therefore a greater net nuclear charge.

57. a. 1+ **b.** 2+ **c.** 6+ **d.** 4+

59. a. In **b.** Si **c.** Pb **d.** C

61. F, S, Si, Ge, Ca, Rb

63. a. [Ne] **b.** [Kr] **c.** [Kr]
d. $[Ar]3d^6$ **e.** $[Ar]3d^9$

65. a. [Ar] Diamagnetic

b. [Ar] | ↿ | ↿ | ↿ | | | Paramagnetic
3d

c. [Ar] | ⥮ | ⥮ | ⥮ | ↿ | ↿ | Paramagnetic
3d

d. [Ar] | ↿ | ↿ | ↿ | ↿ | ↿ | Paramagnetic
3d

67. a. Li **b.** I^- **c.** Cr **d.** O^{2-}

69. O^{2-}, F^-, Na^+, Mg^{2+}

71. a. Br
b. Na
c. cannot tell based on periodic trends
d. P

73. In, Si, N, F

75. a. second and third **b.** fifth and sixth
c. sixth and seventh **d.** first and second

77. a. Na **b.** S **c.** C **d.** F

79. a. Sr **b.** Bi
c. cannot tell based on periodic trends
d. As

81. S, Se, Sb, In, Ba, Fr

83. Br:$1s^22s^22p^63s^23p^64s^23d^{10}4p^5$
Kr:$1s^22s^22p^63s^23p^64s^23d^{10}4p^6$
Krypton's outer electron shell is filled, giving it chemical stability. Bromine is missing an electron from its outer shell and subsequently has a high electron affinity. Bromine tends to be easily reduced by gaining an electron, giving the bromide ion stability due to the filled *p* subshell that corresponds to krypton's chemically stable electron configuration.

85. V:$[Ar]\ 4s^23d^3$
V^{3+}:$[Ar]\ 3d^2$
Both V and V^{3+} contain unpaired electrons in their 3*d* orbitals.

87. A substitute for K^+ would need to exhibit a 1+ electric charge and have similar mass and atomic radius. Na^+ and Rb^+ would not be good substitutes because their radii are significantly smaller and larger, respectively. Based on mass, Ca^+ and Ar^+ are the closest to K^+. Because the first ionization energy of Ca^+ is closest to that of K^+, Ca^+, is the best choice for a substitute. The difficulty lies in Ca's low second ionization energy, making it easily oxidized.

89. Si, Ge

91. a. N:[He] $2s^22p^3$, Mg:[Ne]$3s^2$, O:[He]$2s^22p^4$,%
F:[He] $2s^22p^5$, Al:[Ne] $3s^23p^1$%
b. Mg, Al, O, F, N
c. Al, Mg, O, N, F
d. Aluminum's first ionization energy is lower than Mg because its 3*p* electron is shielded by the 3*s* orbital. Oxygen's first ionization energy is lower than that of N because its fourth 2*p* electron experiences electron–electron repulsion by the other electron in its orbital.

93. For main-group elements, atomic radii decrease across a period because the addition of a proton in the nucleus and an electron in the outermost energy level increases Z_{eff}. This does not happen in the transition metals because the electrons are added to the $n_{highest-1}$ orbital and the Z_{eff} stays roughly the same.

95. Noble gases are exceptionally unreactive due to the stability of their completely filled outer quantum levels and their high ionization energies. The ionization energies of Kr, Xe, and Rn are low enough to form some compounds.

97. 6A: ns^2np^4, 7A: ns^2np^5, group 7A elements require only one electron to achieve a noble gas configuration. Since group 6A elements require two electrons, their affinity for one electron is less negative because one electron will merely give them an np^5 configuration.

99. 85

101. a. One If By Land (O, Ne, I, F, B, Y, La, Nd)
b. Atoms Are Fun (N, U, Fe, Ra, S, Mo, Ta backward)

103. 1.390×10^3 kJ/mol, 86.14 nm

105. a. F **b.** B **c.** B **d.** O

107. a. $d_{Ar} \approx 2$ g/L, $d_{Xe} \approx 6.5$ g/L
b. $d_{118} \approx 13$ g/L
c. mass $= 3.35 \times 10^{-23}$ g/Ne atom, density of Ne atom $= 2.3 \times 10^4$ g/L. The separation of Ne atoms relative to their size is immense.
d. Kr:2.69×10^{22} atoms/L, Ne:2.69×10^{22} atoms/L. It seems Ar will also have 2.69×10^{22} atoms/L. $d_{Ar} = 1.78$ g/L. This corresponds to accepted values.

109. Density increases to the right because, though electrons are added successively across the period, they are added to the 3*d* subshell, which is not a part of the outermost principal energy level. As a result, the atomic radius does not increase significantly across the period, while mass does.

111.

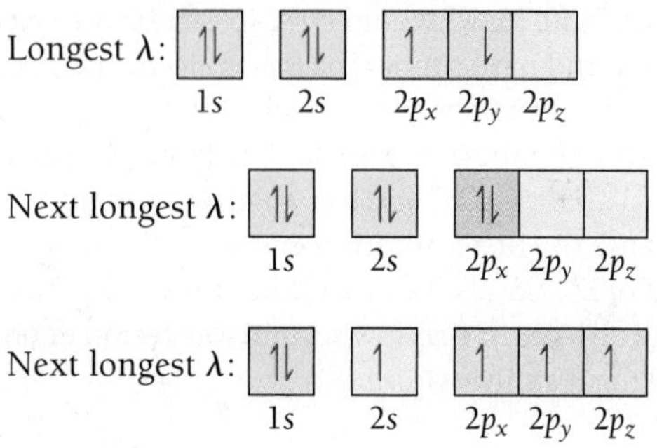

113. 168, noble gas

115. A relatively high effective nuclear charge is found in gallium with its completed 3*d* subshell and in thallium with its completed 4*f* subshell, accounting for the relatively high first ionization energies of these elements.

117. The second electron affinity requires the addition of an electron to something that is already negatively charged. The monoanions of both of these elements have relatively high electron density in a relatively small volume.

119. 120, 170

121. Fr, [Rn] $7s^1$, >265, <376, >1.879, <29
a. $Fr^+(aq)$, $OH^-(aq)$, $H_2(g)$
b. $Fr_2O(s)$
c. FrCl(s)

123. **a.** any group 6A element **b.** any group 5A element **c.** any group 1A element

125. **a.** true **b.** true **c.** false **d.** true

127. Since Ca has valence electrons of $4s^2$, it has a relatively low ionization energy to lose two electrons. F has a highly exothermic electron affinity when gaining one electron but not a second electron because of its $2s^22p^5$ valence electrons. Therefore, calcium and fluoride combine in a 2:1 ratio.

133. **a.** First ionization energy generally increases as you move from left to right across period 3 because effective nuclear charge increases from left to right.
c. Electron affinity generally decreases (becomes more exothermic) from left to right across period 3 because effective nuclear charge increases from left to right.
e. The overall energy change is approximately 150 kJ/mol. The exchange is endothermic.

Chapter 10

35. $1s^2\underline{2s^22p^3}$ ·N̈:

37. **a.** Al **b.** Na^+ **c.** Cl **d.** $[Cl]^-$

39. **a.** $Na^+[F]^-$ **b.** $Ca^{2+}[O]^{2-}$ **c.** $Sr^{2+}2[Br]^-$ **d.** $2\ K^+[O]^{2-}$

41. **a.** SrSe **b.** $BaCl_2$ **c.** Na_2S **d.** Al_2O_3

43. As the size of the alkaline earth metal ions increases, so does the distance between the metal cations and oxygen anions. Therefore, the magnitude of the lattice energy decreases accordingly because the potential energy decreases as the distance increases.

45. One factor of lattice energy is the product of the charges of the two ions. The product of the ion charges for CsF is −1, while that for BaO is −4. Because this product is four times greater, the lattice energy is also four times greater.

47. −708 kJ/mol

49. **a.** H:H, filled duets, 0 formal charge on both atoms
b. Cl—Cl, filled octets, 0 formal charge on both atoms
c. O=O, filled octets, 0 formal charge on both atoms
d. N≡N, filled octets, 0 formal charge on both atoms

51.

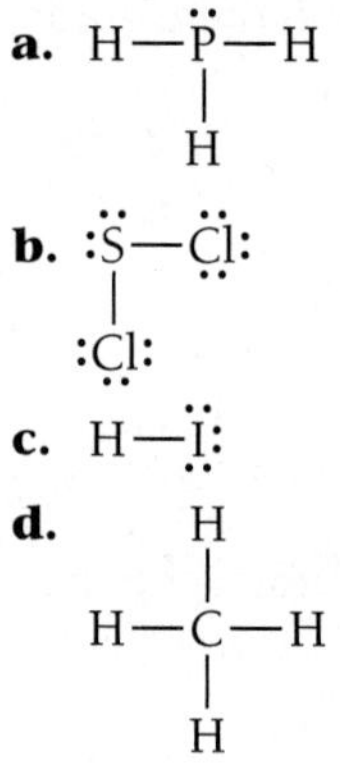

53.

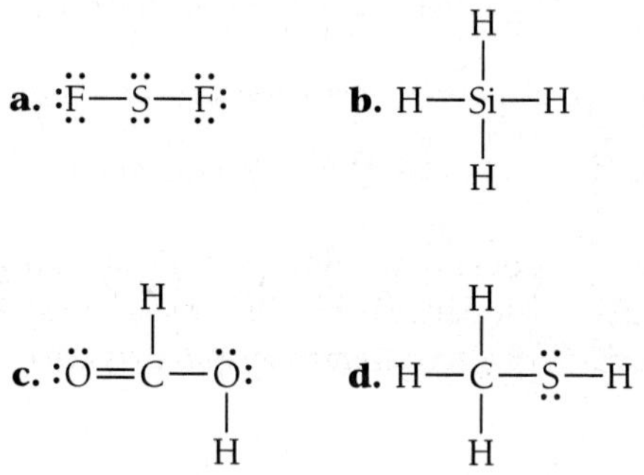

55. **a.** pure covalent
b. polar covalent
c. pure covalent
d. ionic bond

57. :C≡O:, 25%

59.

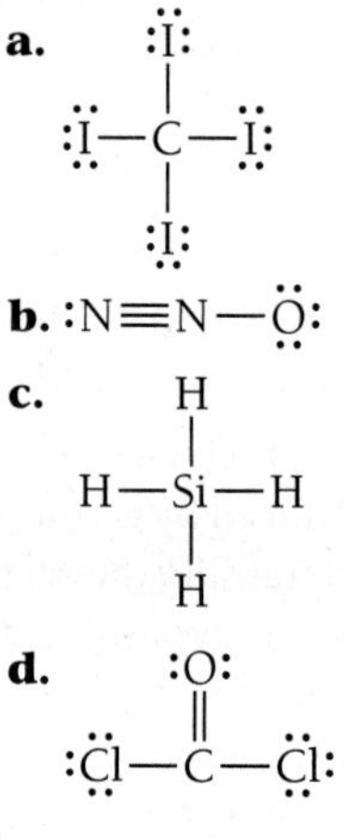

61. a. 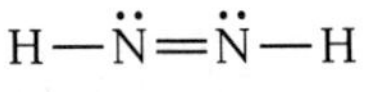 **b.** 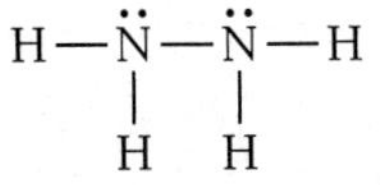

c. 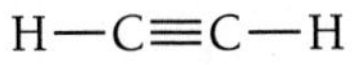 **d.** 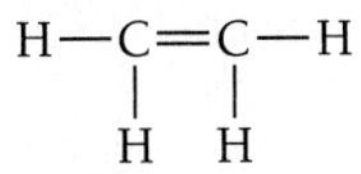

63. a. 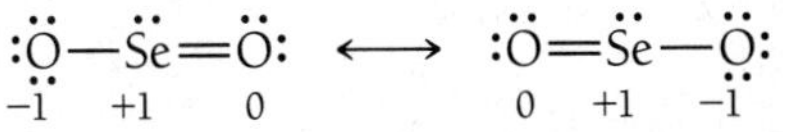

b. 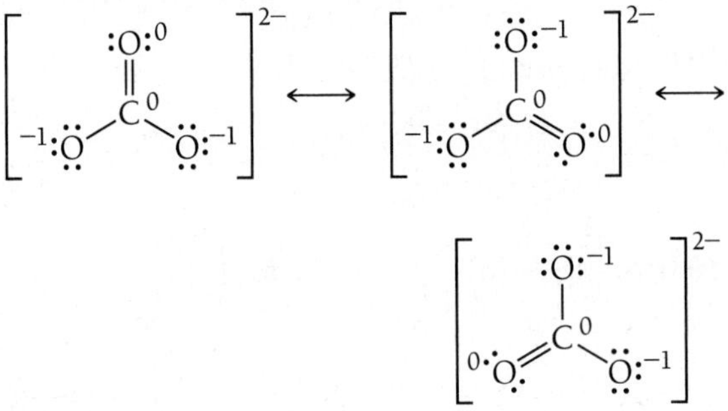

c. 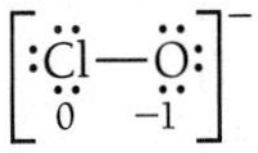

d. 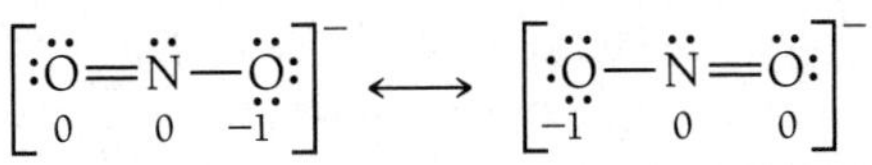

65. 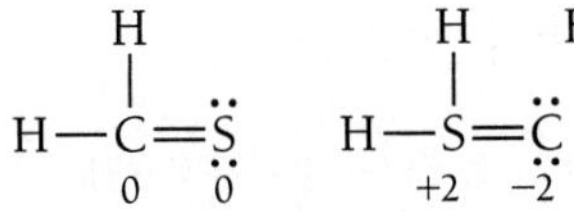 H_2CS is the better structure.

67. :O≡C—Ö: does not provide a significant contribution to the resonance hybrid as it has a +1 formal charge on a very electronegative atom (oxygen).

69. 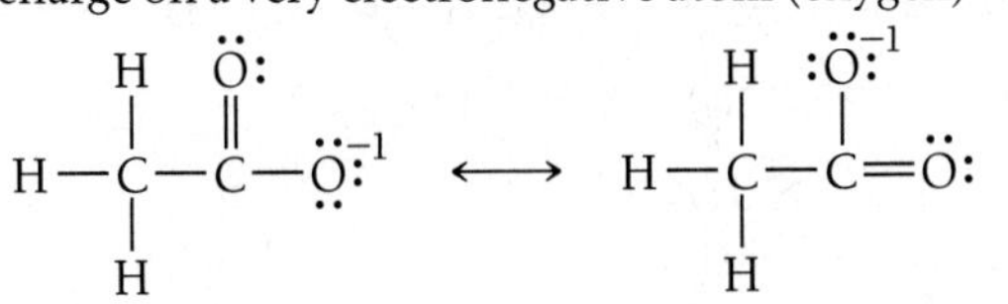

71. N has a formal charge of +1; O has a formal charge of −1.

73. a. 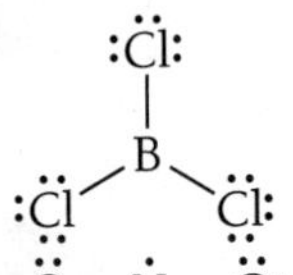

b. 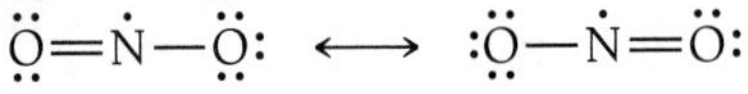

c. 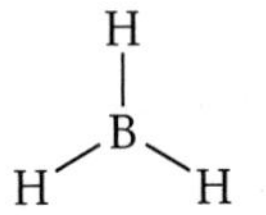

75. a. 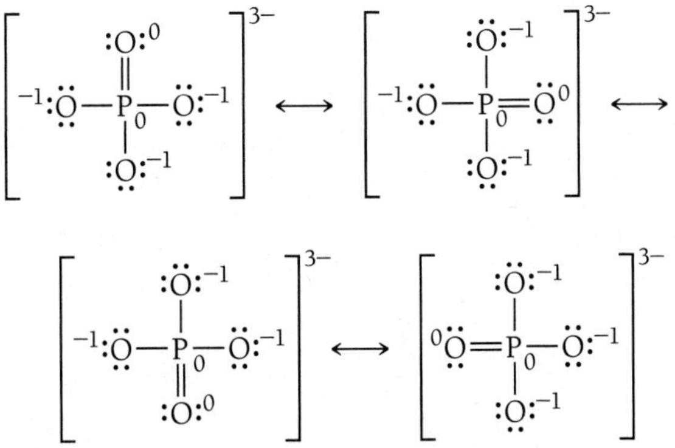

b. 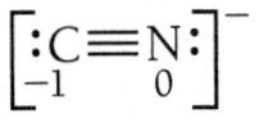

c. 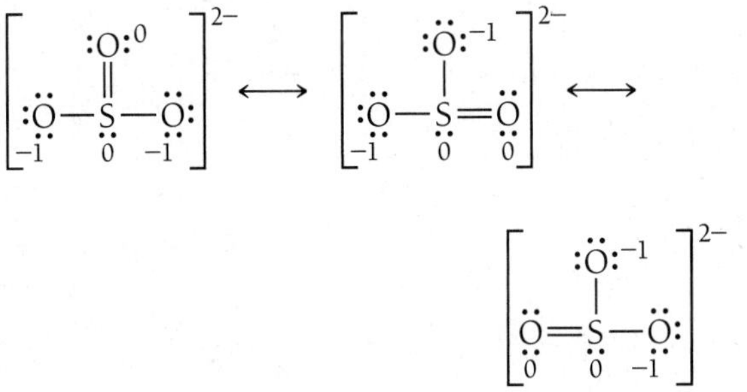

d. 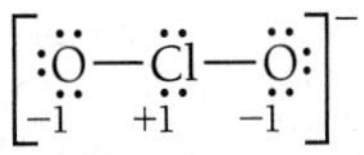

77. a. 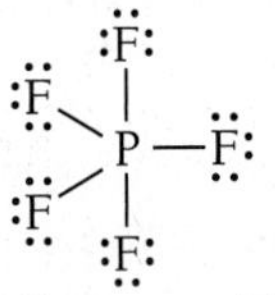

b. 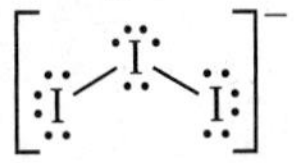

c. 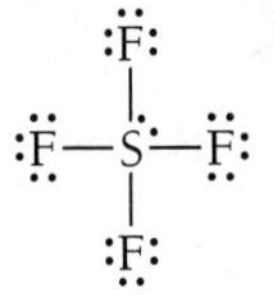

d. 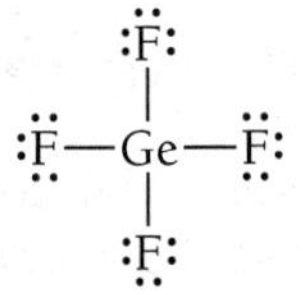

79. H_3CCH_3, H_2CCH_2, HCCH

81. −128 kJ

83. −2812 kJ

85. a. 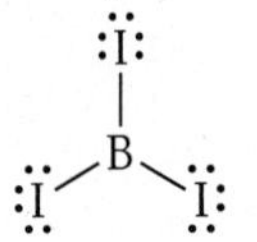

b. 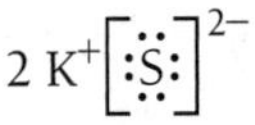

c. 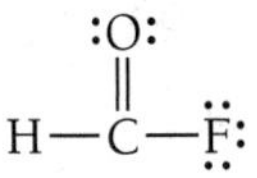

d. 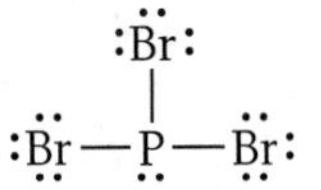

87. a. 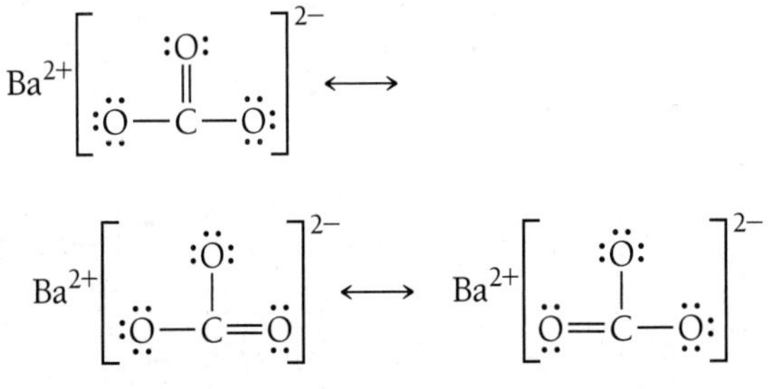

b. 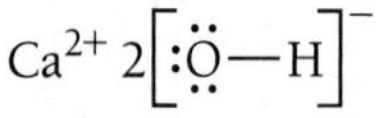

c. 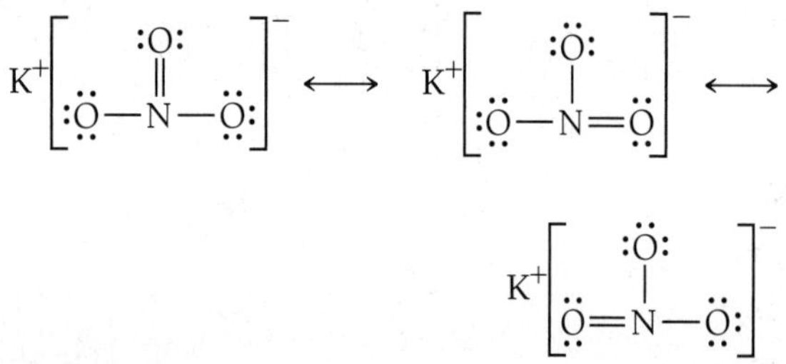

d. 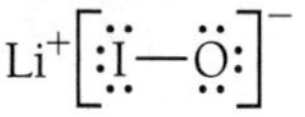

89. a. 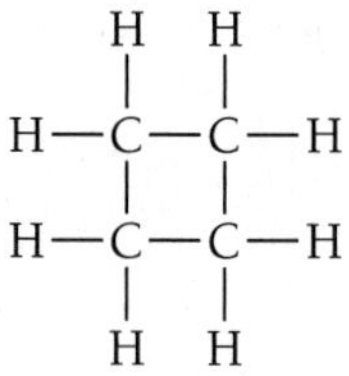

b. 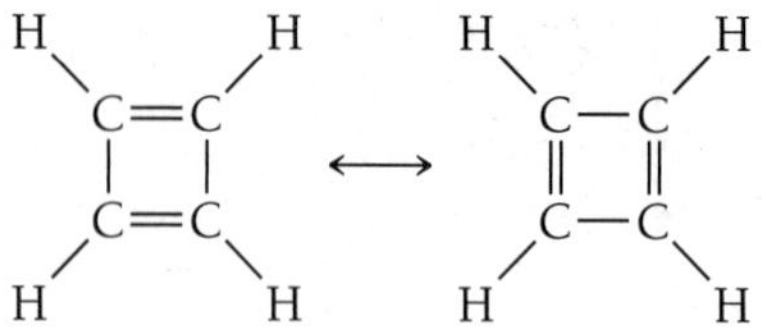

c. 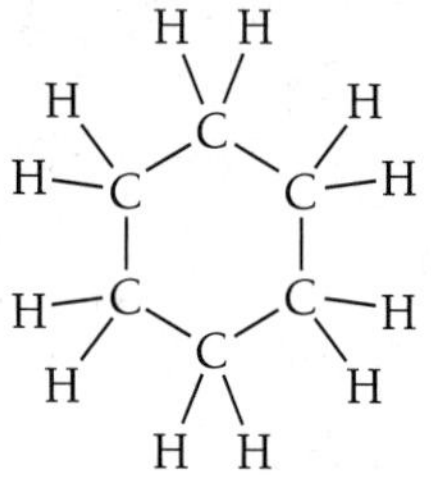

d. 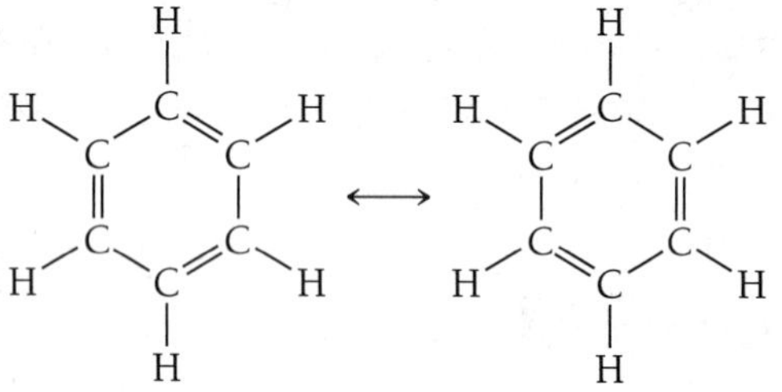

91. CH_2O_2, 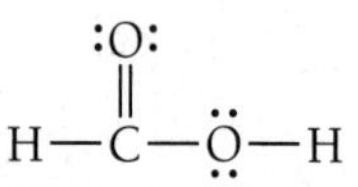

93. The reaction is exothermic due to the energy released when the Al_2O_3 lattice forms.

95. 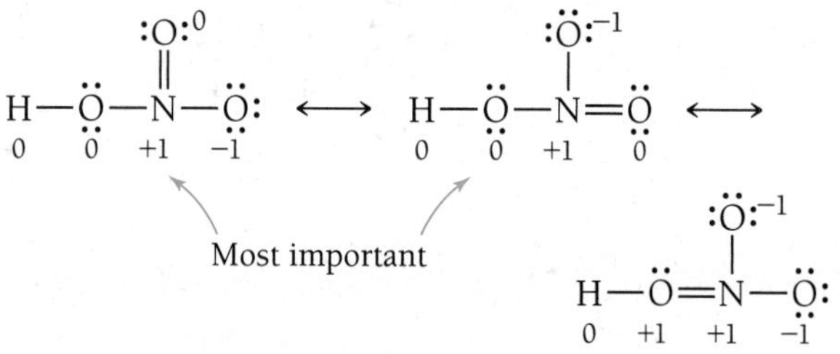

97. 

The fulminate ion is less stable because nitrogen is more electronegative than carbon and should therefore be terminal to accommodate the negative formal charge.

99. a. 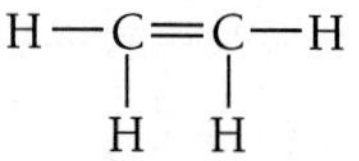

b. 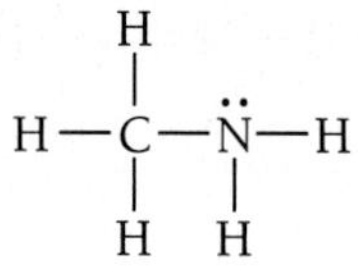

c. 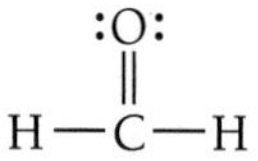

d. 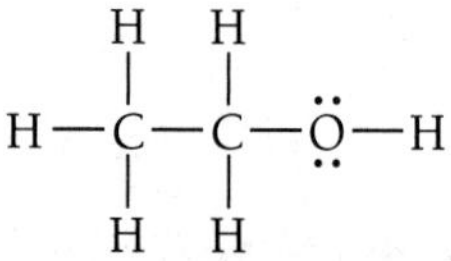

e. 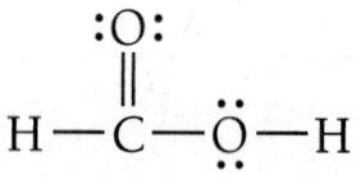

101. 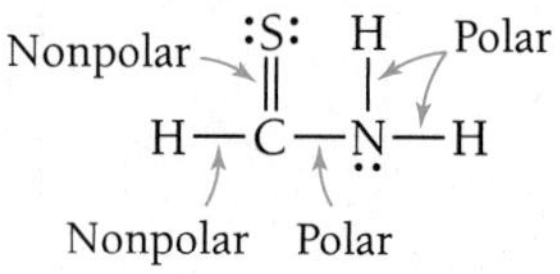

103. a. 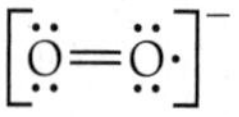

b. 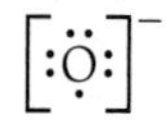

c. 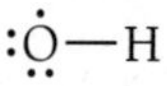

d. 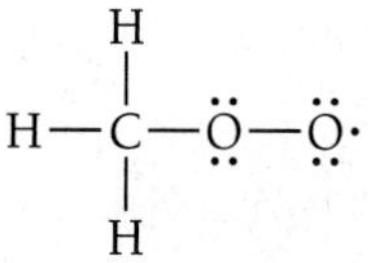

105. $\Delta H_{rxn(H_2)} = -243 \text{ kJ/mol} = -121 \text{ kJ/g}$

$\Delta H_{rxn(CH_4)} = -802 \text{ kJ/mol} = -50.0 \text{ kJ/g}$

CH_4 yields more energy per mole, while H_2 yields more energy per gram.

107. a. 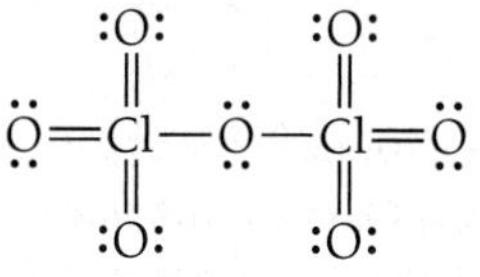 **b.** 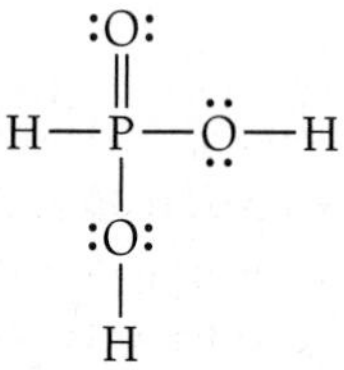

c. 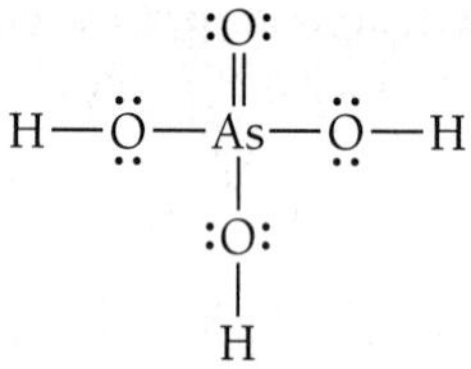

109. Na^+F^-, Na^+O^{2-}, $Mg^{2+}F^-$, $Mg^{2+}O^{2-}$, $Al^{3+}O^{2-}$

111. 333 kJ/mol

113. $H-C\equiv C-H$

115. 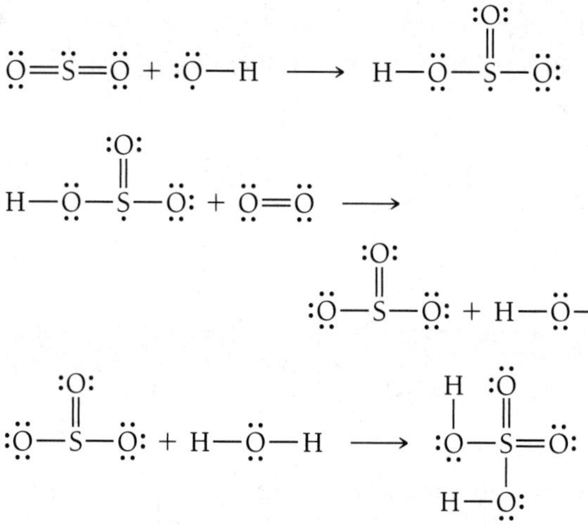

$\Delta H_{rxn} = -172 \text{ kJ}$

117. $r_{HCl} = 113$ pm
$r_{HF} = 84$ pm
These values are close to the accepted values.

119.
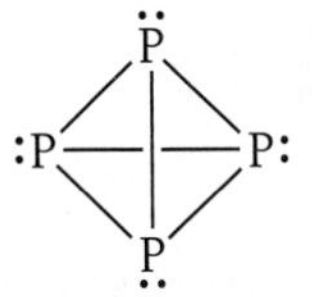

121. 126 kJ/mol

123. The oxidation number of the S atoms bonded directly to hydrogen atoms is −1. The oxidation number of interior S atoms is 0.

125. 536 kJ

127. The compounds are energy rich because a great deal of energy is released when these compounds undergo a reaction that breaks weak bonds and forms strong ones.

129. The theory is successful because it allows us to predict and account for many chemical observations. The theory is limited because electrons cannot be treated as localized "dots."

135. a. The lattice energy generally increases as you move across the period.
c. The increase in ionic radius between Cr^{2+} and Mn^{2+} results in a decrease in lattice energy.

Chapter 11

31. 4

33. a. 4 e^- groups, 4 bonding groups, 0 lone pair
b. 5 e^- groups, 3 bonding groups, 2 lone pairs
c. 6 e^- groups, 5 bonding groups, 1 lone pair

35. a. e^- geometry: tetrahedral molecular geometry: trigonal pyramidal idealized bond angle: 109.5°, deviation
b. e^- geometry: tetrahedral molecular geometry: bent idealized bond angle: 109.5°, deviation
c. e^- geometry: tetrahedral molecular geometry: tetrahedral idealized bond angle: 109.5°, deviation (due to large size of Cl compared to H)
d. e^- geometry: linear molecular geometry: linear idealized bond angle: 180°

37. H_2O has a smaller bond angle due to lone pair–lone pair repulsions, the strongest electron group repulsion.

39. a. seesaw,
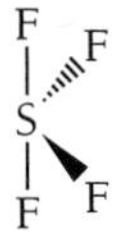

b. T-shape,
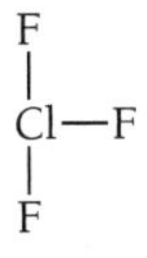

c. linear, F—I—F

d. square planar,
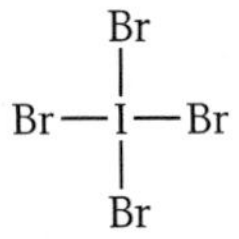

41. a. linear, H—C≡C—H
b. trigonal planar,
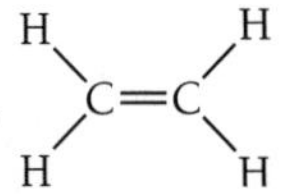

c. tetrahedral,
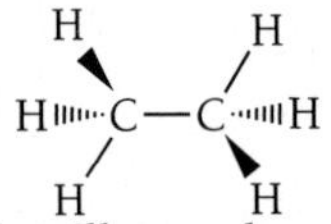

43. a. The lone pair will cause lone pair–bonding pair repulsions, pushing the three bonding pairs out of the same plane. The correct molecular geometry is trigonal pyramidal.
b. The lone pair should take an equatorial position to minimize 90° bonding pair interactions. The correct molecular geometry is seesaw.
c. The lone pairs should take positions on opposite sides of the central atom to reduce lone pair–lone pair interactions. The correct molecular geometry is square planar.

45. a. C: tetrahedral
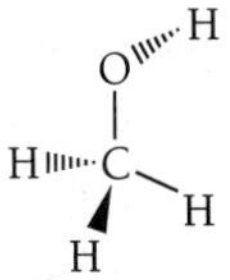

O: bent
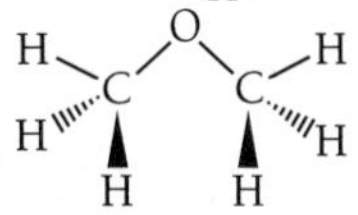

b. C's: tetrahedral
O: bent
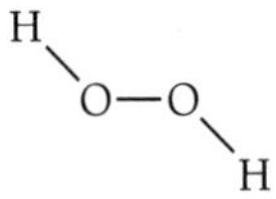

c. O's: bent

47. The vectors of the polar bonds in both CO_2 and CCl_4 oppose each other with equal magnitude and sum to 0.

49. PF_3, polar%
SBr_2, nonpolar%
$CHCl_3$, polar%
CS_2, nonpolar%

51. a. polar **b.** polar
c. nonpolar

53. a. 0 **b.** 3 **c.** 1

55.
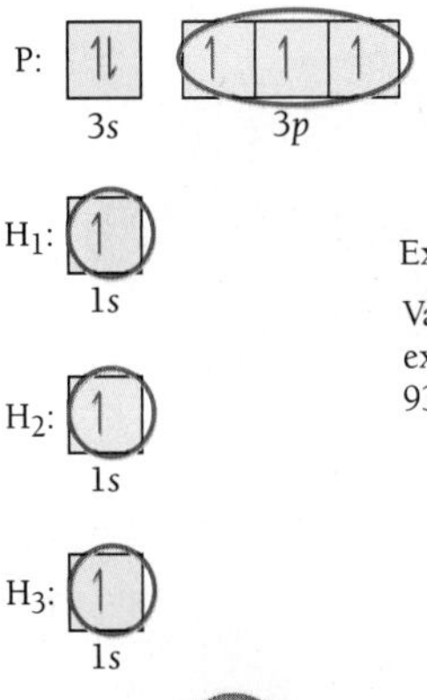

Expected bond angle = 90°

Valence bond theory is compatible with experimentally determined bond angle of 93.3° without hybrid orbitals.

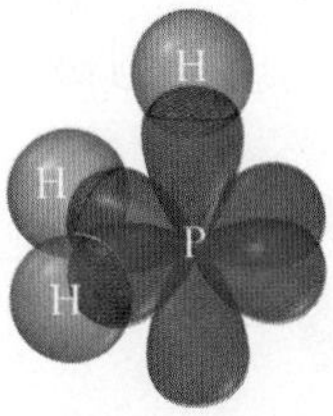

57. 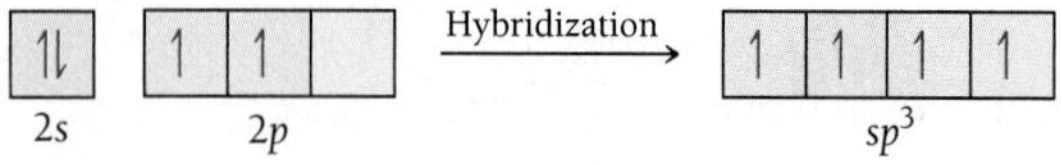

59. *sp*^{2}

61. **a.** *sp*^{3}

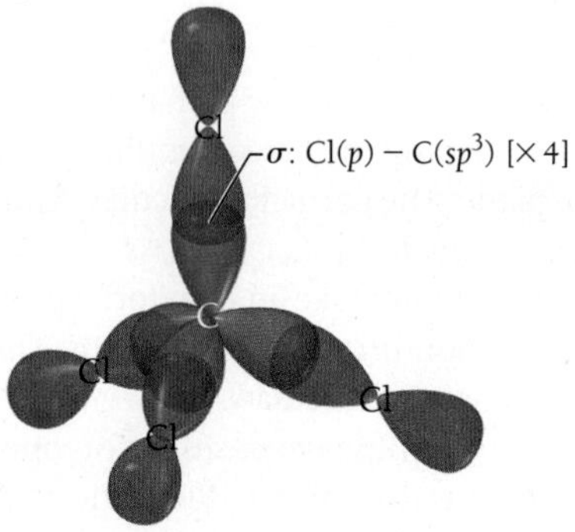

b. *sp*^{3}

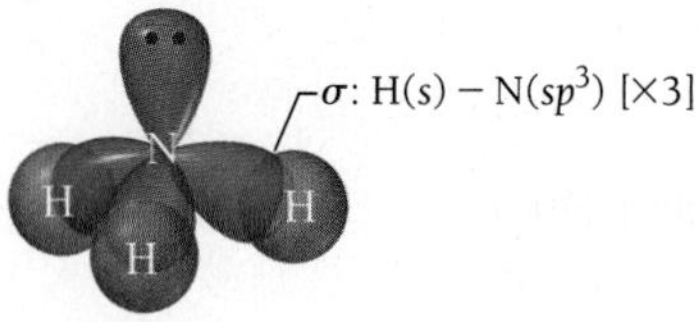

c. *sp*^{3}

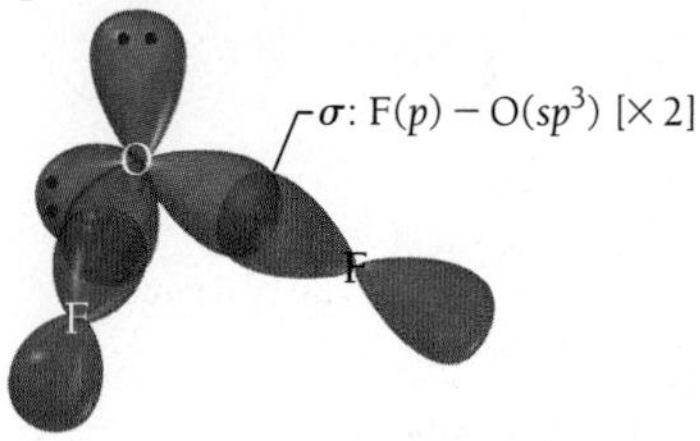

d. *sp*

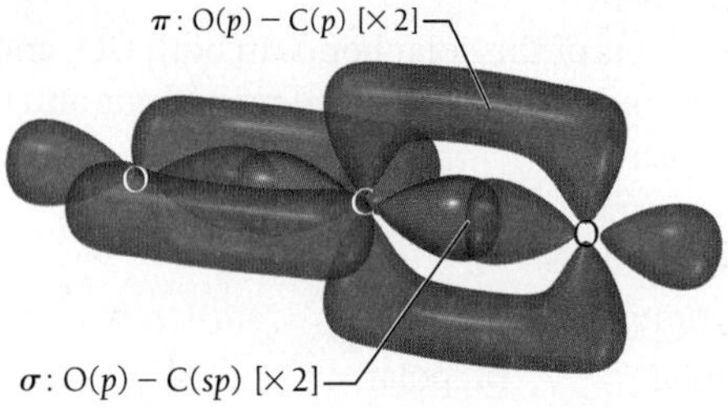

63. **a.** *sp*^{2}

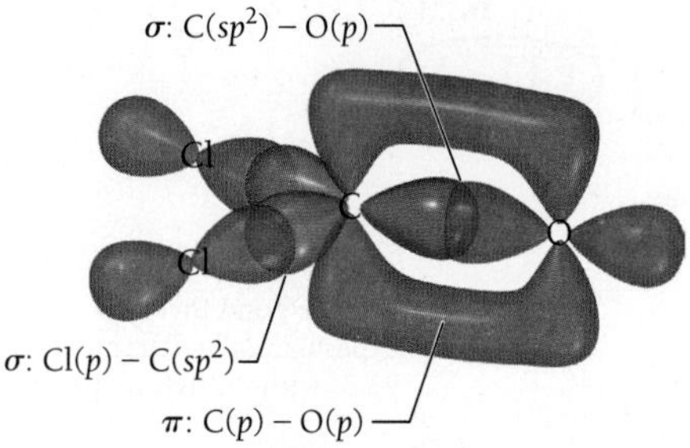

b. *sp*^{3}*d*^{2}

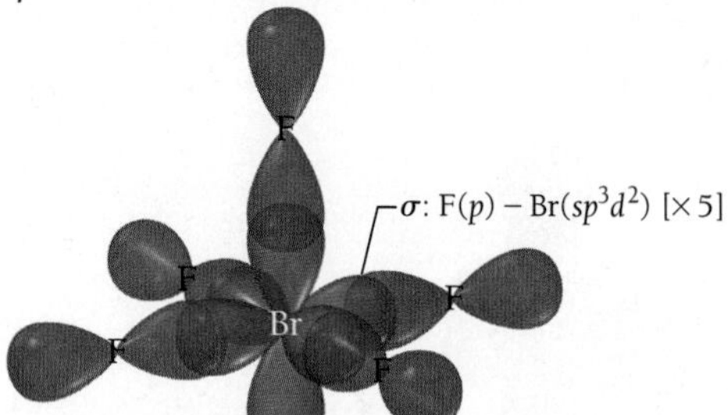

c. *sp*^{3}*d*

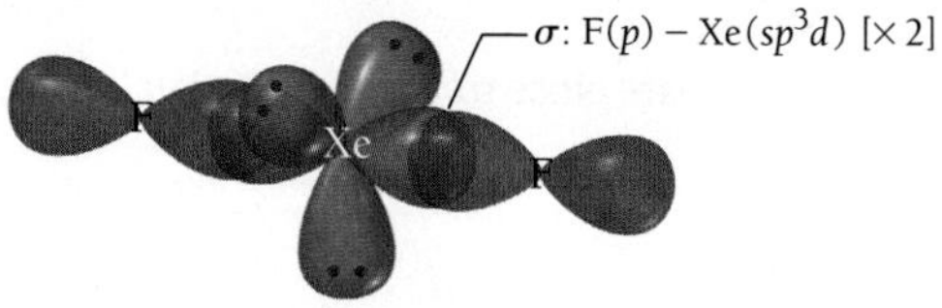

d. *sp*^{3}*d*

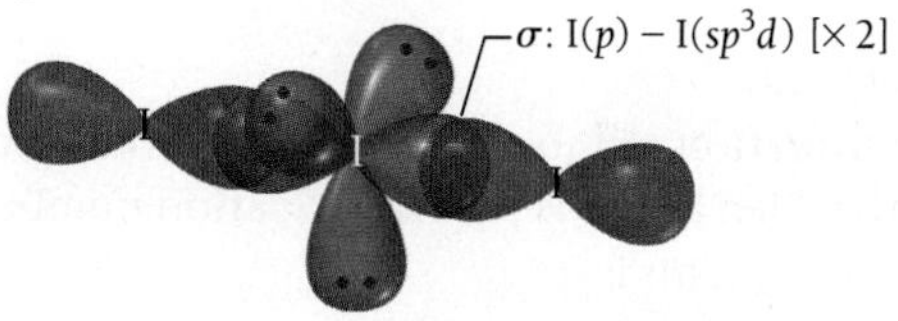

65. **a.** N's:*sp*^{2}

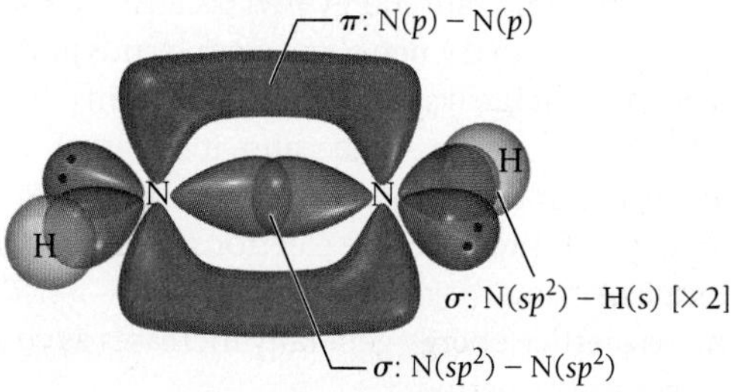

b. N's:*sp*^{3}

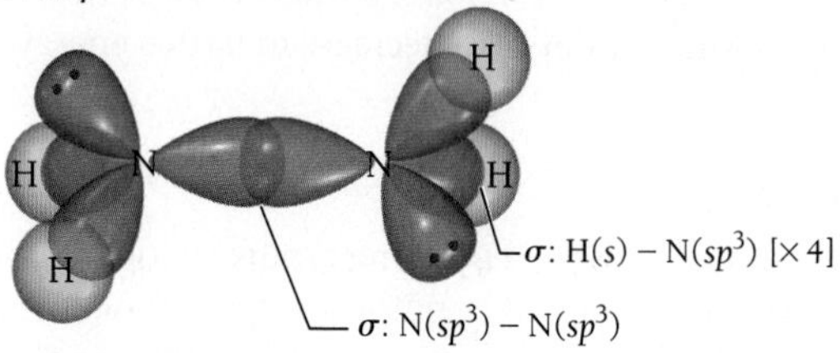

c. C:*sp*^{3}
N:*sp*^{3}

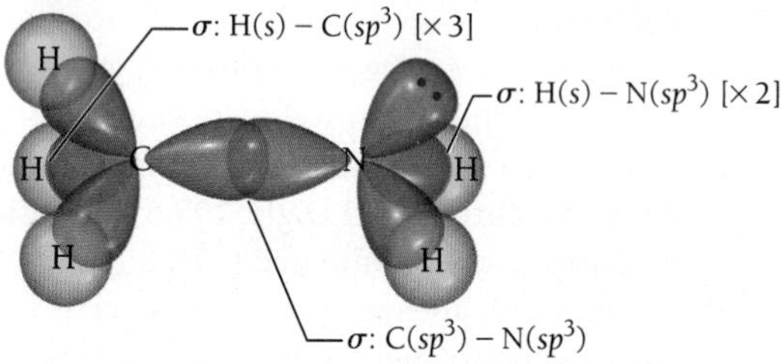

67. 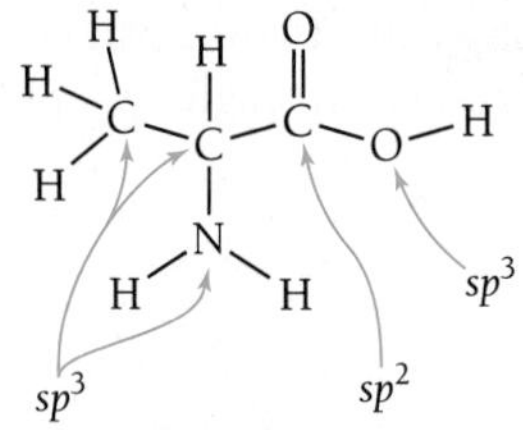

69. 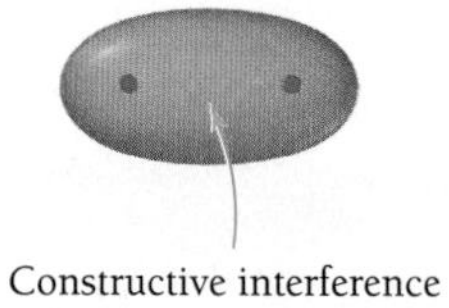

71. Be_2^+

Be_2^-

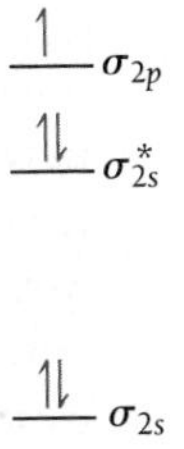

bond order $Be_2^+ = 1/2$
bond order $Be_2^- = 1/2$
Both will exist in gas phase.

73. Bonding

Antibonding

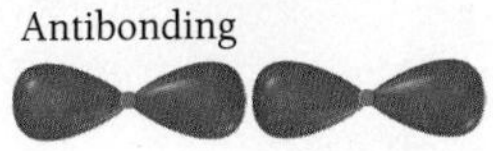

75. a.

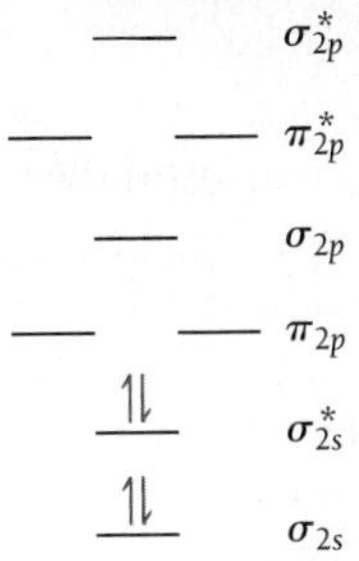

bond order = 0 diamagnetic

b.

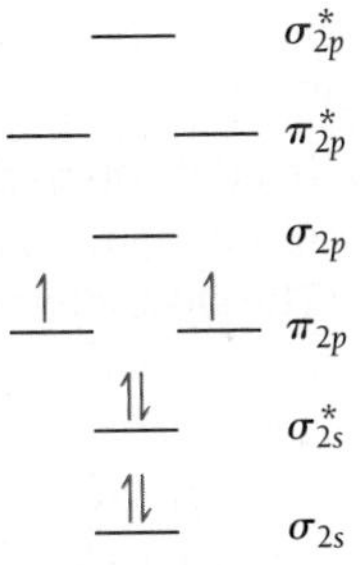

bond order = 1 paramagnetic

c.

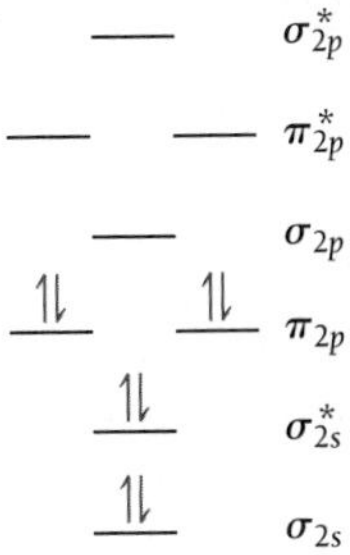

bond order = 2 diamagnetic

d.

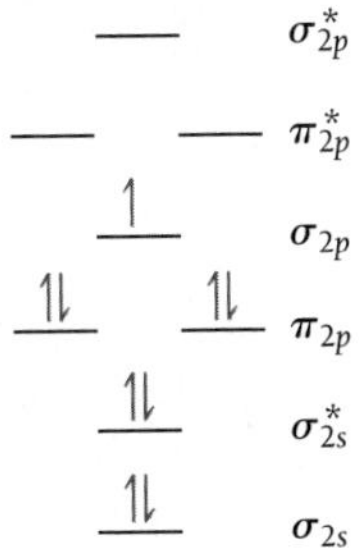

bond order = 2.5 paramagnetic

77. a. not stable **b.** not stable
c. stable **d.** not stable

79. C_2^- has the highest bond order, the highest bond energy, and the shortest bond length.

81.

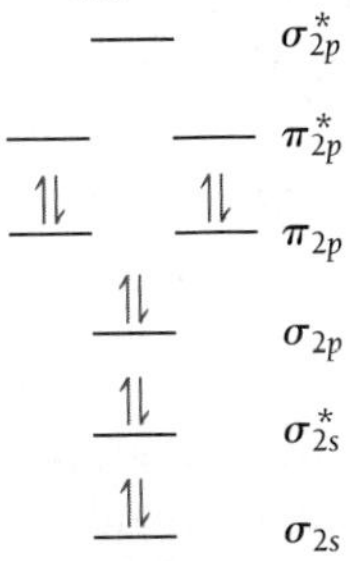

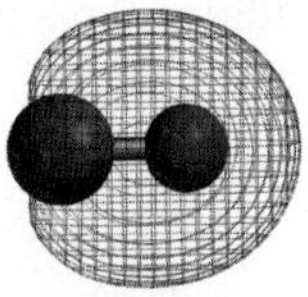

bond order = 3

83. a.

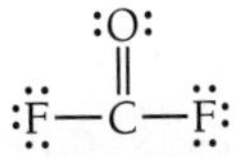

trigonal planar polar C: sp^2

b.

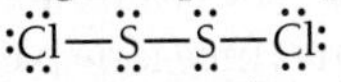

bent polar S's: sp^3

c.

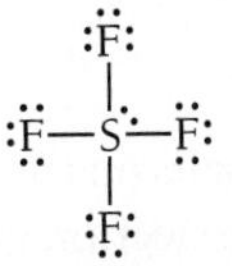

seesaw polar S: sp^3d

85. a.

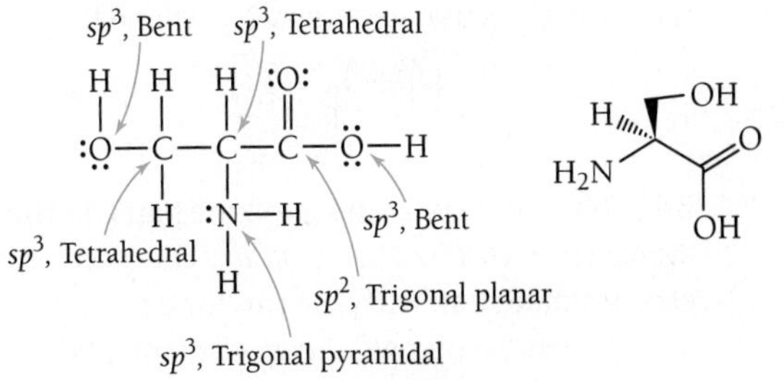

b.

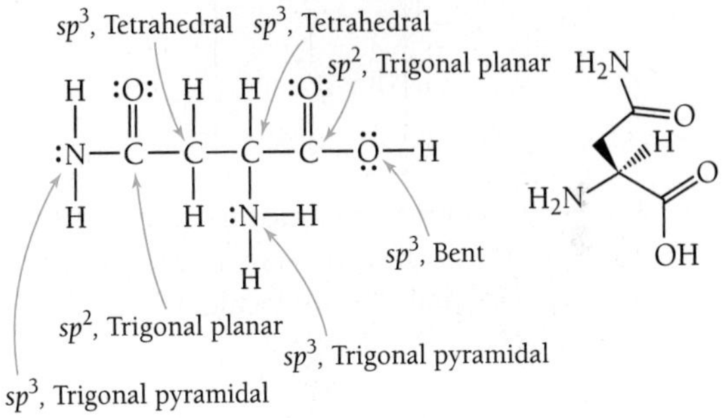

c.

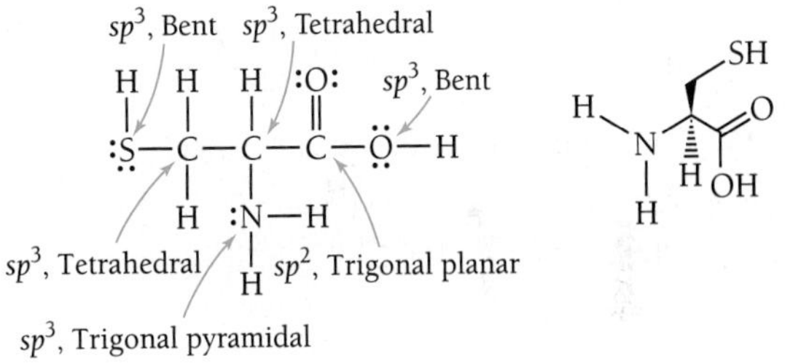

87. σ bonds: 25
π bonds: 4
lone pairs: on O's and N (without methyl group): sp^2 orbitals
on N's (with methyl group): sp^3 orbitals

89. a. water soluble **b.** fat soluble
c. water soluble **d.** fat soluble

91.

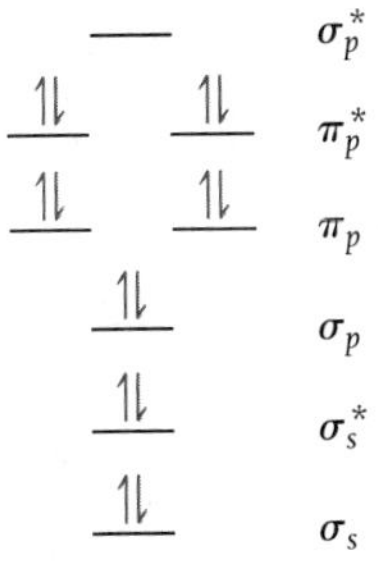

bond order = 1

93. BrF, unhybridized, linear

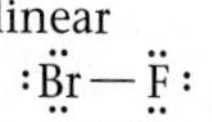

BrF_2^- has two bonds and three lone pairs on the central atom. The hybridization is sp^3d. The electron geometry is trigonal bipyramidal, with the three lone pairs equatorial. The molecular geometry is linear.

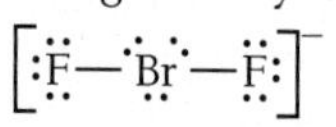

BrF_3 has three bonds and two lone pairs on the central atom. The hybridization is sp^3d. The electron geometry is trigonal bipyramidal, with the two lone pairs equatorial. The molecular geometry is T-shaped.

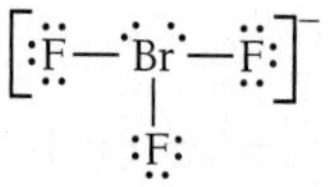

BrF_4^- has four bonds and two lone pairs on the central atom. The hybridization is sp^3d^2. The electron geometry is octahedral, with the two lone pairs on the same axis. The molecular geometry is square planar.

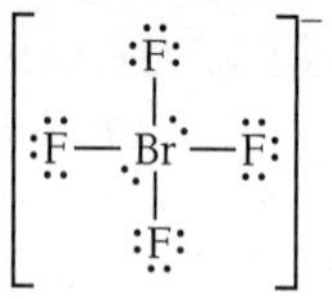

BrF_5 has five bonds and one lone pair on the central atom. The hybridization is sp^3d^2. The electron geometry is octahedral. The molecular geometry is square pyramidal.

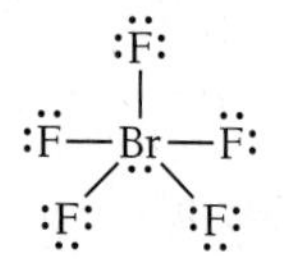

95. The moments of the two Cl's cancel.

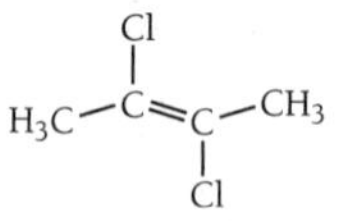

97. a. 10 **b.** 14 **c.** 2

99. According to valence bond theory, CH_4, NH_3, and H_2O are all sp^3 hybridized. This hybridization results in a tetrahedral electron group configuration with a 109.5° bond angle. NH_3 and H_2O deviate from this idealized bond angle because their lone electron pairs exist in their own sp^3 orbitals. The presence of lone pairs lowers the tendency for the central atom's orbitals to hybridize. As a result, as lone pairs are added, the bond angle moves further from the 109.5° hybrid angle and closer to the 90° unhybridized angle.

101. NH_3 is stable due to its bond order of 3.

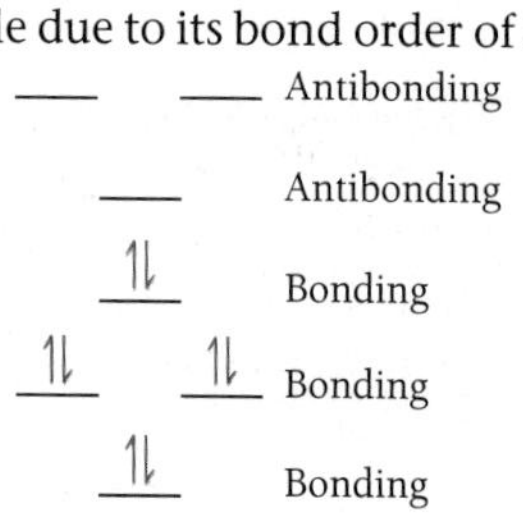

103. In NO_2^+, the central N has two electron groups, so the hybridization is sp and the ONO angle is 180°. In NO_2^- the central N has three electron groups, two bonds and one lone pair. The ideal hybridization is sp^2, but the ONO bond angle should close down a bit because of the lone pair. A bond angle around 115° is a good guess. In NO_2 there are three electron groups, but one group is a single electron. Again, the ideal hybridization would be sp^2, but since one unpaired electron must be much smaller than a lone pair or even a bonding pair, we predict that the ONO bond angle will spread and be greater than 120°. As a guess, the angle is probably significantly greater than 120°.

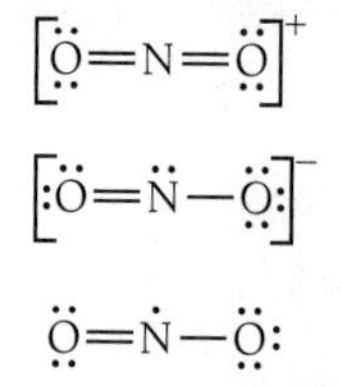

105. In addition to the 2s and the three 2p orbitals, one more orbital is required to make five hybrid orbitals. The closest in energy is the 3s orbital. So the hybridization is s^2p^3. VSEPR predicts trigonal bipyramidal geometry for five identical substituents.

107.

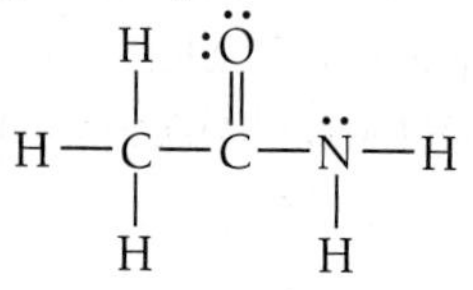

Lewis Structure

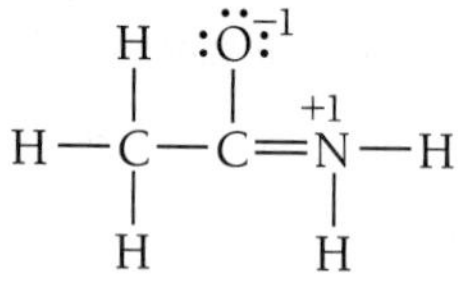

Resonance Structure

Terminal carbon is tetrahedral, central carbon is trigonal planar, and nitrogen is trigonal pyramidal (but resonance structure is trigonal planar).

109. a. This is the best.

b. This statement is similar to **a** but leaves out nonbonding lone-pair electron groups.

c. Molecular geometries are not determined by overlapping orbitals but rather by the number and type of electron groups around each central atom.

111. Lewis theory defines a single bond, double bond, and triple bond as a sharing of two electrons, four electrons, and six electrons, respectively, between two atoms. Valence bond theory defines a single bond as a sigma overlap of two orbitals, a double bond as a single sigma bond combined with a pi bond, and a triple bond as a double bond with an additional pi bond. Molecular orbital theory defines a single bond, double bond, and triple bond as a bond order of 1, 2, or 3, respectively, between two atoms.

118. a. 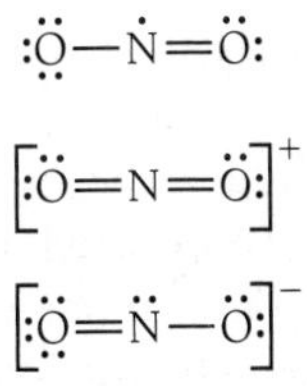

c. 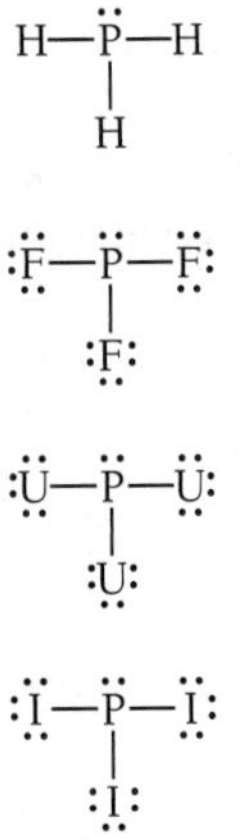

e. The Lewis structures all have four electron groups, one lone pair, and three bonding groups. Based on VESPR, each of these molecules should have a bond angle of slightly less than 109.5 °. However, the atomic radius increases in the following order: H < Cl < I. The increasing radius from H to I can explain the increasing bond angle in these compounds.

Chapter 12

35. a. dispersion
b. dispersion, dipole–dipole, hydrogen bonding
c. dispersion, dipole–dipole
d. dispersion

37. a. dispersion, dipole–dipole
b. dispersion, dipole–dipole, hydrogen bonding
c. dispersion
d. dispersion

39. a, b, c, d, Boiling point increases with increasing intermolecular forces. The molecules increase in their intermolecular forces as follows: **a,** dispersion forces; **b,** stronger dispersion forces (broader electron cloud); **c,** dispersion forces and dipole–dipole interactions; **d,** dispersion forces, dipole–dipole interactions, and hydrogen bonding.

41. a. CH_3OH, hydrogen bonding
b. CH_3CH_2OH, hydrogen bonding
c. CH_3CH_3, greater mass, broader electron cloud causes greater dispersion forces.

43. a. Br_2, smaller mass results in weaker dispersion forces.
b. H_2S, lacks hydrogen bonding
c. PH_3, lacks hydrogen bonding

45. a. not homogeneous
b. homogeneous, dispersion, dipole–dipole, hydrogen bonding, ion–dipole
c. homogeneous, dispersion
d. homogeneous, dispersion, dipole–dipole, hydrogen bonding

47. Water. Surface tension increases with increasing intermolecular forces, and water can hydrogen-bond while acetone cannot.

49. compound A

51. When the tube is clean, water experiences adhesive forces with glass that are stronger than its cohesive forces, causing it to climb the surface of a glass tube. Water does not experience strong intermolecular forces with oil, so if the tube is coated in oil, the water's cohesive forces will be greater and it will not be attracted to the surface of the tube.

53. The water in the 12-cm dish will evaporate more quickly. The vapor pressure does not change, but the surface area does. The water in the dish evaporates more quickly because the greater surface area allows for more molecules to obtain enough energy at the surface and break free.

55. Water is more volatile than vegetable oil. When the water evaporates, the endothermic process results in cooling.

57. 0.405 L

59. 91 °C

61. $\Delta H_{vap} = 24.7$ kJ/mol, bp $= 239$ K

63. 41 torr

65. 27.5 kJ/mol

67. 22.0 kJ

69. 2.7 °C

71. 30.5 kJ

73. a. solid **b.** liquid
c. gas **d.** supercritical fluid
e. solid/liquid **f.** liquid/gas
g. solid/liquid/gas

75. N_2 has a stable liquid phase at 1 atm.

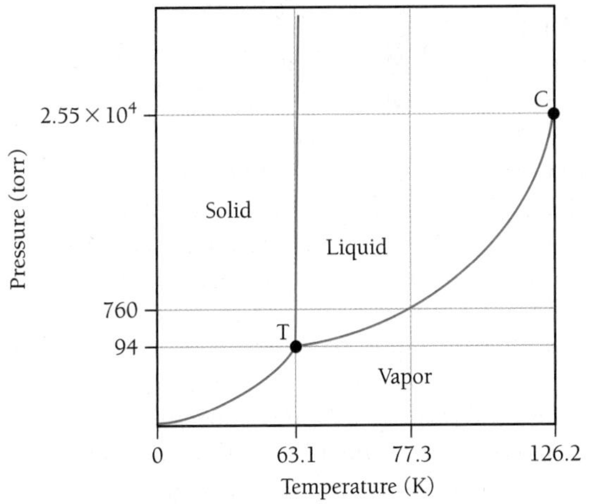

77. a. 0.027 mmHg **b.** rhombic

79. Water has strong intermolecular forces. It is polar and experiences hydrogen bonding.

81. Water's exceptionally high specific heat capacity has a moderating effect on Earth's climate. Also, its high ΔH_{vap} causes water evaporation and condensation to have a strong effect on temperature.

83. The general trend is that melting point increases with increasing mass. This is because the electrons of the larger molecules are held more loosely and a stronger dipole moment can be induced more easily. HF is the exception to the rule. It has a relatively high melting point due to hydrogen bonding.

85. yes, 1.22 g

87. gas $\longrightarrow$ liquid $\longrightarrow$ solid

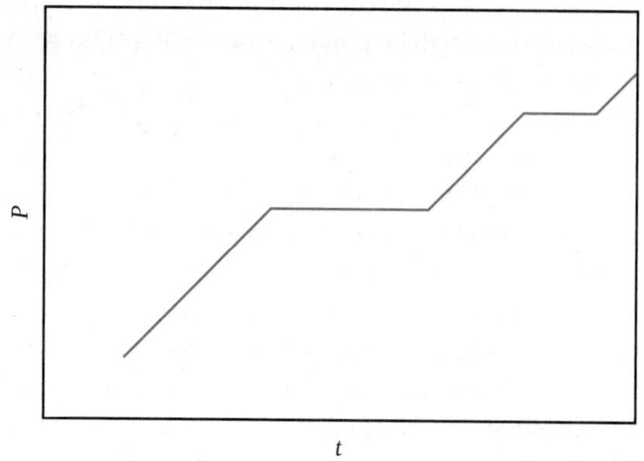

89. 26 °C

91.

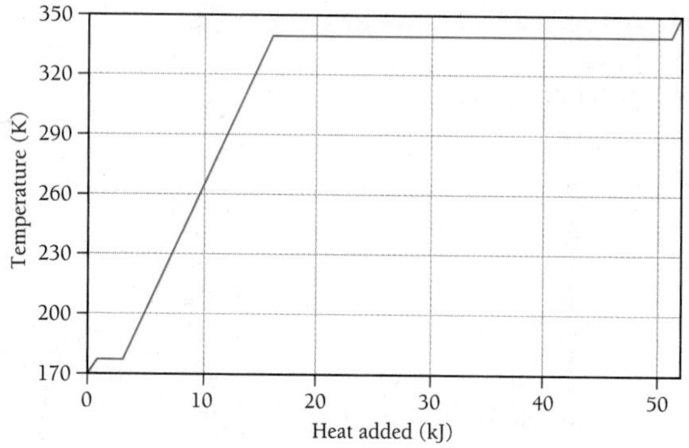

93. 3.4×10^3 g H_2O

95. **a.** $CO_2(s) \longrightarrow CO_2(g)$ at 195 K

b. $CO_2(s) \longrightarrow$ triple point at 216 K $\longrightarrow CO_2(g)$ just above 216 K

c. $CO_2(s) \longrightarrow CO_2(l)$ at somewhat above 216 K $\longrightarrow CO_2(g)$ at around 250 K

d. $CO_2(s) \longrightarrow CO_2(g) \longrightarrow$ supercritical fluid

97. Decreasing the pressure will decrease the temperature of liquid nitrogen. Because the nitrogen is boiling, its temperature must be constant at a given pressure. As the pressure decreases, the boiling point decreases, and therefore so does the temperature. If the pressure drops below the pressure of the triple point, the phase change will shift from vaporization to sublimation and the liquid nitrogen will become solid.

99. 70.7 L

101. 0.48 atm

103.

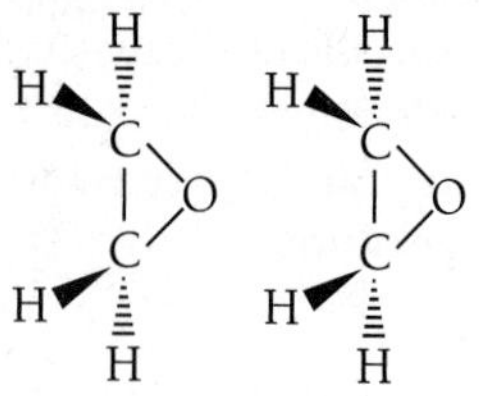

105. The water within a container with a larger surface area will evaporate more quickly because there is more surface area from which the molecules can evaporate. Vapor pressure is the pressure of the gas when it is in dynamic equilibrium with the liquid. The vapor pressure is dependent only on the substance and the temperature. The larger the surface area, the more quickly it will reach the dynamic state.

107. The triple point will be at a lower temperature since the fusion equilibrium line has a positive slope. This means that we will be increasing both temperature and pressure as we travel from the triple point to the normal melting point.

109. The liquid segment will have the least steep slope because it takes the most kJ/mol to raise the temperature of the phase.

111. There are substantial intermolecular attractions in the liquid but virtually none in the gas.

117. **a.** No. Although it does correlate for H_2S, H_2Se, and H_2Te, it does not correlate for H_2O.

c. Water has the highest dipole moment, that together with the small size of the hydrogen atom accounts for the anomalously high boiling point.

Chapter 13

27. 162 pm

29. **a.** 1 **b.** 2 **c.** 4

31. 68%

33. $l = 393$ pm, $d = 21.3$ g/cm^3

35. 134.5 pm

37. 6.0×10^{23} atoms/mol

39. **a.** atomic **b.** molecular **c.** ionic **d.** atomic

41. LiCl(s). The other three solids are held together by intermolecular forces, while LiCl is held together by stronger coulombic interactions between the cations and anions of the crystal lattice.

43. **a.** $TiO_2(s)$, ionic solid

b. $SiCl_4(s)$, larger, stronger dispersion forces

c. Xe(s), larger, stronger dispersion forces

d. CaO, ions have greater charge and therefore stronger coulombic forces

45. TiO_2

47. Cs:1(1) = 1
Cl:8(1/8) = 1
1:1
CsCl
Ba:8(1/8) + 6(1/2) = 4
Cl:8(1) = 8
4:8 = 1:2
$BaCl_2$

49. cesium chloride: none of these; barium(II) chloride: fluorite structure

51. face-centered cubic

53. **a.** nonoxide **b.** silicate **c.** nonoxide

55. boron oxide, B_2O_3

57. Ca: +2; Si: +2; O: −2

59. a. Zn(*s*)
61. 0.807 mol orbitals
63. insulator
65. a. p-type
b. n-type
67. Yes, it has sufficient energy.
69.

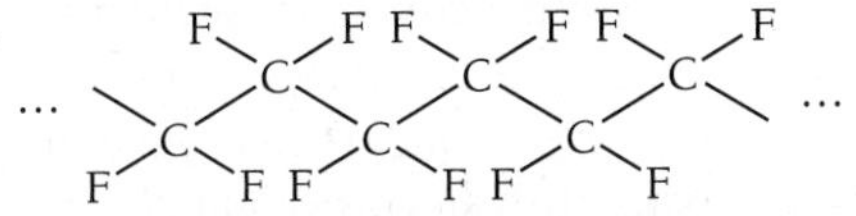

71.

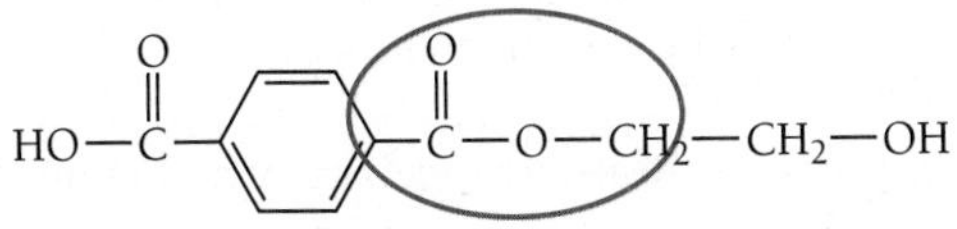

73. H—C ≡ C—H
75.

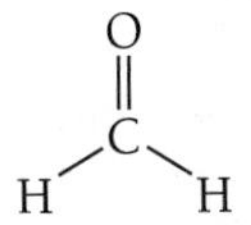

77. CsCl has a higher melting point than AgI because of its higher coordination number. In CsCl, one anion bonds to eight cations (and vice versa), while in AgI, one anion bonds to only four cations.
79. a. $4r$
$c^2 = a^2 + b^2 \; c = 4r, a = l, b = l$
$(4r)^2 = l^2 + l^2$
$16r^2 = 2l^2$
b. $8r^2 = l^2$
$l = \sqrt[3]{8r^2}$
$l = 2\sqrt{2}r$
81. 8 atoms/unit
83. 55.843 g/mol
85. 2.00 g/cm^3
87. body diagonal $= \sqrt{6}r$,
radius $= (\sqrt{3} - \sqrt{2})r/\sqrt{2} = 0.2247r$
89. The higher-level electron transitions with their smaller energy gaps would not give off enough energy to create X-rays.
91. a.

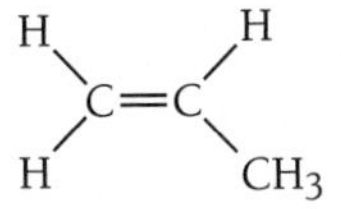

b.

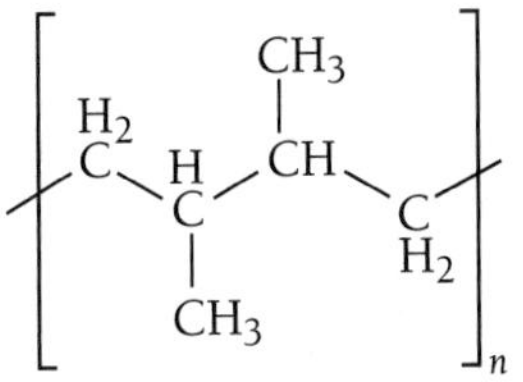

To obtain this structure, the monomer from part a would react in a head-to-head (or tail-to-tail) addition as opposed to the head-to-tail addition that leads to the structure shown in Table 12.3.
93. Because the structure is a face-centered cubic, there are therefore four C_{60} molecules per unit cell. Thus, there must be 3 × 4 = 12 Rb atoms per unit cell, and all sites (tetrahedral and octahedral) are occupied.
95. The liquid must be cooled quickly in order to prevent the formation of an organized crystal structure and instead achieve an amorphous product.
97. Both structures may be viewed as having essentially a face-centered cubic unit cell with half of the tetrahedral holes filled. Diamond, however, consists of only one type of atom (C) and is covalently bound, whereas zinc blende has S^{2-} ions at the face-centered cubic sites and Zn^{2+} ions in the tetrahedral holes, and is held together by ionic forces.
99. d. All of the above would likely lead to an increase in electrical conductivity.
105. a. 20% Cr and 80% Ni; 1405°
a. 97% Cr and 3% Ni; body-centered cubic

Chapter 14

29. a. hexane, toluene, or CCl_4; dispersion forces
b. water, methanol; dispersion, dipole–dipole, hydrogen bonding
c. hexane, toluene, or CCl_4; dispersion forces
d. water, acetone, methanol, ethanol; dispersion, ion–dipole
31. $HOCH_2CH_2CH_2OH$
33. a. water; dispersion, dipole–dipole, hydrogen bonding
b. hexane; dispersion
c. water; dispersion, dipole–dipole
35. a. endothermic
b. The lattice energy is greater in magnitude than the heat of hydration.
c.

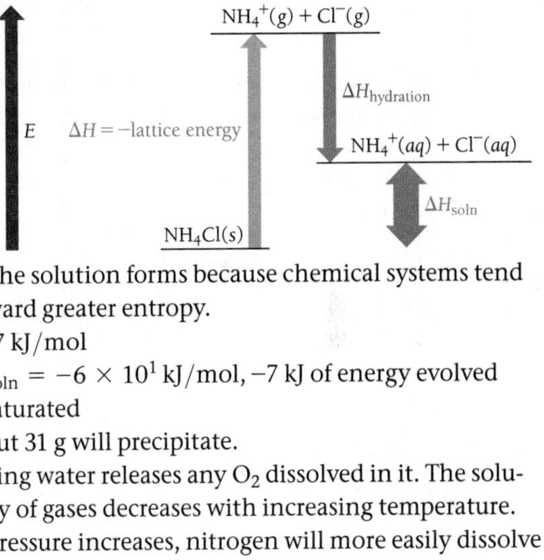

d. The solution forms because chemical systems tend toward greater entropy.
37. −797 kJ/mol
39. $\Delta H_{soln} = -6 \times 10^1$ kJ/mol, −7 kJ of energy evolved
41. unsaturated
43. About 31 g will precipitate.
45. Boiling water releases any O_2 dissolved in it. The solubility of gases decreases with increasing temperature.
47. As pressure increases, nitrogen will more easily dissolve in blood. To reverse this process, divers should ascend to lower pressures.
49. 1.1 g
51. 1.92 M, 2.0 *m*, 10.4%
53. 0.340 L
55. 1.6×10^2 g
57. 1.4×10^4 g
59. Add water to 7.31 mL of concentrated solution until a total volume of 1.15 L is acquired.
61. a. Add water to 3.73 g KCl to a volume of 100 mL.
b. Add 3.59 g KCl to 96.41 g H_2O.
c. Add 5.0 g KCl to 95 g H_2O.
63. a. 0.417 M **b.** 0.444 *m*
c. 7.41% by mass **d.** 0.00794
e. 0.794% by mole

65. 0.89 M

67. 15 m, 0.22

69. The level has decreased more in the beaker filled with pure water. The dissolved salt in the seawater decreases the vapor pressure and subsequently lowers the rate of vaporization.

71. 30.7 torr

73. **a.** $P_{hep} = 24.4$ torr, $P_{oct} = 5.09$ torr
b. 29.5 torr
c. 80.8% heptane by mass, 19.2% octane by mass
d. The vapor is richer in the more volatile component.

75. $P_{chl} = 51.9$ torr, $P_{ace} = 274$ torr, $P_{tot} = 326$ torr. The solution is not ideal. The chloroform–acetone interactions are stronger than the chloroform–chloroform and acetone–acetone interactions.

77. freezing point (fp) $= -1.27$ °C, bp $= 100.349$ °C

79. freezing point (fp) $= 1.0$ °C, boiling point(bp) $= 82.4$ °C

81. 1.8×10^2 g/mol

83. 26.1 atm

85. 6.36×10^3 g/mol

87. **a.** fp $= -0.558$ °C, bp $= 100.154$ °C
b. fp $= -1.98$ °C, bp $= 100.546$ °C
c. fp $= -2.5$ °C, bp $= 100.70$ °C

89. 157 g

91. **a.** –0.632 °C **b.** 5.4 atm **c.** 100.18 °C

93. 2.3

95. 3.4

97. 23.0 torr

99. Chloroform is polar and has stronger solute–solvent interactions than nonpolar carbon tetrachloride.

101. $\Delta H_{soln} = 51$ kJ/mol, –8.7 °C

103. 2.2×10^{-3} M/atm

105. 1.3×10^4 L

107. 0.24 g

109. –24 °C

111. **a.** 1.1% by mass/V **b.** 1.6% by mass/V
c. 5.3% by mass/V

113. 2.484

115. 0.229 atm

117. χ_{CHCl_3}(original) $= 0.657$,
P_{CHCl_3}(condensed) $= 0.346$ atm

119. 1.74 M

121. $C_6H_{14}O_2$

123. 12 grams

125. 6.4×10^{-3} L

127. 22.4 glucose by mass, 77.6 sucrose by mass

129. $P_{iso} = 0.131$ atm, $P_{pro} = 0.068$ atm. The major intermolecular attractions are between the OH groups. The OH group at the end of the chain in propyl alcohol is more accessible than the one in the middle of the chain in isopropyl alcohol. In addition, the molecular shape of propyl alcohol is a straight chain of carbon atoms, while that of isopropyl alcohol is a branched chain and is more like a ball. The contact area between two ball-like objects is smaller than that of two chain-like objects. The smaller contact area in isopropyl alcohol means the molecules don't attract each other as strongly as do those of propyl alcohol. As a result of both of these factors, the vapor pressure of isopropyl alcohol is higher.

131. 0.005 m

133. Na_2CO_3 0.050 M, $NaHCO_3$ 0.075 M

135. The water should not be immediately cycled back into the river. As the water was warmed, dissolved oxygen would have been released, since the amount of a gas able to be dissolved into a liquid decreases as the temperature of the liquid increases. As such, the water returned to the river would lack dissolved oxygen if it was still hot. To preserve the dissolved oxygen necessary for the survival of fish and other aquatic life, the water must first be cooled.

137. **b.** NaCl

144. **a.** The salinity of seawater is generally higher near the equator and lower near the poles.
c. –2.3 °C

Chapter 15

25. **a.** $\text{Rate} = -\dfrac{1}{2}\dfrac{\Delta[\text{HBr}]}{\Delta t} = \dfrac{\Delta[\text{H}_2]}{\Delta t} = \dfrac{\Delta[\text{Br}_2]}{\Delta t}$
b. 1.8×10^{-3} M/s
c. 0.040 mol Br_2

27. **a.** $\text{Rate} = -\dfrac{1}{2}\dfrac{\Delta[\text{A}]}{\Delta t} = -\dfrac{\Delta[\text{B}]}{\Delta t} = \dfrac{1}{3}\dfrac{\Delta[\text{C}]}{\Delta t}$
b. $\dfrac{\Delta[\text{B}]}{\Delta t} = -0.0500$ M/s, $\dfrac{\Delta[\text{C}]}{\Delta t} = 0.150$ M/s

29.

$\Delta[Cl_2]/\Delta t$	$\Delta[F_2]/\Delta t$	$\Delta[ClF_3]/\Delta t$	Rate
−0.012 M/s	−0.036 M/s	0.024 M/s	0.012 M/s

31. **a.** $0 \longrightarrow 10$ s : Rate $= 8.7 \times 10^{-3}$ M/s
$40 \longrightarrow 50$ s : Rate $= 6.0 \times 10^{-3}$ M/s
b. 1.4×10^{-2} M/s

33. **a.** **i.** 1.0×10^{-2} M/s **ii.** 8.5×10^{-3} M/s
iii. 0.013 M/s
b.

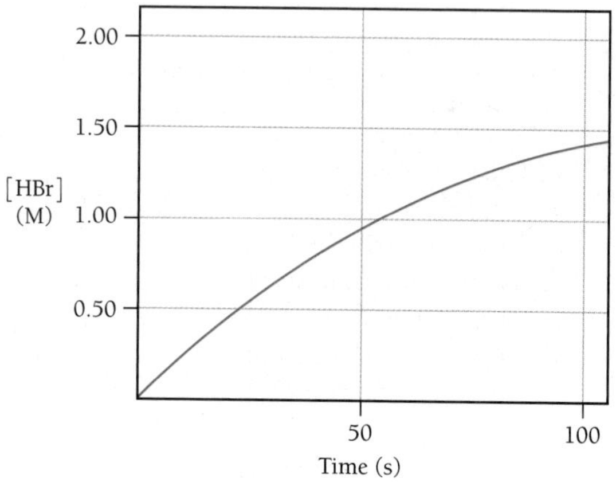

35. **a.** first order
b.

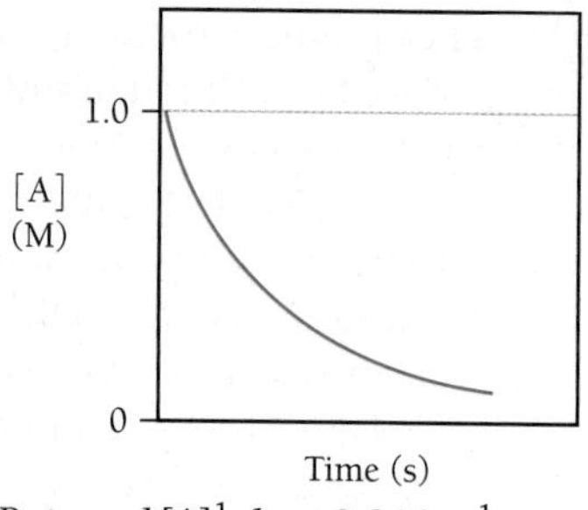

c. Rate $= k[\text{A}]^1$, $k = 0.010\ \text{s}^{-1}$

37. **a.** s^{-1} **b.** $M^{-1} s^{-1}$ **c.** $M \cdot s^{-1}$

39. **a.** Rate = $k[A][B]^2$ **b.** third order
c. 2 **d.** 4
e. 1 **f.** 8

41. second order, Rate = $5.25\ M^{-1} s^{-1}[A]^2$

43. first order, Rate = $0.065\ s^{-1}[A]$

45. Rate = $k[NO_2][F_2]$, $k = 2.57\ M^{-1} s^{-1}$, second order

47. **a.** zero order **b.** first order
c. second order

49. second order, $k = 2.25 \times 10^{-2}\ M^{-1} s^{-1}$, [AB] at 25 s = 0.619 M

51. first order, $k = 1.12 \times 10^{-2}\ s^{-1}$, Rate = 2.8×10^{-3} M/s

53. **a.** $4.5 \times 10^{-3}\ s^{-1}$ **b.** Rate = $4.5 \times 10^{-3}\ s^{-1}[A]$
c. 1.5×10^2 s **d.** [A] = 0.0908 M

55. **a.** 4.88×10^3 s **b.** 9.8×10^3 s
c. 1.7×10^3 s
d. 0.146 M at 200 s, 0.140 M at 500 s

57. 6.8×10^8 yr; 1.8×10^{17} atoms

59.

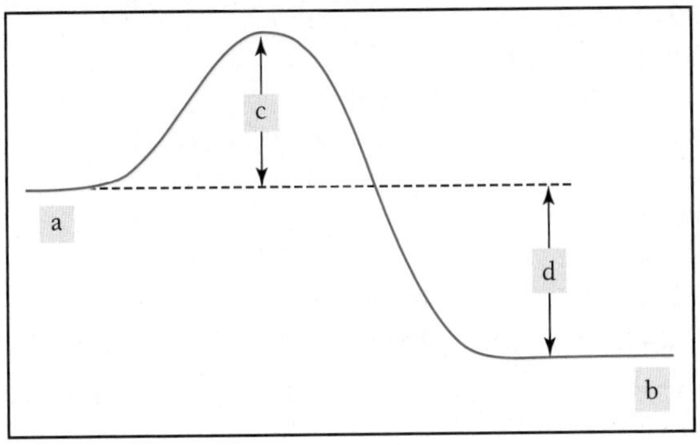

61. $17\ s^{-1}$

63. 61.90 kJ/mol

65. $E_a = 251$ kJ/mol, $A = 7.93 \times 10^{11}\ s^{-1}$

67. $E_a = 23.0$ kJ/mol, $A = 8.05 \times 10^{10}\ M^{-1}s^{-1}$

69. **a.** 122 kJ/mol
b. $0.101\ s^{-1}$

71. 47.85 kJ/mol

73. **a**

75. The mechanism is valid.

77. **a.** $Cl_2(g) + CHCl_3(g) \longrightarrow HCl(g) + CCl_4(g)$
b. $Cl(g)$, $CCl_3(g)$
c. Rate = $k[Cl_2]^{1/2}[CHCl_3]$

79. Heterogeneous catalysts require a large surface area because catalysis can only happen at the surface. A greater surface area means greater opportunity for the substrate to react, which results in a faster reaction.

81. 10^{12}

83. **a.** first order, $k = 0.0462\ hr^{-1}$
b. 15 hr
c. 5.0×10^1 hr

85. 0.0531 M/s

87. rate = $4.5 \times 10^{-4}[CH_3CHO]^2$, $k = 4.5 \times 10^{-4}$, 0.37 atm

89. 219 torr

91. 1×10^{-7} s

93. 1.6×10^2 seconds

95. **a.** 2
b.

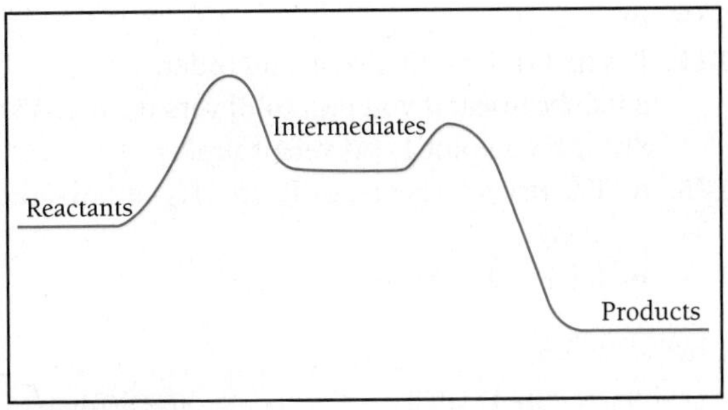

c. first step
d. exothermic

97. **a.** 5.41 s
b. 2.2 s for 25%, 5.4 s for 50%
c. 0.28 at 10 s, 0.077 at 20 s

99. **a.** $E_a = 89.5$ kJ/mol, $A = 4.22 \times 10^{11}\ s^{-1}$
b. $2.5 \times 10^{-5}\ M^{-1} s^{-1}$
c. 6.0×10^{-4} M/s

101. **a.** No
b. No bond is broken, and the two radicals attract each other.
c. Formation of diatomic gases from atomic gases

103. 1.35×10^4 years

105. **a.** Both are valid. For both, all steps sum to overall reaction, and the predicted rate law is consistent with experimental data.
b. Buildup of I(g)

107. rate = $k_2[(k_1/k_{-1})[Br_2]]^{1/2}[H_2]$ The rate law is 3/2 order overall.

109. **a.** 0% **b.** 25% **c.** 33%

111. 174 kJ

113. **a.** second order
b. $CH_3NC + CH_3NC \underset{k_2}{\overset{k_1}{\rightleftharpoons}} CH_3NC^* + CH_3NC$ (fast)

$CH_3NC^* \xrightarrow{k_3} CH_3CN$ (slow)

$k_1[CH_3NC]^2 = k_2[CH_3NC^*][CH_3NC]$

$[CH_3NC^*] = \frac{k_1}{k_2}[CH_3NC]$

$\text{Rate} = k_3 \times \frac{k_1}{k_2}[CH_3NC]$

$\text{Rate} = k[CH_3NC]$

115. Rate = $k[A]^2$

$$\text{Rate} = -\frac{d[A]}{dt}$$

$$\frac{d[A]}{dt} = -k[A]^2$$

$$2\frac{d[A]}{[A]^2} = k\,dt$$

$$\int_{[A]_0}^{[A]} -\frac{1}{[A]^2}d[A] = \int_0^t k\,dt$$

$$\left[\frac{1}{[A]}\right]_{[A]_0}^{[A]} = k[t]_0^t$$

$$\frac{1}{[A]} - \frac{1}{[A]_0} = kt$$

$$\frac{1}{[A]} = kt + \frac{1}{[A]_0}$$

117. $k = 3.20 \times 10^{-4}\ s^{-1}$
119. b)
121. B is first order and A is second order. B will be linear if you plot ln[B] versus time; A will be linear if you plot 1/[A] versus time.
125. **a.** The reaction is first order in CH_4 and first order in O_3.
a. 1.7×10^{-18} M/s

Chapter 16

21. **a.** $K = \frac{[SbCl_3][Cl_2]}{[SbCl_5]}$ **b.** $K = \frac{[NO]^2[Br_2]}{[BrNO]^2}$
c. $K = \frac{[CS_2][H_2]^4}{[CH_4][H_2S]^2}$ **d.** $K = \frac{[CO_2]^2}{[CO]^2[O_2]}$
23. The concentration of the reactants will be greater. No, this is not dependent on initial concentrations; it is dependent on the value of K_c.
25. **a.** figure v
b. The change in the decrease of reactants and increase of products would be faster.
c. No, catalysts affect kinetics, not equilibrium.
27. **a.** 4.42×10^{-5}, reactants favored
b. 1.50×10^{2}, products favored
c. 1.96×10^{-9}, reactants favored
29. 1.3×10^{-29}
31. **a.** 2.56×10^{-23} **b.** 1.3×10^{22}
c. 81.9
33. **a.** $K_c = \frac{[HCO_3^-][OH^-]}{[CO_3^{2-}]}$ **b.** $K_c = [O_2]^3$
c. $K_c = \frac{[H_3O^+][F^-]}{[HF]}$ **d.** $K_c = \frac{[NH_4^+][OH^-]}{[NH_3]}$
35. 136
37.

T(K)	$[N_2]$	$[H_2]$	$[NH_3]$	K_c
500	0.115	0.105	0.439	1.45×10^3
575	0.110	0.249	0.128	9.6
775	0.120	0.140	4.39×10^{-3}	0.0584

39. 234 torr
41. 18
43. 3.3×10^2
45. 764
47. More solid will form.
49. Additional solid will not dissolve.
51. **a.** [A] = 0.20 M, [B] = 0.80 M
b. [A] = 0.33 M, [B] = 0.67 M
c. [A] = 0.38 M, [B] = 1.2 M
53. $[N_2O_4] = 0.0115$ M, $[NO_2] = 0.0770$ M
55. 0.199 M
57. 1.9×10^{-3} M
59. 7.84 torr
61. **a.** [A] = 0.38 M, [B] = 0.62 M, [C] = 0.62 M
b. [A] = 0.90 M, [B] = 0.095 M, [C] = 0.095 M
c. [A] = 1.0 M, [B] = 3.2×10^{-3} M, [C] = 3.2×10^{-3} M
63. **a.** shift left **b.** shift right
c. shift right
65. **a.** shift right **b.** no effect
c. no effect **d.** shift left
67. **a.** shift right **b.** shift left
c. no effect
69. Increase temperature → shift right, decrease temperature → shift left. Increasing the temperature will increase the equilibrium constant.
71. **b, d**
73. **a.** 1.7×10^2
b. $\frac{[Hb{-}CO]}{[Hb{-}O_2]} = 0.85$ or 17/20
CO is highly toxic, as it blocks O_2 uptake by hemoglobin. CO_2 at a level of 0.1% will replace nearly half of the O_2 in blood.
75. **a.** 1.68 atm **b.** 1.41 atm
77. 0.406 g
79. **b, c, d**
81. 0.0144 atm
83. 3.1×10^2 g, 20% yield
85. 0.12 atm
87. 0.72 atm
89. 0.017 g
91. 0.226
93. **a.** 29.3 **b.** 169 torr
95. $P_{NO} = P_{Cl_2} = 429$ torr
97. 1.27×10^{-2}
99. $K_P = 5.1 \times 10^{-2}$
101. Yes, because the volume affects Q.
103. $a = 1, b = 2$
105. $K_c = 1$
111. **a.** For system 1, $K_p = 0.011$; For system 2, $K_p = 91$.
c. System 1 is more likely.

Chapter 17

33. **a.** acid, $HNO_3(aq) \longrightarrow H^+(aq) + NO_3^-(aq)$
b. acid, $NH_4^+(aq) \rightleftharpoons H^+(aq) + NH_3(aq)$
c. base, $KOH(aq) \longrightarrow K^+(aq) + OH^-(aq)$
d. acid, $HC_2H_3O_2(aq) \rightleftharpoons H^+(aq) + C_2H_3O_2^-(aq)$
35. **a.** $H_2CO_3(aq) + H_2O(l) \rightleftharpoons H_3O^+(aq) + HCO_3^-(aq)$
acid, base, conj. acid, conj. base
b. $NH_3(aq) + H_2O(l) \rightleftharpoons NH_4^+(aq) + OH^-(aq)$
base, acid, conj. acid, conj. base
c. $HNO_3(aq) + H_2O(l) \rightleftharpoons H_3O^+(aq) + NO_3^-(aq)$
acid, base, conj. acid, conj. base
d. $C_5H_5N(aq) + H_2O(l) \rightleftharpoons C_5H_5NH^+(aq) + OH^-(aq)$
base, acid, conj. acid, conj. base
37. **a.** Cl^- **b.** HSO_3^- **c.** CHO_2^- **d.** F^-
39. $H_2PO_4^-(aq) + H_2O(l) \rightleftharpoons HPO_4^{2-}(aq) + H_3O^+(aq)$
$H_2PO_4^-(aq) + H_2O(l) \rightleftharpoons H_3PO_4(aq) + OH^-(aq)$
41. **a.** strong **b.** strong
c. strong **d.** weak, $K_a = \frac{[H_3O^+][HSO_3^-]}{[H_2SO_3]}$
43. **a, b, c**
45. **a.** F^- **b.** NO_2^- **c.** ClO^-
47. **a.** 8.3×10^{-7}, basic **b.** 1.2×10^{-10}, acidic
c. 2.9×10^{-13}, acidic

49. **a.** pH = 7.77, pOH = 6.23
b. pH = 7.00, pOH = 7.00
c. pH = 5.66, pOH = 8.34

51.

$[H_3O^+]$	$[OH^-]$	pH	Acidic or Basic
7.1×10^{-4}	1.4×10^{-11}	3.15	Acidic
3.7×10^{-9}	2.7×10^{-6}	8.43	Basic
7.9×10^{-12}	1.3×10^{-3}	11.1	Basic
6.3×10^{-4}	1.6×10^{-11}	3.20	Acidic

53. $[H_3O^+] = 1.5 \times 10^{-7}$ M, pH = 6.81

55. pH = 1.36, 1.35, 1.34. A difference of 1 in the second significant digit in a concentration value produces a difference of 0.01 in pH. Therefore, the second significant digit in value of the concentration corresponds to the hundredths place in a pH value.

57. **a.** $[H_3O^+] = 0.25$ M, $[OH^-] = 4.0 \times 10^{-14}$ M, pH = 0.60
b. $[H_3O^+] = 0.015$ M, $[OH^-] = 6.7 \times 10^{-13}$ M, pH = 1.82
c. $[H_3O^+] = 0.072$ M, $[OH^-] = 1.4 \times 10^{-13}$ M, pH = 1.14
d. $[H_3O^+] = 0.105$ M, $[OH^-] = 9.5 \times 10^{-14}$ M, pH = 0.979

59. **a.** 1.8 g **b.** 0.57 g **c.** 0.045 g

61. 2.21

63. $[H_3O^+] = 2.5 \times 10^{-13}$ M, pH = 2.59

65. **a.** 1.82 (approximation valid)
b. 2.18 (approximation breaks down)
c. 2.72 (approximation breaks down)

67. 2.75

69. 6.8×10^{-6}

71. 0.0063%

73. **a.** 0.42% **b.** 0.60%
c. 1.3% **d.** 1.9%

75. 3.61×10^{-5}

77. **a.** pH = 1.88, percent ionization = 5.1%
b. pH = 2.10, percent ionization = 7.9%
c. pH = 2.26, percent ionization = 11%

79. **a.** 0.939 **b.** 1.07
c. 2.19 **d.** 3.02

81. **a.** $[OH^-] = 0.15$ M, $[H_3O^+] = 6.7 \times 10^{-14}$ M, pH = 13.17, pOH = 0.83
b. $[OH^+] = 0.003$ M, $[H_3O^+] = 3.3 \times 10^{-12}$ M, pH = 11.48, pOH = 2.52
c. $[OH^-] = 9.6 \times 10^{-4}$ M, $[H_3O^+] = 1.0 \times 10^{-11}$ M, pH = 10.98, pOH = 3.02
d. $[OH^-] = 8.7 \times 10^{-5}$ M, $[H_3O^+] = 1.1 \times 10^{-10}$ M, pH = 9.93, pOH = 4.07

83. 13.842

85. 0.104 L

87. **a.** $NH_3(aq) + H_2O(l) \rightleftharpoons NH_4^+(aq) + OH^-(aq)$, $K_b = \frac{[NH_4^+][OH^-]}{[NH_3]}$
b. $HCO_3^-(aq) + H_2O(l) \rightleftharpoons H_2CO_3(aq) + OH^-(aq)$, $K_b = \frac{[H_2CO_3][OH^-]}{[HCO_3^-]}$
c. $CH_3NH_2(aq) + H_2O(l) \rightleftharpoons CH_3NH_3^+(aq) + OH^-(aq)$, $K_b = \frac{[CH_3NH_3^+][OH^-]}{[CH_3NH_2]}$

89. $[OH^-] = 1.6 \times 10^{-3}$ M, pOH = 2.79, pH = 11.21

91. 7.48

93. 6.7×10^{-7}

95. **a.** neutral
b. basic, $ClO^-(aq) + H_2O(l) \rightleftharpoons HClO(aq) + OH^-(aq)$
c. basic, $CN^-(aq) + H_2O(l) \rightleftharpoons HCN(aq) + OH^-(aq)$
d. neutral

97. $[OH^-] = 1.4 \times 10^{-6}$ M, pH = 8.16

99. **a.** acidic, $NH_4^+(aq) + H_2O(l) \rightleftharpoons NH_3(aq) + H_3O^+(aq)$
b. neutral
c. acidic, $Co(H_2O)_6^{3+}(aq) + H_2O(l) \rightleftharpoons Co(H_2O)_5(OH)^{2+}(aq) + H_3O^+(aq)$
d. acidic, $CH_2NH_3^+(aq) + H_2O(l) \rightleftharpoons CH_2NH_2(aq) + H_2O^+(aq)$

101. **a.** acidic **b.** basic
c. neutral **d.** acidic
e. acidic

103. NaOH, $NaHCO_3$, NaCl, NH_4ClO_2, NH_4Cl

105. **a.** 5.13 **b.** 8.87 **c.** 7.0

107. $[K^+] = 0.15$ M, $[F^-] = 0.15$ M, $[HF] = 1.5 \times 10^{-6}$ M, $[OH^-] = 1.5 \times 10^{-6}$ M; $[H_3O^+] = 6.7 \times 10^{-9}$ M

109. $H_3PO_4(aq) + H_2O(l) \rightleftharpoons H_2PO_4^-(aq) + H_3O^+(aq)$, $K_{a_1} = \frac{[H_3O^+][H_2PO_4^-]}{[H_3PO_4]}$
$H_2PO_4^-(aq) + H_2O(l) \rightleftharpoons HPO_4^{2-}(aq) + H_3O^+(aq)$, $K_{a_2} = \frac{[H_3O^+][HPO_4^{2-}]}{[H_2PO_4^-]}$
$HPO_4^{2-}(aq) + H_2O(l) \rightleftharpoons PO_4^{3-}(aq) + H_3O^+(aq)$, $K_{a_3} = \frac{[H_3O^+][PO_4^{3-}]}{[HPO_4^{2-}]}$

111. **a.** $[H_3O^+] = 0.048$ M, pH = 1.32
b. $[H_3O^+] = 0.12$ M, pH = 0.92

113. $[H_2SO_3] = 0.418$ M
$[HSO_3^-] = 0.082$ M
$[SO_3^{2-}] = 6.4 \times 10^{-8}$ M
$[H_3O^+] = 0.082$ M

115. **a.** $[H_3O^+] = 0.50$ M, pH = 0.30
b. $[H_3O^+] = 0.11$ M, pH = 0.96 (*x is small* approximation breaks down)
c. $[H_3O^+] = 0.059$ M, pH = 1.23

117. **a.** HCl, weaker bond
b. HF, bond polarity
c. H_2Se, weaker bond

119. **a.** H_2SO_4, more oxygen atoms bonded to S
b. $HClO_2$ more oxygen atoms bonded to Cl
c. HClO, Cl has higher electronegativity
d. CCl_3COOH, Cl has higher electronegativity

121. S^{2-}; its conjugate acid (H_2S), is a weaker acid than H_2S.

123. **a.** Lewis acid **b.** Lewis acid
c. Lewis base **d.** Lewis base

125. **a.** acid: Fe^{3+}, base: H_2O
b. acid: Zn^{2+}, base: NH_3
c. acid: BF_3, base: $(CH_3)_3N$

127. **a.** weak **b.** strong
c. weak **d.** strong

129. If blood became acidic, the H^+ concentration would increase. According to Le Châtelier's principle, equilibrium would be shifted to the left and the concentration of oxygenated Hb would decrease.
131. All acid will be neutralized.
133. $[H_3O^+]$(Great Lakes) $= 3 \times 10^{-5}$ M, $[H_3O^+]$(West Coast) $= 4 \times 10^{-6}$ M. The rain over the Great Lakes is about eight times more concentrated.
135. 2.7
137. a. 2.000 **b.** 1.52 **c.** 12.95 **d.** 11.12 **e.** 5.03
139. a. 1.260 **b.** 8.22 **c.** 0.824 **d.** 8.57 **e.** 1.171
141. a. $CN^-(aq) + H^+(aq) \rightleftharpoons HCN(aq)$
b. $NH_4^+(aq) + OH^-(aq) \rightleftharpoons NH_3(aq) + H_2O(l)$
c. $CN^-(aq) + NH_4^+(aq) \rightleftharpoons HCN(aq) + NH_3(aq)$
d. $HSO_4^-(aq) + C_2H_3O_2^-(aq) \rightleftharpoons SO_4^{2-}(aq) + HC_2H_3O_2(aq)$
e. no reaction between the major species
143. 0.794
145. $K_a = 1.4 \times 10^{-4}$
147. 6.79
149. 2.14
151. $[A^-] = 4.5 \times 10^{-5}$ M
$[H^+] = 2.2 \times 10^{-4}$ M
$[HA_2^-] = 1.8 \times 10^{-4}$ M
153. 9.28
155. 50.1 g $NaHCO_3$
157. b
159. $CH_3COOH < CH_2ClCOOH < CHCl_2COOH < CCl_3COOH$
166. a. 9.2 g SO_2
c. $S_2O_5^{2-}(aq) + H_2O(l) \rightleftharpoons 2\ HSO_3^-(aq)$
e. 16 g for (a) and 15 g for (b)

Chapter 18

27. d
29. a. 3.62 **b.** 9.11
31. pure water: 2.1%, in $NaC_7H_5O_2$: 0.065%. The percent ionization in the sodium benzoate solution is much smaller because the presence of the benzoate ion shifts the equilibrium to the left.
33. a. 2.14 **b.** 8.32 **c.** 3.46
35. $HCl + NaC_2H_3O_2 \longrightarrow HC_2H_3O_2 + NaCl$
$NaOH + HC_2H_3O_2 \longrightarrow NaC_2H_3O_2 + H_2O$
37. a. 3.62 **b.** 9.11
39. a. 7.60 **b.** 11.18 **c.** 4.61
41. a. 3.86 **b.** 8.95
43. 3.5
45. 3.7 g
47. a. 4.74 **b.** 4.68 **c.** 4.81
49. a. initial 7.00 after 1.70
b. initial 4.71 after 4.56
c. initial 10.78 after 10.66
51. 1.2 g; 2.7 g
53. a. yes **b.** no **c.** yes **d.** no **e.** no
55. a. 7.4 **b.** 0.3 g **c.** 0.14 g
57. $KClO/HClO = 0.79$
59. a. does not exceed capacity
b. does not exceed capacity
c. does not exceed capacity
d. does not exceed capacity
61. i. a. pH = 8
b. pH = 7
ii. a. weak acid
b. strong acid
63. a. 40.0 mL HI for both
b. KOH: neutral, CH_3NH_2: acidic
c. CH_3NH_2
d. Titration of KOH with HI:

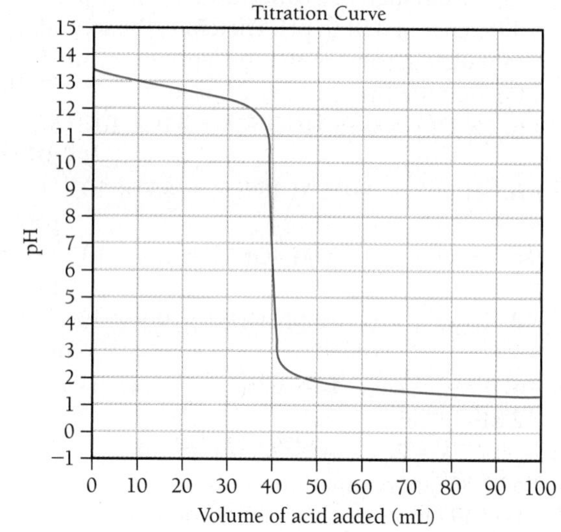

Titration of CH_3NH_2 with HI:

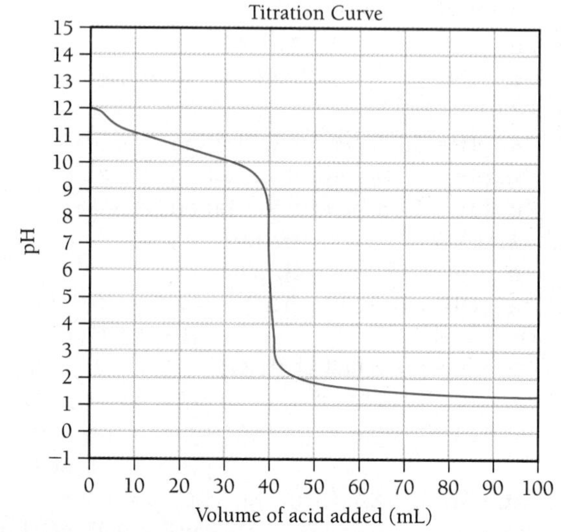

65. a. pH = 9, added base = 30 mL
b. 0 mL **c.** 15 mL
d. 30 mL **e.** 30 mL
67. a. 0.757 **b.** 30.6 mL **c.** 1.038
d. 7 **e.** 12.15
69. a. 13.06 **b.** 28.8 mL **c.** 12.90
d. 7 **e.** 2.07

71. a. 2.86 **b.** 16.8 mL **c.** 4.37
d. 4.74 **e.** 8.75 **f.** 12.17

73. a. 11.94 **b.** 29.2 mL **c.** 11.33
d. 10.64 **e.** 5.87 **f.** 1.90

75. i. (a)
ii. (b)

77. $pK_a = 3,82$ g/mol

79. First equivalence: 22.7 mL
Second equivalence: 45.4 mL

81. The indicator will appear red. The pH range is 4 to 6.

83. a. phenol red, *m*-nitrophenol
b. alizarin, bromothymol blue, phenol red
c. alizarin yellow R

85. a. $BaSO_4(s) \rightleftharpoons Ba^{2+}(aq) + SO_4^{2-}(aq)$, $K_{sp} = [Ba^{2+}][SO_4^{2-}]$
b. $PbBr_2(s) \rightleftharpoons Pb^{2+}(aq) + 2\,Br^-(aq)$, $K_{sp} = [Pb^{2+}][Br^-]^2$
c. $Ag_2CrO_4(s) \rightleftharpoons 2\,Ag^+(aq) + CrO_4^{2-}(aq)$, $K_{sp} = [Ag^+]^2[CrO_4^{2-}]$

87. a. 7.31×10^{-7} M **b.** 3.72×10^{-5} M
c. 3.32×10^{-4} M

89. a. 1.07×10^{-21} **b.** 7.14×10^{-7}
c. 7.44×10^{-11}

91. AX_2

93. 2.07×10^{-5} g/100 mL

95. a. 0.0183 M **b.** 0.00755 M
c. 0.00109 M

97. a. 5×10^{14} M **b.** 5×10^{8} M
c. 5×10^{4} M

99. a. more soluble, CO_3^{2-} is basic
b. more soluble, S^{2-} is basic
c. not, neutral
d. not, neutral

101. precipitate will form, CaF_2

103. precipitate will form, $Mg(OH)_2$

105. a. 0.018 M **b.** 1.4×10^{-7} M
c. 1.1×10^{-5} M

107. a. $BaSO_4$, 1.1×10^{-8} M
b. 3.0×10^{-8} M

109. 8.7×10^{-10} M

111. 5.6×10^{16}

113. 4.03

115. 3.57

117. HCl, 4.7 g

119. a. $NaOH(aq) + KHC_8H_4O_4(aq) \longrightarrow Na^+(aq) + K^+(aq) + C_8H_4O_4^{2-}(aq) + H_2O(l)$
b. 0.1046 M

121. 4.73

123. 176 g/mol; 1.0×10^{-4}

125. 14.2 L

127. 1.6×10^{-7} M

129. 8.0×10^{-8} M

131. 6.29

133. 0.172 M

135. The ratio by mass of dimethyl ammonium chloride to dimethyl amine needed is 3.6.

137. 0.18 M benzoic acid, 0.41 M sodium benzoate

139. 0.78 g $NaCO_3$

141. 1.8×10^{-11} (based on this data)

143. a. 5.5×10^{-25} M **b.** 5.5×10^{-4} M

145. 1.38 L

147. 12.97

149. a. $pH < pK_a$ **b.** $pH > pK_a$
c. $pH = pK_a$ **d.** $pH > pK_a$

151. b

153. a. no difference **b.** less soluble
c. more soluble

160. a. 30.0 mL **a.** 1.0×10^2 g/mol
a. Trimethylamine

Chapter 19

27. a, c

29. System B has the greatest entropy. There is only one energetically equivalent arrangement for System A. However, the particles of System B may exchange positions for a second energetically equivalent arrangement.

31. 29.2 J/K

33. −24.7 J/K

35. a. $\Delta S > 0$ **b.** $\Delta S < 0$
c. $\Delta S < 0$ **d.** $\Delta S < 0$

37. a. $\Delta S_{sys} > 0$, $\Delta S_{surr} > 0$, spontaneous at all temperatures
b. $\Delta S_{sys} < 0$, $\Delta S_{surr} < 0$, nonspontaneous at all temperatures
c. $\Delta S_{sys} < 0$, $\Delta S_{surr} < 0$, nonspontaneous at all temperatures
d. $\Delta S_{sys} > 0$, $\Delta S_{surr} > 0$, spontaneous at all temperatures

39. a. 1.29×10^3 J/K
b. 5.00×10^3 J/K
c. -3.83×10^2 J/K
d. -1.48×10^3 J/K

41. a. −649 J/K, nonspontaneous
b. 649 J/K, spontaneous
c. 123 J/K, spontaneous
d. −76 J/K, nonspontaneous

43. a. 1.93×10^5 J, nonspontaneous
b. -1.93×10^5 J, spontaneous
c. -3.7×10^4 J, spontaneous
d. 4.7×10^4 J, nonspontaneous

45. -2.247×10^6 J, spontaneous

47.

ΔH	ΔS	ΔG	Low Temperature	High Temperature
−	+	−	Spontaneous	Spontaneous
−	−	Temperature dependent	Spontaneous	Nonspontaneous
+	+	Temperature dependent	Nonspontaneous	Spontaneous
+	−	+	Nonspontaneous	Nonspontaneous

49. It increases.

51. **a.** $CO_2(g)$, greater molar mass and complexity
b. $CH_3OH(g)$, gas phase
c. $CO_2(g)$, greater molar mass and complexity
d. $SiH_4(g)$, greater molar mass
e. $CH_3CH_2CH_3(g)$, greater complexity
f. $NaBr(aq)$, aqueous

53. **a.** He, Ne, SO_2, NH_3, CH_3CH_2OH From He to Ne there is an increase in molar mass; beyond that, the molecules increase in complexity.
b. $H_2O(s)$, $H_2O(l)$, $H_2O(g)$; increase in entropy in going from solid to liquid to gas phase.
c. CH_4, CF_4, CCl_4; increasing entropy with increasing molar mass.

55. **a.** -120.8 J/K, decrease in moles of gas
b. 133.9 J/K, increase in moles of gas
c. -42.0 J/K, small change because moles of gas stay constant
d. -390.8 J/K, decrease in moles of gas

57. -89.3 J/K, decrease in moles of gas

59. $\Delta H^\circ_{rxn} = -1277$ kJ, $\Delta S^\circ_{rxn} = 313.6$ J/K, $\Delta G^\circ_{rxn} = -1.370 \times 10^3$ kJ; yes

61. **a.** $\Delta H^\circ_{rxn} = 57.2$ kJ, $\Delta S^\circ_{rxn} = 175.8$ J/K, $\Delta G^\circ_{rxn} = 4.8 \times 10^3$ J/mol; nonspontaneous, becomes spontaneous at high temperatures
b. $\Delta H^\circ_{rxn} = 176.2$ kJ, $\Delta S^\circ_{rxn} = 285.1$ J/K, $\Delta G^\circ_{rxn} = 91.2$ KJ; nonspontaneous, becomes spontaneous at high temperatures
c. $\Delta H^\circ_{rxn} = 98.8$ kJ, $\Delta S^\circ_{rxn} = 141.5$ J/K, $\Delta G^\circ_{rxn} = 56.6$ KJ; nonspontaneous, becomes spontaneous at high temperatures
d. $\Delta H^\circ_{rxn} = -91.8$ kJ, $\Delta S^\circ_{rxn} = -198.1$ J/K, $\Delta G^\circ_{rxn} = -32.8$ kJ; spontaneous

63. **a.** 2.8 kJ **b.** 91.2 kJ **c.** 56.4 kJ **d.** -32.8 kJ
Values are comparable. The method using ΔH° and ΔS° can be used to determine how ΔG° changes with temperature.

65. **a.** -72.5 kJ, spontaneous
b. -11.4 kJ, spontaneous
c. 9.1 kJ, nonspontaneous

67. -29.4 kJ

69. **a.** 19.3 kJ **b.** **(i)** 2.9 kJ **(ii)** -2.9 kJ
c. The partial pressure of iodine is very low.

71. 11.9 kJ

73. **a.** 1.48×10^{90} **b.** 2.09×10^{-26}

75. **a.** -24.8 kJ **b.** 0 **c.** 9.4 kJ

77. **a.** 1.90×10^{47} **b.** 1.51×10^{-13}

79. $\Delta H^\circ = 50.6$ kJ $\Delta S^\circ = 226$ J·K

81. 4.8

83. **a.** + **b.** – **c.** –

85. **a.** $\Delta G^\circ = 175.2$ kJ, $K = 1.95 \times 10^{-31}$, nonspontaneous
b. 133 kJ, yes

87. $Cl_2: \Delta H^\circ_{rxn} = -182.1$ kJ, $\Delta S^\circ_{rxn} = -134.4$ J/K, $\Delta G^\circ_{rxn} = -142.0$ kJ $K = 7.94 \times 10^{24}$
$Br_2: \Delta H^\circ_{rxn} = -121.6$ kJ, $\Delta S^\circ_{rxn} = -134.2$ J/K, $\Delta G^\circ_{rxn} = -81.6$ kJ $K = 2.02 \times 10^{14}$
$I_2: \Delta H^\circ_{rxn} = -48.3$ kJ, $\Delta S^\circ_{rxn} = -132.2$ J/K, $\Delta G^\circ_{rxn} = -8.9$ kJ $K = 37$
Cl_2 is the most spontaneous, and I_2 is the least. Spontaneity is determined by the standard enthalpy of formation of the dihalogenated ethane. Higher temperatures make the reactions less spontaneous.

89. **a.** 107.8 kJ **b.** 5.0×10^{-7} atm
c. spontaneous at higher temperatures, $T = 923.4$ K

91. **a.** 2.22×10^5 **b.** 94.4 mol

93. **a.** $\Delta G^\circ = -689.6$ kJ, ΔG° becomes less negative.
b. $\Delta G^\circ = -665.2$ kJ, ΔG° becomes less negative.
c. $\Delta G^\circ = -632.4$ kJ, ΔG° becomes less negative.
d. $\Delta G^\circ = -549.3$ kJ, ΔG° becomes less negative.

95. With one exception, the formation of any oxide of nitrogen at 298 K requires more moles of gas as reactants than are formed as products. For example, 1 mol of N_2O requires 0.5 mol of O_2 and 1 mol of N_2, 1 mol of N_2O_3 requires 1 mol of N_2 and 1.5 mol of O_2, and so on. The exception is NO, where 1 mol of NO requires 0.5 mol of O_2 and 0.5 mol of N_2:

$$\frac{1}{2}N_2(g) + \frac{1}{2}O_2(g) \longrightarrow NO(g)$$

This reaction has a positive ΔS because what is essentially mixing of the N and O has taken place in the product.

97. 15.0 kJ

99. **a.** Positive, the process is spontaneous. It is slow unless a spark is applied.
b. Positive, although the change in the system is not spontaneous; the overall change, which includes such processes as combustion or water flow to generate electricity, is spontaneous.
c. Positive, the acorn-oak tree system is becoming more ordered, so the processes associated with growth are not spontaneous. But they are driven by spontaneous processes such as the generation of heat by the sun and the reactions that produce energy in the cell.

101. At 18.3 mmHg $\Delta G = 0$, at 760 mmHg $\Delta G^\circ = 55.4$ kJ

103. **a.** 3.24×10^{-3}
b.

$$NH_3 + ATP + H_2O \longrightarrow NH_3{-}P_i + ADP$$
$$NH_3{-}P_i + C_5H_8O_4N^- \longrightarrow C_5H_9O_3N_2 + P_i + H_2O$$
$$NH_3 + C_5H_8O_4N^- + ATP \longrightarrow C_5H_9O_3N_2 + ADP + P_i$$

$\Delta G^\circ = -16.3$ kJ, $K = 7.20 \times 10^2$

105. **a.** -95.3 kJ/mol Since the number of moles of reactants and products is the same, the decrease in volume affects the entropy of both equally, so there is no change in ΔG.
b. 102.8 kJ/mol The entropy of the reactants (1.5 mol) is decreased more than the entropy of the product (1 mol). Since the product is relatively more favored at lower volume, ΔG is less positive.
c. 204.2 kJ/mol The entropy of the product (1 mol) is decreased more than the entropy of the reactant (0.5 mol). Since the product is relatively less favored, ΔG is more positive.

107. $\Delta H^\circ = -93$ kJ, $\Delta S^\circ = -2.0 \times 10^2$ J/K

109. ΔS_{vap} diethyl ether $= 86.1$ J/mol K, ΔS_{vap} acetone $= 88.4$ J/mol K,

ΔS_{vap} benzene $= 87.3\,J/mol\,K$,
ΔS_{vap} chloroform $= 88.0\,J/mol\,K$. Because water and ethanol hydrogen bond, they are more ordered in the liquid and we expect ΔS_{vap} to be more positive.
Ethanol $38600/351.0 = 38600/351.0 = 110\,J/mol\,K$,
$H_2O = 40700/373.2 = 109\,J/mol\,K$

111. c

113. b

115. c

117. ΔG°_{rxn} is negative and ΔG_{rxn} is positive.

123.

a.

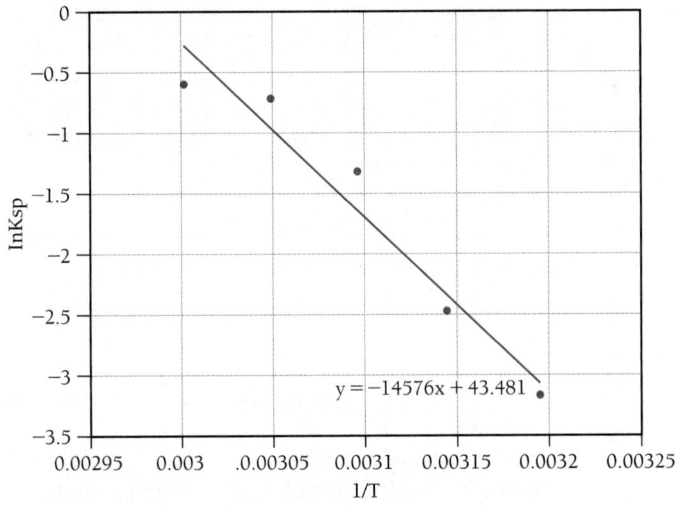

c. 362 J/K

e.

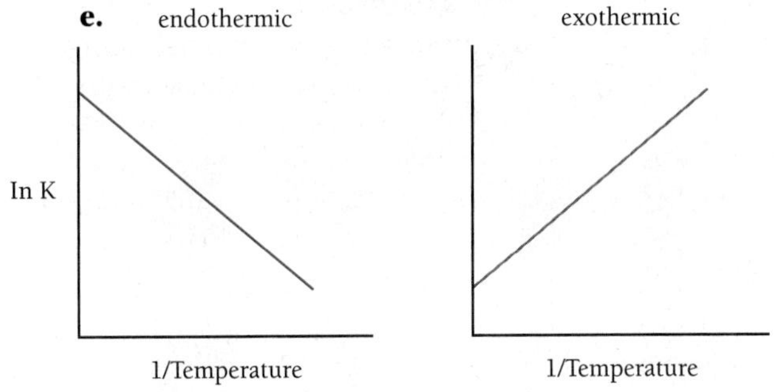

Chapter 20

37. **a.** $3\,K(s) + Cr^{3+}(aq) \longrightarrow Cr(s) + 3\,K^+(aq)$
b. $2\,Al(s) + 3\,Fe^{2+}(aq) \longrightarrow 2\,Al^{3+}(aq) + 3\,Fe(s)$
c. $2\,BrO_3^-(aq) + 3\,N_2H_4(g) \longrightarrow 2\,Br^-(aq) + 3\,N_2(g) + 6\,H_2O(l)$

39. **a.** $PbO_2(s) + 2\,I^-(aq) + 4\,H^+(aq) \longrightarrow Pb^{2+}(aq) + I_2(s) + 2\,H_2O(l)$
b. $5\,SO_3^{2-}(aq) + 2\,MnO_4^-(aq) + 6\,H^+(aq) \longrightarrow 5\,SO_4^{2-}(aq) + 2\,Mn^{2+}(aq) + 3\,H_2O(l)$
c. $S_2O_3^{2-}(aq) + 4\,Cl_2(g) + 5\,H_2O(l) \longrightarrow 2\,SO_4^{2-}(aq) + 8\,Cl^-(aq) + 10\,H^+(aq)$

41. **a.** $H_2O_2(aq) + 2\,ClO_2(aq) + 2\,OH^-(aq) \longrightarrow O_2(g) + 2\,ClO_2^-(aq) + 2\,H_2O(l)$
b. $Al(s) + MnO_4^-(aq) + 2\,H_2O(l) \longrightarrow Al(OH)_4^-(aq) + MnO_2(s)$
c. $Cl_2(g) + 2\,OH^-(aq) \longrightarrow Cl^-(aq) + ClO^-(aq) + H_2O(l)$

43. **a.**

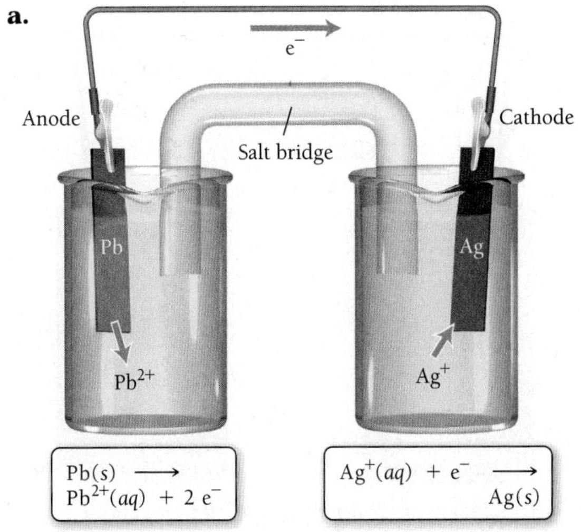

b.

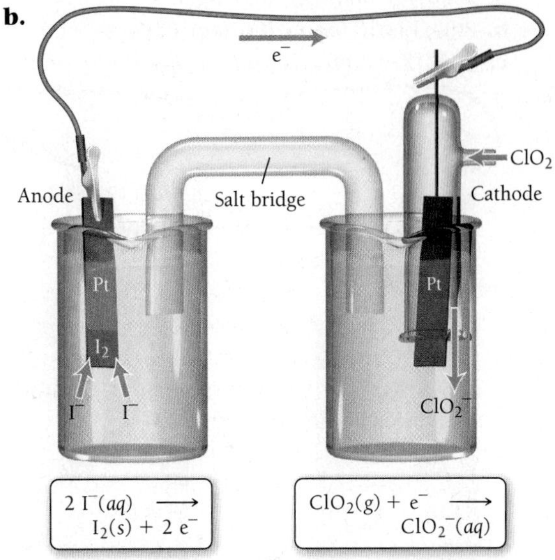

c.

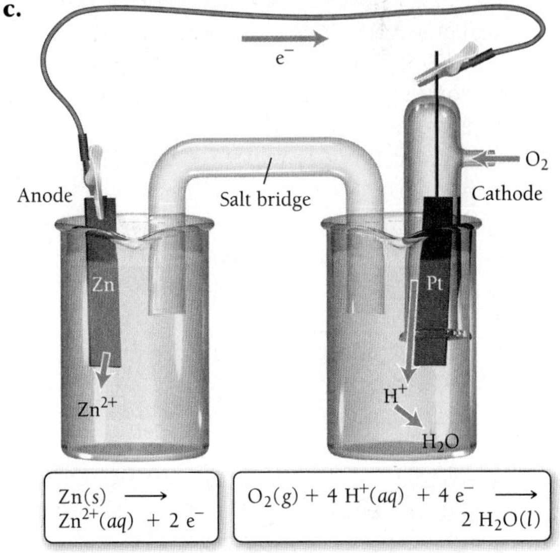

45. **a.** 0.93 V **b.** 0.41 V **c.** 1.99 V

47. **a, c, d**

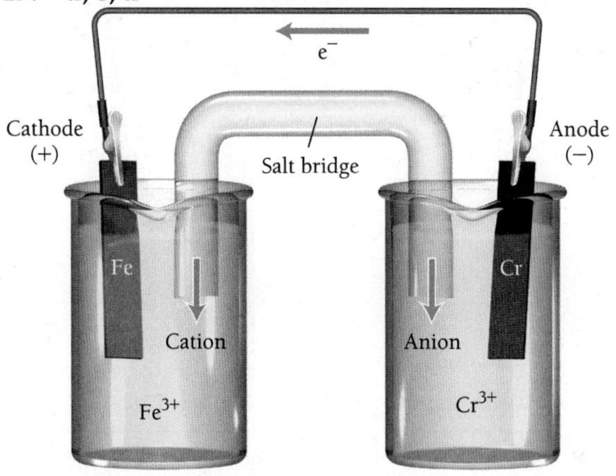

b. $Cr(s) + Fe^{3+}(aq) \longrightarrow Cr^{3+}(aq) + Fe(s), E^\circ_{cell} = 0.69\ V$

49. **a.** $Pb(s)\,|\,Pb^{2+}(aq)\,\|\,Ag^+(aq)\,|\,Ag(s)$
b. $Pt(s), I_2(s)\,|\,I^-(aq)\,\|\,ClO_2^-(aq)\,|\,ClO_2(g)\,|\,Pt(s)$
c. $Zn(s)\,|\,Zn^{2+}(aq)\,\|\,H_2(O)(l)\,|\,H^+(aq)\,|\,O_2(g)\,|\,Pt(s)$

51.

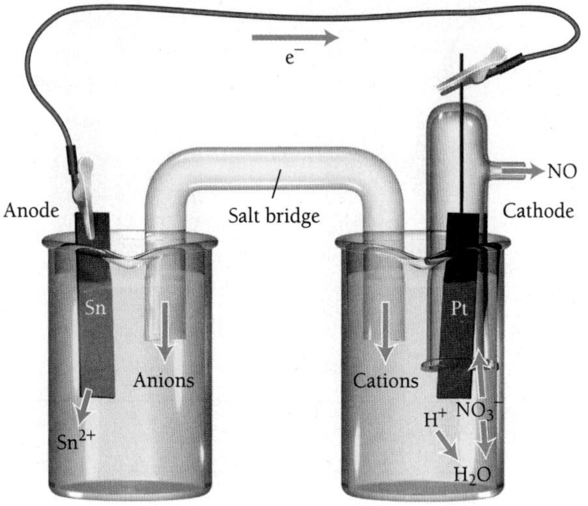

$3\,Sn(s) + 2\,NO_3^-(aq) + 8\,H^+(aq) \longrightarrow$
$3\,Sn^{2+}(aq) + 2\,NO(g) + 4\,H_2O(l), E^\circ_{cell} = 1.10\ V$

53. **b, c** occur spontaneously in the forward direction.

55. aluminum

57. **a.** yes, $2\,Al(s) + 6\,H^+(aq) \longrightarrow 2\,Al^{3+}(aq) + 3\,H_2(g)$
b. no
c. yes, $Pb(s) + 2\,H^+(aq) \longrightarrow Pb^{2+}(aq) + H_2(g)$

59. **a.** yes, $3\,Cu(s) + 2\,NO_3^-(aq) + 8\,H^+(aq) \longrightarrow$
$3\,Cu^{2+}(aq) + 2\,NO(g) + 4\,H_2O(l)$
b. no

61. **a.** −1.70 V, nonspontaneous
b. 1.97 V, spontaneous
c. −1.51 V, nonspontaneous

63. **a**

65. **a.** −432 kJ **b.** 52 kJ
c. -1.7×10^2 KJ

67. **a.** 5.31×10^{75} **b.** 7.7×10^{-10}
c. 6.3×10^{29}

69. 5.6×10^5

71. $\Delta G^\circ = -7.\underline{9}7$ kJ, $E^\circ_{cell} = 0.041$ V

73. **a.** 1.04 V **b.** 0.97 V **c.** 1.11 V

75. 1.87 V

77. **a.** 0.56 V **b.** 0.52 V
c. $[Ni^{2+}] = 0.003$ M, $[Zn^{2+}] = 1.60$ M

79.

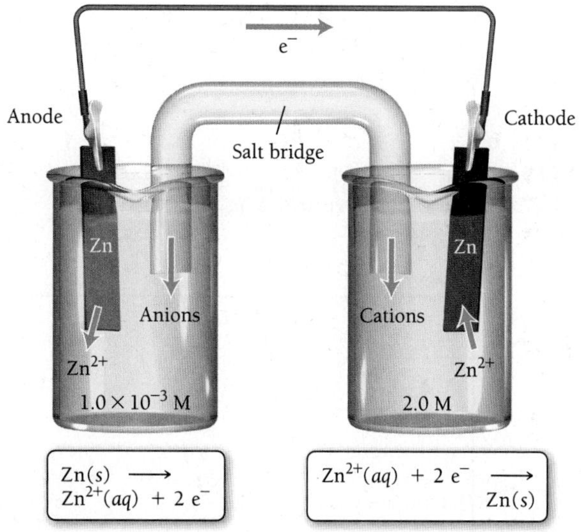

81. $\dfrac{[Sn^{2+}](ox)}{[Sn^{2+}](red)} = 4.2 \times 10^{-4}$

83. 0.3762

85. 1.038 V

87. **a, c** would prevent the corrosion of iron.

89.

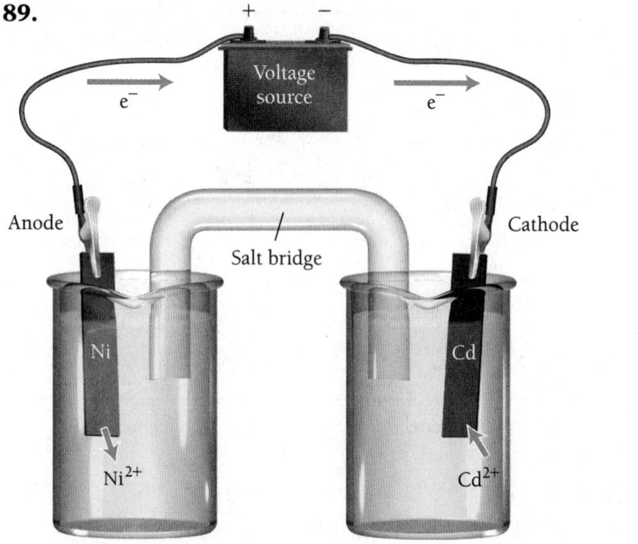

minimum voltage = 0.17 V

91. oxidation: $2\,Br^-(l) \longrightarrow Br_2(g) + 2\,e^-$
reduction: $K^+(l) + e^- \longrightarrow K(l)$

93. oxidation: $2\,Br^-(l) \longrightarrow Br_2(g) + 2\,e^-$
reduction: $K^+(l) + e^- \longrightarrow K(l)$

95. **a.** anode: $2\,Br^- \longrightarrow Br_2(l) + 2\,e^-$
cathode: $2\,H_2O(l) + 2\,e^- \longrightarrow H_2(g) + 2\,OH^-(aq)$
b. anode: $2\,I^-(aq) \longrightarrow I_2(s) + 2\,e^-$
cathode: $Pb^{2+}(aq) + 2\,e^- \longrightarrow Pb(s)$
c. anode: $2\,H_2O(l) \longrightarrow O_2(g) + 4\,H^+(aq) + 4\,e^-$
cathode: $2\,H_2O(l) + 2\,e^- \longrightarrow H_2(g) + 2\,OH^-(aq)$

97.

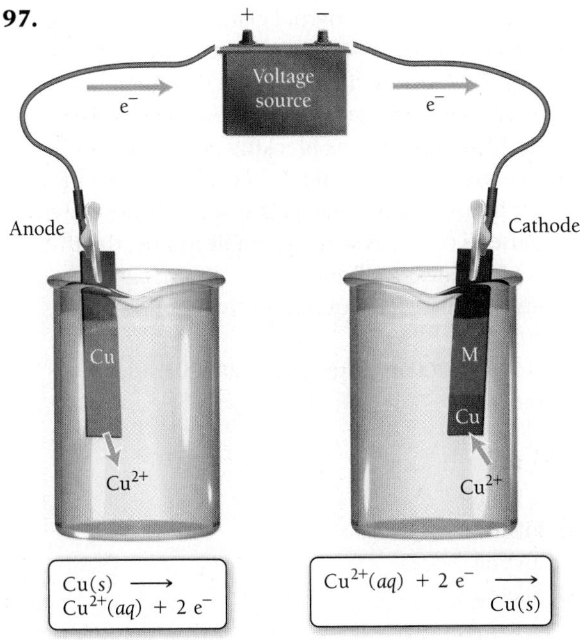

99. 1.8×10^2 s

101. 1.2×10^3 A $E_{cell} = 0.0725$ V, K = 282

103.

$[B^{2+}]$	$[A^{2+}]$	Q	E_{cell}	ΔG_{rxn}
1.00	1.0	1.0	0.0725 V	−14.0 kJ
1.00	1.00×10^{-4}	1.00×10^{-4}	0.191	−36.8 kJ
1.00×10^{-4}	1.0	1.00×10^{4}	−0.0458	8.82 kJ
3.52×10^{-3}	1.0	284	0	0

105. $2\,MnO_4^-(aq) + 5\,Zn(s) + 16\,H^+(aq) \longrightarrow 2\,Mn^{2+}(aq) + 5\,Zn^{2+}(aq) + 8\,H_2O(l)$ 34.9 mL

107. The drawing should show that several Al atoms dissolve into solution as Al^{3+} ions and that several Cu^{2+} ions are deposited on the Al surface as solid Cu.

109. **a.** 68.3 mL
b. cannot be dissolved
c. cannot be dissolved

111. 0.25

113. There are no paired reactions that produce more than about 5 or 6 V.

115. **a.** 2.83 V **b.** 2.71 V **c.** 16 hr

117. 176 hr

119. 0.71 V

121. **a.** $\Delta G^\circ = 461$ kJ, $K = 1.4 \times 10^{-81}$
b. $\Delta G^\circ = 2.7 \times 10^2$ kJ, $K = 2.0 \times 10^{-48}$

123. MCl_4

125. 51.3%

127. pH = 0.85

129. 0.83 M

131. 4.1×10^5 L

133. 435 s

135. 8.39% U

137. The overall cell reaction for both cells is $2\,Cu^+(aq) \longrightarrow Cu^{2+}(aq) + Cu(s)$. The difference in E° is because $n = 1$ for the first cell and $n = 2$ for the second cell. For both cells, $\Delta G^\circ = -35.1$ kJ.

139. **a**

141. ΔG°_{rxn} is positive and E°_{cell} is negative.

147. **a.**

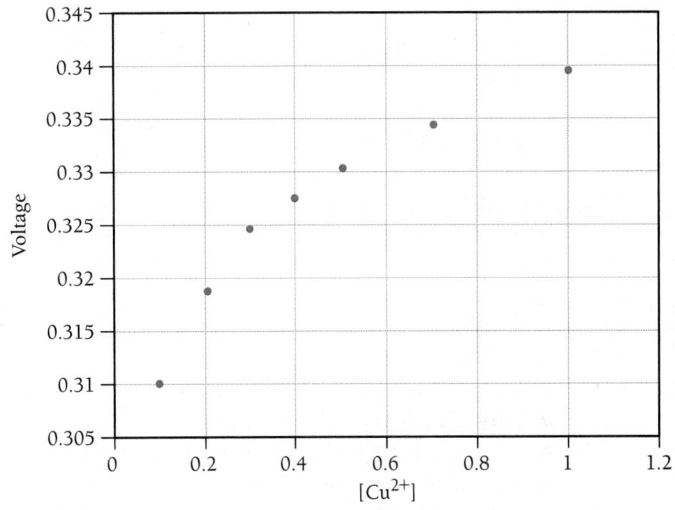

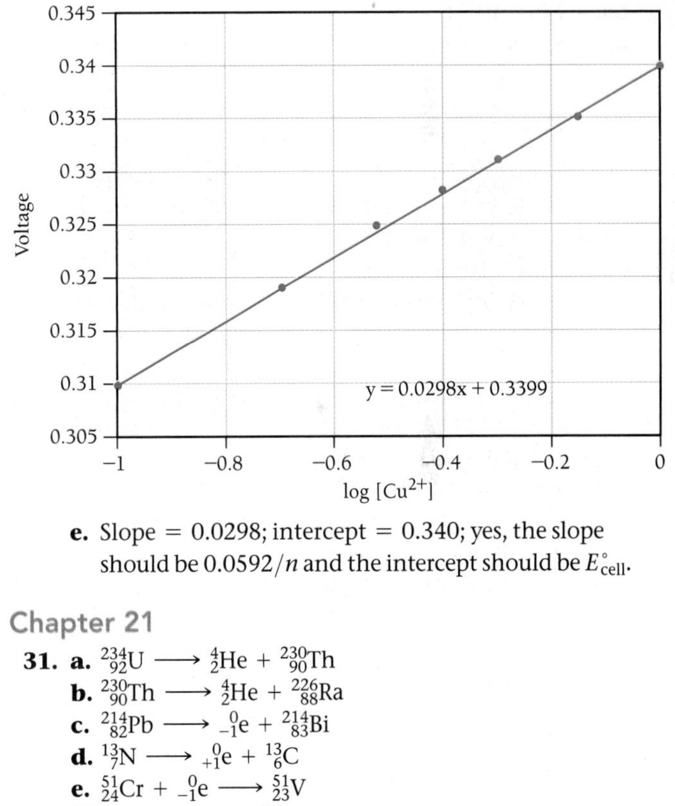

e. Slope = 0.0298; intercept = 0.340; yes, the slope should be $0.0592/n$ and the intercept should be E°_{cell}.

Chapter 21

31. **a.** ${}^{234}_{92}U \longrightarrow {}^{4}_{2}He + {}^{230}_{90}Th$
b. ${}^{230}_{90}Th \longrightarrow {}^{4}_{2}He + {}^{226}_{88}Ra$
c. ${}^{214}_{82}Pb \longrightarrow {}^{0}_{-1}e + {}^{214}_{83}Bi$
d. ${}^{13}_{7}N \longrightarrow {}^{0}_{+1}e + {}^{13}_{6}C$
e. ${}^{51}_{24}Cr + {}^{0}_{-1}e \longrightarrow {}^{51}_{23}V$

33. ${}^{232}_{90}Th \longrightarrow {}^{4}_{2}He + {}^{228}_{88}Ra$
${}^{228}_{88}Ra \longrightarrow {}^{0}_{-1}e + {}^{228}_{89}Ac$
${}^{228}_{89}Ac \longrightarrow {}^{0}_{-1}e + {}^{228}_{90}Th$
${}^{228}_{90}Th \longrightarrow {}^{4}_{2}He + {}^{224}_{88}Ra$

35. **a.** ${}^{221}_{87}Fr$ **b.** ${}^{0}_{-1}e$ **c.** ${}^{0}_{+1}e$ **d.** ${}^{0}_{-1}e$

37. **a.** stable; N/Z ratio is close to 1, acceptable for low Z atoms.
b. not stable; N/Z ratio is much too high for low Z atom.
c. not stable; N/Z ratio is less than 1, much too low.
d. stable; N/Z ratio is acceptable for this Z.

39. Sc, V, and Mn; each have odd numbers of protons. Atoms with an odd number of protons typically have less stable isotopes than those with an even number of protons.

41. **a.** beta decay
b. positron emission
c. positron emission
d. positron emission

43. **a.** Cs-125 **b.** Fe-62

45. 2.34×10^9 years

47. 0.57 g

49. 10.8 hr

51. 2.66×10^3 yr

53. 2.4×10^4 yr

55. 2.7×10^9 yr

57. ${}^{235}_{92}U + {}^{1}_{0}n \longrightarrow {}^{144}_{54}Xe + {}^{90}_{38}Sr + 2\,{}^{1}_{0}n$

59. ${}^{2}_{1}H + {}^{2}_{1}H \longrightarrow {}^{3}_{2}He + {}^{1}_{0}n$

61. ${}^{238}_{92}U + {}^{1}_{0}n \longrightarrow {}^{239}_{92}U$
${}^{239}_{92}U \longrightarrow {}^{239}_{93}Np + {}^{0}_{-1}e$
${}^{239}_{93}Np \longrightarrow {}^{239}_{94}Pu + {}^{0}_{-1}e$

63. ${}^{249}_{98}Cf + {}^{12}_{6}C \longrightarrow {}^{257}_{104}Rf + 4\,{}^{1}_{0}n$

65. 9.0×10^{13} J

67. **a.** mass defect = 0.13701 amu binding energy = 7.976 MeV/nucleon
b. mass defect = 0.54369 amu binding energy = 8.732 MeV/nucleon
c. mass defect = 1.16754 amu binding energy = 8.431 MeV/nucleon

69. 7.228×10^{10} J/g U—235

71. 7.84×10^{10} J/g H—2

73. radiation: 25 J, fall: 370 J

75. 68 mi

77. **a.** ${}^{1}_{1}p + {}^{9}_{4}Be \longrightarrow {}^{6}_{3}Li + {}^{4}_{2}He$ 1.03×10^{11} J/mol
b. ${}^{209}_{83}Bi + {}^{64}_{28}Ni \longrightarrow {}^{272}_{111}Rg + {}^{1}_{0}n$ 1.141×10^{13} J/mol
c. ${}^{179}_{74}W + {}^{0}_{-1}e \longrightarrow {}^{179}_{73}Ta$ 7.59×10^{10} J/mol

79. **a.** ${}^{114}_{44}Ru \longrightarrow {}^{0}_{-1}e + {}^{114}_{45}Rh$
b. ${}^{216}_{88}Ra \longrightarrow {}^{0}_{+1}e + {}^{216}_{87}Fr$
c. ${}^{58}_{30}Zn \longrightarrow {}^{0}_{+1}e + {}^{58}_{29}Cu$
d. ${}^{31}_{10}Ne \longrightarrow {}^{0}_{-1}e + {}^{31}_{11}Na$

81. 2.9×10^{21} beta emissions, 3700 Ci

83. 1.6×10^{-5} L

85. 4.94×10^7 kJ/mol

87. 7.72 MeV

89. ${}^{14}N$

91. 0.15%

93. 1.24×10^{21} atoms

95. 2.42×10^{-12} m

97. −0.7 MeV; there is no coulombic barrier for collision with a neutron.

99. **a.** 1.164×10^{10} kJ
b. 0.1299 g

101. U-235 forms Pb-207 in seven α-decays and four β-decays, and Th-232 forms Pb-208 in six α-decays and four β-decays.

103. 3.0×10^2 K

105. ${}^{21}_{9}F \longrightarrow {}^{21}_{10}Ne + {}^{0}_{-1}e$

107. Nuclide A is more dangerous because the half-life is shorter (18.5 days) and so it decays faster.

109. Iodine is used by the thyroid gland to make hormones. Normally, we ingest iodine in foods, especially iodized salt. The thyroid gland cannot tell the difference between stable and radioactive iodine and will absorb both. KI tablets work by blocking radioactive iodine from entering the thyroid. When a person takes KI, the stable iodine in the tablet gets absorbed by the thyroid. Because KI contains so much stable iodine, the thyroid gland becomes "full" and cannot absorb any more iodine—either stable or radioactive—for the next 24 hours.

115. **a.** 0.34 g at 200 minutes; 0.23 g at 400 minutes
c. 0.63 μg

Chapter 22

33. **a.** alkane
b. alkene
c. alkyne
d. alkene

35.

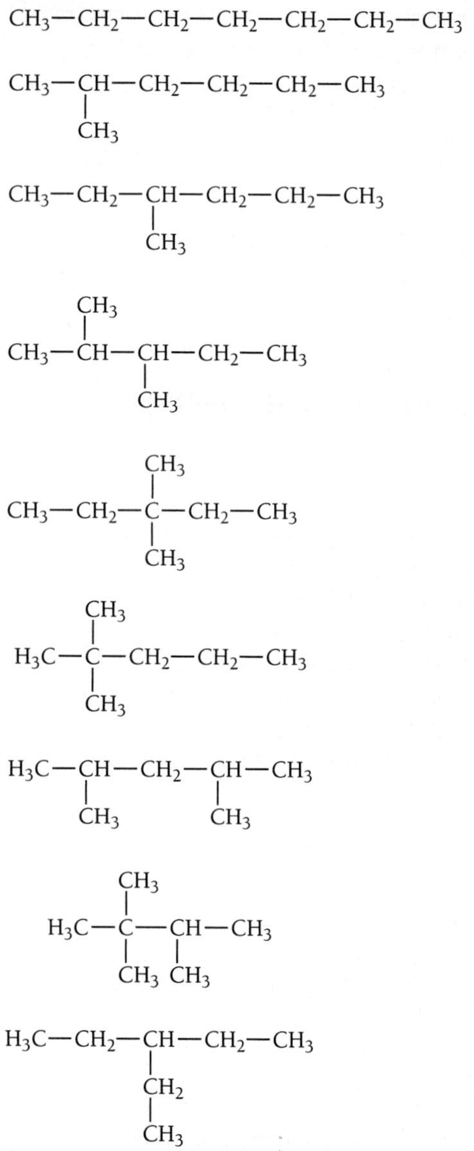

37. **a.** no **b.** yes **c.** yes **d.** no

39. **a.** enantiomers **b.** same **c.** enantiomers

41. **a.** pentane
b. 2-methylbutane
c. 4-isopropyl-2-methylheptane
d. 4-ethyl-2-methylhexane

43. **a.**
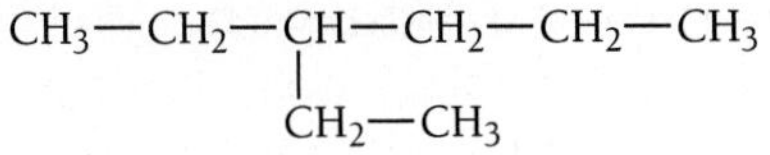
b.
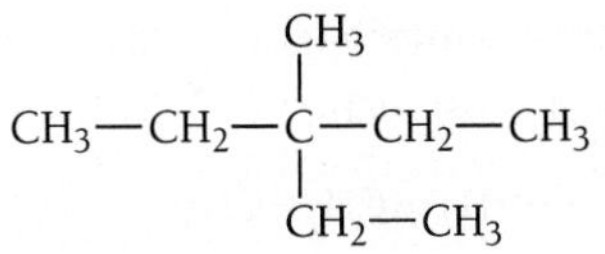
c.
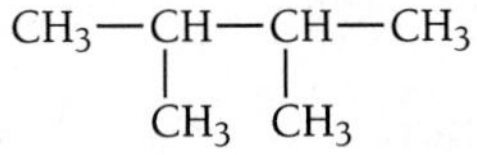
d.
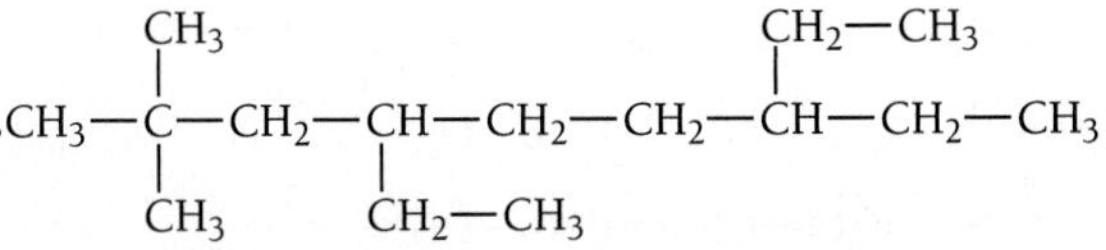

45. **a.** $CH_3CH_2CH_3 + 5\,O_2 \longrightarrow 3\,CO_2 + 4\,H_2O$
b. $CH_3CH_2CH = CH_2 + 6\,O_2 \longrightarrow 4\,CO_2 + 4\,H_2O$
c. $2\,CH{\equiv}CH + 5\,O_2 \longrightarrow 4\,CO_2 + 2\,H_2O$

47. **a.** CH_3CH_2Br
b. $CH_3CH_2CH_2Cl$, $CH_3CHClCH_3$
c.
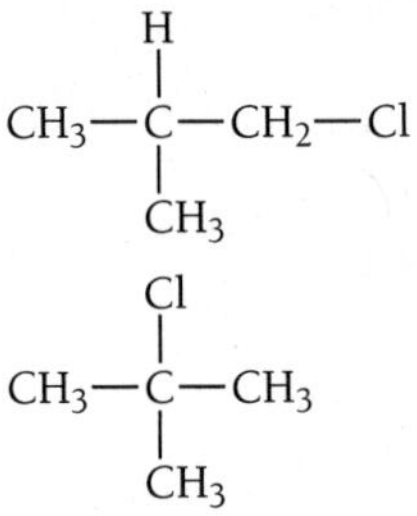

49. $CH_2{=}CH{-}CH_2{-}CH_2{-}CH_2{-}CH_3$
$CH_3{-}CH{-}CH{-}CH_2{-}CH_2{-}CH_3$
$CH_3{-}CH_2{-}CH{=}CH{-}CH_2{-}CH_3$

51. **a.** 1-butene
b. 3,4-dimethyl-2-pentene
c. 3-isopropyl-1-hexene
d. 2,4-dimethyl-3-hexene

53. **a.** 2-butyne
b. 4,4-dimethyl-2-hexyne
c. 3-isopropyl-1-hexyne
d. 3,6-dimethyl-4-nonyne

55. **a.** $CH_3{-}CH_2{-}CH{-}C{\equiv}C{-}CH_2{-}CH_2{-}CH_3$
b.
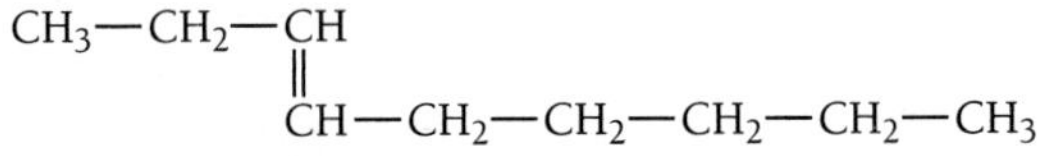
c.
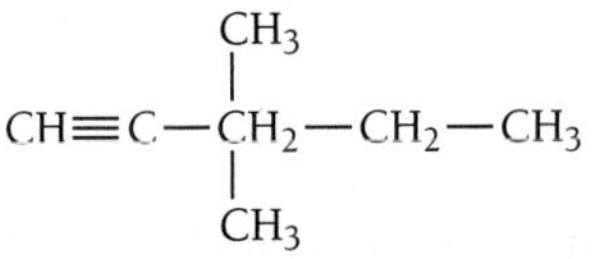
d.
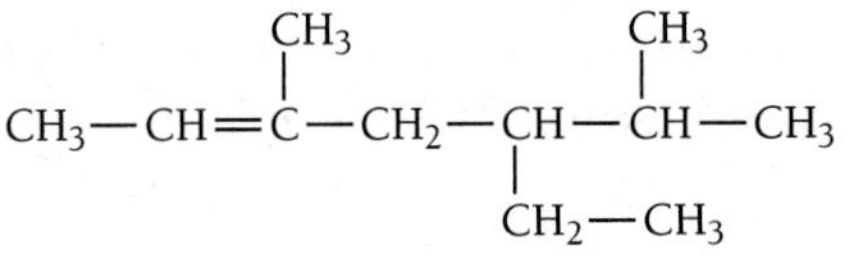

57. **a.**
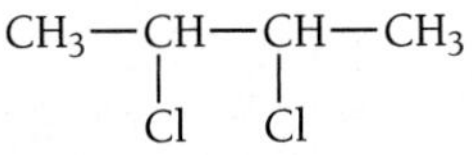
b.
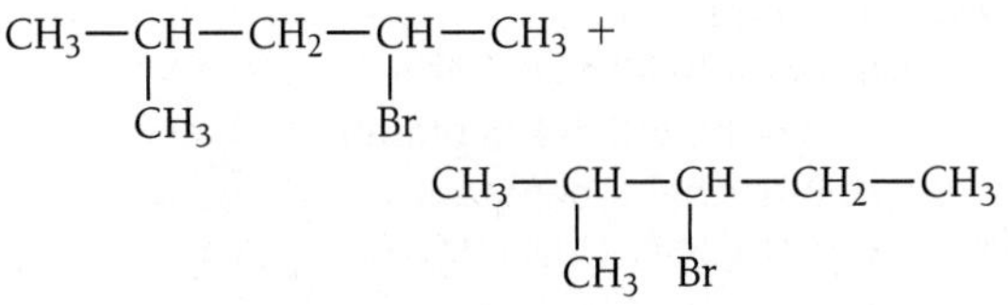
c.
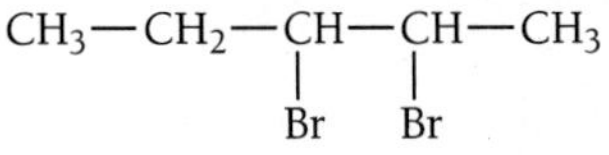
d.
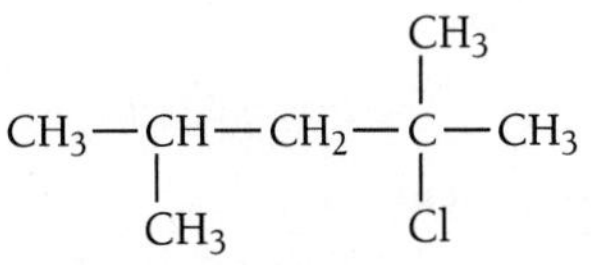

59. **a.** $CH_2{=}CH{-}CH_3 + H_2 \longrightarrow CH_3{-}CH_2{-}CH_3$
b.
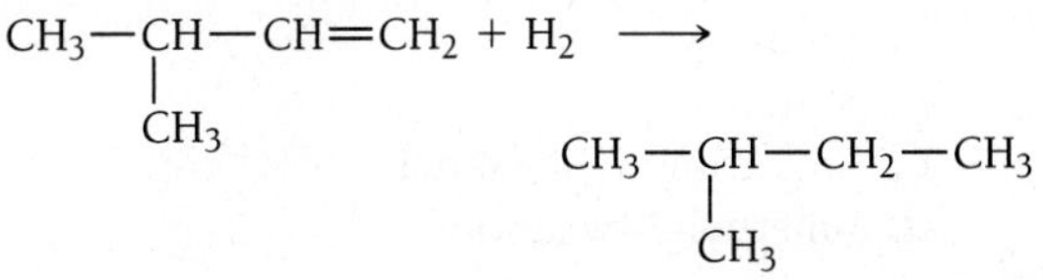
c.
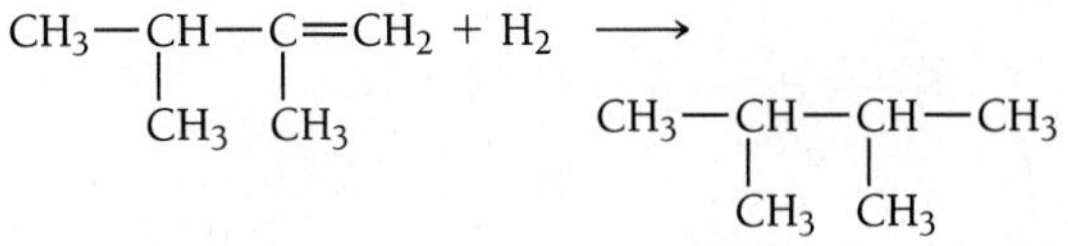

61. **a.** methylbenzene or toluene
b. bromobenzene
c. chlorobenzene

63. **a.** 3,5-dimethyl-7-phenylnonane
b. 2-phenyl-3-octene
c. 4,5-dimethyl-6-phenyl-2-octyne

65. **a.** 1,4-dibromobenzene or *p*-dibromobenzene
b. 1,3-diethylbenzene or *m*-diethylbenzene
c. 1-chloro-2-fluorobenzene or *o*-chlorofluorobenzene

67. **d.**
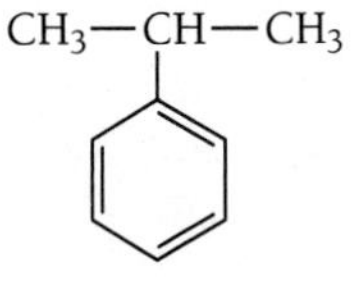
e.
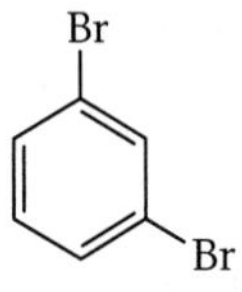
f.

69. **g.**
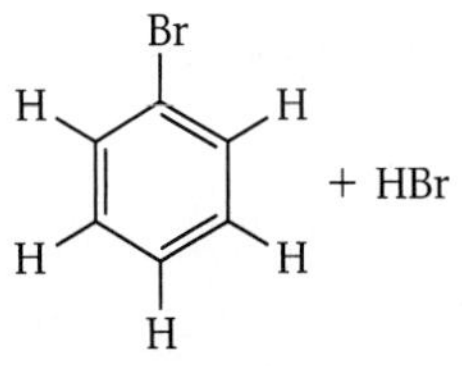
h.
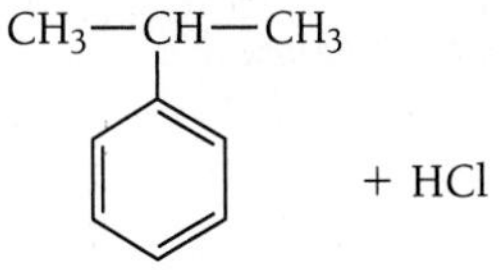

71. **a.** 1-propanol
b. 4-methyl-2-hexanol
c. 2,6-dimethyl-4-heptanol
d. 3-methyl-3-pentanol

73. **a.** $CH_3CH_2CH_2Br + H_2O$
b. 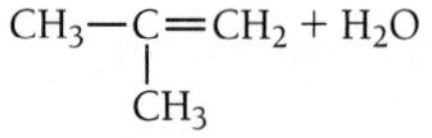
c. $CH_3CH_2ONa + \frac{1}{2}H_2$
d. 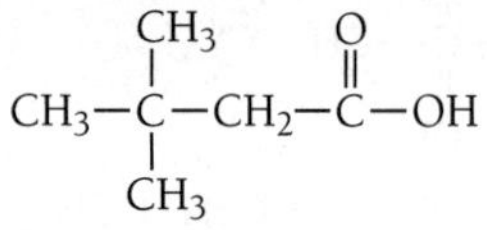

75. **a.** butanone
b. pentanal
c. 3,5,5-trimethylhexanal
d. 4-methyl-2-hexanone

77. 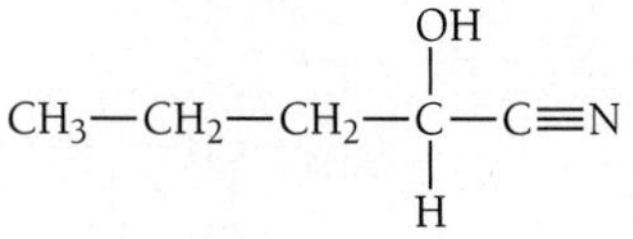

79. **a.** methylbutanoate
b. propanoic acid
c. 5-methylhexanoic acid
d. ethylpentanoate

81. **a.** 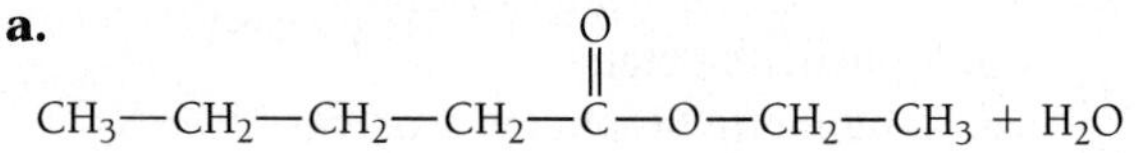
b. 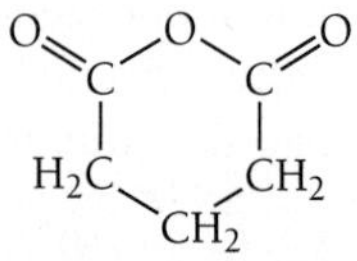 $+ H_2O$

83. **a.** ethyl propyl ether
b. ethyl pentyl ether
c. dipropyl ether
d. butyl ethyl ether

85. **a.** diethylamine
b. methylpropylamine
c. butylmethylpropylamine

87. **a.** acid–base, $(CH_3)_2NH_2^+(aq) + Cl^-(aq)$
b. condensation, $CH_3CH_2CONHCH_2CH_3(aq) + H_2O$
c. acid–base, $CH_3NH_3^+(aq) + HSO_4^-(aq)$

89. **a.** ester, methyl 3-methylbutanoate
b. ether, ethyl 2-methylbutyl ether
c. aromatic, 1-ethyl-3-methylbenzene or *m*-ethylmethylbenzene
d. alkyne, 5-ethyl-4-methyl-2-heptyne
e. aldehyde, butanal
f. alcohol, 2-methyl-1-propanol

91. **a.** 5-isobutyl-3-methylnonane
b. 5-methyl-3-hexanone
c. 3-methyl-2-butanol
d. 4-ethyl-3,5-dimethyl-1-hexyne

93. **a.** isomers **b.** isomers
c. same

95. 558 g

97. **a.** combustion
b. alkane substitution
c. alcohol elimination
d. aromatic substitution

99. **a.** 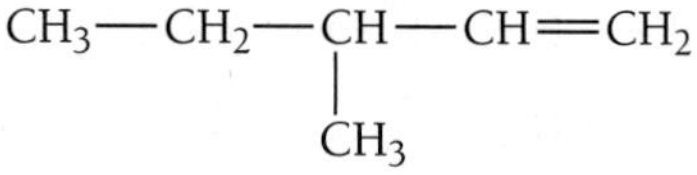
Can exist as a stereoisomer
b. 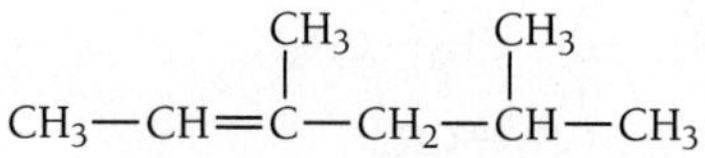
Can exist as a stereoisomer
c. 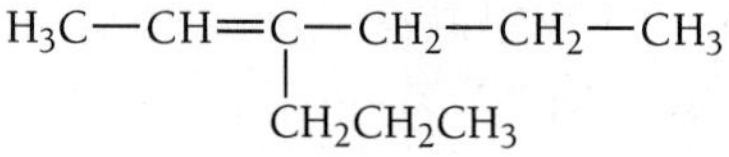
Can exist as a stereoisomer

101. **1.** 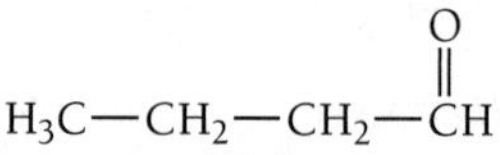
Aldehyde
2. 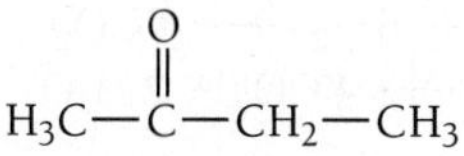
Ketone
3. $H_3C{-}CH{=}CH{-}O{-}CH_3$
Alkene, ether
4. $H_2C{=}CH{-}O{-}CH_2{-}CH_3$
Alkene, ether
5. $H_2C{=}CH{-}CH_2{-}O{-}CH_3$
Alkene, ether
6. $H_3C{-}CH{=}CH{-}CH_2{-}OH$
Alkene, alcohol
7. 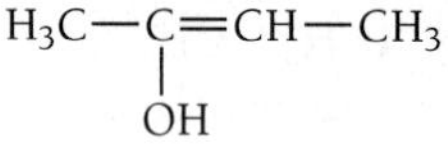
Alkene, alcohol
8. 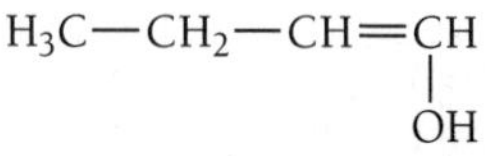
Alkene, alcohol
9. 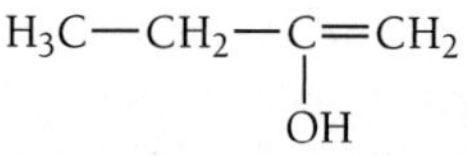
Alkene, alcohol
10. 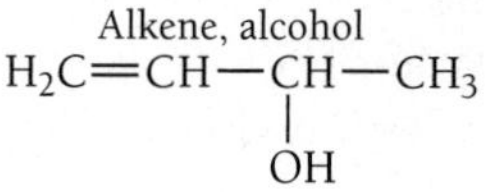
Alkene, alcohol
11. $H_2C{=}CH{-}CH_2{-}CH_2{-}OH$
Alkene, alcohol

103. In the acid form of the carboxylic acid, electron withdrawal by the C=O enhances acidity. The conjugate base, the carboxylate anion, is stabilized by resonance, so the two O atoms are equivalent and bear the negative charge equally.

105. **a.** 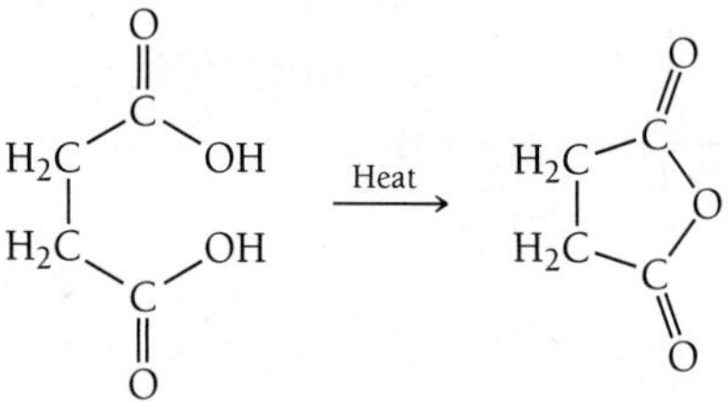

b.

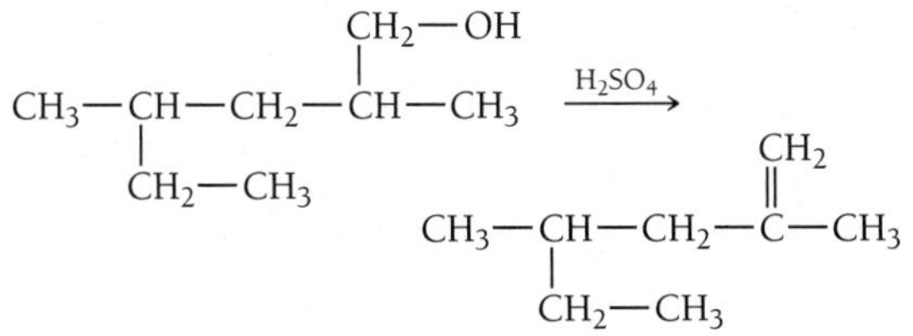

c.

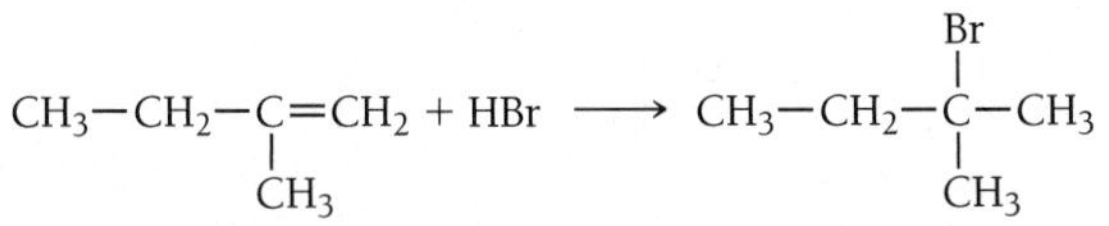

107. a. 3:1

b. 2° hydrogen atoms are more reactive. The reactivity of 2° hydrogens to 1° hydrogens is 11:3.

109.

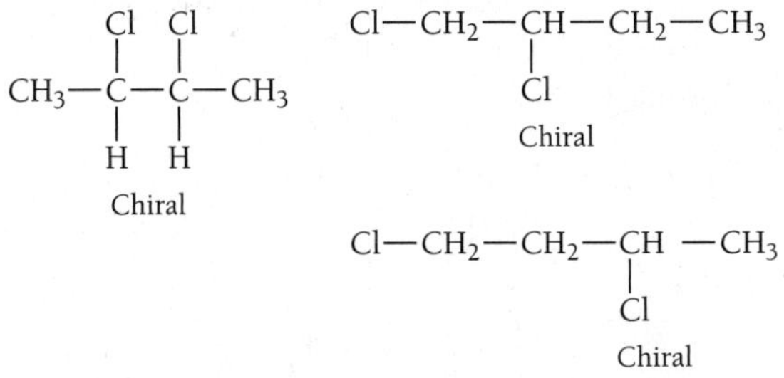

111. The first propagation step for F is very rapid and exothermic because of the strength of the H—F bond that forms. For I the first propagation step is endothermic and slow because the H—I bond that forms is relatively weak.

113.

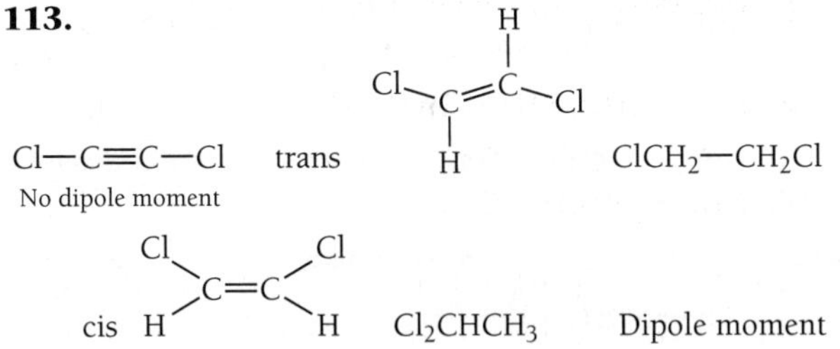

115.

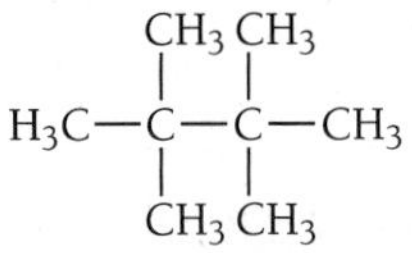

2,2,3,3-tetramethylbutane

121. a. Apple: methylbutanoate; Pear: propyl ethanoate (or propyl acetate); Pineapple: ethyl butanoate

c.

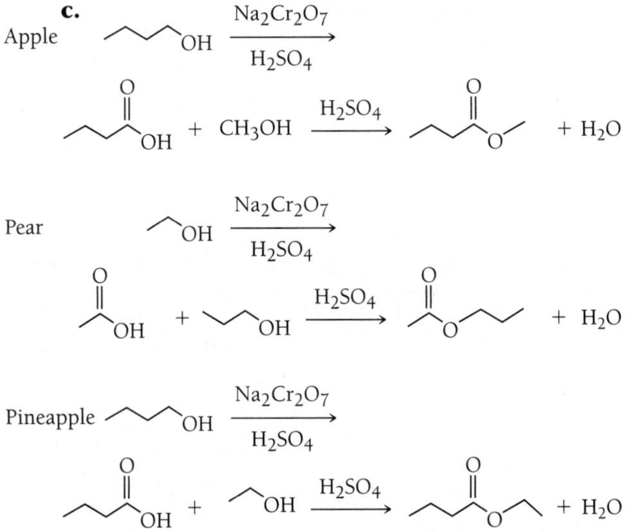

Chapter 23

31. a. saturated fatty acid
b. steroid

33. a. saturated fatty acid
b. not a fatty acid
c. not a fatty acid
d. monounsaturated fatty acid

35.

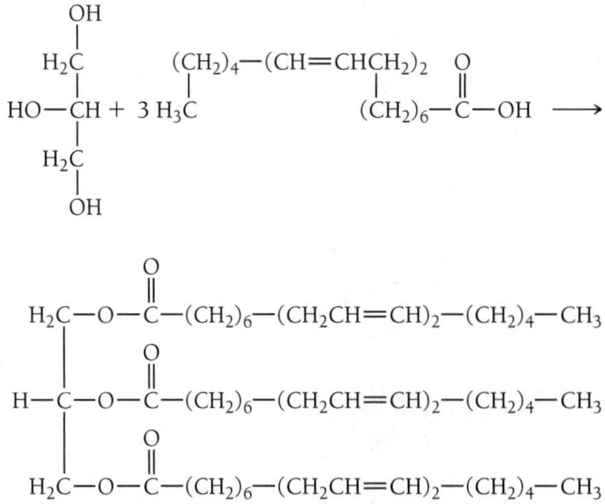

Triglyceride is expected to be an oil.

37. a. monosaccharide **c.** disaccharide

39. a. aldose, hexose **b.** aldose, pentose
c. ketose, tetrose **d.** aldose, tetrose

41. a. 5 **b.** 3 **c.** 1 **d.** 3

43.

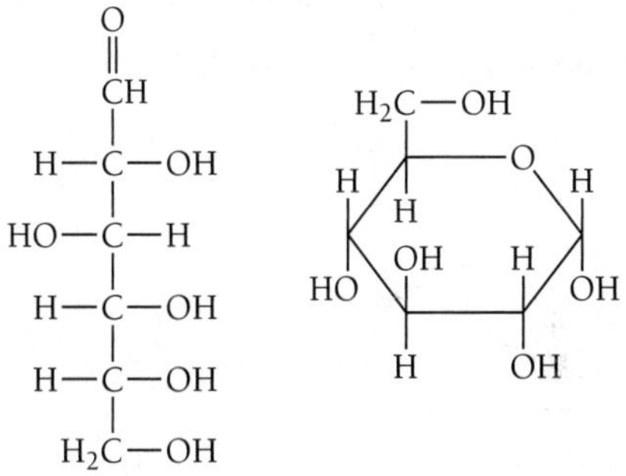

45.

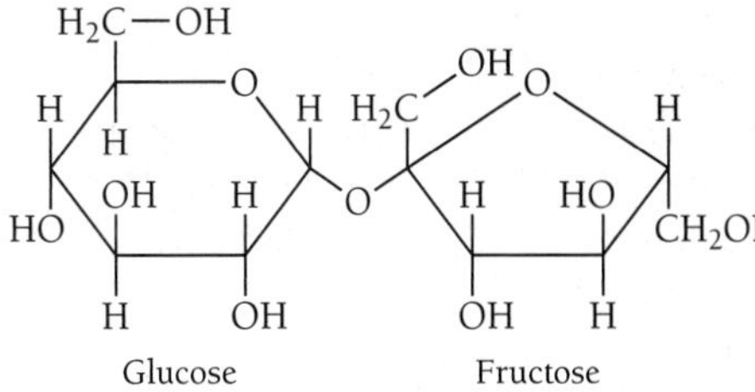

47.

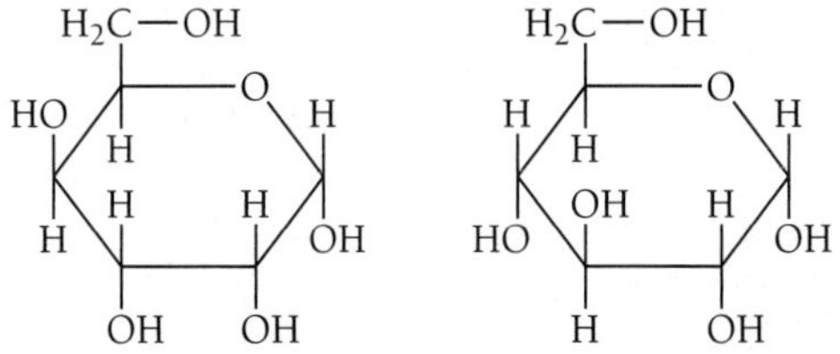

49. a.

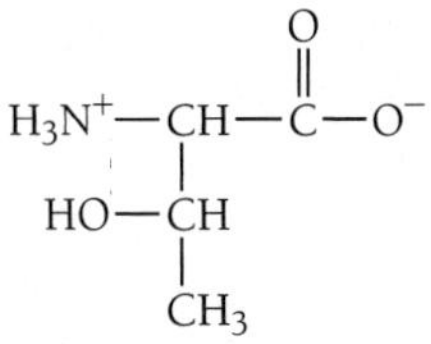

b.

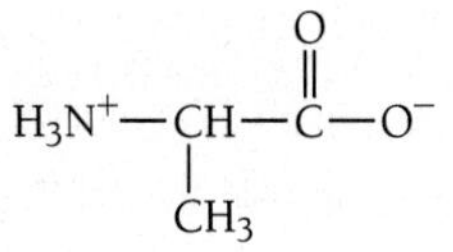

c.

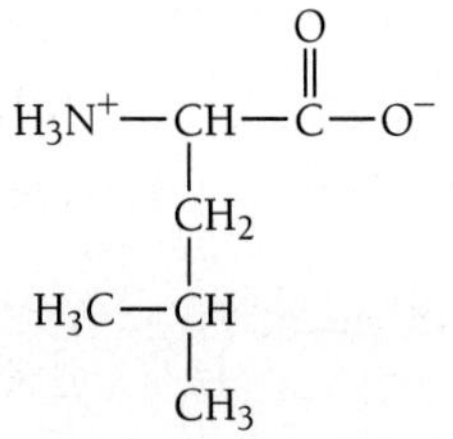

d.

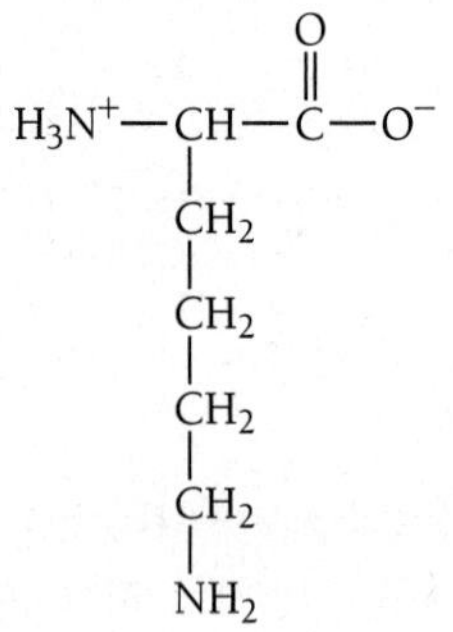

51.

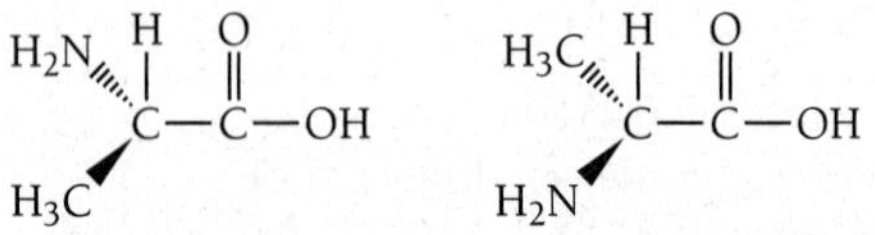

53. 6, Ser-Gly-Cys, Ser-Cys-Gly, Gly-Ser-Cys, Gly-Cys-Ser, Cys-Ser-Gly, Cys-Gly-Ser

55.

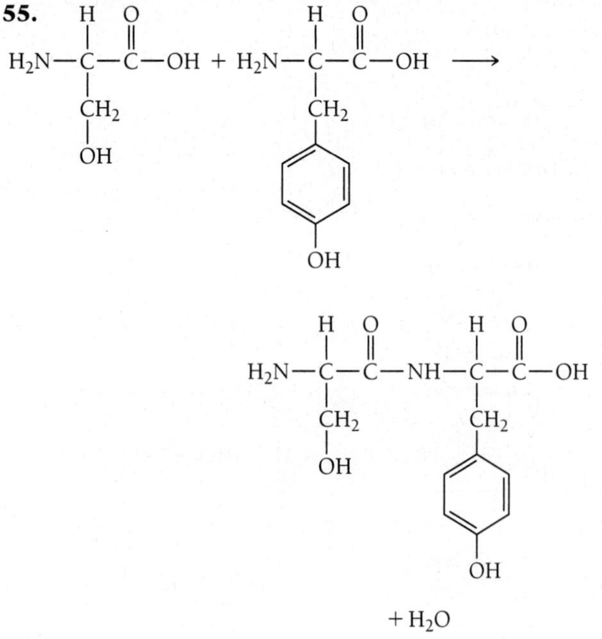

57. **a.**

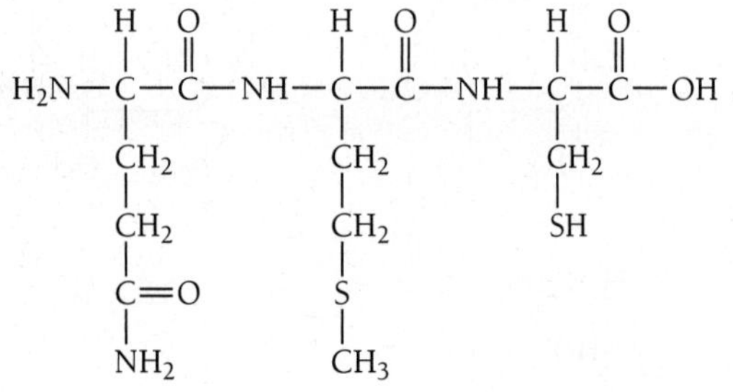

b.

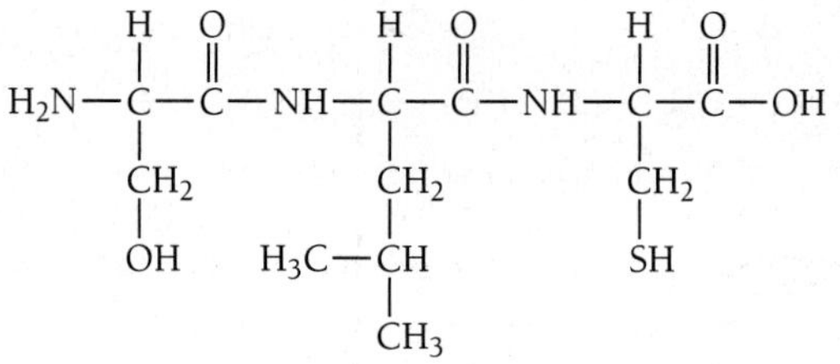

c.

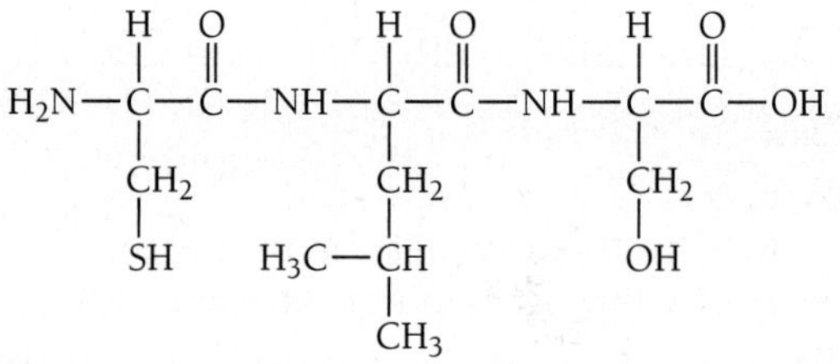

59. tertiary

61. primary

63. **a.** A
b. T

65.

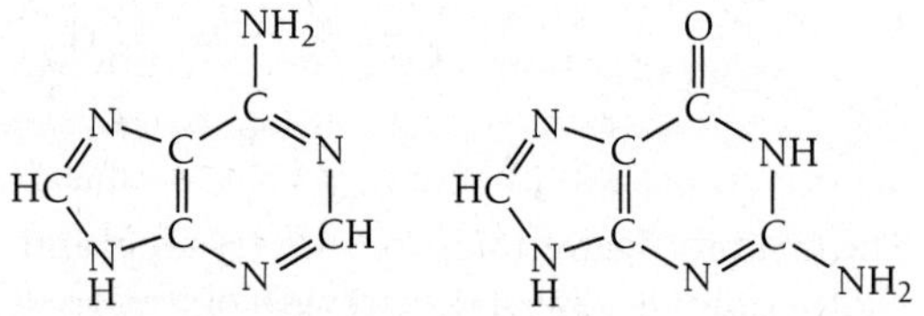

67. A C A T G C G

69. 154 codons, 462 nucleotides

71. **a.** protein
b. carbohydrate
c. lipid

73. A codon is composed of three nucleotides. A codon codes for a specific amino acid, while a gene codes for an entire protein.

75.

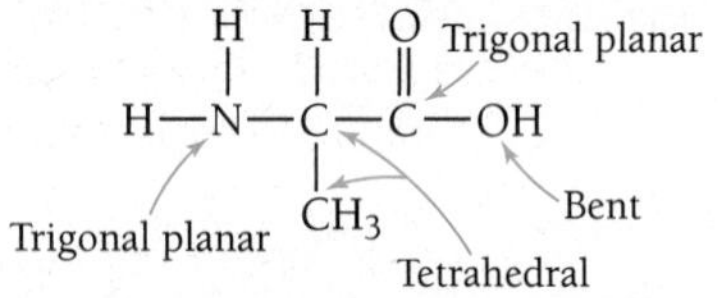

77. valine, leucine, isoleucine, phenylalanine

79. Gly-Arg-Ala-Leu-Phe-Gly-Asn-Lys-Trp-Glu-Cys

81.

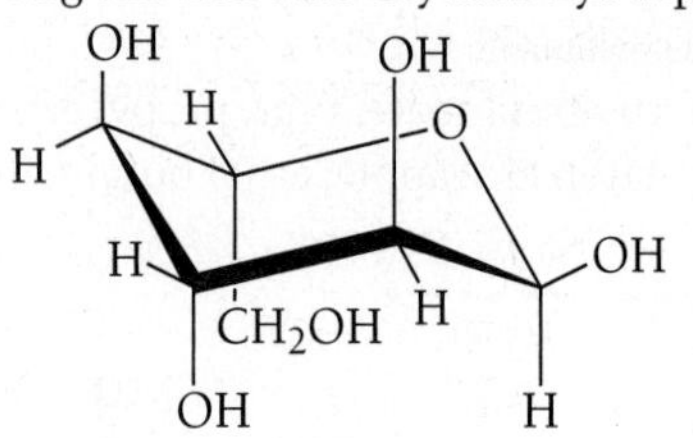

a.

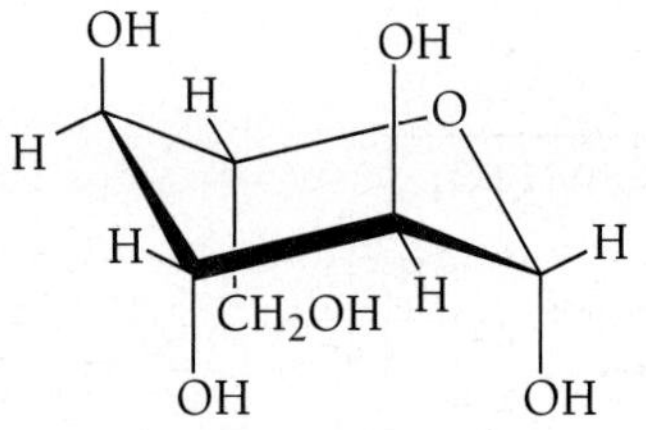

b.

83. As the temperature increases, the favorable entropy for uncoiling a chain becomes dominant. On cooling, the favorable enthalpy of forming hydrogen bonds between paired bases is dominant.

85. When the fake thymine nucleotide is added to the replicating DNA, the chain cannot continue to form because the $-N = N^+ = NH$ group on the sugar prevents future phosphate linkages.

87. $V_{max} = 47.6, K_t = 1.68$

89. $H_3N^+CH_2COO^- + H^+ \rightleftharpoons$
$(H_3N^+CH_2COOH[HA]/[A^-] = 2,$
$H_3N^+CH_2COO^- \rightleftharpoons H_2NCH_2COO^- + H^+[HA]/[A^-]$
$= 0.4, pH = 6.0$

91. A three-base codon codes for a single amino acid. If there are only three bases, there could be 27 different three-base codon arrangements. Therefore, you could theoretically code for the 20 different amino acids needed.

98. **a.**

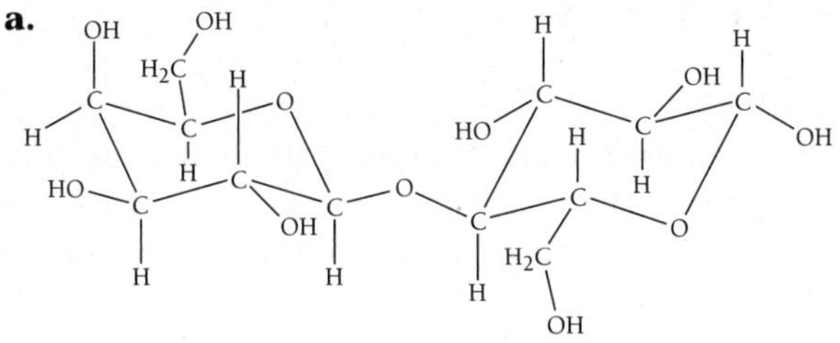

c.

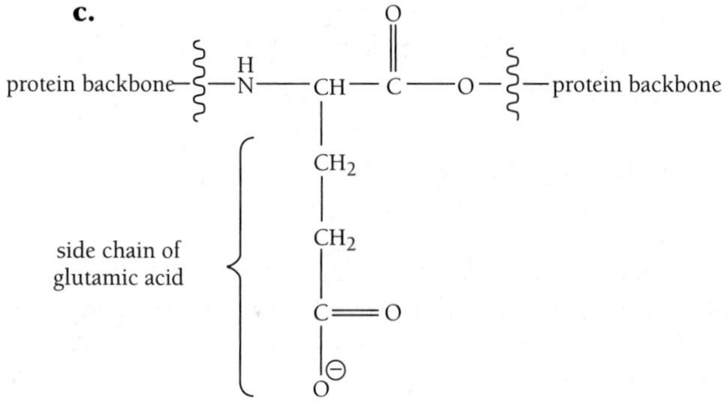

Chapter 24

15. **a.** +4 **b.** +4 **c.** +4

17. $Ca_3Al_2(SiO_4)_3$

19. 4

21. tetrahedrons stand alone, orthosilicates

23. amphibole or double-chain structure; $Ca^{2+}, Mg^{2+}, Fe^{2+}, Al^{3+}$

25. 950 g

27. NCl_3 has a lone pair that BCl_3 lacks, giving it a trigonal pyramidal shape, as opposed to BCl_3's trigonal planar shape.

29. **a.** 6 vertices, 8 faces
b. 12 vertices, 20 faces

31. *closo*-Boranes have the formula $B_nH_n^{2-}$ and form fully closed polyhedra, *nido*-boranes have the formula B_nH_{n+4} and consist of a cage missing a corner, and *arachno*-boranes have the formula B_nH_{n+6} and consist of a cage missing two or three corners.

33. Activated charcoal consists of fine particles, rather than a lump of charcoal, and subsequently has a much higher surface area.

35. Ionic carbides are composed of carbon, generally in the form of the carbide ion, C_2^{2-}, and low-electronegativity metals, such as the alkali and alkaline earth metals. Covalent carbides are composed of carbon and low-electronegativity nonmetals or metalloids, such as silicon.

37. **a.** solid $\longrightarrow$ gas
b. gas $\longrightarrow$ liquid $\longrightarrow$ solid
c. solid $\longrightarrow$ gas

39. **a.** $CO(g) + CuO(s) \longrightarrow CO_2(g) + Cu(s)$
b. $SiO_2(s) + 3\,C(s) \longrightarrow SiC(s) + 2\,CO(g)$
c. $S(s) + CO(g) \longrightarrow COS(g)$

41. **a.** +2 **b.** +4 **c.** +4/3

43. Fixing nitrogen refers to converting N_2 to a nitrogen-containing compound.

45. White phosphorus consists of P_4 molecules in a tetrahedral shape with the atoms at the corners of the tetrahedron. This allotrope is unstable because of the strain from the bond angles. Red phosphorus is much more stable because one bond of the tetrahedron is broken, allowing the phosphorus atoms to make chains with bond angles that are less strained.

47. saltpeter: 13.86% N by mass Chile saltpeter: 16.48% N by mass

49. HN_3 has a positive ΔG_f°, meaning that it spontaneously decomposes into H_2 and N_2 at room temperature. There are no temperatures at which HN_3 will be stable. ΔH_f is positive and ΔS_f is negative, so ΔG_f will always be negative.

51. **a.** $NH_4NO_3(aq) + \text{heat} \longrightarrow N_2O(g) + 2\,H_2O(l)$
b. $3\,NO_2(g) + H_2O(l) \longrightarrow 2\,HNO_3(l) + NO(g)$
c. $2\,PCl_3(l) + O_2(g) \longrightarrow 2\,POCl_3(l)$

53. $NO_3^-, NO_2^-, N_3^-, N_2H_5^+, NH_4^+$

55.

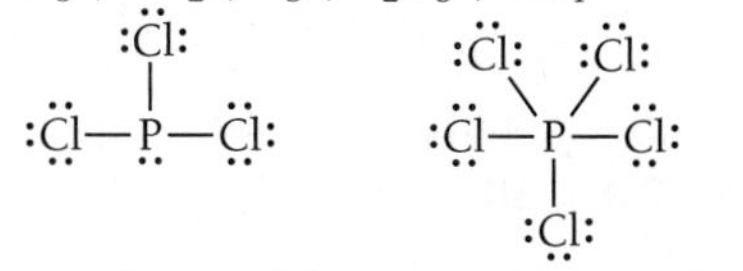

Trigonal pyramidal Trigonal bipyramidal

57. $CO(NH_2)_2 + 2\,H_2O \longrightarrow (NH_4)_2CO_3$
14g

59. P_4O_6 forms if there is only a limited amount of oxygen available, while P_4O_{10} will form with greater amounts of oxygen.

61. The major source of oxygen is the fractionation of air by which air is cooled and liquefied and oxygen is separated from the other components.

63. **a.** superoxide **b.** oxide
c. peroxide

65. Initially, liquid sulfur becomes less viscous when heated because the S_8 rings have greater thermal energy, which overcomes intermolecular forces. Above 150 °C the rings break and the broken rings entangle one another, causing greater viscosity.

67. **a.** 4×10^{-22} g
b. 4.0×10^{-19} g

69. $2\ FeS_2(s) \xrightarrow{heat} 2\ FeS(s) + S_2(g)$
510 L

71. **a.** +2, linear
b. +6, octahedral
c. +6, square pyramidal

73. $Cl_2(g) + 2\ Br^-(aq) \longrightarrow 2\ Cl^-(aq) + Br_2(l)$
Oxidizing agent: Cl_2
Reducing agent: Br^-

75. No, there is not enough HF to dissolve all of the SiO_2. HF is the limiting reagent. 1.6 g SiO_2.

77. 8 kg from lignite, 40 kg from bituminous

79. Chlorine is much more electronegative than iodine, allowing it to withdraw an electron and ionize in solution much more easily.

81. **a.** $rate_{HCl}/rate_{Cl_2} = 1.395$
b. $rate_{HCl}/rate_{HF} = 0.7407$
c. $rate_{HCl}/rate_{HI} = 1.873$

83. $4\ Na_2O_2 + 3\ Fe \longrightarrow 4\ Na_2O + Fe_3O_4$

85. The bond length of the O_2 species increases as electrons are added because they are added to the π^* antibonding orbital. O_2^{2-} is diamagnetic.

87. 2.0 mol of C—C bonds, 715 kJ/mol, 6.9×10^2 kJ/mol. This value calculated from the bond energy is too low because it doesn't include van der Waals attractions between C atoms not directly bonded to each other.

89. −50 kJ/mol

91. **a.** −13.6 kJ/mol **b.** −11.0 kJ/mol
c. −24.8 kJ/mol
Fe_2O_3 is the most exothermic because it has the highest oxidation state and is therefore able to oxidize the most CO per mol Fe.

93. **a.** Ö=C=C=C=Ö
b. *sp*
c. −92 kJ/mol

95. **a.** 7.6×10^{-22} **b.** 1.2×10^{-8}
c. $[N_2H_4] = 0.009$ M, $[N_2H_5^+] = 0.0025$ M, $[N_2H_6^{2+}] = 7.0 \times 10^{-13}$ M

97. The acid is
a. 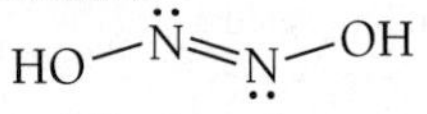

and the base is
b. 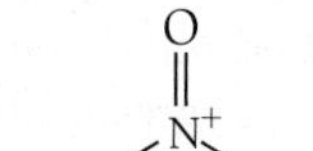

The acid is weaker than nitrous acid because of electron donation by resonance in contributing structures such as
c. 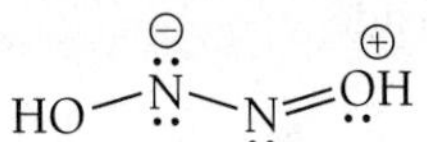

The base is weaker than ammonia because of electron withdrawal by the electronegative nitro group.

99. The triple bond in nitrogen is much stronger than the double bond in oxygen, so it is much harder to break. This makes it less likely that the bond in nitrogen will be broken.

101. Sodium dinitrogen phosphate (NaH_2PO_4) can act as a weak base or a weak acid. A buffer can be made by mixing it with either Na_2HPO_4 or with Na_3PO_4, depending on the desired pH of the buffer solution.

103. F is extremely small, and so there is a huge driving force to fill the octet by adding an electron, giving a −1 oxidation state. Other halogens have access to *d* orbitals, which allows for more hybridization and oxidation state options.

105. SO_3 cannot be a reducing agent because the oxidation state of S is +6, the highest possible oxidation state for S. Reducing agents need to be able to be oxidized. SO_2 can be a reducing agent or an oxidizing agent because the oxidation state of S is +4.

112. **a.** The solubility of H_2S in water decreases as temperature increases.
c. No
e. Copper(II)
f. 4.8 g CuS

Chapter 25

15. Metals are typically opaque, are good conductors of heat and electricity, and are ductile and malleable, meaning they can be drawn into wires and flattened into sheets.

17. aluminum, iron, calcium, magnesium, sodium, potassium

19. Fe: hematite (Fe_2O_3), magnetite (Fe_3O_4)
Hg: cinnabar (HgS)
V: vanadite $[Pb_5(VO_4)Cl]$, carnotite $[K_2(UO_2)_2(VO_4)_2 \cdot 3\ H_2O]$
Nb: columbite $[Fe(NbO_3)_2]$

21. $MgCO_3(s) + heat \longrightarrow MgO(s) + CO_2(g)$
$Mg(OH)_2(s) + heat \longrightarrow MgO(s) + H_2O(g)$

23. The flux is a material that will react with the gangue to form a substance with a low melting point. MgO is the flux.

25. Hydrometallurgy is used to separate metals from ores by selectively dissolving the metal in a solution, filtering out impurities, and then reducing the metal to its elemental form.

27. The Bayer process is a hydrometallurgical process by which Al_2O_3 is selectively dissolved, leaving other oxides as solids. The soluble form of aluminum is $Al(OH)_4^-$.

29. Sponge-powdered iron contains many small holes in the iron particles due to the escaping of the oxygen when the iron is reduced. Water-atomized powdered iron has much smoother and denser particles as the powder is formed from molten iron.

31. **a.** 50% Cr, 50% V by moles; 50.5% Cr, 49.5% V by mass
b. 25% Fe, 75% V by moles; 26.8% Fe, 73.2% V by mass
c. 25% Cr, 25% Fe, 50% V by moles; 24.8% Cr, 26.6% Fe, 48.6% V by mass

33. Cr and Fe are very close to each other in mass, so their respective atomic radii are probably close enough to form an alloy. Also, they both form body-centered cubic structures.

35. A: solid, 20% Cr, 80% Fe
B: liquid, 50% Cr, 50% Fe

37. A: solid (20% Co and 80% Cu overall. Two phases; one is the Cu structure with 4% Co, and the other is the Co structure with 7% Cu. There will be more of the Cu structure).
B: solid (Co structure), 90% Co, 10% Cu

39. C would fill interstitial holes; Mn and Si would substitute for Fe.

41. **a.** Mo_2N **b.** CrH_2

43. **a.** zinc **b.** copper **c.** manganese

45. −19.4 kJ/mol

47. When Cr is added to steel, it reacts with oxygen in steel to prevent it from rusting. A Cr steel alloy would be used in any situation where the steel might be easily oxidized, such as when it comes in contact with water.

49. rutile: 33.3% Ti by moles, 59.9% Ti by mass ilmenite: 20.0% Ti by moles, 31.6% Ti by mass

51. Titanium must be arc-melted in an inert atmosphere because the high temperature and flow of electrons would cause the metal to oxidize in a normal atmosphere.

53. TiO_2 is the most important industrial product of titanium, and it is often used as a pigment in white paint.

55. The Bayer process is a hydrometallurgical process used to separate Al_2O_3 from other oxides. The Al_2O_3 is selectively dissolved by hot, concentrated NaOH. The other oxides are removed as solids, and the Al_2O_3 precipitates out of solution when the solution is neutralized.

57. cobalt and tungsten

59. 3.3 kg Fe, 2.0 kg Ti

61. Four atoms surround a tetrahedral hole, and six atoms surround an octahedral hole. The octahedral hole is larger because it is surrounded by a greater number of atoms.

63. Mn has one more electron orbital available for bonding than does chromium.

65. Ferromagnetic atoms, like paramagnetic ones, have unpaired electrons. However, in ferromagnetic atoms, these electrons align with their spin oriented in the same direction, resulting in a permanent magnetic field.

67. The nuclear charge of the last three is relatively high because of the lanthanide series in which the 4*f* subshell falls between them and the other six metals of the group.

69. **a.** 16.0 cm **b.** 4.95 cm **c.** 14%

71. 92%

73. 5.4×10^7

75. First, roast to form the oxide.

$$4\,CoAsS(s) + 9\,O_2(g) \longrightarrow 4\,CoO(s) + 4\,SO_2(g) + As_4O_6(s)$$

Then reduce the oxide with coke.

$$CoO(s) + C(s) \longrightarrow Co(s) + Co(g)$$

The oxides of arsenic are relatively volatile and can be separated, but they are poisonous.

77. Au and Ag are found in elemental form because of their low reactivity. Na and Ca are group 1 and group 2 metals, respectively, and are highly reactive as they readily lose their valence electrons to obtain octets.

84. **a.** Because they are stronger and harder.
c. Tin, 232 °C; Lead 328 °C
e. Because the melting range is neither too sharp nor too broad. It has a pasty range that helps it to set, but it then hardens quickly.

Chapter 26

17. **a.** $[Ar]\,4s^2 3d^8, [Ar]\,3d^8$
b. $[Ar]\,4s^2 3d^5, [Ar]\,3d^3$
c. $[Kr]\,5s^2 4d^1, [Kr]\,5s^1 4d^1$
d. $[Xe]\,6s^2 4f^{14} 5d^3, [Xe]\,4f^{14} 5d^3$

19. **a.** +5 **b.** +7 **c.** +4

21. **a.** +3, 6 **b.** +2, 6 **c.** +2, 4 **d.** +1, 2

23. **a.** hexaaquachromium(III)
b. tetracyanocuprate(II)
c. pentaaminebromoiron(III) sulfate
d. aminetetraaquahydroxycobalt(III) chloride

25. **a.** $[Cr(NH_3)_6]^{3+}$
b. $K_3[Fe(CN)_6]$
c. $[Cu(en)(SCN)_2]$
d. $[Pt(H_2O)_4][PtCl_6]$

27. **a.** $[Co(NH_3)_3(CN)_3]$, triaminetricyanocobalt(III)
b. $[Cr(en)_3]^{3+}$, tris(ethylenediamine)chromium(III)

29.

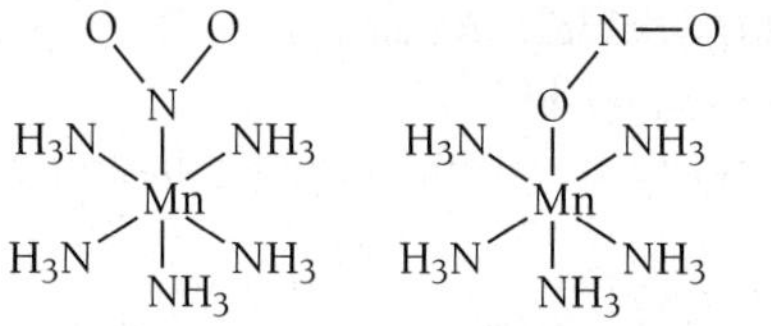

31. $[Fe(H_2O)_5Cl]Cl \cdot H_2O$ pentaaquachloroiron(II) chloride monohydrate
$[Fe(H_2O)_4Cl_2] \cdot 2\,H_2O$, tetraaquadichloroiron(II) dihydrate

33. **b, c, e**

35. **a.** 3
b. No geometric isomers.

37. **a.**

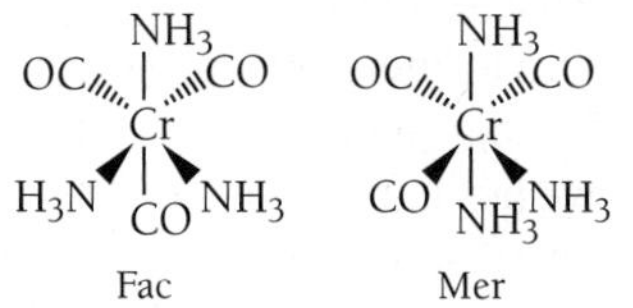

Fac Mer

b.

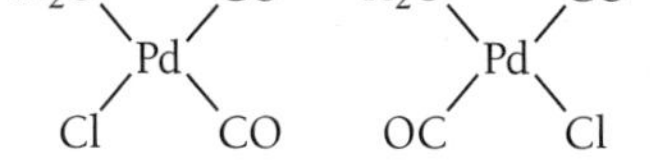

Cis Trans

39. *cis* isomer is optically active.

41. **a.** 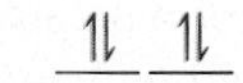

b. 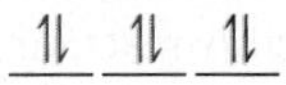

c. 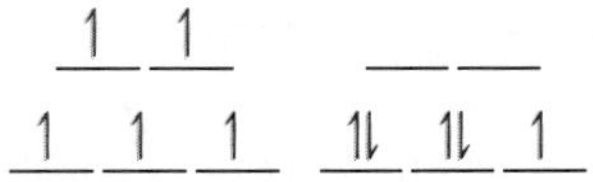

d. 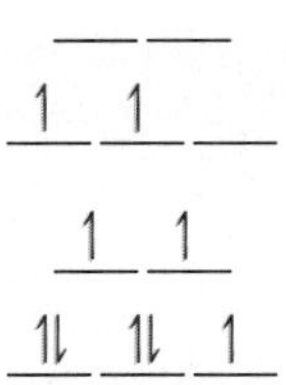

43. 163 kJ/mol

45. $[Co(CN)_6]^{3-} \longrightarrow$ 290 nm, colorless
$[Co(NH_3)_6]^{3+} \longrightarrow$ 440 nm, yellow
$[CoF_6]^{3-} \longrightarrow$ 770 nm, green

47. weak

49. **a.** 4 **b.** 3 **c.** 1

51. 3

53. porphyrin

55. Water is a weak-field ligand that forms a high-spin complex with hemoglobin. Because deoxyhemoglobin is a weak field, it absorbs large-wavelength light and appears blue. Oxyhemoglobin is a low-spin complex and absorbs small-wavelength light, so O_2 must be a strong-field ligand.

57. **a.** $[Ar]4s^1 3d^5$, $[Ar]3d^5$, $[Ar]3d^4$, $[Ar]3d^3$
b. $[Ar]\ 4s^1 3d^{10}$, $[Ar]\ 3d^{10}$, $[Ar]\ 3d^9$

59. **a.** 

b. 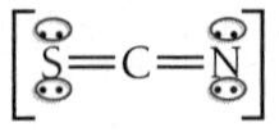

c. 

61. $[MA_2B_2C_2]$ all cis; A trans and B and C cis; B trans and A and C cis; C trans and A and B cis; all trans.
$[MA_2B_3C]$ will have fac–mer isomers.
$[MAB_2C_3]$ will have fac–mer isomers.
$[MAB_3C_2]$ will have fac–mer isomers.
$[MA_3B_2C]$ will have fac–mer isomers.
$[MA_2BC_3]$ will have fac–mer isomers.
$[MA_3BC_2]$ will have fac–mer isomers.
$[MABC_2]$ will have AB cis–trans isomers.
$[MAB_4C]$ will have AC cis–trans isomers.
$[MA_4BC]$ will have BC cis–trans isomers.
$[MABC_4]$ will have AB cis–trans isomers.

63. 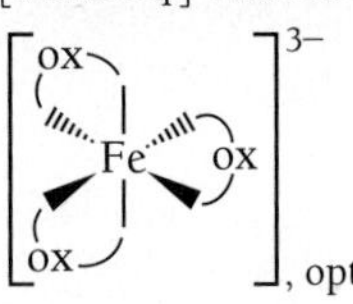
, optical isomers

65. 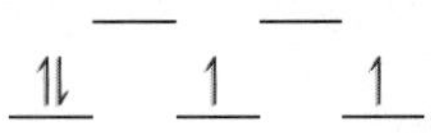
, paramagnetic

67.

1. 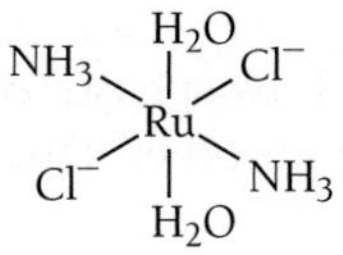
2. 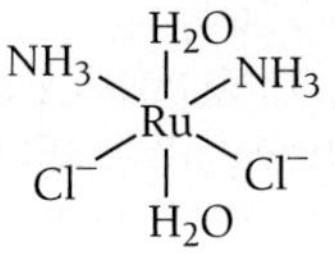
3. 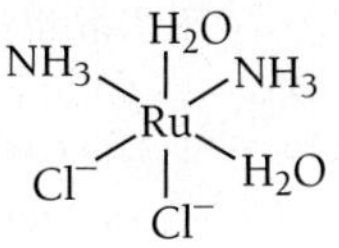
4. 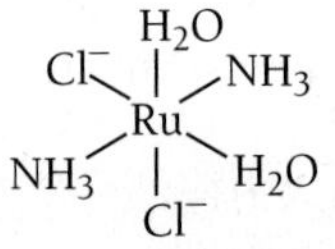
5. 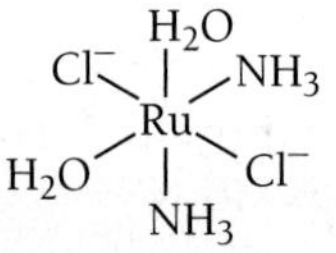

Only structure 3. is chiral. This is its mirror image.

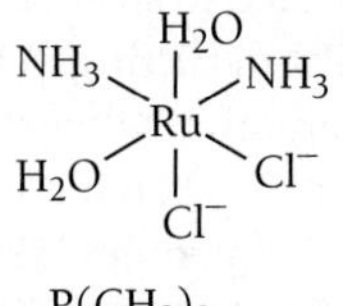

69. 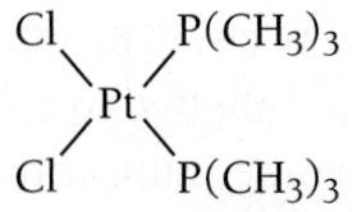
cis-dichlorobis (trimethyl phosphine) platinum(II)

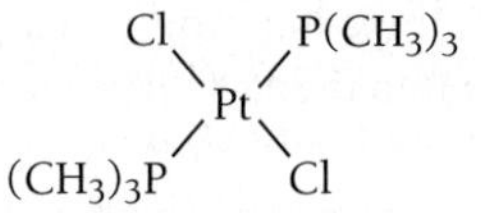
trans-dichlorobis (trimethyl phosphine) platinum(II)

71. ______ d_{z^2}
______ ______ $d_{x^2-y^2}$ and d_{xy}
______ ______ d_{xz} and d_{yz}

73. **a.** 2×10^{-8} M
b. 6.6×10^{-3} M
c. NiS will dissolve more easily in the ammonia solution because the formation of the complex ion is favorable, removing Ni^{2+} ions from the solution and allowing more NiS to dissolve.

75. Prepare a solution that contains both $[MCl_6]^{3-}$ and $[MBr_6]^{3-}$ and see if any complex ions that contain both Cl and Br form. If they do, it would demonstrate that these complexes are labile.

77. pH = 10.1

79. Au

86. **a.** red
c. smaller (because it absorbs at longer wavelengths)
e. The crystal fields splitting energies of the two complexes must be similar (because they have the same color).

APPENDIX IV

Answers to In-Chapter Practice Problems

Chapter 1

1.1. a. The composition of the copper is not changing; thus, being hammered flat is a physical change that signifies a physical property.

b. The dissolution and color change of the nickel indicate that it is undergoing a chemical change and exhibiting a chemical property.

c. Sublimation is a physical change indicative of a physical property.

d. When a match ignites, a chemical change begins as the match reacts with oxygen to form carbon dioxide and water. Flammability is a chemical property.

1.2. a. 29.8 °C

b. 302.9 K

1.3. 21.4 g/cm^3. This matches the density of platinum.

1.3. *For More Practice* 4.50 g/cm^3 The metal is titanium.

1.4. The thermometer shown has markings every 1 °F; thus, the first digit of uncertainty is 0.1. The answer is 103.1 °F.

1.5. a. Each figure in this number is significant by rule 1: three significant figures.

b. This is a defined quantity that has an unlimited number of significant figures.

c. Both 1's are significant (rule 1), and the interior zero is significant as well (rule 2): three significant figures.

d. Only the two 9's are significant, the leading zeroes are not (rule 3): two significant figures.

e. There are five significant figures because the 1, 4, and 5 are nonzero (rule 1) and the trailing zeroes are after a decimal point so they are significant as well (rule 4).

f. The number of significant figures is ambiguous because the trailing zeroes occur before an implied decimal point (rule 4).

1.6. a. 0.381

b. 121.0

c. 1.174

d. 8

1.7. 3.15 yd

1.8. 2.446 gal

1.9. 1.61×10^6 cm^3

1.9. *For More Practice* 3.23×10^3 kg

1.10. 1.03 kg

1.10. *For More Practice* 2.9×10^{-2} cm^3

1.11. 0.855 cm

1.12. 2.70 g/cm^3

1.13. 0.33 ppm/yr; The rate is lower because less fossil fuel was being burned in that era.

Chapter 2

2.1. For the first sample:

$$\frac{\text{mass of oxygen}}{\text{mass of carbon}} = \frac{17.2\text{ g O}}{12.9\text{ g C}} = 1.33 \text{ or } 1.33:1$$

For the second sample:

$$\frac{\text{mass of oxygen}}{\text{mass of carbon}} = \frac{10.5\text{ g O}}{7.88\text{ g C}} = 1.33 \text{ or } 1.33:1$$

The ratios of oxygen to carbon are the same in the two samples of carbon monoxide, so these results are consistent with the law of definite proportions.

2.2. Mass of hydrogen to 1 g of oxygen in water/mass of hydrogen to 1 g of oxygen in hydrogen peroxide = 0.125/0.0625 = 2.00.
The ratio of the mass of hydrogen from one compound to the mass of hydrogen in the other is equal to 2. This is a simple whole number and therefore consistent with the law of multiple proportions.

2.3. a. $Z = 6, A = 13,\ ^{13}_{6}\text{C}$

b. 19 protons, 20 neutrons

2.4. a. N^{3-}

b. Rb^{+}

2.5. 24.31 amu

2.5. *For More Practice* 70.92 amu

2.6. 4.65×10^{-2} mol Ag

2.7. 0.563 mol Cu

2.7. *For More Practice* 22.6 g Ti

2.8. 1.3×10^{22} C atoms

2.8. *For More Practice* 6.87 g W

2.9. $l = 1.72$ cm

2.9. *For More Practice* 2.90×10^{24} Cu atoms

Chapter 3

3.1. a. C_5H_{12}

b. HgCl

c. CH_2O

3.2. a. molecular element

b. molecular compound

c. atomic element

d. ionic compound

e. ionic compound

3.3. K_2S

3.4. AlN

3.5. silver nitride

3.5. *For More Practice* Rb_2S

3.6. iron(II) sulfide

3.6. *For More Practice* RuO_2

3.7. tin(II) chlorate

3.7. *For More Practice* $Co_3(PO_4)_2$
3.8. dinitrogen pentoxide
3.8. *For More Practice* PBr_3
3.9. hydrofluoric acid
3.10. nitrous acid
3.10. *For More Practice* $HClO_4$
3.11. sulfurous acid
3.12. 164.10 amu
3.13. 5.839×10^{20} $C_{13}H_{18}O_2$ molecules
3.13. *For More Practice* 1.06 g H_2O
3.14. 53.29%
3.14. *For More Practice* 74.19% Na
3.15. 83.9 g Fe_2O_3
3.15. *For More Practice* 8.6 g Na
3.16. 4.0 g O
3.16. *For More Practice* 3.60 g C
3.17. CH_2O
3.18. $C_{13}H_{18}O_2$
3.19. C_6H_6
3.19. *For More Practice* $C_2H_8N_2$
3.20. C_2H_5
3.21. C_2H_4O

Chapter 4

4.1. $SiO_2(s) + 3\,C(s) \longrightarrow SiC(s) + 2\,CO(g)$
4.2. $2\,C_2H_6(g) + 7\,O_2(g) \longrightarrow 4\,CO_2(g) + 6\,H_2O(g)$
4.3. $Pb(NO_3)_2(aq) + 2\,KCl(aq) \longrightarrow PbCl_2(s) + 2\,KNO_3(aq)$
4.4. 4.08 g HCl
4.5. 22 kg HNO_3
4.6. H_2 is the limiting reagent, since it produces the least amount of NH_3. Therefore, 29.4 kg NH_3 is the theoretical yield.
4.7. CO is the limiting reagent, since it only produces 114 g Fe. Therefore, 114 g Fe is the theoretical yield: percentage yield = 63.4% yield.
4.8. $2\,C_2H_5SH(l) + 9\,O_2(g) \longrightarrow 4\,CO_2(g) + 2\,SO_2(g) + 6\,H_2O(g)$
4.9. **a.** $2\,Al(s) + 3\,Cl_2(g) \longrightarrow 2\,AlCl_3(s)$
b. $2\,Li(s) + 2\,H_2O(l) \longrightarrow 2\,Li^+(aq) + 2\,OH^-(aq) + H_2(g)$
c. $H_2(g) + Br_2(l) \longrightarrow 2\,HBr(g)$

Chapter 5

5.1. 0.214 M $NaNO_3$
5.1. *For More Practice* 44.6 g KBr
5.2. 402 g $C_{12}H_{22}O_{11}$
5.2. *For More Practice* 221 mL of KCl solution
5.3. 667 mL
5.3. *For More Practice* 0.105 L
5.4. 51.4 mL HNO_3 solution
5.4. *For More Practice* 0.170 g CO_2
5.5. **a.** insoluble
b. insoluble
c. soluble
d. soluble
5.6. $NH_4Cl(aq) + Fe(NO_3)_3(aq) \longrightarrow$ NO REACTION
5.7. $2\,NaOH(aq) + CuBr_2(aq) \longrightarrow Cu(OH)_2(s) + 2\,NaBr(aq)$
5.8. $2\,H^+(aq) + 2\,I^-(aq) + Ba^{2+}(aq) + 2\,OH^-(aq) \longrightarrow 2\,H_2O(l) + Ba^{2+}(aq) + 2\,I^-(aq) H^+(aq) + OH^-(aq) \longrightarrow H_2O(l)$
5.9. Molecular equation:
$HBr(aq) + LiOH(aq) \longrightarrow H_2O(l) + LiBr(aq)$
Net ionic equation:
$H^+(aq) + OH^-(aq) \longrightarrow H_2O(l)$
5.10. $HCHO_2(aq) + OH^-(aq) \longrightarrow H_2O(l) + CHO_2^-(aq)$
5.11. 9.03×10^{-2} M H_2SO_4
5.11. *For More Practice* 24.5 mL NaOH solution
5.12. $2\,HBr(aq) + K_2SO_3(aq) \longrightarrow H_2O(l) + SO_2(g) + 2\,KBr(aq)$
5.12. *For More Practice* $2\,H^+(aq) + S^{2-}(aq) \longrightarrow H_2S(g)$
5.13. **a.** Cr = 0
b. $Cr^{3+} = +3$
c. $Cl^- = -1$, C = +4
d. Br = −1, Sr = +2
e. O = −2, S = +6
f. O = −2, N = +5
5.14. Sn is oxidized and N is reduced.
5.14. *For More Practice* **b.** Reaction b is the only redox reaction. Al is oxidized and O is reduced.
5.15. **a.** This is a redox reaction in which Li is the reducing agent (it is oxidized) and Cl_2 is the oxidizing reagent (it is reduced).
b. This is a redox reaction in which Al is the reducing agent and Sn^{2+} is the oxidizing agent.
c. This is not a redox reaction because no oxidation states change.
d. This is a redox reaction in which C is the reducing agent and O_2 is the oxidizing agent.
5.16. **a.** Yes
b. No

Chapter 6

6.1. 15.0 psi
6.1. *For More Practice* 80.6 kPa
6.2. 2.1 atm at a depth of approximately 11 m
6.3. 123 mL
6.4. 11.3 L
6.5. 1.63 atm, 23.9 psi
6.6. 16.1 L
6.6. *For More Practice* 976 mmHg
6.7. $d = 4.91$ g/L
6.7. *For More Practice* 44.0 g/mol
6.8. 70.7 g/mol
6.9. 0.0610 mol H_2
6.10. 4.2 atm
6.11. 12.0 mg H_2
6.12. 82.3 g Ag_2O
6.12. *For More Practice* 7.10 g Ag_2O
6.13. 6.53 L O_2
6.14. $u_{rms} = 238$ m/s
6.15. $\frac{rate_{H_2}}{rate_{Kr}} = 6.447$

Chapter 7

7.1. $\Delta E = 71\ J$

7.2. $C_s = 0.38 \frac{J}{g \cdot °C}$

The specific heat capacity of gold is 0.128 J/g · °C; therefore, the rock cannot be pure gold.

7.2. *For More Practice* $T_f = 42.1\ °C$

7.3. 37.8 grams Cu

7.4. −122 J

7.4. *For More Practice* $\Delta E = -998\ J$

7.5. $\Delta E_{reaction} = -3.91 \times 10^3\ kJ/mol\ C_6H_{14}$

7.5. *For More Practice* $C_{cal} = 4.55 \frac{kJ}{°C}$

7.6. **a.** endothermic, positive ΔH
b. endothermic, positive ΔH
c. exothermic, negative ΔH

7.7. $-2.06 \times 10^3\ kJ$

7.7. *For More Practice* 33 g C_4H_{10}
99 g CO_2

7.8. $\Delta H_{rxn} = -68\ kJ$

7.9. $N_2O(g) + NO_2(g) \longrightarrow 3\ NO(g),\ \Delta H_{rxn} = +157.6\ kJ$

7.9. *For More Practice*
$3\ H_2(g) + O_3(g) \longrightarrow 3\ H_2O(g),\ \Delta H_{rxn} = -868.1\ kJ$

7.10. **d.** $Na(s) + \frac{1}{2}Cl_2(g) \longrightarrow NaCl(s),\ \Delta H_f^\circ = -411.2\ kJ/mol$
e. $Pb(s) + N_2(g) + 3\ O_2(g) \longrightarrow Pb(NO_3)_2(s),\ \Delta H_f^\circ = -451.9\ kJ/mol$

7.11. $\Delta H_{rxn}^\circ = -851.5\ kJ$

7.12. $\Delta H_{rxn}^\circ = -1648.4\ kJ$
111 kJ emitted (−111 kJ)

7.13. $1.2 \times 10^2\ kg\ CO_2$

Chapter 8

8.1. $5.83 \times 10^{14}\ s^{-1}$

8.2. 2.64×10^{20} photons

8.2. *For More Practice* 435 nm

8.3. **a.** blue < green < red
b. red < green < blue
c. red < green < blue

8.4. $6.1 \times 10^6\ m/s$

8.5. For the 5*d* orbitals:
$n = 5$
$l = 2$
$m_l = -2, -1, 0, 1, 2$
The five integer values for m_l signify that there are five 5*d* orbitals.

8.6. **a.** l cannot equal 3 if $n = 3$. $l = 2$
b. m_l cannot equal −2 if $l = -1$. Possible values for $m_l = -1, 0,$ or 1
c. l cannot be 1 if $n = 1$. $l = 0$

8.7. 397 nm

8.7. *For More Practice* $n = 1$

Chapter 9

9.1. **a.** Cl $1s^22s^22p^63s^23p^5$ or $[Ne]3s^23p^5$
b. Si $1s^22s^22p^63s^23p^2$ or $[Ne]3s^23p^2$
c. Sr $1s^22s^22p^63s^23p^64s^23d^{10}4p^65s^2$ or $[Kr]5s^2$
d. O $1s^22s^22p^4$ or $[He]2s^22p^4$

9.2. There are no unpaired electrons.

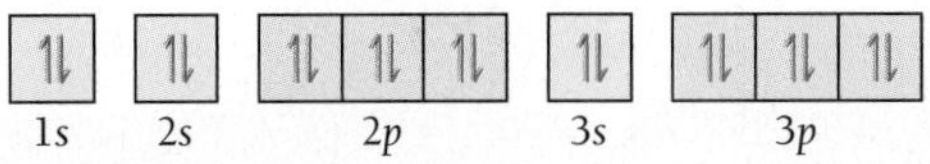

9.3. $1s^22s^22p^63s^23p^3$ or $[Ne]3s^23p^3$. The 5 electrons in the $3s^23p^3$ orbitals are the valence electrons, while the 10 electrons in the $1s^22s^22p^6$ orbitals belong to the core.

9.4. $[Xe]6s^24f^{14}5d^{10}6p^3$

9.4. *For More Practice* $[Kr]5s^24d^{10}5p^5$

9.5. **a.** Sn
b. cannot predict
c. W
d. Se

9.5. *For More Practice* Rb > Ca > Si > S > F

9.6. **a.** $[Ar]4s^03d^7$. Co^{2+} is paramagnetic.

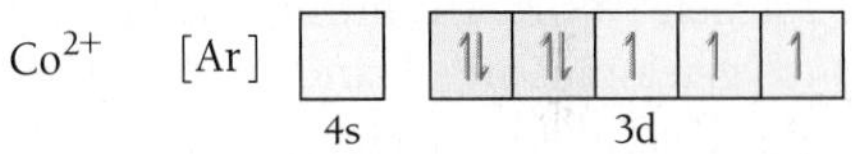

b. $[He]2s^22p^6$. N^{3-} is diamagnetic.

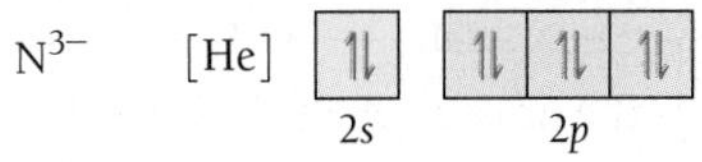

c. $[Ne]3s^23p^6$. Ca^{2+} is diamagnetic.

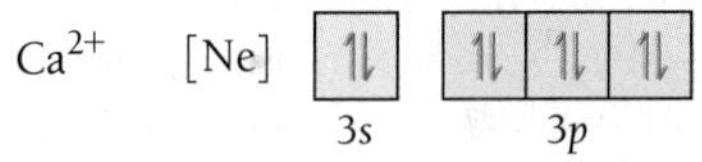

9.7. **a.** K **b.** F^- **c.** Cl^-

9.8. **a.** I **b.** Ca
c. cannot predict **d.** F

9.8. *For More Practice* F > S > Si > Ca > Rb

9.9. **a.** Sn
b. cannot predict based on simple trends (Po is larger)
c. Bi
d. B

9.9. *For More Practice* Cl < Si < Na < Rb

Chapter 10

10.1. Mg_3N_2

10.2. KI < LiBr < CaO

10.2. *For More Practice* $MgCl_2$

10.3. **a.** pure covalent
b. ionic
c. polar covalent

10.4. :C≡O:

10.5. 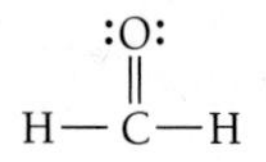

10.6. 

10.7. 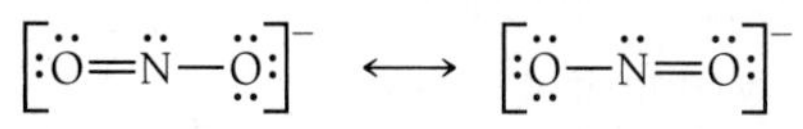

10.8.

Structure	A			B			C		
	:N̈=N=Ö:			:N≡N—Ö: (with lone pairs)			:N̈—N≡O: (with lone pairs)		
number of valence e⁻	5	5	6	5	5	6	5	5	6
number of nonbonding e⁻	−4	−0	−4	−2	−0	−6	−6	−0	−2
$\frac{1}{2}$ (number of bonding e⁻)	−2	−4	−2	−3	−4	−1	−1	−4	−3
Formal charge	**−1**	**−1**	**0**	**0**	**+1**	**−1**	**−2**	**+1**	**+1**

Structure B contributes the most to the correct overall structure of N_2O

10.8. *For More Practice* The nitrogen is +1, the singly bonded oxygen atoms are −1, and the double-bonded oxygen atom has no formal charge.

10.9. 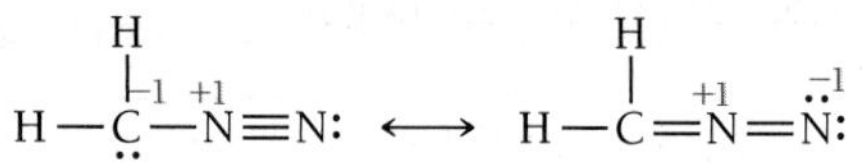

10.10. 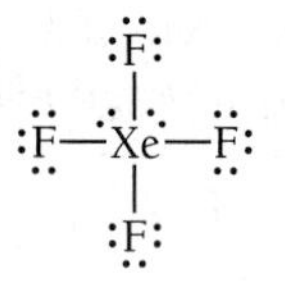

10.10. *For More Practice* 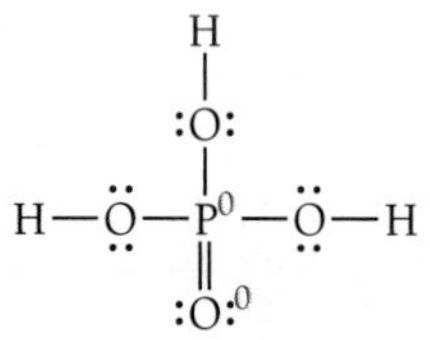

10.11. $CH_3OH(g) + \frac{3}{2} O_2(g) \longrightarrow CO_2(g) + 2\,H_2O(g)$

$\Delta H_{rxn} = -641$ kJ

10.11. *For More Practice* $\Delta H_{rxn} = -8.0 \times 10^1$ kJ

Chapter 11

11.1. tetrahedral

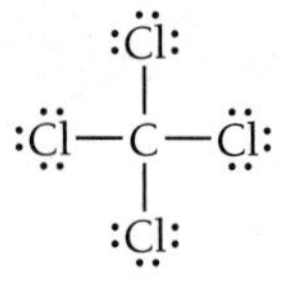

11.2. bent

11.3. linear

11.4.

Atom	Number of Electron Groups	Number of Lone Pairs	Molecular Geometry
Carbon (left)	4	0	Tetrahedral
Carbon (right)	3	0	Trigonal planar
Oxygen	4	2	Bent

11.5. The molecule is nonpolar.

11.6. The xenon atom has six electron groups and therefore has an octahedral electron geometry. An octahedral electron geometry corresponds to sp^3d^2 hybridization (refer to Table 11.3).

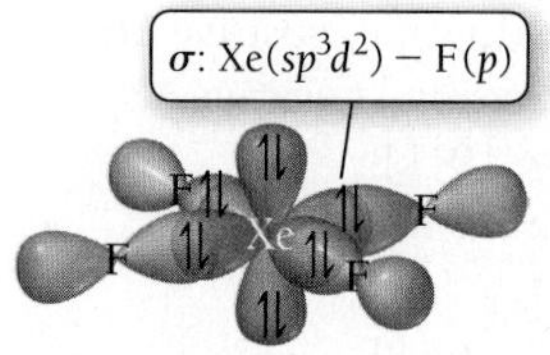

11.7. Since there are only two electron groups around the central atom (C), the electron geometry is linear. According to Table 11.3, the corresponding hybridization on the carbon atom is *sp*.

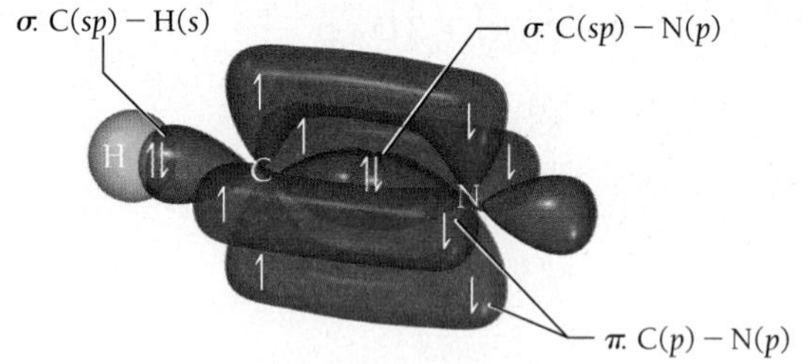

11.8. Since there are only two electron groups about the central atom (C), the electron geometry is linear. The hybridization on C is *sp* (refer to Table 11.3).

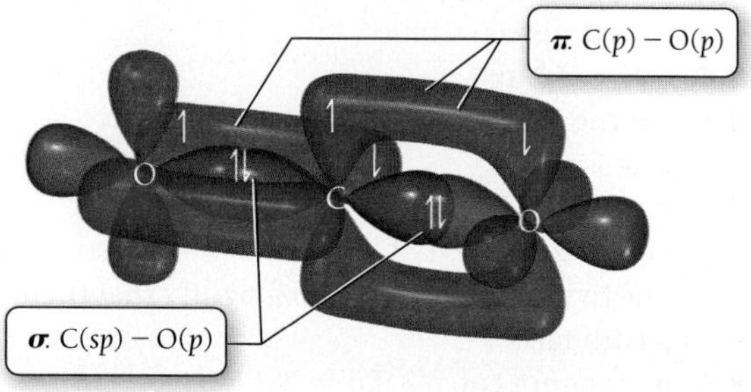

11.8. *For More Practice* There are five electron groups about the central atom (I); therefore, the electron geometry is trigonal bipyramidal and the corresponding hybridization of I is sp^3d (refer to Table 11.3).

11.9. H_2^+ bond order $= +\frac{1}{2}$

Since the bond order is positive, the H_2^+ ion should be stable; however, the bond order of H_2^+ is lower than the bond order of H_2 (bond order $= 1$). Therefore, the bond in H_2^+ is weaker than in H_2.

11.10. The bond order of N_2^+ is 2.5, which is lower than that of the N_2 molecule (bond order $= 3$); therefore, the bond is weaker. The MO diagram shows that the N_2^+ ion has one unpaired electron and is therefore paramagnetic.

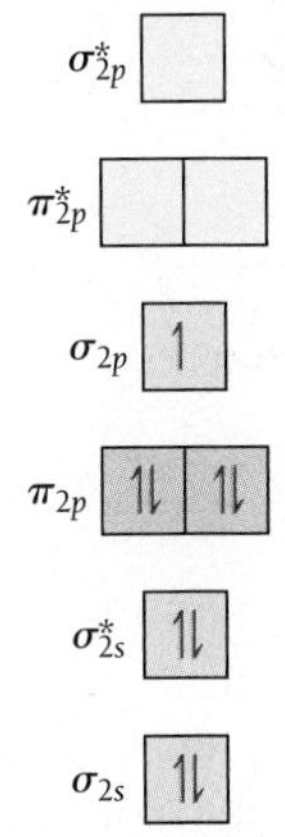

11.10. *For More Practice* The bond order of Ne_2 is 0, which indicates that dineon does not exist.

11.11. The bond order of NO is +2.5. The MO diagram shows that the ion has one unpaired electron and is therefore paramagnetic.

Chapter 12

12.1. **b**, **c**

12.2. HF has a higher boiling point than HCl because, unlike HCl, HF is able to form hydrogen bonds. The hydrogen bond is the strongest of the intermolecular forces and requires more energy to break.

12.3. 5.83×10^3 kJ

12.3. *For More Practice* 49 °C

12.4. 33.8 KJ/mol

12.5. 7.04×10^3 torr

Chapter 13

13.1. 29.4°

13.2. 78.5%

13.3. 3.24×10^{-23} cm^3

13.4. $7.18 \frac{g}{cm^3}$

13.5. Metallic

Chapter 14

14.1. **a.** not soluble
b. soluble
c. not soluble
d. not soluble

14.2. 2.7×10^{-4} M

14.3. 42.5 g $C_{12}H_{22}O_{11}$

14.3. *For More Practice* 3.3×10^4 L

14.4. **a.** $M = 0.415$ M
b. $m = 0.443$ m
c. % by mass $= 13.2\%$
d. $\chi_{C_{12}H_{22}O_{11}} = 0.00793$
e. mole percent $= 0.793\%$

14.5. 0.600 M

14.5. *For More Practice* 0.651 *m*

14.6. 22.5 torr

14.6. *For More Practice* 0.144

14.7. **a.** $P_{benzene} = 26.6$ torr
$P_{toluene} = 20.4$ torr
b. 47.0 torr
c. 52.5% benzene; 47.5% toluene The vapor will be richer in the more volatile component, which in this case is benzene.

14.8. $T_f = -4.8$ °C

14.9. 101.84 °C

14.10. 11.8 atm

14.11. –0.60 °C

14.12. 0.014 mol NaCl

Chapter 15

15.1. $\frac{\Delta[H_2O_2]}{\Delta t} = -4.40 \times 10^{-3}$ M/s

$\frac{\Delta[I_3^-]}{\Delta t} = 4.40 \times 10^{-3}$ M/s

15.2. **a.** Rate $= k[CHCl_3][Cl_2]^{1/2}$. (Fractional-order reactions are not common but are occasionally observed.)
b. $3.5\ M^{-1/2} \cdot s^{-1}$

15.3. 5.78×10^{-2} M

15.4. 0.0277 M

15.5. 1.64×10^{-3} M

15.6. 79.2 s

15.7. $2.07 \times 10^{-5} \frac{L}{mol \cdot s}$

15.8. $6.13 \times 10^{-4} \frac{L}{mol \cdot s}$

15.9. $2\,A + B \longrightarrow A_2B$
Rate $= k[A]^2$

Chapter 16

16.1. $K = \frac{[CO_2]^3[H_2O]^4}{[C_3H_8][O_2]^5}$

16.2. 2.1×10^{-13}

16.2. *For More Practice* 1.4×10^2

16.3. 6.2×10^2

16.4. $K_c = \frac{[Cl_2]^2}{[HCl]^4[O_2]}$

16.5. 9.4

16.6. 1.1×10^{-6}

16.7. $Q_c = 0.0196$
Reaction proceeds to the left.
16.8. 0.033 M
16.9. $[N_2] = 4.5 \times 10^{-3}$ M
$[O_2] = 4.5 \times 10^{-3}$ M
$[NO] = 1.1 \times 10^{-3}$ M
16.10. $[N_2O_4] = 0.005$ M
$[NO_2] = 0.041$ M
16.11. $P_{I_2} = 0.0027$ atm
$P_{Cl_2} = 0.0027$ atm
$P_{ICl_2} = 0.246$ atm
16.12. 1.67×10^{-7} M
16.13. 6.78×10^{-6} M
16.14. Adding Br_2 increases the concentration of Br_2, causing a shift to the left (away from the Br_2). Adding BrNO increases the concentration of BrNO, causing a shift to the right.
16.15. Decreasing the volume causes the reaction to shift right. Increasing the volume causes the reaction to shift left.
16.16. If we increase the temperature, the reaction shifts to the left. If we decrease the temperature, the reaction shifts to the right.

Chapter 17

17.1. a. H_2O donates a proton to C_5H_5N, making it the acid. The conjugate base is therefore OH^-. Since C_5H_5N accepts the proton, it is the base and becomes the conjugate acid $C_5H_5NH^+$.
b. Since HNO_3 donates a proton to H_2O, it is the acid, making NO_3^- the conjugate base. Since H_2O is the proton acceptor, it is the base and becomes the conjugate acid, H_3O^+.
17.2. a. Since $[H_3O^+] < [OH^-]$, the solution is basic.
b. $[H_3O^+] = 1.0 \times 10^{-7}$ M
Neutral solution.
c. $[H_3O^+] = 1.2 \times 10^{-5}$ M
Since $[H_3O^+] > [OH^-]$, the solution is acidic.
17.3. a. 8.02 (basic)
b. 11.85 (basic)
17.4. 4.3×10^{-9} M
17.5. 0.013 M
17.6. 3.28
17.7. 2.72
17.8. 1.8×10^{-6}
17.9. 0.85%
17.10. 2.0×10^{-7} M
17.11. $[OH^-] = 0.020$ M pH = 12.30
17.12. $[OH^-] = 1.2 \times 10^{-2}$ M pH = 12.08
17.13. a. weak base
b. pH-neutral
17.14. 9.07
17.15. a. pH-neutral
b. weak acid
c. weak acid
17.16. a. basic
b. acidic
c. pH-neutral
d. acidic
17.17. 3.83
17.18. $[SO_4^{2}] = 0.00386$ M
pH = 1.945
17.19. 5.6×10^{-11} M

Chapter 18

18.1. 4.44
18.1. *For More Practice* 3.44
18.2. 9.14
18.3. 4.87
18.3. *For More Practice* 4.65
18.4. 9.68
18.4. *For More Practice* 9.56
18.5. hypochlorous acid (HClO); 2.4 g NaClO
18.6. 1.74
18.7. 8.08
18.8. 2.30×10^{-6} M
18.9. 5.3×10^{-13}
18.10. 1.21×10^{-5} M
18.11. $FeCO_3$ will be more soluble in an acidic solution than $PbBr_2$ because the CO_3^{2-} ion is a basic anion, whereas Br^- is the conjugate base of a strong acid (HBr) and is therefore pH-neutral.
18.12. $Q > K_{sp}$; therefore, a precipitate forms.
18.13. 2.9×10^{-6} M
18.14. a. AgCl precipitates first; $[NaCl] = 7.1 \times 10^{-9}$ M
b. $[Ag^+]$ is 1.5×10^{-8} M when $PbCl_2$ begins to precipitate, and $[Pb^{2+}]$ is 0.085 M.
18.15. 9.6×10^{-6} M

Chapter 19

19.1. a. positive
b. negative
c. positive
19.2. 15.2 J/K
19.3. a. −548 J/K
b. ΔS_{sys} is negative.
c. ΔS_{univ} is negative, and the reaction is not spontaneous.
19.3. *For More Practice* 375 K
19.4. $\Delta G = -101.6 \times 10^3$ J
Therefore, the reaction is spontaneous. Since both ΔH and ΔS are negative, as the temperature increases ΔG will become more positive.
19.5. −153.2 J/K
19.6. $\Delta G^\circ_{rxn} = -36.3$ kJ
Since ΔG°_{rxn} is negative, the reaction is spontaneous at this temperature.
19.7. $\Delta G^\circ_{rxn} = -42.1$ kJ
Since the value of ΔG°_{rxn} at the lowered temperature is more negative (or less positive) (which is −36.3 kJ), the reaction is more spontaneous.

19.8. $\Delta G^\circ_{rxn} = -689.6$ kJ
Since ΔG°_{rxn} is negative, the reaction is spontaneous at this temperature.

19.8. *For More Practice* $\Delta G^\circ_{rxn} = -689.7$ kJ (at 25°)
The value calculated for ΔG°_{rxn} from the tabulated values (−689.6 kJ) is the same, to within 1 in the least significant digit, as the value calculated using the equation for ΔG°_{rxn}
$\Delta G^\circ_{rxn} = -649.7$ kJ (at 500.0 K)
You could not calculate ΔG°_{rxn} at 500.0 K using tabulated ΔG°_f values because the tabulated values of free energy are calculated at a standard temperature of 298 K, much lower than 500 K.

19.9. +107.1 kJ

19.10. $\Delta G_{rxn} = -129$ kJ
The reaction is more spontaneous under these conditions than under standard conditions because ΔG_{rxn} is more negative than ΔG°_{rxn}.

19.11. −10.9 kJ

Chapter 20

20.1. $2\,Cr(s) + 4\,H^+(aq) \longrightarrow 2\,Cr^{2+}(aq) + 2\,H_2(g)$

20.2. $Cu(s) + 4\,H^+(aq) + 2\,NO_3^-(aq) \longrightarrow Cu^{2+}(aq) + 2\,NO_2(g) + 2\,H_2O(l)$

20.3. $3\,ClO^-(aq) + 2\,Cr(OH)_4^-(aq) + 2\,OH^-(aq) \longrightarrow 3\,Cl^-(aq) + 2\,CrO_4^{2-}(aq) + 5\,H_2O(l)$

20.4. +0.60 V

20.5. **a.** The reaction *will* be spontaneous as written.
b. The reaction *will not* be spontaneous as written.

20.6. $\Delta G^\circ = -3.63 \times 10^5$ J
Since ΔG° is negative, the reaction is spontaneous.

20.7. 4.5×10^3

20.8. 1.08 V

20.9. *Anode*: $2\,H_2O(l) \longrightarrow O_2(g) + 4\,H^+(aq) + 4\,e^-$
Cathode: $2\,H_2O(l) + 2\,e^- \longrightarrow H_2(g) + 2\,OH^-(aq)$

20.10. 6.0×10^1 min

Chapter 21

21.1. ${}^{216}_{84}Po \longrightarrow {}^{212}_{82}Pb + {}^{4}_{2}He$

21.2. **a.** ${}^{235}_{92}U \longrightarrow {}^{231}_{90}Th + {}^{4}_{2}He$
${}^{231}_{91}Th \longrightarrow {}^{231}_{91}Pa + {}^{0}_{-1}e$
${}^{231}_{91}Pa \longrightarrow {}^{227}_{89}Ac + {}^{4}_{2}He$
b. ${}^{22}_{11}Na \longrightarrow {}^{22}_{10}Ne + {}^{0}_{+1}e$
c. ${}^{76}_{36}Kr + {}^{0}_{-1}e \longrightarrow {}^{76}_{35}Br$

21.2. *For More Practice* Positron emission (${}^{40}_{19}K \longrightarrow {}^{40}_{18}Ar + {}^{0}_{+1}e$) or electron capture (${}^{40}_{19}K + {}^{0}_{+1}e \longrightarrow {}^{40}_{18}Ar$)

21.3. **a.** positron emission
b. beta decay
c. positron emission

21.4. 10.7 yr

21.5. $t = 964$ yr
No, the C-14 content suggests that the scroll is from about A.D. 1000, not 500 B.C.

21.6. 1.0×10^9 yr

21.7. Mass defect = 1.934 amu
Nuclear binding energy = 7.569 MeV/nucleon

Chapter 22

22.1.

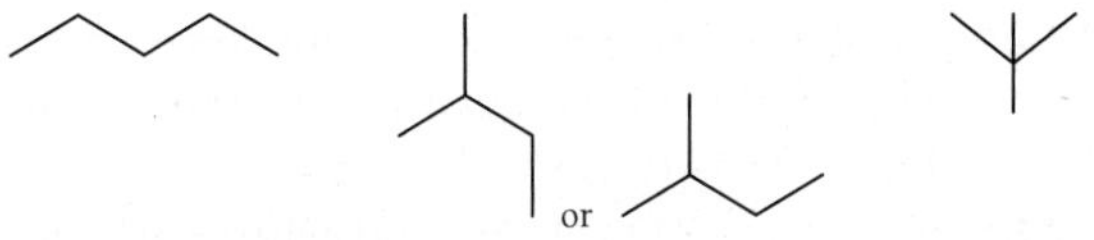

22.2. 3-methylhexane

22.3. 3,5-dimethylheptane

22.4. 2,3,5-trimethylhexane

22.5. **a.** 4,4-dimethyl-2-pentyne
b. 3-ethyl-4,6-dimethyl-1-heptene

22.6. **a.** 2-methylbutane

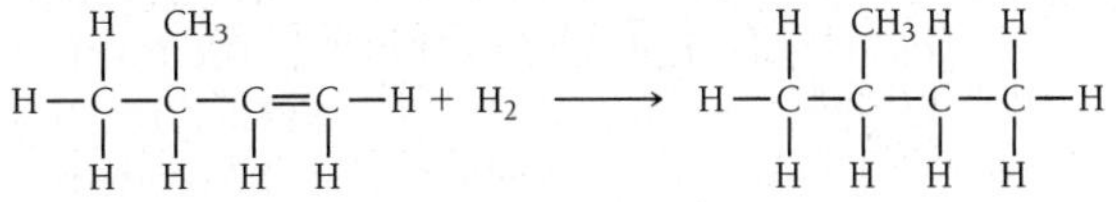

b. 2-chloro-3-methylbutane

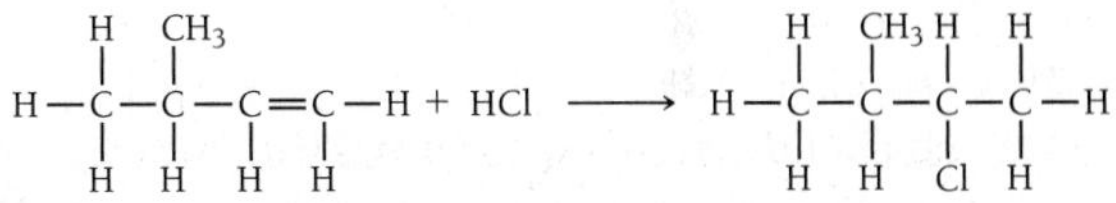

22.7. **a.** Alcohol reacting with an active metal.

$$CH_3CH_2OH + Na \longrightarrow CH_3CH_2ONa + \frac{1}{2}H_2$$

b. dehydration reaction

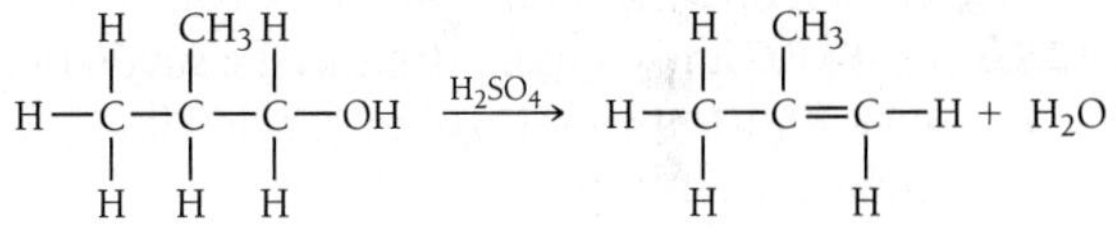

Chapter 23

23.1. Fructose exhibits optical isomerism. It contains three chiral carbons.

23.2.

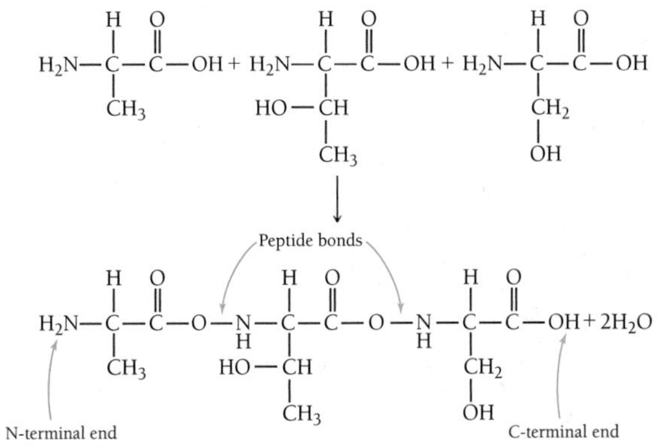

Chapter 24

24.1. $KAlSi_3O_8$

24.2. $x = 2$

24.3. Orthosilicate (or neosilicate): each of the two Be ions has a charge of 2+ for a total of 4+, and the SiO_4 unit has a charge of 4–.

24.4. Inosilicate (or pyroxene): Ca and Mg each have a charge of 2+ for a total of 4+, and the Si_2O_6 unit has a charge of 4– (two SiO_3^{2-} units).

24.5. $2\,H_2S(g) + 3\,O_2(g) \longrightarrow 2\,H_2O(g) + SO_2(g)$
S changes from the −2 to +4 oxidation state.

24.6. The oxidation state for Cl is +7 in ClO_4^- and −1 in Cl^-.

24.7. $I_2(s) + 5\,F_2(g) \longrightarrow 2\,IF_5(g)$

24.8. The electron geometry is tetrahedral, and the shape is bent for ICl_2^+.

24.9. The electron geometry is octahedral for BrF_5, and the molecular geometry is square pyramidal.

24.10. The oxidation number changes from −1 to 0 for the oxidation of the Cl in HCl to Cl_2 and from +5 to +4 for the reduction of the Cl in $NaClO_3$ to ClO_2. The oxidizing agent is $NaClO_3$, and the reducing agent is HCl.

Chapter 25

25.1. At 50 mol% Ni and 1000 °C, this is a solid phase with half of the atoms each Ni and Cu.

25.2. At 50 mol% Ni and 1400 °C, this is a liquid phase with half of the atoms each Ni and Cu.

25.3. At 900 °C and 60 mol% Cr, this is a two-phase region with more Ni-rich face-centered cubic crystals than Cr-rich body-centered cubic crystals. The Ni-rich phase is about 42 mol% Cr and 58 mol% Ni. The Cr-rich phase is about 94 mol% Cr and 6 mol% Ni.

25.4. At 900 °C and 98 mol% Cr, this is a single-phase region with 100 mol% of the Cr-rich body-centered cubic crystals that contains 2% Ni.

Chapter 26

26.1. $[Xe]6s^24f^{14}5d^6$

26.2. $[Kr]5s^04d^3$ or $[Kr]4d^3$

26.3. pentaamminecarbonylmanganese(II) sulfate

26.4. sodium tetrachloroplatinate(II)

26.5. The complex ion $[Cr(H_2O)_3Cl_3]^+$ fits the general formula MA_3B_3, which results in fac and mer isomers.

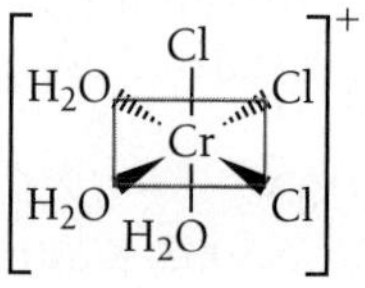

Fac

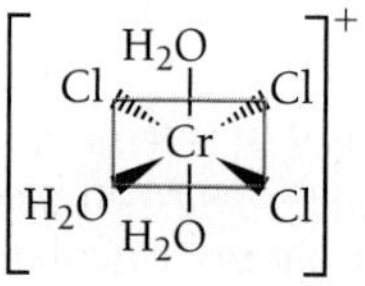

Mer

26.6. The oxalate ligand is a small bidentate ligand, so it will have to occupy two adjacent (cis) positions of the octahedron. There are three ways to arrange the two NH_3 and two Cl^- ligands in the four remaining positions. One has both NH_3 and both Cl^- in cis positions (cis isomer). Another has the NH_3 ligands in a trans arrangement with both Cl^- in cis positions (*trans*-ammine isomer). The third has both NH_3 ligands cis and Cl^- ligands trans (*trans*-chloro isomer).

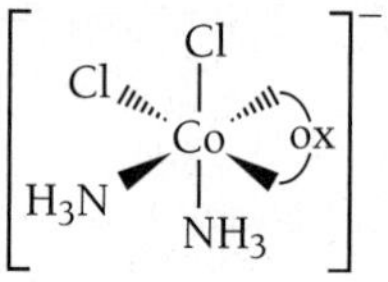

Cis isomer

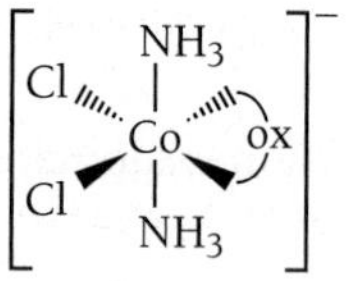

Trans (in NH_3)

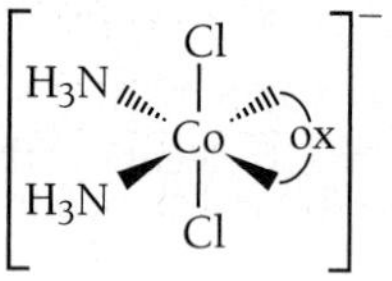

Trans (in Cl^-)

26.7. Both the fac and mer isomers are superimposable (by rotating 180°) on their mirror images, so neither one is optically active.

26.8. 288 kJ/mol

26.9. five unpaired electrons

26.10. one unpaired electron

Glossary

accuracy A term that refers to how close a measured value is to the actual value. (1.7)

acid A molecular compound that is able to donate an H^+ ion (proton) when dissolved in water, thereby increasing the concentration of H_3O^+. (3.6)

acid ionization constant (K_a) The equilibrium constant for the ionization reaction of a weak acid; used to compare the relative strengths of weak acids. (17.4)

acid–base reaction (neutralization reaction) A reaction in which an acid reacts with a base and the two neutralize each other, producing water. (5.7)

acid–base titration A laboratory procedure in which a basic (or acidic) solution of unknown concentration reacts with an acidic (or basic) solution of known concentration in order to determine the concentration of the unknown. (18.4)

acidic solution A solution containing an acid that creates additional H_3O^+ ions, causing $[H_3O^+]$ to increase. (17.5)

activated carbon Very fine carbon particles with high surface area. (24.5)

activated complex (transition state) A high-energy intermediate state between reactant and product. (15.5)

activation energy An energy barrier in a chemical reaction that must be overcome for the reactants to be converted into products. (15.5)

active site The specific area of an enzyme in which catalysis occurs. (15.7)

activity series of metals A listing of metals in order of decreasing activity, decreasing ability to oxidize, and decreasing tendency to lose electrons. (5.9)

actual yield The amount of product actually produced by a chemical reaction. (4.4)

addition polymer A polymer in which the monomers link together without the elimination of any atoms. (13.9)

addition reaction A type of organic reaction in which two substituents are added across a double bond. (22.10)

alcohol A member of the family of organic compounds that contain a hydroxyl functional group (—OH). (3.11, 22.9)

aldehyde A member of the family of organic compounds that contain a carbonyl functional group (C=O) bonded to two R groups, one of which is a hydrogen atom. (22.10)

aldose A sugar that is an aldehyde. (23.3)

aliphatic hydrocarbon A hydrocarbon—including alkanes, alkenes, and alkynes—that does not contain an aromatic ring. (22.3)

alkali metals Highly reactive metals in group 1A of the periodic table. (2.7)

alkaline battery A dry-cell battery that employs half-reactions in a basic medium. (20.7)

alkaline earth metals Fairly reactive metals in group 2A of the periodic table. (2.7)

alkaloid Organic bases found in plants; they are often poisonous. (17.2)

alkane A hydrocarbon containing only single bonds. (3.11, 22.3)

alkene A hydrocarbon containing one or more carbon–carbon double bonds. (3.11, 22.3)

alkyne A hydrocarbon containing one or more carbon–carbon triple bonds. (3.11, 22.3)

alloy A metallic material that contains more than one element. (24.4)

alpha (α) decay The form of radioactive decay that occurs when an unstable nucleus emits a particle composed of two protons and two neutrons. (21.3)

alpha (α) particle A particle released during alpha decay; equivalent to a helium-4 nucleus. (20.3)

α-helix A pattern in the secondary structure of a protein that occurs when the amino acid chain is wrapped tightly in a coil, with the side chains extending outward. (23.5)

aluminosilicates Members of a family of compounds in which aluminum atoms substitute for silicon atoms in some of the silicon lattice sites of the silica structure. (23.3)

amine An organic compound containing nitrogen and derived from ammonia by replacing one or more hydrogen atoms on ammonia with an alkyl group. (22.3)

amino acid An organic compound that contains a carbon atom, called the α-carbon, bonded to four different groups: an amine group, an R group, a carboxylic acid group, and a hydrogen atom. (23.4)

ammonia NH_3, the strong-smelling compound in which nitrogen displays its lowest oxidation state (−3). (24.6)

amorphous A term describing a solid in which atoms or molecules do not have any long-range order. (1.3, 12.2)

ampere (A) The SI unit for electrical current; $1\ A = 1\ C/s$. (20.3)

amphoteric Able to act as either an acid or a base. (17.3)

amplitude The vertical height of a crest (or depth of a trough) of a wave; a measure of wave intensity. (8.2)

angular momentum quantum number (*l*) An integer that determines the shape of an orbital. (8.5)

anion A negatively charged ion. (2.6)

anode The electrode in an electrochemical cell at which oxidation occurs; electrons flow away from the anode. (20.3)

antibonding orbital A molecular orbital that is higher in energy than any of the atomic orbitals from which it was formed. (11.8)

aqueous solution A solution in which water acts as the solvent. (5,2, 14.2)

***arachno*-boranes** Boranes with the formula B_nH_{n+6}, consisting of a cage of boron atoms that is missing two or three corners. (24.4)

arc-melting A method in which a solid metal is melted with an arc from a high-voltage electric source in a controlled atmosphere to prevent oxidation. (25.5)

aromatic hydrocarbon Any hydrocarbon containing a stabilized planar ring of carbon atoms, most commonly a benzene ring. (22.3)

Arrhenius definitions (of acids and bases) According to these definitions, an acid is defined as a substance that produces H^+ ions in aqueous solution, and a base is defined as a substance that produces OH^- ions in aqueous solution. (5.7, 17.3)

Arrhenius equation An equation that relates the rate constant (k) and the temperature in kelvin (T); $k = Ae^{\frac{-E_a}{RT}}$. (15.5)

Arrhenius plot A plot of the natural log of the rate constant ($\ln k$) versus the inverse of the temperature in kelvins ($1/T$) that yields a straight line with a slope of $-E_a/R$ and a y-intercept of $\ln A$. (15.5)

atmosphere (atm) A unit of pressure based on the average pressure of air at sea level; 1 atm = 101,325 Pa. (6.2)

atom A submicroscopic particle that constitutes the fundamental building block of ordinary matter; the smallest identifiable unit of an element. (1.1)

atomic element Elements that exist in nature with single atoms as their basic units. (3.4)

atomic mass (atomic weight) The average mass in amu of the atoms of a particular element based on the relative abundance of the various isotopes; numerically equivalent to the mass in grams of 1 mol of the element. (2.8)

atomic mass unit (amu) A unit used to express the masses of atoms and subatomic particles, defined as 1/12 the mass of a carbon atom containing 6 protons and 6 neutrons. (2.6)

atomic number (*Z*) The number of protons in an atom; the atomic number defines the element. (2.6)

atomic radius The average bonding radius of an atom determined from measurements on a large number of elements and compounds. (9.6)

atomic solids Solids whose composite units are atoms; they include nonbonding atomic solids, metallic atomic solids, and network covalent solids. (13.4)

atomic theory The theory that each element is composed of tiny indestructible particles called atoms, that all atoms of a given element have the same mass and other properties, and that atoms combine in simple, whole-number ratios to form compounds. (1.2, 2.3)

aufbau principle The principle that indicates the pattern of orbital filling in an atom. (9.3)

autoionization The process by which water acts as an acid and a base with itself. (17.5)

Avogadro's law The law that states that the volume of a gas is directly proportional to its amount in moles ($V \propto n$). (6.3)

Avogadro's number The number of ^{12}C atoms in exactly 12 g of ^{12}C; equal to 6.0221179×10^{23}. (2.9)

balanced chemical equation A symbolic representation of a chemical reaction; a balanced equation contains equal numbers of the atoms of each element on both sides of the equation. (4.2)

ball-and-stick molecular model A model that represents atoms as balls and chemical bonds as sticks; how the two connect reflects a molecule's shape. (3.3)

band gap An energy gap that exists between the valence band and conduction band of semiconductors and insulators. (13.8)

band theory A model for bonding in atomic solids based on molecular orbital theory in which atomic orbitals combine and become delocalized over the entire crystal. (13.8)

barometer An instrument used to measure atmospheric pressure. (6.2)

base ionization constant (K_b) The equilibrium constant for the ionization reaction of a weak base; used to compare the relative strengths of weak bases. (17.7)

basic solution A solution containing a base that creates additional OH^- ions, causing the $[OH^-]$ to increase. (17.5)

bent geometry A molecular geometry in which the angle between three bonded atoms is approximately 109° (but could be less). (11.3)

beta (β) decay The form of radioactive decay that occurs when an unstable nucleus emits an electron. (21.3)

beta (β) particle A medium-energy particle released during beta decay; equivalent to an electron. (21.3)

β-pleated sheet A pattern in the secondary structure of a protein that occurs when the amino acid chain is extended and forms a zigzag pattern. (23.5)

bidentate A term describing ligands that donate two electron pairs to the central metal. (26.3)

bimolecular An elementary step in a reaction that involves two particles, either the same species or different, that collide and go on to form products. (15.6)

binary acid An acid composed of hydrogen and a nonmetal. (3.6)

binary compound A compound that contains only two different elements. (3.5)

biochemistry The study of the chemistry that occurs in living organisms. (23.1)

biological effectiveness factor (RBE) A correction factor multiplied by the dose of radiation exposure in rad to obtain the dose in rem. (21.11)

black phosphorus An allotrope of phosphorus with a structure similar to that of graphite; the most thermodynamically stable form. (24.6)

body-centered cubic A unit cell that consists of a cube with one atom at each corner and one atom at the center of the cube. (13.3)

boiling point The temperature at which the vapor pressure of a liquid equals the external pressure. (12.5)

boiling point elevation The effect of a solute that causes a solution to have a higher boiling point than the pure solvent. (14.6)

bomb calorimeter A piece of equipment designed to measure ΔE_{rxn} for combustion reactions at constant volume. (7.5)

bond energy The energy required to break 1 mol of the bond in the gas phase. (10.10)

bond length The average length of a bond between two particular atoms in a variety of compounds. (10.10)

bond order For a molecule, the number of electrons in bonding orbitals minus the number of electrons in nonbonding orbitals divided by two; a positive bond order implies that the molecule is stable. (11.8)

bonding orbital A molecular orbital that is lower in energy than any of the atomic orbitals from which it was formed. (11.8)

bonding pair A pair of electrons shared between two atoms. (10.5)

boranes Compounds composed of boron and hydrogen. (24.4)

Born–Haber cycle A hypothetical series of steps based on Hess's law that represents the formation of an ionic compound from its constituent elements. (10.4)

borosilicate glass (Pyrex®) A type of glass containing boric oxide (B_2O_3). Borosilicate glass expands less when heated and can withstand heating and cooling cycles without shattering. (13.7)

Boyle's law The law that states that volume of a gas is inversely proportional to its pressure $\left(V \propto \frac{1}{P}\right)$. (6.3)

brass A widely used alloy that contains copper and zinc. (25.5)

Brønsted–Lowry definitions (of acids and bases) According to these definitions, an acid is defined as a proton (H^+ ion) donor and a base is defined as a proton acceptor. (17.3)

bronze An alloy of copper and tin that has been used for thousands of years. (25.5)

buffer A solution containing significant amounts of both a weak acid and its conjugate base (or a weak base and its conjugate acid) that resists pH change by neutralizing added acid or added base. (18.2)

buffer capacity The amount of acid or base that can be added to a buffer without causing a large change in pH. (18.3)

calcination Heating an ore in order to decompose it and drive off a volatile product. (25.3)

calorie (cal) A unit of energy defined as the amount of energy required to raise 1 g of water 1°C; equal to 4.184 J. (7.2)

Calorie (Cal) Shorthand notation for the kilocalorie (kcal), or 1000 calories; also called the nutritional calorie, the unit of energy used on nutritional labels. (7.2)

calorimetry The experimental procedure used to measure the heat that evolves in a chemical reaction. (7.5)

capillary action The ability of a liquid to flow against gravity up a narrow tube due to adhesive and cohesive forces. (12.4)

carbides Binary compounds composed of carbon and a low-electronegativity element. (24.5)

carbohydrate A polyhydroxyl aldehyde or ketone. (23.3)

carbon black A fine powdered form of carbon. (24.5)

carbonyl group A functional group consisting of a carbon atom double-bonded to an oxygen atom ($C{=}O$). (22.10)

carboxylic acid An organic acid containing the functional group —COOH. (17.2, 22.11)

catalyst A substance that increases the rate of the reaction but is not consumed by the reaction; it works by providing an alternate mechanism in which the rate-determining step has a smaller activation energy. (15.7)

cathode The electrode in an electrochemical cell at which reduction occurs; electrons flow toward the cathode. (20.3)

cathode ray A stream of electrons produced when a high electrical voltage is applied between two electrodes within a partially evacuated tube. (2.4)

cathode ray tube An evacuated tube containing charged plates to accelerate and view electron beams. (2.4)

cation A positively charged ion. (2.6)

cell potential (cell emf) (E_{cell}) The potential difference between the cathode and the anode in an electrochemical cell. (20.3)

cellulose A polysaccharide that consists of glucose units bonded together by β-glycosidic linkages; the main structural component of plants, and the most abundant organic substance on Earth. (23.3)

Celsius (°C) scale The temperature scale most often used by scientists (and by most countries other than the United States), on which pure water freezes at 0 °C and boils at 100 °C (at sea level). (1.6)

ceramics Inorganic metallic solids that are prepared from powders usually mixed with water, formed into the desired shape, and then heated. (13.7)

chain reaction A series of reactions in which previous reactions cause future ones; in a fission bomb, neutrons produced by the fission of one uranium nucleus induce fission in other uranium nuclei. (21.7)

charcoal A fuel similar to coal that is made by heating wood in the absence of air. (24.5)

Charles's law The law that states that the volume of a gas is directly proportional to its temperature ($V \propto T$). (6.3)

chelate A complex ion that contains either a bi- or polydentate ligand. (26.3)

chelating agent The coordinating ligand of a chelate. (26.3)

chemical bond The sharing or transfer of electrons to attain stable electron configurations for the bonding atoms. (10.3)

chemical change A change that alters the composition of matter; see also **chemical reaction**. (1.4)

chemical energy The energy associated with the relative positions of electrons and nuclei in atoms and molecules. (7.2)

chemical equation A symbolic representation of a chemical reaction; a balanced equation contains equal numbers of the atoms of each element on both sides of the equation. (4.2)

chemical formula A symbolic representation of a compound that indicates the elements present in the compound and the relative number of atoms of each. (3.3)

chemical property A property that a substance displays only by changing its composition via a chemical change. (1.4)

chemical reaction A process by which one or more substances convert to one or more different substances; see also **chemical change**. (4.2)

chemical symbol A one- or two-letter abbreviation for an element; listed directly below an element's atomic number on the periodic table. (2.6)

chemistry The science that seeks to understand the behavior of matter by studying the behavior of atoms and molecules. (1.1)

chiral A term that describes an environment or a molecule that is not superimposable on its mirror image; chiral molecules exhibit optical isomerism. (22.3)

chromosome The DNA-containing structures that occur in the nuclei of living cells. (23.6)

cis–trans (geometric) isomerism A form of stereoisomerism involving the orientation of functional groups in a molecule that contains bonds incapable of rotating. Cis-isomers have two functional groups (or R groups) on the same side of a bond, and trans-isomers have them on opposite sides of a bond. (22.5)

Claus process An industrial process for obtaining sulfur through the oxidation of hydrogen sulfide. (24.8)

Clausius–Clapeyron equation An equation that displays the exponential relationship between vapor pressure and temperature:

$$\ln (P_{vap}) = \frac{-\Delta H_{vap}}{R}\left(\frac{1}{T}\right) + \ln \beta.$$

(12.5)

clay A powdered form of a mineral (such as an aluminosilicate) mixed with water. (13.7)

closo-boranes Boranes that have the formula $B_{12}H_{12}{}^{2-}$ and form the full icosohedral shape. (24.4)

coal A solid, black fuel with high carbon content that is the product of the decomposition of ancient plant material. (24.5)

codon A sequence of three bases in a nucleic acid that codes for one amino acid. (23.6)

coffee-cup calorimeter A piece of equipment designed to measure ΔH_{rxn} for aqueous reactions at constant pressure. (7.7)

coke A solid formed by heating coal in the absence of air that consists primarily of carbon and ash. (24.5)

colligative property A property that depends on the amount of a solute but not on the type. (14.6)

collision frequency A factor in collision theory that represents the number of collisions that occur per unit time. (15.5)

collision model A model of chemical reactions in which a reaction occurs after a sufficiently energetic collision between two reactant molecules. (15.5)

colloidal dispersion (colloid) A mixture in which a dispersed substance is finely dived but not truly dissolved in a dispersing medium. (14.8)

combustion analysis A method of obtaining empirical formulas for unknown compounds, especially those containing carbon and hydrogen, by burning a sample of the compound in pure oxygen and analyzing the products of the combustion reaction. (3.10)

combustion reaction A type of chemical reaction in which a substance combines with oxygen to form one or more oxygen-containing compounds; the reaction often causes the evolution of heat and light in the form of a flame. (4.2)

common ion effect The tendency for a common ion to decrease the solubility of an ionic compound or to decrease the ionization of a weak acid or weak base. (18.2)

common name A nickname of sorts for a compound that gives little or no information about its chemical structure; for example, the common name of $NaHCO_3$ is "baking soda." (3.5)

complementary Capable of precise pairing; in particular, the bases of nucleic acids. (23.6)

complementary properties Properties that exclude one another; that is, the more you know about one, the less you know about the other. For example, the wave nature and particle nature of the electron are complementary. (8.4)

complete ionic equation An equation that lists individually all of the ions present as either reactants or products in a chemical reaction. (5.6)

complex carbohydrate Another term for a polysaccharide based on the fact that it is made up of many simple sugars. (23.3)

complex ion An ion that contains a central metal ion that is bound to one or more ligands. (18.8, 26.3)

composition The basic components that make up a substance. (1.3)

compound A substance composed of two or more elements in fixed, definite proportions. (1.3)

concentrated solution A solution that contains a large amount of solute relative to the amount of solvent. (5.2, 14.5)

concrete A mixture of Portland cement combined with sand and pebbles. (13.7)

condensation The phase transition from gas to liquid. (12.5)

condensation polymer A polymer formed by elimination of an atom or small group of atoms (usually water) between pairs of monomers during polymerization. (13.9)

condensation reaction A reaction in which two or more organic compounds are joined, often with the loss of water or some other small molecule. (22.11)

conduction band In band theory, the band of energy levels that forms from antibonding molecular orbitals. (13.8)

conjugate acid Any base to which a proton has been added. (17.3)

conjugate acid–base pair Two substances related to each other by the transfer of a proton. (17.3)

conjugate base Any acid from which a proton has been removed. (17.3)

constructive interference The interaction of waves from two sources that align with overlapping crests, resulting in a wave of greater amplitude. (8.2)

contact process An industrial method for the production of sulfuric acid. (24.8)

conversion factor A fractional quantity with the units we are converting from on the bottom and the units we are converting to on the top; a conversion factor can be constructed from any two quantities known to be equivalent. (1.8)

coordinate covalent bond The bond formed when a ligand donates electrons to an empty orbital of a metal in a complex ion. (26.3)

coordination compound A neutral compound made when a complex ion combines with one or more counterions. (26.3)

coordination isomers Isomers of complex ions that occur when a coordinated ligand exchanges places with the uncoordinated counterion. (26.4)

coordination number (in a crystal structure) The number of atoms with which each atom in a crystal lattice is in direct contact. (13.3)

coordination number (secondary valence) The number of molecules or ions directly bound to the metal atom in a complex ion. (26.3)

core electrons Those electrons in a complete principal energy level and those in complete *d* and *f* sublevels. (9.4)

corrosion The gradual, nearly always undesired, oxidation of metals that occurs when they are exposed to oxidizing agents in the environment. (20.9)

Coulomb's law A scientific law stating that the potential energy between two charged particles is proportional to the product of the charges divided by the distance that separates the charges. (9.3)

covalent bond A chemical bond in which two atoms share electrons that interact with the nuclei of both atoms, lowering the potential energy of each through electrostatic interactions. (3.2, 10.2)

covalent carbides Binary compounds composed of carbon combined with low-electronegativity nonmetals or metalloids. (24.5)

covalent radius (bonding atomic radius) In nonmetals, one-half the distance between two atoms bonded together, and in metals one-half the distance between two adjacent atoms in a crystal of the metal. (9.6)

critical mass The necessary amount of a radioactive isotope required to produce a self-sustaining fission reaction. (21.7)

critical point The temperature and pressure above which a supercritical fluid exists. (12.8)

critical pressure The pressure required to bring about a transition to a liquid at the critical temperature. (12.5)

critical temperature The temperature above which a liquid cannot exist, regardless of pressure. (12.5)

crystal field theory A bonding model for coordination compounds that focuses on the interactions between ligands and the central metal ion. (26.1)

crystalline A term that describes a solid in which atoms, molecules, or ions are arranged in patterns with long-range, repeating order. (1.3, 12.2)

crystalline lattice The regular arrangement of atoms in a crystalline solid. (13.3)

cubic closest packing A closest-packed arrangement in which the third layer of atoms is offset from the first; the same structure as the face-centered cubic. (13.3)

cyclotron A particle accelerator in which a charged particle is accelerated in an evacuated ring-shaped tube by an alternating voltage applied to each semicircular half of the ring. (21.10)

Dalton's law of partial pressures The law stating that the sum of the partial pressures of the components in a gas mixture must equal the total pressure. (6.6)

de Broglie relation The observation that the wavelength of a particle is inversely proportional to its momentum; $\lambda = \frac{h}{mv}$. (8.4)

decanting A method of separating immiscible liquids by pouring the top layer into another container. (1.3)

degenerate A term describing two or more electron orbitals with the same value of *n* that have the same energy. (9.3)

density (*d*) The ratio of an object's mass (*m*) to its volume (*V*). (1.6)

deposition The phase transition from gas to solid. (12.6)

derived unit A unit that is a combination of other base units. For example, the SI unit for speed is meters per second (m/s), a derived unit. (1.6)

destructive interference The interaction of waves from two sources that are aligned so that the crest of one overlaps the trough of the other, resulting in cancellation. (8.2)

deterministic A characteristic of the classical laws of motion, which imply that present circumstances determine future events. (8.4)

dextrorotatory Capable of rotating the plane of polarization of light clockwise. (22.3)

diamagnetic The state of an atom or ion that contains only paired electrons and is, therefore, slightly repelled by an external magnetic field. (9.7)

diamond An elemental form of carbon in which each carbon atom is covalently bonded to four other carbon atoms at the corners of a tetrahedron. (13.6)

diffraction The phenomena by which a wave emerging from an aperture spreads out to form a new wave front. (8.2)

diffusion The process by which gas molecules spread out in response to a concentration gradient. (6.9)

dilute solution A solution that contains a very small amount of solute relative to the amount of solvent. (5.2, 14.5)

dimensional analysis The use of units as a guide to solving problems. (1.8)

dimer The product that forms from the reaction of two monomers. (13.9)

diode A device that allows the flow of electrical current in only one direction. (13.8)

dipeptide Two amino acids linked together. (23.4)

dipole moment (μ) A measure of the separation of positive and negative charge in a molecule. (10.6)

dipole–dipole force An intermolecular force exhibited by polar molecules that results from the uneven charge distribution. (12.3)

diprotic acid An acid that contains two ionizable protons. (5.7, 17.4)

disaccharide A carbohydrate composed of two monosaccharides. (23.3)

dispersion force An intermolecular force (also referred to as London force) exhibited by all atoms and molecules that results from fluctuations in the electron distribution. (12.3)

distillation The process by which mixtures are heated to boil off the more volatile (easily vaporizable) liquid. The volatile liquid is then recondensed in a condenser and collected in a separate flask. (1.3)

disubstituted benzene A benzene in which two hydrogen atoms have been replaced by other atoms. (22.7)

dose The amount of energy absorbed by bodily tissues as a result of exposure to radiation. (21.11)

double bond The bond that forms when two electrons are shared between two atoms. (10.5)

dry-cell battery A battery that does not contain a large amount of liquid water, often using the oxidation of zinc and the reduction of MnO_2 to provide the electrical current. (20.7)

duet A Lewis symbol with two dots, signifying a filled outer electron shell for the elements H and He. (10.3)

dynamic equilibrium The point at which the rate of the reverse reaction or process equals the rate of the forward reaction or process. (12.5, 14.4, 16.2)

effective nuclear charge (Z_{eff}) The actual nuclear charge experienced by an electron, defined as the charge of the nucleus plus the charge of the shielding electrons. (9.3)

effusion The process by which a gas escapes from a container into a vacuum through a small hole. (6.9)

electrical charge A fundamental property of certain particles that causes them to experience a force in the presence of electric fields. (2.4)

electrical current The flow of electric charge. (20.3)

electrochemical cell A device that uses redox reactions to generate electricity or an electrical current to drive a chemical reaction. (20.3)

electrode A conductive surface through which electrons can enter or leave a half-cell in an electrochemical cell. (20.3)

electrolysis The process in which electrical current drives an otherwise nonspontaneous redox reaction. (20.8)

electrolyte A substance that dissolves in water to form solutions that conduct electricity. (5.4)

electrolytic cell An electrochemical cell that consumes electrical current to drive a nonspontaneous chemical reaction. (20.3)

electromagnetic radiation A form of energy embodied in oscillating electric and magnetic fields. (8.2)

electromagnetic spectrum The range of the wavelengths of all possible electromagnetic radiation. (8.2)

electrometallurgy The use of electrolysis to produce metals from their compounds. (25.3)

electromotive force (emf) The force that results in the motion of electrons due to a difference in potential. (20.3)

electron A negatively charged, low-mass particle found outside the nucleus of all atoms that occupies most of the atom's volume but contributes almost none of its mass. (2.4)

electron affinity (EA) The energy change associated with the gaining of an electron by an atom in its gaseous state. (9.8)

electron capture The form of radioactive decay that occurs when a nucleus assimilates an electron from an inner orbital. (21.3)

electron configuration A notation that shows the particular orbitals that are occupied by electrons in an atom. (9.3)

electron geometry The geometrical arrangement of electron groups in a molecule. (11.3)

electron groups A general term for lone pairs, single bonds, multiple bonds, or lone electrons in a molecule. (11.2)

electronegativity An atom's ability to attract electrons to itself in a covalent bond. (10.6)

element A substance that cannot be chemically broken down into simpler substances. (1.3)

elementary step An individual step in a reaction mechanism. (15.6)

emission spectrum The range of wavelengths emitted by a particular element; used to identify the element. (8.3)

empirical formula A chemical formula that gives the *relative* number of atoms of each element in a compound. (3.3)

empirical formula molar mass The sum of the masses of all the atoms in an empirical formula. (3.10)

enantiomers (optical isomers) Two molecules that are nonsuperimposable mirror images of one another. (22.3, 26.4)

endothermic reaction A chemical reaction that absorbs heat from its surroundings; for an endothermic reaction, $\Delta H > 0$. (7.6)

endpoint The point of pH change where an indicator changes color. (18.4)

energy The capacity to do work. (1.5, 7.2)

English system The system of units used in the United States and various other countries in which the inch is the unit of length, the pound is the unit of force, and the ounce is the unit of mass. (1.6)

enthalpy (*H*) The sum of the internal energy of a system and the product of its pressure and volume. (7.6)

enthalpy (heat) of reaction (ΔH_{rxn}) The enthalpy change for a chemical reaction. (7.6)

enthalpy of solution (ΔH_{soln}) The enthalpy change associated with the formation of a solution. (14.3)

entropy A thermodynamic function that is proportional to the number of energetically equivalent ways to arrange the components of a system to achieve a particular state; a measure of the energy randomization or energy dispersal in a system. (14.2, 18.3)

enzyme A biochemical catalyst made of protein that increases the rates of biochemical reactions. (15.7, 23.4)

equilibrium constant (*K*) The ratio, at equilibrium, of the concentrations of the products of a reaction raised to their stoichiometric coefficients divided by the concentrations of the reactants raised to their stoichiometric coefficients. (16.3)

equivalence point The point in the titration at which the added solute completely reacts with the solute present in the solution; for acid–base titrations, the point in the titration when the number of moles of base is stoichiometrically equal to the number of moles of acid. (5.7, 18.4)

ester A family of organic compounds with the general structure R—COO—R. (22.11)

ester linkage The bonds that form between a carboxylic acid and an alcohol to form an ester, such as those in triglycerides. (23.2)

ether A member of the family of organic compounds of the form ROR. (22.12)

exact numbers Numbers that have no uncertainty and thus do not limit the number of significant figures in any calculation. (1.7)

excess (reactants) The reactants that do not limit the amount of product (4.4)

exothermic reaction A chemical reaction that releases heat to its surroundings; for an exothermic reaction, $\Delta H < 0$. (7.6)

experiment A highly controlled procedure designed to generate observations that may support a hypothesis or prove it wrong. (1.2)

exponential factor A number between zero and one that represents the fraction of molecules that have enough energy to make it over the activation barrier on a given approach. (15.5)

exposure The number of radioactive decay events to which a person is exposed. (21.11)

extensive property A property that depends on the amount of a given substance, such as mass. (1.6)

extractive metallurgy The process by which an elemental metal is extracted from the compounds in which it is found. (25.3)

face-centered cubic A crystal structure that has a unit cell that consists of a cube with one atom at each corner and one atom in the center of every face. (13.3)

Fahrenheit (°F) scale The temperature scale that is most familiar in the United States, on which pure water freezes at 32 °F and boils at 212 °F at sea level. (1.6)

family A group of organic compounds with the same functional group. (3.11)

family (group) Columns within the main-group elements in the periodic table that contain elements that exhibit similar chemical properties. (2.7)

Faraday's constant (*F*) The charge in coulombs of 1 mol of electrons; $F = \frac{96{,}485\ \text{C}}{\text{mol e}^-}$. (20.5)

fatty acid A carboxylic acid with a long hydrocarbon tail. (23.2)

ferromagnetic The state of an atom or ion that is very strongly attracted by an external magnetic field. (25.5)

fibrous protein A protein with a relatively linear structure; fibrous proteins tend to be insoluble in aqueous solutions. (23.5)

filtration A procedure used to separate a mixture composed of an insoluble solid and a liquid by pouring the mixture through filter paper or some other porous membrane or layer. (1.3)

first law of thermodynamics The law stating that the total energy of the universe is constant. (7.3)

flux In pyrometallurgy, material that reacts with the gangue to form a substance with a low melting point. (25.3)

formal charge The charge that an atom in a Lewis structure would have if all the bonding electrons were shared equally between the bonded atoms. (10.8)

formation constant (K_f) The equilibrium constant associated with reactions for the formation of complex ions. (18.8)

formula mass The average mass of a molecule of a compound in amu. (3.8)

formula unit The smallest, electrically neutral collection of ions in an ionic compound. (3.4)

Frasch process An industrial process for the recovery of sulfur that uses superheated water to liquefy sulfur deposits in Earth's crust and bring the molten sulfur to the surface. (24.8)

free energy change of a reaction under nonstandard conditions (ΔG_{rxn}) The free energy change of a reaction under nonstandard conditions; given by the relationship: $\Delta G_{rxn} = \Delta G^\circ_{rxn} + RT \ln Q$ (19.9)

free energy of formation (ΔG°_f) The change in free energy when 1 mol of a compound forms from its constituent elements in their standard states. (19.8)

free radical A molecule or ion with an odd number of electrons in its Lewis structure. (10.9)

freezing The phase transition from liquid to solid. (12.6)

freezing point depression The effect of a solute that causes a solution to have a lower melting point than the pure solvent. (14.6)

frequency (ν) For waves, the number of cycles (or complete wavelengths) that pass through a stationary point in one second. (8.2)

frequency factor The number of times that reactants approach the activation energy per unit time. (15.5)

fuel cell A battery-like device in which reactants, provided from an external source, constantly flow through the battery generating electrical current as they undergo a redox reaction. In a hydrogen-oxygen fuel cell, the oxidation of hydrogen and the reduction of oxygen form water and provide electrical current. (20.7)

fullerenes Carbon clusters, such as C_{60}, bonded in roughly spherical shapes containing from 36 to over 100 carbon atoms. (13.6)

functional group A characteristic atom or group of atoms that impart certain chemical properties to an organic compound. (3.11)

gamma (γ) ray The form of electromagnetic radiation with the shortest wavelength and highest energy. (8.2, 21.3)

gamma (γ) ray emission The form of radioactive decay that occurs when an unstable nucleus emits extremely high frequency electromagnetic radiation. (21.3)

gangue The undesirable minerals that are separated from specific ores. (25.3)

gas A state of matter in which atoms or molecules have a great deal of space between them and are free to move relative to one another; lacking a definite shape or volume, gases always assume the shape and volume of their containers. (1.3)

gas-evolution reaction A reaction in which two aqueous solutions are mixed and a gas forms, resulting in bubbling. (5.7)

Geiger–Müller counter A device used to detect radioactivity, which uses argon atoms that become ionized in the presence of energetic particles to produce an electrical signal. (21.5)

gene A sequence of codons within a DNA molecule that codes for a single protein. (23.6)

geometric (cis–trans) isomerism A form of stereoisomerism involving the orientation of functional groups in a molecule that contains bonds incapable of rotating. Cis-isomers have two functional groups (or R groups) on the same side of a bond, and trans-isomers have them on opposite sides of a bond. (22.5)

geometric isomers For complex ions, isomers that result when the ligands bonded to the metal have a different spatial arrangement. (26.4)

Gibbs free energy (G) A thermodynamic state function related to enthalpy and entropy by the equation $G = H - TS$; chemical systems tend toward lower Gibbs free energy, also called the *chemical potential.* (19.6)

glass An amorphous form of silica with a randomly ordered structure. (13.7)

globular protein A protein that folds into a roughly spherical shape so that its polar side chains are oriented outward and its nonpolar side chains, toward the interior; globular proteins tend to be soluble in water. (23.5)

glycogen A highly branched form of starch. (23.3)

glycolipid A triglyceride composed of a fatty acid, a hydrocarbon chain, and a sugar molecule as the polar section. (23.2)

glycosidic linkage A bond between carbohydrates that results from a dehydration reaction. (23.3)

Graham's law of effusion A scientific law that states the ratio of effusion rates of two gases is equal to the square root of the inverse of their molar masses. (6.9)

graphene A new material that consists of a single sheet of carbon atoms (similar to a sheet from graphite) one atom thick. (13.1)

graphite An elemental form of carbon consisting of flat sheets of carbon atoms, bonded together as interconnected hexagonal rings held together by intermolecular forces, that can easily slide past each other. (13.6)

ground state The lowest energy state in an atom, ion, or molecule. (9.3)

Haber–Bosch process The industrial process for producing ammonia from nitrogen gas and hydrogen gas. (24.6)

half-cell One half of an electrochemical cell where either oxidation or reduction occurs. (20.3)

half-life ($t_{1/2}$) The time required for the concentration of a reactant or the amount of a radioactive isotope to fall to one-half of its initial value. (15.4)

halogens Highly reactive nonmetals in group 7A of the periodic table. (2.7)

heat (q) The flow of energy caused by a temperature difference. (7.2)

heat capacity (C) The quantity of heat required to change a system's temperature by 1 °C. (7.4)

heat of fusion (ΔH_{fus}) The amount of heat required to melt 1 mol of a solid. (12.6)

heat of hydration ($\Delta H_{hydration}$) The enthalpy change that occurs when 1 mol of gaseous solute ions is dissolved in water. (14.3)

heat (or enthalpy) of sublimation (ΔH_{sub}) The amount of heat required to sublime 1 mol of a solid to a gas. (12.6)

heat (or enthalpy) of vaporization (ΔH_{vap}) The amount of heat required to vaporize 1 mol of a liquid to a gas. (12.5)

Heisenberg's uncertainty principle The principle stating that due to the wave–particle duality, it is fundamentally impossible to precisely determine both the position and velocity of a particle at a given moment in time. (8.4)

Henderson–Hasselbalch equation An equation used to easily calculate the pH of a buffer solution from the initial concentrations of the buffer components, assuming that the "*x is small*" approximation is valid; $pH = pK_a + \log\frac{[base]}{[acid]}$. (18.2)

Henry's law An equation that expresses the relationship between solubility of a gas and pressure; $S_{gas} = k_H P_{gas}$. (14.4)

Hess's law The law stating that if a chemical equation can be expressed as the sum of a series of steps, then ΔH_{rxn} for the overall equation is the sum of the heats of reactions for each step. (7.8)

heterogeneous catalysis Catalysis in which the catalyst and the reactants exist in different phases. (15.7)

heterogeneous mixture A mixture in which the composition varies from one region to another. (1.3)

hexagonal closest packing A closest-packed arrangement in which the atoms of the third layer align exactly over those in the first layer. (13.3)

hexose A six-carbon sugar. (23.3)

high-spin complex A complex ion with weak field ligands that have the same number of unpaired electrons as the free metal ion. (26.5)

homogeneous catalysis Catalysis in which the catalyst exists in the same phase as the reactants. (15.7)

homogeneous mixture A mixture with the same composition throughout. (1.3)

Hund's rule The principle stating that when electrons fill degenerate orbitals, they first fill them singly with parallel spins. (9.3)

hybrid orbitals Orbitals formed from the combination of standard atomic orbitals that correspond more closely to the actual distribution of electrons in a chemically bonded atom. (11.7)

hybridization A mathematical procedure in which standard atomic orbitals are combined to form new, hybrid orbitals. (11.7)

hydrate An ionic compound that contains a specific number of water molecules associated with each formula unit. (3.5)

hydrazine N_2H_4, a nitrogen and hydrogen compound in which nitrogen has a negative oxidation state (–2). (24.6)

hydrocarbon An organic compound that contains only carbon and hydrogen. (3.11)

hydrogen azide (HN_3) A nitrogen and hydrogen compound with a higher hydrogen-to-nitrogen ratio than ammonia or hydrazine. (24.6)

hydrogen bond A strong attraction between the H atom on one molecule and the F, O, or N on its neighbor. (12.3)

hydrogen bonding The forming of a hydrogen bond. Hydrogen bonds form when polar molecules containing hydrogen atoms bond directly to small electronegative atoms such as fluorine, oxygen, and nitrogen. (12.3)

hydrogenation The catalyzed addition of hydrogen to alkene double bonds to make single bonds. (15.7)

hydrolysis The splitting of a chemical bond with water, resulting in the addition of H and OH to the products. (23.3)

hydrometallurgy The use of an aqueous solution to extract metals from their ores. (25.3)

hydronium ion H_3O^+; the ion formed from the association of a water molecule with an H^+ ion donated by an acid. (5.7, 17.3)

hydroxyl group An –OH group. (22.9)

hypothesis A tentative interpretation or explanation of an observation; a good hypothesis is *falsifiable*. (1.2)

hypoxia A physiological condition caused by low levels of oxygen, marked by dizziness, headache, shortness of breath, and eventually unconsciousness or even death in severe cases. (6.6)

ideal gas A hypothetical gas that follows the ideal gas law under all conditions. (6.4)

ideal gas constant The proportionality constant of the ideal gas law, R, equal to 8.314 J/mol·K or 0.08206 L·atm/mol·K. (6.4)

ideal gas law The law that combines the relationships of Boyle's, Charles's, and Avogadro's laws into one comprehensive equation of state with the proportionality constant R in the form $PV = nRT$. (6.4)

ideal solution A solution that follows Raoult's law at all concentrations for both solute and solvent. (14.6)

indeterminacy The principle asserting that present circumstances do not necessarily determine future evens in the quantum-mechanical realm. (8.4)

indicator A dye whose color depends on the pH of the solution in which it is dissolved; often used to detect the endpoint of a titration. (5.7, 18.4)

infrared (IR) radiation Electromagnetic radiation emitted from warm objects, with wavelengths slightly larger than those of visible light. (8.2)

insoluble Incapable of dissolving in water or being extremely difficult of solution. (5.4)

integrated rate law A relationship between the concentrations of the reactants in a chemical reaction and time. (15.4)

intensive property A property such as density that is independent of the amount of a given substance. (1.6)

interference The superposition of two or more waves overlapping in space, resulting in either an increase in amplitude (constructive interference) or a decrease in amplitude (destructive interference). (8.2)

interhalogen compounds A class of covalent compounds that contain two different halogens. (24.9)

internal energy (*E*) The sum of the kinetic and potential energies of all the particles that compose a system. (7.3)

International System of Units (SI) The standard unit system used by scientists, based on the metric system. (1.6)

interstitial alloy An alloy in which small, usually nonmetallic atoms fit between the metallic atoms of a crystal. (25.4)

ion An atom or molecule with a net charge caused by the loss or gain of electrons. (2.6)

ion product constant for water (K_w) The equilibrium constant for the autoionization of water; sometimes called the dissociation constant for water. (17.5)

ion–dipole force An intermolecular force that occurs when an ionic compound is mixed with a polar compound. (12.3)

ionic bond A chemical bond formed between two oppositely charged ions, generally a metallic cation and a nonmetallic anion, that are attracted to each other by electrostatic forces. (3.2, 10.2)

ionic carbides Binary compounds composed of carbon combined with low-electronegativity metals. (24.5)

ionic compound A compound composed of cations and anions bound together by electrostatic attraction. (3.2)

ionic solids Solids whose composite units are ions; they generally have high melting points. (13.4)

ionization energy (IE) The energy required to remove an electron from an atom or ion in its gaseous state. (9.7)

ionizing power The ability of radiation to ionize other molecules and atoms. (21.3)

isotopes Atoms of the same element with the same number of protons but different numbers of neutrons and consequently different masses. (2.6)

joule (J) The SI unit for energy: equal to 1 $kg \cdot m^2/s^2$. (7.2)

kelvin (K) The SI standard unit of temperature. (1.6)

Kelvin scale The temperature scale that assigns 0 K (−273 °C or −459 °F) to the coldest temperature possible, absolute zero, which is the temperature at which molecular motion virtually stops. (1.6)

ketone A member of the family of organic compounds that contain a carbonyl functional group ($C{=}O$) bonded to two R groups, neither of which is a hydrogen atom. (22.10)

ketose A sugar that is a ketone. (23.3)

kilogram (kg) The SI standard unit of mass defined as the mass of a block of metal kept at the International Bureau of Weights and Measures at Sèvres, France. (1.6)

kilowatt-hour (kWh) An energy unit used primarily to express large amounts of energy produced by the flow of electricity; equal to 3.60×10^6 J. (7.2)

kinetic energy The energy associated with motion of an object. (1.5, 7.2)

kinetic molecular theory A model of an ideal gas as a collection of point particles in constant motion undergoing completely elastic collisions. (6.8)

lanthanide contraction The trend toward leveling off in size of the atoms in the third and fourth transition rows due to the ineffective shielding of the *f* sublevel electrons. (26.2)

lattice energy The energy associated with forming a crystalline lattice from gaseous ions. (10.4)

law See **scientific law**. (1.2)

law of conservation of energy A law stating that energy can neither be created nor destroyed, only converted from one form to another. (1.5, 7.2)

law of conservation of mass A law stating that matter is neither created nor destroyed in a chemical reaction. (1.2, 2.3)

law of definite proportions A law stating that all samples of a given compound have the same proportions of their constituent elements. (2.3)

law of mass action A law regarding the relationship between the balanced chemical equation and the expression of the equilibrium constant. (16.3)

law of multiple proportions A law stating that when two elements (A and B) form two different compounds, the masses of element B that combine with one gram of element A can be expressed as a ratio of small whole numbers. (2.3)

Le Châtelier's principle The principle stating that when a chemical system at equilibrium is disturbed, the system shifts in a direction that minimizes the disturbance. (16.9)

leaching The process by which a metal is separated out of a mixture by selectively dissolving the metal into solution. (25.3)

leaded glass A type of glass (often called *crystal*) that contains PbO. This type of glass has a higher index of refraction (it bends light more than ordinary glass), which results in more brilliant-looking glassware. (13.7)

lead–acid storage battery A battery that uses the oxidation of lead and the reduction of lead(IV) oxide in sulfuric acid to provide electrical current. (20.7)

lever rule The rule that states that, in a two-phase region, whichever phase is closer to the composition of the alloy is the more abundant phase. (25.4)

levorotatory Being capable of rotating the polarization of light counterclockwise. (22.3)

Lewis acid An atom, ion, or molecule that is an electron pair acceptor. (17.11)

Lewis base An atom, ion, or molecule that is an electron pair donor. (17.11)

Lewis electron-dot structures (Lewis structures) A drawing that represents chemical bonds between atoms in molecules as shared or transferred electrons; the valence electrons of atoms are represented as dots in a Lewis structure. (10.1)

Lewis model A simple model of chemical bonding using diagrams that represent bonds between atoms as lines or pairs of dots. According to this model, atoms bond together to obtain stable octets (eight valence electrons). (10.1)

Lewis symbol The symbol of an element surrounded with dots representing the element's valence electrons. (10.3)

ligand A neutral molecule or an ion that acts as a Lewis base with the central metal ion in a complex ion. (18.8, 26.3)

limiting reactant The reactant that has the smallest stoichiometric amount in a reactant mixture and consequently limits the amount of product in a chemical reaction. (4.4)

linear accelerator A particle accelerator in which a charged particle is accelerated in an evacuated tube by a potential difference between the ends of the tube or by alternating charges in sections of the tube. (21.10)

linear geometry The molecular geometry of three atoms with a 180° bond angle due to the repulsion of two electron groups. (11.2)

linkage isomers Isomers of complex ions that occur when some ligands coordinate to the metal in different ways. (26.4)

lipid A member of the class of biochemical compounds that are insoluble in water but soluble in nonpolar solvents, including fatty acids, triglycerides, and steroids. (23.2)

lipid bilayer A double-layered structure made of phospholipids or glycolipids, in which the polar heads of the molecules interact with the environment and the nonpolar tails interact with each other; a component of many cellular membranes. (23.2)

liquid A state of matter in which atoms or molecules pack about as closely as they do in solid matter but are free to move relative to each other; liquids have a fixed volume but not a fixed shape. (1.3)

liter (L) A unit of volume equal to 1000 cm^3 or 1.057 qt. (1.6)

lithium ion battery A battery that produces electrical current in the form of motion of lithium ions from the anode to the cathode. (20.7)

lone pair A pair of electrons associated with only one atom. (10.5)

low-spin complex A complex ion with strong-field ligands that have fewer unpaired electrons than the free metal ion. (26.5)

magic numbers Certain numbers of nucleons (N or $Z = 2, 8, 20, 28, 50, 82$, and $N = 126$) that confer unique stability. (21.4)

magnetic quantum number (m_l) An integer that specifies the orientation of an orbital. (8.5)

main-group elements Those elements found in the *s* or *p* blocks of the periodic table, whose properties tend to be predictable based on their position in the table. (2.7, 24.2)

manometer An instrument used to determine the pressure of a gaseous sample, consisting of a liquid-filled U-shaped tube with one end exposed to the ambient pressure and the other end connected to the sample. (6.2)

mass A measure of the quantity of matter making up an object. (1.6)

mass defect The difference in mass between the nucleus of an atom and the sum of the separated particles that make up that nucleus. (21.8)

mass number (*A*) The sum of the number of protons and neutrons in an atom. (2.6)

mass percent composition (mass percent) An element's percentage of the total mass of a compound containing the element. (3.9)

mass spectrometry An experimental method of determining the precise mass and relative abundance of isotopes in a given sample using an instrument called a *mass spectrometer*. (2.8)

matter Anything that occupies space and has mass. (1.3)

mean free path The average distance that a molecule in a gas travels between collisions. (6.9)

melting (fusion) The phase transition from solid to liquid. (12.6)

melting point The temperature at which the molecules of a solid have enough thermal energy to overcome intermolecular forces and become a liquid. (12.6)

metal A member of the class of elements that are generally good conductors of heat and electricity, malleable, ductile, and lustrous, and tend to lose electrons during chemical changes. (2.7)

metallic atomic solids Atomic solids held together by metallic bonds; they have variable melting points. (13.4)

metallic bonding The type of bonding that occurs in metal crystals, in which metal atoms donate their electrons to an electron sea, delocalized over the entire crystal lattice. (10.2)

metallic carbides Binary compounds composed of carbon combined with metals that have a metallic lattice with holes small enough to fit carbon atoms. (24.5)

metalloid A member of the class of elements found on the boundary between the metals and nonmetals of the periodic table, with properties intermediate between those of both groups; also called *semimetals*. (2.7)

metallurgy The part of chemistry that includes all the processes associated with mining, separating, and refining metals and the subsequent production of pure metals and mixtures of metals called alloys. (25.1)

meter (m) The SI standard unit of length; equivalent to 39.37 inches. (1.6)

metric system The system of measurements used in most countries in which the meter is the unit of length, the kilogram is the unit of mass, and the second is the unit of time. (1.6)

microwaves Electromagnetic radiation with wavelengths slightly longer than those of infrared radiation; used for radar and in microwave ovens. (8.2)

milliliter (mL) A unit of volume equal to 10^{-3} L or 1 cm^3. (1.6)

millimeter of mercury (mmHg) A common unit of pressure referring to the air pressure required to push a column of mercury to a height of 1 mm in a barometer; 760 mmHg = 1 atm. (6.2)

mineral A homogeneous, naturally occurring, crystalline inorganic solid. (24.3, 25.2)

miscibility The ability to mix without separating into two phases. (12.3)

miscible The ability of two or more substances to be soluble in each other in all proportions. (14.2)

mixture A substance composed of two or more components in proportions that can vary from one sample to another. (1.3)

molality (m) A means of expressing solution concentration as the number of moles of solute per kilogram of solvent. (14.5)

molar heat capacity The amount of heat required to raise the temperature of 1 mol of a substance by 1 °C. (7.4)

molar mass The mass in grams of 1 mol of atoms of an element; numerically equivalent to the atomic mass of the element in amu. (2.9)

molar solubility The solubility of a compound in units of moles per liter. (18.5)

molar volume The volume occupied by 1 mol of a substance; the molar volume of an ideal gas at STP is 22.4 L. (6.5)

molarity (M) A means of expressing solution concentration as the number of moles of solute per liter of solution. (5.2, 14.5)

mole (mol) A unit defined as the amount of material containing 6.0221421×10^{23} particles (Avogadro's number of particles). (2.9)

mole fraction (χ_a) The number of moles of a component in a mixture divided by the total number of moles in the mixture. (6.6)

mole fraction (χ_{solute}) A means of expressing solution concentration as the number of moles of solute per moles of solution. (14.5)

mole percent A means of expressing solution concentration as the mole fraction multiplied by 100%. (14.5)

molecular compound Compounds composed of two or more covalently bonded nonmetals. (3.2)

molecular element Those elements that do not normally exist in nature with single atoms as their basic units; elements with diatomic or polyatomic molecules as their basic unit. (3.4)

molecular equation An equation showing the complete neutral formula for each compound in a reaction. (5.6)

molecular formula A chemical formula that shows the actual number of atoms of each element in a molecule of a compound. (3.3)

molecular geometry The geometrical arrangement of atoms in a molecule. (11.3)

molecular orbital theory An advanced model of chemical bonding in which electrons reside in molecular orbitals delocalized over the entire molecule. In the simplest version, the molecular orbitals are simply linear combinations of atomic orbitals. (11.8)

molecular solids Solids whose composite units are molecules; they generally have low melting points. (13.4)

molecularity The number of reactant particles involved in an elementary step. (15.6)

molecule Two or more atoms joined chemically in a specific geometrical arrangement. (1.1)

monodentate A term that describes ligands that donate only one electron pair to the central metal. (26.3)

monomer A repeating unit in a polymer. (13.9)

monoprotic acid An acid that contains only one ionizable proton. (17.4)

monosaccharide The simplest carbohydrates, with three to eight carbon atoms and only one aldehyde or ketone group. (23.3)

nanotubes Long, tubular structures consisting of interconnected C_6 rings. (13.6)

natural abundance The relative percentage of a particular isotope in a naturally occurring sample with respect to other isotopes of the same element. (2.6)

Nernst equation The equation relating the cell potential of an electrochemical cell to the standard cell potential and the reaction quotient; $E_{cell} = E^{\circ}_{cell} - \frac{0.0592\text{ V}}{n} \log Q$. (20.6)

net ionic equation An equation that shows only the species that actually change during the reaction. (5.6)

network covalent atomic solids Atomic solids held together by covalent bonds; they have high melting points. (13.4)

neutral The state of a solution where the concentrations of H_3O^+ and OH^- are equal. (17.5)

neutron An electrically neutral subatomic particle found in the nucleus of an atom, with a mass almost equal to that of a proton. (2.5)

nickel–cadmium (NiCad) battery A battery that consists of an anode composed of solid cadmium and a cathode composed of NiO(OH)(*s*) in a KOH solution. (20.7)

nickel–metal hydride (NiMH) battery A battery that uses the same cathode reaction as the NiCad battery but a different anode reaction, the oxidation of hydrogens in a metal alloy. (20.7)

nido-boranes Boranes that have the formula B_nH_{n+4} and consist of a cage of boron atoms missing one corner. (24.4)

nitrogen narcosis A physiological condition caused by an increased partial pressure of nitrogen, resulting in symptoms similar to those of intoxication. (6.6)

noble gases The group 8A elements, which are largely unreactive (inert) due to their stable filled *p* orbitals. (2.7)

node A point where the wave function (ψ), and therefore the probability density (ψ^2) and radial distribution function, all go through zero (8.6)

nonbonding atomic radius The distance between the centers of adjacent atoms in direct contact but not bonded together. (9.6)

nonbonding atomic solids Atomic solids held together by dispersion forces; they have low melting points. (13.4)

nonbonding electrons Electrons in a Lewis structure that are not in a chemical bond; also called lone pair electrons. (10.5)

nonbonding orbital An orbital whose electrons remain localized on an atom. (11.8)

nonelectrolyte A compound that does not dissociate into ions when dissolved in water. (5.4)

nonmetal A member of the class of elements that tend to be poor conductors of heat and electricity and usually gain electrons during chemical reactions. (2.7)

nonvolatile Not easily vaporized. (12.5)

normal boiling point The temperature at which the vapor pressure of a liquid equals 1 atm. (12.5)

n-type semiconductor A semiconductor that employs negatively charged electrons in the conduction band as the charge carriers. (13.8)

nuclear binding energy The amount of energy that would be required to break apart the nucleus into its component nucleons. (21.8)

nuclear equation An equation that represents nuclear processes such as radioactivity. (21.3)

nuclear fission The splitting of the nucleus of an atom, resulting in a tremendous release of energy. (21.7)

nuclear fusion The combination of two light nuclei to form a heavier one. (21.9)

nuclear theory The theory that most of the atom's mass and all of its positive charge are contained in a small, dense nucleus. (2.5)

nucleic acid A biological polymer composed of nucleotide units that carries genetic information. (23.6)

nucleons The particles that compose the nucleus and that are protons and neutrons. (21.4)

nucleotides The individual units composing nucleic acids; each consists of a phosphate group, a sugar, and a nitrogenous base. (23.6)

nucleus The very small, dense core of the atom that contains most of the atom's mass and all of its positive charge; composed of protons and neutrons. (2.5)

nuclide A particular isotope of an atom. (21.3)

octahedral geometry The molecular geometry of seven atoms with 90° bond angles. (11.2)

octahedral hole A space that exists in the middle of six atoms on two adjacent close-packed sheets of atoms in a crystal lattice. (25.4)

octet The eight dots around atoms in a Lewis structure that signify a filled outer electron shell for *s* and *p* block elements. (10.3)

octet rule The tendency for most bonded atoms to possess or share eight electrons in their outer shell to obtain stable electron configurations and lower their potential energy. (10.3)

optical isomers (enantiomers) Two molecules that are nonsuperimposable mirror images of one another. (22.3, 26.4)

orbital A probability distribution map, based on the quantum-mechanical model of the atom, used to describe the likely position of an electron in an atom; also, an allowed energy state for an electron. (8.5)

orbital diagram A diagram that gives information similar to an electron configuration but symbolizes an electron as an arrow in a box representing an orbital, with the arrow's direction denoting the electron's spin. (9.3)

ore A rock that contains a high concentration of a specific mineral. (25.2)

organic chemistry The study of carbon-based compounds. (22.1)

organic compound A compound composed of carbon and hydrogen and possibly a few other elements, including nitrogen, oxygen, and sulfur. (3.12)

organic molecule A molecule composed of carbon and hydrogen and a few other elements, including nitrogen, oxygen, or sulfur. (3.11, 22.1)

orientation factor A factor in collision theory (usually between 0 and 1) that represents the fraction of collisions having an orientation that can allow the reaction to occur. (15.5)

orthosilicates Silicates in which tetrahedral SO_4^{4-} ions stand alone. (24.3)

osmosis The flow of solvent from a solution of lower solute concentration to one of higher solute concentration. (14.6)

osmotic pressure The pressure required to stop osmotic flow. (14.6)

Ostwald process An industrial process used for commercial preparation of nitric acid. (24.6)

overall order The sum of the orders of all reactants in a chemical reaction; the sum of the exponents $(m+n)$ in the rate law equation: Rate $= k[A]^m[B]^n$. (15.3)

oxidation The loss of one or more electrons; also the gaining of oxygen or the loss of hydrogen. (5.9)

oxidation state (oxidation number) A positive or negative whole number that represents the "charge" an atom in a compound would have if all shared electrons were assigned to the atom with a greater attraction for those electrons. (5.9)

oxidation–reduction (redox) reaction Reactions in which electrons are transferred from one reactant to another and the oxidation states of certain atoms are changed. (5.9)

oxidizing agent A substance that causes the oxidation of another substance; an oxidizing agent gains electrons and is reduced. (5.9)

oxyacid An acid composed of hydrogen and an oxyanion. (3.6)

oxyanion A polyatomic anion containing oxygen and another element. (3.5)

oxygen toxicity A physiological condition caused by an increased level of oxygen in the blood, resulting in muscle twitching, tunnel vision, and convulsions. (6.6)

ozone O_3, an allotrope of oxygen that is a toxic blue diamagnetic gas with a strong odor. (24.7)

packing efficiency The percentage of volume of a unit cell occupied by the atoms, assumed to be spherical. (13.3)

paramagnetic The state of an atom or ion that contains unpaired electrons and is, therefore, attracted by an external magnetic field. (9.7)

partial pressure (P_n) The pressure due to any individual component in a gas mixture. (6.6)

parts by mass A unit for expressing solution concentration as the mass of the solute divided by the mass of the solution multiplied by a multiplication factor. (14.5)

parts by volume A unit for expressing solution concentration as the volume of the solute divided by the volume of the solution multiplied by a multiplication factor. (14.5)

parts per billion (ppb) A unit for expressing solution concentration in parts by mass in which the multiplication factor is 10^9. (14.5)

parts per million (ppm) A unit for expressing solution concentration in parts by mass in which the multiplication factor is 10^6. (14.5)

pascal (Pa) The SI unit of pressure, defined as 1 N/m^2. (6.2)

Pauli exclusion principle The principle that no two electrons in an atom can have the same four numbers. (9.3)

penetrating power The ability of radiation to penetrate matter. (21.3)

penetration The phenomenon of some higher-level atomic orbitals having significant amounts of probability within the space occupied by orbitals of lower energy level. For example, the 2*s* orbital penetrates into the 1*s* orbital. (9.3)

peptide bond The bond that forms between the amine end of one amino acid and the carboxylic end of another. (23.4)

percent by mass A unit for expressing solution concentration in parts by mass with a multiplication factor of 100%. (14.5)

percent ionic character The ratio of a bond's actual dipole moment to the dipole moment it would have if the electron were transferred completely from one atom to the other, multiplied by 100%. (10.6)

percent ionization The ratio of the ionized acid concentration to the initial acid concentration, multiplied by 100%. (17.6)

percent yield The percentage of the theoretical yield of a chemical reaction that is actually produced; the ratio of the actual yield to the theoretical yield multiplied by 100%. (4.4)

periodic law A law based on the observation that when the elements are arranged in order of increasing mass, certain sets of properties recur periodically. (2.7)

periodic property A property of an element that is predictable based on an element's position in the periodic table. (9.1)

permanent dipole A molecule with a permanent dipole always has a slightly negative charge at one end and a slightly positive charge at the other. (12.3)

pH The negative log of the concentration of H_3O^+ in a solution; the pH scale is a compact way to specify the acidity of a solution. (17.5)

phase With regard to waves and orbitals, the phase is the sign of the amplitude of the wave, which can be positive or negative. (8.6)

phase diagram A map of the state or *phase* of a substance as a function of pressure (on the *y*-axis) and temperature (on the *x*-axis). (12.8)

phenyl group A benzene ring treated as a substituent. (22.7)

phosphine PH_3; a colorless, poisonous gas that smells like decaying fish and has an oxidation state of −3 for phosphorus. (24.6)

phospholipid Compound similar in structure to a triglyceride but in which one fatty acid is replaced by a phosphate group. (23.2)

phosphorescence The long-lived emission of light that sometimes follows the absorption of light by certain atoms and molecules. (21.2)

photoelectric effect The observation that many metals emit electrons when light falls upon them. (8.2)

photon (quantum) The smallest possible packet of electromagnetic radiation with an energy equal to $h\nu$. (8.2)

physical change A change that alters only the state or appearance of a substance but not its chemical composition. (1.4)

physical property A property that a substance displays without changing its chemical composition. (1.4)

pi (π) bond The bond that forms between two *p* orbitals that overlap side to side. (11.7)

p–n junctions Tiny areas in electronic circuits that have p-type semiconductors on one side and n-type on the other. (13.8)

polar covalent bond A covalent bond between two atoms with significantly different electronegativities, resulting in an uneven distribution of electron density. (10.6)

polyatomic ion An ion composed of two or more atoms. (3.4)

polydentate A term that describes ligands that donate more than one electron pair to the central metal. (26.3)

polymer A long chain-like molecule composed of repeating units called monomers. (13.9)

polymorphs The different crystal structures that can sometimes exist for the same compound. (13.4)

polypeptide A chain of amino acids joined together by peptide bonds. (23.4)

polyprotic acid An acid that contains more than one ionizable proton and releases them sequentially. (5.7, 17.9)

polysaccharide A long, chainlike molecule composed of many monosaccharide units bonded together. (23.3)

Portland cement A powdered mixture consisting mostly of limestone ($CaCO_3$) and silica (SiO_2), with smaller amounts of alumina (Al_2O3), iron(III) oxide (Fe_2O_3), and gypsum ($CaSO_4 \cdot 2\,H_2O$). (13.7)

positron The particle released in positron emission; equal in mass to an electron but opposite in charge. (21.3)

positron emission The form of radioactive decay that occurs when an unstable nucleus emits a positron. (21.3)

positron emission tomography (PET) A specialized imaging technique that employs positron-emitting nuclides, such as fluorine-18, as a radiotracer. (21.12)

potential difference A measure of the difference in potential energy (usually in joules) per unit of charge (coulombs). (20.3)

potential energy The energy associated with the position or composition of an object. (1.5, 7.2)

powder metallurgy A process by which metallic components are made from powdered metal. (25.3)

precipitate A solid, insoluble ionic compound that forms in, and separates from, a solution. (5.5)

precipitation reaction A reaction in which a solid, insoluble product forms when two solutions are mixed. (5.5)

precision A term that refers to how close a series of measurements are to one another or how reproducible they are. (1.7)

prefix multipliers Multipliers that change the value of the unit by powers of ten. (1.6)

pressure A measure of force exerted per unit area; in chemistry, most commonly the force exerted by gas molecules as they strike the surfaces around them. (6.1)

pressure–volume work The work that occurs when a volume change takes place against an external pressure. (7.4)

primary structure The sequence of amino acids in a protein chain. (23.5)

primary valence The oxidation state on the central metal atom in a complex ion. (26.3)

principal level (shell) The group of orbitals with the same value of *n*. (8.5)

principal quantum number (*n*) An integer that specifies the overall size and energy of an orbital. The higher the quantum number *n*, the greater the average distance between the electron and the nucleus and the higher its energy. (8.5)

probability density The probability (per unit volume) of finding the electron at a point in space as expressed by a three-dimensional plot of the wave function squared (ψ^2). (8.6)

products The substances produced in a chemical reaction; they appear on the right-hand side of a chemical equation. (4.2)

proton A positively charged subatomic particle found in the nucleus of an atom. (2.5)

p-type semiconductor A semiconductor that employs positively charged "holes" in the valence band as the charge carriers. (13.8)

pure substance A substance made up of only one component and having invariant composition; the particles that compose a pure substance can be individual atoms or groups of atoms joined together. (1.3)

pyrometallurgy A technique of extractive metallurgy in which heat is used to extract a metal from its mineral. (25.3)

pyrosilicates Silicates in which two SO_4^{4-} tetrahedral ions share a corner. (24.3)

pyroxenes Silicates in which SO_4^{4-} tetrahedral ions bond together to form chains. (24.3)

qualitative analysis A systematic way to determine the ions present in an unknown solution. (18.7)

quantitative analysis A systematic way to determine the amounts of substances in a solution or mixture. (18.7)

quantum number One of four interrelated numbers that determine the shape and energy of orbitals, as specified by a solution of the Schrödinger equation. (8.5)

quantum-mechanical model A model that explains the behavior of absolutely small particles such as electrons and photons. (8.1)

quartz A silicate crystal that has a formula unit of SiO_2. (13.6, 24.3)

quaternary structure The way that subunits fit together in a multimeric protein. (23.5)

racemic mixture An equimolar mixture of two optical isomers that does not rotate the plane of polarization of light at all. (22.3)

radial distribution function A mathematical function (corresponding to a specific orbital) that represents the total probability of finding an electron within a thin spherical shell at a distance *r* from the nucleus. (8.6)

radio waves The form of electromagnetic radiation with the longest wavelengths and smallest energy. (8.2)

radioactive The state of those unstable atoms that emit subatomic particles or high-energy electromagnetic radiation. (21.1)

radioactivity The emission of subatomic particles or high-energy electromagnetic radiation by the unstable nuclei of certain atoms. (2.5, 21.1)

radiocarbon dating A form of radiometric dating based on the C-14 isotope. (21.6)

radiometric dating A technique used to estimate the age of rocks, fossils, or artifacts that depends on the presence of radioactive isotopes and their predictable decay with time. (21.6)

radiotracer A radioactive nuclide that has been attached to a compound or introduced into a mixture in order to track the movement of the compound or mixture within the body. (21.12)

random coil A section of a protein's secondary structure that has less regular patterns than α-helixes or β-pleated sheets. (23.5)

random error Error that has equal probability of being too high or too low. (1.7)

Raoult's law An equation used to determine the vapor pressure of a solution; $P_{soln} = \chi_{solv} P^{\circ}_{solv}$. (14.6)

rate constant (*k*) A constant of proportionality in the rate law. (15.3)

rate law A relationship between the rate of a reaction and the concentration of the reactants. (15.3)

rate-determining step The step in a reaction mechanism that occurs much more slowly than any of the other steps. (15.6)

reactants The starting substances of a chemical reaction; they appear on the left-hand side of a chemical equation. (4.2)

reaction intermediate A species that forms in one step of a reaction mechanism and is consumed in another. (15.6)

reaction mechanism A series of individual chemical steps by which an overall chemical reaction occurs. (15.6)

reaction order (*n*) A value in the rate law that determines how the rate depends on the concentration of the reactants. (15.3)

reaction quotient (Q_c) The ratio, at any point in the reaction, of the concentrations of the products of a reaction raised to their stoichiometric coefficients divided by the concentrations of the reactants raised to their stoichiometric coefficients. (16.7)

recrystallization A technique used to purify solids in which the solid is put into hot solvent until the solution is saturated; when the solution cools, the purified solute comes out of solution. (14.4)

red phosphorus An allotrope of phosphorus similar in structure to white phosphorus but in which one of the bonds between two phosphorus atoms in the tetrahedron is broken; red phosphorus is more stable than white. (24.6)

reducing agent A substance that causes the reduction of another substance; a reducing agent loses electrons and is oxidized. (5.9)

reduction The gaining of one or more electrons; also the gaining of hydrogen or the loss of oxygen. (5.9)

refining A process in which the crude material is purified. (25.3)

rem A unit of the dose of radiation exposure that stands for roentgen equivalent man, where a roentgen is defined as the amount of radiation that produces 2.58×10^{-4} C of charge per kg of air. (21.11)

resonance hybrid The actual structure of a molecule that is intermediate between two or more resonance structures. (10.8)

resonance structures Two or more valid Lewis structures that are shown with double-headed arrows between them to indicate that the actual structure of the molecule is intermediate between them. (10.8)

reversible As applied to a reaction, the ability to proceed in either the forward or the reverse direction. (16.2)

reversible process A process that reverses direction upon an infinitesimally small change in some property (such as temperature or pressure) related to the reaction. (19.4)

roasting Heating that causes a chemical reaction between a furnace atmosphere and a mineral in order to process ores. (25.3)

salt An ionic compound formed in a neutralization reaction by the replacement of an H^+ ion from the acid with a cation from the base. (5.7)

salt bridge An inverted, U-shaped tube containing a strong electrolyte (such as KNO_3) that connects two half-cells, allowing a flow of ions that neutralizes charge buildup. (20.3)

saturated fat A triglyceride with no double bonds in the hydrocarbon chain; saturated fats tend to be solid at room temperature. (23.2)

saturated hydrocarbon A hydrocarbon that is saturated (loaded to capacity) with hydrogen; a hydrocarbon containing no double bonds in the carbon chain. (22.4)

saturated solution A solution in which the dissolved solute is in dynamic equilibrium with any undissolved solute; any added solute will not dissolve in a saturated solution. (14.4)

scientific law A brief statement or equation that summarizes past observations and predicts future ones. (1.2)

scintillation counter A device that detects radioactivity using a material that emits ultraviolet or visible light in response to excitation by energetic particles. (21.5)

second (s) The SI standard unit of time, defined as the duration of 9,192,631,770 periods of the radiation emitted from a certain transition in a cesium-133 atom. (1.6)

second law of thermodynamics A law stating that for any spontaneous process, the entropy of the universe increases ($\Delta S_{univ} > 0$). (19.3)

secondary structure The regular periodic or repeating patterns in the arrangement of protein chains. (23.5)

secondary valence The number of molecules or ions directly bound to the metal atom in a complex ion; also called the *coordination number*. (26.3)

seesaw geometry The molecular geometry of a molecule with trigonal bipyramidal electron geometry and one lone pair in an axial position. (11.3)

selective precipitation A process involving the addition of a reagent to a solution that forms a precipitate with one of the dissolved ions but not the others. (18.6)

semiconductor A material with intermediate electrical conductivity that can be changed and controlled. (2.7)

semipermeable membrane A membrane that selectively allows some substances to pass through but not others. (14.6)

shielding The effect on an electron of repulsion by electrons in lower-energy orbitals that screen it from the full effects of nuclear charge. (9.3)

sigma (σ) bond The resulting bond that forms between a combination of any two *s*, *p*, or hybridized orbitals that overlap end to end. (11.7)

significant figures (significant digits) In any reported measurement, the non–place-holding digits (those that are not simply marking the decimal place) that indicate the precision of the measured quantity. (1.7)

silica A silicate crystal that has a formula unit of SiO_2; also called *quartz*. (13.6, 24.3)

silicates Network covalent atomic solids that contain silicon, oxygen, and various metal atoms. (13.6, 24.3)

simple cubic A unit cell that consists of a cube with one atom at each corner. (13.3)

slag In pyrometallurgy, the waste liquid solution that is formed between the flux and gangue; usually a silicate material. (25.3)

smelting A form of roasting in which the product is liquefied, which aids in separation. (25.3)

soda-lime glass A type of glass that is about 70% SiO_2 with the balance being mostly Na_2O and CaO. This type of glass is transparent to visible light (not ultraviolet) and has a high thermal expansion, but it is less expensive to make and form into desired shapes than vitreous silica. (13.7)

solid A state of matter in which atoms or molecules are packed close to one another in fixed locations with definite volume. (1.3)

solubility The amount of a substance that will dissolve in a given amount of solvent. (14.2)

solubility product constant (K_{sp}) The equilibrium expression for a chemical equation representing the dissolution of an ionic compound. (18.5)

soluble Being able to dissolve to a significant extent, usually in water. (5.4)

solute The minority component of a solution. (5.2, 14.1)

solution A homogeneous mixture of two substances. (5.2, 14.1)

solvent The majority component of a solution. (5.2, 14.1)

soot An amorphous form of carbon that forms during the incomplete combustion of hydrocarbons. (24.5)

space-filling molecular model A representation of a molecule in which atoms fill the space between each other to more closely represent how a molecule might appear if scaled to visible size. (3.3)

specific heat capacity (C_s) The amount of heat required to raise the temperature of 1 g of a substance by 1 °C. (7.4)

spectator ion Ions in a complete ionic equation that do not participate in the reaction and therefore remain in solution. (5.6)

spin quantum number (m_s) The fourth quantum number, which denotes the electron's spin as either ½ (up arrow) or −½ (down arrow). (8.5)

spontaneous process A process that occurs without ongoing outside intervention. (19.2)

square planar geometry The molecular geometry of a molecule with octahedral electron geometry and two lone pairs. (11.3)

square pyramidal geometry The molecular geometry of a molecule with octahedral electron geometry and one lone pair. (11.3)

standard cell potential (standard emf) (E°_{cell}) The cell potential for a system in standard states (solute concentration of 1 M and gaseous reactant partial pressure of 1 atm). (20.3)

standard electrode potential The potential of a half-cell in an electrochemical cell. (20.4)

standard enthalpy change (ΔH°) The change in enthalpy for a process when all reactants and products are in their standard states. (7.9)

standard enthalpy (heat) of formation (ΔH°_f) The change in enthalpy when 1 mol of a compound forms from its constituent elements in their standard states. (7.9)

standard entropy change for a reaction (ΔS°_{rxn}) The change in entropy for a process in which all reactants and products are in their standard states. (19.7)

standard free energy change (ΔG°_{rxn}) The change in free energy for a process when all reactants and products are in their standard states. (19.8)

standard hydrogen electrode (SHE) The half-cell consisting of an inert platinum electrode immersed in 1 M HCl with hydrogen gas at 1 atm bubbling through the solution; used as the standard of a cell potential of zero. (20.4)

standard molar entropy ($S°$) A measure of the energy dispersed into 1 mol of a substance at a particular temperature. (19.7)

standard state For a gas, the standard state is the pure gas at a pressure of exactly 1 atm; for a liquid or solid, the standard state is the pure substance in its most stable form at a pressure of 1 atm and the temperature of interest (often taken to be 25 °C); for a substance in solution, the standard state is a concentration of exactly 1 M. (7.9)

standard temperature and pressure (STP) The conditions of $T = 0°C$ (273 K) and $P = 1$ atm; used primarily in reference to a gas. (6.5)

starch A polysaccharide that consists of glucose units bonded together by α-glycosidic linkages; the main energy storage medium for plants. (23.3)

state A classification of the physical form of matter as a solid, liquid, or gas. (1.3)

state function A function whose value depends only on the state of the system, not on how the system got to that state. (7.3)

stereoisomers Molecules in which the atoms are bonded in the same order but have a different spatial arrangement. (22.3, 26.4)

steroid A lipid composed of four fused hydrocarbon rings. (23.2)

stock solution A highly concentrated form of a solution used in laboratories to make less concentrated solutions via dilution. (5.2)

stoichiometry The numerical relationships between amounts of reactants and products in a balanced chemical equation. (4.3)

strong acid An acid that completely ionizes in solution. (5.4, 17.4)

strong base A base that completely dissociates in solution. (17.7)

strong electrolyte A substance that completely dissociates into ions when dissolved in water. (5.4)

strong force Of the four fundamental forces of physics, the one that is the strongest but acts over the shortest distance; the strong force is responsible for holding the protons and neutrons together in the nucleus of an atom. (21.4)

strong-field complex A complex ion in which the crystal field splitting is large. (26.5)

structural formula A molecular formula that uses lines to represent covalent bonds and shows how the atoms in a molecule are connected or bonded to each other. (3.3, 22.3)

structural isomers Molecules with the same molecular formula but different structures. (22.3, 26.4)

sublevel (subshell) Those orbitals in the same principal level with the same value of n and l. (8.5)

sublimation The phase transition from solid to gas. (12.6)

substance A specific instance of matter. (1.3)

substitutional alloy An alloy in which one metal atom substitutes for another in the crystal structure. (25.4)

substrate The reactant molecule of a biochemical reaction that binds to an enzyme at the active site. (15.7)

supersaturated solution An unstable solution in which more than the equilibrium amount of solute is dissolved. (14.4)

surface tension The energy required to increase the surface area of a liquid by a unit amount; responsible for the tendency of liquids to minimize their surface area, giving rise to a membrane-like surface. (12.4)

surroundings In thermodynamics, everything in the universe that exists outside the system under investigation. (7.2)

system In thermodynamics, the portion of the universe that is singled out for investigation. (7.2)

systematic error Error that tends to be consistently either too high or too low. (1.7)

systematic name An official name for a compound, based on well-established rules, that can be determined by examining its chemical structure. (3.5)

temperature A measure of the average kinetic energy of the atoms or molecules that compose a sample of matter. (1.6)

termolecular An elementary step of a reaction in which three particles collide and go on to form products. (15.6)

tertiary structure The large-scale bends and folds produced by interactions between the R groups of amino acids that are separated by large distances in the linear sequence of a protein chain. (23.5)

tetrahedral geometry The molecular geometry of five atoms with 109.5° bond angles. (11.2)

tetrahedral hole A space that exists directly above the center point of three closest-packed metal atoms in one plane and a fourth metal located directly above the center point in the adjacent plane in a crystal lattice. (25.4)

theoretical yield The greatest possible amount of product that can be made in a chemical reaction based on the amount of limiting reactant. (4.4)

theory A proposed explanation for observations and laws, based on well-established and tested hypotheses, that presents a model for the way nature is and tries to show not merely what nature does but why. (1.2)

thermal energy A type of kinetic energy associated with the temperature of an object, arising from the motion of individual atoms or molecules in the object; see also **heat**. (1.5, 7.2)

thermal equilibrium The point at which there is no additional net transfer of heat between a system and its surroundings. (7.4)

thermochemistry The study of the relationship between chemistry and energy. (7.1)

thermodynamics The general study of energy and its interconversions. (7.3)

thermoluminescent dosimeter A device used to measure the dose of radiation to which a person is exposed. (21.5)

third law of thermodynamics The law stating that the entropy of a perfect crystal at absolute zero (0 K) is zero. (19.7)

titration A laboratory procedure in which a substance in a solution of known concentration is reacted with another substance in a solution of unknown concentration in order to determine the unknown concentration; see also **acid–base titration**. (5.7)

torr A unit of pressure named after Evangelista Torricelli and equivalent to 1/760 of an atmosphere (atm). (6.2)

transition elements (transition metals) Those elements found in columns labeled with a number and the letter B in the periodic table whose properties tend to be less predictable based simply on their position in the table. (2.7)

transmutation The transformation of one element into another as a result of nuclear reactions. (21.10)

triglyceride Triesters composed of glycerol with three fatty acids attached. (23.2)

trigonal bipyramidal geometry The molecular geometry of six atoms with 120° bond angles between the three equatorial electron groups and 90° bond angles between the two axial electron groups and the trigonal plane. (11.2)

trigonal planar geometry The molecular geometry of four atoms with 120° bond angles in a plane. (11.2)

trigonal pyramidal geometry The molecular geometry of a molecule with tetrahedral electron geometry and one lone pair. (11.3)

triple bond The bond that forms when three electron pairs are shared between two atoms. (10.5)

triple point The unique set of conditions at which all three phases of a substance are equally stable and in equilibrium. (12.8)

triprotic acid An acid that contains three ionizable protons. (17.4)

T-shaped geometry The molecular geometry of a molecule with trigonal bipyramidal electron geometry and two lone pairs in axial positions. (11.3)

two-phase region The region between the two phases in a metal alloy phase diagram, where the amount of each phase depends on the composition of the alloy. (25.4)

Tyndall effect The scattering of light by a colloidal dispersion. (14.8)

ultraviolet (UV) radiation Electromagnetic radiation with slightly smaller wavelengths than visible light. (8.2)

unimolecular A term that describes a reaction involving only one particle that goes on to form products. (15.6)

unit cell The smallest divisible unit of a crystal that, when repeated in three dimensions, reproduces the entire crystal lattice. (13.3)

units Standard quantities used to specify measurements. (1.6)

unsaturated fat A triglyceride with one or more double bonds in the hydrocarbon chain; unsaturated fats tend to be liquid at room temperature. (23.2)

unsaturated hydrocarbon A hydrocarbon that is not loaded to capacity with hydrogen; a hydrocarbon that includes one or more double or triple bonds. (22.5)

unsaturated solution A solution containing less than the equilibrium amount of solute; any added solute will dissolve until equilibrium is reached. (14.4)

valence band In band theory, the band of energy levels that forms from bonding molecular orbitals. (13.8)

valence bond theory An advanced model of chemical bonding in which electrons reside in quantum-mechanical orbitals localized on individual atoms that are a hybridized blend of standard atomic orbitals; chemical bonds result from an overlap of these orbitals. (11.6)

valence electrons Those electrons that are important in chemical bonding. For main-group elements, the valence electrons are those in the outermost principal energy level. (9.4)

valence shell electron pair repulsion (VSEPR) theory A theory that allows prediction of the shapes of molecules based on the idea that electrons—either as lone pairs or as bonding pairs—repel one another. (11.2)

van der Waals equation The extrapolation of the ideal gas law that considers the effects of intermolecular forces and particle volume in a nonideal gas; $P + a\left(\frac{n}{V}\right)^2 \times (V - nb) = nRT$. (6.10)

van der Waals radius (nonbonding atomic radius) One-half the distance between the centers of adjacent, nonbonding atoms in a crystal. (9.6)

van't Hoff factor (*i*) The ratio of moles of particles in a solution to moles of formula units dissolved. (14.7)

vapor pressure The partial pressure of a vapor in dynamic equilibrium with its liquid. (6.6, 12.5)

vapor pressure lowering (ΔP) The change in vapor pressure that occurs in pure substance upon addition of a solute. (14.6)

vaporization The phase transition from liquid to gas. (12.5)

viscosity A measure of the resistance of a liquid to flow. (12.4)

visible light Those frequencies of electromagnetic radiation that can be detected by the human eye. (8.2)

vitreous (or fused) silica A type of glass that is hard, resists high temperatures, has a low thermal expansion, and is transparent to both visible light and ultraviolet light. (13.7)

volatile Tending to vaporize easily. (1.3, 12.5)

volt The SI unit of potential difference; defined as 1 J/C. (20.3)

voltaic (galvanic) cell An electrochemical cell that produces electrical current from a spontaneous chemical reaction. (20.3)

volume (*V*) A measure of space. Any unit of length, when cubed (raised to the third power), becomes a unit of volume. (1.6)

washing soda The hydrated crystal of sodium carbonate, $Na_2CO_3 \cdot 10\,H_2O$. (24.5)

wave function (*ψ*) A mathematical function that describes the wavelike nature of the electron. (8.5)

wavelength (*λ*) The distance between adjacent crests of a wave. (8.2)

weak acid An acid that does not completely ionize in water. (5.4, 17.4)

weak base A base that only partially ionizes in water. (17.7)

weak electrolyte A substance that does not completely ionize in water and only weakly conducts electricity in solution. (5.4)

weak-field complex A complex ion in which the crystal field splitting is small. (26.5)

white phosphorus An unstable allotrope of phosphorus consisting of P_4 molecules in a tetrahedral shape, with the phosphorus atoms at the corners of the tetrahedron. (24.6)

work (*w*) The action of a force through a distance. (1.5, 7.2)

X-ray Electromagnetic radiation with wavelengths slightly longer than those of gamma rays; used to image bones and internal organs. (8.2)

X-ray crystallography The process of using X-ray diffraction to determine the structure of a crystal. (13.2)

X-ray diffraction A powerful laboratory technique that allows for determining the arrangement of atoms in a crystal and for measuring the distance between them. (13.2)

Photo and Text Credits

Cover "Motorized Molecules Drill Through Cells" Rice University News and Media, August 30, 2017. **Chapter 1** Page 2: Einstein, Albert. "Physics and Reality" (1936). Ideas and Opinions. Trans. Sonja Bargmann. New York: Bonanza, 1954. Page 3: Lavoisier, Antoine. Elements of Chemistry: In a New Systematic Order, Containing All the Modern Discoveries. Trans. Robert Kerr. William Creech, (1796). Page 3: madbit/123rf. Page 3: MeteeChaicharoen/Shutterstock. Page 3: Tomas Abad/Alamy Stock Photo. Page 5: Thomas Samuel Kuhn (1962). "The Structure of Scientific Revolutions" University of Chicago Press. Page 6: madbit/123rf. Page 7: Al Messerschmidt/Getty Images. Page 7: DenisLarkin/Getty Images. Page 7: Sezeryadigar/Getty Images. Page 7: YinYang/Getty Images. Page 9: Michael Dalton/Fundamental Photographs. Page 10: xpixel/Shutterstock. Page 11: Charles D. Winters/Science Source. Page 11: Clark Brennan/Alamy. Page 11: Renn Valo. Page 12: Phovoir/Shutterstock. Page 14: "Mars Climate orbiter failure board release report, numerous NASA actions underway in response," NASA, (Nov. 10, 1999). Page 14: JPL History/NASA. Page 14: ostill/Shutterstock. Page 14: Pixel_Squid/Getty Images. Page 14: Richard Megna/Fundamental Photographs. Page 14: Siede Preis/Getty Images. Page 16: Byron W. Moore/Shutterstock. Page 16: Kevin Carden/Fotolia. Page 16: Marty Honig/Getty Images. Page 16: Monkey Business Images/Shutterstock. Page 20: lukovic photography/Shutterstock. Page 20: Teguh Mujiono/Alamy Stock Vector. Page 21: Richard Megna/Fundamental Photographs. Page 21: Richard Megna/Fundamental Photographs. Page 21: Richard Megna/Fundamental Photographs. Page 21: Stacey Stambaugh. Page 34: Retrieved from: https://www.esrl.noaa.gov/gmd/ccgg/trends/data.html, ftp://aftp.cmdl.noaa.gov/products/trends/co2/co2_mm_mlo.txt. Page 41: Richard Megna/Fundamental Photographs. Page 41: Richard Megna/Fundamental Photographs. Page 41: zoom-zoom/Getty Images. Page 42: Stacey Stambaugh. Page 42: Stacey Stambaugh. Page 42: Stacey Stambaugh. Page 42: Stacey Stambaugh/Pearson Education. Page 42: Warren Rosenberg/Fundamentals Photographs. Page 42: Warren Rosenberg/Fundamentals Photographs. Page 45: Dana Berry, SkyWorks Digital/NASA. **Chapter 2** Page 48: John Dalton (1808). "A New System of Chemical Philosophy" W. Dawson, vol. 1. Page 48: The Natural History Museum/Alamy Stock Photo. Page 50: J Stroscio, R. Celotta/NIST. Page 50: Nobelprize.org. Page 51: Democritus of Abdera. Diogenes Laertius IX, 44. Trans. R. D. Hicks (1925), Vol. 2, 453–5. Page 52: Charles D. Winters/Science Source. Page 52: Charles D. Winters/Science Source. Page 52: Joseph Calev/Shutterstock. Page 54: John Dalton (1808). "A New System of Chemical Philosophy" W. Dawson, vol. 1. Page 54: Richard Phillips Feynman (1994). "Six Easy Pieces: Essentials of Physics Explained by Its Most Brilliant Teacher" Perseus Book Group. Page 55: Richard Megna/Fundamental Photographs. Page 56: Thomson, J. J. (1897). Philosophical Magazine. On cathode rays, 44, 293–317. Page 58: Edward Neville da Costa Andrade/Peter Smith Pub Inc. Page 59: Richard Megna/Fundamental Photographs. Page 60: Jeremy Woodhouse/Getty Images. Page 60: Marijus Auruskevicius/Shutterstock. Page 60: puttapong jitrakyad/Shutterstock. Page 62: Library of Congress. Page 64: NASA. Page 65: Dmitri Mendeleev's Principle in Periodic Law. Page 66: Martyn F. Chillmaid/Science Source. Page 66: Olga Popova/Shutterstock. Page 66: Richard Megna/Fundamental Photographs. Page 67: Charles D. Winters/Science Source. Page 67: Charles D. Winters/Science Source. Page 67: Clive Streeter/Getty Images. Page 67: Eric Schrader/Fundamental Photographs. Page 67: Jeff J Daly/Alamy Stock Photo. Page 67: Matthias Zepper. Page 67: Perennou Nuridsa/Science Source. Page 67: PjrStudio/Alamy Stock Photo. Page 67: Steffen Foerster/Shutterstock. Page 67: Tom Grundy/Shutterstock. Page 67: Vastram/Shutterstock. Page 68: Charles D. Winters/Science Source. Page 68: Charles D. Winters/Science Source. Page 72: Copyright 2018 International Union of Pure Applied Chemistry. Page 72: IUPAC. Pure Appl. Chem. 2011, 83(2), 359–396. Page 74: marekuliasz/Shutterstock. Page 74: Stacey Stambaugh. Page 85: Joseph Stroscio and Robert Celotta/NIST. **Chapter 3** Page 90: Francis Crick (1988). "What Mad Pursuit: A Personal View of Scientific Discovery" Basics Books. Page 92: malerapaso/Getty Images. Page 93: Charles D. Winters/Science Source. Page 93: Charles Falco/Science Source. Page 93: Richard Megna/Fundamental Photographs. Page 98: Charles D. Winters/Science Source. Page 98: Charles Falco/Science Source. Page 99: Stacey Stambaugh. Page 100: Basement Stock/Alamy Stock Photo. Page 100: David Nelson/Alamy Stock Photo. Page 100: razorpix/Alamy Stock Photo. Page 100: Sidney Moulds/Science Source. Page 105: Richard Megna/Fundamental Photographs. Page 105: Richard Megna/Fundamental Photographs. Page 107: Elena Schweitzer/Shutterstock. Page 107: Richard Megna/Fundamental Photographs. Page 108: Andre Jenny Stock Connection Worldwide/Newscom. Page 108: Richard Megna/Fundamental Photographs. Page 113: NASA. Page 115: Richard Megna/Fundamental Photographs. Page 118: David R. Frazier Photolibrary, Inc./Alamy Stock Photo. Page 123: Sinelev/Shutterstock. Page 124: lightpoet/Fotolia. Page 126: Basement Stock/Alamy Stock Photo. **Chapter 4** Page 138: Linus Pauling (1995). Ed. Barbara Marinacci, "Linus Pauling in His Own Words: Selected Writings, Speeches, and Interviews." Simon & Schuster. Page 156: Andrew Lambert/Science Source. Page 157: Richard Megna/Fundamental Photographs. Page 157: Richard Megna/Fundamental Photographs. Page 157: Richard Megna/Fundamental Photographs. Page 157: Richard Megna/Fundamental Photographs. **Chapter 5** Page 166: Karl Raimund Popper (1988). "The Open Universe: An Argument for Indeterminism" Psychology Press. Page 168: PGoodie76/Getty Images. Page 177: Richard Megna/Fundamental Photographs. Page 177: Richard Megna/Fundamental Photographs. Page 177: Richard Megna/Fundamental Photographs. Page 178: Richard Megna/Fundamental Photographs. Page 179: Martyn F. Chillmaid/Science Source. Page 180: Clive Streeter/Getty Images. Page 181: Richard Megna/Fundamental Photographs. Page 185: Chip Clark/Fundamental Photographs. Page 186: Richard Megna/Fundamental Photographs. Page 187: Richard Megna/Fundamental Photographs. Page 187: Richard Megna/Fundamental Photographs. Page 190: Richard Megna/Fundamental Photographs. Page 190: Richard Megna/Fundamental Photographs. Page 190: Richard Megna/Fundamental Photographs. Page 192: Richard Megna/Fundamental Photographs. Page 193: Charles D. Winters/Science Source. Page 193: Charles D. Winters/Science Source. Page 194: Richard Megna/Fundamental Photographs. Page 194: Richard Megna/Fundamental Photographs. Page 199: Philippe Regard/Getty Images. Page 199: Richard Megna/Fundamental Photographs. Page 199: Richard Megna/Fundamental Photographs. Page 199: Richard Megna/Fundamental Photographs. Page 200: Chris Cheadle/Getty Images. Page 204: Charles D. Winters/Science Source. Page 204: Chip Clark/Fundamental Photographs.

Page 208: FlintWaterStudy.org (2015) "Lead Results from Tap Water Sampling in Flint, MI during the Flint Water Crisis". **Chapter 6** Page 223: Renn Valo. Page 210: James Clerk Maxwell (1890). The Scientific Papers of James Clerk Maxwell, Vol. II. Cambridge: Cambridge University Press. Page 215: ERproductions Ltd/Getty Images. Page 220: Carlos Caetano/Shutterstock. Page 220: Richard Megna/Fundamental Photographs. Page 223: Renn Valo. Page 238: U.S. Environmental Protection Agency. Page 258: Chip Clark/Fundamental Photographs. Page 258: Chip Clark/Fundamental Photographs. Page 261: Holme Moss PROCLOUD Results, Centre for Atmospheric, http://www.cas.manchester.ac.uk/resprojects/holmemoss/results/fig2/. **Chapter 7** Page 282: Pearson Education, Inc. Page 262: Feynman, Richard (1964). The Feynman Lectures on Physics; Volume 1. U.S.A: Addison Wesley. ISBN 0-201-02115-3. Print. Page 263: Pearson Education, Inc. Page 265: Pearson Education, Inc. Page 265: Pearson Education, Inc. Page 265: Pearson Education, Inc. Page 265: Pearson Education, inc. Page 266: MOLPIX/Shutterstock. Page 273: Radoslaw Lecyk/Shutterstock. Page 282: Paul Hakimata/Alamy Stock Photo. Page 282: Pearson Education, Inc. Page 293: Richard Megna/Fundamental Photographs. Page 294: U.S. Energy Information Administration. Monthly Energy Review, October, 2017 (Percentages for the 2016 calendar year). Page 295: U.S. Energy Information Administration. Monthly Energy Review, October, 2017. Page 296: United States Environmental Protection Agency. Page 298: Kim Steele/Getty Images. Page 298: NOAA National Geophysical Data Center. Page 298: Sandia National Laboratories. Page 298: Sandia National Laboratories. Page 298: Sjo/Getty Images. Page 306: md8speed/Shutterstock. Page 306: Underworld/Fotolia. **Chapter 8** Page 323: Richard Megna/Fundamental Photographs. Page 310: Quoted in, John R. Gribbin (1984). "In search of Schrödinger's Cat: Quantum Physics and Reality" Bantam Books. Page 310: Quoted in, Werner Heisenberg (1971). "Physics and Beyond: Encounters and Conversartions" Allen and Unwin. Page 310: Science Source/Science Source. Page 310: William Hermanns, Albert Einstein (1983). "Einstein and the Poet: In Search of the Cosmic Man" Branden Press. Page 312: Erwin Schrödinger (1935). The present situation in quantum mechanics: A translation of Schrödinger's "Cat Paradox" paper, translated by John D. Trimmer (Oct. 10, 1980). Proceedings of the American Philosophical Society, Vol. 124, No. 5, Pages 323–338. Page 313: ExcellentPhoto/Getty Images. Page 315: Elena Elisseeva/Shutterstock. Page 315: Matthias Kulka/Getty Images. Page 316: Poznyakov/Shutterstock. Page 316: Sierra Pacific Innovations Corporation. Page 317: Bonita R. Cheshier/Shutterstock. Page 317: Snowleopard1/Getty Images. Page 322: Karin Hildebrand Lau/Shutterstock. Page 323: Wabash Instrument Corp./Fundamental Photographs. Page 324: Alexey Repka/Fotolia. Page 324: Pearson Education, Inc. Page 324: Phil Degginger/Science Source. Page 325: All the data for these spectra is courtesy of the National Institute of Standards and Technology. Page 325: All the data for these spectra is courtesy of the National Institute of Standards and Technology. Page 325: Andrew Lambert/Science Source. Page 325: Andrew Lambert/Science Source. Page 325: Andrew Lambert/Science Source. Page 325: Jerry Mason/Science Source. Page 328: Paul Adrien Maurice Dirac (1935). "The Principles of Quantum Mechanics" Oxford: The Claredon Press. Page 328: Segre Collection/Science Source. Page 330: Stephen Dunn/Getty Images. Page 331: Tim Sharp/Reuters. Page 349: Based on "Critical Wavelength & Broad Spectrum UV Protection" graph from Cosmetic and Plastic Surgery Specialists. Available at http://mycpss.com/critical-wavelength-broad-spectrum-uv-protection/?. **Chapter 9** Page 350: Isaac Asimov (1966). "From Earth to Heaven" Garden City, New York: Doubleday. Page 352: Repin, Ilya Yefimovich. Page 353: Charles D. Winters/Science Source. Page 353: Richard Megna/Fundamental Photographs. Page 381: Charles D. Winters/Science Source. Page 381: Charles D. Winters/Science Source. Page 381: Charles D. Winters/Science Source. Page 381: Dennis S.K. Collection. Page 381: Dorling Kindersley/Getty Images. Page 381: Enricoros. Page 381: Harry Taylor/Getty Images. Page 381: Jumk.de Webprojects. Page 381: Manamana/Shutterstock. Page 381: PjrStudio/Alamy Stock Photo. Page 381: Richard Megna/Fundamental Photographs. Page 381: Ted Kinsman/Science Source. **Chapter 10** Page 392: Karl Raimund Popper (1959). "The Logic of Scientific Discovery" Hutchinson. Page 394: Lawrence Berkeley National Laboratory/Science Source. Page 395: John A. Rizzo/Getty Images. Page 395: Madlen/Shutterstock. Page 395: Richard Megna/Fundamental Photographs. Page 403: Richard Megna/Fundamental Photographs. Page 403: Richard Megna/Fundamental Photographs. Page 419: Chubykin Arkady/Shutterstock. Page 419: Syda Productions/Shutterstock. Page 426: Demarco/Fotolia. Page 435: After C.S.G. Phillips, R. J. P Williams, Inorganic Chemistry, Volume 1, p. 179. **Chapter 11** Page 436: Thomas S. Kuhn (1962). "The Structure of Scientific Revolutions" Vol 2, Issue 2. University of Chicago Press, 1970. Print. Page 438: warrengoldswain /123rf. Page 440: Renn Valo. Page 440: Renn Valo. Page 440: Renn Valo. Page 441: Renn Valo. Page 441: Renn Valo. Page 454: blueee/Fotolia. Page 454: Kip Peticolas/Fundamental Photographs. Page 454: Richard Megna/Fundamental Photographs. Page 479: Richard Megna/Fundamental Photographs. **Chapter 12** Page 494: Quoted in, Philip Ball (1994). "Desinging the Molecular World: Chemistry at the Frontier" Princeton University Press. Page 495: NASA. Page 496: American Physical Society. Page 509: Doug4537/Getty Images. Page 510: Andrei Kuzmik/Shutterstock. Page 510: Stéphane Bidouze/Fotolia. Page 511: Constantin Iosif/Shutterstock. Page 512: Britta Pedersen/picture-alliance/dpa/AP Images. Page 512: Chip Clark/Fundamental Photographs. Page 512: Richard Megna/Fundamental Photographs. Page 514: Maridav/Fotolia. Page 518: Michael Dalton/Fundamental Photographs. Page 522: University of Nottingham. Page 523: Reika/Shutterstock. Page 525: CAN BALCIOGLU/Shutterstock. Page 525: krutar/Shutterstock. Page 525: taffpixture/Shutterstock. Page 529: David Ducros/Science Source. Page 530: Kristen Brochmann/Fundamental Photographs. Page 531: Finnbarr Webster/Alamy Stock Photo. Page 535: Harry Taylor/Getty Images. Page 535: Image Source/Getty Images. Page 535: Tro, Nivaldo Jose. **Chapter 13** Page 542: Ted Kinsman/Science Source. Page 540: Qouted in, Alan L. Mackay (1991). "A Dictionary of Scientific Quotations" CRC Press. Page 542: Ted Kinsman/Science Source. Page 544: Omikron/Science Source. Page 553: Andrew Syred/Science Source. Page 553: Mirka Moksha/Shutterstock. Page 553: showcake/Fotolia. Page 553: yurakp/Fotolia. Page 554: Nivaldo Jose Tro. Page 556: Baris Muratoglu/Getty Images. Page 556: Charles D. Winters/Science Source. Page 558: Alan Curtis/Alamy Stock Photo. Page 558: everything possible/Alamy Stock Photo. Page 559: Lijuan Guo/Fotolia. Page 560: Mathier/Getty Images. Page 561: Dea/A. Dagli Orti/Getty Images. Page 562: jmalov/Getty Images. Page 562: Nikada/Getty Images. Page 562: Richard Megna/Fundamental Photographs. Page 563: Johnny Franzen/Getty Images. Page 563: jwblinn/Shutterstock. Page 566: Comstock Images/Getty Images. Page 566: Luisa Leal Photography/Shutterstock. Page 568: Korta/Fotolia. **Chapter 14** Page 615: David M. Phillips/Getty Images. Page 579: François-Marie Raoult, Comptes Rendus 104, 1430–3 (May 23, 1887), translated by Henry M. Leicester, Herbert S. Klickstein (1952). "A Source Book in Chemistry, 1400–1900" Harvard University Press. Page 580: Mana Photo/Shutterstock. Page 581: Robert Sijan/Getty Images. Page 616: Richard Megna/Fundamental Photographs. Page 591: Richard Megna/Fundamental Photographs. Page 590: Richard Megna/Fundamental Photographs. Page 590: Richard Megna/Fundamental Photographs. Page 590: Richard Megna/Fundamental Photographs. Page 594: Bill Evans/USGS. Page 594: Eric BOUVET/Getty Images. Page 599: Gregory Johnston/Shutterstock. Page 599: Peter Gudella/Shutterstock. Page 599: Robert Brook/Alamy Stock Photo. Page 599: Stockholm Convention on Persistent Organic Pollutants. Page 601: ollo/

Getty Images. Page 608: Clark Brennan/Alamy Stock Photo. Page 611: Gerald A. DeBoer/Shutterstock. Page 615: David M. Phillips/ Getty Images. Page 615: David M. Phillips/Science Source. Page 616: iStock/Getty Images Plus. Page 592: Richard Megna/Fundamental Photographs. Page 616: RubberBall/Alamy Stock Photo. Page 617: alicat/Getty Images. Page 617: CostinT/Getty Images. Page 617: Eric Gevaert/Shutterstock. Page 617: nanjan/Getty Images. Page 617: Spencer Hopkins/Getty Images. Page 618: Inga Leksina/Alamy Stock Photo. Page 618: Kip Peticolas/Fundamental Photographs. **Chapter 15** Page 630: Hinshelwood, C. (1957). Chemical kinetics in the past few decades. Science, 125(3250), 679–682. Page 631: Quade/Pearson. Page 642: Data taken from EPA site (under section 602 of Clean Air Act). Page 663: EPA's National Air Trends. Page 663: Mark R. Schoeberl/NASA GSFC. Page 664: NASA Ozone Watch. Page 664: NASA Ozone Watch. Page 664: Ozone Hole Watch, May 11, 2017. https://ozonewatch.gsfc.nasa.gov/Scripts/big_image.php?date=2017-05-11&hem=S. Page 664: Ozone Hole Watch, September 11, 2017. https://ozonewatch.gsfc.nasa.gov/Scripts/big_image.php?date=2017-09-11&hem=S. **Chapter 16** Page 682: Cited in, Alfred James Lotka (1925). "Elements of Physical Biology" William & Wilkins Company, p. 284. Page 684: Courtesy of Kenneth Eward Illustration. Page 690: Vshivkova/Shutterstock. Page 711: Cited in, Alfred James Lotka (1925). "Elements of Physical Biology" William & Wilkins Company, p. 283. Page 717: Richard Megna/Fundamental Photographs. Page 717: Richard Megna/Fundamental Photographs. **Chapter 17** Page 730: James E. Huheey (1972). "Inorganic Chemnistry: Principles of Structure and Reactivity", Harper and Row. Page 733: Ivaylo Ivanov/Shutterstock. Page 733: Khomulo Anna/Shutterstock. Page 733: kovaleva_ka/Fotolia. Page 734: Stacey Stambaugh. Page 744: David M. Martin, M.D/Science Source. Page 758: Renn Valo. Page 773: Data from Americans use many types of energy, U.S Energy facts Explained, U.S Energy Information Administration. Retrieved from https://www.eia.gov/energyexplained/?page=us_energy_home. Page 774: Hydrogen ion Concentration as pH from Measurements made at the Central Analytical Laboratory, 205, National Atmospheric Deposition Program, National Trends Network, Retrieved from http://nadp.slh.wisc.edu/maplib/pdf/2015/pH_2015.pdf. Page 774: Karol Kozlowski/Shutterstock. Page 774: Richard Megna/Fundamental Photographs. Page 775: U.S. EPA Air Trends. Page 783: Eco Images/Getty Images. **Chapter 18** Page 790: Richard Megna/Fundamental Photographs. Page 786: Witt, O. N (1967) "Solubility," In J. W. Mellor (ed.) Mellor's Modern Inorganic Chemistry, p. 177. London: Longmans, Green & Company. Page 787: Quade/Pearson. Page 790: Richard Megna/Fundamental Photographs. Page 790: Richard Megna/Fundamental Photographs. Page 790: Richard Megna/Fundamental Photographs. Page 802: Ronen/Fotolia. Page 803: Richard Megna/Fundamental Photographs. Page 803: Richard Megna/Fundamental Photographs. Page 803: Richard Megna/Fundamental Photographs. Page 815: Chip Clark/Fundamental Photographs. Page 816: Richard Megna/Fundamental Photographs. Page 819: Bernhard Edmaier/Science Source. Page 819: Sheila Terry/Science Source. Page 822: Santi Rodriguez/Fotolia. Page 823: Charles D. Winters/Science Source. Page 823: Charles D. Winters/Science Source. Page 823: Richard Megna/Fundamental Photographs. Page 828: Charles D. Winters/Science Source. Page 828: Jerry Mason/Science Source. Page 828: Jerry Mason/Science Source. Page 828: Richard Megna/Fundamental Photographs. Page 828: Richard Megna/Fundamental Photographs. Page 833: Richard Megna/Fundamental Photographs. Page 833: Richard Megna/Fundamental Photographs. Page 833: Richard Megna/Fundamental Photographs. **Chapter 19** Page 846: Clausius, R. (1867). The Mechanical Theory of Heat, (ed.) T. A. Hirst. London: J. Van Voorst. Page 848: Filip Miletic/Shutterstock. Page 848: Luminis/Shutterstock. Page 849: Alan Curtis/Alamy Stock Photo. Page 849: BlackJack3D/ Getty Images. Page 851: paradoxdes/Fotolia. Page 851: Pulse/ Getty Images. Page 852: Daderot. Page 852: Richard Megna/Fundamental Photographs. Page 857: Jan Will/Fotolia. Page 878: Ryan McVay/Getty Images. **Chapter 20** Page 896: Originally, Gergory, R.A. (1918). "Discovery or The Spirit and Service of Science," Macmillan. Page 897: Astronaut Images/Getty Images. Page 898: ExcellentPhoto/Getty Images. Page 902: Richard Megna/Fundamental Photographs. Page 902: Richard Megna/Fundamental Photographs. Page 903: Alejandro Díaz Díez/Age Fotostock. Page 913: Richard Megna/Fundamental Photographs. Page 923: Rugged Studio/Shutterstock. Page 924: wojtek/Fotolia. Page 926: NielsDK imageBROKER/Newscom. Page 930: Charles D. Winters/ Science Source. Page 934: Alan Pappe/Getty Images. Page 934: Donovan Reese/Getty Images. Page 934: StockPhotosArt/Shutterstock. Page 935: busypix/Getty Images. Page 935: jazman/Shutterstock. **Chapter 21** Page 972: (i) The DIII-D National Fusion Facility is a Department of Energy user facility, operated by General Atomics under cooperative agreement DE-FC02-04ER54698 and (ii) Image Courtesy of General Atomics. © 2017 General Atomics. Page 949: AFP/Getty Images. Page 963: Antonio Calan ni/AP Photo. Page 961: Baz Ratner/Rueters. Page 978: Cordelia Molloy/Science Source. Page 966: Courtesy of Franklin D. Roosevelt Presidential Library and Museum. Page 957: Courtesy of United States Air Force. Page 986: Craig Ellenwood/Alamy Stock Photo. Page 978: D. Silbersweig/Science Source. Page 973: David Parker/Science Source. Page 973: DOE Photo/Alamy Stock Photo. Page 972: Fox Photos/Getty Images. Page 949: Klaus Guldbrandsen/Science Source. Page 978: LARRY MULVEHILL/Getty Images. Page 967: Marlee90/Getty Images. Page 948: Martin F. Chillmaid/ Science Source. Page 977: Newscom. Page 965: Pictorial Press Ltd/ Alamy Stock Photo. Page 958: Richard J Green/Getty Images. Page 948: Science History Images/Alamy Stock Photo. Page 962: Steve Smith/Shutterstock. Page 967: Stocktrek/Getty Images. Page 968: STR/Associated Press. Page 949: Eve Curie, (1937). "Madame Curie: A Biography," (trans.) Vincent Sheean, Double Day. Page 966: Letter to Franklin D. Roosevelt from Albert Einstein (Part 1). Page 976: Department of Health and Human Services, National Institutes of Health. **Chapter 22** Page 988: Avalon_Studio/Getty Images. Page 990: Eric Isselee/Shutterstock. Page 1003: John Casey/Fotolia. Page 1017: Lyudmila Suvorova/Shutterstock. Page 1008: Pearson Education, Inc. Page 991: Photos.com/Getty Images. Page 1002: pzAxe/Shutterstock. Page 988: Quoted in, Letter to Berzelius 28 January 1835, Alan L. Mackay (1991). "A Dictionary of Scientific Quotations" CRC Press. Page 1018: schankz/ Shutterstock. Page 1020: Tim UR/Fotolia. Page 1020: Yasonya/ Shuttestock. **Chapter 23** Page 1057: Adrian T. Summer/Getty Images. Page 1052: Eye of Science/Science Source. Page 1058: National Cancer Institute. Page 1041: studiomode/Alamy Stock Photo. Page 1041: Valentyn Volkov/Shutterstock. Page 1036: Speech of Francis Crick in Eagle pub at the University of Cambridge. Page 1038: European Journal of Biochemistry, Vol. 114, p. 653–661 (1981). **Chapter 24** Page 1076: Chip Clark/Fundamental Photographs. Page 1091: Courtesy of National Oceanic and Atmospheric Administration (NOAA). Page 1084: GUSTOIMAGES/SCIENCE PHOTO LIBRARY/Getty Images. Page 1082: Klikk/Fotolia. Page 1097: Martyn F. Chillmaid/Science Source. Page 1094: Richard Megna/Fundamental Photographs. Page 1076: SCIMAT/Science Source. Page 1094: W. Chadwick/ USGS. Page 1070: Fuller, Richard Buckminster (1963). "Ideas and Integrities: A Spontaneous Autobiographical Disclosure," Prentice-Hall, p. 75. **Chapter 25** Page 1111: Bjoern Wylezich/123RF. Page 1111: Bruno Barbier/robertharding/Alamy Stock Photo. Page 1115: Courtesy of the Metal Powder Industries Federation. Page 1125: Dirk Hoffmann/Fotolia. Page 1126: Eye of Science/Science Source. Page 1123: Joseph P. Sinnot/Fundamental Photographs. Page 1125: Lance Bellers/Shutterstock. Page 1122: Richard Megna/ Fundamental Photographs. Page 1125: scol22/Fotolia. Page 1110: SPL/Science Source. Page 1125: Vaclav Janousek/Fotolia. Page 1108: William Henry (1817). "The Elements of Experimental

Chemistry," Philadelphia: Webster. **Chapter 26** Page 1136: Asya Babushkina/Shutterstock. Page 1136: boykung/Shutterstock. Page 1136: Harry Taylor/Getty Images. Page 1136: Ileysen/Shutterstock. Page 1146: Richard Megna/Fundamental Photographs. Page 1146: Richard Megna/Fundamental Photographs. Page 1152: Richard Megna/Fundamental Photographs. Page 1152: Richard Megna/Fundamental Photographs. Page 1156: Richard Megna/Fundamental Photographs. Page 1152: Richard Megna/Fundamental Photographs. Page 1152: Richard Megna/Fundamental Photographs. Page 1136: sudjai banthaothuk/Shutterstock. Page 1134: Quoted in George B. Kauffman (1966). "Alfred Werner: Founder of Coordination Chemistry," Springer-Verlag.

Index

A

A. *See* ampere
A. *See* frequency factor; mass number
A. O. Smith Company, 1115
absolute concentration, 800, 802
absolute temperature scale (Kelvin scale), 15–16, 220
absolute zero, 219, 868
absorption spectra, 324–325
accuracy, 25–26
acetaldehyde (ethanal), 126, 1017–1019
acetate, 104
acetic acid
  acid ionization constant for, 739
  buffering by, 789, 790
  as carboxylic acid, 126
  double bonds in, 124
  formula and uses of, 1019
  reaction between salicylic acid and, 1021
  strength of, 177, 187, 738
  structure of, 733
  uses of, 732
acetone, 42, 126
  boiling point of, 514
  charge density plot for, 1019
  dipole–dipole force in, 502–503
  formation of, 1018
  heat of fusion of, 524
  heat of vaporization of, 514
  intermolecular forces in, 583
  as solvent, 584
  structure of, 1017
  volatility of, 513
acetonitrile, 651–652
acetylene (ethyne)
  from calcium carbide, 1082
  formula of, 125, 1004
  hybrid orbitals of, 465–466
  Lewis structure of, 990
  representations of, 97
  structure and properties of, 1003
  triple bonds in, 124
acetylide ion, 1082
acetylsalicylic acid, 489, 1021
acid(s). *See also* acid–base chemistry; acid–base titration
  amino. *See* amino acids
  binary, 108, 770
  carboxylic, 126, 733, 1019–1021
  dilution of, 171
  diprotic, 186, 737, 765, 768–769, 814
  fatty, 1038–1040
  inorganic nomenclature flowchart, 109–110
  metals dissolved in, 107, 913
  naming, 107–109
  nucleic. *See* nucleic acids
  oxyacids, 108–109, 771
  polyprotic, 186, 765–769, 814
  properties of, 734
  rusting promoted by, 934
  strong, 176, 177, 737, 745, 751–752, 803–807, 813
  weak. *See* weak acid(s)
acid anhydride, 1021
acid–base chemistry, 185–191, 730–785. *See also* buffers; pH
  acid–base properties of ions, 758–765
  acid ionization constant, 739–740
  acid rain, 773–775
  acid strength, 737–740, 770–771
  addition to buffer, 794–798
  Arrhenius model of, 186–188, 734–735
  autoionization of water, 740–742
  base solutions, 754–758
  Brønsted–Lowry model of, 735–737, 770, 772
  definitions of, 734–737
  heartburn and, 731–732
  Lewis model of, 772–773, 1079
  molecular structure, 770–771
  nature of, 732–734
  neutralization reactions, 1020–1021
  pOH and other p scales, 743–744
  polyprotic acids, 765–769
  salt solutions as acidic, basic, or neutral, 763–765
  writing equations, 188
acid–base titration, 803–817
  endpoint of, 814
  indicators, 189–191, 814–817
  of polyprotic acids, 814
  of strong acids with strong bases, 803–807
  titration/pH curve, 803–814
  of weak acids with strong bases, 808–813
  of weak bases with strong acids, 813
acid dissociation constant. *See* acid ionization constant(s) (K_a)
acidic solutions, 741, 742, 744, 899–900
acid ionization constant(s) (K_a), 739–740
  magnitude of, 740
  for polyprotic acids, 765–766
  for solutions with anions acting as weak bases, 760
  for weak acids, 745, 749
acidosis, 788
acid rain, 108, 148, 295, 773–775, 1096
acid rebound, 758
acid reflux, 731–732
acquired immune deficiency syndrome (AIDS), 393–394
actinides (inner transition elements), 362, 364–365
activated carbon (activated charcoal), 1081
activated complex (transition state), 651
activation energy (activation barrier), 651–655, 661
active metals, reaction of alcohols with, 1015
active site, 394, 438, 664, 666
activity series of metals, 198–201
actual yield, 150, 151
acute concern, acid rain as, 775
acute radiation damage, 974
addition polymers, 566
addition reactions, 1008–1009, 1018–1019
adducts, 772
adenine, 508, 509, 1055, 1056
adenosine triphosphate (ATP), 891
adhesive forces, 512
adipic acid, 567
Adventure Thru Inner Space (ride), 1–2
aerosols, 223, 617
AES (Auger electron spectroscopy), 347
AIDS (acquired immune deficiency syndrome), 393–394
air
  composition of dry, 226, 228, 229
  fractionation of, 1092
  separation with, 1112
air bags, automobile, 256
air pollution, 238, 295–296
alanine, 1047, 1048
alchemists, 972
alcohol(s), 126, 584, 1013–1016
alcoholic beverages, 1014
aldehydes, 126, 1013, 1016–1019, 1043
aldohexose, 1043
aldose, 1043
aldrin, 599
aliphatic hydrocarbons, 992. *See also* alkanes; alkenes; alkynes
aliquot, 636
alizarin, 817
alizarin yellow R, 817
alkali metals. *See* group 1A metals
alkaline batteries, 923
alkaline earth metals. *See* group 2A metals
alkaloids, 734
alkanes, 124, 992, 998–1002
  n-alkanes, 998–999
  boiling points of, 501–502
  naming, 999–1002
  reactions of, 1007–1008
  viscosity of, 511
Alka-Seltzer, 1084
alkenes, 124, 664, 992, 1002–1009
alkyl groups, 999–1000
alkynes, 124, 992, 1002–1009
allotropes, 869, 1078, 1085, 1094
alloys, 1110, 1116–1121
  copper, 1125, 1126
  interstitial, 1116, 1119–1121
  with limited solubility, 1118–1119
  nickel, 1126
  steel, 1122–1124
  substitutional, 1116–1118
  zinc, 1126
α-carbon, 1047
alpha (α) decay, 949–951, 954
α-helix, 1051, 1052
alpha (α) particles, 57, 58, 950
altitude, 268, 518
aluminosilicates, 562, 1075
aluminum, 62
  activity series of, 200
  density of, 19

aluminum (*cont.*)
from Hall process, 1114
ionization energies of, 378, 379
oxidation of, 934
specific heat of, 273
aluminum acetate, 764
aluminum-based antacids, 758
aluminum hydroxide, 832–833
aluminum ion, 773
aluminum nitrate, 764
aluminum oxide, 562, 1135
amides, 568, 1022
amines, 126, 755, 1013, 1022
amino acids, 432, 488
as building blocks of proteins, 1047–1050
and chymotrypsin, 666
and genetic code, 1056–1057
L-amino acids, 1049
peptide bonding between, 1049–1050
and proteins, 1038, 1059
uses of, 732
ammonia
in Brønsted–Lowry model, 735–736
buffer containing, 798
formation of, 152–154, 714–716, 1085
from Haber–Bosch process, 1086
Henry's law constants for, 593
hybrid orbitals in, 460
ionization of, 754–755
Lewis acid–base model and, 772
as ligand, 1141
molecular and electron geometry of, 442–443
molecular representation of, 97
nitrogen-to-hydrogen mass ratio of, 52–53
pH of, 742
reaction between boron trifluoride and, 772
reaction between silver ion and, 1141
reaction between silver ions and, 829
strength of, 187
uses of, 734
ammonium, 104, 191, 828
ammonium bromide, 764
ammonium chloride, 798
ammonium dichromate, 1123
ammonium nitrate, 104, 586, 1088
ammonium nitrite, 764
ammonium salts, 1022
amorphous solids, 6, 498, 542
ampere (A), 14, 903, 932
amphiboles, 1076, 1077
amphogel, 758
amphoteric substances, 735, 740, 832–833
amplifiers, 565
amplitude, 314
amu (atomic mass unit), 59
amylopectin, 1046
amylose, 1046
Andés, José, 167–168
anemia, sickle-cell, 1052, 1067
angle of reflection, 543
anglesite, 1114
angular momentum, orbital, 479
angular momentum quantum number (*l*), 331, 332, 337
anhydrous compounds, 105
aniline, 755, 842, 1011
anion(s), 64, 93
as conjugate base of acid, 759–760
electrolysis of cations and, 929–930
electron configuration and, 371
periodic table and, 68
radii of, 374
in salts, 763–764
as weak bases, 759–762
in weak diprotic acid solutions, 768–769
anionic ligands, 1143, 1144
anodes, 55
in batteries, 923–926
in electrolytic cell, 927–930
and standard electrode potential, 907
in voltaic cell, 904–905
antacids, 185, 732, 744, 758
Antarctica, ozone hole over, 113, 663, 664
anthracene, 1012
anthracite, 1081
antibodies, radioactively tagged, 947
antibonding orbitals, 472–474, 476, 477
antifluorite structure, 558
antifreeze, 608–611, 787–788
antimony, 66
antiparticles, 952
apatite, 1085
Appalachian red spruce, 108
appendicitis, 947–948
apples, pH of, 742
aqueous (*aq*), 107
aqueous ionic equilibrium, 786–845
acid–base titrations, 803–817
and antifreeze, 787–788
buffers, 788–802
complex ion equilibria, 829–833
pH curves, 803–814
precipitation, 823–826
qualitative chemical analysis, 826–828
solubility equilibria, 817–822
aqueous reactions, 166–209
acid–base, 185–191
enthalpy of reaction for, 285–286
equations for, 183–185
gas-evolution, 191–192
in molecular gastronomy, 167–168
oxidation–reduction, 193–201
precipitation, 179–183
solution concentration, 168–173
solution stoichiometry, 173–174
types of solutions and solubility, 175–179
aqueous solution(s), 581. *See also* acid–base chemistry; buffers; solubility equilibria
balancing redox reactions in, 898–901
concentration of, 168–173
defined, 168
electrolysis in, 930–931
electrolyte and nonelectrolyte, 175–177
heats of hydration and, 588–589
hydroxide and hydronium ions in, 740–741
of ionic compounds, 507
solubility of ionic compounds in, 177–179
standard entropies for, 870
stoichiometry of, 173–174
arachno-boranes, 1080
arc-melting, 1122
arginine, 1048
argon, 61
in air, 228, 229
as atomic solid, 555
ionization energies of, 379
molar volume under pressure, 247–248
on periodic table, 66
relative standard entropy, 870
spontaneous mixing of neon and, 582
van der Waals constants for, 248
Aristotle, 3, 51
aromatic hydrocarbons, 992, 1010–1012
Arrhenius, Svante, 186, 650, 734–735
Arrhenius acids and bases, 186–188, 734–735
Arrhenius equation, 650–656
activation energy, 651–655
collision model of, 655–656
defined, 650
exponential factor, 652
frequency factor, 651–655
two-point form of, 654
Arrhenius plots, 652–655
arsenic, 66
arsenic pentafluoride, 420, 466–467
asbestos, 1076
ascorbic acid, 766
Asimov, Isaac, 350
asparagine, 1048
aspartic acid, 1047, 1048
Aspidin, Joseph, 562
aspirin, 489, 744, 1021
atmosphere
air pollution and, 295–296
carbon dioxide in, 34
Earth's early, 1091
hydrocarbons released into, 419
nitrogen in, 1084
oxygen in, 1091
ozone in, 1093
atmosphere (atm), 213, 214
atom(s), 1–3, 48–89. *See also* periodic table; quantum-mechanical model of atom
Brownian motion of, 48–50
in chemical equations, 142
diamagnetic, 372
early ideas about, 51
electron, discovery of, 55–57
elements and, 50
humans and, 54
interaction energy of, 455–456
interactions among, 394–396
modern atomic theory, 51–55
molar mass, 73–78
moles and number of, 74, 76–77
nuclear theory of, 58
paramagnetic, 371
patterns in elements based on, 65–69
plum-pudding model of, 57, 58
properties of matter and, 0
radioactive, 948
size of. *See* atomic radius(-i)
structure of, 57–59
subatomic particles, 59–65
terminal, 410
atomic bomb, 965–967
atomic elements, 96, 99
atomic machines, 50
atomic mass, 69–73, 111
atomic mass unit (amu), 59
atomic number (*Z*), 60, 63, 949
atomic radius vs., 366–367
beta decay and, 951
electron capture and, 953
first ionization energy vs., 375
and nuclear stability, 956
positron emission and, 953
atomic orbitals, 333
atomic radius and, 366–367
degenerate, 355, 357
electron configurations and, 353–365
energy ordering of for multi-electron atoms, 357
hybridized. *See* Hybridization

linear combination of, 471–475
periodic table and, 362–363
phase of, 341–342
radial distribution functions for, 357
shapes of, 337–342
in valence bond theory, 455–457
atomic radius(-i), 366–370
atomic number vs., 366–367
effective nuclear charge and, 366–370
electronegativity and, 408
of main-group elements, 1072
periodic trends in, 366–370, 383
transition elements and, 369–370
of transition metals, 1138
and unit cell volume/edge length, 548–549
atomic solids, 553, 555–556, 558–561
atomic spectroscopy
Bohr model and, 322–325
described, 334–337
identifying elements with, 324–325
atomic theory, 4, 51–55
of Dalton, 54–55
and law of conservation of mass, 51–52
and law of definite proportions, 52–53, 55
and law of multiple proportions, 53–55
atomic weight, 69–73, 111
atomos, 48, 51
ATP (adenosine triphosphate), 891
atto prefix, 17
attractive strong force, 955
aufbau principle, 358
Auger electron spectroscopy (AES), 347
autoionization of water, 740–742
automobile air bags, 256
average rate of reaction, 634
Avogadro, Amedeo, 73, 221
Avogadro's law, 221–222, 240, 242
Avogadro's number, 73–74, 76
axial positions, 441, 444
azidothymidine (AZT), 1068
azimuthal quantum number, 331

B

Bacon, Francis, 51
bacterial infection, ulcers from, 744
baking powder, 1084
baking soda. *See* sodium bicarbonate
balanced chemical equations, 141–145, 898–901
bald eagles, DDT and, 599
ball-and-stick models, 96, 97
balloons, 220, 222
band gap, 564
band theory, 563–565, 1110
barium, 66, 323, 325
barium chloride hexahydrate, 105
barium fluoride, 818
barium hydroxide, 187, 754
barium sulfate, 403, 818
barometer, 213
base(s), 185. *See also* acid–base chemistry; acid–base titration
complementary, 509, 1056, 1058–1059
in DNA, 1055–1056
organic, 508–509
purine, 1055–1056
pyrimidine, 1055–1056
strong, 754, 756–757, 762, 803–814
weak, 754–757, 759–762, 788–789, 813
base ionization constant (K_b), 755, 760
base-pairing, in DNA, 509, 1056
basic research, 896
basic solutions, 741, 742, 900
battery(-ies), 877, 898, 922–926
Baumgartner, Felix, 211
bauxite, 1114
Bayer process, 1114
The Bazaar (restaurant), 167
Becquerel, Antoine-Henri, 57, 948–949
beer, pH of, 742
bent geometry, 443, 446, 449
benzaldehyde, 1017
benzene, 97, 482, 553–554, 609, 1010–1012
benzoic acid, 739
benzyl acetate, 989, 990
berkelium, 61
beryllium, 62
effective nuclear charge for, 369
electron configuration for, 359
incomplete octets of, 418
ionization energy of, 377–378
Lewis structure of, 396
MO diagram for, 475
molecular geometry, 439
orbital diagram for, 359
beryllium aluminum silicate crystals, 1135–1136
beta (β) decay, 949, 951–952, 954
beta (β) particles, 57, 951
β-pleated sheet, 1051, 1053
bicarbonate ion, 732, 755, 758, 788, 802
bicarbonates, 104, 191
bidentate ligands, 1142
Big Bang Theory, 64
bimolecular elementary step, 657, 658
binary acids, 108, 770
binary compounds, 102–104
binary phase diagrams, 1117–1119
binding energy per nucleon, 970, 971
bioamplification, 598
biochemistry, 1036–1069
amino acids, 1038, 1047–1050
carbohydrates, 1043–1046
defined, 1038
diabetes and human insulin, 1037–1038
DNA replication, 1058–1060
lipids, 1038–1043
nucleic acids, 1054–1057
proteins, 1038, 1046–1057, 1059
biological effectiveness factor (RBE), 975
biological systems, 863, 875
biomolecules, 1156–1158
bisulfate (hydrogen sulfate), 104
bisulfite (hydrogen sulfite), 104, 191
bituminous coal, 1081
black holes, 45
black phosphorus, 1086
black smoker vents, 1091
bleached hair, 199
blood, human, 742, 788, 802
blood pressure, 215
blooming, 554
Blue Ribbon Commission on America's Nuclear Future, 968
body-centered cubic crystal structure, 548
body-centered cubic unit cell, 546–548
Bohr, Neils, 310, 323, 324
Bohr model, 322–325, 331, 339
boiling, 9
boiling point(s)
of *n*-alkanes, 501–502
defined, 517
dipole moment and, 503
of group 4A and 6A compounds, 506
of hydrides, 530
of molecular compounds, 405–406
of noble gases, 501
normal, 518
temperature dependence of, 517–518
of water at different altitudes, 518
boiling point elevation, 608–610
Boltzmann, Ludwig, 852
Boltzmann constant, 852
bomb calorimeter, 279–280
bond(s), 93–94, 392–493
AIDS drugs and models of, 393–394
covalent. *See* covalent bond(s)
double. *See* double bond(s)
electronegativity and, 406–410
electron sea model of, 396, 425–426, 555, 563, 1110
formation of, 394–396
hydrogen bonds vs., 505
ionic. *See* ionic bond(s)
and lattice energy, 398–403
Lewis model, 392, 394–398, 417–421, 462
Lewis structures, 392, 394–398, 410–417
metallic, 395, 396, 425–426, 555–556
molecular orbital theory, 392, 470–483
in morphine, 437–438
nonpolar, 450
peptide, 666, 1049–1050
pi, 462
polar, 406–410, 450–454, 770
rotation about, 463
sigma, 462
single, 95, 404, 422, 425, 464, 1006
strength of, 770
triple. *See* triple bond(s)
valence bond theory, 392, 455–470
VSEPR theory, 436, 438–454, 1099–1100
writing hybridization and bonding schemes, 467–470
bond energy(-ies), 407, 422–425, 455
bonding
of amino acids, 1049–1050
of carbon, 990–991
in coordination compounds, 1150–1155
ionization energies and, 379
bonding atomic radius (covalent radius), 366
bonding electrons, 404
bonding forces, 499–500
bonding orbitals, 472–474, 476, 477
bonding pairs, 404, 443
bonding theories of metals, 1110
bond length, 424–425, 456
bond order, 473–475, 478
bone density, 20
bone scan, 977
boranes, 1080
borax, 1078
boric oxide, 563
Born–Haber cycle, 398–401
boron, 1078–1080
boranes, 1080
boron–oxygen compounds, 1079

boron (*cont.*)
electron configuration for, 359
elemental, 1078–1079
incomplete octet formation by, 418, 420
ionization energy of, 377–378
Lewis structure of, 396
orbital diagram for, 359, 475–478
trihalides, 1079
boron nitride, 562, 1071–1072
boron trifluoride, 772
borosilicate glass, 563
Boy and His Atom, A (film), 50
Boyle, Robert, 51, 216
Boyle's law, 216–218, 221, 240, 242
Bragg's law, 543, 544
Brand, Henning, 1085
brass, 1125, 1126
breathalyzer, fuel-cell, 926
bridging hydrogens, 410
brochanite, 1125
bromate, 105
bromide, 102
bromine
ΔH_f° for compounds containing, 290
on periodic table, 66, 68
properties of, 1097
reaction between fluorine and, 157
reaction between potassium and, 656
bromine pentafluoride, 445
bromine trifluoride, 444
1-bromo-2-chlorobenzene, 1011
bromobenzene, 1010
bromocresol green, 817
bromocresol purple, 817
bromphenol blue, 817
bromthymol blue, 817
Brønsted–Lowry acids and bases, 735–737, 770, 772
bronze, 1125
Brown, Robert, 49–50
Brownian motion, 48–50, 616, 617
buckminsterfullerene, 559
buckyballs, 560
buffer capacity, 802
buffers, 788–802
action of, 796
calculating pH changes in solutions, 794–798
containing a base and its conjugate acid, 798–799
effectiveness of, 799–802
formation of, 789, 798
Henderson–Hasselbalch equation, 791–793
importance of, 786
pH of, 790–791
range for, 801–802
burning, 11
butanal, 1017
butane, 125, 142, 993, 998
butanoic acid, 1019
butanol, 584, 1014, 1018
butanone, 1017, 1018
butene, 1003, 1006
butyl substituent, 1000
1-butyne, 1004
butyric acid, 133, 1039

C

C (heat capacity), 272–274, 279
cadaverine, 1022
cadmium, 924
caffeine, 489, 522
cal (calorie), 266
Cal (Calorie), 266
calamine (zinc silicate), 1126
calcination, 1113
calcite, 100
calcium, 66, 69, 200, 290, 898
calcium acetate, 763
calcium-based antacids, 758
calcium borate, 1078
calcium carbide, 1082
calcium carbonate, 99, 100, 179, 818, 819, 822
calcium fluoride, 555, 817, 818, 820–821, 823
calcium hydroxide, 187, 754, 818
calcium nitrate, 763
calcium oxide, 102, 1082
calcium phosphate, 1090
calcium sulfate, 403, 818, 1096
calcium sulfate hemihydrate, 105
calculations, significant figures in, 23–25
californium, 973–974
calorie (cal), 266
Calorie (Cal), 266
calorimetry, 278–280, 285–286
cancer, 317, 974, 978, 1158
candela, 14
cannon, potato, 272
capillary action, 511–512
caproic acid, 1039
carbaloy, 1124
carbides, 1082–1083
carbohydrates, 1043–1046
carbon, 60, 66, 1081–1084. *See also* hydrocarbons; organic chemistry
activated, 1081
α-, 1047
amorphous, 1081–1082
carbides, 1082–1083
catenation tendency of, 990–992
chemistry of life and, 69
covalent bonds with, 990
double and triple bonds involving, 990–991
electron configuration for, 358, 359
ΔH_f° for compounds containing, 290
hybridization in, 458, 459
inorganic, 1081
Lewis structure of, 396
molar entropies of allotropes of, 869
as network covalent solid, 558–561
orbital diagram for, 358, 359, 477–478
organic compounds, 123–124
uniqueness of, 988, 990–992
carbon-12, 74, 75
carbon-14, 83, 678
carbon-14 dating, 961–962
carbonate(s), 104, 191, 774, 822, 1084
carbonate ion, 178, 179, 755
carbon black, 1082
carbon dioxide, 53, 1083. *See also* dry ice
in air, 228, 229
atmospheric, 296–297
chemical formula for, 94
formula mass of, 111
from fossil fuel combustion, 145–149, 156, 296–297
as greenhouse gas, 140
Henry's law constants for, 593
in Lake Nyos, 594
molar mass of, 111–112
molecular geometry of, 439, 451
phase diagrams of, 529
reaction between water and, 773, 774, 1158
solubility of, 591–592, 1083
stoichiometric determination of, 145–149
structural formula of, 95
supercritical, 522
van der Waals constants for, 248
from volcanoes, 147
carbon disulfide, 555
carbonic acid
in acid rain, 774, 788
and blood buffering system, 802
formation of, 1084
ionization constants for, 766
strength of, 738
uses of, 732
carbonic anhydrase, 802, 1156, 1158
carbonization, 1081
carbon monoxide
in air, 20–21, 34, 238
carbon dioxide vs., 53
in catalytic converter, 662
from combustion of fossil fuels, 296
as ligand, 1141
properties of, 1083–1084
reaction between hydroxyl radical and, 419
reaction between nitrogen dioxide and, 658–659
carbon nanotubes, 1071–1072
carbon oxides, 1083–1084
carbon skeleton formula, 993
carbon tetrachloride, 94, 248, 584, 609
carbonyl chloride (phosgene), 433, 679, 1084
carbonyl group, 1016, 1019
carbonyl sulfide, 1084
carboxylic acids, 126, 733, 1019–1021
Carlsbad Caverns National Park, 822
carnotite, 1111
cars, hybrid, 267
carvone, 1018
cassiterite, 1111
catalysis, 661–666
catalysts, 258, 1008, 1080
catalytic converters, 662–663
catenation, of carbon, 990–992
cathode rays, 55–56
cathode ray tubes, 55
cathodes, 55
in batteries, 923–926
in electrolytic cells, 927–930
and standard electrode potential, 907, 908
in voltaic cells, 904–905
cation(s), 64, 93
as conjugate acids, 762
as counterions, 762
electrolysis of anions and, 929–930
electron configuration and, 365, 371
as Lewis acids, 773
metal, 762–763
periodic table and, 68
radii of, 373
in salts, 763–764
as weak acids, 762–763
cell diagram, 905–906
cell potential (E_{cell}), 904, 917–922
cellular fluids, 580, 581
cellulose, 1045–1046
Celsius (°C) scale, 15–16
cement, 562–563
cementite, 1083
centipoise (cP), 511
centi prefix, 17
ceramics, 540, 561–563
cesium chloride, 401, 557
CFCs. *See* chlorofluorocarbons
Chadwick, James, 59
chain reaction, 965
chalcopyrite, 1114–1115, 1125
charcoal, 19, 1081
charge. *See* electrical charge
charge density plots, 1019
Charles, J. A. C., 219
Charles's law, 218–221, 238, 240

chelate, 1142
chelating agents, 1142, 1156
chemical analysis, coordination compounds used in, 1156
chemical bonds. *See* bond(s); bonding
chemical changes, 9–12. *See also* reaction(s)
chemical cold packs, 282
chemical energy, 13, 264
chemical equations. *See* equation(s)
chemical equilibrium, 683–729
  acid strength and, 737
  dynamic, 685–687
  equilibrium concentrations, 696–699, 701–710
  equilibrium constant, 688–699
  fetal hemoglobin and, 683–685
  heterogeneous, 695–696
  Le Châtelier's principle, 711–718
  reaction quotient, 699–701
chemical formula(s), 94–95
  combustion analysis, 121–123
  for compounds, 120–121
  conversion factors from, 116–117
  determining composition from, 117
  from experimental data, 118–123
  for ionic compounds, 100–101
  from mass percent composition, 114
chemical gradient, 351–352
chemical hand warmers, 263–264, 282
chemical kinetics. *See* reaction rate(s)
chemical potential, 849
chemical properties, 10
  and electron configurations, 359, 364–365
  and valence electrons, 359, 364–365
chemical quantities, 149–155
  in balanced chemical equations, 141–145
  limiting reactant, theoretical yield, percent yield, and reactant in excess, 149–155
  reaction stoichiometry, 145–149
chemical reactions. *See* reaction(s)
chemical sensors, 1134
chemical stoichiometry, 138
chemical symbols, 60–61
chemistry, defined, 2
Chernobyl nuclear accident (1986), 968
cherries, 167–168, 742
chile saltpeter, 1085, 1086
china (ceramic), 562
chiral complexes, 1149
chiral environments, 997
chirality, 996, 997, 1149
χ_{solute}. *See* mole fraction
chlorates, 104, 105, 1092
chlordane, 599
chloride ion, 374, 1141
chloride minerals, 1111
chlorides, 102, 409, 827
chlorine, 60–62, 68
  atomic mass of, 69–70
  catalytic ozone destruction and, 662–664
  electron affinity of, 379, 380
  electron configuration of, 364, 374
  electronegativity of, 408
  elemental, 1099
  ΔH_f° for compounds containing, 290
  ionization energies of, 376, 379
  Lewis structure of, 397, 404
  mass spectrum of, 71
  as molecular element, 98
  properties of, 92, 1097
  reaction between chlorine gas and, 998
  reaction between chloromethane and, 1007
  reaction between iron and, 157
  reaction between potassium and, 397
  van der Waals constants for, 248
chlorine dioxide, 1101
chlorine fluoride, 409
chlorine oxides, 1101
chlorite, 104, 105
1-chloro-3-ethylbenzene, 1011
chlorobenzene, 1010, 1012
chloroethane, 1007, 1008
chlorofluorocarbons (CFCs), 113, 135, 642, 663, 1093
chloroform, 583, 609
chloromethane, 1007
chlorophyll, 1156, 1158
chloropropane, 1009
chlorous acid, 739
chocolate, 554–555
cholesterol, 1042
chromate, 104, 1123
chromate ion, 1123
chromite, 1122
chromium, 66
  activity series of, 200
  cations formed by, 103
  in human body, 1156
  on phase diagrams, 1117–1118
  sources, properties, and products of, 1122–1123
chromium(III) bromide, 103
chromosomes, 1057
chymotrypsin, 666
cinnabar, 1111
cinnamaldehyde, 123, 1017
cisplatin, 1158
cis–trans (geometric) isomerism, 464, 1006–1007, 1147–1148
citric acid, 732, 733, 766, 1020
classical physics, 329–330
Clausius, Rudolf, 846
Clausius–Clapeyron equation, 518–521
Claus process, 1095
clays, 561
Clean Air Act, 20, 108, 296, 775
climate change, 139–140, 296–297
closest-packed crystal structures, 551–552, 555–556
closo-boranes, 1080
Clostridium botulinum, 1089
clouds, polar stratospheric, 663
cloud-to-ground lightning, 898
club soda, 581, 591
coal, 294, 295, 773–774, 1081
cobalt, 103, 1124
cobalt(II) chloride hexahydrate, 105
cobaltite, 1124
cocoa butter, 554–555
codon(s), 1057, 1059
coefficients, 141, 145
coffee, 734, 847, 848
coffee-cup calorimeters, 285–286
cohesive forces, 512
coke, 1081–1083
cold packs, chemical, 282
colemanite, 1078
collagen, 1051
colligative properties, 601–616
  defined, 601
  freezing point depression and boiling point elevation, 608–611
  medical solutions and, 615–616
  osmotic pressure, 611–613
  of strong electrolyte solutions, 613–616
  vapor pressure lowering, 602–603
  of volatile solutions, 605–607
collision(s), 239, 245–246, 248
collision frequency, 655–656
collision model, 239
colloids (colloidal dispersion), 616–618
color, 314–315
  absorption of light energy and, 1136, 1152
  complementary, 1152
  of complex ions, 1152–1153
  of gemstones, 1135–1136
coloring agents, 1156
color wheel, 1152
columbite, 1111
combustion (combustion reactions), 3, 121, 1092
  defined, 155
  fossil fuel, 139–140, 145–149, 294–298
  gasoline, 276–277
  hydrocarbon, 1007
  methane, 141–142, 151, 291–292, 419
  natural gas, 141, 155–156
  propane, 283–284
  writing and balancing equations for, 141–142, 155–156
combustion analysis, 121–123
common brass, 86
common ion effect, 790, 820–821
common names, 101
complementary bases, 509, 1056, 1058–1059
complementary colors, 1152
complementary properties, 329, 331
complete ionic equations, 183–185
complex carbohydrates, 1045–1046
complex ion(s), 829
  color of, crystal field strength and, 1152–1153
  common geometries of, 1143
  coordination compound and, 1140
  formulas of, 1144
  naming, 1143–1144
  valence bond model hybridization schemes in, 1150
complex ion equilibria, 829–833
composition
  of compounds, 113–118
  of dry air, 226, 228, 229
  of humans, 69
  of matter, 5
  and potential energy, 264
compound(s), 90–137
  anhydrous, 105
  atomic-level view of, 96–100
  binary, 102–104
  chemical formulas of, 118–123
  classification of, 97
  composition of, 113–118
  coordination. *See* coordination compound(s)
  defined, 7, 8
  elements vs., 90–93
  formula mass for, 111
  free energy of formation for, 873
  inorganic, 109–110, 123, 991

compound(s) (*cont.*)
insoluble, 178, 823
interhalogen, 157, 1099–1100
ionic. *See* ionic compound(s)
mixtures vs., 92
molar mass of, 111–112
mole concept for, 111–113
molecular. *See* molecular compound(s)
molecular formulas for, 120–121
nonstoichiometric, 576
organic. *See* organic compound(s)
Proust's observations on, 52
representing, 94–96
soluble, 177–179, 823
specific heat of, 273
standard enthalpy of formation for, 290
undergoing gas-evolution reactions, 191
compressibility, of gases, 6–7
concentrated energy, 847–848
concentrated solutions, 168, 169, 595, 602–603, 742
concentration(s). *See also* equilibrium concentration(s); equilibrium constant (*K*)
absolute, 800, 802
and buffer capacity, 802
and buffer effectiveness, 799–800
cell potential and, 917–922
equilibrium constant in terms of, 693–694
from first-order integrated rate law, 644–645
and half-life of reaction, 647
initial, 703–705, 707–710
Le Châtelier's principle on change in, 712–714
and reaction rate, 634, 637–642
relative, 799–800, 802
of solutions, 168–171, 594–601
time and, 642–649
concentration cells, 920–922
concentration units, converting between, 600–601
conceptual plan, 27, 28, 32
concrete, 563
condensation, 513, 514, 860, 1020–1022
condensation polymers, 567, 568
condensed states, 494, 499–509. *See also* liquid(s); solid(s)
conduction band, 564, 565
conductivity, 402–403, 565, 1125
conductors, 1110, 1111
cones, 464
conformation, protein, 1050–1054
coniine, 734
conjugate acid–base pairs, 736–737, 759, 762, 799–800
conservation
of energy, 12, 265, 848
of mass, 3–4, 51–52
constant-pressure calorimetry, 285–286
constant-volume calorimetry, 278–280, 286
constructive interference, 317, 319, 472, 543
consumer products, radiation exposure from, 976
contact process, 1097
contaminants, 531
continuous spectra, 323
contractile proteins, 1046
controlled disequilibrium, 690
coordinate covalent bonds, 420, 456, 1141, 1150
coordination compound(s), 1134, 1136, 1140–1158
applications of, 1155–1158
bonding in, 1150–1155
defined, 1140
naming, 1143–1145
structure and isomerization in, 1145–1150
coordination isomers, 1145
coordination numbers, 546–550, 555, 1140, 1143
Copernicus, Nicolaus, 51
copolymers, 567
copper, 66
activity series of, 198–200
cations formed by, 103
in concentration cells, 920–921
crystal structure of, 1117
density of, 19
ductility of, 426
in human body, 1156
nickel–copper alloy, 1116–1117
refinement of, 1114–1115
sources, properties, and products of, 1125
specific heat of, 273
copper electrolysis cell, 1115
copper ions, 199, 901–905, 918, 920–921
copper nitrate, 1089
copper(II) oxide, 103
copper plating, 932
copper(II) sulfate pentahydrate, 105
copper(II) sulfide, 818
core electrons, 361, 369
corrosion, 933–935, 1126
Coulomb's law, 332, 355–356, 368, 394, 395, 401, 499
counterions, 762, 1140
covalent bond(s), 93, 395, 396
carbon's tendency to form, 990
coordinate, 420, 456, 1141, 1150
directionality of, 405
double, 404
Lewis model of, 394–396
models vs. reality of, 405–406
polar and nonpolar, 406–408
shapes of atomic orbitals and, 337–342
single, 404
stability of, 94
triple, 405
covalent carbides, 1083
covalent radius (bonding atomic radius), 366
cP (centipoise), 511
o-cresolphthalein, 817
Crick, Francis H. C., 90, 509, 543, 1036, 1058
critical mass, 965
critical point, 521–522, 527–529
critical pressure (P_c), 522
critical temperature (T_c), 522
crucible, 562
crystal fields, 1136
crystal field splitting energy, 1152–1153
crystal field theory, 1134, 1151–1155
basic principles of, 1151
and color of complex ions, 1152–1153
defined, 1136
magnetic properties of transition metal complexes, 1153–1155
octahedral complexes in, 1151–1152
tetrahedral and square planar complexes, 1155
crystalline lattice, 93, 545
crystalline solid(s), 6, 498
fundamental types, 552–556
structures of, 556–561
unit cells, 545–552
X-ray crystallography of, 542–544
crystallography, X-ray, 393, 542–544
crystals, 563, 868
crystal structures, of metals, 1116
crystal violet, 817
C_s (specific heat capacity), 273, 530
cubic closest packing, 552
cubic measure, 18
cubic unit cells, 545–552
body-centered, 546–548
face-centered, 546, 549–550, 552
simple, 546–547
Curie, Marie Sklodowska, 57, 61, 62, 946, 949, 972
Curie, Pierre, 949
curium, 61, 62
current, 901–904
cyanato ligand, 1147
cyanide, 104
cyanide ions, 1141
cyanobacteria, 1091
cyano ligand, 1147
cycles per second (cycle/s), 314
cyclohexane, 124, 991
cyclooctasulfur, 1094
cyclotron, 972–974
cysteine, 1048
cytochrome c, 1156, 1157
cytosine, 508, 509, 1055, 1056

D

D (debye), 409
Dalton, John, 4, 48, 50, 51, 53–55, 61–62, 69
Dalton's law of partial pressures, 229–231, 240
data, identifying patterns in, 33–34
data analysis, 33–35
data gathering, integrity in, 26
data interpretation, 33–35
daughter nuclides, 950
Davisson–Germer experiment, 325
d block, periodic table, 362
DDT, 599
Dead Sea Scrolls, 961
de Broglie, Louis, 310, 325
de Broglie relation, 327
de Broglie wavelength, 327
debye (D), 409
decane, 993, 999
decanting, 9
deci prefix, 17
decomposition
of ozone, 419, 661–664
photo-, 419
standard heat of formation for, 291–292
of sugar vs. salt, 991
of water, 52, 298
decompression, risk of, 211–212
deep-freezing, 523
deep-sea diving, 231–232
definite proportions, law of, 52–53, 55
degenerate orbitals, 355, 357
dehydrating agents, 1097
dehydration reactions of alcohols, 1015
delocalization, 413, 471, 563
Democritus, 51
density(-ies)
of bone, 20
calculating, 19
as conversion factor, 30–31
of gases, 226–227
and pressure, 212
probability, 337–339
SI unit for, 18

deoxyribonucleic acid. *See* DNA
deoxyribose, 1055
deposition, 522
derived unit, 17–18
destructive interference, 318, 319, 472, 543
detergents, 1091
deterministic laws, 330
deuterium-tritium fusion reaction, 971
dextrorotatory isomer, 996
diabetes, 1037–1038
diagnostic medical procedures, radioactivity in, 977–978
diamagnetism, 372, 479, 1154
diamond, 3, 6
  conversion to graphite of, 849
  molar entropies of, 869
  as network covalent solid, 556, 558, 559
diastolic blood pressure, 215
diatomic molecule(s), 98
  bond lengths in, 425
  bond order of, 473
  heteronuclear, 480–482
  homonuclear, 475–480
diazomethane, 433
diborane, 410
dichlorobenzene, 1011
dichlorodifluoromethane, 642
1,2-dichloroethane, 463, 464, 1006–1008
1,2-dichlorotetrafluoroethane, 642
dichromate ions, 1123
dichromates, 104, 1123
dieldrin, 599
diethyl ether, 126
  boiling point of, 514
  Clausius–Clapeyron plot for, 519
  formula for, 1021
  freezing point depression/boiling point elevation constants for, 609
  heat of fusion for, 524
  heat of vaporization for, 514
  as solvent, 584
  uses of, 1022
differential rate law, 643. *See also* integrated rate law
diffraction, 318–319, 326–327, 542–544
diffraction patterns, 543
diffusion, 245
digestion, 666, 1041, 1045
dihydrogen phosphate, 104
dihydrogen sulfide (hydrogen sulfide), 456–457, 1094, 1095
dilute solutions, 168, 169, 594–595
dimensional analysis, 26
dimers, 567, 568
dimethyl ether, 505, 1021
dimethylglyoxime, 1156
dinitrogen monoxide (nitrous oxide), 106, 636, 1088
dinitrogen trioxide, 1088
2,4-dinitrophenol, 817
diodes, 565
diopside, 1076
dioxin, 599
dipeptides, 1049
dipolar ions, 1049
dipole–dipole forces, 502–505, 507, 508, 582, 583
dipole moment (μ), 408–409, 415, 451–453, 503
dipoles, 500, 502–503
dipropyl ether, 1022
diprotic acid(s), 186, 737, 765, 768–769, 814
Dirac, P. A. M., 310, 328
dirty dozen chemicals, 598–599
disaccharides, 1045
diseases, water quality and, 531
disequilibrium, controlled, 690
dispersion, colloidal, 616–618
dispersion forces, 500–502, 507, 508, 582, 583
disproportionation, 1089
dissociation, 175, 176, 769
dissociation constant for water. *See* ion product constant for water (K_w)
dissociation energy. *See* bond energy(-ies)
dissolution, 11, 850, 852, 870
distillation, 9, 627
disubstituted benzenes, 1011
disulfide linkages, 1052, 1053
diving, 216–217
DNA (deoxyribonucleic acid), 508–509, 544, 1054–1056, 1058
DNA polymerase, 1059
DNA replication, 1058–1060
DOE. *See* U.S. Department of Energy
doping, 565
Dörbereiner, Johann, 352
d orbitals, 333
  gemstone color and splitting of, 1135, 1136
  for octahedral complexes, 1151, 1152
  shapes of, 340, 341
  for square planar/tetrahedral complexes, 1155
dose, radiation, 975–976
double bond(s), 95, 404
  bond energy of, 422
  bond length of, 425
  carbon's ability to form, 990–991
  covalent, 404
  drawing Lewis structures with, 411
  hydrogenation of, 664
  in Lewis model, 462
  and molecular geometry, 439
  rotation about, 1006
  single bonds vs., 464, 1006
  sp^2 hybridization and, 460–464
  in structural formulas, 994
  in valence bond theory, 460–464
double helix, 1058–1059
double silicate chains, 1076
dowager's hump, 20
drugs (pharmaceuticals), 403, 554, 1158
dry-cell batteries, 922–923
dry ice, 11, 45, 98, 306, 523, 553, 1083
ductility, 66, 380, 426, 1110
duet, 396, 411
DuPont, 568
dynamic equilibrium
  concept of, 685–687
  defined, 685
  population analogy for, 686–687
  in solution, 590
  and vapor pressure, 515–521, 602
dyne, 45

E

E (first ionization energy), 375–378, 383
E (internal energy), 267–269, 272
E. coli, 978
ΔE. *See* internal energy change
EA. *See* electron affinity(-ies)
Eagle Nebula, 64
ears, pressure imbalance and, 213
Earth, 964–965, 1074, 1111
E_{cell} (cell potential), 904, 917–922
E°_{cell} (standard cell potential), 904, 914–917
ectotherms, 632
edge length, unit cell, 548
EDTA (ethylenediaminetetraacetate) ligand, 1141, 1142
effective nuclear charge (Z_{eff}), 356, 366–370
effusion, 245–246
egg-white lysozyme, 1052, 1057
egg whites, pH of, 742
eigenstates, 331
Einstein, Albert, 50, 51, 61, 310, 320, 321, 965–967, 969
einsteinium, 61
eka-aluminum, 353
eka-silicon, 66, 353
elastic collision, 239
eldrin, 599
electrical charge, 55
  of anode/cathode, 904
  in balanced redox reactions, 898
  distribution of, in water, 175
  of electrons, 56–57
  and movement of electrons, 897–898
  properties of, 55
  of subatomic particles, 59, 60
electrical current, 901–904
electrical resistivity, 1110, 1111
electric field, 55, 313
electricity
  driving chemical reactions with, 926–933
  fission for generation of, 967–968
electrochemical cell notation, 905–906
electrochemical cells, 901–906
  concentration cells, 920–922
  equilibrium constant for reactions in, 913–914, 916–917
  predicting spontaneous redox reactions and sketching, 912
  standard free energy change for, 913–915
  standard potential of, 905–910
  with standard vs. nonstandard conditions, 918
electrochemistry, 896–945
  balancing oxidation–reduction equations, 898–901
  batteries, 922–926
  cell potential, free energy, and the equilibrium constant, 913–917
  cell potential and concentration, 917–922
  corrosion, 933–935
  electrolysis, 926–933
  in lightning and batteries, 897–898
  standard electrode potentials, 905–913
  voltaic cells, 901–906
electrodes, 902, 905–906, 935. *See also* standard hydrogen electrode (SHE) half-cell
electrolysis, 926–933
  applications of, 927
  in electrometallurgy, 1114–1115
  predicting products of, 929–932
  of seawater, 1099
  stoichiometry of, 932–933
  of water, 927, 1092
electrolyte(s), 175–177
  rusting promoted by, 934

electrolyte(s) (*cont.*)
  strong, 176, 177, 613–616, 737
  weak, 177, 737
electrolyte solutions, 175–177
electrolytic cells, 902, 926–933
electromagnetic radiation, 313–314, 317, 952. *See also* light
electromagnetic spectrum, 315–317
electrometallurgy, 1114–1115
electromotive force (emf), 903
electron(s)
  bonding, 404
  charge of, 56–57, 59, 60
  core, 361, 369
  delocalization of, 413
  discovery of, 55–57
  electric charge and movement of, 897–898
  excitation of, 334–337
  ions and, 63–65
  Lewis acid–base model and, 772–773
  localization of, 413
  mass of, 55–56, 60, 311–312
  observation of, 311–312
  odd-electron species, 417, 418
  outermost, 369
  photon release by, 335
  position of, 329
  positrons and, 952
  redox reaction with partial transfer of, 193, 194
  shielding and penetration of, 356, 358
  symbol for, 950
  valence, 359, 361–365, 396–398
  velocity of, 329
  wave nature of, 325–331
electron affinity(-ies) (EA), 379–380, 383, 395
electron capture, 949, 953, 954
electron cloud, 500–501
electron configuration(s), 353–365
  chemical properties and, 359, 364–365
  electron spin and Pauli exclusion principle, 354–355
  inner, 359, 363–364
  of inner transition elements, 364–365
  and ion charge, 366
  and magnetic properties of ions, 371–372
  for multielectron atoms, 358–360
  orbital blocks in periodic table, 362–363
  order of electron removal vs. filling in, 371
  outer, 363–364
  sublevel energy splitting in multielectron atoms, 355–357
  of transition metals, 364–365, 1136–1137
  valence electrons, 361–365
  writing, from periodic table, 363–364
electron diffraction experiment, 326–327
electronegativity, 193, 406–410, 771, 1097, 1139
electronegativity difference (ΔEN), 408, 409
electron geometry, 442–447
  hybridization scheme from, 467–470
  linear, 446, 468
  octahedral, 445, 446, 468
  tetrahedral, 442–443, 446, 468
  trigonal bipyramidal, 444–446, 468
  trigonal planar, 446, 468
electron groups
  defined, 438
  five, 441
  four, 439–443
  hybridization scheme and, 467–470
  with lone pairs, 442–447
  and molecular geometry, 439, 447
  repulsion between, 438, 447
  six, 441
  three, 439
  two, 439
electron pairs, 443, 772
electron sea model, 396, 425–426, 555, 563, 1110
electron spin, 354–355
electron transfer, 395
electron volt (eV), 970
electrostatic forces, 55, 955
element(s). *See also* main-group elements; transition metal(s); *specific elements*
  absorption spectra of, 324–325
  atomic, 96, 99
  atomic-level view of, 96–100
  atomic mass of, 69–73
  atoms and, 50
  classification of, 97
  compounds vs., 90–93
  defined, 7, 8
  electron configurations for, 363–364
  emission spectra of, 322–325
  family (group) of, 66
  free energy of formation for, 873
  of life, 69
  molecular, 96, 98
  origin of, 64
  periodic table, 65–69
  proton number in, 60–61
  specific heat of, 273
  standard enthalpy of formation for, 289
  synthetic, 974
  transuranium, 974
elementary steps, 657–658
elimination reactions of alcohols, 1015
emeralds, color of, 1135–1136
emf (electromotive force), 903
emission spectra, 323–325
empirical formula molar mass, 120
empirical formulas, 94–95, 118–123
emulsion, 617
ΔEN (electronegativity difference), 408, 409
enantiomers, 996, 997, 1149
endorphins, 438
endothermic processes
  entropy changes in, 859, 861
  spontaneous, 850–852
  vaporization as, 514
endothermic reaction(s)
  bond energies and, 423
  equilibrium constant for, 716, 717
  exothermic vs., 281–283
  solution formation as, 586, 589
  spontaneity of, 865–866
endpoint, titration, 814
energy(-ies), 12–13. *See also* thermochemistry; *specific types*
  concentrated energy in nature, 847–848
  conservation of, 12, 265, 848
  conversion factors for, 267
  conversion of mass to, 969–971
  defined, 12, 264
  environment and use of, 294–298
  manifestations of, 264
  nature of, 264–266
  nuclear fusion as sun's source of, 971–972
  of photons, 320–321, 335
  "places" for, 857, 870
  and position, 331
  in solution formation, 586–587
  transfer of, 264–266
  units of, 267
  and wavelength/frequency, 321
energy bands, 563–565
energy diagrams, 268–269
engines, pressure–volume work by, 276–277
English system of measurement, 14
enthalpy(-ies) (*H*), 281–284, 850. *See also* bond energy(-ies); heat(s)
enthalpy change (Δ*H*)
  bond energies to estimate, 423–424
  and change in entropy for surroundings, 861–862
  in chemical reactions, 285–294
  defined, 281
  for exothermic vs. endothermic processes, 283
  magnitude/absolute value of, 589
  measuring, 285–286
  relationships involving, 286–289
  spontaneity and, 864–867
  standard, 289–294
  from standard heats of formation, 289–294
  stoichiometry involving, 283–284
  total energy change vs., 281
enthalpy of reaction (ΔH_{rxn}), 285–294
  from average bond energy, 423–424
  measuring, 285–286
  relationships involving, 286–289
  stoichiometry involving, 283–284
enthalpy of solution (ΔH_{soln}), 586–587
entropy(-ies) (*S*), 846, 852–863
  biological systems and, 863
  definition of, 582, 852
  microstates/macrostates and, 853–855
  at relative and absolute zero, 867–868
  relative standard, 868–870
  second law of thermodynamics and, 850–860
  solutions and, 582, 602–603
  units of, 858–859
  of universe, 860
entropy change (Δ*S*)
  in chemical reactions, 867–871
  effect on spontaneity, 864–867
  expansion of ideal gas and, 854–856
  heat transfer and, 858, 860–863
  sign of, 858
  state changes and, 856–860
  in surroundings, 860–863
  temperature and, 861
environment
  acid rain, 108, 773–775
  and energy use, 294–298
  free radicals and, 419
  Lake Nyos carbon dioxide accumulation, 594
  Lewis structure of ozone, 426
  persistent organic pollutants, 598–599
  renewable energy, 298
  water pollution, 531
enzymes, 632, 664–666, 1046
EPA. *See* U.S. Environmental Protection Agency
epsom salts (magnesium sulfate heptahydrate), 105

equation(s)
for acid–base reactions, 188
for aqueous reactions, 183–185
balancing, 898–901
coefficients as conversion factors, 235–236
complete ionic, 183–185
defined, 141
equilibrium constant and changes in, 691–692
for gas-evolution reactions, 192
molecular, 183, 184
net ionic, 184–185
nuclear, 950–953, 965
for oxidation–reduction reactions, 898–901
for precipitation reactions, 182–183
problems involving, 32–33
thermochemical, 283–284
writing and balancing, 141–145
equatorial positions, 441, 444
equilibrium(-a). *See also* aqueous ionic equilibrium; chemical equilibrium; dynamic equilibrium
complex ion, 829–833
controlled disequilibrium, 690
dynamic, 515–521, 590, 602, 685–687
free energy change of reaction under, 879
heterogeneous, 695–696
for pH changes in buffer solutions, 794–796
solubility, 786, 817–822
in solution(s), 589–593
thermal, 272
equilibrium bond length, 456
equilibrium concentration(s)
approximations with, 707–710
and equilibrium constants, 690, 696–699, 708–710
equilibrium constants from, 696–699
finding, 701–710
equilibrium constant (K), 688–695. *See also* acid ionization constant(s) (K_a)
chemical equations and, 691–692
defined, 682, 688
equilibrium concentrations and, 690, 696–699, 708–710
expressing, 688–689
for fetal vs. adult hemoglobin, 684
free energy and, 881–884
magnitude of, 690
reaction quotient vs., 699–701
for redox reaction, 916–917
significance of, 689
temperature and, 696, 883–884
in terms of concentrations, 693–694
in terms of pressure, 692–695
units of, 694
equivalence point, 189, 803–808, 814
Eriochrome black T, 817
errors, 26
erythrosin B, 817
ESA (European Space Agency), 529
esophageal sphincter, 732
ester(s), 126, 1013, 1019–1021
ester linkages, 1040
estimation, 21, 31–32
estradiol, 134, 1042
estrone, 134
ethanal (acetaldehyde), 126, 1017–1019
ethane, 503, 990, 998
ethanoic acid. *See* acetic acid
ethanol, 305, 581
breathalyzer to measure, 926
density of, 19
elimination reaction with, 1015
and ethylene glycol poisoning, 788
freezing point depression/boiling point elevation constants for, 609
hydrogen bonding in, 505–506
isopropyl alcohol vs., 126
oxidation of, 1015, 1018
reaction between hydrobromic acid and, 1015
reaction between oxygen and, 156
solubility of, 583–585
specific heat of, 273
structure and uses of, 1014
ethene
common uses of, 125
double bonds in, 124
formula of, 125, 1003
Lewis structure, 990–991
polymers using, 566
reaction between chlorine gas and, 998
reaction between hydrogen and, 656
space-filling model of, 125
structure and properties of, 1002
ethers, 126, 1013, 1021–1022
ethyl alcohol. *See* ethanol
ethylamine, 126, 755, 1022
ethylbenzene, 1010, 1012
ethyl butanoate, 1020
ethylene. *See* ethene
ethylenediamine ligand, 1141, 1142
ethylenediaminetetraacetate ion, 1156
ethylenediaminetetraacetate (EDTA) ligand, 1141, 1142
ethylene glycol, 42, 608–610, 787–788
ethylmethylamine, 1022
ethyl methyl ether, 1021
ethyl pentanoate, 1019
ethyl propanoate, 1019
ethyl propyl ether, 1022
ethyl substituent, 1000
ethyne. *See* acetylene
European Space Agency (ESA), 529
europium, 61
Eustace, Alan, 211–212
eV (electron volt), 970
evaporation, 514, 850, 851
exact numbers, 22–23
exa prefix, 17
exothermic process(es), 860–862
exothermic reaction(s)
bond energies and, 423
in chemical hand warmers, 264
endothermic vs., 282, 283
equilibrium constant for, 716, 717
solution formation as, 586, 589
spontaneity of, 864, 865
expanded octets, 411, 417, 420–421, 466
experiments, 3
explosives, 1089
exponential factor, 652
exposure, radiation, 974–976
extensive properties, 18
extractive metallurgy, 1112

F

F (Faraday's constant), 914, 932
face-centered cubic crystal structure, 549
face-centered cubic unit cell, 546, 549–550, 552
fac–mer isomerism, 1148
Fahrenheit (°F) scale, 15
falsifiability, 3
family(-ies)
of elements, 66. *See also specific groups*
of organic compounds, 126, 1013
Faraday, Michael, 896
Faraday's constant (F), 914, 932
fats, 1040–1041
fatty acids, 1038–1040
f block, periodic table, 362
FDA. *See* U.S. Food and Drug Administration
feldspar, 1074, 1077
femto prefix, 17
Fermi, Enrico, 965
ferrochrome, 1122
ferromagnetic materials, 1124
ferromanganese, 1124
fertilizers, 1086, 1089–1091
fetal hemoglobin (HbF), 683–685
fetuses, mercury exposure for, 118
Feynman, Richard P., 54, 262
fibrous proteins, 1050–1051, 1053
filtration, 9
fireworks, 324, 1089
first ionization energy (E), 375–378, 383
first law of thermodynamics, 267–272, 848
first-order integrated rate law, 642–644, 649
first-order reaction, 637–638, 649
first-order reaction half-life, 646–648
fish, methylmercury in, 118
fission, nuclear, 965–968
fixation, nitrogen, 1086
flame tests, 325, 828
flash freezing, 530
Flint, Michigan, 208–209
Flintstones, The (TV show), 219
fluids, 73, 522, 580, 581
fluoride, 102
fluoride ions, 371
fluorine, 64, 68
electron configuration of, 359, 371
electronegativity of, 407
elemental, 1098–1099
ΔH_f° for compounds containing, 290
Lewis structure of, 396
orbital diagram for, 359, 477–478
oxidation state for, 195
properties of, 1097
reaction between bromine and, 157
fluorine-18, 977
fluorite (CaF_2) structure, 557–558
fluoroapatite, 1097
fluorspar, 1097
flux, 1113
foam, 617
food, 978, 1089, 1091
food industry, 1091
f orbitals, 340–341
force(s). *See also* intermolecular force(s)
adhesive, 512
cohesive, 512
defined, 44
dispersion, 500–502, 507, 508, 582, 583
electromotive, 903
electrostatic, 55, 955
intramolecular, 405
nondirectional, 402
strong, 955
total, 241
vital, 991
forests, acid rain damage to, 108

formal charge, 410, 414–417
formaldehyde, 439, 503, 1016, 1017
formalin, 1017
formation constant (K_f), 829
formic acid (methanoic acid), 187, 433, 738, 739, 808–813, 1019–1020
formula mass, 111–113
formulas. *See* chemical formula(s)
formula unit, 98
fossil fuel combustion, 139–140, 145–149, 294–298
fossil fuels, acid rain and, 773–774
fossils, 961
fractionation, air, 1092
fragrances, 989–990
francium, 407
Franklin, Rosalind, 543
franklinite, 1126
Frasch process, 1094
free energy, 863–864, 876–877
free energy change of reaction (ΔG), 917
  calculating, 863–864
  under equilibrium conditions, 879
  under nonstandard conditions, 878–881
  standard, 871–884, 914–915, 917
free energy of formation ΔG_f°, 873–874
free radical(s), 418, 419, 433, 1008
freezer burn, 523
freezing, 523–524, 530, 860, 861
freezing point depression, 608–611, 614
frequency (ν), 314–316, 320, 321
frequency factor (A), 651–655
friction, 279
Friday night experiments, 541–542
frogs, antifreeze in, 611
fructose, 134
  conversion of sucrose to, 632, 636, 665
  glycosidic linkages of glucose and, 1045
  molecular formula for, 120
  structure and function of, 1043–1045
fuel(s), 663, 992. *See also* fossil fuel combustion
fuel-cell breathalyzer, 926
fuel cells, 298, 925–926
fuel-cell vehicles, 298
Fukushima Daiichi nuclear accident (2011), 968
Fuller, R. Buckminster, 559, 1070, 1072
fullerenes, 560
Fulton, Robert, 267
functional groups, 125–126, 1013
functionalized hydrocarbons, 125–126
furan, 599
fused silica, 563
fusion, 64, 523–524, 971–972. *See also* melting
fusion curve, 527–529

G

G (Gibbs free energy), 863–867
ΔG. *See* free energy change of reaction
galactose, 1045
galena, 1111
Galileo Galilei, 51
gallium, 66, 353, 378, 565
galvanic cells. *See* voltaic cells
galvanized nails, 935
galvanizing steel, 1126
gamma (γ) rays, 57, 316, 317, 949, 952, 954
gangue, 1112
garnet, 1136
gas(es), 210–261
  Avogadro's law, 221–222, 240, 242
  Boyle's law, 216–218, 221, 240, 242
  Charles's law, 218–221, 238, 240
  in chemical reactions, 235–238
  collecting, over water, 233–235
  compressibility of, 6–7
  entropy change associated with change in state of, 856–860
  greenhouse, 139–140
  ideal. *See* ideal gas(es)
  ideal gas law, 222–225
  kinetic molecular theory of, 238–244
  mean free path and effusion of, 245–246
  mixtures of, 228–235
  molecular comparison with other phases, 496–499
  natural, 294, 295
  noble. *See* noble gas(es)
  partial pressures, 228–235
  on phase diagram, 527–528
  pressure, 212–215
  real, 246–250
  relative standard entropies of, 868
  solubility in water, 591–593
  standard state for, 289, 867
  supersonic skydiving and, 211–212
gas chromatograph, 636
gaseous matter, 6–7
gaseous solutions, 581
gas-evolution reactions, 185, 191–192
gasoline, 13, 276–277, 847–848
gastric juice, pH of, 742
gastroesophageal reflux disease (GERD), 732
gauge pressure, 224, 254
Gay-Lussac's law, 223, 240
Geiger-Müller counter, 957–958
Geim, Andre, 541, 542
gemstones, 1135–1136
gene(s), 1038, 1056–1058, 1060
Genentech, 1038
genetic code, 1056–1057
genetic defects, 974–975
genetic structure, 1057
geodesic dome, 559
geometric isomerism, 464, 1006–1007, 1147–1148
geometry. *See* electron geometry; molecular geometry
GERD (gastroesophageal reflux disease), 732
German brass, 1126
germanium, 66, 353, 361
ΔG_f° (free energy of formation), 873–874
Gibbs free energy (*G*), 863–867. *See also* free energy change of reaction (ΔG)
gibbsite, 100
giga prefix, 17
given information, 28, 32
glass
  as amorphous solid, 6
  boron used in manufacture of, 1079
  density of, 19
  etching, 1099
  properties of, 563
  reaction between hydrofluoric acid and, 1099
  specific heat of, 273
glassblowing, 563
global climate change, 296–297
global warming, 140
globular proteins, 1051, 1053
glucose
  conversion of sucrose to, 632, 636, 665
  glycosidic linkages of fructose and, 1045
  molecular representation of, 97
  oxidation of, 875
  ring formation, 1044–1045
  structure and function of, 1043
glutamic acid, 1048
glutamine, 1048
glycerol, 42, 1040
glycine, 449, 1047, 1048, 1163
glycogen, 1045, 1046
glycolic acid, 788
glycolipids, 1041, 1042
glycosidic linkages, 1045, 1046
gold
  activity series of, 200
  conductivity and resistivity of, 1110
  as crystalline solid, 553
  density of, 18, 19
  electronegativity of, 1139
  from leaching process, 1113
  specific heat of, 273
gold foil experiment, 57–58
gout, 842
gradient, chemical, 351–352
Graham, Thomas, 245
Graham's law of effusion, 245–246
granite, specific heat of, 273
graphene, 541–542, 560
graphite, 3, 542, 556, 558, 849, 869
graphs, interpreting, 34–35
gravitational potential energy, 12
gravitational pull, 14
gravity, 495–496
greenhouse effect, 140
greenhouse gases, 139–140
ground state, 353
group 1A metals (alkali metals)
  defined, 66
  ion formation by, 68
  in nerve signal transmission, 351–352
  orbitals of, 362
  qualitative chemical analysis of, 828
  reactions of, 156–158
  reactivity of, 365
  as reducing agents, 197
group 2A metals (alkaline earth metals)
  defined, 66
  ion formation by, 68
  orbitals of, 362
  reactivity of, 365
  as reducing agents, 197
group 4A compounds, 506
group 5A elements, 195
group 6A compounds, 506, 770
group 6A elements, 195
group 7A elements. *See* halogens
group 7A hydrides, 770
group 8A elements. *See* noble gas(es)
groups, of elements, 66
ΔG_{rxn}°. *See* standard change in free energy
guanine, 508, 509, 1055, 1056

H

H. *See* enthalpy(-ies)
ΔH. *See* enthalpy change
ΔH° (standard enthalpy change), 289–294
H_3O^+. *See* hydronium ion; hydronium ion concentration

Haber, Fritz, 1086
Haber–Bosch process, 1086
Haber process, 892
Hahn, Otto, 965
hair, bleached, 199
half-cell potential, 905–908, 910
half-cells, 902
half-life, of reaction, 646–649, 959–960
half-reaction, activity series, 200
half-reaction method of balancing, 898–901
halides, 1079, 1089–1090
halite. *See* sodium chloride
Hall process, 1114
halogen oxides, 1100–1101
halogens, 68, 362, 1097–1101. *See also specific elements*
  boron–halogen compounds, 1079
  compounds containing, 1099–1101
  diatomic molecules formed by, 404
  electron affinities for, 380
  electronegativity of, 1097
  elemental, 1098–1099
  oxidation states of, 195, 1097, 1098
  reaction between phosphorus and, 1089–1090
  reactions of, 156–158
  reactivity of, 365
  single bonds between nitrogen and, 425
halogen substitution reactions, 1007–1008
Hamiltonian operator, 331
hand warmers, chemical, 263–264, 282
hard water, 179, 819
hardystonite, 1075
harpoon mechanism, 656
hausmannite, 1123
HbF (fetal hemoglobin), 683–685
HDPE (high-density polyethylene), 566
heartburn, 731–732
heat(s), 15, 272–276. *See also* enthalpy(-ies) (*H*)
  at constant volume, 279
  defined, 264, 272
  and entropy change, 858, 860–863
  in first law of thermodynamics, 270–272
  internal energy change and, 270–272
  as product or reactant in reaction, 716–718
  in reactions at constant pressure, 281–284
  in reversible processes, 859
  solutions and changes in, 285
  temperature vs., 272
  thermal energy transfer, 274–276
heat capacity (*C*), 272–274, 279
heat death, 848
heating curves, 518, 524–527
heat of fusion (ΔH_{fus}), 523–524
heat of hydration ($\Delta H_{hydration}$), 588–589
heat of reaction. *See* enthalpy of reaction (ΔH_{rxn})
heat of sublimation (ΔH_{sub}), 524
heat of vaporization (ΔH_{vap}), 514–515, 520, 524
heavy metal poisoning, medical treatment of, 1156
Heisenberg, Werner, 310, 329
Heisenberg's uncertainty principle, 329
heliox, 232
helium, 60, 61, 66
  as atomic element, 96
  bonding radii of, 367
  electron configuration of, 354, 396
  emission spectrum of, 322, 323
  Lewis structure of, 396
  MO diagram for, 473–474
  from nuclear fusion, 64
  in periodic table, 362
  real gas behavior of, 249
  van der Waals constants for, 248
  in water, Henry's law constants for, 593
helium ions, 368
hematite, 1111
heme, 1157
hemlock, 734
hemoglobin
  dispersal of, in blood, 618
  fetal (HbF), 683–685
  as globular protein, 1051
  oxygen-carrying site on, 1134, 1156–1158
  sickle-cell anemia and, 1052
  subunits, 1054
Henderson–Hasselbalch equation, 791–793
Henry, William, 1108
Henry's law, 593
Henry's law constant, 593
heptachlor, 599
heptane, 511, 583, 998, 999
2-heptanone, 1018
Hertz (Hz), 314
Hess's law, 287–289, 398, 587
heterogeneous catalysis, 663–664
heterogeneous equilibria, 695–696
heterogeneous mixtures, 7, 8
heteronuclear diatomic molecules, 480–482
hexaaminecobalt(II), 1153
hexaaminecobalt(III), 1153
hexachlorobenzene, 599
hexagonal closest packing, 551–552
hexagonal unit cells, 545
hexamethylenediamine, 567
hexane, 511, 583–585, 993, 998, 999
3-hexanone, 1017
1-hexene, 1003
hexose, 1043, 1045
1-hexyne, 1004
ΔH_f° (standard enthalpy of formation), 289–294
ΔH_{fus} (heat of fusion), 523–524
$\Delta H_{hydration}$ (heat of hydration), 588–589
high-density polyethylene (HDPE), 566
high-spin complexes, 1154–1155
Hinshelwood, Cyril N., 630
histidine, 1048
HIV (human immunodeficiency virus), 393–394
HIV protease, 393–394, 544
Hoffmann, Roald, 494, 512
homogeneous catalysis, 663–664
homogeneous mixtures, 7, 8. *See also* solution(s)
homonuclear diatomic molecules, 475–480
Hooke, Robert, 216
hormones, 1042, 1046
hot-air balloons, 220
ΔH_{rxn}. *See* enthalpy of reaction
ΔH_{rxn}° (standard enthalpy of reaction), 872–873
ΔH_{sub} (heat of sublimation), 524
Huheey, James E., 730
Human Genome Project, 1036, 1060
human immunodeficiency virus (HIV), 393–394
humans. *See also* medicine
  atoms and, 54
  blood of, 742, 788, 802
  elemental composition of, 69
  nerve cells of, 922
  transition metals in, 1156
Hund's rule, 358, 359, 1153
ΔH_{vap}. *See* heat of vaporization
Hwang Woo Suk, 26
hybrid cars, 267
hybridization, 413–414
  of atomic orbitals, 457–470
  and bonding schemes, 467–470
  defined, 457
  sp, 464–466, 468
  sp^2, 460–464, 468
  sp^3, 458–460, 468
  sp^3d and sp^3d^2, 466–467, 468
  writing hybridization and bonding schemes, 467–470
hybrid orbitals, 455, 457
hybrids, 458
hydrated ionic compounds, 105
hydrates, 105
hydration
  heat of ($\Delta H_{hydration}$), 588–589
  waters of, 105
hydrazine, 305, 1087
hydrides, 530, 770
hydrobromic acid, 108, 187, 737, 1015
hydrocarbons, 124–126, 992–1012
  aliphatic, 992
  alkanes, 124, 992, 998–1002
  alkenes and alkynes, 124, 992, 1002–1007
  aromatic, 992, 1010–1012
  in atmosphere, 419
  functional groups, 1013
  functionalized, 125–126
  names for, 124–125
  polarity of, 454
  reactions of, 1007–1009
  stereoisomerism and optical isomerism of, 995–997
  structures, 993–995
  uses of, 992, 999
  viscosity of, 511
hydrochloric acid
  in Arrhenius model, 735
  in Brønsted–Lowry model, 735
  formula of, 108, 187
  and heartburn, 732
  polar bonds in, 450
  reaction between limestone and, 185
  reaction between metal sulfides and, 1096
  reaction between methylamine and, 1022
  reaction between sodium bicarbonate and, 191, 192
  reaction between sodium hydroxide and, 186
  reaction between zinc and, 107, 913
  stock solutions of, 171
  in stomach, 185
  strength of, 176, 177, 737
  titration with sodium hydroxide of, 803–807
  uses, 206, 732, 733
  and weak acid, 751–752
hydrocyanic acid, 739
hydroelectric power, 298
hydrofluoric acid
  acid ionization constant for, 739
  anions from, 759
  formula of, 187
  reaction between sodium hydroxide and, 187

hydrofluoric acid (*cont.*)
reactivity of, 1099
strength of, 738
uses of, 732
hydrogen
activity series of, 200
bond order for, 473
boron–hydrogen compounds, 1080
bridging, 410
chemistry of life and, 69
electron configuration for, 353, 368
emission spectrum of, 322
ΔH_f° for compounds containing, 290
interaction energy of two atoms of, 455–456
Lewis structure of, 404
as molecular element, 98
in nuclear fusion, 64
oxidation state for, 195
properties of water vs. oxygen and, 91–93
reaction between iodine and, 633–634, 640, 685
reaction between nitrogen monoxide and, 640
reaction between propene and, 1008
reaction of ethene and, 656
as reducing agent, 197
Schrödinger equation for, 331–334
transitions in, 334–337
van der Waals constants for, 248
from water, 875
weighted linear sum of molecular orbitals for, 471–473
hydrogenation, 664, 1008
hydrogen azide, 1087
hydrogen bonding, 505–507, 530, 582, 583, 1053
hydrogen carbonate, 104
hydrogen chloride, 735, 1008, 1009
hydrogen cyanide, 415–416
hydrogen fluoride, 505
dipole moment of, 409
formal charge of, 415
MO diagram for, 481
polar bonding in, 406–407
hydrogen halides, 157
hydrogen–oxygen fuel cell, 925, 926
hydrogen peroxide, 2, 95, 199, 405, 1087
hydrogen phosphate, 104
hydrogen sulfate (bisulfate), 104
hydrogen sulfide (dihydrogen sulfide), 456–457, 1094, 1095
hydrogen sulfite (bisulfite), 104, 191
hydroiodic acid, 187, 737
hydrolysis, 1045
hydrometallurgy, 1113–1114
hydronium ion, 186, 405
hydronium ion concentration
and Arrhenius model, 735
of mixture of acids, 751–753
and pH, 742–743
of strong acids, 745
in water, 740–741
of weak acids, 745–749, 751
hydrophilic molecules, 1041
hydrophobic interactions, 1053
hydrophobic molecules, 1041
hydroxide ion, 185, 735, 740–741, 756–757
hydroxides, 104, 822, 828
hydroxyl group, 1014
hydroxyl radical, 419
hyperbaric oxygen therapy, 1092
hyperosmotic solutions, 615, 626
hypertension, 93, 215
hypochlorite, 104, 105
hypochlorite ion, 99
hypochlorous acid, 739
hyposmotic solutions, 615
hypothesis, 3
hypoxia, 231
Hz (Hertz), 314

I

i (van't Hoff factor), 613–614
ibuprofen, 133
ice, 19, 553, 850–851
ICE tables, 697–699, 703, 745–746
icosahedron, 1078
ideal gas(es), 223, 582, 854–856
ideal gas constant, 223
ideal gas law, 222–225, 693
breakdown of, 246–247
density of gas, 226–227
and intermolecular forces, 248–249
kinetic molecular theory and, 240–242
molar mass of gas, 227–228
molar volume at standard temperature and pressure, 225–226
partial pressure computed from, 229–231
simple gas laws and, 222–223
and volume of gas particles, 247–248
ideal solutions, 605
IE. *See* ionization energy(-ies)
IE_2 (second ionization energy), 375, 378–379
IE_3 (third ionization energy), 375
igneous rocks, 964
ilmenite, 1121, 1122
inches of mercury (in Hg), 214
incomplete octets, 411, 417–420
indeterminacy, 329–331
indicators, 189–191, 803, 814–817
indinavir, 393
inelastic collision, 239
inert platinum electrode, 905–906
infrared (IR) radiation, 316
initial rates, method of, 638–639
inner electron configuration, 359, 363–364
inner transition elements (actinides), 362, 364–365
inorganic carbon, 1081
inorganic chemistry, 1070
inorganic compounds, 109–110, 123, 991
inosilicates (pyroxenes), 1076–1078
insect control, radioactivity for, 979
insoluble compounds, 178, 823
instantaneous dipole (temporary dipole), 500
instantaneous rate of reaction, 634–635
insulated nanowires, 1071–1072
insulators, 562
insulin, 1037–1038, 1051
insulin receptors, 1050
integrated rate law, 642–649
first-order, 642–644, 649
half-life of reaction, 646–649
and radiometric dating, 960–961
second-order, 645–646, 649
zero-order, 646, 649
integrity, in data gathering, 26
intensity, light, 314, 321–322
intensive properties, 18
interaction energy of atoms, 455–456
interference, 317–319, 472, 543
interference pattern, 318–319, 326–328, 543
interhalogen compounds (interhalides), 157, 1099–1100
intermediates, reaction, 657, 659–660
intermolecular force(s), 405, 499–512
capillary action, 511–512
in condensed states, 494, 499–509
dipole–dipole, 502–505, 507, 508, 582, 583
dispersion, 500–502, 507, 508, 582, 583
hydrogen bonding, 505–508, 530, 582, 583
ion–dipole, 507, 508, 582, 583, 588–589
molecular solids and, 553
real gases and, 248–249
solutions and, 582–586
surface tension and, 509–510
viscosity, 511
and water in absence of gravity, 495–496
internal energy (*E*), 267–269, 272
internal energy change (ΔE), 268–272
for chemical reactions, 278–280
enthalpy change vs., 281
and heat/work, 270–272
International Bureau of Weights and Measures, 14
International System of Units (SI), 13–14. *See also* SI unit(s)
International Union of Pure and Applied Chemistry (IUPAC) nomenclature system, 72, 999
internuclear distance, 455–456
interstitial alloys, 1116, 1119–1121
intramolecular forces, 405
intravenous fluids, 73
intravenous solutions, 616
iodate, 105
iodide, 102, 132
iodine, 66, 68
phase diagrams of, 529
properties of, 1097
reaction between hydrogen and, 633–634, 640, 685
iodine-131, 977
iodine monochloride, 657
ion(s), 63–65, 371–379. *See also* anion(s); cation(s); *specific ions*
acid–base properties of, 758–765
complex, 829, 1140
dipolar, 1049
electrolysis of mixture of, 929–930
electron configurations of, 371–372
formation of, with predictable charges, 365–366
ionization energy of, 375–379
isoelectronic series of, 374
magnetic properties of, 371–372
periodic table and, 68–69
polyatomic, 99, 104–105, 196, 410, 412
radii of, 373–375
spectator, 184
ion channels, 351–352
ion–dipole forces, 507, 508, 582, 583, 588–589

ionic bond(s), 93, 395, 406
dipole moment of, 409
electron transfer and, 395
lattice energy and, 398–402
Lewis model of, 397–398
model for, 402–403
nondirectionality of, 405
ionic carbides, 1082
ionic character, 407
ionic compound(s), 100–105
acidity or basicity of, 765
aqueous solutions of, 507
binary, 102–104
conductivity of, 402–403
as drugs, 403
formulas for, 100–101
hydrated, 105
inorganic nomenclature flowchart, 109–110
lattice energy of, 398–402
melting points of, 402–403
naming, 101–105
polyatomic ions in, 104–105
solubility of, 177–179, 817
ionic equations, 184–185
ionic solids, 553, 555–558
ionic solvents, 614–615
ionizable protons, 737
ionization, 176, 177
of acids, 737–738
of polyprotic acids, 765–766
of strong bases, 754
of weak acid, 750–751
of weak bases, 754–756
ionization energy(-ies) (IE), 375–379, 395, 1138
ionizing power, 951, 953
ionizing radiation, 317
ionone, 1018
ion pairing, 613
ion product constant for water (K_w), 741, 760
ion pumps, 351–352
iron
activity series of, 200
as atomic solid, 555
cations formed by, 103
charge of, 102
corrosion of, 934
density of, 19
in human body, 1156
reaction between chlorine and, 157
rusting of, 10
specific heat of, 273
iron-59, 977
iron blue, 1156
iron(II) carbonate, 818, 820
iron(III) chloride, 764
iron(II) disulfide (iron pyrite), 1095
iron(III) fluoride, 764
iron(II) hydroxide, 818
iron sponge, 1115
iron(II) sulfate, 104
iron(II) sulfide, 818, 1096
irradiation, of foods, 978
IR (infrared) radiation, 316
irregular tetrahedron, 444
irreversible reactions, 877
isobutane, 124, 991, 993
isobutyl substituent, 1000
isocyanato ligand, 1147
isocyano ligand, 1147
isoleucine, 1048
isomerism
cis–trans, 464, 1006–1007, 1147–1148
in coordination compounds, 1145–1150
fac–mer, 1148
optical, 995–997, 1044, 1148–1150
isomerization, 464
isomers, 464
coordination, 1145
dextrorotatory, 996
geometric, 1147–1148
levorotatory, 996
linkage, 1145–1147
optical, 1148–1150
retinal, 464
stereo-, 995, 1145
structural, 993–995, 1043–1044, 1145–1147
isopropyl alcohol
boiling point of, 514
functional groups in, 1013
heat of fusion for, 524
heat of vaporization of, 514
methanol vs., 126
oxidized to 2-propanone, 1018
properties of, 40
solubility of, 584
uses of, 1014
isopropyl substituent, 1000
isosmotic (isotonic) solutions, 615–616
isothermal processes, 858
isothiocyanato ligand, 1147
isotones, 86
isotonic solutions, 615–616
isotope(s), 61–63, 373
mass of, 71
natural abundance of, 62, 69
notation for symbolizing, 949, 950
as radiotracers, 977–978
relative abundance of, 71
IUPAC nomenclature system, 72, 999

J

Jaleo (restaurant), 167
Joliot-Curie, Irene and Frederic, 972
joule (J), 266
Joule, James, 266
J-tube, 216

K

k. *See* rate constant(s)
K. *See* equilibrium constant
K (kelvin), 14–16
K_a. *See* acid ionization constant(s)
kaolinite, 561–562
K_b (base ionization constant), 755, 760
kcal (kilocalorie), 266
Kekulé, Friedrich August, 1010
kelvin (K), 14–16
Kelvin scale (absolute scale), 15–16, 220
Kepler, Johannes, 51
keratin, 1051, 1052
kernite, 1078
ketohexose, 1043
ketones, 126, 1013, 1016–1019, 1043
ketose, 1043–1044
Kevlar, 568
K_f (formation constant), 829
kilocalorie (kcal), 266
kilogram (kg), 14
kilojoule (kJ), 266
kilo prefix, 17
kilowatt-hour (kWh), 266
kinetic energy, 12
defined, 45, 264
temperature and, 239, 242–243
transformation of, 265
kinetic molecular theory, 238–244
ideal gas law and, 240–242
postulates of, 238–239
pressure and, 239–240
simple gas laws and, 239–240
temperature and molecular velocities, 242–244
kinetics, chemical. *See* reaction rate(s)
kJ (kilojoule), 266
knowledge, scientific approach to, 3–5
krypton, 66, 248, 366
K_{sp}. *See* solubility product constant
Kuhn, Thomas S., 5, 436
K_w (ion product constant for water), 741, 760
kWh (kilowatt-hour), 266
Kwolek, Stephanie, 568

L

l. *See* angular momentum quantum number
L (liter), 18
lactic acid, 783, 802, 1020
lag time, in photoelectric effect, 318
lakes, acid rain and, 774, 775
λ. *See* wavelength
lanthanide contraction, 1138
lanthanides, 362, 364–365
lateral ideas, exploration of, 542
lattice energy, 398–402
laughing gas, 106
Lavoisier, Antoine, 3, 51, 1091–1092
Lavoisier, Marie, 3
law(s)
of conservation of energy, 12, 265, 848
of conservation of mass, 3–4, 51–52
of definite proportions, 52–53, 55
deterministic, 330
of mass action, 688, 691, 693
of multiple proportions, 53–55
scientific, 3–5
LCAO (linear combination of atomic orbitals), 471–475
LDPE (low-density polyethylene), 566
leaching, 1113
lead, 624
activity series of, 200
cations formed by, 103
density of, 19
on periodic table, 66
specific heat of, 273
uranium/lead dating, 964–965
lead(II) bromide, 818
lead(II) chloride, 818
lead(II) nitrate, 179–181
lead(II) sulfate, 818
lead(II) sulfide, 818, 1096, 1113
lead–acid storage batteries, 923
leaded glass, 563
lead poisoning, 207
Le Châtelier, Henri, 682
Le Châtelier's principle, 517, 711–718, 751, 917
concentration change, 712–714
free energy changes and, 881
population analogy for, 711–712
temperature change, 716–718
volume (or pressure) change, 714–715
lemons, pH of, 742
length, SI unit of, 14, 18
leucine, 1048
Leucippus, 51
lever rule, 1119
levorotatory isomer, 996
Lewis, G. N., 394, 772
Lewis acid–base adduct, 1140–1141
Lewis acids and bases, 772–773, 1079

Lewis electron-dot structures. *See* Lewis structures
Lewis model, 392, 394
of covalent bonding, 394–397
double bonds in, 462
of ionic bonding, 397–398
octet rule exceptions, 417–421
valence electrons represented with dots, 396–398
Lewis structures (Lewis electron-dot structures), 394–397
formal charge and, 414–417
of ionic bonds, 397–398
of molecular compounds, 410–411
of polyatomic ions, 410, 412
resonance and, 412–415
valence electrons in, 396–398
Lewis symbol, 396–398
Lewis theory, 468
Libby, Willard, 961, 962
life
as controlled disequilibrium, 690
effects of radiation on, 974–976
elements of, 69
Life of Pi (Martel), 579
ligand(s), 829, 1140
bidentate, 1142
capable of linkage isomerization, 1145–1147
common, 1141
coordination isomerization and, 1145
geometric isomerism and, 1147–1148
monodentate, 1142
names and formulas of, 1143–1144
polydentate, 1142
strong-field, 1153
used in chemical analysis, 1155
weak-field, 1153
light, 312–322. *See also* photons
absorption of, 324–325
diffraction of, 318–319
electromagnetic spectrum, 315–317
interference, 317–319
particle nature of, 318–322
rotation of polarized, 996–997
visible, 314–316
wave nature of, 313–315
wave–particle duality of, 312, 322
lightning, 60, 313, 897–898
"like dissolves like," 584
limes, pH of, 742
limestone, 100, 108, 185, 774, 819
liming process, 207
limiting reactant, 149–155
linear accelerator, 972–974
linear combination of atomic orbitals (LCAO), 471–475
linear geometry
of complex ions, 1143
electron, 446, 468
molecular, 439, 440, 445, 446, 449
line formulas, 993
line notation, 905
linkage isomers, 1145–1147
linoleic acid, 1039
linolenic acid, 1039
lipid bilayer, 1042
lipids, 1038–1043
liquid(s), 494. *See also specific liquids, e.g.:* water
entropy change associated with change in state of, 856–860
equilibria involving, 695–696
intermolecular forces in, 499–512
molecular comparison with other phases, 496–499
nonvolatile, 513
on phase diagram, 527–528
relative standard entropies of, 868
standard state for, 289, 867
vaporization and vapor pressure of, 512–522
volatile, 513
liquid matter, 6
liquid solutions, 581
liter (L), 18
lithium, 63, 66, 68
activity series of, 200
effective nuclear charge for, 368–369
electron configuration for, 358, 359, 371
energy levels of molecular orbitals in, 564
flame tests for, 325
Lewis structure for, 396
orbital diagram for, 358, 475
lithium bromide, 589
lithium carbonate, 403
lithium chloride, 401
lithium fluoride, 409
lithium hydroxide, 187, 754
lithium ion battery, 924–925
lithium ions, 356, 371
lithium sulfide, 191
litmus paper, 732, 734
lizards, 631–632
localization, 413, 471
logarithm, 742
London, Fritz, 500
London force, 500. *See also* dispersion forces
lone pairs, 404
bonding vs., 443
electron groups with, 442–447
hybridization and, 460
repulsion for, 447
in weak bases, 755, 756
Los Angeles County, carbon monoxide concentrations in, 20–21
low-density polyethylene (LDPE), 566
low-spin complexes, 1154–1155
Lukens, Isaiah, 267
lysine, 1047, 1048
lysozyme, egg-white, 1052, 1057

M

m (meter), 14
m (molality), 595, 596
M (molarity), 168–171, 595–596
Maalox, 758
machines
atomic, 50
perpetual motion, 267
macromolecules, 1038
macroscopic world, 312, 327
macrostates, 853–855
magic numbers, 956
magnesium, 66, 198–199, 378, 379
magnesium-based antacids, 758
magnesium carbonate, 179, 818, 819
magnesium hydroxide, 403, 818, 820, 822
magnesium oxide, 562
magnesium sulfate, 403
magnesium sulfate heptahydrate (epsom salts), 105
magnetic field, 313
magnetic quantum number (m_l), 332
magnetism, 479, 1124, 1153–1155
main-group elements, 66, 67, 1072–1073
atomic radii of, 1072
effective nuclear charge for, 369
electron affinities for, 380
ion formation by, 68
ionization energy of, 376
valence electrons for, 361
malachite, 1125
malic acid, 733
malleability, 66, 380, 426, 1110
manganese, 200, 1123–1124, 1139, 1156
manganese ions, 911
manganese oxides, 1123–1124
Manhattan Project, 965–967
manometer, 214–215
maps, probability distribution, 329–331
Markovnikov's rule, 1009
Mars, 140, 529, 530
Mars Climate Orbiter, 13, 14
Mars Express Orbiter, 529
Marshall, Barry J., 744
Martel, Yann, 579
mass(es). *See also* molar mass
atomic, 69–73, 111
conservation of, 3–4, 51–52
conversion to energy of, 969–971
converting between moles and, 75–77
critical, 965
formula, 111–113
of isotopes, 71
limiting reactant, theoretical yield, and percent yield from, 152–153
molecular, 111
parts by, 595–597
percent by, 595, 596
reaction stoichiometry with, 146–147
SI unit of, 14, 18
of subatomic particles, 59, 60
mass action, law of, 688, 691, 693
mass defect, 969–971
mass number (*A*), 62–63, 949, 971
mass percent composition, 114–115
mass spectrometry, 70–73
materials science, 540
matter. *See also* states of matter
atoms as building blocks of, 51
classification of, 5–9
defined, 5
phases of, 496–499
physical and chemical changes in, 9–12
properties of, 0
wave nature of, 325–331
maximum contaminant levels (MCLs), 531, 599
Maxwell, James Clerk, 210
mean free path, 245–246
measurement, 13–26
reliability of, 20–26
units of, 13–20. *See also* SI unit(s)
mechanical potential energy, 849
medicine
antacids, 758
blood buffering system, 802
blood pressure, 215
bone density, 20
chelating agents, 1156
chymotrypsin in digestion, 666
colligative properties and, 615–616
concentration cells in human nerve cells, 922
coordination compounds, 1158

definition of life, 690
elements of life, 69
ionic compounds as drugs, 403
methylmercury in fish, 118
nuclear, 947–948
oxygen used in, 1092
radiation exposure from diagnostic procedures, 976–978
radioactivity in, 947–948, 976–978
radiotherapy in, 317, 978
ulcers, 744
megaelectron volt (MeV), 970
mega prefix, 17
Meitner, Lise, 965
melanin, 199
melting, 523–524, 850–851. *See also* fusion
melting point(s), 523
of crystalline solids, 554–556
of ionic compounds, 402–403
of molecular compounds, 405–406
Mendeleev, Dmitri, 65–66, 350, 352–353, 361
meniscuses, 512
mercury, 44, 61
absorption spectrum of, 325
as atomic solid, 555
cations formed by, 103
density of, 19
emission spectrum of, 322, 325
in fish, 118
meniscus of, 512
mercury(II) oxide, 1092
mercury(II) sulfide, 1096
messenger RNA (mRNA), 1059
metal(s), 67, 1108–1133. *See also* alloys
activity series of, 198–201
bonding atomic radii for, 366
bonding theories of, 1110
cation, 762–763
cations formed by, 102–104
closest-packed crystal structures in, 555
corrosion of, 934–935
dissolved in acids, 107, 913
electrolysis to plate metals onto other, 927
electron affinities for, 380–381, 395
general properties and natural distribution of, 1110–1111
group 1A. *See* group 1A metals (alkali metals)
group 2A. *See* group 2A metals (alkaline earth metals)
ion formation by, 68
ionization energies of, 395–396
name in anionic complex, 1144
noble, 1110
oxidation states of, 1139
properties of, 66
reaction of alcohols with active, 1015
structures of, 1116
transition. *See* transition metal(s)
vandium contamination of, 1109–1110
metal chlorides, 401, 1099
metal halides, 156, 157
metal hydride, 924
metal hydroxides, 754, 832–833
metallic atomic solids, 553, 555–556
metallic bond(s), 395, 396, 425–426, 555–556
metallic carbides, 1083
metallic character, periodic trends in, 380–383
metalloid(s), 66, 67, 1083
metallurgy, 1112–1116
defined, 1108, 1110
electrometallurgy, 1114–1115
extractive, 1112
hydrometallurgy, 1113–1114
powder, 1115–1116
pyrometallurgy, 1112–1113
separation, 1112
metal nitrates, 1089, 1092
metal nitrides, 1085
metal oxides, 927, 1083, 1092
metal sulfides, 1095–1096
metastable state, nuclei in, 952
meter (m), 14
methanal. *See* formaldehyde
methane
combustion of, 141–142, 151, 291–292, 419
common uses of, 125
methanol vs., 126
molecular formula for, 96, 125
molecular geometry for, 440, 443, 457–459
as organic molecule, 990
space-filling model for, 123, 125
standard enthalpy of formation for, 289
structural formula for, 123, 125
structure and properties of, 998
van der Waals constants for, 248
methanoic acid. *See* formic acid
methanol, 305
functional groups in, 1013
methane vs., 126
reaction between sodium and, 1015
solubility of, 584
uses of, 1014
methionine, 1048
method of successive approximations, 708–710
methyl acetate, 126
methylamine, 755, 1022
methylammonium chloride, 1022
methyl butanoate, 1019, 1020
3-methylhexane, 996
methyl isonitrile, 651–652
methylmercury, in fish, 118
2-methyl-2-pentene, 1004
methyl propanoate, 1019
methyl red, 816, 817
methyl substituent, 1000
metric system, 14
MeV (megaelectron volt), 970
Meyer, Julius Lothar, 352
mica, 1076
micelles, 617–618
Michaelis–Menten equation, 1068
micro prefix, 17
microscope, scanning tunneling, 50
microstates, 853–855
microwaves, 316
milk, 617
milk of magnesia, 742, 758
milligrams solute/per liter, 597
Millikan, Robert, 56–57
Millikan's oil drop experiment, 56–57
milliliter (mL), 18
millimeter of mercury (mmHg), 213, 214
milli prefix, 17
minerals, 1111–1116
Mirai (fuel-cell vehicle), 298
mirex, 599
miscibility, 503–504, 583
mixing, 580–582, 602–603
mixture(s)
compounds vs., 92
defined, 7, 8
electrolysis of cation and anion, 929–930
of gas, 228–235
homogeneous. *See* solution(s)
of polar and nonpolar molecules, 454
separating, 8–9
m_l (magnetic quantum number), 332
mL (milliliter), 18
mmHg (millimeter of mercury), 213, 214
moissanite, 1083
mol% (mole percent), 595, 598
molality (*m*), 595, 596
molar heat capacity, 273
molarity (M), 168–171, 595–596
molar mass, 73–78, 869
of compounds, 111–112
defined, 75
dispersion force and, 501
of gases, 227–228
molecular formula from, 120–121
velocity and, 243
viscosity and, 511
molar solubility, 817–820
molar volume, 225–226, 246–247
mole(s), 14, 73–78
of compounds, 111–113
converting between mass and, 75–77
converting between number of atoms and, 74, 76–77
mole concept, 77–78
and pressure of gases, 237
reaction stoichiometry with, 146
and volume of gases, 221–222
mole concept, 77–78, 111–113
molecular complexity, 870
molecular compound(s), 94, 106–109
formulas for, 106
inorganic nomenclature flowchart, 109–110
ionic vs., 99–100
Lewis structures for, 410–411
melting and boiling points of, 405–406
naming, 106–109
molecular elements, 96, 98
molecular equation, 183, 184
molecular formulas, 94–95, 120–121
molecular gastronomy, 167–168
molecular geometry
bent, 443, 446, 449
electron groups and, 438, 439, 447
of larger molecules, 449–450
linear, 439, 440, 445, 446, 449
lone pairs effect, 442–447
octahedral, 441, 446, 449, 467
polarity and, 450–454
predicting, with VSEPR, 447–450
seesaw, 444, 446, 449
square planar, 445, 446, 448, 449
square pyramidal, 445, 446
tetrahedral, 439–443, 446, 449, 458, 459
trigonal bipyramidal, 441, 446, 449, 466–467
trigonal planar, 439, 440, 446, 449, 460
trigonal pyramidal, 442–443, 446, 448, 449, 453
T-shaped, 444, 446
molecularity, 657–658
molecular mass, 111

molecular models, 96, 113
molecular orbitals
antibonding, 472–474, 476, 477
bonding, 472–474, 476, 477
and energy bands, 563–565
nonbonding, 481
molecular orbital theory, 392, 457, 470–483
linear combination of atomic orbitals, 471–475
period two heteronuclear diatomic molecules, 480–482
period two homonuclear diatomic molecules, 475–480
polyatomic molecules, 482–483
trial mathematical functions in, 470–471
molecular solids, 553–555
molecular structure, acid strength and, 770–771
molecular velocities, 243–244
molecular weight, 111
molecule(s), 1–3
bio-, 1156–1158
chiral, 996, 997
diatomic. *See* diatomic molecule(s)
hydrophobic vs. hydrophilic, 1041
as Lewis acids, 772–773
mass spectrum of, 71–73
molar mass for counting, 111–112
organic, 990
polar, 503–504
polyatomic, 98, 482–483
properties of matter and, 0
shapes of, 438. *See also* molecular geometry
size of, 113
temperature and motion of, 15
mole fraction (χ_{solute}), 229, 232, 595, 598
mole percent (mol%), 595, 598
molybdenite, 1111
molybdenum, functions in human body, 1156
mond process, 1126
Monel (alloy), 1126
monochloropentafluoroethane, 642
monoclinic unit cells, 545
monodentate ligands, 1142
monomeric proteins, 1054
monomers, 565–567
monoprotic acids, 737, 739, 750
monosaccharides, 1043–1045
monosubstituted benzenes, 1010–1011
Monoun, Lake, 594
monounsaturated fats, 1041
monounsaturated fatty acids, 1039
morphinan, 437
morphine, 437–438
Moseley, Henry, 353
motile proteins, 1046
motion
Brownian, 48–50, 616, 617
and kinetic energy, 264
Newton's laws of, 239, 329–330
perpetual, 267
motor oil, 511, 513
Mount Everest, 231
mRNA (messenger RNA), 1059
m_s. *See* spin quantum number
multimeric proteins, 1054
multiple proportions, law of, 53–55
multiwalled nanotubes (MWNT), 560
μ. *See* dipole moment
Mylanta, 185, 758
myristic acid, 1039

N

n. *See* principal quantum numbers; reaction order
N (Newton), 45, 213
names. *See* nomenclature
nano prefix, 17
nanoribbons, 560
nanotechnology, 45, 50
nanotubes, 560–561, 1071–1072
nanowires, insulated, 1071–1072
naphthalene, 133, 1012
National Ambient Air Quality Standards, 238
National Institutes of Health (NIH), 1060
natural abundance of isotopes, 62, 69
natural gas
combustion of, 141, 155–156
reaction between oxygen and, 155–156
U.S. energy from, 294, 295
natural radiation exposure, 976
nature, concentrated energy in, 847–848
Nature of Chemical Bond, The (Pauling), 407
neon, 66, 582
bonding radii of, 367
electron configuration for, 359
emission spectrum of, 322, 324
isotopes of, 62
Lewis structure of, 396
orbital diagram for, 359, 477–478
van der Waals constants for, 248
neopentane, 501
Nernst equation, 917–921
nerve cells, 351–352, 922
nerve signal transmission, 351–352
nesosilicates (orthosilicates), 1075, 1077
net ionic equations, 184–185
network covalent atomic solids, 553, 556, 558–561
neutralization reactions, 1020–1021. *See also* acid-base chemistry
neutral ligands, naming, 1143, 1144
neutral solutions, 741, 742
neutron(s), 59
actual number of, 956
charge of, 60
in isotopes, 61–63
mass of, 59, 60
number of, 949
N/Z ratio and, 955
symbol for, 950
neutron stars, 59, 86
Newlands, John, 352
Newton (N), 45, 213
Newton, Isaac, 51, 540
Newton's laws of motion, 239, 329–330
nickel, 200, 556, 1116–1118, 1125–1126
nickel-cadmium (NiCad) battery, 924
nickel ions, 911
nickel-metal hydride (NiMH) battery, 924
nido-boranes, 1080
NIH (National Institutes of Health), 1060
NiMH (nickel-metal hydride) battery, 924
niobium, 1111
NIO mnemonic, 911, 930
nitrate ion, 178
nitrates, 104, 105, 1089
nitric acid
in acid rain, 160, 773–774
formation of, 1088
formula of, 108, 109, 187
reduction half-reaction for, 913
strength of, 737
structure of, 733
uses of, 732, 1089
nitric oxide (nitrogen monoxide), 725, 870
in catalytic converter, 662
electron density map of, 481
formation of, 1085, 1087
as free radical, 418
MO diagram for, 480–481
reaction between hydrogen and, 640, 660
nitride, 102
nitrite, 104, 105, 1089
nitrito ligand, 1145, 1146, 1147
nitrogen, 1085–1089
in air, 228, 229
chemistry of life and, 69
compounds containing, 290, 1086–1089
electron configuration for, 359
elemental, 1085–1086
Henry's law constants for, 593
ionization energy of, 378
Lewis structure of, 396
as molecular element, 98
orbital diagram for, 359, 477–478
single bonds of halogens with, 425
van der Waals constants for, 248
velocity distribution for temperatures of, 243
in weak bases, 755, 756
nitrogen dioxide, 106, 238, 658–659, 891, 1088
nitrogen hydrides, 1086–1087
nitrogen monoxide. *See* nitric oxide
nitrogen narcosis, 231, 624
nitrogen oxides, 296, 773–774, 1087–1088
nitrogen tetroxide, 712–713, 716–717
nitro ligand, 1145–1147
m-nitrophenol, 817
nitrosamines, 1089
nitrosyl chloride, 655–656
nitrous acid, 739
nitrous oxide (dinitrogen monoxide), 106, 636, 1088
noble gas(es), 66, 68, 362, 365
boiling points of, 501
ionization energy and, 375
standard entropies of, 869
noble metals, 1110
nomenclature
for acids, 107–109
for alcohols, 1014
for aldehydes and ketones, 1017
for alkanes, 999–1002
for alkenes and alkynes, 1003–1006
for aromatic hydrocarbons, 1010–1012
for carboxylic acids and esters, 1019
for coordination compounds, 1143–1145
for ethers, 1021–1022
for hydrocarbons, 124–125
for inorganic compounds, 109–110
for ionic compounds, 101–105
IUPAC system, 72, 999
for molecular compounds, 106–109
Nomex, 574
n-nonane, 511, 999
nonbonding atomic radius (van der Waals radius), 366

nonbonding atomic solids, 553, 555
nonbonding electrons, 404
nonbonding orbitals, 481
nondirectional forces, 402
nonelectrolytes, 605–607
nonelectrolyte solutions, 176, 177
nonideal solutions, 605–607
nonmetal(s), 66, 67, 380, 1070–1107. *See also* halogens; main-group elements; *specific elements*
- bonding atomic radii for, 366
- bonds, types of, 1073
- carbides, 1082–1083
- carbonates, 1084
- carbon oxides, 1083–1084
- electron affinities of, 395
- insulated nanowires, 1071–1072
- ion formation by, 68
- ionization energies of, 395
- silicates, 1074–1078

nonoxide ceramics, 562
nonpolar bonds, 450
nonpolar covalent bonds, 408
nonpolar solvents, 584
nonspontaneous processes, 848–850, 861, 864, 875
nonstandard states, free energy changes for, 878–881
nonstoichiometric compounds, 576
nonvolatile liquids, 513
normal boiling point, 518
normalization, of total intensity, 71
normal science, 5
Novoselov, Konstantin, 541, 542
n-type semiconductors, 565
nuclear binding energy, 969–971
nuclear charge, 356, 366–370
nuclear chemistry, 965–976. *See also* radioactivity
- effects of radiation on life, 974–976
- fission, 965–968
- fusion, 64, 971–972
- mass defect and nuclear binding energy, 969–971
- transmutation and transuranium elements, 972–974

nuclear energy industry, 1079, 1100
nuclear equation(s), 950–953, 965
nuclear fission, 965–968
nuclear fusion, 64, 971–972
nuclear medicine, 947–948
nuclear power, 967–968
nuclear power plants, 967–968
nuclear reactors, 967
nuclear stability, 954–957
nuclear theory of atom, 58
nuclear transmutation, 972–974
nuclear waste, disposal of, 968
nuclear weapons, 965–967
nucleic acids, 73, 1054–1057
nucleon(s), 954–957, 970, 971
nucleotide(s), 508, 1054–1057, 1068
nucleus(-i), 58–59, 946
- in metastable state, 952
- strong force binding, 955

nuclide(s), 949, 950, 959, 970, 971
nylon 6,6, 567, 568
Nyos, Lake, 594
N/Z ratio, 955

O

Obama, Barack, 968
observation, 3
octahedral complexes
- cis-trans isomerism in, 1147–1148
- *d* orbital energy changes for, 1151, 1152
- fac-mer isomerism in, 1148
- high-spin, 1154–1155
- low-spin, 1154–1155
- optical isomerism in, 1149–1150

octahedral geometry
- of complex ions, 1143
- electron, 445, 446, 468
- molecular, 441, 446, 449, 467

octahedral hole, 1120
octane, 146–147, 511, 998, 999
octaves, 352
octet(s), 396–397
- expanded, 411, 417, 420–421, 466
- incomplete, 411, 417–420

octet rule, 396, 406, 417–421
odd-electron species, 417, 418
odors, 989–990, 1017–1018, 1020. *See also* aromatic hydrocarbons
OH^-. *See* hydroxide ion
—OH functional group, 125
oil(s), 511, 513, 1040–1041, 1109–1110
oil drop experiment, Millikan's, 56–57
oleic acid, 1039, 1040
oleum, 1097
olfaction, 990
oligopeptides, 1049
olivines, 1075
On the Revolution of the Heavenly Orbs (Copernicus), 51
opal, 617
opaque, metals as, 1110
operators, algebraic, 331
opioid receptors, 437, 438
Oppenheimer, J. R., 967
optical isomerism, 995–997, 1044, 1148–1150
orbital angular momentum, 479
orbital diagram, 354
orbital overlap. *See* valence bond theory
orbitals, 330. *See also* atomic orbitals; molecular orbitals
order of magnitude estimations, 31–32
ores, 1111–1116
organic bases, 508–509
organic chemistry, 69, 988–1035. *See also* hydrocarbons
- alcohols, 1014–1016
- aldehydes, 1016–1019
- alkanes, 998–1002
- alkenes and alkynes, 1002–1007
- amines, 1022
- carboxylic acids, 1019–1021
- esters, 1019–1021
- ethers, 1021–1022
- fragrances and odors, 989–990
- functional groups, 1013
- ketones, 1016–1019
- and uniqueness of carbon, 988, 990–992

organic compound(s), 123–126, 416–417, 991
organic molecules, 990
orientation factor, 655–656
orthorhombic unit cells, 545
orthosilicates (nesosilicates), 1075, 1077
osmosis, 611, 615
osmosis cell, 611–612
osmotic pressure, 611–613
osteoporosis, 20
Ostwald process, 1088
outer electron configuration, 363–364
outermost electrons, 369
overvoltage, electrolysis of aqueous sodium chloride and, 930–931
oxalate ion, 1141
oxalic acid, 766, 1163
oxidation
- defined, 193, 898
- selective, 913

oxidation-reduction reaction(s), 193–201
- of alcohols, 1015, 1018
- in aqueous solutions, balancing, 898–901
- in batteries, 922–926
- corrosion as undesirable, 934–935
- generating electricity from, 901–906
- identifying, 196–198
- with oxygen, 193
- with partial electron transfer, 193, 194
- spontaneous direction of, 198–201, 910–913, 915
- without oxygen, 193, 194

oxidation state(s) (oxidation number[s]), 194–196, 898
- of halogens in compounds, 1097, 1098
- identifying changes in, 1101
- identifying redox reactions from, 196–198
- of nitrogen compounds, 1086
- of polyatomic ions, 196
- rules for assigning, 195–196
- in sulfur reactions, 1095
- of transition metals, 1139

oxide(s), 102, 1092–1093. *See also specific compounds*
- halogen, 1100–1101
- nitrogen, 773–774, 1087–1088
- phosphorus, 1090
- sulfur, 773–775

oxide ceramics, 562
oxide minerals, 1111
oxidizing agents, 197, 198, 909, 1073, 1092, 1123
oxyacids (oxoacids), 108–109, 771
oxyanions, 104, 108
oxygen, 1091–1093. *See also* ozone
- in air, 228, 229
- boron-oxygen compounds, 1080
- chemistry of life and, 69
- in combustion reactions, 141–142, 155–156
- electron configuration for, 359
- elemental, 1091–1092
- emission spectrum of, 324
- Henry's law constants for, 593
- ΔH_f° for compounds containing, 290
- ionization energy of, 378
- Lewis structure of, 396, 404
- liquid, 479
- orbital diagram for, 359, 477–479
- oxidation state for, 195
- as oxidizing agent, 197
- and oxyacid strength, 771
- paramagnetism of, 479
- partial pressure limits of, 231
- properties of, 60, 66, 91–93
- redox reactions with, 193
- redox reactions without, 193, 194
- in silicate tetrahedron, 1074
- uses for, 1092
- van der Waals constants for, 248

oxygen toxicity, 231, 624
oxygen transport, 1110
oxyhemoglobin, 1162
ozone
as air pollutant, 238
from combustion of fossil fuels, 296
decomposition of, 419, 661–664
from fuel fragments in exhaust, 663
Lewis structure of, 426, 482
molecular orbital model of, 482
properties of, 40
resonance hybrid structure of, 413
use of, 1093
valence bond model of, 482
ozone layer, 642, 1093

P

P (poise), 511
ΔP (vapor pressure lowering), 602–603
Pa (Pascal), 213, 214
packing efficiency, 546–550
palmitic acid, 307, 1039
parabolic troughs, 298
paramagnetism, 371, 479, 1154
parent nuclide, 950
partially hydrogenated vegetable oil, 1008
partial pressures, 228–235
and collecting gases over water, 233–235
Dalton's law of, 229–231, 239–240
deep-sea diving and, 231–232
and equilibrium constant, 692–693
finding equilibrium, 706–707
free energy change of reaction with, 880
particle nature of light, 318–322
parts by mass, 595–597
parts by volume, 595–597
parts per billion by mass (ppb), 595, 597
parts per million by mass (ppm), 595, 597
Pascal (Pa), 213, 214
patchouli alcohol, 990
patina, 1125
Pauli, Wolfgang, 354
Pauli exclusion principle, 354–355, 358
Pauling, Linus, 138, 407
p block, periodic table, 362, 1073–1074
P_c (critical pressure), 522
PCBs (polychlorinated biphenyls), 599
peaches, pH of, 742
penetrating power, 951, 953
penetration, 356
pentaamminebromocobalt(II), 1145
pentaamminechlorocobalt(II), 1145
pentaamminenitritocobalt(III), 1146
pentaamminenitrocobalt(III), 1146
pentagonal bipyramidal geometry, 1100
pentanal, 1017
pentane, 305
common uses of, 125
critical point transition for, 521–522
dynamic equilibrium in, 516–517
formula of, 125, 998
intermolecular forces in, 583
miscibility of water and, 504
molecular formula for, 125
neopentane vs., 501, 502
space-filling model of, 125
structure of, 993
viscosity of, 511
pentanoic acid, 1019
pentanol, 584
2-pentanone, 1017
1-pentene, 1003
1-pentyne, 1004
peptide bond(s), 666, 1049–1050
percent by mass (%), 595, 596
percent ionic character, 409
percent ionization, of weak acid, 750–751
percent mass to volume, 616
percent yield, 150–153
perchlorate, 104, 105
perchloric acid, 187, 737
peridot, 1136
period 2 elements, 475–482
periodic law, 65, 66, 353
periodic property(-ies), 350–391
defined, 352
and development of periodic table, 352–353
effective nuclear charge and, 366–370
electron affinities, 379–380
electron configurations and, 353–365, 371–372
of ions, 371–379
of main-group elements, 1072–1073
metallic character, 380–383
nerve signal transmission and, 351–352
and quantum-mechanical model, 365–366
sizes of atoms, 366–370
summary, 383
transition elements and, 369–370
periodic table, 65–69, 350, 1073. *See also specific elements; specific families or groups*
atomic mass, 69–73
development of, 352–353
ions and, 68–69
modern, 66–68
orbital blocks in, 362–363
organization of, 61
quantum-mechanical theory and, 350, 353–365
writing electron configuration from, 363–364
permanent dipoles, 502–503
permanganate, 104
permanganate ion, 1124
peroxide, 104, 1092
perpetual motion machine, 267
Perrin, Jean, 50, 51
persistent organic pollutants (POPs), 598–599
perturbation theory, 455
PET (positron emission tomography), 977
peta prefix, 17
petroleum, 294, 295
pH. *See also* acid–base chemistry; buffers
of blood, 788, 802
of buffers, 790–791
of mixture of acids, 751–753
of polyprotic acids, 766–768
of salt solutions, 763–765
solubility and, 822
of solution with anion acting as weak base, 760–762
of solution with conjugate acid of weak base, 763
of strong acid solutions, 745
of weak acid solutions, 745–749
of weak bases, 756–757
phase(s)
of matter, 496–499. *See also* gas(es); liquid(s); solid(s)
of orbitals, 341–342
of waves, 317–318
phase diagram(s), 527–530, 1117–1119
phase transition(s), 498–499
condensation, 513, 514, 860, 1020–1022
critical point, 521–522
deposition, 522
entropy and, 856–860
freezing, 523–524, 530
melting or fusion, 523–524
sublimation, 11, 522–524, 638
vaporization, 512–522, 524
pH curves, 803–814
phenol, 739, 1010, 1011
phenolphthalein, 814–815, 817
phenol red, 817
4-phenyl-1-hexene, 1011
phenylalanine, 1047, 1048
phenyl group, 1011
3-phenylheptane, 1011
pH meters, 814
phosgene (carbonyl chloride), 433, 679, 1084
phosphate(s), 104, 207, 828, 1090–1091
phosphate links, in nucleic acids, 1056
phosphatidylcholine, 1041, 1042
phosphide, 102
phosphine, 1089
phospholipids, 1041, 1042
phosphorescence, 948
phosphoric acid, 732, 738, 766, 1090–1091
phosphorus, 1085
black, 1086
chemistry of life and, 69
compounds, 1089–1091
elemental, 1085–1086
ionization energies of, 379
as molecular element, 98
red, 1085
silicon doped with, 565
white, 1085, 1090
phosphorus-30, 953
phosphorus-32, 977
phosphorus halides, 1089–1090
phosphorus oxides, 1090
phosphorus oxychloride, 1090
phosphorus oxyhalides, 1090
phosphorus pentachloride, 441
photochemical smog, 296
photoelectric effect, 318–322
photons, 320–321, 335
photosynthesis, 147–148, 305, 1083, 1091, 1156, 1158
pH scale, 730, 742–743
phyllosilicates, 1077
physical changes, 9–12
physical property, 10
physics, classical, 329–330
π^*_{2p} antibonding orbital, 476, 477
π_{2p} bonding orbital, 476, 477
pi (π) bonds, 462
pico prefix, 17
PIR mnemonic, 911, 930
pK_a scale, 744
Planck, Max, 310, 320
Planck's constant, 320
plane-polarized light, 996–997
plastic(s), 540, 565–568
platinum, 19, 905–906
Plato, 3, 51
plum-pudding model, 57, 58
plums, pH of, 742
p-n junctions, 565
pOH scale, 743–744
poise (P), 511
polar bonds, 406–410, 450–454, 770

polar covalent bonds, 406–407
polarimetry, 636
polarity
bond, 406–410, 770
molecular shape and, 450–454
polarized light, 636, 996–997
polar molecules, 503–504
polar solvents, 584
polar stratospheric clouds (PSCs), 663
pollutant(s), 108, 598–599, 1096
pollution, 238, 295–296, 531, 662–663
polonium, 61, 949
polyatomic ion(s), 99, 104–105
balancing chemical equations containing, 144–145
Lewis structures for, 410, 412
oxidation numbers in, 196
polyatomic molecules, 98, 482–483
polychlorinated biphenyls (PCBs), 599
polycyclic aromatic hydrocarbons, 1011–1012
polydentate ligands, 1142
polyethylene, 566, 567
polyethylene terephthalate, 567
polymer(s), 565–568, 1038
polymorphism, 554
polypeptides, 1049
polypropylene, 567
polyprotic acids, 186, 765–769, 814
polysaccharides, 1045–1046
polystyrene, 567
polyunsaturated fatty acids, 1039
polyurethane, 567
polyvinyl chloride (PVC), 566, 567
Popper, Karl, 392
POPs (persistent organic pollutants), 598–599
p orbitals, 333, 340
2*p*, 340, 342, 356–357
and properties of main-group elements, 1073–1074
porphyrin, 1134, 1157
Portland cement, 562–563
position
in classical mechanics, 329–330
and energy as complementary properties, 331
and potential energy, 264
and velocity as complementary properties, 331
positron, 952–953
positron emission, 949, 952–954
positron emission tomography (PET), 977
potassium, 66
activity series of, 200
flame tests for, 325
Lewis structure of, 397
reaction between bromine and, 656
reaction between chlorine and, 397
potassium bromide, 763
potassium chloride, 100, 102, 401, 1111
potassium hydroxide, 187, 589, 734, 754
potassium iodide, 179–181, 403, 824
potassium ions, 351–352, 922
potassium nitrate, 591
potassium nitrite, 763
potassium permanganate, 403
potato cannon, 272
potential difference, 903–904, 914
potential energy
of charged particles, 394–396
Coulomb's law and, 499
defined, 12, 264
exothermic chemical reactions and, 283
and law of conservation of energy, 13
solution formation and, 582
stability of covalent bond and, 94
transformation of, 265
pounds per square inch (psi), 213
powder metallurgy, 1115–1116
power, units raised to, 30
ppb (parts per billion by mass), 595, 597
ppm (parts per million by mass), 595, 597
precipitate, 168, 179
precipitation (precipitation reactions), 179–183, 823–826
in molecular gastronomy, 168
qualitative analysis by, 826–828
reaction quotient and, 823–824
selective, 824–826
from supersaturated solution, 590
writing equations for, 182–183
precision, 22, 25–26
pre-exponential factor (frequency factor), 651–655
prefixes, 17, 105, 106, 1000
pressure(s), 212–215. *See also* gas(es); partial pressures
blood, 215
calculating, 240–242
critical, 522
defined, 212
dynamic equilibrium and, 516
equilibrium constant in terms of, 693–694
free energy for water vs., 879
gas amount and, 237
gas solubility in water and, 592–593
gauge, 224, 254
heat in reactions at constant, 281–284
kinetic molecular theory and, 239–240
Le Châtelier's principle on change in, 714–715
manometer to measure, 214–215
molecular collisions and, 212–213
osmotic, 611–613
particle density and, 212
phase changes and, 498
and reaction rates, 636
SI unit of, 213–214
STP, 225–226
temperature and, 223
total, 224, 230–231
units of, 213–214
vapor, 233, 515–521, 605–607, 614–615
volume and, 216–218
pressure–volume work, 276–278
Priestley, Joseph, 1091
primary structure, protein, 1051, 1052, 1054
primary valence, 1140
principal level (principal shell), 333
principal quantum numbers (*n*), 331, 332, 376
principles, 4
probability density, 337–339
probability distribution maps, 329–331
problem solving, 26–33
product(s)
in chemical equation, 141
in chemical stoichiometry, 139
concentration of, 634
and law of conservation of mass, 51
proline, 1048
proof, of alcoholic beverages, 1014
propanal, 1017
propane, 163
burning of, 11
combustion of, 283–284
common uses of, 125
formation of, 1008
formula of, 125, 998
ionic compounds vs., 98
liquid, 498
space-filling model of, 125
structure of, 124, 991
propanoic acid, 1019, 1020
2-propanol. *See* isopropyl alcohol
propanone. *See* acetone
propene, 994, 1003, 1008, 1009
property(-ies)
extensive and intensive, 18
periodic. *See* periodic property(-ies)
physical, 10
propylene glycol, 787
propyl substituent, 1000
propyne, 994, 1004
protactinium-234, 956
protease inhibitors, 394
protective proteins, 1046
protein(s), 393–394, 1046–1057. *See also* amino acids
defined, 1038
digestion of, 666
fibrous, 1050–1051
functions, 1046
functions of, 438
globular, 1051
mass spectrum of, 73
monomeric, 1054
multimeric, 1054
nucleic acids as blueprints for, 1054–1057
structure of, 1050–1054
synthesis of, 1059
proton(s), 44, 58
actual number of, 956
Brønsted–Lowry definition of acids and bases and, 735–736, 770, 772
charge of, 59, 60
ionizable, 737
mass of, 59, 60
number of, in elements, 60–61
N/Z ratio and, 955
repulsive electrostatic force among, 955
symbol for, 950
Proust, Joseph, 52, 54
PSCs (polar stratospheric clouds), 663
pseudogout, 842
psi (pounds per square inch), 213
ψ (wave function), 331
p-type semiconductors, 565
pumps, ion, 351–352
pure compounds, 289
pure substances, 7, 8
purine bases, 1055–1056
PVC (polyvinyl chloride), 566, 567
pyrene, 1012
Pyrex®, 273, 563
pyridine, 755
pyrimidine bases, 1055–1056
pyrolusite, 1123–1124
pyrometallurgy, 1112–1113

pyrosilicates (sorosilicates), 1075, 1077
pyroxenes (inosilicates), 1076–1078

Q

Q (reaction quotient), 699–701, 823–824
quadratic equations, 703
qualitative analysis, 826
qualitative chemical analysis, 826–828
quantitative analysis, 826
quantized energy, 324
quantum, of light, 320–321
quantum-mechanical model of atom, 311–349
  and atomic spectroscopy, 334–337
  atomic spectroscopy and Bohr model, 322–325
  explanatory power of, 365–366
  nature of light, 312–322
  nodes and wave functions, 340
  periodic table and, 350, 353–365
  Schrödinger equation for hydrogen atom, 331–334
  Schrödinger's cat and, 311–312
  shapes of atomic orbitals, 337–342
  wave nature of matter and, 325–331
quantum-mechanical strike zone, 330, 331
quantum mechanics, 66
quantum numbers, 331–334, 354–355
quarks, 973
quartz, 553, 561, 1074
quaternary structure, protein, 1051, 1054

R

racemic mixture, 996
radial distribution functions, 338–340, 357
radiation
  in cancer treatment, 317
  electromagnetic, 313–314, 317. *See also* light
  of hydrogen energy, 334–337
  infrared, 316
  ionizing, 317
  ultraviolet, 316, 426
radiation dose, 975–976
radiation exposure, 974–976
radicals, 418, 419, 433, 1008
radioactive atoms, 948
radioactive decay, 957–965
radioactive decay series, 956–957
radioactivity, 946–965. *See also* nuclear chemistry
  defined, 948
  detecting, 957–958
  discovery of, 57, 948–949
  kinetics of radioactive decay and radiometric dating, 958–965
  in medicine, 947–948, 976–978
  other applications, 978–979
  types of, 949–954
  and valley of stability, 954–957
radiocarbon dating, 961–963
radiometric dating, 961–963
radiotherapy, 978
radiotracers, 977–978
radio waves, 316
radium, 949, 1111
radium-228, 951
radon-220, 959
rain, acid, 108, 148, 295, 773–775, 1096
rainwater, pH of, 742
Rana sylvatica (wood frogs), 611
random coils, 1053
random errors, 26
Raoult, François-Marie, 578
Raoult's law, 603–607
rapture of the deep (nitrogen narcosis), 231, 624
rate constant(s) (*k*), 637, 639, 650
rate-determining steps, 658–659
rate law, 637–642
  containing intermediates, 659–660
  determining order of reaction, 638–641
  differential, 643
  for elementary steps, 657–658
  first-order reaction, 637–638, 649
  integrated, 642–649, 960–961
  overall, 658–659
  reaction order for multiple reactants, 640–642
  second-order reaction, 637–639, 649
  zero-order reaction, 637–639, 649
RBE (biological effectiveness factor), 975
reactant(s)
  in chemical equation, 141
  in chemical stoichiometry, 139
  concentration of, 634
  and law of conservation of mass, 51
  limiting, 149–155
  reaction order for multiple, 640–642
reactant in excess, 150, 151, 155
reaction(s), 138–165. *See also* free energy change of reaction (Δ*G*); *specific types*
  of alcohols, 1014–1016
  of aldehydes and ketones, 1018–1019
  of alkali metals, 156–158
  of amines, 1022
  of aromatic hydrocarbons, 1012
  of carboxylic acids and esters, 1020–1021
  climate change and fossil fuel combustion, 139–140
  defined, 138, 141
  direction of, 699–701
  enthalpy changes for, 285–294, 423–424
  entropy changes in, 867–871
  examples of, 155–158
  gases in, 235–238
  half-life of, 646–649, 959–960
  of halogens, 156–158
  heat evolved in, at constant pressure, 281–284
  of hydrocarbons, 1007–1009
  internal energy change for, 278–280
  limiting reactant, theoretical yield, percent yield, and reactant in excess, 149–155
  rates of. *See* reaction rate(s)
  spontaneity of, 848–850
  standard enthalpy change for, 291–294, 872–873
  standard entropy change for, 867–873
  stoichiometry for, 145–155
  writing and balancing equations for, 141–145
reaction intermediates, 657, 659–660
reaction mechanisms, 656–661
reaction order (*n*), 637–642
reaction quotient (*Q*), 699–701, 823–824
reaction rate(s), 630–681
  average, 634
  catalysis, 661–666
  defined, 632–635
  instantaneous, 634–635
  integrated rate law, 642–649
  measuring, 636
  of radioactive decay and radiometric dating, 958–965
  rate law, 637–642, 658–659
  and reactant/product concentrations, 634
  reaction mechanisms and, 656–661
  in reptile movement, 631–632
  temperature effect on, 650–656
  thermodynamics and, 849, 850
reaction stoichiometry, 145–155
  enthalpy change and, 283–284
  for gases, 235–238
  limiting reactant, 149–155
  mass-to-mass conversions, 146–147
  mole-to-mole conversions, 146
  percent yield, 150–153
  theoretical yield, 149–155
reactivity, of halogens, 1097
real gas(es), 246–250
rechargeable batteries, 924–925
recrystallization, 591
red blood cells, 615
Redheffer, Charles, 267
Redheffer's perpetual motion machine, 267
redox reactions. *See* oxidation–reduction reaction(s)
red phosphorus, 1085
reducing agents, 197, 198, 909
reduction, 193, 898. *See also* oxidation–reduction reaction(s)
refining, 1112, 1114–1115
reflection, angle of, 543
refractory materials, 562
relative abundance, of isotopes, 71
relative concentration, 799–800, 802
relative solubility, 820
relative standard entropies, 868–870
relative zero, 867–868
reliability, of measurements, 20–26
rem (roentgen equivalent man), 975
renewable energy, 298
repulsive electrostatic force, among protons, 955
resistivity, of metals, 1110, 1111
resonance, 410, 412–415
resonance hybrids, 413
resonance stabilization, 413
resonance structures, 412–417, 1010
resting potential, 922
retina, 464
11-*cis*-retinal, 346
retinal isomers, 464
reversible reactions, 685, 686, 858, 859, 877
R group (side chains) of amino acids, 1047
rhodochrosite, 1123
rhomohedral unit cells, 545
ribonucleic acid (RNA), 1055

ribose, 1055
ribosomes, 1059
ripening agent, ethene as, 1002
ritonavir, 554
RNA (ribonucleic acid), 1055
roasting, 1113
rock candy, 591
rocks, uranium/lead dating of, 964
rock salt structure, 557
rods, 464
roentgen, 975
roentgen equivalent man (rem), 975
Roman Pantheon, 562
Roosevelt, Franklin, 965–967
root mean square velocity, 243–244
rotation, of polarized light, 996–997
rotational energy, 857, 870
Ru-92, 953
rubbing alcohol. *See* isopropyl alcohol
rubidium, 66
rubies, color of, 1135–1136
rusting, 10, 934
Rutherford, Ernest, 57–59, 61, 949, 972
rutherfordium, 61
rutile, 1111, 1121, 1122
Rydberg, Johannes, 323
Rydberg constant, 323, 332
Rydberg equation, 323, 333, 335

S

S. *See* entropy(-ies)
$S°$ (standard molar entropies), 867–871
s (second), 14–15
ΔS. *See* entropy change
Sacramento, California, 273
sacrificial electrode, 935
SAE scale, 511
Safe Drinking Water Act (SDWA), 531, 626
salicylic acid, 1021
Salmonella, irradiation of foods to kill, 978
salt(s)
  acid–base properties of, 758–765
  from acid–base reactions, 186, 187
  density of, 19
  electrolysis of molten, 929
  organic compounds vs., 123
  solutions as acidic, basic, or neutral, 763–765
  table. *See* sodium chloride
salt bridges, 904–905, 1053
saltpeter, 1085
salt water, 175–177
sand, specific heat of, 273
San Francisco, California, 273
Sanger, Frederick, 1038
Saran, 574
saturated fats, 1041
saturated fatty acid, 1039
saturated hydrocarbons. *See* alkanes
saturated solution, 590, 823
s block, periodic table, 362
scanning tunneling microscope (STM), 50
Schrödinger, Erwin, 310, 312
Schrödinger equation, 331–334, 354, 470–471
Schrödinger's cat, 311–312
science, 5
scientific approach to knowledge, 3–5
scientific law, 3–5
scientific notation, 17
scientific revolution, 5
scintillation counter, 958
SCN^- ligand, chemical analysis with, 1156
screening (shielding), 356, 358, 368–369
scuba diving, 216–217, 231–232
SDWA (Safe Drinking Water Act), 531, 626
seawater, 579–581, 824, 1099
sec-butyl substituent, 1000
second (s) (unit), 14–15
secondary structure, protein, 1051–1054
secondary valence, 1140
second ionization energy (IE_2), 375, 378–379
second law of thermodynamics, 848, 850–860
second-order integrated rate law, 645–646, 649
second-order reaction, 637–639, 649
second-order reaction half-life, 648, 649
seed crystals, 555
seesaw geometry, 444, 446, 449
selective oxidation, 913
selective precipitation, 824–826
selenium, 61
semiconductor(s), 66, 540, 563–565
semipermeable membrane, 611–612
sensors, chemical, 1134
separation, in metallurgy, 1112
serine, 1047, 1048
SHE half-cell, 905–908, 910
—SH groups, 199
shielding (screening), 356, 358, 368–369
Shroud of Turin, 963
SI (International System of Units), 13–14
sickle-cell anemia, 1052, 1067
sievert (Sv), 975
sigma (σ) bonds, 462
σ^*_{2p} antibonding orbital, 476, 477
σ_{2p} bonding orbital, 476, 477
significant figures, 22–25, 742
silica, 561, 563, 1074, 1077
silicate ceramics, 561–562
silicate glass, 563
silicates, 561, 1074–1078
silicon, 66, 361, 379, 565, 992
silicon carbide, 562, 1083
silicon dioxide, 555, 556
silicon nitride, 562
silicon oxide, 1083
silk, 1053
silver, 71, 200, 273, 290, 371
silver brass, 1126
silver bromide, 818
silver chloride, 132, 178, 817, 818, 831
silver chromate, 818
silver iodide, 818
silver ions, 829, 1141
silver nitrate, 178, 403, 824
silver plating, 927
simple carbohydrates, 1043–1045
simple cubic structure, 546–547, 1120
simple cubic unit cell, 546–547
single bond(s), 95
  bond energy of, 422
  bond length of, 425
  covalent, 404
  double bonds vs., 464, 1006
single-nucleotide polymorphisms (SNPs), 1060
single-walled nanotubes (SWNT), 560
sintering, 1115
SI unit(s)
  base units, 13–14
  of density, 18
  derived units, 17–18
  of energy, 266
  of length, 14, 18
  of mass, 14, 18
  prefix multipliers, 17
  of pressure, 213–214
  of speed, 17
  of temperature, 15–16
  of time, 14–15
  of volume, 18
skunk, smell of, 990
skydiving, supersonic, 211–212
SLAC (Stanford Linear Accelerator), 972–973
slag, 1113
smell, sense of, 989–990
smelting, 1113
smithsonite, 1126
smog, photochemical, 296
smoke, 617
snorkels, extra-long, 219
snowflake, 542
SNPs (single-nucleotide polymorphisms), 1060
soap, 454, 616–617
Socrates, 734
soda ash, 100
soda-lime glass, 563
sodium, 61, 66
  activity series of, 200
  charge of, 101
  electron affinity of, 380
  electron configuration of, 359, 373
  electronegativity of, 408
  electron sea model for, 425, 426
  emission spectrum of, 324
  flame tests for, 325
  ΔH_f° for compounds containing, 290
  ionization energies of, 375, 376, 378, 379
  Lewis structure of, 397
  properties of, 92
  reaction between methanol and, 1015
  reaction between sulfur and, 397
sodium acetate, 590, 789, 790, 823
sodium alginate, 168
sodium bicarbonate (baking soda)
  as antacid, 206
  carbon dioxide from, 1084
  ions from dissociation of, 758
  in laundry detergents, 207
  in medicine, 403
  polyatomic ions in, 99
  reaction between hydrochloric acid and, 191, 192
  uses of, 734
sodium borates, 1078
sodium carbide, 1082
sodium carbonate, 179, 734
sodium chlorate, 1101
sodium chloride
  acidity of solutions containing, 763
  from alkali metal reaction, 156
  Born–Haber cycle for production of, 398–401
  chemical formula for, 94
  conductivity of, 402–403
  as crystalline solid, 553, 555
  decomposition of sugar vs., 991
  density of, 19
  electrolysis of, 929–931
  formation of, 51–52, 93, 1111
  formula unit for, 98–99
  as ionic compound, 100
  lattice energy of, 398–402
  melting of, 402–403
  properties of sodium and chlorine vs., 92
  reaction between potassium iodide and, 180–181
  from redox reaction, 193–194
  in seawater, 580–581

sodium chloride (*cont.*)
solute and solvent interactions in solution, 175
unit cell for, 557
in water, 507, 581, 586, 589–590, 601, 602
sodium chlorite, 1101
sodium fluoride, 403, 763, 820–821
sodium hydroxide
in Arrhenius model, 735
formula of, 187
pH of, 742
reaction between hydrochloric acid and, 186
reaction between hydrofluoric acid and, 189
reaction between propanoic acid and, 1020
reaction between water and, 586, 1015
strength of, 754
and sulfurous acid, 814
titration with formic acid, 808–813
titration with hydrochloric acid, 803–807
uses of, 734
sodium hypochlorite, 99
sodium iodide, 930
sodium ion(s)
cations vs., 64
electron configuration of, 373
in human nerve cells, 922
nerve signal transmission and, 351–352
solubility and, 178
sodium methoxide, 1015
sodium nitrite, 99, 104, 1089
sodium oxide, 111
sodium phosphate compounds, 1091
sodium sulfide, 1096
soft drinks, pH of, 742
solar power, 298
solar-powered electrolytic cell, 927
solid(s), 494, 541–577. *See also* crystalline solid(s)
amorphous, 498
ceramics, cement, and glass, 561–563
entropy change associated with change in state of, 856–860
equilibria involving, 695–696
and graphene's discovery, 541–542
intermolecular forces in, 499–512
ionic, 553, 555–558
molecular comparison with other phases, 496–499
network covalent atomic, 558–561
on phase diagram, 527–528
polymers, 565–568
properties of, 497
relative standard entropies of, 868
semiconductors, 563–565
solubility of, temperature dependence of, 591
standard state for, 289, 867
sublimation and fusion of, 522–524
unit cells and basic structures of, 545–552
X-ray crystallography of, 542–544
solid aerosols, 617
solid emulsion, 617
solid matter, 6, 7
solid solution, 581
solubility
alloys with limited, 1118–1119
of amphoteric metal hydroxides, 832–833
complex ion equilibria and, 831–832
defined, 581
effect of intermolecular forces on, 582–586
and entropy, 582
of gases in water, 591–593
molar, 817–820
relative, 820
temperature dependence of, 591
solubility equilibria, 786, 817–822
common ion effect on, 820–821
molar solubility, 817–820
pH and, 822
solubility product constant (K_{sp}), 817–820
molar solubility and, 817–820
and reaction quotient, 823–824
relative solubility and, 820
solubility rules, 178, 817
soluble compounds, 177–179, 823
solute(s), 168, 580
interactions between, 175, 582–583
interactions with solvents, 605
intermolecular forces acting on, 582–586, 605
van't Hoff factors for, 613–614
solution(s), 579–629. *See also* acid–base chemistry; aqueous solution(s)
boiling point elevation, 608–610
colligative properties of, 601–616
colloids, 616–618
concentrated, 168, 169, 595, 602–603, 742
concentration of, 168–171, 594–601
defined, 168, 580
dilute, 168, 169, 594–595
dilution of, 171–173
electrolyte, 175–177
energetics of formation, 586–589
entropy and, 582, 602–603
equilibrium processes in, 589–593
freezing point depression, 608–611
gaseous, 581
hyperosmotic, 615, 626
hyposmotic, 615
ideal, 605
intermolecular forces in, 582–586
intravenous, 616
isosmotic (isotonic), 615–616
liquid, 581
molarity of, 168–171
neutral, 741, 742
nonelectrolyte, 176, 177
nonideal, 605–607
saturated, 590, 823
separation using, 1112
solid, 581
standard state for substances in, 867
stock, 171–172
supersaturated, 590, 823
thirsty, 579–581, 602–603
transition metal ions in, 829–833
unsaturated, 590, 823
vapor pressure of, 605–607
solution stoichiometry, 173–174
solvent(s), 168, 580
interactions between, 582–583, 605
interactions of solutes and, 175, 582–583
intermolecular forces acting on, 582–586, 605
nonpolar, 584
polar, 584
soot, 1082
s orbitals, 333, 337–340
1*s*, 337–338, 342
2*s*, 339–340, 356–357
3*s*, 339–340
sorosilicates (pyrosilicates), 1075, 1077
sound, speed of, 313
sp hybridization, 464–466, 468
sp^2 hybridization, 460–464, 468
sp^3d hybridization, 466–467, 468
sp^3d^2 hybridization, 467, 468
sp^3 hybridization, 458–460, 468
space-filling molecular models, 96, 97, 113
specific heat capacity (C_s), 273, 530
spectator ions, 184
spectra, 323–325
spectrochemical series, 1153
spectrometers, 636
spectroscopy, 636
speed, SI unit for, 17
sphalerite, 1111, 1126
spherification, 167–168
sphygmomanometer, 215
spin-pairing, 456–457
spin quantum number (m_s), 332, 333, 354–355
spin up and spin down, 354
spontaneity
change in Gibbs free energy as criterion for, 864
conditions for, 883
effect of ΔS, ΔH, and temperature on, 864–867
in oxidation–reduction reactions, 198–201, 901–906, 910–913, 915
spontaneous process(es), 848–850
decrease in Gibbs free energy and, 864
endothermic, 850–852
exothermic, 860
making nonspontaneous processes into, 875
mixing, 580–582
in voltaic (or galvanic) cells, 901–906
square planar complexes, 1147–1148, 1155
square planar geometry
of complex ions, 1143
molecular, 445, 446, 448, 449
square pyramidal geometry, 445, 446
S°_{rxn} (entropy change for a reaction), 867–873
stability, valley of, 954–957
stainless steels, 1122, 1123
stalactites, 822
stalagmites, 822
standard atomic weight, 69–73, 111
standard cell potential (E°_{cell}), 904, 914–917
standard change in free energy (ΔG°_{rxn}), 871–884
calculating, 871–877
and change in free energy, 917
and equilibrium constant, 881–884
from free energies of formation, 873–874
and "free energy" concept, 876–877
with nonstandard conditions, 878–881

and standard cell potential, 914–915, 917
from standard enthalpies of formation, 872–873
for stepwise reaction, 875–876
standard electrode potentials, 905–913
and direction of redox reaction, 910–913
and solubility of metals in acids, 913
standard cell potential from, 905–910
standard emf. *See* standard cell potential (E°_{cell})
standard enthalpy change (ΔH°), 289–294
standard enthalpy of formation (ΔH°_f), 289–294
standard enthalpy of reaction (ΔH°_{rxn}), 291–292, 872–873
standard entropy change for a reaction (S°_{rxn}), 867–873
standard free energies of formation, 873–874
standard heat of formation, 289–294
standard hydrogen electrode (SHE) half-cell, 905–908, 910
standard molar entropies (S°), 867–871
standard state, 289–290, 867, 878
standard temperature and pressure (STP), molar volume at, 225–226
Stanford Linear Accelerator (SLAC), 972–973
starch, 1045, 1046
stars, neutron, 59, 86
state function, 267–269, 853
states of matter, 5–7
changing between, 498–499. *See also* phase transition(s)
in chemical equations, 141
critical point for, 521–522
differences between, 496–498
entropy change associated with change in, 856–860
stationary states, 324, 325
steady state, 962
steam burn, 514
stearic acid, 1039–1040
steel
galvanizing, 1126
production of, 1090, 1092, 1124
stainless, 1122, 1123
steel alloys, 1122–1124
stepwise reactions, standard change in free energy for, 875–876
stereoisomerism, 1147–1150
geometric, 1006–1007, 1147–1148
optical, 995–997, 1044, 1148–1150
stereoisomers, 995, 1145
Stern–Gerlach experiment, 371
steroids, 1042
STM (scanning tunneling microscope), 50
stock solutions, 171–172
stoichiometry, 138, 145–155
defined, 141
of electrolysis, 932–933
involving enthalpy change, 283–284
molar volume and, 236–238
for pH changes in buffer solutions, 794, 796
reaction, 145–155, 235–238, 283–284
solution, 173–174
storage proteins, 1046
STP (standard temperature and pressure), molar volume at, 225–226
Strassmann, Fritz, 965
strong acid(s), 176, 177, 737
hydronium ion sources in, 745
pH of, mixed with weak acid, 751–752
titration with strong base, 803–807
titration with weak base, 813
strong base(s), 754, 756
cations as counterions of, 762
hydroxide ion concentration and pH of, 756–757
titration of diprotic acid with, 814
titration with strong acid, 803–807
titration with weak acid, 808–813
strong electrolytes, 176, 177, 613–616, 737
strong-field complexes, 1151
strong-field ligands, 1153
strong force, 956
strontium, 66
strontium hydroxide, 754
structural formulas, 95, 993–995
structural isomers, 993–995, 1043–1044, 1145–1147
structural proteins, 1046
Structure of Scientific Revolutions, The (Kuhn), 5
styrene, 1011
subatomic particles, 59–65. *See also* electron(s); neutron(s); proton(s)
sublevels (subshells), 333, 355–357
sublimation, 11, 522–524, 638
sublimation curve, 527–529
subscripts, 141
substance(s), 5, 7–9
substituents, 999–1000
substitutional alloys, 1116–1118
substitution reactions, 1007–1008, 1012, 1015
substrate, 664–665
successive approximations, method of, 708–710
succimer, 207
sucrase, 665
sucrose
catalytic breakup of, 665
dehydration of, 1097
density of, 19
glycosidic linkage in, 1045
hydrolysis of, 632, 636
sugar(s), 123
decomposition of salt vs., 991
density of, 19
dissolution of, 11
in nucleic acids, 1055
solubility of, 591
and water, 175–177
sulfate, 104
sulfide(s), 102, 191, 822, 827–828, 1111. *See also specific compounds*
sulfites, 104, 191
sulfonic acid groups, 199
sulfur, 60
elemental, 1094–1095
ΔH°_f for compounds containing, 290
hydrogen and metal sulfides, 1095–1096
ionization energies of, 379
Lewis structure of, 397
as molecular element, 98
on periodic table, 66
reaction with sodium, 397
uses of, 1093–1097
sulfur dioxide, 238, 775, 1095, 1096
sulfur fluoride, 444
sulfur hexafluoride, 420, 441, 467
sulfuric acid
acid–base reactions involving, 186
in acid rain, 160, 773–774
expanded octets of, 420–421
formula of, 187
ionization constants for, 766
reaction between lithium sulfide and, 191
reaction between potassium hydroxide and, 189
strength of, 737
structure of, 733
uses of, 732, 1096–1097
sulfurous acid, 109, 738, 765–766, 814
sulfur oxides, 296, 773–775
sun, 298, 848, 971–972
supercritical fluid, 522
supernova, 64
superoxide, 1092
supersaturated solution, 590, 823
supersonic skydiving, 211–212
surface tension, 509–510
surfactants, 1090
surroundings. *See also* thermochemistry
energy exchange of systems and, 278–279
energy flow in, 265, 266, 269, 270
entropy change in, 860–863
suspensions, 758
Sv (sievert), 975
sweating, 514
SWNT (single-walled nanotubes), 560
sylvite. *See* potassium chloride
synthetic elements, 974
system(s). *See also* thermochemistry
energy exchange of surroundings and, 278–279
energy flow in, 265, 266, 269, 270
state of, 269
systematic error, 26
systematic names, 101
systolic blood pressure, 215

T

table salt. *See* sodium chloride
talc, 1077
tantalite, 1111
tantalum, 1111
tapas, 167
tartaric acid, 133
T_c (critical temperature), 522
technetium-99, 952
technetium-99m, 977
tectosilicates, 1077
tellurium, 353
telomers, 1068
temperature(s)
absolute zero, 219
boiling point and, 517–518
critical, 522
defined, 272
entropy change and, 858, 861
equilibrium constant and, 696, 883–884
gas solubility in water and, 591–592
global, 140
heat capacity and, 272–274
heat vs., 272
intermolecular forces and, 500
and ion product constant for water, 741
kinetic energy and, 239, 242–243

temperature(s) (*cont.*)
Le Châtelier's principle on change in, 716–718
molecular velocities and, 243–244
phase changes and, 498
pressure and, 223
reaction rate and, 650–656
scale conversions, 16
SI unit of, 15–16
solubility of solids and, 591
spontaneity and, 864–867
standard change in free energy from, 872–873
STP, 225–226
and thermal energy, 264
vapor pressure and, 233, 517–518, 521
viscosity and, 511
volume and, 218–221
water's moderating effect on, 530
tempering, of chocolate, 554–555
temporary dipole (instantaneous dipole), 500
10W-40 oil, 511
tera prefix, 17
terminal atoms, 410
termolecular steps, 657, 658
tert-butyl substituent, 1000
tertiary structure, protein, 1051, 1053, 1054
testosterone, 1042
tetracene, 1012
tetragonal unit cells, 545
tetrahedral complex(es), 1150, 1155
tetrahedral geometry, 96
of complex ions, 1143
electron, 442–443, 446, 468
molecular, 439–443, 446, 449, 458, 459
tetrahedral hole, 557, 1120
tetrahedrons, 440, 444, 561, 1074
tetrapeptide, 1049
tetraphosphorus decaoxide, 1090
tetraphosphorus hexaoxide, 1090
thallium-201, 977
theoretical yield, 149–155
theories, laws vs., 4–5
therapeutic agents, 1158
therapeutic techniques, radioactivity in, 977
thermal conductivity, of metals, 1111
thermal energy, 12, 496, 630. *See also* heat(s)
defined, 264
dispersal of, 582
dissipation of, 847–848
distribution of, 652
in exothermic reactions, 283
and temperature, 264
transfer of, 274–276
vaporization and, 512–513
thermal equilibrium, 272
thermal shock, 562
thermite reaction, 293
thermochemical equations, 283–284
thermochemistry, 262–309. *See also* energy(-ies)
of chemical hand warmers, 263–264
enthalpy, 281–284
enthalpy change for chemical reactions, 285–294
environmental impacts of energy use, 294–298
first law of thermodynamics, 267–272
internal energy change for chemical reactions, 278–280
and nature of energy, 264–266
pressure–volume work, 276–278
quantifying heat, 272–276
thermodynamics, 846–895. *See also* equilibrium(-a)
chemical reactions, 867–877
concentrated energy in nature, 847–848
defined, 267
entropy in, 852–863, 867–871
and equilibrium constant, 881–884
first law of, 267–272, 848
free energy change of reaction under non-standard conditions, 878–881
Gibbs free energy, 863–867
heat transfer, 860–863
reaction rate and, 849, 850
of reversible reaction, 877
second law of, 848, 850–860
of spontaneous vs. nonspontaneous processes, 848–850
standard change in free energy, 871–884
state changes, 856–860
third law of, 867–871
thermoluminescent dosimeters, 957
thiocyanate ion, 1141
thiocyanato ligand, 1147
thiol groups, 199
third ionization energy (IE_3), 375
third law of thermodynamics, 867–871
thirsty solutions, 579–581, 602–603
Thomson, J. J., 55–57
thorium-234, decay of, 956
threonine, 1048
threshold frequency, 320, 321
thymine, 508, 509, 1055, 1056
thymol blue, 817
thymolphthalein, 817
thyroid gland, radiotracer used for, 977
time
concentration and, 642–649
product/reactant concentrations as function of, 634
SI unit of, 14–15
tin, 61, 103, 200, 1125
titanium, 19, 1121–1122
titanium oxide, 1122
titration, 189–191, 636. *See also* acid–base titration
titration curves, 803–814
Tokamak fusion reactor, 972
toluene, 553–554, 584, 1011
torr, 213
Torricelli, Evangelista, 213
total force, of a gas, 241
total intensity, normalization of, 71
total pressure, 224, 230–231
toxaphene, 599
Toyota Mirai (fuel-cell vehicle), 298
trajectory, 329–330
trans–cis isomers. *See* geometric isomerism
trans-fats, 1008
transition(s). *See also* phase transition(s)
in Bohr model, 324, 325
in hydrogen atom, 334–337
quantum-mechanical orbital, 334
transition metal(s), 66, 67, 102, 364–365, 1134–1165
atomic radii and, 369–370
and colors of rubies and emeralds, 1135–1136
coordination compounds, 1140–1158
crystal structures for, 1116
functions in human body, 1156
inner, 362, 364–365
ion formation by, 68
properties of, 1136–1139
sources, products, and properties of, 1121–1126
valence electrons for, 362
transition metal ions, 371–372
transition state (activated complex), 651
translational energy, 857, 870
transmutation, nuclear, 972–974
transport proteins, 1046
transuranium elements, 974
tremolite, 1076–1077
triads, 352
1,1,2-trichloro-1,2,2-trifluoroethane, 642
trichlorofluoromethane, 642
triclinic unit cells, 545
triglycerides, 1040–1041
trigonal bipyramidal geometry, 1100
electron, 444–446, 468
molecular, 441, 446, 449, 466–467
trigonal planar geometry
electron, 446, 468
molecular, 439, 440, 446, 449, 460
trigonal pyramidal geometry, 442–443, 446, 448, 449, 453
trihalides, 1079
trimethylamine, 1022
triolein, 1041
tripeptide, 1049
triple bond(s), 405
bond energy of, 422
bond length of, 425
carbon's ability to form, 990–991
covalent, 405
drawing Lewis structures with, 411
sp hybridization and, 464–466
in structural formulas, 994
triple point, 527–529
triprotic acids, 738, 765–766
tristearin, 1040–1041
trona, 100
tryptophan, 1048
T-shaped geometry, 444, 446
Tums, 758
tungsten carbide, 1083
turquoise, 1136
two-phase region, 1118–1119
Tyndall effect, 618
tyrosine, 1048

U

ulcers, 744
ultraviolet (UV) radiation, 316, 426
uncertainty principle, 328–329
unimolecular elementary step, 657, 658
unit cells, 545–552
for closest-packed structures, 551–552
cubic, 545–552
for ionic solids, 556–558
unit conversion problems, 26–31
United States, energy consumption in, 294–295, 773
U.S. Department of Agriculture (USDA), 978
U.S. Department of Energy (DOE), 146, 294, 1060
U.S. Environmental Protection Agency (EPA), 118, 238, 296, 531, 599

U.S. Food and Drug Administration (FDA), 118, 978, 1041
units of measurement, 13–20. *See also* SI unit(s)
universe
 age of, 965
 dissipation of energy in, 848
 entropy of, 860, 863
unsaturated fat, 1041
unsaturated fatty acids, 1040
unsaturated hydrocarbons, 1002–1009. *See also* alkenes; alkynes
unsaturated solutions, 590, 823
unsaturation, effect of, 1040
uracil, 1055
uranic rays, 949
uranium, 60, 1111
uranium-235, 83, 965–969
uranium-238, 678, 950, 956, 965
uranium fuel rods, 968
uranium/lead dating, 964–965
urea, 162, 991
USDA (U.S. Department of Agriculture), 978
UV (ultraviolet) radiation, 316, 426

V

V (volt), 903
ν. *See* frequency
valence, 1140
valence bands, 564, 565
valence bond theory, 392, 455–470
 bonding in coordination compounds and, 1150
 double bonds in, 460–464
 hybridization of atomic orbitals, 457–470
 Lewis model and, 462
 Lewis theory and, 468
 orbital overlap in, 455–457
valence electrons, 361–365, 396–398
valence shell electron pair repulsion (VSEPR) theory, 436–454, 1100–1101
 bent geometry, 443, 446, 449, 453
 linear geometry, 439, 440, 445, 449, 453
 lone pairs effect, 442–447
 molecular shape and polarity, 450–454
 octahedral geometry, 441, 445, 446, 449, 467
 predicting molecular geometries with, 447–450
 seesaw geometry, 444, 446, 449
 square planar geometry, 445, 446, 448, 449
 square pyramidal geometry, 445, 446
 summary of, 445
 tetrahedral geometry, 439–443, 446, 449, 453, 458, 459
 trigonal bipyramidal geometry, 441, 444–446, 449, 466–467
 trigonal planar geometry, 439, 440, 446, 449, 453, 460
 trigonal pyramidal geometry, 442–443, 446, 448, 449, 453
 T-shaped geometry, 444, 446
valine, 1048
valley of stability, 954–957
vanadinite, 1111
vanadium, 371, 1109–1110, 1117–1118
vanadium ions, 371
vandate compounds, 1110
van der Waals, Johannes, 248
van der Waals constants, 248
van der Waals equation, 249
van der Waals radius, 366
vanillin, 1017
van't Hoff factor (*i*), 613–614
vaporization, 512–522
 Clausius–Clapeyron equation and, 518–521
 critical point, 521–522
 energetics of, 514–515
 heat of, 514–515, 520, 524
 process of, 512–513
 vapor pressure and dynamic equilibrium, 515–521
vaporization curve, 527–529
vapor pressure, 233
 defined, 516
 and dynamic equilibrium, 515–521, 602
 of solutions, 605–607
 and strong electrolytes, 614–615
 temperature and, 233, 518–519, 521
vapor pressure lowering (ΔP), 602–603
variational method, 471
vector addition, 452
vector quantities, 451
velocity(-ies)
 in classical mechanics, 329–330
 of electron, 329
 molecular, 243–244
 and position as complementary property, 331
 root mean square, 243–244
Venus (planet), 140
Venus of Dolni, 561
vibrational energy, 870
vinegar, 733
viscosity, 511
visible light, 314–316
vision, 464
vital force, 991
vitalism, 991
vitamins, 489
vitreous silica, 563
volatility, 9, 45, 513, 605–607
volt (V), 903
voltaic (galvanic) cells, 901–906
 anode, cathode, and salt bridge in, 904–905
 batteries as, 922–926
 concentration cells, 920–922
 current and potential difference in, 903–904
 electrochemical cell notation, 905–906
 electrolytic cells vs., 928–929
volume
 constant-volume calorimetry, 278–280, 286
 gas amount and, 221–222
 Le Châtelier's principle on change in, 714–715
 molar, 225–226, 236–238, 246–247
 parts by, 597–598
 percent mass to, 616
 pressure and, 216–218
 pressure–volume work, 276–278
 of real gas particles, 247–248
 SI unit for, 18
 stoichiometry and, 236–238
 temperature and, 218–221
 unit cell, 548–549
VSEPR theory. *See* valence shell electron pair repulsion theory

W

W (watt), 266
Warren, J. Robin, 744
washing soda, 1084
water, 2, 9
 amphotericity of, 740
 Arrhenius definition of acids and bases and, 735
 autoionization of, 740–742
 boiling point of, 514, 518
 charge distribution in, 175
 chemical formula for, 94–95
 collecting gases over, 233–235
 decomposition of, 52, 298
 density of, 19
 electrolysis of, 927, 1092
 empirical formula for, 118–119
 entropy of surroundings and freezing of, 860, 861
 ethanol mixed with, 583
 formation of, 156
 from fossil fuel combustion, 295
 free energy change for, 878–880
 freezing point depression/boiling point elevation constants for, 609
 geometry of, 443, 451
 gravity and behavior of, 495–496
 hard, 179, 819
 heat capacity of, 273, 274
 heating curve for, 524–527
 heat of fusion for, 523–524
 heat of vaporization of, 514
 hexane mixed with, 583–584
 hydrogen bonding in, 506, 530
 Lewis structure of, 404, 405
 as ligand, 1141
 on Mars, 529, 530
 meniscus of, 512
 obtaining hydrogen from, 875
 phase diagram for, 527–529
 polarity of, 451, 454, 504, 584
 properties of, 91–93, 530–531
 reaction between calcium and, 898
 reaction between carbon dioxide and, 773, 774
 reaction of alkali metals and, 156, 157
 real gas behavior of, 249
 in seawater, 580–581
 sodium chloride in, 507, 581, 586, 589–590, 601, 602
 solubility in, 584, 591–593
 specific heat of, 273
 spherical droplets of, 510
 states of, 496
 and sugar, 175–177
 thermal energy distributions for, 512–513
 van der Waals constants for, 248
 viscosity of, 511
water atomization, 1115
water pollution, 531
waters of hydration, 105
water softeners, 626
water vapor, condensation of, 514
Watson, James D., 509, 543, 1036, 1058
watt (W), 266
wave function (ψ), 331
wavelength (λ), 314
 de Broglie, 327
 energy and, 321
 frequency and, 315, 321
wave nature
 of electrons, 325–331
 of light, 313–315
 of matter, 325–331

wave–particle duality of light, 312, 322
weak acid(s), 177
  acid ionization constants for, 738–740, 745–746
  in buffer solution, 788–789
  cations as, 762–763
  diprotic, 768–769
  hydronium ion sources in, 745–749, 751
  percent ionization of, 750–751
  pH of mixtures containing, 751–753
  titration with strong base, 808–813
weak base(s), 754–757
  anions as, 759–762
  in buffer solution, 788–789
  hydroxide ion concentration and pH of, 756–757
  titration with strong acid, 813
weak electrolytes, 177, 737
weak-field complexes, 1151
weak-field ligands, 1153
weather, 212–213
weighing, 21, 111–112
weight, 14
  atomic, 69–73, 111
  molecular, 111
weighted linear sum, of molecular orbitals, 471–473
Werner, Alfred, 1134, 1140, 1143
western bristlecone pine trees, 962
wet chemistry, 826
wetting agent, 1112
whipped cream, 617
white light spectrum, 314, 315, 322–323
white phosphorus, 1085, 1090
Wilhelmy, Ludwig, 632, 636
Wilkins, Maurice, 543
willemite, 1075
window glass, 563
wind power, 298
wines, pH of, 742
Winkler, Clemens, 66
Witt, Otto N., 786
Wöhler, Friedrich, 988, 991
wood alcohol. *See* methanol
wood frogs (*Rana sylvatica*), 611
work
  defined, 12, 264
  in first law of thermodynamics, 270–272
  internal energy change and, 270–272
  pressure–volume, 276–278

X

xenon
  as atomic solid, 555
  as crystalline solid, 553
  nonideal behavior of, 248–249
  on periodic table, 66
  van der Waals constants for, 248
xenon difluoride, 445
x is small approximation, 708, 710, 746–748, 769, 791–793
X-ray crystallography, 393, 542–544
X-ray diffraction, 542–544
X-rays, 316, 317, 948

Y

yield of reactions
  actual, 150, 151
  percent, 150–153
  theoretical, 149–155
Yucca Mountain, Nevada, 968

Z

Z. *See* atomic number
Z_{eff} (effective nuclear charge), 356, 366–370
zeolites, 1085
zero entropy, 868
zero-order integrated rate law, 646, 649
zero-order reaction, 637–639, 649
zero-order reaction half-life, 648–649
zinc
  activity series of, 200
  alloy of copper and, 1126
  crystal structure of, 556
  in dry-cell batteries, 922–923
  electrochemical cell of copper ions and, 918
  in galvanized nails, 935
  in human body, 1156
  reaction between copper ions and, 901–905
  reaction between hydrochloric acid and, 107, 913
  sources, properties, and products of, 1126
zinc blende structure, 557, 559
zinc ions, 372
zinc oxide, 403, 1113
zinc phosphate, 1126
zinc silicate (calamine), 1126
zinc sulfide, 557, 559, 1096
zwitterion, 1049